NON-LEAGUE CLUB DIRECTORY 2019-20

(42nd Edition)

EDITORS
MIKE & TONY WILLIAMS

NON-LEAGUE CLUB DIRECTORY 2019-20

ISBN 978-1-869833-99-2

Editors
Mike Williams
(Tel: 01548 531 339)
mwpublishing@btconnect.com
Tony Williams
Email: t.williams320@btinternet.com

Published by MW Publishing
(Tel: 01548 531 339)
Email: mwpublishing@btconnect.com

Printed by
CPI William Clowes - Suffolk

Sales & Distribution
MWPublishing (01548 531 339)

Front Cover: Pagham's Scott Murfin is well tackled by hosts', K Sports, Steve Rothery, during their FA Cup Extra Preliminary Round tie which ended in a 2-2 draw. Photo: Alan Coomes.

I am delighted to write a few words on behalf of my friend Tony Williams.

I first met Tony when we were both doing our National Service, Tony was serving in the AirForce and I was in the Army. It was at sometime in this period around 1958 that we played together for an FA XI, and we forged a friendship that has lasted all these years.

Roger Hunt (centre) playing for an FA XI.

Tony went on to become heavily involved in Non-League Football and has had many well deserved acknowledgments for his endeavours. He is still, along with his son Mike, producing the Non-League Club Directory now in it's 42nd year, some achievement!

Before the Army, I played for Stockton Heath which is now Warrington Town and while I was stationed at Larkhill I played for Devizes Town. These clubs, along with all Non-League clubs, are the backbone of English football. Looking back through Tony's books are familiar names of footballers who, like me, plied their trade in Non-League hoping for a break. For some footballers it's their record to show their grandchildren their achievements.

I wish Mike and his new office boy, now the 80-year-old Tony and all the family continued success in the years to come with this unique book.

Roger Hunt MBE

P.S. Tony, who was a perfectly placed steward at Wembley in 1966, always says the ball was over the line!

CONTENTS

THE 2018-19 SEASON

STEP 1

STEP 2

STEP 3 & 4

STEP 5/6

STEP 7+

'A SIGN OF THE TIMES'

On Thursday 18th July I, along with others, made the heart wrenching decision to fold Loddiswell Athletic Football Club - just over 45 years since the day the club was formed. Personally I'd invested 18 years into the club as a player, manager and committee member, with the last five being the toughest.

At the pinnacle of our history we enjoyed several years in the top half of the South Devon Premier Division, winning the league cup along the way. However, it was when this successful crop of players started retiring that things started to change. With those hanging up their boots went the commitment that is needed just to put an eleven on the field let alone win anything. The attitude of the majority (sadly) today seems to be that they are doing you a favour if they decide to turn out on a Saturday afternoon!

Somehow with a young side, of an ever changing starting eleven we managed to survive relegation from the premier for several years - truth be known we wanted to go down!

However, when it did finally happen we saw this as a chance to re-group and along with a new manager we hoped we could build again for future success.

Brian Birch was like a breath of fresh air when he arrived last July, an old school manager with the same outlook on football as I'd grown up with. His enthusiasm was infectious, and we started 2018-19 with great expectations.

Unfortunately, even with Brian at the helm a core of only six committed players out of the 56 signed on, saw inconsistent results and a final position of 11th in Division One.

Brian worked hard during the closed season to recruit the right players - ie: ones that if they signed would actually turn up to play/train - and added to the six from last year it was looking good. However, several attempts by Brian to organise friendlies and even training soon saw that word 'commitment' rise it's ugly head again. I was therefore not overly surprised when, on Thursday 18th, I got the dreaded call from Brian saying he couldn't continue any longer. From that moment I knew we only had one choice, backed up by my fellow committee members, later that day I contacted the league to tell them we were folding the club.

When I started playing in our league there were eight divisions, for the 2019-20 campaign it starts with only four. We're not the first and we certainly won't be the last to fold. Players today are just not interested in committing their time to a club, on or off the field. What upsets me the most though is that Brian, who came with such enthusiasm and worked tirelessly to give the lads a great platform from which to play their football, has now retired from local football completely - his passion has been extinguished by the lack of others commitment!

It will be a strange feeling not being involved with a club this season. I have had offers to join other clubs but have decided to take a year out to just enjoy watching local football without the 'stress'. I certainly won't miss the phone calls hours before kick-off from a desperate manager trying to put an eleven together.

V.A.R. - GOOD FOR OUR LEVEL OF THE GAME?

I've yet to be convinced that the introduction of V.A.R. is a positive for football. For 'man handling' during corners and tackles in the penalty area, yes I can see it has it's use. But for me disallowing a goal, sometimes up to five minutes after it was scored, because the 'blue line' shows the back of a players heel was in an offside position is just going to kill the spirit of players and fans alike.

I almost gave up on the recent Women's World Cup because of it, luckily I didn't and I got to watch some fantastic quarter finals which were strangely devoid of V.A.R. (I presume even FIFA were not impressed!)

This season we'll see V.A.R. in the Premier League, we shall see how it goes but if it starts to effect the flow and excitement of the game I can see many turning to local football for their 'fix'.

Let's hope so!

Mike Williams

A LIFE TIME OF PASSION

I realise how lucky I have been to spend a lifetime involved with the sport I love.

Parents were happy for their boys to play on the local council pitches in 1946. I was only 7 years old, but was thrilled when invited to join the older local lads kicking a football around in the Devon village of Whitchurch, just outside Tavistock.

I was the youngest, but seemed capable of joining in and was often picked quickly when the older lads were sorting out the teams. I loved playing and it seemed to come naturally.

Everything about the game excited me and when my father took me to a war battered Plymouth Argyle to see a 3-3 draw with Doncaster Rovers, I was hooked.

Since then, within an ever changing world of football I have enjoyed playing, coaching, managing, organising sponsorship and then compiling, writing and editing football features, magazines and books.

What career could possibly have been more fun ? I realise how lucky I have been!

I am thrilled to say my son Michael shows the game just as much love and respect while looking after our Non-League Club Directory. A publication that is celebrating its 42nd edition and helps promote the wonderful competitions below The Football League.

Tony Williams

SPECIAL ACKNOWLEDGMENTS

'OUR TEAM' OF PHOTOGRAPHERS
Peter Barnes, Keith Clayton, Alan Coomes,
Bill Wheatcroft and Gordon Whittington.

FA COMPETITIONS DEPARTMENT
Chris Darnell and Scott Bolton

CONTRIBUTORS
Arthur Evans, Colin Startup, Richard Rundle (Football Club History Database), and the many league and club officials that have been kind enough to supply the necessary information.
Thank you one and all

I must also give an extra special acknowledgment to Cyril Windiate (seated), retiring as Chairman of the Kent County League after 35 years at the helm. Cyril has been involved in football for over 60 years and has received both the FA 50 Year Long Service award and Kent FA Council 50 year award for his services to football.

The Kent County member clubs honoured Cyril at the recent Presentation evening, and he was also presented with a letter of appreciation from the Football Association which was presented by Ray Lewis, Chairman of the FA Leagues Committee.
During this time Cyril has been a strong supporter of the Directory and has helped us promote the Non-League game via his league. From my Dad and myself thank you for everything you have done for us and we hope you enjoy your retirement.

Non-League Pyramid (Steps 1-7) 2019-20

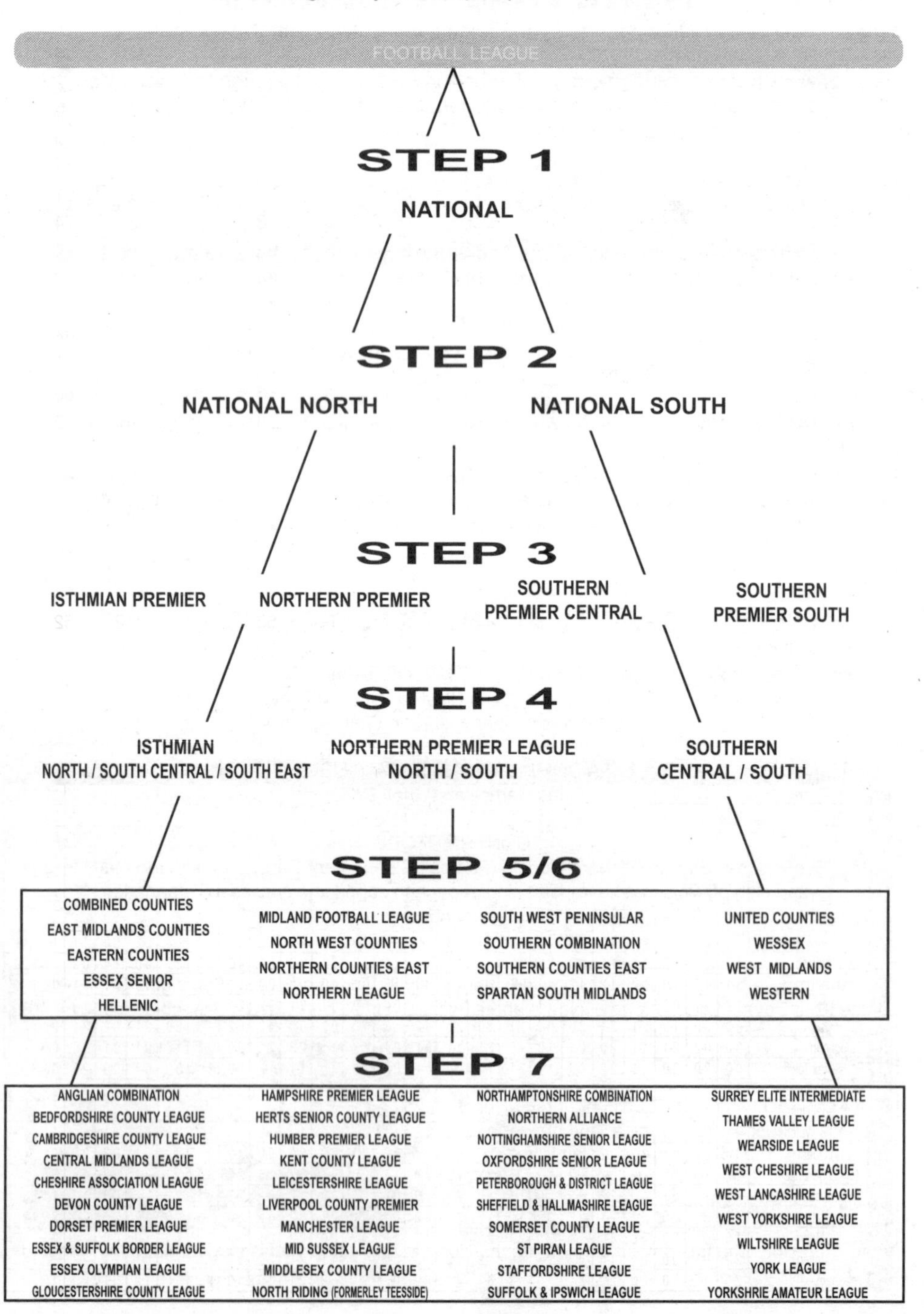

NATIONAL LEAGUE TABLE 2018-19

		P	W	D	L	F	A	GD	Pts
1	Leyton Orient	46	25	14	7	73	35	38	89
2	Solihull Moors	46	25	11	10	73	43	30	86
3	Salford City (Play-off winners)	46	25	10	11	77	45	32	85
4	Wrexham	46	25	9	12	58	39	19	84
5	AFC Fylde	46	22	15	9	72	41	31	81
6	Harrogate Town	46	21	11	14	78	57	21	74
7	Eastleigh	46	22	8	16	62	63	-1	74
8	Ebbsfleet United	46	18	13	15	64	50	14	67
9	Sutton United	46	17	14	15	55	60	-5	65
10	Barrow	46	17	13	16	52	51	1	64
11	Bromley	46	16	12	18	68	69	-1	60
12	Barnet	46	16	12	18	45	50	-5	60
13	Dover Athletic	46	16	12	18	58	64	-6	60
14	Chesterfield	46	14	17	15	55	53	2	59
15	FC Halifax Town	46	13	20	13	44	43	1	59
16	Hartlepool United	46	15	14	17	56	62	-6	59
17	Gateshead (demoted to Nat N)	46	19	9	18	52	48	4	57*
18	Dagenham & Redbridge	46	15	11	20	50	56	-6	56
19	Maidenhead United	46	16	6	24	45	70	-25	54
20	Boreham Wood	46	12	16	18	53	65	-12	52
21	Aldershot Town	46	11	11	24	38	67	-29	44
22	Havant & Waterlooville	46	9	13	24	62	84	-22	40
23	Braintree Town	46	11	8	27	48	78	-30	38*
24	Maidstone United	46	9	7	30	37	82	-45	34

		1	2	3	4	5	6	7	8	9	10	11	12	13	14	15	16	17	18	19	20	21	22	23	24
1	Aldershot Town		0-2	0-0	1-1	3-2	1-0	0-2	2-1	2-0	0-2	1-3	0-0	0-2	3-0	0-2	1-1	2-0	1-2	0-1	0-0	0-1	0-3	2-1	0-0
2	Barrow	2-1		0-2	1-2	1-1	1-0	3-2	0-1	2-3	0-0	0-3	1-1	1-2	0-0	2-2	1-0	3-0	2-3	1-0	2-0	3-2	1-2	2-1	0-0
3	Barnet	2-0	3-1		1-1	1-1	1-1	0-2	2-1	2-0	0-3	1-2	1-1	1-2	1-1	1-0	0-0	2-2	0-0	0-2	1-0	1-3	2-0	0-1	1-2
4	Boreham Wood	0-2	1-1	1-0		2-1	1-1	1-0	1-0	0-1	0-0	3-3	1-1	1-1	2-1	2-4	0-4	1-3	1-0	0-1	3-1	2-3	2-2	1-2	0-2
5	Bromley	2-2	2-1	0-1	0-2		2-4	3-3	0-2	2-2	5-1	0-1	3-2	1-0	2-2	1-1	4-0	4-0	2-1	2-0	1-0	0-2	0-2	2-1	2-0
6	Braintree Town	0-1	0-2	4-0	1-1	2-4		1-3	2-0	2-1	0-4	1-2	2-1	2-0	0-2	0-4	1-1	3-4	1-5	0-1	0-2	1-0	0-3	2-2	0-1
7	Chesterfield	3-0	0-0	0-1	3-2	1-1	1-0		2-0	0-0	3-3	2-3	0-0	0-3	1-0	0-1	1-1	0-0	0-1	4-1	1-3	2-0	0-4	3-0	1-1
8	Dagenham & Redbridge	1-1	0-0	0-1	4-4	3-0	1-0	1-1		1-3	1-3	2-0	2-1	0-2	1-1	2-1	1-2	3-1	2-1	1-2	2-2	0-0	1-1	1-0	1-2
9	Dover Athletic	1-0	0-2	1-2	1-1	1-1	3-0	0-0	0-2		1-1	1-2	2-1	1-2	2-1	2-3	2-1	4-3	0-0	3-1	2-0	1-4	0-2	3-0	0-1
10	Ebbsfleet United	3-1	1-0	1-0	3-2	1-2	4-2	0-1	0-1	0-1		3-0	1-3	0-1	4-0	0-2	0-0	1-1	2-0	1-1	3-0	0-1	0-1	0-1	4-2
11	Eastleigh	1-2	0-1	0-3	1-0	1-0	2-1	1-1	1-0	2-2	0-1		0-0	1-0	0-1	2-1	3-2	2-1	1-1	2-0	2-0	1-1	1-2	3-2	1-3
12	AFC Fylde	3-0	0-0	1-0	2-1	2-1	3-0	0-1	1-1	4-0	2-0	4-2		1-0	0-2	0-0	4-2	6-2	1-3	2-0	2-1	0-2	3-1	2-2	2-0
13	Gateshead	3-0	0-2	2-1	1-1	2-0	0-1	1-0	2-0	2-1	1-1	0-1	0-1		1-1	2-3	2-1	0-0	1-1	1-0	0-1	2-1	1-2	0-0	1-1
14	FC Halifax Town	0-0	2-0	3-0	1-1	2-2	0-0	1-1	2-1	1-0	0-0	0-1	0-0	1-0		1-1	1-2	0-0	1-1	3-0	0-1	0-0	2-0	0-1	2-1
15	Harrogate Town	4-1	4-2	2-0	0-1	1-0	3-1	1-1	1-1	2-2	1-2	4-0	1-2	2-0	1-2		3-1	3-2	0-3	2-2	1-0	0-1	3-1	2-2	0-0
16	Hartlepool United	1-1	0-0	1-3	2-0	1-2	2-1	1-0	1-2	3-2	0-1	1-1	1-2	2-1	2-1	2-2		1-1	1-1	1-2	2-1	3-2	0-1	2-3	1-0
17	Havant & Waterlooville	2-1	2-0	0-2	0-0	0-3	2-1	1-2	3-0	0-0	3-3	2-2	1-1	0-1	2-1	1-2	1-2		1-2	5-2	7-0	1-1	0-1	1-2	2-3
18	Leyton Orient	0-0	2-2	3-1	1-0	3-1	0-0	3-1	1-0	3-0	1-1	3-2	2-0	2-0	2-2	2-0	0-0	4-0		3-0	0-1	0-3	3-0	0-1	1-0
19	Maidstone United	0-2	1-0	2-1	1-2	0-1	0-2	1-1	0-3	0-1	0-2	1-3	1-1	2-3	0-1	0-2	1-1	2-0	1-2		2-4	0-2	1-3	0-1	1-1
20	Maidenhead United	4-3	1-1	0-1	1-0	2-2	0-1	2-0	1-1	1-0	1-1	2-0	0-6	1-3	3-0	1-2	0-1	2-1	0-2	3-2		0-3	1-2	1-0	0-2
21	Salford City	4-0	3-1	0-0	3-1	2-1	2-2	3-2	1-2	1-3	1-1	0-2	0-1	1-1	2-1	3-2	3-0	3-0	1-1	1-0	3-0		2-0	2-0	2-0
22	Solihull Moors	1-0	0-1	2-2	0-0	5-0	2-1	2-2	2-0	2-2	2-1	4-1	1-2	1-0	0-0	2-0	0-1	3-2	0-0	5-0	1-0	0-0		2-2	1-0
23	Sutton United	2-1	0-1	0-0	0-4	1-0	0-3	1-1	1-0	2-2	1-0	1-0	0-0	4-2	1-1	2-1	2-2	2-2	1-2	2-2	0-1	2-1	2-2		3-0
24	Wrexham	2-0	1-3	1-0	3-0	2-2	3-1	1-0	1-0	0-1	4-1	2-0	0-0	3-1	0-0	2-1	1-0	1-0	0-2	1-0	1-0	5-1	1-0	1-0	

AFC FYLDE MATCH RESULTS 2018-19

Date	Comp	Opponents	H/A	Att:	Result		Goalscorers	Pos
Aug 4	NL	Bromley	H	1227	W	2 - 1	Bond 45 Rowe 68	
7	NL	Wrexham	A	5777	D	0 - 0		
11	NL	Havant & Waterlooville	A	1182	D	1 - 1	Rowe 24 (Pen)	
14	NL	Solihull Moors	H	1257	W	3 - 1	Rowe 4 Bond 19 Toure 67	
18	NL	Dover Athletic	H	1258	W	4 - 0	Rowe 41 85 (Pen) Cardle 50 Hardy 91	
25	NL	Sutton United	A	1770	D	0 - 0		2
27	NL	Harrogate Town	H	1709	D	0 - 0		3
Sept 1	NL	Ebbsfleet United	A	1395	W	3 - 1	Rowe 49 57 Toure 86	3
4	NL	Salford City	H	2941	L	0 - 2		5
8	NL	Eastleigh	A	1750	D	0 - 0		7
15	NL	Aldershot Town	H	1470	W	3 - 0	Croasdale 43 Tasdemir 45 Cardle 62	5
22	NL	Barnet	A	1101	D	1 - 1	Philliskirk 25	8
25	NL	FC Halifax Town	A	1197	D	0 - 0		9
29	NL	Braintree Town	H	1535	W	3 - 0	Tasdemir 11 Philliskirk 50 Rowe 68	7
Oct 6	NL	Chesterfield	A	4021	D	0 - 0		7
13	NL	Maidstone United	H	1507	W	2 - 0	Byrne 68 Birch 89	6
20	**FAC 4Q**	**Chesterfield**	**H**	**1092**	**L**	**1 - 3**	**Rowe 12**	
27	NL	Maidenhead United	A	1372	W	6 - 0	Rowe 4 32 (Pen) Toure 55 Tasdemir 75 Philliskirk 86 Bond 88	6
30	NL	Gateshead	H	1470	W	1 - 0	Rowe 90+3	5
Nov 3	NL	Leyton Orient	H	2142	L	1 - 3	Rowe 20	6
17	NL	Dagenham & Redbridge	A	1328	L	1 - 2	Bond 1	6
24	NL	Boreham Wood	H	1345	W	2 - 1	Rowe 87 Tasdemir 88	6
27	NL	Hartlepool United	A	1721	W	2 - 1	Rowe 44 Gnahoua 74	4
Dec 1	NL	Sutton United	H	1401	D	2 - 2	Bond 36 Toure 81	5
8	NL	Dover Athletic	A	927	L	1 - 2	Rowe 26	6
15	**FAT 1P**	**Stratford Town**	**H**	**491**	**W**	**5 - 1**	**Tasdemir 4 84 Williams 19 90+3 Rowe 45**	
22	NL	Ebbsfleet United	H	1474	W	2 - 0	Croasdale 28 Rowe 80	5
26	NL	Barrow	A	1582	D	1 - 1	Bond 38	5
29	NL	Harrogate Town	A	1603	W	2 - 1	Rowe 47 90 (Pen)	3
Jan 1	NL	Barrow	H	2194	D	0 - 0		4
5	NL	Bromley	A	1102	L	2 - 3	Rowe 9 Gnahoua 58	5
12	**FAT 2P**	**Biggleswade Town**	**H**	**594**	**W**	**1 - 0**	**Haughton 42**	
19	NL	Wrexham	H	2912	W	2 - 0	Hemmings 44 55	4
26	NL	Solihull Moors	A	1588	W	2 - 1	Rowe 52 74	4
Feb 5	**FAT 3P**	**Ramsbottom United**	**A**	**743**	**D**	**5 - 5**	**Tasdemir 11 48 Haughton 34 Tunnicliffe 45+1 Bond 87**	
9	NL	Maidstone United	A	2033	D	1 - 1	Davies 85 (og)	4
12	**FAT 3Pr**	**Ramsbottom United**	**H**	**913**	**W**	**4 - 1**	**Rowe 35 68 Tunnicliffe 45 Tasdemir 50**	
16	NL	Chesterfield	H	2175	L	0 - 1		4
19	NL	Havant & Waterlooville	H	1192	W	6 - 2	Croasdale 20 Tunnicliffe 45+3 69 Rowe 57 Crawford 75 Hemmings 90+1	
23	**FAT 4P**	**Barnet**	**H**	**795**	**D**	**0 - 0**	**(Won 4-1 on penalties aet)**	
Mar 2	NL	Maidenhead United	H	1402	W	2 - 1	Rowe 31 Crawford 57	4
9	NL	Boreham Wood	A	493	D	1 - 1	Byrne 71	5
12	NL	Hartlepool United	H	1272	W	4 - 2	Rowe 3 79 Kerr 56 (og) Walters 90	4
16	**FAT SF1**	**Stockport County**	**H**	**2605**	**D**	**0 - 0**		
23	**FAT SF2**	**Stockport County**	**A**	**6054**	**W**	**3 - 2**	**Rowe 65 (pen) Croasdale 85 Reid 89**	
26	NL	Leyton Orient	A	4696	L	0 - 2		5
30	NL	Aldershot Town	A	1280	D	0 - 0		5
Apr 2	NL	Dagenham & Redbridge	H	1275	D	1 - 1	Rowe 40	5
6	NL	Eastleigh	H	1525	W	4 - 2	Bradley 20 Tunnicliffe 50 Haughton 67 Reid 77	5
9	NL	Gateshead	A	470	W	1 - 0	Haughton 31	4
13	NL	Braintree Town	A	331	L	1 - 2	Tunnicliffe 85	5
19	NL	Barnet	H	1489	W	1 - 0	Rowe 21	5
22	NL	Salford City	A	3338	W	1 - 0	Reid 31	4
27	NL	FC Halifax Town	H	1891	L	0 - 2		5
May 1	**PO Q**	**Harrogate Town**	**H**	**1560**	**W**	**3 - 1**	**Croasdale 10 Bond 15 Bradley 90**	
5	**PO SF**	**Solihull Moors**	**A**	**3681**	**W**	**1 - 0**	**Philliskirk 2**	
11	**PO F**	**Salford City**	**N**	**8049**	**L**	**0 - 3**		
M 18	**FAT Final**	**Leyton Orient**	**N**	**42962**	**W**	**1 - 0**	**Rowe 60**	

GOALSCORERS	SG	CSG	Pens	Hat tricks	Total		SG	CSG	Pens	Hat tricks	Total
Rowe	26	4	5		33	Bradley	2	1			2
Tasdemir	7	1			9	Byrne	2	1			2
Bond	8	1			8	Cardle	2	1			2
Tunnicliffe	5	1			6	Crawford	2	1			2
Croasdale	5	1			5	Gnahoua*	2	1			2
Haughton	4	2			4	Opponent	2	1			2
Philliskirk	4	1			4	Williams	1	1			2
Toure	4	1			4	Birch	1	1			1
Hemmings	2	1			3	Hardy	1	1			1
Reid	3	1			3	Walters	1	1			1

No.	Lynch	Francis-Angol	Byrne	Tunnicliffe	Bond	Hardy	Croasdale	Rowe	Philliskirk	Cardle	Burke	Toure	Tasdemir	Griffiths	Hemmings	Birch	Kane (L)	Kellerman (L)	Brewitt	Green	Williams (L)	Haughton	Gnahoua (L)	Montrose	Bloomfield (L)	Stanley	Bradley	Odusina (L)	Crawford (L)	Sang	Reid	Walters
1	x	x	x	x	x	xs	x	x	x	xs	x	sx	sx	s	s	s																
2	x	x	x	xs	x	xs	x	x	x	xs	x	sx	sx	s	s	sx																
3	x	x	x		xs	sx	x	x	xs	sx	x	xs	s	s	sx	xs	x															
4	x	x	x		x	xs	x	x	xs	xs	x	sx	sx	s	s	sx	x															
5	x	x	x		x	x	x	x	x	xs	xs	sx	s	s	s	sx	x															
6	x	x	x		x	x	x	x		xs	xs	sx	s	s	sx	sx	x	xs														
7	x	x	x	s	x	xs	x	x		xs	x	sx	sx		sx	s	x	xs														
8	x	x	x	sx	x	xs	x	x		s	x	sx	s		xs		x	xs	sx													
9	x	x	x	x	xs	xs	x	x	sx	s	x	sx	s		xs			x	sx													
10	x		x	x	s	sx	x	x	x	xs	x	sx	sx		xs	x		xs	s													
11	x	x	x	x	sx	sx	x	x	x	xs	xs	sx	xs		s			x	s													
12	x	x	x	x	sx		x	x	x	x			xs	s	sx	x		xs	s	s												
13	x	x	x	x	sx		x	x	x	xs			xs		sx	x	s	xs	s	s												
14	x	xs	x	x	sx	sx	x	x	x	xs			xs		sx	x	s	x	s													
15	x	x	x	x	s		x	x	x	xs			s		sx	x	s	x	xs		sx											
16	x	x	x	x	xs	xs	x	x	x	x	s		s		sx	x		s	sx													
17	x	x	x	x	s	x	xs	x	xs	x	s	sx	sx	s	x	x		s	s													
18	x	x	x	x	x		x	xs	x	xs	s	xs	sx		sx	x			s			sx										
19	x	x	x	x	x		x	x	x	sx	s	xs	sx		s	xs			s			x										
20	x	x	x	x	x		x	xs	x	sx	xs	sx	xs		sx	s			s			x										
21	x		x	x	xs		xs	x	x		x	x	sx		sx	s		sx	s		xs	x										
22	x	x	x	x			x	x	xs		x	xs	sx		sx	s		sx	s		xs	x										
23	x	x	x	x	x		xs	x	x		x	xs	s		sx				sx		s	xs	sx									
24	x	x	x	x	x		x	x	x		xs	sx			sx				sx		s	xs	xs	s								
25	x	x	x	x			xs	x	x		x	sx	s					xs	s		sx	x	xs	sx								
26		x	x	s	sx		xs	xs			s		x	x		x		sx	x		x	xs	sx	x								
27	x	x	x	sx	x		xs	x	s		x		sx			s			x		sx	xs	xs	x								
28	x	x	x	s	x		x	x	s		x		sx			s			x		sx	x	xs	xs								
29	x	x	x	sx	x		x	x	xs		x		sx			sx			x	s	s	xs	xs									
30	x	x	x	x	sx		xs	x	x		x		sx		sx	s			x		s	xs	xs									
31	x	x	x	xs	xs			x	x		xs		s		s	sx			x			x	x	sx	sx							
32	s	x	s	x	sx			x	x				xs	x		x			x	sx		x	xs	x		s						
33	x		x	x	sx		x	x	sx				s		x	xs			sx	s		xs		xs			x	x				
34	x	x	x	x	sx	s	x	x	x						xs	s			sx			xs					xs	x	sx			
35		x	x	x	x	s	s	x	s				x	x		s				s		x						x	x	x		
36	x	x	x	x	s		x	x	x				s		xs							xs					x	x	s		sx	sx
37	x	xs	x	x	x	xs	x	xs	s				x			x				sx		sx						sx	x	s		
38	x	x	x	x	s		x	x	xs				sx		xs							x					x	xs	s		sx	sx
39	x	x	x	x	x		x	xs	s				sx		sx	x						xs					xs	s	x		sx	
40	x	x	x	x	x		xs	xs	sx		s		xs			x				sx		x						s	x		sx	
41	x	x	x	x	s		x	x	s				sx		xs	x						xs						sx	x		x	s
42	x	x	x	x	xs		x	xs	sx				sx		s	x						x					xs	s	x		sx	
43	x	x	x	x			x	x	xs				sx		s	x			sx			xs						s	x		xs	sx
44	x	x	x	x		xs	x	x	sx				xs	s		xs			s			x						sx	x		sx	
45	x	x	x	x		x	x	x	x					s		xs			s			xs						sx	sx	s	x	
46	x	x	x	x		xs	x	x	x						sx				s			sx					sx	xs	s		xs	x
47	x	x	x	x	xs	xs	x	x	x		s				sx	x						xs							s		sx	sx
48	x	xs	x	x	s	xs	x	x	x		sx					x						xs					x		s		sx	sx
49	x	x		x	sx	s	x	x	x		x		s			sx			xs			xs					xs		sx		x	
50	x	x	x	x	sx	s	x	xs	x				sx			x						xs					x		s		xs	sx
51	x	x	x	x	s	sx	x	x	xs				sx			xs						x					x		s		xs	sx
52	x	x	x	x	x	sx	x	x	sx		x		sx			s						xs					xs		xs		s	
53	x	x	x	x	x	s	x	xs	sx		x		s									sx					x	sx			xs	xs
54				sx	s	x		s	x		sx		sx	x	x	x			xs			xs						x	x		x	xs
55	x	x	x	x	x	s	x	x	xs		x			s								xs					x	s	sx		sx	
56	x	x	x	x	x	s	x	x	x		x			s								sx					xs	s	s		x	
57	x	x	x	x	xs	sx	x	x	x		xs			s								sx					x	s	sx		xs	
58	x	x	xs	x	x	s	x	x	x					s		xs			sx			xs						sx	sx		x	
x	54	51	54	45	24	5	46	48	32	3	21	1	3	4	3	20	6	4	7	0	1	14	1	3	0	0	9	5	9	1	6	1
xs	0	3	1	2	8	12	8	9	9	12	7	5	8	0	7	7	0	7	3	0	2	21	7	2	0	0	6	2	1	0	6	2
sx	0	0	0	4	11	7	0	0	7	3	2	14	23	0	18	7	0	3	9	3	4	6	2	2	1	0	1	6	6	0	9	7
s	1	0	1	3	9	8	1	1	6	2	7	0	14	14	9	11	3	2	15	5	4	0	0	1	0	1	0	7	8	2	1	1

x - Played full 90 minutes
xs - Substituted off
sx - Substituted on
s - Non-playing Substitute

ALDERSHOT TOWN MATCH RESULTS 2018-19

Date	Comp	Opponents	H/A	Att:	Result		Goalscorers	Pos
Aug 4	NL	Barnet	H	2409	D	0 - 0		
7	NL	Chesterfield	A	4930	L	0 - 3		
11	NL	Soihull Moors	A	867	L	0 - 1		
14	NL	Dagenham & Redbridge	H	1917	**W**	2 - 1	Rendell 3 Fenelon 54	
18	NL	Harrogate Town	A	1774	L	0 - 2		
25	NL	Ebbsfleet United	A	1233	L	1 - 3	McClure 7	22
27	NL	Sutton United	H	1904	**W**	2 - 1	Rendall 45 Berkeley-Agyepong 65	20
Sept 1	NL	Wrexham	A	4648	L	0 - 2		20
5	NL	Havant & Waterlooville	A	1989	L	1 - 2	Rendell 90	21
8	NL	Bromley	H	1768	**W**	3 - 2	Rendell 17 Holman 65 Rowe 87	18
15	NL	AFC Fylde	A	1470	L	0 - 3		19
22	NL	Dover Athletic	H	1619	**W**	2 - 0	May 18 67	17
25	NL	Maidstone United	H	1619	L	0 - 1		19
29	NL	Hartlepool United	A	3251	D	1 - 1	McClure 63	19
Oct 6	NL	FC Halifax Town	H	1625	**W**	3 - 0	May 8 McDonnell 20 Gallagher 47	18
13	NL	Eastleigh	A	2349	**W**	2 - 1	Johnson 36 (og) Rendell 39	16
20	**FAC 4Q**	**Kettering Town**	**H**	**1634**	**W**	**2 - 0**	**Rendell 16 McDonnell 82**	
27	NL	Gateshead	A	703	L	0 - 3		16
30	NL	Boreham Wood	H	1419	D	1 - 1	McDonnell 45+2	15
Nov 3	NL	Braintree Town	H	1618	**W**	1 - 0	McDonnell 83	13
10	**FAC 1P**	**Bradford City**	**H**	**2455**	**D**	**1 - 1**	**Fowler 12**	
17	NL	Salford City	A	2875	L	0 - 4		15
20	**FAC 1Pr**	**Bradford City**	**A**	**2248**	**D**	**1 - 1**	**Howell 108 (Lost 1-4 on pens)**	
24	NL	Barrow	H	1549	L	0 - 2		16
27	NL	Leyton Orient	A	4289	D	0 - 0		16
Dec 1	NL	Ebbsfleet United	H	1663	L	0 - 2		17
8	NL	Harrogate Town	A	1362	L	1 - 4	McDonnell 14	17
15	**FAT 1P**	**Bedford Town**	**H**	**784**	**D**	**3 - 3**	**Fenelon 22 McDonagh 44 Wanadio 85**	
18	**FAT 1Pr**	**Bedford Town**	**A**	**485**	**L**	**0 - 7**		
22	NL	Wrexham	H	1866	D	0 - 0		18
26	NL	Maidenhead United	A	1853	L	3 - 4	Grant 24 66 McDonnell 89 (Pen)	19
29	NL	Sutton United	A	2216	L	1 - 2	Grant 23	19
Jan 1	NL	Maidstone United	H	2090	D	0 - 0		19
19	NL	Chesterfield	H	2120	L	0 - 2		22
26	NL	Dagenham & Redbridge	A	1652	D	1 - 1	Mensah 64	22
Feb 9	NL	Eastleigh	H	2096	L	1 - 3	Mensah 57	22
12	NL	Solihull Borough	H	1199	L	0 - 3		22
16	NL	FC Halifax Town	A	1650	D	0 - 0		22
23	NL	Braintree Town	A	829	**W**	1 - 0	Grant 64	22
Mar 2	NL	Gateshead	H	1885	L	0 - 2		22
9	NL	Barrow	A	1156	L	1 - 2	McDonnell 58	22
12	NL	Leyton Orient	H	1989	L	1 - 2	Rendell 72 (pen)	22
16	NL	Salford City	H	1668	L	0 - 1		22
23	NL	Boreham Wood	A	809	**W**	2 - 0	Goddard 60 Rendell 80 (pen)	22
26	NL	Barnet	A	1064	L	0 - 2		22
30	NL	AFC Fylde	H	1280	D	0 - 0		22
Apr 6	NL	Bromley	A	1521	D	2 - 2	Grant 25 Howell 51	22
13	NL	Hartlepool United	H	1589	D	1 - 1	Grant 10	22 (R)
19	NL	Dover Athletic	A	1348	L	0 - 1		22
22	NL	Havant & Waterlooville	H	1446	**W**	2 - 0	Mensah 14 McClure 25	21
27	NL	Maidstone United	A	1929	**W**	2 - 0	McClure 56 Mensah 86	21

GOALSCORERS	SG	CSG	Pens	Hat tricks	Total
Rendell	8	2	2		8
McDonnell	7	2	1		7
Grant	5	2			6
McClure	4	2			4
Mensah*	4	2			4
May	2	1			3
Fenelon	2	1			2
Howell	2	1			2
Berkeley-Agyepong	1	1			1
Fowler	1	1			1
Gallagher	1	1			1
Goddard	1	1			1
Holman	1	1			1
McDonagh	1	1			1
Opponent	1	1			1
Rowe	1	1			1
Wanadio	1	1			1

Cole	Kinsella	McDonnell	Fowler	Fenelon	Bernard (L)	Rowe	Booty	Holman	Berkeley-Agyepong	Smith C (L)	Osborne	Rendell	Wanadio	McClure	Gallagher	Mannion (L)	Lelan	Howell	Oualah	Legg (L)	May (L)	McCoy	Osho (L)	Barrett (L)	Grant	McDonagh (L)	Bozier	Hall	Woodward	Rabbetts	Smith M	Hedley	Howorth	Hounto	Wylie	Tuson-Firth	Quintyne	Black	Finney	Goddard	Mensah (L)	Menayese (L)	Elokobi	Arnold N	No.
x	x	x	x	xs	x	x	x	xs	x	xs	sx	sx	sx	s	s																														1
x	x	x	x	xs	x	sx	x	sx	s	s	xs	x	sx	x	xs																														2
s	x	s	x		xs	x	x	xs	x	sx	xs	sx	x	sx		x	x																												3
s	x	sx	xs	xs	x	sx	x	x	sx			x	xs	s		x	x	x																											4
x	x		x	x	x	s	xs	xs	x	s		x	sx	sx	s		x	x																											5
x	xs	x			x	sx		xs	sx	x		sx	x	xs	x		x	x	s																										6
x	x	x	x	sx	x	s	xs	s	x			x	xs		sx		x	x	s																										7
x	x	x	x	sx	x	sx	xs	sx	xs	s		x	xs		s		x	x																											8
x	x	x	x	xs	xs	x	s	sx	x	s		x	sx		x		x	s																											9
s	x	xs	x			x	sx	sx	x	sx		x	xs		x		x	xs		x																									10
s	x	x	x		sx	x	s	x	xs	x			sx	sx	x		xs	xs		x																									11
x	x	x	x		x		xs	sx	x		x		x	xs	sx			sx			xs																								12
x	x	x	x		x		x	sx	x		xs		x	xs	s		sx	s		s	x																								13
x	x	x	x		s		x		xs			sx	xs	x	sx		x	sx		s	xs	x																							14
x	x	x	x	sx			x	sx				xs		xs	xs	s	s	sx			x	x	x																						15
x	x	xs	x	sx			xs	s				x		x	xs	s	sx	sx			x	x	x																						16
s	**x**	**x**	**x**	**xs**	**s**		**x**	**s**				**x**	**sx**	**xs**	**sx**	**x**	**s**	**x**				**x**	**x**																						17
s	x	x	x	sx			xs					x	sx	x	xs	x	s	s			x	x	x																						18
s	x	x	x	xs	x		s					x	sx	xs	x	x	x	sx			x	s																							19
s	x	xs	x	xs	s		sx					x	xs		x	x	sx	sx			x	x	x																						20
s	**x**	**x**	**x**	**s**	**s**		**xs**		**sx**			**x**	**sx**	**xs**	**x**	**x**	**s**	**sx**				**x**	**x**	**xs**																					21
	x	x	x	sx			sx		xs			xs	s		x	x	sx	s			x	x	x	xs																					22
s	**x**	**x**	**x**	**xs**	**xs**		**x**		**xs**				**s**	**sx**	**xs**	**x**	**x**	**sx**				**sx**	**x**	**sx**																					23
s	x			xs			xs		x				s	x	xs	x	x	sx			sx	x	x	x	sx																				24
s	x	x		sx	x				sx				s	xs	x	x		x			xs	x	x	sx	xs																				25
	x	x		sx	x								sx		xs	x	s	x			x	x	x	xs	x																				26
	x	xs			x		x				sx		x	sx	x	x	x					xs		sx	xs	x																			27
	x	**x**		**xs**	**x**		**x**				**xs**		**x**	**x**	**x**	**x**	**x**								**sx**		**sx**																		28
																												x	**x**	**x**	**xs**	**x**	**x**	**x**	**x**	**xs**	**xs**	**x**							29
s	x	x			s		x				xs		x	xs	x	x	sx					x			sx	x	s												x						30
s	x	x			s		x				s		x	x	x	x	x					x			x		s												x						31
x	x	x			x		sx						x	x	x	s	s					x			xs	x	s												x						32
	xs	x			x		sx				s		x	x	x	x	sx					xs			x	x	s												x						33
		xs			x		x						x	sx	x	x	sx	xs				xs			sx	x	s												x	x					34
	x	x			x		x						sx	sx	s	x	x	x				s				x	s												x	xs	xs				35
s	xs	x			x		x					sx	sx		sx	x	s	xs								xs													x	x	x	x			36
s		x			x		x					xs			sx	x	s	xs							sx	sx													x	xs	x	x	x		37
x		sx			x		x					x			xs		xs	x							sx	sx													s	x	xs	x	x		38
x		sx			x		x		sx			x			x	s	xs	x				s			xs														sx	xs		x	x		39
x				sx	x		x		sx						xs		xs	x				s			xs	sx													s	x	x	x	x		40
x		xs		sx	x		x		xs						sx		s	x								sx		s											x	xs	x	x	x		41
x		x			x		xs		xs			x		sx	s	s		x							sx														s	x	x	x	x		42
x		x			xs		x		x			x		s	sx	s		x							sx														s	xs	x	x	x		43
s					x		x		xs			xs		sx	x	x		x				s			sx														sx	x	xs	x	x		44
		x			xs		x		xs			x		sx	sx	x		x				s			sx														s	x	x	x	x		45
		sx			s		x		sx			x		xs	xs	x		x				x				s													s	x	x	x	x		46
		x			x	sx			sx			xs		s	xs	x		xs				s			x	sx													x	x	x	x			47
s		xs			x	sx	x		sx			x			s	x		x							xs	sx													x	xs	x	x			48
x	sx	x			xs	x			x						x										x	s		s											xs	x	xs	x	sx	sx	49
x	x	s			xs		x					x		x				x							s			s											x	sx	xs	x	x	sx	50
x	xs	sx			x	sx	xs					x		x	xs			x							s			s												sx	x	x	x		51
22	32	32	21	1	29	6	27	2	11	2	1	22	11	11	19	26	16	21	0	2	8	15	11	1	5	6	0	1	1	1	0	1	1	1	1	0	0	1	12	10	11	16	12	0	x
0	4	7	1	10	7	0	10	4	9	1	5	5	6	10	12	0	4	6	0	0	3	3	0	3	6	1	0	0	0	0	1	0	0	0	0	1	1	0	1	6	5	0	0	0	xs
0	1	5	0	10	1	7	5	7	9	2	2	5	12	10	9	0	7	9	0	0	1	1	0	3	10	6	1	0	0	0	0	0	0	0	0	0	0	0	2	2	0	0	1	2	sx
18	0	2	0	1	7	2	3	3	1	4	2	0	4	4	7	6	9	4	2	2	0	7	0	0	2	2	6	4	0	0	0	0	0	0	0	0	0	0	6	0	0	0	0	0	s

Also Played: Lluka - 18/12 (sx); Montague - 18/12 (sx); Arsenio - 18/12 (s); Taylor - 18/12 (s).

x - Played full 90 minutes
xs - Substituted off
sx - Substituted on
s - Non-playing Substitute

BARNET MATCH RESULTS 2018-19

Date	Comp	Opponents	H/A	Att:	Result	Goalscorers	Pos
Aug 4	NL	Aldershot Town	A	2409	D 0 - 0		
7	NL	Braintree Town	H	1507	D 1 - 1	Coulthirst 62	
11	NL	Eastleigh	H	1028	L 1 - 2	Adams 90	
14	NL	Harrogate Town	A	1381	L 0 - 2		
18	NL	Ebbsfleet United	H	1217	L 0 - 3		
25	NL	Chesterfield	A	4685	**W** 1 - 0	Taylor 90	
27	NL	Dagenham & Redbridge	H	1522	**W** 2 - 1	Fonguck 41 Barham 63	
Sept 1	NL	Dover Athletic	A	1037	**W** 2 - 1	Barham 4 Harrison 26	
4	NL	Bromley	A	1568	**W** 1 - 0	Sweeney 21	13
8	NL	Maidenhead United	H	1569	**W** 1 - 0	Walker 3	9
15	NL	Leyton Orient	A	5607	L 1 - 3	Fonguck 24	11
22	NL	AFC Fylde	H	1101	D 1 - 1	Coulthirst 20	12
25	NL	Havant & Waterlooville	H	965	D 2 - 2	Coulthirst 13 (Pen) 81	12
29	NL	Wrexham	A	4727	L 0 - 1		13
Oct 6	NL	Solihull Moors	H	1054	**W** 2 - 0	Fonguck 59 90+9	11
20	**FAC 4Q**	**Braintree Town**	**H**	**1057**	**W 4 - 2**	**Tutonda 6 Taylor J 16 Johnson 79 Alexander 84**	
27	NL	Barrow	A	1135	**W** 2 - 0	Duku 16 Fonguck 36	12
30	NL	Salford City	H	1243	L 1 - 3	Fonguck 43	12
Nov 3	NL	Maidstone Town	H	1424	L 0 - 2		12
11	**FAC 1P**	**Bristol Rovers**	**H**	**1705**	**D 1 - 1**	**Robson 16**	
18	NL	Hartlepool United	A	3545	**W** 3 - 1	Duku 24 25 Walker 90+4	11
21	**FAC1Pr**	**Bristol Rovers**	**A**	**2740**	**W 2 - 1**	**Robson 75 Harrison 77**	
24	NL	Gateshead	H	940	L 1 - 2	Taylor J 57	11
Dec 2	**FAC 2P**	**Stockport County**	**H**	**2826**	**W 1 - 0**	**Sparkes 8**	
8	NL	Ebbsfleet United	A	1320	L 0 - 1		15
15	**FAT 1P**	**Bath City**	**H**	**413**	**W 3 - 2**	**Fonguck 1 Duku 10 Mason-Clark 24**	
22	NL	Dover Athletic	H	1011	**W** 2 - 0	Taylor J 56 da Silva Vilhete 90+1	14
26	NL	Boreham Wood	A	1894	L 0 - 1		15
John Still retires from football management after 42 years - Darren Currie takes temporary charge.							
29	NL	Dagenham & Redbridge	A	1775	**W** 1 - 0	Coulthirst 34	13
Jan 1	NL	Boreham Wood	H	2087	D 1 - 1	Mason-Clark 68	14
6	**FAC 3P**	**Sheffield United**	**A**	**9906**	**W 1 - 0**	**Coulthirst 21 (Pen)**	
12	**FAT 2P**	**Dorchester Town**	**H**	**878**	**W 2 - 1**	**Coulthirst 50 Robson 81**	
19	NL	Braintree Town	A	700	L 0 - 4		16
Darren Currie is given the managers job on a permanent basis.							
28	**FAC 4P**	**Brentford**	**H**	**6215**	**D 3 - 3**	**Coulthirst 50 53 Sparkes 75**	
Feb 3	**FAT 3P**	**Carshalton Athletic**	**A**	**938**	**D 3 - 3**	**Coulthirst 7 20**	
5	**FAC 4Pr**	**Brentford**	**A**	**6954**	**L 1 - 3**	**Tutonda 74**	
9	NL	Sutton United	H	1316	L 0 - 1		17
12	**FAT 3Pr**	**Carshalton Athletic**	**H**	**606**	**W 2 - 1**	**Coulthirst 7 20**	
16	NL	Solihull Moors	A	1747	D 2 - 2	Fonguck 4 Coulthirst 59	19
19	NL	Sutton United	A	1917	D 0 - 0		17
23	**FAT 4P**	**AFC Fylde**	**A**	**795**	**D 0 - 0**	**(Lost 1-4 on penalties aet)**	
26	NL	Chesterfield	H	902	L 0 - 2		19
Mar 2	NL	Barrow	H	1022	**W** 3 - 1	Johnson 5 Coulthirst 62 Jones 74 (og)	17
5	NL	FC Halifax Town	A	1085	L 0 - 3		19
9	NL	Gateshead	A	655	L 1 - 2	Mason-Clark 23	19
12	NL	FC Halifax Town	H	702	D 1 - 1	Fonguck 24	19
16	NL	Hartlepool United	H	1269	D 0 - 0		20
19	NL	Harrogate Town	H	849	**W** 1 - 0	Tarpey 30	17
23	NL	Salford City	A	2452	D 0 - 0		17
26	NL	Aldershot Town	H	1064	**W** 2 - 0	Mason-Clark 46 Coulthirst 85	16
30	NL	Leyton Orient	H	3648	D 0 - 0		16
Apr 2	NL	Eastleigh	A	1579	**W** 3 - 0	Coulthirst 24 62 (pen) Mason-Clark 52	13
6	NL	Maidenhead United	A	1491	**W** 1 - 0	Elito 44	12
9	NL	Maidstone Town	A	1471	L 1 - 2	Elito 1	12
13	NL	Wrexham	H	1594	L 1 - 2	Coulthirst 70	13
19	NL	AFC Fylde	A	1489	L 0 - 1		15
22	NL	Bromley	H	1744	D 1 - 1	Coulthirst 71	14
27	NL	Havant & Waterlooville	A	1003	**W** 2 - 0	Alexander 48 Barham 70	12

GOALSCORERS	SG	CSG	Pens	Hat tricks	Total
Coulthirst	15	2	3		20
Fonguck	8	3			9
Mason-Clark	5	1			5
Duku	3	1			4
Taylor J	4	1			4
Barham	3	2			3
Robson	3	1			3
Alexander	2	1			2
Elito	2	2			2
Harrison	2	1			2
Johnson	2	1			2
Sparkes	2	1			2
Tutonda	2	1			2
Walker	2	1			2
Adams	1	1			1
da Silva Vilhete*	1	1			1
Opponent	1	1			1
Sweeney	1	1			1
Tarpey	1	1			1

No.	Cousins	Alexander	Johnson	Robson	Adams	Harrison	Sparkes	Fonguck	Elito	Walker	Sweeney	Coulthirst	Mason-Clark	Taylor Jack	Matrevics	Tutonda	Payne	Kyei	Barham	Azaze	Box	Jules (L)	Boucaud	Taylor	Duku (L)	Reynolds	Tarpey	Bettamer	Vilhete	Akinola	Huffer (L)	Smith	Charles	Ricardo	Hinckson-Mars	Vasiliou A
1	X	X	X	X	X	X	X	XS	XS	XS	X	SX	SX	SX	S	S																				
2	X	X	X	X	X	X	X	S	XS	XS	X	SX	SX	X	S		S																			
3	X	X	X	X	X	X	XS	S	XS	SX	X	X	SX	X	S	S																				
4	X	X	X	X		XS	SX	S		SX	X	X	X	X	S	S		XS																		
5	X	X		X	X	XS	X	X	XS	SX	X	SX	XS		S	X	S		SX																	
6	X	X	X	X	X	X	S	X			X	SX	XS	SX	S	X	S		XS																	
7	X	X	X	X	X	X	S	X			X	SX	SX	XS	S	X	S		XS																	
8	X	X	X	X	X	X	S	X		SX	X		S	X	S	X	S		XS																	
9	X	X	X	X	X	X	S	XS		SX	X		S	X		X	SX		XS	S																
10	X	X	X	X	X	X	S	XS		XS	X		SX	X			XS	SX		S	SX															
11	X	X	X	X	X		S	XS		XS	X		SX	X	S	XS	SX	SX	X																	
12	X	X		X	X			X	S	SX	X	X	SX	XS	S	X	S		XS			X														
13	X	X		X	X			X		X	XS	X	S		S	X	SX		S			X	SX	XS												
14	X	X		X	X		X	X	S				XS	X	S	X	S	SX	X			X														
15	X	X		X	X		S	X	S	XS	X		SX	X	S	X			SX			X			XS											
16	X	X	SX	X	X		S	X	S	X	X		SX	XS	S	XS			SX			X			XS		S									
17	X	X	X	X	X			X		XS	X		S	X	S	XS			SX						XS	SX	SX									
18	X	X	X	X	X			X		XS	XS		S	X	S	X			SX						XS	SX	SX									
19	X	X	X	X	X			X		XS	S	SX	SX	X	S	XS			SX							X	XS									
20	X	X	X	X	X	SX	SX	XS		SX	X	S		X	S	S									XS	X	S	XS								
21	X	X	X	X	X	SX	S	X	S	SX	X			X	S										XS	X		XS								
22	X	X	X	X	X	SX	SX	XS	S	SX	X	S	S	X	S										XS	X		XS								
23	X	X	X	X	XS	X	SX	XS	S	XS	X			X	S										SX	X		SX								
24	X	X	X	X	SX	XS	X	XS	SX	XS	X	S	S	X	S										SX	X		S								
25	X	XS	X	X	X	XS	S	X	SX		X	SX	SX	X	S											X		XS								
26	X		X	X	SX		XS	XS	SX		X	SX	X	X	S	X									XS	X		S								
27	X	X	X		X	SX		X	X		X	S	XS	X	S										XS	X		S	SX							
28	X	X	X	X	X	X		XS	SX		X	XS	S	X	S	S			SX							X										
29	X	X	X	X	X	SX		S	XS		X	XS	XS	X	S	SX										X				SX						
30	X	X	X	X	X	SX		S	X		X	X	XS	X	S	S										XS				SX						
31	X	X	X	X	X	SX		SX	XS	S	X	XS	XS	X	S	SX										X		S		S						
32	X	X	X	X	X	S		SX	XS		XS	X	XS	X	S	SX										X				SX						
33	X	X	X	X	X	SX	S		XS	SX	X	X	XS	X	SX	S										X										
34		X	X	X		S	SX	XS	XS		X	X	X	X	S	X	S						SX					S			X	S				
35	S	X	X	X		S	X	XS	X		X	X	XS	SX		X							XS					SX			X		SX			
36	X	X	XS	X		S	SX	XS	X		X	X	XS	X	S	X	S						SX					S		SX						
37	X	X		X		SX		SX	X		X	X	XS	XS		X	S						X							SX	S		X			
38	S	X		X		S	X	XS	X		X	X	XS			X							XS	SX				SX			X		SX			
39	S	SX		X		SX	X	XS	X		X	XS	SX			XS							S	X		X					X		X			
40	S	S	X	X			XS	X	X		X	X	XS				S		SX				SX	X		X					X					
41	X	S	X	X				X	XS		X	X	XS		S				SX				XS	X		X				SX			SX			
42	X	S	X	XS				X	XS		X	X	SX						SX	S			SX	X		X				X			XS			
43	X	X	X	X		S		X	XS		X	XS	SX		S				X				X	SX		X				S						
44	X	XS	X	X				XS	X		X	X	S		S	SX			XS					X		X	SX			SX						
45	X	X	X				X	S	X		X	X	XS		S	S							XS	X		X	SX						SX			
46	X	X	X				XS	X	SX		X		XS		S	S			S				X	X		X	X			SX						
47	X	X	X	S				X	S		X	XS	XS		S				SX				X	X		X	X			SX						
48	X	X	X	SX			SX	XS			X	X	X						S	S			XS	X		X	XS			SX						
49	X	X	X	SX			X	SX			X	XS	XS						S	S			X	X		X	XS			SX						
50	X	XS	X	SX			SX	XS	SX		X	X	X							S			X	X		X	XS			X						
51	X	XS	X	SX				X	SX		XS	X	X							S			XS	X		X	X			S				SX		
52	X	X	X	X			SX	XS	X		XS	X	XS		S									X		X	SX			S				SX		
53	X	X	X	X				S	X			XS	XS		S	SX			SX					X		X	XS			SX						
54	X	X		X				XS	XS		X	X	XS		S	X			SX					X		X				SX			S		SX	
55	X	S	X	X				SX	XS		XS	X	XS	SX	S								X	X		X	SX							X		
56	X	X	X	SX				S	XS		X	XS	X	X	S								XS	X		X	SX			SX						
57	X	X	XS	S			XS	XS				X	X	X	S						SX		X			X				SX				X		SX
58	X	X	X	X								XS	SX	X	S	X			XS		S		XS	X		X				SX						SX
x	53	48	46	47	29	10	10	22	12	2	47	24	8	31	0	18	0	0	3	0	0	5	8	18	0	34	3	0	0	2	5	0	2	2	0	0
xs	0	4	2	1	1	4	5	21	15	10	6	10	23	4	0	5	1	1	7	0	0	0	8	1	9	1	5	4	0	0	0	0	1	0	0	0
sx	0	1	1	5	2	10	9	5	7	10	0	8	15	4	1	5	3	3	13	0	2	0	5	2	2	2	7	3	1	16	0	0	4	2	1	2
s	4	4	0	2	0	6	11	8	8	1	1	4	9	0	45	9	11	0	4	7	1	0	1	0	0	0	2	6	0	4	1	1	1	0	0	0

x - Played full 90 minutes
xs - Substituted off
sx - Substituted on
s - Non-playing Substitute

BARROW MATCH RESULTS 2018-19

Date	Comp	Opponents	H/A	Att:	Result		Goalscorers	Pos
Aug 4	NL	Havant & Waterlooville	H	1389	**W**	3 - 0	Hindle 40 72 Smith T 58	
7	NL	FC Halifax Town	A	1654	L	0 - 2		
11	NL	Leyton Orient	A	4304	D	2 - 2	Hindle 4 Correia 85	
14	NL	Chesterfield	H	1701	**W**	3 - 2	Hindle 7 Smith T 69 72	
18	NL	Maidstone United	A	2003	L	0 - 1		
25	NL	Braintree Town	A	1232	**W**	1 - 0	Rooney 7	
27	NL	Salford City	A	3012	L	1 - 3	Taylor 20	
Sept 1	NL	Solihull Moors	H	1260	L	1 - 2	Smith T 90	
4	NL	Hartlepool United	A	3361	D	0 - 0		15
8	NL	Dagenham & Redbridge	H	1171	L	0 - 1		15
15	NL	Boreham Wood	A	564	D	1 - 1	Rooney 81	15
22	NL	Maidenhead United	H	1520	**W**	2 - 0	Rooney 25 Smith T 74	13
25	NL	Gateshead	H	1053	L	1 - 2	Smith T 25	15
29	NL	Dover Athletic	A	814	**W**	2 - 0	Hindle 69 83	14
Oct 6	NL	Sutton United	H	1203	**W**	2 - 1	Hindle 2 Burgess 42	12
13	NL	Bromley	A	2211	L	1 - 2	De Sousa 56	13
20	**FAC 4Q**	**Chorley**	**A**	**1734**	**L**	**2 - 3**	**Burgess 16 Smith T 45+2**	
27	NL	Barnet	H	1135	L	0 - 2		13
30	NL	Harrogate Town	A	1268	L	2 - 4	Rooney 32 Smith T 77	14
Nov 3	NL	Ebbsfleet United	A	1277	L	0 - 1		17
17	NL	Eastleigh	H	1102	L	0 - 3		17
24	NL	Aldershot Town	A	1549	**W**	2 - 0	Smith T 27 Hindle 84	15
27	NL	Wrexham	H	851	D	0 - 0		14
Dec 1	NL	Braintree Town	A	482	**W**	2 - 0	Agustien 10 Smith T 63	12
8	NL	Maidstone United	H	804	**W**	1 - 0	Smith T 62	12
15	**FAT 1P**	**FC Halifax Town**	**H**	**578**	**L**	**1 - 2**	**Brown 80 (og)**	
22	NL	Solihull Moors	A	958	**W**	1 - 0	Rooney 74	11
26	NL	AFC Fylde	H	1582	D	1 - 1	Hindle 75	12
29	NL	Salford City	H	2311	**W**	3 - 2	Blyth 15 (pen) 90+4 Agustien 82	11
Jan 1	NL	AFC Fylde	A	2194	D	0 - 0		11
5	NL	Havant & Waterlooville	A	1074	L	0 - 2		11
19	NL	FC Halifax Town	H	1142	D	0 - 0		12
26	NL	Chesterfield	A	4626	D	0 - 0		11
Feb 9	NL	Bromley	H	1130	D	1 - 1	Angus 16	11
16	NL	Sutton United	A	1892	**W**	1 - 0	Kay 90	11
23	NL	EBBsfleet United	H	1058	D	0 - 0		12
Mar 2	NL	Barnet	A	1022	L	1 - 3	Jameson 80	12
5	NL	Leyton Orient	H	1130	L	2 - 3	Kay 71 Turner 75	13
9	NL	Aldershot Town	H	1156	**W**	2 - 1	Angus 32 Rooney 90+6 (pen)	11
12	NL	Wrexham	A	4613	**W**	3 - 1	Jones 3 Blyth 24 Hardcastle 45+3	11
16	NL	Eastleigh	A	1738	**W**	1 - 0	Hindle 29	11
23	NL	Harrogate Town	H	1934	D	2 - 2	Hardcastle 19 Rooney 22 (pen)	11
30	NL	Boreham Wood	H	1415	L	1 - 2	Hindle 37	11
Apr 6	NL	Dagenham & Redbridge	A	2173	D	0 - 0		11
13	NL	Dover Athletic	H	1351	L	2 - 3	Rooney 44 Hardcastle 67	11
19	NL	Maidenhead United	A	1820	D	1 - 1	Hindle 19	11
22	NL	Hartlepool United	H	3007	**W**	1 - 0	Kay 28	11
27	NL	Gateshead	A	798	**W**	2 - 0	Rooney 8 22	10

GOALSCORERS	SG	CSG	Pens	Hat tricks	Total
Hindle	10	2			12
Smith T	10	3			11
Rooney	9	2	2		10
Blyth	2	1	1		3
Hardcastle	3	1			3
Kay	3	1			3
Agustien	2	1			2
Angus	2	1			2
Burgess	2	1			2
Correia	1	1			1
Jameson	1	1			1
Jones	1	1			1
Opponent	1	1			1
Sousa	1	1			1
Taylor	1	1			1
Turner	1	1			1

Firth	Jones D (3)	Taylor	Granite	Hindle	Rooney	Kay	Brown	Wilson	Turner	Smith T (L)	Waterson	Burgess (L)	Correia	Elsdon	Barthram	Jameson (L)	Pollard	Jennings	Molyneux	Carroll-Burgess (L)	Blyth	Dixon	Norrington-Davies (L)	Holden (L)	Mulholland	Sousa	Sloan	Agustien	Dyson	McFarlane (L)	Hird	Angus (L)	Wade (L)	Hardcastle	Stephens	Saltmer	Reid	Dawson	Philpot	No.
x	x	x	x	xs	x	xs	x	x	x	xs	sx	sx	sx	s	s																									1
x	x	x	x	x	x	x	x	xs	xs	x	s	s	sx	sx	sx																									2
x	x	x	x	x	x	xs	x		xs	xs	sx	sx	sx		s	x	s																							3
x	x	xs	x	x	x	x	xs			x	x	sx	s		sx	x		sx	s																					4
x	x	x	x	x	x	sx	x			x		xs	sx		s	xs	s		sx	xs																				5
x	x	x	x	x	x	xs	sx			x	xs	sx	sx		xs	s		s	x																					6
x	x	x	x	xs	x	xs	x			x	x	sx	s		sx	s		s	x																					7
x	x	x	x	x	x	s	x			x	x	x	s		s	s		s	x																					8
x	x	x	x	x	x	x	x			xs		x	s		s	s		s	x		sx																			9
x	x	x	x	xs	x	x	x			x		x			s	s		s	x		sx	s																		10
x	x	x	x	sx	x	x	x			xs		xs			s	sx		s			sx		x	xs																11
x	xs	x		sx	x	xs	x			x		x			sx	x		s	s		sx		x	xs																12
x	x	x		sx	x	xs	xs			x		x			sx	x		s	s		sx		x	xs																13
x	x	x	x	sx	x	xs	x			xs		x			sx	s		s			sx		x	xs																14
x	x	x	x	x	xs					xs		xs						sx	x		sx		x	x	sx															15
x	x	x	xs	x	x	sx	x	sx		x		xs			sx	s			xs			s				x														16
x	x	x		x	xs	sx	x	x		x		x			s	s		s	s			s	x		sx	xs														17
x	x	x		sx	x	xs	xs	x		x		x			sx	s			sx			s	x			xs														18
x	x	x		sx	x	xs	x	s		x		sx			s	x			xs				x		xs	sx														19
s		x		x	x	xs	x	x				x			s	x			s			x	x		sx	x	s													20
	xs		x	sx	sx	sx	x	x	xs	x		xs							s		s	x	x			x		x												21
	x	x	x	sx	xs	sx	s	x		xs		s			x			sx			x	x	x					xs												22
		x	x	sx	x	sx	sx	xs		xs		s			x	x					x	x	x			s		xs												23
	x	x	x	sx	xs	s	s			xs		sx			x	x		sx			x	x	x					xs												24
	x	xs		sx	xs		s	x	sx	xs		s			x	x		sx			x	x	x					x												25
x	x			sx	x	x	xs	x	xs			xs		x	sx	s			x		x						s	sx												26
	x	x	x	sx	x	s		xs	xs						x	sx		s			x	x	x					xs	sx											27
	x	x	x	sx	xs	sx	s		x						x	x		s			xs	x	x					xs	sx											28
	x	x	x	xs	xs	sx	s					s			x	x		s			x	x	x					x	sx											29
	x	x	x	xs	xs	sx	s					sx			x	x		sx	s		x	x	x					xs												30
	x	x	x	sx	xs	sx	s								x	x		sx		s	xs	x	x					xs		x										31
	x	x	xs	sx	xs	sx	s					x		x	x				s		x	x	x								sx	xs								32
	x	x	s	sx	sx	xs	sx		xs					x	x				x		xs	x									x	x	s							33
	x	x		xs	xs	sx	x							x	x			s			x	x					s				x	x		sx	s					34
	x	x		xs	x	x	x					sx		s	x	s			s			x					sx				x	x		xs						35
	x	x		x	x	xs	x					sx			x	x		s	s		sx	x					s					xs		x						36
	x			sx	x	xs	x		sx			s			x	x		x	s		x	x					s					xs		x						37
	x			sx	xs	x	x		sx			sx				x		x	x		xs	x					s					xs		x		s				38
	x	x		sx	x	x	xs		xs			s			x	sx		sx			s	x									xs	x		x						39
	x	x		sx	x	xs			s						sx	x		x	sx		x	x	x									xs		x		s				40
	x	x		xs	x	x								sx		x		x	s		xs	x	x											x		s	sx	s		41
	x	x		x	x	x								s		x		x	sx			x	x								s			x		s	s		x	42
	x	x		x	x	xs								s	sx	s		x	s			x	x								x			x			sx		xs	43
	x	x	x	xs	x	xs								s	sx				s			x	x				s				x			x			sx		x	44
	x	x	x	x	x									s	x	s			s			x	x				s				x			x			s		x	45
		x	x	xs	x	xs	sx							s	s	x			s			x	x								x	sx		x					x	46
		x	x	x	x	sx	x							s	s	s			s			x	x								x	xs		x					x	47
		x	xs	x	x	xs	sx							s	xs	sx			sx		s	x	x								x			x					x	48
20	41	42	26	17	34	11	22	8	2	14	3	10	0	4	17	20	0	6	9	0	12	28	29	1	0	3	0	3	0	1	9	4	0	13	0	0	0	0	6	x
0	2	2	3	10	12	18	5	3	7	10	1	6	0	0	2	1	0	0	2	1	5	0	0	4	1	2	0	7	0	0	1	6	0	1	0	0	0	0	1	xs
0	0	0	0	21	2	13	5	1	3	0	2	11	5	2	12	4	0	8	5	0	8	0	0	0	3	1	1	1	3	0	1	1	0	1	0	0	3	0	0	sx
1	0	0	1	0	0	3	8	1	1	0	1	7	4	9	12	14	2	15	17	1	3	4	0	0	0	1	8	0	0	0	1	0	1	0	1	4	2	1	0	s

x - Played full 90 minutes
xs - Substituted off
sx - Substituted on
s - Non-playing Substitute

BOREHAM WOOD MATCH RESULTS 2018-19

Date	Comp	Opponents	H/A	Att:	Result		Goalscorers	Pos
Aug 4	NL	Dagenham & Redbridge	H	833	**W**	1 - 0	Balanta 52	
7	NL	Havant & Waterlooville	A	1348	D	0 - 0		
11	NL	Wrexham	A	4356	L	0 - 3		
14	NL	Gateshead	H	608	D	1 - 1	Stephens 45	
18	NL	Leyton Orient	A	3767	L	0 - 1		
25	NL	FC Halifax Town	H	572	**W**	2 - 1	Umerah 78 90	
27	NL	Maidstone United	A	2035	**W**	2 - 1	Balanta 60 Umerah 85	
Sept 1	NL	Braintree Town	H	578	D	1 - 1	Fyfield 35	
4	NL	Chesterfield	H	737	**W**	1 - 0	Fyfield 8	10
8	**SCC2**	**Dunfermline Athletic**	**H**		**D**	**0 - 0**	**Lost 5-6 on pens**	
15	NL	Barrow	H	564	D	1 - 1	Murtagh 90	12
18	NL	Sutton United	A	1677	**W**	4 - 0	Balanta 3 Murtagh 6 Shaibu 23 Umerah 53	7
22	NL	Salford City	A	2006	L	1 - 3	Umerah 55	10
25	NL	Eastleigh	A	1306	L	0 - 1		11
29	NL	Harrogate Town	H	566	L	2 - 4	Ugwu 11 60	12
Oct 6	NL	Hartlepool United	A	2988	L	0 - 2		14
13	NL	Maidenhead United	H	684	**W**	3 - 1	Murtagh 45 Umerah 75 Shaibu 85	11
20	**FAC 4Q**	**Dagenham & Redbridge**	**H**	**408**	**D**	**2 - 2**	**Umerah 15 (pen) Shaibu 85**	
23	**FAC 4Qr**	**Dagenham & Redbridge**	**A**	**792**	**W**	**1 - 0**	**Fyfield 45**	
27	NL	Bromley	H	629	**W**	2 - 1	Shaibu 45 Ugwu 60	11
30	NL	Aldershot Town	A	1419	D	1 - 1	Stephens 90+1	11
Nov 3	NL	Solihull Borough	A	803	D	0 - 0		11
10	**FAC 1P**	**Southport**	**A**	**1460**	**L**	**0 - 2**		
17	NL	Ebbsfleet United	H	724	D	0 - 0		10
24	NL	AFC Fylde	A	1345	L	1 - 2	Ugwu 58	10
27	NL	Dover Athletic	H	407	L	0 - 1		11
Dec 8	NL	Leyton Orient	H	1602	**W**	1 - 0	Ilesanmi 4	11
15	**FAT 1P**	**Torquay United**	**H**	**207**	**W**	**3 - 1**	**Shaibu 65 98 113 (aet)**	
18	NL	FC Halifax Town	A	913	D	1 - 1	Shaibu 4	11
22	NL	Braintree Town	A	371	D	1 - 1	Shaibu 50	12
26	NL	Barnet	H	1894	**W**	1 - 0	Ash 88	11
29	NL	Maidstone United	H	630	L	0 - 1		12
Jan 1	NL	Barnet	A	2087	D	1 - 1	Ash 85 (Pen)	12
5	NL	Dagenham & Redbridge	A	1043	D	4 - 4	Kanu 14 Shakes 31 Shaibu 35 Ash 87	12
12	**FAT 2P**	**Blyth Spartans**	**A**	**712**	**L**	**0 - 1**		
19	NL	Havant & Waterlooville	H	511	L	1 - 3	Kanu 70	12
26	NL	Gateshead	A	562	D	1 - 1	Shields 43	14
Feb 9	NL	Maidenhead United	A	1113	L	0 - 1		15
16	NL	Hartlepool United	H	679	L	0 - 4		15
19	NL	Wrexham	H	645	L	0 - 2		16
Mar 2	NL	Bromley	A	1326	**W**	2 - 0	Gabriel 41 Kanu 90	16
9	NL	AFC Fylde	H	493	D	1 - 1	Fyfield 57	17
12	NL	Dover Athletic	A	743	D	1 - 1	Shaibu 4	16
16	NL	Ebbsfleet United	A	1110	L	2 - 3	Murtagh 9 Ash 85	17
23	NL	Aldershot Town	H	809	L	0 - 2		18
26	NL	Solihull Borough	H	478	D	2 - 2	Gabriel 26 Kanu 88	20
30	NL	Barrow	A	1415	**W**	2 - 1	Murtagh 19 Shaibu 34 (pen)	18
Apr 6	NL	Sutton United	H	508	L	1 - 2	Shakes 29	19
13	NL	Harrogate Town	A	1216	**W**	1 - 0	Champion 9	18 (s)
19	NL	Salford City	H	854	L	2 - 3	Gabriel 26 (pen) Murtagh 70	19
22	NL	Chesterfield	A	4384	L	2 - 3	Murtagh 28 Shaibu 59 (pen)	19
27	NL	Eastleigh	H	502	D	3 - 3	Gabriel 39 Ash 58 Murtagh 77	20

GOALSCORERS	SG	CSG	Pens	Hat tricks	Total
Shaibu	11	2	2	1	13
Murtagh	8	3			8
Umerah	6	2	1		7
Ash	5	2	1		5
Fyfield	4	2			4
Gabriel	4	1	1		4
Kanu*	4	1			4
Ugwu	3	1			4
Balanta	3	1			3
Shakes	2	1			2
Stephens	2	1			2
Champion	1	1			1
Ilesanmi	1	1			1
Shields	1	1			1

No.	Huddart	Woodards	Ilesanmi	Ricketts	Parry	Stephens	Shakes	Champion	Murtagh	Ash	Balanta	Thomas	Fyfield	Jeffers	Smith C	Clifford	Balcombe (L)	Shaibu (L)	Umerah (L)	Burbidge	Hackett-Fairchild (L)	Ugwu (L)	Gibbs	Ndiaye	Morgan	Creese	Kanu	Shields (L)	Courtnage	Legg (L)	Gabriel	Cooper (L)	Smith K
1	x	x	x	x	x	x	x	x	x	xs	x	sx	s	s	s	s																	
2		x	x	x	x	x	x	x	x	sx	x	s	s		s	s	x	xs															
3		xs	x	x	x	x	sx	x	x	sx	x	s	s		sx		x	xs	xs														
4		x	s	xs	sx	x	x	x	x	s	x	sx	x		s		x	xs	x														
5		xs	sx	x	sx	x	x	x	x	s	xs	sx	x		xs		x		x	s													
6		xs	x	x	s	x	x	x	x	s	x	sx	x		s		x		x	s													
7		xs	sx	x	s	x	x	x	x	sx	x	xs	x		s		x		x	s													
8	s		x	x	s	x	x	x	x	s	x	x	x		s		x	sx	xs														
9	x		x	x	sx	x	x	xs	x	s	x	xs	x		s			sx	x	s													
10																																	
11	x	sx	x	x	x	x	x	s	x		x		x		s		s		xs		xs												
12	x	xs	sx	x	sx	x	x	x	x		xs		x		s		s	x	sx		xs												
13	x	xs	x	x	s	x	x	x	x			sx	x				s	xs	x			sx											s
14	x	xs	sx	xs	x	x	x		x			sx	x		x		s	s	x			x	s										
15	x		x		x	x	x	x	x			sx	x		xs		s	sx	xs			x	s	s									
16	s		x		x		x	x	x			xs	x		x		x	sx	x			x	s	s	s								
17	x		x	x	x		x	x	x			sx	x		xs			sx	xs	s		x	s	s									
18	**x**		**x**	**x**	**x**		**x**	**x**	**x**		**x**	**s**	**x**					**sx**	**xs**	**s**		**x**	**s**	**s**									
19	**x**		**x**	**x**	**x**		**x**	**x**	**x**			**x**	**x**					**sx**	**xs**	**s**		**x**	**s**	**s**		**s**							
20	x	sx	xs	x	x	s	x	x				x	x		x			xs	sx	s	xs	sx											
21	x	xs		x	x	sx	x	x				x	x		xs			sx	x	s	s	x	s										
22	x	xs		x	x	x	x	x	xs			sx	x					sx	x	s	sx	xs	s										
23	**x**	**xs**	**s**	**x**	**x**	**x**	**x**		**xs**	**sx**		**x**	**x**		**sx**			**sx**	**x**	**s**		**xs**		**s**									
24	x	xs	x	x	s	x	x	x	x	sx		sx	x					xs	sx			xs											s
25	x	xs	x	x	x		x	x	x	s		sx	x		s			sx	xs	s		x											
26	x	xs	sx	x	s	x	x	x	x	sx		xs	x		s			x	sx			xs											
27	x		x	x	s	x	x	x	x	x		x	x		s			sx		s		xs		s									
28	**x**		**x**	**x**	**sx**	**x**	**x**	**x**	**xs**	**xs**		**x**	**x**		**s**			**sx**		**s**		**x**		**s**									
29	x		x	x	x	x	x	x	xs	s		sx	sx		xs			x		s		x		s									
30	x	s	x	x	s	x	x	x	x	sx		x	x		s			xs		s		x											
31	x	xs	x	x	s	x	x	x	x	sx		sx	x		s			xs		s		x											
32	x	s	x	x	xs	x	x	x	x	xs		sx	sx		xs			sx		s		x											
33	x	xs	x	x	s	x	x	x	x			sx	x		s			x		s		xs											
34	x	sx	x	x	s	x	x	x	xs	sx		sx	x					x		s							xs	xs					
35		**sx**	**x**	**x**	**s**		**x**	**x**	**xs**	**sx**		**x**	**x**					**x**		**x**							**xs**		**s**				
36		xs	xs	x	s	x	x	x		sx		sx	x					xs		s		sx					x	x		x			
37		s	x	x	x		x	x	x	s		sx	x					sx		s		x					xs	xs		x			
38	s	x	x	xs	x		x	x	x	sx		s	x					sx				xs					xs	sx		x			
39	x	s	x	x	x		sx	x	x	sx		x	x							s		s					x	xs			xs		
40	x	s	x	x	x		xs	x	x	sx		x	x					sx				s					x			s	xs		
41	x	s	x	x	s	x	sx	x	x	sx			x					xs									x	x		s	xs		
42	x	s	x	x	s	x	sx	x	x	x		sx	x					xs									x	xs		s			
43	x	s	x	x	s	x	sx	x	x	x			x					x									xs	sx		s		xs	
44	x	sx	x	x	s	x	x	x	xs	sx			x					xs									x			s	sx	xs	
45	s	xs	x		s	x	sx	x	x	xs			x					sx									xs	sx		x	x	x	
46	s	x	x	x	s	x	x	x	x	sx			x					x									sx			x	xs	s	
47	s	x	x		x	x	x	x	x	sx			x					xs									sx	s		x	xs	s	
48	s	s	x	x	s	x	x	x	x	sx			x					x									sx			x	xs	xs	
49	x	xs	x	xs	sx	x	x	x	x	sx			x					xs									sx			s	x	s	
50	x		x	x	sx	xs	x	x	x	sx			x					xs									sx			s	x	s	xs
51	s	x	x	s	x		sx	x	x	sx		sx	x					xs									xs	xs		x		xs	
52	x	x	x				x	x	x	sx		xs	x					xs							s		sx	s		s	x		x
x	34	8	40	41	22	36	43	47	41	3	10	11	46	0	3	0	8	9	11	1	0	14	0	0	0	0	6	2	0	8	4	1	1
xs	0	18	2	4	1	1	1	1	7	4	2	5	0	0	6	0	0	17	8	0	3	7	0	0	0	0	7	5	0	0	6	4	1
sx	0	5	5	0	7	1	7	0	0	23	0	20	2	0	2	0	0	18	4	0	1	3	0	0	0	0	6	3	0	0	1	0	0
s	8	9	2	1	20	1	0	1	0	8	0	4	3	1	16	2	5	1	0	23	1	2	8	9	2	1	0	2	1	8	0	4	2

x - Played full 90 minutes
xs - Substituted off
sx - Substituted on
s - Non-playing Substitute

BRAINTREE TOWN MATCH RESULTS 2018-19

Date	Comp	Opponents	H/A	Att:	Result		Goalscorers	Pos
Aug 4	NL	FC Halifax Town	H	621	L	0 - 2		
7	NL	Barnet	A	1507	D	1 - 1	Taylor 34 (og)	
11	NL	Chesterfield	A	4927	L	0 - 1		
14	NL	Hartlepool United	H	606	D	1 - 1	Bettamer 90+5	
18	NL	Havant & Waterlooville	H	407	L	3 - 4	Grant 31 72 Bettamer 38	
25	NL	Barrow	A	1232	L	0 - 1		
27	NL	Maidenhead United	H	576	L	0 - 2		
Sept 1	NL	Boreham Wood	A	578	D	1 - 1	Bettamer 48	23
4	NL	Dagenham & Redbridge	A	1081	L	0 - 1		24
8	NL	Wrexham	H	802	L	0 - 1		24
15	NL	Gateshead	A	578	**W**	1 - 0	Ellul 55	23
22	NL	Maidstone United	H	807	L	0 - 1		23
25	NL	Leyton Orient	H	2574	L	1 - 5	Della Verde 23	24
29	NL	AFC Fylde	A	1535	L	0 - 3		24
Oct 6	NL	Eastleigh	H	418	L	1 - 2	Bettamer 72	24
Manager Brad Quinton leaves by mutual agreement, former manager Hakan Hayrettin put in temporary charge.								
13	NL	Salford City	A	2710	D	2 - 2	Bettamer 45 74	24
20	**FAC 4Q**	**Barnet**	**A**	**1057**	**L**	**2 - 4**	**Grant 44 Della-Verde 66**	
27	NL	Dover Athletic	H	575	**W**	2 - 1	Amaluzor 13 Grant 78 (Pen)	23
30	NL	Bromley	A	1008	**W**	4 - 2	Gomis 6 Grant 29 84 Della Verde 48	23
Nov 3	NL	Aldershot Town	A	1618	L	0 - 1		23
Hakan Hayrettin made permanent manager.								
17	NL	Solihull Moors	H	822	L	0 - 3		23
24	NL	Harrogate Town	A	1454	L	1 - 3	Amaluzor 26	24
27	NL	Sutton United	H	439	D	2 - 2	Barrington 31 Crook 72	24
Dec 1	NL	Barrow	H	482	L	0 - 2		24
8	NL	Havant & Waterlooville	A	858	L	1 - 2	Woodford 76 (og)	24
22	NL	Boreham Wood	H	371	D	1 - 1	Della Verde 30	24
26	NL	Ebbsfleet United	A	1231	L	2 - 4	Ellul 5 Morton 48 (Pen)	24
29	NL	Maidenhead United	A	1218	**W**	1 - 0	James 68	24
Jan 1	NL	Ebbsfleet United	H	752	L	0 - 4		24
5	NL	FC Halifax Town	A	1302	D	0 - 0		24
8	**FAT 1P**	**Salisbury**	**A**	**502**	**L**	**1 - 2**	**Allen 29**	
19	NL	Barnet	H	700	**W**	4 - 0	Morton 6 (Pen) 33 59 (Pen) Allen I 84	24
Hakan Hayrettin leaves the club and joins Maidstone as John Still's assistant. Danny Searle takes over as manager.								
26	NL	Hartlepool United	A	2769	L	1 - 2	Amaluzor 39	24
Feb 9	NL	Salford City	H	765	**W**	1 - 0	Morton 90+3	24
16	NL	Eastleigh	A	2000	L	1 - 2	James 42	24
23	NL	Aldershot Town	H	829	L	0 - 1		24
Mar 2	NL	Dover Athletic	A	1053	L	0 - 3		24
5	NL	Chesterfield	H	482	L	1 - 3	Allen L 64 (pen)	24
9	NL	Harrogate Town	H	362	L	0 - 4		24
12	NL	Sutton United	A	1525	**W**	3 - 0	Henry 61 Kelly 77 Eyoma 89	24
16	NL	Solihull Moors	A	1003	L	1 - 2	Henry 22	24
23	NL	Bromley	H	673	L	2 - 4	Lyons-Foster 54 Sagaf 90+3	24
30	NL	Gateshead	H	291	**W**	2 - 0	Henry 44 (pen) Cerulli 88	23 (R)
Apr 6	NL	Wrexham	A	4221	L	1 - 3	Henry 40	24
13	NL	AFC Fylde	H	331	**W**	2 - 1	Sagaf 32 Richards 77	23
19	NL	Maidstone United	A	1908	**W**	2 - 0	Sagaf 2 (pen) Henry 85	23
22	NL	Dagenham & Redbridge	H	909	**W**	2 - 0	Cerulli 77 Sagaf 86	23
27	NL	Leyton Orient	A	8241	D	0 - 0	Deducted 3 points after the season ended.	23

GOALSCORERS	SG	CSG	Pens	Hat tricks	Total
Bettamer	5	2			6
Grant	4	2	1		6
Henry	5	2	1		5
Morton	3	1	3		5
Della Verde	4	1			4
Sagaf	4	3			4
Amaluzor	3	1			3
Allen L	2	1	1		2
Cerulli*	2	1			2
Ellul	2	1			2
James	2	1			2
Opponent	2	1			2
Allen I*	1	1			1
Barrington	1	1			1
Crook	1	1			1
Eyoma	1	1			1
Gomis	1	1			1
Kelly	1	1			1
Lyons-Foster	1	1			1
Richards	1	1			1

Killip	Muleba	Webber (L)	Durojaiye	Clark	Hill	Allen L	Bettamer	Pattisson	Della-Verde	Ochieng	Thompson	Rowe	Grant	Ellul	Bettache	Lyons-Foster	Frimpong	Crook	Gabriel	James (L)	Nieskens	Sagaf	Amaluzor	Cass	Barrington	Gomis (L)	Legg (L)	Richards	Okosieme	Morton (L)	Clayton-Phillips (L)	Borg (L)	Curran (L)	Eleftheriou (L)	Atkinson (L)	Allen I	Matsuzaka	Henry	Kelly	Gibson	Eyoma (L)	Eze	Temple	Cerulli	No.
x	x	x	x	x	x	xs	x	x	xs	xs	sx	sx	sx	s	s																														1
x	x	x	x	x	sx	xs		x	x		xs	sx	sx	xs	s	x	s																												2
x	x	x	x	x	x	sx	sx	x	xs	s	x	xs			s	x	s																												3
x	x	x	xs	x	xs	x	x	x	sx	s		xs			s	x	sx																												4
x	xs		x	x	x	x	x	sx	xs	sx		s	xs		x	x	sx																												5
x	x		x	x	x	x	x	sx	sx	s	xs		xs		s	x		xs																											6
x			xs	x	x		x	x	xs	x	sx		sx		s	x	s	sx	x																										7
x		x	s	s		x	x	sx	sx							x		xs	x	x	x	x	xs																						8
x		x		s		x	xs	s	sx			sx	sx			xs		xs	x	x	x	x	x																						9
x		s		s		xs	x				xs		sx	xs		x		sx	x	x	x	x	x																						10
x	x			sx		s	x	s	sx			sx	xs	xs				x	x	x	x	x	xs																						11
x	x			s		sx	x	s	sx			s	xs	x				x	x	x	x	xs	x																						12
x	x			x			x	s	x			xs	s	xs				xs	x	x	x	sx																							13
x	x	s		s		x	xs	x	sx		sx	xs	sx	x					x	xs	x	x																							14
x	x	s				x	x	s	sx		xs		sx	x		x	s		x	xs		x		x																					15
x	x					sx	x	xs	x		s		xs	x		x	xs		x	x		s	sx	sx																					16
x	**x**					**s**		**xs**	**x**	**s**	**xs**		**x**	**x**	**s**	**x**			**x**	**xs**	**x**	**sx**	**sx**		**sx**																				17
	x	s				sx		sx	xs				xs	x		x			x	x		x	x	sx	s	xs																			18
	x	s				s		sx	x	sx			x	x		x			x	xs		x	xs	sx		xs																			19
	x	s				s		sx	xs	s			x	x		x			x	x		x	xs	sx		x																			20
	x					x		xs	xs		sx			x		x		sx	x		s	x	xs	s		x	x																		21
	x					xs		sx		x				x		x		sx	x		s	s	xs	sx	x	xs	x	x																	22
	x					s								x		x		xs	x		x	s	xs	xs	x		x	x	sx																23
	x	sx						xs	s	s				xs				x	x			xs			x		x	x	x	x	sx														24
	sx								x					x		x		s	x			s	x		xs		x	x	x	x	s	xs													25
x									xs					x		x		sx	x	x		s	x		x			x	sx	x	s	xs	s												26
x						s			xs					x		x		sx	x	x		sx			x			xs	xs	x	sx	x	s												27
x	x					sx			xs					x		x			x	x		sx	xs		sx			x		x	s	xs	s												28
x	x					s			xs							xs			x	x		s	x		sx			x	x	x	sx	xs	sx												29
x						xs			sx			sx				x			x	x			x		xs			x		x		s		x	x										30
x						**x**				**x**						**x**			**x**			**x**	**x**		**sx**			**xs**		**x**		**x**	**x**												31
x						x			s			xs				x			x	x		sx	x					xs		x		s	s	x	x	sx									32
x						x			sx			xs				x			x	x		s	x		sx			xs		x				x	x	s	s								33
x						s										x			x	x		s	x					x		x		s		x	x	sx	s	xs	x						34
x						sx			sx							x			xs	x		s						xs		x		sx		x	x	xs	s	x	x						35
x						x			x			sx				x			x	x		s						s		x		s		x		sx	x	xs	xs						36
x						s										x			x	x		x						s		x		x		xs		s	sx	x	x						37
x						x			sx			sx				x				x		xs						s		xs		x		x	x	xs	x	sx							38
x						x						s				x				x		xs						sx				xs		x	x	x	s	x	xs	sx	sx				39
x						xs						s				xs				x		s						x				x		x	x	sx	sx	x	xs	sx	x				40
x						xs													sx	x		sx						x				xs		x	x	xs	x	x		s	x	sx			41
x						x										x				x		sx						xs				xs		x	x	x	sx	x			x	s	s	s	42
x																x				xs		x						x				sx		x		xs	x	x			x	s	s	sx	43
x																x						xs						x				sx		x	x	x	xs	x			x	s	s	s	44
x																x						x						x				x		x	x	sx	x	x		s	xs	s		s	45
x																x				xs		x						x						x	x	x	x	x		s		s	s	sx	46
x																x				xs		x						x						x	x	xs	x	xs		s		sx	sx	sx	47
x																x				x		x						x				sx		x	xs	xs	x	x		s		s	s	sx	48
40	21	6	5	8	5	15	12	6	7	3	1	0	3	15	1	38	0	3	30	26	9	17	12	1	5	2	5	17	3	14	0	6	1	17	14	4	8	11	3	0	5	0	0	0	x
0	1	0	2	0	1	7	2	4	11	1	5	6	6	5	0	3	1	5	1	7	0	5	8	1	2	3	0	6	1	1	0	7	0	1	1	6	1	3	3	0	1	0	0	0	xs
0	1	1	0	1	1	6	1	7	12	2	4	7	7	0	0	0	2	6	1	0	0	7	2	5	5	0	0	1	2	0	3	4	1	0	0	5	3	1	0	2	1	2	1	4	sx
0	0	6	1	5	0	9	0	5	2	6	1	4	1	1	7	0	4	1	0	0	2	11	0	1	1	0	0	3	0	0	3	4	4	0	0	2	4	0	0	5	0	6	5	3	s

Also Played: Rrapaj - 14/08 (sx) 18/08 (s) 25/08 (sx) 27/08 (xs). Blackmore - 01/09 (s) 20/10 (s) 05/01 (s) 02/03 (s) 16/03 (s). Charles - 08/09 (sx) 25/09 (sx). Jones - 27/10 (x) 30/10 (x) 3/11 (x). Wabo (L) - 17/11 (sx) 24/11 (sx) 27/01 (sx) 01/12 (sx) 08/12 (sx). Bailey - 08/01 (s). Iyayi - 08/01(s). Lamb - 08/01(s). Wray - 08/01(s). Osborne - 02/03 (x) 05/03 (s). Karic (L) - 06/04 (x) 13/04 (x) 19/04 (xs) 22/04 (x) 27/04 (x). Smith K - 06/04 (sx) 13/04 (s) 19/04 (sx) 22/04 (s).

x - Played full 90 minutes
xs - Substituted off
sx - Substituted on
s - Non-playing Substitute

BROMLEY MATCH RESULTS 2018-19

Date	Comp	Opponents	H/A	Att:	Result		Goalscorers	Pos
Aug 4	NL	AFC Fylde	A	1227	L	1 - 2	Higgs 63	
7	NL	Dover Athletic	H	1303	D	2 - 2	Johnson D 3 Sutherland 89 (Pen)	
11	NL	Harrogate Town	H	1061	D	1 - 1	Porter 12	
14	NL	Eastleigh	A	1478	L	0 - 1		
18	NL	Gateshead	H	1078	**W**	1 - 0	Ogedi-Uzokwe 88	
25	NL	Wrexham	A	5714	D	2 - 2	Sutherland 69 (Pen) Summerfield 90 (og)	
27	NL	Havant & Waterlooville	H	1413	**W**	4 - 0	Bugiel 9 33 Ogedi-Uzokwe 58 73	
Sept 1	NL	Maidenhead United	A	1201	D	2 - 2	Sutherland 90+1 (Pen) Porter 90+2	
4	NL	Barnet	H	1568	L	0 - 1		16
8	NL	Aldershot Town	A	1768	L	2 - 3	Ogedi-Uzokwe 30 Fowler 45+3 (og)	16
15	NL	Salford City	H	2020	L	0 - 2		18
22	NL	Solihull Borough	A	648	L	0 - 5		19
25	NL	Ebbsfleet United	A	1204	**W**	2 - 1	Ogedi-Uzokwe 15 Sutherland 31 (Pen)	17
29	NL	FC Halifax Town	H	1143	D	2 - 2	Sutherland 14 Porter 81	17
Oct 6	NL	Maidstone United	A	2294	**W**	1 - 0	Ogedi-Uzokwe 11	16
13	NL	Barrow	H	2211	**W**	2 - 1	Bugiel 8 Raymond 75	15
20	**FAC 4Q**	**Gloucester City**	**A**	**621**	**W**	**1 - 0**	**Raymond 50**	
27	NL	Boreham Wood	A	629	L	1 - 2	Bugiel 27	15
30	NL	Braintree Town	H	1008	L	2 - 4	Quigley 18 Bugiel 58	17
Nov 3	NL	Hartlepool United	H	1516	**W**	4 - 0	Sutherland 12 (Pen) 78 (Pen) Bugiel 63 Porter 85	14
10	**FAC 1P**	**Peterborough United**	**H**	**3107**	**L**	**1 - 3**	**Johnson R 40**	
17	NL	Leyton Orient	A	6058	L	1 - 3	Goddard 41	16
24	NL	Dagenham & Redbridge	H	1162	L	0 - 2		17
27	NL	Chesterfield	A	3729	D	1 - 1	Porter 35	18
Dec 8	NL	Gateshead	A	680	L	0 - 2		18
15	**FAT 1P**	**Sutton United**	**H**	**776**	**W**	**2 - 1**	**Hooper 60 Porter 62 (Match awarded to Sutton after Bromley played an ineligible player.**	
22	NL	Maidenhead United	H	1073	**W**	1 - 0	Holland 41	17
26	NL	Sutton United	A	2086	L	0 - 1		17
29	NL	Havant & Waterlooville	A	1341	**W**	3 - 0	Hooper 37 Holland 63 Coulson 86	17
Jan 1	NL	Sutton United	H	1428	**W**	2 - 1	Hooper 33 Goodman 89	16
5	NL	AFC Fylde	H	1102	**W**	3 - 2	Hooper 25 81 Sutherland 29 (Pen)	13
8	NL	Wrexham	H	1061	**W**	2 - 0	Okoye 21 Porter 44	11
19	NL	Dover Athletic	A	1216	D	1 - 1	Mekki 39	11
26	NL	Eastleigh	H	1381	L	0 - 1		12
Feb 9	NL	Barrow	A	1130	D	1 - 1	Hooper 54	12
16	NL	Maidstone United	H	2589	**W**	2 - 0	Hooper 31 90+5	12
23	NL	Hartlepool United	A	2985	**W**	2 - 1	Okoye 30 Coulson 45	11
Mar 2	NL	Boreham Wood	H	1326	L	0 - 2		11
5	NL	Harrogate Town	A	789	L	0 - 1		11
9	NL	Dagenham & Redbridge	A	1186	L	0 - 3		14
12	NL	Chesterfield	H	910	D	3 - 3	Johnson R 56 Hooper 60 87	12
23	NL	Braintree Town	A	673	**W**	4 - 2	Porter 16 Coulson 21 Raymond 45+1 Hooper 66	13
30	NL	Salford City	A	2314	L	1 - 2	Hooper 85 (pen)	15
Apr 2	NL	Leyton Orient	H	3047	**W**	2 - 1	Sutherland 49 (pen) Hackett-Fairchild 63	12
6	NL	Aldershot Town	H	1521	D	2 - 2	Hooper 4 63	13
13	NL	FC Halifax Town	A	1303	D	2 - 2	Coulson 51 Brindley 84	14
19	NL	Solihull Borough	H	1536	L	0 - 2		13
22	NL	Barnet	A	1744	D	1 - 1	Higgs 49	13
27	NL	Ebbsfleet United	H	1352	**W**	5 - 1	Porter 21 Sutherland 51 (pen) Brindley 56 Hooper 64 Coulson 90+1	11

GOALSCORERS	SG	CSG	Pens	Hat tricks	Total
Hooper	10	3	1		14
Sutherland	9	2	9		10
Porter	8	1			8
Bugiel	5	4			6
Ogedi-Uzokwe	5	1			6
Coulson	5	1			5
Raymond	3	2			3
Brindley	2	1			2
Higgs	2	1			2
Holland	2	1			2
Johnson R	2	1			2
Okoye	2	1			2
Opponent	2	1			2
Goddard	1	1			1
Goodman	1	1			1
Hackett-Fairchild	1	1			1
Johnson D	1	1			1
Mekki	1	1			1
Quigley	1	1			1

Gregory	Adebyo-Rowling	Johnson R	Sutherland	Johnson D	Holland	Raymond	Bugiel	Higgs	Okoye	Porter	Taylor	Meekums	Ogedi-Uzokwe	Huxter	Goodman	Enver	Goddard (L)	Wood	Mekki	De Silva	Luque (L)	Brindley	Rooney (L)	Quigley	Craske	Dunne	Najia	Okoh	Barham (L)	Coulson	Hines	Hooper (L)	Sarpong-Wiredu (L)	Lewis	Philpot	Nakov	Hackett-Fairchild (L)	Ojeman	Ogunmekan	No.
x	xs	x	x	x	x	x	xs	xs	x	x	sx	sx	sx	s	s																									1
x	x	x	x	x	x	x	x	xs	sx	xs	xs	sx	sx	s	s																									2
x	x	x	x	xs	x	x	x		sx	x	sx	xs	x	s	s	s																								3
x	x	x	x	s	x	x	x	x		x	sx	xs	xs	s	sx	s																								4
x	xs	x	x	sx		x	xs	x	x	x	s	sx	sx	s	x		xs																							5
x	xs	x	x	s		x	xs	s	x	x	sx	sx	sx		x		xs	x																						6
x	sx	xs		sx		x	x	x	xs	x	sx	s	x	s	x		xs	x																						7
x	s	x	sx	s		x	xs	xs	x	x	sx	sx	x		x		xs	x																						8
x	xs	x	xs	s		x		sx	x	x	sx	s	x		x		xs	x	sx																					9
x	sx	xs		s		x		x	x	x	sx	xs	x		x		xs	x	sx	s																				10
x	xs		sx	s	x	x	xs	x		xs	s		x		x		sx	x	x	sx																				11
x		x	x	sx	x	xs	xs	xs		x	s	s	x		x		sx	x			sx																			12
x		sx	x		x	x	xs	sx		x		sx	x	s	xs			x		s	xs	x																		13
			x	s	x		xs	x	x	x	sx	sx	x	x				xs		sx	xs		x																	14
x		sx	x		x	x		sx	xs	x	xs	s	x					x	xs		s	sx	x																	15
x			x		x	x	xs	sx	s	xs	sx		x		s		sx	x	xs			x	x																	16
x		**s**	**x**		**x**	**x**	**xs**	**sx**	**sx**	**x**	**sx**	**s**		**s**	**s**		**x**	**xs**	**xs**			**x**	**x**																	17
x			x		x	xs	x		sx	xs			x		s		xs	x	sx	s		x	x	sx																18
x			x		x	x	sx		sx	x			xs		s		xs	x	sx	s		x	xs	x																19
x		x	x		x	x	xs			x			sx		sx		s	x	xs	sx		x	s	xs																20
x		**x**	**x**		**x**	**x**	**xs**		**xs**	**x**					**s**		**sx**	**x**	**xs**			**x**	**s**	**sx**	**sx**	**s**	**s**													21
x		x			x				x	x			x		sx	s	x	x			sx	x	s	xs		xs		s												22
x		xs	x		x			sx	x	sx			x		s		xs	x	sx			x	s	xs					x											23
x		xs	x		x			xs	x	x			sx		xs		sx	x	s			x		s		sx			x											24
x		x	x		x	sx			xs	sx			s		s			x	sx			x							xs	xs	x	x								25
x		**sx**	**x**		**x**	**x**			**s**	**x**			**sx**		**x**		**s**	**x**	**xs**			**x**		**sx**						**xs**		**xs**								26
x		sx	x		x	x			sx	xs			s		x			x	xs			x							sx	xs	s	x								27
x		xs	x		x	x			x	x			xs		s		s	x	sx			x		sx						xs	sx									28
x		s	x		x	x	s		xs	xs			sx		sx			x	xs			x								x	sx	x								29
x		s	x		x	x	s		x	x			sx		sx			x	xs			xs								xs	sx	x								30
x		s	x		x	x	sx		xs	x			s		sx			x	xs			x								xs	sx	x								31
x		s	x		x	x	sx		x	x		s			s			x	xs			x								xs	sx	x								32
x		s	x		x	x	sx		x	xs					sx			x	xs	sx		x				s				xs		x								33
x		sx	x		x	x	sx	s		x					x			x	xs	s		xs				s				x		x								34
x			x		x	x	sx	s	x	xs					s			x				x								xs		x	xs	sx	sx					35
x			x		xs	x	xs	sx	x	x					sx			x				x								xs		x	s		sx	s				36
x		sx	x			x	xs	sx	x	xs					x			x				x				s				x		xs	s		sx					37
x		sx				x	xs	xs	x	x					xs			x				x				s				x		x	sx	sx	s					38
x		x				x	x	sx	x	xs		s						x				x				s				xs		x	x	sx	s					39
x		x	xs			x	x	sx	xs			s						x				x				sx				x		x	x	s	s					40
x		x	xs		xs	x	sx	sx				s						x				x				x				x		x	sx	s			xs			41
x		x	sx		x	x	sx	s		xs								x				x				s				x		xs	xs	sx			x			42
x		x	xs		x	x	sx	s	sx	xs								x				x				s				x		x	sx				xs			43
x		x	x		x	x	sx	s	sx	xs								x				x				s				x		x	s				xs			44
x			xs		x	x	sx	sx	x	xs								x				x			s	s				x		x	sx				xs			45
x		x	xs		x	sx	sx	x	sx	xs								x				x			s	s				x		x	xs							46
x		x	x		x	x		xs		x						s		x				x				sx				x			xs			s		sx	s	47
x		xs	x		x	x		x	sx	x						s		x				x				s				x		x				s			s	48
x		xs	x		x	xs		x	sx	x								x				x				s				x	sx	xs	sx			s				49
48	3	21	35	2	37	40	7	9	20	30	0	0	14	1	12	0	2	42	1	0	0	33	5	1	0	1	0	0	2	14	1	19	2	0	0	0	1	0	0	x
0	5	7	6	1	2	3	15	7	7	15	2	3	3	0	3	0	9	2	13	0	2	2	1	3	0	1	0	0	1	11	0	4	4	0	0	0	4	0	0	xs
0	2	7	3	3	0	2	12	12	11	2	11	7	9	0	8	0	5	0	7	4	2	1	0	4	1	3	0	0	1	0	6	0	5	4	3	0	0	1	0	sx
0	1	6	0	7	0	0	2	6	2	0	3	9	3	8	13	5	3	0	1	5	1	0	4	1	2	13	1	1	0	0	1	0	3	2	3	4	0	0	2	s

x - Played full 90 minutes
xs - Substituted off
sx - Substituted on
s - Non-playing Substitute

CHESTERFIELD MATCH RESULTS 2018-19

Date	Comp	Opponents	H/A	Att:	Result		Goalscorers	Pos
Aug 4	NL	Ebbsfleet United	A	2041	W	1 - 0	Hines 65 (Pen)	7
7	NL	Aldershot Town	H	4930	W	3 - 0	Carter 9 39 Fortune 81 (Pen)	1
11	NL	Braintree Town	H	4927	W	1 - 0	Weston 59	2
14	NL	Barrow	A	1701	L	2 - 3	Hines 14 Evans 50	5
18	NL	Salford City	A	3595	L	2 - 3	Hines 43 Fortune 59	8
25	NL	Barnet	H	4685	L	0 - 1		11
27	NL	Hartlepool United	A	3773	L	0 - 1		15
Sept 1	NL	Leyton Orient	H	4735	L	0 - 1		16
4	NL	Boreham Wood	A	737	L	0 - 1		17
8	NL	Dover Athletic	H	4303	D	0 - 0		17
15	NL	Dagenham & Redbridge	A	1273	D	1 - 1	Weston 13	16
22	NL	Gateshead	H	4210	L	0 - 3		18
25	NL	Maidenhead United	H	3681	L	1 - 3	Fortune 67 (Pen)	20
29	NL	Maidstone United	A	2438	D	1 - 1	Fortune 74	20
Oct 6	NL	AFC Fylde	H	4021	D	0 - 0		20
13	NL	FC Halifax Town	A	2191	D	1 - 1	Denton 79	19
20	**FAC 4Q**	**AFC Fylde**	**A**	**1092**	**W**	**3 - 1**	**Evans 17 Denton 28 (Pen) 70**	
27	NL	Wrexham	H	5662	D	1 - 1	Smith J 90	19
30	NL	Sutton United	A	1852	D	1 - 1	Smith J 89	19
Nov 3	NL	Harrogate Town	A	2291	D	1 - 1	Smith J 57	19
10	**FAC 1P**	**Billericay Town**	**H**	**2952**	**D**	**1 - 1**	**Maguire 17**	
17	NL	Havant & Waterlooville	H	4082	D	0 - 0		19
20	**FAC 1Pr**	**Billericay Town**	**A**	**2493**	**W**	**3 - 1**	**Denton 40 65 87**	
24	NL	Eastleigh	A	1774	D	1 - 1	Hallam 41	21
27	NL	Bromley	H	3729	D	1 - 1	Hines 90 (Pen)	21
Dec 2	**FAC 2P**	**Grimsby Town**	**H**	**4537**	**L**	**0 - 2**		
8	NL	Salford City	H	5085	W	2 - 0	Kiwomya 2 59	20
15	**FAT 1P**	**Basford United**	**H**	**1276**	**W**	**5 - 1**	**Kiwomya 12 Denton 34 61 Smith J 53 Shaw 58**	
22	NL	Leyton Orient	A	4755	L	1 - 3	Kiwomya 35	20
26	NL	Solihull Moors	H	4877	L	0 - 4		22
Martin Allen sacked as manager.								
29	NL	Hartlepool United	H	4752	D	1 - 1	Barry 75	21
Jan 1	NL	Solihull Moors	A	1375	D	2 - 2	Fortune 47 Shaw 68	21
5	NL	Ebbsfleet United	H	4123	D	3 - 3	Denton 64 Fortune 83 Evans 90+5	22
John Sheridan leaves Carlisle United to take up the vacant managers position.								
12	**FAT 2P**	**Bedford Town**	**H**	**2213**	**W**	**1 - 0**	**Denton 89**	
19	NL	Aldershot Town	A	2120	W	2 - 0	Evans 44 78	21
26	NL	Barrow	H	4626	D	0 - 0		21
Feb 2	**FAT 3P**	**Brackley Town**	**H**	**2054**	**L**	**0 - 2**		
9	NL	FC Halifax Town	H	4523	W	1 - 0	Boden 68 (pen)	20
16	NL	AFC Fylde	A	2175	W	1 - 0	Fortune 13	17
23	NL	Harrogate Town	H	4661	L	0 - 1		19
26	NL	Barnet	A	902	W	2 - 0	Carter 15 Kiwomya 81	17
Mar 2	NL	Wrexham	A	7106	L	0 - 1		19
5	NL	Braintree Town	A	482	W	3 - 1	Boden 14 83 Carter 21	16
9	NL	Eastleigh	H	4319	L	2 - 3	Hollis 32 Boden 47	18
12	NL	Bromley	A	910	D	3 - 3	Binnom-Williams 44 Boden 82 Rowley 90+1	18
16	NL	Havant & Waterlooville	A	1097	W	2 - 1	Evans 52 Boden 90 (pen)	16
23	NL	Sutton United	H	4311	W	3 - 0	Denton 28 55 Boden 48	15
30	NL	Dagenham & Redbridge	H	4377	W	2 - 0	Smith J 47 Boden 50	12
Apr 6	NL	Dover Athletic	A	1348	D	0 - 0		14
13	NL	Maidstone United	H	4592	W	4 - 1	Barry 18 Boden 68 De Havilland 84 (og) Maguire 90	12
19	NL	Gateshead	A	1208	L	0 - 1		12
22	NL	Boreham Wood	H	4384	W	3 - 2	Denton 43 85 Boden 49 (pen)	12
27	NL	Maidenhead United	A	1555	L	0 - 2		14

GOALSCORERS	SG	CSG	Pens	Hat tricks	Total
Denton	8	2	1	1	14
Boden*	9	6	3		10
Fortune	7	2	2		7
Evans	5	1			6
Kiwomya	4	1			5
Smith J	5	3			5
Carter	3	1			4
Hines	4	2	2		4
Barry	2	1			2
Maguire	2	1			2
Shaw	2	1			2
Weston	2	1			2
Binnom-Williams	1	1			1
Hallam	1	1			1
Hollis	1	1			1
Opponent	1	1			1
Rowley	1	1			1

Jalal	Evans	Smith G	Weir	Barry	Nelson	Talbot	Weston	Carter	Hines	Ugwu	Fortune	Maguire	Muggleton	Wedgbury	Shaw	Binnom-Williams	Anyon	Reid	Amantchi	Burton (L)	Rowley	Hollis (L)	Denton	Smith J (L)	Kayode (L)	Render	Ofoegbu	Kiwomya (L)	Wakefield	Holmes	Hallam (L)	Beestin (L)	Sharman	Rawson	Yarney (L)	Dodds	Chapman (L)	Boden	McKay (L)	No.
X	X	XS	XS	X	X	X	X	X	X	XS	SX	SX	SX	S	S																									1
X	X		X	S	X	X	X	X	XS	XS	SX	X	S	SX	SX	XS																								2
X	X	S	XS	SX	X	X	X	X	XS	XS	X		SX	SX	S	X																								3
X	X	SX	X		X	X	X	X	XS		XS	SX	S	XS	SX	X	S																							4
X	X		XS	SX	XS	X	X	XS	X		X	X	SX		SX		S	X	S																					5
S	X		XS	XS	X	X	X		X	SX	X	XS	SX					X		X	SX	S																		6
	XS		XS	S	X	X	X		X	X	SX	S	XS		SX			SX		X	X	X																		7
	X		X	S	X	X	X		X	XS	SX	XS	SX			X		SX		X	XS	S																		8
	S		XS	SX	X	X	X		X		XS	X			X	XS		SX	SX	X	S	X																		9
X	SX		S	X	X	X	X		SX	XS		XS			X	X		SX		S	XS	X																		10
X	X		X	SX		X	XS		XS		S	SX	SX		XS	X		X		S		X	X																	11
X			SX		X	XS	X	X	SX			S	S		XS	X		XS				X	X	X	SX															12
X			XS		X	X	X	X			XS	X	SX		SX	X					S	S	X	XS	SX															13
	X						X	XS			SX	X	X		XS	X		S		X	X	S	X	X	SX	S														14
	X						X				XS	X	X		X	XS		SX	SX	X	X	S	X	X	S		S													15
	X						X		SX		SX	X	X		XS	SX		XS		X	X	S	X	X	S			XS												16
	X				S		X		SX		S	X	X		XS	XS	S	SX	SX	X	X	X	XS					X	S											17
	XS						X		X		S	X	XS		SX	X		S	SX	X	X	X	XS	X				SX												18
	S						XS		SX		S	X	X		X	XS		SX	SX	X	X	X	XS	X				X												19
	X				S		X		XS		S	X	X		XS	SX		SX		X	X	X	SX	X				XS												20
	X				S		XS		X		XS	X	S		SX	X	S	XS	SX	X	X	X	SX	X				S												21
	X						XS				XS	X	SX		X	X	S	XS	SX	X	X	X	SX	X				S												22
					S		X		XS		S	X	X		XS	X	S	SX	SX	X	XS	X	X	X				SX		S										23
				X			X					X	SX		XS	X	S	S	SX	X	X	X	X	X				S			XS									24
				X	S		XS		X			X	XS		SX		S	SX	SX	X	X	X	XS	X							X									25
	X			X	S		X		SX		S		S		XS	X	S		SX	X	SX	X	XS	X				X			XS									26
	X		SX	X	S		X						S		X	X	S		XS	X		X	XS	X				X			SX									27
	X			X									S		XS	X			S	X	SX	X	XS	XS			SX	X			X	X	SX							28
	X				S		X						XS		X	X	S		X	X	SX	X	XS	X			SX	XS				SX								29
	X		SX		XS		XS						S		X	X	S	X	XS	X	X	X		X			SX					SX								30
	X		S	X			X								X	X	S	XS	XS	X	XS	X		X								SX	SX	SX						31
	X		SX	X			X				XS				X	X	S	S		X		X		X				SX				XS	XS	SX						32
	X		SX	XS			X				X				X	X	S	SX		X		X	SX	X								XS	XS	S						33
X	X		XS		S		X				X		S		X	X	S	X			XS	X	XS	X								XS								34
X	X		X	XS			X				XS				X	X	S	SX			SX	X	SX	X				XS				S								35
X	X		X	XS			X				XS				X	X	S	SX			SX	X	SX	X				XS				S								36
X	X						X								SX	XS	S	XS			X	X	SX	X				X	S			XS			X	SX				37
X	X		X				X				XS				X		S	S				X	SX	X											X		X	XS	SX	38
X	X		X	SX			X				XS				XS	S	S					X	SX	X											X		X	XS	SX	39
X			X				XS	SX			XS	X			XS	SX	S					X	SX	X											X		X	X	S	40
X	X		X				X	XS				S				SX	S	SX				X	XS	X				SX							X		X	XS		41
X	X		XS				X				XS	S			SX	X	S	SX				X	SX	X											X		XS	X		42
X	X		XS				XS	XS				SX			SX	SX	S	S				X	X	X											X		X	X		43
X	X		XS				X	XS			SX	S			SX	SX	S					X	X	X											X		X	XS		44
X	X						X				XS				XS	X	S	SX			X	X	SX	XS				SX							X			X	S	45
X	X		XS	X			X	SX			SX				S	SX		S			XS	X	XS												X		X	X		46
X	X		SX				SX	XS			SX	XS			S		S				X	X	XS	X											X		X	X		47
X	X		S				X	SX			S	X			SX			SX			XS	X	X	X											X		XS	XS		48
S	X		X	SX				XS			X	X			XS		X	X				X	SX					SX							X		S		XS	49
	X		SX	X			XS	SX				X			S		X				XS	X	X	SX											XS		X	X	S	50
X	X		X	X				XS			XS	XS			S			X				X	SX	X				SX									SX	X	S	51
X	X		SX	X			XS	SX							SX						X	X	X	XS				S							X		X	XS	S	52
X	X		X	X			S	XS							XS		S				SX	X	SX					X							X		X	SX	XS	53
27	42	0	13	14	11	12	38	6	9	1	6	20	7	0	15	26	2	7	1	24	17	42	13	33	0	0	0	7	0	0	2	1	0	0	15		11	8	0	x
0	2	1	12	4	2	1	10	9	6	5	15	5	4	1	15	6	0	6	3	0	8	0	12	4	0	0	0	5	0	0	2	4	2	0	1		2	6	2	xs
0	1	1	8	6	0	0	1	5	6	1	9	4	9	2	14	7	0	17	11	0	7	0	15	1	3	0	3	7	0	0	1	3	2	2	0		1	1	2	sx
2	2	1	3	3	9	0	1	0	0	0	8	5	9	1	6	1	29	7	2	2	2	6	0	0	2	1	1	4	2	1	0	2	0	1	0		1	0	5	s

x - Played full 90 minutes
xs - Substituted off
sx - Substituted on
s - Non-playing Substitute

DAGENHAM & REDBRIDGE MATCH RESULTS 2018-19

Date	Comp	Opponents	H/A	Att:	Result		Goalscorers	Pos
Aug 4	NL	Boreham Wood	A	833	L	0 - 1		
7	NL	Maidstone United	H	1405	L	1 - 2	Romain 80	
11	NL	Maidenhead United	H	1069	D	2 - 2	McQueen 67 Romain 87	
14	NL	Aldershot Town	A	1917	L	1 - 2	Kandi 73	
18	NL	FC Halifax Town	A	1364	L	1 - 2	Adeloye 33	
25	NL	Hartlepool United	H	1212	L	1 - 2	McQueen 36	
27	NL	Barnet	A	1522	L	1 - 2	Romain 1	24
Sept 1	NL	Salford City	H	1114	D	0 - 0		24
4	NL	Braintree Town	H	1081	**W**	1 - 0	Kandi 84 (Pen)	22
8	NL	Barrow	A	1171	**W**	1 - 0	Romain 90	21
15	NL	Chesterfield	H	1273	D	1 - 1	Kandi 79	20
22	NL	Eastleigh	A	1538	L	0 - 1		22
25	NL	Solihull Moors	A	753	L	0 - 2		22
29	NL	Ebbsfleet United	H	1225	L	1 - 3	Mullings 42	22
Oct 6	NL	Gateshead	A	687	L	0 - 2		22
13	NL	Wrexham	H	1601	L	1 - 2	Walker 45 (og)	22
20	**FAC 4Q**	**Boreham Wood**	**A**	**408**	**D**	**2 - 2**	**Adeloye 90 (pen) Pennell 90+3**	
23	**FAC 4Qr**	**Boreham Wood**	**H**	**792**	**L**	**0 - 1**		
27	NL	Harrogate Town	H	1446	**W**	2 - 1	McQueen 39 42	21
30	NL	Dover Athletic	A	924	**W**	2 - 0	Adeloye 11 Phipps 44	20
Nov 3	NL	Sutton United	A	1909	L	0 - 1		22
17	NL	AFC Fylde	H	1328	**W**	2 - 1	Wilkinson 28 Munns 64	21
24	NL	Bromley	A	1162	**W**	2 - 0	Wilkinson 17 Balanta 84	19
27	NL	Havant & Waterlooville	H	1054	**W**	3 - 1	Wilkinson 8 50 Balanta 75	17
Dec 1	NL	Hartlepool United	A	2030	**W**	2 - 1	Goodliffe 90 Robinson 90+2	15
8	NL	FC Halifax Town	H	1098	D	1 - 1	Munns 60	14
15	**FAT 1P**	**Ebbsfleet United**	**A**	**720**	**W**	**1 - 0**	**Balanta 29**	
22	NL	Salford City	A	2082	**W**	2 - 1	Wilkinson 39 Balanta 67	15
26	NL	Leyton Orient	H	3694	**W**	2 - 1	McQueen 77 Nunn 87	13
29	NL	Barnet	H	1775	L	0 - 1		14
Jan 1	NL	Leyton Orient	A	6001	L	0 - 1		15
5	NL	Boreham Wood	H	1043	D	4 - 4	Wilkinson 41 Gordon 43 74 Balanta 45	16
12	**FAT 2P**	**Salford City**	**A**	**1061**	**L**	**0 - 2**		
19	NL	Maidstone United	A	2188	**W**	3 - 0	Smith 22 Wilkinson 73 Reynolds 90+1	13
26	NL	Aldershot Town	H	1652	D	1 - 1	Wilkinson 49	13
Feb 9	NL	Wrexham	A	5366	L	0 - 1		14
16	NL	Gateshead	H	1209	L	0 - 2		14
23	NL	Sutton United	H	1322	**W**	1 - 0	Wilkinson 71	14
Mar 2	NL	Harrogate Town	A	1262	D	1 - 1	Wilkinson 90	14
5	NL	Maidenhead United	A	1156	D	1 - 1	Kandi 85	15
9	NL	Bromley	H	1186	**W**	3 - 0	Balanta 3 Wilkinson 14 Kandi 72	13
12	NL	Havant & Waterlooville	A	713	L	0 - 3		15
26	NL	Dover Athletic	H	1084	L	1 - 3	Wright 69	17
30	NL	Chesterfield	A	4377	L	0 - 2		19
Apr 2	NL	AFC Fylde	A	1275	D	1 - 1	Balanta 18	18
6	NL	Barrow	H	2173	D	0 - 0		18
13	NL	Ebbsfleet United	A	1551	**W**	1 - 0	Adeloye 24	17
19	NL	Eastleigh	H	1315	**W**	2 - 0	Harfield 44 Kandi 52	16
22	NL	Braintree Town	A	909	L	0 - 2		18
27	NL	Solihull Moors	H	1370	D	1 - 1	Wilkinson 46	18

GOALSCORERS	SG	CSG	Pens	Hat tricks	Total
Wilkinson	11	3			12
Balanta	6	2			6
Kandi	6	1	1		6
McQueen	4	1			5
Adeloye	4	1	1		4
Romain	4	2			4
Gordon	1	1			2
Munns	2	1			2
Goodliffe	1	1			1
Harfield	1	1			1
Mullings	1	1			1
Nunn	1	1			1
Opponent	1	1			1
Pennell	1	1			1
Phipps	1	1			1
Reynolds	1	1			1
Robinson	1	1			1
Smith	1	1			1
Wright	1	1			1

No.	Justham	Gordon	Robinson	Donovan (L)	Kandi	Romain	Goodliffe	Phipps	Wright	Hoyte	Harfield	Reynolds	Blanchfield	Davey	Moore	Bonds	Hyde	Adeloye	McQueen	Pennell	Leighton	Mullings (L)	Bellamy	Nunn	Munns	Onaraise (L)	Smith	Balanta	Wilkinson (L)	Clark	Najia	Loft (L)
1	x	x	x	x	x	x	x	xs	x	x	xs	sx	sx	s	s	s																
2	x	x	x	xs	x	x		xs	x	x	sx	x	sx	x	s	s	s															
3	x	x	x	xs	xs	x		s	x	x	x	xs	sx	x	s			sx	sx													
4	x	x	x	xs	sx	x		xs	x	s	sx	sx		x	s			x	x	xs												
5	x	x	x		xs	sx	x		x	sx		xs		x	s	s		x	x	xs	sx											
6	x	xs	x	xs	sx	x	x		x	s		sx		x	s		sx	xs	x	x												
7	x	x	x		sx	x	x		x	x	sx	xs		x	s		s	sx	xs		xs											
8	x	x	x	s		x	x		x	sx	x	sx		xs	s			sx	x	xs	xs											
9	x	x	x	s	sx	x	x		x	sx	x	xs			s			xs	xs	x	sx											
10	x	x	x	xs	sx	x	xs	sx	x	x	x	sx	s		s			xs		x												
11	x	x	x	s	x	x	x	sx	x	x	xs	sx			s			xs	sx	xs												
12	x	x	x	xs	x	x	x	sx	x	xs	s	sx			s			xs	sx	x												
13	x	x	x	xs	xs	x	x	sx	x	x	sx	s			s				s	x	x											
14	x	xs	x	x	sx	x	x		x	s				x	s			s	x	x		xs	sx									
15	x		x	xs	xs	x			x	s		sx		x	s				xs	x		x	sx	x	sx							
16	x	x	x		sx	x			x	s	xs	sx			s				xs	x		x	x	xs	sx							
17	x	xs	x	x	xs		x		x		sx	x		s	s			sx	s	x	s	xs		x	sx							
18	x		x	xs	sx		x	s	x	s	x	sx		x	s			xs	x	x		xs			sx							
19	x		x	sx			x	xs				sx			s			x	x	s		s		x	xs	x	x	x				
20	x		x	sx			x	x		s		sx			s			xs	x	x		sx		x	xs	x		xs				
21	x		x	sx			xs	x		s		sx			s			xs	x	x		sx		x	xs	x		x				
22	x	sx	x		sx		x	x	s						s			sx	x	x				x	xs	x		xs	xs			
23	x	sx	x		sx		x	x	s						s			sx	x	x				x	xs	x		xs	xs			
24	x		x		sx		x	x			sx				s			s	x	x				xs	xs	x		x	xs	sx		
25	x		x		sx		x	xs			sx				s			sx	x	x				xs	xs	x		x	x	s		
26	x	s	xs		sx			xs			sx				s			sx	x					x	xs	x		xs	x	x		
27		x			sx		x	x	sx	x	s				x			s	x						xs	x		xs	x	x	s	
28	x	x			sx		x	x	sx	x	s				s			s	x						xs	x		xs	x	x		
29	x	x			s		x	x	s		sx				s				x			s		x	xs	x		x	x	x		
30	x	x					x	xs	x	s	xs	sx	sx		s							sx		xs		x		x	x	x		
31	x	x					x		x	x		sx	s		s				x			sx			xs	xs	s	x	x	x		
32	x	x			sx		x		x	sx	sx				s			s	x					xs	xs	x		x	xs	x		
33	x	x			xs		x		xs	xs	sx				s				x			sx	sx		x	x	s	x		x		
34	x	x	x		sx				sx		s	sx			s				x					x	xs	x	x	xs	xs	x		
35	x	sx	x		sx		s		s			xs			s				x					x	xs	x	x		x	x		x
36	x	x	x		sx		xs		x		sx	x			s				sx					x		x	s		xs	x		xs
37	x	x	x		sx		xs		s		sx	x			s				x						xs	x	s		x	x		x
38	x	x	x		sx		x		sx		s				s			xs	x						x	x	s		x	x		xs
39	x	x	x		sx		x		sx		sx				s			xs	x						xs	x	s		x	x		xs
40	x	x	x		sx		sx	s	x		x				s			xs	x							x	x	s	x	xs		
41	x	x			sx		x	sx	x		s				s			sx	x						x	x	x	xs	xs			xs
42	x	xs	xs		x		x	sx	x		x				s			sx	x					s	sx	x	x	xs				
43	x	x	x		sx				sx		sx				s			s						x	x	x	xs	x	xs	x		xs
44	x	x	x		x		x		x		sx			s	s			sx						xs	sx	x		xs		x		xs
45	x		x		x			sx	x		x			s	s			sx						x	xs	x	x	xs		x		s
46	x		sx		sx				x		x				s			s	s					xs	xs	x	x	x	x	x		x
47	x		x		xs				x		x			s	s			xs	sx						s	x	x	x	sx	x		x
48	x		x		x				x		x			s	s			sx	s						s	x	x	xs	x	x		x
49	s	x			sx		x	xs		x	s		xs	x	x	sx		x	x				sx	xs	x							
50	x		x		x		s		x		x				s			s	s						s	x	x	x	x	x		x
x	48	30	38	3	9	15	31	8	31	11	12	4	0	10	2	0	0	4	29	16	1	2	1	14	5	30	11	13	15	21	0	6
xs	0	4	2	9	7	0	4	8	1	2	4	5	1	1	0	0	0	12	4	4	2	3	0	8	19	1	1	12	8	1	0	6
sx	0	3	1	3	27	1	1	7	6	4	16	16	4	0	0	1	1	13	5	0	2	5	4	0	6	0	0	0	1	1	0	0
s	1	1	0	3	1	0	2	3	5	9	7	1	2	6	48	3	2	8	5	1	1	2	0	1	3	0	6	1	0	1	1	1

x - Played full 90 minutes
xs - Substituted off
sx - Substituted on
s - Non-playing Substitute

DOVER ATHLETIC MATCH RESULTS 2018-19

Date	Comp	Opponents	H/A	Att:	Result		Goalscorers	Pos
Aug 4	NL	Wrexham	H	1359	L	0 - 1		
7	NL	Bromley	A	1303	D	2 - 2	Allen 35 Lokko 72	
11	NL	Gateshead	A	693	L	1 - 2	Allen 25	
14	NL	Havant & Waterlooville	H	997	W	4 - 3	Nortey 36 Allen 67 (Pen) Brundle 78 Lokko 86	
18	NL	AFC Fylde	A	1258	L	0 - 4		
25	NL	Eastleigh	H	844	L	1 - 2	Brundle 65	
27	NL	Leyton Orient	A	4641	L	0 - 3		
Sept 1	NL	Barnet	H	1037	L	1 - 2	Brundle 65	
4	NL	Ebbsfleet United	H	1127	D	1 - 1	Essam 34	23
8	NL	Chesterfield	A	4303	D	0 - 0		23
15	NL	Solihull Moors	H	823	L	0 - 2		24
22	NL	Aldershot Town	A	1619	L	0 - 2		24
25	NL	Sutton United	A	1694	D	2 - 2	Brundle 36 (Pen) Schmoll 87	23
29	NL	Barrow	H	814	L	0 - 2		23
Chris Kinnear sacked as manager.								
Oct 6	NL	Salford City	H	1127	L	1 - 4	Gomis 50	23
Andy Hessenthaler appointed manager.								
13	NL	Harrogate Town	A	1865	D	2 - 2	Effiong 46 60	23
20	**FAC 4Q**	**Concord Rangers**	**A**	**446**	**W**	**1 - 0**	**Effiong 86**	
27	NL	Braintree Town	A	575	L	1 - 2	Lokko 68	24
30	NL	Dagenham & Redbridge	H	924	L	0 - 2		24
Nov 3	NL	Maidenhead United	H	872	W	2 - 0	Lokko 37 Reason 74	24
10	**FAC 1P**	**Bury**	**A**	**2355**	**L**	**0 - 5**		
17	NL	FC Halifax Town	A	1356	L	0 - 1		24
24	NL	Hartlepool Town	H	1027	W	2 - 1	Gomis 20 Effiong 38	23
27	NL	Boreham Wood	A	407	W	1 - 0	Effiong 56	23
Dec 1	NL	Eastleigh	A	1430	D	2 - 2	Effiong 21 Reason 56	23
8	NL	AFC Fylde	H	927	W	2 - 1	Effiong 83 90+3	21
15	**FAT 1P**	**Havant & Waterlooville**	**H**	**327**	**D**	**2 - 2**	**Pavey 62 Jeffrey 90+2**	
22	NL	Barnet	A	1011	L	0 - 2		21
26	NL	Maidstone United	H	1937	W	3 - 1	Brundle 58 Gomis 75 Effiong 80	20
29	NL	Leyton Orient	H	2270	D	0 - 0		20
Jan 1	NL	Maidstone United	A	3087	W	1 - 0	Allen 86	18
5	NL	Wrexham	A	4817	W	1 - 0	Jeffrey 87	18
8	**FAT 1Pr**	**Havant & Waterlooville**	**A**	**229**	**W**	**1 - 0**	**Pavey 19**	
12	**FAT 2P**	**Harrogate Town**	**H**	**463**	**L**	**1 - 2**	**Effiong 12**	
19	NL	Bromley	H	1216	D	1 - 1	Lokko 29	19
26	NL	Havant & Waterlooville	A	1024	D	0 - 0		19
Feb 2	NL	Gateshead	H	1037	L	1 - 2	Lokko 8	19
9	NL	Harrogate Town	H	997	L	2 - 3	Allen 79 Reason 81	21
16	NL	Salford City	A	2498	W	3 - 1	McNamara 25 Doe 59 Reason 81	20
23	NL	Maidenhead United	A	1244	L	0 - 1		20
Mar 2	NL	Braintree Town	H	1053	W	3 - 0	Pavey 18 Reason 57 Brundle 72	20
9	NL	Hartlepool Town	A	3431	L	2 - 3	Pavey 28 Reason 39	20
12	NL	Boreham Wood	H	743	D	1 - 1	Brundle 11	20
16	NL	FC Halifax Town	H	897	W	2 - 1	Pavey 25 Jeffrey 61	19
26	NL	Dagenham & Redbridge	A	1084	W	3 - 1	Allen 21 Gomis 28 Pavey 50	19
30	NL	Solihull Moors	A	1338	D	2 - 2	Pavey 4 Doe 44	20
Apr 6	NL	Chesterfield	H	1348	D	0 - 0		20
13	NL	Barrow	A	1351	W	3 - 2	Brundle 73 Jeffrey 85 Modeste 90+2	19 (s)
19	NL	Aldershot Town	H	1348	W	1 - 0	Lewis 88	17
22	NL	Ebbsfleet United	A	1723	W	1 - 0	Pavey 52	15
27	NL	Sutton United	H	1103	W	3 - 0	Lewis 15 Effiong 76 Passley 90 (pen)	13

GOALSCORERS	SG	CSG	Pens	Hat tricks	Total
Effiong	9	4			11
Brundle	8	1	1		8
Pavey	8	3			8
Allen	6	3	1		6
Lokko	6	1			6
Reason	6	2			6
Gomis	4	1			4
Jeffrey	4	1			4
Doe	2	1			2
Lewis	2	1			2
Essam	1	1			1
McNamara	1	1			1
Modeste	1	1			1
Nortey	1	1			1
Passley	1	1	1		1
Schmoll	1	1			1

Walker	Passley	Connors	Lokko	Essam	Brundle	Allen	Effiong	Nortey	Schmoll	Gomis	Diarra	Daniel	Okosieme	Lewington	Smith D	Fazakerley	Jeffrey	Tajbakhsh	Smith G (L)	Massanka	Sho-Silva	Barry (L)	Lewis	Debayo (L)	Adebowale	Reason	Taylor	Huckle	Worgan	Wratten	Smith J	Earls	Pavey	Bedford	Doe	Modeste	McNamara (L)	No.
x	x	x	x	x	x	x	xs	x	x	xs	sx	sx	s	s	s																							1
x	x	x	x	x	x	x	xs	xs	x	x	s	sx	sx		s	s																						2
x	x	x	x	x	x	xs	xs	xs	x	x	s	sx	sx			s	sx																					3
x	x	x	x	x	x	x	xs	x	x	xs	s	sx	s			s	sx																					4
x	x	xs	x	x	x	x	xs	x	x	xs	sx	sx	s			s	sx																					5
x	x	x	x	xs	x	x	xs	xs	x		sx	sx	s			s	sx	x																				6
x	x	x	x	x	x	x	sx	sx	x		s	x	s			s	xs	xs																				7
x	x	s	xs	x	x	x	sx	xs	x		sx	s					sx	x	x	xs																		8
x	x	sx		x	x	xs	sx	x	x		x	sx	s				s	xs	x		xs																	9
x	xs	x		x	x	x	sx	sx	x		x	sx	s				xs	x		s	xs																	10
x		s		x	x		sx	x	x		x	x	x		sx	s	xs		x	s	xs																	11
x	x	s		xs	x	xs		sx	x		x	sx	s		sx			x	x		x	xs																12
x	x			x	x	s	x		x	s	x	sx	x		xs			x	xs		sx	s																13
x	xs			x	x	sx	xs	s	x	x	x	sx	x		s				xs		x	sx																14
x		x		x	x	sx	sx	x	s	x		xs	x			sx	s		x		xs	xs																15
x	x		x	x	x	x	xs	sx		xs			sx				x			sx	s		x	xs	s													16
x	x		x	x	x	xs	x	xs	s	xs		sx	sx							s	sx		x	x	s													17
x	x		x	x	x		x	xs		xs	sx	s								sx			x	xs	s	sx	x											18
x	x		x	x	x	x	x	s			sx	xs								s			x	x		sx	xs											19
x	x		x		x	xs	x	sx			x	s											x	xs	xs	sx	x	sx	s									20
x	x		x		x	x	xs	sx		x	x	sx											xs	x	xs			s		sx	s	s						21
x	x		x		x	x	x	sx		xs	sx												x	x	s	xs	x	s	s									22
x	x		x		x	x	xs	sx		xs	s						sx				sx		x	x		xs	x		s									23
x	x		x		x	xs	x	sx		xs							sx						x	x	s	x	xs		s				sx					24
x	x		x		x	x	x	s		x	s						x				s		x			xs	x		s				sx					25
x	x		x		x	xs	x	sx		x	s	s					x						x			xs	x		s				sx					26
s	sx		s		x		sx	x		sx	x	xs					x									xs	x		x		xs		x	x				27
x	x		x		x	xs	x	sx		xs	s						xs						x				x		s				sx		sx	x		28
x	x		x		x	sx	xs	s		x							xs						x			x	x		s				sx		sx	xs		29
x			x		x	s	x	xs		x	s						sx						x	x		x			s				x	s	x			30
x			x		x	sx	x	xs		x	s						sx						x	xs		x			s				xs		x	sx		31
x			x		x	xs	x	x			s						sx						x	x		x			s				xs	s	x	sx		32
s			s		x	xs	sx	x			x	xs					x						x	x		sx	s		x				x	x				33
x	sx		sx		x	xs	x	x			x	s					x				s		x	xs		sx							x	xs				34
x			x		x	xs	xs	x		x	sx						sx						x	x		xs	sx						s		x	s		35
x			x		x	xs	x	xs			s												x	x		xs	sx		s				sx		x	sx	x	36
x			x		x	xs	x	xs			s						sx						x	x		x	sx						sx		x	s	xs	37
x			x		x	x	x														s		x	xs	s	x	x		s				sx		x	sx	xs	38
x			x			xs	xs	sx		x	s						sx						x			x	x		s				sx		x	xs	x	39
x			x		x	x	x	s		x	sx						sx						x	s			xs						sx		x	xs	xs	40
			x		x	xs	sx	sx		x							sx						x	s		x	x		x				xs		x	xs	s	41
s	sx		x		x	x	sx	s		x							xs						x	s		x	x		x				xs				x	42
	s		x		x	xs	sx	sx		x							xs						x	sx		xs	x		x				x		s		x	43
	s		x		x	xs	sx	sx		x		s					xs						x			x	x		x				xs		sx		x	44
s	x		x		x	x	sx	sx		xs		s					sx						x			xs	x		x				xs		x			45
s	x		x		x	xs	sx	s		x							sx						x			xs	x		x				xs		x	sx		46
s	x		x		x		x	sx		x		s					sx						xs			xs	x		x				xs		x	sx		47
s	xs		x		x	sx	x	x				s					sx						x			xs	x		x				xs		x	sx		48
s			x		x	x	xs	x	s			sx					x						x	xs	x	s	x		x				sx					49
s	x		x		x	xs	sx	s				s					x						x		s	x	x		x				x		x			50
x	x		x		x	x	sx					sx					x						xs	s		xs	x		s				xs	sx	x			51
39	29	8	40	17	50	20	20	13	14	19	11	2	4	0	0	0	9	5	5	0	2	0	32	12	1	12	22	0	12	0	0	0	6	2	16	1	5	x
0	3	1	1	2	0	20	14	10	0	11	0	4	0	0	1	0	8	2	2	1	4	2	3	7	2	13	3	0	0	0	1	0	10	1	0	4	3	xs
0	3	1	1	0	0	5	16	17	0	1	9	15	4	0	2	1	19	0	0	2	3	1	0	1	0	5	3	1	0	1	0	0	11	1	3	7	0	sx
9	2	3	2	0	0	2	0	8	3	1	14	10	8	1	3	7	2	0	0	4	4	1	0	4	7	1	1	2	15	0	1	1	1	2	1	2	1	s

x - Played full 90 minutes
xs - Substituted off
sx - Substituted on
s - Non-playing Substitute

EASTLEIGH MATCH RESULTS 2018-19

Date	Comp	Opponents	H/A	Att:	Result		Goalscorers	Pos
Aug 4	NL	Solihull Moors	H	1354	L	1 - 2	McCallum 77 (pen)	18
7	NL	Sutton United	A	1725	L	0 - 1		23
11	NL	Barnet	A	1028	W	2 - 1	Green 20 McCallum 64	14
14	NL	Bromley	H	1478	W	1 - 0	Yeates 5	11
18	NL	Wrexham	H	1717	L	1 - 3	McCallum 68	15
25	NL	Dover Athletic	A	844	W	2 - 1	Williamson 19 McCallum 37	13
27	NL	Ebbsfleet United	H	1663	L	0 - 1		16
Sept 1	NL	Harrogate Town	A	1158	L	0 - 4		17
4	NL	Maidenhead United	A	1212	L	0 - 2		18
8	NL	AFC Fylde	H	1750	D	0 - 0		19
15	NL	Hartlepool United	A	3302	D	1 - 1	McCallum 70	17
22	NL	Dagenham & Redbridge	H	1538	W	1 - 0	Wynter 89	16
25	NL	Boreham Wood	H	1306	W	1 - 0	Yeates 80	14
29	NL	Gateshead	A	655	W	1 - 0	Hare 77	11
Oct 6	NL	Braintree Town	A	418	W	2 - 1	McCallum 15 Zebroski 37	10
Manager Andy Hessenthaler leaves to rejoin Dover Athletic, Ben Strevens takes temporary charge.								
13	NL	Aldershot Town	H	2349	L	1 - 2	McCallum 6	10
20	**FA 4Q**	**Hampton & Richmond Boro'**	**H**	**740**	**L**	**0 - 1**		
27	NL	FC Halifax Town	A	1343	W	1 - 0	Hare 58	10
30	NL	Leyton Orient	H	1938	D	1 - 1	Hare 35	10
Nov 3	NL	Salford City	H	2253	D	1 - 1	Williamson 47	10
Ben Strevens named as permanent manager.								
17	NL	Barrow	A	1102	W	3 - 0	McCullum 14 48 Williamson 43	9
24	NL	Chesterfield	H	1774	D	1 - 1	Wynter 11	9
27	NL	Maidstone United	A	1570	W	3 - 1	Jones 45+3 McCallum 60 85	9
Dec 1	NL	Dover Athletic	H	1430	D	2 - 2	Williamson 2 McCallum 86	9
8	NL	Wrexham	A	4105	L	0 - 2		9
15	**FAT 1P**	**Hemel Hempstead Town**	**A**	**234**	**L**	**1 - 2**	**Dennett 85**	
22	NL	Harrogate Town	H	1622	W	2 - 1	Williamson 27 Miley 82	9
26	NL	Havant & Waterlooville	A	1884	D	2 - 2	McCallum 37 40	9
29	NL	Ebbsfleet United	A	1305	L	0 - 3		10
Jan 1	NL	Havant & Waterlooville	H	2104	W	2 - 1	Johnson 56 Hare 85	10
5	NL	Solihull Moors	A	829	L	1 - 4	McCullum 53	10
19	NL	Sutton United	H	1872	W	3 - 2	Boyce 10 Hare 61 Williamson 88	10
26	NL	Bromley	A	1381	W	1 - 0	Boyce 88	8
Feb 9	NL	Aldershot Town	A	2096	W	3 - 1	Hollands 42 McCallum 70 72	9
16	NL	Braintree Town	H	2120	W	2 - 1	McCallum 14 17	8
23	NL	Salford City	A	2329	W	2 - 0	McCallum 25 52	5
Mar 2	NL	FC Halifax Town	H	3323	L	0 - 1		7
9	NL	Chesterfield	A	4319	W	3 - 2	McCullum 44 Boyce 59 Jones 83	8
12	NL	Maidstone United	H	1642	W	2 - 0	Zebroski 43 Yeates 85	6
16	NL	Barrow	H	1738	L	0 - 1		7
30	NL	Hartlepool United	H	1863	W	3 - 2	Williamson 2 Wynter 14 Hobson 48	7
Apr 2	NL	Barnet	H	1579	L	0 - 3		7
6	NL	AFC Fylde	A	1525	L	2 - 4	Wynter 10 McCallum 15	7
9	NL	Leyton Orient	A	5203	L	2 - 3	McCallum 6 21	7
13	NL	Gateshead	H	1698	W	1 - 0	Johnson 16	7
19	NL	Dagenham & Redbridge	A	1315	L	0 - 2		7
22	NL	Maidenhead United	H	2146	W	2 - 0	McCallum 28 (pen) Yeates 38	7
27	NL	Boreham Wood	A	502	D	3 - 3	Dennett 30 Gobern 47 McKinight 51	7
May 1	**PO Q**	**Wrexham**	**A**	**6723**	**W**	**1 - 0**	**Hollands 109 (aet)**	
5	**PO SF**	**Salford City**	**A**	**2963**	**D**	**1 - 1**	**McCallum 57 (lost 3-4 on pens aet)**	

GOALSCORERS	SG	CSG	Pens	Hat tricks	Total
McCallum	20	3	2		27
Williamson	7	1			7
Hare	5	2			5
Wynter	4	1			4
Yeates	4	1			4
Boyce	3	2			3
Hollands	2	1			2
Johnson	2	1			2
Jones	2	1			2
Zebroski	2	1			2

	SG	CSG	Pens	Hat tricks	Total
Dennett	1	1			1
Gobern	1	1			1
Green	1	1			1
Hobson	1	1			1
McKnight	1	1			1
Miley	1	1			1

Stack	Hare	Green	Hollands	Boyce	Johnson	Wynter	Gobern	Yeates	Williamson	McCallum	Zebroski	Miley	Constable	Wood	Dowling	Joey Jones	Flitney	Dennett	Baughan	Bearwish	Strevens	Payne (L)	Stryjek (L)	Harvey	Cotton	Scorey	Simm	McKnight	Southwood (L)	Hobson (L)	Matthews (L)	No.
x	x	x	x	xs	x	x	xs	x	xs	x	sx	sx	sx	s	s																	1
x	x	x	xs	xs	x	x	x	x	xs	x	sx	sx		s	sx	s																2
x	x	x	x	x	x	x	xs	sx	sx	xs	xs	x	s		sx		s															3
x	x	x	s		x	x	x	xs	xs	x	x	x	sx	sx			s	s														4
x	x	x	xs	sx	x	x	sx	x	xs	x	xs	x	sx				s	s														5
x	x	x	sx		x	x	x	xs	xs	x		x	sx			x	s	s	s													6
	x	x	x	x		x	xs	x		x		x	x				x	sx	s	s												7
x	x	x	xs	xs	x		x	x		x	x	x				sx	s	sx	s	sx												8
x	x	x	x		x	x	x	x			x	x					s	x	s		s	s										9
x	x		x	s	x	x	xs	x		x	sx	x	xs			sx	s	s				x										10
x	x		s	s	x	x	x	x		x	sx	x	s			x	s	xs				x										11
	x	x	s	s	x	x	xs	xs		x	sx	x	sx			x		sx				xs	x									12
	x	x	s	sx	x	x	xs	xs			x	x	sx			xs	s	sx				x	x									13
	x	x		x	x	x	xs	xs	sx	sx	xs	x	sx				s	s				x	x									14
	x	x	sx	x	x	x	xs	x	sx	xs	xs	x	sx				s	s					x									15
		x	s	xs	x	xs	x	x	sx	x	x	x	sx			x	s	s					x									16
			x	**x**		**x**	**x**	**x**	**xs**	**x**		**x**	**sx**			**x**	**x**	**xs**	**s**	**sx**				**s**	**s**							17
	x	x	x	x		x	xs	x	xs	x		x				sx	s	sx		s			x	s								18
	x	x	x	x		x	xs	x	x	x	sx	xs				sx	s	s		s			x									19
	x	x	x	x	x	x		x	xs	xs	sx		sx			x	s	s		s			x									20
	x		x	x	x	x	sx	xs	xs	xs		x				x	s	sx	s	sx			x									21
	x		x	x	x	x	sx	x	xs	x		xs				x	s	sx	s	s			x									22
	xs		x	x		x	x	xs	x	xs	s	x	sx			x	x	sx	sx	s												23
		x	x	x	x	sx	xs	x	xs	x		x	sx			xs	s	sx		s			x									24
	x	sx	x	x	x	x	x	x	xs	x	s	xs				s		sx		s			x									25
	x	**x**	**x**	**x**				**x**	**x**	**x**	**xs**	**x**				**x**	**s**	**sx**	**s**				**x**			**s**	**s**					26
	x	x	x	xs	x	x	sx	xs	xs	x	s	sx				x		s					x					sx				27
	x	x	x	x	x	x	sx	xs	xs	xs	sx	sx				x		s										s	x			28
	x			xs	x	x	x	x	xs	sx	sx	x				x		sx		s				s				xs	x			29
	x			x	x	x	x	x	xs	x	s	x				x		s		s				s				sx	x			30
	x		sx	x	x	x	xs	x	xs	x	sx	xs				x		s		s								sx	x			31
	x	x	x	x	x	x	sx	xs	xs	xs	sx	s				x				s								sx	x			32
	x	x	x	x	x	x	sx	xs	x		xs	sx				x				s						s		s	x			33
	x	x	x	x	x	x	sx	x	xs	xs	sx	sx				x				s								s	x			34
	x	x	xs	x	xs	x		x		xs	x	sx				x		s		sx						s		sx	x			35
	x	x	x	x		x	xs	xs		xs	x					x		sx	s	sx				s				sx	x			36
	x	xs	x	x		x	xs	x	sx	x	xs	sx				x		s		s								sx	x			37
	x	s	x	x		x	x	xs	sx	xs	xs	x				x		s										sx	x	sx		38
	x	sx	x	x	x	x	x	xs	sx	x	xs	xs						s										sx	x	s		39
	x	x	xs	x	x	xs	x	x	sx	x	xs	sx						s										sx	x	s		40
	x	x	x	x		x	sx	xs	x		sx	sx				xs		s										s	x	x	xs	41
	x	x	x	x		x	sx	x	xs	sx	sx	x						s										s	x	xs	xs	42
	x	x		x		x	xs	x	xs	xs	sx	x				sx		s										s	x	xs	sx	43
	x	x		x			sx	sx	xs	x	sx	xs				x	s	s										xs	x	x	x	44
	x	x		x	x		s	s	xs	xs	sx	x				x		s										sx	x	x	x	45
	x	x	s	x		x	s	xs	sx	x	sx	x				x												sx	x	xs	xs	46
	x	x	x	x	x	x	sx	xs	xs	x	sx	s				xs												s	x		sx	47
			x	s		xs	x				x	x					x	xs	xs	sx				sx		sx		x	s	x	x	48
	xs	**x**	**x**	**x**	**x**	**x**	**sx**	**xs**	**xs**	**x**	**sx**	**s**				**xs**												**sx**	**x**		**sx**	49
	x	**x**	**xs**	**x**	**x**	**x**	**xs**	**xs**	**xs**	**x**	**sx**	**sx**																**sx**	**x**	**s**	**sx**	50
10	44	36	29	35	34	42	16	27	5	29	8	28	1	0	0	25	4	1	0	0	0	4	14	0	0	0	0	1	22	4	3	x
0	2	1	6	6	1	3	16	19	26	13	10	6	1	0	0	5	0	3	1	0	0	1	0	0	0	0	0	2	0	3	3	xs
0	0	2	3	2	0	1	13	2	9	3	21	11	13	1	2	5	0	13	1	6	0	0	0	1	0	1	0	14	0	1	4	sx
0	0	1	6	4	0	0	2	1	0	0	4	3	2	2	1	2	20	23	9	15	1	1	0	5	1	3	1	7	1	3	0	s

x - Played full 90 minutes
xs - Substituted off
sx - Substituted on
s - Non-playing Substitute

EBBSFLEET UNITED MATCH RESULTS 2018-19

Date	Comp	Opponents	H/A	Att:	Result	Goalscorers	Pos
Aug 4	NL	Chesterfield	H	2041	L 0 - 1		21
7	NL	Leyton Orient	A	4710	D 1 - 1	Whitely 90+1	18
11	NL	Hartlepool United	A	3182	**W** 1 - 0	Whitely 71	9
14	NL	Sutton United	H	1506	L 0 - 1		15
18	NL	Barnet	A	1217	**W** 3 - 0	Kedwell 44 Whitely 66 Shields 88	10
25	NL	Aldershot Town	H	1233	**W** 3 - 1	Shields 35 81 Drury 72	7
27	NL	Eastleigh	A	1663	**W** 1 - 0	Kedwell 45	6
Sept 1	NL	AFC Fylde	H	1395	L 1 - 3	Whitely 76	9
4	NL	Dover Athletic	A	1127	D 1 - 1	McQueen 12	11
8	NL	Gateshead	H	1392	L 0 - 1		13
15	NL	Wrexham	A	4718	L 1 - 4	Kedwell 48	14
22	NL	Havant & Waterlooville	H	1141	D 1 - 1	Cheek 27	14
25	NL	Bromley	H	1204	L 1 - 2	Powell 45+2	16
29	NL	Dagenham & Redbridge	A	1225	**W** 3 - 1	Bush 4 Kedwell 31 57 (Pen)	15
Oct 6	NL	Harrogate Town	H	1169	L 0 - 2		15
13	NL	Solihull Moors	A	1505	L 1 - 2	Bush 33	17
20	**FAC 4Q**	**Worthing**	**H**	**1011**	**W 4 - 0**	**Coulson 30 40 Winfield 51 McQueen 81**	
27	NL	Salford United	A	2498	D 1 - 1	Whitely 35	17
30	NL	Maidstone United	H	2003	D 1 - 1	Clark 57	15
Nov 3	NL	Barrow	H	1277	**W** 1 - 0	Kedwell 35	15
Daryl McMahon sacked as manager, Garry Hill named as his replacement.							
10	**FAC 1P**	**Cheltenham Town**	**H**	**1624**	**D 0 - 0**		
17	NL	Boreham Wood	A	724	D 0 - 0		14
20	**FAC 1Pr**	**Cheltenham Town**	**A**	**1435**	**L 0 - 2**		
24	NL	FC Halifax Town	H	1104	**W** 4 - 0	Cheek 24 90 Bush 40 Kedwell 47 (Pen)	13
27	NL	Maidenhead United	A	1055	D 1 - 1	Cheek 14	10
Dec 1	NL	Aldershot Town	A	1663	**W** 2 - 0	Cheek 48 Kedwell 67 (Pen)	10
8	NL	Barnet	H	1320	**W** 1 - 0	Kedwell 84	10
15	**FAT 1P**	**Dagenham & Redbridge**	**H**	**720**	**L 0 - 1**		
22	NL	AFC Fylde	A	1474	L 0 - 2		10
26	NL	Braintree Town	H	1231	**W** 4 - 2	Kedwell 1 13 Graham 45+4 McDonald 63	10
29	NL	Eastleigh	H	1305	**W** 3 - 0	Cheek 2 Kedwell 10 Whitely 37	9
Jan 1	NL	Braintree Town	A	752	**W** 4 - 0	McDonald 3 Cheek 22 61 Whitely 79	9
5	NL	Chesterfield	A	4123	D 3 - 3	Cheek 21 (Pen) McDonald 40 Graham 45	9
19	NL	Leyton Orient	H	3020	**W** 2 - 0	King 22 Bush 63	8
26	NL	Sutton United	A	2108	L 0 - 1		10
Feb 9	NL	Solihull Moors	H	1325	L 0 - 1		10
16	NL	Harrogate Town	A	1488	**W** 2 - 1	Cheek 8 Drury 87	10
19	NL	Hartlepool United	H	1265	D 0 - 0		10
23	NL	Barrow	A	1058	D 0 - 0		10
Mar 2	NL	Salford United	H	1708	L 0 - 1		10
12	NL	Maidenhead United	H	811	**W** 3 - 0	Whitely 51 Cheek 58 79	10
16	NL	Boreham Wood	H	1110	**W** 3 - 2	King 5 Magri 21 Bush 52	10
23	NL	Maidstone United	A	3002	**W** 2 - 0	Ugwu 20 Cheek 90	9
26	NL	FC Halifax Town	A	1073	D 0 - 0		8
30	NL	Wrexham	H	1523	**W** 4 - 2	Pearson 10 (og) Cheek 40 44 Ugwu 85	8
Apr 6	NL	Gateshead	A	798	D 1 - 1	Bush 64	8
13	NL	Dagenham & Redbridge	H	1551	L 0 - 1		8
19	NL	Havant & Waterlooville	A	1097	D 3 - 3	Kedwell 46 Cheek 50 Magri 56	8
22	NL	Dover Athletic	H	1723	L 0 - 1		8
27	NL	Bromley	A	1352	L 1 - 5	Drury 62	8

GOALSCORERS	SG	CSG	Pens	Hat tricks	Total
Cheek	12	3	1		16
Kedwell	11	2	3		13
Whitely	8	2			8
Bush	6	1			6
Drury	3	1			3
McDonald	3	1			3
Shields	2	2			3
Coulson	1	1			2
Graham	2	1			2
King	2	1			2
Magri	2	1			2
McQueen	2	1			2
Ugwu	2	1			2
Clark	1	1			1
Opponent	1	1			1
Powell	1	1			1
Winfield	1	1			1

Ashmore	King	Magri	Payne	Weston	Bush	Whitely	Drury	Adams	Wilson	Kedwell	Cheek	Shields	Powell	Miles	McQueen	Coulson	Winfield	Rance	Graham	Clark	Allassani (L)	McDonald	Moncur	Omar	Ugwu (L)	Achuba	No.
X	X	X	X	X	X	X	XS	XS	XS	X	SX	SX	SX	S	S												1
X	X	X	S	XS	X	SX	X	XS		X	SX	X	X	S	XS	SX											2
X	X	X	SX	X	X	SX	X	XS		XS	SX	X	X	S	XS	S											3
X	X	X		SX	X	X	XS	SX		X	XS	X	X	S	SX	S	XS										4
X	X	X		XS	SX	XS	X	X		X	S	X	XS		S	SX	X	SX									5
X	X	X		X	SX	XS	X	XS		XS	SX	X	S		S	SX	X	X									6
X	X	X		XS	SX	XS	X	XS		X	S	X	SX		S	SX	X	X									7
X	X	X		X	S	SX	XS	XS		X	S	X	SX		SX	XS	X	X									8
X	X	SX		X	X	X	SX		S	SX	XS	X	X		XS	S	XS	X									9
X	X	X			XS	X	X		X	X	SX	XS	S	S	XS	SX		X	SX								10
X	X	X		X	SX	X	X	XS		XS	SX	S			S	XS		X	SX	X							11
X		SX		X	X	X		X		S	XS	SX	XS		SX	S	X	X	XS	X							12
X		X		X	X	X		X		SX	XS	SX	XS	S	SX	S	X	X	XS								13
X		S		X	X	X		X		XS	SX	S	SX			SX	X	XS	X	X	XS						14
X		SX		X	X	X		XS		X	SX	S	SX			S	X	X	XS	X	XS						15
X	S	X	X		X	XS	X			X	SX	SX		S		X	X	XS	S	X							16
X	**S**	**X**	**X**	**SX**	**X**	**XS**	**X**	**S**	**S**	**X**		**SX**		**S**	**SX**	**XS**	**X**	**XS**		**X**							17
X		X	X	X	X	XS	X	S	S	X		SX		S	SX	XS	X			X							18
X		X	X	X	X	X		XS	S	X	S	SX		S	SX	XS	X			X							19
X		X	X	X	X	XS	XS	SX	SX	X		SX		S	S	XS	X			X							20
X	**SX**	**X**	**X**	**XS**	**X**	**X**		**XS**	**SX**	**X**	**S**	**S**		**S**	**SX**	**XS**	**X**		**S**	**X**							21
X	S	X	X		X	X	X		S	XS	SX	XS			SX	XS	X			X	SX						22
X	**X**	**X**	**X**		**X**	**XS**	**X**		**S**	**X**	**SX**	**XS**		**S**	**SX**	**XS**	**X**		**SX**	**S**							23
X	X		X	XS	X	X	XS	SX	X	XS	X			S		S	X		SX		SX						24
X	X	S	X	XS	X	XS	XS	SX	X	X	X			S		SX	X					SX					25
X	X	X	X	X	X	XS		X	X	X	XS			S		SX		S	S			SX					26
X	X	X	X	XS	X	XS	S	X	X	X	XS			S				SX	SX			SX					27
X	**X**	**X**	**XS**	**S**	**X**	**X**	**SX**	**XS**	**X**	**X**	**X**			**S**				**SX**	**X**								28
X	X	X	X		XS	XS	XS	X	SX	X	SX			S			X	S	X			SX					29
X	SX	X	X	SX	XS		X	XS	X	X	S						XS	SX	X			X	S				30
X	X	X	X	X	X	XS	X	SX	SX	XS	X							XS	S			S	SX				31
X	X	X	XS		X	SX	X	XS	X	S	X			S				SX	X			XS	SX				32
X	X	X	X	SX	X	SX	X	XS	X	SX	X							S	XS			XS	S				33
X	X	X	X	S	X	SX	XS	X	X	X	XS			S				SX	XS			SX					34
X	X	X	X	SX	X	SX	X	X	X	XS	XS			S				S	XS			SX					35
X	X	X	X	SX	X	X	XS	S	XS	XS	SX			S				X	SX			X					36
X	X	X	X	X	X	XS	X	X	X	SX	XS			S								SX	S	S			37
X	X	X	X	X	X	SX	X	S	X	SX	XS			S				X				XS	S				38
X	X	X	X	X	X	XS	X	X	X	SX	X			S									S	S			39
X	X	X	X	X		SX	X	XS	X	X	X			S					X				S	S			40
X	X	X	XS	X		X		XS	XS	SX	X			S					X				SX	SX	X		41
X	X	X	X	SX	X	SX		X	X	S	XS						SX	X	XS				S		X		42
X	X	X	X	X	X	XS			X	SX	X			S				X	SX				S	S	XS		43
X	X	X	X	XS	X	S	SX	XS	X	SX	XS							X	SX				S		X		44
X	X	X	X	X	X	XS	SX	SX	X	S	XS							XS	SX				S		X		45
X	X	X	X	X	X	SX	SX	XS		SX	XS						X	XS	S				S		X		46
X	X	X	X	X	X	X	SX	S	XS	SX	XS						S	XS	SX						X		47
X		X	SX	X	X	SX	X	XS	XS	X	XS			S			X	X	SX				S				48
X		X	X	X	X	SX	XS	SX	X	X	SX			S				X	XS				S		XS		49
S		XS		X	X	X	X	SX	S	X	SX			X				X	X				XS	XS		SX	50
9	35	43	31	27	40	18	23	12	20	26	10	8	4	1	0	1	21	17	8	11	0	2	0	0	6	0	x
0	0	1	3	8	3	17	10	19	5	9	16	3	3	0	4	9	3	7	8	0	2	3	1	1	2	0	xs
0	2	3	2	7	4	13	6	8	4	11	15	8	5	0	10	8	1	6	11	0	2	7	3	1	0	1	sx
1	3	2	1	2	1	1	1	5	7	4	6	4	2	31	6	7	1	4	5	1	0	1	13	4	0	0	s

x - Played full 90 minutes
xs - Substituted off
sx - Substituted on
s - Non-playing Substitute

FC HALIFAX TOWN MATCH RESULTS 2018-19

Date	Comp	Opponents	H/A	Att:	Result		Goalscorers	Pos
Aug 4	NL	Braintree Town	A	621	W	2 - 0	Edwards 42 Clarke 65	
7	NL	Barrow	H	1654	W	2 - 0	Southwell 43 Brown 88	
11	NL	Maidstone United	H	1534	W	3 - 0	King 40 Tomlinson 51 Southwell 70 (pen)	
14	NL	Salford City	A	2632	L	1 - 2	Kosylo 73	
18	NL	Dagenham & Redbridge	H	1364	W	2 - 1	Kosylo 29 Edwards 59	
25	NL	Boreham Wood	A	572	L	1 - 2	Clarke 70	
27	NL	Gateshead	H	1688	W	1 - 0	Preston 45	
Sept 1	NL	Sutton United	A	1789	D	1 - 1	Southwell 62	4
4	NL	Wrexham	A	5377	D	0 - 0		4
8	NL	Leyton Orient	H	1927	D	1 - 1	Southwell 64 (pen)	5
15	NL	Maidenhead United	A	1306	L	0 - 3		9
22	NL	Hartlepool United	H	2360	L	1 - 2	Hanson 88	11
25	NL	AFC Fylde	A	1197	D	0 - 0		10
29	NL	Bromley	A	1143	D	2 - 2	Staunton 60 Preston 90	10
Oct 6	NL	Aldershot Town	A	1625	L	0 - 3		13
13	NL	Chesterfield	H	2191	D	1 - 1	Kosylo 69	14
20	**FAC 4Q**	**Warrington Town**	**A**	**929**	**D**	**2 - 2**	**Clarke 4 Kosylo 72**	
23	**FAC 4Qr**	**Warrington Town**	**H**	**844**	**W**	**2 - 0**	**Preston 15 Southwell 65**	
27	NL	Eastleigh	H	1343	L	0 - 1		14
30	NL	Solihull Moors	A	915	D	0 - 0		13
Nov 3	NL	Havant & Waterlooville	A	1258	L	1 - 2	Maher 79	16
10	**FAC 1P**	**Morecombe**	**A**	**1736**	**D**	**0 - 0**		
17	NL	Dover Athletic	H	1356	W	1 - 0	Kosylo 40	12
20	**FAC 1Pr**	**Morecombe**	**H**	**1218**	**W**	**1 - 0**	**King 12**	
24	NL	Ebbsfleet United	A	1104	L	0 - 4		14
Dec 1	**FAC 2P**	**AFC Wimbledon**	**H**	**2044**	**L**	**1 - 3**	**Hanson 86 (og)**	
8	NL	Dagenham & Redbridge	A	1098	D	1 - 1	Clarke 80	16
15	**FAT 1P**	**Barrow**	**A**	**578**	**W**	**2 - 1**	**Brown 39 Edwards 88**	
18	NL	Boreham Wood	H	913	D	1 - 1	Southwell 43	
22	NL	Sutton United	H	1319	L	0 - 1		19
26	NL	Harrogate Town	A	2310	W	2 - 1	Clarke 55 Southwell 88	17
29	NL	Gateshead	A	830	D	1 - 1	Preston 1	17
Jan 1	NL	Harrogate Town	H	1696	D	1 - 1	Edwards 90+1	17
5	NL	Braintree Town	H	1302	D	0 - 0		17
12	**FAT 2P**	**Solihull Moors**	**H**	**798**	**D**	**2 - 2**	**Southwell 64 Kosylo 83**	
15	**FAT 2Pr**	**Solihull Moors**	**A**	**355**	**L**	**0 - 1**		
19	NL	Barrow	A	1142	D	0 - 0		17
26	NL	Salford City	H	2115	D	0 - 0		16
Feb 9	NL	Chesterfield	A	4523	L	0 - 1		16
16	NL	Aldershot Town	H	1650	D	0 - 0		18
19	NL	Maidstone United	A	1813	W	1 - 0	Quigley 86	15
23	NL	Havant & Waterlooville	H	1181	D	0 - 0		15
Mar 2	NL	Eastleigh	A	3323	W	1 - 0	Ferry 77	15
5	NL	Barnet	H	1085	W	3 - 0	Rodney 35 Ferry 60 Duku 73	12
12	NL	Barnet	A	702	D	1 - 1	Rodney 72	14
16	NL	Dover Athletic	A	897	L	1 - 2	Kosylo 64	14
23	NL	Solihull Moors	H	1563	W	2 - 0	Duku 14 Rodney 83	14
26	NL	Ebbsfleet United	H	1073	D	0 - 0		13
30	NL	Maidenhead United	H	1336	L	0 - 1		14
Apr 6	NL	Leyton Orient	A	5458	D	2 - 2	Duku 9 Rodney 45+1	15
13	NL	Bromley	H	1303	D	2 - 2	Staunton 27 Rodney 75	15
19	NL	Hartlepool United	A	3018	L	1 - 2	Rodney 14	18
22	NL	Wrexham	H	2577	W	2 - 1	Quigley 29 Rodney 90+2	16
27	NL	AFC Fylde	A	1891	W	2 - 0	Brown 38 Birch 41 (og)	15

GOALSCORERS	SG	CSG	Pens	Hat tricks	Total
Southwell	8	2	2		8
Kosylo	7	2			7
Rodney	7	4			7
Clarke	5	1			5
Edwards	4	1			4
Preston	4	1			4
Brown	3	1			3
Duku	3	1			3
Ferry	2	1			2
King	2	1			2
Opponent	2	1			2
Quigley	2	1			2
Staunton	2	1			2
Hanson	1	1			1
Maher	1	1			1
Tomlinson	1	1			1

No.	Johnson	Duckworth	Sellers	Clarke	Brown	Staunton	Southwell	Edwards	Tomlinson	Preston	Maher	Kosylo	King	Rowley	Leacock-McLeod	Hanson	Odelusi	Lenighan	Berrett	Skarz (L)	Wootton (L)	Ferry (L)	Quigley (L)	Hardy (L)	Duku (L)	Rodney (L)	Gondoh (L)	Freedman
1	X	X	X	X	X	X	X	XS	X	XS	X	SX	SX	S	S	S												
2	X	X	XS	X	X	XS	X	X	X	XS	X	SX	SX	S	S	SX												
3	X	X		X	X		XS	X	X	SX	X	XS	X	S	SX	X	S											
4	X	X		X	X		X	X	XS	SX	X	XS	SX	S	SX	X	S	XS										
5	X		X	X	X		XS	XS	X	SX	X	XS	SX	S	S	X	SX	X										
6	X			X	X		X	XS	X	SX		X	SX	S	S	X	S	X	X	X								
7	X			X	X		XS	SX	X	X		X	S	S	S	X	S	X	X	X								
8	X			X	X		X	SX	XS	X	S	X	S	S		X	S	X	X	X								
9	X			X	X		XS	X		X	SX	X	SX	S	S	X	S	XS	X	X								
10	X		S	X	X		XS	X		XS	SX	X	S	S		X	SX	X	X	X								
11	X		SX	X	X		X	SX		X	X	X	S	S		X	XS	S	X	XS								
12	X		X	X	X		XS	XS		X	SX	X	S	S	S	X	SX	X	X									
13	X	S	X	X		S	X	X		X	X		S	S	SX	X	XS	X	X									
14	X	S	X	X		SX	XS	X		X	XS		S	S		X	X	X	X		SX							
15	X	S	X	X		SX	X	SX		XS	X		SX	S		X	X	XS	X		XS							
16	X	SX		X		X	XS	X			XS	X	SX	S		X	S	SX	XS	X	X							
17	X	X	X	X		X	XS	SX				X	SX	S	S	S	X	XS		X								
18	X		X	X		X	X	X		XS		X	X	S	S	X	SX	S		X								
19	X		X	X	S	X	X	X			X	X	X	S	S	X	SX	S		XS								
20	X		X	X	X	X	X	X			X	X	X	S	S	X	S	S										
21	X		X	X	X	XS	X	X			X	X	X	S	S	X	SX	S		S								
22	X		X	X	X	X	XS	SX		SX	X		X	S	S	X	XS			X								
23	X		S	X	X	X	XS	SX		SX	X	X	XS	S	SX	X	XS			X								
24	X	S	X	X	X	X	XS	SX		XS	X	X	X	S	S	X	SX	S										
25	X	S	X	X	X	X	X	SX		X	X	X	XS	S		X	SX			S								
26	X	S	X	X	X	X	XS	SX		X	X	X	XS	S	SX	X	S			S								
27	X	S	X	X	X	X	XS	SX		X	X	X		S	XS	X	S			SX								
28	X	SX	X	X	X		X	SX	S	X	X			S	XS	XS	XS					X						
29	X	S	X	X	X		X	S	SX	X	X			S	X	X	XS					X						
30	X	S	X	X	X		XS	SX	SX	X	X	X		S	S	X	XS					X						
31	X	X	X	X	X	S	X	S	SX	X	X	X		S	S		XS					X						
32	X	X	X	X	X	S	X	SX	XS	X	X	X		S		S	S					X						
33	X	S	X	X	X	S	XS	SX	X	X	X	X		S		X	S					X						
34	X	S		X	X	S	XS	SX		X	X	X		S		X	S			X		X	X					
35	X	X		X	X		X	SX		XS	X	X	SX	S		S			X	X		S	XS					
36	X		X	X	X	S	XS	SX		SX	X	X	XS	S		X			SX			X	XS					
37	X	X		X	X		XS	SX	SX	SX	X	X	XS	S					X	X		S	XS					
38	X	X		X	X		XS	SX	SX	SX	X	X	XS	S					X	X		S	XS					
39	X	X		X	X	S		SX	SX	XS	X	X	XS	S					X	X		S	X					
40	X	X	X	X	X	S		SX	XS	X	X	X		S					X			S	XS	SX				
41	X	X	X	X	X	S	XS	SX	XS	SX	X	X		S					X				SX	XS				
42	X	X	X	X	X	SX		XS		SX	X	X		S		S			X			SX	XS	XS				
43	X	X	X	X	X	S				S	X	X	SX	S								X	SX	XS	XS	X		
44	X	X	X	X	X	SX				S	X	X	SX	S								XS	XS	XS	SX	X		
45	X	X		X	X			S		SX	X	XS	SX	S		SX				X		X		XS	XS	X		
46	X	X		X	X	S				S	X	X	X	S					XS	X			XS		SX	X	SX	
47	X	X		X	X	X				S	X	XS	SX	S					XS	X			SX		XS	X	SX	
48	X	XS		X	X	X				SX	XS	X	SX	S					X	X			SX		XS	X	S	
49	X			X	X	XS		SX		SX		X	X	S		X			XS	X			SX		X	XS	S	
50	X			X	X	X		S		S		X	X	S		X			X	X			SX		XS	X	S	
51	X			X	X	X				S		X	X	S		X			X	X			S		XS	X	SX	S
52	X			X	X	X				S		X	X	S		XS			X	X			S		XS	X	SX	SX
53	X			X	X	S				SX	X	X	X	S					X	X			XS		SX	X	XS	S
54	X			X	X	S		S		X	X	X	X	S					X	X					X	X	S	S
X	54	19	28	54	47	17	18	12	7	19	39	41	14	0	1	32	3	8	23	25	1	10	2	0	2	11	0	0
XS	0	1	1	0	0	3	21	5	5	8	3	5	7	0	2	2	8	4	4	2	1	1	9	5	7	1	1	0
SX	0	2	1	0	0	4	0	24	6	15	3	2	15	0	5	2	8	1	1	1	1	1	6	1	3	0	4	1
S	0	11	2	0	1	13	0	5	1	7	1	0	7	54	16	5	13	6	0	3	0	5	2	0	0	0	4	3

x - Played full 90 minutes
xs - Substituted off
sx - Substituted on
s - Non-playing Substitute

GATESHEAD TOWN MATCH RESULTS 2018-19

Date	Comp	Opponents	H/A	Att:	Result	Goalscorers	Pos
Aug 4	NL	Maidenhead United	A	1264	**W** 3 - 1	Olley 17 Boden 48 Armstrong 55	2
7	NL	Salford City	H	1243	**W** 2 - 1	Armstrong 37 (pen) 68	3
11	NL	Dover Athletic	H	693	**W** 2 - 1	Tinkler 35 Armstrong 87	3
14	NL	Boreham Wood	A	608	D 1 - 1	Rigg 88	2
18	NL	Bromley	A	1078	L 0 - 1		5
25	NL	Leyton Orient	H	1052	D 1 - 1	Armstrong 77	6
27	NL	FC Halifax Town	A	1688	L 0 - 1		11
Sept 7	NL	Maidstone United	H	564	**W** 1 - 0	Boden 88 (pen)	8
4	NL	Harrogate Town	H	846	L 2 - 3	Kerr 35 Rigg 52	12
8	NL	Ebbsfleet United	A	1392	**W** 1 - 0	Bush 13 (og)	8
15	NL	Braintree Town	H	578	L 0 - 1		10
22	NL	Chesterfield	A	4210	**W** 3 - 0	Boden 18 68 Rigg 43	9
25	NL	Barrow	A	1053	**W** 2 - 1	Boden 45 Olley 47	6
29	NL	Eastleigh	H	655	L 0 - 1		9
Oct 6	NL	Dagenham & Redbridge	H	687	**W** 2 - 0	Rigg 18 White 20	8
13	NL	Havant & Waterlooville	A	1250	**W** 1 - 0	Rigg 56	7
20	**FAC 4Q**	**Dunston UTS**	**A**	**2520**	**W 4 - 0**	**Olley 5 Rigg 15 Boden 44 Molyneux 78**	
27	NL	Aldershot Town	H	703	**W** 3 - 0	Olley 20 Boden 33 White 77	7
30	NL	AFC Fylde	A	1470	L 0 - 1		7
Nov 3	NL	Wrexham	A	4421	L 1 - 3	Armstrong 88	8
10	**FAC 1P**	**Rochdale**	**A**	**2415**	**L 1 - 2**	**Mellish 49**	
17	NL	Sutton United	H	794	D 0 - 0		8
24	NL	Barnet	A	940	**W** 2 - 1	Boden 20 Armstrong 77	7
Dec 1	NL	Leyton Orient	A	4636	L 0 - 2		7
8	NL	Bromley	H	680	**W** 2 - 0	Armstrong 16 Kerr 52	7
18	**FAT 1P**	**Salford City**	**A**	**380**	**L 1 - 3**	**Armstrong 89**	
22	NL	Maidstone United	A	2131	**W** 3 - 2	Molyneux 25 56 Tinkler 33	7
26	NL	Hartlepool United	H	2678	**W** 2 - 1	Armstrong 13 33	7
29	NL	FC Halifax Town	H	830	D 1 - 1	Boden 63	7
Jan 1	NL	Hartlepool United	A	3468	L 1 - 2	Anderson 61 (og)	7
5	NL	Maidenhead United	H	581	L 0 - 1		8
8	NL	Solihull Moors	H	519	L 1 - 2	Boden 56 (pen)	8
Steve Watson quits as manager to join York City, Ben Clark is named as his replacement.							
19	NL	Salford City	A	2055	D 1 - 1	Boden 44	9
26	NL	Boreham Wood	H	562	D 1 - 1	Boden 73	9
Feb 2	NL	Dover Athletic	A	1037	**W** 2 - 1	Kerr 79 Olley 90+4	7
9	NL	Havant & Waterlooville	H	531	D 0 - 0		8
16	NL	Dagenham & Redbridge	A	1209	**W** 2 - 0	Rigg 41 (pen) 55	6
23	NL	Wrexham	H	1228	D 1 - 1	Rigg 40	8
Mar 2	NL	Aldershot Town	A	1885	**W** 2 - 0	Thomson 63 Salkeld 85	6
9	NL	Barnet	H	655	**W** 2 - 1	Olley 48 White 72	7
12	NL	Solihull Moors	A	924	L 0 - 1		8
16	NL	Sutton United	A	1722	L 2 - 4	Olley 44 46	8
30	NL	Braintree Town	A	291	L 0 - 2		9
Apr 6	NL	Ebbsfleet United	H	798	D 1 - 1	Mellish 4	10
9	NL	AFC Fylde	H	470	L 0 - 1		10
13	NL	Eastleigh	A	1698	L 0 - 1		10
19	NL	Chesterfield	H	1208	**W** 1 - 0	Rigg 27 (pen)	9
22	NL	Harrogate Town	A	1629	L 0 - 2		9
27	NL	Barrow	H	798	L 0 - 2	Deducted 9 points after the season ended.	17

GOALSCORERS	SG	CSG	Pens	Hat tricks	Total
Boden	11	2	2		12
Armstrong	9	3	1		11
Rigg	9	2	2		10
Olley	7	1			8
Kerr	3	1			3
Molyneux	2	1			3
White	3	1			3
Mellish	2	1			2
Opponent	2	1			2
Tinkler	2	1			2

	SG	CSG	Pens	Hat tricks	Total
Salkeld	1	1			1
Thomson	1	1			1

Pears (L)	Kerr	Tinkler	Forbes	Thomson	Mellish	White	Olley	O'Donnell	Boden	Armstrong	Maloney	Hunter	Salkeld	Foden	Devitt	Rigg	Williamson	Barrow	Molyneux	McManus	Lumsden	McGeoch	Clark	Hayhurst	Slater	No.
x	x	x	xs	x	x	xs	x	x	xs	x	sx	sx	sx	s	s											1
x	x	x	s	s	x	x	x	x	x	x	s	x	xs	s	sx											2
x	x	x	s		xs	xs	x	sx	x	x		x	xs	s	sx	sx	x									3
x	x	x		sx	x	xs	x	x	x	x		s	xs	s	s	sx	x									4
x	x	x		sx	x	sx	x	x	x	x	s	x	xs	s	s	xs										5
x	x	x		xs	x	sx	x	x	s	x	xs	x	sx	s	s	x										6
x	x	x	s	sx	x	x	x	x	x	x		xs	xs	s	s	sx										7
x	x	x	sx	s	x	x	x	x	x		s	xs	xs	s	sx	x										8
x	x	x	x	sx	x	x	x		x		s	s	xs	s	x	x		s								9
x	xs	x	x	sx	x	x	x	x	x			s		s	sx	x			xs	s						10
x	x	x	x		x	x	x	x	x			s	x	s	s	x	s	s								11
x	x	x	s		x	x	x	sx	x			sx	sx	s		xs	x	xs	xs							12
x	x	x	s		x	x	x	x	x			sx	s	s		x	s	x	xs							13
x	x	x	s		x	x	x		x			s	sx	s	s	x	x	xs	x							14
x	x	x	s		x	x	x		xs			x	sx	s	s	x	x	x	s							15
x	x	s	sx		x	xs	x	xs	x			x		s	sx	x	x	x	s							16
x	**x**	**x**	**s**		**xs**	**x**	**x**	**sx**	**xs**	**sx**		**x**	**s**	**s**	**s**	**xs**	**x**	**x**	**sx**							17
x	x	x		s	x	x	x	s	xs	sx		x		s		xs	x	x	sx							18
x	x	x		s	x	xs	x	s	sx	x		x		s		xs	x	x	sx							19
x	x	x		s	sx	x	x	s	x	x		xs		s		xs	x	x	sx							20
x	**x**	**x**	**s**	**s**	**x**	**x**	**x**	**s**	**xs**	**x**		**xs**		**s**	**s**	**sx**	**x**	**x**	**sx**							21
x	x	x		s	x	xs	x	s	sx	x		x		s		xs	x	x	sx							22
x	x	xs		sx	x	x	x	s	xs	x		s		s		sx	x	x	x							23
x	x	x			xs	x	x	sx	x	x		s		s	s	sx	x	x	xs							24
x	x	x	s	s	x	x		s	s	x		x		s		x	x	x	x							25
s	**x**	**x**		**s**		**xs**	**sx**	**xs**	**sx**	**x**		**x**		**x**	**sx**	**x**	**x**	**x**	**xs**							26
x	x	x		s	xs	x		x	x	xs		x	s	s	sx	sx		x	x							27
x	x	x		s	x	x		sx	xs	x		x		s	s	sx	x	xs	x							28
	x	x	s	s	x			x	x	x		x	s	x	s	x	x		x		s					29
	x	x		x	x			xs	x			x	sx	x	s	x	x		x		s	sx				30
x	x	x	xs	x	x				x			x	x	s	s	x	x					sx	s	s		31
x	x	x	xs	s	x	x			x		s	x	sx	s	x	x	x					s				32
x	x	x	s	s	x	x			x		x	x	sx	s	s	xs	x	x								33
x	x	x	sx	s	x	x	sx		x		xs	xs	x	s	s	x	x									34
x	x	x	x	x	x	x	x				s	s	s	s	s	x	x	x								35
x	x	x	x	x	x	x	x				s	s	s	s	x	x		x				s				36
x	x	x	x	xs	x	x	xs				s	sx	sx	s	s	x	x	x								37
x	x	x	x	xs	x	x	xs				s	sx	sx	s	s	x	x	x								38
x		x	x	xs	x	x	xs	s			s	sx	sx		x	x	x	x			s					39
x		x	xs	x	x	xs	x	s			sx	sx	s	s	x	x	x	x								40
x		x		xs	x	x	xs	sx			sx	xs	sx	s	x	x	x	x				s				41
x		x		x	x	x	x	xs			s	x	sx	s	x	xs		x				sx			s	42
x		x	s	x	x	x	x				sx	xs	x	s	xs	x		x				sx			s	43
x		x	sx	x	x	x	x	s			s	xs	x	s	x	x		x				s				44
x		x	s	x	x	x	x	sx			sx	xs	s	s	xs	x	x	x								45
x		x	x	x	x	x	xs	s			sx	s	sx	s	xs	x	x	x								46
x		x	xs	x	x	x	x	s			s	sx	s	s	x	x	x	x								47
x		x		xs	xs	x	x	sx			sx	xs	sx	s	x	x	x	x				s				48
x		x		sx	x	x	x	sx			sx	xs	xs	s	xs	x	x	x				s				49
6	37	47	9	12	42	36	34	12	22	17	1	20	5	3	10	30	34	30	7	0	0	0	0	0	0	x
0	1	1	5	6	5	8	5	4	7	1	2	11	8	0	4	9	0	3	5	0	0	0	0	0	0	xs
0	0	0	4	7	1	2	2	9	3	2	8	8	15	0	7	8	0	0	6	0	0	4	0	0	0	sx
1	0	1	14	15	0	0	0	12	2	0	13	10	9	45	20	0	2	2	2	1	3	6	1	1	2	s

x - Played full 90 minutes
xs - Substituted off
sx - Substituted on
s - Non-playing Substitute

HARROGATE TOWN MATCH RESULTS 2018-19

Date	Comp	Opponents	H/A	Att:	Result		Goalscorers	Pos
Aug 4	NL	Sutton United	H	1378	D	2 - 2	Muldoon 60 Langmead 86	9
7	NL	Hartlepool United	A	3623	D	2 - 2	Knowles 60 Howe 90	11
11	NL	Bromley	A	1061	D	1 - 1	Knowles 73	12
14	NL	Barnet	H	1381	**W**	2 - 0	Emmett 23 Kitching 26	9
18	NL	Aldershot Town	A	1774	**W**	2 - 0	Knowles 57 Kinsella 63 (og)	7
25	NL	Solihull Moors	H	1180	**W**	3 - 1	Kitching 7 Thomson 75 Howe 78	3
27	NL	AFC Fylde	A	1709	D	0 - 0		4
Sept 1	NL	Eastleigh	H	1158	**W**	4 - 0	Muldoon 25 47 Beck 80 87	2
4	NL	Gateshead	A	846	**W**	3 - 2	Knowles 23 (Pen) Muldoon 56 Williams 85	1
8	NL	Havant & Waterlooville	H	1709	**W**	3 - 2	Howe 12 Knowles 52 Muldoon 57	1
15	NL	Maidstone United	A	2222	**W**	2 - 0	Howe 17 Muldoon 44	1
22	NL	Leyton Orient	H	2584	L	0 - 3		2
25	NL	Wrexham	H	2387	D	0 - 0		3
29	NL	Boreham Wood	A	566	**W**	4 - 2	Thomson 19 Williams 51 Ilesanmi 53 (og) Emmett 74	3
Oct 6	NL	Ebbsfleet United	A	1169	**W**	2 - 0	Howe 30 Williams 71	3
13	NL	Dover Athletic	H	1865	D	2 - 2	Williams 27 Langmead 90	4
20	**FAC 4Q**	**Wrexham**	**H**	**1540**	**D**	**0 - 0**		
23	**FAC 4Qr**	**Wrexham**	**A**	**2550**	**L**	**0 - 2**		
27	NL	Dagenham & Redbridge	A	1446	L	1 - 2	Leesley 83	5
30	NL	Barrow	H	1268	**W**	4 - 2	Jameson 53 (og) Muldoon 56 Falkingham 58 Beck 69	4
Nov 3	NL	Chesterfield	H	2291	D	1 - 1	Williams 90+7	4
24	NL	Braintree Town	H	1454	**W**	3 - 1	Muldoon 44 Thomson 64 Woods 90+3	4
27	NL	Salford City	H	1208	L	2 - 3	Muldoon 9 Kitching 25	5
Dec 1	NL	Maidenhead United	A	1090	**W**	2 - 1	Howe 11 Langmead 77	3
4	NL	Solihull Moors	A	794	L	0 - 2		3
8	NL	Aldershot Town	H	1362	**W**	4 - 1	Burrell 32 54 70 Muldoon 90+1	3
15	**FAT 1P**	**York City**	**H**	**1336**	**W**	**2 - 1**	**Knowles 27 Kitching 66**	
22	NL	Eastleigh	A	1622	L	1 - 2	Leesley 2	5
26	NL	FC Halifax Town	H	2310	L	1 - 2	Howe 37	6
29	NL	AFC Fylde	H	1603	L	1 - 2	Beck 82	6
Jan 1	NL	FC Halifax Town	A	1696	D	1 - 1	Thomson 6	6
5	NL	Sutton United	A	1841	L	1 - 2	Thomson 60	7
12	**FAT 2P**	**Dover Athletic**	**A**	**463**	**W**	**2 - 1**	**Muldoon 15 64**	
19	NL	Hartlepool United	H	2000	**W**	3 - 1	Kerry 4 Muldoon 50 Beck 68	6
Feb 2	**FAT 3P**	**Stockport County**	**H**	**1142**	**L**	**2 - 4**	**Keane 17 (og) Thomson 88**	
9	NL	Dover Athletic	A	997	**W**	3 - 2	Beck 6 84 Thomson 90+2	7
16	NL	Ebbsfleet United	H	1488	L	1 - 2	Muldoon 50	9
23	NL	Chesterfield	A	4661	**W**	1 - 0	Burrell 8	7
Mar 2	NL	Dagenham & Redbridge	H	1262	D	1 - 1	Howe 55	8
5	NL	Bromley	H	789	**W**	1 - 0	Muldoon 90+4	6
9	NL	Braintree Town	A	362	**W**	4 - 0	Emmett 1 Beck 10 56 Thomson 37	6
16	NL	Maidenhead United	H	1105	**W**	1 - 0	Beck 53	6
19	NL	Barnet	A	849	L	0 - 1		6
23	NL	Barrow	A	1934	D	2 - 2	Muldoon 47 Howe 69	6
27	NL	Salford City	H	1700	L	0 - 1		6
30	NL	Maidstone United	H	1134	D	2 - 2	Beck 21 Muldoon 62 (pen)	6
Apr 6	NL	Havant & Waterlooville	A	937	**W**	2 - 1	Woods 42 Thomson 81	6
13	NL	Boreham Wood	H	1216	L	0 - 1		6
19	NL	Leyton Orient	A	6665	L	0 - 2		6
22	NL	Gateshead	H	1629	**W**	2 - 0	Thewlis 41 Beck 55	6
27	NL	Wrexham	A	3690	L	1 - 2	Beck 11	6
May 1	**PO Q**	**AFC Fylde**	**A**	**1560**	**L**	**1 - 3**	**Burke 53 (og)**	

GOALSCORERS	SG	CSG	Pens	Hat tricks	Total
Muldoon	15	4	2		17
Beck	10	2			13
Howe	9	2			9
Thomson	9	2			9
Knowles	6	2	1		6
Opponent	5	1			5
Williams	5	3			5
Burrell	2	1		1	4
Kitching	4	1			4
Emmett	3	1			3
Langmead	3	2			3
Leesley	2	1			2
Woods	2	1			2
Falkingham	1	1			1
Kerry	1	1			1
Thewlis	1	1			1

Belshaw	Fallowfield	Howe (L)	Emmett	Kitching (L)	Burrell	Falkingham	Thomson	Muldoon	Williams	Knowles	Langmead	Leesley	Cracknell	Agnew	Kerry	Parker	Beck	Sutton (L)	Thewlis	Woods	Lees	Senior (L)	Mottley-Henry (L)	No.
x	xs	x	x	x	x	x	x	xs	x	x	sx	sx	s	s	s									1
x		x	x	x	x	x	x	xs	x	x	x	sx	s	s	s	s								2
x		x	x	x	x	x	xs	xs	x	x	x	sx	s	s	sx	s								3
x		x	x	x	x	x	x	xs	sx	xs	x	x	s	sx	s	s								4
x		x	x	x	x	x	xs	xs	sx	xs	x	x	s	sx	sx	s								5
x		x	x	x	x	x	x	xs	s	xs	x	x	s	sx	s		sx							6
x		x		x	x	xs	xs	x	sx	xs	x	x	s	sx	x	s	sx							7
x		x		x	x		x	xs	sx	xs	x	xs	s	x	x	s	sx	sx						8
x		x		x	x		xs	x	sx	xs	x	x	s	xs	x	s	sx	sx						9
x		x		x	x		x	xs	sx	xs	x	x	s	xs	x	s	sx	sx						10
x		x		x	x		x	xs	sx	xs	x	x	s	x	x	s	sx	s						11
x		x		x	x	x	x	x	sx	x	x		s	s	x	s	xs	s						12
x		x		x	x	x	xs	x	sx	xs	x	x	s	s	x		sx	s						13
x		x	sx	x	x	x	xs	xs	x	s	x	x	s	sx	xs		sx							14
x		x	xs	x	x	x	x	xs	x		x	x	s	sx	s		sx		s					15
x		x	x	x	x	x	x	xs	xs		x	x	s	s	s		sx		sx					16
x	**x**	**s**	**x**	**x**	**x**	**x**	**xs**	**sx**	**xs**		**x**	**x**	**s**	**sx**	**s**		**sx**		**xs**					17
x	**s**	**x**	**x**	**x**	**x**	**x**	**s**	**sx**	**xs**		**x**	**x**	**s**	**xs**	**sx**		**sx**		**xs**					18
x		x	x	x	x	x	x	s	s		x	x	s	s	s		x		x					19
x	xs	x	xs	x	x	x	x	x	sx		sx	x	s	s	sx		xs							20
x	x	x	x	x	x	x	xs	xs	sx		s	x	s	s	sx		x							21
x	x	x	x	x	x	x	x	xs	s		s	xs	s		sx		x			sx				22
x	s	x	x	x	x	x	x	xs		sx	x		s		s		x		xs	sx				23
x	x	x	x		x	x	xs	xs	s	sx	x	x	s		s		x			sx				24
x	x	x	x		x	x	xs	xs	sx	sx	x	x	s		s		xs			sx				25
x	x	x	xs	x	x	x	x	x	sx	xs		x	s		s		s			sx				26
x	**x**		**xs**	**x**	**x**	**x**	**x**	**xs**	**sx**	**xs**	**x**	**x**	**s**		**sx**		**s**			**sx**				27
x	x	x	xs	x	x	x	x	s	sx	xs		x	s		xs		sx			sx				28
x	x	x	sx	x	x	x	s	xs	sx	xs		x	s		x		sx			xs				29
x		x	s	x	x	x	sx	xs	sx	xs	x	x	s		x		sx			xs				30
x	x	x	x		x	x	x	sx	s		x	xs	s		x		x			s	s			31
x	x	x	xs	s	x	x	x	sx	sx		x	xs	s		xs		x			sx				32
x	**x**	**x**	**xs**	**x**	**x**	**x**	**x**	**xs**	**s**	**sx**	**s**		**s**		**x**		**x**			**sx**				33
x	x	x	xs	x	x	x	x	xs	sx	sx		s	s		x		xs			sx				34
x	**x**	**xs**	**xs**	**x**	**x**	**x**	**x**	**xs**	**sx**			**sx**	**s**		**x**		**x**			**s**		**sx**		35
x	x	sx	x	x	x	x	x	xs	sx				s		xs		x			s		xs	sx	36
x	x	x	x	x	x	x	xs	xs	sx				s		x		x			s		s	sx	37
x	x	x	xs	s	x	x	x	xs	sx		x		s		x		x			s			sx	38
x	x	x	x	s	x	x	x	xs	sx		x		s		xs		x			s			sx	39
x	x	x	x	s	x	x	x	x	s		x		s	s	x		x			s				40
x	x	x	xs		x	x	x	xs	sx		x		s	sx	x		xs			sx		s		41
x	x	x	x		x	x	x	x	s		x	s	s	s	x		x					s		42
x	x	x	xs		x	x	xs	x			x	sx	s	s	x		x			sx		s		43
x	xs	x	xs		x	x	xs	x	sx		x	sx	s	s	x		x					sx		44
x	x	x	xs	s	x	xs	sx	x	sx		x	x	s		x		x			s				45
x	x	x		s	x	x	sx	x	sx		x	x	s	xs	x		xs			s				46
x	s	x		x	x	x	x	x			x	x	s	sx	xs		s		sx	xs				47
x	s	x		x	x	x	xs	xs	sx		x	x	s	x			sx		sx	xs				48
x	x	x	xs	x	x	x	s	sx		sx		sx	s		x		xs		x			xs		49
x	xs	x		x	x	x	sx	sx		s			s	sx	x		x		xs	xs		x		50
s		s		x	s	s	x	x	x		x	x	x	x			x		s	x	x			51
x	**x**	**x**	**x**	**x**	**x**	**x**	**sx**	**xs**		**sx**		**sx**	**s**	**s**			**x**		**xs**			**xs**		52
51	26	47	22	39	51	45	30	14	6	4	37	28	1	4	24	0	21	0	2	1	1	1	0	x
0	4	1	15	0	0	2	14	30	3	14	0	4	0	4	6	0	7	0	5	5	0	3	0	xs
0	0	1	2	0	0	0	5	6	29	7	2	8	0	10	7	0	16	3	3	12	0	2	4	sx
1	4	2	1	6	1	1	3	2	8	2	3	2	51	14	12	10	3	3	2	9	1	4	0	s

x - Played full 90 minutes
xs - Substituted off
sx - Substituted on
s - Non-playing Substitute

HARTLEPOOL UNITED MATCH RESULTS 2018-19

Date	Comp	Opponents	H/A	Att:	Result		Goalscorers	Pos
Aug 4	NL	Maidstone United	A	2599	D	1 - 1	Noble 42	11
7	NL	Harrogate Town	H	3623	D	2 - 2	Muir 53 Cassidy 70	12
11	NL	Ebbsfleet United	H	3182	L	0 - 1		16
14	NL	Braintree Town	A	606	D	1 - 1	Muir 25	18
18	NL	Maidenhead United	H	2925	**W**	2 - 1	James 47 Featherstone 60	14
25	NL	Dagenham & Redbridge	A	1212	**W**	2 - 1	Woods 48 Noble 63 (pen)	12
27	NL	Chesterfield	H	3773	**W**	1 - 0	Featherstone 17	8
Sept 1	NL	Havant & Waterlooville	A	1272	**W**	2 - 1	Noble 23 (pen) 90 (pen)	7
4	NL	Barrow	H	3361	D	0 - 0		6
8	NL	Solihull Moors	A	1311	**W**	1 - 0	Noble 58	4
15	NL	Eastleigh	H	3302	D	1 - 1	Muir 24	6
22	NL	FC Halifax Town	A	2360	**W**	2 - 1	Noble 52 (pen) Featherstone 64	5
25	NL	Salford City	A	2420	L	0 - 3		8
29	NL	Aldershot Town	H	3251	D	1 - 1	Muir 33	8
Oct 6	NL	Boreham Wood	H	2988	**W**	2 - 0	Davies 34 82	6
13	NL	Leyton Orient	A	6871	D	0 - 0		8
20	**FAC 4Q**	**Kidsgrove Athletic**	**H**	**2703**	**W**	**1 - 0**	**Muir 8**	
27	NL	Sutton United	H	2788	L	2 - 3	Muir 47 Noble 50	9
30	NL	Wrexham	A	4665	L	0 - 1		9
Nov 3	NL	Bromley	A	1516	L	0 - 4		9
10	**FAC 1P**	**Gillingham**	**A**	**2224**	**D**	**0 - 0**		
18	NL	Barnet	H	3545	L	1 - 3	Kioso 10	12
21	**FAC 1Pr**	**Gillingham**	**H**	**1873**	**L**	**3 - 4**	**Magney 21 McLaughlin 32 O'Neill 114**	
24	NL	Dover Athletic	A	1027	L	1 - 2	Hawkes 84	12
27	NL	AFC Fylde	H	1721	L	1 - 2	Noble 84 (pen)	13
Matthew Bates sacked as manager, Director of Football, Craig Hignett, takes temporary charge.								
Dec 1	NL	Dagenham & Redbridge	H	2030	L	1 - 2	Noble 13 (pen)	14
8	NL	Maidenhead United	A	1157	**W**	1 - 0	Hawkes 17	13
Richard Money is appointed full-time manager.								
15	**FAT 1P**	**Leamington**	**A**	**334**	**W**	**1 - 0**	**Donaldson 64**	
22	NL	Havant & Waterlooville	H	3024	D	1 - 1	Noble 18	13
26	NL	Gateshead	A	2678	L	1 - 2	Noble 87 (pen)	14
29	NL	Chesterfield	A	4752	D	1 - 1	James 45+2	16
Jan 1	NL	Gateshead	H	3468	**W**	2 - 1	Noble 7 (pen) McLaughlin 66	14
5	NL	Maidstone United	H	2929	L	1 - 2	Cassidy 5	14
12	**FAT 2P**	**Telford United**	**H**	**1920**	**L**	**1 - 2**	**Anderson 90+6**	
19	NL	Harrogate Town	A	2000	L	1 - 3	Kabamba 57	15
Richard Money moves 'upstairs' at the club with Craig Hignett taking over as manager.								
26	NL	Braintree Town	H	2769	**W**	2 - 1	Kabamba 52 Hawkes 59 (pen)	15
Feb 9	NL	Leyton Orient	H	3297	D	1 - 1	Kabamba 45+4	13
16	NL	Boreham Wood	A	679	**W**	4 - 0	Kabamba 7 88 Hawkes 50 57 (pen)	13
19	NL	Ebbsfleet United	A	1265	D	0 - 0		13
23	NL	Bromley	H	2985	L	1 - 2	Noble 90+4	11
Mar 2	NL	Sutton United	A	1923	D	2 - 2	Kitching 65 James 75	13
9	NL	Dover Athletic	H	3431	**W**	3 - 2	Hawkes 70 (pen) 73 (pen) Molyneux 90+1	12
12	NL	AFC Fylde	A	1272	L	2 - 4	Donaldson 46 Hawkes 75	13
16	NL	Barnet	A	1269	D	0 - 0		12
23	NL	Wrexham	H	3888	**W**	1 - 0	Hawkes 24 (pen)	12
30	NL	Eastleigh	A	1863	L	2 - 3	Kitching 6 Kabamba 71	13
Apr 6	NL	Solihull Moors	H	2981	L	0 - 1		16
13	NL	Aldershot Town	A	1589	D	1 - 1	Holohan 80	16
19	NL	FC Halifax Town	H	3018	**W**	2 - 1	James 32 Molyneux 54	14
22	NL	Barrow	A	3007	L	0 - 1		17
27	NL	Salford City	H	3582	**W**	3 - 2	Featherstone 50 Kabamba 69 James 75	16

GOALSCORERS	SG	CSG	Pens	Hat tricks	Total
Noble	12	2	8		13
Hawkes	7	1	5		9
Kabamba*	6	4			7
Muir	6	2			6
James	5	1			5
Featherstone	4	1			4
Cassidy	2	1			2
Davies	1	1			2
Donaldson	2	1			2
Kitching	2	1			2
McLaughlin	2	1			2
Molyneux	2	1			2
Holohan	1	1			1
Kioso	1	1			1
Magney	1	1			1
O'Neill	1	1			1
Woods	1	1			1

Loach	Magnay	Davies	Noble	Kitching	Kioso	Donaldson	Featherstone	Muir	James	Cassidy	Hawkes	Dinanga (L)	Newton	Woods	Anderson	McLaughlin	Laing	Richardson	Catterick	Hawkins	Murphy	O'Neill (L)	Butler (L)	Rodgers (L)	Miller	Scott	Raynes (L)	Molyneux (L)	Kabamba (L)	Amos (L)	Cunningham	Kerr	Edgar	Holohan	Bale	No.
X	X	X	X	X	X	X	XS	XS	XS	X	SX	SX	SX	S	S																					1
X	X	X	X	X	X	X	XS	XS	X	X		S	SX	S	S	SX																				2
X	X	XS	X	X	XS	S	S	XS	X	XS		SX	SX			X	SX	X																		3
X	X		XS	X	X	X	X	X	XS	SX		S	SX	XS	X	SX	S																			4
X	X		X	X	X	X	X	X	XS	SX		S	S	XS	X	SX	S																			5
X	X		X	X	X	X	X	X	X			SX	S	XS	X	SX	S		S																	6
X	X		X	X	X	X	X	XS	X	S		SX	S	XS	X	SX	S																			7
X	X		XS	X	X	X	X	X	XS		S	SX	SX	XS	X	SX		S																		8
X	X		X	X	X	X	X	X	X		S	S	S	XS	X	SX		S																		9
X	X		X	X	X	X	X	X	X		S	S	S	SX	X	XS		S																		10
X	X		X	X	X	XS	X	X	XS		S	SX	S	SX	X	XS		SX																		11
X	X	XS	X	X	X		X	XS	XS		SX	SX	S	S	X	X		SX																		12
X	X	X	X	X			X	XS	X		S	SX	XS	SX	X	X		S		S																13
X	XS	X	X	X	X	X	X	XS	X		SX	S	S	XS	SX	SX																				14
X	X	X	X	X	XS	X	X	X	X		S	S		S	SX	X				S																15
X	X	X	XS	X	X	X	X	X	XS		SX	SX	SX	XS				S		S																16
X	**X**	**X**	**XS**	**X**	**X**	**X**	**X**	**XS**	**X**		**SX**	**SX**		**XS**	**S**	**SX**		**S**	**S**	**S**																17
X	X	X	X	X	X	X	XS	X	X		S	SX		SX	S	XS				S																18
X	X	X	X	S	X	X	XS	XS	SX		SX	X	SX		X	XS				S																19
X	X		X	XS	X	X	X	XS	SX		SX	X	SX		XS	X		S			S															20
X	**X**		**X**	**X**		**XS**	**X**	**SX**	**XS**		**S**	**XS**	**SX**	**S**	**X**	**X**		**X**	**S**		**S**	**SX**														21
X			X	X	X	X	X	SX	X		S	SX	S		X	XS		X				XS	S													22
X	**X**	**XS**	**X**	**X**	**S**	**X**	**XS**	**SX**	**XS**		**S**	**XS**	**SX**		**SX**	**X**		**X**	**S**			**SX**														23
X	X			X	X	X	X	SX	XS		SX	SX			X	X		XS	S			XS	S													24
X	X		SX	X	S	X	X	SX	X		XS		XS		X	XS		X				SX	S													25
X	X		X	XS	X	X	X	XS	X		XS	SX	SX			SX		X				S	S													26
X	X		X	X	XS	X	X	X	X		XS	S			X	SX		SX				S	S													27
X	**X**			**X**		**X**	**X**	**X**	**SX**		**XS**	**XS**				**X**		**X**	**S**		**S**	**SX**		**X**	**S**											28
X	X	X	X	X		X	XS	X	XS		SX		SX		S	X		SX		S				XS												29
X	X	X	X	X		X	S	X	SX		SX		XS		S	S		X		XS				X												30
X	X		X	X	S	X	SX	X	X		XS		S		X	S		X				S		X												31
X	X		X	X	SX	X	X	X	X		XS				X	SX		XS	S				S			S										32
X	XS		X	X	SX	X	S	SX	X	X	XS				X	S		X	S					X												33
X	**X**			**XS**	**SX**	**X**	**X**	**X**	**X**		**SX**				**SX**	**XS**		**XS**	**S**					**X**		**S**				**X**						34
X	XS			X	SX	X	XS	S	XS	X	SX				SX			X									X	X	X	S						35
X				SX	X	X	X	S	SX	SX	X				X			XS	S								X	X	XS	XS						36
X			SX	S	X	X	X	S	X		X				XS					S							X	XS	X	X	SX					37
X			XS	SX	X	X	X	SX	XS		XS				X			S		SX					S				X	X	X					38
X			X	SX	X	X	X	SX	XS		XS				X			S		S								SX	X	XS	X					39
X			X	SX	X	X	X	XS			SX				X			S								S		SX	X	XS	XS					40
X			X	X		X	X	S	X		X				X				S	S								SX	X	S	XS	X				41
X			XS	XS		X	X	S	X		X				X				S	SX								SX	X	SX		X	XS			42
X			SX	S	XS	X	X	S	X		X				X					S								X	X	S		X	X			43
X			XS	S	X	X	SX	S	X		XS				X													X	X	S		X	X	SX		44
X			XS	SX	X	X	X	S	SX		XS				X													X	X		XS	X		S	SX	45
X			XS	XS	X	XS	X	SX	X		SX				X													X	X	S		S	X	SX		46
X			XS	SX	X	X	X	S	X						XS				S									X	X			X	X	SX		47
X				X	X	X	X	SX	X						S				S									XS	X	S		X	X	XS	SX	48
X			SX		X	X	X	S	X						X				S									XS	X	S		X	X	XS	SX	49
X			SX		X	X	X	SX	XS		SX				S													X	X	XS		X	X	XS	S	50
X			XS	X	XS	X	X	S	X		SX				X			SX										X	X				XS	SX	S	51
51	31	11	29	34	32	45	39	17	29	4	5	2	0	0	31	10	0	11	0	0	0	0	0	5	0	0	3	9	16	3	2	9	7	0	0	x
0	3	3	11	5	5	3	7	12	15	1	11	3	3	9	3	7	0	4	0	1	0	2	0	1	0	0	0	3	1	4	3	0	2	3	0	xs
0	0	0	5	6	4	0	2	11	6	3	16	14	12	4	5	12	1	5	0	2	0	4	0	0	0	0	0	4	0	1	1	0	0	4	3	sx
0	0	0	0	4	3	1	3	11	0	1	10	8	10	5	8	3	4	10	15	11	3	3	6	0	2	3	0	0	0	7	0	1	0	1	2	s

x - Played full 90 minutes
xs - Substituted off
sx - Substituted on
s - Non-playing Substitute

HAVANT & WATERLOOVILLE MATCH RESULTS 2018-19

Date	Comp	Opponents	H/A	Att:	Result	Goalscorers	Pos
Aug 4	NL	Barrow	A	1389	L 0 - 3		
7	NL	Boreham Wood	H	1348	D 0 - 0		
11	NL	AFC Fylde	H	1182	D 1 - 1	Kabamba 48	
14	NL	Dover Athletic	A	997	L 3 - 4	Fogden 48 Pavey 50 Lewis 52	
18	NL	Braintree Town	A	407	**W** 4 - 3	Williams 1 Rose 45 Kabamba 90+4 Rutherford 90+6	
25	NL	Salford City	H	1679	D 1 - 1	Pavey 22	
27	NL	Bromley	A	1413	L 0 - 4		
Sept 1	NL	Hartlepool United	H	1272	L 1 - 2	Woodford 83	21
5	NL	Aldershot Town	H	1989	**W** 2 - 1	Lewis 27 Robinson 83	18
8	NL	Harrogate Town	A	1709	L 2 - 3	Kabamba 6 63	20
15	NL	Sutton United	H	1273	L 1 - 2	Kabamba 32	21
22	NL	Ebbsfleet United	A	1141	D 1 - 1	Cosgrove 2	21
25	NL	Barnet	A	965	D 2 - 2	Robinson A 71 92	21
29	NL	Solihull Moors	H	1115	L 0 - 1		21
Oct 6	NL	Wrexham	A	4323	L 0 - 1		21
13	NL	Gateshead	H	1250	L 0 - 1		21
20	**FAC 4Q**	**Metropolitan Police**	**A**	**400**	**L 0 - 1**		
27	NL	Leyton Orient	A	5043	L 0 - 4		22
30	NL	Maidenhead United	H	952	**W** 7 - 0	Cordner 8 Williams 41 Rutherford 63 80 Pavey 64 66 Bradley 85	22
Nov 3	NL	FC Halifax Town	H	1258	**W** 2 - 1	Cordner 48 Rutherford 64	20
17	NL	Chesterfield	A	4082	D 0 - 0		20
24	NL	Maidstone United	H	1308	**W** 5 - 2	Rutherford 11 63 85 Ayunga 35 Bradley 54	18
27	NL	Dagenham & Redbridge	A	1054	L 1 - 3	Ayunga 85	19
Dec 1	NL	Salford City	A	2181	L 0 - 3		19
8	NL	Braintree Town	H	858	**W** 2 - 1	Rutherford 55 90	19
15	**FAT 1P**	**Dover Athletic**	**A**	**327**	**D 2 - 2**	**Kabamba 28 Rutherford 70**	
22	NL	Hartlepool United	A	3024	D 1 - 1	Frost 12	18
26	NL	Eastleigh	H	1884	D 2 - 2	Robinson A 80 Strugnell 89	18
29	NL	Bromley	H	1341	L 0 - 3		18
Jan 1	NL	Eastleigh	A	2104	L 1 - 2	Jalloh 82	20
5	NL	Barrow	H	1074	**W** 2 - 0	Lewis 55 Williams 90+1	19
8	**FAT 1Pr**	**Dover Athletic**	**H**	**229**	**L 0 - 1**		
19	NL	Boreham Wood	A	511	**W** 3 - 1	Paterson 9 Robinson A 16 Jalloh 90	18
26	NL	Dover Athletic	H	1024	D 0 - 0		18
Feb 9	NL	Gateshead	A	531	D 0 - 0		18
16	NL	Wrexham	H	1658	L 2 - 3	Quigley 16 (pen) Rutherford 69	21
19	NL	AFC Fylde	A	1192	L 2 - 6	Paterson 14 (pen) Rutherford 87	21
23	NL	FC Halifax Town	A	1181	D 0 - 0		21
Mar 2	NL	Leyton Orient	H	2058	L 1 - 2	Rutherford 67	21
9	NL	Maidstone United	A	1901	L 0 - 2		21
12	NL	Dagenham & Redbridge	H	713	**W** 3 - 0	Rutherford 3 Harris 74 Lewis 90	21
16	NL	Chesterfield	H	1097	L 1 - 2	Paul 27	21
26	NL	Maidenhead United	A	1230	L 1 - 2	Paterson 89	21
30	NL	Sutton United	A	1816	D 2 - 2	Cordner 39 59	21
Apr 6	NL	Harrogate Town	H	937	L 1 - 2	Paterson 22 (pen)	21
13	NL	Solihull Moors	A	1179	L 2 - 3	Quigley 1 Gudger 86 (og)	21 (R)
19	NL	Ebbsfleet United	H	1097	D 3 - 3	Rutherford 21 44 McNamara 45+3	21
22	NL	Aldershot Town	A	1446	L 0 - 2		22
27	NL	Barnet	H	1003	L 0 - 2		22

GOALSCORERS	SG	CSG	Pens	Hat tricks	Total		SG	CSG	Pens	Hat tricks	Total
Rutherford	11	2		1	16	Quigley	2	1	1		2
Kabamba	5	2			6	Cosgrove	1	1			1
Robinson A	4	1			5	Fogden	1	1			1
Cordner	3	2			4	Frost*	1	1			1
Lewis	4	1			4	Harris	1	1			1
Paterson*	4	1	2		4	McNamara	1	1			1
Pavey	3	1			4	Opponent	1	1			1
Williams	3	1			3	Paul	1	1			1
Ayunga	2	2			2	Rose	1	1			1
Bradley	2	1			2	Strugnell	1	1			1
Jalloh	2	1			2	Woodford	1	1			1

No.	Young	Williams	Stock	Harris	Fogden	Pavey	Kabamba	Tarbuck	Robinson A	Rose	Robinson P	Lewis	Carter	Huggins	Woodford	Rutherford	Cosgrove	Strugnell	Sekajja	Simpson (L)	Dudzinski	Ridge	Cordner (L)	Wood (L)	Bradley (L)	Boerstra Leeflang	Ayunga (L)	Frost (L)	Paul	Jalloh	Molyneaux L	Robertson (L)	James (L)	Patterson	Quigley (L)	Banjo	Šarkić (L)	Donovan (L)	Bilboe (L)	McNamara (L)
1	x	xs	x	x	x	xs	x	x	x	x	xs	sx	sx	sx	s	s																								
2	x	xs	xs	x	x	x	xs	x	x	x	x	s	sx	sx	s	sx																								
3	x	x	x	x	x	xs	xs	x	xs	x	x	sx	sx		s	s	sx																							
4	x	x	x	x	x	sx	xs	sx	xs	x	x	x	sx		s	s		xs																						
5	x	x	x	x	x	xs	x	xs	s	x		x	s	s	x	sx	sx																							
6	x	xs	x	xs	x	xs	x	xs		x	sx	x	s		x	sx	s	sx																						
7	x	x	sx		x	x	x		xs	x	x	sx	xs	s	x	s	sx	xs																						
8	x	xs	x	x	x	s	x	x		xs	x	xs	x		sx	sx	s		sx																					
9	x	x	xs	x	xs	xs	x	s	sx		x	x			x	s	sx	x	sx																					
10	x	x		x		sx	x	s	xs		x	x		x	x	s	xs	xs	sx	sx																				
11	x	x	x	x		sx	x	sx		s	x	x		xs	x	sx	xs		xs	s																				
12		x	x	x		sx	x	s	sx			xs		x	x	s	xs		sx		x	xs	x																	
13		x	x	x		x	x	sx			sx	x		xs	xs		s		sx	s	x	xs	x																	
14		xs		x		xs	x	x	x	s		xs		s	x		sx	sx	x	sx	x		x																	
15			x	xs		sx	x	x	x	s	s	xs		x	x		sx	sx	xs		x		x																	
16			x			x	x	x	x	x	x	s			sx		sx	s	sx		x		x	xs	xs															
17						x	x	x	x	xs	x	x			x		sx	sx	sx		x			xs	xs															
18			x	xs		sx	x	x			s	x		sx	s		xs	x	xs		x		x	x	sx															
19		xs	x			x	xs	x	x		xs			sx	s	sx	s	x			x		x	x	sx															
20		xs	x			xs	sx	x	x		x			s	s	xs	sx	x			x		x	x	sx															
21		x	x			x	sx	xs	x		x			s	sx	xs	s	x			x		x		xs	sx														
22		x	x				sx	s				xs		sx	x	x	s	x	sx		x		x		x	xs	xs													
23		xs	x				sx	sx	xs					s	x	x	sx	x	s		x		x		x	xs	x													
24			x	x			sx	x	x			xs		s	x	xs	s	x	sx		x			xs		sx	x													
25		xs	x				xs	x	x		xs	s		s	sx	x	sx				x		x	x	sx		x													
26		x	x	xs			x	s	x	s		x			sx	x		x			x		x		x			s	s											
27		x	xs	x			x	sx	x			xs			s	xs		x			x		x	sx	s			x	sx											
28		x		xs	sx		x	sx	x			x			s	sx	xs	x			x		x		s			x	xs											
29		sx					xs	x	x	x		s				x		x			x		x	xs	s	xs		sx	x	sx										
30		x			sx		x	x	x			xs			x	xs		x	s		x		x		sx			xs	s	sx										
31		x			sx		x	xs	x			x			x	xs		x	s		x		x		s			xs	sx	sx										
32		x			xs		x	x		x		x		s	xs	sx		sx	xs		x		x					sx	x		s									
33		x			xs				x	sx		x			s	x			s		x		x					sx	xs	sx		x	x	xs						
34		x			xs				x	sx		x			s	xs			s		x		x					sx	xs	sx		x	x	x						
35		x			x				x	x		xs			s	sx		sx	s		x		x						x	sx			xs	xs	x					
36		xs		s	x				x	x					s	x		sx	sx		x		x						x	xs			xs	sx	x					
37		xs		xs	x				x	s		x			x	sx		x			x		x						xs	s			sx	x	sx					
38		x			x				xs	x		x			s	x		x	s		x		x						sx	sx			xs	sx	xs					
39				s	x				x	x		xs			sx	x		x	sx		x		x						s	xs			xs	sx	x					
40				s	x				x	x		xs	sx		xs	x		x	s		x		x						sx	xs				sx	x					
41				xs	x				x	sx		sx	xs	x	sx	x		x			x		x						x	s				s	xs					
42				x	x					sx		x	xs	x	s	x		x			x		x						xs	s				sx	xs	sx				
43		x		x	x					sx		x	xs	s	s	x		x					x							sx				sx	xs		x	xs		
44		x		s	x							s	xs		xs	x		x					x						sx	sx				xs	sx			x	x	x
45		x		xs						x	xs	sx	s		s	x							x						x	sx				xs	sx			x	x	x
46		x		s	sx				x	x		sx	x		s	x		x					x						s						xs			xs	x	x
47		x			x							x	x	s	x	x		x					x						xs	s	s				sx	s			x	x
48		x			x				x			xs	sx	xs	x	x		x			x		x						sx	sx	s			s	xs					
49		xs		xs	x				xs	sx			x	sx	x	x		x			s		x						x		s				sx				x	
x	11	27	20	16	21	7	21	16	27	17	12	20	4	5	19	19	0	26	1	0	32	0	36	4	3	0	3	2	7	0	0	2	2	2	4	0	1	2	5	4
xs	0	12	3	9	4	7	6	4	7	2	4	12	5	3	4	7	5	3	4	0	0	2	0	4	3	3	1	2	6	3	0	0	4	4	6	0	0	2	0	0
sx	0	1	1	0	4	6	5	6	2	6	2	6	6	6	7	10	11	7	11	2	0	0	0	1	5	2	0	4	6	11	0	0	1	6	5	1	0	0	0	0
s	0	0	0	5	0	1	0	5	1	5	2	5	3	11	18	7	7	1	8	2	1	0	0	0	4	0	0	1	4	4	4	0	0	2	0	1	0	0	0	0

x - Played full 90 minutes
xs - Substituted off
sx - Substituted on
s - Non-playing Substitute

LEYTON ORIENT MATCH RESULTS 2018-19

Date	Comp	Opponents	H/A	Att:	Result		Goalscorers	Pos
Aug 4	NL	Salford City	A	2156	D	1 - 1	Hogan 8 (og)	12
7	NL	Ebbsfleet United	H	4710	D	1 - 1	Brophy 18	13
11	NL	Barrow	H	4304	D	2 - 2	Bonne 55 80	13
14	NL	Maidstone United	A	3037	**W**	2 - 1	Koroma 10 Ekpiteta 35	16
18	NL	Boreham Wood	H	3767	**W**	1 - 0	Bonne 69 (pen)	9
25	NL	Gateshead	A	1052	D	1 - 1	Ekpiteta 89	9
27	NL	Dover Athletic	H	4641	**W**	3 - 0	McAnuff 50 Koroma 81 Harrold 90+2	5
Sept 1	NL	Chesterfield	A	4735	**W**	1 - 0	Dayton 78	5
4	NL	Solihull Moors	H	4250	**W**	3 - 0	Lee 45 Bonne 85 Harrold 90	2
8	NL	FC Halifax Town	A	1927	D	1 - 1	Alabi 90	3
15	NL	Barnet	H	5607	**W**	3 - 1	Coulson 11 Dayton 68 Bonne 78	3
22	NL	Harrogate Town	A	2584	**W**	3 - 0	Bonne 23 McAnuff 36 69	1
25	NL	Braintree Town	A	2574	**W**	5 - 1	Bonne 8 (pen) 63 70 Ekpiteta 41 Koroma 57	1
29	NL	Sutton United	H	5627	L	0 - 1		2
Oct 6	NL	Maidenhead United	A	2016	**W**	2 - 0	Bonne 11 Alabi 30	2
13	NL	Hartlepool United	H	6871	D	0 - 0		3
20	**FAC 4Q**	**Maidstone United**	**A**	**1906**	**L**	**0 - 2**		
27	NL	Havant & Waterlooville	H	5043	**W**	4 - 0	Coulson 13 Lewis 18 (og) Lee 39 Bonne 60	1
30	NL	Eastleigh	A	1938	D	1 - 1	Bonne 66	3
Nov 3	NL	AFC Fylde	A	2142	**W**	3 - 1	Bonne 5 Koroma 43 51	2
17	NL	Bromley	H	6058	**W**	3 - 1	McAnuff 56 Koroma 59 Bonne 77	1
24	NL	Wrexham	A	6248	**W**	2 - 0	Bonne 86 Brophy 90	1
27	NL	Aldershot Town	H	4289	D	0 - 0		1
Dec 1	NL	Gateshead	H	4636	**W**	2 - 0	Koroma 59 Bonne 90+6	1
8	NL	Boreham Wood	A	1602	L	0 - 1		1
15	**FAT 1P**	**Beaconsfield Town**	**H**	**1177**	**W**	**4 - 0**	**Elokobi 16 Brophy 55 Clay 76 Gorman 83**	
22	NL	Chesterfield	H	4755	**W**	3 - 1	Koroma 8 Ekpiteta 62 Bonne 85	1
26	NL	Dagenham & Redbridge	A	3694	L	1 - 2	Koroma 73	1
29	NL	Dover Athletic	A	2270	D	0 - 0		1
Jan 1	NL	Dagenham & Redbridge	H	6001	**W**	1 - 0	Bonne 32	1
5	NL	Salford City	H	6937	L	0 - 3		1
12	**FAT 2P**	**Wrexham**	**A**	**1949**	**W**	**1 - 0**	**Harrold 63 (pen)**	
19	NL	Ebbsfleet United	A	3020	L	0 - 2		1
26	NL	Maidstone United	H	5488	**W**	3 - 0	Maguire-Drew 33 Bonne 56 90+5 (pen)	1
Feb 2	**FAT 3P**	**Blyth Spartans**	**H**	**1842**	**W**	**1 - 0**	**Turley 84**	
9	NL	Hartlepool United	A	3297	D	1 - 1	McAnuff 22	1
16	NL	Maidenhead United	H	5337	L	0 - 1		3
23	**FAT 4P**	**Brackley Town**	**A**	**1563**	**W**	**2 - 1**	**Harrold 74 Happe 83**	
Mar 2	NL	Havant & Waterlooville	A	2058	**W**	2 - 1	Maguire-Drew 35 Coulson 73	3
5	NL	Barrow	A	1130	**W**	3 - 2	Ling 13 Simpson 47 Maguire-Drew 69	2
9	NL	Wrexham	H	6643	**W**	1 - 0	Ekpiteta 72	1
12	NL	Aldershot Town	A	1989	**W**	2 - 1	Coulson 35 38	1
16	**FAT SF1**	**AFC Telford United**	**H**	**3622**	**W**	**1 - 0**	**Bonne 54**	
23	**FAT SF2**	**AFC Telford United**	**A**	**3478**	**W**	**2 - 1**	**Harrold 6 Coulson 77**	
26	NL	AFC Fylde	H	4696	**W**	2 - 0	Ekpiteta 15 Bonne 24 (pen)	1
30	NL	Barnet	A	3648	D	0 - 0		1
Apr 2	NL	Bromley	A	3047	L	1 - 2	Coulson 45+2	1
6	NL	FC Haliffax Town	H	5458	D	2 - 2	Koroma 45+2 Harrold 90+4	2
9	NL	Eastleigh	H	5203	**W**	3 - 2	Koroma 10 Bonne 57 Brophy 61	1
13	NL	Sutton United	A	3339	**W**	2 - 1	Happe 64 Bonne 90 (pen)	1
19	NL	Harrogate Town	H	6665	**W**	2 - 0	Coulson 3 Harrold 90+3	1
22	NL	Solihull Moors	A	3681	D	0 - 0		1
27	NL	Braintree Town	H	8241	D	0 - 0		1
M 18	**FAT Final**	**AFC Fylde**	**N**	**42962**	**L**	**0 - 1**		

GOALSCORERS	SG	CSG	Pens	Hat tricks	Total
Bonne	20	5	5	1	24
Koroma	10	2			11
Coulson	7	1			9
Harrold	7	1	1		7
Ekpiteta	6	1			6
McAnuff	4	1			5
Brophy	4	1			4
Maguire-Drew	3	1			3
Alabi	2	1			2
Dayton	2	1			2
Happe	2	1			2
Lee	2	1			2
Opponent	2	1			2
Clay	1	1			1
Elokobi	1	1			1
Gorman	1	1			1
Ling	1	1			1
Simpson	1	1			1
Turley	1	1			1

Brill	Ling	Coulson	Lawless	Widdowson	Elokobi	Koroma	Clay	McAnuff	Alabi	Bonne	Brophy	Dayton	Lee	Ekpiteta	Sargeant	Happe	Judd	Harrold	Gorman	Sweeney J	Lumeka (L)	Sotiriou	Janata	Maguire-Drew	Turley (L)	Ogie	Shabni B	Simpson	No.
x	xs	x	xs	x	x	xs	x	x	x	x	sx	sx	sx	s	s														1
x	x	x	xs	x	xs	sx	x	x	x	x	xs	s	sx	sx	s														2
x	x	x	s	x		sx	x	x	xs	x	x	sx	xs	x	s	s													3
x	sx	x	sx	x		x	x		sx	x	xs	xs	x	x	s	s	xs												4
x	s	xs	sx	x		x	x	x	sx	x		xs	xs	x	s	sx	x												5
x		x		x		x	x	x	sx	x		xs	xs	x	s	s	xs	sx	sx										6
x		x	x	x		x	xs	x		x		xs	x	x	s	s	x	sx	sx										7
x		x		x		xs	x	x		x		x	x	x	s	s	x	sx	s		s								8
x		x	sx	x		x	x	xs		x		xs	xs	x	s	s	x	sx			sx								9
x		x	s	x		x	xs	x	sx	x		xs	x	x	s	s	x	sx											10
x		x		x		xs	x	x	sx	xs		x	xs	x	s	s	x	sx	sx										11
x		x		x		xs	xs	x	sx	xs		x	x	x	s	s	x	sx	sx										12
x		x		x		x	xs	x	sx	x	sx	xs	xs	x	s	s	x		sx										13
x	s	x		x		x	x	x	sx	x	sx	xs	xs	x	s		xs		sx										14
x	s	x		x			x	x	xs	x	sx	xs	xs	x	s		x	sx	sx										15
x	sx	x	s	x		sx	x	x	x	x	xs	xs		x	s		xs	sx											16
x	x	x	xs			sx	s	sx	sx	x	x		x	x	s	xs		xs	x			s							17
x	xs	x				x	x	x	sx	x	sx	xs	xs	x	s	s	x		sx										18
x		x				x	x	x	s	x	x	xs	x	x	s	s	x	sx	s										19
x		x		x		x	x	x	sx	x	sx	xs	xs	x	s	s		s	x										20
x		x		x		x	x	x	sx	x	sx	xs		xs	s	sx	x	s	xs										21
x		x		x		x	x	x	sx	x	sx	xs		x		s	x	s	xs				s						22
x		x		x		x	xs	x	sx	x	sx	xs		x		s	x	s	x				s						23
x	xs	x	sx	x		x	x	x	sx	x	sx	xs		x		s			xs				s						24
x	xs	x	sx	x		x	x	x	sx	x	sx	xs		x	s	s			xs										25
x	x		x		x	x	xs		xs	s	x			s	s	x		x	sx	x		sx							26
x	x	x		x		x	x	x	sx	xs	xs		xs	x	s	s		sx	sx										27
x	x	x	s	x		x	x		xs	x	x		xs	x	s	s		sx	sx										28
x	x	x	sx	x		x			sx	x	xs		x	x	s	s		xs	x			s							29
x	x	x	sx	x		x		x	s	x	xs		x	x	s	s		sx	xs										30
x	x	xs	sx	x		x		x		x	x		xs	x	s	sx		s	xs					s					31
x			x		x	sx			x		xs		x	xs	s	x	x	x	sx	sx		s		xs					32
x	x		x	x	xs	x	sx		s	x	x		xs		s	x		sx						xs	sx				33
x	x		sx	x		xs	x	x		x	sx		xs		s	x	s	sx						xs	x				34
x	sx		x						xs		x				s	x	x	x	x	xs		sx		xs	x	sx	s		35
x			sx	x			x	x	sx	x	x		xs		s	x	x	xs				s			x	s			36
x	x			x			x	x		x	x		xs	s	s	x		sx	sx					sx	xs			xs	37
x	x	sx					x	x		x	x		s	xs	s	x	xs	sx	xs					sx				x	38
x	x	x		x			x	x		x	s		sx	x	s	x		sx						xs	s			xs	39
x	x	x		x			x	x		x	sx		sx	x	s	xs		s						xs	sx			xs	40
x	xs	sx		x			x	x		x	sx			x	s	x		sx	s					xs	x			xs	41
x	x	x		x			x	x		x	sx	sx		x	s	x		xs	s					xs	s				42
x	xs	sx				sx	x	x	s	x	x	sx		x	s	x		xs	xs						x				43
x		x		x		xs	x	x	sx	xs	sx		s	x	s	x		x	s						x				44
x		x		x		xs	x	x	sx	x	xs	sx		x	s	x			sx						xs			s	45
x		x	xs	x		xs	x	xs	s	x	x	sx	sx	x	s	x												sx	46
x		x	xs	x		sx	x		sx	x	x	s	x	x	s	x			s									xs	47
x	s	x	xs	x		x	x			x	x	sx	xs		s	x		sx						sx				x	48
x	xs	x	xs	x		x	x			x	x	sx		x	s	x		sx						s				s	49
x	xs	x		x		xs	x			x	x	sx	sx	x	s	x		sx	xs									s	50
x		x		x		xs	x	x		x	x		s	x	s	x		sx						sx	sx			s	51
x		xs		x		x	x	xs		x	x		sx	x	s	x		sx						sx	xs			s	52
x		x		x		xs	x	xs		x	xs		sx	x	s	x		sx						sx	x			s	53
x	s	x		x		x	x	xs		x	x		sx	x	s	xs		sx						sx	xs				54
54	16	41	5	46	3	27	41	37	4	47	20	3	11	42	0	22	17	4	5	1	0	0	0	0	7	0	0	2	x
0	8	3	7	0	2	11	6	5	5	4	9	18	18	3	0	3	5	5	9	1	0	0	0	8	4	0	0	5	xs
0	3	3	10	0	0	7	1	1	22	0	16	9	9	1	0	3	0	26	14	1	1	2	0	7	3	1	0	1	sx
0	5	0	4	0	0	0	1	0	5	1	1	2	3	3	51	21	1	6	6	0	1	4	3	2	2	1	1	6	s

x - Played full 90 minutes
xs - Substituted off
sx - Substituted on
s - Non-playing Substitute

MAIDENHEAD UNITED MATCH RESULTS 2018-19

Date	Comp	Opponents	H/A	Att:	Result		Goalscorers	Pos
Aug 4	NL	Gateshead	H	1264	L	1 - 3	Kerr 90+2 (og)	22
7	NL	Solihull Moors	A	730	L	0 - 1		24
11	NL	Dagenham & Redbridge	A	1069	D	2 - 2	Obiley 15 Owusu 81	22
14	NL	Wrexham	H	1584	L	0 - 2		24
18	NL	Hartlepool United	A	2925	L	1 - 2	Massey 80	24
25	NL	Maidstone United	H	1339	**W**	3 - 2	Upward 2 Clifton 77 De Havilland 90 (og)	20
27	NL	Braintree Town	A	576	**W**	2 - 0	Clifton 27 Obileye 45	18
Sept 1	NL	Bromley	H	1201	D	2 - 2	Clifton 33 Kelly 62	18
4	NL	Eastleigh	H	1212	**W**	2 - 0	Kelly 44 45	14
8	NL	Barnet	A	1569	L	0 - 1		14
15	NL	FC Halifax Town	H	1306	**W**	3 - 0	Kelly 12 36 Clifton 18	13
22	NL	Barrow	A	1520	L	0 - 2		15
25	NL	Chesterfield	A	3681	**W**	3 - 1	Rodrigues Alves 8 45+3 Upward 69	13
29	NL	Salford City	H	1726	L	0 - 3		16
Oct 6	NL	Leyton Orient	H	2016	L	0 - 2		17
13	NL	Boreham Wood	A	684	L	1 - 3	Bird 77	18
20	**FAC 4Q**	**Chippenham Town**	**A**	**706**	**D**	**1 - 1**	**Smith 61**	
15	**FAC 4Qr**	**Chippenham Town**	**H**	**738**	**W**	**1 - 0**	**Clifton 74**	
27	NL	AFC Fylde	H	1372	L	0 - 6		18
30	NL	Havant & Waterlooville	A	952	L	0 - 7		18
Nov 3	NL	Dover Athletic	A	872	L	0 - 2		21
10	**FAC 1P**	**Portsmouth**	**H**	**3205**	**L**	**0 - 4**		
24	NL	Sutton United	A	1606	**W**	1 - 0	Clifton 85	20
27	NL	Ebbsfleet United	H	1055	D	1 - 1	Cole R 73	20
Dec 1	NL	Harrogate Town	H	1090	L	1 - 2	Clifton 25	20
8	NL	Hartlepool United	H	1157	L	0 - 1		22
22	NL	Bromley	A	1073	L	0 - 1		22
26	NL	Aldershot Town	H	1853	**W**	4 - 3	Clifton 28 Kelly 51 Odametey 54 Kilgour 62	21
29	NL	Braintree Town	H	1218	L	0 - 1		22
Jan 1	NL	Aldershot Town	A	2090	D	0 - 0		22
5	NL	Gateshead	A	581	**W**	1 - 0	Clerima 29	20
8	**FAT 1P**	**Oxford City**	**H**	**352**	**L**	**1 - 2**	**Owusu 52**	
19	NL	Solihull Moors	H	1180	L	1 - 2	Clifton 40 (pen)	20
26	NL	Wrexham	A	4323	L	0 - 1		20
Feb 9	NL	Boreham Wood	H	1113	**W**	1 - 0	Akintunde 74	19
16	NL	Leyton Orient	A	5337	**W**	1 - 0	Clifton 53	16
23	NL	Dover Athletic	H	1244	**W**	1 - 0	Clifton 13	16
Mar 2	NL	AFC Fylde	A	1402	L	1 - 2	Upward 10	18
5	NL	Dagenham & Redbridge	H	1156	D	1 - 1	Kilgour 90	18
9	NL	Sutton United	H	1210	**W**	1 - 0	Upward 90+5	16
12	NL	Ebbsfleet United	A	811	L	0 - 3		17
16	NL	Harrogate Town	A	1105	L	0 - 1		18
26	NL	Havant & Waterlooville	H	1230	**W**	2 - 1	Upward 62 Clifton 86	18
30	NL	FC Halifax Town	A	1336	**W**	1 - 0	Obiley 72 (pen)	17
Apr 6	NL	Barnet	H	1491	L	0 - 1		17
13	NL	Salford City	A	2419	L	0 - 3		20 (s)
19	NL	Barrow	H	1820	D	1 - 1	Fondop-Talum 75	20
20	NL	Eastleigh	A	2146	L	0 - 2		20
27	NL	Chesterfield	H	1555	**W**	2 - 0	Obileye 70 Clifton 77	19

GOALSCORERS	SG	CSG	Pens	Hat tricks	Total
Clifton	13	2	1		13
Kelly	4	2			6
Upward	5	1			5
Obileye	4	1	1		4
Alves	1	1			2
Opponent	2	1			2
Owusu	2	1			2
Akintunde	1	1			1
Bird	1	1			1
Clerima	1	1			1
Cole R	1	1			1
Fondop-Talum	1	1			1
Kilgour	2	1			2
Massey	1	1			1
Odametey	1	1			1
Smith	1	1			1

Pentney	Clerima	Massey	Odametey	Kilman	Obileye	Mulley	Comley	Worsfold	Bird	Kelly	Owusu	Alves	Clifton	Steer	Smith	Peters	Cole C	Sheckleford	Akintunde	Upward	Archer (L)	Hamann	Kilgour	Ofori-Twumasi	Cole R (L)	Tarpey (L)	Keetch	Nombe (L)	Fondop-Talom (L)	Mason	Gabriel R	No.
x	x	x	x	x	x	xs	x	xs	x	xs	sx	sx	sx	s	s																	1
x	x	x	x	s	x	s	xs	x	xs	sx	xs	sx	sx	x	x																	2
x	x	x	x		x	sx	x	x	xs	s	x	s	x	xs	sx	s																3
x	x		x		x	s	x	x	x	sx	xs	s	xs		x		x	sx	s													4
x	x	x	x		x	sx	x	xs	xs	sx	xs	s	sx		s		x			x												5
x	x	x	x		x	sx	xs	xs	xs	sx		sx	x	x	s				s	x												6
x	x	x	x		x	xs			s	xs	sx	x	xs		sx	s	x		sx	x												7
x	x	x	x		x	x				xs	xs	s	xs	x	s		sx		sx	x	sx											8
x	x	x	x		x	sx		s		xs	xs	s		x	x				sx	x	x											9
x	x	x	x		x	xs		sx		x	xs	sx		x	s		s		sx	x	xs											10
x	x	x	x		x	sx	x	x		x	sx		xs	xs	s				s	xs	sx											11
x	x	x	x				x	x	sx	x	sx		x	xs	sx		xs		s	xs	s											12
x	x	xs	sx		x		x	x	sx	s	s	x	sx		x				xs	x	xs											13
x	x		x		x		xs	x	s	x	sx	xs	x		x		sx		sx	xs	s											14
x	x	x	x		x	s	x	xs	xs	x		sx	sx		s		x		xs		sx											15
x	x	x	x		x	xs		x	sx	sx	s	s		x	x		sx		xs		xs											16
x	x	x	x		x	sx	x	xs	xs	sx	s	s	x	x	x		s		s	s												17
x	x	x	x		x	s	x	xs	s	xs	sx	s	x		xs		x		sx	sx		s										18
x	x	x	x		x	sx	xs	x	xs		s	s		x	x				xs	sx	sx											19
x	x	x	x		x	x	x	sx	sx		xs	xs	xs	x		s	sx		s													20
	x	x	x		x	xs	x		xs	sx	sx	sx	x	x			s		xs	s		x										21
x	x	x	x		x	s	xs	s	sx	x	sx	s	xs	x					sx	xs		s	x									22
x	xs	x			x		x	x	x	xs	s	sx	sx	x		s							x	x	s							23
x		x	xs		x		x	x	s	sx	s	s	x	x									x	x	sx	xs						24
x	x	x	sx		xs		x		x	sx	s	sx	xs	x		s							x	x	xs							25
x	x	x	sx		xs		x	xs	sx	x	s		xs	x		s							x	x	sx							26
x	x	x	x		x			xs	s	x	s		x	x					sx				xs	x	sx		s					27
x	xs	x	x		x				sx	xs	x	s	xs	x					s				x	x	sx	sx						28
x	x	x	x		xs				sx	xs	xs	sx	x	x					s				x	x	s	sx						29
x	x	x	x		s		x	xs	x	xs		s		x					sx				x	x	sx	s						30
x	x	x	x		xs		x		xs	sx		s	sx	x		s			xs	sx			x	x								31
x	sx	x	x		sx		x			xs	sx	xs		x		s			xs	xs			x	x			sx					32
x		x	x				x		sx		sx	s	x	x		s			xs	xs			x	x			s	x				33
x	s	x	x				x		sx	sx	sx	s	xs	x					xs	x			x	x				xs				34
x	s	x	x				x		sx	xs	s		xs	x		s			sx	x			x	x				x				35
x	x	x			x		x		s	sx	sx		xs	x					xs	x			x					xs	sx	s		36
x	x	x	sx		xs		x			s	s		xs	x					x	x			x	sx				xs	sx			37
x	x	x	sx		xs		x			sx	s		xs	x					xs	x			x	s				x	sx			38
x	x	x	x		s		xs			xs	sx		xs	x					sx	x			x	s				x	sx			39
x	x	x	x		x		x	sx		sx	s		s	xs					xs	x				x				s	x			40
x	x	x	x		xs		xs	sx		sx	xs	s	x					x	s	x				x				sx				41
x	x	x	sx		x		xs	sx		sx	s	s	x	x					xs	x				x				xs				42
x	x	x	x		x		x		sx	sx	s		xs	x					xs	x				x				s			s	43
x	x		x		x		x		s	xs	s	s	sx	x					sx					x				x	xs		x	44
x	x	x	x				x	sx	sx	xs	s	s	x						sx					x				xs	xs		x	45
x	x	x	x		xs		x	sx		xs			x	x					sx	xs				x				s	sx		s	46
x	x	x	x				x	xs	s	xs	s		sx	s					sx					x				x	x		x	47
x	x	x	x				x		s	xs	sx	s	x	xs					sx					x				xs	x		sx	48
x	x	x	x		xs		x		s	sx	xs		x	x					sx					x				s	xs		sx	49
48	42	45	40	1	30	2	33	11	5	8	2	2	17	33	8	0	5	1	1	17	1	1	17	23	0	0	0	6	3	0	3	x
0	2	1	1	0	9	5	8	10	9	17	10	3	16	5	1	0	1	0	14	7	3	0	1	0	1	1	0	6	3	0	0	xs
0	1	0	6	0	1	7	0	7	13	18	14	9	9	0	3	0	4	1	17	3	4	0	0	1	5	2	1	1	5	0	2	sx
0	2	0	0	1	2	5	0	2	10	3	18	21	1	2	7	10	3	0	9	2	2	2	0	2	2	1	2	4	0	1	2	s

x - Played full 90 minutes
xs - Substituted off
sx - Substituted on
s - Non-playing Substitute

MAIDSTONE UNITED MATCH RESULTS 2018-19

Date	Comp	Opponents	H/A	Att:	Result	Goalscorers	Pos
Aug 4	NL	Hartlepool United	H	2599	D 1 - 1	Turgott 41 (Pen)	13
7	NL	Dagenham & Redbridge	A	1405	W 2 - 1	Turgott 41 51	5
11	NL	FC Halifax Town	A	1534	L 0 - 3		10
14	NL	Leyton Orient	H	3037	L 1 - 2	Mullings 80	16
18	NL	Barrow	H	2003	W 1 - 0	Mullings 6	13
25	NL	Maidenhead United	A	1339	L 2 - 3	Turgott 45 57 (Pen)	16
27	NL	Boreham Wood	H	2035	L 1 - 2	Paxman 45	19
Manager Jay Saunders leaves the club by mutual consent.							
Sept 1	NL	Gateshead	A	564	L 0 - 1		19
4	NL	Sutton United	H	1838	L 0 - 1		19
8	NL	Salford City	A	2273	L 0 - 1		22
Harry Wheeler appointed new manager 11/09/2018							
15	NL	Harrogate Town	H	2222	L 0 - 2		22
22	NL	Braintree Town	A	807	W 1 - 0	Turgott 90 (Pen)	20
25	NL	Aldershot Town	A	1619	W 1 - 0	Turgott 25	18
29	NL	Chesterfield	H	2438	D 1 - 1	Turgott 31	18
Oct 6	NL	Bromley	H	2294	L 0 - 1		19
13	NL	AFC Fylde	A	1507	L 0 - 2		20
20	**FAC 4Q**	**Leyton Orient**	**H**	**1906**	**W 2 - 0**	**Turgott 54 Romain 76**	
27	NL	Solihull Moors	H	2106	L 1 - 3	Turgott 9	20
30	NL	Ebbsfleet United	A	2003	D 1 - 1	De Havilland 75	21
Nov 3	NL	Barnet	A	1424	W 2 - 0	Turgott 28 Omotayo 80	18
10	**FAC 1P**	**Macclesfield Town**	**H**	**2169**	**W 2 - 1**	**Powell 51 Turgott 69 (Pen)**	
17	NL	Wrexham	H	2626	D 1 - 1	Walton 64	18
24	NL	Havant & Watervoolville	A	1308	L 2 - 5	Paxman 77 Turgott 78	22
27	NL	Eastleigh	H	1570	L 1 - 3	Phillips 89	22
Dec 1	**FAC 2P**	**Oldham Athletic**	**H**	**3560**	**L 0 - 2**		
8	NL	Barrow	A	804	L 0 - 1		23
15	**FAT 1P**	**Woking**	**H**	**1245**	**D 1 - 1**	**Shields 71**	
18	**FAT 1Pr**	**Woking**	**A**	**602**	**W 3 - 2**	**Phillips 37 Cassidy 47 De Havilland 116 (aet)**	
22	NL	Gateshead	H	2131	L 2 - 3	Cassidy 79 McLennon 82	23
26	NL	Dover Athletic	A	1937	L 1 - 3	Robinson 7	23
Harry Wheeler is sacked as manager, Tristan Lewis and Simon Walton take temporary charge.							
29	NL	Boreham Wood	A	630	W 1 - 0	Cassidy 7	23
Jan 1	NL	Dover Athletic	H	3087	L 0 - 1		23
5	NL	Hartlepool United	A	2929	W 2 - 1	Powell 4 40	23
12	**FAT 2P**	**Oxford City**	**H**	**1156**	**W 1 - 0**	**Richards 36**	
15	NL	Maidenhead United	H	1829	L 2 - 4	De Havilland 14 62	23
19	NL	Dagenham & Redbridge	H	2188	L 0 - 3		23
John Still comes out of retirement to take up the managers job with Hakan Hayrettin joining as his assistant.							
26	NL	Leyton Orient	A	5488	L 0 - 3		23
Feb 5	**FAT 3P**	**Salford City**	**A**	**701**	**D 1 - 1**	**Phillips 22**	
9	NL	AFC Fylde	H	2033	D 1 - 1	Philliskirk 60 (og)	23
12	**FAT 3Pr**	**Salford City**	**H**	**880**	**W 3 - 0**	**Phillips 9 Romain 59 De Havilland 88**	
16	NL	Bromley	A	2589	L 0 - 2		23
19	NL	FC Halifax Town	H	1813	L 0 - 1		23
23	**FAT 4P**	**Stockport County**	**A**	**2585**	**D 1 - 1**	**Cassidy 17**	
26	**FAT 4Pr**	**Stockport County**	**H**	**1140**	**L 0 - 3**		
Mar 2	NL	Solihull Moors	A	956	L 0 - 5		23
9	NL	Havant & Watervoolville	H	1901	W 2 - 0	Embery 33 Powell 42	23
12	NL	Eastleigh	A	1642	L 0 - 2		23
16	NL	Wrexham	A	3604	L 0 - 1		23
23	NL	Ebbsfleet United	H	3002	L 0 - 2		23
30	NL	Harrogate Town	A	1134	D 2 - 2	Amaluzor 45 52	24
Apr 6	NL	Salford City	H	2050	L 0 - 2		24 (R)
9	NL	Barnet	H	1471	W 2 - 1	Amaluzor 46 Swaine 70	23
13	NL	Chesterfield	A	4592	L 1 - 4	Turgott 36	24
19	NL	Braintree Town	H	1908	L 0 - 2		24
22	NL	Sutton United	A	1858	D 2 - 2	Turgott 54 (pen) 90+5 (pen)	24
27	NL	Aldershot Town	H	1929	L 0 - 2		24

GOALSCORERS	SG	CSG	Pens	Hat tricks	Total
Turgott	13	3	6		16
De Havilland	4	1			5
Cassidy	4	1			4
Phillips	4	1			4
Powell	3	1			4
Amaluzor	2	1			3
Mullings	2	2			2
Paxman	2	1			2
Romain	2	1			2
Embery	1	1			1
McLennon	1	1			1
Omotayo	1	1			1
Opponent	1	1			1
Richards	1	1			1
Robinson	1	1			1
Shields	1	1			1
Swaine	1	1			1
Walton	1	1			1

Worgan	Ofori-Twumasi	De Havilland	Lewis	McLennon	Finney	Muldoon	Phillips	Turgott	Loza	Quigley	Paxman	Mullings	Wynter	Efete	Richards	Coker	Walton	Cassidy (L)	Durojaiye	Doyle (L)	Wilson	Omotayo (L)	Powell	Romain	Strizovic	Smith (L)	Swaine	Tajbakhsh	Wishart	Shields (L)	Robinson	Worner (L)	Wassmer (L)	Edobor (L)	Ross (L)	Taylor (L)	Meredith (L)	Henry (L)	Davies (L)	Donnellan S	Lewington	Amaluzor	Donnellan L	Embery	No.
x	x	x	x	x	x	xs	xs	x	x	xs	sx	sx	sx	s	s																														1
x	x	xs	x	x	x	xs	sx	x	x	xs	xs	sx	sx	s		s																													2
x	x	x	x	x	xs	xs	s	x	xs	sx	sx	x	x	s		sx																													3
x	x	x	x	s	x	xs	xs	x	xs	x	sx	sx	s	x		sx																													4
x	x	x	x	s		x	sx	x	sx	sx	xs	xs	x	x		xs																													5
x	x	x	x	s	s	xs	s	x	sx	sx	x	x	x	x		xs																													6
x	x	x	x	s	x	xs	sx	x		x	xs	s	sx	x		x																													7
x	x	x		xs	x	x	x	x	sx	sx	xs	x	s	xs		sx																													8
x	x	x	xs	s	x	x	x		x		sx	x	xs	x	s	sx																													9
x	x	x			x	x	x		x		xs	x	xs	x	sx	sx																													10
x	x	x	x	sx	x		x			sx	xs	x	s	x	s	xs	x																												11
x	s	x	x		x		sx	x	x		xs	xs					x	sx	xs	x	s																								12
x	s	x	x		x		sx	xs	sx		x	s					x	x	xs	x	x																								13
x		x	x	s	x		x	x	s	sx	xs						x	xs	s	x	x																								14
x	s	x	xs		x	sx	sx	x		sx	x						xs	x	s	x	x	xs																							15
x		x		s	x	xs	sx	x			x						xs	x	s	xs	sx	sx	x																						16
x	x	x		s	x	xs	sx	x			xs						x	x	sx	x			xs	sx	s																				17
x	xs	x		sx	x	xs	s	x			x						x	x		xs		sx	x	sx	s																				18
	sx	x		s	x	sx	x	x			x						xs	xs	s	x		sx		x		x	xs																		19
	s	x		x	x	s	x	x			xs						x	x	sx			sx	x	xs	s	x																			20
	s	x		x	x	s	x	x			xs						x	x	sx				xs	x	s	x		sx																	21
		x		x	x	sx	xs	x			xs						x	x	sx				xs	x	s	x	sx	s																	22
		x		x	x	sx	s	x			x						xs	x	sx				xs	x	s	x	xs	sx																	23
		x		s	x		x	xs									x	x	xs				x	x	s	x	s	sx	x	sx															24
		x		x	xs	sx	x				x				s			x	xs				x	x	s	x		x																	25
		s		x		xs	x				sx						xs	x					s	sx			x	sx	x	x	x	x	xs												26
		sx		x	s	x	x				x				s		x	x					x	xs	s			sx	xs	x		x													27
		sx		x	sx		x				xs						x	x					xs	x	s		sx	xs	x	x		x		s											28
				xs		xs	x				xs						x	x					sx	x	s		sx	sx	x	x	x	x	s												29
		s		x		s	x				sx						x	x					s	sx			x	xs	xs	x	xs	x	x												30
		x		x		x	x				xs				s			x					x	sx	s			xs	x		s	x	x	sx											31
		x		x		x	x				xs				sx		s	x					x	x	s			xs			sx	x	x	sx											32
		x		x		x	x				x				s		s						x	sx			s	xs			xs		x	sx	x	x									33
		x				x	x				x				xs		sx						x	x	s		x	xs						x	x										34
		x		xs		x	x				x				s		s						x	sx			sx	sx			x		xs	x	x	xs									35
		x					xs				sx				s		xs						x	x			x	sx	x		xs		s	x	x	x									36
		x		x			xs				s				s		x						x	sx			x	s	x		x			s	x	x	x								37
		x		s		x	xs				x				s		x						x		s		s	sx	x								x	x	x	x					38
		x				xs	x				sx						x	x					xs	s				sx	x		sx						xs	x	x	x	s				39
		x				xs	x				xs				sx		xs						x	x	s		s	sx	x								sx	x	x	x					40
		x				xs	x											x					x	sx				xs	x		xs			s		sx		x	x	x	s	sx			41
		x		x		s	x				s							x					x	xs							sx			sx			x	xs	x	xs	sx	x			42
		xs					x				x						sx	x					x	xs	s		x		x					s			s		x	x	x		sx		43
						xs	x	sx			x						xs	x					x						x					xs			sx	s	x	x	x		sx		44
		x				x	x	xs			s						x						x	x					x								s	x		x	s	xs	sx	sx	45
		x				sx	x	x															x	x			x		x							sx	s	s	xs	x	x		s	xs	46
		x				sx	xs	x															x	x					x							x	s	s	x	x	x	sx	s	xs	47
		x					x	x			s						x						x						x							x	s	s	x	x	x	xs	s	sx	48
		x					sx	x									x	x					x		s		s		x							xs		x	x	x		xs	s	sx	49
		x					sx	x							s		x	x					x				x		sx							xs		s	x	x	x	xs		s	50
		x					s	x							s		xs	x					x	sx	s		x									x			x	x	x	xs		sx	51
		x				sx	x	x									xs	xs					x	sx			x		x							x		s		s	x	x		s	52
		x				s	x	x							sx								x	xs	s		x		x							xs			x		x	x		sx	53
						x	x	x							xs		sx	s					xs	sx			x		x							x		s	x		x	sx		xs	54
		x				x	sx	x							xs		s						xs	x			x		x					s				x	x		s	x		sx	55
		x				x	x	xs															x	x			x							x		xs		s			x	x		sx	56
18	12	47	11	17	21	16	33	29	5	2	15	6	3	7	0	1	21	26	0	6	3	0	29	17	0	7	14	1	22	5	4	7	4	4	5	8	3	7	15	13	11	5	0	0	x
0	1	2	2	3	2	14	7	4	2	2	17	2	2	1	3	3	10	3	4	2	0	1	8	5	0	0	2	7	2	0	4	0	2	1	0	5	1	1	1	1	0	5	0	3	xs
0	1	2	0	2	1	8	11	1	4	7	8	3	3	0	4	5	3	1	5	0	1	4	1	12	0	0	4	11	1	1	3	0	0	4	0	2	2	0	0	0	1	3	3	7	sx
0	5	2	0	11	2	5	5	0	1	0	4	2	3	3	13	1	4	1	4	0	1	0	2	1	20	0	5	2	0	0	1	0	2	5	0	0	5	8	0	1	4	0	4	2	s

Also Played: Funnell - 18/08 (s) 27/08 (s) 01/09 (s) 04/09 (s) 08/09 (s). Capel 08/09 (s). Robins 08/09 (s) 15/09 (s).
Wabo (L) - 22/09 (sx) 25/09 (s) 29/09 (sx). Dale - 20/10 (s) 10/11 (s) 12/01 (s) 27/04 (sx). Williams 20/10 (s) 10/11 (s) 01/12 (s) 13/04 (s).
Florence - 01/12 (sx). Tingle - 01/12 (s) 26/02 (s). Fagg - 12/01 (sx). Bates 12/01 (s). Philpot - 19/01 (sx). Gilbert - 27/04 (s). Rollings - 27/04 (s).

x - Played full 90 minutes
xs - Substituted off
sx - Substituted on
s - Non-playing Substitute

SALFORD CITY MATCH RESULTS 2018-19

Date	Comp	Opponents	H/A	Att:	Result		Goalscorers	Pos
Aug 4	NL	Leyton Orient	H	2156	D	1 - 1	Gaffney 47	14
7	NL	Gateshead	A	1243	L	1 - 2	Rooney 11	17
11	NL	Sutton United	A	1898	L	1 - 2	Piergianni 20	21
14	NL	FC Halifax Town	H	2632	W	2 - 1	Rooney 11 83	14
18	NL	Chesterfield	H	3595	W	3 - 2	Rooney 19 Piergianni 56 Whitehead 89	12
25	NL	Havant & Waterlooville	A	1679	D	1 - 1	Rooney 53	14
27	NL	Barrow	H	3012	W	3 - 1	Rooney 29 Pond 62 Lloyd-McGoldrick 65 (pen)	10
Sept 1	NL	Dagenham & Redbridge	A	1114	D	0 - 0		11
4	NL	AFC Fylde	A	2941	W	2 - 0	Walker 26 Rooney 69	9
8	NL	Maidstone United	H	2273	W	1 - 0	Mullings 47 (og)	6
15	NL	Bromley	A	2020	W	2 - 0	Gaffney 36 Walker 61	4
22	NL	Boreham Wood	H	2006	W	3 - 1	Walker 3 Shelton 21 Gaffney 52	4
25	NL	Hartlepool United	H	2420	W	3 - 0	Lloyd-McGoldrick 64 Rooney 69 Walker 75	2
29	NL	Maidenhead United	A	1726	W	3 - 0	Wiseman 24 Rooney 26 Rodney 90	1
Oct 6	NL	Dover Athletic	A	1127	W	4 - 1	Rooney 18 20 56 Piergianni 66	1
13	NL	Braintree town	H	2710	D	2 - 2	Gaffney 1 Rooney 90	1
20	**FAC 4Q**	**Marine**	**A**	**1709**	**W**	**2 - 1**	**Whitehead 40 Gaffney 57**	
27	NL	Ebbsfleet United	H	2498	D	1 - 1	Gaffney 38	2
30	NL	Barnet	A	1243	W	3 - 1	Gaffney 45+1 Walker 47 Shelton 64	1
Nov 3	NL	Eastleigh	A	2253	D	1 - 1	Maynard 90	3
11	**FAC 1P**	**Shrewsbury Town**	**A**	**4351**	**D**	**1 - 1**	**Rooney 27**	
17	NL	Aldershot Town	H	2875	W	4 - 0	Rooney 2 35 65 (Pen) Gaffney 46	2
21	**FAC 1Pr**	**Shrewsbury Town**	**H**	**2432**	**L**	**1 - 3**	**Rooney 77**	
24	NL	Solihull Moors	A	2216	D	0 - 0		2
27	NL	Harrogate Town	H	1206	W	3 - 1	Whitehead 11 Gaffney 44 57	2
Dec 1	NL	Havant & Waterlooville	H	2181	W	3 - 0	Rooney 22 Politic 23 Whitehead 90+5	2
8	NL	Chesterfield	A	5085	L	0 - 2		2
18	**FAT 1P**	**Gateshead**	**H**	**380**	**W**	**3 - 1**	**Dieseruvwe 35 Rodney 80 84**	
22	NL	Dagenham & Redbridge	H	2082	L	1 - 2	Piergianni 13	2
26	NL	Wrexham	A	8283	L	1 - 5	Whitehead 90+5	4
29	NL	Barrow	A	2311	L	2 - 3	Green 59 Touray 84	5
Jan 1	NL	Wrexham	H	4044	W	2 - 0	Green 23 Gaffney 60	3
5	NL	Leyton Orient	A	6937	W	3 - 0	Piergianni 6 81 Gaffney 8	2
12	**FAT 2P**	**Dagenham & Redbridge**	**H**	**1061**	**W**	**2 - 0**	**Rodney 33 Dieseruvwe 83**	
19	NL	Gateshead	H	2055	D	1 - 1	Lloyd-McGoldrick 28 (pen)	3
26	NL	FC Halifax Town	A	2115	D	0 - 0		2
Feb 5	**FAT 3P**	**Maidstone United**	**H**	**701**	**D**	**1 - 1**	**Dieseruvwe 35**	
9	NL	Braintree town	A	765	L	0 - 1		5
12	**FAT 3Pr**	**Maidstone United**	**A**	**880**	**L**	**0 - 3**		
16	NL	Dover Athletic	H	2498	L	1 - 3	Politic 9	5
23	NL	Eastleigh	H	2329	L	0 - 2		6
Mar 2	NL	Ebbsfleet United	A	1708	W	1 - 0	Piergianni 32	5
5	NL	Sutton United	H	1686	W	2 - 0	Dieseruvwe 12 Piergianni 55	5
9	NL	Solihull Moors	H	2476	W	2 - 0	Hogan 55 Green 82	4
16	NL	Aldershot Town	A	1668	W	1 - 0	Redmond 44	4
23	NL	Barnet	H	2452	D	0 - 0		4
27	NL	Harrogate Town	A	1700	W	1 - 0	Redmond 49 (pen)	3
30	NL	Bromley	H	2314	W	2 - 1	Maynard 88 Pond 90+4	2
Apr 6	NL	Maidstone United	A	2050	W	2 - 0	Rooney 13 42	1
13	NL	Maidenhead United	H	2419	W	3 - 0	Dieseruvwe 11 Touray 27 Rooney 45 (pen)	2
19	NL	Boreham Wood	A	854	W	3 - 2	Piergianni 7 Hogan 22 Green 88	2
22	NL	AFC Fylde	H	3338	L	0 - 1		2
27	NL	Hartlepool United	A	3582	L	2 - 3	Rooney 3 Dieseruvwe 87	3
May 5	**PO SF**	**Eastleigh**	**H**	**2963**	**D**	**1 - 1**	**Piergianni 43 (won 4-3 on pens aet)**	
11	**PO F**	**AFC Fylde**	**N**	**8049**	**W**	**3 - 0**	**Dieseruvwe 15 Piergianni 53 Touray 61**	

GOALSCORERS	SG	CSG	Pens	Hat tricks	Total
Rooney	17	4	2	2	23
Gaffney	11	3			12
Piergianni	10	2			11
Dieseruvwe	7	1			7
Walker	5	3			5
Whitehead	5	2			5
Green	4	2			4
Rodney	3	1			4
Lloyd-McGoldrick	3	1	2		3
Touray	3	1			3
Hogan	2	1			2
Maynard	2	1			2
Politic	2	1			2
Pond	2	1			2
Redmond	2	1			2
Shelton	2	1			2
Opponent	1	1			1

Neal	Wiseman	Touray	Rooney	Piergianni	Hogan	Maynard	Lloyd-McGoldrick	Walker	Whitehead	Gaffney	Haughton	Mafuta	Crocombe	Shelton	Pond	Hooper	Rodney	Glynn	Askew	Moncrieffe	Jones	Politic (L)	Lockett	Nolan (L)	Dieseruwwe	Brockbank (L)	Green	Muscatt (L)	Linganzi	Doyle A	Foulds M	Adetiloye	Dyson	James-Taylor	Ogunrinde	Neave	Shepherd	Redmond	No.
x	x	x	x	x	x	x	xs	xs	x	x	sx	sx	s	s	s																								1
x	x	x	x	x	xs	x		x	x	x		sx	s	s	s	s																							2
x	x	x	x	x	x	x		sx	x	xs	sx	xs	s	xs	s		sx																						3
x	x	x	x	x	sx	x	xs	sx	x	x	xs	s	s		x		s																						4
x	x	x	x	x	sx	x	xs	xs	x	xs	s	sx	s		x		sx																						5
x	x	x	x	x	xs	x	x	sx	x	xs		s	s	s	x		sx																						6
x	xs	x	x	x	sx	sx	x	xs	x	x	s	x	s		x		s																						7
x	x	x	x	x	sx	x	x	xs	x	xs	s	sx	s		x		sx																						8
x	x	x	x	x	sx			x	x	xs	xs		s	x	x	s	sx	s																					9
x	x	x	x	x	sx		xs	xs	x	xs	sx		s	x	x	s	sx																						10
x	x	x	x	x	sx	sx	xs	xs	x	x	s		s	x	x		s																						11
x	x	x	xs	x	sx	sx	xs	xs	x	x	s		s	x	x		sx																						12
x	x	x	xs	x	sx	sx	xs	xs	x	x	s		s	x	x		sx																						13
x	x	x	xs	x	sx	sx	xs	xs	x	x	s		s	x	x		sx																						14
x	x	x	xs	x	sx	s	xs	xs	x	x	sx		s	x	x		sx																						15
x	x	x	x	x	sx		xs	x	x	x	sx		s	xs	xs		sx		s																				16
x	**x**	**x**	**x**	**x**	**x**	**x**	**xs**	**xs**	**x**	**x**	**s**		**s**			**s**	**sx**		**sx**	**s**	**s**																		17
x	x	x	x	x	s	s	xs	xs	x	x			s	x	x		sx					sx																	18
x	x	x	x	x	sx	sx	xs	xs	x	x			s	x	x		s					s																	19
x	x	x	x	x	sx	sx	xs	xs	x	x			s	xs	x					s		sx																	20
x	**x**	**x**	**x**	**x**	**sx**	**x**	**xs**	**sx**	**x**	**xs**			**s**		**x**	**s**	**sx**			**s**		**xs**	**s**																21
x	x	x	xs	x	sx		x		x	xs			s	x	x					sx		x	s																22
x	**x**	**x**	**x**	**x**	**sx**	**sx**	**xs**	**x**	**x**	**x**			**s**		**x**	**s**				**s**		**xs**	**s**																23
x	x	x	x	x	sx	x	x	xs	x	x			s		x		s							s	s														24
x	x	x	x	x	sx	xs	xs	xs	x	x			s		x							sx		sx	s														25
x	x	x	xs	x	sx		x	x	x	xs			s		x							sx		xs	sx	s													26
x	x	xs	x	x	sx		x	x	x	xs			s		x							sx		xs	sx	s													27
s	**s**	**x**		**x**	**x**		**xs**	**x**	**sx**	**sx**		**xs**	**x**				**sx**					**x**		**x**	**xs**	**x**													28
x	x	x	x	x	sx		xs	x	x	xs		s	s		x							xs			sx		sx												29
x	x	x	x	x	sx		x	x	x	sx		xs	s		xs		sx							s			x												30
x	x	x	x	x	x		xs		x	s		x	s		xs									sx	sx	s	x												31
x	x	x	s	x	x		s	x	x	xs			s		x									x	sx	sx	xs												32
x	x	x	sx	x	x		s	x	xs	x			s		x		sx							x	s		xs												33
s	**s**		**xs**	**x**	**x**		**x**			**s**			**x**				**x**	**x**	**x**		**x**			**x**	**sx**			**x**											34
x	x	x	sx	x	x		xs	x		xs			s		xs		sx	sx						x			x	s											35
x	x	x	x	x			xs	x	x	sx			s		x		s				s				sx		xs	x											36
s			**xs**		**x**		**s**					**x**	**x**				**sx**	**x**	**x**	**sx**	**x**	**xs**			**x**			**x**	**xs**	**sx**									37
x	x	x		x	xs		sx	sx	x	x			s		x							xs			sx		x	xs	s										38
												x	**x**				**x**	**x**	**xs**	**x**	**x**				**xs**					**x**	**x**	**xs**	**sx**	**sx**	**sx**	**s**	**s**		39
x	x	x		x	s	sx	sx	x	x	x			s		x							xs			sx		xs		xs										40
x	x	x		x	x	sx	xs	x	x	x			s					s							sx		xs		xs									sx	41
x	x	x		x	x	x	s	s		sx		x	s		x						s				xs		x											x	42
x	x	x		x	x	x	s	sx		sx		x	s		x						s				xs		xs											x	43
x	x	x		x	x	x	s			sx		x	s		x				s		s				x		xs											x	44
x	x	x	sx	x	x	x	s			sx		x	s		x						s				xs		xs											x	45
x	xs		sx	x	x	x	s	x	sx	sx		xs	s		x										x		xs											x	46
x	x	x	s	x	x	x		s	s	xs		x	s		x										x		sx											x	47
x	x	x	xs	x	xs	x		sx	s	sx		x	s		x										xs		sx											x	48
x	x	x	xs	x	x	x		sx	sx	sx		xs	s		x										x		s											xs	49
x	x	x	xs	x	x	x		sx	sx	s		xs	s		x										x		sx											xs	50
x	x	x	x	x	x			s	sx			x	s		xs										xs		sx		x									xs	51
x	xs	x	x	x	x	x		sx		sx		x	s		x										xs		sx		s									xs	52
x	x	x	xs	xs	x	x	x	s	x			xs	s												sx		x		sx									sx	53
x	**xs**	**x**	**x**	**x**	**x**	**x**		**sx**	**sx**	**sx**		**xs**	**s**		**xs**		**sx**								**xs**													**x**	54
x	**x**	**x**		**x**	**x**	**x**		**s**	**xs**	**sx**		**xs**	**s**	**sx**	**x**		**sx**								**xs**													**x**	55
51	47	50	28	52	24	23	10	16	36	21	0	12	4	10	39	0	2	3	2	1	3	2	0	5	6	1	6	3	1	1	1	0	0	0	0	0	0	9	x
0	4	1	12	1	4	1	23	16	2	14	2	9	0	3	6	0	0	0	1	0	0	6	0	2	10	0	9	1	3	0	0	1	0	0	0	0	0	4	xs
0	0	0	4	0	23	10	2	11	6	13	5	4	0	1	0	0	21	1	1	2	0	5	0	2	11	1	6	0	1	1	0	0	1	1	1	0	0	2	sx
3	2	0	2	0	2	2	8	5	2	3	8	3	51	3	3	6	6	2	2	4	6	1	3	2	3	3	1	1	2	0	0	0	0	0	0	1	1	0	s

x - Played full 90 minutes
xs - Substituted off
sx - Substituted on
s - Non-playing Substitute

SOLIHULL MOORS MATCH RESULTS 2018-19

Date	Comp	Opponents	H/A	Att:	Result		Goalscorers	Pos
Aug 4	NL	Eastleigh	A	1354	W	2 - 1	Yussuf 80 Sweeney 83	5
7	NL	Maidenhead United	H	730	W	1 - 0	Yussuf 28	4
11	NL	Aldershot Town	H	867	W	1 - 0	Wright 50	4
14	NL	AFC Fylde	A	1257	L	1 - 3	Maxwell 47	6
18	NL	Sutton United	H	763	D	2 - 2	Wright 69 Storer 82	6
25	NL	Harrogate Town	A	1180	L	1 - 3	Yussuf 11	10
27	NL	Wrexham	H	2412	W	1 - 0	Gudger 81	7
Sept 1	NL	Barrow	A	1260	W	2 - 1	Maxwell 84 Yussuf 89	6
4	NL	Leyton Orient	A	4250	L	0 - 3		8
8	NL	Hartlepool United	H	1311	L	0 - 1		11
15	NL	Dover Athletic	A	823	W	2 - 0	Hylton 72 Wright 79	8
22	NL	Bromley	H	648	W	5 - 0	Gudger 2 Carter 10 Wright 19 45+2 Osborne 72	6
25	NL	Dagenham & Redbridge	A	753	W	2 - 0	Wright 20 Hylton 89	5
29	NL	Havant & Waterlooville	A	1115	W	1 - 0	Yussuf 90+3	5
Oct 6	NL	Barnet	A	1054	L	0 - 2		5
13	NL	Ebbsfleet United	H	1505	W	2 - 1	Hylton 19 Maxwell 83	5
20	**FAC 4Q**	**Witton Albion**	**A**	**681**	**W**	**2 - 0**	**Yussuf 39 Daly 82**	
27	NL	Maidstone United	A	2106	W	3 - 1	Wright 2 Yussuf 8 Hylton 75	4
30	NL	FC Halifax Town	H	915	D	0 - 0		6
Nov 3	NL	Boreham Wood	H	803	D	0 - 0		5
11	**FAC 1P**	**Hitchin Town**	**A**	**3148**	**W**	**2 - 0**	**Yussuf 72 (Pen) Wright 78**	
17	NL	Braintree Town	A	822	W	3 - 0	Wright 46 Yussuf 53 (Pen) Stenson 58	4
24	NL	Salford City	H	2216	D	0 - 0		5
30	**FAC 2P**	**Blackpool**	**H**	**3005**	**D**	**0 - 0**		
Dec 4	NL	Harrogate Town	H	794	W	2 - 0	Gudger 36 Yussuf 85 (pen)	5
8	NL	Sutton United	A	1728	D	2 - 2	Osborne 33 49	5
15	**FAT 1P**	**Southport**	**A**	**767**	**W**	**1 - 0**	**Murphy 54**	
18	**FAC 2Pr**	**Blackpool**	**A**	**1441**	**L**	**2 - 3**	**Yussuf 33 51 (Pen) (aet)**	
22	NL	Barrow	H	958	L	0 - 1		4
26	NL	Chesterfield	A	4877	W	4 - 0	Blissett 4 29 Gudger 70 Hylton 83	3
29	NL	Wrexham	A	6220	L	0 - 1		3
Jan 1	NL	Chesterfield	H	1375	D	2 - 2	Hylton 36 Gudger 49	4
5	NL	Eastleigh	H	829	W	4 - 1	Wright 25 Blissett 35 Hylton 55	3
8	NL	Gateshead	A	519	W	2 - 1	Daly 22 Carter 53	3
12	**FAT 2P**	**FC Halifax Town**	**A**	**798**	**D**	**2 - 2**	**Yussuf 47 Blissett 58**	
15	**FAT 2Pr**	**FC Halifax Town**	**H**	**355**	**W**	**1 - 0**	**Blissett 59**	
19	NL	Maidenhead United	A	1180	W	2 - 1	Daly 30 Yussuf 90+3	2
26	NL	AFC Fylde	H	1588	L	1 - 2	Osborne 67	3
Feb 5	**FAT 3P**	**Hemel Hempstead Town**	**A**	**438**	**W**	**5 - 0**	**Hawkridge 6 Yussuf 41 64 Hylton 80 86**	
9	NL	Ebbsfleet United	A	1325	W	1 - 0	Yussuf 51	2
12	NL	Aldershot Town	A	1199	W	3 - 0	Blissett 14 73 90+4	1
16	NL	Barnet	H	1747	D	2 - 2	Blissett 73 Storer 90+4	1
23	**FAT 4P**	**AFC Telford United**	**H**	**1577**	**L**	**1 - 2**	**Osborne 74**	
Mar 2	NL	Maidstone United	H	956	W	5 - 0	Hylton 9 26 33 (pen) Carter 14 Yussuf 90+2	2
9	NL	Salford City	A	2476	L	0 - 2		3
12	NL	Gateshead	H	924	W	1 - 0	Blissett 62	2
16	NL	Braintree Town	H	1003	W	2 - 1	Daly 38 Yussuf 77 (pen)	2
23	NL	FC Halifax Town	A	1563	L	0 - 2		2
26	NL	Boreham Wood	A	478	D	2 - 2	Blissett 8 Yussuf 70	2
30	NL	Dover Athletic	H	1338	D	2 - 2	Wright 38 Williams 90+1	3
Apr 6	NL	Hartlepool United	A	2981	W	1 - 0	Yussuf 59	3
13	NL	Havant & Waterlooville	H	1179	W	3 - 2	Williams 24 Gudger 73 Wright 89	3
19	NL	Bromley	A	1536	W	2 - 0	Osborne 15 Wright 59	3
22	NL	Leyton Orient	H	3681	D	0 - 0		3
27	NL	Dagenham & Redbridge	A	1370	D	1 - 1	Hylton 55	2
May 5	**PO SF**	**AFC Fylde**	**H**	**3681**	**L**	**0 - 1**		

GOALSCORERS	SG	CSG	Pens	Hat tricks	Total
Yussuf	19	2	5		21
Hylton	10	2	1	1	13
Wright	12	3			13
Blissett*	8	3		1	11
Gudger	6	1			6
Osborne	5	1			5
Daly	4	1			4
Carter	3	1			3
Maxwell	3	1			3
Storer	2	1			2
Williams	2	1			2
Hawkridge	1	1			1
Murphy	1	1			1
Stenson	1	1			1
Sweeney	1	1			1

Boot	Daly	Gudger	Osborne	Reckord	Williams	Storer	Carter	Yussuf	Thomas	Wright	Hylton	Carline	Sweeney	Maxwell	Murphy	Willock	Coyle	Tibbetts (L)	O'Keeffe (L)	Flowers	Stenson	Blissett	Boney (L)	Hawkridge	Vaughan	Agboola (L)	Sbarra	No.
x	x	xs	x	x	x	x	x	x	xs	xs	sx	sx	sx	s	s													1
x	x		x	x	x	x	xs	xs		x	xs	x	sx	sx	s	sx	s											2
x	x		xs		x	x	x	xs	sx	x	xs	x	sx	x	sx	s	s											3
x	x		x	x	x	x	xs	x		x		x	xs	sx	sx	s	s	s										4
x	x		x	x	x	x	x	xs		x	sx	s	sx	xs	s	s			x									5
x	x	sx	x	x	x	x	xs	xs		x	xs	s	sx	sx	s				x									6
x	x	x	x	x	x	x	x	xs		x	xs	sx	s	s	s				sx									7
x	x	x	xs	x	x	x	xs	x		xs	x	sx	s	sx	sx				s									8
x	x	x	sx	x	x	x	x	xs	s	xs	sx	sx		x	s				xs									9
x	x	x	x		x	x	x	xs	sx	xs	x	xs	sx	s	s				sx									10
x	x	x	xs		x		x	sx	x	x	xs	x	s	xs	sx			s	sx									11
x	x	x	x	x	xs		xs	sx	x	x	xs	sx	s	sx	s				x									12
x	x	x	x	x	x			xs		x	sx	xs	s	x	sx			s	x	s								13
x	x	x	xs	x	x	x	x	sx	xs	x	xs	sx		s					sx	s								14
x		x		x	x	x	x	xs	xs	x	sx	sx		sx	s				xs	s								15
x	x	x	sx	x	x	xs	x	xs	sx	x	xs	sx		x					s	s								16
x	x	xs	s	x	x	x	s	xs	xs	sx	x	s		x	x				sx	sx								17
x	x		xs	x	x		x	xs	sx	x	xs	s		x	s				sx	x	sx							18
x	x		x	x	x	xs	x	x	sx	xs	xs	s		sx					s	x	sx							19
x	x	x	xs	x	x	x	x	xs	sx	x		sx		sx					s	s	xs							20
x	x	x	xs	x	x	x	xs	x	xs	x		sx		sx	sx				s	s								21
x	x	x	x	x		xs	x	xs	sx	x		sx		sx	s				x	s	xs							22
x	x	x		x	x	x	x	xs	sx	xs	sx	sx		x	s					s	xs							23
x	x	x	xs	x	x	x	x	x	sx	xs	sx	s		xs	s				sx	s								24
x	x	x	x	x	x	x	xs	sx	sx	x	xs	s		sx						s	xs							25
x	xs	x	x	xs		x	x	xs	s	x	x	sx		s					x	sx	sx							26
x		xs	s		x	s	x	sx	x	s		x		x	x				x	x	x							27
x	x	x	x	xs	x	x	x	xs	sx	xs	xs	sx		sx	sx				s	s								28
x	x	x	x	x	x	x	xs	xs	s	x	xs	sx		sx						s	sx							29
x	x	x	x	x	x	xs	x	sx		xs	sx	s		x						s	sx	xs						30
x	x	x	x	x	x	x	x	sx		xs	sx	s		xs						s	sx	xs						31
x	x	x	x	x		xs	x	xs		s	x	sx		sx						xs	sx	x	s					32
x	x	x	xs	x	x	x	x	sx		x	xs	s		sx						s	sx	xs						33
x	x	x	xs	x	x	x	x	sx		xs	x	s		sx						s	sx	xs						34
x	s	x	sx	s	x		x	xs		sx	sx	x		xs						x	xs	x		x				35
x	x	x	x	x	x	x		sx		xs	xs	s		x						s	sx	xs		sx				36
x	x	x	x	x	x	x	xs	sx		xs	sx	s		sx							s	x		xs				37
x	x	x	x	x	x	x	xs	sx		x	xs	s		sx						s		xs		sx				38
x	s	x	s	xs	sx	xs	sx	x		xs	sx	x		x						x		x		x				39
x	x	x	x	x	x	x	xs	xs		x	xs	s		sx								sx		sx	s			40
x	x	x	x	x	sx	x	x	xs			sx	sx								s		x		xs	xs	s		41
x	x	x	x	x	s	x	xs	xs			xs	sx								s	sx	x		sx	x			42
x	x	x	x	xs	x	x	x	sx	s		xs	sx								s	xs	x		sx				43
x	x	x	x		s	xs	x	sx		x	xs	x		sx							s	xs		sx	x			44
x	x	x	x	x	s	x	x	sx		x	xs	s		s								x		s	x			45
x	x	x	x	x	s	x	xs	sx		xs	xs	sx		sx							s	x			x			46
x	x	x	x	x	s	x	x	sx		xs	xs	sx		s								x			x			47
x	x	x		xs	sx	x	x	sx		xs	sx	x		s							s	x		xs	x			48
x	x	x	xs	x	x	x	x	xs			xs	s		s							sx	x		sx			sx	49
x	x	x	x	x	x	x	xs	sx		xs	xs	sx		s								x		s			sx	50
x		x	xs	x	x	x	x	xs		xs	sx	x		sx							s	x		s			sx	51
x		x		x	x	x	x	xs		x	s	x		sx							sx	xs		xs	s		sx	52
x	x	x	xs	x	x	x	x	x		xs	sx	sx										xs		s	s		sx	53
x	x	x	x	x	x	x	x	xs		xs	sx	s										sx		s	x		s	54
x	x	s			x		s			s	x	x		x						x	sx	xs		x	x	s	x	55
x	x	x	x	x	x	x	xs	xs		x	sx	s										sx		sx	xs		s	56
56	49	45	32	44	44	42	36	8	3	26	7	12	0	12	2	0	0	0	7	6	1	14	0	3	8	0	1	x
0	1	3	13	5	1	7	15	28	5	21	25	2	1	5	0	0	0	0	2	1	6	10	0	4	2	0	0	xs
0	0	1	3	0	3	0	1	19	11	2	18	23	6	23	7	1	0	0	7	2	14	3	0	8	0	0	5	sx
0	2	1	3	1	5	1	2	0	4	3	1	19	5	10	13	3	3	3	6	21	5	0	1	5	3	2	2	s

x - Played full 90 minutes
xs - Substituted off
sx - Substituted on
s - Non-playing Substitute

SUTTON UNITED MATCH RESULTS 2018-19

Date	Comp	Opponents	H/A	Att:	Result		Goalscorers	Pos
Aug 4	NL	Harrogate Town	A	1378	D	2 - 2	Clough 39 Collins 90+3 (Pen)	10
7	NL	Eastleigh	H	1725	W	1 - 0	Collins 31 (Pen)	6
11	NL	Salford City	H	1898	W	2 - 1	Eastmond 35 Lafayette 63	6
14	NL	Ebbsfleet United	A	1506	W	1 - 0	Eastmond 33	3
18	NL	Solihull Moors	A	763	D	2 - 2	Lafayette 25 Wright 76	4
25	NL	AFC Fylde	H	1770	D	0 - 0		5
27	NL	Aldershot Town	A	1904	L	1 - 2	Lafayette 90 (Pen)	9
Sept 1	NL	FC Halifax Town	H	1789	D	1 - 1	Davis 55	10
4	NL	Maidstone United	A	1838	W	1 - 0	Lafayette 9	7
8	**SCC2**	**Airdrieonians**	**A**	**831**	**W**	**1 - 0**	**Wright 21**	
15	NL	Havant & Waterlooville	A	1273	W	2 - 1	Wright 60 Beautyman 77	7
18	NL	Boreham Wood	H	1677	L	0 - 4		8
22	NL	Wrexham	H	2050	W	3 - 0	Collins 15 (Pen) Cadogan 35 Eastmond 51	7
25	NL	Dover Athletic	H	1694	D	2 - 2	Eastmond 2 Bailey 18	7
29	NL	Leyton Orient	A	5627	W	1 - 0	Ayunga 49	6
Oct 6	NL	Barrow	A	1203	L	1 - 2	Thomas 90	9
13	**SCC3**	**Bohemians**	**A**	**1130**	**D**	**0 - 0**	**(Lost 4-3 on pens)**	
20	**FAC 4Q**	**Wealdstone**	**A**	**1082**	**W**	**2 - 1**	**Collins 65 (pen) Drinan 90+3**	
27	NL	Hartlepool United	A	2788	W	3 - 2	Thomas 21 Bolarinwa 63 Eastmond 79	8
30	NL	Chesterfield	H	1852	D	1 - 1	Ayunga 37	8
Nov 3	NL	Dagenham & Redbridge	H	1909	W	1 - 0	Cadogan 56	7
10	**FAC 1P**	**Slough Town**	**H**	**1830**	**D**	**0 - 0**		
17	NL	Gateshead	A	794	D	0 - 0		7
20	**FAC 1Pr**	**Slough Town**	**A**	**1360**	**D**	**1 - 1**	**Taylor 9**	
24	NL	Maidenhead United	H	1606	L	0 - 1		8
27	NL	Braintree Town	A	439	D	2 - 2	Clough 75 Collins 86 (Pen)	8
Dec 1	NL	AFC Fylde	A	1401	D	2 - 2	Pearce 74 Cadogan 88	8
8	NL	Solihull Moors	H	1728	D	2 - 2	Brown W 35 Davis 74	8
15	**FAT 1P**	**Bromley**	**A**	**776**	**L**	**1 - 2**	**Thomas-Asante 22** (Reinstated after Bromley were found to have played an ineligible playe	
22	NL	FC Halifax Town	A	1319	W	1 - 0	Eastmond 90+4	8
26	NL	Bromley	H	2086	W	1 - 0	Collins 54	8
29	NL	Aldershot Town	H	2216	W	2 - 1	Beautyman 4 Williams 6	8
Jan 1	NL	Bromley	A	1428	L	1 - 2	Davis 11	8
5	NL	Harrogate Town	H	1841	W	2 - 1	Ayunga 19 Beautyman 82	6
12	**FAT 2P**	**Spennymoor Town**	**A**	**760**	**L**	**0 - 3**		
19	NL	Eastleigh	A	1872	L	2 - 3	Toure 43 Williams 66	7
26	NL	Ebbsfleet United	H	2108	W	1 - 0	Toure 90+4	6
Feb 9	NL	Barnet	A	1316	W	1 - 0	Dobson 36	6
16	NL	Barrow	H	1892	L	0 - 1		7
19	NL	Barnet	H	1917	D	0 - 0		6
23	NL	Dagenham & Redbridge	A	1322	L	0 - 1		9
Mar 2	NL	Hartlepool United	H	1923	D	2 - 2	Deacon 27 Toure 56	9
5	NL	Salford City	A	1686	L	0 - 2		9
9	NL	Maidenhead United	A	1210	L	0 - 1		9
12	NL	Braintree Town	H	1525	L	0 - 3		9
16	NL	Gateshead	H	1722	W	4 - 2	Kearny 51 Dobson 63 (pen) Beckwith 86 89	9
Manager Paul Doswell steps down to take a break with Ian Baird taking over for the rest of the season.								
23	NL	Chesterfield	A	4311	L	0 - 3		10
30	NL	Havant & Waterlooville	H	1816	D	2 - 2	Collins 5 (pen) Beckwith 67	10
Apr 6	NL	Boreham Wood	A	508	W	2 - 1	Beautyman 15 Eastmond 90+5	9
13	NL	Leyton Orient	H	3339	L	1 - 2	Ayunga 52	9
19	NL	Wrexham	A	5264	L	0 - 1		10
22	NL	Maidstone United	H	1858	D	2 - 2	Kearny 9 Williams 76	10
27	NL	Dover Athletic	A	1103	L	0 - 3		9

GOALSCORERS	SG	CSG	Pens	Hat tricks	Total
Collins	7	2	5		7
Eastmond	7	2			7
Ayunga	4	1			4
Beautyman	4	1			4
Lafayette	4	1	1		4
Cadogan	3	1			3
Davis	3	1			3
Toure	3	2			3
Williams	3	1			3
Wright	3	2			3
Beckwith	2	1			2
Clough	2	1			2
Dobson	2	1	1		2
Kearny	2	1			2
Thomas	2	1			2
Bailey	1	1			1
Bolarinwa	1	1			1
Brown W	1	1			1
Deacon	1	1			1
Drinan	1	1			1
Pearce	1	1			1
Taylor	1	1			1
Thomas-Asante	1	1			1

No.	Butter	Bennett	Thomas	Eastmond	Collins	Clough	Bolarinwa	Lafayette	Taylor	Beautyman	Bailey	Wright	Drinan (L)	Wishart	Beckwith	Davis	Cadogan	Brown W	Ayunga	Worner	Lema	Dundas	Brown S	Thomas-Asante (L)	McQueen	Pearce	Mason	Williams (L)	Toure	Ziger (L)	Mbeta	Dobson	Ikebuassi	Deacon	Kearney	Green	Bellikli	Barden
1	x	xs	x	x	x	x	x	xs	xs	x	x	sx	sx	sx	s	s																						
2	x	x	x	x	x	x	xs	x	sx	s		xs	sx	x	s	xs	sx																					
3	x	x	x	x	x	x	s	xs	sx	s		xs	sx	x	sx	x	xs																					
4	x	x		x	x	x	sx	xs	xs			s	x	x	sx	x	xs	sx	s																			
5	x	x		x	x		sx	x	xs			sx	xs		sx		xs	s	s																			
6	x	x		x	x	x	x	xs	x	sx		sx	sx	xs	s	x	xs	s																				
7	x		x	x	x	x	sx	sx	xs	x		xs	xs	s	x	x	sx	s																				
8	x	x	s	x		x	x	xs	sx	s		sx	x	x	x	xs	sx	xs																				
9	x	x	s	x		x	s	xs	x	x		sx	sx	x	x	sx		xs	xs																			
10			**x**	**sx**	**x**		**x**		**x**	**x**	**x**	**xs**	**s**	**xs**	**x**	**sx**	**sx**	**xs**	**s**	**x**																		
11	x	x	x	x		x		xs	xs	x	sx	x		s	x	xs	sx	s	sx																			
12	x	x		x		x		xs	xs	x	sx	x	sx	x	x	xs	s	s	sx																			
13	x	x	x	x	xs	x	sx		s	s	x	xs	sx		sx		x	x	xs																			
14	x	x	x	x	xs	x	xs	s	sx	s	x	x	sx		sx			xs	x																			
15	x	x	x	x		x	sx	s		s	x	xs	x	sx	x	xs		sx	xs																			
16	x	x	x			x	sx	xs	sx	xs			x	x		xs	sx	x	x	s	s																	
17	**s**	**x**	**x**	**x**		**x**	**xs**	**sx**	**x**	**s**			**x**	**x**		**sx**	**sx**	**xs**	**xs**	**x**																		
18	**x**	**x**	**x**	**x**	**x**	**x**	**xs**		**xs**	**sx**	**x**		**x**	**sx**		**s**	**xs**		**sx**	**s**																		
19	x	x	x	x	x	x	x		s	sx			x	sx	s	xs	xs	sx	xs																			
20	x	x	x	x	x	x	x			s	sx		x	s	s	xs	x	sx	xs																			
21	x	x	x	x	x	xs	xs		s	s	x		x	sx	sx		x	sx	xs																			
22	**x**	**xs**	**x**	**x**	**x**	**x**	**x**		**s**	**s**	**sx**		**xs**	**s**	**sx**	**x**	**x**	**sx**	**xs**	**s**																		
23		x	x		x	x	xs		x	xs			sx	xs	x	s	s	x	sx	x		sx																
24		**x**	**x**	**x**	**x**	**x**	**sx**		**xs**	**x**			**sx**	**s**	**x**	**sx**	**sx**	**xs**	**xs**	**x**			**s**															
25	x	xs	x	x	x	x			x	x	sx			s			sx	xs		s		xs		x	sx													
26	x	xs	xs	x	x	x			sx	sx	x						x	s		s		xs		x	x	sx												
27	x		x	x	x	x			x	sx	x					xs	sx	xs		s		s		xs	sx	x												
28	x	x		x	x				xs	s	x				s	x	sx	x				x		xs	sx	x	s											
29	**x**	**x**		**x**	**x**	**x**			**xs**	**sx**	**x**				**sx**	**x**	**xs**						**s**	**x**	**sx**	**xs**	**s**											
30	x	x	xs	x	x		sx		sx	xs	x				s	x	s		xs						sx	x		x										
31	x	x		x	x		sx		s	x	x				sx	x			xs					s	s	x		x	xs									
32	x	x		x	x		sx		sx	x	x				s	x			xs					sx	s	x		xs	xs									
33	x	x	xs	x	xs		sx			x	x				sx	xs			x						s	x	s	x	sx									
34		x		x			xs			x	x				x	sx			xs	x	s			sx	sx	x	s	x	xs									
35		**x**		**x**			**sx**			**x**	**x**				**x**	**x**		**s**	**x**		**s**			**xs**	**x**	**x**	**s**			**x**	**s**							
36		x	x	xs			sx			x	x				x	xs			s	x					sx	sx	s	x	xs			x						
37		x	x				xs			x	x				x	x			sx	x	s				sx	s		xs	x			x	s					
38		x	sx	x	x		sx			x	xs				x	xs			s	x					s			x	xs			x		sx				
39		x		x	x		sx			xs					x				xs	x	s					x	s	xs	x			x		sx	sx			
40	s	x		x	x		x									x			x	x	s						s	xs	x			x		x	sx	s		
41	s	x		x	x		sx								x	x			x	x	s						s	xs	x			xs		x	sx			
42		xs	x	x	x		xs			x					x	x			sx	x								sx	xs			sx		x		s	s	
43		xs	x	x	x		x			x					x	xs			s	x								sx	xs			sx		x		s	sx	
44	s		x	x	x		sx			x	xs				x	sx			sx	x								xs	x			xs		x			s	
45	s		x		x		xs			x	x				x	x			sx	x								s	xs			sx		x	sx		xs	
46	s	x	x				x			x					x	xs			s	x								xs	sx			x		x	x		s	sx
47	s	x	xs				x			x					x				sx	x	s							xs	sx			x		x	x		sx	xs
48	x	x	x	x	x		s			x					x				x	s								xs	xs			sx		sx	sx			xs
49	x	x		x			x			x					x				s	s							s	sx	x			x		xs	xs		sx	x
50	xs	x		x			x			x									x	sx	s						s	x	sx			x		x	xs		s	x
51		x	sx	x			x			x									xs	x	s						s	x	x			xs		x	sx		sx	xs
52		xs	sx	x			x			x									s	x	s						sx	x	x			xs		xs	x		sx	x
53			x				xs			x	sx								x	x	x						xs	x	x		s	sx		sx		s	xs	x
x	31	40	29	44	32	25	15	2	7	28	20	3	9	8	24	16	5	4	9	20	1	1	0	3	2	9	0	10	9	1	0	9	0	10	3	0	0	4
xs	1	7	4	1	3	1	11	9	10	4	2	6	3	3	0	14	7	8	15	0	0	2	0	3	0	1	1	9	9	0	0	4	0	2	2	0	2	3
sx	0	0	3	1	0	0	17	2	8	6	6	5	10	5	10	6	11	6	9	1	0	1	0	2	8	2	1	3	4	0	0	5	0	4	6	0	5	1
s	7	0	2	0	0	0	3	2	5	11	0	1	1	6	8	3	3	7	9	8	11	1	2	1	4	1	12	1	0	0	2	0	1	0	0	4	4	0

x - Played full 90 minutes
xs - Substituted off
sx - Substituted on
s - Non-playing Substitute

WREXHAM MATCH RESULTS 2018-19

Date	Comp	Opponents	H/A	Att:	Result		Goalscorers	Pos
Aug 4	NL	Dover Athletic	A	1359	W	1 - 0	Fondop-Talom 29	8
7	NL	AFC Fylde	H	5777	D	0 - 0		9
11	NL	Boreham Wood	H	4356	W	3 - 0	Maguire-Drew 25 Pyke 66 Fondop-Talom 84	5
14	NL	Maidenhead United	A	1584	W	2 - 0	Fondop-Talom 14 Maguire-Drew 27	1
18	NL	Eastleigh	A	1717	W	3 - 1	Smith 9 Wynter 13 (og) Fondop-Talom 82	1
25	NL	Bromley	H	5714	D	2 - 2	Fondop-Talom 31 Pyke 65	1
27	NL	Solihull Moors	A	2412	L	0 - 1		2
Sept 1	NL	Aldershot Town	H	4648	W	2 - 0	Beavon 62 Maguire-Drew 78	1
4	NL	FC Halifax Town	H	5377	D	0 - 0		3
8	NL	Braintree Town	A	802	W	1 - 0	Pearson 66	2
15	NL	Ebbsfleet United	H	4718	W	4 - 1	Holroyd 6 Beavon 12 Pyke 19 Pearson 45+2	2
22	NL	Sutton United	A	2050	L	0 - 3		3
25	NL	Harrogate Town	A	2387	D	0 - 0		4
29	NL	Barnet	H	4727	W	1 - 0	Beavon 42	4
Oct 6	NL	Havant & Waterlooville	H	4323	W	1 - 0	Pyke 31	4
13	NL	Dagenham & Redbridge	A	1601	W	2 - 1	Young 43 Summerfield 67	2
20	**FAC 4Q**	**Harrogate Town**	**A**	**1540**	**D**	**0 - 0**		
23	**FAC 4Qr**	**Harrogate Town**	**H**	**2550**	**W**	**2 - 0**	**Wright 62 Young 76**	
27	NL	Chesterfield	A	5662	D	1 - 1	Walker 20 (Pen)	3
30	NL	Hartlepool United	H	4665	W	1 - 0	Young 20	2
Nov 3	NL	Gateshead	H	4421	W	3 - 1	Kerr 18 (og) Walker 68 Pyke 90+2	1
11	**FAC 1P**	**Weston-super-Mare**	**A**	**1170**	**W**	**2 - 0**	**Summerfield 51 Beavon 81**	
17	NL	Maidstone United	A	2626	D	1 - 1	Walker 71	3
24	NL	Leyton Orient	H	6248	L	0 - 2		3
27	NL	Barrow	A	851	D	0 - 0		3
Dec 1	**FAC 2P**	**Newport County**	**H**	**5295**	**D**	**0 - 0**		
Manager Sam Ricketts leaves to take up the position at Shrewsbury Town, assistant Graham Barrow takes temporary charge								
8	NL	Eastleigh	H	4105	W	2 - 0	Jennings 2 Grant 58	4
11	**FAC 2Pr**	**Newport County**	**A**	**4143**	**L**	**0 - 4**		
15	**FAT 1P**	**Boston United**	**H**	**1083**	**W**	**3 - 0**	**Holroyd 1 Fondop 10 Rutherford 31**	
Graham Barrow made permanent manager.								
22	NL	Aldershot Town	A	1866	D	0 - 0		3
26	NL	Salford City	H	8283	W	5 - 1	Pearson 3 Wright 24 Walker 45 Tollitt 86 Holroyd 90+3	2
29	NL	Solihull Moors	H	6220	W	1 - 0	Rutherford 49	2
Jan 1	NL	Salford City	A	4044	L	0 - 2		2
5	NL	Dover Athletic	H	4817	L	0 - 1		4
8	NL	Bromley	A	1061	L	0 - 2		4
12	**FAT 2P**	**Leyton Orient**	**H**	**1949**	**L**	**0 - 1**		
19	NL	AFC Fylde	A	2912	L	0 - 2		5
26	NL	Maidenhead United	H	4323	W	1 - 0	Young 65	5
Graham Barrow resigns as manager. Bryan Hughes is named as his replacement.								
Feb 9	NL	Dagenham & Redbridge	H	5366	W	1 - 0	Beavon 74	3
16	NL	Havant & Waterlooville	A	1658	W	3 - 2	Pearson 48 Wright 58 Jennings 60	2
19	NL	Boreham Wood	A	645	W	2 - 0	Tollitt 56 64	1
23	NL	Gateshead	A	1228	D	1 - 1	Stockton 90+3	1
Mar 2	NL	Chesterfield	H	7106	W	1 - 0	Wright 62	1
9	NL	Leyton Orient	A	6643	L	0 - 1		2
12	NL	Barrow	H	4613	L	1 - 3	Kennedy 77	3
16	NL	Maidstone United	H	3604	W	1 - 0	Tollitt 49	3
23	NL	Hartlepool United	A	3888	L	0 - 1		3
30	NL	Ebbsfleet United	A	1523	L	2 - 4	Beavon 49 Pearson 82	4
Apr 6	NL	Braintree Town	H	4221	W	3 - 1	Grant 18 Pearson 59 Wright 66	4
13	NL	Barnet	A	1594	W	2 - 1	Wright 47 McGlashan 86	4
19	NL	Sutton United	H	5264	W	1 - 0	Kennedy 78	4
22	NL	FC Halifax Town	A	2577	L	1 - 2	Holroyd 40	5
27	NL	Harrogate Town	H	3690	W	2 - 1	Oswell 42 Deverdics 80	4
May 1	**PO Q**	**Eastleigh**	**H**	**6723**	**L**	**0 - 1**	**(aet)**	

GOALSCORERS	SG	CSG	Pens	Hat tricks	Total
Beavon	6	1			6
Fondop-Talom	6	4			6
Pearson	6	2			6
Wright	6	2			6
Pyke	5	1			5
Holroyd	4	1			4
Tollitt	3	1			4
Walker	4	1	1		4
Young	4	1			4
Maguire-Drew	3	2			3
Grant	2	1			2
Jennings	2	1			2
Kennedy	2	1			2
Opponent	2	1			2
Rutherford	2	1			2
Summerfield	2	1			2
Deverdics	1	1			1
McGlashan	1	1			1
Oswell	1	1			1
Smith	1	1			1
Stockton	1	1			1

Lainton (L)	Jennings	Smith	Pearson	Summerfield	Young	Fondop-Talom	Rutherford	Roberts	Wright	Beavon	Pyke (L)	Carrington	Maguire-Drew (L)	Dibble	Tharme	Holroyd	Deverdics	Burgess (L)	Hinds (L)	Lawlor	Walker (L)	Grant (L)	Sargent	Thorn	Beaumont	Tollitt (L)	Stockton (L)	Oswell	Kennedy	Simpson	McGlashan (L)	Agustien	Spyrou (L)	No.
X	X	X	X	X	X	XS	XS	X	X	XS	SX	SX	SX	S	S																			1
X	X	X	X	X	X	XS	X	X	X	SX	SX	S	XS	S	S																			2
X	X	X	X	X	XS	X	SX	XS	X	XS	SX	SX	X	S	S																			3
X	X	X	X	X		XS	X		X	SX	XS	X	XS	S	S	SX	SX																	4
X	X	X	X	X		X	XS		X	SX	XS	X	XS	S	S	SX	SX																	5
X	XS	X	X	X	SX	X			X	XS	SX	X	X	S	SX	S	XS																	6
X		XS	X	XS	X	XS		X	X		X	X	SX	S	SX	X		SX	S															7
X			X	X	SX	X	SX	X	X	X	SX	X	XS	S	XS	S	XS																	8
X	X		X	X	SX	XS	XS		X	SX	X	X	XS	S		SX				X	S													9
X	X		X	X	XS	XS	SX	X	SX	X	SX		X	S		S				X	XS													10
X	X		X	XS	SX	SX	X	X	SX	X	XS		S	S		XS				X	X													11
X	X		X	X	SX	SX	XS	X	SX	XS	X		S	S		X				X	XS													12
X			X	X	SX	X	XS	X	XS	SX		X	XS	S		SX	S			X	X													13
X			X	X	SX	SX	SX	X	X	X		X	XS	S		XS	S			X	XS													14
X			X	X	X		SX	X	SX	XS	X	X	XS	S	S		SX			X	XS													15
X			X	X	X	SX	SX	X	SX	XS	X	X	XS	S			S			XS	X													16
X			X	XS	X	XS	X	X	X	SX	SX	X	SX	S	XS		S	S	S		X													17
X	X				X	SX	SX	X	XS	XS	X	X	XS	S	S	S	S	SX		X	X													18
X	SX		X		X	XS	X	X	X	SX	XS	XS	S	S		SX				X	X													19
X	X		X		X	SX	SX	X	X	XS	X		XS	S		S	SX			X	XS													20
X	X		X	X	X	S	X	X	SX	XS	SX			S		XS	SX			X	XS													21
X	X		X	X	X	S	X	X	SX	XS	SX			S		XS	SX			X	XS													22
X	X		X	X	X	XS	XS	X	XS	SX	X	S	SX	S						X	SX													23
X	SX		X	X	X	SX	XS	X	S	XS	XS	X	SX	S						X	X													24
X	X		X	X	X	SX	SX	X	S	XS	XS		S	S						X	X	X												25
X	SX	S	X	X	SX	SX	XS	X	XS	XS		X		S		S	S			X	X	X												26
X	X	X		X	SX	SX	X	XS	X	XS		X		S		SX	S			X		XS												27
X	X		X	XS	X	SX	X		X	XS		X		S		SX	SX			X		XS	S	S	S									28
S	X			X		X	XS		X	S		X		X		X	X			X	X	S	SX	S										29
X	X		X	X		S	XS		X	XS		X	S	S		SX	SX			X	X	X												30
X	X	S	X	X			XS		X	XS		X		S		SX	SX			X	X	XS				SX								31
X	X		X	XS	SX		X	SX	X	XS		X		S		S				X	XS	X				SX								32
X	X		X	X	SX		X	SX	XS	XS		XS		S		S				X	X	X				SX								33
X	X		X	X	XS		X	X	SX	XS		S		S		SX				X	XS	X				SX								34
X	X		X	X	X		XS	X	XS		SX	S		S						X		X				SX	SX	XS						35
S	X			X	X		SX	X	XS		SX	XS		X		S				X	X					SX	X	XS						36
X			X	X	SX		X	X	X	XS	SX	X		S						X	XS	XS					SX	S						37
X	X		X	XS	SX		X	X	X	XS	XS			S		SX				X	X	S						SX						38
X	X		X		XS		SX	X	X	SX		SX		S		S				X	X	XS				X	XS							39
X	X		X		X		X		X			X		S		SX	S			X	XS					X	S	XS	SX					40
X	X				X		X		X			X		S	S	SX	S			X	X					XS	SX	XS	X					41
	X				X		X		XS			XS		X	S	SX	SX			X	X					XS	SX	X	X	S				42
X	X		X		X		X	S	X	XS				S		SX				X	X					XS	S	SX	X					43
X	X		X		X		X	S	X	XS				S						X	XS	SX				XS	SX	SX	X					44
X	X				X		SX	X	X	XS				S		SX				X		S				X	SX	XS	X		XS			45
X	X		X		X		X	S	X	SX				S		XS	XS			X		SX				XS			X		SX			46
X	X		X		X		X	S	X	SX				S		X	S			X									X		XS	XS	SX	47
X	X		X		SX		X	X	X	SX		X		S		S				X								SX			XS	XS	XS	48
X	SX		X		X		X	X	X	XS		X		S		X				XS		XS						SX	SX		S			49
X	S		X	SX	X		XS	X	X	XS		X		S		X						XS						SX	X		SX			50
X	S		X	SX	X		XS	X	X	XS		X		S		X						XS						SX	X		SX			51
X	X		X	XS	X		SX	X	X	SX		S		S		XS						X						XS	X		SX			52
	X			XS			X	X	S			X		X	X		SX						X	SX			SX	XS		S		X	XS	53
X	X		X	XS	X		SX	X	X	XS		S		S		X						XS						SX	X		SX			54
50	39	7	46	29	30	6	24	35	35	4	8	28	3	4	1	8	1	0	0	38	19	8	1	0	0	3	1	1	11	0	0	1	0	X
0	1	1	0	9	4	9	14	2	8	29	7	4	11	0	2	6	3	0	0	2	12	9	0	0	0	5	1	7	0	0	3	2	2	XS
0	4	0	0	2	14	11	14	2	8	13	12	3	5	0	2	16	11	2	0	0	1	2	1	1	0	6	7	8	2	0	5	0	1	SX
2	2	2	0	0	0	3	0	4	3	1	0	6	5	50	9	11	10	1	2	0	1	3	1	2	1	0	2	1	0	2	1	0	0	S

x - Played full 90 minutes
xs - Substituted off
sx - Substituted on
s - Non-playing Substitute

NATIONAL LEAGUE PLAY-OFF FINAL

AFC Fylde 0 - 3 Salford City

Lynch (Fylde) is still airbourne as Piergianni (Salford) celebrates. Photo: Keith Clayton.

Byrne (Fylde) blocks Dieseruvwe (Salford)
Photo: Keith Clayton.

Photo: Peter Barnes.

Photo: Peter Barnes.

NATIONAL LEAGUE NORTH TABLE 2018-19

		P	W	D	L	F	A	GD	Pts
1	Stockport County	42	24	10	8	77	36	41	82
2	Chorley (Play-off winners)	42	24	9	9	83	41	42	81
3	Brackley Town	42	22	11	9	72	40	32	77
4	Spennymoor Town	42	22	10	10	78	48	30	76
5	Altrincham	42	20	11	11	85	56	29	71
6	Blyth Spartans	42	20	9	13	74	62	12	69
7	Bradford (Park Avenue)	42	18	11	13	71	61	10	65
8	AFC Telford United	42	17	14	11	64	55	9	65
9	Chester	42	16	14	12	60	62	-2	62
10	Kidderminster Harriers	42	17	9	16	68	62	6	60
11	Boston United	42	17	7	18	62	60	2	58
12	York City	42	16	10	16	58	63	-5	58
13	Leamington	42	13	15	14	57	60	-3	54
14	Southport	42	13	14	15	58	55	3	53
15	Alfreton Town	42	13	12	17	53	67	-14	51
16	Darlington	42	12	14	16	56	62	-6	50
17	Hereford	42	11	16	15	47	58	-11	49
18	Curzon Ashton	42	13	10	19	44	71	-27	49
19	Guiseley	42	9	17	16	46	60	-14	44
20	Ashton United	42	9	8	25	43	86	-43	35
21	FC United Of Manchester	42	8	10	24	49	82	-33	34
22	Nuneaton Borough	42	4	7	31	38	96	-58	19

		1	2	3	4	5	6	7	8	9	10	11	12	13	14	15	16	17	18	19	20	21	22
1	Alfreton Town		0-7	2-0	3-1	1-1	0-1	0-1	2-1	2-2	0-1	0-0	2-3	0-1	1-1	3-3	1-2	3-1	1-7	3-1	1-1	1-1	2-3
2	Altrincham	3-1		3-0	1-1	0-2	1-2	1-1	5-3	4-0	0-2	3-3	1-2	1-1	1-1	2-1	2-2	4-0	0-2	1-0	0-1	3-1	3-0
3	Ashton United	0-2	1-1		0-3	1-1	1-5	0-2	0-5	0-3	1-2	2-2	1-0	1-0	0-0	0-1	2-1	0-0	3-0	1-2	0-6	3-4	0-2
4	Blyth Spartans	1-1	2-1	2-0		3-0	1-3	1-2	1-2	8-1	3-2	0-1	0-3	2-0	2-3	3-3	0-2	4-1	2-2	2-1	3-2	1-0	2-1
5	Boston United	0-1	1-2	2-1	4-0		1-3	2-2	0-2	0-2	4-1	0-2	2-1	1-0	3-1	0-2	1-1	2-1	0-2	1-2	1-3	2-2	2-0
6	Brackley Town	3-1	1-2	3-1	1-1	2-0		3-0	2-2	2-2	2-0	2-4	1-0	2-0	2-0	3-1	2-2	3-1	4-1	2-0	1-0	3-1	0-0
7	Bradford (Park Avenue)	1-1	2-3	3-2	1-1	1-0	1-0		1-0	2-0	2-2	2-2	2-3	1-2	1-0	1-2	2-1	1-0	1-0	2-2	1-1	1-2	1-3
8	Chorley	3-1	4-1	0-1	2-4	1-1	2-0	3-2		0-0	2-0	3-2	4-0	3-0	1-0	3-0	3-0	2-0	1-2	4-0	2-0	1-1	1-0
9	Chester	3-2	1-2	4-1	2-0	4-1	0-0	5-3	0-0		0-1	3-1	0-0	1-1	3-0	3-1	1-1	3-2	0-0	0-0	0-6	2-1	2-2
10	Curzon Ashton	3-2	0-6	2-4	1-3	1-3	1-1	1-1	0-1	0-3		1-1	3-1	1-0	0-1	1-1	1-1	0-1	0-5	0-3	0-2	2-1	1-0
11	Darlington	0-1	0-3	2-1	1-1	1-0	0-2	1-0	1-1	0-1	1-2		2-0	0-0	2-2	3-0	1-1	1-2	1-2	0-0	0-1	3-0	5-1
12	FC United Of Manchester	1-1	1-2	3-4	1-2	0-3	1-1	2-2	1-4	0-2	2-0	1-2		3-3	2-2	0-1	0-2	0-4	1-3	1-1	1-2	1-2	3-3
13	Guiseley	0-1	2-2	1-1	1-3	4-5	2-1	1-5	0-2	1-1	1-0	1-0	3-0		1-1	0-0	1-1	2-1	1-1	0-1	1-1	1-1	1-1
14	Hereford	2-1	1-1	0-2	3-0	0-2	0-2	1-2	1-1	2-0	1-2	4-2	1-3	1-0		1-0	2-1	2-2	0-3	0-3	2-2	1-1	1-1
15	Kidderminster Harriers	0-1	3-2	3-3	3-1	1-2	2-0	3-0	0-4	4-1	1-1	5-2	1-2	1-2	2-1		1-2	4-1	2-1	1-4	2-1	0-0	1-2
16	Leamington	3-1	3-0	1-0	1-2	2-0	0-0	4-2	1-1	1-0	0-1	2-2	2-2	2-2	2-2	0-4		3-0	0-2	1-0	0-1	2-2	0-1
17	Nuneaton Borough	1-2	0-2	0-1	1-3	1-5	1-3	0-6	0-1	2-3	2-4	1-2	1-0	1-3	0-0	1-1	0-2		0-2	1-4	0-3	1-2	2-2
18	Spennymoor Town	1-1	4-4	5-0	2-2	1-0	2-1	0-2	1-0	2-0	0-0	2-2	2-0	3-2	0-2	2-1	1-0	3-1		1-1	1-3	2-3	3-0
19	Southport	2-1	1-3	2-2	0-1	2-3	0-0	2-2	5-3	3-0	2-2	0-0	0-0	1-0	1-0	2-2	5-1	1-1	1-1		0-1	0-4	1-2
20	Stockport County	0-1	2-0	2-1	0-1	0-2	1-1	3-0	3-0	1-1	2-0	2-0	5-1	1-1	1-1	1-0	3-1	2-2	1-0	3-2		3-2	3-1
21	AFC Telford United	0-0	1-1	2-1	1-1	1-0	2-1	0-2	1-1	3-1	3-1	3-1	1-3	1-1	1-1	0-1	4-1	3-1	2-1	1-0	1-1		2-1
22	York City	1-2	0-1	2-0	2-0	2-2	2-1	1-4	1-4	0-0	1-1	4-0	2-0	4-2	1-2	0-3	2-2	2-0	2-3	1-0	1-0	1-0	

AFC TELFORD UNITED MATCH RESULTS 2018-19

Date	Comp	Opponents	H/A	Att:	Result	Goalscorers	Pos
Aug 4	NLN	Southport	H	1274	**W** 1 - 0	Morgan-Smith 66	
7	NLN	Kidderminster Harriers	A	1778	D 0 - 0		
11	NLN	Guiseley	A	504	D 1 - 1	Brown 76	
14	NLN	Brackley Town	H	1097	**W** 2 - 1	Udoh 15 Knights 72	
18	NLN	Spennymoor Town	A	600	**W** 3 - 2	Udoh 56 58 Deeney 77	
25	NLN	Chester	H	1876	**W** 3 - 1	McQuilkin 14 Udoh 19 76	
27	NLN	Leamington	A	812	D 2 - 2	Dawson 34 Brown 47	
Sept 1	NLN	Ashton United	H	1148	**W** 2 - 1	Udoh 64 85	
8	NLN	Darlington	A	1212	L 0 - 3		2
15	NLN	Stockport County	H	1415	D 1 - 1	Cowans 88	3
22	**FAC 2Q**	**Bedford Town**	**H**	**737**	**W 3 - 1**	**Udoh 17 72 90**	
29	NLN	Blyth Spartans	A	590	L 0 - 1		5
Oct 6	**FAC 3Q**	**Warrington Town**	**A**	**543**	**L 1 - 2**	**Udoh 90**	
13	NLN	Chorley	H	1258	D 1 - 1	Cowans 1	5
20	NLN	Curzon Ashton	A	299	L 1 - 2	Brown 61	7
27	NLN	York City	H	1384	**W** 2 - 1	Knights 73 Morley 90	6
30	NLN	Hereford	H	1804	D 1 - 1	Udoh 35	8
Nov 3	NLN	Alfreton Town	A	545	D 1 - 1	Sutton 51	8
10	NLN	Boston United	H	1146	**W** 1 - 0	Sutton 23	6
17	NLN	FC United of Manchester	A	964	**W** 2 - 1	Knights 22 Morgan-Smith 56	3
23	**FAT 3Q**	**Darlington**	**A**		**W 2 - 0**		
Dec 1	NLN	Bradford Park Avenue	H	1468	L 0 - 2		5
8	NLN	Altrincham	A	895	L 1 - 3	Udoh 25	7
15	**FAT 1P**	**Farsley Celtic**	**H**	**452**	**W 4 - 3**	**Udoh 33 Barnett 59 Royle 75 Cowans 82**	
22	NLN	Chester	A	2079	L 1 - 2	Morgan-Smith 19	
26	NLN	Nuneaton Borough	H	1524	**W** 3 - 1	Daniels 41 Udoh 43 Knights 54	
29	NLN	Leamington	H	1196	**W** 4 - 1	Daniels 11 Morgan-Smith 20 (Pen) 79 Udoh 90	
Jan 1	NLN	Nuneaton Borough	A	763	**W** 2 - 1	Brown 79 Cowans 82	
5	NLN	Spennymoor Town	H	1205	**W** 2 - 1	Daniels 27 (Pen) Knights 64	4
12	**FAT 2P**	**Hartlepool United**	**A**	**1920**	**W 2 - 1**	**Morgan-Smith 7 Udoh 67**	
19	NLN	Kidderminster Harriers	H	1714	L 0 - 1		
26	NLN	Southport	A	1052	**W** 4 - 0	Royle 24 Dinanga 32 Udoh 50 Deeney 90	
Feb 2	**FAT 3P**	**Spennymoor Town**	**A**	**571**	**W 2 - 1**	**Sutton 55 Brown 75**	
9	NLN	Brackley Town	A	601	L 1 - 3	Dinanga 44	
12	NLN	Guiseley	H	900	D 1 - 1	Udoh 11	
16	NLN	Stockport County	A	4708	L 2 - 3	Sutton 34 Daniels 63	
19	NLN	Ashton United	A	195	**W** 4 - 3	Morgan-Smith 20 52 Udoh 30 76	5
23	**FAT 4P**	**Solihull Moors**	**A**	**1577**	**W 2 - 1**	**Morgan-Smith 25 Udoh 89**	
Mar 2	NLN	Boston United	A	993	D 2 - 2	Udoh 10 Street 90	7
5	NLN	Darlington	H	1052	**W** 3 - 1	Barnett 13 Morgan Smith 16 Udoh 45	6
9	NLN	FC United of Manchester	H	1672	L 1 - 3	Deeney 90	7
16	**FAT SF1**	**Leyton Orient**	**A**	**3622**	**L 0 - 1**		
23	**FAT SF2**	**Leyton Orient**	**H**	**3478**	**L 1 - 2**	**Deeney 39**	
26	NLN	Bradford Park Avenue	A	384	**W** 2 - 1	McQuilkin 57 Udoh 60	6
30	NLN	Blyth Spartans	H	1211	D 1 - 1	Udoh 18	7
Apr 6	NLN	Chorley	A	1286	D 1 - 1	Daniels 87 (pen)	7
9	NLN	Altrincham	H	982	D 1 - 1	Brown 90+1 (pen)	7
13	NLN	Curzon Ashton	H	1507	**W** 3 - 1	Morley 28 29 Brown 49	7
20	NLN	Hereford	A	2623	D 1 - 1	Sutton 62	
22	NLN	Alfreton Town	H	1564	D 0 - 0		8
27	NLN	York City	A	2864	L 0 - 1		8

GOALSCORERS	SG	CSG	Pens	Hat tricks	Total
Udoh	20	4		1	26
Morgan-Smith	8	2	1		10
Brown	7	2	1		7
Daniels	5	2	2		5
Knights	5	1			5
Sutton	5	2			5
Cowans	4	1			4
Deeney	4	1			4
Morley	2	1			3
Barnett	2	1			2
Dinanga	2	1			2
McQuilkin	2	1			2
Royle	2	1			2
Dawson	1	1			1
Streete	1	1			1

Bramley (L)	White	Morley	Streete	Sutton	Deeney	Cowans	McQuilkin	Morgan -Smith	Udoh	Knights	Sears (L)	Royle	Brown	Martinez	Dawson	Lilly	Barnes-Homer	Smith Dominic	Wycherley	Cockerill-Mollett (L)	Ellis	McKenna (L)	McAtee (L)	Barnett (L)	Ceesay (L)	Yusifu	Bursik (L)	Dinanga	No.
x	x	xs	x	x	x	x	xs	x	xs	x	sx	sx	sx	s	s														1
x	x		x	x	x	xs	x	x	sx	xs	x	sx	xs	s	sx	s													2
	x		x	x	x	xs	x	x	xs	x	x	sx	sx	x	s	s	s												3
	x		x	x	x	x	xs	sx	xs	x	x	sx	xs	x	sx		s	s											4
x	x		x	x	x	s	xs	xs	xs	x	x	x	sx		sx			sx	s										5
x	x	xs	x	x	x	x	xs	xs	x	x		s	sx		sx			sx	s										6
x	x		sx	x	x	x	s		x	sx	xs	x	x		xs		s	x	s										7
x	x		x	x	x	xs	x		x	x		sx	xs		sx	s	sx	xs	s										8
xs	x		x	x	x	x	xs		x	x			xs		sx		sx	x	sx										9
x	x		x	x	x	x	xs		x	x		sx	xs		sx		sx	s	s	xs									10
x	x		x	x	x	x	x		x	s		x	x		x	s	s	s	s		s	s							11
x	x		x	x	x	xs	xs	s	x	x		sx	s		sx		xs		s	x									12
x	x	x	x	x	x	s	x	x	x	s		x	s		s		s	s	s				x						13
x	xs	x	x	x	x	sx		s	x	x		xs	sx		sx	x			s				x						14
x	x	xs	x	x	x	sx	xs	sx		x		s	x		sx	xs			s				x						15
s	sx	x	x	x	x	x	s	x	x	xs		xs	sx		sx	xs			x										16
s	x	xs	x	x	x	x	sx	xs	x	x		xs	sx		sx			s	x										17
s	x	x	x	x	x	x	s	x	x	xs		x	sx		s			s	x										18
s	x	x	x	x		x	x	xs		xs		x	xs		sx		sx	s	x					sx					19
s	x	x	x	x	sx	x	xs	xs	xs	x		x	sx					s	x					sx					20
																													21
s	x			x	x	x	x	xs	x	xs		x	sx					xs	x					sx	sx	s			22
	x		x	x	x	x	xs	sx	x	x		xs	s					s	x					xs	sx	sx			23
	x	x	x	x	x	x	xs	sx	xs	s		sx	xs				sx		x					x	s				24
	x	x	x	x	x	xs	xs	xs	x	sx		s	sx						x					sx	x	s			25
	x	sx	x	x	x	s	s	x	xs	xs		x	sx						x					x	x	s			26
	x	sx	x		x	sx	sx	x	x	xs		x	s				s	x	x					xs	xs				27
	x	s	x	s	x	sx	sx	x	x	x		xs	sx					x	x					x	x				28
	x	sx	x	x	x	x	x	sx	x	xs		sx	s											s	xs		x	xs	29
	x	sx	x	x	x	s	sx	x	x	x		x	sx				s		x					xs	xs				30
	x	s	xs	x	x	sx	x		x	x		s	s											x	x		x	s	31
	x	x		x	x	sx	x	sx	xs			x	sx			s			s					x	xs		x	xs	32
	x	x		x	x	xs	x	xs		sx		x	xs	s		s	sx		x					x	sx				33
	x	xs	sx	x	x	s	xs	s	x	sx		x	sx											x	xs		x	x	34
	x	xs	x	x	x	x	sx	s	x	xs		x	sx											sx	s		x	xs	35
	x	s	x	x	x	xs	xs	sx	x	s		x	s											x	x		x	sx	36
	x	x	x	x	x	xs	x	xs	x	x		s	s											sx	s		x	sx	37
	x	xs	x	x	x			x	xs	xs		x	sx	s		s	sx		x					x	sx				38
	x	x	x	x	x		sx	x	x	x		xs	s		sx				xs					xs			sx	s	39
	x	sx	xs	x	x		x	x	xs	x		s	sx		sx									xs	x		x	s	40
	x	s	x	x	x		x	xs	x	xs		s	sx		sx									x	xs		x	sx	41
	x	xs	x	x			x	xs	x	x		x	sx	s		s		sx	x					xs	sx				42
	x		xs	x	x		xs	x	x	sx		xs	sx	s			s	sx	x					x	x				43
	x		sx	x	x		x	sx	sx			x	sx		s			x	x		s			x	sx			sx	44
	x		sx	x	x		x	s	x	xs		sx	s		s			x						x	xs		x	xs	45
	xs	s	x	x	x		x	sx	x	x		xs	sx		s			xs						sx	x		x		46
	x	xs	x	x	x		xs	xs	x	x		s	sx		sx			s						x			x	sx	47
	x	x	x	x			x	sx	s	x		x	xs		sx			s			sx			xs			x	xs	48
	x	x	x	x		sx	x	sx	xs	x		x	xs		s			s						xs			x	sx	49
	x	xs	s	x		x	x	xs	x	xs		s	sx		sx			x						x			x	sx	50
	x	xs	xs	x	x	x	x	xs	x	sx		s	s					x						sx			x	sx	51
12	47	14	38	48	44	19	22	14	33	25	4	21	3	2	1	1	0	8	18	1	0	0	3	15	8	0	16	1	x
1	2	11	4	0	0	8	16	14	11	13	1	8	10	0	1	2	1	3	1	1	0	0	0	8	7	0	0	5	xs
0	1	5	4	0	1	7	6	11	2	6	1	10	26	0	19	0	7	4	1	0	1	0	0	8	6	1	1	8	sx
6	0	5	1	1	0	5	4	5	1	4	0	10	11	6	8	8	8	12	11	0	2	1	0	1	3	3	0	3	s

x - Played full 90 minutes
xs - Substituted off
sx - Substituted on
s - Non-playing Substitute

ALFRETON TOWN MATCH RESULTS 2018-19

Date	Comp	Opponents	H/A	Att:	Result	Goalscorers	Pos
Aug 4	NLN	Kidderminster Harriers	H	754	D 3 - 3	Platt 31 Denton 45 Johnson 85 (Pen)	
7	NLN	Brackley Town	A	505	L 1 - 3	Peniket 59	
11	NLN	York City	A	2501	W 2 - 1	Denton 12 Bateson 14	
14	NLN	Curzon Ashton	H	421	L 0 - 1		
18	NLN	Blyth Spartans	H	465	W 3 - 1	Denton 11 65 Platt 67	
25	NLN	Stockport County	A	2868	W 1 - 0	Denton 8	
27	NLN	Southport	H	546	W 3 - 1	Platt 6 Denton 79 Johnson 89 (Pen)	
Sept 1	NLN	Darlington	A	1269	W 1 - 0	Johnson 2	
8	NLN	Guiseley	H	634	L 0 - 1		
15	NLN	Chorley	A	1298	L 1 - 3	Johnson 33	
22	**FAC 2Q**	**Sutton Coldfield Town**	**A**	**284**	**D 2 - 2**	**Peniket 53 Bacon 61**	
25	**FAC 2Qr**	**Sutton Coldfield Town**	**H**	**194**	**W 3 - 0**	**Bacon 17 54 Sinnott 28**	
29	NLN	Bradford Park Avenue	H	487	L 0 - 1		9
Oct 6	**FAC 3Q**	**Mickleover Sports**	**A**	**505**	**W 2 - 1**	**Sinnott 32 (Pen) Peniket 45**	
13	NLN	Altrincham	A	1123	L 1 - 3	Peniket 60	12
20	**FAC 4Q**	**St Neots Town**	**H**	**645**	**W 4 - 0**	**Bateson 5 21 Clifton 17 (pen) 27 (pen)**	
27	NLN	Chester	A	1619	L 2 - 3	Styche 7 Johnson 20	
30	NLN	FC United of Manchester	A	1531	D 1 - 1	Clifton 88	15
Nov 3	NLN	AFC Telford United	H	545	D 1 - 1	Sinnott 74	16
11	**FAC 1P**	**Fleetwood Town**	**H**	**827**	**L 1 - 4**	**Sinnott 70**	
17	NLN	Nuneaton Borough	H	1673	W 3 - 1	Chettle 45 72 Hobson 89	12
24	**FAT 3Q**	**Farsley Celtic**	**H**	**214**	**L 0 - 2**		
20	NLN	Leamington	H	316	L 1 - 2	Shiels 80	
Dec 1	NLN	Hereford	A	2082	L 1 - 2	Hobson 87	14
4	NLN	Ashton United	A	154	W 2 - 0	Peniket 61 Styche 74	
8	NLN	Spennymoor Town	H	235	L 1 - 7	Styche 43	13
22	NLN	Stockport County	H	825	D 1 - 1	Styche 66	
26	NLN	Boston United	A	1393	W 1 - 0	Styche 6	
29	NLN	Southport	A	1023	L 1 - 2	Styche 53 (Pen)	
Jan 1	NLN	Boston United	H	665	D 1 - 1	Hotte 90	
5	NLN	Blyth Spartans	A	676	D 1 - 1	Allan 33	
12	NLN	Darlington	H	648	D 0 - 0		15
19	NLN	Brackley Town	H	369	L 0 - 1		
26	NLN	Kidderminster Harriers	A	1315	W 1 - 0	Styche 25	
Feb 2	NLN	York City	H	655	L 2 - 3	Styche 35 (pen) 51	
9	NLN	Curzon Ashton	A	204	L 2 - 3	Styche 7 Wilde 33	
16	NLN	Chorley	H	536	W 2 - 1	Clarke 54 O'Brien 55	15
23	NLN	Guiseley	A	402	W 1 - 0	Sinnott 35	15
Mar 2	NLN	Ashton United	H	413	W 2 - 0	Johnson 72 Bacon 84	15
9	NLN	Nuneaton Borough	A	517	W 2 - 1	Shiels 67 Sinnott 87	11
23	NLN	Spennymoor Town	A	1083	D 1 - 1	Sinnott 74 (pen)	13
30	NLN	Bradford Park Avenue	A	465	D 1 - 1	Styche 76	12
Apr 6	NLN	Altrincham	H	538	L 0 - 7		14
9	NLN	Hereford	H	434	D 1 - 1	Peniket 68	13
13	NLN	Leamington	A	523	L 1 - 3	Sinnott 74	14
20	NLN	FC United of Manchester	H	733	L 2 - 3	Peniket 29 Allan 44	
22	NLN	AFC Telford United	A	1564	D 0 - 0		15
27	NLN	Chester	H	530	D 2 - 2	Wilde 65 81	15

GOALSCORERS	SG	CSG	Pens	Hat tricks	Total
Styche	10	5	2		11
Sinnott	8	2	2		8
Peniket	7	2			7
Denton	5	3			6
Johnson	6	2	2		6
Bacon	3	2			4
Bateson	2	1			3
Clifton	2	1	2		3
Platt	3	1			3
Wilde	2	1			3
Allan	2	1			2
Chettle	1	1			2
Hobson	2	2			2
Shiels	2	1			2
Clarke	1	1			1
Hotte	1	1			1
O'Brien	1	1			1

Ramsbottom	Clifton	Wilde	Platt	Lane	Shiels	Johnson	Hotte	Denton	Peniket	King	Chettle	Bateson	Bacon	Nicholson	Clarke	Middleton	Gowling (L)	Clackstone	Riley	Sinnott	Hobson	Hird Adrian	Styche	Lynch	Allan (L)	Curry (L)	O'Brien	Collins	Smith (L)	Wagner	Blake (L)	Hinchley	Brough	Grice	Ridley	No.
x	x	x	x	x	x	x	xs	x	x	xs	sx	sx	s	s	s																					1
x	x	xs	x	x	x	xs	x	x	x	xs	sx	sx	s	s		sx																				2
x	x	x	x	xs	x		x	x	x	x		xs			sx	sx																				3
x	x	x	x		x		xs	x	xs	xs	sx	x	sx	s	sx	s	x																			4
x	x	x	xs		x		x	x	xs	s	x	xs	sx	s	sx	sx	x																			5
x	x	x	x		x	sx	x	x	xs	s	xs		sx	s		sx	x	sx																		6
x	x	x	x		x	x	x	x	x		x		s	s		s	x	s	s																	7
x	x	x	xs		x	x	x	x	x		xs		s	s		sx	x	sx	sx																	8
x	x	x	xs			x	xs	x	x		s	x	sx	s		sx	x	s	x																	9
x	x	x	s		x	x	x		x		sx	s	s	s			x	s	x	s																10
x	**x**	**x**	**x**		**x**		**x**		**x**	**xs**	**s**	**x**	**sx**	**s**	**sx**		**x**	**s**	**s**	**xs**																11
x	**sx**	**xs**	**sx**		**x**	**s**	**xs**		**x**	**s**	**sx**	**xs**	**x**	**s**	**x**		**x**	**x**	**s**	**x**																12
x	s	x	s		x	x	x		x		s	x	x	s	s		x	x		x																13
x	**x**	**x**	**sx**		**x**	**xs**	**x**		**x**		**s**	**x**	**s**	**s**	**sx**	**s**	**x**	**x**	**s**	**xs**																14
x	x	x	x		x	x			x		sx	sx		s	s		x	xs	s	x	xs															15
x	**xs**	**x**	**s**		**xs**	**x**	**x**		**x**		**s**	**x**	**sx**	**s**	**x**		**xs**	**sx**	**sx**	**s**		**x**														16
x	x	x	s		x	x	x		x			x		s			x	sx		s	sx	x	xs													17
x	x	x			x	xs	xs		x			x		s			s	sx		sx	sx	x	xs	x												18
x		xs	sx		x	xs			x			x		s	xs		s	x		x	sx	x	sx	x												19
x		**x**	**s**		**x**	**x**	**x**		**x**		**sx**	**xs**	**sx**	**s**	**xs**		**s**	**x**	**x**	**x**																20
x		x	s		x	x	sx		xs		x	sx		s				x	x	x	sx			xs	xs											21
x	**x**	**xs**	**sx**		**x**		**xs**				**x**	**x**		**s**	**sx**			**sx**	**x**		**xs**		**x**	**s**	**x**											22
x	sx	x	s		x		x		sx		x	x		s				xs	x	sx	xs			xs	x											23
x	x		x				xs		x		sx	xs		s	s			xs	x		sx		sx	x	x	x										24
x	xs		x				sx		x		x	s		s				x	x		sx		xs	x	x	x	s									25
x	x				s		s		x		s			s				x	xs		s		xs	x	x	x	x	x								26
x	x	x	sx		x		sx		xs			x		s						s	sx		xs	x	x	xs		x								27
x	x	x	x		x		sx		x		s	x		s						sx	s		xs	x	x	xs										28
x	x	x	x		x		s		x		sx	xs		s						sx	s		x		x	x		xs								29
x	x		x		x		x		x			xs		s	s			s		sx	s		x	x	x	x										30
x			x		x				x			x	s	s	s			x	x	x	s		x	x	x		s									31
x			x		x	sx			x			sx		s				x	x	xs			x	x	xs		s		x	s						32
x		xs	x		x	sx			x			xs		s				sx	x	s			x	x	x		s		x							33
x		x	x		x	x			xs			sx		s				x	x	s			xs	x	sx		s		x							34
x		x	x		x	x	s							s	x			xs	x	sx			x	xs			sx		x		s					35
x		x	x		x	x	s					s			xs			xs	x	sx			x	xs	sx		sx		x							36
x		x			xs	x	x				s			s	x			x	x	x				x	s		sx		x							37
x		x			x	x	x		sx		s		xs	s				sx	x	x				xs	sx		sx		x							38
x		x			x	x	x		xs				sx	s	sx			x	x	x				xs	s		s		x							39
x		x	s		x	x	xs		x				xs		s			x	x	x			sx	sx			s		x							40
x		x	x		x	x			xs		s		sx	s	x			x	x	x				xs	s		sx									41
x		x	x		x	x	sx		sx				xs		x			x	x	xs			sx	s		xs	s									42
x		x	x		xs	x	sx		sx				s		xs			x	x	x			xs	s		x	sx									43
x	sx	x	x			xs	x		x				x	s	x				x	sx			s	xs	s	x										44
s	x	xs	x				x		x				xs	x	x				x	x			sx	s	sx	x	s									45
x	x		x		x		x		x				sx	s	xs					x			x		xs	x	sx					s	s			46
x	x	x	x		xs		x		x				sx	s						x			xs		x	x	s					s	sx			47
s		x	x				x		x				xs	x					x	x					x	x	xs					sx	sx	s	s	48
46	25	35	27	2	37	21	23	9	32	1	6	14	3	2	8	0	13	17	24	17	0	4	9	13	13	11	1	2	9	0	0	0	0	0	0	x
0	2	6	3	1	4	5	8	0	8	4	2	8	5	0	5	0	1	5	1	4	3	0	9	8	3	3	1	1	0	0	0	0	0	0	0	xs
0	3	0	5	0	0	3	6	0	4	0	9	6	11	0	7	6	0	8	2	8	7	0	5	1	4	0	7	0	0	0	0	1	2	0	0	sx
2	1	0	8	0	1	1	4	0	0	3	10	3	8	41	7	3	3	5	5	6	5	0	1	4	4	0	10	0	0	1	1	2	1	1	1	s

x - Played full 90 minutes
xs - Substituted off
sx - Substituted on
s - Non-playing Substitute

ALTRINCHAM MATCH RESULTS 2018-19

Date	Comp	Opponents	H/A	Att:	Result		Goalscorers	Pos
Aug 4	NLN	Leamington	H	1047	D	2 - 2	Hulme 46 53	
7	NLN	Southport	A	1268	**W**	3 - 1	Goulding 50 Johnston 70 Hulme 76	
11	NLN	Spennymoor Town	A	698	D	4 - 4	White 21, Jones 32 Hancock 48 77	
14	NLN	FC United of Manchester	H	1704	L	1 - 2	Hulme 54	
18	NLN	Boston United	H	1067	L	0 - 2		
25	NLN	Darlington	A	1450	**W**	3 - 0	Johnston 30 (Pen) Hulme 51 61	
27	NLN	Guiseley	H	1149	D	1 - 1	Hulme 56	
Sept 1	NLN	Blyth Spartans	A	635	L	1 - 2	Hancock 26	
8	NLN	Curzon Ashton	H	955	L	0 - 2		15
15	NLN	Bradford Park Avenue	A	454	**W**	3 - 2	Peers 6 Johnston 55 Harrop 62	12
22	**FAC 2Q**	**Whitley Bay**	**H**	**680**	**W**	**5 - 0**	**Hulme 28 Moult 55 Hannigan 66 Peers 74 84**	
29	NLN	Kidderminster Harriers	A	1517	L	2 - 3	Johnston 23 Harrop 52	15
Oct 6	**FAC 3Q**	**Bradford Park Avenue**	**H**	**780**	**W**	**4 - 2**	**Hampson 36 Moult 44 Jones 62 Hulme 86**	
13	NLN	Alfreton Town	H	1123	**W**	3 - 1	Dale 3 Harrop 9 Hulme 24	13
20	**FAC 4Q**	**Stockport County**	**A**	**2981**	**L**	**0 - 2**		
27	NLN	Ashton United	H	930	**W**	3 - 0	Johnston 12 56 Dale 87	11
30	NLN	Nuneaton Borough	H	695	**W**	4 - 0	Dale 45 Johnston 46 58 Hancock 90	9
Nov 3	NLN	Hereford	A	2220	D	1 - 1	Hancock 90	10
10	NLN	Chester	A	2388	**W**	2 - 1	Hulme 11 64	8
17	NLN	York City	H	685	**W**	3 - 0	Hancock 57 90 Moult 83	7
24	**FAT 3Q**	**Bradford Park Avenue**	**H**	**570**	**W**	**4 - 0**	**Johnston 13 (pen) Hulme 34 Hancock 53 Mantack 77**	
Dec 1	NLN	Brackley Town	A	510	**W**	2 - 1	Richman 39 White 52	4
8	NLN	AFC Telford United	H	895	**W**	3 - 1	Hancock 17 86 Hampson 74	3
15	**FAT 1P**	**Stockport County**	**H**	**988**	**L**	**0 - 1**		
22	NLN	Darlington	H	1076	D	3 - 3	Hancock 10 Harrop 45 Hemmings 65	
26	NLN	Stockport County	A	4549	L	0 - 2		
29	NLN	Guiseley	A	791	D	2 - 2	Hemmings 51 Hampson 89	
Jan 1	NLN	Stockport County	H	3383	L	0 - 1		
5	NLN	Boston United	A	684	**W**	2 - 1	Hancock 24 Hulme 34	
12	NLN	Chorley	A	1675	L	1 - 4	Harrop 23 CHECK SUBS	7
19	NLN	Southport	H	1102	**W**	1 - 0	Moult 59	
26	NLN	Leamington	A	564	L	0 - 3		
Feb 9	NLN	FC United of Manchester	A	2215	**W**	2 - 1	Johnston 29 White 83	
16	NLN	Bradford Park Avenue	H	1328	D	1 - 1	Hancock 22	
19	NLN	Spennymoor Town	H	696	L	0 - 2		7
23	NLN	Curzon Ashton	A	506	**W**	6 - 0	Johnston 29 Williams 36 Piggott 47 54 72 Ceesay 49	7
Mar 2	NLN	Chester	H	1714	**W**	4 - 0	Piggott 51 Hancock 62 69 Johnston 90	5
5	NLN	Blyth Spartans	H	718	D	1 - 1	Johnston 20	7
9	NLN	York City	A	2618	**W**	1 - 0	Hancock 81	6
30	NLN	Kidderminster Harriers	H	1095	**W**	2 - 1	Jones J 10 Johnson 19 (og)	6
Apr 6	NLN	Alfreton Town	A	538	**W**	7 - 0	Ceesay 8 87 Hulme 31 89 Johnston 39 (pen) Hancock 60 Jones J 90	5
9	NLN	AFC Telford United	A	982	D	1 - 1	Hulme 11	5
13	NLN	Chorley	H	1597	**W**	5 - 3	Hulme 9 Hannigan 50 Densmore 71 83 Poole 88 (pen)	5
16	NLN	Brackley Town	H	787	L	1 - 2	Harrop 38	5
20	NLN	Nuneaton Borough	A	530	**W**	2 - 0	Hancock 53 Harrop 90+1	
22	NLN	Hereford	H	1407	D	1 - 1	Hulme 53	5
27	NLN	Ashton United	A	484	D	1 - 1	Moult 19	5
May 1	**PO Q**	**Blyth Spartans**	**H**	**1698**	**D**	**2 - 2**	**Johnston 35 (pen) Hancock 90+3 (won 7-6 on pens aet)**	
5	**PO SF**	**Chorley**	**A**	**3446**	**D**	**1 - 1**	**Hancock 67 (lost 1-3 on pens aet)**	

GOALSCORERS	SG	CSG	Pens	Hat tricks	Total
Hancock	16	2			20
Hulme	15	3			19
Johnston	13	3	4		15
Harrop	7	2			7
Moult	5	1			5
Jones J	4	2			4
Piggott	2	2		1	4
Ceesay	2	1			3
Dale	3	3			3
Hampson	3	1			3
Peers	2	2			3
White	3	1			3
Densmore	1	1			2
Hannigan	2	1			2
Hemmings	2	1			2
Goulding	1	1			1
Mantack*	1	1			1
Opponent	1	1			1
Poole	1	1	1		1
Richman	1	1			1
Williams	1	1			1

Thompson T	Daniels (L)	White	Moult	Jones	Johnston	Hulme	Hancock	Hampson	Goulding	Harrop	Peers	Williams	Richman	Wynne	Harrison	Hannigan	Densmore	Dale (L)	Downing	Poole	Harris	Thompson J	Gabidon	Scott	Mantack	Langley (L)	Hemmings (L)	Sang (L)	Elliott	Waterston (L)	Drench	Piggott (L)	Ceesay (L)	Fawns	Dolan	Sass- (L)	Chadwick		No.
x	xs	x	x	x	x	x	xs	x	x	xs	sx	sx	sx	s	s																								1
x	xs	x	x	x	x	xs	sx	x	x	xs	sx	x	sx	s	s																								2
x	sx	xs	x	x	x	x	xs	x	x	sx	s	xs	x	s	sx																								3
x	xs		x	s	x	x		x	s	x	sx	x	s	s	x	x	x																						4
x	sx	x	x	s	xs	x	x	xs	x	xs	sx	sx	x	s		x																							5
s	sx	x	x	x	xs	x	x		s	sx		xs		x		x	x	xs	sx																				6
s	xs	x	x	x		x			s	x		x		x	s	x	x	x	s	sx																			7
s		x	x	x		x	xs		s	xs	sx	x	s	x		x	x	x		sx																			8
s			x	x	x		x		sx	x	xs	xs	x	x	s	x	xs	sx			sx																		9
s		x	x	x	x	s	x		s	sx	xs	x	x	x		x		xs		sx																			10
s		**x**	**xs**	**x**	**xs**	**x**	**xs**	**s**	**s**	**x**	**sx**	**x**	**x**	**x**		**x**		**sx**		**sx**		**s**																	**11**
s		x	x	x	x	sx	sx	x	s	x	xs	xs		x		x		xs		sx																			12
x		**x**	**x**	**x**	**xs**	**x**	**sx**	**x**	**s**	**x**	**sx**	**xs**		**s**		**x**	**s**	**xs**		**sx**		**s**																	**13**
x		x	x	xs	x	x	sx	x	sx	xs	s	x		s		x		xs		sx																			14
x		**x**	**x**	**x**	**x**	**x**	**sx**	**x**	**s**	**xs**	**sx**	**xs**	**s**	**s**		**x**	**s**	**xs**		**sx**																			**15**
x		x	x	x	xs	x	x	x		x	s		sx	s		x	s	sx		xs																			16
x		x	x	x	x	x	x	x	s	xs	sx		sx	s		x	s	xs																					17
x		x	x	x	x	x	x	x		xs			sx	s		x	s	xs					sx	s															18
x		x	x	x	xs	x	x	x		x				s		x	sx	x					s	s															19
x		x	x	x	x	x	x	x					x	s		x	s	x						s	s	s													20
x		**x**	**x**	**x**	**xs**	**x**	**xs**	**x**		**sx**			**x**	**s**		**x**	**sx**	**x**							**sx**	**s**													**21**
x		x	x	x	x	x	x	x		s			x	s		x	s						s		x	s													22
x		xs	x	x	xs	x	x	x		sx			x	s		x	sx								xs	s	sx												23
s			**x**	**s**	**sx**	**x**	**x**	**sx**				**xs**	**x**	**x**	**x**		**x**						**sx**		**xs**	**x**	**xs**												**24**
x			x	x	x		x	x		x		s	x	s		x	x								s	s	x	s											25
x			x	x	x		x	x		xs		xs	sx	s	sx	xs	x								s		x	sx											26
x			x	x	xs		x	x		sx		s	x	s	s	x	x								sx		x	xs											27
x		x	x	x	x	x	x	x				s	x	s	s	x	s								xs			sx											28
x		xs	x	x	xs	x	x	x		xs		sx	x			x	sx			sx					s				s										29
x		x	x	x	x	x	x	x		x			x			x																							30
x		x	x	x	x	xs	x	x		xs		sx	x		s	x	s								s			sx											31
x		x	x	xs	x	x	x	x		xs		sx	xs		sx	x	s								s					sx									32
		x	x	sx	x		x	xs		xs		x	sx		xs	x														sx	x	x	s	s					33
s		s	x	x	xs		x	x		x			x			x	x			s											x	xs	sx	sx					34
s		x	x	x	x		xs	x		sx		xs	s			x	s														x	x	x	sx					35
x		xs	xs	x	x		x	x				x	sx			x	sx														s	x	x	s	s				36
x		x	xs	x	x	sx	x	x				x	sx			x	s														s	xs	xs		sx				37
x		x	x	x	x	sx	x	x		sx		x		s		x	s															xs	xs		s				38
x		x	x	xs	x	x	xs	x		sx		x	sx			x	s																xs		s	sx			39
x		x	x	x	xs	x	x	x				x	s			x	sx														s		xs		s		sx		40
x		x	x	x	xs	x	xs	xs		s		x	sx			x				sx											s		x				sx		41
x		x	x	x	xs	xs	xs			sx		x	sx			x	x			s													x			sx	s		42
x		x	x	x	xs	x				xs		xs	sx			x	x			sx											s		x		s		sx		43
x			x	xs	x	x	sx	xs		xs		x	sx		sx	x	x			s													x				s		44
x		xs	x		x	x	xs	sx		sx		x	s		x	x	x			sx															s		x		45
x			x			x	sx	x		xs		s	sx	s	x	x	x			xs													x		sx		xs		46
			xs	x	sx	s	x	sx		xs		x	x	x		s	x			x													sx		xs		x		47
x			**x**	**x**	**x**	**xs**	**x**	**xs**		**sx**		**xs**	**sx**	**s**	**sx**	**x**	**x**			**sx**													**xs**						**48**
x			**x**	**x**	**xs**	**xs**	**x**	**x**		**sx**		**xs**	**sx**	**s**	**sx**	**x**	**x**			**sx**													**xs**						**49**
37	0	32	45	39	28	31	29	33	4	11	0	18	18	9	4	43	17	5	0	1	0	0	0	0	1	1	3	0	0	0	3	3	7	0	0	0	2		x
0	4	5	4	4	16	5	10	5	0	17	3	12	1	0	1	1	1	8	0	2	0	0	0	0	3	0	1	1	0	0	0	3	6	0	1	0	1		xs
0	3	0	0	1	2	3	7	3	2	13	9	5	17	0	6	0	6	3	1	14	1	0	2	0	2	0	1	3	0	2	0	0	2	2	2	2	3		sx
0	0	1	0	3	0	2	0	1	10	2	3	4	6	24	7	1	14	0	1	3	0	2	2	3	6	5	0	1	1	0	5	0	1	2	6	0	2		s

x - Played full 90 minutes
xs - Substituted off
sx - Substituted on
s - Non-playing Substitute

ASHTON UNITED MATCH RESULTS 2018-19

Date	Comp	Opponents	H/A	Att:	Result		Goalscorers	Pos
Aug 4	NLN	Nuneaton Borough	H	273	D	0 - 0		
7	NLN	FC United of Manchester	A	1562	**W**	4 - 3	Chadwick 7 (Pen) Tomsett 50 Evangelinos 58 McHale 85	
11	NLN	Kidderminster Harriers	A	1335	D	3 - 3	Chadwick 3 Regan 6 Evangelinos 73	
14	NLN	York City	H	545	L	0 - 2		
18	NLN	Brackley Town	H	180	L	1 - 5	Hobson 90	
25	NLN	Southport	A	881	D	2 - 2	Chadwick 8 Jackson 14	
27	NLN	Darlington	H	456	D	2 - 2	Chadwick 8 Jackson 23	
Sept 1	NLN	AFC Telford United	A	1148	L	1 - 2	McAtee 38	
8	NLN	Chorley	H	425	L	0 - 5		
15	NLN	Hereford	A	2195	**W**	2 - 0	Chadwick 16 20	18
22	**FAC 2Q**	**Trafford**	**H**	**240**	**W**	**3 - 0**	**Chadwick 23 (Pen) Jackson 82 Evangelinos 90+**	
29	NLN	Leamington	H	192	**W**	2 - 1	Jackson 18 Martin 90	14
Oct 6	**FAC 3Q**	**King's Lynn Town**	**A**	**622**	**W**	**1 - 0**	**Howarth 72**	
13	NLN	Spennymoor Town	A	708	L	0 - 5		17
20	**FAC 4Q**	**Southport**	**A**	**770**	**L**	**1 - 2**	**Sheridan 61**	
27	NLN	Altrincham	A	930	L	0 - 3		18
30	NLN	Chester	A	1646	L	1 - 4	Jackson 90	19
Nov 3	NLN	Boston United	H	227	D	1 - 1	Tomsett 88	20
6	NLN	Guiseley	H	218	**W**	1 - 0	Regan 69	17
17	NLN	Bradford Park Avenue	A	1427	L	2 - 3	Jackson 3 Martin 19	20
24	**FAT 3Q**	**Boston United**	**H**	**187**	**L**	**0 - 5**		
Dec 4	NLN	Alfreton Town	H	154	L	0 - 2		
8	NLN	Blyth Spartans	A	588	L	0 - 2		21
18	NLN	Stockport County	H	830	L	0 - 6		
22	NLN	Southport	H	286	L	1 - 2	Richards 75 (og)	
26	NLN	Curzon Ashton	A	457	**W**	4 - 2	Sheridan 13 Chadwick 47 74 Askew 66	
29	NLN	Darlington	A	1407	L	1 - 2	Tomsett 88	
Jan 1	NLN	Curzon Ashton	H	457	L	1 - 2	Ennis 38 (Pen)	
5	NLN	Brackley Town	A	431	L	1 - 3	Jones J 90	21
19	NLN	FC United of Manchester	H	845	**W**	1 - 0	Chalmers 75	
26	NLN	Nuneaton Borough	A	655	**W**	1 - 0	Hobson 63	
Feb 9	NLN	York City	A	2150	L	0 - 2		
16	NLN	Hereford	H	405	D	0 - 0		
19	NLN	AFC Telford United	H	195	L	3 - 4	Sheridan 31 Mantack 70 72	20
23	NLN	Chorley	A	1326	**W**	1 - 0	Regan 59	20
26	NLN	Kidderminster Harriers	H	226	L	0 - 1		20
Mar 2	NLN	Alfreton Town	A	413	L	0 - 2		20
9	NLN	Bradford Park Avenue	H	265	L	0 - 2		21
23	NLN	Blyth Spartans	H	215	L	0 - 3		21
26	NLN	Stockport County	A	3257	L	1 - 2	Tomsett 72	21
30	NLN	Leamington	A	601	L	0 - 1		21
Apr 6	NLN	Spennymoor Town	H	208	**W**	3 - 0	Sheridan 15 Mantack 17 Hobson 19	20
13	NLN	Guiseley	A	655	D	1 - 1	Sheridan 82	20
19	NLN	Chester	H	468	L	0 - 3		21
22	NLN	Boston United	A	942	L	1 - 2	Reed 31	21 (R)
27	NLN	Altrincham	H	484	D	1 - 1	Tomsett 2	20

GOALSCORERS	SG	CSG	Pens	Hat tricks	Total
Chadwick	7	2	2		9
Jackson*	6	2			6
Sheridan	5	2			5
Tomsett	5	1			5
Evangelinos	3	2			3
Hobson	3	1			3
Mantack	2	1			3
Regan	3	1			3
Martin	2	1			2
Askew	1	1			1
Chalmers	1	1			1
Ennis	1	1	1		1
Howarth*	1	1			1
Jones J	1	1			1
McAtee	1	1			1
McHale	1	1			1
Opponent	1	1			1
Reed	1	1			1

Ollerenshaw	Bakare	Regan	Chalmers	Hill	Lees	Sheridan	Sephton	Chadwick	Dixon	Tomsett	Evangelinos	McAtee	McHale	Roberts	Anghel	Jacobs	Hobson	Pilling (L)	Jackson	Platt	Hickman (L)	Jones C	Ashworth	Sangha (L)	Baines	Martin	Howarth	Budtz	Holgate (L)	Kay	Aires-Mendes	Askew (L)	Crowther	Goulding	Jones J (L)	Ennis	Crowley	McMahon	Reed	Swaby-Neain (L)	Sefil (L)	Mantack	Jennings	Dimaio (L)	No.
x	xs	x	x	x	x	x	x	xs	xs	x	sx	sx	sx	s	s																														1
x		x	x	x	x	x	x	xs	xs	x	sx	xs	sx	s	sx																														2
x		x	xs	x	x	x	x	x	sx	x	xs	sx		s	xs	sx	s																												3
x		x	x	x	x	x	x		s	x	xs	sx	x	s	xs	s	sx																												4
	sx	x	x	x	x	x	x	x		xs	xs	sx	xs		s		sx																												5
	s	x	x	x		x		x		x	s	sx	s		sx	x	xs	x	xs	x																									6
		x	x	sx	sx	xs	xs	x		x	s	sx			s	x	x	x	x	xs																									7
	x	x	x	x	x		sx			x	sx	xs	s		s	xs	xs	x	x	sx																									8
x		x	x	s	x		s			xs	sx	xs	sx				x		sx	x	x	xs	x																						9
		x	x	s	sx	xs	x	xs			s		xs		sx		x	x	sx		x		x	x																					10
		x	**x**	**s**	**sx**	**xs**	**xs**	**xs**			**sx**				**sx**		**xs**	**x**	**x**		**x**	**s**	**x**	**x**																					**11**
		x	x	s	s	x	s	x							x		x	x	x		x		s	x	x	sx																			12
		x	**x**	**sx**	**x**	**x**		**x**					**xs**		**xs**			**x**	**x**			**s**	**sx**	**xs**	**x**		**sx**																		**13**
		xs	xs	sx	x	x				x					s				x				sx	xs	x	s	x	x	x																14
		x	**x**	**sx**	**x**	**xs**		**x**		**x**			**sx**	**s**	**s**			**x**	**x**				**x**	**xs**	**x**	**s**	**s**				**x**														**15**
		x	x	s	sx	x		x		x			xs					x	xs				sx	s	x	sx			x	xs															16
		s	x	x	s	x		x		xs			xs					x	x				x	sx	x	sx			sx	xs															17
		x	xs	xs	x	x		x		sx					s			x	x				sx		x	sx			s	xs		x													18
		x		x	x	x		xs		x					s			x	x			sx	xs		x	sx					s	x													19
		x	x	x	x	x				x				s	s			x	x				x			x	s			s		x	s												20
																																													21
		x	sx	sx						x				s	x			x	x				x			xs	sx			x		xs	s	x											22
		x	sx	s		x		xs		x				s	xs			x	x								sx			x			sx	x	x										23
		x	x	sx				xs		x				xs				x								xs	sx			x		x	sx	x	x										24
		x	x	s		x		x		x				s	sx			x								xs	s			x		x	s	x	x										25
		x	x	sx		xs		xs		x				s	x			x									s			x	s	x	sx	x	x										26
		x	xs	sx		xs		x		x				s	xs			x								sx				x		x	s	x	x	sx									27
		x		s		x		xs		x				s	sx			x								x				x		x	sx	x	x	sx	x								28
x		xs	xs							x				x	sx											x				x		x	sx	x	x	x									29
		xs	x					xs		sx				sx	s		x						x			x				x			s	x		xs	x	x	sx						30
			s			sx		sx		xs				s			xs						x			x				x				x		xs	x	x	sx	x	x				31
			s			xs				sx				s			xs						x			x				x				x		sx		x	sx	x	x	x	xs		32
		x	s			x		sx		sx				s									x			x				xs				x			x	x	sx			xs	xs		33
		x	sx			x				s							x						x			xs				xs				x			x	x	s	xs		sx	sx	x	34
		x	x			xs				s				s			xs						x							x				x			x	x	sx	sx		xs	x	sx	35
		x	x			x				sx				s			xs						x							s				x			x	x	sx	s		x	xs	x	36
		x	xs			xs				sx				s									x			s				x				x			x	x	sx	sx		x	xs	x	37
		x	x			sx				sx					s		x						x							xs				x			x	x	sx	s		xs	xs	x	38
		x	x		s	xs				sx							xs													x	x			x		sx	x			sx		x	xs	x	39
x		x	x		x	x				x							x													x	s			x			x		xs	s		sx			40
		x	x		x	xs				x				s			xs													x				x		s		x	sx	x		sx		x	41
		x	x		x	xs				x				sx			xs																	x		sx	x	x	sx			xs		x	42
		x	x		x	x				x				s			x						s							s				xs		s	x	x	sx			x		x	43
		x	xs		x	x				x				s			x						x							s				x		s		x	sx	sx		xs		x	44
		x	s		x	x				x				s			sx						xs							xs				x		s		x	x	x		sx		x	45
		x	x			x				x				sx	sx		xs						x							x						xs		x				x		x	46
7	1	39	29	10	19	25	6	12	0	27	0	0	1	1	3	2	10	20	13	2	4	0	18	3	8	7	1	1	2	17	2	9	0	23	7	1	13	15	1	4	2	6	1	11	x
0	1	3	7	1	0	12	2	10	2	4	3	3	5	1	5	1	11	0	2	1	0	1	2	3	0	4	0	0	0	7	0	1	0	1	0	3	0	0	1	1	0	5	6	0	xs
0	1	0	3	8	4	2	1	2	1	8	5	6	4	3	8	1	3	0	2	1	0	1	4	1	0	6	4	0	1	0	0	0	5	0	0	5	0	0	12	4	0	4	1	1	sx
0	1	1	4	8	3	0	2	0	1	2	3	0	2	22	11	1	1	0	0	0	0	2	2	1	0	3	4	0	1	4	3	0	5	0	0	4	0	0	1	3	0	0	0	0	s

Also Played: Woodford - 07/08 (s) 05/01 (s) 06/04 (s) 27/04 (s). Carnell - 18/08 (x). Turner - 18/08 (s) 22/09 (s) 06/10 (s). Watson - 13/10 (sx). Steadman (L) - 04/12 (xs) 08/12 (xs) 18/12 (s). Harris - 18/12 (s). Slew - 05/01 (sx). Freeland - 26/03 (s) 30/03 (s).

x - Played full 90 minutes
xs - Substituted off
sx - Substituted on
s - Non-playing Substitute

BLYTH SPARTANS MATCH RESULTS 2018-19

Date	Comp	Opponents	H/A	Att:	Result	Goalscorers	Pos
Aug 4	NLN	Hereford	A	2836	L 0 - 3		
7	NLN	Bradford Park Avenue	H	661	L 1 - 2	Reid 87	
11	NLN	Chester	H	737	W 8 - 1	Maguire 14 92 Green 18 Holmes 40 Reid 55 Howson 61 (og) Wrightson 66 Buddle 75	
15	NLN	Darlington	A	1631	D 1 - 1	Maguire 5	
18	NLN	Alfreton Town	A	465	L 1 - 3	Dale 24 (Pen)	
25	NLN	Chorley	H	725	L 1 - 2	Dale 78 (Pen)	
27	NLN	York City	A	2696	L 0 - 2		
Sept 1	NLN	Altrincham	H	635	W 2 - 1	Reid 25 Rivers 83	
8	NLN	Kidderminster Harriers	A	1570	L 1 - 3	Horsfall 59 (og)	
15	NLN	Leamington	H	596	L 0 - 2		
22	**FAC 2Q**	**Nantwich Town**	**A**	**371**	**D 3 - 3**	**Reid Holmes Fewster**	
25	**FAC 2Qr**	**Nantwich Town**	**H**	**491**	**W 1 - 0**	**Maguire**	
29	NLN	AFC Telford United	H	590	W 1 - 0	Maguire 45	18
Oct 6	**FAC 3Q**	**Gainsborough Trinity**	**A**	**428**	**W 2 - 1**	**Reid Dale**	
13	NLN	Boston United	A	1081	L 0 - 4		19
20	**FAC 4Q**	**York City**	**H**	**1378**	**L 0 - 1**		
27	NLN	Southport	A	820	W 1 - 0	Dale 52	
30	NLN	Guiseley	A	613	W 3 - 1	Cunningham 3 Maguire 35 82	17
Nov 3	NLN	FC United of Manchester	H	832	L 0 - 3		17
10	NLN	Brackley Town	A	415	D 1 - 1	Reid 67	17
17	NLN	Curzon Ashton	H	1146	W 3 - 2	Fewster 58 Maguire 70 Rivers 74	16
20	NLN	Stockport County	H	531	W 3 - 2	Cowan 24 (og) Reid 28 Oliver 47	
23	**FAT 3Q**	**Marske United**	**H**		**W 4 - 1**	**Maguire x3 Dale (pen)**	
Dec 1	NLN	Nuneaton Borough	A	505	W 3 - 1	Maguire 26 50 Rivers 46	10
8	NLN	Ashton United	H	588	W 2 - 0	Reid 53 Dale 87	9
15	**FAT 1P**	**Lancaster City**	**A**	**149**	**W 3 - 0**	**Liddle Maguire Holmes**	
22	NLN	Chorley	A	1076	W 4 - 2	Reid 38 (Pen) Maguire 44 Holmes 74 (Pen) 83	
26	NLN	Spennymoor Town	H	1133	D 2 - 2	Maguire 22 Reid 66	
29	NLN	York City	H	1122	W 2 - 1	Reid 15 (Pen) Fewster 84	
Jan 1	NLN	Spennymoor Town	A	1129	D 2 - 2	Cunningham 62 Reid 64 (Pen)	
5	NLN	Alfreton Town	H	676	D 1 - 1	Dale 37 (200th goal for the club)	8
12	**FAT 2P**	**Boreham Wood**	**H**	**712**	**W 1 - 0**	**Maguie 26 (150th goal for the club)**	
19	NLN	Bradford Park Avenue	A	373	D 1 - 1	Reid 26	
26	NLN	Hereford	H	783	L 2 - 3	Green 73 Fewster 90	
Feb 2	**FAT 3P**	**Leyton Orient**	**A**	**1842**	**L 0 - 1**		
9	NLN	Darlington	H	1579	L 0 - 1		
16	NLN	Leamington	A	523	W 2 - 1	Green 1 Maguire 7	11
23	NLN	Kidderminster Harriers	H	705	D 3 - 3	Maguire 2 88 Buddle 90	11
26	NLN	Chester	A	1382	L 0 - 2		
Mar 2	NLN	Brackley Town	H	651	L 1 - 3	Maguire 8	14
5	NLN	Altrincham	A	718	D 1 - 1	Dale 27	14
23	NLN	Ashton United	A	215	W 3 - 0	Green 2 Laing 12 Maguire 30	12
30	NLN	AFC Telford United	A	1211	D 1 - 1	Maguire 88	11
Apr 1	NLN	Curzon Ashton	A	218	W 3 - 1	Green 4 Maguire 33 Rivers 86	11
6	NLN	Boston United	H	632	W 3 - 0	Liddle 40 Reid 50 Maguire 78	10
9	NLN	Nuneaton Borough	H	557	W 4 - 1	Reid 10 Green 44 Wrightson 63 Nicholson 89	8
13	NLN	Stockport County	A	5665	W 1 - 0	Maguire 19	8
19	NLN	Guiseley	H	915	W 2 - 0	Green 12 Buddle 89	
22	NLN	FC United of Manchester	A	1971	W 2 - 1	Rivers 16 Wrightson 90	6
27	NLN	Southport	H	1491	W 2 - 1	Dale 6 70 (2x pen)	6
May 1	**PO Q**	**Altrincham**	**A**	**1698**	**D 2 - 2**	**Rivers 11 Nicholson 28 (Lost 7-6 on pens aet)**	

GOALSCORERS	SG	CSG	Pens	Hat tricks	Total
Maguire	20	4		1	26
Reid	15	4	3		15
Dale	9	2	5		10
Green	7	1			7
Rivers	6	2			6
Holmes	4	1	1		5
Fewster	4	1			4
Buddle	3	1			3
Opponent	3	1			3
Wrightson	3	1			3
Cunningham	2	1			2
Liddle	2	1			2
Nicholson	2	1			2
Laing	1	1			1
Oliver	1	1			1

Jameson	Oliver	Reid	Rivers	Liddle	Buddle	Dale	Maguire	Green	Nicholson	Brotherton	Horner	Fewster	Holmes	Skirpan	Watson	Wrightson	Cunningham	Ardelean	Butler	Watson	Mullen	Pybus	Laing	Foden (L)	Atkinson (L)	Armstrong	Hutchinson	No.
x	x	x	x	x	x	xs	xs	x	x	xs	sx	sx	sx	s	s													1
x	x	x	xs	x	x	x	x	x	x		s	sx	xs	s	s	sx												2
x	sx	x	xs	x	x	x	x	xs	x		sx		xs	s	s	sx	x											3
x	x	xs	xs		x		xs	x	x		sx		x	s	x	sx	x	sx	s									4
x	xs	x			x	x	x	x	x		sx		xs	s	x	sx	xs	sx	s									5
x	x	x	x		x	x	x	x	x		s	s	x	s	xs	s		s										6
x	x	x	xs		x	x	x	x	xs		xs			s	x	sx		s	sx		sx							7
x	s	x	x	x	x	x	x	x			x			s		s	x	s	s	x								8
x	x	x	x	x	x	x	x		x		xs			s	s	sx	x				s	s						9
x	sx	x	x	x	s	xs	xs		x		x	x			s	sx	x			x	s							10
x	**s**	**x**	**xs**	**x**	**x**	**xs**			**x**		**s**	**x**	**xs**	**s**	**sx**	**sx**	**s**	**sx**		**x**	**x**							11
x	**sx**	**x**		**x**	**x**	**sx**	**sx**	**xs**	**x**		**s**	**xs**	**x**	**s**	**s**	**x**	**s**			**x**	**xs**							12
x		x	sx		x	x	x	xs	x		sx	sx	xs	s	x	xs	s			x								13
x	**sx**	**x**	**sx**		**x**	**xs**	**x**	**x**	**x**			**sx**	**xs**		**x**	**xs**				**x**								14
x	sx	xs			x	xs	x	x	x			sx	x		x	x	sx			xs	s							15
x	**x**	**x**	**sx**	**xs**		**x**	**x**		**x**	**s**	**s**	**sx**	**xs**	**s**	**s**	**sx**				**x**	**xs**		**x**					16
x	x	xs	sx	x	x	x	xs	sx				sx		s	s	xs	x			x	x							17
x	x	sx	xs	x	x	x	xs	xs				sx		s		sx	x			s	x		x					18
x	xs	sx	x	x	x	x	x	xs				sx		s		s	x			s	x		x					19
x	xs	x		x	x	x	x	sx			xs	s		s	sx		s			x	x		x					20
x	sx	x	x	x		x	x	x			x	xs			s	s	s			x	s		x					21
x	x	x	xs	x		x	xs	xs			x	sx			s	sx	x			x	sx		s					22
x	**sx**	**x**	**s**	**x**	**xs**	**x**	**x**	**xs**			**x**	**xs**	**sx**		**s**	**sx**				**x**	**x**							23
x	x	xs	x	x		x	xs	xs	x		s	sx	sx		x		x			s	sx							24
x	x	x	x	x	s	x	x	x	s		x	s	s				x			x	s							25
x	**x**	**x**	**x**	**x**	**x**		**x**				**x**		**x**							**x**	**x**							26
x	x	x	sx	x	x		x	xs	s		x	s	sx		s		xs			x	x							27
x	x	x	x	x	x		x	s	s		x	s	x		s		s			x	x							28
x	xs	x	x	x	x		xs	x	x		s	sx	xs		s	sx	x			sx								29
x	x	x	s	x	x		x	x	s		x	xs	s		s	sx	x			x								30
x	x		xs	x	x	x	x		s		x	sx	x		s	sx	s			x	x							31
x	**x**	**x**	**sx**	**x**	**x**	**x**	**xs**	**xs**	**x**			**sx**	**xs**		**s**	**s**				**x**	**sx**							32
x	x	x	sx	x	x	x	x	xs	x			s	xs			s				x	s		sx					33
x	xs	x		x	x	x	x	x	x			sx	xs			sx			s	s	s		x					34
x	**x**	**xs**		**x**	**x**	**x**	**x**	**xs**	**x**		**s**	**sx**	**sx**			**sx**				**xs**	**s**		**x**					35
x	x	x		xs	sx	x	x	xs	x		s	sx	sx			xs				x	s		x					36
x	s	sx	x		x	x	xs	x	x		x	sx	xs			sx			s		xs		x					37
x	sx	sx	x		x	x	x	xs	x		s	s	xs			sx				x	xs		x					38
x	s	sx	xs		x	x	x	x	x		s	sx	xs			sx				x	xs		x					39
	x	xs	x		x	sx	x	xs	s		x		xs			sx			sx	x	s		x	x				40
x	s	xs	x	s	x	x	xs	x	x		x		sx			s			sx		x		x					41
x	x		xs	x	x	sx	x	x	s		x		xs			s				s	xs		x		s			42
x	x	sx	sx	x		x	x	x	x		s		s			s				x	x		x		xs			43
x		x	x	x	sx	sx	xs	xs	s		x		xs			sx				s	x		x		x			44
x		x	x	x	sx	xs	xs	xs	x		s					sx			s	sx	x		x		x			45
x		x	s	xs	x	xs	x	x	sx		x					x				sx	xs		x		s	sx		46
x			x	x	x	x	xs	xs	x		sx					sx			s	x	x				x	s	s	47
x	sx		xs	x	x	x	xs	xs	x		s					sx		sx		x	x				x		s	48
x	sx		x	x	x	x	xs	xs	x		s		sx			sx				x	x				xs		s	49
x	sx		xs	x	x	x	x	xs	x		s		sx			sx				x	xs		s		x			50
x	**xs**	**sx**	**x**	**x**	**x**		**xs**	**xs**	**x**		**sx**		**xs**			**sx**				**x**			**sx**		**x**		**s**	51
50	24	31	21	36	40	33	32	20	32	0	17	2	7	0	7	3	13	0	0	30	17	0	18	1	6	0	0	x
0	6	7	12	3	1	7	17	22	1	1	3	4	18	0	1	4	2	0	0	2	8	0	0	0	2	0	0	xs
0	11	7	8	0	3	4	1	2	1	0	7	19	9	0	2	28	1	4	3	3	4	0	2	0	0	1	0	sx
0	5	0	3	1	2	0	0	1	8	1	16	7	3	17	17	9	7	3	7	6	10	1	2	0	2	1	4	s

x - Played full 90 minutes
xs - Substituted off
sx - Substituted on
s - Non-playing Substitute

BOSTON UNITED MATCH RESULTS 2018-19

Date	Comp	Opponents	H/A	Att:	Result		Goalscorers	Pos
Aug 4	NLN	Guiseley	H	1231	W	1 - 0	Johnson 76	
7	NLN	Leamington	A	656	L	0 - 2		
11	NLN	FC United of Manchester	A	1686	W	3 - 0	Abbott 23 85 Johnson 77	
14	NLN	Nuneaton Borough	H	1200	W	2 - 1	Arnold 45 Wafula 74	
18	NLN	Altrincham	A	1067	W	2 - 0	Marriott 49 Arnold 89	
25	NLN	Spennymoor Town	H	1210	L	0 - 2		
27	NLN	Bradford Park Avenue	A	573	L	0 - 1		
Sept 1	NLN	Kidderminster Harriers	H	1129	L	0 - 2		
8	NLN	Stockport County	A	3050	W	2 - 0	Rose 23 Arnold 71	
15	NLN	Chester	H	1188	L	0 - 2		9
22	**FAC 2Q**	**Peterborough Sports**	**H**	**935**	**L**	**0 - 2**		
29	NLN	Curzon Ashton	A	305	W	3 - 1	Walker 64 Rose 73 Wright 90	7
Oct 13	NLN	Blyth Spartans	H	1081	W	4 - 0	Smith Greg 12 Walker 64 Allott 77 Abbott 79	4
20	NLN	Darlington	A	1860	L	0 - 1		6
27	NLN	Hereford	H	1137	W	3 - 1	Allott 49 Hine 57 Slew 86	
30	NLN	Brackley Town	H	922	L	1 - 3	Slew 65	7
Nov 3	NLN	Boston United	A	227	D	1 - 1	Qualter 12	7
10	NLN	AFC Telford United	A	1146	L	0 - 1		9
17	NLN	Southport	H	1146	L	1 - 2	Allott 80	9
24	**FAT 3Q**	**Ashton United**	**A**	**187**	**W**	**5 - 0**		
Dec 1	NLN	Chorley	A	1047	D	1 - 1	Walker 31	9
8	NLN	York City	H	1143	W	2 - 0	Walker 51 Allott 63	8
15	**FAT 1P**	**Wrexham**	**A**	**1083**	**L**	**0 - 3**		
26	NLN	Alfreton Town	H	1393	L	0 - 1		
29	NLN	Bradford Park Avenue	H	1061	D	2 - 2	Davies 51 (Pen) Wright 54	
Jan 1	NLN	Alfreton Town	A	665	D	1 - 1	Walker 2	
5	NLN	Altrincham	H	694	L	1 - 2	Davies 80 (Pen)	
12	NLN	Kidderminster Harriers	A	1549	W	2 - 1	Wright 6 Davies 39 (Pen)	12
19	NLN	Leamington	H	885	D	1 - 1	Davies 36 (pen)	
26	NLN	Guiseley	A	725	W	5 - 4	Allott 15 Rollins 22 28 Abbott 70 Gibbens 76	
29	NLN	Spennymoor Town	A	544	L	0 - 1		
Feb 2	NLN	FC United of Manchester	H	1070	W	2 - 1	Allott 17 Walker 62	
9	NLN	Nuneaton Borough	A	655	W	5 - 1	Allott 15 Walker 38 47 Wroe 60 Rollins 72	
16	NLN	Chester	A	1648	L	1 - 4	Davies 72	9
Mar 2	NLN	AFC Telford United	H	993	D	2 - 2	Davies 61 (pen) Allott 85	10
5	NLN	Stockport County	H	1073	L	1 - 3	Davies 77	10
9	NLN	Southport	A	1025	W	3 - 2	Wright J 63 Allott 77 Walker 89	10
16	NLN	Chorley	H	1007	L	0 - 2		10
23	NLN	York City	A	2594	D	2 - 2	Rollins 60 Wright 78	9
30	NLN	Curzon Ashton	H	1406	W	4 - 1	Wright J 1 Wright M 24 Davies 44 (pen) Clare 90+4	10
Apr 6	NLN	Blyth Spartans	A	632	L	0 - 3		11
13	NLN	Darlington	H	1035	L	0 - 2		11
19	NLN	Brackley Town	A	755	L	0 - 2		
22	NLN	Ashton United	H	942	W	2 - 1	Clare 2 Cresswell 34	11
27	NLN	Hereford	A	2232	W	2 - 0	Clare 33 Abott 76 (pen)	11

GOALSCORERS	SG	CSG	Pens	Hat tricks	Total
Allott	10	1	1		10
Walker	8	2			9
Davies	8	3	6		8
Abbott	3	1			4
Rollins	3	1			4
Wright M	4	1			4
Arnold	3	2			3
Clare	3	2			3
Johnson	2	1			2
Rose*	2	1			2
Slew	2	2			2
Wright J	2	1			2
Cresswell	1	1			1
Gibbens	1	1			1
Hine	1	1			1
Marriott	1	1			1
Qualter	1	1			1
Smith Gregg	1	1			1
Wafula	1	1			1
Wroe	1	1			1

Willis	Middleton	Jackson	Thanoj	Harris	Qualter	Arnold	Abbott	Margetts	Marriott	Wafula	Walker	Johnson	Roberts	McCombe	Gough	Lees (L)	Westcarr	Davies	Keane	Wright (L)	Rose (L)	Ceesay	Norris	Smith Gr	Allott	Hine	Slew	Malkowski	Jones (L)	Parkshouse (L)	Rowe	Agnew (L)	Thewlis (L)	Gibbens (L)	Rollins Jay	Chisholm	Chettle (L)	Wroe	Parkin	Wright (L)	Smith Ge (L)	Clare	Cresswell	Hawkes (L)	No.
x	x	x	x	x	x	xs	x	xs	xs	x	sx	sx	sx	s	s																														1
x	xs	x	x	x	x	x	x	xs	x	xs	sx	sx	s		s	sx																													2
x	x	x	x	x	x	x	x	s	xs	xs	sx	xs	sx			s	sx																												3
x	x	x	x	x	x	xs	x	s	xs	x	sx	xs	s			sx	sx																												4
x	x	x	x	x		xs	x	s	xs	x	xs	s	sx		sx	x	sx																												5
x	x		x	x	s	xs	x	sx	xs	xs	x	s			x	x	sx	sx																											6
x	s		x	x	x		x	xs	xs	xs	x	sx			x	s	sx	x	sx																										7
x	sx		x	x	x		x		s	xs	x	sx	xs		x	s	xs	x	sx																										8
x	x	x	xs		x	x	x	s	s	sx	x					sx		x		x	xs	s																							9
x	x	x	x	s	x	xs	x	sx	s	s	x							x		x	xs	sx																							10
x	**x**	**x**		**x**	**x**	**xs**	**xs**	**s**	**sx**	**s**	**x**	**s**			**s**			**x**		**x**	**xs**		**sx**	**sx**																					11
x	x	x		x	x		x		s	xs	xs	s			sx			x		sx	sx		xs	x																					12
x	x	x	x	s	x		x			xs	x	sx						x					s	xs	xs	sx	sx																		13
x	x	x	x		x		x				x	sx						x		sx			s	xs	x	xs	s	sx																	14
		x	x	s	x		x				xs	s						x		sx			sx	xs	x	xs	sx	x	x																15
		x	x	s	x		x				xs							x		sx			s	xs	x	xs	sx	x	x	sx															16
		x	x	sx	x		sx				xs							x		x			xs	s	x	s	xs	x	x	sx															17
x	xs	x	x	x	x													x		sx			xs		x	s	xs	s	x	sx	sx														18
x	s	x	x	s	x							sx						x		sx			x		x	xs	xs		x	s	x														19
																																													20
x		x	x	x	x		x				xs							x		xs					x		s	s				xs	sx	sx	sx										21
x		x	x	x	x		x				xs							x		xs					x		sx	s			sx	xs		s	sx										22
x		**x**	**x**	**x**	**x**		**x**			**s**	**xs**							**x**		**xs**					**xs**		**sx**	**s**				**x**		**sx**	**sx**										23
x		x	x	x	x		x			x	x							x		x							xs	s						s	sx										24
x		x	x	sx	x		x			sx	xs							x		x					xs		sx				s			x	xs	s									25
x		x	x	sx	x		x			sx	xs							x		xs					x		s	s						x	xs	sx									26
x		x	x	s	x		xs			sx	xs							x		x					x		sx							x	s	sx	xs								27
x		x	x	sx	x		x			x	s							x		x					xs		sx	s						x	xs		s								28
x		x	x	sx	x		xs			xs	sx	s						x		x					x		sx							x	xs		s								29
x		x	x	sx	x		xs			x	sx	s						x		xs					xs									x	x		s	sx							30
x		x	x	sx	x		xs			x	sx	s						x		x					x									xs	xs		s	sx							31
x		x	x	x	x		xs			xs	sx	sx						x		sx					x		s								xs		s	x							32
x		x	x	x	x		sx			s	x	sx						x		x					xs		sx								xs			xs	s						33
x		x	x	x	x		sx			sx	xs	sx						x		xs					xs		s								x			x	s						34
x	s	x	x	x	x		xs			xs	sx	s						x		sx					x										x			x	s						35
x	x	x	x	s	x		s	sx		s	x							x		xs					x										sx			x		xs					36
x	x	x	x	sx	x		sx			x	sx	s						x		s					xs										xs			x		xs					37
x	x		xs	s	x		x			x	sx							x		s					x										x			s		xs	x	sx			38
x		sx	xs		x		x			sx	x	s						x		x							s								xs			x			x	sx	xs		39
x		sx	sx		x		x			s	xs	s						x		x															xs			x		xs	x	sx	x		40
x	s	sx	xs		x		xs			sx	xs							x		x															x			x			x	sx	x	s	41
x	x	sx	x		x		xs			x		xs						xs		x															x			sx	s		x			sx	42
x	x	x	x		x		xs					sx						x		xs							s								x			xs	s		x	sx		sx	43
x	x	x	sx		x		x					sx						sx		xs															x			xs	s		xs	x	x	s	44
x	x	x	x		x		x					sx																							x			x	s		x	xs		xs	45
41	18	36	36	19	42	3	27	0	1	10	12	0	0	0	3	2	0	35	0	15	0	0	1	1	16	0	0	3	5	0	1	1	0	6	9	0	0	9	0	0	7	1	3	0	x
0	2	0	4	0	0	6	10	3	6	10	14	3	1	0	0	0	1	1	0	9	3	0	3	4	8	4	4	0	0	0	0	2	0	1	10	0	1	3	0	4	1	1	1	1	xs
0	1	4	2	8	0	0	4	3	1	7	11	13	3	0	2	3	5	2	2	8	1	1	2	1	0	1	10	1	0	3	2	0	1	2	5	2	0	3	0	0	0	5	0	2	sx
0	4	0	0	8	1	0	1	5	4	6	1	12	2	1	3	3	0	0	0	2	0	1	3	1	0	2	7	7	0	1	1	0	0	2	1	1	5	1	7	0	0	0	0	2	s

Also Played: Gray - 27/04 (sx).

x - Played full 90 minutes
xs - Substituted off
sx - Substituted on
s - Non-playing Substitute

BRACKLEY TOWN MATCH RESULTS 2018-19

Date	Comp	Opponents	H/A	Att:	Result	Goalscorers	Pos
Aug 4	NLN	Bradford Park Avenue	A	369	L 0 - 1		
7	NLN	Alfreton Town	H	505	W 3 - 1	Murombedzi 5 13 Ndlovu 69	
11	NLN	Darlington	H	570	L 2 - 4	Armson 6 Ndlovu 48	
14	NLN	AFC Telford United	A	1097	L 1 - 2	Smith 89	
18	NLN	Ashton United	A	180	W 5 - 1	Armson 16 55 Walker G 74 Ndlovu 79 (Pen) Smith 89	
25	NLN	York City	H	580	D 0 - 0		
27	NLN	Nuneaton Borough	A	480	W 3 - 1	Armson 19 Ndlovu 60 Fairlamb 81	
Sept 1	NLN	Chorley	H	530	D 2 - 2	Franklin 35 Ndlovu 41	
8	NLN	Hereford	H	830	W 2 - 0	Armson 15 Ndlovu 51	
15	NLN	Curzon Ashton	A	220	D 1 - 1	Armson 33	7
22	**FAC 2Q**	**Nuneaton Borough**	**A**	**491**	**D 1 - 1**	**Ndlovu 30**	
25	**FAC 2Qr**	**Nuneaton Borough**	**H**	**325**	**W 2 - 0**	**Ndlovu 28 Hall 37**	
29	NLN	Southport	H	590	W 2 - 0	Myles-Tebbutt 23 Armson 32	6
Oct 6	**FAC 3Q**	**Marine**	**H**	**371**	**L 2 - 3**	**Walker A Lowe**	
13	NLN	Guiseley	A	751	L 1 - 2	Fairlamb 11	9
20	NLN	Spennymoor Town	H	447	W 4 - 1	Hall 14 Armson 53 88 Nti 72	5
27	NLN	FC United of Manchester	A	1858	D 1 - 1	Armson 60	
30	NLN	Boston United	A	922	W 3 - 1	Byrne 26 90 Hall 33	5
Nov 3	NLN	Chester	H	650	D 2 - 2	Franklin 50 Byrne 59	5
10	NLN	Blyth Spartans	H	415	D 1 - 1	Lowe 83	7
17	NLN	Stockport County	A	3449	D 1 - 1	Ndlovu 61	8
24	**FAT 3Q**	**Nuneaton Borough**	**H**		**W 3 - 0**		
Dec 1	NLN	Altrincham	H	510	L 1 - 2	Walker G 41	8
8	NLN	Kidderminster Harriers	A	1288	L 0 - 2		10
15	**FAT 1P**	**Hayes & Yeading United**	**H**	**268**	**W 4 - 2**	**Walker A 48 Nti 66 Lowe 84 Jeffers 90+1**	
22	NLN	York City	A	2119	L 1 - 2	Dean 26	
26	NLN	Leamington	H	570	D 2 - 2	Armson 33 Dean 38	
29	NLN	Nuneaton Borough	H	506	W 3 - 1	Lowe 34 McAlinden 37 Armson 70	
Jan 1	NLN	Leamington	A	623	D 0 - 0		
5	NLN	Ashton United	H	431	W 3 - 1	Jeffers 21 (Pen) Dean 44 Lowe 57	10
12	**FAT 2P**	**Hereford**	**A**	**1569**	**W 3 - 1**	**Byrne 14 (pen) Ndlovu 46 Jeffers 65**	
19	NLN	Alfreton Town	A	369	W 1 - 0	Nti 89	
26	NLN	Bradford Park Avenue	H	487	W 3 - 0	Baker 24 78 Ndlovu 59	
Feb 2	**FAT 3P**	**Chesterfield**	**A**	**2054**	**W 2 - 0**	**Ndlovu 52 Armson 76**	
9	NLN	AFC Telford United	H	601	W 3 - 1	Armson 23 Ndlovu 40 Baker 43	
12	NLN	Chorley	A	790	L 0 - 2		
16	NLN	Curzon Ashton	H	490	W 2 - 0	Baker 14 53	4
20	NLN	Darlington	A	915	W 2 - 0	Smith W (og) Nti 78	
23	**FAT 4P**	**Leyton Orient**	**H**	**1563**	**L 1 - 2**	**Ndlovu 24**	
Mar 2	NLN	Blyth Spartans	A	651	W 3 - 1	Byrne 25 (pen) 37 Dean 30	4
9	NLN	Stockport County	H	1107	W 1 - 0	Ndlovu 76	4
23	NLN	Kidderminster Harriers	H	845	W 3 - 1	Armson 4 Ndlovu 71 Bryne 78 (pen)	5
26	NLN	Hereford	A	1512	W 2 - 0	Baker 18 Hickman 74 (og)	3
30	NLN	Southport	A	791	D 0 - 0		3
Apr 6	NLN	Guiseley	H	585	W 2 - 0	Byrne 45 Hall 48	3
13	NLN	Spennymoor Town	A	669	L 1 - 2	Byrne 45 (pen)	3
16	NLN	Altrincham	A	787	W 2 - 1	Ndlovu 70 Hannigan 90+4 (og)	3
19	NLN	Boston United	H	755	W 2 - 0	Armson 44 Byrne 50 (pen)	3
22	NLN	Chester	A	1592	D 0 - 0		3
27	NLN	FC United of Manchester	H	935	W 1 - 0	Nti 86	3
May 5	**PO SF**	**Spennymoor Town**	**H**	**1271**	**D 0 - 0**	**(Lost 4-5 on pens aet)**	

GOALSCORERS	SG	CSG	Pens	Hat tricks	Total
Ndlovu	17	3	1		17
Armson	14	2			16
Byrne	8	2	5		10
Baker	4	1			6
Lowe	5	1			5
Nti	5	1			5
Dean	4	2			4
Hall	4	1			4
Jeffers	3	1	1		3
Opponent	3	1			3
Fairlamb	2	1			2
Franklin	2	1			2
Murombedzi	1	1			2
Smith	2	2			2
Walker A	2	1			2
Walker G	2	1			2
McAlinden	1	1			1
Myles	1	1			1

No.	Lewis	Lowe	Franklin	Byrne	Graham	Dean	Walker G	Armson	Smith	Ndlovu	Murombedzi	Fairlamb	Nti	Myles	Walker A	Hall	Noon	Lobjoit	Jeffers	Staff	Finch	McAlinden (L)	Morgan (L)	Jackson (L)	Baker	Sterling-James (L)	Prosser (L)
1	X	X	X	X	XS	X	X	X	XS	X	XS	SX	SX	SX	S	S											
2	X	X	X	X	S	X	X	X	S	X	X	S	S	S	X	X											
3	X	X	X	X	S	X	XS	X	S	X	XS	SX	SX	SX	X	XS											
4	X	X	X	X	S	X	XS	XS	SX	X	XS	SX	S	SX	X	X											
5	X	X	X	X	S	X	XS	X	SX	X	X	SX	S	S	X	X											
6	X	X	X	X	S	X	XS	X	SX	XS	XS	SX	S	SX	X	X											
7	X	XS	X	X	S	X	S	XS	SX	XS	SX	X	SX	X	X	X											
8	X	XS	X	X	S	X	SX	XS	S	X	SX	XS	SX	X	X	X											
9	X	XS	X	X	S	X	SX	X	SX	XS		XS	SX	X	X	X	S										
10	X	XS	X	X	S	X		XS	SX	X		X	SX	X	X	X	S	S									
11	X	SX	SX	X		X	X	SX		X		XS	XS	X	X	X	S		XS								
12	X	X	X	X		X	SX	XS		XS	S	XS	SX	X	X	X	S		SX								
13	X	X	X	X		X		X		X	S	X	S	X	X	X	S		S	S							
14	X	X	X	X		X		X		XS	SX	XS	SX	XS	X	X	S		SX	S							
15	X	XS	S	X		X	X	SX		X	X	X	SX	S	X	X	S		XS								
16	X	SX	XS	X		X	X	X		S	XS	SX	X	SX	X	X	S		XS								
17	X	SX	XS	X		X	X	X		SX	X	SX	XS	S	X	X	S		XS								
18	X	X	X	X		X	XS	XS		X	X	SX	SX	S	X	X	S		S								
19	X	XS	XS	X		X	X	XS		X	X	SX	SX	SX	X	X	S		S								
20	X	X	SX	X		X	X	X		X	XS	X	SX	SX	XS	XS	S		S								
21	X	X	X	X		X	X	X		X	SX	S	S	X	XS	X	S		S								
22																											
23	X	X	XS	X		X	X			XS	XS	SX	SX	X	X	X	S		SX								
24	X	X	S	X		X	X			XS	X	SX	X	X	XS	X			SX		S						
25	X	X	S	X		X	X			SX	S	X	XS	X	X	X			SX			XS	S				
26	X	X	S	X		X	X	SX			SX	XS	XS	XS	X	X			SX			X	S				
27	X	X		X		X	X	X		XS	S	SX	SX	XS	X	X			SX			XS	S				
28	X	X		X		X	X	X		X	SX	SX	S	S	X	XS			S			X	XS				
29	X	X	X	X		X	X	XS		X	X	S	S	S	X				X			SX	S				
30	X	XS	X	X		X	X	XS		XS	X	SX	S	SX	X				X			SX	S				
31	X	X	XS	X		X	X	X		X	XS	SX	SX	SX	X				XS			S					
32	X	X		X		X	XS	X		X		SX	SX	S	X				X		S			X	X		
33	X	X		X		X	X	XS		XS		SX	SX	X	SX				S					X	X	XS	
34	X	XS		X		X	X	X		XS		SX	SX	X	X		S		SX					X		XS	
35	X	XS		X		X	X	X		X		SX	SX	X	X	X			S					S	XS	S	
36	X	X		X		X	X	XS		X	S	SX	SX	XS	X	X			S						X	S	
37	X	X		X		X	X	SX		X		X		X	X	X			S					S	XS		
38	X	X		X		X	X	S			S	X	SX	X	X	X			XS					S	X	S	
39	X	X		X		X	X	X		X	S	X	SX	XS	X	X			S					S		S	
40	X	XS		X		X	X	XS		X	S	SX	SX	X	X	X								S	XS	SX	
41	X	X		X		X	XS	X		X	SX	SX	SX	X	XS	X								S	XS	S	
42	X	XS		X		X		XS		X	X	SX	SX	X	X	X			S					S	XS		SX
43	X	X		X		X		XS		X	X	SX	SX	XS	X	X			S					S	XS		SX
44	X	XS		X		X	SX	X		X	XS	SX	SX	X	X	X								S	XS		S
45	X	XS		X		X	X	X		XS	XS	SX	SX	X	X	X			S							SX	S
46	X	X		X		X		X		X	X	XS	SX	XS	X	X			S					S		SX	S
47	X	X		X		X	X	X		X	X	SX	S	S	XS	X								S	XS	SX	
48	X	XS		X		X	X	XS		X	X	SX	SX	SX	X	X								S	XS	S	
49	X	X		X		X	X	X		X	X	SX	S	S	XS	X								S	XS	SX	
50	X	X		X		X	X	X		X	X	SX	SX	SX	XS	X								S	XS		S
51	X	X	S	X		X	X			X	X	SX		XS	XS	X								S	XS	SX	SX
X	50	33	17	50	0	50	32	26	0	33	17	9	2	21	40	40	0	0	3	0	0	2	0	3	4	0	0
XS	0	14	5	0	1	0	7	15	1	12	10	7	4	8	8	3	0	0	6	0	0	2	1	0	12	2	0
SX	0	3	2	0	0	0	4	4	6	2	7	31	31	11	1	0	0	0	8	0	0	2	0	0	0	6	3
S	0	0	5	0	9	0	1	1	3	1	8	3	11	10	1	1	15	1	15	2	2	1	5	15	0	6	4

x - Played full 90 minutes
xs - Substituted off
sx - Substituted on
s - Non-playing Substitute

BRADFORD PARK AVENUE MATCH RESULTS 2018-19

Date	Comp	Opponents	H/A	Att:	Result		Goalscorers	Pos
Aug 4	NLN	Brackley Town	H	369	W	1 - 0	McKenna 45	
7	NLN	Blyth Spartans	A	661	W	2 - 1	Beesley 11 85	
11	NLN	Leamington	H	524	L	2 - 4	Killock 90 Johnson 90	
14	NLN	Spennymoor Town	H	392	W	1 - 0	McKenna 26	
18	NLN	Stockport County	H	825	D	1 - 1	Nowakowski 88	
25	NLN	Hereford	A	2601	W	2 - 1	Branson 22 Johnson 80 (Pen)	
27	NLN	Boston United	H	573	W	1 - 0	Johnson 15 (Pen)	
Sept 2	NLN	FC United of Manchester	A	1814	D	2 - 2	Killock 23 Senior 55 (og)	
8	NLN	Chester	A	1693	L	3 - 5	McKenna 4 Beesley 43 Johnson 52	
15	NLN	Altrincham	H	454	L	2 - 3	Killock 39 Branson 52	4
22	**FAC 2Q**	**Darlington**	**A**	**1037**	**W**	**1 - 0**	**Lowe 24**	
29	NLN	Alfreton Town	A	487	W	1 - 0	Branson 71	3
Oct 6	**FAC 3Q**	**Altrincham**	**A**	**780**	**L**	**2 - 4**	**Beesley 30 (Pen) Killock 38**	
13	NLN	Kidderminster Harriers	H	529	L	1 - 2	Branson 61	6
20	NLN	Nuneaton Borough	A	823	W	6 - 0	Branson 23 Wroe 33 Spencer 42 Beesley 64 (Pen) 87 Hurst 73	3
27	NLN	Chorley	H	554	W	1 - 0	Beesley 77	
30	NLN	Darlington	H	625	D	2 - 2	Johnson 21 Clee 39	3
Nov 3	NLN	York City	A	2289	W	4 - 1	Beesley 26 (Pen) 47 Spencer 50 McKenna 82	2
10	NLN	Curzon Ashton	A	314	D	1 - 1	Beesley 64	1
17	NLN	Ashton United	H	1427	W	3 - 2	Knight 84 Killock 85 90	1
24	**FAT 3Q**	**Altrincham**	**A**	**570**	**L**	**0 - 4**		
Dec 1	NLN	AFC Telford United	A	1468	W	2 - 0	Knight 52 Spencer 90	1
8	NLN	Southport	H	532	D	2 - 2	Branson 17 Johnson 74	1
22	NLN	Hereford	H	448	W	1 - 0	Knight 70	
26	NLN	Guiseley	A	1150	W	5 - 1	Johnson 3 Beesley 19 27 55 (Pen) Branson 59	
29	NLN	Boston United	A	1061	D	2 - 2	Knight 36 McKenna 90	
Jan 1	NLN	Guiseley	H	665	L	1 - 2	Johnson 65	
5	NLN	Stockport County	A	4105	L	0 - 3		
12	NLN	FC United of Manchester	H	713	L	2 - 3	Johnson 38 Knight 77	2
19	NLN	Blyth Spartans	H	373	D	1 - 1	Branson 77	
26	NLN	Brackley Town	A	487	L	0 - 3		
Feb 16	NLN	Altrincham	A	1328	D	1 - 1	East 84	
23	NLN	Chester	H	705	W	2 - 0	Beesley 1 35	5
Mar 2	NLN	Curzon Ashton	H	426	D	2 - 2	Beesley 34 (pen) 61	6
5	NLN	Leamington	H	303	W	2 - 1	Branson 3 Langstaff 40	5
9	NLN	Ashton United	A	265	W	2 - 0	Johnson 68 Spencer 90	5
19	NLN	Spennymoor Town	A	749	W	2 - 0	Branson 24 Beesley 85	4
23	NLN	Southport	A	949	D	2 - 2	Platt 15 (og) Beesley 32	4
26	NLN	AFC Telford United	H	384	L	1 - 2	Branson 75	5
30	NLN	Alfreton Town	H	465	D	1 - 1	Havern 86	4
Apr 6	NLN	Kidderminster Harriers	A	1606	L	0 - 3		6
13	NLN	Nuneaton Borough	H	429	W	1 - 0	Beesley 57 (pen)	6
19	NLN	Darlington	A	1310	L	0 - 1		
22	NLN	York City	H	775	L	1 - 3	Knight 54	7
27	NLN	Chorley	A	1575	L	2 - 3	Beesley 36 (pen) Johnson 55	7
May 1	**PO Q**	**Spennymoor Town**	**A**	**1509**	**L**	**0 - 1**		

GOALSCORERS	SG	CSG	Pens	Hat tricks	Total
Beesley	14	2	7	1	21
Branson	11	2			11
Johnson	11	2	2		11
Killock	5	1			6
Knight	6	2			6
McKenna	5	1			5
Spencer	4	1			4
Opponent	2	1			2
Clee	1	1			1
East	1	1			1
Havern	1	1			1
Hurst	1	1			1
Langstaff	1	1			1
Lowe	1	1			1
Nowakowski	1	1			1
Wroe	1	1			1

Drench	Toulson	Lowe	Wroe	Killock	Havern	McKenna	Branson	Beesley	Dawson	Clee	Spencer	Johnson	Boshell	Ross	Nowakowski	Atkinson	Knight	Anderson	Hurst	East	Andrew (L)	Langstaff (L)	Crichlow-Noble	Dickinson	Lewis-Potter (L)	No.
x	x	x	xs	x	x	x	x	x	xs	xs	sx	sx	sx	s	s											1
x	x	x	x	x	x	xs	x	x	xs	xs	sx	sx	s	sx	s											2
x	x		xs	x	x	x	x	x	x	x	sx	sx	s	x	s	s										3
x		xs	sx	x	x	x	x	x	xs	sx	x	xs	s	x	sx		s									4
x			sx	x	x	x	x	x	xs	x	xs	xs	s	x	sx	s	sx									5
x	s		x	x	x		x	x	sx	x	xs	xs	sx	x	sx	s	xs									6
x	sx		x	x	x		x	x	sx	x	xs	xs	s	x	sx	s	xs									7
x		sx	x	x	x	x	x	x	s	x	xs	xs	sx	x	s		s									8
x		x	x	x	xs	xs	x	x	s	xs	sx	x	s	x	sx		sx									9
x	x	xs	xs	x	x	x	x	x	xs	x	sx	sx	s	s	sx											10
	sx	**x**	**x**	**x**	**x**	**xs**	**x**	**x**	**xs**	**xs**	**sx**	**sx**		**x**	**s**	**x**	**s**									11
x	s	x	x	x	x	x	x	x	x	x	s		s	x	s		s									12
x	**s**	**x**	**x**	**x**	**xs**	**x**	**x**	**x**	**xs**	**x**	**sx**	**s**	**sx**	**x**	**s**		**s**	**s**								13
x	sx	x	xs	x	x		x	xs			xs	x	sx	x	sx	s	x									14
x	s	x	xs	x	x		x	x		sx	x	xs		x	sx	s	xs		sx							15
x	s	x	x	x	x	sx	x	x		sx	xs	xs		x	sx		xs		s							16
x	s	xs	xs	x	x	sx	x	x		sx	x	x		x	s		xs		sx							17
x	s		x	x	x	sx	x	x		x	xs	xs		x	s	s	x		sx							18
x	s		xs	x	x	sx	x	x		x	x	xs		x	s	s	x		sx							19
x	s	s	x	x	x	xs	x	x		x	xs			x	sx	s	x		sx							20
																										21
x	x	x	x	x	x	s		x	s	x	sx	xs		s	xs		x		s							22
x	x	x	xs		x	s	x	x	s	xs	sx	x		x	sx		x		s							23
x	x	x	xs	sx	x	sx	x	x	s	x	sx	xs		x			xs		s							24
x	x	x	sx	s	x	sx	x	x	s	xs	sx	xs		x			xs		x							25
x	s	x	xs	x	x	sx	x	x		sx	s	xs		x	sx		x		xs							26
x	xs	x	s	s	x	sx	x	x		x	sx	xs		x	sx		x		xs							27
s	x	x	sx	x		sx	x	x		xs	s	xs		x	sx	x	x		xs							28
x	xs	x	x	x		xs	x	x	s			x		x	sx	s	x		sx							29
x	s	x	xs	x			x	x	s	x	x	xs		x	sx	s	x		sx							30
x		x		xs	x		x	x	s	xs	x	xs		x	sx	s	x		sx	sx						31
	s			xs	x		x	x		x	x	xs		x	s		x		xs	sx	x	sx	sx			32
	sx	s		x	x			x		xs	x			x	x		xs		x	sx	x	xs	sx	s		33
	s	s		x	x		xs	x		x	x			x			x		x	sx	x	x		s		34
		x		x	x		x	x		sx	x	s		x	sx		xs		xs	sx	x	xs	s			35
	s			x	x		x	xs		x	x	sx		x	sx		x		xs	sx	x	xs	s			36
	s	sx		x	x		x	x		xs	x	sx		x	sx		x		xs	xs	x		s			37
	sx	s		xs	x		x	xs		x	x	x		x	x		x			sx	x		s	s		38
	xs	xs			x		x	x		sx	x	x		x	sx		x		xs	s	x		sx	s		39
	s	x			x			x		x	x	xs		x	x		xs		sx	xs	x		sx	s	sx	40
	s	x		s	x		x	x		x	sx	sx		x	sx		xs		xs	xs	x		xs			41
		xs		x	x		x	x		x	xs	sx		x	sx		xs		s	sx	x		x		s	42
	s			x	x		x	x		xs	sx	sx		x	s		x		xs	xs	x		x		sx	43
	s	x		x	x		x	x			sx	xs		x	xs		x		sx	xs	x		s		sx	44
		x		x	x		x	x		sx	x	xs		x	xs		xs		s	sx	x		s		sx	45
	s	**x**			**x**		**x**	**x**		**xs**	**x**	**sx**		**x**	**sx**		**x**		**sx**	**xs**	**x**		**s**		**xs**	46
28	9	25	13	34	40	8	41	42	2	22	17	7	0	41	3	2	21	0	3	0	15	1	2	0	0	x
0	3	5	11	3	2	5	1	3	7	12	9	21	0	0	3	0	13	0	10	6	0	3	1	0	1	xs
0	5	2	4	1	0	9	0	0	2	8	15	11	5	1	24	0	2	0	11	9	0	1	4	0	4	sx
1	20	4	1	3	0	2	0	0	9	0	3	2	8	3	12	12	5	1	6	1	0	0	7	5	1	s

x - Played full 90 minutes
xs - Substituted off
sx - Substituted on
s - Non-playing Substitute

CHESTER MATCH RESULTS 2018-19

Date	Comp	Opponents	H/A	Att:	Result		Goalscorers	Pos
Aug 4	NLN	Spennymoor Town	H	2191	D	0 - 0		
6	NLN	Curzon Ashton	A	977	**W**	3 - 0	Grand 22 Dudley 37 Pritchard 60	
11	NLN	Blyth Spartans	A	737	L	1 - 8	Stopforth 70	
25	NLN	AFC Telford United	A	1886	L	1 - 3	Grand 81	
Sept 1	NLN	Guiseley	A	806	D	1 - 1	Moran 90	
8	NLN	Bradford Park Avenue	H	1693	**W**	5 - 3	Mooney 6 74 Dudley 11 90 (Pen) Mahon 33	
11	NLN	FC United of Manchester	H	2045	D	0 - 0		
15	NLN	Boston United	A	1188	**W**	2 - 0	Howson 51 Mooney 59	14
18	NLN	Kidderminster Harriers	H	1512	**W**	3 - 1	Dudley 6 (Pen) Hughes 52 81	9
22	**FAC 2Q**	**City of Liverpool**	**H**	**1806**	**W**	**4 - 0**	**Pritchard 43 45 Murray 71 Noble 90**	
29	NLN	Chorley	A	2028	D	0 - 0		8
Oct 2	NLN	Hereford	H	1705	**W**	3 - 0	Hughes 15 Pritchard 72 Smalley Deane 87	5
6	**FAC 3Q**	**Dunston UTS**	**A**	**873**	**L**	**3 - 4**	**Smalley Deane 35 Mooney 44 60**	
27	NLN	Alfreton Town	H	1619	**W**	3 - 2	Roberts G 4 (Pen) 67 90	
30	NLN	Ashton United	H	1646	**W**	4 - 1	Dudley 2 60 Howson 31 Mahon 71	6
Nov 3	NLN	Brackley Town	A	650	D	2 - 2	Mooney 58 90	6
6	NLN	Nuneaton Borough	H	1462	**W**	3 - 2	Livesey 17 Dudley 20 Mooney 49	5
10	NLN	Altrincham	H	2388	L	1 - 2	Grand 52	5
13	NLN	York City	A	2319	D	0 - 0		4
17	NLN	Leamington	A	975	L	0 - 1		6
24	**FAT 3Q**	**Southport**	**A**	**914**	**D**	**0 - 0**		
27	**FAT 3Qr**	**Southport**	**H**	**654**	**L**	**0 - 2**		
Dec 1	NLN	Darlington	H	1934	**W**	3 - 1	Asante 27 49 69	3
8	NLN	Stockport County	A	3714	D	1 - 1	Asante 33	4
22	NLN	AFC Telford United	H	2079	**W**	2 - 1	Asante 24 Dudley 51	
26	NLN	Southport	A	1644	L	0 - 3		
29	NLN	Hereford	A	2775	L	0 - 2		
Jan 1	NIN	Southport	H	1984	D	0 - 0		
5	NLN	FC United of Manchester	A	2260	**W**	2 - 0	Dudley 16 Roberts 90	
12	NLN	Guiseley	H	1759	D	1 - 1	Dudley 55	5
19	NLN	Curzon Ashton	H	1671	L	0 - 1		
26	NLN	Spennymoor Town	A	863	L	0 - 2		
Feb 9	NLN	KIdderminster Harriers	A	1769	L	1 - 4	Asante 37	
16	NLN	Boston United	H	1648	**W**	4 - 1	Asante 21 Dudley 43 Mahon 62 Waring 73	
23	NLN	Bradford Park Avenue	A	705	L	0 - 2		8
26	NLN	Blyth Spartans	H	1382	**W**	2 - 0	Mahon 67 Waring 74	
Mar 2	NLN	Altrincham	A	1714	L	0 - 4		9
9	NLN	Leamington	H	1983	D	1 - 1	McKenna 47	9
27	NLN	Darlington	A	1116	**W**	1 - 0	Grand 40	9
30	NLN	Chorley	H	1979	D	0 - 0		9
Apr 6	NLN	Nuneaton Borough	A	688	**W**	3 - 2	Asante 4 Livesey 51 90+3	9
9	NLN	Stockport County	H	2565	L	0 - 6		10
13	NLN	York City	H	1772	D	2 - 2	Newton 48 (og) Waring 73	10
19	NLN	Ashton United	A	468	**W**	3 - 0	Murray 31 Livesey 46 Waring 63	
22	NLN	Brackley Town	H	1592	D	0 - 0		9
27	NLN	Alfreton Town	A	530	D	2 - 2	Asante 13 Waring 68	9

GOALSCORERS	SG	CSG	Pens	Hat tricks	Total
Dudley	9	2	2		11
Asante*	7	3		1	9
Mooney	5	2			8
Waring	5	1			5
Grand	4	1			4
Livesey	3	1			4
Mahon	4	1			4
Pritchard	3	1			4
Roberts G	2	1	1	1	4
Hughes	2	1			3
Howson	2	1			2
Murray	2	1			2
Smalley Deane	2	2			2
McKenna	1	1			1
Moran	1	1			1
Noble	1	1			1
Opponent	1	1			1
Stopforth	1	1			1

Shenton	Tuton	Stopforth	Roberts G	Howson	Grand	Mooney (L)	Livesey (L)	Dudley (L)	Pritchard	Smalley Do	Mahon	Moran	Downes	Brown	Thomson	Hughes	Burton	Marsh-Hughes	Waters	King	Noble	Miller	Smalley De	Jordan	Roberts	Murray	Crilly	Jones D	Cottrell	Dieseruvwe (L)	Dawson	Asante (L)	Green	Jackson	McAllister	McKenna	Waring	Crawford J	No.
x	x	x	x	x	x	xs	x	x	x	x	sx	s	s	s	s																							1
x	xs	x	x	x	x	xs	x	x	x	xs	sx	s	s	sx	sx																							2
x		x	x	x	x	xs	x	x	x	xs	s	s			s	x	sx	s																				3
x		x		s	x	s	xs	x	x	x	xs	sx			sx	xs	x	sx	x																			4
x		x		x	x	xs		x		x	xs	x			s	x	xs	sx		s	sx	sx																5
x		x		x	x	xs		x	sx	xs	xs	x			s	xs	x				s		sx	sx														6
x		x	s	x	x	xs	s	x	sx	x	xs	x			s	x	x							sx	s													7
x		x	x	x	x	xs	x	x	s	xs	x	sx				sx	xs							sx		s												8
x		x	x	x	x	xs	x	xs	sx		x	x				sx		s	s	s				sx		xs												9
x		x	xs	x	x		x		x		x	xs			sx	xs		sx		s	sx					x	s	s	s									10
x		x		x	x	xs	x		s		x	x			s	x	x				s		sx	sx		xs												11
x		x		x	x	xs	x		sx		x	x			s	xs	x				s		sx	sx		xs												12
x				x		x	x																x																13
x		x	x	x	x	x		x	sx	xs	x	x			s								x	s		s				sx										14
x		x	x	x	x	xs	x	x	sx	s	x	x											s	sx		xs				sx										15
x		x	x	xs	x	x	x	xs	sx	s	x	x											sx	sx		s				xs										16
x		x	x	x	x	xs	x	xs	sx	sx	xs	x											s	s		sx				x										17
x			x	x	x	x	x	x	xs	s	x	xs									sx		sx	sx		s				xs										18
x		x	x	x	x	x	x	xs	s	xs	x	sx									s		sx							xs	sx									19
x		x	x	x	x	x	x	xs	s	s	x	x									s		sx							sx	xs									20
																																							21
x		x	x	x	x	xs	x	x			sx				x			sx		s	s		sx	xs							xs									22
x		x			x	x	x				xs			s	x			sx			x		sx			s					sx	xs								23
x		x	x	x	x		xs	xs			x			s	x			s			sx		sx			s					x	x								24
x		x		x	x	sx		x			xs	x			x			s			x		sx								xs	xs	s	sx						25
x			x	x	x	x		x			x	x			xs			s	s		xs		sx								x		sx	s						26
x			x	x	x	xs		x			xs	x			xs			sx	sx		s		sx								s		x	x						27
x			x	x	x	xs		x			x	s						sx	x		s		xs			s					sx		x	x						28
x			xs	x	x	xs	x	x			xs	sx						s	sx		xs		s			s							x	x						29
x			x	x	x	xs	x	x			x	s		sx					sx		s		xs			s								x	x					30
x			x	xs	x	x	x				x				s		s	x	s				sx										sx	x	x	xs			31
x			x	x	x	sx	x				s				x		x		s				sx										sx	xs	xs	xs	x		32
x			x	x		sx	x	x			x			s	x		x	sx	x				s			s						xs					xs		33
x			xs	x		xs	x	x			x				s		x	sx	x							s						xs	sx	x			sx		34
x			x	x		x	x	x			xs				s		x	sx	x	s						sx								x	s		x		35
x			x	x		xs	x	x			xs				s		x	sx	x	s						sx								x	sx		xs		36
x			x	x	s	xs	x	x			xs						x	sx	x													s		x	sx	s	xs		37
x			x	x	s	s	x	x			x							s	x		s											xs		x	x	x	sx		38
x			x	s	x	sx	x	x			xs							s	x							sx						xs		x	x	xs	sx		39
x			x	s	x	xs	x	x			xs							s	x													xs	sx	x	x	sx	sx		40
x			x	s	x	xs	x	xs			sx							s	x													xs	sx	x	x	x	sx		41
x			x	sx	x	sx	x	xs			x						s		x													xs	s	x	x	xs	sx		42
x			x	s	x		x	sx			xs				x		xs		x							sx							xs	x		s	x	sx	43
x			xs	x	x		x	xs			sx				s		xs		x							x							sx	x		s	x	sx	44
x			x	x	x			sx			xs				s		x		x							xs							sx	x	s	sx	x	xs	45
x			x	x	x		s	x			xs						x		x							sx						x	s	x		s	x	s	46
45	1	22	32	36	38	10	33	27	5	4	20	14	0	0	7	4	13	1	16	0	2	0	2	0	0	2	0	0	0	1	2	2	3	18	7	2	6	0	x
0	1	0	4	2	0	22	2	9	1	6	17	2	0	0	2	4	4	0	0	0	2	0	2	1	0	5	0	0	0	3	3	9	1	1	1	4	3	1	xs
0	0	0	0	1	0	5	0	2	8	1	5	4	0	2	3	2	1	12	3	0	4	1	15	9	0	6	0	0	0	3	3	0	8	1	2	2	6	2	sx
0	0	0	1	5	2	2	2	0	4	4	2	5	2	4	14	0	2	10	4	6	10	0	4	2	1	11	1	1	1	0	1	1	3	1	2	4	0	1	s

x - Played full 90 minutes
xs - Substituted off
sx - Substituted on
s - Non-playing Substitute

CHORLEY MATCH RESULTS 2018-19

Date	Comp	Opponents	H/A	Att:	Result		Goalscorers	Pos
Aug 4	NLN	York City	H	1520	W	1 - 0	Blakeman 38	
7	NLN	Guiseley	A	701	W	2 - 0	Newby A 38 Blakeman 72	
11	NLN	Nuneaton Borough	A	511	W	1 - 0	Carver 44	1
14	NLN	Southport	H	1368	W	4 - 0	Teague 6 Blakeman 17 (Pen) Newby A 33 Priestly 47 (og)	1
18	NLN	Hereford	H	1542	W	1 - 0	Wilson 90	1
25	NLN	Blyth Spartans	A	725	W	2 - 1	Newby A 66 Wilson 70	1
27	NLN	Curzon Ashton	H	1571	W	2 - 0	Almond 50 Carver 90	1
Sept 1	NLN	Brackley Town	A	530	D	2 - 2	O'Keefe 66 83	1
8	NLN	Ashton United	A	425	W	5 - 0	O'Keefe 11 Blakeman 31 Carver 36 Almond 46 Newby E 85	1
15	NLN	Alfreton Town	H	1298	W	3 - 1	Challoner 21 Blakeman 28 60	1
22	**FAC 2Q**	**Leek Town**	**H**	**746**	**W**	**3 - 0**		
29	NLN	Chester	H	2028	D	0 - 0		1
Oct 6	**FAC 3Q**	**Peterborough Sports**	**A**	**404**	**W**	**3 - 0**		
13	NLN	AFC Telford United	A	1258	D	1 - 1	Wilson 83	1
20	**FAC 4Q**	**Barrow**	**H**	**1734**	**W**	**3 - 2**	**Challoner 46 Almond 67 Carver 71**	
27	NLN	Bradford Park Avenue	A	554	L	0 - 1		1
30	NLN	Stockport County	A	2653	L	0 - 3		1
Nov 3	NLN	Spennymoor Town	H	1212	L	1 - 2	Newby E 59	1
11	**FAC 1P**	**Doncaster Rovers**	**H**	**3239**	**D**	**2 - 2**	**O'Keefe 2 Meppen-Walter 43**	
17	NLN	Kidderminster Harriers	A	2090	W	4 - 0	Wilson 26 58 Newby E 45 Teague 69	2
20	**FAC 1Pr**	**Doncaster Rovers**	**A**	**3048**	**L**	**0 - 7**		
24	**FAT 3Q**	**Stockport County**	**A**	**1245**	**L**	**0 - 3**		
Dec 1	NLN	Boston United	H	1047	D	1 - 1	Meppen-Walters 58	2
8	NLN	Leamington	A	568	D	1 - 1	O'Keefe 90+4	2
15	NLN	Darlington	H	737	W	3 - 2	Carver 55 Teague 67 Newby A 68	1
22	NLN	Blyth Spartans	H	1076	L	2 - 4	O'Keefe 45 Newby E 55	
26	NLN	FC United of Manchester	A	2366	W	4 - 1	Carver 6 75 Wilson 60 65	
29	NLN	Curzon Ashton	A	490	W	1 - 0	Carver 13	
Jan 1	NLN	FC United of Manchester	H	2021	W	4 - 0	Newby E 51 76 O'Keefe 79 83	
5	NLN	Hereford	A	2168	D	1 - 1	O'Keefe 59	
12	NLN	Altrincham	H	1675	W	4 - 1	Newby A 54 84 Wilson 64 Meppen-Walter 90	1
19	NLN	Guiseley	H	1314	W	3 - 0	Wilson 10 Blakeman 48 Newby A 61	1
26	NLN	York City	A	2669	W	4 - 1	Leather 8 Meppen-Walter 16 Wilson 76 Newby A 83	1
Feb 9	NLN	Southport	A	1542	L	3 - 5	Newby A 29 56 Newby E 90	
12	NLN	Brackley Town	H	790	W	2 - 0	Carver 38 Blakeman 63 (pen)	
16	NLN	Alfreton Town	A	536	L	1 - 2	Carver 37	
23	NLN	Ashton United	H	1326	L	0 - 1		1
26	NLN	Nuneaton Borough	H	961	W	2 - 0	Newby A 63 Blakeman 90 (pen)	1
Mar 2	NLN	Darlington	A	1213	D	1 - 1	Wilson 90	1
9	NLN	Kidderminster Harriers	H	1474	W	3 - 0	Wilson 4 60 Carver 66	1
16	NLN	Boston United	A	1007	W	2 - 0	Carver 34 Newby E 78	1
23	NLN	Leamington	H	1507	W	3 - 0	Carver 31 78 Almond 90	1
30	NLN	Chester	A	1979	D	0 - 0		1
Apr 6	NLN	AFC Telford United	H	1286	D	1 - 1	Teague 9	1
13	NLN	Altrincham	A	1597	L	3 - 5	Teague 52 69 Meppen-Walters 78	2
19	NLN	Stockport County	H	3597	W	2 - 0	Teague 15 Carver 60	1
22	NLN	Spennymoor Town	A	1261	L	0 - 1		2
27	NLN	Bradford Park Avenue	H	1575	W	3 - 2	Almond 44 54 89	2
May 5	**PO SF**	**Altrincham**	**H**	**3446**	**D**	**1 - 1**	**Wilson 83 (won 3-1 on pens aet)**	
12	**PO F**	**Spennymoor Town**	**H**	**3594**	**D**	**1 - 1**	**Leather 102 (won 4-3 on pens aet)**	

GOALSCORERS	SG	CSG	Pens	Hat tricks	Total
Carver	13	3			15
Wilson	11	3			14
Newby A	9	4			11
Blakeman	8	2	3		9
O'Keefe	7	2			9
Newby E	7	1			8
Almond	5	1		1	7
Teague	6	3			7
Meppen-Walters	5	1			5
Challoner	2	1			2
Leather	2	1			2
Opponent	1	1			1

Belford	Challoner	Blakeman	Teague	Leather	Meppen-Walter	Newby A	O'Keefe	Carver	Wilson	Newby E	Almond	Whitham	Short	Anson	Fletcher	Urwin (L)	Jordan	Cottrell	Eccles	Glynn (L)	Noble-Lazarus	Wilson	Lussey	O'Brien	Lenehan	Hooper	Baines	Lee	McMillan	McGurk	Tuton (L)	Hanley	No.
x	x	x	x	x	x	x	x	xs	xs	xs	sx	sx	sx	s	s																		1
x	x	xs	x	x	x	xs	x	xs	x	x	sx	sx	sx	s	s																		2
	x	x	x	x	s	xs	x	xs	sx	x	xs	sx	s		sx	x	x																3
	x	x	x	x	x	x	xs	xs	sx	x	xs	s	sx	s		x		sx															4
	x	x	x	xs	sx	x	x	x	sx	xs	xs		s		s	x	x	sx															5
	x	xs	x	x	sx	x	x	x	xs	x	s	s		xs		x	xs	sx															6
	x		x	x	x	x	x	x	sx	xs	xs	sx	xs	s		x		sx	s														7
	x		x	x		s	x	x	x	x	sx	s	xs	x		x	s	x	s														8
	x	x	x	x	x		xs	x	x	x	xs	sx	s	sx		x		sx	s														9
	x	xs	x	x	x		x	x	x	xs	xs	sx		s		x	s	sx		sx													10
																																	11
	x	x	x	x	x		x	x	x	x	xs	s		s	s	x		sx	s														12
																																	13
	x	x	x	x	x	sx		xs	x	x	sx	xs		s		x	s	x		s													14
	x	x	x	x	x	xs	x	x		x	xs	sx		s		x	s	s	s	sx	s												15
	x	x	x	x	xs	xs	x	x	sx	x	x	s		s		x		s		sx													16
	x	x	x	xs	x	xs	x	x	sx	x	xs	sx		s		x		s		sx													17
	x	x	x	xs	x	s	x	sx	x	x	x	s		s		x		s		x													18
	x	x	x	x	x	s	xs	x	s	x	xs	sx		s		x	s	sx	s	xs													19
	x	x	x		x	s	xs	x	xs	xs	sx	sx		s		x	x	x		sx													20
		x	x	xs	x		x			xs	x	sx		x		x	sx	x	s		sx	xs	s	s	s								21
																																	22
		x	xs		x	x	x	x	sx	x	xs	s		x		x	x	s					s			sx							23
	x	x			x	sx	x	xs		x	x	s		xs		x	x	xs				sx	s			sx							24
	x	x	x			xs	x	x	s	x	x	s		x		xs	x	sx	sx							s							25
	x	x	x		s	x	x	x	xs	x	sx						x	s	x							sx	xs	s					26
	x	x	xs		sx	xs	x	x	x	x							xs	sx	s							sx	x	s	x				27
	x	x	x		x	sx	x	xs	xs	x	s							x	s							sx	x	s	x				28
	x	x	xs	sx	x	xs	x	x	x	xs	sx							sx	s							s	x		x				29
	x	x	x	s	x	x	x	xs	xs	x	sx					x		sx	s							sx	x						30
	x	x	x	x	x	x	x	x	xs	x		s				x		s	s							sx	s						31
	x	xs	x	x	x	x	x	x	xs	x						x	s	sx	s							s				sx			32
	x	x	x	x	x	xs	x	x	xs	xs						x	s	sx	s							sx				sx			33
	x	x	x	xs	x	x	x	x	xs	xs	sx					x	s	s								sx				sx			34
	x	x	x	x	x	xs	x	xs	xs	x	s					x	s	sx								s				sx			35
	x	x	xs	s	x	x	x	x	sx		sx			s		x	x	xs								sx				xs			36
	xs	x	x	xs	xs	x	x	x	x	x	sx					x	sx	s								s				sx			37
	x	x	x		x	x	x	xs	sx	xs	xs			s		x	x	sx								sx				s			38
	x	x	x		x	x	xs	x	sx	x	xs			s		x	xs	s								sx				sx			39
	x	x	x	xs	x	x		xs	xs	x	s			sx		x	s	x								sx				sx			40
	x	x	x	x	x	x		xs	xs	x	sx			s		x	sx	x	s											s			41
	x	xs	x	x	x		x	xs	x	xs	sx			s		x	sx	x	s											sx			42
	x	x	x	xs	x		xs	x		x	sx			s		x	sx	x	s											sx	xs		43
	xs	x	x	x	x			x	xs	x	sx	x				x	sx	x								s				s	sx		44
		x	x	xs	x	x		xs	x	x	sx	sx		s		x	xs	x								s					sx		45
	x	x	x	x	x	x	sx	xs	xs	xs	sx			s		x	s	x													sx		46
	x	x	xs	x	x	x	sx	x	xs	xs	sx	s		s		x	sx	x															47
		x		xs	x	x	sx	xs		x	x			x		x	x	xs	s							sx					sx	s	48
	xs	x	x	x	x	x	sx	xs	x	xs	sx			s		x	s	x													sx		49
	x	x	x	x	x	x	sx	x	xs	x	sx			s		x	s	xs								s							50
2	40	40	40	25	38	23	31	28	13	32	6	1	0	5	0	40	10	14	1	1	0	0	0	0	0	0	4	0	3	0	0	0	x
0	3	5	5	10	2	10	6	17	17	14	13	1	2	2	0	1	4	4	0	1	0	1	0	0	0	0	1	0	0	1	1	0	xs
0	0	0	0	1	3	3	5	1	10	0	20	12	3	2	1	0	7	16	1	5	1	1	0	0	0	14	0	0	0	9	5	0	sx
0	0	0	0	2	2	4	0	0	2	0	4	11	3	24	4	0	13	10	18	1	1	0	3	1	1	8	1	3	0	3	0	1	s

x - Played full 90 minutes
xs - Substituted off
sx - Substituted on
s - Non-playing Substitute

CURZON ASHTON MATCH RESULTS 2018-19

Date	Comp	Opponents	H/A	Att:	Result		Goalscorers	Pos
Aug 4	NLN	Darlington	A	1488	**W**	2 - 1	Fawns 25 Hughes 53	
6	NLN	Chester	H	977	L	0 - 3		
11	NLN	Hereford	H	416	L	0 - 1		
14	NLN	Alfreton Town	A	421	**W**	1 - 0	Guest 90	
18	NLN	York City	A	2192	D	1 - 1	Guest 58	
25	NLN	Kidderminster Harriers	H	353	D	1 - 1	Brooke 37	
27	NLN	Chorley	A	1571	L	0 - 2		
Sept 1	NLN	Nuneaton Borough	H	221	L	0 - 1		
8	NLN	Altrincham	A	955	**W**	2 - 0	Hughes 42 Crankshaw 57	
15	NLN	Brackley Town	H	220	D	1 - 1	Crankshaw 80	15
22	**FAC 2Q**	**Radcliffe**	**A**	**381**	**W**	**2 - 1**	**Guest 24 Cummins 51**	
29	NLN	Boston United	H	305	L	1 - 3	Morgan 18	16
Oct 6	**FAC 3Q**	**Southport**	**H**	**408**	**L**	**1 - 2**	**Morgan 71**	
13	NLN	Leamington	A	705	**W**	1 - 0	Morgan 5 (Pen)	15
20	NLN	AFC Telford United	H	299	**W**	2 - 1	Brooke 4 McJannet 65	10
27	NLN	Spennymoor Town	A	564	D	0 - 0		
30	NLN	Southport	A	580	D	2 - 2	Crankshaw 66 Brooke 72	11
Nov 3	NLN	Stockport County	H	1487	L	0 - 2		11
10	NLN	Bradford Park Avenue	H	314	D	1 - 1	Crankshaw 68	11
17	NLN	Blyth Spartans	A	1146	L	2 - 3	Brooke 23 Crankshaw 32 (Pen)	13
24	**FAT 3Q**	**Basford United**	**A**	**266**	**L**	**1 - 2**		
John Flanagan sacked as manager. Head Coach, Mark Bradshaw, is promoted to the vacant position.								
Dec 8	NLN	FC United of Manchester	A	1645	L	0 - 2		15
22	NLN	Kidderminster Harriers	A	1407	D	1 - 1	Morton 76	
26	NLN	Ashton United	H	457	L	2 - 4	Fawns 27 Shaw 53	
29	NLN	Chorley	H	490	L	0 - 1		
Jan 1	NLN	Ashton United	A	457	**W**	2 - 1	Crankshaw 62 Brooke 66	
5	NLN	York City	H	427	**W**	1 - 0	Shenton 60	
12	NLN	Nuneaton Borough	A	915	**W**	4 - 2	Crankshaw 21 (Pen) Reilly 60 Hunt 77 Wall 90 (Pen)	16
19	NLN	Chester	A	1671	**W**	1 - 0	Crankshaw 76	
26	NLN	Darlington	H	394	D	1 - 1	Reilly 47	
Feb 2	NLN	Hereford	A	2081	**W**	2 - 1	Reilly 64 Miller 88	
9	NLN	Alfreton Town	H	204	**W**	3 - 2	Reilly 48 Reily (og) McAtee 83	
16	NLN	Brackley Town	A	490	L	0 - 2		
23	NLN	Altrincham	H	506	L	0 - 6		13
Mar 2	NLN	Bradford Park Avenue	A	426	D	2 - 2	Brooke 43 McJannet 58	15
4	NLN	Guiseley	H	271	**W**	1 - 0	Reilly 25	12
23	NLN	FC United of Manchester	H	1075	**W**	3 - 1	Miller 39 80 Hunt 49	11
26	NLN	Guiseley	A	420	L	0 - 1		11
30	NLN	Boston United	A	1406	L	1 - 4	Reilly 41	14
Apr 1	NLN	Blyth Spartans	H	218	L	1 - 3	Hunt 49	14
6	NLN	Leamington	H	202	D	1 - 1	McJannett 14	13
13	NLN	AFC Telford United	A	1507	L	1 - 3	Crankshaw 74 (pen)	15
19	NLN	Southport	H	380	L	0 - 3		
22	NLN	Stockport County	A	6001	L	0 - 2		18
27	NLN	Spennymoor Town	H	328	L	0 - 5		18

GOALSCORERS	SG	CSG	Pens	Hat tricks	Total
Crankshaw	9	2	3		9
Brooke	6	1			6
Reilly	6	3			6
Guest	3	2			3
Hunt	3	1			3
McJannet	3	1			3
Miller	2	1			3
Morgan	3	3	1		3
Fawns	2	1			2
Hughes	2	1			2

	SG	CSG	Pens	Hat tricks	Total
Cummins	1	1			1
McAtee	1	1			1
Morton	1	1			1
Opponent	1	1			1
Shaw	1	1			1
Shenton	1	1			1
Wall	1	1	1		1

Mason	Morton	McJannet (L)	Hunt	Shaw	Rowney	Guest	Marshall	Sharp	Fawns	Hughes	Brooke	Ali	Baillie	Crankshaw	McKenzie	Cummins	O'Leary	Samizadeh	Deakin	Morgan	Purdham	Khoury	Wall	Merrill	Muir	Boyles	Balde	Shenton	McAtee (L)	Racchi	Dickin	Reilly (L)	Thornley	Miller	Lindfield	Earing (L)	Deakin	McCoy	Danaher	Senior	Wardle	No.
x	x	x	x	x	x	x	xs	xs	x	xs	sx	sx	sx	s	s																											1
x	x	x	x	x	x	x	xs	xs	xs	x	sx	s	s	sx	sx																											2
x		x	x	x	x	x	xs		xs	x	xs	s	x	sx	sx	sx	s																									3
x	xs	x	x	x	x	x	x		s	xs	x	s	x	sx		s		sx																								4
x	x	x	x	x	xs	x	xs		s	x	x	sx	xs	sx		s		sx																								5
x	x		x	x	x	x	xs		s	x	xs	sx		s		sx	x	xs	sx																							6
x	x	x	x	x	x	x			sx	x	xs	xs		sx		sx	s	xs	s																							7
x	x	x	x	x	x	x	xs		sx	x	xs	s	s	sx		sx		xs																								8
x	x	x	x	x	xs	x	sx		sx	xs		s	sx	x		x	s	xs																								9
x	x		x	s	xs	x	sx		s	x		xs	sx	x		x	x	xs		sx																						10
x						x										x																										11
x	x	x	x	s	sx	x	xs		s	xs	sx	x		x		xs		sx		x																						12
xs	xs	x	x	s	x	x	x		x	s	sx	x	sx	s		xs		s		x	sx																					13
		x	x	x	x	x			sx	xs	xs	sx	x	x		sx	s			xs	x	s																				14
x		x	x	x	x	x			s	xs	xs	sx	x	xs		sx	s			x		sx																				15
x		x	x	x	x	x			sx	xs		x	x	xs		x					s	sx	s	s																		16
x		x	x	x	x	x			s	x	x	sx	xs	xs		sx				xs		sx	s																			17
x	x	x	x	x	xs	x			s	x	x	x		sx		s				x		s	s																			18
x	x		x		x				x	xs	x	x		xs		x	x					sx	sx	s	s	s																19
x	x		x	sx	xs	x			xs	x	x	x		x		sx	x			s		s	s																			20
																																										21
																																										22
x	x	x	x	s	xs	x			sx		xs	x		x		sx	x						sx	s			xs															23
x	x	x	x	x	x	x			xs		xs			x			s					sx	s	xs				sx	sx													24
x	x	x	x	x	x	x			x		x											xs	s	s	s			sx		x	s											25
x	x	x	x	x	x	x			x		x			sx								s	xs		s			sx		xs	s											26
x	x	x	x	xs	x	x					x	x		xs			s					s	x		s			sx		sx												27
x		xs	x		x				s		x	x		x									x					x	s	sx		xs	x	sx	s							28
x		x	x		x				s		x	x		x									x					sx	sx			xs	x	s	s	xs						29
x		x	x		x				s		x	x		x									x					sx	s			xs	x	sx	s	xs						30
x		x	x		xs				sx		xs	x		x									xs					sx	sx			x	x	s	s	x						31
x		x	x		xs						x	x		x									x	s				s	sx			xs	x	sx		xs	sx					32
x		x	x		xs							xs		x			xs						x	s				s	x			x	x	sx		sx	sx					33
x		x	x	x							s			x									x					sx	xs	xs		xs	x	x			sx	s	sx			34
x		x	x	x	sx						x			xs									xs	s				sx	xs			x	x	x			sx		s			35
x		x	x	s	x						x			x									x					s	sx			xs	x	x			s		s	x		36
x		x	x	sx	x						xs			x									xs					s	sx			xs	x	x			sx		s	x		37
x		x	x	x	x						x			xs									xs		s			sx	sx			xs	x	x			sx		s			38
x		x	x	s	xs						x			x									xs					s	sx			xs	x	x			sx			x	sx	39
x		xs	x	sx	x						xs									sx			x					xs	sx			x	x	x			s			x	s	40
x		s	x	x	xs						x									sx			x					xs	sx			x	x				xs	s		x	sx	41
x		x	x	sx	x						xs									s			xs					sx	x			x	x				xs	s		x	sx	42
x		x	x	s	x						x			x						sx		sx	xs	s					xs				x				sx			x	xs	43
x			x	x	x						xs			xs								sx	x	sx					x				x	sx			s	s		xs	x	44
x		x	x	s	x						xs											sx	xs	x					xs				x	sx			sx	s		x	x	45
x					x						x			xs			x					sx	x	x	s			s	x				x	sx			xs	s		x		
42	17	34	42	22	29	24	2	0	5	10	20	13	5	18	0	5	6	0	0	4	1	0	12	2	0	0	0	1	4	1	0	6	19	7	0	1	0	0	0	9	2	x
1	2	2	0	1	11	0	7	2	4	8	14	3	2	9	0	2	1	5	0	2	0	1	9	1	0	0	1	2	4	2	0	9	0	0	0	3	3	0	0	1	1	xs
0	0	0	0	4	2	0	2	0	7	0	4	6	4	8	2	9	0	3	1	4	1	9	2	1	0	0	0	11	10	2	0	0	0	7	0	1	9	0	1	0	3	sx
0	0	1	0	8	0	0	0	0	11	1	1	5	2	3	1	3	7	1	1	2	1	5	6	8	6	1	0	6	2	0	2	0	0	2	4	0	3	6	4	0	1	s

x - Played full 90 minutes
xs - Substituted off
sx - Substituted on
s - Non-playing Substitute

DARLINGTON UNITED MATCH RESULTS 2018-19

Date	Comp	Opponents	H/A	Att:	Result	Goalscorers	Pos
Aug 4	NLN	Curzon Ashton	H	1488	L 1 - 2	Ainge 13	
7	NLN	Spennymoor Town	A	1768	D 2 - 2	Thompson 17 (Pen) Styche 39	
11	NLN	Brackley Town	A	570	**W** 4 - 2	Styche 2 21 23 Ainge 27	
15	NLN	Blyth Spartans	H	1631	D 1 - 1	Styche 41	
18	NLN	Kidderminster Harriers	A	1522	L 2 - 5	Ainge 53 Nicholson 69	
25	NLN	Altrincham	H	1450	L 0 - 3		
27	NLN	Ashton United	A	456	D 2 - 2	Thompson 54 (Pen) Saunders 76	
Sept 1	NLN	Alfreton Town	H	1269	L 0 - 1		
8	NLN	AFC Telford United	H	1212	**W** 3 - 0	Nicholson 35 Saunders 78 Thompson 90 (Pen)	
15	NLN	Southport	A	1019	D 0 - 0		17
22	**FAC 2Q**	**Bradford Park Avenue**	**H**	**1037**	**L 0 - 1**		
29	NLN	Stockport County	H	1507	L 0 - 1		19
Oct 13	NLN	FC United of Manchester	A	1978	**W** 2 - 1	Saunders 16 48	16
20	NLN	Boston United	H	1860	**W** 1 - 0	Willis 11 (og)	13
27	NLN	Leamington	A	765	D 2 - 2	Ainge 18 Saunders 32	
30	NLN	Bradford Park Avenue	A	625	D 2 - 2	Nicholson 2 18	14
Nov 3	NLN	Guiseley	H	1307	D 0 - 0		14
17	NLN	Hereford	H	2211	D 2 - 2	Syers 53 Nicholson 84	14
23	**FAT 3Q**	**AFC Telford United**	**H**	**770**	**L 0 - 2**		
Dec 1	NLN	Chester	A	1934	L 1 - 3	Wheatley 56	17
8	NLN	Nuneaton Borough	H	1064	L 1 - 2	Nicholson 60 CHECK SUBS	17
15	NLN	Chorley	A	737	L 2 - 3	Nelson 39 85	17
22	NLN	Altrincham	A	1076	D 3 - 3	Elliott T 8 Saunders 25 Nicholson 44	
26	NLN	York City	H	2286	**W** 5 - 1	Nelson 31 52 (Pen) Saunders 37 Nicholson 61 Hughes 80	
29	NLN	Ashton United	H	1407	**W** 2 - 1	Nelson 37 83	
Jan 1	NLN	York City	A	3265	L 0 - 4		
5	NLN	Kidderminster Harriers	H	1123	**W** 3 - 0	Thompson 11 Smith 50 Nicholson 52	
12	NLN	Alfreton Town	A	648	D 0 - 0		13
19	NLN	Spennymoor Town	H	1664	L 1 - 2	Thompson 17 (Pen)	
26	NLN	Curzon Ashton	A	394	D 1 - 1	Elliott T 70	
Feb 9	NLN	Blyth Spartans	A	1579	**W** 1 - 0	Thompson 35 (Pen)	
16	NLN	Southport	H	1462	D 0 - 0		
20	NLN	Brackley Town	H	915	L 0 - 2		16
Mar 2	NLN	Chorley	H	1213	D 1 - 1	Kneeshaw 41	16
5	NLN	AFC Telford United	A	1052	L 1 - 3	Saunders 88	16
9	NLN	Hereford	A	2294	L 2 - 4	Elliott T 11 Thompson 37	17
23	NLN	Nuneaton Borough	A	620	**W** 2 - 1	Thompson 13 Nicholson 48	18
27	NLN	Chester	H	1116	L 0 - 1		17
30	NLN	Stockport County	A	4807	L 0 - 2		18
Apr 6	NLN	FC United of Manchester	H	1407	**W** 2 - 0	Holness 42 Thompson 59	18
13	NLN	Boston United	A	1035	**W** 2 - 0	Elliott C 58 Jackson 60	18 (s)
19	NLN	Bradford Park Avenue	H	1310	**W** 1 - 0	Thompson 80	
22	NLN	Guiseley	A	1258	L 0 - 1		16
27	NLN	Leamington	H	1145	D 1 - 1	Nicholson 43	16

GOALSCORERS	SG	CSG	Pens	Hat tricks	Total
Nicholson	10	2			11
Thompson	10	2	5		10
Saunders	7	2			8
Nelson*	3	2	1		6
Styche	3	3		1	5
Ainge	4	1			4
Elliott T	3	1			3
Elliott C	1	1			1
Holness	1	1			1
Hughes	1	1			1
Jackson	1	1			1
Kneeshaw	1	1			1
Opponent	1	1			1
Smith	1	1			1
Syers	1	1			1
Wheatley	1	1			1

No.	Madison	Trotman	O'Hanlon	Hughes	Collins	Galbraith	Elliott T	Wheatley	Styche	Ainge	Nicholson	Henshall	Saunders	Syers	Bancroft	Vaulks	Thompson	Burn J	Dunn	Glover	Banks	Morrison	Kaba	Burn A	Lycett	Alderson	Stansfield	Hall	Lingthep	Hemming (L)	Kokolo (L)	Wollerton (L)	Nelson (L)	Smith (L)	Palmer	Muggleton (L)	Kneeshaw	Turner (L)	Holness	Jackson	Elliott C	Bascome
1	x	x	x	xs	x	x	x	x	x	x	xs	sx	sx	s	s	s																										
2	x	x	x		x	x	x	x	xs	xs	sx	xs	sx	sx	s	s	x																									
3	x	x		sx	x	x	x	x	xs	x	sx	xs	sx	s		s	xs	x																								
4	x	x	s	s	x	x	x	x	x	x	s	xs	s	sx			x	x																								
5	x	x	sx	sx	xs	x	x	x	x	xs	sx	xs	s	s			x	x																								
6	x	x	x	xs	sx	xs	x		x	x	x		sx	sx			x	x	s	s																						
7	x	x	x	s			x		x	x	x		x	x	s		x	x		s	s	s																				
8	x	x		x			x		x	x	x		x	x	s		x	x		s	s	s	s																			
9	x	x	x	x			x	xs			x	s	x	x			x	x		sx		s		s	s																	
10	x	x	x	x		s	x		x		x	xs	sx	x			x	x		s		s		s																		
11	**x**	**x**	**x**	**x**		**x**	**x**		**x**	**x**	**xs**	**xs**	**sx**	**sx**			**x**			**s**				**s**	**s**	**s**	**s**															
12	x	x	x	x		x	x	x	x	sx	sx		xs	xs		s	x			s				s																		
13	x	x	x	x		x	x	x		xs	sx	xs	x	s			x	sx		s								sx														
14	x	x		x		x	x	x		x	x	xs	xs	sx			xs	s		s	sx			sx																		
15	x	x		x		x	xs	x		x	x	xs	x	sx			x	sx		s								s	s													
16		x		x		x	x	x		xs	x	sx	x	sx			xs	x		s							s	s		x												
17		x		x		x	x	x		x	x	x	x	s			x			s				s				s	s	x												
18	s	x	x	x		x	x	x		sx	x	s	xs	x			x	s		s										x												
19	**s**	**x**	**xs**	**x**		**x**	**x**	**xs**		**xs**	**x**	**sx**	**sx**	**x**			**x**	**s**		**sx**										**x**												
20	x	x	s	x		x	x	x			x	xs	x				x			s				x			s	s	sx													
21	x	x	x			x	x	x			x		x				x	x		s		s		s	s				s		x											
22	x	x				x		x			x		xs				x	x													xs	x	x									
23	x	x	sx			x	x				xs	s	x				sx	x										s			xs		x	x	x							
24	x	x	x	x		x	x				x	s	xs				sx							s				s				sx	xs	x	x							
25	x	x	x	x		x	x				xs	sx	xs				sx							s							s	s	x	x	x							
26	x	x	sx	xs		x	x	x		s	sx		x				sx														xs	s	xs	x	x							
27	x	x		x		x	x	x		sx	xs		xs				x	s										s			x	sx		x	sx							
28	x	x	s			x	x	x		x	x	sx	x				x	s		s								s			xs			x								
29	x	x	x			x	x	x		x	x	sx	xs				x	s		s								s			s			x								
30	x	x				x	x	xs		x	xs	sx	x				x														sx			x	x							
31	x	x	sx	x		x	x	sx		x	xs	s	sx				xs																	x	x	xs	s					
32	x	x	sx	x		xs	x	s		x	xs		sx				x											s						x	s	xs	sx					
33	x	x	x	x			x	xs		xs	x	xs	sx				x			s											s			x	sx		sx					
34	s	x		s		x	x	x		x	sx	sx	x				xs														sx			x	xs		xs	x				
35	s	x				x	x	x		x		s	x				x			s											s			x	x		xs	x				
36	s	x				x	x			x	xs	x	sx				x			s									s		s			x	x		x	x				
37	s	x				x	x			x	x	xs	sx				x	s																	x		xs	x	x	sx	s	
38	s	x				x	x			x	x	s	x				x																		x		x	x	x	s	s	s
39	s	x				x	x			x	x	sx	xs				x	s																	x		xs	x		x	sx	sx
40	s					x	x	sx		x	xs	sx	xs				x																		x		xs	x	x	x	sx	s
41		x				x	xs			x	xs	xs	sx				x	s																	x		sx	x	x	x	sx	s
42	s	x				x	sx			x	x		sx				x	s																	xs		xs	x	x	x	x	s
43	s	x				x	xs	sx		x	xs	sx	xs				x	s																				x	x	x	x	sx
44		x				xs	x	xs		x	x		xs				x					s					sx	s	sx									x	x	x	sx	
x	29	43	15	19	4	36	39	21	9	26	23	2	16	6	0	0	34	12	0	0	0	0	0	1	0	0	0	0	0	4	2	1	3	14	13	0	2	11	7	6	2	0
xs	0	0	1	3	1	3	3	5	2	6	12	13	12	1	0	0	5	0	0	0	0	0	0	0	0	0	0	0	0	0	4	0	2	0	2	2	6	0	0	0	0	0
sx	0	0	5	2	1	0	1	3	0	3	7	11	14	7	0	0	4	2	0	2	1	0	0	1	0	0	1	1	2	0	2	2	0	0	2	0	3	0	0	1	4	2
s	1	0	3	3	0	1	0	1	0	1	1	7	2	5	4	4	0	11	1	19	2	6	1	8	3	1	3	11	4	0	5	2	0	0	1	0	1	0	0	1	2	4

x - Played full 90 minutes
xs - Substituted off
sx - Substituted on
s - Non-playing Substitute

FC UNITED OF MANCHESTER MATCH RESULTS 2018-19

Date	Comp	Opponents	H/A	Att:	Result		Goalscorers	Pos
Aug 4	NLN	Stockport County	A	4577	L	1 - 5	Willoughby 72	
7	NLN	Ashton United	H	1562	L	3 - 4	Willoughby 19 Winter 31 Banister 32	
11	NLN	Boston United	H	1686	L	0 - 3		
14	NLN	Altrincham	A	1704	W	2 - 1	Dickinson 65 Willoughby 81	
25	NLN	Leamington	H	1727	L	0 - 2		
27	NLN	Spennymoor Town	A	863	L	0 - 2		
Tom Greaves resigns as Manager with Dave Chadwick taking temporary charge.								
Sept 2	NLN	Bradford Park Avenue	H	1814	D	2 - 2	Litchfield 62 Willoughby 90 (Pen)	
8	NLN	Southport	H	1967	D	1 - 1	Willoughby 35	
11	NLN	Chester	A	2045	D	0 - 0		
15	NLN	Guiseley	A	907	L	0 - 3		
22	**FAC 2Q**	**Colne**	**H**	**1130**	**W**	**2 - 0**	**Donohue 2 Willoughby 39**	
29	NLN	Nuneaton Borough	A	638	L	0 - 1		22
Oct 6	**FAC 3Q**	**Witton Albion**	**H**	**1234**	**L**	**1 - 2**	**Banister 32**	
13	NLN	Darlington	H	1978	L	1 - 2	Brierley 12	22
20	NLN	Kidderminster Harriers	A	1860	W	2 - 1	Banister 19 32	21
Neil Reynolds is appointed new manager.								
27	NLN	Brackley Town	H	1858	D	1 - 1	Potts 30	
30	NLN	Alfreton Town	H	1531	D	1 - 1	Wallen 20	20
Nov 3	NLN	Blyth Spartans	A	832	W	3 - 0	Willoughby 19 Peers 21 Mansell 90	19
10	NLN	Hereford	A	259	W	3 - 1	Peers 24 Smith H 27 (og) Willoughby 29	18
17	NLN	AFC Telford United	H	964	L	1 - 2	Peers 28	19
24	**FAT 3Q**	**Hereford**	**A**	**1067**	**L**	**1 - 3**	**Banister 15**	
Dec 1	NLN	York City	A	2583	L	0 - 2		20
8	NLN	Curzon Ashton	H	1645	W	2 - 0	Wallen 2 Willoughby 65	18
22	NLN	Leamington	A	725	D	2 - 2	Wallen 31 Willoughby 45	
26	NLN	Chorley	H	2366	L	1 - 4	Lynch 14	
29	NLN	Spennymoor Town	H	2069	L	1 - 3	Potts 23	
Jan 1	NLN	Chorley	A	2021	L	0 - 4		
5	NLN	Chester	H	2260	L	0 - 2		
12	NLN	Bradford Park Avenue	A	713	W	3 - 2	Sharp 45 Banister 64 Willoughby 65	20
19	NLN	Ashton United	A	845	L	0 - 1		
26	NLN	Stockport County	H	2987	L	1 - 2	Willoughby 9	
Feb 2	NLN	Boston United	A	1070	L	1 - 2	Sharp 8	
9	NLN	Altrincham	H	2215	L	1 - 2	Whitham 77	
16	NLN	Guiseley	H	1775	D	3 - 3	Willoughby 28 76 (pen) Peers 83	
23	NLN	Southport	A	1665	D	0 - 0		21
Mar 2	NLN	Hereford	H	2058	D	2 - 2	Sharp 11 Willoughby 90	21
9	NLN	AFC Telford United	A	1672	W	3 - 1	McHale 35 Willoughby 53 Peers 60	20
23	NLN	Curzon Ashton	A	1075	L	1 - 3	Willoughby 11	20
26	NLN	York City	H	1670	D	3 - 3	Whitham 9 37 Willoughby 48	20
30	NLN	Nuneaton Borough	H	1697	L	0 - 4		20
Apr 6	NLN	Darlington	A	1407	L	0 - 2		21
13	NLN	Kidderminster Harriers	H	1760	L	0 - 1		21
20	NLN	Alfreton Town	A	733	W	3 - 2	Myers 11 Willoughby 36 Baird 78	20
22	NLN	Blyth Spartans	H	1971	L	1 - 2	Bannister 87	20 (R)
27	NLN	Brackley Town	A	935	L	0 - 1		21

GOALSCORERS	SG	CSG	Pens	Hat tricks	Total
Willoughby	18	4	2		19
Bannister	6	2			7
Peers	5	2			5
Sharp	3	1			3
Wallen	3	2			3
Whitham	2	1			3
Potts	2	1			2
Baird	1	1			1
Brierley	1	1			1
Dickinson	1	1			1
Donohue	1	1			1
Litchfield	1	1			1
Lynch	1	1			1
Mansell	1	1			1
McHale*	1	1			1
Myers	1	1			1
Opponent	1	1			1
Winter	1	1			1

Cellin (L)	Senior	O'Halloran	Baird	Lynch	Banister	Winter	Dickinson	Willoughby	Logan	Tattum	Crawford	Litchfield	Greaves	Racchi	Ashworth	Simoes	Kay	Palinkas	Donohue	Carnell	Thompson (L)	Jones	Mansell (L)	Priestly (L)	Brierley	Lonsdale	Perrin (L)	Grimshaw	Allinson	Potts	Wallen	Peers	Milligan	White	Richards (L)	Sharp	Morton	Jallow	Mohammed (L)	Sass-Davies (L)	Whitham (L)	Fisher (L)	Harris	Myers	No.
x	xs	x	x	x	x	x	xs	x	x	sx	sx	s	s																																1
x	s	x	s	x	xs	x	xs	x	sx	x	xs	sx	sx	x	x																														2
x	x	x	sx	xs	s	x	sx	x		xs	x	s	x	x	x	s																													3
x	sx	x	x	x	s		x	x		x	x	s	xs	x	s		x	s																											4
x	s	x	x	x	s	sx	x	x	sx	x	xs	xs	sx	xs			x																												5
x		x	x	x	x	xs	s	x	xs	x	sx	s	x			sx	x																												6
x	xs	x	x	x	s			x	xs	sx	sx	x			x	s	x		x																										7
		x	x	xs	sx		s	x	s	x	s	sx					x		x	x	x	x	xs																						8
		x	x		s		sx	x	s	x	sx	s					x		xs	x	x	x	xs	x																					9
	x	x	x		s	xs	sx	x	sx	s		xs							x	x	xs	x		x																					10
		x		x	x	x		x	xs			sx				sx	x		x	x	x	sx		x																					11
	sx	x		xs	sx	x		x	s		x	sx								x	x	x		xs	xs	s																			12
		x		x	x	x		x		x	xs					sx			xs	xs	x	x	sx				sx																		13
	xs	x		x	x					x	sx							sx	x		x	xs	x		xs	s	x	s																	14
	x	x		x	x						sx					xs			x		x				x	x	s		x																15
	x	x			x						sx					x		s	x		x		xs	x	s		s		x	x	x														16
	x	x	s	x	s			x			sx					xs			xs		x		x		sx	s			x	x	x														17
	x	x	s	x	sx			x			sx					sx			xs		x		sx						x	x	x	xs	s												18
	x	x	s	x	sx			x			sx					xs			x		x		sx						x	x	x	xs	s												19
	x	x	s	x	sx			xs								x			sx		x	s							x	x	x	x	sx	xs											20
	x	x		x	xs			x			sx					x													x	xs	x	xs	sx	x											21
	x	x	s	x	sx			x								x									sx				x	x	xs	xs	s	sx	x										22
	x	x		x	sx			xs								xs		s	xs						s				x	x	x	x		sx	x	sx									23
	x	x		x	sx			x										s	xs						s				x	x	x	xs	s	sx	x	x									24
	x	x		x	s			x								xs		s	xs						s				x	x	x	sx	s	sx	x	x									25
	x	x		xs	s	x		sx										sx	xs										x	x	xs	x	s	sx	x	x									26
		x		x	s	x		x								xs		xs	xs										x	x	sx	x	s	s	x	sx									27
		x		x	x	x		x								x		s	sx						s				x	s	xs				xs	x	x	sx							28
	s	x			xs	x		x			sx					xs		s							sx				x	sx	x					xs	x		x	x					29
	sx	x			x	x		x			s							s											x		xs					x	xs		x	x	xs				30
	x	x			x	x		x										s	xs										x		xs					sx		s	x	x	x				31
		xs			xs			x			s							s	x										x		x	sx				xs	x		x	x	x				32
				sx		xs		x											x										s		sx	x				sx	x		x	x	x	x	xs	xs	33
	s	x		x	x	x		x											sx										sx		s	sx				xs	x		xs	x	x	x			34
		x		x	s	s		x											xs										s		x	xs				s	x		s	x	x	x	x		35
		x		x	sx	sx		x											sx										s		x	x				xs	x		s	x	xs	x	xs		36
		x		x	xs	x		xs											x									sx	s		x	sx				s	x		x			x		sx	37
		x		x	x	x		xs											xs												x	sx				s	x		x		sx	x	s	sx	38
		x		x	x	x		x											sx												sx	s				sx	x		x		xs	x	s	xs	39
		x		s	x			x											sx									s			xs	sx				sx	xs		x		x	x	x	x	40
		x		x	sx			x										x	sx									x		x	s	x				s			x			x		sx	41
		x		x	x			x										xs	sx									x		xs		s				s		sx	x			x		x	42
		x	x		x			x	sx										xs									sx		x		x				xs		sx	x			x		xs	43
		x	x	s	x	sx		x	sx										xs									s		x		xs				x		sx	x			x		xs	44
		xs	x	x	sx	x		x	s										sx									s		x		sx				xs		xs	x			x		x	45
7	15	42	11	30	17	17	2	37	1	8	3	1	2	3	3	5	7	1	11	5	12	5	2	4	1	1	1	2	18	15	15	8	0	1	6	6	10	0	14	8	6	13	2	3	x
0	3	2	0	4	5	3	2	4	3	1	3	2	1	1	0	7	0	2	14	1	1	1	3	1	2	0	0	0	0	2	6	7	0	1	1	6	2	1	1	0	3	0	2	4	xs
0	3	0	1	1	11	3	3	1	5	2	12	4	2	0	0	4	0	2	9	0	0	1	3	0	3	0	1	2	1	1	3	7	2	5	0	6	0	4	0	0	1	0	0	3	sx
0	4	0	6	2	11	1	2	0	4	1	3	5	1	0	1	2	0	10	0	0	0	1	0	0	5	3	2	4	4	1	2	2	7	1	0	5	0	1	2	0	0	0	2	0	s

Also Played: Barnes - 04/08 (xs). Dempsey - 04/08 (sx). Affleck - 27/08 (s) 02/09 (s) 20/10 (s). Egan - 15/09 (sx) 20/10 (sx). Bongwanga - 13/10 (sx) 20/10 (s) 27/10 (sx) 20/04 (s). Healey - 20/10 (xs). Roache - 24/11 (sx) 01/12 (xs). Hmami (L) - 19/01 (sx) 26/01 (sx) 02/02 (sx). McGiveron - 19/01 (sx) 26/01 (sx) 02/02 (sx) 09/02 (s). McHale - 09/03 (xs) 23/03 (xs) 26/03 (xs) 30/03 (xs). Ozono - 06/04 (xs) 13/04 (sx) 20/04 (s). West - 06/04 (xs) 13/04 (xs).

x - Played full 90 minutes
xs - Substituted off
sx - Substituted on
s - Non-playing Substitute

GUISELEY MATCH RESULTS 2018-19

Date	Comp	Opponents	H/A	Att:	Result		Goalscorers	Pos
Aug 4	NLN	Boston United	A	1231	L	0 - 1		
7	NLN	Chorley	H	701	L	0 - 2		
11	NLN	AFC Telford United	H	504	D	1 - 1	Morrison 90	
14	NLN	Stockport County	A	2923	D	1 - 1	Felix 22	
18	NLN	Leamington	A	485	D	2 - 2	Clayton 47 Liburd 89	
25	NLN	Nuneaton Borough	H	528	**W**	2 - 1	Purver 66 Felix 90+3	
27	NLN	Altrincham	A	1149	D	1 - 1	Halls 71	
Sept 1	NLN	Chester	H	806	D	1 - 1	Garner 87	
8	NLN	Alfreton Town	A	634	**W**	1 - 0	Liburd 11	
15	NLN	FC United of Manchester	H	907	**W**	3 - 0	Hatfield 28 Liburd 47 62	10
22	**FAC 2Q**	**Staveley Miners Welfare**	**A**	**437**	**W**	**4 - 0**	**Smith 35 James 53 70 90**	
29	NLN	York City	A	2331	L	2 - 4	James 3 Smith 84	13
Oct 6	**FAC 3Q**	**Cleethorpes Town**	**A**	**255**	**D**	**2 - 2**	**Hatfield 62 James 67**	
9	**FAC 3Qr**	**Cleethorpes Town**	**H**	**384**	**W**	**2 - 1**	**Hatfield 58 (pen) Odejayi 76**	
13	NLN	Brackley Town	H	751	**W**	2 - 1	James 9 Clayton 88	10
20	**FAC 4Q**	**Stourbridge**	**H**	**633**	**W**	**3 - 1**	**Thornton 28 Walters 75 Felix 80**	
27	NLN	Kidderminster Harriers	H	697	D	0 - 0		
30	NLN	Blyth Spartans	H	613	L	1 - 3	James 19 (Pen)	13
Nov 3	NLN	Darlington	A	1307	D	0 - 0		13
6	NLN	Ashton United	A	218	L	0 - 1		14
11	**FAC 1P**	**Cambridge United**	**H**	**1097**	**W**	**4 - 3**	**Hatfield 25 Moyo 40 Felix 48 James 55**	
17	NLN	Spennymoor Town	H	2090	D	1 - 1	Liburd 59	15
24	**FAT 3Q**	**Lancaster City**	**A**	**259**	**D**	**2 - 2**	**Liburd 26 Thorton 90+3**	
Dec 3	**FAC 2P**	**Fleetwood Town**	**H**	**2324**	**L**	**1 - 2**	**Purver 33**	
11	**FAT 3Qr**	**Lancaster City**	**H**		**L**	**1 - 2**	**Liburd 9**	
22	NLN	Nuneaton Borough	A	872	**W**	3 - 1	Liburd 2 48 Felix 64	
26	NLN	Bradford Park Avenue	H	1150	L	1 - 5	Purver 64	
29	NLN	Altrincham	H	791	D	2 - 2	Heaton 73 Hatfield 84	
Jan 1	NLN	Bradford Park Avenue	A	665	**W**	2 - 1	Odejayi 45 Liburd 70	
5	NLN	Leamington	H	683	D	1 - 1	Odejayi 18	
8	NLN	Southport	A	701	L	0 - 1		
12	NLN	Chester	A	1759	D	1 - 1	Odejayi 19	18
19	NLN	Chorley	A	1314	L	0 - 3		
22	NLN	Hereford	H	481	D	1 - 1	Odejayi 26	
26	NLN	Boston United	H	725	L	4 - 5	Odejayi 18 90 Liburd 20 47	
Feb 9	NLN	Stockport County	H	1296	D	1 - 1	Cantrill 56	
12	NLN	AFC Telford United	A	900	D	1 - 1	Smith 50	
16	NLN	FC United of Manchester	A	1775	D	3 - 3	Heaton 15 Liburd 33 Hatfield 66	
23	NLN	Alfreton Town	H	402	L	0 - 1		19
Mar 2	NLN	Southport	H	761	L	0 - 1		19
4	NLN	Curzon Ashton	A	271	L	0 - 1		19
23	NLN	Hereford	A	2261	L	0 - 1		19
26	NLN	Curzon Ashton	H	420	**W**	1 - 0	Purver 76	19
30	NLN	York City	H	1304	D	1 - 1	James 77	19
Apr 2	NLN	Spennymoor Town	A	603	L	2 - 3	Garner 26 Hatfield 70	19
6	NLN	Brackley Town	A	585	L	0 - 2		19
13	NLN	Ashton United	H	655	D	1 - 1	James 79 (pen)	19
19	NLN	Blyth Spartans	A	915	L	0 - 2		19
22	NLN	Darlington	H	1258	**W**	1 - 0	Felix 17	19 (s)
27	NLN	Kidderminster Harriers	A	1354	**W**	2 - 1	Halls 44 (pen) Dyche 68	19

GOALSCORERS	SG	CSG	Pens	Hat tricks	Total
Liburd	9	2			12
James	8	3	2	1	10
Hatfield	7	2	1		7
Odejayi	6	2			7
Felix	6	1			6
Purver	4	1			4
Smith	3	2			3
Clayton	2	1			2
Garner	2	1			2
Halls	2	1	1		2
Heaton	2	1			2
Thorton	2	1			2
Cantrill	1	1			1
Dyche	1	1			1
Morrison	1	1			1
Moyo	1	1			1
Walters	1	1			1

No.	Green	Moyo	Heaton	James	Garner	Halls	Purver	Hatfield	Liburd	Clayton	Thompson	Odejayi	Felix	Morrison	Dyche	Thornton	Worsnop	Kennedy	Smith Scott	Hussain	Walters	Harvey	Newall	Hogg	Young	Cummings (L)	Walsh (L)	Dewhurst (L)	Cantrill (L)	Langley (L)	Ceesay	Starčenko	Digie	Francis	Boateng	Barkers	Archer	Fowler (L)
1	x	x	x	x	x	x	xs	x	x	xs	xs	sx	sx	sx	s	s																						
2	x	x	x	x	x	x	xs	xs	xs	sx	x	x	sx	sx	s	s																						
3		x	x	xs	x	x	xs	x	x	sx	xs	s	x	sx	sx	s	x																					
4		x	x	x	x	x	sx	xs	s	s	s	x	x	x	x	s	x																					
5		x	x	x	x		x		sx	xs	x	sx	xs	xs	sx	x	x	s	s																			
6	x	x	x	x	x	x	sx		x	s	xs	sx	x		xs	s		xs		sx																		
7	x	x	x	x	x	x	x	s	x	sx	sx	x	x		xs	s				s																		
8	x	x	x	x	x	x	x	s	x	sx		xs	x		x	s			s	s																		
9	x	x	x	x	x	x	x	sx	x	s					s	x		s	sx		xs	xs																
10	x	xs	x	x		x	x	x	x	s					s	x		sx	sx	sx	xs	xs																
11	x	xs	x	x		x	x	x	xs	sx					sx		s	x	x	sx		xs	s	s	s													
12	x	x	x	x		x	x	xs		x		s		sx	s	x		xs	sx		sx	xs																
13	x	x	x	x		x	x	x		s		x		s	s	x	s		x		s	x			s													
14	x	x	x	xs		x	x	x		s		x		sx		x	s		xs	s	sx	x			s													
15	x	x	x	x		x	x	x		sx		xs	sx	sx	s	x			xs		s	xs																
16	x	x	x	xs		x	x	x		s		x	sx	xs	s	x	s		s		sx	x				s												
17	x	x	x	s			x	x		sx		xs	x	s		x	s		s		x	x				x												
18	x	x	x	x		s	x	xs		sx		xs	sx	x		x			sx		xs	s				x												
19	x	x	x	x		x	x	x		x		s	x	s		x					sx	s				s	xs											
20	x	x	x	x		x	x	x		xs		sx	xs	s		x					sx	s				s	x											
21	x	x	x	x		x	xs	x	xs	s		sx	x	s		x	s				sx	sx				s	xs											
22		x	x	x		x	x	x	x	sx			x	s		s	x		s		x	s				x												
23	s	x	x	x		x	xs	xs	x	sx			x			x	x		s		xs	sx					sx											
24	x	x	x	x		xs	x	xs	x	sx			xs	s		x	s		s		sx	s				x	sx											
25	s	x	x	x			xs	sx	x	sx				sx		xs	x		s		x						xs											
26	x	xs	x	x		x	x	x	x	s		s	xs	sx					x			s				x	sx											
27	x		x	xs		x	x	x	x	sx		s	x			sx			xs		s	xs				x	sx											
28	s		x	x		x	x	x	x	s		sx	xs			x			x		sx	s					xs	x										
29	s	x	x	x		x	x	x	x	s		x	sx			x			xs		s						s	x										
30	s	x	x	x		x	x		xs	sx		xs	x	sx		x			xs		sx		s					x										
31	s	xs	x	x		x	x		x	sx		xs	x	sx		x			xs		sx		s					x										
32	s	xs	x			x	sx		x	s		x	xs	x		sx				s								x	x	x								
33			x	x		x	x		x	sx		xs	xs	x		sx	s		sx									x	x	xs	s							
34		x	xs	x		x	sx	x	sx	x		x	xs	s		sx			s									x	x	xs								
35		x	x	s		x	x	x	x	sx		x		sx		xs	s		xs									x	x			s						
36		x	x	x		x		x	xs	sx		x																x	x	x			x					
37		x	x	sx		x	x	s	x	s		x		s		sx			xs									x	x	xs			x					
38		x	x	xs	x		sx	x	x	s		x		s		sx			x									x	x				xs	s				
39		x	x		x		x	x	x	sx		xs		xs	sx	s												x	x				xs	sx	s			
40		x	x		x	x	x	xs	x	sx		xs	xs	s	sx													x	s				x	sx				
41		s	x		x	x		sx	x	s		s	x	xs	x													x	x	x		sx				xs		
42		xs		sx	x	x	sx			sx		s	x	xs	x													x	x	x			s			xs	x	
43		sx		x	x	x	x			s		sx	xs	sx	xs													x	x	x			s			x	xs	
44				x	x	x	x	sx				x	xs	sx	xs	s												x	x	x			s			xs		sx
45		x		x	x	x	xs	sx				x	xs	sx	s													x	x	x			s			xs		sx
46		x	x	x	x	x	x	xs					xs	sx	s	sx												x		x			s			s		x
47		x		x	x	x	x	x		s		x	x		s		s											x	x	x			s					s
48		x		xs	x	x	x	xs		sx		xs	x		sx	s												x	x	x			s					sx
49		x		x	x	x	x	x		sx		xs	xs		sx	s	s											x	x				x					s
50		x	s	x		x	x	x					xs	s	x	xs												x	x			s	x			sx	sx	
x	21	38	41	36	21	43	35	25	24	3	2	16	17	4	5	19	6	1	5	0	3	4	0	0	0	6	1	23	17	10	0	0	5	0	0	1	1	1
xs	0	6	1	6	0	1	7	9	5	3	3	11	15	5	4	3	0	2	8	0	4	6	0	0	0	0	4	0	0	3	0	0	2	0	0	4	1	0
sx	0	1	0	2	0	0	6	5	2	23	1	7	6	15	7	7	0	1	5	3	10	2	0	0	0	0	4	0	0	0	0	1	0	2	0	1	1	3
s	7	1	1	2	0	1	0	3	1	17	1	7	0	12	11	12	11	2	9	4	4	7	3	1	3	4	1	0	1	0	1	2	7	1	1	1	0	2

x - Played full 90 minutes
xs - Substituted off
sx - Substituted on
s - Non-playing Substitute

HEREFORD MATCH RESULTS 2018-19

Date	Comp	Opponents	H/A	Att:	Result		Goalscorers	Pos
Aug 4	NLN	Blyth Spartans	H	2836	W	3 - 0	White 29 McGrath 44 Richards 74	
7	NLN	Nuneaton Borough	A	895	D	0 - 0		
11	NLN	Curzon Ashton	A	416	W	1 - 0	White 79	
14	NLN	Leamington	H	2781	W	2 - 1	White 51 (Pen) Bird 85	
18	NLN	Chorley	A	1542	L	0 - 1		
25	NLN	Bradford Park Avenue	H	2601	L	1 - 2	White 90 (Pen)	
Sept 1	NLN	York City	H	2558	D	1 - 1	McGrath 65	
8	NLN	Brackley Town	A	830	L	0 - 2		
Peter Beadle is sacked as manager.								
15	NLN	Ashton United	H	2195	L	0 - 2		16
22	**FAC 2Q**	**Truro City**	**H**	**1441**	**D**	**0 - 0**		
26	**FAC 2Qr**	**Truro City**	**A**	**250**	**W**	**4 - 3**	**McGrath 42, Sainty 60 Jackson 85, Thomas 113 (aet)**	
29	NLN	Spennymoor Town	H	2159	L	0 - 3		17
Oct 2	NLN	Chester	A	1705	L	0 - 3		17
Gloucester City manager Marc Richards is appointed head coach.								
Oct 6	**FAC 3Q**	**Welling United**	**H**	**1330**	**L**	**0 - 2**		
13	NLN	Stockport County	A	3646	D	1 - 1	Dinsley 52	18
27	NLN	Boston United	A	1137	L	1 - 3	Lloyd 65	
30	NLN	AFC Telford United	A	1804	D	1 - 1	Lloyd 22	18
Nov 3	NLN	Altrincham	H	2220	D	1 - 1	Roberts 52	18
10	NLN	FC United of Manchester	H	259	L	1 - 3	Roberts 81	20
13	NLN	Southport	H	1512	L	0 - 3		21
17	NLN	Darlington	A	2211	D	2 - 2	Owen-Evans 15 50	21
24	**FAT 3Q**	**FC United of Manchester**	**H**	**1067**	**W**	**3 - 1**	**Cullinane-Liburd 47 O'Sullivan 48 Symons 76**	
Dec 1	NLN	Alfreton Town	H	2082	W	2 - 1	Symons 18 Roberts 90	18
15	**FAT 1P**	**Billericay Town**	**H**	**1097**	**W**	**2 - 1**	**Owen-Evans 37 (pen) Lloyd 81**	
22	NLN	Bradford Park Avenue	A	448	L	0 - 1		
26	NLN	Kidderminster Harriers	H	3210	W	1 - 0	Roberts 80 (Pen)	
29	NLN	Chester	H	2775	W	2 - 0	Greenslade 30 Symons 72	
Jan 1	NLN	Kidderminster Harriers	A	2745	L	1 - 2	Roberts 17	
5	NLN	Chorley	H	2168	D	1 - 1	Gowling 90	19
12	**FAT 2P**	**Brackley Town**	**H**	**1569**	**L**	**1 - 3**	**Gowling 90**	
19	NLN	Nuneaton Borough	H	2112	D	2 - 2	Owen-Evans 25 52 (pen)	
22	NLN	Guiseley	A	481	D	1 - 1	Richards 47	
26	NLN	Blyth Spartans	A	783	W	3 - 2	Owen-Evans 8 Oates 62 Lloyd 84	
Feb 2	NLN	Curzon Ashton	H	2081	L	1 - 2	Greenslade 52	
5	NLN	York City	A	2370	W	2 - 1	Greenslade 77 Waite 80	
9	NLN	Leamington	A	1150	D	2 - 2	Waite 33 Owen-Evans 45 (pen)	
16	NLN	Ashton United	A	405	D	0 - 0		18
Mar 2	NLN	FC United of Manchester	A	2058	D	2 - 2	Symons 17 Richards 56	18
9	NLN	Darlington	H	2294	W	4 - 2	Thomas 58 Finn 66 Owen-Evans 70 Smith L 89	16
23	NLN	Guiseley	H	2261	W	1 - 0	Gowling 79	16
26	NLN	Brackley Town	H	1512	L	0 - 2		16
30	NLN	Spennymoor Town	A	830	W	2 - 0	Smith L 32 Owens-Evans 42 (pen)	16
Apr 6	NLN	Stockport County	H	3025	D	2 - 2	Liburd R 65 Cowan 90+2 (og)	16
9	NLN	Alfreton Town	A	434	D	1 - 1	Owen-Evans 57 (pen)	15
13	NLN	Southport	A	1002	L	0 - 1		17
20	NLN	AFC Telford United	H	2623	D	1 - 1	Liburd R 7	
22	NLN	Altrincham	A	1407	D	1 - 1	Owen-Evans 64	17
27	NLN	Boston United	H	2232	L	0 - 2		17

GOALSCORERS	SG	CSG	Pens	Hat tricks	Total
Owen-Evans	9	1	3		11
Roberts	5	2	1		5
Lloyd	4	2			4
Symons	4	1			4
White	4	2	2		4
Gowling	3	2			3
Greenslade	3	2			3
McGrath	3	1			3
Richards	3	1			3
Liburd R	2	1			2
Smith L	2	1			2
Thomas	2	1			2
Waite	2	2			2
Bird	1	1			1
Culliane-Liburd	1	1			1
Dinsley	1	1			1
Finn	1	1			1
Jackson	1	1			1
O'Sullivan	1	1			1
Oates*	1	1			1
Opponent	1	1			1
Sainty	1	1			1

Horsell	Green	Cullinane-Liburd	Greenslade	McGrath	Richards	Thomas	Murphy	White	Smith L	Myrie-Williams	Hall	Dinsley	Bird	Smith H (L)	Sainty	Hockey	Franklin	Reffell	Mayebi	Larri	Harrison (L)	Jackson	McLeod	Marston	Yates (L)	Wassall (L)	Lloyd (L)	O'Sullivan	Owen-Evans	Roberts	Finn	Symons	Dielna	Gowling	Wharton	Oates (L)	Waite	Radovanovic	Wesolowski	Ebbutt	Hill	Hickman	Ezewele (L)	Liburd	No.
x	x	x	x	x	x	x	x	x	xs	x	sx																																		1
x	x	x	x	xs	xs	x	x	x	xs	x	sx	sx	sx	s	s																														2
x		x	x	xs	xs	x	x	x	x		xs	sx	sx	x	sx	s	s																												3
x	s	x	x	x	x	x	x	x	xs		xs	s	sx	x				sx	s																										4
x	x	x		x	xs	x	x	x	xs		xs	sx	sx	s				sx	s																										5
x	x	x	xs	x	x	x	x	x	sx			sx	sx					xs		xs																									6
x	x	x	x	x	x	x	xs	xs	sx	x		sx	sx	s					s	xs																									7
x	x	x	x	x	x	x	x	x	sx	xs	s	sx	xs	s					s																										8
x	xs	x	x	x		x	xs	x	sx	x	sx		x	sx	s				s	xs																									9
x		x	x	x		x		x	x				x	x							x	x																							10
x	x		x	x		x	sx	x		sx	xs		xs	x	xs		s			sx	xs	sx	s	s																					11
x	s	x	x	x	xs	x		x		sx	xs		xs	x	x					sx	s	sx																							12
x	s	x	x	x	x	x		xs			x	sx	xs	x	s					sx	s	x																							13
x	s	x	x	x	x	x	x	s			x	x	s	x			s			s	s	x																							14
	x	sx	x		xs	x	x	xs				x	s	x			s			s		sx			x	x	x																		15
	x	s	x	sx	xs	xs		sx	x			xs										s			x	x	x	x	sx																16
s		x	x	x		x	s	sx	x													s			x	x	x	x	x	xs	s														17
s	s	x	x			x	x	sx						x								s			x	x	x	x	xs	xs	sx														18
	x		x	s		x	x	s				sx		x								s			x	xs	x	xs	x	x	sx														19
		x	x	x	s	x	xs	sx						x											x	s	x	sx	x	xs	xs	sx													20
s	s	x	x	x	s	x	xs							x											x		xs	sx	x	x	sx	x													21
		x	x	x										x											x		x	sx	x			x													22
s		x	x			x	s	s				x		x											x		x	xs	x	sx	x	x	s												23
s		x	x			x						x		x											x		x	sx	x	sx	xs	x	s	s					xs						24
s		x	x			x	s					x													x		xs	x	x	sx	xs	x	sx	x	s										25
s		x	x		sx	x						x													x		xs	xs	x	sx	xs	x	s	x	sx										26
s		x	x		sx	x								sx											x		x	xs	x	xs	xs	x	s	x	sx										27
s		x	x		sx	x						xs		s											x		xs	sx	x	x	xs	x		x	sx										28
s		x	x		sx	x						xs		s				sx							x			sx	x	x	xs	x		x	xs										29
		x	x		xs	x						s		s				sx							x			sx	x	xs	xs	x	sx	x	x										30
		s	x		sx	x						x		x				sx							x		xs	s	x	sx	xs	x		x	xs										31
		x	x		x	x								x				sx							x		xs	x	x	s	s	x	s	x	s										32
		xs	x		x	xs								x											x		sx	xs	x	s	sx	x	s	x	sx	x									33
		x	xs		x	xs								x											x		sx	x	x	sx	x	xs		x	s	x	s								34
		x	x		x	x						s		xs											x		xs	x	x	sx	s			x	s	x	sx								35
		x	x		x	x			s																x		xs	x	x	s	s	sx		x	s	x	x								36
		x	xs		xs	x								s											x		xs	x	x	sx	sx	x		x	sx	x		s							37
		x	x		xs	x																			x			x	x	xs	sx	x		x	sx	x			s	s	s				38
		x	x		x	x			sx																x			x	x	x	sx	x		x	s	x			s		s				39
		x	x		xs				sx								s								x			x	x	sx	xs	x		x					xs	sx		x	s		40
		x	x		x				x																x			x	x	s	sx	xs		xs	s		sx		xs			x	sx		41
		x	x		sx	x			xs																x			xs	x		x	sx			s		s				s	x	x	x	42
		x	x		sx	x																			x			sx	x		xs	x		x	xs		sx				s	xs	s	x	43
		x	x		x																				x			sx	x		sx	xs		x	xs		x		s		s	x	s	x	44
		x	x		x																				x			sx	xs		x	sx		x	x		xs		s		s	x	s	x	45
		x	x		xs	x																			x			xs			sx	x		x	s		x		sx		s	x	s	x	46
		x	x		xs	x																			x			sx	x		sx	x		x	s		x		s			x	s	xs	47
		x	x		xs	x																			x			x	x		sx	xs		x	sx		sx		s			xs	s	x	48
14	10	42	44	16	16	40	11	11	5	4	2	7	2	19	1	0	0	0	0	0	1	3	0	0	34	4	10	14	29	5	4	20	0	22	2	7	4	0	0	0	0	7	1	6	x
0	1	1	3	2	13	3	4	3	5	1	5	3	4	1	1	0	0	1	0	3	1	0	0	0	0	1	9	7	2	6	11	4	0	1	4	0	1	0	3	0	0	2	0	1	xs
0	0	1	0	1	7	0	1	4	6	2	3	8	6	2	1	0	0	6	0	3	0	3	0	0	0	0	2	11	1	9	12	4	2	0	7	0	4	0	1	1	0	0	1	0	sx
10	6	2	0	1	2	0	3	3	1	0	1	3	2	8	3	1	5	0	5	2	3	4	1	1	0	1	0	1	0	4	4	0	6	1	10	0	2	1	6	1	7	0	7	0	s

x - Played full 90 minutes
xs - Substituted off
sx - Substituted on
s - Non-playing Substitute

KIDDERMINSTER HARRIERS MATCH RESULTS 2018-19

Date	Comp	Opponents	H/A	Att:	Result		Goalscorers	Pos
Aug 4	NLN	Alfreton Town	A	754	D	3 - 3	Bradley 22 Richards 47 Ironside 66	
7	NLN	AFC Telford United	H	1778	D	0 - 0		
11	NLN	Ashton United	H	1335	D	3 - 3	Taylor 50 Chambers 77 Richards 90	
18	NLN	Darlington	H	1522	**W**	5 - 2	Ironside 30 (pen) 38 Williams 62 Horsfall 73 Weeks 90	
25	NLN	Curzon Ashton	A	353	D	1 - 1	Chambers 74	
27	NLN	Stockport County	H	1756	**W**	2 - 1	Taylor 36 O'Connor 76	
Sept 1	NLN	Boston United	A	1129	**W**	2 - 0	Williams 14 Chambers 22	
8	NLN	Blyth Spartans	H	1570	**W**	3 - 1	Chambers 37 Horsfall 43 Williams 70	
15	NLN	York City	A	2404	**W**	3 - 0	Williams 12 45 Ironside 55	2
18	NLN	Chester	H	1512	L	1 - 3	Williams 72 (Pen)	2
22	**FAC 2Q**	**Atherstone Town**	**H**	**1212**	**W**	**5 - 0**	**Bradley 34 56 68 Ironside 53 (Pen) Richards 87**	
29	NLN	Altrincham	H	1517	**W**	3 - 2	Williams 1 Bradley 35 Chambers 44	2
Oct 6	**FAC 3Q**	**Stourbridge**	**A**	**1527**	**L**	**2 - 3**	**Williams 12 Ironside 53 (Pen)**	
13	NLN	Bradford Park Avenue	A	529	**W**	2 - 1	Williams 81 89	2
20	NLN	FC United of Manchester	H	1860	L	1 - 2	Williams 4	2
27	NLN	Guiseley	A	697	D	0 - 0		2
30	NLN	Leamington	A	782	**W**	4 - 0	Bradley 18 Weeks 20 Chambers 35 Vaughan 62	2
Nov 3	NLN	Southport	H	1513	L	1 - 4	O'Connor 68	4
10	NLN	Nuneaton Borough	A	654	D	1 - 1	O'Connor 66	3
17	NLN	Chorley	H	2090	L	0 - 4		5
24	**FAT 3Q**	**York City**	**H**	**784**	**L**	**1 - 3**	**Vaughan 66**	
Dec 8	NLN	Brackley Town	H	1288	**W**	2 - 0	Chambers 11 62	6
22	NLN	Curzon Ashton	H	1407	D	1 - 1	Bradley 90	
26	NLN	Hereford	A	3210	L	0 - 1		
29	NLN	Stockport County	A	3784	L	0 - 1		
Jan 1	NLN	Hereford	H	2745	**W**	2 - 1	Richards 20 Weeks 47	
5	NLN	Darlington	A	1123	L	0 - 3		
8	NLN	Spennymoor Town	A	575	L	1 - 2	Philips 45	
12	NLN	Boston United	H	1549	L	1 - 2	Ironside 32	9
19	NLN	AFC Telford United	A	1714	**W**	1 - 0	Clayton-Phillips 3	
26	NLN	Alfreton Town	H	1315	L	0 - 1		
Feb 9	NLN	Chester	H	1769	**W**	4 - 1	Weeks 42 Ironside 45 Johnson 71 Williams 87	
16	NLN	York City	H	1598	L	1 - 2	Ironside 75	
23	NLN	Blyth Spartans	A	705	D	3 - 3	Clayton-Phillips 7 Ironside 22 (pen) Williams 71	
26	NLN	Ashton United	A	226	**W**	1 - 0	Daniels 63	9
Mar 2	NLN	Nuneaton Borough	H	1539	**W**	4 - 1	Chambers 26 78 88 Ironside 47 (pen)	8
9	NLN	Chorley	A	1474	L	0 - 3		8
16	NLN	Spennymoor Town	H	1436	**W**	2 - 1	Chambers 21 50	8
23	NLN	Brackley Town	A	845	L	1 - 3	Ironside 37 (pen)	8
30	NLN	Altrincham	A	1095	L	1 - 2	Ironside 39	8
Apr 6	NLN	Bradford Park Avenue	H	1606	**W**	3 - 0	Ironside 18 78 Chambers 78	8
13	NLN	FC United of Manchester	A	1760	**W**	1 - 0	Ironside 32 (pen)	9
19	NLN	Leamington	H	1515	L	1 - 2	Ironside 5	
22	NLN	Southport	A	956	D	2 - 2	Butterfield 61 Ironside 75 (pen)	10
27	NLN	Guiseley	H	1354	L	1 - 2	Ironside 79 (pen)	10

GOALSCORERS	SG	CSG	Pens	Hat tricks	Total
Ironside	17	7	8		19
Chambers	10	2		1	14
Williams	11	4	1		13
Bradley	5	2		1	7
Richards	4	1			4
Weeks	4	1			4
O'Connor	3	2			3
Clayton-Phillips	2	1			2
Horsfall	2	1			2
Taylor	2	1			2
Vaughan	2	1			2
Butterfield	1	1			1
Daniels	1	1			1
Johnson	1	1			1
Philips	1	1			1

Hall	Vaughan	Austin	O'Connor	Horsfall	Johnson	Weeks	Daniels	Ironside	Chambers	Bradley	Richards	Williams	Taylor	Baxendale	Digie	Truslove	Stratford	Wagner	Taylor -Randle	Palmer	Cummings	White	Brooks	Higginson	Penn	Waring (L)	Phillips	Butterfield	Heaton (L)	Clayton-Phillips (L)	McAlinden (L)	Lowth	Weaver (L)	Boucher (L)	Flowers (L)	Thomas (L)	No.
x	x	x	x	x	x	x	x	x	xs	x	sx	s	s	s	s																						1
x	x	x	x	x	x	x	xs	x	xs	xs	sx	sx	s	sx	s																						2
x	x	xs	x	x	xs	x	xs	x	x	x	sx	sx	sx	s	s																						3
x	x	sx	x	x	x	x	xs	x	xs		sx	x	xs	sx	s	s																					4
x	x	s	x	x	x	x	x	xs	x		sx	x	x	s	s		s																				5
x	x	sx	x	x	x	x	x	xs	x		sx	x	xs	s	s		s																				6
x	x	sx	x	x	x	x	x	xs	x	sx	sx	x	xs	s	s																						7
x	x	s	x	x		x	x	xs	xs	sx	sx	xs	x	sx	x			s																			8
x	x	s	x	x	s	x	x	xs	xs	sx	sx	xs	x	sx	x																						9
x	x	s	x	x	s	x	x	xs	x	sx	sx	x	x	s	xs																						10
x	**x**	**x**	**x**	**x**	**x**	**x**		**xs**	**s**	**xs**	**sx**	**xs**		**x**	**s**		**sx**		**sx**	**s**	**s**																11
x	x	x	x	x	x	x	x	sx	xs	xs	sx	xs		sx	s					s																	12
x	**x**	**x**	**x**		**x**	**x**	**x**	**sx**	**x**	**xs**	**sx**	**x**	**s**	**s**	**xs**					**s**		**s**	**s**														13
x	x	xs	x	x		x	x	xs	xs		sx	x	sx	sx	x					s				s													14
x	x	xs	x	x	x	xs	x	sx	xs		sx	x	s	sx	s																						15
x	x	s	x	x	x	x	x	sx	xs	xs	sx	x	x	s	s																						16
x	x	s	x	x	x	x	x	sx	xs	xs	sx	xs	x	sx	s																						17
x	xs	sx	x	x	xs	x	x	sx	x	xs	sx	x	x	s	s																						18
x	x	s	x	x	x		x	sx	xs	xs	sx	x	x	xs	s										sx												19
x	x	sx	xs	x	sx	xs	x		x	x	sx	x	xs	s				s							x												20
x	**x**	**x**		**x**	**x**	**sx**	**x**		**x**	**x**	**x**	**x**	**s**	**s**				**s**		**s**					**xs**												21
x	x	x		x	x	x			xs	x	xs	x		sx				s		s					x	sx	s										22
x	x	x		x	x	x	sx		x	x	xs	x		s						s					xs	sx	s										23
x	x	x	s	x	x	x	xs		x	xs	xs	x		sx											sx	sx											24
x	x	x	s	x	x	x			x	x	xs			xs						s		s			x	sx	sx										25
x	x	x	x	x	x	x			xs		x		s	s								s			x	x	sx	s									26
x	x	xs	x	x	x	x			x		x			sx								s			xs	x	s	sx	s								27
x	x	xs		x		x		x	x		xs			sx						s		sx		s	x		x	sx	xs								28
x	x	xs		x		x		x	xs	x	sx			sx										s	x		xs	s	x	sx							29
xs	x	x		x		x		x	xs								s			sx				x	xs			sx	x	x	sx	s					30
	x	sx		x	xs	x		x	x										s					sx	xs			sx	xs	x	x		x	s			31
x		x		x	x	x		x	xs			sx	x			sx						sx		s				x		xs	xs		s				32
x		x		x	x		xs	x			s	sx	x											s				x		x	x		s				33
x		x		x	x		sx	x	xs		s	xs	x			s								s	x			x	s	xs							34
x		x		x	x		x	x	x		s	x	x				s			s				s	x				s		x						35
x		x		x	x		x	x	xs		sx	xs	x						sx					s	xs			sx	s		x						36
x		x		x	x		x	xs	xs		sx	xs	x							s				s	x			sx	sx		x						37
x		xs		sx	x		x	xs	x		s	x	x							s					sx			xs			x				x	sx	38
x		xs		x	x	sx		xs	x		sx		x				s			s				s	x						x				x	x	39
x				x	x	xs		xs	x		sx	x	x							s				s	sx			x			xs				x	sx	40
x		x		x	x			x	xs		s	xs	x							s				s	sx			x			x				x	sx	41
		x		x	x			xs	xs		sx	x	x							x				s	s			x	s		x				x	sx	42
		x		x	x			x	x		sx	x	x							x		s		s	sx			x	s		xs				xs		43
s		x		x				x	xs		sx	x	xs				s			x		sx		xs	x			x	sx		x						44
s		x		x		sx		x	x		sx	x					s			x		xs		s	xs			x	x		x						45
39	30	23	21	43	32	28	21	17	21	8	3	23	20	1	3	0	0	0	0	4	0	0	0	1	11	2	1	9	3	3	11	0	1	0	5	1	X
1	1	8	1	0	3	3	5	13	22	9	5	9	5	2	2	0	0	0	0	0	0	1	0	1	7	0	1	1	2	2	3	0	0	0	1	0	XS
0	0	6	0	1	1	3	2	7	0	4	29	4	2	13	0	1	1	0	2	1	0	3	0	1	6	4	2	6	2	1	1	0	0	0	0	4	SX
2	0	7	2	0	2	0	0	0	1	0	5	1	6	13	14	2	7	4	1	15	1	5	1	15	1	0	3	2	6	0	0	1	2	1	0	0	S

x - Played full 90 minutes
xs - Substituted off
sx - Substituted on
s - Non-playing Substitute

LEAMINGTON MATCH RESULTS 2018-19

Date	Comp	Opponents	H/A	Att:	Result		Goalscorers	Pos
Aug 4	NLN	Altrincham	A	1047	D	2 - 2	Edwards 28 Gitting 48	
7	NLN	Boston United	H	656	**W**	2 - 0	Stenson 15 English 71	
11	NLN	Bradford Park Avenue	H	524	**W**	4 - 2	Stenson 44 59 Gitting 48 Dwyer 90	
14	NLN	Hereford	A	2781	L	1 - 2	Edwards 19	
18	NLN	Guiseley	H	485	D	2 - 2	Stenson 36 English 65	
25	NLN	FC United of Manchester	A	1727	**W**	2 - 0	Dunbar 9 Stenson 70	
27	NLN	AFC Telford United	H	812	D	2 - 2	Stenson 7 (Pen) Hood 60	
Sept 1	NLN	Stockport County	A	2680	L	1 - 3	Mace 39	
8	NLN	Spennymoor Town	H	545	L	0 - 2		
15	NLN	Blyth Spartans	A	596	**W**	2 - 0	Edwards 5 Dunbar 32	8
22	**FAC 2Q**	**Stourbridge**	**A**	**467**	**L**	**2 - 3**	**Stenson x2**	
29	NLN	Ashton United	A	192	L	1 - 2	Obeng 1	11
Oct 13	NLN	Curzon Ashton	H	705	L	0 - 1		14
27	NLN	Darlington	H	765	D	2 - 2	Bishop 63 (Pen) Edwards 70	
30	NLN	Kidderminster Harriers	H	782	L	0 - 4		16
Nov 3	NLN	Nuneaton Borough	A	662	**W**	2 - 0	Bishop 8 Dunbar 32	12
17	NLN	Chester	H	975	**W**	1 - 0	Bishop 83	11
20	NLN	Alfreton Town	A	316	**W**	2 - 1	Edwards 42 Dunbar 82	
24	**FAT 3Q**	**Witton Albion**	**H**	**332**	**W**	**2 - 1**	**Bishop 30 (pen) Dwyer 90+2**	
Dec 4	NLN	York City	A	1938	D	2 - 2	Bishop 70 85	
8	NLN	Chorley	H	568	D	1 - 1	Bishop 31	12
15	**FAT 1P**	**Hartlepool United**	**H**	**344**	**L**	**0 - 1**		
22	NLN	FC United of Manchester	H	725	D	2 - 2	Bishop 3 41	
26	NLN	Brackley Town	A	570	D	2 - 2	Bishop 17 (Pen) Dunbar 74	
29	NLN	AFC Telford United	H	1196	L	1 - 4	Bishop 4	
Jan 1	NLN	Brackley Town	H	623	D	0 - 0		
5	NLN	Guiseley	H	683	D	1 - 1	Murphy J 45	
12	NLN	Southport	A	892	L	1 - 5	Edwards 34	14
19	NLN	Boston United	A	885	D	1 - 1	Bishop 31	
22	NLN	Stockport County	H	604	L	0 - 1		
26	NLN	Altrincham	H	564	**W**	3 - 0	English 13 Bishop 31 (pen) 44	
Feb 9	NLN	Hereford	H	1150	D	2 - 2	Edwards 44 Bishop 84 (pen)	
16	NLN	Blyth Spartans	H	523	L	1 - 2	Bishop 58 (pen)	
23	NLN	Spennymoor Town	A	786	L	0 - 1		17
Mar 2	NLN	York City	H	801	L	0 - 1		17
5	NLN	Bradford Park Avenue	A	303	L	1 - 2	Obeng 25	17
9	NLN	Chester	A	1983	D	1 - 1	Obeng 83	18
16	NLN	Southport	H	452	**W**	1 - 0	Bishop 7	16
23	NLN	Chorley	A	1507	L	0 - 3		18
30	NLN	Ashton United	H	601	**W**	1 - 0	Flanagan 71	17
Apr 6	NLN	Curzon Ashton	A	202	D	1 - 1	Bishop 83	17
13	NLN	Alfreton Town	H	523	**W**	3 - 1	Gittings 35 Murphy J 53 Edwards 69	16
19	NLN	Kidderminster Harriers	A	1515	**W**	2 - 1	Edwards 10 English 32	
22	NLN	Nuneaton Borough	H	623	**W**	3 - 0	Bishop 18 20 61	14
27	NLN	Darlington	A	1145	D	1 - 1	Bishop 78	13

GOALSCORERS	SG	CSG	Pens	Hat tricks	Total
Bishop	17	3	5	1	22
Edwards	9	2			9
Stenson	6	3	1		8
Dunbar	5	1			5
English	4	1			4
Gittings	3	1			3
Obeng	3	2			3
Dwyer	2	1			2
Murphy J	2	1			2
Flanagan	1	1			1
Hood	1	1			1
Mace	1	1			1

No.	Breeden	English	Gudger	Clarke	Mace	Hood	Dunbar	Gittings	Stenson	Edwards	Obeng	Taylor C	Dwyer	Bowen	Morris	Magunda	Steele	James	Lane	Caswell	Nicholson	Naylor	Jay	Flanagan	Bishop	Murphy J (L)	Newey	Wilding (L)	Taylor M	Sweeney (L)	Hodge	Murphy B	Parker (L)
1	x	x	x	x	x	x	xs	x	xs	x	xs	sx	sx	sx	s	s																	
2	x	x	xs	x	x	x	x	x	xs	x	sx	x	s	sx	s	sx																	
3	x	x		x	x	x	x	x	x	xs	s	xs	sx	x	s	sx	sx																
4	x	x	s	x	x	x	x		x	x	x	s	s	x	s	x	s																
5	x	x	x	x	x	x	x	xs	x	x	sx	xs		s	s	sx	s																
6	x	x	xs	x	x	x	xs	x	x	xs	sx	x	s	sx	s	sx																	
7	x	x		x	x	x	x	x	xs	x	s	x	sx	x	s	s	s																
8	x	x		xs	x	x	xs	x	x	x	sx	x	s	xs	sx	sx		s															
9	x	x		x		x	x	x	x	x	s	xs	sx	x		s		s	x	s													
10	x	x		x		x	x	x	xs	x	x	s	sx	x				s	x		s	s											
11	**x**	**x**		**xs**		**x**	**xs**	**x**	**x**	**x**	**xs**	**sx**	**sx**	**x**		**sx**		**s**	**x**		**s**	**s**	**s**										
12	x	x		x	x	s	x	x	x	x	x	s	s	x		s			x					s									
13	x	x	xs		x	x	xs	x	x	x		sx	sx	x		xs			s					sx	s								
14	x	x	xs	xs	x		x	x		x	xs	s	x	sx				s	x					sx	sx								
15	x	x	x	x	x	s	s	x		x	x	x	x	s					x					s	s								
16	x	x	x	sx	x	x	x	x		x		sx		sx				s	s					xs	xs								
17	x	x	x	sx	x	x	x	x		x	s	x		s				s	s					xs	x								
18	x	x	x	sx	x	x	x	x		x	sx	x		s				s	s					xs	xs								
19	**x**	**x**	**x**	**x**	**x**	**x**	**xs**	**s**		**x**	**sx**	**x**	**sx**	**s**					**s**					**x**	**xs**								
20	x	x	x	s	x	xs	x	x		xs	sx	xs	sx	s					sx					x	x								
21	x	x	x	sx	x	s	xs	x		x	sx	x	sx	s					x					xs	xs								
22	**x**	**x**	**xs**	**s**	**x**	**s**	**x**	**x**		**xs**	**sx**	**xs**	**sx**	**sx**					**x**					**x**	**x**								
23	x	x	x	sx	x	s	xs	xs		x	sx	x	s	s					x					x	x								
24	x	x	x	x	x	s	x	x		x	sx	x		s					x					sx	x	sx							
25	x	xs	x	xs	x	sx	xs	sx		x	sx	s		s					x					x	x	x							
26	x		xs	sx	x	x	xs	x		x	sx	s	s	sx					x					xs	x	x							
27	x	s		x	x		xs	x		x	sx	s		x				s	x			s		x	x	x							
28	x	sx		xs	x		xs	x		x	sx	sx		xs				s	x					x	x	x	s						
29	x	x			x		xs	x		x	x	sx		x				s	x			s			x	x	s						
30	x	x		xs	x	x		s		x	x	sx		s					x					xs	x	x	s	sx					
31	x	x		x	x	x		x		xs	x	sx		s					x					s	xs	xs		sx	sx				
32	x	x	s	x	x	x		x		x	x							s	x					s	x	x		s	sx				
33	x	x	x	sx	x	x		xs		x	xs								s					xs	x	x	s	sx	sx				
34	x	x	x	xs	x	x				x	x								s					sx	x	x	s	x	s				
35	x	x	xs	x	x	x				x	sx	s							sx					sx	x	x	s	xs		xs			
36	x	x	xs	xs	x	x				x	x	sx						s	sx					xs	x	x	s	s					
37	x	x	x	x	x	x					xs								s					x	x	x	s	s		s	x	sx	
38	x	x	x	x	x	x		sx			xs	sx							sx					xs	x		s	x			xs		s
39	x			x	x	x		sx		x	sx	s							x					x	x	xs	s	xs			x		s
40	x	x	x	x	x	x		xs		xs	xs	s							s					sx	x	x		sx			sx		
41	x	x	xs	x	x	x		xs		x	xs	s						s	sx					sx	x	x					sx		
42	x	x	x	xs	x			xs		x	xs	s							x					sx	x	x	s	sx			sx		
43	x	x	x	x	x			xs		xs	xs	s							x					sx	x	x		sx			sx		s
44	x	x	x	x	x			s		xs	s	xs							x					sx	xs			x			sx		sx
45	x	x	s	xs	x	xs				x	s	xs							x					sx	x	x		x			sx		sx
x	45	40	20	24	42	29	15	26	9	35	10	11	2	10	0	1	0	0	23	0	0	0	0	9	24	17	0	4	0	0	2	0	0
xs	0	1	9	10	0	2	13	7	4	8	10	7	0	2	0	1	0	0	0	0	0	0	0	9	6	2	0	2	0	1	1	0	0
sx	0	1	0	7	0	1	0	3	0	0	17	10	11	7	1	6	1	0	5	0	0	0	0	11	1	1	0	6	3	0	6	1	2
s	0	1	3	2	0	6	1	3	0	0	6	13	7	12	7	4	3	14	9	1	2	4	1	4	2	0	11	3	1	1	0	0	3

x - Played full 90 minutes
xs - Substituted off
sx - Substituted on
s - Non-playing Substitute

NUNEATON BOROUGH MATCH RESULTS 2018-19

Date	Comp	Opponents	H/A	Att:	Result		Goalscorers	Pos
Aug 4	NLN	Ashton United	A	273	D	0 - 0		
7	NLN	Hereford	H	895	D	0 - 0		
11	NLN	Chorley	H	511	L	0 - 1		
14	NLN	Boston United	A	1200	L	1 - 2	Andoh 82	
18	NLN	Southport	H	459	L	1 - 4	Angus 82	
25	NLN	Guiseley	A	528	L	1 - 2	Andoh 23	
27	NLN	Brackley Town	H	480	L	1 - 3	Mitchell 74	
Sept 1	NLN	Curzon Ashton	A	221	**W**	1 - 0	Angus 8	
15	NLN	Spennymoor Town	A	725	L	1 - 3	Angus 4 (Pen)	22
22	**FAC 2Q**	**Brackley Town**	**H**	**491**	**D**	**1 - 1**	**Mitchell 55**	
25	**FAC 2Qr**	**Brackley Town**	**A**	**325**	**L**	**0 - 2**		
29	NLN	FC United of Manchester	H	638	**W**	1 - 0	Andoh 85	20
Oct 2	NLN	York City	H	501	D	2 - 2	Angus 10 83	20
20	NLN	Bradford Park Avenue	H	823	L	0 - 6		20
27	NLN	Stockport County	A	2802	D	2 - 2	McGurk 7 Addison 78	
30	NLN	Altrincham	A	695	L	0 - 4		21
Nov 3	NLN	Leamington	H	662	L	0 - 2		22
6	NLN	Chester	A	1462	L	2 - 3	Baker 60 McGurk 81	22
10	NLN	Kidderminster Harriers	H	654	D	1 - 1	Davies 77	22
17	NLN	Alfreton Town	A	1673	L	1 - 3	Angus 43	22
Manager Nicky Eaden leaves by mutual consent, with Assistant manager, Lee Fowler, taking over.								
24	**FAT 3Q**	**Brackley Town**	**A**	**350**	**L**	**0 - 3**		
Dec 1	NLN	Blyth Spartans	H	505	L	1 - 3	Angus 85	22
Lee Fowler left the club by mutual consent. Jimmy Ginnelly is named new manager.								
8	NLN	Darlington	A	1064	**W**	2 - 1	Edmunds 44 Angus 70	22
22	NLN	Guiseley	H	872	L	1 - 3	Angus 11	
26	NLN	AFC Telford United	A	1524	L	1 - 3	Calveley 90	
29	NLN	Brackley Town	A	506	L	1 - 3	Edmunds 27	
Jan 1	NLN	AFC Telford United	H	763	L	1 - 2	Edmunds 20	
5	NLN	Southport	A	976	D	1 - 1	Ceesay 54	
12	NLN	Curzon Ashton	H	915	L	2 - 4	Ceesay 4 Addison 88	22
19	NLN	Hereford	A	2112	D	2 - 2	Calveley 30 38	22
26	NLN	Ashton United	H	655	L	0 - 1		22
Feb 9	NLN	Boston United	H	655	L	1 - 5	Edmunds 79 (pen)	22
16	NLN	Spennymoor Town	H	510	L	0 - 2		22
23	NLN	York City	A	2355	L	0 - 2		22
26	NLN	Chorley	A	961	L	0 - 2		22
Mar 2	NLN	Kidderminster Harriers	A	1539	L	1 - 4	Townsend 38	22
9	NLN	Alfreton Town	H	517	L	1 - 2	Edmunds 72	22
23	NLN	Darlington	H	620	L	1 - 2	Addison 28	22
30	NLN	FC United of Manchester	A	1697	**W**	4 - 0	Allen 17 Townsend 19 Lussey 63 Caton 85	22
Apr 6	NLN	Chester	H	688	L	2 - 3	Addison 36 Calveley 86	22 (R)
9	NLN	Blyth Spartans	A	557	L	1 - 4	Allen 85	22
13	NLN	Bradford Park Avenue	A	429	L	0 - 1		22
20	NLN	Altrincham	H	530	L	0 - 2		22
22	NLN	Leamington	A	623	L	0 - 3		22
27	NLN	Stockport County	H	4054	L	0 - 3		22

GOALSCORERS	SG	CSG	Pens	Hat tricks	Total
Angus	8	3	1		9
Edmunds	5	2	1		5
Addison	4	1			4
Calveley	3	1			4
Andoh	3	1			3
Allen	2	1			2
Ceesay*	2	2			2
McGurk	2	1			2
Mitchell	2	1			2
Townsend	2	1			2
Baker	1	1			1
Caton	1	1			1
Davies	1	1			1
Lussey	1	1			1

No.	Gray	Burns	Hurst	Wesolowski	Addison	Carter	Calveley (L)	Richards	Panayiotou	Tudur-Jones	Angus (L)	Tweed	Mitchell (L)	Andoh	Etheridge	Wharton	Freestone (L)	Basso	Obeng	Belford C	Kelly-Evans	Baker	McGurk	Benjamin	Davies (L)
1	x	x	x	xs	x	x	x	x	x	xs	xs	sx	sx	sx	s	s									
2	x	x	x		x	x	x	x	x	sx	xs	s	x	s	s	s	x								
3		x	x		x	x	xs	x	x	s		s	x	sx	x	x	xs	s	sx						
4	x	x	x	sx		x	xs	xs	x	xs		sx	x	sx	s	s	x		x						
5	x	x	x	xs		x	sx	xs	x		xs	sx	xs	x	s	s	x		x						
6		x				x	x	x	x		xs	xs	sx	xs			x	s	x	x	sx				
7		x			x	x	x	x	x		x	sx	sx	xs			x	s	xs	x					
8		x			x		x	x	x		x	s	x	s		s	x	s	s	x		x			
9		x		xs	x			x			x		sx	s			x	s	x	x	sx	x	xs	sx	
10		**x**		**xs**	**x**			**x**					**x**	**sx**		**s**	**x**	**s**	**x**	**x**	**x**	**x**	**xs**	**sx**	
11		**xs**			**x**	**x**		**x**					**x**	**sx**		**sx**	**sx**	**s**	**x**	**x**	**x**	**x**	**xs**	**xs**	
12						x	x	x			x		sx	xs		x		s	x	x	x		xs	sx	x
13				s		x	x	x	s		x			x		x		s	x	x	x	s	xs	s	x
14				s		xs	x	x	sx		x			xs		xs			x	x	x	sx	x	s	x
15				xs	x	x	x	x	sx		x			s	x	x		s	x		sx		x	s	xs
16				x	x	xs	x	x	s		x		s		x	x		s	x		x		x	s	sx
17				x	x	x	x	xs	s		x	s			x	s		s			x	x		sx	x
18				xs	x	x	x	sx	x		xs					xs		s	x	x	x	x	sx	sx	s
19					x	x	x	x	x		x	s				s		s	x	x	x	x	x	s	sx
20				x	x		x	x			x	s						s	x	x	xs	x	x		xs
21					**x**		**x**		**x**		**x**	**sx**			**s**			**s**		**x**	**xs**	**x**	**x**		
22							x		x		x							s		x	x	x	xs		
23					x		x		x		x							s		x	sx	x	x		s
24					x		x		x		x									x	s	x	xs		
25					x		x		xs		x							s	x	x	x	x			
26					x		x		sx		x							s	x	x	x	x			
27					x		x		s		x							s	x	x	x	x			
28					x		x											s	x	x	x	x			
29					x		x											s	x	x	xs	x			
30					x		x												x	x	s				
31					x		x												x	x	sx				
32					x		x												x	x					
33					x		x												xs	x	sx				
34					x		x												x	x	s				
35					x		x												x	x	x				
36					x		xs												x	x	x				
37					x		x												x	x	sx				
38					x		x												x	x	x				
39					x		x												x	x					
40					x		x												x	x	sx				
41					x		xs													x	x				
42					x		x												x	x	x				
43																			x	x	x				
44																				x	x				
45																			x	x	xs				
x	4	10	5	3	35	14	34	16	14	0	18	0	6	2	4	5	8	0	32	37	21	17	7	0	4
xs	0	1	0	6	0	2	4	3	1	2	5	1	1	4	0	2	1	0	2	0	4	0	7	1	2
sx	0	0	0	1	0	0	1	1	3	1	0	5	5	5	0	1	1	0	1	0	8	1	1	5	2
s	0	0	0	2	0	0	0	0	4	1	0	6	1	4	5	8	0	23	1	0	3	1	0	5	2

No.	Jennings	Edmunds	Morrison-Derbyshire	Kelly	Lyne	Leek	Hildreth	Lussey	Ceesay (L)	Sharpe	Baxendale (L)	Lundstram (L)	Allen (L)	Belford T	Birch	Townsend	Barlone	Caton	Halil	Dunkley
1																				
2																				
3																				
4																				
5																				
6																				
7																				
8																				
9																				
10																				
11																				
12																				
13																				
14																				
15																				
16																				
17																				
18																				
19																				
20	sx	sx																		
21	**x**			**x**	**x**															
22		x	x	x	x	sx														
23		xs	x	x	x	sx														
24		xs	xs	x	x	sx	sx													
25	sx	s	sx	x	xs	sx	x													
26	sx	xs	sx		xs	xs	x													
27	s	x	s		sx	x	x	xs												
28		x	s		s	s	x	x	x	x										
29		x	s	sx	s	sx	x	xs	x	x										
30		xs	s			sx			x	x	x	x	x	s						
31		xs	s				sx		x	x	xs	x	x	s						
32		x	s							x	x	x	x	s	x					
33		x	x							x	x	x	x	s	xs	sx				
34		xs	xs							x	x	x	x	s	xs	sx				
35		xs	sx							x	xs	x	x	s	s	xs				
36		x	sx					x		x	sx	x	xs	s	sx	x				
37		xs	x					x		x	s	x	sx	s	s	xs	x			
38		xs	x					x		x		x	sx	s				xs	s	sx
39		xs	s					x		x		x	x	s		x		xs	sx	sx
40		x	s					xs		x		x	xs	s		x		xs		sx
41		x	x					xs		x		x		sx				x		
42		xs	x					xs		x			xs	sx			x		sx	sx
43		x						x		x		x	x	sx			x	xs	sx	xs
44		x	x					x		xs		x	x	sx			x	x	xs	sx
45		x	x					x		x		x	xs	sx			x	x	s	sx
x	1	12	9	5	4	1	5	8	4	17	4	15	9	0	1	3	5	3	0	0
xs	0	11	2	0	2	1	0	5	0	1	2	0	4	0	2	2	0	4	1	1
sx	3	1	4	1	1	6	2	0	0	0	1	0	2	5	1	2	0	0	3	6
s	1	1	8	0	2	1	0	0	0	0	1	0	0	11	2	0	0	0	2	0

Also Played: Coyle (L) - 25/08 (sx) 27/08 (sx). Onyeak - 25/08 (s) 27/08 (s) 01/09 (x) 15/09 (xs). Blackham - 22/09 (s) 25/09 (s) 29/09 (s) 20/10 (sx). Corcoran - 22/09 (s) 25/09 (s). Fowler - 29/09 (s). Edobor - 24/11 (s) 01/12 (s) 08/12 (s) 22/12 (s). Prior (L) - 19/01 (x) 26/01 (xs) 09/02 (xs). Lavelle-Moore - 26/01 (sx) 09/02 (sx) 16/02 (s) 23/02 (sx) 26/02 (sx). Nabay - 16/02 (sx) 23/02 (sx) 26/02 (sx) 02/03 (s). Eccleston - 06/04 (sx) 09/04 (sx).

x - Played full 90 minutes
xs - Substituted off
sx - Substituted on
s - Non-playing Substitute

SOUTHPORT MATCH RESULTS 2018-19

Date	Comp	Opponents	H/A	Att:	Result		Goalscorers	Pos
Aug 4	NLN	AFC Telford United	A	1274	L	0 - 1		
7	NLN	Altrincham	H	1268	L	1 - 3	Richards 55	
11	NLN	Stockport County	H	1736	L	0 - 1		
14	NLN	Chorley	A	1368	L	0 - 4		
18	NLN	Nuneaton Borough	A	459	W	4 - 1	Sampson 3 45 Charles 40 88	
25	NLN	Ashton United	H	881	D	2 - 2	Astles 54 Gilchrist 75	
27	NLN	Alfreton Town	A	546	L	1 - 3	Osborne 76	
Sept 1	NLN	Spennymoor Town	H	821	D	1 - 1	Astles 17	
8	NLN	FC United of Manchester	A	1967	D	1 - 1	Green 80	
15	NLN	Darlington	H	1019	D	0 - 0		20
22	**FAC 2Q**	**Farsley Celtic**	**A**	**306**	**W**	**3 - 0**	**Winnard 46 Charles 58 Green 65**	
29	NLN	Brackley Town	A	590	L	0 - 2		21
Oct 6	**FAC 3Q**	**Curzon Ashton**	**A**	**408**	**W**	**2 - 1**	**Charles 45+2 Sampson 58**	
13	NLN	York City	H	1149	L	1 - 2	Charles 8	21
20	**FAC 4Q**	**Ashton United**	**H**	**770**	**W**	**2 - 1**	**Bauress 3 Green 82**	
27	NLN	Blyth Spartans	A	820	L	0 - 1		22
30	NLN	Curzon Ashton	H	580	D	2 - 2	Morgan 14 Charles 80	22
Nov 3	NLN	Kidderminster Harriers	A	1513	W	4 - 1	Sampson 4 33 Gilchrist 23 Charles 34	21
10	**FAC 1P**	**Boreham Wood**	**H**	**1460**	**W**	**2 - 0**	**Winnard 29 Gilchrist 70**	
13	NLN	Hereford	A	1512	W	3 - 0	Charles 24 (Pen) Winnard 45 Archer 67	20
17	NLN	Boston United	A	1146	W	2 - 1	Sampson 16 Astles 90	18
24	**FAT 3Q**	**Chester**	**H**	**914**	**D**	**0 - 0**		
27	**FAT 3Qr**	**Chester**	**A**	**654**	**W**	**2 - 0**	**Morgan 52 Archer 55**	
Dec 2	**FAC 2P**	**Tranmere Rovers**	**A**	**4701**	**D**	**1 - 1**	**Bauress 70**	
8	NLN	Bradford Park Avenue	H	532	D	2 - 2	Winnard 13 Bauress 77	19
15	**FAT 1P**	**Solihull Moors**	**H**	**767**	**L**	**0 - 1**		
17	**FAC 2Pr**	**Tranmere Rovers**	**H**	**5414**	**L**	**0 - 2**		
22	NLN	Ashton United	A	286	W	2 - 1	Sampson 2 Morgan 71	
26	NLN	Chester	H	1644	W	3 - 0	Morgan 40 89 Bauress 45	
29	NLN	Alfreton Town	H	1023	W	2 - 1	Gilchrist 1 Sampson 37	
Jan 1	NLN	Chester	A	1984	D	0 - 0		
5	NLN	Nuneaton Borough	H	976	D	1 - 1	Archer 90	
8	NLN	Guiseley	H	701	W	1 - 0	Sampson 54	
12	NLN	Leamington	H	892	W	5 - 1	Bauress 47 70 Morgan 66 Charles 78 89	11
19	NLN	Altrincham	A	1102	L	0 - 1		
26	NLN	AFC Telford United	H	1052	L	0 - 4		
Feb 9	NLN	Chorley	H	1542	W	5 - 3	Sampson 11 89 Green 20 Charles 28 (pen) 38	
16	NLN	Darlington	A	1462	D	0 - 0		
19	NLN	Stockport County	A	3724	L	2 - 3	Richards 19 Charles 32	
23	NLN	FC United of Manchester	H	1665	D	0 - 0		14
Mar 2	NLN	Guiseley	A	761	W	1 - 0	Sampson 52	13
5	NLN	Spennymoor Town	A	660	D	1 - 1	Sampson 81	13
9	NLN	Boston United	H	1025	L	2 - 3	Bauress 14 Archer 84	14
16	NLN	Leamington	A	452	L	0 - 1		14
23	NLN	Bradford Park Avenue	H	949	D	2 - 2	Archer 52 Gilchrist 90	15
30	NLN	Brackley Town	H	791	D	0 - 0		15
Apr 6	NLN	York City	A	2174	L	0 - 1		15
13	NLN	Hereford	H	1002	W	1 - 0	Platt 58	13
19	NLN	Curzon Ashton	A	380	W	3 - 0	Charles 46 Sampson 74 Wood 78	
22	NLN	Kidderminster Harriers	H	956	D	2 - 2	Charles 45+1 65	13
27	NLN	Blyth Spartans	A	1491	L	1 - 2	Platt 55	14

GOALSCORERS	SG	CSG	Pens	Hat tricks	Total
Charles	12	2	2		16
Sampson	11	2			14
Bauress	6	2			7
Morgan	5	2			6
Gilchrist	5	1			5
Archer	5	1			5
Green	4	1			4
Winnard	4	2			4
Astles	3	1			3
Platt	2	1			2
Richards	2	1			2
Osborne	1	1			1
Wood	1	1			1

Richards	Priestly	Lynch	Astles	Langley	Osborne	Lowe	Green	Sampson	Phenix	Morgan	Charles	Gilchrist	Mueller	Winnard	Corbett	Parry	Ogle (L)	Dobie	Bauress	Hollins	Kinsella	Bosma	Homson-Smith	Tibbetts	Wood (L)	Edwards	Archer (L)	Davies	Mohammed (L)	Lacey	Crowley	Mapmosa	Russell	Whittle	Owens	McHale	Ennis	Platt	Doyle	No.
x	x	x	x	x	xs	x	xs	x	xs	sx	sx	sx	s	s																										1
x	s	x	x	x	s	x	s	sx	xs	x	x	x	x		s																									2
x	x	x		x	x	xs	s	x	sx	x	s	xs	x	sx		s																								3
x	xs	x		x	xs	s	sx	x	s	x	sx	xs	x	x		sx																								4
x		sx	x	x	sx	xs	xs	x	sx	x	x	s	s	x		xs																								5
x	s	sx	x	x	x	xs	x	x	s		x	sx	sx			xs	x																							6
x	x		x	s	x		xs	x	xs	x	x	sx	s				x	sx	s																					7
x	s	x	x	x	x		s	x	sx	x	xs	xs	s				x		sx																					8
s	s	x	x	x	s		sx	x		x	x	xs	s	x			x		x																					9
x		x	x		sx		xs	x	s	x	x	sx	s	x			x		xs	s																				10
x		x	x	s			x	x	s	xs	x	sx	sx	x		s	xs		xs	sx	s																			11
x		x	x	s			x	x	s	x	x	s	s	x			x		x			s																		12
x		x	x	s			xs	x	s	x	x	s	s	x		s	x		x		s		sx																	13
x		x	x	s			sx	x		x	x	sx	s	x			x		xs			xs	s																	14
x		x	x	s			x	x		x	xs	s	s	x		s	x		x		s		sx	s																15
x			x	s			x	x		x	x	s	s	x			x		xs				sx	s	x															16
x	s			x			s	x		x	x	x	s	x			x		xs				sx	s	x															17
x	s						s	x		x	x	xs	s	x			x		x				sx	s	x	x														18
x							sx	x		x	xs	xs		x			x		xs				sx		x	x	sx													19
x				s			s	x		x	x	xs		x			x		xs				s		x	x	sx	sx												20
x			sx				sx	x		x	x		s	x			x		x				sx		x	xs	xs	s												21
x			x				sx	x		x	x		s	x		s	x		xs				sx	s	x		xs													22
x			x				xs	s		x	xs		sx	x		sx	x		xs				sx	s	x		x													23
x			xs				sx	x		x	x	s	s	x		sx	x		x				s	s	x	xs	s													24
x							sx	sx		x	x	xs	s	x		s	x		x				s		x	x	xs													25
							s						x			x					s		x	x			s		x	xs	x	x	sx	x	x	xs	sx			26
xs			x				sx	x		x	x	sx	s	x		s	x		x				s	s	xs	xs	sx													27
x			sx				x	x		x	xs			x			xs		x				s		x	x	sx	s	s											28
			xs				sx	s		x	x	x		x		s	x		x				s		x	x	x		s											29
x			x				sx	x		x	x	xs		x		sx			xs				s		x	x	s		s											30
x			xs				xs	xs		x	sx	sx				x	x						sx		x	x	x	s	s											31
x							s	x		xs	xs	x		x		sx	x		xs				sx		x	x	sx		s											32
s								sx		x	xs	xs		x		x	x		x				sx	s	x	x	xs	sx												33
sx							sx	x		x	x	xs		xs		x	x		xs				sx	s	x	x		s												34
xs							xs	x		x	x	s		sx		x	x		x				s		xs	x	s			sx										35
x							xs	x		x	xs	sx				x	x		x				sx	s	x		xs	s		sx										36
sx			x				xs	x		x	xs	xs					x						sx	s	x	x	sx			s								x		37
s			x				xs	x		x	x	xs				x							sx	s	x	x	sx			s								x		38
x			x					sx		x	x	sx				xs							sx	s	x	x	xs	s		xs								x		39
s			x				xs	x		x	x	xs				s	x						sx		xs	x	sx			sx								x		40
s			x				sx	x		x	x	xs				sx	x		xs				s			x	sx			xs								x		41
s			x				sx	x		x	x					xs	x		x				s	s		x	xs			sx								x		42
xs			x				s	x		x	x					x	x		xs				sx	s			sx	sx		xs								x		43
			x				sx	xs		x	x					xs	x		xs				sx	s	x		x	sx										x	s	44
x			x				xs			x	x	sx				s	x		xs				sx	s	x		x	s										x		45
x			x				x			x	x			s		x	x						s	s	x		x	s		s								x		46
x			x				x	sx		x	xs						x						sx	s	xs	xs	x	s		sx								x		47
s			x				x	x		x	sx					x	x		x				s	s		x	xs			s								x		48
x							x	x			x			xs		s	x		sx				xs	s	x	x		sx		xs								sx		49
x			x				sx	x		x	x					x	x		x				s	s	xs	s		s										x		50
xs			x				sx			s	x					x	x		s				x	s	x	x		x		s								x		51
35	3	12	32	9	4	2	10	38	0	44	35	4	4	25	0	12	40	0	17	0	0	0	2	1	26	21	7	1	1	0	1	1	0	1	1	0	0	14	0	x
4	1	0	3	0	2	3	13	2	3	2	10	15	0	2	0	5	2	0	16	0	0	1	1	0	5	4	8	0	0	5	0	0	0	0	0	1	0	0	0	xs
2	0	2	2	0	2	0	17	5	3	1	4	11	3	2	0	6	0	1	2	1	0	0	22	0	0	0	10	5	0	5	0	0	1	0	0	0	1	1	0	sx
7	6	0	0	8	2	1	9	2	6	1	1	7	18	2	1	11	0	0	2	1	4	1	14	24	0	1	4	10	5	5	0	0	0	0	0	0	0	0	1	s

x - Played full 90 minutes
xs - Substituted off
sx - Substituted on
s - Non-playing Substitute

SPENNYMOOR TOWN MATCH RESULTS 2018-19

Date	Comp	Opponents	H/A	Att:	Result		Goalscorers	Pos
Aug 4	NLN	Chester	A	2191	D	0 - 0		
7	NLN	Darlington	H	1768	D	2 - 2	Anderson 32 Taylor 89	
11	NLN	Altrincham	H	698	D	4 - 4	Anderson 11 Boyes 40 Henry 68 Taylor 84	
14	NLN	Bradford Park Avenue	A	392	L	0 - 1		
18	NLN	AFC Telford United	H	600	L	2 - 3	Anderson 30 Foley 86	
25	NLN	Boston United	A	1210	W	2 - 0	Ramshaw 18 Taylor 79	
27	NLN	FC United of Manchester	H	863	W	2 - 0	Taylor 59 (Pen) Boyes 89	
Sept 1	NLN	Southport	A	821	D	1 - 1	Taylor 90	
8	NLN	Leamington	A	545	W	2 - 0	Boyes 86 Anderson 90	
15	NLN	Nuneaton Borough	H	725	W	3 - 1	Taylor 2 (Pen) Ramshaw 45 Johnson 57	5
22	**FAC 2Q**	**Witton Albion**	**A**	**322**	**L**	**1 - 2**	**Hall 90**	
29	NLN	Hereford	A	2159	W	3 - 0	Anderson 21 Taylor 43 Boyes 86	4
Oct 13	NLN	Ashton United	H	708	W	5 - 0	Curtis 9 Henry 32 Anderson 45 Johnson 59 Boyes 87	3
20	NLN	Brackley Town	A	447	L	1 - 4	Anderson 11	4
27	NLN	Curzon Ashton	H	564	D	0 - 0		
30	NLN	York City	H	1063	W	3 - 0	Brogan 18 Taylor 25 88	4
Nov 3	NLN	Chorley	A	1212	W	2 - 1	Atkinson 66 Taylor 70 (Pen)	3
17	NLN	Guiseley	A	2090	D	1 - 1	Taylor 43 (Pen)	4
24	**FAT 3Q**	**Halesowen Town**	**H**	**502**	**W**	**8 - 2**	**Boyes 10 24 38 Ramshaw 20 90 Taylor 42 Tuton 45 Morris 85 (og)**	
Dec 8	NLN	Alfreton Town	A	235	W	7 - 1	Taylor 6 (Pen) 45 55 Brogan 33 Chandler 34 Tuton 63 Johnson 85	
11	NLN	Stockport County	H	659	L	1 - 3	Brogan 72	5
15	**FAT 1P**	**Barwell**	**H**	**295**	**W**	**4 - 0**	**Taylor 26 51 Anderson 65 76**	
26	NLN	Blyth Spartans	A	1133	D	2 - 2	Anderson 56 Johnson 74	
29	NLN	FC United of Manchester	A	2069	W	3 - 1	Kempster 76 Atkinson 78 Anderson 90	
Jan 1	NLN	Blyth Spartans	H	1129	D	2 - 2	Atkinson 18 Johnson 40	
5	NLN	AFC Telford United	A	1205	L	1 - 2	Taylor 56	
8	NLN	Kidderminster Harriers	H	575	W	2 - 1	Johnson 44 Hall 49	6
12	**FAT 2P**	**Sutton United**	**H**	**760**	**W**	**3 - 0**	**Taylor 24 62 Johnson 81**	
19	NLN	Darlington	A	1664	W	2 - 1	Taylor 53 Brogan 67	
26	NLN	Chester	H	863	W	2 - 0	Hall 30 Taylor 79	
29	NLN	Boston United	H	544	W	1 - 0	Taylor 54	
Feb 2	**FAT 3P**	**AFC Telford United**	**H**	**571**	**L**	**1 - 2**	**Taylor 59**	
16	NLN	Nuneaton Borough	A	510	W	2 - 0	Taylor 77 Anderson 85	
19	NLN	Altrincham	A	696	W	2 - 0	Anderson 38 Ramshaw 63	
23	NLN	Leamington	H	786	W	1 - 0	Anderson 32	3
Mar 2	NLN	Stockport County	A	6311	L	0 - 1		3
5	NLN	Southport	H	660	D	1 - 1	Taylor 87	3
16	NLN	Kidderminster Harriers	A	1436	L	1 - 2	Taylor 49	3
19	NLN	Bradford Park Avenue	H	749	L	0 - 2		3
23	NLN	Alfreton Town	H	1083	D	1 - 1	Taylor 21	3
30	NLN	Hereford	H	830	L	0 - 2		5
Apr 2	NLN	Guiseley	H	603	W	3 - 2	Henry 5 7 Ramshaw 38	4
6	NLN	Ashton United	A	208	L	0 - 3		4
13	NLN	Brackley Town	H	669	W	2 - 1	Hall 42 Taylor 76	4
19	NLN	York City	A	2871	W	3 - 2	Curtis 40 Harrison 54 Hall 78	4
22	NLN	Chorley	H	1261	W	1 - 0	Taylor 90+3	4
27	NLN	Curzon Ashton	A	328	W	5 - 0	Taylor 17 Hibbs 45 Ramshaw 53 Harrison 66 Boyes 87	4
May 1	**PO Q**	**Bradford Park Avenue**	**H**	**1509**	**W**	**1 - 0**	**Hawkins 75**	
5	**PO SF**	**Brackley Town**	**A**	**1271**	**D**	**0 - 0**	**(won 3-1 on pens aet)**	
12	**PO F**	**Chorley**	**A**	**3594**	**D**	**1 - 1**	**Taylor 105 (lost 3-4 on pens aet)**	

GOALSCORERS	SG	CSG	Pens	Hat tricks	Total
Taylor	27	6	5	1	32
Anderson	13	3			14
Boyes	7	2		1	9
Johnson	7	1			7
Ramshaw	6	1			7
Hall	5	2			5
Brogan	4	2			4
Henry	3	1			4
Atkinson	3	2			3
Curtis	2	1			2
Harrison	2	1			2
Tuton	2	1			2
Chandler	1	1			1
Foley	1	1			1
Hawkins	1	1			1
Hibbs	1	1			1
Kempster	1	1			1
Opponent	1	1			1

	Johnson	Brogan	Taylor	Ramshaw	Chandler	Foley	Williams	Anderson	Curtis	Thackray	Henry	Hibbs	King	Boyes	Elliot	Hayes	Atkinson	Tuton	Hall	Jackson	Bayne	Kempster (L)	Agnew (L)	Harrison (L)	Hawkins (L)	Diamond (L)	Webb	Miller	No.
X	X	X	X	X	X	XS	X	XS	X	X	SX	SX	S	S	S														1
X	XS	X	X	X	X	XS	X	X	X	X	S	S		SX	S	SX													2
X	XS	X	X	X	X	S	X	X	X	X	SX	S		X	S	S													3
X	SX	X	X	X	X	SX	X	XS	X	S	XS	SX		XS	S		X												4
X	SX	X	X	X	XS	SX	XS	X	X	S	X	SX		XS	S		X												5
X	SX	X	XS	X	X	SX			X	S	X	X		SX	S		X	XS	SX										6
X	XS	X	X	X	X	S			X		X	X		SX		S	X	X	SX	S									7
X	XS	X	X	X	X				X	SX	X	X		SX	S	S	XS	X	S										8
X	XS	X	X	X	X		S	SX	X	X	X	X		SX	S	S		XS											9
X	XS	X	XS	X	X			SX	X	X	X	X		SX	S		S	XS	SX										10
X	XS	XS	X	X	X		S	SX	X	X	X	X		SX	S		S	XS	SX										11
X	SX	X	X	XS	X		S	XS	X	X	X	X		SX			S	X		S									12
X	SX	X	XS	X	X			X	X	X	XS	X		SX	S		S	XS	SX										13
X	SX	XS	X	X	X			XS	X	X	X	X		S	S		SX	XS	SX										14
X	SX	X	X	X	X		S	XS		X	X	X		SX	S	S	X	XS											15
X	XS	X	X	X	X			X	XS	X	X	XS		SX	S	S	SX	SX											16
X	XS	X	X	X	X		X	XS	X	X				SX	S	S	X	SX			S								17
X	XS	X	X	X	X		S	XS	X	XS	SX	X		SX	S		X	SX											18
	X	X		XS	X	XS		SX		X	S	X	X		X	S		X	XS	SX			SX						19
X	X	X	X		XS		SX	S	X	X	X	X		X	S			XS	S										20
X	XS	X	X	X			S	SX	X	X	X	X		XS	S			XS	SX			SX							21
X	SX	XS	XS	X	X		S	X	X	X	X	X		SX	S			SX	XS										22
X	SX	X	X	X	X			XS	X	X	X	X		SX	S		S	S	XS										23
X	XS	X		X	X			SX	X	S	XS	X		X	S		X	XS	SX			SX							24
X	XS	X	XS	XS	X			X	X	S	X	X		SX	S		X		SX			SX							25
X	XS	X	X		X		SX	XS	X	S	X	XS		X			X	SX	S			SX							26
X	XS	X	X	S			X		X	X	X			SX	S		X	XS	X		S	SX							27
X	XS	X	X	XS	X		X		X	S	X			SX	S		X	SX	XS			SX							28
X	XS	X	XS	X	X		X	SX	X	S	X			SX	S		X	SX	XS										29
X	XS	X	XS	X	X		X	X	X	S				SX	S		X	S	X				SX						30
X	SX	X	X	X	X		X	XS	X	SX				S	S		XS	XS	SX				X						31
X	X	X	X	X	X		X	S	X	XS	XS	SX		SX	S			SX	XS										32
X	XS	X	XS	X	X		X	X	X	S	SX			SX	S				SX				XS	X					33
X	X	X	XS	X	X		X	XS	X	S	X			SX	S				SX				S	X					34
X	XS	X	X	X	X		X	XS	X	S	X			SX				S	SX				S	X					35
X	XS	XS	X	X	X		X	XS	X	S	X			SX	S			SX	SX					X					36
X	XS	X	X	X	X		X	X	X	S	XS			S	S			SX	SX					X					37
X		X	X	X	X		X	XS	X	S	XS	SX		SX	S			XS	SX					X					38
X		X	X	X	X		X	XS	X	S	SX	S		XS	S			SX	X					X					39
X		X	X		X		SX		X	SX	X	XS		S	S			SX	XS					XS	X	X			40
X			X		X		X		X	X		XS	S	SX	S		X		X						X	X	S	S	41
X			X	XS	X		X		X	S	X	S		SX	S		X		X					SX	X	XS			42
X	SX		X	X	X		X		X		X	SX		SX	S		X		XS					S	XS	XS			43
X		X	X	X			X	SX	X		X	S		SX	S		X		X					S	XS	XS			44
X		X	X	X	X		X	XS	X	SX	X			S	S				SX					X	SX	XS			45
X		X	X	X	X		XS			X	X	SX	S	S	S				X					X	XS	SX			46
X			XS	XS	XS		S			X		X	X	SX	S		SX		X					X	X	X	SX		47
X		X	X	X	X		X	S	X	XS		SX		SX	S		S		XS					X	X				48
X		X	X	X	XS		X	SX	X	S		XS		SX	S		S		X					X	X				49
X	SX	X	X	X	X		X	SX	X			XS		SX	S		SX		XS					XS	XS				50
50	5	41	38	40	42	0	26	10	46	20	30	19	1	5	0	0	19	3	9	0	0	0	1	12	6	3	0	0	X
0	22	4	11	5	5	2	2	16	1	3	6	6	0	4	0	0	2	14	9	0	0	0	1	2	4	4	0	0	XS
0	12	0	0	0	0	3	4	9	0	4	5	8	0	34	0	1	4	12	18	0	0	7	1	1	1	1	1	0	SX
0	0	0	0	1	0	2	8	3	0	19	1	5	3	7	46	7	7	3	3	2	2	0	2	2	0	0	1	1	S

x - Played full 90 minutes
xs - Substituted off
sx - Substituted on
s - Non-playing Substitute

STOCKPORT COUNTY MATCH RESULTS 2018-19

Date	Comp	Opponents	H/A	Att:	Result		Goalscorers	Pos
Aug 4	NLN	FC United of Manchester	H	4577	W	5 - 1	Mulhern 12 Warburton 29 45 Turnbull 89 Mantack 90	
7	NLN	York City	A	3218	L	0 - 1		
11	NLN	Southport	A	1736	W	1 - 0	Dimaio 85	
14	NLN	Guiseley	H	2923	D	1 - 1	Walker 60	
18	NLN	Bradford Park Avenue	A	825	D	1 - 1	Warburton 78	
25	NLN	Alfreton Town	H	2868	L	0 - 1		
27	NLN	Kidderminster Harriers	A	1756	L	1 - 2	Mulhern 56	
Sept 1	NLN	Leamington	H	2680	W	3 - 1	Bell 27 Dimaio 59 Stephenson 65	
8	NLN	Boston United	H	3050	L	0 - 2		
15	NLN	AFC Telford United	A	1415	D	1 - 1	Dimaio 33	12
22	**FAC 2Q**	**South Shields**	**A**	**1707**	**W**	**2 - 1**	**Walker 37 Bell 90+1**	
29	NLN	Darlington	A	1507	W	1 - 0	Bell 29	10
Oct 6	**FAC 3Q**	**Corby Town**	**H**	**1935**	**W**	**3 - 0**	**Warburton 53 Mulhern 57 82**	
13	NLN	Hereford	H	3646	D	1 - 1	Mulhern 79	11
20	**FAC 4Q**	**Altrincham**	**H**	**2981**	**W**	**2 - 0**	**Mulhern 41 Warburton 68**	
27	NLN	Nuneaton Borough	H	2802	D	2 - 2	Thomas 57 Walker 67 (Pen)	
30	NLN	Chorley	H	2653	W	3 - 0	Warburton 72 78 89	10
Nov 3	NLN	Curzon Ashton	A	1487	W	2 - 0	Walker 43 (Pen) Osborne 75	9
10	**FAC 1P**	**Yeovil Town**	**A**	**2550**	**W**	**3 - 1**	**Warburton 34 Bell 38 Mulhern 62**	
17	NLN	Brackley Town	H	3449	D	1 - 1	Mulhern 90	10
20	NLN	Blyth Spartans	A	531	L	2 - 3	Thomas 34 Mulhern 66	
24	**FAT 3Q**	**Chorley**	**H**	**1245**	**W**	**3 - 0**	**Palmer 18 Stott 53 Thomas 55**	
Dec 2	**FAC 2P**	**Barnet**	**A**	**2826**	**L**	**0 - 1**		
8	NLN	Chester	H	3714	D	1 - 1	Walker 45	
11	NLN	Spennymoor Town	A	659	W	3 - 1	Warburton 35 Walker 41 Bell 95	11
15	**FAT 1P**	**Altrincham**	**A**	**988**	**W**	**1 - 0**	**Palmer 22**	
18	NLN	Ashton United	A	830	W	6 - 0	Warburton 24 48 Kirby 28 52 Mulhern 31 (Pen) Turnbull 90	
22	NLN	Alfreton Town	A	825	D	1 - 1	Bell 80	
26	NLN	Altrincham	H	4549	W	2 - 0	Stott 24 Mulhern 51	
29	NLN	Kidderminster Harriers	H	3784	W	1 - 0	Miniham 87	
Jan 1	NLN	Altrincham	A	3383	W	1 - 0	Warburton 27	
5	NLN	Bradford Park Avenue	H	4105	W	3 - 0	Warburton 6 Stephenson 67 Mulhern 73	
12	**FAT 2P**	**Truro City**	**H**	**1677**	**W**	**5 - 0**	**Warburton 3 17 27 65 Stephenson 29**	
19	NLN	York City	H	4664	W	3 - 1	Warburton 4 22 75	2
22	NLN	Leamington	A	604	W	1 - 0	Stephenson 37	
26	NLN	FC United of Manchester	A	2987	W	2 - 1	Mulhern 44 Stott 88	
Feb 2	**FAT 3P**	**Harrogate Town**	**A**	**1142**	**W**	**4 - 2**	**Thomas 21 Mulhern 22 79 Warburton 48**	
9	NLN	Guiseley	A	1296	D	1 - 1	Stephenson 42	
16	NLN	AFC Telford United	H	4708	W	3 - 2	Bell 10 Warburton 50 69	
19	NLN	Southport	H	3724	W	3 - 2	Keane 45 Stephenson 50 Walker 53	2
23	**FAT 4P**	**Maidstone United**	**H**	**2585**	**D**	**1 - 1**	**Warburton 28**	
26	**FAT 4Pr**	**Maidstone United**	**A**	**1140**	**W**	**3 - 0**	**Kirby 64 83 Keane 90+3**	
Mar 2	NLN	Spennymoor Town	H	6311	W	1 - 0	Walker 72	2
5	NLN	Boston United	A	1073	W	3 - 1	Stephenson 54 Osborne 66 Mulhern 81	1
9	NLN	Brackley Town	A	1107	L	0 - 1		2
16	**FAT SF1**	**AFC Fylde**	**A**	**2605**	**D**	**0 - 0**		
23	**FAT SF2**	**AFC Fylde**	**H**	**6064**	**L**	**2 - 3**	**Bell 25 Palmer 88**	
26	NLN	Ashton United	H	3257	W	2 - 1	Bell 36 Thomas 67	2
30	NLN	Darlington	H	4807	W	2 - 0	Thomas 44 Keane 65	2
Apr 6	NLN	Hereford	A	3025	D	2 - 2	Thomas 26 Bell 27	2
9	NLN	Chester	A	2565	W	6 - 0	Bell 9 33 Walker 19 82 (pen) Stephenson 69 Keane 87	1
13	NLN	Blyth Spartans	H	5665	L	0 - 1		1
20	NLN	Chorley	A	3597	L	0 - 2		2
22	NLN	Curzon Ashton	H	6001	W	2 - 0	Palmer 6 Warburton 26	1
27	NLN	Nuneaton Borough	A	4054	W	3 - 0	Palmer 37 Warburton 45+1 Thomas 78	1

GOALSCORERS	SG	CSG	Pens	Hat tricks	Total		SG	CSG	Pens	Hat tricks	Total
Warburton	18	4		3	27	Stott	3	1			3
Mulhern	14	3	1		16	Osborne	2	1			2
Bell	11	2			12	Turnbull	2	1			2
Walker	9	2	3		10	Mantack	1	1			1
Stephenson	8	2			8	Miniham	1	1			1
Thomas	8	3			8						
Palmer	5	2			5						
Keane	4	1			4						
Kirby	2	1			4						
Dimaio	3	1			3						

No.	Hinchliffe	Cowan	Duxbury	Keane	Miniham	Mulhern	Stephenson	Turnbull	Walker	Warburton	Palmer	Bell	Dimaio	Mantack	Ormson	Smalley	Downing	Askew (L)	Kirby	Thomas	Osborne	Stott (L)	Etches	Czubik	Robinson	Jackson	Baines	Gilchrist (L)
1	X	X	X	X	X	XS	XS	X	X	XS	X	SX	SX	SX	S	S												
2	X	X	XS	X	X	X	XS	X		XS	X	SX	SX	SX	S	X	S											
3	X	X		X	X	XS	X	XS	X	XS	X	SX	SX	SX	S	X	S											
4	X	X		X	X	XS	XS	X	X	X		SX	SX	SX	S		XS	X	S									
5	X	S		X	X	XS	SX	X	X	X		SX	XS	SX	S	X		X	XS									
6	X	S		XS	X	XS		X	X	X	X	X	SX		S	X		XS	SX	SX								
7	X	X		X	X	SX	SX	XS	X	X	X	X	S		S	SX		XS	XS									
8	X	X		X		XS	X		X	SX	X	XS	XS	SX	S	X	SX	S		X								
9	X	X	SX	XS	SX	XS	X		X	SX	X	X	X		S	XS	S			X								
10	X	X	X	X	X	XS	XS		X	SX	X	SX	XS	S	S				SX	X								
11	X	X	X	X	X	XS	XS		X	S	X	SX	XS	SX	S		S		S	X	SX							
12	X	X	X	XS	X		XS		X	XS	X	X	SX	S	S					SX	X	SX						
13	X	X	X	XS	SX	SX	X		X	SX	X	XS	S	S	S	S				XS	X	X						
14	X	XS	X		SX	X	XS		X	XS	X	SX	SX		S	S				X	X	X						
15	X	SX	XS	SX	X	X	XS		X	XS	X	S	SX	S	S	S				X	X	X						
16	X	S	X	S	X	X	X		X	XS	X	SX	SX		S					XS	X	X						
17	X		X	X	X	SX	XS		X	SX	X	XS	SX		S		S			X	XS	X						
18	X	X	X	X	X	SX	SX		X	X	X	XS	SX		S		S			XS	XS							
19	X	X	X	X	X	SX	S		X	XS	X	XS	SX		S		SX			X	XS		S	S				
20	X	X	X	X	X	SX	SX	S	XS	X	X	XS	SX		S					X	XS							
21	X	X	X	X	XS	X		S	XS	XS	X	SX	SX		S					X	X	SX						
22	X	X	X	X	S	XS	SX	XS	SX	XS	X	SX			S					X	X	X						
23	X	X		XS	XS	X	X	S	X	SX	X	SX	SX		S		S			X	XS	X			S			
24	X	SX	X	X	X	XS	SX	S	X	X	X	SX			S					XS	XS	X						
25	X	SX	X	X	S	XS		X	X	XS	X	SX			S				XS	X	SX	X						
26	X	X	X	X	S	XS	SX	SX		X	X	SX			S				XS	X	XS	X						
27	X	X	X	X	SX	XS	S	X		XS	X	SX			S				X	XS	SX	X						
28	X	XS	X	X	S	XS		XS	SX	X	X	SX			S				X	X	SX	X						
29	X		X	X	X	XS	SX	X	SX	XS	X	SX			S				XS	X	S	X						
30	X	SX	X		X	XS	XS	X	XS	X	X	XS			S					XS	X	X				S		
31	X	SX	X	X	X	XS	SX	X		XS	X	S			S				X	XS	SX	X						
32	X	S	X	X	X	XS	X	XS		XS	X	SX	SX		S					X	SX	X						
33	X	S	X	X	X	X	XS	XS	SX	XS	X				S				SX	X	SX	X						
34	X	SX	X	X	X	XS	X		X	XS	X	SX			S				SX	XS	S	X						
35	X	SX	X	X	X	X	X		X	XS	X	S			S				S	XS	SX	X						
36	X	SX	X	X	X	X	XS	S	X	XS	X				S				SX	XS	SX	X						
37	X	SX	X	X	X	XS	XS	SX	X	XS	X				S				SX	X	S						X	
38	X	S	X		X	XS	X	SX	X	XS	X				S				SX	X	SX						X	
39	X		XS	X	X	SX	X	SX	X	X	X	XS			S				S	X	S						X	
40	X		X	X	X	SX	XS	SX	X	XS	X	XS			S				S	X	SX						X	
41	X		XS	X	X	SX	X	SX	X	X	X	XS			S				SX	X	S						XS	
42	X	X	X	X	SX	XS	SX	X	X		X	SX			S				XS	XS	X						S	
43	X			X	X	SX	SX	SX	X	XS	X	XS			S				XS	X	S	X					X	
44	X	X	X	X	SX	X	XS	X	SX	X	XS				S				S	X	SX	X						
45	X	X	SX	X	XS	X		S	X	SX	X				S				XS	SX	X	X					XS	
46	X	S	X	X	X		X	S	X	SX	X	X			S					XS	X	X					S	
47	X	S	X	X	X	SX	XS	SX	X	SX	X	XS			S					XS	X	X						
48	X	X	X	SX	S	SX	XS	X	X	XS	X	XS			S					X	SX	X						
49	X	X	X	X	SX		SX	X	S	XS	X	XS			S					XS	X	X						SX
50	X	X	X	X	S	SX	XS	SX	XS	SX	X	XS			S					X	X	X						
51	X	SX	X	SX	XS		X	X	X	XS	X	XS			S					X	SX	X						S
52	X	XS	X	XS	S	SX	X	X	X	SX	X	XS			S					X	SX	X						
53	X		X	X	XS	SX	XS	X	SX	X	X	XS			S				SX	X	S	X						
54	X		X	SX	SX	X	SX	XS	X	XS	X				S				XS	X	X	X						S
55	X	S	X	X	X	XS	SX	X	X	XS	X	SX			S				XS	X	SX							
X	55	25	41	41	34	12	15	18	39	14	52	5	1	0	0	5	0	2	3	32	15	32	0	0	0	0	5	0
XS	0	3	4	6	5	24	19	7	4	28	1	18	4	0	0	1	1	2	10	14	7	0	0	0	0	0	2	0
SX	0	10	2	4	8	15	14	9	6	11	0	22	16	7	0	1	2	0	9	3	16	2	0	0	0	0	0	1
S	0	9	0	1	7	0	2	7	1	1	0	3	2	4	55	4	7	1	6	0	7	0	1	1	1	1	2	2

x - Played full 90 minutes
xs - Substituted off
sx - Substituted on
s - Non-playing Substitute

YORK CITY MATCH RESULTS 2018-19

Date	Comp	Opponents	H/A	Att:	Result		Goalscorers	Pos
Aug 4	NLN	Chorley	A	1520	L	0 - 1		
7	NLN	Stockport County	H	3218	**W**	1 - 0	York 76	
11	NLN	Alfreton Town	H	2501	L	1 - 2	Langstaff 68	
14	NLN	Ashton United	A	545	**W**	2 - 0	Langstaff 76 Tait 84	
18	NLN	Cuzon Ashton	H	2192	D	1 - 1	Parkin 76	
Martin Gray sacked as manager, club's Youth Team Manager, Sam Collins, is made caretaker.								
25	NLN	Brackley Town	A	580	D	0 - 0		
27	NLN	Blyth Spartans	H	2696	**W**	2 - 0	Parkin 80 (Pen) Moke 90	
Sept 1	NLN	Hereford	A	2558	D	1 - 1	Langstaff 25	
15	NLN	Kidderminster Harriers	H	2404	L	0 - 3		14
22	**FAC 2Q**	**Ashton Athletic**	**H**	**1020**	**W**	**5 - 0**	**Ferguson 2 Burrow 15 Tait 38 Harris 45 York 63**	
29	NLN	Guiseley	H	2331	**W**	4 - 2	Langstaff 16 Burrow 37 Newton 77 82	12
Oct 2	NLN	Nuneaton Borough	A	501	D	2 - 2	Wright 74 Parkin 85	9
6	**FAC 3Q**	**St Ives Town**	**H**	**1243**	**W**	**3 - 0**	**Wright 9 Burrow 50 56**	
Caretaker Sam Collins is given the manager's job.								
13	NLN	Southport	A	1149	**W**	2 - 1	Burrow 42 Heslop 83	8
20	**FAC 4Q**	**Blyth Spartans**	**A**	**1378**	**W**	**1 - 0**	**Burrow 11**	
27	NLN	AFC Telford United	A	1384	L	1 - 2	Langstaff 36	9
30	NLN	Spennymoor Town	A	1063	L	0 - 3		12
Nov 3	NLN	Bradford Park Avenue	H	2289	L	1 - 4	Newton 61	15
10	**FAC 1P**	**Swindon Town**	**A**	**3744**	**L**	**1 - 2**	**Ferguson 43**	
13	NLN	Chester	H	2319	D	0 - 0		12
17	NLN	Altrincham	A	685	L	0 - 3		17
24	**FAT 3Q**	**Kidderminster Harriers**	**A**	**784**	**W**	**3 - 1**	**Burrow 2 51 (pen) Hawkins 22**	
Dec 1	NLN	FC United of Manchester	H	2583	**W**	2 - 0	Harris 35 Burrow 86	13
4	NLN	Leamington	H	1938	D	2 - 2	Burrow 56 61 (Pen)	
8	NLN	Boston United	A	1143	L	0 - 2		14
15	**FAT 1P**	**Harrogate Town**	**A**	**1336**	**L**	**1 - 2**	**Bray 21**	
22	NLN	Brackley Town	H	2119	**W**	2 - 1	Moke 16 Burrow 49 (Pen)	
26	NLN	Darlington	A	2286	L	1 - 5	Wright 66	
29	NLN	Blyth Spartans	A	1122	L	1 - 2	Wright 36	
Jan 1	NLN	Darlington	H	3265	**W**	4 - 0	Burrow 31 (Pen) Bencherif 41 83 Wright 63	
5	NLN	Cuzon Ashton	A	427	L	0 - 1		
Sam Collins steps down as manager. Gateshead manager, Steve Watson, resigns and takes up the vacant position.								
19	NLN	Stockport County	A	4664	L	1 - 3	Kempster 73	17
26	NLN	Chorley	H	2669	L	1 - 4	Burrow 35	
Feb 2	NLN	Alfreton Town	A	655	**W**	3 - 2	Newton 11 Kempster 84 Burrow 88 (pen)	
5	NLN	Hereford	H	2370	L	1 - 2	Kempster 9	
9	NLN	Ashton United	H	2150	**W**	2 - 0	Burrow 83 89	
16	NLN	Kidderminster Harriers	A	1598	**W**	2 - 1	Griffiths 31 Burgess 83	
23	NLN	Nuneaton Borough	H	2355	**W**	2 - 0	York 57 Bencherif 78	12
Mar 2	NLN	Leamington	A	801	**W**	1 - 0	Kempster 11	11
9	NLN	Altrincham	H	2618	L	0 - 1		12
23	NLN	Boston United	H	2594	D	2 - 2	Newton 24 Langstaff 38	14
26	NLN	FC United of Manchester	A	1670	D	3 - 3	Langstaff 29 77 York 72	14
30	NLN	Guiseley	A	1304	D	1 - 1	McLaughlin 10	13
Apr 6	NLN	Southport	H	2174	**W**	1 - 0	Langstaff 32	12
13	NLN	Chester	A	1772	D	2 - 2	Moke 36 McLaughlin 64	12
19	NLN	Spennymoor Town	H	2871	L	2 - 3	Kempster 51 Newton 66	
22	NLN	Bradford Park Avenue	A	775	**W**	3 - 1	McLaughlin 67 Burrow 80 Langstaff 90+1	12
27	NLN	AFC Telford United	H	2864	**W**	1 - 0	Burrow 50	12

GOALSCORERS	SG	CSG	Pens	Hat tricks	Total		SG	CSG	Pens	Hat tricks	Total
Burrow	15	3	5		19	Ferguson	2	1			2
Langstaff	9	2			10	Harris	2	1			2
Newton	5	1			6	Tait	2	1			2
Kempster	5	2			5	Bray	1	1			1
Wright	5	3			5	Burgess	1	1			1
York	4	1			4	Griffiths	1	1			1
Bencherif	2	1			3	Hawkins	1	1			1
McLaughlin	3	1			3	Heslop	1	1			1
Moke	3	1			3						
Parkin	3	1	1		3						

Bartlett	Griffiths	Newton	Bencherif	Tait	Penn	Kempster	Heslop	Burrow	Wright	York	Moke	Langstaff	Parkin	Ferguson	Whitley	Allan	Parslow	Law	McAughtrie	Harris	Dyer	Hawkins (L)	Davis	Bray (L)	Harrison	Digie (L)	Ironside (L)	Agnew (L)	Bradbury (L)	Burgess (L)	McLaughlin (L)	Mirfin (L)	Moon (L)	No.
x	x	x	x	x	xs	x	x	xs	x	xs	sx	sx	sx	s	s																			1
x	x	x	x	x	x	x	xs	xs	xs	x	sx	sx	sx	s	s																			2
x	x	x	x	x	x	xs		xs	x	x	x	sx	sx	sx	s	s																		3
x	x		x	x	xs			x	xs	x	xs	x	sx	sx	s	x	s	sx																4
x	x		x	x	xs		x	sx	sx	xs	x	xs	x	s	s	x		sx																5
x	x		x	x	x		x	sx	sx	sx		xs	xs	x	s	s		x	xs															6
x	x		x	x	x		x	sx	xs	xs	sx	xs	sx	x	s	s		x																7
x	x		x	x	sx		x		xs	sx	xs	x	xs	x	s		s	x	sx															8
x	x	sx	x	x			x	s	xs	sx	xs	x	sx	x	s			x	xs															9
x	**x**	**x**		**xs**	**sx**		**xs**	**x**	**s**	**sx**	**x**	**xs**	**s**	**x**	**s**	**s**	**sx**	**x**		**x**														10
x	xs	x	sx	x	sx		x	x	s	sx	xs	xs	s	x				x		x														11
x	xs	x	s	x	s		x	xs	sx	sx	x	xs	sx	x				x		x														12
x		**x**	**x**	**xs**	**sx**	**sx**	**x**	**xs**	**xs**	**s**	**s**	**s**	**sx**	**x**			**s**	**x**		**x**	**x**													13
x		x	x		x		x	x	xs		s	sx	sx	xs	s	sx		x		x	xs													14
x	**x**	**x**	**sx**	**x**	**x**		**x**	**x**	**s**	**sx**	**sx**	**xs**	**s**		**s**	**x**		**xs**		**xs**	**s**													15
x	s	x	x	x	x	s		x	sx		sx	xs		x		sx		x		xs	x													16
x	x	x	x	x	xs			x	sx	xs	x	xs	sx			s		sx		x	s													17
x	xs	x	sx	x				x	xs		xs	sx	sx	s		x		x		x	s	x												18
x	**x**	**x**	**s**					**x**	**s**		**x**	**sx**	**sx**	**x**	**s**			**xs**		**sx**	**xs**	**x**	**x**	**xs**	**s**									19
x	x	x						xs			x	sx	sx	s				x		s	s	x		x		x	xs							20
x	x	x						x			x	sx	sx	s				x		sx	s	xs	x	xs		x	xs							21
x	**x**	**x**		**xs**				**x**	**s**	**s**	**x**	**s**		**sx**				**sx**		**xs**	**x**	**x**	**x**	**x**										22
x	x	xs		s				x	s		x	s		sx						x	x	x	x	xs		x	sx							23
x	x	x		x				x	xs		x	sx		s				s		x		sx	x	xs		x	s							24
x	x	x		x				x		sx	xs	xs		s				s		xs		x	x	sx		x	sx							25
x	**x**			**s**				**x**		**x**		**sx**		**x**			**s**	**xs**		**sx**	**x**	**xs**	**x**	**xs**		**x**	**sx**							26
x			s	x				x	sx	x	x	sx	s	x			x	x			x		s	xs			xs							27
x		sx		xs				x	sx	x	x		s	xs			x	x			x			x		s	xs	sx						28
x			x				sx	x	xs		xs	x		x	s			xs		sx	x		s			x	sx	x						29
x			x				x	xs	xs		x	x		x	s			x		s	s		x	sx			sx	x						30
x	xs		x					x	x		x	xs		x	s			x		sx	s		x			s	sx	x						31
x	x	x	x	s		x		x	xs	sx	xs	s	sx	x	s			x										x						32
x	s	s	x	x		xs		x	xs	x		sx	sx	x	s														x	x	x			33
x	xs	x	xs			x		x	sx	sx				s	s			x		sx									x	xs	x	x		34
x	s	x				xs		x	sx	x				sx	s		xs	x		x									x	sx	xs	x		35
x	x	x	s			x		x	xs	x	xs		sx	x	s			sx		s										x		x		36
x	x	x	s			x		x		x	x		s	x	s			s		s										x	x	x		37
x	x	x	sx			x		x	s	xs	x			x	s			s		sx										x	x	xs		38
x	x	x	x			x		x		xs	x		s	x	s			sx		s	s									x	x			39
x	xs	x	sx			xs		x		x	xs		sx	x	s			s		sx										x	x	x		40
x	x	x	s			sx		x		sx	xs	xs	xs	x	s					sx										x	x	x		41
x	x	x	x	s		xs		sx		sx	x	x	xs	x	s						s									x	x			42
x	x	x	s	x		xs		x		s	x	x	s	x	s					sx										x	x			43
	x	x	s			x		x	xs	sx		x	s	x	x			s		s										x	x		x	44
s	x	x	s			xs		xs	sx	s	x	x	sx	x	x															x	x		x	45
s	x	x		s		sx		x		sx	xs	x		x	x			xs		sx										xs	x		x	46
s	x	x		x		x		x		xs		x		x	x			s		sx	s									x	x		s	47
s	x	x		x		xs		x		sx	x			x	x			s		xs	sx									x	x		s	48
43	33	34	20	22	7	10	12	34	3	11	22	11	1	30	5	4	2	20	0	10	8	6	9	3	0	7	0	4	3	13	14	6	3	x
0	6	1	1	4	4	8	2	8	15	7	12	12	4	2	0	0	1	5	2	5	2	2	0	6	0	0	4	0	0	2	1	1	0	xs
0	0	2	5	0	4	3	1	4	10	15	5	12	19	5	0	2	1	6	1	12	1	1	0	2	0	0	6	1	0	1	0	0	0	sx
4	3	1	9	5	1	1	0	1	7	4	2	4	9	9	28	5	4	8	0	6	10	0	2	0	1	2	1	0	0	0	0	0	2	s

x - Played full 90 minutes
xs - Substituted off
sx - Substituted on
s - Non-playing Substitute

National North action between Brackley Town and Guiseley. Photo: Bill Wheatcroft.

Alfreton Town v FC United in the National League North. Photo: Bill Wheatcroft.

Boston Utd v Alfreton Town.

Alfreton Town v Southport. Photos: Bill Wheatcroft.

NATIONAL LEAGUE SOUTH TABLE 2018-19

		P	W	D	L	F	A	GD	Pts
1	Torquay United	42	27	7	8	93	41	52	88
2	Woking (Play-off winners)	42	23	9	10	76	49	27	78
3	Welling United	42	23	7	12	70	47	23	76
4	Chelmsford City	42	21	9	12	68	50	18	72
5	Bath City	42	20	11	11	58	36	22	71
6	Concord Rangers	42	20	13	9	69	48	21	70*
7	Wealdstone	42	18	12	12	62	50	12	66
8	Billericay Town	42	19	8	15	72	65	7	65
9	St Albans City	42	18	10	14	67	64	3	64
10	Dartford	42	18	10	14	52	58	-6	64
11	Slough Town	42	17	12	13	56	50	6	63
12	Oxford City	42	17	5	20	64	63	1	56
13	Chippenham Town	42	16	7	19	57	64	-7	55
14	Dulwich Hamlet	42	13	10	19	52	65	-13	49
15	Hampton & Richmond Borough	42	13	10	19	49	66	-17	49
16	Hemel Hempstead Town	42	12	12	18	52	67	-15	48
17	Gloucester City	42	12	11	19	35	54	-19	47
18	Eastbourne Borough	42	10	12	20	52	65	-13	42
19	Hungerford Town	42	11	9	22	45	72	-27	42
20	Truro City	42	9	12	21	63	87	-24	39
21	East Thurrock United	42	10	7	25	42	63	-21	37
22	Weston-super-Mare AFC	42	8	11	23	50	80	-30	35

		1	2	3	4	5	6	7	8	9	10	11	12	13	14	15	16	17	18	19	20	21	22
1	Bath City		1-2	5-0	2-0	1-1	1-2	2-1	1-0	1-0	3-0	1-0	0-1	4-1	1-0	2-0	0-3	3-2	1-1	1-1	0-2	1-1	2-0
2	Billericay Town	0-2		1-2	0-1	1-1	1-1	1-1	2-0	3-2	1-0	1-3	2-1	1-2	2-3	3-2	3-2	0-2	3-2	1-0	2-0	0-4	4-2
3	Chippenham Town	2-2	2-0		0-1	4-1	1-2	1-2	2-3	2-0	1-0	3-2	1-1	3-1	0-1	1-0	0-0	2-1	2-1	3-1	1-4	2-2	1-3
4	Chelmsford City	1-0	5-1	1-0		2-2	2-1	2-2	3-2	1-0	2-0	2-0	2-1	4-1	2-1	0-1	2-4	0-0	0-2	0-3	0-0	2-0	2-2
5	Concord Rangers	2-1	2-2	1-1	3-0		2-0	0-0	3-0	1-1	2-0	4-0	2-1	4-0	0-1	2-2	2-1	0-1	3-0	2-2	0-5	1-1	3-0
6	Dartford	3-0	2-1	0-1	1-0	1-1		2-1	2-2	2-0	2-0	2-2	0-0	2-1	3-2	1-1	3-2	0-2	1-1	0-3	1-0	2-0	2-1
7	Dulwich Hamlet	0-2	2-2	2-0	1-3	0-1	2-0		2-1	2-1	0-1	0-2	3-3	3-1	0-1	0-1	1-0	0-2	3-2	1-1	2-1	1-3	3-3
8	Eastbourne Borough	0-0	0-2	2-1	1-1	1-2	6-0	2-1		0-2	1-2	2-2	3-0	3-1	2-2	2-4	1-2	2-4	2-2	0-3	1-0	1-2	1-1
9	East Thurrock United	1-0	2-1	2-1	2-0	0-2	2-2	0-0	0-1		2-0	0-0	1-2	2-1	0-1	1-0	2-4	1-2	2-2	0-1	4-1	0-1	2-3
10	Gloucester City	0-0	1-4	3-2	0-0	1-2	1-2	1-1	2-2	1-0		0-0	1-1	0-0	1-0	1-2	0-0	0-0	0-2	0-0	0-1	3-4	1-3
11	Hampton & Richmond Borough	0-1	0-2	2-1	1-1	1-4	0-1	2-0	0-0	1-0	0-1		1-2	0-3	2-4	1-1	0-1	0-3	2-2	2-1	2-1	0-3	3-1
12	Hemel Hempstead Town	0-3	0-2	4-2	3-5	2-2	1-2	1-0	3-2	3-2	2-1	1-1		0-0	2-1	1-1	1-1	1-4	1-1	0-1	1-1	0-2	0-2
13	Hungerford Town	0-0	2-2	2-1	0-6	2-1	1-0	1-2	2-0	1-1	1-2	2-0	0-3		1-1	1-2	5-0	0-2	1-4	1-1	0-1	1-1	0-1
14	Oxford City	1-2	2-3	1-1	1-3	2-0	2-1	4-1	0-0	3-1	0-1	3-5	2-1	1-2		1-3	2-1	1-0	4-0	3-0	0-1	1-2	3-0
15	Slough Town	0-0	2-1	2-2	1-0	1-0	2-2	1-2	1-1	3-1	1-2	1-1	1-0	2-0	2-0		2-2	0-0	1-2	0-1	1-0	0-1	2-1
16	St Albans City	0-2	2-1	2-3	3-1	2-0	2-0	1-0	1-1	2-1	1-2	2-3	2-1	3-2	1-0	3-2		0-4	2-2	0-0	2-0	1-1	2-0
17	Torquay United	1-0	2-2	0-1	3-1	4-1	2-0	5-2	2-0	2-0	2-1	0-2	2-0	0-1	7-2	4-0	4-1		4-2	3-2	3-1	2-2	1-2
18	Truro City	1-1	0-4	1-2	0-3	1-3	3-1	3-2	2-0	1-3	1-2	0-2	1-2	2-3	2-0	3-3	2-1	1-3		1-2	2-2	0-1	3-3
19	Wealdstone	3-3	1-1	1-0	2-3	1-1	1-1	1-3	0-3	3-0	2-0	2-1	2-1	1-0	0-2	0-3	2-2	0-3	3-0		1-3	1-0	4-1
20	Welling United	2-1	0-3	2-1	2-0	0-1	2-0	2-0	1-0	2-0	3-1	4-0	1-1	3-1	3-2	2-1	2-2	2-0	5-3	1-1		3-3	3-1
21	Woking	1-3	2-1	2-0	1-1	1-2	0-1	1-2	2-0	3-0	1-2	3-1	3-1	3-0	3-2	0-1	2-1	3-3	3-1	0-2	2-0		2-1
22	Weston-super-Mare AFC	0-2	2-3	0-1	0-3	1-2	3-1	1-1	0-1	1-1	0-0	0-2	1-2	0-0	1-1	2-0	2-3	2-2	1-1	0-5	0-1	2-4	

BATH CITY MATCH RESULTS 2018-19

Date	Comp	Opponents	H/A	Att:	Result		Goalscorers	Pos
Aug 4	NLS	Dartford	H	828	L	1 - 2	Mann 9	
7	NLS	Torquay United	A	2151	L	0 - 1		
11	NLS	Hampton & Richmond Boro	A	408	**W**	1 - 0	Rigg 61	
14	NLS	Gloucester City	H	775	**W**	3 - 0	Brunt 3 20 Stearn 62	
18	NLS	Dulwich Hamlet	H	869	**W**	2 - 1	Brunt 50 72	
25	NLS	Chelmsford City	A	764	L	0 - 1		
27	NLS	Weston-super-Mare	H	1022	**W**	2 - 0	Rigg 56 Raynes 62	
Sept 1	NLS	East Thurrock United	A	203	L	0 - 1		
8	NLS	Hungerford Town	H	689	**W**	4 - 1	Brunt 25 30 (Pen) Straker 36 Cundy 53	
15	NLS	Oxford City	A	402	**W**	2 - 1	Mann 63 Raynes 90	5
22	**FAC 2Q**	**Banbury United**	**A**	**654**	**W**	**2 - 0**	**Stearn 30 42**	
29	NLS	Welling United	H	1585	L	0 - 2		8
Oct 6	**FAC 3Q**	**Lewes**	**H**	**628**	**W**	**3 - 0**	**Brunt 45 Mann 51 Smith 71**	
13	NLS	St Albans City	A	1432	**W**	2 - 0	Brunt 10 Mann 33	5
20	**FAC 4Q**	**Weston-super-Mare**	**A**	**1053**	**L**	**0 - 1**		
27	NLS	Woking	A	1562	**W**	3 - 1	Mann 6 Cundy 23 Straker 38 (Pen)	
30	NLS	Truro City	A	140	D	1 - 1	Straker 48 (Pen)	
Nov 3	NLS	Hemel Hempstead Town	H	916	L	0 - 1		5
10	NLS	Wealdstone	A	901	D	3 - 3	Stearn 4 13 75	8
17	NLS	Eastbourne Borough	H	783	**W**	1 - 0	Cundy 35	6
25	**FAT 3Q**	**Horsham**	**A**	**328**	**W**	**2 - 1**	**Batten 10 Rigg 68**	
Dec 8	NLS	Concord Rangers	H	546	D	1 - 1	Rigg 48	
11	NLS	Billericay Town	H	545	L	1 - 2	Stearn 9	
15	**FAT 1P**	**Barnet**	**A**	**413**	**L**	**2 - 3**	**Efete 34 Mann 64**	
22	NLS	Chelmsford City	H	637	**W**	2 - 0	Straker 6 (Pen) Smith 90	
26	NLS	Chippenham Town	A	1445	D	2 - 2	Stearn 30 Brunt 74	
29	NLS	Weston-super-Mare	A	833	**W**	2 - 0	Cundy 21 Raynes 52	
Jan 1	NLS	Chippenham Town	H	1727	**W**	5 - 0	Straker 18 (Pen) Stearn 22 28 Cundy 33 Mann 54	
5	NLS	Dulwich Hamlet	A	3104	**W**	2 - 0	Smith 73 Stearn 80	
8	NLS	Slough Town	A	520	D	0 - 0		
12	NLS	East Thurrock United	H	772	**W**	1 - 0	Rigg 54	
19	NLS	Torquay United	H	3492	**W**	3 - 2	Hinds 9 Straker 82 Brunt 86	3
26	NLS	Gloucester City	A	519	D	0 - 0		
Feb 9	NLS	Dartford	A	1034	L	0 - 3		
16	NLS	Concord Rangers	A	284	L	1 - 2	Rigg 90	
23	NLS	Slough Town	H	866	**W**	2 - 0	Hinds 28 Morton 90	6
Mar 2	NLS	Truro City	H	1408	D	1 - 1	Straker 3	6
9	NLS	Hemel Hempstead Town	A	413	**W**	3 - 0	Stearn 34 68 70	6
12	NLS	Hampton & Richmond Boro	H	576	**W**	1 - 0	Batten 23	3
16	NLS	Wealdstone	H	966	D	1 - 1	Pryce 66	3
23	NLS	Eastbourne Borough	A	587	D	0 - 0		5
30	NLS	Woking	H	1710	D	1 - 1	Watkins 72	5
Apr 6	NLS	Welling United	A	711	L	1 - 2	Rigg 59	5
13	NLS	St Albans City	H	1059	L	0 - 3		5
19	NLS	Hungerford Town	A	576	D	0 - 0		5
22	NLS	Oxford City	H	1164	**W**	1 - 0	Smith 60	5
27	NLS	Billericay Town	A	1109	**W**	2 - 0	Cundy 57 Smith 60	5
May 1	**PO Q**	**Wealdstone**	**H**	**2201**	**L**	**1 - 3**	**Mann 82**	

GOALSCORERS	SG	CSG	Pens	Hat tricks	Total
Stearn	8	2		2	14
Brunt	7	2			10
Mann	8	1			8
Rigg	7	1			7
Straker	7	2	3		7
Cundy	6	2			6
Smith	5	2			5
Raynes	3	1			3
Batten	2	1			2
Hinds	2	1			2
Efete	1	1			1
Morton	1	1			1
Pryce*	1	1			1
Watkins	1	1			1

Clarke	Straker	Batten	Watkins	Rigg	Brunt	Stearn	Mann	Cundy	Raynes	Morton (L)	Mills	Artus	Richards	Ball	Hodges	Amankwaah	Smith T (L)	Ollis	Efete (L)	Rees (L)	Wiles-Richards	Moore (L)	Baghdadi (L)	Matthews	Hinds (L)	Davies (L)	Romanski (L)	Pryce (L)	Pearson (L)	No.
x	x	x	x	xs	xs	x	x	x	x	x	sx	sx	s	s	s															1
x	x	x	xs	x	sx	x	xs	x	x	x	x	sx	s	s	s															2
x	x	x	x	x	sx	x	x	x	x	x	xs	s	s	s	s															3
x	x	x	xs	xs	xs	x	x	x	x	x	sx	sx	sx	s																4
x	x	xs	xs	x	x	xs	x	x	x	x	sx	sx	s	sx	s															5
x	x	x	x	x	xs		x	x	x	x	sx	x	s	s	s	s														6
x	x	x	xs	x	xs		x	x	x	x	sx	x	sx	s	s	s														7
x	x	x	sx	x	x	x	xs	x	x	x	s	x	s		s	s														8
x	x	x	xs	x	xs	x	x	x	x	x	sx	sx	s		s	s														9
x	x	x	xs	x	x	x	x	x	x	xs	sx	sx	s		s	s														10
x	**x**	**x**	**sx**	**xs**	**x**	**xs**	**x**	**x**	**x**		**xs**	**x**	**s**	**s**	**s**	**s**	**sx**	**sx**												11
x	x	x		xs	x	x	x	x	x		sx	s	xs	s	s	sx	x													12
x	**x**	**x**			**xs**	**x**	**x**	**x**	**x**		**sx**	**x**	**s**	**s**	**s**	**s**	**x**		**x**											13
x	x	x	s		x	x	x	x	s	x		x		s	s	s	x		x											14
x	**x**	**x**	**s**	**s**	**x**	**x**	**x**	**x**	**sx**	**x**		**x**		**s**	**s**	**s**	**xs**		**x**											15
x	x	x			sx	xs	xs	x		x		x				s	x		x	sx										16
x	x	x			sx	xs	x	x	x	x		x		s	s	sx	x		x	s										17
x	x			sx	x	sx	x	x	x	x		xs				xs	x		x	s	s									18
x	x	x		xs	sx	x	xs	x	x	x		x					sx		x	s	s									19
x	x	x		x	s	xs	x	x	x	xs		x					sx		x		s	sx	s							20
	x	**x**		**x**	**xs**	**x**	**x**	**x**	**x**	**x**		**xs**					**sx**				**x**	**sx**	**s**	**s**						21
x	x	x		xs	sx	x	xs	x	x			x				s	x		x		s	s	sx							22
x	x	x			xs	x	x	x	x			x	s				x		x		s	sx	s							23
x	**x**	**x**			**xs**	**x**	**x**	**x**	**x**			**x**	**s**			**s**	**xs**		**x**		**s**	**sx**	**sx**							24
x	x	x			x	x	x	x	x			x	s			s	x	s	x		s									25
x	x	x			xs	x	x	x	x			x	s			s	x	sx	x		s									26
x	x	x				x	x	x	x	sx	s	xs	s			x	xs	sx	x		s									27
x	x	x			sx	xs	x	x	x	x	s	xs	s			x	sx		x		s									28
x		x	sx			x	x	x	x	x		x	sx	s		x	xs		xs		s									29
x	x	x		sx		x	x	x	x			x	sx	s		xs	xs				s				x					30
x	x	x	sx	x	sx	xs	x	x	x			x	s	s			xs				s				x					31
x	x	x	sx	x	sx	xs		x	x			x		s		xs	sx				s				xs	x				32
x	x	x	s		s	sx	x	x	x	x		x					s				s				x	xs	x			33
x	x	x	sx			x		x	x	x		x	s				x				s				xs	s	x			34
x	x	x	xs	sx	sx	sx	x	x		x		xs				s	xs				s				x	x				35
x	x	x	s	x	sx	xs	xs	x	x	x		s					sx				s				x		x			36
x	x	x	xs	x	sx	sx	xs	x	x	x				s			s				s				x		x			37
x	x	x	sx	xs	xs	sx		x	x	x		x		sx		s					s				x		x			38
x	x	x			x	x		x	x	x		x		sx		s	sx				s				xs		xs			39
x	x	x			x	xs		x	x	x		x		s		s	s				s				x		x	sx		40
x	x	x	sx			x		x	x	x		xs		s		s	sx				s				x		xs	x		41
x	x	x	x			xs		x	x	x				s		x	x				s				x		s	sx		42
x	x	x	xs	xs		sx	sx	x	x	x						x	x				s				xs		s	sx		43
x	x	x	xs	xs		sx	x	x	x	x						x	x				s						s	sx	s	44
x	x	x	xs	xs	sx	x	xs	x	x	x		sx		s			x				s				sx					45
x	x	x	sx	xs	xs	sx		x	x	x		x		s			x				s				xs			sx		46
x	x	x			xs	xs	sx	x	x	x		x		sx			x				s				xs		s	sx		47
x	**x**	**x**		**sx**	**x**	**xs**	**sx**	**x**	**x**	**x**		**xs**		**s**			**x**				**s**				**x**			**sx**		48
47	47	46	4	14	12	25	29	48	44	34	1	27	0	0	0	6	18	0	15	0	1	0	0	0	11	2	6	1	0	x
0	0	1	11	11	13	13	8	0	0	2	2	7	1	0	0	3	7	0	1	0	0	0	0	0	6	1	2	0	0	xs
0	0	0	9	4	13	8	3	0	1	1	9	7	4	4	0	2	9	3	0	1	0	4	2	0	1	0	0	7	0	sx
0	0	0	4	1	2	0	0	0	1	0	3	3	18	23	15	19	3	1	0	3	30	1	3	1	0	1	4	0	1	s

x - Played full 90 minutes
xs - Substituted off
sx - Substituted on
s - Non-playing Substitute

BILLERICAY TOWN MATCH RESULTS 2018-19

Date	Comp	Opponents	H/A	Att:	Result		Goalscorers	Pos
Aug 4	NLS	Truro City	A	362	**W**	4 - 0	Robinson 5 20 65 67	
7	NLS	Concord Rangers	H	1351	D	1 - 1	Emmanuel 90	
11	NLS	Wealdstone	H	1152	**W**	1 - 0	Robinson 31	
14	NLS	Welling United	A	742	**W**	3 - 0	Coombes 23 (Pen) Walton 51 Robinson 59	
18	NLS	Weston-super-Mare	H	790	**W**	4 - 2	Robinson 4 81 Howells 51 Emmanuel 65	
25	NLS	Chippenham Town	A	547	L	0 - 2		
Harry Wheeler is sacked as manager.								
27	NLS	St Albans City	H	1356	**W**	3 - 2	Doe 41 Robinson 45 Kennedy 70	
Sept 1	NLS	Woking	A	1925	L	1 - 2	Robinson 12 (Pen)	
8	NLS	Hemel Hempstead Town	A	821	**W**	2 - 0	Cunnington 48 Emmanuel 90	
15	NLS	Dartford	H	1431	D	1 - 1	Robinson 49 (Pen)	2
Dean Brennan steps down from Hemel Hempstead to become the new Billericay Town manager.								
22	**FAC 2Q**	**Burnham**	**H**	**667**	**W**	**4 - 1**	**Hunte 2 Emmanuel 8 74 Deering 90**	
29	NLS	Hampton & Richmond Boro'	A	886	**W**	2 - 0	Robinson 5 Kizzi 57	1
Oct 6	**FAC 3Q**	**Whitehawk**	**H**	**609**	**W**	**9 - 1**	**Kizzi 2 Robinson 8 63 Shokunbi 15 Deering 30 Emmanuel 35 45 53 Shooman 73 (og)**	
13	NLS	Gloucester City	H	1420	**W**	1 - 0	Emmanuel 41	1
20	**FAC 4Q**	**Taunton Town**	**H**	**976**	**D**	**2 - 2**	**Emmanuel 17 39**	
24	**FAC 4Qr**	**Taunton Town**	**A**	**1582**	**W**	**1 - 0**	**Deering 43**	
27	NLS	Dulwich Hamlet	H	1384	D	1 - 1	Lafayette 19	
30	NLS	East Thurrock United	H	832	**W**	3 - 2	Coombes 63 70 Lafayette 73	1
Nov 3	NLS	Torquay United	A	2046	D	2 - 2	Cunnington 50 69	1
10	**FAC 1P**	**Chesterfield**	**A**	**2952**	**D**	**1 - 1**	**Emmanuel 52**	
17	NLS	Hungerford Town	A	353	D	2 - 2	Inaman 17 90	2
20	**FAC 1Pr**	**Chesterfield**	**H**	**2493**	**L**	**1 - 3**	**Kizzi 63**	
24	**FAT 3Q**	**Hampton & Richmond Boro'**	**A**	**298**	**W**	**1 - 0**	**Robinson 73**	
Dec 1	NLS	Oxford City	H	874	L	2 - 3	Robinson 15 Lafayette 73	4
8	NLS	Eastbourne Borough	A	574	**W**	2 - 0	Lafayette 32 (Pen) Aransibia 49	
11	NLS	Bath City	A	545	**W**	2 - 1	Emmanuel 14 Deering 71	
15	**FAT 1P**	**Hereford**	**A**	**1097**	**L**	**1 - 2**	**Lafayette 4**	
22	NLS	Woking	H	1220	L	0 - 4		
26	NLS	Chelmsford City	A	1404	L	1 - 5	Coombes 52	
29	NLS	St Albans City	A	769	L	1 - 2	Coombes 54	
Jan 1	NLS	Chelmsford City	H	1646	L	0 - 1		
5	NLS	Weston-super-Mare	A	568	**W**	3 - 2	Coombes 8 (Pen) 35 Cadogan 61	
12	NLS	Chippenham Town	H	4582	L	1 - 2	Coombes 38	
Dean Brennan sacked as manager. Harry Wheeler returns (147 days after he was dismissed).								
19	NLS	Concord Rangers	A	668	D	2 - 2	Smith C 37 Emmanuel 59	7
26	NLS	Welling United	H	1129	**W**	2 - 0	Cadogan 49 Coombes 61	
29	NLS	Slough Town	H	509	**W**	3 - 2	Emmanuel 40 Kizzi 49 Coombes 70	
Feb 9	NLS	Truro City	H	820	**W**	3 - 2	Emmanuel 3 23 Deering 70	
16	NLS	Eastbourne Borough	H	910	**W**	2 - 0	Coombes 23 Hamilton 77 (og)	
23	NLS	Oxford City	A	335	**W**	3 - 2	Emmanuel 57 Loza 60 Kizzi 68	
25	NLS	Wealdstone	A	906	D	1 - 1	Waldren 53	3
Mar 2	NLS	East Thurrock United	A	484	L	1 - 2	Coombes 5	
9	NLS	Torquay United	H	1324	L	0 - 2		7
16	NLS	Slough Town	A	759	L	1 - 2	Emmanuel 44	7
23	NLS	Hungerford Town	H	898	L	1 - 2	Coombes 50 (pen)	7
30	NLS	Dulwich Hamlet	A	3243	D	2 - 2	Kizzi 16 Emmanuel 27	7
Apr 6	NLS	Hampton & Richmond Boro'	H	829	L	1 - 3	Emmanuel 69	8
13	NLS	Gloucester City	A	392	**W**	4 - 1	Wassmer 60 Emmanuel 65 83 90+4 (pen)	6
20	NLS	Hemel Hempstead Town	H	964	**W**	2 - 1	Kizzi 33 Emmanuel 63	6
22	NLS	Dartford	A	1325	L	1 - 2	Robinson 56 (pen)	7
27	NLS	Bath City	H	1109	L	0 - 2		8

GOALSCORERS	SG	CSG	Pens	Hat tricks	Total
Emmanuel	18	4	1	2	25
Robinson	12	3	3		17
Coombes	11	2	3		13
Kizzi	7	1			7
Deering	5	1			5
Lafayette	5	2	1		5
Cunnington	2	1			3
Cadogan	2	1			2
Inman	1	1			2
Opponent	2	1			2
Aransibia	1	1			1
Doe	1	1			1
Howells	1	1			1
Hunte	1	1			1
Kennedy	1	1			1
Loza	1	1			1
Shokunbi	1	1			1
Smith C	1	1			1
Waldren	1	1			1
Walton	1	1			1
Wassmer	1	1			1

Julian	Kizzi	Kennedy	Doe	Inman	Deering	Modeste	Waldren	Robinson	Coombes	Howells	O'Hara	Cunnington	Walton	Emmanuel	Eyong	Potter	Wells	Hayles	Gerring	Hunte	Shokunbi (L)	Lafayette	Stewart (L)	Jahraldo-Martin	Coveney (L)	Clifford	Rooney (L)	Aransibia (L)	Gordon-Stearn	Murrell-Williamson	Smith M	Doyley	Cadogan	Smith C	Minhas	Efete	Loza	Debrah (L)	Wassmer	Davies	Kpakawa	Kelly	Paxman	No.
X	X	X	X	X	X	X	XS	XS	XS	X	SX	SX	SX	S	S																													1
X	X	XS	X	X	X	XS	S	X	XS	X	X	SX	S	SX		SX																												2
X	X		X	X	X		X	X	X	X	XS	SX	SX	S	S	X	S																											3
	X		X	X	XS		X	XS	X	X	SX	S	X	SX	SX	XS	X	S																										4
	X		X	X	XS		X	X	XS	X	X	SX	XS	SX		SX	X	S	S																									5
S	X	XS		X	X		XS	X	SX	SX	X	XS	X		S	SX	X	X																										6
X	XS	X	X	SX	X	SX	X	X		XS	X	S	S			SX		X	XS																									7
X		X	X	X	XS	XS	X	X	SX	X	SX	S	SX		X	SX		S																										8
X	X	X	X	S	XS		X	XS	XS	X	S	SX		SX		X		X		SX																								9
X	XS	X	X	X	XS	SX	XS	X	S	X		X		S		SX		X		SX																								10
S	**SX**	**X**	**S**	**XS**	**SX**	**X**	**X**	**SX**	**XS**	**S**	**X**	**S**		**X**		**X**	**X**	**X**		**XS**																								11
X	X	X	X	SX	X	XS	SX	XS		X	X	SX		X			S	XS		S																								12
X	**X**	**S**	**X**	**SX**	**X**	**S**	**SX**	**X**		**X**	**X**	**S**		**XS**		**X**	**S**	**XS**		**SX**	**XS**																							13
X	X	SX	X	S	X		S	X		X	XS	SX		XS		X	S	X			X																							14
X	**X**		**X**	**SX**	**X**	**SX**	**S**			**X**	**SX**	**S**		**X**		**X**	**S**				**XS**	**X**	**XS**	**S**	**XS**																			15
X	**X**	**X**	**X**	**SX**	**XS**	**XS**	**SX**			**X**	**X**	**S**		**XS**			**S**	**X**			**S**	**X**	**S**	**SX**																				16
X	X	X			X		XS			X	X	SX		XS				XS			S	X	SX	SX	S																			17
X	X	X		X	X		SX		SX	X	XS	S		XS		XS					SX	X	X	S																				18
X	X	X	X	S	XS		SX	S	X	XS	X	SX		X				X			XS			SX																				19
X	**X**	**X**	**X**	**SX**	**X**	**S**	**X**	**XS**		**X**	**SX**			**XS**			**S**	**XS**		**S**	**S**	**X**		**SX**																				20
X	X		X	X	X	X	S	X	S	X	X	S		S						S		X				X																		21
X	**X**	**X**	**X**	**X**	**X**	**XS**	**XS**	**X**	**S**	**X**	**S**	**S**		**SX**			**S**			**SX**	**S**	**X**																						22
X	**X**	**X**	**XS**	**X**	**X**	**SX**	**X**	**XS**	**SX**	**X**	**SX**			**X**						**S**	**S**					**XS**																		23
X	X	X			X	SX	XS	X		X				XS				SX		SX	S	X				XS	X	S																24
X	X				X		X		XS	X	SX			X		SX				S	SX	X				XS	X	XS	S															25
X	X	X			X		X			X				X		X				S	SX	XS		S		SX	X	XS	S															26
X	**X**	**X**			**XS**		**X**			**X**				**X**		**X**				**SX**	**S**	**XS**		**S**		**SX**	**X**	**X**	**S**															27
X	X	XS			S		X		SX	X				X		XS				SX	S	X		SX		X	XS	X																28
X	X	X					SX		SX	X				X		XS				S	XS	X		X		S	X	X	S															29
X	X	X					X		X	XS				XS		X				S		X		S		X	X	SX	S	SX														30
S	X	X					X		XS	SX				XS		S						X				X	X	SX		SX	X	XS	X											31
S	X	XS							X	X				SX		X				S						XS	XS	X		SX	X		X	X	SX									32
S	X				S				X	X				XS		X								S		XS		SX			X		X	X	SX	X	X							33
X	X								XS	X				X		S								X		XS	X	SX			S		SX	X	S	X		X						34
X	X				S		XS		XS	X				X		SX						X				SX	X				S		XS	SX		X			X					35
X	X				SX		X		X	X				X		SX						XS					X				S		XS	S		X		SX	X					36
X	X				X		X		X	X				XS		SX						SX					X					S	S	S		X	XS		X					37
X	X				XS		X		XS	X	S			XS		SX						SX					S					X		SX		X	X		X					38
X	X				XS		X		X	X	S			XS		SX						SX					SX				S	X				X	XS		X					39
X	X						X		XS	X	S			X		SX						XS					SX				S	XS	SX			X	X		X					40
X		S					XS		X	XS				X		X						SX					XS					X	SX			X	X		X	S				41
X	X				SX		XS	X		X	SX			SX		XS						XS					S					S	X			X	X		X					42
X	X						XS	X		X	SX			X	S							X					S					XS	SX			X	X				X			43
X	X						X		XS	XS	SX			XS	S							SX					S					X	SX			X	X				X	X		44
X	X						X		S	X		SX		XS	S							S					SX					XS				X	XS				X	XS	X	45
X	X						X		X	XS		SX		XS	S	SX						SX					S									X	X				X	XS	X	46
	X				XS		SX	XS	XS	X		SX		X								SX									X					X	S		X		X	S	X	47
	X				XS		SX	XS	XS	X		SX		X		SX						S									X					X	S		X		X		X	48
	X	S			SX		S	XS	SX	X		X		XS		X											XS				X					X	SX		X				XS	49
	X	XS			X		XS	X	SX	X		X			S	SX															X					S	SX		X		XS		X	50
39	45	20	18	12	20	3	23	15	11	41	11	3	2	18	1	13	4	8	0	0	1	15	1	2	0	4	11	4	0	0	7	4	4	3	0	17	8	1	12	0	6	1	5	X
0	2	5	1	1	12	5	11	9	14	6	3	1	1	17	0	5	0	4	1	1	4	5	1	0	1	6	4	2	0	0	0	4	2	0	0	0	3	0	0	0	1	2	1	XS
0	1	1	0	6	4	5	8	1	8	2	10	13	3	7	1	16	0	1	0	7	3	7	1	5	0	3	3	4	0	3	0	0	5	2	2	0	2	1	0	0	0	0	0	SX
5	0	3	1	3	3	2	5	1	4	1	5	10	2	4	8	2	8	3	1	9	8	2	1	6	1	1	5	1	5	0	5	2	1	2	1	1	2	0	0	1	0	1	0	S

x - Played full 90 minutes
xs - Substituted off
sx - Substituted on
s - Non-playing Substitute

CHELMSFORD CITY MATCH RESULTS 2018-19

Date	Comp	Opponents	H/A	Att:	Result		Goalscorers	Pos
Aug 4	NLS	Torquay United	H	1058	D	0 - 0		
7	NLS	Dartford	A	1220	L	0 - 1		
11	NLS	Hungerford Town	A	279	W	6 - 0	Anderson 34 Church 48 Murphy 57 Spillane 59 Fenwick 69 (Pen) Wraight 86	
13	NLS	Dulwich Hamlet	H	991	D	2 - 2	Murphy 25 Fenwick 57	
18	NLS	Hampton & Richmond Boro'	A	495	D	1 - 1	Murphy 90 (Pen)	
25	NLS	Bath City	H	764	W	1 - 0	Murphy 45 (Pen)	
27	NLS	Hemel Hempstead Town	A	625	W	5 - 3	Wraight 9 Church 66 Swaine 67 Murphy 83 Whelpdale 90	
Sept 1	NLS	Slough Town	H	754	L	0 - 1		
8	NLS	Welling United	H	806	D	0 - 0		
15	NLS	Wealdstone	A	856	W	3 - 2	Spillane 27 Murphy 36 Wraight 50	8
22	**FAC 2Q**	**Worthing**	**H**	**563**	**L**	**1 - 2**	**Whelpdale 51**	
29	NLS	St Albans City	H	711	L	2 - 4	Nasha 9 Murphy 11	12
Oct 13	NLS	Woking	A	1663	D	1 - 1	Whelpdale 35	14
27	NLS	Oxford City	A	302	W	3 - 1	Murphy 30 87 Fenwick 61	
30	NLS	Concord Rangers	A	691	L	0 - 3		
Nov 3	NLS	Eastbourne Borough	H	668	W	3 - 2	Fenwick 3 38 Church 27	
5	NLS	Chippenham Town	H	547	W	1 - 0	Wraight 45	4
17	NLS	Truro City	H	757	L	0 - 2		11
24	**FAT 3Q**	**Oxford City**	**A**	**212**	**L**	**0 - 4**		
Dec 1	NLS	Gloucester City	H	631	W	2 - 0	Wraight 27 Nasha 49	8
8	NLS	East Thurrock United	A	338	L	0 - 2		
11	NLS	Weston-super-Mare	A	541	W	3 - 0	Wraight 38 90 Murphy 71	
22	NLS	Bath City	A	637	L	0 - 2		
26	NLS	Billericay Town	H	1404	W	5 - 1	Fenwick 6 Wraight 16 Murphy 27 57 60	
29	NLS	Hemel Hempstead Town	H	720	W	2 - 1	Fenwick 33 Wraight 36	
Jan 1	NLS	Billericay Town	A	1646	W	1 - 0	Murphy 74	
5	NLS	Hampton & Richmond Boro'	H	784	W	2 - 0	Murphy 22 27	
12	NLS	Slough Town	A	765	L	0 - 1		
19	NLS	Dartford	H	1023	W	2 - 1	Giles 85 Murphy 89	4
26	NLS	Dulwich Hamlet	A	2826	W	3 - 1	Whelpdale 4 59 Kennedy 90	
Feb 2	NLS	Hungerford Town	H	943	W	4 - 1	Whelpdale 19 26 Murphy 85 Wraight 90	
16	NLS	East Thurrock United	H	1358	W	1 - 0	Murphy 43	
23	NLS	Gloucester City	A	361	D	0 - 0		4
Mar 2	NLS	Concord Rangers	H	1179	D	2 - 2	Fenwick 18 Whelpdale 79	3
9	NLS	Eastbourne Borough	A	533	D	1 - 1	Giles 64	4
16	NLS	Weston-super-Mare	H	973	D	2 - 2	Whelpdale 30 Isaac 33	5
23	NLS	Truro City	A	506	W	3 - 0	Murphy 35 70 (pen) Isaac 58	4
30	NLS	Oxford City	H	1029	W	2 - 1	Murphy 46 Spillane 62	4
Apr 2	NLS	Torquay United	A	2852	L	1 - 3	Reynolds 32	4
6	NLS	St Albans City	A	922	L	1 - 3	Whelpdale 42	4
13	NLS	Woking	H	1611	W	2 - 0	Murphy 43 Cascaval 72	4
19	NLS	Welling United	A	934	L	0 - 2		4
22	NLS	Wealdstone	H	954	L	0 - 3		4
27	NLS	Chippenham Town	A	503	W	1 - 0	Murphy 16	4
May 5	**PO Q**	**Welling United**	**A**	**1912**	**L**	**2 - 3**	**Fenwick 44 Giles 83**	

GOALSCORERS	SG	CSG	Pens	Hat tricks	Total
Murphy	19	5	3	1	24
Whelpdale	8	2			10
Wraight	9	2			10
Fenwick	8	2	1		9
Church	3	1			3
Giles	3	1			3
Spillane	3	1			3
Isaac	2	2			2
Nasha	2	1			2
Anderson	1	1			1
Caşcaval	1	1			1
Kennedy	1	1			1
Reynolds	1	1			1
Swaine	1	1			1

No.	Worner (L)	Omozusi	Swaine	Church	Fenwick	Reason	Wraight	Anderson	Nasha	Young	Murphy	Miles	Porter	Foy (L)	Ohman	Haines	Spillane	Barnum-Bobb	Whelpdale	Batt	McDonald	Giles	Amoo	Chiedozie	Silverman	Khinda-John	Sotiriou (L)	Isaac	Maynard-Brewer (L)	Caşcaval	O'Reilly	Sho-Silva (L)	Kennedy (L)	Cosgrave	Gregan	Knott	Wright	Reynolds (L)
1	x	x	x	x	xs	xs	x	x	xs	x	x	sx	sx	sx	s	s																						
2	x	x		x	x	xs	x	x	xs	xs	x	sx	sx	s		s	x	sx																				
3	x	x		x	xs	sx	x	x	s		xs		x	sx		s	x	x	xs	sx																		
4	x	x		x	xs	sx	x	x	xs		x	s		sx		s	x	x	xs	sx																		
5		x	x	xs	xs	x	x	x			x	sx	s			s	x	sx	xs	sx	x																	
6		x	x	xs	sx	xs	x	x			x	sx	x	s		s		x	xs		x	sx																
7		x	xs	x	xs	sx	x	x		x	x	x	xs	s				s	sx		x	sx																
8		x	x	x	sx	xs	x	x			x	sx	xs				s	x	xs	s	x	sx																
9		x	x	x	xs	s	xs	x		x	x	sx	xs				x		sx	sx	x	s																
10		x		x	sx	s	xs	x	xs	x	x	sx	xs				x		sx		x	x	s															
11		**xs**	**x**	**x**	**s**	**sx**	**x**	**x**		**x**	**x**	**xs**	**s**				**x**	**s**	**sx**		**x**	**xs**	**s**	**s**														
12		x	x	x	sx	s	x	xs	xs	xs	x		sx				x		x		x		s	sx														
13		x	x	x	sx	s	sx	x	xs	x	xs		sx				x		x		x	s		xs														
14		xs		x	x		sx	x	xs	s	x	sx	xs				x	x	x		x	s			sx													
15				x	x		x	x	xs	s	xs		s				x	xs	x		x	sx				x	sx	sx										
16				x	x		x	x		s	x	sx	x				x	s	x		x	s				x	s	xs										
17					xs		x	sx	s	x	x	sx	x				x	x	x		x	sx				xs	s	xs										
18		x		sx	x		x		s	sx	x	xs	xs				x	s	x		x	sx				xs		x										
19		**x**		**x**	**x**				**sx**	**x**			**xs**									**x**						**x**			**x**							
20		x		x			x	x	xs	x		sx	x			s		s				x				s		x	x	x	s							
21		x		x	xs		x	x	xs	x			xs				sx	s	sx			x						s	x	x		sx						
22		x		xs	sx		x	x	s		x						x	x	sx			xs				s		sx	x	x		xs						
23		x		xs	x		x	x	sx	s			s				x	xs	x			x				s		sx	x	x								
24		xs		xs	x		x	x	s		xs		sx				x	sx	x			s						x	x	x			sx					
25		x		x	xs		x	x			xs		s				x	s	xs			sx						x	x	x		sx	sx					
26		x		x	xs		x	xs			xs		sx				x	s	x		x	s						x		x		sx	sx					
27		x		x	xs		x		sx	x	xs		s				x		x		x	s						xs		x			sx	sx				
28		xs		x	xs		x	x		s			s				x	sx	x		x	sx						x		x			xs	sx				
29		x		xs			x	x		xs	x		s					s	x		x	sx				s		x		x			sx	xs				
30				xs	x		x	x			xs		sx				x	xs	x		x	s				s		x		x			sx	sx				
31		x		x	xs		x	xs			x		sx				x	s	xs		x	sx		s				x		x				sx				
32		x		x	xs		x			s	xs	sx	x				x		x		x	x		sx		s				xs				sx				
33		x		xs	xs		x			x	x	sx	x				x	s	x		x	xs		sx		s								sx				
34		x		x	x					s	x		s				x	s	x		x	xs		s				x		x				sx	x			
35		x		s	xs		sx				x		x				x	s	x		x	xs		sx				x		x				sx	xs			
36		xs		x	x		x	xs		sx	x		s				x		x		x			s				xs		x				sx		sx		
37				sx	x		x	xs			xs						x	x	x			sx				s		x		x				s		xs	x	sx
38				sx	x		x	x		s	xs						x	x	xs			s						xs		x				sx		x	x	sx
39				s	xs		x	xs		s	sx						x	x	x			sx						x		x				sx		x	x	xs
40		x		x	x		xs	xs		sx	x						xs	x	x		x	sx						s						s		x		sx
41		x		x	s			x		s	xs		x				x	sx	xs		x	xs		sx				x		x								sx
42		x		x				x		s	xs		x				x	s	x		x	xs		sx				x		xs				sx				sx
43		x		sx			sx	x		x	x		x					s	x		x	sx		xs				xs		x				s				xs
44		s		sx	x		xs	x			xs		x				x	x	x		x	sx		s						x						xs		sx
45		**x**		**s**	**xs**		**x**	**xs**			**x**		**xs**				**x**	**s**	**x**		**x**	**sx**						**sx**		**x**						**x**		**sx**
x	4	32	8	28	15	1	33	29	0	13	25	1	12	0	0	0	35	12	26	0	31	6	0	0	0	2	0	16	6	22	1	0	0	0	1	4	3	0
xs	0	5	1	8	18	4	4	8	10	3	14	2	9	0	0	0	1	3	9	0	0	7	0	2	0	2	0	6	0	2	0	1	1	1	1	2	0	2
sx	0	0	0	5	6	4	4	1	3	3	1	13	8	3	0	0	1	5	6	4	0	16	0	6	1	0	1	4	0	0	0	3	6	12	0	1	0	7
s	0	1	0	3	2	4	0	0	5	11	0	1	10	3	1	7	1	16	0	1	0	9	3	5	0	8	2	2	0	0	1	0	0	3	0	0	0	0

x - Played full 90 minutes
xs - Substituted off
sx - Substituted on
s - Non-playing Substitute

CHIPPENHAM TOWN MATCH RESULTS 2018-19

Date	Comp	Opponents	H/A	Att:	Result		Goalscorers	Pos
Aug 4	NLS	Hemel Hempstead Town	A	510	L	2 - 4	Chambers 28 36	
7	NLS	Slough Town	H	593	**W**	1 - 0	Jarvis 68	
11	NLS	Welling United	H	498	L	1 - 4	Chambers 22	
14	NLS	Truro City	A	159	**W**	2 - 1	Richards 45 Jarvis 75	
18	NLS	Eastbourne Borough	A	505	L	1 - 2	McDonald 32	
25	NLS	Billericay Town	H	547	**W**	2 - 0	Jarvis 54 Guthrie 65	
27	NLS	Hampton & Richmond Boro'	A	491	L	1 - 2	Richards 90	
Sept 1	NLS	Concord Rangers	H	497	**W**	4 - 1	Evans 58 McDonald 60 76 Jarvis 83	
8	NLS	Torquay United	A	1454	**W**	1 - 0	Smith Matt 25	
15	NLS	Gloucester City	H	597	**W**	1 - 0	Guthrie 84	6
22	**FAC 2Q**	**Swindon Supermarine**	**H**	**384**	**D**	**2 - 2**		
25	**FAC 2Qr**	**Swindon Supermarine**	**A**	**364**	**W**	**1 - 0**	**Jarvis 66**	
29	NLS	Dulwich Hamlet	A		L	0 - 2		10
Oct 10	**FAC 3Q**	**Hendon**	**H**	**402**	**W**	**4 - 1**	**Jarvis 20 McCootie 32 45+1 Rigg 55**	
13	NLS	Dartford	H	565	L	1 - 2	Jarvis 44	11
20	**FAC 4Q**	**Maidenhead United**	**H**	**706**	**D**	**1 - 1**	**Jones 90+5**	
23	**FAC 4Qr**	**Maidenhead United**	**A**	**738**	**L**	**0 - 1**		
27	NLS	East Thurrock United	H	502	**W**	2 - 0	McCootie 52 62	
30	NLS	Oxford City	A	246	D	1 - 1	Jarvis 47	
Nov 3	NLS	Woking	H	732	D	2 - 2	Chambers 37 55	12
5	NLS	Chelmsford City	A	547	L	0 - 1		12
10	NLS	St Albans City	A	584	**W**	3 - 2	Chambers 2 Jarvis 55 McCootie 84	10
17	NLS	Wealdstone	H	618	**W**	3 - 1	Parselle 11 Smile 82 (Pen) Chambers 90	8
24	**FAT 3Q**	**Wingate & Finchley**	**H**	**280**	**D**	**1 - 1**	**Jarvis**	
27	**FAT 3Qr**	**Wingate & Finchley**	**A**	**90**	**L**	**2 - 3**	**Opponent 12 Chambers 79**	
Dec 1	NLS	Weston-super-Mare	H	581	L	1 - 3	Jarvis 34	10
8	NLS	Hungerford Town	A	239	L	1 - 2	Jarvis 22	
22	NLS	Concord Rangers	A	253	D	1 - 1	Guthrie 90	
26	NLS	Bath City	H	1445	D	2 - 2	McCootie 15 Guthrie 19	
29	NLS	Hampton & Richmond Boro'	H	535	**W**	3 - 2	Chambers 8 Richards 30 Jarvis 51	
Jan 1	NLS	Bath City	A	1727	L	0 - 5		
5	NLS	Eastbourne Borough	H	504	L	2 - 3	Guthrie 60 McCootie 90	
12	NLS	Billericay Town	A	4582	**W**	2 - 1	Jarvis 22 Chambers 72	
19	NLS	Slough Town	A	605	D	2 - 2	Evans 55 Rigg 76	12
26	NLS	Truro City	H	539	**W**	2 - 1	Jarvis 9 11	
Feb 5	NLS	Welling United	A	248	L	1 - 2	Chambers 15	
9	NLS	Hemel Hempstead Town	H	469	D	1 - 1	McCootie 55	
16	NLS	Hungerford Town	H	582	**W**	3 - 1	Jarvis 58 70 McCootie 90	
23	NLS	Weston-super-Mare	A	654	**W**	1 - 0	Jarvis 59	9
Mar 2	NLS	Oxford City	H	522	L	0 - 1		10
9	NLS	Woking	A	1728	L	0 - 2		11
16	NLS	St Albans City	H	439	D	0 - 0		11
23	NLS	Wealdstone	A	902	L	0 - 1		12
30	NLS	East Thurrock United	A	206	L	1 - 2	Chambers 86	12
Apr 6	NLS	Dulwich Hamlet	H	532	L	1 - 2	McCootie 86	12
13	NLS	Dartford	A	1014	**W**	1 - 0	George 78	13
19	NLS	Torquay United	H	1906	**W**	2 - 1	Evans 24 McCootie 69	12
22	NLS	Gloucester City	A	409	L	2 - 3	Ossai 12 Smile 31 (pen)	12
27	NLS	Chelmsford City	H	503	L	0 - 1		13

GOALSCORERS	SG	CSG	Pens	Hat tricks	Total
Jarvis	17	2			19
Chambers	11	2			12
McCootie	9	2			11
Guthrie	5	2			5
Evans	3	1			3
McDonald	2	1			3
Richards	3	1			3
Rigg	2	1			2
Smile	2	1	1		2
George	1	1			1

	SG	CSG	Pens	Hat tricks	Total
Jones	1	1			1
Opponent	1	1			1
Ossai	1	1			1
Parselle	1	1			1
Smith	1	1			1

[illegible]	Rigg	McDonald	Tindle	Richards	Jarvis	Compton	Guthrie	Parselle	Chambers	Smile	Jones	Ferguson	Smith	McCootie	Ellington	Evans	Sandell	Henry (L)	Gunner (L)	House (L)	Klukowski	Thompson	Drewitt B	Beeden	Horgan	Edwards (L)	Milloy R	Ekongo	Sparkes (L)	Felix	Davies (L)	Rutty	Ossai	Lea	George	No.
x	x	x	x	x	x	x	xs	xs	x	x	sx	sx	s	s	s																					1
x	x	x	x	x	x	x	x	x	x	x		s	s	s		s	s																			2
	x		x	x	x		x	x	x	x	s	x	s	s	s	s	x	x																		3
	x	x	x	x	x		sx	s	sx	x	s	xs	x	xs		x	s	x																		4
	xs	x	x	x	x		sx	sx	x	xs	s	xs	x	s		x	sx	x																		5
		x		x	x	s	xs	x	sx	x	x		x	xs	s	x	sx	x	s																	6
		x		x	x	sx	xs	x	xs	sx	x		x	x	s	x	sx	x	s																	7
	sx	x		x	xs	xs	x	x	sx		x		x	xs	sx	x		x																		8
	x	x		x	x	x	x	x	s	s	x		x		s	x			s	x	s															9
	x	x		x	x	xs	x	x	s	sx	xs		x	sx	s	xs				x	sx															10
																																				11
	x	x		x	x	xs	x	x	s	s	x		s	sx	s	x					x	x	s	s												12
	x	x		x	x	s		x	s	sx	x		x	x		x				x	xs			s	s											13
	x	x		x	x			x	sx	x	xs		x	xs		xs			sx	x	s	s		sx	s											14
	x			x	x			x	x	x	xs	s	sx				xs		x	x	xs			sx	s	sx										15
	x	x		x	x	sx	xs	x	sx	x	sx	s	s	xs					x	x	xs			s			s									16
	x	xs		x	x	xs	x	x	sx	x	s		sx	x					x	x	s			s				s								17
	x			x	xs	xs		x	sx	x	x		x	x	s				xs	x				s		sx			sx							18
	x	x		x	x	s		x	s	x	x		x	x					x	x				s		s			s							19
	x	x		x	x	x		x	x	x	s		s		s				x	x						s			s	x						20
		x		x	x	x		x	x	x	sx		xs		s				x	x						s		s	sx	xs						21
	x	x		x	x	x		x	x	x			xs	sx		x				x						sx			s	s	s					22
	x	xs		x	x	xs		x	x	x	sx	sx	s	s		x			x	x									s							23
	x	x		x	x	sx		x	xs	x	sx	sx	xs	x		s			xs	x	s															24
s	x			x	sx	x		x	x	xs	x	xs	sx	xs		x			sx	x	s															25
s				x	x	s		x	x	x	x		x	xs		sx			x	x	s			s						x						26
s	x			x	x	x		x	x	x	s	s	x	x		x			s	x	s															27
s		x		x	x	s	x	x	s	x	s	x		x					x	x											x	s				28
s		x		x	x	sx	xs	x	sx		s		x	xs		sx			x	x											xs		x			29
s	x			x	x	x	xs	x	xs		s		x	s		sx			x	x											x		sx			30
s	x	xs		x	x	xs	x	x		xs				x		sx			x	x											sx		sx			31
x	x			x	xs	xs	x	x	x		sx		sx	sx		x								s	s						xs		x			32
x	x			x	x	x	x	x	xs	x	s			sx		x								s	s							s	x			33
x	x	s		x	x	x	x	x	x	x	s			s					s													s	x			34
x	x			x	x	s	x	x	x	x	s			x	s	x			s													s	x			35
x	x			x	x	s	x	x	x	x	s			x		x			s													s	x	s		36
x	x			x	x	s	x	x	x	x	s			x		x			s												s		x		s	37
x	x			x	x	sx	x	x	x	x				x		x			s												s	s	x		s	38
x	x			x	x	xs		x	sx	x	s			xs		x			sx		s										x		x		s	39
x	x			x	x	s		x	xs	x				x		x			sx		s										x	s	xs		sx	40
x	x			x	x	s	s	x	s	x				s		xs			x		sx										x		x		x	41
	x			x	x			x	x	x				sx		x			x	x	s				s						xs	s	sx		xs	42
s	x			x	x			x	x	x				xs		xs			xs	x	sx										sx	s	x		sx	43
x	x		x	s	x			x	sx	x				xs		x			xs	s	xs										sx		x		sx	44
	x		x		x			x	xs	x		s		sx		x			sx	x	xs										s	x	xs		sx	45
x	x		x		xs			x	sx	x		s		x		x			s						s						x	x	xs		sx	46
x	x		x	s	xs			x	sx	xs		s		xs		x			sx												x	x	x		sx	
x	x		x	s	sx			x	xs	x		s		sx		x			s												xs	x	x		x	
x	x		x	s	x	sx		x	sx	x				xs		x			s												xs	x	x		s	
17	40	20	11	42	41	11	16	45	20	35	10	2	15	15	0	27	1	6	14	24	1	1	0	0	0	0	0	0	0	2	7	5	15	0	2	x
0	1	3	0	0	5	9	6	1	7	4	3	3	3	13	0	4	1	0	4	0	5	0	0	0	0	0	0	0	0	1	5	0	3	0	1	xs
0	1	0	0	0	2	6	2	1	13	3	6	3	4	8	1	4	3	0	6	0	3	0	0	2	0	3	0	0	2	0	3	0	3	0	6	sx
8	0	1	0	4	0	10	1	1	7	2	15	8	7	8	11	3	2	0	12	1	10	1	1	9	7	3	1	2	4	1	4	9	0	1	4	s

x - Played full 90 minutes
xs - Substituted off
sx - Substituted on
s - Non-playing Substitute

CONCORD RANGERS MATCH RESULTS 2018-19

Date	Comp	Opponents	H/A	Att:	Result		Goalscorers	Pos
Aug 4	NLS	Gloucester City	H	326	W	2 - 0	Wall 26 79	
7	NLS	Billericay Town	A	1351	D	1 - 1	Wall 78	
11	NLS	Dulwich Hamlet	A	822	W	1 - 0	Midson 34	
14	NLS	Dartford	H	526	W	2 - 0	Wall 3 Theobalds 77	
18	NLS	Hungerford Town	H	312	W	4 - 0	Hayes 30 Midson 40 43 Wall 45	
25	NLS	Wealdstone	A	786	D	1 - 1	Wall 35	
27	NLS	Welling United	H	637	L	0 - 5		
Sept 1	NLS	Chippenham Town	A	497	L	1 - 4	Wall 33	
8	NLS	Woking	H	608	D	1 - 1	Knott 90	
15	NLS	St Albans City	A	582	L	0 - 2		13
22	**FAC 2Q**	**Margate**	**H**	**219**	**W**	**2 - 0**	**Midson Topley**	
29	NLS	Truro City	H	242	W	3 - 0	Wall 36 Pollock 61 Midson 67	9
Oct 6	**FAC 3Q**	**Beaconsfield Town**	**H**	**184**	**W**	**2 - 1**	**Shaw Midson**	
13	NLS	Oxford City	A	256	L	0 - 2		10
20	**FAC 4Q**	**Dover Athletic**	**H**	**446**	**L**	**0 - 1**		
27	NLS	Weston-super-Mare	A	489	W	2 - 1	Nash 54 Midson 62	
30	NLS	Chelmsford City	H	691	W	3 - 0	Midson 8 Wall 21 Nash 23	
Nov 3	NLS	Slough Town	A	683	L	0 - 1		
13	NLS	Eastbourne Borough	H	262	W	3 - 0	Midson 29 82 Kyei 62	6
17	NLS	Torquay United	A	1937	L	1 - 4	Abdulla 83	10
24	**FAT 3Q**	**Wealdstone**	**H**	**281**	**L**	**2 - 3**	**Minshull 66 Wall 69**	
Dec 1	NLS	Hemel Hempstead Town	H	258	W	2 - 1	Wall 38 Nash 70	5
4	NLS	Hampton & Richmond B'	H	212	W	4 - 0	Blackman 5 Nash 14 (Pen) 90 Midson 40	
8	NLS	Bath City	A	546	D	1 - 1	Blackman 49	
22	NLS	Chippenham Town	H	253	D	1 - 1	Blackman 75	
26	NLS	East Thurrock United	A	286	W	2 - 0	Green 45 Wall 49	
29	NLS	Welling United	A	611	W	1 - 0	Sterling 1	
Jan 1	NLS	East Thurrock United	H	412	D	1 - 1	Blackman 17	
5	NLS	Hungerford Town	A	170	L	1 - 2	Blackman 69	
12	NLS	Wealdstone	H	492	D	2 - 2	Wall 11 84	
19	NLS	Billericay Town	H	668	D	2 - 2	Wall 4 Midson 90 (Pen)	6
26	NLS	Dartford	A	984	D	1 - 1	Midson 49 (pen)	
Feb 2	NLS	Dulwich Hamlet	H	457	D	0 - 0		
16	NLS	Bath City	H	284	W	2 - 1	Wall 2 10	
23	NLS	Hemel Hempstead Town	A	505	D	2 - 2	Pollock 58 Luque 60	10
Mar 2	NLS	Chelmsford City	A	1179	D	2 - 2	Wall 36 Midson 51	9
5	NLS	Gloucester City	A	178	W	2 - 1	Henry 75 (og) Minshull 90	9
9	NLS	Slough Town	H	312	D	2 - 2	Minshull 44 Wall 56	9
16	NLS	Hampton & Richmond B'	A	391	W	4 - 1	Midson 9 (pen) 65 Green 60 Luque 90	8
23	NLS	Torquay United	H	627	L	0 - 1		9
30	NLS	Weston-super-Mare	H	214	W	3 - 0	Midson 18 Luque 33 Ashford 50	8
Apr 6	NLS	Truro City	A			A - A	After a serious injury to Truro's Michael Herve (score was 1-0)	
13	NLS	Oxford City	H	207	L	0 - 1		10
16	NLS	Truro City	A	416	W	3 - 1	Wall 28 Midson 45 Ashford 57	7
19	NLS	Woking	A	1819	W	2 - 1	Wall 30 Luque 36	7
22	NLS	St Albans City	H	480	W	2 - 1	Ashford 14 Wall 19	6
27	NLS	Eastbourne Borough	A	545	W	2 - 1	Essam 37 Luque 39	6

GOALSCORERS	SG	CSG	Pens	Hat tricks	Total
Wall	19	3			22
Midson	15	3	3		18
Blackman	5	3			5
Luque	5	1			5
Nash	4	2	1		5
Ashford	3	1			3
Minshull	3	2			3
Green	2	1			2
Pollock	2	1			2
Abdulla	1	1			1

	SG	CSG	Pens	Hat tricks	Total
Essam	1	1			1
Hayes	1	1			1
Knott	1	1			1
Kyei	1	1			1
Opponent	1	1			1
Shaw	1	1			1
Sterling	1	1			1
Theobalds	1	1			1
Topley	1	1			1

	Clohessy	Shaw	Blackman	Minshull	Sterling	Hayes	Green	Wall	Midson	Knott B	Pollock	Smith	Awotwi	Moore	Theobalds	Boakye-Yiadom	Confrey	Littlejohn	Topley	Popo	Froud	Sullivan	Knott S	Clark	Glover	Harris	Armstrong	Hurford	Nash (L)	Abdulla	Essam (L)	Kyei (L)	Gardner	Hunt	Davidson	White (L)	Luque	Ashford	Maloney	Kennedy (L)	No.
	x	x	x	x	x	xs	xs	x	x	x	sx	sx	s	s	s																										1
	x	x	x	x	x	xs	xs	x	x	x	s	s	s		sx	sx																									2
	x	x	x		x	xs	xs	x	x	xs	x	sx		s	sx	sx	s																								3
	x	x	xs		x	xs	xs	x	x	x	x	sx			sx	sx	s	s																							4
	x	x	xs		x	xs	xs	x	x	x	x	sx			sx	sx	s	s																							5
	x	x	x	sx	x	xs	xs	x	x	xs	x	s			sx	sx			s																						6
	x	x	x	sx	x	s	sx	x	x	xs	x	s			xs	xs				sx																					7
	x	x	x	x	x	x	x	x	x	x	s	s			s	s				s																					8
	xs	x	xs	x	x	sx	s	x	x	x	x	sx		s					sx	xs																					9
		x	x	x	x	sx	sx	x	xs	x	x	xs					s		sx	xs																					10
		x	**x**	**x**	**x**	**sx**	**x**	**x**	**x**	**x**	**x**	**s**					**s**	**s**	**sx**	**x**	**sx**	**s**																			11
		x	x	x	x		xs	xs	x	x	x	sx					s		sx	x	s		s																		12
		x	**x**	**x**	**x**		**x**	**x**	**x**	**x**	**x**	**sx**							**sx**	**x**	**s**		**sx**		**s**	**s**	**s**														13
		x	x	x			x	x	x	s	x	x							x	s	s			x	s			s													14
		x	**x**	**x**	**x**		**x**	**x**	**x**		**sx**	**s**							**x**	**x**	**s**	**s**	**sx**	**x**	**s**	**s**															15
		x	x	x	x		xs	xs	x		sx			s					xs	x			sx	x	s				sx												16
		x	x	x	x		xs	x	xs		sx								sx	x			s	x	s				x	s											17
			x	x	x		x		x		sx								s	x	s		xs	x	s	s			x	x											18
x	sx	x	x	x	x		xs		xs		sx	s								x					s				x	sx	x	xs									19
x	sx	x	x	x	x		x	sx	x		s									x					s				x	sx	x	x									20
x	**sx**	**x**	**x**	**x**	**x**		**x**	**x**	**x**		**sx**			**s**						**x**	**s**				**s**				**x**		**x**										21
x	x	x	x	x	x		s	xs	sx		sx									sx					s				x	xs	x	xs									22
x		xs	x	s	x		sx	x	x		sx			s						x					s				x	xs	x										23
x		x	x	x			xs	x	x	s	x			sx			s			x	s								xs	x			sx								24
x		x	x	x	x		xs	x	x		s	s		sx			s			x									x	x			s								25
x		x	x	x	x		xs	x	x		sx	sx		s			s			x									xs	xs				sx							26
x		x	x	x	x		xs		x		sx			s			s			x	s								x	x	x			s							27
x		x	x	x	x		xs		x		x			sx			s			x	s								x	s	x			s							28
x		x	x	x	x		x		x		sx			xs						x	s									sx	x			s	xs						29
x		x	x	x	x		sx	x	x		s			s						x										xs	x		sx	s		xs					30
x		x	x	x			x	x	x		x			s						x	s									s	x		xs	s		sx					31
x		x	x	x	x		xs		x		sx			s						x										s	x		x	s		sx	xs				32
x		x	xs		x		x		xs		sx			s						x						s				x	x		x	s		sx	x				33
x		x	x		x		xs	x	x		sx								sx	xs	s									x	x		sx	s			x				34
x			x		x		xs	x	xs		x	sx							sx	x						s				xs	x		sx	s			x				35
x			x		x		xs	x	x		x	sx							x	x	s										x		sx	s			xs				36
x			x	x	x		x	x	x		xs	sx							s	x	s										x		s	s							37
x			x	x	x		sx	x	xs		sx	x							sx						s						x		s					xs	xs		38
x			x	s	x		xs	xs	x		s	x								x										sx	x		s				sx	x	x		39
x			x	sx	x		sx		x		s	x								x					s					xs	x		s				xs	x	x		40
x			xs	sx	x		xs	s	x		s	x								x										sx	x						xs	x	x	sx	41
x			x	sx	x		xs	sx	x		s	xs								x											x		s				xs	x	x	sx	42
x			x	x	x		sx	xs	x			x		s						x											x		sx				sx	xs	xs	s	43
x			x	sx	x		s	xs	x			x								x										sx	x		sx				xs	xs	x	s	44
x			x	sx	x		s	xs	x			x								x										sx	x		sx				xs	x	xs	s	45
x			sx	sx	x		xs	sx	s		x	x																		xs	x		x				x		x	xs	46
6	9	32	40	29	43	1	12	27	38	10	17	9	0	0	0	0	0	0	3	31	0	0	0	5	0	0	0	0	10	6	25	1	3	0	0	0	4	5	6	0	x
0	1	1	5	0	0	6	23	7	6	3	1	2	0	1	1	1	0	0	1	3	0	0	1	0	0	0	0	0	2	7	0	2	1	0	1	1	7	3	3	1	xs
0	3	0	1	8	0	3	7	3	1	0	16	11	0	3	5	5	0	0	9	2	1	0	3	0	0	0	0	0	1	7	0	0	8	1	0	3	2	0	0	2	sx
0	0	0	0	2	0	1	4	1	1	2	9	8	2	13	2	1	11	3	3	2	14	2	2	0	13	5	1	1	0	4	0	0	6	11	0	0	0	0	0	3	s

x - Played full 90 minutes
xs - Substituted off
sx - Substituted on
s - Non-playing Substitute

DARTFORD MATCH RESULTS 2018-19

Date	Comp	Opponents	H/A	Att:	Result		Goalscorers	Pos
Aug 4	NLS	Bath City	A	828	W	2 - 1	Bradbrook 45 Sam-Yorke 87 (Pen)	
7	NLS	Chelmsford City	H	1220	W	1 - 0	Bradbrook 77	
11	NLS	Hemel Hempstead Town	H	974	D	0 - 0		
14	NLS	Concord Rangers	A	526	L	0 - 2		
18	NLS	Wealdstone	H	981	L	0 - 3		
25	NLS	Hungerford Town	A	226	L	0 - 1		
27	NLS	East Thurrock United	H	1114	W	2 - 0	Bonner 38 Greenhalgh 73	
Sept 1	NLS	St Albans City	A	658	L	0 - 2		
8	NLS	Eastbourne Borough	H	1005	D	2 - 2	Sherringham 23 (Pen) Bradbrook 90	
15	NLS	Billericay Town	A	1431	D	1 - 1	Philpot 90	16
22	**FAC 2Q**	**AFC Uckfield Town**	**A**	**500**	**W**	**3 - 1**	**Bradbrook Sheringham Murphy**	
29	NLS	Weston-super-Mare	H	906	W	2 - 1	Noble 14 Philpot 66	15
Oct 6	**FAC 3Q**	**Oxford City**	**A**	**312**	**L**	**1 - 4**	**Bradbrook 82**	
13	NLS	Chippenham Town	A	565	W	2 - 1	Philpot 23 Ibrahim 59	13
20	NLS	Dulwich Hamlet	H	1578	W	2 - 1	Philpot 45 Sheringham 60 (Pen)	6
27	NLS	Truro City	A	87	L	1 - 3	Oyenuga 90	
Nov 3	NLS	Gloucester City	A	320	W	2 - 1	Sheringham 45 Greenhalgh 48	
13	NLS	Oxford City	H	766	W	3 - 2	Coker 5 Wynter 15 Sheringham 30	
17	NLS	Hampton & Richmond Boro'	A	724	W	1 - 0	Sheringham 11	5
24	**FAT 3Q**	**Eastbourne Borough**	**A**	**340**	**D**	**1 - 1**		
27	**FAT 3Qr**	**Eastbourne Borough**	**H**	**404**	**L**	**2 - 3**		
Dec 4	NLS	Torquay United	H	917	L	0 - 2		
8	NLS	Slough Town	H	1466	D	1 - 1	Coker 52	
22	NLS	Hungerford Town	H	901	W	2 - 1	Philpot 12 Noble 70	
26	NLS	Welling United	A	1912	L	0 - 2		
29	NLS	East Thurrock United	A	442	D	2 - 2	Sheringham 8 Bradbrook 74	
Jan 1	NLS	Welling United	H	1725	W	1 - 0	Vint 86	
5	NLS	Wealdstone	A	420	D	1 - 1	Bradbrook 70	
12	NLS	St Albans City	H	1018	W	3 - 2	Bradbrook 21 Roberts 39 88	
19	NLS	Chelmsford City	A	1023	L	1 - 2	Roberts 4	8
26	NLS	Concord Rangers	H	984	D	1 - 1	Greenhalgh 28	
Feb 5	NLS	Woking	A	1190	W	1 - 0	Vint 90	
9	NLS	Bath City	H	1034	W	3 - 0	Noble 16 Sheringham 26 Roberts 56	
16	NLS	Slough Town	A	701	D	2 - 2	Greenhalgh 13 McQueen 56	
23	NLS	Woking	H	1720	W	2 - 0	McQueen 23 Roberts 70	7
Mar 2	NLS	Dulwich Hamlet	A	2779	L	0 - 2		7
5	NLS	Hemel Hempstead Town	A	360	W	2 - 1	Roberts 80 89	6
9	NLS	Gloucester City	H	1061	W	2 - 0	Roberts 44 Sheringham 83	5
16	NLS	Torquay United	A	2284	L	0 - 2		6
23	NLS	Hampton & Richmond Boro'	H	1103	D	2 - 2	Sheringham 59 (pen) McQueen 90+2	6
30	NLS	Truro City	H	1010	D	1 - 1	Bradbrook 62	6
Apr 6	NLS	Weston-super-Mare	A	535	L	1 - 3	Hayes 71	6
13	NLS	Chippenham Town	H	1014	L	0 - 1		8
20	NLS	Eastbourne Borough	A	731	L	0 - 6		
22	NLS	Billericay Town	H	1325	W	2 - 1	Murphy 88 90+2	9
27	NLS	Oxford City	A	378	L	1 - 2	Vint 33	10

GOALSCORERS	SG	CSG	Pens	Hat tricks	Total
Sherringham	10	3	3		10
Bradbrook	9	2			9
Roberts	6	2			8
Philpot	5	2			5
Greenhalgh	4	1			4
McQueen*	3	2			3
Murphy	2	1			3
Noble	3	1			3
Vint	3	1			3
Coker	2	1			2
Bonner	1	1			1
Hayes	1	1			1
Ibrahim	1	1			1
Oyenuga	1	1			1
Sam-Yorke	1	1	1		1
Wynter	1	1			1

No.	Oyenuga	Vint	Noble	Bonner	Onyemah	Driver	Greenhalgh	Bradbrook	Philpot	Issac	Ighorae	Sam-Yorke	Murphy	Roast	Mensah	Cue	Nicholls	Knowles (L)	Sheringham	Ba (L)	Yao (L)	Wynter (L)	Coker (L)	Fulton	Johnson	Vose (L)	Gilles	Hayes	Darbyshire	Fisher	Roberts	Crook	Healy	Smith	Leveson	McQueen (L)	Darren	Walsh	Smoker	Wells	Evans	Calvert	Pugh
1	x	x	x	x	x	x	x	x	xs	xs	sx	sx	s	s	s																												
2		x	x	x	x	x	xs	x	xs	xs	sx	x	sx	sx	s	s																											
3	s	x	x	x	x	x	xs		x	xs	sx	x	sx	sx	xs	s																											
4	xs	x		x	x	x	x	x	s	s	sx	x	xs	x	s	sx																											
5	x	x		x	x	x	x		s	xs	sx	xs	x	x	s	sx	s																										
6	sx	x		x	xs	xs	x	x	x	s	s	sx	x	sx	x	xs																											
7	x	x	xs	x	x	x	x	x	xs	sx	s	sx	xs	s	sx																												
8	xs	x	x	x	x		xs	x		sx	sx	sx	xs		s			x	x																								
9	s	s	x	x	x		x	x		x	sx	sx		xs	s			xs	x	x																							
10	s	x	x	x	x		x		sx	x	sx	xs	s	xs			s	x		x																							
11			**x**	**x**	**x**		**x**	**x**		**x**			**sx**						**x**																								
12	sx	s	x	x	x		x	x	xs	xs		sx	sx				s			xs	x	x																					
13			**x**	**x**	**x**		**x**	**x**		**x**			**sx**						**x**																								
14	s	x	x	x			x	x	xs	xs		sx	xs						x		x	x	s	s																			
15		x	x	x	sx		x	x	xs	s			xs				s		x		s	x	sx		x																		
16	sx	x		x	x		xs	x	x				xs						x			x	s		x	x	s	sx															
17	sx	x	x	x	x		x		xs			s	sx						x			x	xs		x	x	s	s															
18	s	x	x	x	x		xs	sx	x			s	s						x			x	xs		x	x		sx															
19	s	x	x	xs	x		xs	sx	xs				sx						x			x	x		x	x	s	sx															
20																																											
21																																											
22	x	x	x	x	xs		x		sx								s					x	x		x	x	s	sx	xs	s													
23	xs	x	x	x	x		sx	s	sx										xs			x	x		x	x		s	xs		sx												
24	sx	x	x	x	x	s	x	s	xs													x	xs		x	x		sx	sx		xs												
25	sx	x	x	x	x		x	x	xs										s			x	sx		x	x		xs	s		s												
26	sx	x	x	x	x	s	x	sx	xs										x			x	xs		x	x		s			s												
27	s	x	x	x	xs		x	x	sx										x			sx	xs		x	x		sx	s		xs												
28	sx	x		x		s	x	x	x													x	x		x	x	s	xs	sx		xs												
29		xs		x	s	s	x	x	sx										sx			x	sx		x	x		xs	sx		x	x											
30	sx	x		x		s	x												x			x	sx		x	x		xs			xs	x	x	s	s								
31	sx	x	x	x			x	x				s					s		xs			x	xs		x	x		sx			x				s								
32	sx	x	xs	x	s		x	x					s						x			x	sx		x	x		xs			xs	sx											
33	sx	x	x	x	s		x	x				s	sx						xs			x	sx		x	x		xs			xs												
34		x	x	x	s		x	x					sx									x	sx		x	x		xs			xs	sx		s		xs							
35		x	x	x	x		x	x					sx										sx		x	x		xs			xs	sx		s		xs	s						
36		x	x	x	x	sx	x	x					s										sx		xs	x					x	x			s	xs	s						
37		x	x	x	x		xs	x					sx						sx				sx		x	x		xs			x				s	xs		s					
38		x		x	s	x	x	x					sx						sx			s	sx		x	x		xs			x		x			xs							
39		x		x		x	xs						sx						sx			x	sx		x	x		xs			x	s	x			xs							
40		x	x	x	xs	s	xs						sx						x			x	s		sx	x		xs			x	x				sx							
41		x	x	x		s	sx	x											x			x	s		x	x		x			xs	xs				sx			s				
42		s	x	x		xs	x	x					x									x	sx		x	x		x								x			s	s	s		
43			x	x		x	x	xs					xs									x	sx		x	x		x						s	s	x			s			sx	
44		xs	xs	x		x	x						sx									x	x		x	s		xs					x	sx	s				x			sx	
45		x	x	x		x	x						sx						xs			x	sx		x	s		x						s		xs			x	s			
46		x	x	x		x	xs						sx						xs			x	sx		x			x						s		x			x	s		s	
x	4	36	32	43	23	12	32	27	5	4	0	3	3	2	1	0	0	2	16	2	2	27	5	0	28	26	0	5	0	0	7	4	4	0	0	3	0	0	3	0	0	0	
xs	3	2	3	1	4	2	10	1	11	6	0	2	7	2	1	1	0	1	5	1	0	0	6	0	1	0	0	13	2	0	9	1	0	0	0	7	0	0	0	0	0	0	
sx	12	0	0	0	1	1	2	3	5	2	8	7	17	3	1	2	0	0	4	0	0	1	16	0	1	0	0	7	3	0	1	3	0	1	0	2	0	0	0	0	0	2	
s	7	3	0	0	5	7	0	2	2	3	2	4	5	2	6	2	6	0	1	0	1	1	4	1	0	2	5	3	2	1	2	1	0	6	6	0	2	1	3	3	1	1	

x - Played full 90 minutes
xs - Substituted off
sx - Substituted on
s - Non-playing Substitute

DULWICH HAMLET MATCH RESULTS 2018-19

Date	Comp	Opponents	H/A	Att:	Result		Goalscorers	Pos
Aug 4	NLS	Welling United	A	1057	L	0 - 2		
7	NLS	East Thurrock United	H	727	**W**	2 - 1	Tomlin 71 Akinyemi 90	
11	NLS	Concord Rangers	H	822	L	0 - 1		
13	NLS	Chelmsford City	A	991	D	2 - 2	Clunis 4 Carew 45	
18	NLS	Bath City	A	869	L	1 - 2	Clunis 8	
25	NLS	Gloucester City	H	747	L	0 - 1		
27	NLS	Slough Town	A	1010	**W**	2 - 1	Akinyemi 56 Clunis 86	
Sept 1	NLS	Hampton & Richmond Boro'	H	815	L	0 - 2		
8	NLS	Wealdstone	H	1101	D	1 - 1	Cook 80	
15	NLS	Woking	A	1859	**W**	2 - 1	Chambers 3 Allen I 77	18
22	**FAC 2Q**	**Tonbridge Angels**	**H**	**569**	**W**	**3 - 1**	**Ferguson 35 Green 44 Akinyemi 87**	
29	NLS	Chippenham Town	H	717	**W**	2 - 0	Akinyemi 52 69	16
Oct 6	**FAC 3Q**	**Eastbourne Borough**	**A**	**570**	**L**	**3 - 4**	**Akinyemi 79 Clunis 83 Eshun 85**	
13	NLS	Hungerford Town	A	357	**W**	2 - 1	Green 53 Eshun 76	13
20	NLS	Dartford	A	1578	L	1 - 2	Akinyemi 19	16
27	NLS	Billericay Town	A	1384	D	1 - 1	Ferguson 70	
Nov 3	NLS	St Albans City	H	850	**W**	1 - 0	Clunis 27	
6	NLS	Weston-super-Mare	H	386	D	3 - 3	Vose 9 Ferguson 49 Carew 52 (Pen)	
11	NLS	Truro City	A	165	L	2 - 3	Carew 41 Clunis 54	
17	NLS	Oxford City	H	320	L	0 - 1		15
24	**FAT 3Q**	**Welling United**	**A**	**478**	**D**	**1 - 1**	**Carew (pen)**	
28	**FAT 3Qr**	**Welling United**	**H**	**219**	**W**	**2 - 1**	**Green 4 Akinyemi 75**	
Dec 1	NLS	Torquay United	H	1441	L	0 - 2		17
8	NLS	Hemel Hempstead Town	A	494	L	0 - 1		
15	**FAT 1P**	**Wingate & Finchley**	**A**	**202**	**L**	**0 - 2**		
22	NLS	Gloucester City	A	342	D	1 - 1	Thompson 33	
26	NLS	Eastbourne Borough	H	3000	**W**	2 - 1	Carew 61 Clunis 74	
29	NLS	Slough Town	H	2900	L	0 - 1		
Jan 1	NLS	Eastbourne Borough	A	702	L	1 - 2	Akinyemi 45	
5	NLS	Bath City	H	3104	L	0 - 2		
12	NLS	Hampton & Richmond Boro'	A	919	L	0 - 2		
19	NLS	East Thurrock United	A	301	D	0 - 0		17
26	NLS	Chelmsford City	H	2826	L	1 - 3	Green 7	
Feb 2	NLS	Concord Rangers	A	457	D	0 - 0		
9	NLS	Welling United	H	2353	**W**	2 - 1	Green 14 Sheriff 86	
16	NLS	Hemel Hempstead Town	H	2849	D	3 - 3	Thompson 5 37 Sheriff 89 (pen)	
23	NLS	Torquay United	A	2655	L	2 - 5	Akinyemi 65 (pen) Green 70	18
Mar 2	NLS	Dartford	H	2779	**W**	2 - 0	Mascoll 27 Sheriff 90	16
9	NLS	St Albans City	A	1088	L	0 - 1		17
16	NLS	Truro City	H	1960	**W**	3 - 2	Akinyemi 36 Ferguson 48 Wanadio 85	15
23	NLS	Oxford City	A	579	L	1 - 4	Akinyemi 90	16
30	NLS	Billericay Town	H	3243	D	2 - 2	Akinyemi 80 (pen) Okuonghae 90+5	15
Apr 6	NLS	Chippenham Town	A	532	**W**	2 - 1	Akinyemi 36 (pen) 80	15
13	NLS	Hungerford Town	H	2841	**W**	3 - 1	Thompson 21 Cook 38 Hunte 42	15
20	NLS	Wealdstone	A	1245	**W**	3 - 1	Hunte 19 Cook 39 Akinyemi 82 (pen)	
22	NLS	Woking	H	2648	L	1 - 3	Tajbakhsh 90	15
27	NLS	Weston-super-Mare	A	669	D	1 - 1	Tajbakhsh 78	14

GOALSCORERS	SG	CSG	Pens	Hat tricks	Total
Akinyemi	13	4	4		15
Clunis	7	2			7
Carew	5	2	2		5
Green	5	1			5
Ferguson	4	1			4
Thompson*	3	1			4
Cook	3	2			3
Sheriff	3	2	1		3
Eshun	2	1			2
Hunte	2	2			2
Tajbakhsh	2	2			2
Allen	1	1			1
Chambers	1	1			1
Mascoll	1	1			1
Okuonghae	1	1			1
Tomlin	1	1			1
Vose	1	1			1
Wanadio	1	1			1

No.		Ming	Abrahams	Kargbo	Okuonghae	Pappoe	Cook	Carew	Akinyemi	Ferguson	Lawrence	Green	Vose	Figueira	Tomlin	May	Taylor	Clunis	Onovwigun	Kamara	Tangara	Guimaraes	Deen-Conteh	Chambers	Allen I	Nash	Eshun (L)	Toure Cheick	Splatt Jamie	Banton (L)	Baguelo'rich	Thompson	Sardinha	Erskine	Essuman (L)	Sheriff	Mavila	Pryce (L)	Jorgenson	Mascoll	Tajbakhsh	Wanadio (L)	Hunte (L)	Allen C
1	x	x	xs	x	x	x	xs	x	xs	x	x	sx	sx	sx	s	s																												
2	x	x		x	x	x	xs	s	sx	x	s	x	x	x	xs	s	s																											
3	x	x		x	x	x	xs		sx	x	s		x	xs	x	sx	xs	sx	s																									
4	x	x		x	x	x	xs	xs	sx	sx	sx		x	s	s	xs	x	x																										
5	x	x	s	x	x	x	x	xs	sx	sx			x	s	xs	s	x	x																										
6	x	sx	xs	x		xs	x	x	xs				x	sx	sx		x	x		x	s	s																						
7	x	x		x		s	x	x	sx			sx	x	xs	xs		x	x	s	x		s																						
8	x	xs		x			x	xs	xs	x		sx	x		sx		x	x		x		s	s	sx																				
9	x	x		x	x		sx	s		x		x	x		s	x	s	sx						x	xs	xs																		
10	x	x		xs	x		x	s	s	x		x	x			xs	s	sx						x	sx	x																		
11	x	x		x					sx	x		x			x	x		x							x																			
12	x	sx		xs	x		sx	sx	xs	x		x	x		x		x	xs						x	s	s																		
13	x				x				x	x			x		x			x						x	x		x																	
14	x	sx	s		x		sx	x	xs	x		x	x			sx	x	xs				s		x			xs																	
15	x	s	s	s	x		xs	x	x	x		x	x		sx		x					s		x			x																	
16	x	x	s	x	x		s	x	x	x		x	xs		sx	s		x						x			s																	
17	x	sx		xs	x		s	x		x		x	x		s	xs	x	x						x	s		sx																	
18	x	sx		xs	x		sx	x		x		x	xs		xs	sx	x	x						x	s		s																	
19	x	x			x		sx	x		xs		x	x		sx	xs	s	x				s		x	x		s																	
20	x	x		x			s	x	x	s		x	x		s	s	x	x						x	x			s																
21	x	x		s	x		x	x	s	s		x	x		x	s		x						x	s			x																
22	x	x			x			x	sx			x			x			x						x				x																
23	x	x		x	x		x	x	sx	s			x		xs	s		x						x	s			x	s															
24	x	xs		s			s	xs	sx	sx		x	x		xs		x	x						x	x			x		s														
25	x	sx		x			s	x	x	x		x			sx	sx	x	xs							xs			x		xs			s											
26	x	sx					x	sx	xs	x		x	xs		sx			x	x									xs		s	x	x	s											
27	x	sx					xs	x	sx	x		x					s	x	x					x				x		x	s	xs	s											
28	x	s					x	x	sx	x		x			sx			x	x					x				xs		xs	s	xs	s											
29	x	s					x	x	xs	x		x			sx		sx	x	xs					x				x		xs	s			sx										
30	x	s					x	x	sx	x		x	sx				x	sx						x				xs		x	s	xs		xs										
31	x						sx	xs	sx	x		x	x				x	x						x				s		s				x	xs	x	s							
32	x				x		x		sx	x		sx	x				s	x	xs					x				s			x			sx		xs	xs							
33	x				x		x		sx	x		x	sx				x	xs	sx					x				s				xs			s	sx	x							
34	x				x		x		sx	x		x	x				x	x	s									xs				xs			sx	s	x	sx						
35	x				x		x		xs	sx		x	xs				x	x	sx					x								xs			s	sx	x	s						
36					x		x		xs	sx		x	xs				x	x	s					x								xs			s	sx	x	sx	x					
37					xs		xs		sx	s		x	sx				x	x						x							sx	xs						s	x	x	x	x		
38	x						s		xs	x		xs	sx				x	x	sx					x								s			x	sx				x	x	xs		
39	x						sx		xs	x		x	xs				x	x	s					x								s			x	sx				x	xs	xs		
40	x						x		x	x		xs	sx				x	x	s					x								s			xs	s				x	x	sx		
41	x				sx		x		x	x							xs	x	s					x								s			x	sx				x	xs	xs	sx	
42	x				x		sx		x	x		x	x				xs	x	s					x								x								xs	sx	s		s
43	x				x		sx		xs	x			sx				x	x						x							s	xs								x	x	s	xs	sx
44	x				x		x		x	x			sx				x							x							s	xs			s					x	x	sx	xs	sx
45	x				x		x		xs	x			sx				x					s									x	xs			s					x	x	sx	xs	sx
46	x				x		x		x	x			sx				x					s									xs	xs			s					x	x	sx	xs	sx
47	x				x		x		x	x			xs				xs	x				s									x	sx			sx					x	x	sx		s
x	45	15	0	14	29	5	22	18	11	34	1	29	23	1	6	2	27	33	3	3	0	0	0	32	5	1	2	7	0	2	4	2	0	1	3	1	4	0	2	10	8	1	0	0
xs	0	2	2	4	1	1	7	5	13	1	0	2	7	2	6	4	4	4	2	0	0	0	0	0	2	1	1	4	0	3	1	12	0	1	2	1	1	0	0	1	2	3	4	0
sx	0	8	0	0	1	0	9	2	17	5	1	4	10	2	9	4	1	4	3	0	0	0	0	1	1	0	1	0	0	0	1	1	0	2	2	6	0	2	0	0	1	5	1	4
s	0	4	4	3	0	1	6	3	2	4	2	0	0	2	5	7	6	0	8	0	1	9	1	0	5	1	3	4	1	3	6	4	4	0	6	2	1	2	0	0	0	2	0	2

x - Played full 90 minutes
xs - Substituted off
sx - Substituted on
s - Non-playing Substitute

EAST THURROCK UNITED MATCH RESULTS 2018-19

Date	Comp	Opponents	H/A	Att:	Result		Goalscorers	Pos
Aug 4	NLS	Woking	H	532	L	0 - 1		
7	NLS	Dulwich Hamlet	A	727	L	1 - 2	Orsi-Dadomo 31	
11	NLS	Torquay United	A	1620	L	0 - 2		
14	NLS	Eastbourne Borough	H	267	L	0 - 1		
18	NLS	Gloucester City	A	210	L	0 - 1		
25	NLS	Slough Town	H	327	W	1 - 0	Orsi-Dadomo 79	
27	NLS	Dartford	A	1114	L	0 - 2		
Sept 1	NLS	Bath City	H	203	W	1 - 0	Artus 89 (og)	
8	NLS	St Albans City	H	326	L	2 - 4	Higgins 26 (Pen) Simmons 32	
15	NLS	Welling United	A	547	L	0 - 2		
22	**FAC 2Q**	**Whitehawk**	**H**	**154**	**L**	**2 - 3**	**Michael-Percil 36 Moncur 62**	
29	NLS	Wealdstone	H	274	L	0 - 1		20
Oct 20	NLS	Hungerford Town	H	1578	W	2 - 1	Michael-Percil 90 Sheeham 90+3	19
27	NLS	Chippenham Town	A	502	L	0 - 2		
30	NLS	Billericay Town	A	832	L	2 - 3	Derry 33 Higgins 55	
Nov 3	NLS	Truro City	H	235	D	2 - 2	Moncur 51 Higgins 90	
17	NLS	Hemel Hempstead Town	H	299	L	1 - 2	Higgins 32 (Pen)	21
20	NLS	Weston-super-Mare	A	465	D	1 - 1	Batt 61	
24	**FAT 3Q**	**Salisbury**	**A**	**465**	**L**	**1 - 2**	**Marlow 56**	
Dec 1	NLS	Hampton & Richmond Boro'	A	377	L	0 - 1		22
8	NLS	Chelmsford City	H	338	W	2 - 0	Marlow 1 Higgins 21	
11	NLS	Oxford City	A	174	L	1 - 3	Higgins 46	
22	NLS	Slough Town	A	581	L	1 - 3	Scott 25	
26	NLS	Concord Rangers	H	286	L	0 - 2		
29	NLS	Dartford	H	442	D	2 - 2	Derry 33 43	
Jan 1	NLS	Concord Rangers	A	412	D	1 - 1	Derry 84	
5	NLS	Gloucester City	H	242	W	2 - 0	Hayles 10 Ashford 61	
12	NLS	Bath City	A	772	L	0 - 1		
19	NLS	Dulwich Hamlet	H	301	D	0 - 0		21
26	NLS	Eastbourne Borough	A	459	W	2 - 0	Higgins 8 (pen) Ashford 20	
Feb 9	NLS	Woking	A	1613	L	0 - 3		
16	NLS	Chelmsford City	A	1358	L	0 - 1		
23	NLS	Hampton & Richmond Boro'	H	301	D	0 - 0		
26	NLS	Torquay United	H	452	L	1 - 2	Harris 17	21
Mar 2	NLS	Billericay Town	H	484	W	2 - 1	Hayles 12 35	20
9	NLS	Truro City	A	429	W	3 - 1	Hayles 3 Marlow 46 Nasha 70	20
16	NLS	Oxford City	H	202	L	0 - 1		20
23	NLS	Hemel Hempstead Town	A	442	L	2 - 3	Higgins 61 Hayles 62	21
30	NLS	Chippenham Town	H	206	W	2 - 1	Higgins 63 77	21
Apr 6	NLS	Wealdstone	A	764	L	0 - 3		21
13	NLS	Weston-super-Mare	H	210	L	2 - 3	Higgins 19 Scott 80	21
19	NLS	St Albans City	A	920	L	1 - 2	Nasha 72	21
22	NLS	Welling United	H	566	W	4 - 1	Higgins 15 37 Nzengo 47 Hayles 90	21 (R)
27	NLS	Hungerford Town	A	485	D	1 - 1	Batt 23	21

GOALSCORERS	SG	CSG	Pens	Hat tricks	Total
Higgins	11	3	3		13
Hayles	5	3			6
Derry	3	2			4
Marlow	3	1			3
Ashford	2	1			2
Batt	2	1			2
Michael-Percil	2	1			2
Moncur	2	1			2
Nasha	2	1			2
Orsi-Dadomo	2	1			2
Scott	2	1			2
Harris	1	1			1
Nzengo	1	1			1
Opponent	1	1			1
Sheeham	1	1			1
Simmons	1	1			1

Giddens	Harris	Stephen	Konchesky	Burns	Scott	Marlow	Lee	Orsi-Dadomo	Derry	Levett	Simmons	Kellum	Knight	Knott	Miller	Egan (L)	Southam	Higgins	Moncur	Bedford (L)	Michael-Percil	Boswell	Batt	Ekpiteta	Hession-Harris	Nzengo	Sheehan	Prestege	Can	McLeod-Urquhart	Marsh-Brown	Mudd	Hayles	Diallo	Merzook	Omrore	Ebwa	Osborn	Ashford	Nasha	Yasar	Olaniran	Dobson	No.
x	x	x	x	x	x	x	x	xs	x	xs	sx	sx	s	s																														1
x	x	xs	x	x	x	s	x	x	xs	xs	x	sx	sx	s	sx																													2
x	x	sx	x	x	x	xs	x	xs	x		x	s	s		sx	x																												3
x	x	s	x	x	x	x	x	sx	x		sx	s	s		xs	x	xs																											4
x	x	s	x	x	x	xs	x	sx	x		xs	s	sx		x	x																												5
x	x	x		x	x	xs	x	sx	sx		xs	s	s			x		x	x																									6
x	x	x		x	x	s	x	xs	xs		sx	sx	s		s	xs		x	x																									7
x	x	x		x	x	xs	x	s	sx		s				x	sx		x	sx	xs	xs																							8
x	sx	x		x	x	xs	x	s	sx		xs				x	x		x	sx	s	xs																							9
x		x		x	x	xs	x	sx	xs						xs	x		x	sx	sx	x																							10
x		**xs**		**x**	**x**	**x**	**x**		**sx**		**xs**				**x**				**sx**		**x**	**sx**	**xs**																					11
x	x	xs		x	x	sx	x		sx		s				x			x	x		x			x	s																			12
x	s				x	x	x		xs						sx			x	s		sx				x	x	x	x	xs															13
x	s				x	s	x		x						x			x	x		x				s	x	x	x																14
x	x				x	x	x		xs									xs	s		sx				x	x	x	sx	sx	xs														15
x	x				x	x	x											x	sx		s		xs		xs	x	x	sx	s	x	s													16
x	x				x	x	x		x									x	xs		sx				s	xs	x	s		x	sx													17
x	x				x	x	x		xs									x	s		sx		sx		s	s	x	x		x	x													18
x	**x**				**xs**	**x**	**x**		**sx**										**s**		**x**		**xs**		**sx**		**x**	**x**		**x**	**xs**	**sx**												19
x	x	x		x	x	x	x												s		xs				sx	s		x		x	xs	sx												20
x				x	x	x	x		sx									x	s		xs		xs		s	s	x	sx		x	x													21
x				xs	x	x	x		xs									xs	sx		sx				s	sx	x	s		x	x		x											22
x				x	x	x	x		sx														xs			sx	x	x					xs	x	xs	sx	s							23
x	x			x		x	xs		x									xs					sx			x	x	xs				sx		x	s	s	sx							24
x	x				x		xs		sx									x					s			x	x	x				s	x	x		s	s	x						25
x	x				x	s			x														xs			x	x	x				s	xs	x		s		x	sx					26
x				s	x	x			x														sx			x	x	x				s	x	x			s	xs	x					27
x				sx	x	x			x														s			x	x	xs					xs	x			s	x	x	sx				28
x	sx			xs	x	x			xs									sx					s			sx	x	s					x	x				xs	x	x				29
x	xs				x	x	sx		sx									xs					sx			xs	x	x						x					x	x				30
x	x			x	x	x	s		s									x					s			s	x	s						x				x	x	x				31
x	x			x	x	x												x					sx			sx	x	xs						x				x	xs		s			32
x	x			x	x	xs	s											x					s			s	x	x					x	x				xs	sx	sx				33
x	x			x		xs	x											x					s			x	x	sx						x				sx	xs	x		s		34
x	x			x	x		sx											x					s			s	x	xs					x	x				xs	sx	x				35
x	x			x	x	x	s											xs					s			s	x	s					x	x				x		x			sx	36
x	x			x	x	xs	sx											x					sx			x	x	sx					x					s		xs			xs	37
x	xs			x	x		sx											x					s	s		sx	x	xs					x	x				xs		x			sx	38
x	x			x	x	x	s											x					s	s		x	x	sx					x					xs		xs			sx	39
x	x			x	x	xs	sx											xs					s	s			x	sx					xs	x				x		x			xs	40
x	xs			x	x		xs											x					s	s			x	sx					x	x				x		x			sx	41
x	x			x	x		x											x					sx	s		s	x	sx						x				x		xs			xs	42
x	x			xs	x		sx											x					s	s		sx	x						x	x				x		x			xs	43
x	x				x													sx					xs	x		x	x						x					x		x			x	44
44	30	7	5	28	41	22	25	1	10	0	2	0	0	0	6	6	0	24	4	0	5	0	0	2	2	13	31	11	0	7	3	0	13	19	0	0	0	11	5	11	0	0	1	x
0	3	3	0	3	1	10	3	3	8	2	4	0	0	0	2	1	1	6	1	1	4	0	7	0	1	2	0	5	1	1	2	0	4	0	1	0	0	6	2	3	0	0	4	xs
0	2	1	0	1	0	1	6	4	10	0	3	3	2	0	3	1	0	2	6	1	5	1	7	0	2	6	0	9	1	0	1	3	0	0	0	1	1	1	3	2	0	0	4	sx
0	2	2	0	1	0	4	4	2	1	0	2	4	5	2	1	0	0	0	6	1	1	0	13	6	6	8	0	5	1	0	1	3	0	0	1	3	4	1	0	0	1	1	0	s

x - Played full 90 minutes
xs - Substituted off
sx - Substituted on
s - Non-playing Substitute

EASTBOURNE BOROUGH MATCH RESULTS 2018-19

Date	Comp	Opponents	H/A	Att:	Result	Goalscorers	Pos
Aug 4	NLS	Oxford City	A	282	D 0 - 0		
7	NLS	Welling United	H	585	W 1 - 0	Dawes 19	
11	NLS	Truro City	H	512	D 2 - 2	Walker 23 West 83	
14	NLS	East Thurrock United	A	267	W 1 - 0	Dawes 32	
18	NLS	Chippenham Town	H	505	W 2 - 1	Walker 19 Odubade 74	
25	NLS	St Albans City	A	510	D 1 - 1	West 14	
27	NLS	Woking	H	927	L 1 - 2	Wills 62	
Sept 1	NLS	Weston-super-Mare	A	824	W 1 - 0	Martin 77	
8	NLS	Dartford	A	1005	D 2 - 2	Martin 12 Odubade 47 (Pen)	
15	NLS	Slough Town	H	645	L 2 - 4	Walker 44 Cox 64	
22	**FAC 2Q**	**Brantham Athletic**	**A**	**285**	**W 1 - 0**	**Odubade 56**	
29	NLS	Gloucester City	A	227	D 2 - 2	Ransom 73 Gardiner 87	11
Oct 6	**FAC 3Q**	**Dulwich Hamlet**	**H**	**570**	**W 4 - 3**	**Rutherford 5 Hall 16 43 Cox 29 (Pen)**	
13	NLS	Torquay United	H	929	L 2 - 4	Rutherford 36 Cox 77	15
20	**FAC 4Q**	**Slough Town**	**H**	**802**	**L 1 - 2**	**Rutherford 70**	
27	NLS	Eastbourne Borough	H	481	W 3 - 0	Rutherford 4 49 72	
30	NLS	Hampton & Richmond Boro'	H	428	D 2 - 2	Torres 4 Cox 31 (Pen)	
Nov 3	NLS	Chelmsford City	A	668	L 2 - 3	Cox 40 (Pen) Hall 87	
10	NLS	Hungerford Town	H	447	W 3 - 1	Hall 48 76 Odubade 55 (Pen)	
13	NLS	Concord Rangers	A	262	L 0 - 3		
17	NLS	Bath City	A	783	L 0 - 1		14
24	**FAT 3Q**	**Dartford**	**H**	**340**	**D 1 - 1**		
27	**FAT 3Qr**	**Dartford**	**A**	**404**	**W 3 - 2**	**Cox 43 67 Gardiner 90+2**	
Dec 1	NLS	Wealdstone	A	719	W 3 - 0	Hall 23 87 Cox 25	12
8	NLS	Billericay Town	H	574	L 0 - 2		
15	**FAT 1P**	**Dorchester Town**	**H**	**215**	**L 0 - 4**		
22	NLS	St Albans City	H	550	L 1 - 2	Cox 18	
26	NLS	Dulwich Hamlet	A	3000	L 1 - 2	Walker 90	
29	NLS	Woking	A	2024	L 0 - 2		
Jan 1	NLS	Dulwich Hamlet	H	702	W 2 - 1	Rollinson 28 Quigley 59	
5	NLS	Chippenham Town	A	504	W 3 - 2	Quigley 33 37 Wills 67	
12	NLS	Weston-super-Mare	H	486	D 1 - 1	Wills 18	
19	NLS	Welling United	A	445	L 0 - 1		14
26	NLS	East Thurrock United	H	459	L 0 - 2		
Feb 2	NLS	Truro City	A	341	L 0 - 2		
9	NLS	Oxford City	H	451	D 2 - 2	Walker 30 Cox 64 (pen)	
16	NLS	Billericay Town	A	910	L 0 - 2		
23	NLS	Wealdstone	H	720	L 0 - 3		15
Mar 2	NLS	Hampton & Richmond Boro'	A	420	D 0 - 0		15
9	NLS	Chelmsford City	H	533	D 1 - 1	Ljubicic 3	16
16	NLS	Hungerford Town	A	196	L 0 - 2		17
23	NLS	Bath City	H	587	D 0 - 0		17
30	NLS	Hemel Hempstead Town	A	486	L 2 - 3	Walker 45+2 57	17
Apr 6	NLS	Gloucester City	H	511	L 1 - 2	Walker 51	17
13	NLS	Torquay United	A	4538	L 0 - 2		17
19	NLS	Dartford	H	731	W 6 - 0	Walker 14 43 68 (pen) Wills 25 Jordan 60 West 61	17
22	NLS	Slough Town	A	905	D 1 - 1	Cotton 90+5	18 (s)
27	NLS	Concord Rangers	H	545	L 1 - 2	Bingham 53	18

GOALSCORERS	SG	CSG	Pens	Hat tricks	Total
Walker	8	2	1	1	11
Cox	9	2	4		10
Hall	4	1			7
Rutherford	4	4		1	6
Odubade	4	1	2		4
Wills	4	2			4
Quigley*	2	2			3
West	3	1			3
Dawes	2	1			2
Gardiner	2	1			2
Martin	2	2			2
Bingham	1	1			1
Cotton	1	1			1
Jordan	1	1			1
Ljubicic	1	1			1
Ransom	1	1			1
Rollinson	1	1			1
Torres	1	1			1

	Hamilton	Campbell	Wills	Ransom	Gardiner	Hall	Torres	Walker	Dawes	Martin	Odubade	West	Simpemba	Pollard	Briggs	Cox	Pearson	Day	Shaw	Bridges	Adebayo-Rowling	Rutherford (L)	Blackmore	Earl	Santos	Freeman	Liddle (L)	Rollinson (L)	Adebowale (L)	Howes (L)	Quigley (L)	Cotton	Rents	Myles-Meekums (L)	Jordan (L)	Ljubicic (L)	Gharbaoui	Bingham	No.
	x	x	x	x	x	x	x	x	xs	xs	sx	sx	s	s	s																								1
		x	x	x	x	x	x	xs	xs	sx	sx	sx		x	s	xs	s																						2
		x	x	x	x	xs	xs	xs	x	sx	sx	sx		s	s	x		x																					3
	x	x	x	x	x	x	sx	x	xs	sx	sx	xs		s		sx		s																					4
	x	x	x	x	x	sx	x	xs	xs	xs	sx	sx		s		x		s																					5
	sx	x	x	x	x		sx	xs	x	xs	sx	x		s	s	x		xs																					6
	x	x	x	x	x	xs	x		xs	sx	x	s	sx	s		x		s																					7
	x	x	x	x	x	x	x		x	sx	xs	sx	s	s		xs		s																					8
	x	x	x	xs	x	x	x	sx	xs	x	sx		sx	s		xs		s																					9
	x	x	x		x	sx	x	x		xs	x	sx		xs	s	x		s	s																				10
			x	x	x	x	x	xs	xs	s	sx	xs	sx	s		x		sx	s	s																			11
		xs	x	x	x	x	xs	xs		sx	sx	sx	s	s		x					x	x																	12
		x	x	x	x	x	x	xs			sx					x					x	x																	13
		xs	x	x	x	x	sx	xs			sx	xs	s	sx	s	x					x	x																	14
		x	x	x	x	xs	xs	xs	sx	s	s	sx	sx		s	x			s		x	x																	15
		x	x	x	x	x	xs	s	sx	s	xs	sx		s		x					x	x																	16
		x	x	x	x	xs	x	xs	xs		sx	sx		s	sx	x					x		s																17
		x	x	x	x	x	x	x	xs		sx	s		s	s	x					x		s																18
		x	x	x	x	x	xs	xs			xs	sx			sx	x					x		sx	s	s														19
		x	x	x	x	x	xs	xs	s		sx	sx			s	x					x				s	x													20
		x	x	x	x	x	x	s			s	s			s	x					x		s				x	x											21
																																							22
		x	x	x	x	x	sx	sx	s			xs			sx	xs					x		s				xs	x											23
		x	x	x	x	x	x	sx	sx						s	xs					x		s				xs	xs	sx										24
		x	x	x	x	x	xs	sx	sx	s					s	x					x						xs	xs	sx										25
		x	xs	x	x	x	x	sx	sx						s	x					x		s				xs	x	s										26
		x	x	sx	x	x	s	xs	x						s	x					x		s				s	x	x										27
		xs	x	x	x	x	x	sx	xs						s	x					x		s				sx	xs	sx										28
		x	x	x	x	xs	s	sx	xs						sx	x					x		s				sx	xs	x										29
		x	x	x	x	x	x	s	sx						sx	xs					x		s				sx	xs		x	x								30
	s	x	x	x	x		xs	x	xs						sx	x					x		s	s				sx		x	x								31
	s	x	x	x	x	xs		xs	sx			sx			sx	x					x		s					sx		x	x								32
	s	x	x	x	x	x		x	xs			xs			sx						x		s		s					x	x	sx							33
	s		x	x	x	x		xs	sx			s			sx	x					x		s							x	x		x	xs					34
	s		x	x	x	xs		sx	xs			s			s	x					x									x			x	sx	x	x			35
	x	x	x	x	s	x		xs	sx			s			x	x							s							x				s	x	x			36
	x	x	x	x	x				xs			x							s				x		sx					x		sx		xs		x	s		37
	xs	x	x	x	x				sx	xs		x			sx	x							xs	sx	s					x				s		x			38
x	s	x	x	sx	x	x				x		x			s	xs					x		s	s											x	x			39
x	sx	x	x	s	x	x				xs		x			s						x			s											x	x		x	40
x	s	x	x	x		xs	sx	sx		xs		x									x			s	sx										x	xs		x	41
x	xs	x	x	sx			x	sx		xs		x			sx						x				s					s					x	x		xs	42
x	sx	x	x	s	x		x	xs		sx		x				sx					xs									s					x	x		xs	43
	s	x	x	s	x		x	xs	sx			x				sx					x			s						x					x	x		xs	44
	x	x	x	x			x	xs	xs	xs		x			sx				s		x		s							x						sx		sx	45
		x	x				x	x	xs	x		xs			sx				s		x		s							x		sx			x			sx	46
			x	x	x		x	x		xs		x			sx				s		x		s							x		sx			x		s	xs	47
	xs	xs	x	x			x	x	s	x		x			s						x			s						x		sx			x			sx	48
3	10	39	46	38	41	26	23	9	4	4	2	12	0	1	1	27	0	1	0	0	32	5	1	0	0	1	1	4	2	14	5	0	2	0	11	9	0	2	x
0	3	4	1	1	0	8	8	19	17	10	3	6	0	1	0	7	0	1	0	0	1	0	1	0	0	0	4	5	0	0	0	0	0	2	0	1	0	4	xs
0	3	0	0	3	0	2	5	10	11	7	14	13	4	1	14	3	0	1	0	0	0	0	1	1	2	0	3	2	3	0	0	5	0	1	0	1	0	3	sx
0	8	0	0	3	1	0	2	3	3	4	2	6	4	13	19	0	1	6	7	1	0	0	19	7	5	0	1	0	1	2	0	0	0	2	0	0	2	0	s

x - Played full 90 minutes
xs - Substituted off
sx - Substituted on
s - Non-playing Substitute

GLOUCESTER CITY MATCH RESULTS 2018-19

Date	Comp	Opponents	H/A	Att:	Result	Goalscorers	Pos
Aug 4	NLS	Concord Rangers	A	326	L 0 - 2		
7	NLS	Oxford City	H	312	**W** 1 - 0	Jackson 64	
11	NLS	Slough Town	H	353	L 1 - 2	Mawford 70	
14	NLS	Bath City	A	775	L 0 - 3		
18	NLS	East Thurrock United	H	210	**W** 1 - 0	Seymour 34	
25	NLS	Dulwich Hamlet	A	747	**W** 1 - 0	Smerdon 47	
27	NLS	Torquay United	H	720	D 0 - 0		
Sept 1	NLS	Hungerford Town	A	235	**W** 2 - 1	Smerdon 23 Liddiard 50	
8	NLS	Truro City	H	314	L 0 - 2		
15	NLS	Chippenham Town	A	597	L 0 - 1		
23	**FAC 2Q**	**Plymouth Parkway**	**H**	**349**	**W 3 - 1**	**Robert 1 Williams H 67 Jackson 79**	
29	NLS	Eastbourne Borough	H	227	D 2 - 2	Parker 31 Liddiard 90	17
Manager Marc Richards leaves to become head coach at Hereford FC.							
Oct 6	**FAC 3Q**	**Dorking Wanderers**	**H**	**333**	**D 3 - 3**		
9	**FAC 3Qr**	**Dorking Wanderers**	**A**	**563**	**W 3 - 0**		
Chris Todd named as the new manager.							
13	NLS	Billericay Town	A	1420	L 0 - 1		18
20	**FAC 4Q**	**Bromley**	**H**	**621**	**L 0 - 1**		
27	NLS	Welling United	A	600	L 1 - 3	Parker 77	
29	NLS	Wealdstone	A	675	L 0 - 2		
Nov 3	NLS	Dartford	H	320	L 1 - 2	Avery 41	
10	NLS	Hemel Hempstead Town	A	456	L 1 - 2	Hanks 90	
14	NLS	Woking	H	291	**W** 4 - 3	Jackson 36 42 Gerring 38 (Og) Knowles 68	
17	NLS	St Albans City	H	299	D 0 - 0		19
25	**FAT 3Q**	**Biggleswade Town**	**H**	**236**	**L 1 - 3**		
Dec 1	NLS	Chelmsford City	A	631	L 0 - 2		19
8	NLS	Hampton & Richmond B'	H	269	D 0 - 0		
22	NLS	Dulwich Hamlet	H	342	D 1 - 1	Williams H 88	
26	NLS	Weston-super-Mare	A	747	D 0 - 0		
29	NLS	Torquay United	A	3071	L 1 - 2	Bailey 88	
Jan 1	NLS	Weston-super-Mare	H	371	L 1 - 3	Bailey 48	
5	NLS	East Thurrock United	A	242	L 0 - 2		
12	NLS	Hungerford Town	H	393	D 0 - 0		
19	NLS	Oxford City	A	313	**W** 1 - 0	Hanks 41 (Pen)	20
26	NLS	Bath City	H	519	D 0 - 0		
Feb 12	NLS	Slough Town	A	463	**W** 2 - 1	Robert 51 Thomas 76	
16	NLS	Hampton & Richmond B'	A	465	**W** 1 - 0	Robert 54	
23	NLS	Chelmsford City	H	361	D 0 - 0		19
Mar 2	NLS	Wealdstone	H	396	D 0 - 0		19
5	NLS	Concord Rangers	H	178	L 1 - 2	Russe 26	19
9	NLS	Dartford	A	1061	L 0 - 2		19
16	NLS	Hemel Hempstead Town	H	216	D 1 - 1	Robert 44	19
23	NLS	St Albans City	A	845	**W** 2 - 1	Jackson 58 Robert 71	18
30	NLS	Welling United	H	283	L 0 - 1		20
Apr 6	NLS	Eastbourne Borough	A	511	**W** 2 - 1	Noel-Williams 63 Jackson 89	18
13	NLS	Billericay Town	H	392	L 1 - 4	Noel-Williams 18	18
20	NLS	Truro City	A	684	**W** 2 - 1	Robert 38 Jackson 76	18
22	NLS	Chippenham Town	H	409	**W** 3 - 2	Robert 72 Hanks 74 (pen) Jackson 76	17 (s)
27	NLS	Woking	A	1881	**W** 2 - 1	Jackson 81 Robert 85	17

GOALSCORERS	SG	CSG	Pens	Hat tricks	Total
Jackson	8	2			9
Robert	8	3			8
Hanks	4	1	3		4
Bailey	2	2			2
Liddiard	2	1			2
Noel-Williams	2	1			2
Parker	2	1			2
Smerdon	2	1			2
Williams H	2	1			2
Avery	1	1			1
Knowles	1	1			1
Mawford	1	1			1
Opponent	1	1			1
Russe	1	1			1
Seymour	1	1			1
Thomas	1	1			1

	Liddiard	Deaman	Hanks	Avery	Hamilton	Seymour (L)	Knowles	Jackson	Mawford J	Page	Parker	Williams M	Edge	Smerdon	Lawrence	Kelly	Morford W	Hannah	Williams H	Robert (L)	Green	Przybek (L)	Wright	Warwick (L)	Bailey (L)	Unwin	Sesay (L)	Weir	Wollacott (L)	Hussaini (L)	Thomas	Robbins	Pearce (L)	Hodges (L)	Kotwica	Law (L)	Russe (L)	Nesbeth	Lapworth	Peck	King T	Noel-Williams	Henry (L)	Spark	No.
	X	X	X	X	X	X	X	X	X	XS	SX	S	S	S	S																														1
	X	X	X	X	X	XS	X	X	X	X	SX	S	S		S	S																													2
	X	XS	X	X	X	SX	X	XS	X	X	X	S	SX		S	S																													3
	X	XS	X	X	X	SX			XS	X	XS	X	X	SX	SX	S	S																												4
		SX	X	X		XS		S	X	X	X	X	X	X	SX	XS	S	S																											5
	X	S	X	X	SX	XS			S	X	X	X	X	XS	SX	X	S																												6
	X	S	X	X	X	XS			X	SX	X		X	X	S	X	S																												7
	X	S	X	X	X	XS	SX		XS	SX	XS	S	X	X	SX	X																													8
	X	S	X		X	X	S		XS	SX	X	X	XS	X	SX	XS			SX																										9
	X	S	X	X	X	XS	XS				X	X	X	X	SX	S	S		SX																										10
		X	**X**	**X**	**X**		**XS**	**SX**		**S**	**X**	**S**	**X**	**X**	**XS**		**S**	**S**	**SX**	**X**	**S**																								11
	X	X	XS	X	X	SX	SX		S	SX	X	S	X	X	XS					XS																									12
																																													13
																																													14
																																													15
			X	X	XS	X	X	XS	SX	SX	X		X		S	S		X	X	X	S																								16
	X	**X**	**X**	**X**	**X**		**XS**	**X**	**X**	**S**	**XS**	**S**	**X**		**SX**			**X**	**SX**		**S**																								17
	X	X	XS	X	X						XS		XS	SX	S	S			SX	X		X	XS	SX																					18
	X	X		X	X				XS		X		SX					X	SX	X		X	XS	SX																					19
	X	XS	X	X	XS		X	S	S		X		SX	X					XS	XS		X	X	SX																					20
		X	X	X			X	S	SX		XS			X					X		S	X	X	X	XS	SX																			21
	X	SX	X	X			X	X	S					X					X				XS	SX	X	S	X	XS																	22
	X	X	X	X			X	X	SX					X					XS		S		XS	SX	X	S	X																		23
	X	X	X	X	S		XS	X	SX					X					SX				SX	S	XS			X	X	XS															24
	X		X	X	X		X	SX	X					XS					XS				XS		SX			X	X	SX	S	S													25
	S		X	X	X		X	X	X		SX								SX				XS		SX			XS	X		XS	S	X												26
	SX		X	X	X		X	S	X		X								XS				XS		SX	S			X		X	S	X												27
	X		X	X	X		S	SX	X		XS								SX				XS		SX			S	X		X	X	XS												28
	SX			X	X		XS	XS	X		XS								S				SX		X			X	X		X	X	SX												29
	X		X		X		S	X	X		S								X		S		SX		X			X	X		XS	X													30
			X	X	X		X	XS	SX		XS			X					S	SX					X				X			S		X	XS	SX									31
			X	X	X			X			X			X					SX						X				X		XS	S		X	XS	SX									32
			X	X	X			XS	X		X								SX	X									X		SX	S		X	XS		X	S								33
			X	X	X				X		X			X		SX			S	XS									X		X			S	X		X	S	S							34
			S	X	X		X		X		X			X					S	X						S			X		XS			SX	X		X		S							35
			SX	X			XS		X		XS			X						X						SX			X		X			X	X		X			S						36
			X	X	X			SX	X		X			X					SX	X						S					SX			XS	XS		X				X	S				37
			X	X	X			S	X		X			X					S	X						S					SX			X	XS		X		S				X			38
			X	X	X		SX	SX	XS		X			X					S	X														X	X		XS						X			39
			X	X	XS		SX	X	X		XS			SX						X											S			X	XS		X					S	SX	X		40
			XS	X	X		SX	X	X		X									X														X	SX		X			S		XS	X		41
			X	X	X		X	X	X		XS			SX						X														X	S					S	S	X	X		42
			X	X	X		X	X	X					SX						X						S					XS			XS	SX							XS	X	SX	43
			XS	X	X		X	XS	X		SX			X						X						S					XS				SX					SX	X	X		S	44
			X	X	X			X	X		SX			SX						X						S					XS			X	X					S	X	XS		S	45
			SX	X	X		X	X	XS		SX			X						X											S			X	XS					S	X	X		S	46
			X	X	X		X	X			XS			X						X						SX					X			S	SX						X			XS	47
4	20	10	35	42	34	3	18	16	24	5	20	5	10	23	0	3	0	3	4	18	0	4	2	1	6	0	2	4	13	0	6	3	2	11	5	0	8	0	0	0	5	3	6	0	x
0	0	3	4	0	3	6	6	6	6	1	12	0	2	2	2	2	0	0	4	3	0	0	8	0	2	0	0	2	0	1	7	0	1	2	7	0	1	0	0	0	0	3	0	1	xs
0	2	2	2	0	1	3	5	5	5	5	6	0	3	6	7	1	0	0	12	1	0	0	3	5	4	3	0	0	0	1	3	0	1	1	4	2	0	0	0	1	0	1	0	1	sx
0	1	5	1	0	1	0	3	5	4	2	1	7	2	1	6	6	6	2	6	0	6	0	0	1	0	9	0	1	0	0	3	6	0	2	1	0	0	2	3	5	2	1	0	3	s

lso Played: Ferguson - 20/10 (s) 29/10 (s). Webb - 10/11 (s). King D - 14/11 (s). Bainbridge - 23/02 (s).

x - Played full 90 minutes
xs - Substituted off
sx - Substituted on
s - Non-playing Substitute

HAMPTON & RICHMOND BOROUGH MATCH RESULTS 2018-19

Date	Comp	Opponents	H/A	Att:	Result		Goalscorers	Pos
Aug 4	NLS	Slough Town	A	866	D	1 - 1	Joseph 3	
7	NLS	Hemel Hempstead Town	H	570	L	1 - 2	Dickson 31	
11	NLS	Bath City	H	408	L	0 - 1		
14	NLS	St Albans City	A	585	**W**	3 - 2	Murrell-Williamson 34 MacLaren 49 Dickson 66	
18	NLS	Chelmsford City	H	495	D	1 - 1	Dickson 45	
25	NLS	Torquay United	A	1571	**W**	2 - 0	Murrell-Williamson 25 Dickson 83	
27	NLS	Chippenham Town	H	491	**W**	2 - 1	Miller-Rodney 65 Dickson 87	
Sept 1	NLS	Dulwich Hamlet	A	815	**W**	2 - 0	Dundas 31 Dickson 57 (Pen)	
8	NLS	Weston-super-Mare	H	672	**W**	3 - 1	Dundas 20 Dickson 26 Joseph 62	
15	NLS	Truro City	A	138	**W**	2 - 0	Dickson 35 Dundas 38	
22	**FAC 2Q**	**Burgess Hill Town**	**H**	**422**	**W**	**3 - 0**	**Dickson 41 Murrell-Williamson 66 Whichelow 85**	
29	NLS	Billericay Town	H	886	L	0 - 2		4
Oct 6	**FAC 3Q**	**AFC Hornchurch**	**H**	**316**	**W**	**1 - 0**	**Wellard**	
13	NLS	Wealdstone	A	1163	L	1 - 2	Maclaren 19	6
20	**FAC 4Q**	**Eastleigh**	**A**	**740**	**W**	**1 - 0**	**Dickson 85**	
27	NLS	Hungerford Town	A	227	L	0 - 2		
30	NLS	Eastbourne Borough	A	428	D	2 - 2	Miller-Rodney 32 Dickson 38	
Nov 3	NLS	Oxford City	H	471	L	2 - 4	Connors 54 90	
10	**FAC 1P**	**Oldham Athletic**	**H**	**2720**	**L**	**1 - 2**	**Dickson 15 (Pen)**	
17	NLS	Dartford	H	724	L	0 - 1		17
24	**FAT 3Q**	**Billericay Town**	**H**	**298**	**L**	**0 - 1**		
Dec 1	NLS	East Thurrock United	H	377	**W**	1 - 0	Murrell-Williamson 90	16
4	NLS	Concord Rangers	A	212	L	0 - 4		
8	NLS	Gloucester City	A	269	D	0 - 0		
15	NLS	Welling United	H	323	**W**	2 - 1	Dickson 45 54	
22	NLS	Torquay United	H	799	L	0 - 3		
26	NLS	Woking	A	2516	L	1 - 2	Bray 58	
29	NLS	Chippenham Town	A	535	L	2 - 3	Whichelow 73 88	
Jan 1	NLS	Woking	H	1497	L	0 - 3		
5	NLS	Chelmsford City	A	784	L	0 - 2		
12	NLS	Dulwich Hamlet	H	919	**W**	2 - 0	Whichelow 5 Dickson 12	
19	NLS	Hemel Hempstead Town	A	415	D	1 - 1	Dundas 76	16
26	NLS	St Albans City	H	605	L	0 - 1		
Feb 9	NLS	Slough Town	H	607	D	1 - 1	Barrington 90	
16	NLS	Gloucester City	H	465	L	0 - 1		
23	NLS	East Thurrock United	A	301	D	0 - 0		16
Mar 2	NLS	Eastbourne Borough	H	420	D	0 - 0		17
9	NLS	Oxford City	A	509	**W**	5 - 3	Barrington 9 Dickson 22 58 Joseph 45 Sotiriou 90	15
12	NLS	Bath City	A	576	L	0 - 1		15
16	NLS	Concord Rangers	H	391	L	1 - 4	Dickson 33 (pen)	16
23	NLS	Dartford	A	1103	D	2 - 2	Sprague 8 Dickson 81	15
30	NLS	Hungerford Town	H	442	L	0 - 3		16
Apr 6	NLS	Billericay Town	A	829	**W**	3 - 1	Sotiriou 8 (pen) Bray 12 Joseph 90	16
13	NLS	Wealdstone	H	725	**W**	2 - 1	Sotiriou 24 55	16
20	NLS	Weston-super-Mare	A	705	**W**	2 - 0	Sotiriou 14 Hill 82	
22	NLS	Truro City	H	509	D	2 - 2	Joseph 26 Sotiriou 47 (pen)	14
27	NLS	Welling United	A	505	L	0 - 4		15

GOALSCORERS	SG	CSG	Pens	Hat tricks	Total
Dickson	17	8	2		19
Sotiriou	5	4	2		6
Joseph	5	1			5
Dundas	4	3			4
Murrell-Williamson	4	1			4
Whichelow	3	1			4
Barrington*	2	1			2
Bray	2	1			2
Connors	1	1			2
MacLaren	2	1			2
Miller-Rodney	2	1			2
Hill	1	1			1
Sprague	1	1			1
Wellard	1	1			1

No.		McLeod-Urquhart	Sprague	Wellard	Bray	Bowry (L)	Joseph	Maclaren	Dundas	Dickson	Murrell-Williamson	Uchechi	Roberts	Burns	Corcoran	Eggleton	Miller-Rodney	Mavilla	Downer	Whichelow	Hammond	Randall	Obi	Hill	Mambo	Connors (L)	Cox	Ruddick	Oliyide	Sole (L)	Orlu (L)	Syla (L)	Kyei (L)	Barrington	Sotiriou (L)	Manesio	Crawford	Maynard-Brewer (L)	Simpson (L)	Kyprianou	Hope
1	x	x	x	x	x	x	xs	x	x	x	xs	sx	sx	s	s	s																									
2	x	x	x	x	x	x	xs	xs	x	x	xs	sx	sx	s	s	sx																									
3	x		x	x	x	s	x	x	xs	x	xs	sx	sx	s	x	x	s																								
4	x		x	x	x	sx	xs	x	x	xs	xs	sx		s	x	s	x	sx																							
5	x		xs	x	x	x	x	x	x	xs	xs	s			x		sx	sx	sx	s																					
6	x			x		s	x	x	x	x	xs	s			x	s	s	x	x	sx	x																				
7	x			x	x	s		x	x	x	s	xs	s			x	x	x		sx	x	s																			
8	x			xs	x	s	sx		xs	x	xs	x			x	sx	x	x	x	sx	s																				
9	x			s	x		x		x	x	s	x		s	x		x	x	x	x	sx		s																		
10	x			x	x	s	xs		x	xs	sx	xs			x		x	x	x	s	sx		sx																		
11	s			xs	x		xs	s	x	x	xs	sx		x	x		x	x	x	sx	s	s	sx																		
12	x			xs	x		xs	sx	x	x	xs	sx			x		x	x	x	sx	s	s																			
13	x			x	x		sx	xs		x	xs	sx		s	x		x	x	x	xs	sx	s	s	s																	
14	x			xs	x		sx	x	x	sx	x	s			xs		x	x	x	xs	sx			s																	
15	x			x	x		xs		x	xs	xs	sx		s	s		x	x	x	s	x	sx		s	sx																
16	x			x	x		x		x	x	x	sx		s	s		x	xs	x		xs			sx	s																
17	x			x	x		x		sx	x	s	x			xs		x	x			sx		s	s	x	xs															
18	x			xs	x		x	sx	x	x	sx	xs			xs		x	sx		s	s				x	x															
19	x			sx	x		x	xs	xs	xs	sx	s		s	x		x	x			s	s	sx		x	x															
20	x		s	xs	x		x			x	xs	sx			s		x	x	s		x	sx			x	x															
21	x		s	x	x		sx			x	xs	x			xs			x	s	s	sx				x	x		x													
22	x		sx	xs			xs			xs	sx	x			s			x	x		x		sx		s	x	x	x													
23	x		sx	x			s			x	xs	x			xs			x	s		sx		sx		xs	x	x	x													
24	x		x	x	x		s			x	xs	xs						sx	x		s		sx			xs	x	x	sx												
25	x		x		x		s		x	x	s	sx					xs	sx	x					sx		xs	x	x		xs											
26	x		xs		x				x	x	sx				s		x		xs	sx				s		x	x	x	sx	xs											
27	x			s	x				x	x	x	s			xs		x	sx		sx				sx		x	x		xs	xs											
28	x		s	sx	x			s	x								x	x		sx				x		x	x	xs	x	s	x										
29	x		x	x	s			sx	x	sx							x			xs				x		s	xs	x	xs	sx	x										
30	x		x	sx	x			xs	xs	x							x			sx				s		x	x	xs	s	sx	x										
31	x		x	s	sx		sx		x	xs							x			xs				sx			x	x	s		x	x	xs								
32	x		x	s	s		xs		x	s							x			xs				s			x	x	sx		x	x	x								
33	x		xs	s	x		xs	sx	sx	x							x		x	x				sx			x		s			x	xs								
34	x		s	s	x			s	x	x							x		x	xs				sx		x	x					x	x	sx							
35	x		x	s	xs		xs	x	x	sx							s		x	sx				sx			xs	x				x		x							
36	x		x	x	x		sx	x	x	sx							s			s				xs		sx	x	x						x	xs						
37	x			x	x		sx	x	sx	x					s		s			s				xs		x	x	x						xs	x						
38	x		sx	x	x		xs	x	x	xs					s		x							sx		x		x	s					xs	sx						
39	x		x	x	x		xs		s	x					xs		x			sx				sx		x		s						x		xs	sx				
40	x		sx	x	x		xs	xs	x	x							x			s				sx		x		xs	s					x			sx				
41	s		x	x	x		xs	xs	sx	x							x			xs				s		x		x									sx	x	xs		
42			xs	s	x		x	x	sx	x							x			s				sx		x		x							sx		xs	x	xs		
43			x		x		sx	x	xs								sx		sx	xs				xs		x		x							x		s	x	s	x	
44			x	sx	x			xs	x								x		x					xs		x		x	s					sx	x		sx	x	s		
45			x	s	x		sx	xs	xs								x		xs					x		x		x	s						x		sx	x	sx		
46			x	xs	x		xs	s	s								x							x		x		x						sx	xs		x	x	sx		sx
47	x		xs	sx	x		x	x	xs	sx							s		x					x		x		x						s	xs		sx				
x	40	2	18	22	40	3	11	14	27	28	3	6	0	1	11	2	32	17	18	2	5	0	0	5	5	22	14	20	1	0	5	5	2	4	4	0	1	6	0	1	0
xs	0	0	5	8	1	0	16	8	7	8	15	4	0	0	7	0	1	1	2	8	1	0	0	4	1	3	2	3	2	3	0	0	2	2	3	1	1	0	2	0	0
sx	0	0	4	5	1	1	9	4	5	5	5	11	3	0	0	2	2	6	2	11	7	2	6	11	1	1	0	0	3	2	0	0	0	3	2	0	6	0	2	0	1
s	2	0	4	9	2	5	3	4	2	1	4	5	1	9	9	3	6	0	3	9	6	5	3	8	2	1	0	1	7	1	0	0	0	1	0	0	1	0	2	0	0

x - Played full 90 minutes
xs - Substituted off
sx - Substituted on
s - Non-playing Substitute

HEMEL HEMPSTEAD TOWN MATCH RESULTS 2018-19

Date	Comp	Opponents	H/A	Att:	Result	Goalscorers	Pos
Aug 4	NLS	Chippenham Town	H	510	W 4 - 2	Oliyide 7 48 Cawley 40 Osborn 88	
7	NLS	Hampton & Richmond Boro'	A	570	W 2 - 1	Connolly 37 Watt 90	
11	NLS	Dartford	A	974	D 0 - 0		
14	NLS	Hungerford Town	H	489	D 0 - 0		
18	NLS	Woking	H	613	L 0 - 2		
25	NLS	Welling United	A	481	D 1 - 1	Parkes 9	
27	NLS	Chelmsford City	H	625	L 3 - 5	Parkes 13 75 Clifford 52	
Sept 1	NLS	Torquay United	A	1409	L 0 - 2		
8	NLS	Billericay Town	H	821	L 0 - 2		
15	NLS	Weston-super-Mare	A	511	W 2 - 1	Roberts 14 79	
Dean Brennan steps down as manager to take up the post at Billericay FC, Jordan Parkes & Darren Ward take over as caretakers.							
22	**FAC 2Q**	**Bowers Pitsea**	**A**	**215**	**W 6 - 1**	**Watt 10 43 80 (Pen) Roberts 30 Olliyide 48 Cawley 58 (Pen)**	
29	NLS	Oxford City	H	425	W 2 - 1	Kaloczi 28 Roberts 35	14
Oct 6	**FAC 3Q**	**Ramsgate**	**H**	**307**	**W 5 - 0**	**Parkes 12 Connolly 30 McCall Oliyide x2**	
13	NLS	Truro City	A	86	W 2 - 1	McCall 9 Yakubu 82	12
20	**FAC 4Q**	**Oxford City**	**H**	**762**	**D 1 - 1**	**Roberts 51**	
23	**FAC 4Qr**	**Oxford City**	**A**	**450**	**L 0 - 5**		
27	NLS	Eastbourne Borough	A	481	L 0 - 3		
30	NLS	Slough Town	H	468	D 1 - 1	Mendy 86	
Nov 3	NLS	Bath City	A	916	W 1 - 0	Cawley 74	
10	NLS	Gloucester City	H	456	W 2 - 1	Sinclair 13 Cawley 58	
13	NLS	Wealdstone	H	703	L 0 - 1		
17	NLS	East Thurrock United	A	299	W 2 - 1	Sinclair 49 52	9
24	**FAT 3Q**	**Lewes**	**A**	**325**	**D 2 - 2**	**Cawley 20 46**	
27	**FAT 3Qr**	**Lewes**	**H**	**137**	**W 3 - 2**	**Snelus 15 Knowles 30 Day 65 (og)**	
Dec 1	NLS	Concord Rangers	A	258	L 1 - 2	Knowles 44	11
8	NLS	Dulwich Hamlet	H	494	W 1 - 0	Parkes 45	
15	**FAT 1P**	**Eastleigh**	**H**	**234**	**W 2 - 1**	**Cawley 69 Parkes 83 (pen)**	
22	NLS	Welling United	H	474	D 1 - 1	Shulton 70	
26	NLS	St Albans City	A	1486	L 1 - 2	Sinclair 35	
29	NLS	Chelmsford City	A	720	L 1 - 2	Cawley 1	
Jan 1	NLS	St Albans City	H	949	D 1 - 1	Howe 66	
12	**FAT 2P**	**Wingate & Finchley**	**H**	**454**	**W 4 - 2**	**Ward D 19 45+2 Watt 33 51**	
19	NLS	Hampton & Richmond Boro'	H	415	D 1 - 1	Parkes 26	15
26	NLS	Hungerford Town	A	252	W 3 - 0	Parkes 16 Cawley 33 Watt 36	
Feb 5	**FAT 3P**	**Solihull Moors**	**H**	**438**	**L 0 - 5**		
9	NLS	Chippenham Town	A	469	D 1 - 1	Parkes 33	
12	NLS	Torquay United	H	624	L 1 - 4	Musonda 90	
16	NLS	Dulwich Hamlet	A	2849	D 3 - 3	Howe 12 Parkes 28 30	
19	NLS	Woking	A	1673	L 1 - 3	Amu 48	
23	NLS	Concord Rangers	H	505	D 2 - 2	Amu 5 Musonda 12	13
Mar 2	NLS	Slough Town	A	669	L 0 - 1		14
5	NLS	Dartford	H	360	L 1 - 2	Parkes 88	14
9	NLS	Bath City	H	413	L 0 - 3		14
16	NLS	Gloucester City	A	216	D 1 - 1	Monlouis 77	14
23	NLS	East Thurrock United	H	442	W 3 - 2	Amu 41 Parkes 74 (pen) 84	14
30	NLS	Eastbourne Borough	H	486	W 3 - 2	Rowe 15 Amu 60 Parkes 90+1	13
Apr 6	NLS	Oxford City	A	332	L 1 - 2	Amu 43	14
13	NLS	Truro City	H	436	D 1 - 1	Watt 23	14
20	NLS	Billericay Town	A	964	L 1 - 2	Amu 48	
22	NLS	Weston-super-Mare	H	503	L 0 - 2		16
27	NLS	Wealdstone	A	823	L 1 - 2	Williams 36	16

GOALSCORERS	SG	CSG	Pens	Hat tricks	Total		SG	CSG	Pens	Hat tricks	Total
Parkes	12	2	2		15	Clifford	1	1			1
Cawley	7	2	1		9	Kaloczi	1	1			1
Watt	5	1	1	1	8	Mendy	1	1			1
Amu	6	3			6	Monlouis	1	1			1
Oliyide	3	1			5	Opponent	1	1			1
Roberts	4	3			5	Osborn	1	1			1
Sinclair	3	1			4	Rowe	1	1			1
Connolly	2	1			2	Shulton	1	1			1
Howe	2	1			2	Snelus	1	1			1
Knowles	2	1			2	Williams	1	1			1
McCall	2	1			2	Yakubu	1	1			1
Musonda	2	1			2						
Ward D	1	1			2						

No.	Walker	Howe	Connolly	Parkes	Ward D	Yakubu	Kaloczi	Shulton	Oliyide	Cawley	Watt	McCall	Hamblin	Osborn	Paulin	Doyley	Dymond	Prestedge	Collins	Sheringham	Clifford	Roberts	Jahraldo-Martin	Cotter	Ibie	Nolan	Mendy Matteo	Murphy	Ward T	Swain	Sinclair	Knowles (L)	Sneius	Muyembe	Kpohomouh	Tomlinson (L)	Musonda (L)	Lobjoit	Amu	Monlouis	Read (L)	Boness	Williams	Randall	Rowe
1	x	x	x	x	x	x	x	xs	xs	x	xs	sx	sx	sx	s																														
2	x		x	x		x	x		xs	x	x	s	xs	sx	s	x	xs	sx																											
3	x	sx	x	x	x	x	xs		xs	x	x	sx		sx	s	xs	s	x																											
4	x	x	s	sx	x		xs	xs	x	sx		x	x	sx	s		x		x	xs																									
5	x	x	x	x		x	s		xs	xs	x	s	x	sx				xs		sx	x	sx																							
6	x	x		x	x	xs	x		sx	x	x	s	sx	s				x		sx	xs	xs																							
7	x	x	x	x			x		x	sx	x	s	x	sx	s			x		xs	xs	s																							
8	x	s	x	x	x		x		s	x	x	x	x	s	s			s			x		x																						
9	x	xs	x	x	x		xs		sx	x	x	xs	x	sx		sx		s			x	s																							
10	x		x	sx	x	x	xs		sx	xs	x	s	s	s		x					x	x	x																						
11	x		x	s		x	x		sx	x	x	x		s	s	x		s			x	x		x																					
12	x		x	sx		x	x		sx	x		x	s	xs	s	x					xs	xs	sx	x																					
13	x	sx	xs	x	s	x	s		x	xs		x	x	xs	s						x	sx	s	x	sx																				
14	x	s	x	x	s	x	x		x			x	x	x	s							x		x	s	s																			
15	x	sx	x	x	x		x		xs	xs	sx		x		s	s					sx	x		x	s	s	sx																		
16	x	sx	xs	x	x	sx	x		x	x	s		xs		s	s					xs	x		x	s		sx																		
17	x	x		x	s	x	xs		xs	sx				xs	s	x						sx		x	sx			x	x																
18	x	x		x	x	x	x		xs	x					s	x								x	s		sx	s	x																
19	x	x		x	x	x	x		sx	x					s	x								x	sx		sx	xs	x	s															
20	x	x	sx	x	x	x	xs			x						xs								x	sx		sx	xs		s	x														
21	x	x	x	x	x	x	s	x		x				s	s									xs			sx			s	x	x													
22	x	x	x	x	x	x	x	x						x	s	s						x					s			s	x	s													
23	x		x	x	x	x	x	x	s	x				x	s										s	s					x		x												
24	x		x	x		x	x		s	x				xs										x	sx	s					x	x	x	s											
25	x		x	x	x	x		x	s	x				s										x		s				s	x	x	x												
26	x		x	x	x	x		x		x				xs										x			s			s		x	sx	s	x										
27	x	x	x	x	x	x		x		x	sx			s	s									xs			s					xs	x			sx									
28	x	x	x	x	x	x		x		x	sx			xs	s												s			sx	sx		xs			xs									
29	x	x	x	x	x	x	s	x		x	xs			s																s	x	sx	x			s									
30	x	x		x	x	x	xs	x		x	x				s															x	x	s	s			sx									
31	x	x	x	x	x	x	s	x		x	sx				s															x	x	s	s			xs									
32	x	x	x	xs	x	x	sx	x		sx	x				s										s						x		xs			s	x								
33	x	x	x	x	x	x	s	x		sx	x				s															s	x		xs			s	x								
34	x	x	xs	x	x	sx	s	x		xs	xs																			s	x		x				x	sx	sx						
35	x	x		x	x	x	sx	xs		x	x		s		s									s							x		xs				x	sx							
36	x	x		x	x	s	x	x		x	x													x						s			xs		s		x	s	sx						
37	x	x		x	x		x	xs		s	x		xs		s									x						sx					xs		x	sx							
38	x	x		x	x		sx	x			x		s		s									x						x			s		x		x	x	sx						
39	x	x		x	x	sx	sx	xs		s			xs											x			s			x			x				x	x	sx						
40	x	x		x	x			s					x		s									x						s			s		x		x	xs	x	x	sx				
41	x	xs		x	x						sx				s									x			s			sx			sx		x		x	xs	xs	x	x				
42	x		sx	x	x								x											x			sx			s			sx		x		x	xs	xs	x	xs	s			
43	x		x	x	x			x					xs											x			sx			sx			xs		x			xs	s	x	sx	s			
44	x	sx	x	x	x			sx			x		x											xs									s		xs				x	x	s	s	x		
45	x	xs	x	x	x						x													s									s		x		x		x	x		s	xs	sx	sx
46	x	sx	x	x							x		s											x									sx		x		x		xs	xs		s	sx	xs	x
47	x	sx	x	x							x		x											x									s		xs				x	x		s	sx	xs	x
48	x	xs	x	x	sx						xs		x											x									s		x				x	xs		s	sx	sx	x
49	x	sx	xs	x	x						x		s											x						x					x				x	sx		s	sx	xs	xs
50	x	xs	x	x							xs		x											x	sx					x	sx			s	x				x	x		s			
51	x	x	xs	x									x											x	sx					x	sx			s	xs					x		s	x	x	
x	51	26	31	46	37	27	17	16	5	24	21	6	15	3	0	7	1	3	1	0	6	6	2	27	0	0	0	1	3	7	13	4	7	0	11	0	13	2	7	9	1	0	2	1	3
xs	0	5	5	1	0	1	7	5	7	5	5	1	5	6	0	2	1	1	0	2	4	2	0	3	0	0	0	2	0	0	0	1	6	0	4	2	0	4	3	2	1	0	1	3	1
sx	0	8	2	3	1	3	4	1	6	5	5	2	2	7	0	1	0	1	0	2	1	3	1	0	7	0	8	0	0	4	3	1	4	0	0	2	0	3	4	1	2	0	4	2	1
s	0	2	1	1	3	1	7	1	4	2	1	5	6	8	29	3	1	3	0	0	0	2	1	2	6	5	6	1	0	12	0	3	8	4	1	3	0	1	1	0	1	10	0	0	0

Also Played: Day 04/08 (s) 07/08 (sx). Dean - 30/10 (s). Nketia - 27/11 (s). Waters - 01/12 (s) 08/12 (s). Baker - 22/04 (s) 27/04 (s).

x - Played full 90 minutes
xs - Substituted off
sx - Substituted on
s - Non-playing Substitute

HUNGERFORD TOWN MATCH RESULTS 2018-19

Date	Comp	Opponents	H/A	Att:	Result	Goalscorers	Pos
Aug 4	NLS	St Albans City	A	566	L 2 - 3	Rose 4 Bradbury 50 (pen)	
7	NLS	Wealdstone	H	435	D 1 - 1	Bradbury 72 (pen)	
11	NLS	Chelmsford City	H	279	L 0 - 6		
14	NLS	Hemel Hempstead Town	A	489	D 0 - 0		
18	NLS	Concord Rangers	A	312	L 0 - 4		
25	NLS	Dartford	H	226	**W** 1 - 0	Lynch 58	
27	NLS	Truro City	A	200	**W** 3 - 2	Ten-Grotenhuis 11 66 70	
Sept 1	NLS	Gloucester City	H	235	L 1 - 2	Lynch 57	
8	NLS	Bath City	A	689	L 1 - 4	Lynch 64 (pen)	
15	NLS	Torquay United	H	620	L 0 - 2		
25	**FAC 2Q**	**Wantage Town**	**H**	**166**	**D 1 - 1**		
29	NLS	Slough Town	A	772	L 0 - 2		19
Oct 2	**FAC 2Qr**	**Wantage Town**	**A**	**330**	**D 2 - 2**	**(Won 4-1 on pens)**	
6	**FAC 3Q**	**Wealdstone**	**H**	**306**	**L 1 - 2**		
13	NLS	Dulwich Hamlet	H	357	L 1 - 2	Orsi-Dadomo 25	19
20	NLS	East Thurrock United	A	1578	L 1 - 2	Orsi-Dadomo 41	20
27	NLS	Hampton & Richmond Boro'	H	227	**W** 2 - 0	Orsi-Dadomo 19 Martin 66	
30	NLS	Woking	A	1381	L 0 - 3		
Nov 3	NLS	Weston-super-Mare	H	217	L 0 - 1		
10	NLS	Eastbourne Borough	A	447	L 1 - 3	Bailey 4	
17	NLS	Billericay Town	H	353	D 2 - 2	Rose 66 Martin 90	20
24	**FAT 3Q**	**Dorchester Town**	**A**	**258**	**L 0 - 1**		
Dec 1	NLS	Welling United	A	404	L 1 - 3	Johnston-Schuster 45	20
8	NLS	Chippenham Town	H	239	**W** 2 - 1	Kavanagh 66 Foxley 90	
22	NLS	Dartford	A	901	L 1 - 2	Ekpiteta 90	
26	NLS	Oxford City	H	299	D 1 - 1	Foxley 64	
29	NLS	Truro City	H	260	L 1 - 4	Kavanagh 20	
Jan 1	NLS	Oxford City	A	374	**W** 2 - 1	Whittingham A 50 Johnston-Schuster 77	
5	NLS	Concord Rangers	H	170	**W** 2 - 1	Foxley 18 86	
12	NLS	Gloucester City	A	393	D 0 - 0		
19	NLS	Wealdstone	A	740	L 0 - 1		19
26	NLS	Hemel Hempstead Town	H	252	L 0 - 3		
Feb 2	NLS	Chelmsford City	A	943	L 1 - 4	Kavanagh 49	
9	NLS	St Albans City	H	216	**W** 5 - 0	Orsi-Dadomo 21 45 Foxley 30 Jones Matt 72 Whittingham A 75	
16	NLS	Chippenham Town	A	582	L 1 - 3	Orsi-Dadomo 6	
23	NLS	Welling United	H	220	L 0 - 1		20
Mar 2	NLS	Woking	H	547	D 1 - 1	Whittingham A 55	21
9	NLS	Weston-super-Mare	A	517	D 0 - 0		21
16	NLS	Eastbourne Borough	H	196	**W** 2 - 0	Kavanagh 42 Ekpiteta 85	20
23	NLS	Billericay Town	A	898	**W** 2 - 1	Orsi-Dadomo 86 (pen) 90	20
30	NLS	Hampton & Richmond Boro'	A	442	**W** 3 - 0	Rusby 27 89 Whittingham A 79	18
Apr 6	NLS	Slough Town	H	408	L 1 - 2	Orsi-Dadomo 64	19
13	NLS	Dulwich Hamlet	A	2841	L 1 - 3	Ekpiteta 80	20
19	NLS	Bath City	H	576	D 0 - 0		19
22	NLS	Torquay United	A	5351	**W** 1 - 0	Leigh-Gilchrist 89	19
27	NLS	East Thurrock United	H	485	D 1 - 1	Chesmain 90+4	19

GOALSCORERS	SG	CSG	Pens	Hat tricks	Total
Oris-Dadomo	7	3	1		9
Foxley	4	1			5
Kavanagh	4	1			4
Whittingham A	4	1			4
Ekpiteta	3	1			3
Lynch	3	2	1		3
Ten-Grotenhuis	1	1		1	3
Bradbury	2	2	2		2
Johnston-Schuster	2	1			2
Martin	2	1			2
Rose	2	1			2
Rusby	1	1			2
Bailey	1	1			1
Chesmain	1	1			1
Jones Matt	1	1			1
Leigh-Gilchrist	1	1			1

Andresson (L)	Johnston-Schuster	Jones Mat	Ten-Grotenhuis	Ekpiteta	Rusby	Rose	Whittingham A	Bradbury (L)	Whittingham R	Fragata	Cooney	McCready	Ouldridge	Lynch	Herring	Foxley	Bailey	Driscoll (L)	Moore-Azille	Weaver (L)	Orsi-Dadomo	Martin	Rees	Elms	Kavanagh (L)	Hargreaves	Anderson	Luyambula (L)	Willmoth	Jones Mike	Leigh-Gilchrist (L)	Chesmain (L)	No.
x	x	x	x	x	x	x	x	x	x	x	s	s	s	s	s																		1
x	x	x	s	x	x	xs	x	x	x	x	s	s	s	sx	x																		2
x	x	x	s	x	x		xs	x	x	xs	s		sx	sx	x	x																	3
x	x	sx	xs	x	x		x	x	sx	sx	xs		x	s	x	x	s																4
						sx	x	x		sx			xs			x		x															5
	x	x	x	x	x	xs	x	s	x	sx	s		s	x	s	x		x															6
	x	x	x	x	x	xs	x	sx	x	sx			s	xs	s	x	s	x															7
	x	x	x	x	x	s	xs	x	x	sx			s	x	s	x	sx	x															8
s	x	x	xs		x	x	xs	sx	x	sx			sx	xs		x	s	x	x														9
x	x	x	sx	xs	sx	x	sx		x	xs			xs	x	s	x	s		x														10
																																	11
	x	x	x	x	x	xs	sx		xs	x		s	sx		sx	x	xs		s	x													12
																																	13
																																	14
	x	x	s	x	x	x	x		x	s			s		x	s	s		x	x	x												15
	x	x	x	x	x	xs	sx		xs	sx				sx	x	xs	s			x	x												16
	x	x		x	x	xs	s		x	s				sx	x	x	s			x	x	x	s										17
	x	x	s	x	x	x	s		x	s				s	x	x	s			x	x	x											18
	x	xs	sx	x	x	xs	s		x					sx	x	x	s			x	x	x		s									19
	x	xs	x	x	sx	s	x		x	s				sx	xs	sx	xs			x	x	x											20
	x	x	x	x	x	xs	sx		xs	s				sx		s	x			x	x	x	s										21
																																	22
	xs	x	s	x	x		s		xs					s	x	x				x	x	x			xs	sx							23
	xs	x	s	x	x		sx		s					s	x	x				x	x	x			x	x	s						24
		x	sx	x	xs	sx	sx		x						s	x	s		xs	x	x	x				xs	x						25
		x	s	x	xs	sx	sx		xs							x	s		x	x	xs	x			sx	x	x						26
			s	xs	sx	sx	sx		xs							x	s		x		x	x			xs	x	x	x					27
	x	x	x		x		x									x					x	x				x	x	x					28
	x	x	x		x	s	x		sx							x	s		s		x	x	s			x	xs	x					29
	x	x	xs		x		xs		sx							x	sx				xs	x			sx	x	x	x					30
	x	x			x		xs		x				sx		s	x	sx		s		sx	x			x	xs	x	x					31
	x	x		s	sx		xs		xs				sx						x		xs	x	s		x	x	sx	x					32
	x	s		xs	x		xs		sx				s		s	x	x				sx	x			x	x	x	x					33
	x	x	sx	xs	x		xs									xs	s				x	x	s		x	x	sx	x	sx				34
	xs	xs	sx	x	x		x									x	s				x	x	s		x	x	sx	x	s				35
	xs	xs		x	x		x		s				s	sx		x	sx				x	x			x		xs	x	sx				36
	x	x	s	x	x		x		sx				s	sx							xs	x			xs		x	x	sx	xs			37
	x	x	sx	x	x		x		xs				sx	sx		x					xs	x	s	s				x	xs				38
	x	xs		x	sx		xs							sx		x					xs	x	s		x	x		x	s	x	sx		39
	x			x	x	s	x		sx				s	x	s	x	s				x					x		x	xs	x			40
	x			x	x		x		s					xs		x					xs		s		sx	x		x	s	x	sx	x	41
	xs			x	x		x		s					sx		x					x		s		x	x		x	s	x	sx	xs	42
	x		sx	x	x		xs							sx		x					x		s			xs		x	s	x	x	x	43
	x		x	x	x		x							xs		sx	s				sx		s			x		x	s	x	xs	x	44
	x		x	x	x		x						s	sx		xs	s				xs		s			x		x		x	sx	x	45
	x		xs	x	x		xs						s	sx		sx	sx				x		s			xs		x		x	x	x	46
5	33	26	12	31	34	5	19	6	15	3	0	0	1	4	10	30	2	5	6	12	20	22	0	0	9	16	8	20	0	8	2	5	x
0	5	5	4	4	2	8	11	0	8	2	1	0	2	4	1	3	2	0	1	0	8	0	0	0	3	4	2	0	2	1	1	1	xs
0	0	1	7	0	5	4	8	2	6	7	0	0	6	15	1	3	5	0	0	0	3	0	0	0	3	1	3	0	3	0	4	0	sx
1	0	1	9	1	0	4	4	1	4	5	4	3	12	5	9	2	18	0	3	0	0	0	14	2	0	0	1	0	6	0	0	0	s

x - Played full 90 minutes
xs - Substituted off
sx - Substituted on
s - Non-playing Substitute

OXFORD CITY MATCH RESULTS 2018-19

Date	Comp	Opponents	H/A	Att:	Result		Goalscorers	Pos
Aug 4	NLS	Eastbourne Borough	H	282	D	0 - 0		
7	NLS	Gloucester City	A	312	L	0 - 1		
11	NLS	Woking	A	1502	L	2 - 3	Paterson 17 62 (Pen)	
14	NLS	Torquay United	H	520	**W**	1 - 0	Sinclair 30	
18	NLS	St Albans City	H	323	**W**	2 - 1	Paterson 25 Fleet 68	
25	NLS	Weston-super-Mare	A	502	D	1 - 1	Tshimanga 82	
27	NLS	Wealdstone	H	466	**W**	3 - 0	Tshimanga 72 Paterson 81 84	
Sept 1	NLS	Welling United	A	465	L	2 - 3	Tshimanga 10 Paterson 82	
8	NLS	Slough Town	A	832	L	0 - 2		
15	NLS	Bath City	H	402	L	1 - 2	Ashby 69	
22	**FAC 2Q**	**Cray Valley PM**	**H**	**142**	**W**	**5 - 0**	**Tshimanga 14 McEachran 16 63 78 Paterson 35**	
29	NLS	Hemel Hempstead Town	A	425	L	1 - 2	McEachran 68	18
Oct 6	**FAC 3Q**	**Dartford**	**H**	**312**	**W**	**4 - 1**	**Tshimanga 22 53 63 Bawling 64**	
13	NLS	Concord Rangers	H	256	**W**	2 - 0	Ashby 45 Sinclair 75	17
20	**FAC 4Q**	**Hemel Hempstead Town**	**A**	**762**	**D**	**1 - 1**	**Walker 70 (og)**	
23	**FAC 4Qr**	**Hemel Hempstead Town**	**H**	**405**	**W**	**5 - 0**	**Fleet 20 Sinclair 59 90+4 Fasanmade 74 Wiltshire 79**	
27	NLS	Chelmsford City	H	302	L	1 - 3	Tshimanga 17	
30	NLS	Chippenham Town	H	246	D	1 - 1	Musonda 76	
Nov 3	NLS	Hampton & Richmond Boro'	A	471	**W**	4 - 2	McEachran 3 Tshimanga 31 Oastler 45 Wiltshire 86	
10	**FAC 1P**	**Tranmere Rovers**	**A**	**4206**	**D**	**3 - 3**	**Tshimanga 39 66 82**	
13	NLS	Dartford	A	766	L	2 - 3	Oastler 17 McEachran 73	
17	NLS	Dulwich Hamlet	A	320	**W**	1 - 0	Self 51	16
20	**FAC 1Pr**	**Tranmere Rovers**	**H**	**1172**	**L**	**0 - 2**		
24	**FAT 3Q**	**Chelmsford City**	**H**	**212**	**W**	**4 - 0**	**Tshimanga 13 (Pen) 53 Nombe 74 McEachran 85**	
Dec 1	NLS	Billericay Town	A	874	**W**	3 - 2	Wiltshire 44 Lafayette 47 (og) Nombe 58	15
8	NLS	Truro City	H	242	**W**	4 - 0	Tshimanga 34 (Pen) Oastler 61 Nombe 70 Otudeko 90	
11	NLS	East Thurrock United	H	174	**W**	3 - 1	Tshimanga 16 49 McEachran 76	
22	NLS	Weston-super-Mare	H	290	**W**	3 - 0	Fleet 30 Oastler 62 Tshimanga 80	
26	NLS	Hungerford Town	A	299	D	1 - 1	Wiltshire 11	
29	NLS	Wealdstone	A	711	**W**	2 - 0	Tshimanga 4 69	
Jan 1	NLS	Hungerford Town	H	374	L	1 - 2	Tshimanga 52	
5	NLS	St Albans City	A	658	L	0 - 1		
8	**FAT 1P**	**Maidenhead United**	**A**	**352**	**W**	**2 - 1**	**Tshimanga 58 (Pen) 99 (aet)**	
12	**FAT 2P**	**Maidstone United**	**A**	**1156**	**L**	**0 - 1**		
19	NLS	Gloucester City	H	313	L	0 - 1		13
26	NLS	Torquay United	A	2467	L	2 - 7	Ashby 68 Tshimanga 71	
Feb 9	NLS	Eastbourne Borough	A	451	D	2 - 2	Tshimanga 10 Oastler 70	
12	NLS	Welling United	H	214	L	0 - 1		
16	NLS	Truro City	A	436	L	0 - 2		
23	NLS	Billericay Town	H	335	L	2 - 3	Tshimanga 36 45	14
Mar 2	NLS	Chippenham Town	A	522	**W**	1 - 0	Tshimanga 51	13
9	NLS	Hampton & Richmond Boro'	H	509	L	3 - 5	Ashby 16 Tshimanga 36 Thomas-Asante 41	13
12	NLS	Woking	H	347	L	1 - 2	Tshimanga 14	13
16	NLS	East Thurrock United	A	202	**W**	1 - 0	Wiltshire 18	13
23	NLS	Dulwich Hamlet	H	579	**W**	4 - 1	Thomas-Asante 12 Wiltshire 20 Tshimanga 25 (pen) 41 (pen)	13
30	NLS	Chelmsford City	A	1029	L	1 - 2	Wiltshire 90+4	14
Apr 6	NLS	Hemel Hempstead Town	H	332	**W**	2 - 1	Bawling 45 Tshimanga 58	13
13	NLS	Concord Rangers	A	207	**W**	1 - 0	Thomas-Asante 53	12
20	NLS	Slough Town	H	530	L	1 - 3	Tshimanga 41 (pen)	
22	NLS	Bath City	A	1164	L	0 - 1		13
27	NLS	Dartford	H	378	**W**	2 - 1	McEachran 51 Tshimanga 59	12

GOALSCORERS	SG	CSG	Pens	Hat tricks	Total
Tshimanga	25	4	6	2	34
McEachran	7	2		1	9
Paterson	5	2	1		7
Wiltshire	7	2			7
Oastler	5	1			5
Ashby	4	1			4
Sinclair	3	1			4
Fleet	3	1			3
Nombe	3	3			3
Thomas-Asante	3	1			3
Bawling	2	1			2
Opponent	2	1			2
Fasanmade	1	1			1
Musonda	1	1			1
Otudeko	1	1			1
Self	1	1			1

No.	King	Jones	Godwin-Malife	Sinclair	Ruddick	Oastler	Ashby	Fleet	Paterson	McEachran	Wiltshire	Tshimanga	Jefford	Ibrahim	Fasanmade	Krasniqi	Grantham	Stewart	Atkinson	Carter	Caro	Lobjoit	Bawling	Otudeko	Musonda (L)	Nombe (L)	Self	Barrett	O'Donoghue	Case	Dielna (L)	Moore-Azille	Thomas-Asante	Vine	James (L)	Hopkins (L)
1	x	x	xs	x	x	x	xs	x	x	x	xs	sx	sx	sx	s	s																				
2	x	x	xs	x	x	x	sx	xs	x	x	sx	x	xs	sx	s	s																				
3	x	s	x	xs	x	x	x	x	x	x	sx	xs	x	sx	s	s																				
4	x	sx	xs	xs	x	x	x	x	x	x	sx	xs	x	sx	s	s																				
5	x	x	x	xs		x	xs	x	x	x	sx	x			sx	xs	sx																			
6	x	x	xs		sx	x		x	x	x	x	x	xs		sx		s	xs	sx																	
7	x	x	x		x	x		x	x	x	x	x	s		sx	s	s	s	xs																	
8	x	x	x		x	x		x	x	x	xs	x	x		sx	s	s		s	s																
9	x				x	x	xs	x	x	x	x	x	x		sx	sx		xs		s	s															
10	x	x	x		x		x	x	x	xs	x	x	xs		sx	sx		s	s	s																
11	**x**	**x**	**xs**		**s**	**x**	**x**	**x**	**xs**	**x**	**xs**	**x**	**x**		**sx**	**s**		**sx**		**sx**	**s**															
12	x	xs		x	x	x	x	x		x	sx	x	x	s	sx					s	s															
13	**x**	**sx**	**x**	**xs**	**s**	**x**	**x**	**x**		**xs**	**x**	**xs**	**x**	**s**	**sx**					**s**	**s**	**sx**	**x**													
14	x	sx	x	x		x	x	x		xs	x	xs	x	s	sx					s		sx	xs													
15	**x**	**s**	**x**	**x**	**s**	**x**	**x**	**x**		**x**	**x**	**xs**	**x**	**s**	**sx**					**s**	**s**		**xs**	**sx**												
16	**x**	**x**	**x**	**x**	**sx**	**x**	**x**	**x**		**xs**	**x**	**xs**	**xs**	**s**	**sx**					**sx**	**s**		**s**	**s**												
17	x	xs	x	x		x	xs	x		x	xs	x	x		sx					s			sx	s	sx											
18	x	s	xs	x		x	x	x		x	sx	x	x		s						s		s		x	x										
19	x	sx	x			x	x	x		x	x	xs	xs		sx						s		sx	s	x	xs										
20	**x**	**sx**	**x**			**x**	**x**	**x**		**x**	**x**	**x**	**x**		**s**					**s**	**s**		**s**	**s**	**x**	**xs**										
21	x	xs	x			x	sx	x		sx	x	x	sx		s								s	xs	x	x	xs									
22	x	x	x				x	sx		x	x	sx			xs					s	s		xs	xs	x	sx	x									
23	**x**	**sx**	**xs**			**x**	**x**	**x**		**xs**	**xs**	**x**	**x**		**s**					**s**	**s**		**sx**	**sx**	**x**	**x**										
24	**x**	**x**	**x**			**x**	**xs**	**x**		**x**	**x**	**x**	**xs**		**sx**									**sx**		**x**										
25	x	x	x			x		x		x	x	xs	x		sx						s		sx	s		xs	x	s								
26	x	x	x			x		x		xs	x	xs	xs		sx						s		sx	sx		x	x	s								
27	x	x	x			x		x		x	x	x			sx					s	s		sx	xs		xs	x	s								
28	x	x	x			x	s	x			xs	x			xs					x			sx	sx		xs	x	s	sx							
29	x	x	x			x	sx	x			x	x			sx					xs			s	xs		x	x	s	s							
30	x	x	x				x	x			x	x	x		sx					s			x	s		xs	x	s	s							
31	x	x	x				x	x			x	x	x		sx					s			xs	s		x	x	s	s							
32	x	x	x				x	x				x	x		xs					x			x	sx			x	s	s							
33	**x**	**x**	**x**				**x**	**x**				**x**	**x**		**x**					**x**	**s**		**x**	**xs**				**sx**	**s**							
34	**x**	**x**	**x**			**x**	**x**	**x**		**sx**		**x**	**xs**		**x**		**s**			**sx**			**xs**	**sx**				**xs**	**s**							
35	x	x	x			x	xs	x		x	xs	x			x		s			s			sx				sx	s		x						
36	x					x	x	x		x	x	x			x					xs	s		sx				sx	sx	s	x						
37	x	x				x	x	x		xs	xs	x									sx		sx				s			s	x	x	x	s		
38	x	x				x	x	x		xs	xs	x									s		sx				sx			s	x	x	x	sx		
39		x				x	x	x			x	x			sx						x		xs				sx			s	x	x	xs	sx		
40	x	x				x	x				x	x			sx						s		x				xs	s	s	s	x	x	x			
41		x				x	x				x	x									x		xs				x	s	s	s	x	x	xs		sx	sx
42		x				x	x	sx			x	x									x		s				xs		s	sx	xs	x	x		xs	sx
43	x	x				x	x	xs			xs	x									s		sx				x			x	sx	xs	x		s	sx
44	x	x				x	x	x			x	x									s		s				x			s	x	x	x		s	s
45	x	x				x	x	x			xs	x									s		sx				xs		s	x		x	xs		sx	sx
46	x	x				x	x	x			x	x									s		sx				xs		s	xs		x	x		sx	
47	x	x				x	x	x			xs	x			sx						s		x				x		s	s		x	x		s	
48	x	x				x	x	x			x	xs			sx						s		xs				x		s	sx		x	xs		sx	
49	x	x				x		x		sx	xs	x			s						s		x				x		xs	sx		x	xs		sx	
50	x	x				x	s	x		sx	sx	x			xs						s		sx				x			xs		x	x		xs	
51	x					x	x	x		sx	x	x			sx					s	s		xs				x		s	x		xs	x			
x	48	36	26	8	9	45	33	45	10	22	28	39	18	0	4	0	0	0	0	3	3	0	7	0	6	7	17	0	0	5	6	13	10	0	0	0
xs	0	3	7	4	0	0	6	2	1	8	13	10	8	0	4	1	0	2	1	2	0	0	9	5	0	6	5	1	1	2	1	2	5	0	2	0
sx	0	6	0	0	2	0	3	2	0	5	7	2	2	4	26	2	1	1	1	3	1	2	15	7	1	1	4	2	1	3	1	0	0	2	5	4
s	0	3	0	0	3	0	2	0	0	0	0	0	1	5	9	7	5	2	2	16	27	0	7	7	0	0	1	11	15	7	0	0	0	1	3	1

x - Played full 90 minutes
xs - Substituted off
sx - Substituted on
s - Non-playing Substitute

SLOUGH TOWN MATCH RESULTS 2018-19

Date	Comp	Opponents	H/A	Att:	Result		Goalscorers	Pos
Aug 4	NLS	Hampton & Richmond Boro'	H	866	D	1 - 1	Harris W 25	
7	NLS	Chippenham Town	A	593	L	0 - 1		
11	NLS	Gloucester City	A	353	W	2 - 1	Togwell L 23 Harris B 69	
14	NLS	Weston-super-Mare	H	651	W	2 - 1	Flood 78 Coles 84	
18	NLS	Torquay United	H	1244	D	0 - 0		
25	NLS	East Thurrock United	A	327	L	0 - 1		
27	NLS	Dulwich Hamlet	H	1010	L	1 - 2	Soares 47	
Sept 1	NLS	Chelmsford City	A	754	W	1 - 0	Flood 70	
8	NLS	Oxford City	H	832	W	2 - 0	Dobson 16 (Pen) Fleet 60 (og)	
15	NLS	Eastbourne Borough	A	645	W	4 - 2	Stevens 16 20 63 Dobson 31 (Pen)	
22	**FAC 2Q**	**Sholing**	**H**	**465**	**D**	**2 - 2**	**Harris B 9 Dobson 26 (Pen)**	
25	**FAC 2Qr**	**Sholing**	**A**	**327**	**W**	**3 - 0**	**Togwell L 93 Dobson 96 Jackman 109 (aet)**	
29	NLS	Hungerford Town	H	772	W	2 - 0	Stevens 35 Dobson 47	5
Oct 6	**FAC 3Q**	**Bristol Manor Farm**	**H**	**481**	**D**	**2 - 2**	**Stevens 10 Flood 63**	
9	**FAC 3Qr**	**Bristol Manor Farm**	**A**	**541**	**W**	**4 - 0**	**Wells 15 Harris W 35 Stevens 51 Soares 82**	
13	NLS	Welling United	A	953	L	1 - 2	Dobson 46	7
20	**FAC 4Q**	**Eastbourne Borough**	**A**	**802**	**W**	**2 - 1**	**Harris B 7 Dobson 58**	
27	NLS	St Albans City	A	779	L	2 - 3	Stevens 10 Flood 87	
30	NLS	Hemel Hempstead Town	A	468	D	1 - 1	Stevens 81	
Nov 3	NLS	Concord Rangers	H	683	W	1 - 0	Dobson 4 (Pen)	
10	**FAC 1P**	**Sutton United**	**A**	**1830**	**D**	**0 - 0**		
17	NLS	Woking	H	1465	L	0 - 1		
20	**FAC 1Pr**	**Sutton United**	**H**	**1360**	**D**	**1 - 1**	**Dobson 81 (Won 8-7 on pens)**	
24	**FAT 3Q**	**Weston-super-Mare**	**H**	**426**	**L**	**2 - 3**	**Harris B 31 39**	
Dec 2	**FAC 2P**	**Gillingham**	**H**	**2084**	**L**	**0 - 1**		
8	NLS	Dartford	A	1466	D	1 - 1	Jackman 37	
11	NLS	Truro City	H	416	L	1 - 2	Dobson 4	
22	NLS	East Thurrock United	H	581	W	3 - 1	Flood 2 30 Dobson 74	
26	NLS	Wealdstone	A	1059	W	3 - 0	Harris B 10 (Pen) Nisbet 15 Hollis 53	
29	NLS	Dulwich Hamlet	A	2900	W	1 - 0	Togwell S 63	
Jan 1	NLS	Wealdstone	H	995	L	0 - 1		
5	NLS	Torquay United	A	2364	L	0 - 4		
8	NLS	Bath City	H	520	D	0 - 0		
12	NLS	Chelmsford City	H	765	W	1 - 0	Dunn 40	
19	NLS	Chippenham Town	H	605	D	2 - 2	Harris W 23 Flood 37	10
26	NLS	Weston-super-Mare	A	667	L	0 - 2		
29	NLS	Billericay Town	A	509	L	2 - 3	Harris B 43 87	
Feb 9	NLS	Hampton & Richmond Boro'	A	607	D	1 - 1	Togwell L 25	
12	NLS	Gloucester City	H	463	L	1 - 2	Lench 13	
16	NLS	Dartford	H	701	D	2 - 2	Harris B 2 Fraser 58	
23	NLS	Bath City	A	866	L	0 - 2		12
Mar 2	NLS	Hemel Hempstead Town	H	669	W	1 - 0	Togwell L 71	12
9	NLS	Concord Rangers	A	312	D	2 - 2	Amartey 79 Togwell S 90	12
16	NLS	Billericay Town	H	759	W	2 - 1	Lench 31 Williams 68 (pen)	12
23	NLS	Woking	A	2543	W	1 - 0	Amartey 20	11
30	NLS	St Albans City	H	744	D	2 - 2	Togwell S 22 Togwell I 75	11
Apr 6	NLS	Hungerford Town	A	408	W	2 - 1	Nisbet 2 Ekpiteta 31 (og)	11
13	NLS	Welling United	H	802	W	1 - 0	Clifford 72	11
20	NLS	Oxford City	A	530	W	3 - 1	Harris W 6 Wells 84 Amertey 87	
22	NLS	Eastbourne Borough	H	905	D	1 - 1	Clifford 90 (pen)	11
27	NLS	Truro City	A	552	D	3 - 3	Lench 45 Harris W 74 Roberts 75	11

GOALSCORERS	SG	CSG	Pens	Hat tricks	Total		SG	CSG	Pens	Hat tricks	Total
Dobson	11	5	4		11	Nesbit	2	1			2
Harris B	7	1	1		9	Opponent	2	1			2
Stevens	6	2		1	8	Soares	2	1			2
Flood	6	1			7	Wells	2	1			2
Harris W	5	1			5	Coles	1	1			1
Togwell L	5	1			5	Dunn	1	1			1
Amartey	3	1			3	Fraser	1	1			1
Lench	3	1			3	Hollis	1	1			1
Togwell S	3	1			3	Roberts	1	1			1
Clifford	2	1			2	Williams	1	1	1		1
Jackman	2	1			2						

Turner	Jackman	Wells	Togwell S	Nisbet	Togwell L	Dobson	Dunn	Harris B	Flood	Harris W	Davies	Coles	Soares	Fraser	Williams	Smart	Hollis	Stevens (L)	Pierson	Phillips	Scott Mark	Noel-Williams	Lench	Wood (L)	Roberts	Clifford (L)	Amarty	No.
x	x	x	x	x	xs	xs	x	xs	x	x	sx	sx	sx	s	s													1
x	s	x	x	x	xs		sx	xs	x	xs	x	sx	x	x	sx	s												2
x	x	x		x	x	s	x	sx	xs	sx	x	s	xs	sx	xs		x											3
x	x		x	s	sx	x	xs	xs	sx	x	x	sx	s	x	xs		x											4
x		x	x	x	x	xs	x	sx	x	sx	sx	xs	xs	x	s		s											5
x	x	x	s	x	x	sx	xs		x	xs	x	sx	sx	s	xs		x											6
x		x	x	s	xs	x	x	xs	sx	sx	sx	x	xs	x	s		x											7
x	x	x	x	x	x	xs	sx	xs	sx	x	x	s		sx			s	xs										8
x	x	x	x	x	x	xs	xs	sx	xs	x			sx	sx	s		s	x										9
x	x	x	x	x	xs	x		xs	sx	x	sx		s	sx	s		x	xs										10
x	**s**	**x**	**x**		**x**	**xs**		**xs**	**sx**	**sx**	**x**		**x**	**x**	**sx**	**s**	**x**	**xs**	**s**									11
x	**x**	**x**	**x**	**x**	**x**	**x**		**xs**	**sx**	**x**	**x**		**s**	**s**	**sx**	**s**		**xs**										12
x	x	x	x	x	xs	xs			x	x	x		sx	sx	sx	s		xs										13
x	**x**	**x**	**x**	**x**	**x**	**x**		**sx**	**xs**	**xs**	**xs**		**sx**	**sx**	**s**		**s**	**x**	**s**									14
x	**s**	**x**	**x**	**x**	**x**	**xs**		**sx**	**sx**	**x**	**s**		**sx**	**x**	**xs**		**x**	**xs**										15
x	s	x	x	xs	x	x		s	sx	x	s		s	x	x		x	x										16
x	**x**	**x**	**x**	**x**	**x**	**x**	**s**	**xs**	**sx**	**sx**	**sx**		**xs**	**s**	**s**		**x**	**xs**		**s**								17
x	x	x	x	x	xs	xs	s	xs	sx	x	sx		sx	s			x	x										18
x	x	s	x	x	x	s	x	s	x	sx	x		xs	x			s	x										19
x	x	s	x	x	x	xs	sx	sx	xs	x	x		s	x			sx	xs										20
x	**x**	**x**	**x**	**x**	**x**	**xs**	**sx**	**xs**		**x**	**x**		**s**	**s**	**sx**	**s**	**s**	**x**		**s**								21
x	x	x	x	x	xs		x	xs	sx	x	xs		sx	sx	s		s	x										22
x	**x**	**x**	**x**	**x**	**x**	**x**	**sx**	**sx**	**xs**	**xs**	**xs**		**s**	**s**	**sx**		**s**	**x**		**s**								23
x		**s**	**x**	**xs**	**sx**	**x**	**x**	**xs**	**x**	**s**	**s**		**x**	**x**	**x**		**x**	**sx**										24
x	**x**	**x**	**x**	**xs**	**x**	**x**	**sx**		**xs**	**xs**	**x**		**sx**	**s**	**s**	**s**		**x**			**s**							25
x	x	x	x	s	x	xs	sx	x	s	x	x		sx		xs		x			s								26
x	xs	x	x	sx	xs	x	x	x		x	sx	sx	s	s	xs		x											27
x	x	x	x	x	x	x	sx	xs	xs	x	xs		s		sx		s					sx						28
x	x	x	x	x	x	s	x	xs	xs	s	xs		sx		sx		x					sx						29
x		x	x	x	x	x	xs	s	x	x	sx		s	x	s		x					s						30
x		x	x	x	sx	x	xs	xs	x	x	x		s	xs	sx		s					sx						31
x	x	x		xs	x	sx	xs	x	x	xs	sx		sx	s			x					s						32
x	x	x	x	s	x	s	x	x		x	x		x	s	s		x					s						33
x	x	x	x	sx	x		xs		x	x	xs		xs	sx	s		x					s	sx					34
x	x	x	x	s	x		x		x	xs	xs		xs	sx	sx		x			s			sx					35
x	x	x	x	xs	x		x	xs	x	x	s		sx	sx			xs			s			sx					36
x	x	s	x	s			xs	x	s	x	x		x	x	sx		x			s			x					37
x	x	x	x	x	x		x	xs	xs	xs			sx	sx		s							x	sx	s			38
x	x	x	x	x	x		x	x	xs	xs			s	s	sx					s			x	sx				39
x	s	x	x	x	x		s	xs	sx	x			sx	x	xs								x	sx		x		40
x	sx	x	x	x	x		sx			x			xs	xs	x		s			s			xs	sx		x		41
x	x	x	x	x	x		s		sx	x			s	s	xs								x		xs	x	sx	42
x	x	x		x	x		x		x	x			s	s	s		x						s			x	sx	43
x	x	x	x	x	x		s			x			s	s	x		x			s			x		s		x	44
x	x	x		x	x		sx						s	sx	xs		x			s			x		sx	xs	xs	45
x	x	x	x	x	x		sx			sx			s	s	xs		x			s			x			xs	x	46
x	sx	x	x		x		xs			x			s	x	s		x						xs		sx	sx	xs	47
x	x	x	x	x	x		xs			xs			s	sx	sx					s			x		sx	x	xs	48
x	s	x	x	x	xs		x			xs			sx	x	sx								x		sx	xs	x	49
x	x	x	x	x	xs		s			xs			sx	s	x		x						x		sx	sx	x	50
x	sx	x	x	s	x			s		sx			sx	x	xs		x						xs		x	x	xs	51
51	36	46	46	35	37	14	16	6	14	28	16	1	5	16	5	0	27	9	0	0	0	0	11	0	1	6	4	x
0	1	0	0	5	10	11	10	19	10	12	7	1	8	2	11	0	1	8	0	0	0	0	3	0	1	3	4	xs
0	3	0	0	2	3	2	11	7	13	8	9	5	18	13	14	0	1	1	0	0	0	3	3	4	5	2	2	sx
0	6	4	1	7	0	4	6	4	2	2	4	2	19	17	14	7	11	0	2	13	1	4	1	0	2	0	0	s

x - Played full 90 minutes
xs - Substituted off
sx - Substituted on
s - Non-playing Substitute

ST ALBANS CITY MATCH RESULTS 2018-19

Date	Comp	Opponents	H/A	Att:	Result		Goalscorers	Pos
Aug 4	NLS	Hungerford Town	H	566	W	3 - 2	Gabriel 15 81 Diedhiou 90	
7	NLS	Woking	A	1671	L	1 - 2	Moyo 80	
11	NLS	Weston-super-Mare	A	523	W	3 - 2	Banton Z 26 72 Gabriel 39	
14	NLS	Hampton & Richmond Boro'	H	585	L	2 - 3	Wyatt 19 Merson 59 (Pen)	
18	NLS	Oxford City	A	323	L	1 - 2	Sho-Silva 60	
25	NLS	Eastbourne Borough	H	510	D	1 - 1	Gabriel 11	
27	NLS	Billericay Town	A	1356	L	2 - 3	Moyo 21 Gabriel 39	
Sept 1	NLS	Dartford	H	658	W	2 - 0	Sambou 48 Da Costa 90	
8	NLS	East Thurrock United	A	326	W	4 - 2	Merson 25 90 Sho-Silva 88 Da Costa 90	
15	NLS	Concord Rangers	H	582	W	2 - 0	Noble 42 Kiangebeni 74	
29	NLS	Chelmsford City	A	711	W	4 - 2	Gabriel 47 (Pen) 52 (Pen) 64 67	6
Oct 2	**FAC 2Q**	**Corinthian-Casuals**	**H**	**403**	**D**	**1 - 1**	**Moyo 44**	
6	**FAC 2Qr**	**Corinthian-Casuals**	**A**	**112**	**W**	**3 - 0**	**Gabriel 10 14 Diedhiou 79**	
10	**FAC 3Q**	**Taunton Town**	**A**	**595**	**L**	**2 - 5**	**Gabriel 61 Bender 76**	
13	NLS	Bath City	H	1432	L	0 - 2		9
27	NLS	Slough Town	H	779	W	3 - 2	Kamdjo 44 59 Moyo 83	
30	NLS	Welling United	H	508	W	2 - 0	Da Costa 9 Moyo 68	
Nov 3	NLS	Dulwich Hamlet	A	850	L	0 - 1		
10	NLS	Chippenham Town	H	584	L	2 - 3	Moyo 40 (Pen) 62	
13	NLS	Torquay United	A	1589	L	1 - 4	Kamdjo 9	
17	NLS	Gloucester City	A	299	D	0 - 0		12
24	**FAT 3Q**	**Weymouth**	**A**	**518**	**D**	**1 - 1**	**Sambou 47**	
27	**FAT 3Qr**	**Weymouth**	**H**	**174**	**L**	**0 - 2**		
Dec 8	NLS	Wealdstone	H	730	D	0 - 0		
22	NLS	Eastbourne Borough	A	550	W	2 - 1	Moyo 52 Knight 58	
26	NLS	Hemel Hempstead Town	H	1486	W	2 - 1	Moyo 21 81	
29	NLS	Billericay Town	H	769	W	2 - 1	Bender 19 Merson 90	
Jan 1	NLS	Hemel Hempstead Town	A	949	D	1 - 1	Banton Z 87	
5	NLS	Oxford City	H	658	W	1 - 0	Moyo 86	
8	NLS	Truro City	A	272	L	1 - 2	Merson 57	
12	NLS	Dartford	A	1018	L	2 - 3	Banton Z 34 Merson 45	
19	NLS	Woking	H	1017	D	1 - 1	Moyo 31	9
26	NLS	Hampton & Richmond Boro'	A	605	W	1 - 0	Banton Z 62	
Feb 9	NLS	Hungerford Town	A	216	L	0 - 5		
16	NLS	Wealdstone	A	1001	D	2 - 2	Diedhiou 15 Sole 90	
23	NLS	Truro City	H	724	D	2 - 2	Clark 50 Diehiou 90	11
Mar 2	NLS	Welling United	A	581	D	2 - 2	Banton Z 10 Merson 82	11
9	NLS	Dulwich Hamlet	H	1088	W	1 - 0	Merson 18	10
12	NLS	Weston-super-Mare	H	341	W	2 - 0	Sambou 57 67	9
16	NLS	Chippenham Town	A	439	D	0 - 0		10
23	NLS	Gloucester City	H	845	L	1 - 2	Clark 36	10
30	NLS	Slough Town	A	744	D	2 - 2	Moyo 45 Bender 80	10
Apr 6	NLS	Chelmsford City	H	922	W	3 - 1	Moyo 45 48 Da Costa 55	10
13	NLS	Bath City	A	1059	W	3 - 0	Kamdjo 15 Merson 54 Wyatt 90+2	7
19	NLS	East Thurrock United	H	920	W	2 - 1	Kamdjo 85 90+8	
22	NLS	Concord Rangers	A	480	L	1 - 2	Kaloczi 41	8
27	NLS	Torquay United	H	1974	L	0 - 4		9

GOALSCORERS	SG	CSG	Pens	Hat tricks	Total
Moyo	12	2	1		15
Gabriel	7	2	2		12
Merson	8	2	1		9
Banton Z	5	1			6
Kamdjo	4	2			6
Da Costa	4	2			4
Diedhiou	4	2			4
Sambou	3	1			4
Bender	3	1			3
Clark	2	1			2
Sho-Silva	2	1			2
Wyatt	2	1			2
Kaloczi	1	1			1
Kiangebeni	1	1			1
Knight	1	1			1
Noble	1	1			1
Sole	1	1			1

No.	Snedker	Herd	Bender	Noble	Diedhiou	Moore-Azille	Da Costa	Sambou	Gabriel	Moyo	Kiangebeni	Merson	Banton Z	Michael-Percil	Joseph	Sage	Wyatt	Sho-Silva	Bonfield	Knight	Kamdjo	Gardiner-Smith	Sinfield	Banton J (L)	McCorkell	Clark	McLeod-Urquhart	Sanderson	Sole (L)	Ewington	Shulton	Kaloczi	Joyce-Dwarika	Geller
1	x	x	x	x	x	xs	x	x	x	xs	x	sx	sx	s	s	s																		
2	x	x	x	xs	xs		sx	x	x	sx	x	xs	s	s	x	x	s																	
3	x	x	x	xs		s	s	x	x	xs	sx	sx	xs	sx	x	x	x																	
4	x		x			xs	xs	x	x	x	x	sx	x	sx	x	s	xs	sx	s															
5	x	x	x	x		s	sx	x	sx	x	s	x	xs	s	xs			x																
6	x	x	x	x			s	x	x	xs	xs	sx	sx	s	x	s	x	x																
7	x	x				s	xs	x	x	x	x	sx	sx	s	x	xs	x	x																
8	x	x	x	x	s		sx	x	xs	xs	xs	sx	s				x	x		x	sx													
9	x	xs	x	x	s		sx	xs	xs	x	sx	x	sx				x	x		x	s													
10	x	x	x	x	x		s	sx	sx	xs	x	xs	s				x	xs		x	s													
11	x	x	x	s	x		x	x	xs	sx	x	s	s				x			x	x	s												
12	**x**	**x**	**x**	**x**	**x**		**sx**	**x**	**sx**	**xs**	**sx**	**xs**	**xs**				**x**			**x**	**s**		**s**											
13	**x**	**s**	**x**	**xs**	**x**		**x**	**sx**	**x**	**xs**	**x**	**sx**	**s**				**x**			**x**	**x**													
14	**x**	**xs**	**x**	**xs**	**x**		**sx**	**sx**	**x**	**x**	**x**	**sx**	**s**				**x**			**x**	**xs**	**s**												
15	x	sx	x	s	x		x	x	xs	sx	x	xs	sx				xs			x	x	s												
16	x		xs	xs	x		x	x		x	s	s	sx				x			x	x	s		sx										
17	x	x	x	xs	x		xs	x		x	s	s	sx				x			x	x	s		sx										
18	x	xs	x	xs	x		x	x		xs	s	sx	sx				x			x	x	s		sx										
19	x	xs	x	xs	x		sx	x	sx	x	s	sx					x			x	x	s		xs										
20	x	x	x	s	x			x	sx	x	xs	xs					x			x	x	s			s									
21	x	x	x	s	x		x	xs	x	x	s	s					x			x	x	s		sx										
22	**x**	**x**	**x**	**x**	**x**		**xs**	**x**	**sx**	**xs**	**x**	**s**	**sx**				**x**			**x**		**s**		**s**										
23	**x**		**xs**	**xs**	**x**		**x**	**x**	**sx**	**x**	**x**	**sx**	**xs**				**x**			**x**	**s**	**sx**												
24	x	x		x	x		sx	x		x	xs	xs	sx				x		s	x	s	s				x								
25	x	x	s	xs	sx		xs	sx		x	sx						x			x	x	s		xs		x	x							
26	x	x	s	x	sx		xs	s		x	s	s	x				x			x	x					x	x							
27	x	x	xs	xs	s		x	x		x	sx	sx	xs				x			x		s				x		sx						
28	x	s	s		x		sx	x		x	xs	x	x				x		s	x		s				x		x						
29	x		xs		x		sx	xs		x	x	x	x				x		s	x		s				x	s	sx						
30	x		x		sx		sx	sx		x	xs	xs	xs				x			x	x	s				x	x	s						
31	x		x		x		sx	xs		x	sx	x	xs				sx			x		s				x	x	x						
32	x		x		x		x	x		x	s		x				x		s	x		s				x	x	sx						
33	x		x		x		xs	x		x	s		x				x		s	x						x	x	s	sx					
34	x	sx	x		x		xs	x		s			x				x		s	xs	sx					xs	x	sx	x					
35	x	x	x		x		s	xs		x		sx	xs				x			x	sx					x	xs	s	sx					
36	x	xs	x		x		sx	s		x		sx	xs				xs			x	x					x	s		sx	x				
37	x	sx	x		x		sx	xs		sx		x	x				x			s	xs					x	x		s	xs				
38	x	x	x		x		sx	x		x		x	xs				x			x						sx	s	s	s	xs				
39	x	x	x		x		xs	x		x		xs	x				x		s	x						s	s		sx	sx				
40	x	x	x				s	x		x		x	xs				xs		s	x						x	x		sx	sx				
41	x	xs	x				sx	x		x		x					xs		s	x	sx					x	s		sx		x	xs		
42	x		x				sx	s		x		xs					x		s	x	x					x			xs		x	x	sx	s
43	x		x				xs	x		xs		sx					x		s	x	x					x			sx		x	x	s	s
44	x		x		sx		xs	x				xs					x		s	x	x					x			sx		xs	x	sx	
45	x		x		xs		xs	x		sx		xs					x		s	x	x					x			sx			x	sx	s
46	x		x		x		xs	x		sx		xs					xs		s	x	x					x			sx		s	x	sx	
47	x				sx		x	x		xs		s					x		s	xs	x					x			x		xs	x	sx	sx
x	47	22	37	10	28	0	11	33	9	28	12	9	9	0	5	2	37	5	0	37	19	0	0	0	0	21	9	2	2	1	3	6	0	0
xs	0	6	4	11	2	2	13	6	4	11	6	12	11	0	1	1	6	1	0	2	2	0	0	2	0	1	1	0	1	2	2	1	0	0
sx	0	3	0	0	5	0	17	5	7	6	6	15	10	2	0	0	1	1	0	0	4	1	0	4	0	1	0	4	10	2	0	0	5	1
s	0	2	3	4	3	3	5	3	0	1	9	7	6	5	1	3	1	0	16	1	5	18	1	1	1	1	5	4	2	0	1	0	1	3

x - Played full 90 minutes
xs - Substituted off
sx - Substituted on
s - Non-playing Substitute

TORQUAY UNITED MATCH RESULTS 2018-19

Date	Comp	Opponents	H/A	Att:	Result		Goalscorers	Pos
Aug 4	NLS	Chelmsford City	A	1058	D	0 - 0		
7	NLS	Bath City	H	2151	W	1 - 0	Davis 80	
11	NLS	East Thurrock United	H	1620	W	2 - 0	Keating 44 52	
14	NLS	Oxford City	A	520	L	0 - 1		
18	NLS	Slough Town	A	1244	D	0 - 0		
25	NLS	Hampton & Richmond Boro'	H	1571	L	0 - 2		
27	NLS	Gloucester City	A	720	D	0 - 0		
Sept 1	NLS	Hemel Hempstead Town	H	1409	W	2 - 0	Reid 77 Hall 84	
8	NLS	Chippenham Town	H	1454	L	0 - 1		
Gary Owers is sacked as manager. Gary Johnson is named as his replacement.								
15	NLS	Hungerford Town	A	620	W	2 - 0	Reid 26 Hall 62	
22	**FAC 2Q**	**Lymington Town**	**A**	**639**	**W**	**7 - 0**	**Og 36 Reid 38 Keating 56 Regis 59 Williams 79 83 Andrews 90**	
29	NLS	Woking	H	2281	D	2 - 2	Reid 80 86	13
Oct 6	**FAC 3Q**	**Brightlingsea Regent**	**A**	**470**	**W**	**3 - 0**	**Reid 15 (Pen) Hall 67 Andrews 81**	
13	NLS	Eastbourne Borough	A	929	W	4 - 2	Andrews 54 Reid 57 83 90	8
20	**FAC 4Q**	**Winchester City**	**H**	**2202**	**W**	**4 - 1**	**Kalala 37 Janneh 41 Lemonheigh-Evans 45 55**	
27	NLS	Wealdstone	A	1241	W	3 - 0	Edwards 45 Essuman 47 Reid 82	
30	NLS	Weston-super-Mare	A	1730	D	2 - 2	Janneh 50 Edwards 81	
Nov 3	NLS	Billericay Town	H	2046	D	2 - 2	Janneh 21 44	
10	**FAC 1P**	**Woking**	**H**	**2419**	**L**	**0 - 1**		
13	NLS	St Albans City	H	1589	W	4 - 1	Reid 6 59 Bender 14 (og), Andrews 60	
17	NLS	Concord Rangers	H	1937	W	4 - 1	Janneh 2 23 34 Reid 43	4
24	**FAT 3Q**	**Basingstoke Town**	**A**	**472**	**D**	**1 - 1**	**Reid (Won 5-3 on pens)**	
Dec 1	NLS	Dulwich Hamlet	A	1441	W	2 - 0	Reid 71 Janneh 78	3
4	NLS	Dartford	A	917	W	2 - 0	Keating 71 Reid 88	
8	NLS	Welling United	H	2460	W	3 - 1	Andrews 3 Janneh 15 Koue Niate 54	
15	**FAT 1P**	**Boreham Wood**	**A**	**207**	**L**	**1 - 3**	**Janneh 48**	
22	NLS	Hampton & Richmond Boro'	A	799	W	3 - 0	Lumbombo-Kalala 15 49 Janneh 69	
26	NLS	Truro City	H	3863	W	4 - 2	Lemonheigh-Evans 26 Lumbombo-Kalala 31 Hall 34 Janneh 49	
29	NLS	Gloucester City	H	3071	W	2 - 1	Hanks 9 (og) Koue Niate 25	
Jan 1	NLS	Truro City	A	2760	W	3 - 1	Reid 21 77 Lumbombo-Kalala 87	
5	NLS	Slough Town	H	2364	W	4 - 0	Wynter 48 Andrews 64 Keating 87 Hall 90	
19	NLS	Bath City	A	3492	L	2 - 3	Hall 42 Reid 65	1
26	NLS	Oxford City	H	2467	W	7 - 2	Janneh 7 21 Reid 23 79 Andrews 35 42 58	1
Feb 12	NLS	Hemel Hempstead Town	A	624	W	4 - 1	Janneh 32 Andrews 46 Hall 83 Reid 89	1
16	NLS	Welling United	A	808	L	0 - 2		
23	NLS	Dulwich Hamlet	H	2655	W	5 - 2	Reid 6 45 (pen) Janneh 15 45 Lumbombo-Kalala 56	
26	NLS	East Thurrock United	A	452	W	2 - 1	Janneh 54 Keating 90	1
Mar 2	NLS	Weston-super-Mare	H	2682	L	1 - 2	Reid 71	1
9	NLS	Billericay Town	A	1324	W	2 - 0	Lumbombo-Kalala 79 Reid 82	1
16	NLS	Dartford	H	2284	W	2 - 0	Reid 29 62	1
23	NLS	Concord Rangers	A	627	W	1 - 0	Cameron 71	1
30	NLS	Wealdstone	H	2934	W	3 - 2	Lumbombo-Kalala 29 Reid 37 Koue Niate 71	1
Apr 2	NLS	Chelmsford City	H	2852	W	3 - 1	Lemonheigh-Evans 25 Reid 65 Andrews 78	1
6	NLS	Woking	A	4589	D	3 - 3	Reid 9 Janneh 80 Wynter 90	1
13	NLS	Eastbourne Borough	H	4538	W	2 - 0	Lemonheigh-Evans 23 Andrews 83	1 (C)
19	NLS	Chippenham Town	A	1906	L	1 - 2	Koszela 57	1
22	NLS	Hungerford Town	H	5351	L	0 - 1		1
27	NLS	St Albans City	A	1974	W	4 - 0	Kalala 1 90+2 Reid 9 Edwards 63	1

GOALSCORERS	SG	CSG	Pens	Hat tricks	Total
Reid	24	5	1	1	32
Janneh	14	4		1	19
Andrews	10	2		1	12
Kalala	8	2			10
Hall	7	2			7
Keating	5	1			6
Lemonheigh-Evans	4	1			5
Edwards	3	2			3
Koue Niate	3	1			3
Opponent	3	1			3
Williams	1	1			2
Wynter	2	1			2
Cameron	1	1			1
Davis	1	1			1
Essuman	1	1			1
Koszela	1	1			1
Regis	1	1			1

No.	MacDonald	Cameron	Koue Niate	Dickson	Regis	Reid	Williams	Essuman	Hall	Davis	Wynter	Keating	Bawling	Burton	Wright	Sokolik	Nabi	Banton	Bass (L)	Andrews (L)	Edwards (L)	Sendles-White	Janneh (L)	Lemonheigh-Evans (L)	Kalala	Koszela	Baxter	Vincent (L)
1	x	x	x	x	xs	xs	x	x	x	x	x	sx	sx	s	s	s												
2	x	x	x	x	xs	xs	x		x	x	x	sx		s	s	x	sx	s										
3	x	x	x	x	sx	s	x		x	x	x	x	s	s		xs	x	s										
4	x	x	x	x	s	s	x		x	x	x	x	s	s	s		x	x										
5	s	x	x	x	s	xs	xs	x	x	x	xs		sx		sx		x	sx	x									
6	s	x		xs	s	x	xs	x	x	x	x	sx	sx		sx		x	xs	x									
7	s	x		x	xs	xs	sx	x	x	x	sx	x	x		sx		xs	s	x									
8	s	x			x	xs	xs	x	x	x	x	sx	sx		s			s	x	x	x							
9	s	x			x	x	sx	x	x	x	x	xs	s		s			sx	x	x	x							
10	s	x			x	xs	sx	x	x	x	x	xs	s		sx			sx	x	x	xs							
11	x	x	sx		x	xs	sx		x	x	x	xs	s		s			s		x	x	xs	sx					
12	s	x	s		xs	x	sx		x	x	xs	xs							x	x	x	x	sx	sx				
13	x	x	xs			x		sx	x	x		sx		s	sx					x	xs	x	xs	x				
14	x	x	x			x	sx	sx	x	x		sx		s						x	x	xs	xs		xs			
15	x	x	x			x	sx	xs	x	x	sx	sx		s							x		xs	x	xs			
16	x	x	x	xs		x	sx	x		x	s	sx		s			sx				x		xs	x	xs			
17	x	x	x	xs		x	s	xs		x	sx	sx		s			sx				x		x	x	xs			
18	x	x	x	x		x	sx			x	x	x		s		s	s						x	x	xs	s		
19	x	x	x	x		x	sx			x	x	sx		s						xs		s	xs	x	xs	sx	s	
20	x	x	x			x	sx			x	xs	xs		s			s			x		sx	x	x	x	s		
21	x	x	x			x	s			x	xs	x		s			sx			xs	sx	sx	x	x	xs			
22	x	x	x			x	sx			x	x	xs		s			sx			x	sx	s	x	x	xs			
23	x	x	xs	sx		x	s	sx		x	x	xs							s	x		s	x	x	x			
24	s	x	x	sx		x	s		sx	x	xs	x							x	xs		sx	x	x	xs			
25	x	x	x	sx		x		s	sx	x	xs	x							s	xs		sx	x	x	xs			
26	x	x	sx			x		sx	xs	x	x	x		s						xs		x	sx	sx	xs	xs		
27	x		xs			x		sx	x	x	x			s			sx			x		x	xs	xs	x	sx		
28	x	x	x			x		s	x	x	x			s			s			xs		sx	xs	x	x	sx		
29	x	x	x			x		sx	x	x	xs			s			s			x		xs	x		x	sx		
30	x	x		sx		x		s	x	xs	x	sx		s						xs		x	x	x	x	s		
31	x	x		sx		x		s	x	x	x	sx		s			s			x		x	xs	x	xs			
32	x	x	s	s		x			x	x	x	sx		s						xs	sx	x	x	x	x			
33	x	x	s	sx		x			xs	x	x	sx		s						xs	sx		x	x	xs			
34	x	x	s	s		x			x	x	x	xs		s						x		x	xs	x	sx			sx
35	x	x	sx	s		x			x	x	x	xs						s		xs		xs	x	x	sx			sx
36	x		x	s		x			x	x	x	sx		s						xs		x	x	x	xs	s		sx
37	x		x	s		x			x	x	x	sx		s						xs		xs	x	x	x	s		sx
38	x	x	x	s		x			x	x	x	sx		s						xs			x	x	x	s		sx
39	x	x	x	sx		xs			x	x	x	xs		s						xs			x	x	sx	s		sx
40	x	x	x	sx		x			xs	x	x	xs		s						s		sx	x	x	xs			sx
41	x	x		sx		x			x	x	x	x		s						s		x	x	x	xs	s		s
42	x	x	sx	sx		x			x	x	x	xs		s								xs	x	x	x	s		s
43	x	x	x	xs		x			xs	x	x	x		s						sx				x	xs	sx		sx
44	x	x	x	sx		x			xs	x	x	xs		s						sx		s	x	x	xs			sx
45	x	x	x	sx		x				xs	x			s						x	s	sx	x	xs	xs	sx		x
46	x	x	x	sx		x			s	xs	x			s						xs	sx	x		x	xs	sx		x
47	x	x	x	xs		x			s	x	x			s						x	sx	s		x	x	sx		xs
48	x	x	xs	xs		xs			s	x	x			s						x	sx	sx		x	x	sx		x
x	40	45	28	8	4	37	4	8	29	45	35	10	1	0	0	1	4	1	8	17	8	11	22	31	12	0	0	3
xs	0	0	4	6	4	9	3	2	5	3	7	13	0	0	0	1	1	1	0	15	2	6	9	2	20	1	0	1
sx	0	0	4	13	1	0	12	6	2	0	3	17	4	0	5	0	6	3	0	2	7	8	3	2	3	9	0	9
s	8	0	4	6	3	2	4	4	3	0	1	0	5	36	6	2	5	6	2	2	1	5	0	0	0	9	1	2

x - Played full 90 minutes
xs - Substituted off
sx - Substituted on
s - Non-playing Substitute

TRURO CITY MATCH RESULTS 2018-19

Date	Comp	Opponents	H/A	Att:	Result		Goalscorers	Pos
Aug 4	NLS	Billericay Town	H	362	L	0 - 4		
7	NLS	Weston-super-Mare	A	568	D	1 - 1	Palmer 59	
Lee Hodges resigns as manager - Ben Harding is put in temporary charge.								
11	NLS	Eastbourne Borough	A	512	D	2 - 2	Harvey T 19 Pittman 40 (Pen)	
14	NLS	Chippenham Town	H	159	L	1 - 2	Thompson 65	
18	NLS	Welling United	H	159	D	2 - 2	Thompson 65 Lewington 90	
25	NLS	Woking	A	1574	L	1 - 3	Richards J 6	
27	NLS	Hungerford Town	H	200	L	2 - 3	Pittman 2 Harvey T 75	
Sept 1	NLS	Wealdstone	A	743	L	0 - 3		
Taunton Town boss Leigh Robinson is named as the new manager.								
8	NLS	Gloucester City	A	314	**W**	2 - 0	Yates 38 (og) Harding 77	
15	NLS	Hampton & Richmond Boro'	H	138	L	0 - 2		
22	**FAC 2Q**	**Hereford**	**A**	**1441**	**D**	**0 - 0**		
26	**FAC 2Qr**	**Hereford**	**H**	**250**	**L**	**3 - 4**	**Lewington 1 Pitman 13 30 (aet)**	
29	NLS	Concord Rangers	A	242	L	0 - 3		21
Oct 13	NLS	Hemel Hempstead Town	H	86	L	1 - 2	Rooney D	21
27	NLS	Dartford	H	87	**W**	3 - 1	Harvey T 33 44 Grimes 45	
30	NLS	Bath City	H	140	D	1 - 1	Harvey T 3	
Nov 3	NLS	East Thurrock United	A	235	D	2 - 2	Harvey T 43 Rooney D 71	
11	NLS	Dulwich Hamlet	H	165	**W**	3 - 2	Allen 2 Pittman 14 Gilchrist 86	
17	NLS	Chelmsford City	A	757	**W**	2 - 0	Richards J 6 Harvey T 14 (Pen)	
24	**FAT 3Q**	**Greenwich Borough**	**H**	**39**	**W**	**3 - 0**	**Riley-Lowe x2 Keats 80**	
Dec 8	NLS	Oxford City	A	242	L	0 - 4		
11	NLS	Slough Town	A	416	**W**	2 - 1	Rooney D 27 45	
15	**FAT 1P**	**Weston-super-Mare**	**H**	**255**	**W**	**4 - 0**	**Rooney D 14 87 Harvey T 18 62**	
26	NLS	Torquay United	A	3863	L	2 - 4	Harvey T 16 Lewington 84	
29	NLS	Hungerford Town	A	260	**W**	4 - 1	Harvey T 11 (Pen) 25 (P) 28 67	
Jan 1	NLS	Torquay United	H	2760	L	1 - 3	Lewington 5	
5	NLS	Welling United	A	420	L	3 - 5	Harvey T 48 70 Hurst 82	
8	NLS	St Albans City	H	272	**W**	2 - 1	Harvey T 76 Rooney L 90+2	
12	**FAT 2P**	**Stockport County**	**A**	**1677**	**L**	**0 - 5**		
19	NLS	Weston-super-Mare	H	403	D	3 - 3	Richards J 19 Herve 40 47	
26	NLS	Chippenham Town	A	539	L	1 - 2	Richards J 82	
Feb 2	NLS	Eastbourne Borough	H	341	**W**	2 - 0	Riley-Lowe 6 Herve 80	
5	NLS	Wealdstone	H	251	L	1 - 2	Harvey T 45	
9	NLS	Billericay Town	A	820	L	2 - 3	Grimes 35 49	
16	NLS	Oxford City	H	436	**W**	2 - 0	Rowthorn 22 Rooney D 71	
23	NLS	St Albans City	A	724	D	2 - 2	Harvey T 48 (pen) Riley-Lowe 53	
26	NLS	Woking	H	718	L	0 - 1		17
Mar 2	NLS	Bath City	A	1408	D	1 - 1	Harvey T 80	18
9	NLS	East Thurrock United	H	429	L	1 - 3	Grimes 4	18
16	NLS	Dulwich Hamlet	A	1960	L	2 - 3	Battle 58 Riley-Lowe 80	18
23	NLS	Chelmsford City	H	506	L	0 - 3		19
Leigh Robinson sacked as manager - Paul Wilkinson is appointed caretaker until the end of the season.								
30	NLS	Dartford	A	1010	D	1 - 1	Grimes 33	19
Apr 6	NLS	Concord Rangers	H			A - A	After a serious injury to Michael Herve (score was 0-1)	
13	NLS	Hemel Hempstead Town	A	436	D	1 - 1	Lewington 89	19
16	NLS	Concord Rangers	H	416	L	1 - 3	Harvey T 45	19
20	NLS	Gloucester City	H	684	L	1 - 2	Harvey T 90	20
22	NLS	Hampton & Richmond Boro'	A	509	D	2 - 2	Harvey T 67 Richards J 90	20
27	NLS	Slough Town	H	552	D	3 - 3	Thompson 17 Harvey 90+1 (pen) Turner 90+4 (og)	20

GOALSCORERS	SG	CSG	Pens	Hat tricks	Total
Harvey T	18	4	4	1	24
Rooney D	5	2			7
Grimes*	4	1			5
Lewington	5	1			5
Richards J	5	2			5
Riley-Lowe	4	1			5
Pittman	4	1	1		4
Herve*	2	1			3
Thompson	3	2			3
Opponent	2	1			2
Allen	1	1			1
Battle	1	1			1
Gilchrist	1	1			1
Harding	1	1			1
Hurst	1	1			1
Keats	1	1			1
Palmer	1	1			1
Rooney L	1	1			1
Rowthorn	1	1			1

Wollacott (L)	Thompson	Palmer	Bignot	Richards J	Smallcombe (L)	Hartridge (L)	Lewington	Gardner	Pittman (L)	Richards R	Riley-Lowe	Harvey T	Harvey C	Palfrey	Keats	Rooney L	Booth	Copp	Harding	Gerring (L)	Bentley (L)	Allen	Rooney D	Rivers	Grimes	Leigh-Gilchrist (L)	Buse	Hurst	Battle (L)	Meaker	Rowthorn (L)	Herve	Ziboth-Mengba	Bentley A	Banton (L)	Regis	Diau B	Andre (L)	Warwick (L)	No.
x	x	x	x	x	x	x	x	x	x	x																														
	x	x	x	x	x	x	s		x	x	x	x	x	s	s	s	s																							
	x	x	x	x	x	x	sx		xs	xs	x	xs	x	s	sx	sx		s																						
x	x	x	x	x	s	x	sx		xs	xs	x	x		s	xs	sx		sx																						
x	x	x	s	x	s	x	sx	xs	x		x	x		x	s		xs	sx																						
x	x	x	s	x	s	x	x	x	s		x	x		x		s	x	s																						
x	xs	x	x	x	xs	x	x	sx	xs		x	x		s		sx	s	sx																						
x	x	x	x	x	s	x	x		xs	sx	x			s	xs	sx	sx		xs																					
x	x	x	s	x	s	sx	s		s	x	x	x			xs	x			x	x																				
x	x	x	s	x		sx	sx		sx	x	x	xs		s	x	xs			xs	x																				
							x		**x**																															
x	x	xs	x	x	sx		sx		x	xs	x			sx	xs			s	x	x																				
x	x	x		x					sx	s	x			s	x	x			s		xs	x	x																	
	x			x			xs		sx	x	x	x	x	s			s		x		s	x	x		x															
	x	s		xs						x	x	x	x	s	sx	xs		s	x		sx	x	x		x															
	x		s	x						s	x	x		sx	xs	xs			xs		sx	x	x	x	x	sx														
	x			x			x		x	s	x			s	sx		xs		xs		sx	x	xs	x	x	sx														
	x		s	x			x		s	x	x	x		s	sx		s				x	x	xs	x		x														
	x		**s**	**x**			**xs**		**sx**		**x**	**x**		**sx**	**sx**		**x**				**x**	**x**	**xs**			**xs**	**x**													
	x		s	x			sx		x	xs	x	x		sx	xs		s				xs		x	x	x	sx														
	x		s	x			x		s		x	x		s	xs		sx				sx	x	x	x	x	xs														
	x		**s**	**x**			**x**		**sx**	**x**	**x**	**xs**			**xs**		**sx**		**sx**		**x**	**xs**	**x**				**x**													
	x			xs			x			x	x	x			xs		s		sx		s	x	xs	x	x	sx		sx												
	x			x			x		sx	sx	x	xs				s			xs		s	x	xs	x	x	x		sx												
	x						xs				x	x			sx	sx	xs				x	x	sx	x	x	xs		x												
	x						xs		sx	s	x	x			s	sx	x				xs	x	x	x	x			x	sx											
				x			x				x	x			s	sx	xs				s	x	x	x	x			x	x											
	x		**s**	**x**			**x**				**x**	**x**			**xs**	**sx**	**x**				**x**		**x**				**x**		**x**	**s**										
	x			x			x				x	x		s	s	sx	sx				s			x	x			x	xs		x	xs								
	x			x			xs				x	x			sx	sx	xs				s			x	x			x	s		xs	x	sx							
	x			x			x				x	x			s	s			s			x		x	x			x	s		x	x	s							
	x			x			x				x	x			sx	sx			s			xs		x	x			xs	sx		x	xs	s							
	x			x			xs				x	x				sx		sx	x			sx	s	x	x				x		x	xs	s							
	x			x							x	x				xs		sx	s			x	xs	x	x				s		x	sx	s	x						
	x			x							x	x				sx		sx	sx			x	xs	x	x				s		x	xs	s	x						
	x			x			x				x	x				sx		x	xs			x	sx	x	x				s		s		sx	x						
	x			x			xs				x	x				x			xs			s	x	x	x				x	s	x		sx	s	sx					
	x			x			xs				x	x		s		xs			sx			x	xs	x	x				xs	s			sx	x	sx					
	xs			x			x				x		x	sx		x							x		x				x	s		x	s	x	x					
	sx						xs				x	x	x	xs		x		x					x	sx	x				s				s	x	xs	x	sx			
				x			x				x	x		x	s	xs		xs					xs	s	x						sx	x			xs	sx		x	sx	
	x			x			x				x	x		xs		x	sx					x	x	s	x						s				xs		sx	x	s	
	x			x			xs				x	x		sx		sx	x	s				xs	sx		x						sx					xs	x	x	s	
	xs			x			sx				x	x		sx		x	x	xs				x	x		x						s					s	xs	x	sx	
	x			x			x				x	x		s		xs	x	sx				xs	xs		x										sx	sx	s	x	xs	
	x			x			x				x	x		x	sx	x	xs	s					x	s	x								sx		s	xs		x		
10	39	11	7	40	3	8	22	2	7	9	44	35	6	4	2	8	7	2	5	3	5	20	16	20	29	2	3	6	5	0	7	4	0	6	1	1	1	6	0	x
0	3	1	0	2	1	0	10	1	4	4	0	4	0	2	10	7	6	2	7	0	3	4	10	0	0	3	0	1	2	0	1	4	0	0	3	2	1	0	1	xs
0	1	0	0	0	1	2	7	1	7	2	0	0	0	7	9	15	5	7	4	0	4	1	3	1	0	4	0	2	2	0	2	1	5	0	3	2	2	0	2	sx
0	0	1	11	0	5	0	2	0	4	4	0	0	0	15	7	4	6	6	4	0	6	1	1	3	0	0	0	0	6	4	3	0	7	1	1	1	1	0	2	s

No. 1 2 3 4 5 6 7 8 9 10 11 12 13 14 15 16 17 18 19 20 21 22 23 24 25 26 27 28 29 30 31 32 33 34 35 36 37 38 39 40 41 42 43 44 45 46 47

x - Played full 90 minutes
xs - Substituted off
sx - Substituted on
s - Non-playing Substitute

WEALDSTONE MATCH RESULTS 2018-19

Date	Comp	Opponents	H/A	Att:	Result		Goalscorers	Pos
Aug 4	NLS	Weston-super-Mare	H	750	**W**	4 - 1	White 2 Pratt 7 86 Hudson-Odoi 30	
7	NLS	Hungerford Town	A	435	D	1 - 1	Pratt 29	
11	NLS	Billericay Town	A	1152	L	0 - 1		
13	NLS	Woking	H	1323	**W**	1 - 0	Lench 85	
18	NLS	Dartford	A	981	**W**	3 - 0	Bubb 17 32 Monakana 53	
25	NLS	Concord Rangers	H	786	D	1 - 1	Green 20	
27	NLS	Oxford City	A	466	L	0 - 3		
Sept 1	NLS	Truro City	H	743	**W**	3 - 0	Hudson-Odoi 17 Bubb 69 78	
8	NLS	Dulwich Hamlet	A	1101	D	1 - 1	Hudson-Odoi 23 (Pen)	
15	NLS	Chelmsford City	H	856	L	2 - 3	Porter 51 (og) Brown 65	
22	**FAC 2Q**	**Great Wakering Rovers**	**H**	**402**	**W**	**2 - 0**		
29	NLS	East Thurrock United	A	274	**W**	1 - 0	Slew 87	7
Oct 6	**FAC 3Q**	**Hungerford Town**	**A**	**306**	**W**	**2 - 1**	**Bubb 66 Shomotun 80**	
13	NLS	Hampton & Richmond Boro'	H	1163	**W**	2 - 1	Pratt 1 Bubb 15	4
20	**FAC 4Q**	**Sutton United**	**H**	**1082**	**L**	**1 - 2**	**Bubb 50 (pen)**	
27	NLS	Torquay United	H	1241	L	0 - 3		
29	NLS	Gloucester City	H	675	**W**	2 - 0	Bubb 55 Pratt 86	
Nov 3	NLS	Welling United	A	507	D	1 - 1	Stevens 21	
10	NLS	Bath City	H	901	D	3 - 3	Straker 75 (og) Charles 85 (pen) 90	
13	NLS	Hemel Hempstead Town	A	703	**W**	1 - 0	Pratt 33	
17	NLS	Chippenham Town	A	618	L	1 - 3	Charles 87	
24	**FAT 3Q**	**Concord Rangers**	**A**	**281**	**W**	**3 - 2**	**Okimo 14 Shomotun 23 Green 63**	
Dec 1	NLS	Eastbourne Borough	H	719	L	0 - 3		
8	NLS	St Albans City	A	730	D	0 - 0		
15	**FAT 1P**	**Biggleswade Town**	**A**	**258**	**L**	**1 - 2**	**Smith 32 (pen)**	
26	NLS	Slough Town	H	1059	L	0 - 3		
29	NLS	Oxford City	H	711	L	0 - 2		
Jan 1	NLS	Slough Town	A	995	**W**	1 - 0	Stevens 48	
5	NLS	Dartford	H	420	D	1 - 1	McKeown 90	
12	NLS	Concord Rangers	A	492	D	2 - 2	Pratt 31 82	
19	NLS	Hungerford Town	H	740	**W**	1 - 0	Stevens 15	
26	NLS	Woking	A	2075	**W**	2 - 0	Allarakhia 11 Pratt 23	
Feb 5	NLS	Truro City	A	251	**W**	2 - 1	Smith 60 (pen) Green 75	
16	NLS	St Albans City	H	1001	D	2 - 2	Smith 45 (pen) Pratt 47	
23	NLS	Eastbourne Borough	A	720	**W**	3 - 0	Pratt 32 Allarakhia 45 Green 80	
25	NLS	Billericay Town	H	906	D	1 - 1	Sheppard 20	8
Mar 2	NLS	Gloucester City	A	396	D	0 - 0		8
5	NLS	Weston-super-Mare	A	546	**W**	5 - 0	Mensah 6 52 Stevens 37 Allarakhia 61 Smith 79	8
9	NLS	Welling United	H	811	L	1 - 3	Green 14 (pen)	8
16	NLS	Bath City	A	966	D	1 - 1	Cundy 28 (og)	9
23	NLS	Chippenham Town	H	902	**W**	1 - 0	Brown 31	8
30	NLS	Torquay United	A	2934	L	2 - 3	Monakana 41 Okimo 73	9
Apr 6	NLS	East Thurrock United	H	764	**W**	3 - 0	Green 1 58 Mensah 68	7
13	NLS	Hampton & Richmond Boro'	A	725	L	1 - 2	Smith 65 (pen)	9
20	NLS	Dulwich Hamlet	H	1245	L	1 - 3	Grant 86	
22	NLS	Chelmsford City	A	954	**W**	3 - 0	Green 32 Allarakhia 49 Cascaval 54 (og)	10
27	NLS	Hemel Hempstead Town	H	823	**W**	2 - 1	Grant 47 Sheppard 56	7
May 1	**PO Q**	**Bath City**	**A**	**2201**	**W**	**3 - 1**	**Sheppard 10 Monakana 62 Pratt 90+5**	
5	**PO SF**	**Woking**	**A**	**2917**	**L**	**2 - 3**	**Grant 3 Stevens 19**	

GOALSCORERS	SG	CSG	Pens	Hat tricks	Total
Pratt	10	2			12
Bubb	6	3	1		8
Green	7	1	1		8
Smith	5	2	4		5
Stevens	5	1			5
Allarakhia	4	1			4
Opponent	4	1			4
Charles	2	1	1		3
Grant	3	1			3
Hudson-Odoi	3	2	1		3
Mensah	2	1			3
Monakana	3	1			3
Sheppard	3	2			3
Brown	2	1			2
Okimo	2	1			2
Shomotun	2	1			2
Lench	1	1			1
McKeown	1	1			1
Slew*	1	1			1
White	1	1			1

Norrn	Tyler	Grant	Stevens	Okimo	Poku	White (L)	Ahmidi	Pratt	Green	Hudson-Odoi	Sheppard	Bubb	Mambo	Lench	Monakana	Brown	Clark	Wilson	Mitchell	Shomoton (L)	Slew	Wheeler	Charles	Mensah	Payne (L)	Regis	Roberts (L)	Smith	Azeez	Samizadeh	Kowalkowski	McKeown	Medford-Smith (L)	Obi	Allarakhia (L)	Paterson	Cox	Antwi	Scott	No.
x	x	x	x	x	x	x	x	x	xs	x	sx	s	s	s	s																									1
x	x		x	x	x	xs	xs	x	xs	x	x	sx	s	sx	sx	s																								2
x	x	x	x	x	x	x	xs	x	sx	x		s	s		x		s	s																						3
x	x	x	x	x	x	xs	x	x	xs			sx	s	sx	xs		s		sx																					4
x	x	x	x	x	x	sx	x	x	x			xs	s	s	xs		s		sx																					5
x	x	x		x	x	s	xs	x	x	sx		xs	x	sx	xs			s	sx																					6
x	x	x	x	x	x	xs		x	x	xs		s		x	sx		sx	s																						7
x	x	x	x	x	x		xs	x	x	xs	sx	xs	s	sx	s				sx																					8
x	x	x	x	x	x		x	x	s	x				xs	xs	sx		s	sx	s																				9
x	x	x	x	x	x		xs	xs	x	xs	s	x		sx	sx	sx		s																						10
																																								11
x		x	x	x	x		x		s	x	x			xs	sx	x		s		x	sx																			12
x		**x**	**x**	**x**	**x**		**x**		**x**	**x**	**x**	**x**	**s**	**sx**	**sx**		**s**	**s**		**x**	**sx**	**s**																		13
x		x	x	x	x		x	x	xs		x	x		sx			s	s		x	s		s																	14
x	**s**	**x**	**x**	**x**	**x**		**x**	**x**	**xs**	**s**	**x**	**x**		**s**				**s**		**x**	**s**	**s**	**sx**																	15
x	x		x	x	x			x	xs	sx	xs	x		xs			s	s		x			sx	sx																16
x	x		x	xs	x			x	s	x	sx	x					s	x		x	s		s	x																17
x	x		xs		x			x	sx	xs	x	x					s	x		sx	s		s	x	x															18
x	x			x	x			x	sx	xs	s	xs			s			x		sx			sx	x	x	xs														19
x	x		x	x	x			x	x	s	xs	x			s			x					s	sx	x	s														20
x	x		x	x	x			x	x	s	s	xs			sx			xs		sx			sx	xs	x															21
x	**x**		**x**	**x**	**x**			**x**	**xs**	**x**		**s**			**s**			**x**		**x**			**sx**	**sx**	**s**			**xs**												22
	x		x	x	x			xs	x	xs		sx			sx			x		x				s	s		x	x	sx											23
x	x		x	x	x			xs	xs	sx	xs				x			s		sx				sx	x	s		x												24
x			**x**	**x**	**x**			**xs**	**sx**	**xs**	**x**				**s**			**x**						**x**		**s**		**x**		**sx**	**sx**	**xs**								25
x			x	x	x			xs	x	sx	x			x	x			s										s		xs	sx		x	s						26
x			x	x	x				x	s	x			sx	sx			x						s				xs			xs	sx	x	xs						27
x			x	x	x			x	x	xs	x			sx	xs			s						x				s			sx		x	s						28
x			x	x	x			xs	x		x			s	xs			s	x					x				s				sx	x	sx						29
x			x	x	x			x	x						sx				x					xs				sx				xs	x	sx	xs					30
x			x	x	x			x	x	s	x				xs				s					xs				sx	sx			sx	x		xs					31
x			x	x	x			xs	x		x				s				sx					x				x	sx			s	x		xs	s				32
x			x	x	x			x	x						s		x		sx					xs				x				sx	x		xs	s				33
x			x	x	x			x	x		x				s	sx			s					xs				x	s			s	x		x					34
x			x	x	x			xs	x		x				s	s			sx					sx				xs				sx	x		xs	s				35
x		x	x	x	x			xs	x		x				sx	xs			s					xs				sx				sx	s		x					36
x	s	x	x	x	x			xs	x		x				sx	sx								xs				x				sx			xs	s				37
x	x	xs	x	x	x			xs	x		sx					sx								x				x				sx			xs	s				38
x	sx	x	xs	x	x			x	x		x					x								xs				s	sx						x	s	s			39
x		x		x	x			x	x		x				sx	x	s							xs				x							x	s		s		40
x	x	x		x	x			xs	x		x				s	x	s							sx				x	s						x	s				41
x	x	x		x	x			sx	x		x				x	xs	s							s				x	s						x	s				42
x	x	x		x	x			xs	x		xs				xs	sx	s							sx				x	sx						x	s				43
x	x	x		x	x			sx	x						x	xs	sx							xs				x	sx						xs	s				44
x	x	x	x	x	x			xs	x		s				x	xs	sx							s				x							sx	s				45
x	x	x	x	x	x			sx	x						s	xs	s							x				x	sx						xs	s				46
x	x	x	x	x	x			sx	x		x				sx	xs	s							s				x	s						xs					47
xs	**x**	**x**	**x**	**x**	**x**			**sx**	**x**		**xs**				**x**	**xs**	**s**							**sx**				**x**								**sx**		**s**		48
	x	**x**	**x**	**x**	**x**			**xs**	**x**		**x**				**x**	**sx**	**s**	**s**				**s**		**sx**				**xs**											**x**	49
45	29	26	39	46	48	2	8	25	33	8	23	8	1	2	8	4	1	8	2	8	0	0	0	9	5	0	1	17	0	0	0	0	10	0	7	0	0	0	1	x
1	0	1	2	1	0	3	5	15	8	8	5	5	0	3	8	7	0	1	0	0	0	0	0	10	0	1	0	4	0	1	1	2	0	1	10	0	0	0	0	xs
0	1	0	0	0	0	1	0	5	4	4	4	3	0	9	13	7	3	0	8	4	2	0	5	9	0	0	0	3	7	1	3	8	0	2	1	1	0	0	0	sx
0	2	0	0	0	0	1	0	0	3	5	4	4	7	4	12	2	16	15	3	1	4	3	4	5	2	3	0	4	4	0	0	2	1	2	0	13	1	2	0	s

x - Played full 90 minutes
xs - Substituted off
sx - Substituted on
s - Non-playing Substitute

WELLING UNITED MATCH RESULTS 2018-19

Date	Comp	Opponents	H/A	Att:	Result		Goalscorers	Pos
Aug 4	NLS	Dulwich Hamlet	H	1057	W	2 - 0	Audel 52 Jebb 67	
7	NLS	Eastbourne Borough	A	585	L	0 - 1		
11	NLS	Chippenham Town	A	498	W	4 - 1	Kiernan 12 81 Goldberg 35 (Pen) Audel 40	
14	NLS	Billericay Town	H	742	L	0 - 3		
18	NLS	Truro City	A	159	D	2 - 2	Audel 15 Goldberg 75	
25	NLS	Hemel Hempstead Town	H	481	D	1 - 1	Kiernan 18	
27	NLS	Concord Rangers	A	637	W	5 - 0	Kiernan 15 Jebb 45 Goldberg 52 McCallum 59 Audel 67	
Sept 1	NLS	Oxford City	H	465	W	3 - 2	Kiernan 31 Ijaha 71 Achempong 90	
8	NLS	Chelmsford City	A	806	D	0 - 0		
15	NLS	East Thurrock United	H	547	W	2 - 0	Kiernan 17 Jebb 26	
22	**FAC 2Q**	**Chesham United**	**H**	**465**	**W**	**2 - 1**	**Jebb 35 McCallum 78**	
29	NLS	Bath City	A	1585	W	2 - 0	McCallum 25 Mills 81	3
Oct 6	**FAC 3Q**	**Hereford**	**A**	**1330**	**W**	**2 - 0**	**Audel Kiernan**	
13	NLS	Slough Town	H	953	W	2 - 1	Coombes 2 83 (Pen)	2
20	**FAC 4Q**	**Woking**	**A**	**1281**	**L**	**0 - 1**		
27	NLS	Gloucester City	H	600	W	3 - 1	Kiernan 4 L'Ghoul 49 Paterson 67	
30	NLS	St Albans City	A	508	L	0 - 2		
Nov 3	NLS	Wealdstone	H	507	D	1 - 1	Mills 90	
17	NLS	Weston-super-Mare	H	622	W	3 - 1	Ijaha 6 Paterson 21 L'Ghoul 90	
24	**FAT 3Q**	**Dulwich Hamlet**	**H**	**478**	**D**	**1 - 1**		
28	**FAT 3Qr**	**Dulwich Hamlet**	**A**	**219**	**L**	**1 - 2**		
Dec 1	NLS	Hungerford Town	H	404	W	3 - 1	Goldberg 33 L'Ghoul 75 Mills 90	
8	NLS	Torquay United	A	2460	L	1 - 3	Goldberg 60 (pen)	
15	NLS	Hampton & Richmond B'	A	323	L	1 - 2	Mills 82	
22	NLS	Hemel Hempstead Town	A	474	D	1 - 1	McCallum 86	
26	NLS	Dartford	H	1912	W	2 - 0	Hill 38 Mills 82	
29	NLS	Concord Rangers	H	611	L	0 - 1		
Jan 1	NLS	Dartford	A	1725	L	0 - 1		
5	NLS	Truro City	H	420	W	5 - 3	Goldberg 14 (pen) Braham-Barrett 28 Paterson 31 Mills 46 56	
9	NLS	Woking	A	1483	L	0 - 2		
19	NLS	Eastbourne Borough	H	445	W	1 - 0	Kiernan 73	
26	NLS	Billericay Town	A	1129	L	0 - 2		
Feb 5	NLS	Chippenham Town	H	248	W	2 - 1	Kiernan 71 Hill 80	
9	NLS	Dulwich Hamlet	A	2353	L	1 - 2	Goldberg 89	
12	NLS	Oxford City	A	214	W	1 - 0	Goldberg 20 (pen)	
16	NLS	Torquay United	H	808	W	2 - 0	Barham 45 Ijaha 51	
23	NLS	Hungerford Town	A	220	W	1 - 0	Mills 61	
Mar 2	NLS	St Albans City	H	581	D	2 - 2	Hill 55 59	5
9	NLS	Wealdstone	A	811	W	3 - 1	Kiernan 30 90 Goldberg 50	3
16	NLS	Woking	H	807	D	3 - 3	Audel 14 17 Kiernan 43	4
23	NLS	Weston-super-Mare	A	572	W	1 - 0	Goldberg 84 (pen)	3
30	NLS	Gloucester City	A	283	W	1 - 0	Acheampong 84	3
Apr 6	NLS	Bath City	H	711	W	2 - 1	Audel 2 Mills 86	3
13	NLS	Slough Town	A	802	L	0 - 1		3
19	NLS	Chelmsford City	H	934	W	2 - 0	Goldberg 1 37 (pen)	3
22	NLS	East Thurrock United	A	566	L	1 - 4	Bettamer 45	3
27	NLS	Hampton & Richmond B'	H	505	W	4 - 0	McCallum 4 Kieran 35 Bettamer 72 Bray 78 (og)	3
May 5	**PO SF**	**Chelmsford City**	**H**	**1912**	**W**	**3 - 2**	**Goldberg 27 Audel 34 Kieran 90+6 (pen)**	
12	**PO F**	**Woking**	**A**	**4865**	**L**	**0 - 1**		

GOALSCORERS	SG	CSG	Pens	Hat tricks	Total
Kiernan	13	3	1		15
Goldberg	12	2	6		13
Audel	8	1			9
Mills	8	1			9
McCallum	5	2			5
Hill	3	1			4
Jebb	4	2			4
Ijaha	3	1			3
L'Ghoul	3	1			3
Achempong	2	1			2
Bettamer	2	2			2
Coombes	1	1			2
Paterson	2	1			2
Barham	1	1			1
Braham-Barrett	1	1			1
Opponent	1	1			1

Wills	Gibbons	Braham-Barrett	Ijaha	Ambroisine	Audel	McCallum	Mendy	Mills (L)	Jebb	L'Ghoul	Kiernan	Kissock	Goldberg	Banya	Orlu	Pinney	Acheampong	Johnson	McDonald	Hurst	Quebe	Mendes	Newton	Anau	Hill	Coombes (L)	Paterson	Agyemang	Marsh-Brown	Genovesi (L)	McNamara (L)	Rooney	Barham (L)	Leacock-McLeod	Oyebanjo	Ming	Bettamer (L)	Hajizadeh	No.
x	x	x	xs	x	x	x	x	x	xs	xs	sx	sx	sx	s	s																								1
x	x	x	xs	x	x	xs	xs	x	x	x	sx	sx	sx		s	s																							2
x	x	x	x		xs	sx	sx	x	x	s	x	xs	xs		x	s	sx																						3
x	x	x	xs		xs	sx	s	x	x	sx	x	x	xs		x	s	sx																						4
x	xs	x	xs		x	s	s	x	x	sx	x	x	sx	sx	xs		x																						5
x		x	s		x	sx	s	x	x	xs	x	x	x	x		s	x	s																					6
x		x	sx		x	x	sx	x	xs	s	x	xs	xs	x		sx	x																						7
x		x	xs	s	x	xs	sx	x	x	sx	x		xs	x		s	x		sx																				8
x			x	s	x	sx	x	x	x	xs	xs		s	x		s	x			x	sx																		9
x		x	x	x	x	sx	sx	x	xs	x	xs	sx	xs						s	x		s																	10
x	s	x	xs	x	x	x	sx	x	x	xs		xs		x		s				x	s		sx	sx															11
x		x		s	x	xs	x	x	x	x		x				s				x	s			sx	x	s													12
x	sx	x	sx	s	x		x	x	x	xs	x	xs	s			s				xs	s			sx	x														13
x	x		sx	s	x		xs	sx	xs	x	x		xs	x										sx	x	x	s												14
x	xs	x	sx	s	x	s	x	x		x	x	xs	sx	s						s	s			x	x														15
x	x	x		s	x			s		x	xs		sx	s								x			x	xs	x	x	sx										16
x	x	x		s	x		x	sx		x	xs		xs	s										s	x		x	x	sx										17
x		x	xs	x	x		s	sx		x	x		xs		s									sx			x	x	s	x									18
x			x	x	x		s	x		x	x	s	sx		sx												xs	x	s	x	xs								19
																																							20
																																							21
x		x	x	x	x	sx		sx		xs	x	xs	x		s												xs	sx		s	x								22
x		xs	x		x	sx	x	x		xs	xs	sx	x		x								s		s		sx				x								23
x			x		x	x	xs	sx			xs	s	x				s						sx	sx	x		xs			x	x								24
x	xs				x	x	xs	sx		sx	s	x	x				x						s	sx	x		xs					x							25
x			sx		x	xs	x	x		xs	sx	x	xs				s						sx	s	x					x	x								26
x			s		x	xs	x	x		x	sx	xs	x				s						sx	sx	x					x	xs								27
x		x	x		x		s	x		xs	xs	sx	sx				x						sx	x	x						s	xs							28
x		x	xs		x	s	sx	x			sx	xs	x				sx							x	x		x			s	x								29
x		x	x		x	sx	xs	x			sx	xs	xs				s						s		x		x	sx			x								30
x		x	x		x	xs	x	sx			xs		xs				sx								x			sx			x		x						31
x	x	x	x		x	s		x			x		xs				x							x	xs			s					sx	sx					32
x	x	x	x		x	sx		x			xs		sx				sx							s	x			x					xs	xs					33
x	x	xs	xs		x	xs	x	x			x		sx				x								sx			x					sx						34
x	x	x	x		x	sx	x	x			sx		xs		s		x											xs					x						35
x	x	x	x		xs	xs	x	x			x		sx		sx		x							sx				s					xs						36
x	x	x	x			x	xs	x			x		xs		x		x							sx	sx			s							s				37
x	xs	x	x		x	x	x	x			x		xs		xs								s	sx	sx			s							sx				38
x		x			x	x				sx	x		xs				x				s		sx	xs	x			x		x									39
x		x			x	xs	x			sx	x		xs				x				s		x	sx	x			s		x									40
x			x		x	xs	xs				x		x				x						sx	sx	x			s		x						x			41
x		sx	x			x	xs	x			xs		xs		x		x						s	sx						x		s				x	sx		42
x		x	x		x	xs	x	xs			x		xs		s		x							sx						s		sx				x	sx		43
x		x	x		x	s	x	x		xs	x		sx		x		s								s					x		sx					xs		44
x		x	xs		x	xs	x	xs			x		x		x		sx						s							s		sx				x	sx		45
x		s			s		xs	s			sx		x		x								x	sx	x			x		x		xs				x	x		46
x	x	x	xs		x	x		x	xs	sx	xs		s				x							sx	sx					s							x		47
x	x	x	x		x	x	x	x		s	x		xs				xs							s	sx												sx	s	48
x	x	x	x		x	xs	xs	x		sx	x		xs		s									sx	x												sx	s	49
47	16	35	22	7	41	11	19	33	10	10	25	6	10	6	8	0	18	0	0	4	0	1	2	4	20	1	5	8	0	11	7	1	2	0	0	5	2	0	x
0	4	2	11	0	3	13	10	2	5	10	11	9	21	0	2	0	1	0	0	1	0	0	0	1	1	1	4	1	0	0	2	2	2	1	0	0	1	0	xs
0	1	1	5	0	0	10	6	7	0	8	8	5	11	1	2	1	6	0	1	0	1	0	7	18	5	0	1	3	2	0	0	3	2	1	1	0	5	0	sx
0	1	1	2	8	1	5	6	2	0	3	1	2	3	4	7	9	5	1	1	1	6	1	6	4	2	1	1	6	2	5	1	1	0	0	1	0	0	2	s

x - Played full 90 minutes
xs - Substituted off
sx - Substituted on
s - Non-playing Substitute

WESTON-SUPER-MARE MATCH RESULTS 2018-19

Date	Comp	Opponents	H/A	Att:	Result		Goalscorers	Pos
Aug 4	NLS	Wealdstone	A	750	L	1 - 4	Phipps 22	
7	NLS	Truro City	H	568	D	1 - 1	Cane 64	
11	NLS	St Albans City	H	523	L	2 - 3	Nurse 17 Welch 23	
14	NLS	Slough Town	A	651	L	1 - 2	Welch 42	
18	NLS	Billericay Town	A	790	L	2 - 4	Cane 73 Lee 77	
25	NLS	Oxford City	H	502	D	1 - 1	Welch 72	
27	NLS	Bath City	A	1022	L	0 - 2		
Sept 1	NLS	Eastbourne Borough	H	824	L	0 - 1		
8	NLS	Hampton & Richmond Boro'	A	672	L	1 - 3	Lucas 67 (Pen)	
15	NLS	Hemel Hempstead Town	H	511	L	1 - 2	Cane 45	
22	**FAC 2Q**	**Salisbury**	**H**	**315**	**D**	**2 - 2**	**Bower 21 Lucas 45 (Pen)**	
25	**FAC 2Qr**	**Salisbury**	**A**	**551**	**W**	**3 - 2**	**OG 22 Llewellyn 110 Nurse 113 (aet)**	
29	NLS	Dartford	A	906	L	1 - 2	Hill 45+2	22
Oct 6	**FAC 3Q**	**Coggeshall Town**	**H**	**288**	**W**	**1 - 0**	**Phipps 90+1**	
20	**FAC 4Q**	**Bath City**	**H**	**1053**	**W**	**1 - 0**	**Hill 13**	
27	NLS	Concord Rangers	H	489	L	1 - 2	Lee 87	
30	NLS	Torquay United	H	1730	D	2 - 2	Bower 34 Ash 88	
Nov 3	NLS	Hungerford Town	A	217	W	1 - 0	Ash 64 (Pen)	
6	NLS	Dulwich Hamlet	H	386	D	3 - 3	Hill 27 Lucas 81 84	
11	**FAC 1P**	**Wrexham**	**H**	**1170**	**L**	**0 - 2**		
17	NLS	Welling United	A	622	L	1 - 3	Llewellyn 18	
20	NLS	East Thurrock United	H	465	D	1 - 1	Scott 27 (og)	
24	**FAT 3Q**	**Slough Town**	**A**	**423**	**W**	**3 - 2**	**Jackson 13 Nurse 34 Hill 69**	
Dec 1	NLS	Chippenham Town	A	581	W	3 - 1	Jackson 15 Diallo 30 Hill 79	
8	NLS	Woking	H	614	L	2 - 4	Lee 43 Byrne 80	
11	NLS	Chelmsford City	H	541	L	0 - 3		22
15	**FAT 1P**	**Truro City**	**A**	**255**	**L**	**0 - 4**		
22	NLS	Oxford City	A	290	L	0 - 3		22
26	NLS	Gloucester City	H	747	D	0 - 0		22
29	NLS	Bath City	H	833	L	0 - 2		22
Jan 1	NLS	Gloucester City	A	371	W	3 - 1	Jackson 52 Lucas 74 Phipps 89	22
5	NLS	Billericay Town	H	568	L	2 - 3	Jackson 28 90	22
12	NLS	Eastbourne Borough	A	486	D	1 - 1	Hill 83	22
19	NLS	Truro City	A	403	D	3 - 3	Phipps 9 Myrie-Williams 43 55	22
26	NLS	Slough Town	H	667	W	2 - 0	Cane 48 Jackson 51	22
Feb 16	NLS	Woking	A	1624	L	1 - 2	Welch 90	22
23	NLS	Chippenham Town	H	654	L	0 - 1		22
Mar 2	NLS	Torquay United	A	2682	W	2 - 1	Hill 9 Bray 84	22
5	NLS	Wealdstone	H	546	L	0 - 5		22
9	NLS	Hungerford Town	H	517	D	0 - 0		22
12	NLS	St Albans City	A	341	L	0 - 2		22
16	NLS	Chelmsford City	A	973	D	2 - 2	Bower 46 Jackson 70	22
23	NLS	Welling United	H	572	L	0 - 1		22
30	NLS	Chelmsford City	A	214	L	0 - 3		22
Apr 6	NLS	Dartford	H	535	W	3 - 1	Nurse 15 Jackson 27 40	22
13	NLS	East Thurrock United	A	210	W	3 - 2	Jackson 44 Llewellyn 72 Bray 82	22
20	NLS	Hampton & Richmond Boro'	H	705	L	0 - 2		22 (R)
22	NLS	Hemel Hempstead Town	A	503	W	2 - 0	Cane 45+3 Bray 46	22
27	NLS	Dulwich Hamlet	H	669	D	1 - 1	Edwards 44 (og)	22

GOALSCORERS	SG	CSG	Pens	Hat tricks	Total
Jackson	8	2			10
Hill	7	2			7
Cane	5	1			5
Lucas	4	1	2		5
Nurse	4	1			4
Phipps	4	1			4
Welch	4	2			4
Bower	3	1			3
Bray	3	1			3
Lee	3	1			3
Llewellyn	3	1			3
Opponent	3	1			3
Ash	2	2	1		2
Myrie-Williams	1	1			2
Byrne	1	1			1
Diallo	1	1			1

[illegible]	McGrory	Nurse (L)	Cane	Pope	Lee	Swallow	Diallo	Lucas	Welch	Phipps	Byrne	Hill	Kingston	Morris-Edwards	Goodall	Llewellyn	Parsons (L)	Plummer	Harris	Bower (L)	Ash (L)	Thomas-Barker	Jackson	Myrie-Williams	Parkinson-Harvey	Dowling (L)	Harrison (L)	Bray (L)	Harper	Ferguson	No.
x	xs	x	x	x	x	x	x	xs	x	x	sx	sx	s	s	s																1
x		x	x	x	x	x	x	x	xs	x	x	sx	s	s	s	s															2
x	sx	x	x	x	x	x	x	xs	xs	xs	s	sx	s				x	sx													3
x	sx		xs	x	x	xs	x		x	x	x	x	s	sx	s		xs	sx													4
x	x		x	x	x	x	x		x	x	x	x		s	s			sx	s												5
x	sx	x	x	x		x	x	xs	xs	sx	x	xs		s	s			sx		x											6
x	sx	x	x	x	sx	x	x	x	xs		xs	sx		s	s			xs		x											7
x	xs	x	x	x	s	x	sx	x	x	sx	xs	xs		s				sx		x											8
x	xs	x	xs	x	x	sx	sx	xs	x	s	x	s						sx		x	x										9
x	s	x	x	x	x	xs	x	sx	x	s	x	sx				s				x	xs										10
x	x	x	x		x	sx	x	x	x	xs		sx		s		s		xs		x											11
x	xs	x	x	xs	sx	x	x	x	xs	xs	sx	sx		s		sx				x											12
	s	x	x	x	xs	sx	x	xs		sx	x	x	x	s		sx				x	xs										13
x	x	x	x	x	x	s		xs	xs	sx	s	x	s	s		sx		x		x											14
x	x	x	s	x	x	s	x	sx	x	xs	x	x		s		s				x		s									15
x	x	x	sx	x	x	sx	x	xs	xs		x		s	s		s				x	x										16
x	x	x	x	x	x	xs	x	sx	x		s		s	s		s				x	x										17
x	x	x	x	x		xs	x	s	x		x	sx	s	s		s				x	x										18
x	x	x	x	x		x	x	sx	xs	s	x	xs		s		sx				x		s									19
x	xs	x	x	x		xs	x	sx	xs	sx	x	x	s	s	s	sx				x		s									20
x	x	x		x	x	sx		sx			x	x	s	s		x				x		s	xs	xs							21
x	xs	x	sx	x	x	sx	sx	s			x	x	s			xs				x			xs	x							22
x	s	x	x	x	x	s	x	sx			x	x	s			s				x			x	xs							23
x	s	x	x	x	x	sx	x	sx		s	x	xs				sx				x			xs	xs							24
x	xs	x	x	x	xs	s		sx		s	x	x				sx				x		s	x	x							25
x	s	x	x	x	x	xs		sx		sx	x	x				xs				x		s	x		s						26
x	xs	xs	xs	x		x		sx		sx	x					x				x		sx	x	x							27
x		xs	xs	x		s	x	s		sx	x	sx				sx	xs			x			x	x		x					28
x	s	x	x	x	s	s	x	s		sx		xs					x			x			x	x		x					29
x		x	x	x	x	s	x	sx		sx	s	xs				s	x						xs	x		x					30
x		x	x		x	s	x	xs		sx	x	x		s	s	sx	x						xs	x							31
x		x			x	s	x	x		s	x	xs		s	s	sx	x						x	x			x				32
x		x	x			s	x	xs		xs	x	sx			s	sx	x						x	x			x				33
x		x	x	s			x	sx	s	xs	x	x			s	sx	x						x	xs			x				34
x		x	x	s	s		x	sx	s	xs	x	x				s	x						x	x			x				35
x		x	xs	x	xs		s	s	sx	sx	sx	x					x						x	x			x	xs			36
x		x	xs	x	sx			s	x	sx	x	sx				s	x						xs	x			x	xs			37
x		xs	sx	x	x		x	sx	xs	s	x	xs				s	x							x			x	sx			38
x		sx	s	x	xs		x	s	xs	sx	x	xs					x						sx	x			x	x			39
x		xs	x		x		x	s	sx	sx	x	x				sx	x							x			x	xs			40
x		xs	s		x		x	x	sx		x	sx				s	x			x			x	xs			x		s		41
x		x	s	x	x		x	xs	s		x	s				sx	x			x			x				x		s		42
x		x	x	xs	x		x	xs	sx		x	sx				sx	x			x		s	xs						s		43
x		x	x	x	x		x	xs	sx		x	xs				sx				x		s					xs		s	sx	44
x		x	x	x	x			s	sx		x	s			xs	x				x			x				sx	xs	s		45
x		x	x	x	x			s	sx		x	s			x	x							x				x	xs	s		46
x		x	x	x	x			s	sx		x				xs	x						s	x				x	x	s	s	47
x		x	x	s							x	x			x	x						sx	xs				x	x	xs	sx	48
		x	x	x	s			sx	xs			x	x		x	x						sx			s		x	x	xs	s	49
47	9	41	34	38	29	10	34	7	11	4	37	18	2	0	3	7	16	1	0	29	4	0	16	15	0	3	15	4	0	0	x
0	8	5	6	2	4	6	0	12	12	7	2	10	0	0	2	2	2	2	0	0	2	0	8	5	0	0	1	5	2	0	xs
0	4	1	3	0	3	7	3	16	8	15	3	13	0	1	0	16	0	6	0	0	0	3	1	0	0	0	1	1	0	2	sx
0	6	0	4	3	4	10	1	11	3	7	4	4	12	19	11	13	0	0	1	0	0	9	0	0	2	0	0	0	7	2	s

x - Played full 90 minutes
xs - Substituted off
sx - Substituted on
s - Non-playing Substitute

WOKING MATCH RESULTS 2018-19

Date	Comp	Opponents	H/A	Att:	Result		Goalscorers	Pos
Aug 4	NLS	East Thurrock United	A	532	W	1 - 0	Kretzschmar 90 (Pen)	
7	NLS	St Albans City	H	1671	W	2 - 1	Hyde 82 Gayle 86	
11	NLS	Oxford City	H	1502	W	3 - 2	Kretzschmar 43 (Pen) Hyde 60 Hodges 79	
13	NLS	Wealdstone	A	1323	L	0 - 1		
18	NLS	Hemel Hempstead Town	A	613	W	2 - 0	Kretzschmar 65 Ofori-Achempong 75	
25	NLS	Truro City	H	1574	W	3 - 1	Ferdinard 64 Cook 67 77	
27	NLS	Eastbourne Borough	A	927	W	2 - 1	Kretzschmar 5 (Pen) Ferdinard 86	
Sept 1	NLS	Billericay Town	H	1925	W	2 - 1	Kretzschmar 16 (Pen) 72	
8	NLS	Concord Rangers	A	608	D	1 - 1	Luer 29	
15	NLS	Dulwich Hamlet	H	1859	L	1 - 2	Bradbury 70	
22	**FAC 2Q**	**Tooting & Mitcham United**	**H**	**1001**	**W**	**4 - 0**	**Bradbury 20 48 69 Little 90+2**	
29	NLS	Torquay United	A	2281	D	2 - 2	Kretzschmar 25 Hyde 39	2
Oct 6	**FAC 3Q**	**Kempston Rovers**	**H**	**944**	**W**	**3 - 2**	**Gayle 38 Hyde 44 45+2**	
13	NLS	Chelmsford City	H	1663	D	1 - 1	Loza 57	3
20	**FAC 4Q**	**Welling United**	**H**	**1281**	**W**	**1 - 0**	**Gerring 77**	
27	NLS	Bath City	H	1562	L	1 - 3	Kretzschmar 31 (pen)	
30	NLS	Hungerford Town	H	1381	W	3 - 0	Hyde 15 48 (pen) Gerring 66	
Nov 3	NLS	Chippenham Town	A	732	D	2 - 2	Loza 70 (pen) 90	
10	**FAC 1P**	**Torquay United**	**A**	**2419**	**W**	**1 - 0**	**Kretzschmar 48 (Pen)**	
14	NLS	Gloucester City	A	291	L	3 - 4	Kretzschmar 36 89 Hyde 44	
17	NLS	Slough Town	A	1465	W	1 - 0	Gerring 30	
24	**FAT 3Q**	**Folkestone Invicta**	**H**	**805**	**W**	**2 - 0**	**Edser 18 Hodges 35**	
Dec 2	**FAC 2P**	**Swindon Town**	**A**	**3654**	**W**	**1 - 0**	**Hyde 54**	
Dec 8	NLS	Weston-super-Mare	A	614	W	4 - 2	Loza 6 26 65 (pen) Little 16	
15	**FAT 1P**	**Maidstone United**	**H**	**1245**	**D**	**1 - 1**	**Edser 74**	
18	**FAT 1Pr**	**Maidstone United**	**A**	**602**	**L**	**2 - 3**	**Eyoma 42 Hodges 79 (aet)**	
22	NLS	Billericay Town	A	1220	W	4 - 0	Gerring 14 Hyde 21 Loza 43 Kretzschmar 62	
26	NLS	Hampton & Richmond B'	H	2516	W	3 - 1	Hyde 27 Edser 45 Luer 90	
29	NLS	Eastbourne Borough	H	2024	W	2 - 0	Edser 2 Gardiner 57 (og)	
Jan 1	NLS	Hampton & Richmond B'	A	1497	W	3 - 0	Luer 3 26 66 (pen)	
6	**FAC 3P**	**Watford**	**H**	**5717**	**L**	**0 - 2**		
9	NLS	Welling United	H	1483	W	2 - 0	Cook 23 Luer 83	
19	NLS	St Albans City	A	1017	D	1 - 1	Cook 36	
26	NLS	Wealdstone	H	2075	L	0 - 2		
Feb 5	NLS	Dartford	H	1190	L	0 - 1		
9	NLS	East Thurrock United	H	1613	W	3 - 0	Tarpey 19 Luer 35 Hyde 90	
16	NLS	Weston-super-Mare	H	1624	W	2 - 1	Hodges 9 Allassani 75	
19	NLS	Hemel Hempstead Town	H	1673	W	3 - 1	Tarpey 4 13 (pen) Bradbury 87	
23	NLS	Dartford	A	1720	L	0 - 2		
26	NLS	Truro City	A	718	W	1 - 0	Little 29	2
Mar 2	NLS	Hungerford Town	A	547	D	1 - 1	Casey 61	2
9	NLS	Chippenham Town	H	1728	W	2 - 0	Hyde 17 44	2
12	NLS	Oxford City	A	347	W	2 - 1	Little 25 Bradbury 90	1
16	NLS	Welling United	A	807	D	3 - 3	Jolley 20 Allassani 76 90	1
23	NLS	Slough Town	H	2543	L	0 - 1		2
30	NLS	Bath City	A	1710	D	1 - 1	Kretzschmar 18	2
Apr 6	NLS	Torquay United	H	4589	D	3 - 3	Luer 7 24 Cadogan 64	2
13	NLS	Chelmsford City	A	1611	L	0 - 2		2
19	NLS	Concord Rangers	H	1819	L	1 - 2	Kretzschmar 64 (pen)	2
22	NLS	Dulwich Hamlet	A	2648	W	3 - 1	Diarra 45 Allassani 57 61	2
27	NLS	Gloucester City	H	1881	L	1 - 2	Little 45	2
May 5	**PO SF**	**Wealdstone**	**H**	**2917**	**W**	**3 - 2**	**Diarra 78 Kretzschmar 86 Hyde 90+3**	
12	**PO F**	**Welling United**	**H**	**4865**	**W**	**1 - 0**	**Little 42**	

GOALSCORERS	SG	CSG	Pens	Hat tricks	Total
Hyde	12	2	1		15
Kretzschmar	13	2	7		15
Luer	6	2	1	1	9
Loza	4	1	2	1	7
Bradbury	4	2		1	6
Little	6	1			6
Allassani*	3	1			5
Cook	3	2			4
Edser	4	1			4
Gerring	4	1			4
Hodges	4	1			4
Tarpey	2	1	1		3
Diarra	2	1			2
Ferdinard	2	2			2
Gayle	2	1			2
Cadogan	1	1			1
Casey	1	1			1
Eyoma	1	1			1
Jolley	1	1			1
Ofoir-Achempong	1	1			1
Opponent	1	1			1

Schotterl	Spence	Casey	Jolley	Gayle	Collier	Kretzschmar	Ferdinard	Hyde	Saraiva	Wheeler	Young	Hodges	Khinda-John	Luer	Mason	Ofori-Acheampong	Cook	Little (L)	Appau	Wassmer	Hayes (L)	Bradbury (L)	Ross	Hester-Cook	Loza (L)	Gerring	Makoma (L)	Edser (L)	Taylor (L)	Eyoma (L)	Leighton (L)	Dunn	Murrell-Williamson	Tarpey (L)	Hudson-Odoi	Allassani (L)	Kamara	Durojaiye	Diarra (L)	Glynn (L)	Ferry (L)	Cadogan (L)	No.
x	x	x	x	x	x	x	x	x	xs	xs	sx	sx	s	s	s																												1
x	x	x	x	x	x	xs	x	x	s	xs	sx	sx	sx	xs	s																												2
x	x	x	xs	x	x	x	x	x	s	sx	xs	sx	sx	xs	s																												3
x	x	x		x	x	x	x	xs	sx	xs	sx	xs	x		s	sx	s																										4
x		x		x	x	x	x			sx	xs	s	s	xs	s	x	x	x	sx																								5
x		x		x	x	x	x			xs	sx	sx	sx	xs	s	x	x	x	s																								6
x	s	x			x	x	x			x	sx	xs	x	x	s	s	x	x	s																								7
x	sx	x			x	x	x	s		x	sx	xs	xs	xs	s	sx	x	x																									8
x	s	x			x	x	x			x	sx	xs	x	xs		sx	x	x		sx	s																						9
x	xs			sx	x	x	x	sx		xs	sx	x	xs	s			x	x			s	x																					10
x	**x**	**x**		**x**	**x**	**x**	**s**	**sx**		**xs**	**sx**	**s**	**s**	**xs**		**sx**	**x**	**x**			**s**	**xs**																					11
s	x	x		x	x	x	x	xs		x	s	s	s	x		sx	x						x																				12
s	**s**	**x**		**x**	**x**	**x**	**s**	**xs**		**s**	**s**	**xs**	**x**	**sx**		**sx**	**x**						**x**	**x**	**x**																		13
s		x		x	x	x		x		xs		sx		s		s	x						x	s	x	x	x																14
s	**s**	**x**		**x**		**x**		**xs**		**xs**	**s**	**sx**	**s**	**sx**		**sx**	**x**						**x**	**x**	**xs**	**x**		**x**															15
s		x		x	s	x		xs		xs		x		sx		sx	x						x	sx		x	xs	x															16
s	s	x			x	s		x		x		sx		xs		x	x						x	x		x	s	x															17
s	s				x	sx		xs		s		sx		xs		x	x						x	x	x	x		x															18
s	**s**	**x**		**sx**	**x**	**x**		**x**		**s**		**s**		**s**		**s**	**x**	**x**					**x**	**xs**	**x**	**x**		**x**															19
s	s	x		x		x		x		xs		s		sx		sx	x	x					x		xs	x		x															20
	s	x			x	x		s		sx		xs		x	s	sx	x	x					x	xs		x		x															21
s	**s**	**x**		**s**	**x**	**xs**		**x**		**sx**		**x**		**xs**			**x**	**x**					**x**	**sx**		**x**		**x**															22
s	**s**	**x**	**x**	**s**	**x**	**x**		**xs**		**sx**		**s**		**sx**		**s**	**x**	**x**					**x**		**x**	**x**		**x**															23
		x	x		x	x		xs		sx		sx		sx			x	x					x		xs	x		x															24
s	**s**	**x**	**x**		**x**	**x**		**sx**		**sx**		**xs**		**sx**			**x**						**x**			**x**		**x**		**xs**	**xs**												25
s	**s**	**x**	**x**		**x**	**x**				**sx**		**sx**		**xs**			**x**						**x**	**sx**		**x**		**x**		**xs**	**xs**												26
		x	x		x	x		xs		sx							x						x		xs	x		xs	x	sx	sx												27
s		x	x		x	x		xs				sx		sx			x						x		xs	x		xs	x	sx	s												28
s		x	x		x			xs		sx		sx		s			x						x		xs	x		x	x	xs	sx												29
s		x	x		x	xs		s				x		xs			x						x		sx	x		xs	x	sx	sx												30
s	**s**	**x**	**x**		**x**			**x**		**s**		**sx**		**xs**			**x**	**sx**				**sx**	**x**	**s**	**x**	**x**		**xs**	**xs**														31
s		x	x	s	x			s		sx		x		sx			x	x				xs	x		xs			x	x														32
	s	x	x	s	x			xs		xs		sx		sx			x	x				x	x			x			x			s											33
	s	x	x	s	x	xs				sx		x		x			x	x				sx	x			x						s	xs										34
	s	x	x	sx	x							x		sx			x	x				xs	x			x						s	xs	x	s								35
		x	x	sx	x			sx				x		x			xs	x				sx	x			x						s	s	xs	xs								36
	x	x	x	x	x			sx				xs		x			x					sx	x									s		xs	sx	xs	s						37
		x	x	x	x			sx				x		x			x					sx	x	s		x						s		xs	s	xs							38
		x	xs	x	x	sx		sx				x		x			x					sx	x			x						s		xs		xs	s						39
		x		s	x	sx		x				x		s			x	x				s	x			x						s		x		xs		x					40
		x	sx	s	x			x				xs		x				xs				sx	x			x						s		xs		sx		x	x				41
		x	sx		x	x		xs				s		x	s		s	xs				sx	x			x										x		x	x				42
		x	s		x	x				s		x		x	s		sx	x				sx	x			x										xs		x	xs				43
		x	x		x	x		x		s		xs			s		s	xs				sx	x			x										sx		x	x				44
		x	s		xs	x		x		s		x			s		x					sx	x			x										x		x	sx	xs			45
		x			s	x		xs				sx		sx			x						x			x										s		x	x	s	xs	x	46
		x			sx	x						s		x	s		x	xs				s	x			x										s		x	x		x	x	47
		x	s	s	x	x								x	s		x	x				sx	x													sx		x	x		xs	xs	48
		x		s	x	x						sx		xs	s		x	x				sx	x													sx		x	x		xs	xs	49
		x			s	xs		sx				sx		xs	s		x	x					x			x										xs		x	x		sx	x	50
		x			sx		x	xs				x		s	sx		x	xs				sx	xs			x												s	x		x	x	51
		x			**s**	**x**	**sx**	**sx**				**sx**		**x**	**s**		**x**	**x**					**x**			**x**										**xs**		**xs**	**x**			**xs**	52
		x			**s**	**x**	**x**	**xs**				**sx**			**s**		**x**	**x**				**sx**	**x**			**x**										**xs**		**sx**	**x**			**xs**	53
11	7	51	19	16	43	34	13	13	0	5	0	14	4	14	0	4	44	25	0	0	0	2	41	4	6	36	1	14	6	0	0	0	0	2	0	2	0	11	11	0	2	4	x
0	1	0	2	0	1	5	0	16	1	11	2	10	2	15	0	0	1	5	0	0	0	3	1	2	7	0	1	4	1	3	2	0	2	5	1	8	0	1	1	1	3	4	xs
0	1	0	2	4	2	3	1	9	1	12	9	19	3	12	1	10	1	1	1	1	0	15	0	3	1	0	0	0	0	3	3	0	0	0	1	4	0	1	1	0	1	0	sx
18	17	0	3	9	5	1	2	4	2	7	3	8	5	7	19	4	3	0	2	0	3	2	0	3	0	0	1	0	0	0	1	9	1	0	2	2	2	1	0	1	0	0	s

x - Played full 90 minutes
xs - Substituted off
sx - Substituted on
s - Non-playing Substitute

Salford City take the lead with Dieseruvwe's goal against Maidenhead United in the National League. Photo: Bill Wheatcroft.

Havant's Wes Fogden has his shot saved by the feet of Chesterfield's Shwan Jalal. Photo: Bill Wheatcroft.

Chesterfield deal with this Maidstone attack. Photo: Bill Wheatcroft.

National League action between Leyton Orient and Chesterfield. Photo: Bill Wheatcroft.

NATIONAL LEAGUE, NORTH AND SOUTH PLAYERS 2018-19

If a player featured on a team sheet during the 2018-19 season, in the starting 11 or as an unused substitute, then they should be contained within the following pages.

Appearance details, for National League (Step 1 & 2) games, FA Cup and FA Trophy are all included in the players' totals as well as any goals scored.
The key for appearances is as follows: X = starting 11 SX = sub on S = unused sub.
Note, there are a few missing line-ups, mainly in the early rounds of the FA Trophy so some players/ clubs totals will be out by one or two.

Also included is the position of the player, their age and their club history. Within this section (L) denotes 'On Loan', Lx2 denotes two loan periods within the same season. The word dual denotes the player was signed for two clubs for the same period of time.

Over 2,200 players laced up their boots to play for their respective clubs during the 2018-19 season.

Harrogate Town enjoyed a debut season at the pinnacle of Non-League football by qualifying for the play-offs, and all achieved with only 25 players, the fewest used across the three National divisions. Gateshead and Blyth Spartans were the next to use their players sparingly, both with 26.

At the other end of the National League Maidstone United had 58 different players looking for the winning formula to keep them up. Whilst in the National North, FC United of Manchester were equally as desperate to put a side together to push them back up the division using 57 players but all to no avail.

Daniel Udoh scores one of his 26 goals of the season to give AFC Telford a 1-0 lead over Blyth Spartans during this National League North match. Photo: Bill Wheatcroft.

2018-19 NATIONAL. NORTH & SOUTH PLAYERS

SURNAME	FIRSTNAME	AGE	POSITION	CLUB PLAYED FOR	APPEARANCES X	SX	S	Ap	Gls
Abbott	Bradley	24	Midfielder	Boston United	37	4	1	41	4
Barnsley (Y), Harrogate (L), Chester (L), Barrow (L), Buxton, Boston U									
Abdulla	Ahmed	27	Midfielder	Concord Rangers	13	7	4	20	1
West Ham (Y), Swindon (L), Dag & Red (L), Barnet, Whitehawk, Staines, Whitehawk, Concord R									
Abrahams	Tanasheh		Midfielder	Dulwich Hamlet	2		4	2	
Wingate, Dulwich H									
Acheampong	Anthony	29	Defender	Welling United	19	6	5	25	2
Welling, Barnet, Ebbsfleet, Maidstone, Dulwich, Welling (L), Welling									
Achuba	Mathew		Defender	Ebbsfleet United		1		1	
Ebbsfleet (Y)									
Adams	Charlee	24	Midfielder	Barnet	30	2		32	1
Birmingham, Lincoln (L), Lincoln (L),Kilmarnock (L), Dagenham & R, Barnet									
Adams	Ebou	23	Midfielder	Ebbsfleet United	31	8	5	39	
Dartford, Norwich, Braintree (L), Shrewsbury (L), Leyton Orient (L), Ebbsfleet									
Addison	Miles	30	Defender	Nuneaton Borough	35			35	4
Derby (Y), Barnsley (L), Bournemouth (L), Bournemouth, Rotherham (L), Scunthorpe (L), Blackpool (L), Peterborough, Kilmarnock, Nuneaton									
Adebayo-Rowling	Tobi	22	Defender	Bromley	8	2	1	10	
				Eastbourne Borough	33			33	
Brighton, Eastbourne B, Peterborough, Sligo Rovers, Cork City, Bromley, Eastbourne B (L), Eastbourne B									
Adebowale	Emmanuel (Manny)	21	Defender	Dover Athletic	3		7	3	
				Eastbourne Borough (L)	2	3	1	5	
West Ham, Sheffield United, Goole AFC (L), Sheffield FC (L), Dover, Bognor Regis (L), Eastbourne B (L)									
Adeloye	Tomi	23	Forward	Dagenham & Redbridge	16	13	8	29	4
Stoke, Macclesfield (L), Chelmsford, Dover, Welling, Altrincham, FC Utd, Hartlepool, Whitehawk, Dagenham & R									
Adetiloye	Sam		Defender	Salford City	1			1	
Salford (Y)									
Affleck	Steven	19	Defender	FC United of Manchester			3		
FC United, West Didsbury (L)									
Agboola	Manny	20	Goalkeeper	Solihull Moors (L)			2		
Reading (Y), Oxford U (Y), Hampton & R (L), Leatherhead (L), Solihull (L)									
Agnew	Liam	24	Midfielder	Harrogate Town	8	10	14	18	
				Boston United (L)	3			3	
				York City (L)	4	1		5	
				Spennymoor (L)	2	1	2	3	
Sunderland (Y), Boston (L), Boston, Harrogate, Boston (L), York (L), Spennymoor (L)									
Agustien	Kemy	32	Midfielder	Barrow	10	1		11	2
Willem II (Y), AZ Alkmaar, Roda JC (L), Birmingham (L), RKC Waalwijk (L), Swansea, Crystal P (L), Brighton, Vendsyssel FF, Hamilton, FC Dordrecht, Global Cebu, SV TEC, Nuneaton, Barrow, Wrexham									
Agustien	Kemy	32	Midfielder	Wrexham	3			3	
Agyemang	Montel	22	Midfielder	Welling United	9	3	6	12	
Leyton O, Grays (L), Malden & T, East Thurrock, Wealdstone, Welling									
Ahmidi	Wadah		Midfielder	Wealdstone	13			13	
Maidenhead, Staines, Wealdstone									
Ainge	Simon	31	Forward	Darlington	32	3	1	35	4
Bradford, Halifax (L), Cambridge U (L), Guiseley, Luton (L), Halifax, Bradford PA, Harrogate T, Wrexham (L), Darlington									
Akinola	Simeon	26	Forward	Barnet	2	16	4	18	
Boreham W, Harrow, Braintree, Barnet									
Akintunde	James	23	Forward	Maidenhead United	15	17	9	32	1
Cambridge U (Y), Histon (L), Brackley (L), Needham (L), Chester, Maidenhead									
Akinyemi	Dipo	21	Forward	Dulwich Hamlet	24	17	2	41	15
Stevenage (Y), Aldershot (L), St Albans (L), Dulwich H (L), Dulwich H									
Al Hussaini	Zaid		Midfielder	Gloucester City (L)	1	1		2	
Derby, Gloucester (L)									
Alabi	James	24	Forward	Leyton Orient	9	22	5	31	2
Stoke, Scunthorpe (L), Mansfield (L), Forest Green (L), Scunthorpe (L), Accrington (L), Ipswich, Grimsby (L), Chester, Tranmere, Dover (L), Leyton Orient									
Alderson	Lewis	17	Defender	Darlington			1		
Darlington (Y)									
Alexander	Cheye	24	Defender	Barnet	52	1	4	53	2
Port Vale, Concord R, Bishop's St., Aldershot, Barnet									
Ali	Mahamud	24	Midfielder	Curzon Ashton	16	6	5	22	
Curzon A									
Allan	Tom	24	Defender	York City	4	2	5	6	
York (Y), Hucknall (L), Harrogate T (L), Gateshead, Alfreton, York, Alfreton (L)									

Key: X - Started; SX - Sub on; S - Non-playing Sub; Ap - Total Appearances; Gls - Total goals.

SURNAME	FIRSTNAME	AGE	POSITION	CLUB	X	SX	S	Ap	Gls
					APPEARANCES				
Allan	Tom	24	Defender	Alfreton Town (L)	16	4	4	20	2
Allarakhia	Tarryn	21	Forward	Wealdstone (L)	17	1		18	4
Colchester, Crawley, Wealdstone (L)									
Allassani	Reise	23	Forward	Ebbsfleet United (L)	2	2		4	
				Woking (L)	10	4	2	14	5
Crystal Pal (Y), Bromley (L), Dulwich, Coventry, Ebbsfleet (L), Woking (L)									
Allen	Charlie	27	Midfielder	Dulwich Hamlet		4	2	4	
Dag & Red (Y), Notts Co, Gillingham, Tamworth (L), Margate, Farnborough, Dulwich H									
Allen	Ifeanyi (Iffy)	25	Midfielder	Dulwich Hamlet	7	1	5	8	1
				Braintree Town	10	5	2	15	1
Barnet, Yeovil, Torquay (L), Aldershot, Wrexham, Bromley, Wealdstone (L), Dulwich H, Braintree									
Allen	Jamie	24	Forward	Dover Athletic	40	5	2	45	6
Fleetwood, AFC Fylde (L), Stalybridge (L), Southport, Dover									
Allen	Luke	26	Midfielder	Braintree Town	22	6	9	28	2
Tottenham (Y), Cambridge U (Y), Cambridge C (L), Hemel (L), Hemel, St Albans, Tonbridge A, Braintree									
Allen	River	23	Midfielder	Truro City	24	1	1	25	1
Plymouth (Y), Gosport (L), Gateshead, Bodmin, Truro									
Allen	Taylor	18	Forward	Nuneaton Borough (L)	13	2		15	2
Leicester (Y), Nuneaton (L)									
Allinson	Lloyd	25	Goalkeeper	FC United of Manchester	18	1	4	19	
Huddersfield (Y), Chesterfield, FC United									
Allott	Gavin	32	Forward	Boston United	24			24	10
Guiseley, Goole, Boston U									
Almeida Santos	Ricardo Alexandre	23	Defender	Barnet	2	2		4	
Dag & Red, Billericay (L), Thurrock, Peterborough, Barnet									
Almond	Louis	27	Forward	Chorley	19	20	4	39	7
Blackpool (Y), Cheltenham (L), Barrow (L), Barrow (L), Barrow (L), Hyde U (L), Hyde U (L), Hyde U, Southport, Tranmere, Southport (L), York, Chorley									
Alves	Herson Rodrigues	22	Forward	Maidenhead United	5	9	21	14	2
Inverness (Y), Brentford (Y), Hampton & R (L), Sutton (L), Maidenhead									
Amaluzor (Formerly Nwogu)	Justin	22	Forward	Braintree Town	20	2		22	3
				Maidstone United	10	3		13	3
Dartford (Y), Barnet, Hayes & Y (L), Hemel (L), Hemel (L), Hampton & R (L), Bognor (L), Braintree, Maidstone									
Amankwaah	Kevin	37	Defender	Bath City	9	2	19	11	
Bristol C, Torquay (L), Cheltenham (L), Yeovil (L), Yeovil, Swansea, Burton (L), Rochdale, Exeter, Northampton, Salisbury, Sutton U, Bath									
Amantchi	Levi	18	Forward	Chesterfield	4	11	2	15	
Chesterfield (Y)									
Amartey	Francis	20	Forward	Slough Town	8	2		10	3
Slough (Y)									
Ambroisine	Yannis	28	Defender	Welling United	7		8	7	
Leatherhead, Whitehawk, Welling									
Amoo	Jerry	21	Forward	Chelmsford City			3		
Hemel H, Chelmsford									
Amos	Danny	19	Defender	Hartlepool United (L)	7	1	7	8	
Doncaster (Y), Buxton (L), Hartlepool (L)									
Amu	Arel	23	Midfielder	Hemel Hempstead Town	10	4	1	14	6
Matlock, Arlesey, Welling, Dunstable, Hemel H									
Anau	Julien	24	Forward	Welling United	5	18	4	23	
Larne, Carrick Rangers, Welling									
Anderson	Joe	29	Defender	Chelmsford City	37	1		38	1
Fulham, Woking (L), Lincoln (L), Lincoln, Cambridge U, Bromley, Maidstone, Chelmsford									
Anderson	Mark	30	Midfielder	Spennymoor Town	26	9	3	35	14
Fort Lauderdale, North Carolina, Spennymoor									
Anderson	Myles	29	Defender	Hartlepool United	34	5	8	39	
Leyton OrientAberdeen, Blackburn R, Aldershot (L), Exeter, Monza, Chievo, Barrow, Torquay, Chester (L), Chester, Hartlepool									
Anderson	Tommy	19	Midfielder	Hungerford Town	10	3	1	13	
Hungerford (Y)									
Anderson				Bradford Park Avenue		1			
Bradford PA									
Andersson	Jokull	17	Goalkeeper	Hungerford Town (L)	5		1	5	
Reading (Y), Hungerford (L)									
Andoh	Enoch Ebo	26	Forward	Nuneaton Borough	6	5	4	11	3
FC Porto (Y), AEL (Cyp), Port Vale, Whitehawk, Nuneaton, Macclesfield									
Andre	Alexis	22	Goalkeeper	Truro City (L)	6			6	
Schiltigheim (Fra), Bristol R, Truro (L)									

2018-19 NATIONAL. NORTH & SOUTH PLAYERS

SURNAME	FIRSTNAME	AGE	POSITION	CLUB PLAYED FOR	X	SX	S	Ap	Gls
					APPEARANCES				
Andrew	Charlie	19	Goalkeeper	Bradford Park Avenue (L)	15			15	
Hull (Y), Bradford PA (L)									
Andrews	Jake	21	Midfielder	Torquay United (L)	32	2	2	34	12
Bristol C (Y), Chippenham (L), Cheltenham (L), Torquay (L)									
Anghel	Ionut-Casian		Midfielder	Ashton United	8	8	11	16	
Ashton U									
Angus	Dior	25	Forward	Nuneaton Borough (L)	23			23	9
				Barrow (L)	10	1		11	2
Solihull, Kidderminster, Worcester (L), Solihull, Stratford, Redditch U, Port Vale, Tamworth (L), Nuneaton (L), Barrow (L)									
Anson	Adam	22	Defender	Chorley	7	2	24	9	
Wigan Athletic, Macclesfield Town, Wigan Athletic, Chorley									
Antwi	Jean-Paul		Defender	Wealdstone			2		
Wealdstone									
Anyon	Joe	32	Goalkeeper	Chesterfield	2		29	2	
Port Vale (Y), Lincoln C, Morecambe (L), Shrewsbury, Macclesfield (L), Unattached, Crewe, Scunthorpe, Chesterfield									
Appau	Declan	19	Midfielder	Woking		1	2	1	
Woking									
Aransibia	Devonte	20	Midfielder	Billericay Town (L)	6	4	1	10	1
Norwich (Y), Billericay (L)									
Archer	Jordan	25	Forward	Maidenhead United (L)	4	4	2	8	
				Southport (L)	15	10	4	25	5
Bedworth United, Stourbridge, Chester, Bury, Maidenhead (L), Southport (L)									
Archer	Lewis	20	Forward	Guiseley	2	1		3	
Guiseley									
Ardelean	Andrei-Vasile	21	Midfielder	Blyth Spartans		4	3	4	
Team Northumbria, Blyth S									
Armson	James	29	Midfielder	Brackley Town	41	4	1	45	16
Nuneaton, Solihull, Brackley									
Armstrong	Luke	22	Forward	Gateshead (L)	18	1		19	11
Middlesbrough (Y), Birmingham, Cowdenbeath, Blyth Sp, Middlesbrough, Gateshead (L), Accrington (L)									
Armstrong	Rhys			Blyth Spartans		1	1	1	
Blyth S									
Armstrong	Taylor		Defender	Concord Rangers		1			
Concord R									
Arnold	Nathan	31	Midfielder	Boston United	9			9	3
Mansfield (Y), Hyde U, Alfreton, Cambridge U, Grimsby (L), Grimsby, Lincoln, Salford (L), Boston U									
Arnold	Nick	25	Defender	Aldershot Town		2		2	
Reading, Wycombe (L), Woking, Whitehawk, Aldershot									
Arsenio	Danilo		Midfielder	Aldershot Town			1		
Aldershot (Y)									
Artus	Frankie	30	Midfielder	Bath City	34	7	3	41	
Exeter, Brentford, Kettering, Cheltenham, Grimsby, Hereford, Bath									
Asante	Akwasi	26	Forward	Chester (L)	11		1	11	9
Birmingham, Northampton (L), Shrewsbury (L), Shrewsbury (L), Kidderminster, Solihull M, Grimsby, Solihull M (L), Tamworth, Chester (L)									
Ash	Bradley	23	Forward	Boreham Wood	7	23	8	30	5
				Weston-s-Mare (L)	6			6	2
Weston-s-Mare, Barnsley, Weston-s-Mare (L), Boreham W (L), Boreham W, Weston-s-Mare (L)									
Ashby	Josh	23	Midfielder	Oxford City	39	3	2	42	4
Oxford U (Y), Telford (L), Brackley (L), Oxford C (L), Oxford C									
Ashford	Sam		Forward	East Thurrock United	7	3		10	2
				Concord Rangers	8			8	3
Witham, East Thurrock, Concord R									
Ashmore	Nathan	29	Goalkeeper	Ebbsfleet United	49		1	49	
Havant & W, Gosport B, Ebbsfleet									
Ashworth	Luke	29	Defender	FC United of Manchester	3		1	3	
				Ashton United	20	4	2	24	
Wigan (Y), Leyton O (L), Leyton O, Rotherham, Harrogate, Halifax, Hyde, Chester (L), FC United, Stalybridge, FC United, Ashton U									
Askew	Josh	21	Defender	Salford City	3	1	2	4	
				Stockport County (L)	4		1	4	
				Ashton United (L)	10			10	1
Blackburn (Y), Ramsbottom (L), Salford, Stockport (L), Ashton U (L)									
Astles	Ryan	24	Defender	Southport	35	2		37	3
Rhyl, Northwich V, Chester, Southport									

Key: X - Started; SX - Sub on; S - Non-playing Sub; Ap - Total Appearances; Gls - Total goals.

SURNAME	FIRSTNAME	AGE	POSITION	CLUB	X	SX	S	Ap	Gls
					APPEARANCES				
Atkinson	David	26	Defender	Blyth Spartans	8		2	8	
Middlesbrough (Y), Hartlepool (L), Carlisle (L), Carlisle, Blyth S, ÍBV (Icel), Blyth S, ÍBV, Blyth S (L)									
Atkinson	Jack		Goalkeeper	Bradford Park Avenue	2		12	2	
Halifax (Y), Bradford PA									
Atkinson	Mike	24	Midfielder	Oxford City	1	1	2	2	
York, Farsley, Northallerton, Scarborough, Oxford C									
Atkinson	Rob	32	Defender	Spennymoor Town	21	4	7	25	3
Barnsley, Scarborough (L), Halifax (L), Grimsby (L), Grimsby, Fleetwood, Accrington (L), Accrington, Guiseley, Bradford PA (L), Spennymoor									
Atkinson	Robert	20	Defender	Braintree Town (L)	15			15	
Basingstoke, Fulham, Braintree (L)									
Audel	Thierry	32	Defender	Welling United	44		1	44	9
Triestina, Pisa, Macclesfield, Crewe, Lincoln (L), Lincoln (L), Macclesfield, Notts Co, Barrow, Welling									
Austin	Sam	22	Midfielder	Kidderminster Harriers	31	6	7	37	
Burton, Telford (L), Leamington (L), Kidderminster									
Avery	Sam	30	Defender	Gloucester City	42			42	1
Shortwood, Gloucester									
Awotwi	Koko		Midfielder	Concord Rangers		2			
Welling, Concord R									
Ayunga	Jonah	22	Forward	Sutton United	24	9	9	33	4
				Havant & Waterlooville (L)	4			4	2
Dorchester, Brighton, Burgess Hill (L), Sligo Rovers (L), Galway (L), Sutton, Havant & W (L)									
Azaze	Aymen	17	Goalkeeper	Barnet			7		
Barnet (Yth)									
AzeEz	Femi		Midfielder	Wealdstone		7	4	7	
Wealdstone (Y)									
Ba	Amadou	21	Forward	Dartford (L)	3			3	
Le Harve (Y), Southend, Dartford (L)									
Bacon	Declan		Forward	Alfreton Town	8	11	8	19	4
Bottesford, Alfreton									
Baghdadi	Mohammed	22	Midfielder	Bath City (L)		2	3	2	
Eintracht Braunschweig (Ger), Bristol R, Poole (L), Weston-s-Mare (L), Bath (L), Norderstedt (Ger)									
Bagueloc'rich	Jay		Defender	Dulwich Hamlet	5	1	6	6	
Fulham (Y), Dulwich H									
Bailey	Callum		Forward	Braintree Town			1		
Braintree (Y)									
Bailey	Dan		Midfielder	Hungerford Town	4	5	18	9	1
Hungerford									
Bailey	Nicky	34	Midfielder	Sutton United	21	6		27	1
Sutton U, Barnet, Southend, Charlton, Middlesbrough, Millwall, Barnet, Sutton U									
Bailey	Odin	19	Midfielder	Gloucester City (L)	8	4		12	2
Birmingham (Y), Gloucester (L)									
Baillie	James	23	Defender	Curzon Ashton	7	4	2	11	
Crewe (Y), Nantwich (L), Curzon A									
Bainbridge	Lewis		Midfielder	Gloucester City			1		
Gloucester									
Baines	Lewis	20	Defender	Ashton United (L)	8			8	
				Chorley (L)	5		1	5	
				Stockport County (L)	7		2	7	
Fleetwood (Y), Bamber B (L), Ashton U (L), Ashton U (L), Chorley (L), Stockport (L)									
Baird	Sam	20	Defender	FC United of Manchester	11	1		12	1
FC United (Y), Droylsden (L)									
Bakare	Mathias		Midfielder	Ashton United	2	1	1	3	
Aveley, VCD Ath, Billericay T, Brentwood, Aveley, Stalybridge, Conah's Q, Ashton U, Hendon, Halesowen									
Baker	Carl	36	Midfielder	Nuneaton Borough	17	1	1	18	1
Prescot C, Southport, Morecambe, Stockport, Coventry, MK Dons, Portsmouth, Nuneaton, Brackley									
Baker	Carl	36	Midfielder	Brackley Town	16			16	6
Baker	Jake		Defender	Hemel Hempstead Town		2			
Hemel H									
Balanta	Angelo	29	Midfielder	Boreham Wood	12			12	3
				Dagenham & Redbridge	25		1	25	6
QPR, Wycombe (L), MK Dons (L), MK Dons (L), MK Dons (L), Yeovil (L), Bristol R, Carlisle, Boreham W, Dagenham & R									
Balcombe	Ellery	19	Goalkeeper	Boreham Wood (L)	8		5	8	
Brentford (Y), Boreham W (L)									

2018-19 NATIONAL. NORTH & SOUTH PLAYERS

SURNAME	FIRSTNAME	AGE	POSITION	CLUB PLAYED FOR	X	SX	S	Ap	Gls
					APPEARANCES				
Balde	Rachid	19	Midfielder	Curzon Ashton (L)	1			1	
Stoke (Y), Curzon A (L)									
Bale	Adam	20	Midfielder	Hartlepool United	3	2	3		
Sunderland (Y), Hartlepool									
Ball	Danny	27	Defender	Bath City		4	23	4	
Bristol C (Y), Bath									
Bancroft	Matthew	21	Goalkeeper	Darlington			4		
Darlington									
Banjo	David	28	Midfielder	Havant & Waterlooville	1	1	1		
Arbroath, Farnborough, Montrose, Berwick, Selkirk, Elgin, Havant & W									
Banks	Ciaran		Defender	Darlington		1	2	1	
Darlington									
Bannister	Jack		Midfielder	FC United of Manchester	22	11	11	33	7
Widnes, FC United									
Banton	Jason	26	Midfielder	Torquay United	2	3	6	5	
				St Albans City (L)	2	4	1	6	
				Dulwich Hamlet (L)	5		3	5	
Arsenal (Y), Blackburn (Y), Liverpool (Y), Leicester (Y), Burton (L), Crystal Palace, Plymouth (L), MK Dons (L), Plymouth, Wycombe, Hartlepool (L), Notts Co (L), Crawley, Partick (L), Woking, Torquay, St Albans (L), Dulwich H (L), Truro (L)									
Banton	Zane	23	Forward	St Albans City	20	10	6	30	6
Luton (Y), Concord R (L), Hemel H (L), Boreham W (L), Hemel H (L), St Albans (L), St Albans									
Banya	Charles	25	Midfielder	Welling United	6	1	4	7	
Fulham, Woking (L), Crawley, Woking (L), Maidstone, Billericay, Margate, Welling									
Barden	Jonathan	26	Defender	Sutton United	7	1		8	
ÍBV, Ottawa Fury, St Louis, Sutton U									
Barham	Jack	23	Forward	Barnet	10	13	4	23	3
				Bromley (L)	3	1		4	
				Welling United (L)	4	2		6	1
Heybridge Swifts, Tilbury, Thurrock, Greenwich, Barnet, Bromley (L), Welling (L)									
Barkers	Dylan	19	Midfielder	Guiseley	5	1	1	6	
Solihull (Y), Guiseley									
Barlone	Luke		Forward	Nuneaton Borough	5			5	
Barwell, Nuneaton									
Barnes	Bradley	30	Midfielder	FC United of Manchester	1			1	
Chester, Colwyn Bay (L), AFC Fylde, Salford, Warrington, FC United									
Barnes-Homer	Matthew	33	Forward	AFC Telford United	1	7	8	8	
Aldershot (Y), Hednesford, Bromsgrove, Willenhall, Wycombe, Kidderminster, Luton (L), Luton, Rochdale (L), Nuneaton, Ostersund (Swe), Macclesfield, Forest GR, Cambridge U, Tamworth (L), Whitehawk, Macclesfield (L), Aldershot, Wilmington (US), Brackley, Telford, Halesowen (DReg)									
Barnett	Ryan	19	Midfielder	AFC Telford United (L)	23	8	1	31	2
Shrewsbury (Y), Telford (L)									
Barnum-Bobb	Jazzi	23	Defender	Chelmsford City	15	5	16	20	
Cardiff, Newport Co (L), Newport Co, Torquay (L), Chelmsford									
Barrett	Ben		Midfielder	Oxford City	1	2	11	3	
Oxford C									
Barrett	Josh	20	Midfielder	Aldershot Town (L)	4	3		7	
Reading (Y), Coventry (L), Aldershot (L)									
Barrington	Marcel	23	Forward	Braintree Town	7	5	1	12	1
				Hampton & Richmond Borough	6	3	1	9	2
Stoke (Y), Harrow B (L), Leicester, Nuneaton (L), Bishop's S (L), Walton C, Tooting & M, Margate, Grays, Tooting & M, Hendon, Braintree, Hampton & R									
Barrow	Scott	30	Defender	Gateshead	33		2	33	
Tamworth, Macclesfield, Newport, Gateshead									
Barry	Bradley	24	Defender	Chesterfield	18	6	3	24	2
				Dover Athletic (L)	2	1	1	3	
Brighton (Y), Swindon, Chesterfield, Dover (L)									
Barthram	Jack	25	Midfielder	Barrow	19	12	12	31	
Tottenham, Swindon, Cheltenham, Barrow									
Bartlett	Adam	33	Goalkeeper	York City	43		4	43	
Hereford, Gateshead, Hartlepool, Darlington, York									
Bascome	Osagi	20	Forward	Darlington		2	4	2	
Darlington									
Bass	Alex	21	Goalkeeper	Torquay United (L)	8		2	8	
Portsmouth (Y), Salisbury (L), Torquay (L)									

Key: X - Started; SX - Sub on; S - Non-playing Sub; Ap - Total Appearances; Gls - Total goals.

SURNAME	FIRSTNAME	AGE	POSITION	CLUB	X	SX	S	Ap	Gls
Basso	Adriano	44	Goalkeeper	Nuneaton Borough		23			
Atletico-PR (Bra), Woking, Bristol C, Wolves, Hull, Truro, FC United, Radcliffe B, Nuneaton									
Bates	Jake		Defender	Maidstone United		1			
Maidstone (Y)									
Bateson	Curtis	23	Forward	Alfreton Town	22	6	3	28	3
Scunthorpe (Y), Gainsborough (L), Gainsborough (L), North Ferriby, Gainsborough, Alfreton									
Batt	Shaun	32	Forward	Chelmsford City		4	1	4	
				East Thurrock United	7	7	13	14	2
Peterborough, Millwall, Crawley (L), Leyton O (L), Leyton O, Barnet, Chelmsford, East Thurrock									
Batten	Jack	23	Defender	Bath City	47			47	2
Bath									
Battle	Alex	20	Forward	Truro City (L)	7	2	6	9	1
Plymouth, Truro (L)									
Baughan	Callum		Defender	Eastleigh	1	1	9	2	
Eastleigh (Y)									
Bauress	Bradley	23	Midfielder	Southport	33	2	2	35	7
Blackburn, Colwyn Bay, Witton, Barrow, Southport									
Bawling	Alfred Bobson	23	Midfielder	Torquay United	1	4	5	5	
				Oxford City	16	15	7	31	2
Watford, Crawley, Woking, Torquay, Oxford C (L), Oxford C									
Baxendale	James	26	Midfielder	Kidderminster Harriers	3	13	13	16	
Leeds (Y), Doncaster, Buxton (L), Hereford (L), Walsall, Mansfield (L), Mansfield, Orange Co, Alfreton, Kidderminster, Nuneaton (L)									
Baxendale	James	26	Midfielder	Nuneaton Borough (L)	6	1	1	7	
Baxter	Josh		Defender	Torquay United			1		
Torquay (Y)									
Bayne	Josh		Defender	Spennymoor Town		2			
Spennymoor									
Bearwish	Tom	19	Forward	Eastleigh		6	15	6	
Eastleigh (Y)									
Beasant	Sam	31	Goalkeeper	Concord Rangers	46			46	
Maidenhead, Woking, Billericay, Woking, Stevenage, Cambridge U, Braintree, Chelmsford, Concord R									
Beaumont	Bobby		Defender	Wrexham			1		
Wrexham (Y)									
Beautyman	Harry	27	Midfielder	Sutton United	32	5	11	37	4
Leyton O, Sutton U, Welling, Peterborough, Northampton, Stevenage, Sutton U									
Beavon	Stuart	35	Forward	Wrexham (L)	33	13	1	46	6
Didcot, Weymouth, Wycombe, PNE, Burton (L), Burton, Coventry, Wrexham (L)									
Beck	Mark	25	Forward	Harrogate Town	28	16	3	44	13
Carlisle (Y), Falkirk (L), Yeovil, Wrexham (L), Darlington, Harrogate									
Beckwith	Dean	35	Defender	Sutton United	24	9	8	33	2
Gillingham, Margate (L), Hereford U, Northampton, Luton, Eastleigh, Sutton U, Maidstone (L)									
Bedford	Joe	21	Midfielder	East Thurrock United (L)	1	1	1	2	
				Dover Athletic	3	1	2	4	
Southend, East Thurrock (L), Dover									
Beeden	Jon	27	Defender	Chippenham Town	2	9	2		
Chippenham									
Beesley	Jake	22	Forward	Bradford Park Avenue	45			45	21
Chesterfield (Y), Salford, Boston U (L), Bradford PA									
Beestin	Alfie	21	Forward	Chesterfield (L)	5	3	2	8	
Tadcaster, Doncaster, Chesterfield (L)									
Belford	Cameron	30	Goalkeeper	Chorley	2			2	
				Nuneaton Borough	37			37	
Coventry (Y), Tamworth (L), Bury, Worcester (L), Southend (L), Southend (L), Accrington (L), Tamworth, Mansfield, Rushall, Swindon, Wrexham, Stranraer (L), Stranraer, Forest GR, Chorley, Nuneaton									
Belford	Tyrell	25	Goalkeeper	Nuneaton Borough	5	11	5		
Liverpool (Y), Swindon, Southport (L), Oxford C, Nuneaton									
Bell	Nyal	22	Forward	Stockport County	23	22	3	45	12
Rochdale (Y), Chester (L), Gateshead, Chester (L), Alfreton (L), Stockport									
Bellamy	Liam	27	Midfielder	Dagenham & Redbridge	1	4		5	
Charlton,Brentford, Cray W (L), Ebbsfleet (L), Ebbsfleet, Dover, Aldershot, Farnborough, Dover, Dagenham & R									
Bellikli	Neset	20	Midfielder	Sutton United	2	5	4	7	
AFC Wimbledon (Y), Sutton Common, Sutton U									
Belshaw	James	28	Goalkeeper	Harrogate Town	51		1	51	
Walsall (Y), Blue Devils (US), Chicago Fire, Nuneaton, Tamworth, Harrogate									

2018-19 NATIONAL. NORTH & SOUTH PLAYERS — **APPEARANCES**

SURNAME	FIRSTNAME	AGE	POSITION	CLUB PLAYED FOR	X	SX	S	Ap	Gls
Bencherif	Hamza	31	Midfielder	York City	21	5	9	26	3
Lincoln C, Macclesfield, Notts Co, Plymouth, JS Kabylie (Alg)Lincoln C, Halifax, Wrexham, York									
Bender	Thomas	26	Defender	St Albans City	41		3	41	3
Colchester, Accrington (L), Chelmsford (L), Millwall, Welling (L), Dartford, Forest GR, St Albans (L), St Albans									
Benjamin	Shane	38	Forward	Nuneaton Borough	1	5	5	6	
Redditch U, Stafford R, Nuneaton									
Bennett	Dale	29	Defender	Sutton United	46			46	
Watford (Y), Wealdstone (L), Kettering (L), Brentford (L), AFC Wimbledon (L), Yeovil (L), Forest GR, Sutton U									
Bentley	Aaron	23	Defender	Truro City	6		1	6	
Plymouth (Y), Alfreton (L), Truro									
Bentley	Jordan	20	Defender	Truro City (L)	8	4	6	12	
Plymouth (Y), Sutton U (L), Truro (L)									
Berkeley-Agyepong	Jacob Kwame	22	Midfielder	Aldershot Town	20	9	1	29	1
Cystal Palace (Yth), Aldershot									
Bernard	Dominic	22	Defender	Aldershot Town (L)	36	1	7	37	
Birmingham (Yth), Aldershot (L)									
Berrett	James	29	Midfielder	FC Halifax Town	27	1		28	
Huddersfield (Y)Carlisle, Yeovil, York, Grimsby, FC Halifax									
Bettache	Mahrez	25	Midfielder	Braintree Town	1		7	1	
Fulham (Y), Corinthian-C, Hendon, Corinthian-C, Braintree									
Bettamer	Mohamed	26	Forward	Braintree Town	14	1		15	6
				Barnet	4	3	6	7	
				Welling United (L)	3	5		8	2
Watford (Y), London Tigers, Hayes & Y, Hampton & R, Al-Ahli Ben (Libya), Staines, Braintree, Barnet, Welling (L)									
Bignot	Paul	33	Defender	Truro City	7		11	7	
Crewe , Kidderminster (L), Kidderminster, Newport Co, Blackpool, Plymouth (L), Grimsby, Solihull M, Newport Co, Barrow, Telford, Truro									
Bilboe	Laurence	21	Goalkeeper	Havant & Waterlooville (L)	5			5	
Rotherham (Y), Havant & W (L)									
Bingham	Josh	24	Forward	Eastbourne Borough	6	3		9	1
Central Coast Mariners (Aus), Eastbourne B									
Binnom-Williams	Jerome	24	Defender	Chesterfield	32	7	1	39	1
Crystal P (Y), Forest Green (L), Southend (L), Burton (L), Leyton O (L), Peterborough, Chesterfield									
Birch	Aaron	24	Midfielder	Nuneaton Borough	3	1	2	4	
Nuneaton									
Birch	Arlen	22	Defender	AFC Fylde	27	7	11	34	1
Everton (Yth), Burnley (Yth), AFC Fylde									
Bird	Jamie	21	Forward	Hereford FC	6	6	2	12	1
Cardiff (Y), Weston (L), Hereford									
Bird	Ryan	31	Forward	Maidenhead United	14	13	10	27	1
Burnham, Portsmouth, Cambridge U (L), Cambridge U, Hartlepool (L), Yeovil, Eastleigh, Newport Co, Dover, Maidenhead									
Bishop	Colby	24	Forward	Leamington	30	1	2	31	22
Notts Co (Y), Gloucester (L), Worcester, Boston U, Leamington									
Black	John		Forward	Aldershot Town	1			1	
Aldershot (Y)									
Blackham	Jack		Midfielder	Nuneaton Borough	1	3	1		
Nuneaton									
Blackman	Sam		Midfielder	Concord Rangers	45	1		46	5
Leatherhead, Margate, Concord R									
Blackmore	Daniel		Defender	Eastbourne Borough	2	1	19	3	
Eastbourne B									
Blackmore	David	30	Goalkeeper	Braintree Town			5		
Godalming, Retired, Braintree									
Blake	Nyle	20	Forward	Alfreton Town (L)			1		
Mansfield (Y), Alfreton (L)									
Blakeman	Adam	27	Midfielder	Chorley	45			45	9
Bolton Wanderers, Hyde United, Ayr United, SouthportChorley									
Blanchfield	James	21	Midfielder	Dagenham & Redbridge	1	4	2	5	
Arsenal, Ipswich,Aldershot (L), Dagenham & R									
Blissett	Nathan	28	Forward	Solihull Moors	24	3		27	11
Romulus, Kidderminster, Cambridge U (L), Hednesford (L), Bristol R (L), Bristol R, Tranmere (L), Lincoln (L), Torquay, Plymouth, Macclesfield (L), Macclesfield, Solihull									
Bloomfield	Mason	22	Forward	AFC Fylde (L)		1		1	
Dagenham & R, Chatham (L), Erith & Bel (L), Maldon & Tiptree (L), Chelmsford, Billericay, Grays, Witham,Brentwood, Aveley, Dagenham & R, Norwich, Hamilton Ac (L)AFC Fylde (L)									

Key: X - Started; SX - Sub on; S - Non-playing Sub; Ap - Total Appearances; Gls - Total goals.

SURNAME	FIRSTNAME	AGE	POSITION	CLUB	X	SX	S	Ap	Gls
					APPEARANCES				
Blyth	Jacob	26	Forward	Barrow	17	8	3	25	3
Nuneaton Griff, Bedworth U, Leamington, Leicester, Burton (L), Notts Co (L), Northampton (L), Burton (L), Cambridge U (L), Blackpool (L), Motherwell, Barrow									
Boakye-Yiadom	Nana	23	Midfielder	Concord Rangers	1	5	1	6	
West Ham (Y), Barnsley (Y), Leatherhead, Waltham F (L), Waltham F, Dulwich H, Leatherhead (L), Concord R									
Boateng	Kwame	20	Defender	Guiseley			1		
Bradford (Y), Guiseley									
Boden	Scott	29	Forward	Gateshead	29	3	2	32	12
				Chesterfield	14	1		15	10
Chesterfield, Macclesfield (L), Macclesfield, Halifax, Newport Co, Inverness CT, Wrexham, Gateshead, Chesterfield									
Boerstra Leeflang	Djamel	27	Midfielder	Havant & Waterlooville	3	2		5	
Vitesse Delft (Nth), Deltras Sidoarjo (IDN), Haaglandia Zon (Nth), Haaglandia Zat, Valletta (Malta), QFC (Malta), New Radiant (Maldives), Lija Ath (Malta), Perseru S (IDN), Havant & W, Lienden (Nth)									
Bolarinwa	Tom	29	Midfielder	Sutton United	26	17	3	43	1
Sutton U, Grimsby, Sutton U (L), Sutton U									
Bond	Andy	33	Midfielder	AFC Fylde	32	11	9	43	8
Crewe , Barrow, Colchester, Crewe (L), Bristol R (L), Chester, Stevenage, Chorley, Crawley, AFC Fylde									
Bonds	Elliot	19	Midfielder	Dagenham & Redbridge	1	3	1		
Dagenham & R (Y)									
Boness	Danny	21	Goalkeeper	Hemel Hempstead Town		10			
Hemel H									
Boney	Myles	21	Goalkeeper	Solihull Moors (L)			1		
Blackpool (Y), Nantwich (L), Solihull (L)									
Bonfield	Alfie	18	Goalkeeper	St Albans City			16		
Wealdstone, St Albans									
Bonne	Macauley	23	Forward	Leyton Orient	51		1	51	24
Colchester, Lincoln (L), Woking (L), Leyton Orient									
Bonner	Thomas	31	Defender	Dartford	44			44	1
Hinckley U, Ilkeston, Dartford, Cambridge U, Dover (L), Ebbsfleet, Dartford									
Boot	Ryan	24	Goalkeeper	Solihull Moors	56			56	
Port Vale (Y), Worcester (L), Norton U (L), Newcastle T (L), Worcester (L), Worcester (L), Macclesfield (L), Solihull									
Booth	Austen		Defender	Truro City	13	5	6	18	
Truro									
Booty	Regan	21	Midfielder	Aldershot Town (L)	37	5	3	42	
Huddersfield (Yth), Aldershot (L)									
Borg	Oscar	21	Defender	Braintree Town (L)	13	4	4	17	
Boshell	Danny	38	Midfielder	Bradford Park Avenue	5	8	5		
Oldham (Y), Bury (L), Stockport, Grimsby, Chesterfield, Guiseley, Altrincham (L), Altrincham, Guiseley, Bradford PA									
Bosma	Bouwe		Midfielder	Southport	1		1	1	
Eastbourne B, Southport									
Boswell	Ryan		Defender	East Thurrock United	1		1		
East Thurrock, RomfordEast Thurrock									
Boucaud	Andre	34	Midfielder	Barnet	16	5	1	21	
QPR, Reading, Peterborough (L), Peterborough (L), Peterborough, Aldershot (L), Kettering, York (L), York, Luton, Notts Co (L), Notts Co, Dagenham & R, Barnet									
Boucher	Kieran	19	Goalkeeper	Kidderminster Harriers (L)		1			
Aston Villa (Y), Lye (L), Halesowen (L), Kidderminster (L)									
Bowen	James	23	Defender	Leamington	12	7	12	19	
Cheltenham, Gloucester (L), Gloucester (L), Hereford, Solihull M, Hereford, Leamington									
Bower	Matthew	20	Defender	Weston-super-Mare (L)	29			29	3
Cheltenham (Y), Weston (Lx2),									
Bowry	Daniel	21	Defender	Hampton & Richmond Borough (L)	3	1	5	4	
Charlton (Y), Hampton & R (L)									
Box	Martyn	17	Defender	Barnet		2	1	2	
Barnet (Yth)									
Boyce	Andrew	29	Defender	Eastleigh	41	2	4	43	3
Gainsborough, Lincoln, Scunthorpe (L), Scunthorpe, Grimsby (L), Grimsby (L), Hartlepool (L), Notts Co (L), Grimsby, Eastleigh									
Boyes	Adam	28	Forward	Spennymoor Town	9	34	7	43	9
York, Kidderminster (L), Scunthorpe, Boston U, Barrow, Gateshead, Guiseley (L), Guiseley, Bradford PA, Spennymoor									
Boyles	Travis	19	Forward	Curzon Ashton			1		
Curzon A									
Bozier	Matt		Defender	Aldershot Town		1	6	1	
Aldershot (Y)									

2018-19 NATIONAL. NORTH & SOUTH PLAYERS

SURNAME	FIRSTNAME	AGE	POSITION	CLUB PLAYED FOR	X	SX	S	Ap	Gls
Bradbrook	Elliot	34	Midfielder	Dartford	28	3	2	31	9
Dartford									
Bradbury	Harvey	20	Forward	Hungerford Town (L)	1			1	1
				Hungerford Town (L)	5	2	1	7	1
				Woking (L)	5	15	2	20	6
Watford, St Albans (L), Hungerford (L), Oxford U, Hungerford (Lx2), Woking (L),									
Bradbury	Thomas	21	Defender	York City (L)	3			3	
Dundee, York (L)									
Bradley	Alex	20	Midfielder	Havant & Waterlooville (L)	6	5	4	11	2
WBA (Y), Havant & W (L), Burton (L)									
Bradley	Daniel	28	Midfielder	Kidderminster Harriers	17	4		21	7
				AFC Fylde	15	1		16	2
Aston Villa (Y), Tamworth, Kidderminster, Alfreton, Barnet, Alfreton, AFC Fylde, Kidderminster, AFC Fylde									
Braham-Barrett	Craig	30	Defender	Welling United	37	1	1	38	1
Welling, Grays, Farnborough, Havant & W, Sutton U, Macclesfield, Cheltenham (L), Cheltenham, Ebbsfleet, Woking (L), Whitehawk (L), Dover, Braintree, Welling (L), Chelmsford, Welling									
Bramley	Max	21	Goalkeeper	AFC Telford United (L)	13		6	13	
Leicester (Y), Telford (L)									
Branson	Connor	27	Defender	Bradford Park Avenue	42			42	11
Barnlsey (Y), Guiseley, Golden Eagles (US), Pittsburgh, Bradford PA									
Bray	Alexander	23	Midfielder	York City (L)	9	2		11	1
				Weston-s-Mare (L)	9	1		10	3
Swansea (Y), Plymouth (L), Rotherham (L), Rotherham, Forest GR (L), York (L), Weston-s-Mare (L)									
Bray	Rian	20	Defender	Hampton & Richmond Borough	41	1	2	42	2
Millwall (Y), Welling (L), Bishop's S (L), Hendon, Hampton & R									
Breeden	Tony	31	Goalkeeper	Leamington	45			45	
Leamington, Kidderminster, Tamworth, Leamington, Solihull, Leamington									
Brewitt	Tom	22	Defender	AFC Fylde	10	9	15	19	
Liverpool (Yth), Middlesbrough (Yth), AFC Fylde									
Bridges				Eastbourne Borough		1			
Eastbourne B									
Brierley	Theo	21	Midfielder	FC United of Manchester	3	3	5	6	1
Stoke (Y), Glossop, Buxton, FC United									
Briggs	Andrew	18	Midfielder	Eastbourne Borough	1	14	19	15	
Eastbourne B									
Brill	Dean	33	Goalkeeper	Leyton Orient	54			54	
Luton, Gillingham (L), Oldham, Barnet, Luton, Inverness Cal (L), Inverness Cal, Motherwell, Colchester, Leyton Orient									
Brindley	Richard	26	Defender	Bromley	35	1		36	2
Norwich (Y), Chelmsford, Chesterfield, Rotherham, Scunthorpe (L), Oxford U (L), Colchester (L), Colchester, Barnet, Bromley									
Brockbank	Harry	20	Defender	Salford City (L)	1	1	3	2	
Bolton (Y), Salford (L)									
Brogan	Stephen	31	Defender	Spennymoor Town	45			45	4
Rotherham (Y), Stalybridge (L), Alfreton, Stalybridge, Guiseley, Forest GR, Southport, Stalybridge, Gainsborough, North Ferriby, Boston U, Spennymoor									
Brooke	Ryan	28	Forward	Curzon Ashton	34	4	1	38	6
Oldham (Y), Barrow (L), Telford (L), Altrincham, Curzon A, Nantwich, Curzon A									
Brooks	Myles		Midfielder	Kidderminster Harriers		1			
Kidderminster (Y), Bromsgrove Sp (L)									
Brophy	James	24	Midfielder	Leyton Orient	29	16	1	45	4
Swindon, Leyton Orient (L)Leyton Orient									
Brotherton	Sam	22	Defender	Blyth Spartans	1		1	1	
Wanderers (NZ), Sunderland (Y), Blyth S, North Carolina (US)									
Brough	Morgan		Forward	Alfreton Town		2	1	2	
Alfreton (Y)									
Brown	Andre	23	Forward	AFC Telford United	13	26	11	39	7
Crewe (Y), Worcester (L), Rushall (L), Kidderminster, Telford									
Brown	Connor	26	Defender	Barrow	27	5	8	32	
Sheffield U, Oldham, Carlisle (L), Guiseley, York, Barrow									
Brown	Matt	29	Defender	FC Halifax Town	47		1	47	3
Manchester C, Chesterfield, Southport (L), Chester (L), Chester, Halifax									
Brown	Nathan	20	Forward	Chester		2	4	2	
Man City, Chester									
Brown	Sebastian	29	Goalkeeper	Sutton United			2		
AFC Wimbledon, Woking (L), Bromley, Whitehawk (L), Hampton & R, Whitehawk, Hampton & R, Sutton U									

Key: X - Started; SX - Sub on; S - Non-playing Sub; Ap - Total Appearances; Gls - Total goals.

2018-19 NATIONAL. NORTH & SOUTH PLAYERS — APPEARANCES

SURNAME	FIRSTNAME	AGE	POSITION	CLUB	X	SX	S	Ap	Gls
Brown	Stefan	29	Forward	Wealdstone	11	7	2	18	2
Totton, Basingstoke, Hungerford, Maidenhead, Hungerford, Wealdstone									
Brown	Wayne	30	Midfielder	Sutton United	12	6	7	18	1
Fulham (Y), Brentford (L), TPS (Fin) (L), Bristol R (L), Bristol R, TPS, SLK Seinajoki, Newcastle (Aus), Sutton U									
Brundle	Mitch	24	Midfielder	Dover Athletic	50			50	8
Yeovil, Bristol C, Cheltenham, Braintree, Hemel H (L), Gateshead, Dover									
Brunt	Ryan	26	Forward	Bath City	25	13	2	38	10
Stoke (Y), Nantwich (L), Luton (L), Tranmere (L), Leyton O (L), Bristol R (L), Bristol R, York (L), Stevenage (L), Plymouth (L), Plymouth, Exeter, Bath									
Bubb	Bradley	31	Forward	Wealdstone	13	3	4	16	8
Farnborough, Aldershot, Woking (L), Havant & W, Oxford C, Ebbsfleet, Wealdstone									
Buddle	Nathan	25	Defender	Blyth Spartans	41	3	2	44	3
Hartlepool (Y), Blyth S, Carlisle, Gateshead, Blyth S									
Budtz	Jan	40	Goalkeeper	Ashton United	1			1	
BK Avarta (Den), Nordsjaelland, Doncaster, Wolves (L), Hartlepool, Eastwood, Stalybridge, Buxton, Gainsborough, Worksop, Gainsborough, Buxton, Ashton U									
Bugiel	Omar	24	Forward	Bromley	22	12	2	34	6
Forest Green Rovers, Bromley (L), Bromley									
Burbidge	Fred		Goalkeeper	Boreham Wood	1		23	1	
Boreham W									
Burgess	Luke	20	Midfielder	Barrow (L)	16	11	7	27	2
Wigan (Y), Chorley (L), Barrow (L)									
Burgess	Scott	22	Midfielder	Wrexham (L)		2	1	2	
				York City (L)	15	1		16	1
Bury (Y), Stalybridge (L), Bergsoy IL (Nor) (L), Macclesfield (L), Wrexham (L), York (L)									
Burke	Luke	21	Defender	AFC Fylde	28	2	7	30	
Wigan Athletic, Barrow, AFC Fylde (L), AFC Fylde									
Burn	Aaron	18	Goalkeeper	Darlington	1	1	8	2	
Darlington									
Burn	Jonathan	23	Defender	Darlington	12	2	11	14	
Middlesbrough (Y), Oldham (L), Kilmarnock (L), Bristol R, York (L), Darlington									
Burns	Charlie	24	Goalkeeper	Hampton & Richmond Borough	1		9	1	
MK Dons, Hayes & Y (L), Galway U, Hampton & R									
Burns	Danny	21	Defender	Nuneaton Borough	11			11	
Cambridge U (Y), Cambridge C (L), Lowestoft (L), Bishop's S (L), Lowestoft (L), Buxton, Gateshead, Blyth (L), Nuneaton									
Burns	Lee	36	Defender	East Thurrock United	31	1	1	32	
Dartford, East Thurrock									
Burrell	Warren	29	Midfielder	Harrogate Town	51		1	51	4
Mansfield (Y), Harrogate, Sheffield FC, Leek, Buxton, Harrogate									
Burrow	Jordan	26	Forward	York City	42	4	1	46	19
Chesterfield, Morecambe, Stevenage, Lincoln, Halifax, Gateshead, York									
Bursik	Josef	18	Goalkeeper	AFC Telford United (L)	16	1		17	
AFC Wimbledon (Y), Stoke, Hednesford (L), Telford (L)									
Burton	Callum	22	Goalkeeper	Chesterfield (L)	24		2	24	
Shrewsbury (Y), Market D (L), Workington (L), Nuneaton (L), Southport (L), Nuneaton (L), AFC Telford (L), Hull, Salford (L), Chesterfield (L)									
Burton	George		Goalkeeper	Torquay United			36		
Torquay									
Burton	Scott			Chester	17	1	2	18	
Salford, Chester									
Buse	Will		Goalkeeper	Truro City	3			3	
Truro									
Bush	Chris	26	Defender	Ebbsfleet United	43	4	1	47	6
Brentford, Wimbledon (L), Wimbledon, Gateshead, Hereford, Welling, Lincoln, Chelmsford, Ebbsfleet									
Butler	Jack	18	Midfielder	Blyth Spartans		3	7	3	
Blyth Spartans									
Butler	James	19	Defender	Hartlepool United (L)		6			
Stoke (Y), Hartlepool (L)									
Butler	Jamie	27	Goalkeeper	Sutton United	31		7	31	
Met Police, Concord R, Hemel H, Braintree (L), Sutton U									
Butterfield	Milan	21	Midfielder	Kidderminster Harriers	10	6	2	16	1
Walsall (Y), Leamington (L), Kidderminster									
Byrne	Alex	22	Midfielder	Weston-super-Mare	39	3	4	42	1
Exeter (Y), Weston (L), Truro (L), Weston									
Byrne	Neill	26	Defender	AFC Fylde	55		1	55	2
Nottingham Forest, Rochdale, Barrow (L), Southport (L), Telford, Macclesfield, Gateshead, AFC Fylde									

2018-19 NATIONAL. NORTH & SOUTH PLAYERS

SURNAME	FIRSTNAME	AGE	POSITION	CLUB PLAYED FOR	X	SX	S	Ap	Gls
Byrne	Shane	26	Midfielder	Brackley Town	50			50	10
Leicester (Y), Bury (L), Bury, Bray W, Corby, Nuneaton, Brackley									
Ca caval	Adrian	31	Defender	Chelmsford City	24			24	1
Academia (Mol), Kaisar (L) (Kaz), Veris (Mol), Costuleni, AGMK (Uzb), Neftchi, Dinamo-Auto (Mol), Luch Vlad (Rus), Naxxar Lions (Malta), Vikingur (F Isle), Chelmsford									
Cadogan	Kieron	28	Midfielder	Sutton United	11	11	3	22	3
				Billericay Town	6	5	1	11	2
				Woking (L)	8			8	1
Crystal Palace, Burton (L), Rotherham (L), Aldershot (L), Barnet (L), Sutton U, Billericay, Woking (L)									
Calveley	Mike	19	Midfielder	Nuneaton Borough (L)	38	1		39	4
Port Vale (Y), Nuneaton (L)									
Calvert	Jack			Dartford			1		
Dartford (Y)									
Cameron	Kyle	22	Defender	Torquay United	45			45	1
Newcastle (Y), York (L), Newport Co (L), Queen OTS (L), Torquay									
Campbell	Kristian		Defender	Eastbourne Borough	43			43	
Merstham, Bromley, Bognor R (Lx2), Eastbourne B									
Can	Gokhan	22	Midfielder	East Thurrock United	1	1	1	2	
Ankaragucu U21 (Tur), East Thurrock									
Cane	Jacob	25	Midfielder	Weston-super-Mare	40	3	4	43	5
Exeter (Y), Weston									
Cantrill	George		Defender	Guiseley (L)	17		1	17	1
Sheff Utd (Y), Guiseley (L)									
Capel	Elliott	19	Midfielder	Maidstone United		1			
Maidstone									
Cardle	Joe	32	Midfielder	AFC Fylde	15	3	2	18	2
Burnley, Port Vale, Clyde (L), Airdrie, Dunfermline, Raith, Ross Co, Dunfermline, AFC Fylde									
Carew	Ashley	33	Midfielder	Dulwich Hamlet	23	2	3	25	5
Gillingham (Y), Worthing (L), Beckenham, Fisher, Barnet, Eastleigh (L), Bromley, Ebbsfleet, Cambridge U, Dover, Whitehawk (L), Dulwich H									
Carline	George	26	Midfielder	Solihull Moors	14	23	19	37	
Solihull M									
Carnell	David	34	Goalkeeper	Ashton United	1			1	
				FC United of Manchester	6			6	
Curzon A, Stalybridge, Hyde, Curzon A, FC United, Ashton U, FC United									
Caro	Steven		Goalkeeper	Oxford City	3	1	27	4	
Oxford C									
Carrington	Mark	32	Defender	Wrexham	32	3	6	35	
Crewe, MK Dons, Hamilton, Bury, Wrexham									
Carroll-Burgess	Nathan		Midfielder	Barrow	1		1	1	
Barrow (Y)									
Carter	Ashley	23	Defender	Nuneaton Borough	16			16	
Wolves (Y), Chesterfield (L), Tamworth (L), Kidderminster, Alvechurch, Nuneaton									
Carter	Charlie	22	Midfielder	Chesterfield	15	5		20	4
Woking (Y), Chipstead (L), Chesterfield									
Carter	Darren	35	Midfielder	Solihull Moors	51	1	2	52	3
Birmingham, Sunderland (L), West Brom, Preston, Millwall (L), Cheltenham, Northampton, Forest Green, Solihull M									
Carter	Michael		Defender	Havant & Waterlooville	9	6	3	15	
Hamble Club, FC Sholing, Gosport, Havant & W									
Carter	Tom		Forward	Oxford City	5	3	16	8	
Oxford C									
Carver	Marcus	25	Forward	Chorley	45	1		46	15
Accrington Stanley, Marine, FC Halifax Town, Barrow, AFC Fylde, ChorleyChorley									
Case	Ryan		Defender	Oxford City	7	3	7	10	
Havant & W, Dorchester, Braintree, Basingstoke, Wealdstone, Basingstoke, Poole, Eastbourne B, Bath, Gosport B, Oxford C									
Casey	Josh	27	Defender	Woking	51			51	1
Salisbury, Hampton & R, Woking									
Cass	Jake	25	Forward	Braintree Town	2	5	1	7	
Egham T, Chalfont S.P, Bishop's S, Braintree									
Cassidy	Jake	26	Forward	Hartlepool United	5	3	1	8	2
				Maidstone United (L)	29	1	1	30	4
llandudno J, Airbus, Wolves, Tranmere (Lx3), Notts Co (L), Southend (L), Oldham, Guiseley, Hartlepool, Maidstone (Lx2)									
Caswell	Bradley		Goalkeeper	Leamington			1		
Leamington									

Key: X - Started; SX - Sub on; S - Non-playing Sub; Ap - Total Appearances; Gls - Total goals.

SURNAME	FIRSTNAME	AGE	POSITION	CLUB	X	SX	S	Ap	Gls
					APPEARANCES				
Caton	James	25	Forward	Nuneaton Borough	7			7	1
Blackpool (Y), Accrington (L), Chester (L), Shrewsbury, Southport (L), Mansfield (L), Wrexham (L), Lincoln (L), Southport, Dover, Darlington, Nuneaton									
Catterick	Ryan	20	Goalkeeper	Hartlepool United			15		
Hartlepool									
Cawley	Steve	27	Midfielder	Hemel Hempstead Town	29	5	2	34	9
Bishop's S, Concord R, Hemel H									
Ceesay	Kieran	18	Forward	Guiseley			1		
Man Utd (Y), Guiseley (Y)									
Ceesay	Yusifu	24	Forward	Boston United (L)		1	1	1	
				AFC Telford United (L)	1	3	1		
				Nuneaton Borough (L)	4			4	2
				Altrincham (L)	13	1	2	14	3
Alvechurch, Blackpool, Boston (L), Telford (L), Nuneaton (L), Alvechurch (L), Altrincham (L)									
Cerulli	Alfie		Forward	Braintree Town		4	3	4	2
Braintree (Y)									
Chadwick	Matthew		Forward	Ashton United	22	2		24	9
				Altrincham	3	3	2	6	
Stalybridge, Mossley, Chadderton, Radcliffe B, Ashton U, Salford, Ashton United, Altrincham									
Chalaye	Tom		Defender	Aldershot Town		1		1	
Aldershot (Y)									
Challoner	Matt	25	Defender	Chorley	43			43	2
Blackpool, Northwich Victoria, SouthportChorley									
Chalmers	Aaron	28	Midfielder	Ashton United	36	3	4	39	1
Oldham (Y), Macclesfield (Y), Hibernian, Mossley, Droylsden (L), Stockport S, Southport, Droylsden (L), New Mills (L), Hyde, Northwich, Stalybridge, Ashton U									
Chambers	Ashley	29	Forward	Kidderminster Harriers	43		1	43	14
Leicester (Y), Wycombe (L), Grimsby (L), York (L), York, Cambridge U, Dagenham & R (L), Dagenham & R, Grimsby, Nuneaton (L), Nuneaton, Kidderminster									
Chambers	Karnell	21	Midfielder	Chippenham Town	27	13	7	40	12
Cheltenham, Gloucester, Chippenham									
Chambers	Michael	24	Defender	Dulwich Hamlet	32	1		33	1
Crystal P (Y), Welling (L), Welling, Dulwich H									
Champion	Tom	33	Midfielder	Boreham Wood	48		1	48	1
Dartford, Cambridge U, Barnet, Lincoln (L), Boreham W									
Chandler	Jamie	30	Midfielder	Spennymoor Town	47			47	1
Darlington, Gateshead, Spennymoor									
Chapman	Ellis	18	Midfielder	Chesterfield (L)	13	1	1	14	
Leicester (Y), Lincoln C, Chesterfield (L)									
Charles	Ashley	20	Midfielder	Barnet	3	4	1	7	
Charles	Dion	23	Forward	Southport	45	4	1	49	16
Blackpool, Fylde (L), Fylde, Fleetwood, Halifax (L), Southport									
Charles	Elliott	28	Forward	Braintree Town		2		2	
Barnet (Y), Farnborough (L), Lewes (L), Hemel (L), Kettering, Dover, Concord R, Hendon, Eastbourne, Dover, Eastbourne, Hendon, Ware, Hampton & R, Braintree, Wealdstone									
Charles	Elliott	28	Forward	Wealdstone		5	4	5	3
Cheek	Michael	27	Forward	Ebbsfleet United	26	15	6	41	16
Heybridge S, Stanway R, Chelmsford, Braintree, Dagenham & R, Ebbsfleet									
Cheidu Dixon	Bohan	29	Midfielder	Ashton United	2	1	1	3	
Accrington, Lincoln, Stalybridge, Fylde, Halifax, Stockport, Ashton U, Warrington									
Chesmain	Noah	21	Defender	Hungerford Town (L)	6			6	1
Millwall,Welling (L), Boreham W (L), Colchester, Hitchin (L), Hungerford (L)									
Chettle	Callum	22	Midfielder	Alfreton Town	8	9	10	17	2
				Boston United (L)	1		5	1	
Peterborough, AFC Fylde (L), Alfreton, Boston U (L)									
Chiedozie	Jordan	29	Forward	Chelmsford City	2	6	5	8	
Bournemouth, Dorchester (L), Poole (Lx2), Concord R, Cambridge U, Dartford (L), Braintree (L), Boreham W, Concord R, Margate, Chelmsford									
Chisholm	Tai-Reece	19	Midfielder	Boston United (L)		2	1	2	
Birmingham (Y), Barnsley U23, Boston U (L)									
Church	Anthony	32	Midfielder	Chelmsford City	36	5	3	41	3
Boston U, Grimsby, Alfreton (L), Chelmsford, Bishop's S, Chelmsford									
Clackstone	Josh	22	Midfielder	Alfreton Town	22	8	5	30	
Hull,Notts Co (L), Halifax (L), Alfreton									
Clare	Tom	19	Forward	Boston United	2	5		7	3
Boston U									

2018-19 NATIONAL. NORTH & SOUTH PLAYERS

SURNAME	FIRSTNAME	AGE	POSITION	CLUB PLAYED FOR	APPEARANCES X	SX	S	Ap	Gls
Clark	Ben	36	Defender	Gateshead			1		
Sunderland (Y), Hartlepool, Gateshead									
Clark	James		Forward	Wealdstone	1	3	16	4	
Didcot, Hungerford, Wealdstone									
Clark	Kenny	30	Defender	Ebbsfleet United	11		1	11	1
				Dagenham & Redbridge	22	1	1	23	
Dagenham & R, Thurrock, Chelmsford, Dartford,Ebbsfleet, Dagenham & R									
Clark	Michael	21	Defender	Braintree Town	8	1	5	9	
				Concord Rangers	5			5	
				St Albans	22	1	1	23	2
Leyton Orient, East Thurrock (L), Braintree, Concord R, St Albans									
Clarke	Danny	34	Midfielder	Alfreton Town	13	7	7	20	1
Hull United, Frickley, Hall Road R, Winterton R, North Ferriby, Halifax, Alfreton									
Clarke	Joe	30	Midfielder	Leamington	34	7	2	41	
Redditch, Darlington, Solihull, Wrexham, Kidderminster, Brackley (L), Brackley, Tamworth, Leamington									
Clarke	Nathan	35	Defender	FC Halifax Town	54			54	5
Huddersfield, Colchester (L), Oldham (L), Bury (L), Leyton O, Bradford, Coventry, Grimsby, FC Halifax									
Clarke	Ryan	37	Goalkeeper	Bath City	47			47	
Bristol R, Southend (L), Kidderminster (L), Forest Green (L), Salisbury, Northwich, Oxford U, Northampton, AFC Wimbledon, Eastleigh, Torquay, Bath									
Clay	Craig	27	Midfielder	Leyton Orient	47	1	1	48	1
Chesterfield, Barrow (L), Alfreton (L), York, Halifax, Worksop, Grimsby, Motherwell, Leyton Orient									
Clayton	Paul	34	Forward	Guiseley	6	23	17	29	2
Gainsborough, Alfreton, Harrogate (L), Harrogate, Alfreton, Shaw Lane, Guiseley									
Clayton-Phillips	Nick	19	Forward	Braintree Town (L)	3	3	3		
				Kidderminster Harriers (L)	5	1		6	2
WBA (Y), Braintree (L), Kidderminster (L)									
Clee	Nicky	35	Midfielder	Bradford Park Avenue	34	8		42	1
Hyde U, Altrincham, Guiseley, Harrogate, Altrincham, Bradford PA									
Clerima	Remy	29	Defender	Maidenhead United	44	1	2	45	1
Histon, Braintree, Maidenhead									
Clifford	Billy	26	Midfielder	Boreham Wood			2		
				Hemel Hempstead Town	10	1		11	1
				Billericay Town	10	3	1	13	
				Slough Town (L)	9	2		11	1
Chelsea (Y), Colchester (L), Yeovil (L), Royal Antwerp (L), Walsall, Boreham W, Crawley, Boreham W, Hemel H, Billericay, Slough (L)									
Clifton	Adrian	30	Midfielder	Maidenhead United	33	9	1	42	13
Maidenhead, Havant & W, Maidenhead									
Clifton	James	27	Defender	Alfreton Town	27	3	1	30	3
Brackley, Oxford C, Nuneaton, Boston, Alfreton									
Clohessy	Sean	32	Defender	Concord Rangers	10	3		13	
Gillingham, Salisbury (L), Salisbury, Southend, Kilmarnock, Colchester, Leyton O, Braintree, Leatherhead, Concord R									
Clough	Charlie	28	Defender	Sutton United	25			25	2
Bristol R (Y), Mangotsfield (L), Newport Co (L), Bath (L), Bath (L), Dorchester, Sutton U, Forest GR, Barnet, Sutton U, DPMM FC (Brunei)									
Clunis	Nyren		Midfielder	Dulwich Hamlet	37	4		41	7
Dulwich H (Y)									
Cockerill-Mollett	Callum	20	Defender	AFC Telford United (L)	2			2	
Walsall (Y), Telford (L), Chasetown (L)									
Coker	Andre	21	Forward	Maidstone United	4	5	1	9	
				Dartford (L)	11	16	4	27	2
Crystal Palace, Maidstone (L), Maidstone, Dartford (L)									
Cole	Chinua	25	Defender	Maidenhead United	6	4	3	10	
Staines, Eastleigh, Hampton & R, Torquay, Hampton & R, Harrow B, Maidenhead, Released									
Cole	Jake	33	Goalkeeper	Aldershot Town	22		18	22	
QPR, Hayes (L), Farnborough, Plymouth, Woking, Aldershot									
Cole	Reece	21	Midfielder	Maidenhead United (L)	1	5	2	6	1
Brentford (Y), Newport Co (L), Yeovil (L), Maidenhead (L), Macclesfield (L)									
Coles	Perry		Forward	Slough Town	2	5	2	7	1
Slough									
Collier	Nathan	33	Midfielder	Woking	44	2	5	46	
Hampton & R, Dartford, Eastbourne B, Hampton & R, Dartford, Woking									
Collins	Dominic	28	Defender	Darlington	5	1		6	
PNE (Y), Crawley (L), Northwich V (L), Northwich V, Chester, Hereford, Southport, AFC Fylde, Darlington									
Collins	Jamie	34	Midfielder	Sutton United	34			34	7
Watford, Newport Co, Aldershot, Forest Green, Eastleigh, Sutton U									

Key: X - Started; SX - Sub on; S - Non-playing Sub; Ap - Total Appearances; Gls - Total goals.

SURNAME	FIRSTNAME	AGE	POSITION	CLUB	X	SX	S	Ap	Gls
Collins	Michael	33	Midfielder	Alfreton Town	3			3	
Huddersfield, Scunthorpe, Wimbledon (L), Oxford U, York, Leyton Orient, Halifax, Bradford (Coach/Manager), Alfreton									
Collins	Roddy	24	Defender	Hemel Hempstead Town	1			1	
Monaghan U, St Pat's, Athlone (L), Brackley, Drogheda, Waterford, Hemel H, Hayes & Y									
Comley	James	28	Midfielder	Maidenhead United	41			41	
Crystal Palace, St Albans, Maidenhead									
Compton	Jack	30	Midfielder	Chippenham Town	20	6	10	26	
Havant & W, Weston-s-Mare, Falkirk, Bradford (L), St Johnstone (L), Portsmouth, Colchester, Hartlepool, Yeovil, Newport Co, Bath, Chippenham									
Confry	Danny		Goalkeeper	Concord Rangers		11			
Concord R									
Connoly	Kyle		Defender	Hemel Hempstead Town	36	2	1	38	2
Hemel H									
Connors	Jack	24	Defender	Dover Athletic	9	1	3	10	
Fulham, Dagenham & R, Hendon (L), Boreham W (L), Ebbsfleet, Dover, Hampton & R (Lx2)									
Connors	Jack	24	Defender	Hampton & Richmond Borough (L)	25	1	1	26	2
Constable	James	34	Forward	Eastleigh	2	13	2	15	
Chippenham, Walsall, Kidderminster (L), Kidderminster, Shrewsbury, Oxford U (L), Oxford U, Eastleigh, Poole (L)									
Cook	Anthony	29	Midfielder	Dulwich Hamlet	29	9	6	38	3
Dagenham & R, Chelmsford, Bromley, Ebbsfleet, Woking (L), Dulwich H									
Cook	Jack	25	Defender	Woking	45	1	3	46	4
Worthing, Hampton & R, Woking									
Coombes	Adam	27	Midfielder	Billericay Town	25	8	4	33	13
				Welling United (L)	2		1	2	2
Chelsea, Yeovil (L), Notts Co, Bromley, Welling, Sutton U, Hampton & R (L), Welling, Billericay, Welling (L)									
Cooney	Tommy		Defender	Hungerford Town	1		4	1	
Boston U, Cefn Druids, Margate, Bognor R, Hungerford, Leatherhead									
Cooper	Charlie	22	Midfielder	Boreham Wood (L)	5		4	5	
Birmingham (Y), Forest GR (L), York (L), Forest GR (L), Forest GR, Newport Co (L), Boreham W (L)									
Copp	Jordan	25	Midfielder	Truro City	4	7	6	11	
Plymouth (Y), Truro, Weymouth, Truro									
Corbett	Zac	23	Midfielder	Southport			1		
Rhyl, FC United, Southport									
Corcoran	Luis		Forward	Nuneaton Borough		2			
Nuneaton (Y)									
Corcoran	Michael	31	Defender	Hampton & Richmond Borough	18		9	18	
Rushden & D, Dover, Brackley, Ebbsfleet, Wealdstone, Chelmsford, Hendon, Hampton & R									
Cordner	Tyler	20	Defender	Havant & Waterlooville (L)	36			36	4
Bournemouth (Y), Havant & W (L)									
Correia	Raul	26	Forward	Barrow		5	4	5	1
Chorley, Blackpool, Guiseley (L), York (L), Barrow									
Cosgrave	Aaron	19	Forward	Havant & Waterlooville	5	11	7	16	1
				Chelmsford City	1	12	3	13	
West Ham (Y), Colchester (Y), Coggeshall, Havant & W, Chelmsford									
Cotter	Kevan	20	Midfielder	Hemel Hempstead Town	32		3	32	
Luton, Oxford C (L), Hemel H									
Cotton	Josh		Goalkeeper	Eastleigh			1		
Eastleigh (Y)									
Cotton	Nico	22	Midfielder	Eastbourne Borough	5		5	1	
Southend, Eastbourne B									
Cottrell	Jake	31	Midfielder	Chorley	18	16	10	34	
FC United, Chorley									
Cottrell	James		Midfielder	Chester			1		
Stoke (Y), Chester (Y)									
Coulson	Josh	30	Defender	Leyton Orient	44	3		47	9
Cambridge U, Leyton Orient									
Coulson	Luke	25	Midfielder	Ebbsfleet United	10	8	7	18	2
				Bromley	25			25	5
Cardiff, Oxford C, Eastleigh, Barnet, Ebbsfleet, Bromley									
Coulthirst	Shaq	24	Forward	Barnet	34	8	4	42	20
Tottneham (Yth), Leyton O (L), Torquay (L), Southend (L), York (L), Wigan (L), Peterborough, Mansfield (L), Barnet									
Courtnage	James	35	Goalkeeper	Boreham Wood			1		
Staines, Boreham W									
Cousins	Mark	32	Goalkeeper	Barnet	53		4	53	
Fulham, Colchester U, Dagenham & R, Barnet									

2018-19 NATIONAL. NORTH & SOUTH PLAYERS

SURNAME	FIRSTNAME	AGE	POSITION	CLUB PLAYED FOR	X	SX	S	Ap	Gls
Coveney	Joe	20	Defender	Billericay Town (L)	1		1	1	
Man City (Y), Nottm Forest, Billericay (L)									
Cowan	Dan	27	Defender	Stockport County	28	10	9	38	
Macclesfield, Chorley (L), Stockport									
Cowans	Henry	23	Midfielder	AFC Telford United	27	7	5	34	4
Aston Villa (Y), Stevenage (L), Telford									
Cox	Dean	31	Midfielder	Eastbourne Borough	34	3		37	10
Brighton, Leyton O, Crawley, Eastbourne B									
Cox	Sam	28	Midfielder	Wealdstone			1		
				Hampton & Richmond Borough (L)	16			16	
Cheltenham, Histon (L), Torquay (L), Barnet, Boreham W (L), Hayes & Y, Boreham W, Wealdstone, Hampton & R (L)									
Coyle	Callum	23	Midfielder	Solihull Moors			3		
				Nuneaton Borough (L)	2		2		
Solihull M, Nuneaton (L)									
Cracknell	Joe	25	Goalkeeper	Harrogate Town	1		51	1	
Hull (Y), Scarborough Ath (L), Bradford, Bradford PA (L), Harrogate									
Crankshaw	Oliver	20	Midfielder	Curzon Ashton	27	8	3	35	9
Curzon A									
Craske	Billy	19	Forward	Bromley		1	2	1	
Plymouth (Y), Bromley									
Crawford	Harry	27	Forward	Hampton & Richmond Borough	2	6	1	8	
Southend, Dartford, Barnet, Dartford (L), Dartford, Boreham W, St Albans, Dover, Welling, Hampton & R									
Crawford	Jamal	21	Midfielder	FC United of Manchester	6	12	3	18	
				Chester	1	2	1	3	
Llandudno, FC United, Chester									
Crawford	Tom	20	Midfielder	AFC Fylde (L)	10	6	8	16	2
Stoke City, Chester, Notts Co, AFC Fylde (L)									
Creese	Daniel		Forward	Boreham Wood			1		
Boreham W (Y)									
Crellin	Billy	18	Goalkeeper	FC United of Manchester (L)	7			7	
Fleetwood (Y), FC United (L)									
Cresswell	Ryan	31	Defender	Boston United	4			4	1
Sheffield U, Halifax (L), Rotherham (L), Morecambe (L), Macclesfield (L), Bury, Rotherham, Southend, Fleetwood, Northampton, Eastleigh, Boston U									
Crichlow-Noble	Romoney	20	Defender	Bradford Park Avenue	3	4	7	7	
Bradford PA									
Crilly	Stuart		Midfielder	Chester			1		
Oldham (Y), Chester (Y)									
Croasdale	Ryan	24	Midfielder	AFC Fylde	54		1	54	5
PNE, Tamworth (L), Sheffield Wed, Kidderminster, AFC Fylde									
Crocombe	Max	25	Goalkeeper	Salford City	4		51	4	
MK Dons (Y), Luton (Y), Buckingham T, Oxford U (Y), Nuneaton (L), Barnet (L), Southport (L), Carlisle, Salford									
Crook	Billy	28	Midfielder	Braintree Town	8	6	1	14	1
				Dartford	5	3	1	8	
Peterborough (Y), Weymouth (L), Histon (L), Tooting & M, Carshalton, Met Police, Enfield T, Braintree, Dartford									
Crowley	Oliver	23	Defender	Southport	1			1	
				Ashton United	13			13	
Rossendale, Stalybridge, FC United, Southport, Ashton U									
Crowther	Ryan	30	Forward	Ashton United		5	5	5	
Stockport (Y),, Liverpool, Stalybridge, Ashton U, Hyde, Fleetwood, Hyde (L), Halifax, Altrincham, Ashton U									
Cue	Alfie	20	Midfielder	Dartford	1	2	2	3	
Dartford, Leatherhead (L)									
Cullinane-Liburd	Jordan	24	Defender	Hereford FC	43	1	2	44	1
Redditch, Solihull M, Rushall, Hereford									
Cummings	Declyn		Midfielder	Kidderminster Harriers		1			
Kidderminster (Y)									
Cummings	Joe	20	Defender	Guiseley (L)	6		4	6	
Charlton (Y), Guiseley (L)									
Cummins	Niall	32	Forward	Curzon Ashton	7	9	3	16	1
Curzon A, Marine (L)									
Cundy	Robbie	23	Defender	Bath City	48			48	6
Oxford U, Gloucester (L), Oxford C (L), Southport (L), Gloucester, Bath									
Cunningham	Aaron	21	Defender	Blyth Spartans (L)	15	1	7	16	2
				Hartlepool United	5	1		6	
Hartlepool (Y), Blyth S (L)									

Key: X - Started; SX - Sub on; S - Non-playing Sub; Ap - Total Appearances; Gls - Total goals.

SURNAME	FIRSTNAME	AGE	POSITION	CLUB	X	SX	S	Ap	Gls
					APPEARANCES				
Cunnington	Adam	31	Forward	Billericay Town	4	13	15	17	3
Solihull, Kettering, Dag & Red (L), Dag & Red, Alfreton (L), Tamworth, Cambridge U, Bristol R (L), Ebbsfleet, Woking (L), Bromley, Billericay									
Curran	Taylor	18	Defender	Braintree Town (L)	1	1	4	2	
Southend, Braintree (L), Swindon									
Curry	Adam	22	Defender	Alfreton Town (L)	14			14	
South Shields, Hull, Boston (L), Spennymoor (L), Alfreton (L)									
Curtis	James	37	Defender	Spennymoor Town	47			47	2
Gateshead, Spennymoor									
Czubik	Szymon	19	Forward	Stockport County		1			
Stockport (Y)									
Da Costa	Khale	25	Midfielder	St Albans City	24	17	5	41	4
Harlow, Concord R, St Albans									
Dale	Charlie		Midfielder	Maidstone United	1	3	1		
Maidstone (Y)									
Dale	Owen	20	Forward	Altrincham (L)	13	3		16	3
Crewe (Y), Witton (L)Altrincham (L)									
Dale	Robert	34	Forward	Blyth Spartans	40	4		44	10
West Alloment, Blyth S, Whitley B, Blyth S									
Daly	Liam	31	Defender	Solihull Moors	50		2	50	4
Evesham, Corby, Redditch, Solihull M, Halesowen, Leamington, Barwell, Leamington, Solihull M, Kidderminster, Solihull M									
Danaher	George	19	Forward	Curzon Ashton		1	4	1	
Curzon A									
Daniel	Kadell	25	Midfielder	Dover Athletic	6	15	10	21	
Crystal Palace, Charlton, Hayes & Y (L), Torquay (L), Woking, Welling, Dover									
Daniels	Billy	24	Forward	Kidderminster Harriers	26	2		28	1
Coventry (Y), Cheltenham (L), Notts Co, Nuneaton, Kidderminster									
Daniels	Brendon	25	Forward	Altrincham (L)	4	3		7	
				AFC Telford United	15	6	3	21	5
Crewe (Y), Leicester, Blackburn, Chester, Tamworth, Harrogate, AFC Fylde, Alfreton, Port Vale, Altrincham (L), Telford (L), Telford									
Darbyshire	Dan	21	Forward	Dartford	2	3	2	5	
Dartford									
Davey	Alex	24	Defender	Dagenham & Redbridge	11		6	11	
Chelsea, Scunthorpe (L), Peterborough (L), Stabæk (Norway) (L), Crawley (L), Cheltenham, Torquay (L), Boreham W, Dagenham & R									
Davidson	Correy	25	Midfielder	Concord Rangers	1			1	
Bohemians, Carrick, Ards, AFC Sudbury, Walthamstow, Bishop's S, Concord R									
Davies	Andrew	34	Defender	Hartlepool United	14			14	2
Middlesbrough (Y), QPR (L), Derby (L), Southampton, Stoke, PNE (L), Sheffield U (L), Walsall (L), Middlesbrough (L), Crystal P (L), Bradford (L), Bradford, Ross Co, Hartlepool, Dundee									
Davies	Aron	21	Defender	Maidstone United (L)	16			16	
Bristol C (Y), Fulham (Y), Maidstone (L)									
Davies	Ben	38	Defender	Boston United	36	2		38	8
Walsall (Y), Kidderminster, Chester, Shrewsbury, Notts Co, Derby, Sheff Utd (L), Sheff Utd, Portsmouth, Grimsby, Boston U									
Davies	Leon	19	Defender	Bath City (L)	3		1	3	
Cambridge U (Y), Bath (L)									
Davies	Liam	22	Midfielder	Southport	1	5	10	6	
Tranmere, Chester, Southport, Marine (L)									
Davies	Rhys	18	Defender	Nuneaton Borough (L)	6	2	2	8	1
				Chippenham Town (L)	12	3	4	15	
Shrewsbury (Y), Nuneaton (L), Chippenham (L)									
Davies	Rob	32	Midfielder	Billericay Town			1		
Wrexham (Y), WBA (Y), Kidderminster (L), Barakaldo CF (Sp), Hednesford, Oxford U, Worcester, Billericay, Concord R (L)									
Davies	Scott	31	Midfielder	Slough Town	23	9	4	32	
Reading (Y), Wycombe (L), Yeovil (L), Wycombe (L), Bristol R (L), Crawley, Aldershot (L), Oxford U, Wealdstone, Oxford C, Chelmsford, Slough									
Davis	Joe	25	Defender	York City	9		2	9	
Port Vale (Y), Luton (L), Leicester, Fleetwood (L), Fleetwood, Port Vale, York									
Davis	Kenny	31	Midfielder	Sutton United	29	6	3	35	3
Grays, Braintree, Boreham W, Sutton U									
Davis	Liam	32	Defender	Torquay United	48			48	1
Coventry, Peterborough (L), Northampton, Oxford U, Yeovil, Cleethorpes T, Cheltneham, Torquay									
Dawes	Lloyd	24	Defender	Eastbourne Borough	21	11	3	32	2
Whitehawk, Worthing, Eastbourne B									
Dawson	Adam	26	Forward	AFC Telford United	2	19	8	21	1
Bury (Y), Wigan, Accrington (L), FC United, Barrow, Leicester, Notts Co (L), Nuneaton (L), Bristol R (L), Kidderminster, Tranmere (L), Nuneaton, Eastleigh, Tranmere, Darlington (L), Southport, Telford, Macclesfield									

2018-19 NATIONAL. NORTH & SOUTH PLAYERS

SURNAME	FIRSTNAME	AGE	POSITION	CLUB PLAYED FOR	X	SX	S	Ap	Gls
					APPEARANCES				
Dawson	Christopher	24	Midfielder	Bradford Park Avenue	9	2	9	11	
Leeds (Y), Rotherham, Viking (L), Scarborough, Bradford PA									
Dawson	Lucas	25	Midfielder	Chester	5	3	1	8	
Stoke, Carlisle, Nuneaton, AFC Telford, Chester									
Dawson	Tom		Forward	Barrow			1		
Barrow (Y)									
Day	Thomas	21	Defender	Hemel Hempstead Town	1	1	1		
				Eastbourne Borough	2	1	6	3	
Barnet, Hemel H (L), Hemel H, Eastbourne B									
Dayton	James	30	Midfielder	Leyton Orient	21	9	2	30	2
Crystal Palace, Yeovil (L), Crawley (L), Kilmarnock, Oldham, St Mirren (L), Swindon, Cheltenham, Leyton Orient									
De Havilland	Will	24	Defender	Maidstone United	49	2	2	51	5
Millwall, Sheffield W, Wycombe, Aldershot (L), Maidstone (L)Maidstone									
De Silva	Kyle	25	Forward	Bromley		4	5	4	
Crystal P (Y), Barnet (L), Notts Co, FC Eindhoven, Bromley									
Deacon	Roarie	27	Midfielder	Sutton United	12	4		16	1
Arsenal (Y), Sunderland, Stevenage, Crawley, Sutton U, Dundee, Sutton U									
Deakin	Kevin (Danny)	25	Forward	Curzon Ashton		1	1	1	
Sheff Wed (Y), Sheff Utd (Y), Detroit City, Orlando City, Detroit City, Curzon A, Buxton (DR)									
Deakin	Reece	22	Forward	Curzon Ashton	3	9	3	12	
Airbus UK, Morecambe, Greenwich, Curzon A									
Deaman	Jack	26	Defender	Gloucester City	13	2	5	15	
Wrexham, Birmingham, Cheltenham (L), Eastbourne B, Cheltenham, Telford (L), Basingstoke, Gloucester, Salford (L), Hereford, Gloucester									
Dean	Gareth	29	Defender	Brackley Town	50			50	4
Nuneaton, Solihull, Brackley									
Dean	Tom	18	Midfielder	Hemel Hempstead Town		1			
Hemel H									
Debayo	Josh	22	Defender	Dover Athletic (L)	19	1	4	20	
Chelsea (Y), Southampton (Y), Leicester, Cheltenham, Dover (L)									
Debrah	Jesse		Defender	Billericay Town (L)	1	1		2	
Millwall (Y), Billericay (L)									
Deen-Conteh	Aziz	26	Defender	Dulwich Hamlet			1		
Chelsea, FC Ergotelis, Port Vale, Boston (L), Zaria Balti, FC Zugdidi, Dover, Dulwich H									
Deeney	Ellis	27	Defender	AFC Telford United	44	1		45	4
Aston Villa (Y), Kettering, Worcester, Tamworth, Telford									
Deering	Sam	28	Midfielder	Billericay Town	32	4	3	36	5
Newport, Oxford U, Barnet (L), Whitehawk, Ebbsfleet, Billericay									
Della-Verde	Lyle	24	Midfielder	Braintree Town	18	12	2	30	4
Southend (Y), Fulham (Y), Bristol R (L), Fleetwood, Crawley, Welling, Concord R, Dartford, Braintree									
Dempsey	Matt	29	Defender	FC United of Manchester	1		1		
Bradford PA, Shaw Lane A, Hyde, Scarborough A, Ossett A, FC United									
Dennet	Oliver	20	Forward	Eastleigh	4	13	23	17	1
Eastleigh (Y), Bashley (L)									
Densmore	Shaun	30	Defender	Altrincham	18	6	14	24	2
Everton (Y), Altrincham									
Denton	Tom	29	Forward	Alfreton	9			9	6
				Chesterfield	25	15		40	14
Wakefield, Huddersfield, Woking (L), Cheltenham (L), Wakefield (L), Alfreton, North Ferriby, Halifax, Alfreton, Chesterfield									
Derry	Tom	24	Forward	East Thurrock United	18	10	1	28	4
Gillingham (Y), Chelmsford (L), Eastbourne B (L), Eastbourne B, Aldershot, Hayes & Y, East Thurrock									
Devericks	Nicky	31	Midfielder	Wrexham	4	11	10	15	1
Gretna, Barnet, Alfreton, Dover, Hartlepool, Dover (L), Wrexham									
Devitt	Tom	22	Defender	Gateshead	14	7	20	21	
Lionsbridge (US), Gateshead									
Dewhurst	Marcus	18	Goalkeeper	Guiseley (L)	23			23	
Sheff Utd (Y), Guiseley (L)									
Diallo	Ibrahima	26	Defender	East Thurrock United	19			19	
Billericay, Burgess H, East Thurrock									
Diallo	Nabi	28	Forward	Weston-super-Mare	34	3	1	37	1
Weston, Aldershot, Bath, Dover, Bath, Weston									
Diamond	Jack	19	Forward	Spennymoor Town (L)	7	1		8	
Sunderland (Y), Spennymoor (L)									

Key: X - Started; SX - Sub on; S - Non-playing Sub; Ap - Total Appearances; Gls - Total goals.

SURNAME	FIRSTNAME	AGE	POSITION	CLUB	X	SX	S	Ap	Gls
					APPEARANCES				
Diarra	Moussa	29	Defender	Dover Athletic	11	9	14	20	
				Woking (L)	12	1		13	2
St Albans, Hemel H, Hampton & R (L), Hampton & R, Barrow, Dover, Woking (L)									
Diau	Brandan		Forward	Truro City	2	2	1	4	
Burgess H, Truro									
Dibble	Christian	25	Goalkeeper	Wrexham	4		50	4	
Bury, Barnsley, Nuneaton (L), Chelmsford (L), Boston Utd, Nuneaton, Chorley (L), Wrexham									
Dickin	Josh	18	Defender	Curzon Ashton			2		
Curzon A									
Dickinson	Liam	33	Forward	FC United of Manchester	4	3	2	7	1
Trafford, Stockport S, Stockport, Derby, Huddersfield (L), Blackpool (L), Leeds (L), Brighton, Peterborough (L), Barnsley, Walsall (L), Rochdale (L), Southend, Stockport, Stalybridge, Guiseley, Bradford PA (L), Bradford PA, Stalybridge, FC United, Droylsden									
Dickinson	Steve	46	Goalkeeper	Bradford Park Avenue		5			
Southport, Bradford PA, Southport, Kendal T (L), Ossett T, Guiseley, Bradford PA									
Dickson	Christopher	34	Forward	Hampton & Richmond Borough	36	5	1	41	19
Charlton (Y), Bristol R (L), Gillingham (L), Nea Salamis (Cyp), AEL, Shanghai SIPG, Dag & Red, Paphos (Cyp), Enosis, Ermis, Sutton U, Chelmsford, Hampton & R									
Dickson	Ryan	32	Midfielder	Torquay United	14	13	6	27	
Brentford (Y), Southampton, Yeovil (L), Leyton O (L), Bradford (L), Colchester, Crawley, Yeovil, Torquay									
Diedhiou	Dave	30	Defender	St Albans City	30	5	3	35	4
Hendon, St Albans									
Dielna	Joel	28	Forward	Hereford FC		2	6	2	
				Oxford City (L)	7	1		8	
Vannes (Fra), Blackpool, CD Gerena (Spa), Solihull M, Telford, Nuneaton, Hereford, Oxford C (L)									
Dieseruvwe	Emmanuel	25	Forward	Salford City	16	11	3	27	7
				Chester (L)	4	3		7	
Sheffield W (Y), Hyde (L), Fleetwood (L), Chesterfield (L), Chesterfield, Mansfield (L), Kidderminster, Boston U (L), Salford, Chester (L)									
Digie	Kennedy	22	Forward	Kidderminster Harriers	5		14	5	
				York City (L)	7		2	7	
				Guiseley	7		7	7	
Kidderminster, Hednesford (L), Worcester (L), Nuneaton (L), York (L), Guiseley									
Dimaio	Connor	23	Midfielder	Stockport County	5	16	2	21	3
				Ashton United (L)	11	1		12	
Sheff Utd (Y), Chesterfield, Stockport, Ashton U (L)									
Dinanga	Marcus	21	Forward	Hartlepool United (L)	5	14	8	19	
				AFC Telford United	6	8	3	14	2
Burton (Y), Mickleover (L), Matlock (L), Telford (L), Hartlepool (L), Telford									
Dinsley	Calvin	28	Midfielder	Hereford FC	10	8	3	18	1
Redditch, Kidderminster, Gloucester, Hereford									
Dixon	Joel	25	Goalkeeper	Barrow	28		4	28	
Sunderland, Workington (L), Hartlepool (L), Boston (L), Gateshead (L), Barrow									
Dobie	Joshua	21	Defender	Southport		1		1	
Southport									
Dobson	James	27	Midfielder	Slough Town	25	2	4	27	11
				Sutton United	13	5		18	2
Oxford U (Y), North Leigh, Slough, Sutton U									
Dobson	Reece		Forward	East Thurrock United	5	4		9	
Needham, East Thurrock									
Dodds	Louis	32	Forward	Chesterfield		1		1	
Port Vale, Shrewsbury, Chesterfield, Port Vale (L),									
Doe	Scott	30	Defender	Billericay Town	19		1	19	1
				Dover Athletic	16	3	1	19	2
Weymouth, Dagenham & Redbridge, Boreham Wood, Dagenham & Redbridge, Whitehawk (L), Boreham W, Billericay, Dover									
Dolan	Callum	18	Midfielder	Altrincham	1	2	6	3	
Man Utd (Y), Blackburn (Y), Stockport T, Altrincham									
Donaldson	Ryan	28	Midfielder	Hartlepool United	48		1	48	2
Newcastle, Hartlepool (L), Tranmere (L), Gateshead, Cambridge U, Plymouth, Hartlepool									
Donnellan	Leo	20	Midfielder	Maidstone United	3	4	3		
QPR (Y), Dagenham & R, Worcester, Maidstone									
Donnellan	Shaun	22	Defender	Maidstone United	14		1	14	
WBA (Y), Worcester (L), Stevenage (L), Dagenham & R (L), Walsall (L), Yeovil, Maidstone									
Donohue	Michael	21	Forward	FC United of Manchester	25	9		34	1
Everton (Y), Barrow (L), Stoke (L), Fleetwood, Tamworth (L), FC United									

2018-19 NATIONAL. NORTH & SOUTH PLAYERS — APPEARANCES

SURNAME	FIRSTNAME	AGE	POSITION	CLUB PLAYED FOR	X	SX	S	Ap	Gls
Donovan	Harry	21	Midfielder	Dagenham & Redbridge (L)	12	3	3	15	
				Havant & Waterlooville (L)	4			4	
Arsenal (Y), Millwall (Y), Dagenham & R (L), Havant & W (L)									
Dowling	George	20	Defender	Eastleigh (L)		2	1	2	
				Weston-super-Mare (L)	3			3	
Bristol C (Y), Weston-S-M (L), Torquay (L), Eastleigh (L), Weston (L)									
Downer	Simon	37	Defender	Hampton & Richmond Borough	20	2	3	22	
Leyton O, Aldershot (L), Weymouth, Grays, Rushden, Sutton U, Maidenhead, Sutton U, Hampton & R									
Downes	Alex	19	Defender	Chester			2		
Chester									
Downing	Bay	23	Forward	Altrincham		1	1	1	
Tampa Spartans (US), Altrincham, Salisbury (dual)									
Downing	Jordan	21	Defender	Stockport County	1	2	7	3	
Stockport									
Doyle	Alex		Defender	Salford City	1	1		2	
Salford (Y)									
Doyle	Jack	22	Defender	Maidstone United (L)	6	2		8	
Blackburn (Y), Derry (L), Maidstone (L)									
Doyle	Lewis		Midfielder	Southport			1		
Southport									
Doyley	Lloyd	36	Defender	Hemel Hempstead Town	9	1	3	10	
				Billericay Town	8		2	8	
Watford (Y), Rotherham, Colchester, Hemel H, Billericay									
Drench	Steven	33	Goalkeeper	Bradford Park Avenue	28		1	28	
				Altrincham	3		5	3	
Blackburn (Y), Morecambe, Southport, Cambridge U (L), Leigh Genesis, Guiseley, Halifax, Bradford PA, Altrincham									
Drewitt	Ben		Goalkeeper	Chippenham Town		1			
Chippenham									
Drinan	Aaron	21	Forward	Sutton United (L)	12	10	1	22	1
Cork (Y), Waterford, Ipswich, Sutton U (L), Waterford (L)									
Driscoll	Liam	20	Goalkeeper	Hungerford Town (L)	5			5	
Reading (Y), Hungerford (L)									
Driver	Callum	26	Defender	Dartford	14	1	7	15	
West Ham (Y), Burton (L), Wycombe, Whitehawk (L), Dartford, Maidstone, Hemel H (L), Hemel H, Welling, Dartford									
Drury	Andy	35	Midfielder	Ebbsfleet United	33	6	1	39	3
Sittingbourne, Ebbsfleet, Lewes, Stevenage, Luton, Ipswich, Crawley (L), Crawley, Luton, Eastleigh, Ebbsfleet									
Duckworth	Michael	27	Defender	FC Halifax Town	20	2	11	22	
York, Harrogate Railway, Bradford PA, Hartlepool, Fleetwood, Morecambe (L), Halifax									
Dudley	Anthony	23	Forward	Chester (L)	36	2		38	11
Bury (Y), Guiseley (Lx2), Macclesfield (L), Salford, Chester (L)									
Dudzinski	Ben	23	Goalkeeper	Havant & Waterlooville	32		1	32	
Durham City, Hartlepool, Darlington (L), Lowestoft, Havant & W									
Duku	Manny	26	Forward	Barnet (L)	9	2		11	4
				FC Halifax Town (L)	9	3		12	3
Legmeervogels, FC Abcoude, FC Breukelen, VV Eemdijk, Chesham, Hemel H, King's Langley, Banbury, Hayes & Y, Cheltenham, Barnet (L), FC Halifax (L)									
Dunbar	Kieran	22	Midfielder	Leamington	28		1	28	5
Fleetwood, Stalybridge, Telford, Leamington (L), Leamington									
Dundas	Craig	38	Forward	Sutton United	3	1	1	4	
				Hampton & Richmond Borough (L)	17	1		18	3
				Hampton & Richmond Borough	17	4	2	21	1
Sutton U, Hampton & R (L), Hampton & R									
Dunkley	Dimitri		Forward	Nuneaton Borough	1	6		7	
Dunn	James	21	Goalkeeper	Woking			9		
Eastern Suburbs (NZ), Woking									
Dunn	Kieran		Midfielder	Darlington			1		
Darlington									
Dunn	Simon	25	Midfielder	Slough Town	26	11	6	37	1
Basingstoke, Slough									
Dunne	Alan	36	Defender	Bromley	2	3	13	5	
Millwall, Leyton O, Bromley									

Key: X - Started; SX - Sub on; S - Non-playing Sub; Ap - Total Appearances; Gls - Total goals.

SURNAME	FIRSTNAME	AGE	POSITION	CLUB	APPEARANCES			Ap	Gls
Durojaiye	Scott	26	Defender	Braintree Town	7		1	7	
				Maidstone United	4	5	4	9	
				Woking	12	1	1	13	
Tottenham (Y), Norwich, Falkirk, Brechin (L), Enfield T, Hayes & Y, Hungerford, Hayes & Y, Haringey, Welling, Braintree, Maidstone, Woking									
Duxbury	Scott		Defender	Stockport County	45	2		47	
Blackburn (Y), Burnley (Y), PNE (Y), Stockport, Northwich V, Stockport									
Dwyer	Anthony	22	Forward	Leamington	2	11	7	13	2
Telford, Hednesford, Leamington									
Dyche	Jack	21	Forward	Guiseley	9	7	11	16	1
Scunthorpe, Bradford PA (L), Boston U (L), Guiseley, Farsley (L),									
Dyer	Nathan	18	Defender	York City	10	1	10	11	
York (Y)									
Dymond	Connor	24	Midfielder	Hemel Hempstead Town	2		1	2	
Crystal P (Y), Barnet (L), Newport Co (L), Bromley, Welling, Hemel H									
Dyson	Olly	19	Midfielder	Barrow		3		3	
Barrow (Y)									
Dyson	Taylor		Midfielder	Salford City		1		1	
Salford (Y)									
Earing	Jack	20	Midfielder	Curzon Ashton (L)	4	1		5	
Bolton (Y), Curzon A (L)									
Earl	James	31	Goalkeeper	Eastbourne Borough	1	7	1		
Eastbourne B									
Earls	Harry		Goalkeeper	Dover Athletic			1		
Dover (Y)									
East	Danny	27	Defender	Bradford Park Avenue	6	9	1	15	1
Hull City, Northampton (L), Gillingham (L), Portsmouth, Aldershot (L), Grimsby, Guiseley, Bradford PA									
Eastmond	Craig	28	Midfielder	Sutton United	44	1		45	7
Arsenal, Millwall (L), Wycombe (L), Colchester (L), Colchester, Yeovil, Sutton U									
Ebbut	Cameron		Forward	Hereford FC		1	1	1	
Birmingham (Y), Bristol R, Hereford									
Eccles	Danny	22	Goalkeeper	Chorley	1	1	18	2	
Carlisle (Y), Barrow, Bradford PA, Kendal, Congleton, Chorley									
Eccleston	Nathan	28	Forward	Nuneaton Borough	1	1		2	
Liverpool (Y), Huddersfield (L), Charlton (L), Rochdale (L), Blackpool, Tranmere (L), Carlisle (L), Coventry (L), Partick, Kilmarnock, Bekescsaba (Hun), Nuneaton									
Edgar	David	32	Defender	Hartlepool United	9			9	
Newcastle, Burnley, Swansea (L), Swansea (L), Birmingham, Huddersfield (L), Sheff Utd (L), Vancouver Whitecaps, Nashville, Ottawa Fury, Hartlepool									
Edge	Jamie	25	Midfielder	Gloucester City	12	3	2	15	
Gloucester, Cirencester, Hereford, Cirencester, Weston-s-Mare, Hereford, Gloucester									
Edmunds	Ryan		Midfielder	Nuneaton Borough	23	1	1	24	5
Sutton Coldfield, Nuneaton									
Edobor	Jarvis	19	Defender	Maidstone United (L)	5	4	5	9	
Chalfont St. P, Brentford, Maidstone (L)									
Edobor	Obaro	19		Nuneaton Borough		4			
Nuneaton (Y)									
Edser	Toby	20	Midfielder	Woking (L)	18			18	4
Nottm Forest, Woking (L), Port Vale (L)									
Edwards	Jack	27	Midfielder	Leamington	43			43	9
Leamington, Solihull M, Leamington									
Edwards	Jonathan	22	Forward	FC Halifax Town	17	24	5	41	4
Peterborough, Ilkeston (L), Scarborough (L), St Albans (L), Hull, Accrington (L), Woking (L), FC Halifax									
Edwards	Jordan	19	Midfielder	Chippenham Town (L)	3	3	3		
Norwich, Swindon, Chippenham (L)									
Edwards	Liam	22	Defender	Southport	25		1	25	
Stoke (Y), Southport									
Edwards	Opanin	20	Midfielder	Torquay United (L)	10	7	1	17	3
Bristol C, Bath (L), Solihull M (L), Bath (L), Torquay (L)									
Edwards	Preston	32	Goalkeeper	Dulwich Hamlet	45			45	
Liverpool (Y), Millwall, Dover (L), Grays, Ebbsfleet, Boreham W (L), Dulwich H									
Efete	Michee	22	Defender	Maidstone United	8		3	8	
				Bath City (L)	15	1		16	1
				Billericay Town (L)	17		1	17	
Norwich, Torquay (L), Maidstone, Bath (L), Billericay (L)									

2018-19 NATIONAL. NORTH & SOUTH PLAYERS — APPEARANCES

SURNAME	FIRSTNAME	AGE	POSITION	CLUB PLAYED FOR				Ap	Gls
Effiong	Inih	28	Forward	Dover Athletic	34	16		50	11
Boreham W, Barrow, Woking, Ross Co, Dover									
Egan	Alfie	21	Midfielder	East Thurrock United (L)	7	1		8	
AFC Wimbledon, Sutton U (L), East Thurrock (L)									
Egan	Leighton	19	Midfielder	FC United of Manchester	2		2		FC
United (Y)									
Eggleton	Jake	20	Defender	Hampton & Richmond Borough	2	2	3	4	
West Ham (Y), Hendon, Hampton & R									
Ekongo	Enock		Defender	Chippenham Town		2			
Chippenham									
Ekpiteta	Calvin		Midfielder	East Thurrock United	2		6	2	
East Thurrock, Aveley (L), Wingate (L)									
Ekpiteta	Marvel	23	Defender	Hungerford Town	35		1	35	3
Chelmsford, Bishop's S, East Thurrock, Hungerford									
Ekpiteta	Marvin	23	Defender	Leyton Orient	45	1	3	46	6
Chelmsford, Concord R, E Thurrock, Leyton Orient									
Eleftheriou	Andrew	21	Defender	Braintree Town (L)	18			18	
Watford (Y), Sandefjord (Nor) (L), Braintree (L)									
Elito	Medy	28	Midfielder	Barnet	27	7	8	34	2
Colchester (Yth), Cheltenham (L), Dagenham & R (L), Cheltenham (L), Dagenham & R, VVV-Venlo, Newport Co, Cambridge U, Barnet									
Ellington	Lewis	20	Forward	Chippenham Town	1	11	1		
Bristol R (Y), Chippenham									
Elliot	Chris	26	Goalkeeper	Spennymoor Town		46			
Bradford C (Y), Harrogate (L), Harrogate, Alfreton, Spennymoor									
Elliott	Ben		Forward	Altricham			1		
Altrincham (Y)									
Elliott	Christopher	18	Forward	Darlington	2	4	2	6	1
Chelsea (Y), Leicester (Y), Darlington									
Elliott	Tom	24	Midfielder	Darlington	42	1		43	3
Worksop, Nuneaton, Darlington									
Ellis	Jud		Midfielder	AFC Telford United	1	2	1		
Ellesmere, Stafford R, Market D, Telford, Sutton C (L), Hednesford (L)									
Ellul	Joe	30	Defender	Braintree Town	20		1	20	2
East Thurrock, Billericay, Braintree									
Elms	Josh		Forward	Hungerford Town			2		
Hungerford									
Elokobi	George	33	Defender	Leyton Orient	5			5	1
				Aldershot Town	12	1		13	
Dulwich H, Colchester, Chester (L), Wolves, Nottingham F (L), Bristol C, Oldham, Colchester, Braintree (L), Leyton Orient, Aldershot									
Elsdon	Matty	21	Defender	Barrow	4	2	9	6	
Sunderland (Y), Middlesbrough (Y), Inverness C (L), Barrow									
Embery	Jake		Forward	Maidstone United	3	7	2	10	1
Herne Bay, Maidstone									
Emmanuel	Moses	29	Forward	Billericay Town	35	7	4	42	25
Brentford, Woking (L), Woking, Bromley, Dover, Sutton, Maidenhead (L), Billericay									
Emmett	Jack	25	Midfielder	Harrogate Town	37	2	1	39	3
Harrogate									
English	Junior	33	Midfielder	Leamington	41	1	1	42	4
Solihull, Brackley (L), Worcester, Leamington									
Ennis	Paul	29	Forward	Southport		1		1	
				Ashton United	4	5	4	9	1
Stockport, Stalybridge, Bala, Colwyn, Guiseley, Stalybridge, Hednesford, Curzon A, Shaw Lane, Southport, Ashton U									
Enver	Aiden		Midfielder	Bromley			5		
Bromley									
Erskine	Jacob	30	Forward	Dulwich Hamlet	2	2		4	
Dorchester, Gillingham, Ebbsfleet, Hampton & R, Dartford, Whitehawk, Bromley, Maidenhead, Dulwich H									
Eshun	Kingsley		Forward	Dulwich Hamlet (L)	3	1	3	4	2
AFC Wembley, QPR (Y), St Albans (L), Dulwich H (L)									
Essam	Connor	26	Defender	Dover Athletic	19			19	1
				Concord Rangers (L)	25			25	1
Gillingham, Luton (L), Crawley, Dartford (L), Dover, Leyton O, Dover (L), Eastleigh, Woking (L), Dover (L), Dover, Concord R (L)									

Key: X - Started; SX - Sub on; S - Non-playing Sub; Ap - Total Appearances; Gls - Total goals.

SURNAME	FIRSTNAME	AGE	POSITION	CLUB	APPEARANCES				
								Ap	Gls
Essuman	George	22	Defender	Torquay United	10	6	4	16	1
				Dulwich Hamlet (L)	5	2	6	7	
Hemel H, Aveley, Leverstock Green, London Colney, Waltham F, Ware, Maldon & Tiptree, Grays, VCD Ath, Dover,Oxford C (L), Whitehawk (L), Margate (L), Torquay, Dulwich H (L)									
Etches	Adam		Forward	Stockport County		1			
Stockport									
Etheridge	Ross	24	Goalkeeper	Nuneaton Borough	4		5	4	
Derby (Y), Crewe (L), Stalybridge (L), Accrington, Doncaster, Alfreton (L), Lincoln (L), Nuneaton, Stratford (L)									
Evangelinos	Nic	25	Forward	Ashton United	3	5	3	8	3
Leicester (Y), Rugby T, Banbury, West Didsbury, Ashton U									
Evans	Alfie			Dartford			3		
Dartford (Y)									
Evans	Dean		Midfielder	Chippenham Town	35	4	3	39	3
Weymouth, Chippenham									
Evans	Will	27	Defender	Chesterfield	44	1	2	45	6
Swindon, Hereford (L), Hereford, Newport Co (L), Eastleigh, Aldershot, Chesterfield									
Ewington	James		Forward	St Albans City	3	2		5	
St Albans									
Eyoma	Aaron	21	Midfielder	Woking (L)	3	3		6	1
				Braintree Town (L)	6	1		7	1
Arsenal (Y), Derby, Woking (L), Braintree (L)									
Eyong	Tambeson	29	Midfielder	Billericay Town	1	1	8	2	
Hornchurch, Canvey Is, Dover, Canvey Is, Bishop's St, Billericay									
Eze	Ikechi		Midfielder	Braintree Town		2	6	2	
Braintree (Y)									
Ezewele	Louis	22	Defender	Hereford FC (L)	1	1	7	2	
Wolves (Y), Bristol R (Y), Redditch, Tamworth, Hereford (L)									
Fagg	Tommy		Forward	Maidstone United	1		1		
Maidstone (Y)									
Fairlamb	Luke	25	Midfielder	Brackley Town	16	31	3	47	2
Corby, Brackley									
Falkingham	Josh	28	Midfielder	Harrogate Town	47		1	47	1
Leeds (Y), St Johnstone, Arbroath, Dunfermline, Darlington, Harrogate									
Fallowfield	Ryan	23	Midfielder	Harrogate Town	30		4	30	
Hull (Y), Harrogate (L), Harrogate, Matlock (L), North Ferriby, Harrogate									
Fasanmade	Craig	19	Midfielder	Oxford City	8	26	9	34	1
Reading (Y), Oxford C									
Fawns	Mason	20	Midfielder	Curzon Ashton	9	7	11	16	2
				Altrincham		2	2	2	
Man City (Y), Blackburn (Y), Oldham (Y), Ashton U (L), AFC Fylde (L), Curzon A, Altrincham, Trafford									
Fazakerley	Loui	34	Defender	Dover Athletic		1	7	1	
Eastbourne B, Welling, Dover									
Featherstone	Nicky	30	Midfielder	Hartlepool United	46	2	3	48	4
Hull, Grimsby (L),Hereford, Walsall, Scunthorpe, Hartlepool									
Felix	Kaine	23	Forward	Guiseley	32	6		38	6
St Neots, Boston U, York, Stockport (L), Leamington, Brackley, Guiseley									
Felix	Nuno		Defender	Chippenham Town	3		1	3	
Chippenham, Taunton, Chippenham									
Fenelon	Shamir	24	Forward	Aldershot Town	11	10	1	21	2
Brighton, Torquay (L), Rochdale (L), Tranmere (L), Dagenham & R (L), Crawley, Whitehawk (L), Aldershot									
Fenwick	Scott	29	Forward	Chelmsford City	33	6	2	39	9
Hartlepool, Tranmere (L), York, Darlington, Naxxar Lions (Malta), Chelmsford									
Ferdinand	Kane	26	Midfielder	Woking	13	1	2	14	2
Southend, Peterborough, Northampton (L), Luton (L), Cheltenham (L), Dagenham & R, East Thurrock, Woking									
Ferguson	Alex	24	Forward	Chippenham Town	5	3	8	8	
Swindon (Y), Chippenham									
Ferguson	Dan	18	Defender	Weston-super-Mare	2	2	2		
Weston (Y)									
Ferguson	David	25	Defender	York City	32	5	9	37	2
Darlington, Sunderland, Boston U (L), Blackpool, Shildon, Darlington, York									
Ferguson	Miles			Gloucester City			2		
Gloucester									
Ferguson	Nathan	23	Midfielder	Dulwich Hamlet	35	5	4	40	4
Dag & Red, Chelmsford (L), Grays, Burton, Dartford (L), Port Vale, Southport (L), Bromley, Dulwich H									

2018-19 NATIONAL. NORTH & SOUTH PLAYERS

SURNAME	FIRSTNAME	AGE	POSITION	CLUB PLAYED FOR	APPEARANCES X	SX	S	Ap	Gls
Ferry	James	22	Midfielder	FC Halifax Town (L)	11	1	5	12	2
				Woking (L)	5	1		6	
Brentford (Y), Wycombe (L), Welling (L), Stevenage, Nuneaton (L), FC Halifax (L), Woking (L)									
Fewster	Bradley	23	Forward	Blyth Spartans	6	19	7	25	4
Middlesbrough (Y), PNE (L), York (L), Hartlepool (L), Spennymoor, Blyth S									
Figueira	Walter	24	Forward	Dulwich Hamlet	3	2	2	5	
Hayes & Y, Platanias (Gr), Acharnaikos (L), Moura (Por), Dulwich H									
Finch	Jack	22	Midfielder	Brackley Town			2		
Coventry (Y), Kidderminster, Brackley									
Finn	Kyle	20	Midfielder	Hereford FC	15	12	4	27	1
Coventry (Y), Hereford (L), Hereford									
Finney	Alex	23	Defender	Maidstone United	23	1	2	24	
				Aldershot Town	13	2	6	15	
Leyton Orient, Bolton, QPR, Maidstone (L), Maidstone, Aldershot									
Firth	Andrew	22	Goalkeeper	Barrow	20		1	20	
Liverpool, Chester (L), Barrow									
Fisher	Andy	21	Goalkeeper	FC United of Manchester (L)	13			13	
Blackburn (Y), FC United (L)									
Fisher	Taylor		Midfielder	Dartford			1		
Dartford									
Flanagan	Reece	24	Midfielder	Leamington	18	11	4	29	1
Walsall (Y), Leamington (L), Leamington									
Fleet	Reece	27	Midfielder	Oxford City	47	2		49	3
Oxford C, Solihull, Oxford C									
Fletcher	Wes	28	Forward	Chorley	0	1	4	1	
Liverpool (Y), Burnley (Y), Grimsby (L), Stockport (L), Accrington (L), Crewe (L), Yeovil (L), York, Motherwell, New Saints, Chorley									
Flintney	Ross	35	Goalkeeper	Eastleigh	4		20	4	
Fulham, Brighton (L), Brighton (L), Doncaster (L), Barnet, Grays, Dover, Gillingham, Eastleigh, Whitehawk, Bromley, Eastleigh									
Flood	Chris	29	Midfielder	Slough Town	25	13	2	38	7
Salisbury, Crawley, Forest GR (L), Dorchester, Eastleigh, Maidenhead (L), Winchester, Basingstoke, Gosport B, Slough									
Florence	Dylan		Midfielder	Maidstone United	1		1		
Dagenham & R (Y), Maidstone (Y)									
Flowers	Harry	23	Defender	Solihull Moors	7	2	21	9	
				Kidderminster Harriers (L)	6			6	
Brocton, Burnley (Y), Guiseley, Solihull, Kidderminster (L)									
Foden	Mark	23	Goalkeeper	Gateshead	3		45	3	
				Blyth Spartans (L)	1			1	
Hartlepool (Y), St Mirren (Y), Ross Co (Y), Stirling (L), Stenhousemuir (L), Gateshead, Blyth S (L)									
Fogden	Wes	31	Midfielder	Havant & Waterlooville	25	4		29	1
Brighton (Y), Bognor (L), Dorchester (L), Dorchester, Havant & W, Bournemouth, Portsmouth, Yeovil, Havant & W									
Foley	David	32	Forward	Spennymoor Town	2	3	2	5	1
Hartlepool, Barrow (L), Puerto Rico Islanders, Fort Launderdale, Spennymoor									
Fondop-Talom	Mike	25	Forward	Wrexham	15	11	3	26	6
Whitehawk, Billericay, Oxford C, Guiseley, Halifax (L)Wrexham, Maidenhead (L)									
Fondop-Talom	Mike	25	Forward	Maidenhead United (L)	6	5		11	1
Fonguck	Wesley	21	Midfielder	Barnet	43	5	8	48	9
Barnet (Yth), Hendon (L), Hampton & R (L),									
Forbes	Elliot	20	Midfielder	Gateshead	14	4	14	18	
Gateshead (Y), Benfield (L)									
Fortune	Marc-Antoine	37	Forward	Chesterfield	21	9	8	30	7
AS Angouleme, LOSC Lille, Rouen (L), Stade Brest, FC Utrecht, AS Nancy, WBA (L), Celtic, WBA, Doncaster (L), Wigan, Coventry, Southend, Chesterfield									
Foulds	Markell		Defender	Salford City	1			1	
Salford (Y)									
Fowler	George		Defender	Aldershot Town	22			22	1
Ipswich, Aldershot (L), Aldershot									
Fowler	Lee	35	Midfielder	Nuneaton Borough		1			
Coventry (Y), Huddersfield, Scarborough (L), Burton, Newport Co (L), Forest GR, Kettering, Oxford U, Cirencester, Halesowen, Forest GR, Wrexham, Fleetwood, Doncaster, Forest GR (L), Burton (L), Kidderminster, TNS, Cefn Druids, Nuneaton, Crawley (L), Wrexham, Tamworth (L), Telford, Nuneaton (Asst Man)									
Fowler	Michael	18	Midfielder	Guiseley (L)	1	3	2	4	
Sunderland (Y), Burnley (Y), Fleetwood, Guiseley (L)									
Foxley	Darren		Forward	Hungerford Town	33	3	2	36	5
Hungerford									

Key: X - Started; SX - Sub on; S - Non-playing Sub; Ap - Total Appearances; Gls - Total goals.

SURNAME	FIRSTNAME	AGE	POSITION	CLUB	X	SX	S	Ap	Gls
								APPEARANCES	
Foy	Matthew	20	Forward	Chelmsford City (L)	3	3	3		
Cambridge U (Y), Chelmsford (L)									
Fragata	Alex		Midfielder	Hungerford Town	5	7	5	12	
Hungerford									
Francis	Akeel	20	Forward	Guiseley		2	1	2	
Rotherham (Y), North Ferriby (L), Accrington, Guiseley									
Francis-Angol	Zaine	25	Defender	AFC Fylde	54			54	
Tottenham, Motherwell, Kidderminster, AFC Fylde									
Franklin	Connor	31	Defender	Brackley Town	22	2	5	24	2
Leicester (Y), Nuneaton, Hinckley U, Alfreton, Nuneaton, Solihull, Brackley									
Franklin	Harry	19	Midfielder	Hereford FC			5		
Hereford (Y)									
Fraser	Sean	38	Defender	Slough Town	18	13	17	31	1
Slough									
Freeland	Adam		Defender	Ashton United			2		
Kidsgrove, Ashton U									
Freedman	Harry		Midfielder	FC Halifax Town		1	3	1	
FC Halifax (Y)									
Freeman	Stacey	26	Defender	Eastbourne Borough	1			1	
Lewes, Eastbourne B									
Freestone	Lewis	19	Defender	Nuneaton Borough (L)	9	1		10	
Peterborough, St Albans (L), Guiseley (L), Nuneaton (L)									
Frimpong	Christian	20	Defender	Braintree Town	1	2	4	3	
Swindon (Y), Braintree									
Frost	Tyler	19	Midfielder	Havant & Waterlooville (L)	4	4	1	8	1
Reading (Y), Havant & W (L)									
Froud	Kiah		Midfielder	Concord Rangers	1	14	1		
Concord R (Y)									
Fulton	Henri		Defender	Dartford			1		
Dartford									
Funnell	Matt	19	Goalkeeper	Maidstone United		5			
Crystal P (Y), Maidstone (L), Maidstone									
Fyfield	Jamal	30	Defender	Boreham Wood	46	2	3	48	4
York, Grimsby, Welling, Wrexham, Gateshead, Boreham W									
Gabidon	Dontai	18	Forward	Altrincham		2	2	2	
Altrincham (Y)									
Gabriel	Ralston	27	Forward	St Albans City	13	7		20	12
				Boreham Wood	10	1		11	4
Haringey B, St Albans, Haringey B, Boreham W									
Gabriel	Ricky	27	Defender	Braintree Town	31	1		32	
				Maidenhead United	3	2	2	5	
Dover, Brimsdown, Enfield T, Braintree, Maidenhead									
Gaffney	Rory	29	Forward	Salford City	35	13	3	48	12
Mervue Utd (Eire), Limerick FC, Cambridge U, Bristol R (L), Bristol R, Salford									
Galbraith	Terry	29	Defender	Darlington	39		1	39	
Darlington									
Gallagher	Jake	26	Midfielder	Aldershot Town	31	9	7	40	1
Millwall, Welling, Aldershot									
Gardiner	Tom	24	Defender	Eastbourne Borough	41		1	41	2
Dartford, St Albans, Wealdstone, Eastbourne B									
Gardiner-Smith	Jacob	21	Midfielder	St Albans City		1	18	1	
St Albans									
Gardner	Joe	28	Forward	Concord Rangers	4	8	6	12	
Concord R, Braintree, East Thurrock, Heybridge, Concord R									
Gardner	Lloyd		Midfielder	Truro City	3	1		4	
Buckland, Bideford, Buckland, Truro, Buckland									
Garner	Scott	29	Defender	Guiseley	21			21	2
Leicester, Mansfield, Grimsby, Cambridge U, Lincoln (L), Boston, Halifax, Guiseley									
Gayle	Ian	26	Defender	Woking	16	4	9	20	2
Dag & Red, Histon (L), Whitehawk (L), St Albans (L), St Albans (L), Bishop's S (L), Welling (L), Braintree, Welling, Wealdstone, Woking									
Geller	Thomas		Midfielder	St Albans City		1	3	1	
St Albans									
Genovesi	Caden	19	Defender	Welling United (L)	11		5	11	
QPR, Whitehawk (L), Welling (L)									

SURNAME	FIRSTNAME	AGE	POSITION	CLUB PLAYED FOR	APPEARANCES			Ap	Gls
George	Adriel	22	Midfielder	Chippenham Town	3	6	4	9	1
Oxford U (Y), Mansfield, Mickleover (L), Hednesford (L), North Ferriby (L), Chippenham									
Gerring	Ben	28	Defender	Billericay Town	1		1	1	
				Truro City (L)	3			3	
				Woking	36			36	4
Cambridge U, Taunton, Truro, Bideford, Hayes & Y, Gosport, Hayes & Y, Truro, Margate, Hayes & Y, Bideford, Torquay, Weston-s-Mare (L), Truro (L), Truro, Billericay, Truro (L), Woking									
Gharbaoui	Ayman			Eastbourne Borough		2			
Eastbourne B									
Gibbens	Lewis		Defender	Boston United (L)	7	2	2	9	1
Mansfield (Y), Boston U (L)									
Gibbons	Jordan	25	Midfielder	Welling United	20	1	1	21	
QPR, Inverness (L), Yeovil, Phoenix Rising, Whitehawk, Welling									
Gibbs	Jack		Defender	Boreham Wood			8		
Boreham W (Y), Northwood (L)									
Gibson	Jayden		Midfielder	Braintree Town		2	5	2	
Braintree (Y)									
Giddens	Jack	27	Goalkeeper	East Thurrock United	44			44	
Leyton O (Y), Grindavik (Ice), Tooting & M, Tilbury, Billericay, East Thurrock									
Gilbert	Jacob		Midfielder	Maidstone United		1			
Maidstone (Y)									
Gilchrist	Jason	24	Forward	Southport	19	11	7	30	5
				Stockport County (L)	1	2	1		
Burnley (Y), Droylsden (L), Accrington (L), Chester (L), FC United, Southport, Stockport C (L)									
Giles	Jonny	25	Midfielder	Chelmsford City	13	16	9	29	3
Oxford U, Southport (L), Oxford C (L), Aldershot (L), Chelmsford									
Gilles	Liam		Defender	Dartford			5		
Dartford									
Gittings	Callum	33	Midfielder	Leamington	33	3	3	36	3
Kidderminster, Solihull, Telford, Leamington									
Glover	Josh		Goalkeeper	Concord Rangers		13			
Concord R									
Glover	Mitchell	18	Midfielder	Darlington		2	19	2	
Nuneaton, Darlington									
Glynn	Kieran	21	Midfielder	Salford City	3	1	2	4	
				Chorley (L)	2	5	1	7	
				Woking (L)	1		1	1	
FC United, Salford, Chorley (L), Woking (L)									
Gnahoua	Arthur	26	Forward	AFC Fylde (L)	8	2		10	2
Stalybridge, Macclesfield, CF Gava, Kidderminster, Shrewsbury, AFC Fylde (L)									
Gobern	Oscar	28	Midfielder	Eastleigh	32	13	2	45	1
Southampton (Y), MK Dons (L), Huddersfield, Chesterfield (L), QPR, Doncaster (L), Mansfield, Ross Co, Yeovil, Eastleigh									
Goddard	John	26	Forward	Bromley (L)	11	5	3	16	1
				Aldershot Town	16	2		18	1
Reading (Y), Hayes & Y, Woking, Swindon, Stevenage, Bromley (L), Aldershot Town									
Godwin-Malife	Udoka		Defender	Oxford City	33			33	
Oxford C, Forest GR									
Goldberg	Bradley	25	Forward	Welling United	31	11	3	42	13
Charlton (Y), Bromley (L), Hastings, Bromley, Hastings, Dag & Red, Bromley (L), Bristol R (L), Bromley (L), Bromley, Welling									
Gomis	Bedsente	31	Midfielder	Dover Athletic	30	1	1	31	4
FC Lens, Puertollano, Almeria, Southend, Sutton, Barrow, Dover									
Gomis	Virgil	20	Forward	Braintree Town (L)	5			5	1
Nottingham F (Y), Braintree (L)									
Gondoh	Ryan	22	Defender	FC Halifax Town (L)	1	4	4	5	
Barnet, Maldon, Colchester, FC Halifax (L)									
Goodall	Jack	20	Defender	Weston-super-Mare	5		11	5	
Weston									
Goodliffe	Ben	19	Defender	Dagenham & Redbridge (L)	35	1	2	36	1
Boreham Wood (Y), Wolves, Dagenham & R (L)									
Goodman	Jake	25	Defender	Bromley	15	8	13	23	1
Millwall, Luton (L), Aldershot (L), AFC Wimbledon (L), Margate, Braintree, Maidenhead, Bromley									
Gordon	Liam	20	Defender	Dagenham & Redbridge	34	3	1	37	2
Dagenham & R, Whitehawk (L)									
Gordon-Stearn	Ciara		Goalkeeper	Billericay Town			5		
Billericay									

Key: X - Started; SX - Sub on; S - Non-playing Sub; Ap - Total Appearances; Gls - Total goals.

2018-19 NATIONAL. NORTH & SOUTH PLAYERS

SURNAME	FIRSTNAME	AGE	POSITION	CLUB	APPEARANCES			Ap	Gls
Gorman	Dale	22	Midfielder	Leyton Orient	14	14	6	28	1
Letterkenny Rovers (Eire), Stevenage (Y), Leyton Orient									
Gough	Jordan	28	Defender	Boston United	3	2	3	5	
Gresley, Solihull M, Brackley, AFC Telford, Chester, Boston U									
Gould	Matt	25	Goalkeeper	Spennymoor Town	50			50	
Hawkes Bay (NZ), Cheltenham, Livingston, Stenhousemuir (L), Stourbridge, Spennymoor									
Goulding	Liam	23	Defender	Altrincham	4	2	10	6	1
				Ashton United	24			24	
Accrington (Y), Belper (L), Witton (L), Ashton U (L), Marine (L), Wealdstone (L), Wealdstone, Warrington, Altrincham, Witton (L), Ashton U (L), Ashton U									
Gowling	Josh	35	Defender	Alfreton Town (L)	14		3	14	
				Hereford FC	23		1	23	3
West Brom, Herfolge, Bournemouth, Carlisle, Hereford (L), Gillingham (L), Gillingham, Lincoln (L), Lincoln, Kidderminster (L), Kidderminster, Grimsby (L), Grimsby, Torquay, Alfreton (L), Hereford									
Graham	Bagasan	26	Midfielder	Ebbsfleet United	16	11	5	27	2
Cheltenham, Telford (L), Chelmsford, Ebbsfleet, Chelmsford (L)									
Graham	Luke	33	Defender	Brackley Town	1		9	1	
Northampton (Y), Billericay (L), Aylesbury U (L), Kettering (L), Forest GR (L), Kettering, King's Lynn (L), Mansfield, York (L), York, Kettering, Luton (L), Forest GR, Hereford U, Alfreton, Brackley, Kettering									
Grand	Simon	35	Defender	Chester	38		2	38	4
Rochdale, Carlisle, Grimsby, Morecambe, Northwich, Fleetwood, Mansfield (L), Aldershot (L), Southport, AFC Telford, Barrow, Salford, AFC Fylde, Chester									
Granite	Josh	27	Defender	Barrow	29		1	29	
Stockport Sports, Mossley, Trafford, Ashton Utd, Barrow									
Grant	Freddie	22	Defender	Wealdstone	27			27	3
Oxford U (Y), Farnborough (L), Oxford C, Wealdstone									
Grant	Reece	24	Forward	Braintree Town	9	7	1	16	6
				Aldershot Town	11	10	2	21	6
Wealdstone, Northwood (L), Heybridge, Braintree, Kingstonian (L), Aldershot									
Grant	Robert (Bobby)	28		Wrexham	17	2	3	19	2
Accrington (Y), Scunthorpe, Rochdale (L), Accrington (L), Rochdale, Blackpool, Fleetwood (L), Shrewsbury (L), Fleetwood, Wrexham (L), Wrexham									
Grantham	Alex		Goalkeeper	Oxford City		1	5	1	
Oxford C									
Gray	Louis	23	Goalkeeper	Nuneaton Borough	4			4	
Wrexham (Y), Rhyl (L), Cefn Druids (L), Everton, Carlisle (L), Nuneaton, Carlisle									
Gray	Taylor	18	Defender	Boston United		1		1	
Boston U (Y)									
Greaves	Tom	32	Forward	FC United of Manchester	3	2	1	5	
Bradford PA, FC United (L), FC United, Hyde									
Green	Danny	30	Midfielder	Concord Rangers	35	7	4	42	2
Dag & Red, Charlton, MK Dons (L), MK Dons, Luton, Chelmsford, Concord R									
Green	Danny	28	Midfielder	Wealdstone	41	4	3	45	8
Bishop's S, St Albans, Braintree, Boreham W, Dag & Red, Bishop's S, Maidenhead, Margate, Wealdstone									
Green	Devarn	22	Forward	Southport	23	17	9	40	4
Blackburn, Tranmere, Warrington (L), Southport									
Green	George	23	Forward	Chester	4	8	3	12	
Everton (Y), Tranmere (L), Oldham, Burnley, Kilmarnock (L), Salford (L), Viking, Nuneaton, Chester									
Green	Joe	23	Goalkeeper	Guiseley	21		7	21	
Mustangs (US)Newport Co, Handsworth P, Scarborough Ath, Guiseley									
Green	Kieran	21	Midfielder	Blyth Spartans	42	2	1	44	7
Hartlepool, Gateshead (L), Gateshead, Blyth S (Lx2), Blyth S									
Green	Matt	32	Forward	Salford City	15	6	1	21	4
Newport (Y), Cardiff, Darlington (L), Oxford U (L), Torquay, Oxford U, Cheltenham (L), Mansfield (L), Mansfield, Birmingham, Mansfield, Lincoln C, Salford									
Green	Michael	34	Defender	Gloucester City			6		
Gloucester									
Green	Mike	30	Defender	Eastleigh	37	2	1	39	1
Bristol R, Port Vale, Eastleigh									
Green	Nathan	27	Defender	Dulwich Hamlet	31	4		35	5
Lewes, Billericay, Tonbridge A, Dag & Red, St Albans (L), Dartford, Margate, Dulwich H									
Green	Ryan		Defender	Sutton United			4		
Sutton U (Y)									

2018-19 NATIONAL. NORTH & SOUTH PLAYERS

SURNAME	FIRSTNAME	AGE	POSITION	CLUB PLAYED FOR	APPEARANCES			Ap	Gls
Green	Ryan	38	Defender	Hereford FC	11		6	11	
Wolves (Y), Torquay (L), Millwall, Cardiff (L), Sheff Wed, Hereford, Bristol R, Hereford, Port Talbot, Merthyr, Hereford									
Green	Sheldon	17	Forward	AFC Fylde		3	5	3	
AFC Fylde (Y)									
Greenhalgh	Ben	27	Midfielder	Dartford	42	2		44	4
Welling, Ebbsfleet, Inverness, Maidstone, Concord R, Maidstone, Hemel H (L), Concord R, Dartford									
Greenslade	Danny	25	Defender	Hereford FC	47			47	3
Bristol R (Y), Bath (L), Gloucester (L), Weston (L), Weston, Hereford FC									
Gregan	Chris		Defender	Chelmsford City	2			2	
Chelmsford									
Gregory	David	24	Goalkeeper	Bromley	48			48	
Crystal Palace, Eastbourne (L), Leyton O (L), Cambridge U, Bromley									
Grice	Harvey			Alfreton Town			1		
Alfreton (Y)									
Griffiths	Kallum	29	Defender	York City	39		3	39	1
Spennymoor, York									
Griffiths	Russell	23	Goalkeeper	AFC Fylde	4		14	4	
Everton (Yth), Northwich Vic (L), Colwyn (L), Halifax (L), Cheltenham (L), Motherwell (L), Motherwell, AFC Fylde									
Grimes	Nick	21	Defender	Truro City	29			29	5
Exeter (Y), Slimbridge, Cinderford, Truro									
Grimshaw	Jack		Midfielder	FC United of Manchester	2	2	4	4	
FC United (Y)									
Gudger	Alex	26	Defender	Solihull Moors	48	1	1	49	6
Brackley, Solihull M									
Gudger	Connor	26	Defender	Leamington	29		3	29	
Hinckley U, Tamworth, Hinckley U (L), Barwell, Worcester, Barwell (L), Leamington									
Guest	Joe	24	Midfielder	Curzon Ashton	24			24	3
Curzon A, Oakleigh C (Aus)									
Guimares	Caio		Forward	Dulwich Hamlet			9		
Dulwich H									
Gunner	Callum	20	Midfielder	Chippenham Town (L)	18	6	12	24	
Swindon (Y), Bradford, Chippenham (L)									
Guthrie	James		Midfielder	Chippenham Town	22	2	1	24	5
Highworth, Chippenham									
Hackett-Fairchild	Recco	20	Forward	Boreham Wood (L)	3	1	1	4	
				Bromley (L)	5			5	1
Dagenham & R (Y), Dulwich (L), Charlton (Y), Boreham W (L), Bromley (L)									
Haines	Mark	29	Defender	Chelmsford City			7		
Chelmsford, Bishop's S (L)									
Hajizadeh	Mohammad	22	Goalkeeper	Welling United			2		
Welling									
Halil	Bekir		Midfielder	Nuneaton Borough	1	3	2	4	
Nuneaton									
Hall	Asa	32	Midfielder	Torquay United	34	2	3	36	7
Birmingham , Boston (L), Shrewsbury (L), Luton, Oxford U, Shrewsbury, Aldershot (L), Oxford U (L), Cheltenham, York (L), Barrow, Torquay									
Hall	Brandon	25	Goalkeeper	Kidderminster Harriers	40		2	40	
Charlton (Y), Nike Acad, St Mirren, Hayes & Y, Ebbsfleet, Lewes (L), Woking, Kidderminster									
Hall	Cameron	17	Goalkeeper	Darlington		1	11	1	
Darlington									
Hall	Connor	26	Defender	Brackley Town	43		1	43	4
Biggleswade T, Brackley T									
Hall	Lewis	23	Midfielder	Hereford FC	7	3	1	10	
Bristol C (Y), Gloucester (L), Gloucester, Hereford FC									
Hall	Ryan	24	Forward	Spennymoor Town	18	18	3	36	5
Workington, Curzon Ashton, Spennymoor									
Hall	Ryan	31	Midfielder	Eastbourne Borough	34	2		36	7
Bromley, Southend, Leeds, Sheff Utd (L), Bromley (L), MK Dons, Rotherham, Notts Co (L), Luton, Bromley, Merstham, Welling, Eastbourne B									
Hall	Ryan		Goalkeeper	Aldershot Town	1		4	1	
Aldershot (Y)									
Hallam	Jordan	20	Forward	Chesterfield (L)	4	1		5	1
Sheffield U (Y), Southport (L), Viking FK (L), Chesterfield (L)									
Halls	Andy	27	Defender	Guiseley	44		1	44	2
Stockport, Macclesfield, Chester, Guiseley									

Key: X - Started; SX - Sub on; S - Non-playing Sub; Ap - Total Appearances; Gls - Total goals.

2018-19 NATIONAL. NORTH & SOUTH PLAYERS

SURNAME	FIRSTNAME	AGE	POSITION	CLUB	APPEARANCES			Ap	Gls
Hamann	Nick	31	Goalkeeper	Maidenhead United	1		2	1	
Basingstoke, Braintree, Woking, Hemel H, Maidenhead									
Hamblin	Tom	32	Defender	Hemel Hempstead Town	20	2	6	22	
Gloucester, Wealdstone, Hemel H									
Hamilton	Marvin	30	Defender	Eastbourne Borough	13	3	8	16	
APEP (Cyp), Eastbourne B, Whitehawk, Dartford, Eastbourne B, Whitehawk, Margate, Whitehawk, Eastbourne B									
Hamilton	Spencer		Defender	Gloucester City	37	1	1	38	
Gloucester									
Hammond	James	29	Defender	Hampton & Richmond Borough	6	7	6	13	
Colchester, Wealdstone, Concord R, Maidenhead, Hendon (L), Hampton & R									
Hampson	Connor	26	Midfielder	Altrincham	38	3	1	41	3
Curzon Ashton, Stockport, Altrincham									
Hancock	Josh	28	Midfielder	Altrincham	39	7		46	20
Witton, Telford, Witton (L), Witton, Salford, Nantwich, Altrincham									
Hanford	Dan	28	Goalkeeper	Southport	50			50	
Hereford, Floriana, Carlisle, Gateshead, Southport									
Hanks	Joe	24	Midfielder	Gloucester City	39	2	1	41	4
Cheltenham, Gloucester (L), Gloucester (L), Gloucester									
Hanley	Raheem	25	Defender	Chorley			1		
Man Utd (Y), Blackburn (Y), Swansea, Northampton, Halifax (L), Connah's QN, Chorley									
Hannah	Andrew	22	Goalkeeper	Gloucester City	3		2	3	
Plymouth (Y), Gloucester, Paulton (L)									
Hannigan	Tom	30	Midfielder	Altrincham	44		1	44	2
Vauxhall M (Y), AFC Fylde, Altrincham									
Hanson	Jacob	21	Defender	FC Halifax Town	34	2	5	36	1
Huddersfield, Bradford, Halifax (L)Halifax (L)Halifax									
Happe	Daniel	20	Defender	Leyton Orient	25	3	21	28	2
Leyton Orient, Gateshead (L)									
Hardcastle	Lewis	20	Midfielder	Barrow (L)	8	1		9	2
Blackburn (Y), Salford (L), Port Vale (L), Barrow (L), Barrow									
Hardcastle	Lewis	20	Midfielder	Barrow	6			6	1
Harding	Ben	34	Midfielder	Truro City	12	4	4	16	1
Wimbledon (Y), MK Dons, Forest GR (L), Aldershot (L), Grays (L), Aldershot, Wycombe, Northampton (L), Northampton, Torquay, Gosport, Truro									
Hardy	James	23	Forward	AFC Fylde	17	7	8	24	1
				FC Halifax Town (L)	5	1		6	
Man City (Y), AFC Fylde, FC Halifax (L)									
Hare	Josh	24	Defender	Eastleigh	46			46	5
Gillingham, Eastbourne, Maidstone, Eastleigh									
Harfield	Ollie	21	Defender	Dagenham & Redbridge	16	16	7	32	1
Bournemouth, Poole (L), Boreham W (L), Dagenham & R									
Hargreaves	Cameron	20	Defender	Hungerford Town (L)	20	1		21	
Bristol R (Y), Hungerford (L)									
Harper	Ashley	21	Defender	Weston-super-Mare	2		7	2	
Bristol C (Y), Weston (L), Bristol R, Weston,									
Harris	Alex	24	Midfielder	York City	15	12	6	27	2
Hibernian, Dundee (L), Queen of the Sth (L), Falkirk, York									
Harris	Ben	28	Forward	Slough Town	25	7	4	32	9
Team Wellington (NZ), Slough									
Harris	Callum	23	Midfielder	Altrincham		1		1	
				Ashton United			1		
Man City (Y), Blackburn (Y), Nike Acad, Wolves, Macclesfield, Central FC (Tr&Tab), Patro Eisden (Bel), Altrincham, Trafford (dual), Winsford (dual), Ashton U									
Harris	Cameron		Midfielder	Concord Rangers		5			
Concord R									
Harris	Charlie	23	Midfielder	Weston-super-Mare		1			
Brighton, Aldershot (L), Barnsley, Maidstone, Eastbourne B, Weston									
Harris	Danny	32	Midfielder	East Thurrock United	33	2	2	35	1
Newport Co, Bishop's S, Dartford, East Thurrock									
Harris	Ed	28	Defender	Havant & Waterlooville	25		5	25	1
QPR (Y), Hayes & Y (L), AFC Wimbledon, Dover, Havant & W									
Harris	Robert	31	Defender	FC United of Manchester	4		2	4	
Queen of the South, Blackpool. Rotherham (L), Sheff Utd, Fleetwood (L), Bristol R, Telford, FC United									
Harris	Spencer	28	Defender	Boston United	19	8	8	27	
Huddersfield (Y), Curzon A, Ossett T, Perth SC (Aus),Guiseley, Buxton (L), Bradford PA, Farsley, Shaw Lane, Boston U									

2018-19 NATIONAL. NORTH & SOUTH PLAYERS

APPEARANCES

SURNAME	FIRSTNAME	AGE	POSITION	CLUB PLAYED FOR	X	SX	S	Ap	Gls
Harris	Warren	28	Midfielder	Slough Town	40	8	2	48	5
Staines, Slough									
Harrison	Ben	28	Defender	Altrincham	5	6	7	11	
Barnton, Lostock Gralam, Witton, Nantwich, Telford, Nantwich, Altrincham, Trafford (Dual), Witton (L)									
Harrison	Byron	31	Forward	Barnet	14	10	6	24	2
Havant & W, Worthing, Boreham Wd, Harrow B, Ashford (Mx), Carshalton, Stevenage, AFC Wimbledon, Cheltenham, Chesterfield, Stevenage (L), Barrow, Sutton U (L), Barnet									
Harrison	Reiss	17	Defender	York City			1		
York (Y)									
Harrison	Scott	25	Defender	Spennymoor Town (L)	14	1	2	15	2
Darlington, Sunderland, Bury (L), Hartlepool (L), Hartlepool (L), Hartlepool, Falkirk, Spennymoor (L)									
Harrison	Tom		Defender	Hereford FC (L)	2		3	2	
				Weston-super-Mare (L)	16	1		17	
Yate (Y), Paulton, Bristol C, Hereford (L), Weston (L)									
Harrold	Matt	34	Forward	Leyton Orient	9	26	6	35	7
Harlow, Brentford, Dagenham & R (L), Grimsby (L), Yeovil, Southend, Wycombe, Shrewsbury, Bristol R, Crawley, Cambridge U (L), Leyton Orient									
Harrop	Max	25	Midfielder	Altrincham	28	13	2	41	7
Bury (Y), Blyth S (L), Hinckley U (L), Tamworth (L), Nantwich, Altrincham									
Hartridge	Alex	20	Defender	Truro City (L)	8	2		10	
Exeter (Y), Truro (L), Truro (Lx2), Truro (Lx2),									
Harvey	Alex-Ray	29	Midfielder	Guiseley	10	2	7	12	
Burnley, Fleetwood Town (L), Fleetwood Town (L), Barrow (L), Barrow, Guiseley									
Harvey	Cory	20	Goalkeeper	Truro City	6			6	
Plymouth (Y), Truro									
Harvey	Lewis	18	Defender	Eastleigh		1	5	1	
Eastleigh (Y), Wimborne (L), Weymouth (L), Gosport (L)									
Harvey	Tyler	23	Forward	Truro City	39			39	24
Plymouth (Y), Salisbury (L), Bath (L), Wrexham, Bath (L), Truro									
Hatfield	Will	27	Midfielder	Guiseley	34	5	3	39	7
Leeds, York (L), Accrington (L), Accrington, Halifax (L), Guiseley									
Haughton	Nick	24	Midfielder	Salford City	2	5	8	7	
				AFC Fylde	35	6		41	4
Bolton (Y), Runcorn Town, Fleetwood, Nantwich (L), Salford (L), Chorley (L), Salford, AFC Fylde									
Havern	Gianluca	30	Defender	Bradford Park Avenue	42			42	1
Stockport (Y), Mansfield, Stockport, Mossley, Ashton U, Hyde, Altrincham, Telford, Bradford PA									
Hawkes	Cameron	19	Midfielder	Boston U (L)	1	2	2	3	
Bradford C (Y), Boston U (L)									
Hawkes	Josh	20	Midfielder	Hartlepool United	16	16	10	32	9
Hartlepool									
Hawkins	Lewis	25	Defender	Hartlepool United	1	2	11	3	
				York City (L)	8	1		9	1
				Spennymoor Town (L)	10	1		11	1
Horden CW, Hartlepool, York (L), Spennymoor (L)									
Hawkridge	Terry	29	Midfielder	Solihull Moors	7	8	5	15	1
Tranmere (Y), Carlton, Hucknall, Carlton, Gainsborough, Scunthorpe, Mansfield (L), Lincoln C (L), Lincoln C, Notts Co, Solihull									
Hayes	Kevin		Forward	Spennymoor Town	1	7	1		
Spennymoor									
Hayes	Nichols	20	Goalkeeper	Woking (L)			3		
Norwich (Y), Woking (L)									
Hayes	Ryan	33	Midfielder	Concord Rangers	7	3	1	10	1
				Dartford	18	7	3	25	1
Dartford, Concord R, Dartford									
Hayhurst	Finley	21	Midfielder	Gateshead			1		
Sutherland Sharks (Aus), Gateshead, North Shields (L)									
Hayles	Rickie	34	Defender	Billericay Town	12	1	3	13	
				East Thurrock United	17			17	6
Hornchuch, Thurrock, East Thurrock, Canvey Isle, Hornchurch, Lowestoft, Bishop's S, East Thurrock, Welling, Billericay, East Thurrock									
Healey	Liam		Midfielder	FC United of Manchester	1			1	
FC United									
Healy	Joe	32	Midfielder	Dartford	4			4	
Welling, Maidstone, Dover, Welling, Dartford									
Heaton	Josh	22	Defender	Kidderminster Harriers (L)	5	2	6	7	
PNE (Y), Tamworth (L), Colne (L), Droylsden, Stalybridge, Bamber B, Ramsbottom, Darlington, St Mirren, Kidderminster (L)									

Key: X - Started; SX - Sub on; S - Non-playing Sub; Ap - Total Appearances; Gls - Total goals.

SURNAME	FIRSTNAME	AGE	POSITION	CLUB	APPEARANCES			Ap	Gls
Heaton	Niall	22	Defender	Guiseley	42		1	42	2
Bradford, Bradford PA (L), Alfreton, Nuneaton, Guiseley									
Hedley	George		Defender	Aldershot Town	1			1	
Aldershot (Y)									
Hemming	Zac	19	Goalkeeper	Darlington (L)	4			4	
Middlesbrough (Y), Darlington (L)									
Hemmings	Ashley	28	Midfielder	AFC Fylde	10	18	9	28	3
				Altrincham (L)	4	1		5	2
Wolves (Yth), Cheltenham (L), Torquay (L), Plymouth (L), Walsall, Burton (L), Dagenham & R, Mansfield, Boston U, Salford, AFC Fylde, Altrincham (L)									
Henry	Dion	21	Goalkeeper	Maidstone United (L)	8		8	8	
Peterborough (Y), Soham R (L), Boston U (L), Crystal P, Maidstone (L)									
Henry	Korrey	19	Forward	Braintree Town	14	1		15	5
West Ham (Y), Yeovil, Braintree									
Henry	Shane		Midfielder	Spennymoor Town	36	5	1	41	4
Spennymoor									
Henry	Will	20	Goalkeeper	Chippenham Town (L)	6			6	
				Gloucester City (L)	6			6	
Swindon (Y), Hampton & R (L), Chippenham (L), Gloucester (L)									
Henshall	Alex	25	Midfielder	Darlington	15	11	7	26	
Swindon (Y), Man City (Y), Chesterfield (L), Bristol R (L), Ipswich (L), Ipswich, Blackpool (L), Kilmarnock, Margate, Braintree, Nuneaton, Darlington									
Herd	Ben	33	Defender	St Albans City	28	3	2	31	
Shrewsbury, Aldershot, Boreham W, Hemel H, St Albans									
Herring	Ian	35	Midfielder	Hungerford Town	11	1	9	12	
Swindon (Y), Chippenham, Salisbury, Weston-s-Mare (L), Northwich V, Forest GR, Eastleigh, Chippenham (L), Hungerford									
Herve	Michael	23	Midfielder	Truro City	8	1		9	3
PSG II, Orleans II, Truro									
Heslop	Simon	32	Midfielder	York City	14	1		15	1
Barnsley, Kidderminster (L), Tamworth (L), Northwich (L), Halifax (L), Grimsby (L), Kettering (L), Luton (L), Oxford U, Stevenage, Mansfield, Torquay, Wrexham, York, Eastleigh (L)									
Hession-Harris	Frankie		Midfielder	East Thurrock United	3	2	6	5	
East Thurrock									
Hester-Cook	Charlie	19	Midfielder	Woking	6	3	3	9	
Woking (Y)									
Hibbs	Jake	23	Midfielder	Spennymoor Town	25	8	5	33	1
Halifax, Droylsden (L), Hyde (L), Telford (L), Bradford PA (L), Spennymoor									
Hickman	Jak	20	Forward	Ashton United (L)	4			4	
				Hereford FC (L)	9			9	
Coventry (Y), Ashton U (L), Hereford (L)									
Higgins	Sam	29	Forward	East Thurrock United	30	2		32	13
Fisher, Bishop's S, Chelmsford, East Thurrock, Dartford, East Thurrock, Concord R, Bromley, East Thurrock									
Higginson	Harry	18	Defender	Kidderminster Harriers	2	1	15	3	
Kidderminster (Y)									
Higgs	Jordan	22	Midfielder	Bromley	16	12	6	28	2
Bromley, Carshalton, Bromley,									
Hildreth	Lee	30	Midfielder	Nuneaton Borough	5	2		7	
Tamworth, Nuneaton									
Hill	Gethyn	24	Forward	Weston-super-Mare	28	13	4	41	7
Cinderford, Weston									
Hill	Jahquil	22	Goalkeeper	Hereford FC			7		
Mansfield (Y), Ilkeston, Stafford R, Rushall, Oakville BD (Can), Hereford									
Hill	Josh	27	Defender	Braintree Town	6	1		7	
				Welling United	21	5	2	26	4
Ilkeston T, Coalville T, Worksop, Dartford, Boreham W, Hemel (L), Havant & W (L), St Albans, Wealdstone, Braintree, Welling									
Hill	Matt	38	Defender	Ashton United	11	8	8	19	
Bristol City (Y), PNE, Wolves, QPR (L), Barnsley, Blackpool, Sheff Utd (L), Sheff Utd, Tranmere, Bradford PA, Ashton U, Stafford									
HIll	Ryan	21	Midfielder	Hampton & Richmond Borough	9	11	8	20	1
Stoke (Y), Hampton & R									
Hinchley	Kieron		Defender	Alfreton Town		1	2	1	
Alfreton (Y)									
Hinchliffe	Ben	30	Goalkeeper	Stockport County	55			55	
PNE (Y), Kendal (L), Tranmere (L), Derby, Oxford U, Worcester, Kendal, Bamber B, Northwich V, AFC Fylde, Stockport									
Hinckson-Mars	Malakai	20	Forward	Barnet		1		1	
Barnet (Y), Chelsea (Y), Crystal P (Y) (L), Derby (Y) (L), Barnet, Farnborough (L), Hanwell (L)									

2018-19 NATIONAL. NORTH & SOUTH PLAYERS

APPEARANCES

SURNAME	FIRSTNAME	AGE	POSITION	CLUB PLAYED FOR				Ap	Gls
Hindle	Jack	25	Forward	Barrow	27	21		48	12
Radcliffe B, Colwyn, Barrow									
Hinds	Freddie	20	Forward	Wrexham (L)			2		
				Bath City (L)	17	1		18	2
Luton (Y), Bristol C, Cheltenham (L), Wrexham (L), Bath (L)									
Hine	Josh	28	Forward	Boston United	4	1	2	5	1
Burscough, Vauxhall M, Skelmersdale, Chorley, Salford, Stalybridge (L), Warrington, Southport, Marine & Boston U (dual)									
Hines	Zavon	30	Forward	Chesterfield	15	6		21	4
				Bromley	1	6	1	7	
West Ham, Coventry (L), Burnley, Bournemouth (L), Bradford, Dagenham & R, Southend, Maidstone, Chesterfield, Bromley									
Hird	Adrian (Sam)	31	Defender	Alfreton Town	4			4	
				Barrow	10	1	1	11	
Leeds (Y), Doncaster (L), Doncaster, Grimsby (L), Chesterfield, Alfreton, Barrow									
Hmami	Josh	19	Midfielder	FC United of Manchester (L)	3		3		
Accrington, TNS, FC United (L)									
Hobson	Craig	31	Forward	Ashton United	7	2	1	9	2
				Alfreton Town	3	7	5	10	2
				Ashton United	14	1		15	1
Kendal Town, Stalybridge, Stockport, Lincoln (L), Guiseley, Chester, Altrincham, Aberystwyth, Ashton U, Alfreton, Ashton U									
Hobson	Shaun	20	Defender	Eastleigh (L)	7	1	3	8	1
Burnley, Bournemouth, Eastbourne B (L), Chester (L), Eastleigh (L)									
Hockey	Adam		Midfielder	Hereford FC			1		
Hereford Lads Club, Hereford, Mangotsfield (L)									
Hodge	Elliot	23	Midfielder	Leamington	3	6		9	
Lincoln (Y), Gainsborough (L), Telford (L), Notts Co, Alfreton (L), Burton, Leamington									
Hodges	Harry	19	Defender	Gloucester City (L)	13	1	2	14	
Plymouth (Y), Gloucester (L)									
Hodges	Keiran	20	Goalkeeper	Bath City			15		
Bristol R (Y), Paulton R, Bath									
Hodges	Paul	26	Forward	Woking	24	19	8	43	4
Hartley, Woking									
Hogan	Liam	30	Defender	Salford City	28	23	2	51	2
Stockport Sports, Halifax, Fleetwood, Macclesfield (L), Tranmere, Gateshead, Salford									
Hogg	Luke		Midfielder	Guiseley			1		
Doncaster (Y), Guiseley, Stocksbridge (L)									
Holden	Rory	21	Forward	Barrow (L)	5			5	
Derry City (Y), Bristol C (Y), Barrow (L)									
Holgate	Harrison	18	Defender	Ashton United (L)	2	1	1	3	
Fleetwood (Y), Ashton U (L)									
Holland	Jack	27	Defender	Bromley	39			39	2
Bromley, Crystal Palace, Eastbourne (L), Bromley,									
Hollands	Danny	33	Midfielder	Eastleigh	35	3	6	38	2
Chelsea, Torquay (L), Bournemouth, Charlton, Swindon (L), Gillingham (L), Portsmouth (L), Portsmouth, Crewe, Eastleigh									
Hollins	Andrew	19	Defender	Southport		1	1	1	
Rochdale (Y), Southport									
Hollis	Guy	28	Defender	Slough Town	28	1	11	29	1
Carshalton, Godalming, Slough									
Hollis	Haydon	26	Defender	Chesterfield (L)	42		6	42	1
Notts Co (Y), Barrow (L), Darlington (L), Forest Green, Chesterfield (L)									
Holman	Dan	29	Forward	Aldershot Town	6	7	3	13	1
Braintree, Colchester, Wrexham (L), Aldershot (L), Dover (L), Woking (L), Cheltenham (L), Cheltenham, Boreham W (L), Leyton O (L), Aldershot									
Holmes	Jack		Midfielder	Chesterfield			1		
Chesterfield (Y)									
Holmes	Jamie	21	Forward	Blyth Spartans	25	9	3	34	5
Newcastle (Y), South Shields, Blyth S									
Holness	Omar	25	Defender	Darlington	7			7	1
Real Salt Lake, Real Monarchs (L), Bethlehem Steel, Darlington									
Holohan	Gavan	27	Midfielder	Hartlepool United	3	4	1	7	1
Hull, Alfreton, Drogheda, Cork, Galway Utd, Waterford, Hartlepool									
Holroyd	Chris	32	Forward	Wrexham	14	16	11	30	4
Chester, Cambridge U, Brighton (L), Brighton, Stevenage (L), Bury (L), Rotherham, Preston, Macclesfield (L), Morecambe, Macclesfield, Wrexham									
Holworth	Dan		Defender	Aldershot Town	1			1	
Aldershot (Y)									

Key: X - Started; SX - Sub on; S - Non-playing Sub; Ap - Total Appearances; Gls - Total goals.

APPEARANCES

SURNAME	FIRSTNAME	AGE	POSITION	CLUB				Ap	Gls
Homson-Smith	Morgan		Midfielder	Southport	3	22	14	25	
Southport									
Hood	Jamie	35	Defender	Leamington	31	1	6	32	1
Barwell, Leamington									
Hooper	James	22	Midfielder	Salford City			6		
				Chorley		14	8	14	
Rochdale (Y), FC United (L), Stockport (L), Carlisle, FC United, Radcliffe B, Salford, Chorley									
Hooper	Jonathan	25	Forward	Bromley (L)	23			23	14
Newcastle (Y), Workington (L), Northampton, Alfreton (L), Farnborough (L), Havant & W, Port Vale, Northampton (L), Grimsby, Bromley (L)									
Hope	Jamie	17	Midfielder	Hampton & Richmond Borough	1		1		
Hampton & R (Y)									
Hopkins	Albie	19	Midfielder	Oxford City (L)		4	1	4	
Oxford U (Y), Oxford C (L)									
Horgan	Gary	42	Defender	Chippenham Town		7			
Swindon Sup, Hungerford, Chippenham									
Horner	Lewis	27	Midfielder	Blyth Spartans	20	7	16	27	
Hibernian, East Stirling (L), Inverness, Blyth S									
Horsell	Martin	32	Goalkeeper	Hereford FC	14		10	14	
Bristol R (Y), Torquay, Yate, Tiverton, RRFC Montegnee (Bel), Weymouth, Mangotsfield, Yate, Hereford, Swindon Sup									
Horsfall	Fraser	22	Defender	Kidderminster Harriers	43	1		44	2
Huddersfield, Stalybridge (L), Salford (L), Gateshead (L), Kidderminster (L)Kidderminster									
Hotte	Nathan	31	Defender	Alfreton Town	31	6	4	37	1
Hull, Scarborough, Farsley Celtic, Bradford PA, North Ferriby, Halifax, Alfreton									
Hounto	Nico		Midfielder	Aldershot Town	1			1	
Aldershot (Y)									
House	Bradley	20	Goalkeeper	Chippenham Town (Lx2)	24		1	24	
WBA (Y), Chippenham (Lx2)									
Howarth	Ramirez	21	Forward	Ashton United	1	4	4	5	1
Blackburn (Y), Bamber Bridge (L), Skelmersdale (L)SkelmersdaleAshton U,Colne (L)									
Howe	Callum	25	Defender	Harrogate Town (L)	48	1	2	49	9
Scunthorpe, Gateshead (L), Alfreton (L), Lincoln, Southport (L), Eastleigh (L),Port Vale, Harrogate (L)									
Howe	Joe	31	Midfielder	Hemel Hempstead Town	31	8	2	39	2
Ebbsfleet, Bromley, Leatherhead, Hemel H									
Howell	Luke	32	Midfielder	Aldershot Town	27	9	4	36	2
Gillingham, MK Dons, Lincoln (L), Lincoln, Dagenham & R, Boreham W, Dagenham & R, Aldershot									
Howells	Jake	28	Midfielder	Billericay Town	47	2	1	49	1
Luton, Yeovil (L), EastleighDagenham & R, Ebbsfleet (L), Billericay									
Howes	Sam	21	Goalkeeper	Eastbourne Borough (L)	14		2	14	
West Ham (Y), Wealdstone (L), Hampton & R (L), Watford, Hampton & R (L), Eastbourne B (L)									
Howson	Steve	33	Defender	Chester	38	1	5	39	2
Ramsbottom, Salford, Curzon A, Southport, Chester									
Hoyte	Gavin	29	Defender	Dagenham & Redbridge	13	4	9	17	
Arsenal, Watford (L), Brighton (L), Lincoln (L), AFC Wimbledon (L), Dagenham & R, Gillingham, Barnet, Eastleigh, Dagenham & R									
Huckle	Ryan	19	Defender	Dover Athletic (L)		1	2	1	
Gillingham (Y), Ramsgate (L), Dover (L)									
Huddart	Ryan	22	Goalkeeper	Boreham Wood	34		8	34	
Charlton (Y), Arsenal (Y), Eastleigh (L), Boreham									
Hudson-Odoi	Bradley	30	Forward	Wealdstone	16	4	5	20	3
				Woking	1	1	2	2	
Hereford, Grays (L), Histon, Grays (L), Met Police, Wealdstone, Sutton U, Maidstone (L), Hampton & R (L), Eastleigh (L), Hampton & R, Wealdstone, Woking,									
Huffer	William	20	Goalkeeper	Barnet (L)	5		1	5	
Leeds (Y), Barnet (L)									
Huggins	Josh	28	Defender	Havant & Waterlooville	8	6	11	14	
Aldershot, Hampton & R, Farnborough, Havant & W, Maidenhead, Farnborough, Havant & W									
Hughes	Connor	26	Midfielder	Curzon Ashton	18		1	18	2
Oldham (Y), Hyde, Halifax, Bradford PA (L), Worcester, Warrington, Stalybridge, Curzon A, Atherton Col (L)									
Hughes	Liam	26	Midfielder	Darlington	22	2	3	24	1
Cambridge U, Inverness CT, Barrow, Guiseley, Billericay, Darlington									
Hughes	Matty	26	Forward	Chester	8	2		10	3
Skelmersdale, Fleetwood, Chester (L), AFC Fylde, Chorley, Chester									
Hulme	Jordan	28	Midfielder	Altrincham	36	3	2	39	19
Padiham, Ramsbottom, Salford, Altrincham									

2018-19 NATIONAL. NORTH & SOUTH PLAYERS

SURNAME	FIRSTNAME	AGE	POSITION	CLUB PLAYED FOR	X	SX	S	Ap	Gls
Hunt	Jonathan	31	Defender	Curzon Ashton	42			42	3
Curzon A									
Hunt	Louie		Forward	Concord Rangers	1	11	1		
Concord R									
Hunte	Connor	22	Midfielder	Billericay Town	1	7	9	8	1
				Dulwich Hamlet (L)	4	1		5	2
Chelsea (Y), Wolves, Stevenage (L), Billericay, Dulwich (L)									
Hunter	Jack	21	Midfielder	Gateshead	31	8	10	39	
Newcastle (Y), Gateshead									
Hurford	Danny		Defender	Concord Rangers		1			
Concord R									
Hurst	Alex	19	Forward	Bradford Park Avenue	13	11	6	24	1
Bradford PA									
Hurst	James	27	Defender	Nuneaton Borough	5			5	
				Welling United	5		1	5	
Portsmouth, West Brom, Blackpool (L), Shrewsbury (L), Chesterfield (L), Birmingham (L), Shrewsbury (L), Crawley, Northampton (L), Hednesford, Torquay, Guiseley (L), Telford, Dover, Wrexham, Nuneaton, Welling, Sutton C									
Hurst	Nick		Midfielder	Truro City	7	2		9	1
Truro									
Hussain	Tabish	18	Forward	Guiseley		3	4	3	
Guiseley (Y)									
Hutchinson	Ryan	26	Midfielder	Blyth Spartans			4		
St Johnstone, Blyth S									
Huxter	Max		Goalkeeper	Bromley	1		8	1	
Bromley (Y), Cray W (L), Burgess H (L), Burgess H (L),									
Hyde	Jake	28	Forward	Woking	29	9	4	38	15
Swindon, Weymouth (L), Weymouth (L), Barnet, Hayes & Yeading, Dundee, Dunfermline, Dundee, Barnet, York, Stevenage, Maidenhead (L), Maidenhead, Woking									
Hyde	Tyrique	20	Midfielder	Dagenham & Redbridge	1	2	1		
Dagenham & Redbridge, Whitehawk (L), Ware (L)									
Hylton	Jermaine	25	Forward	Solihull Moors	32	18	1	50	13
Swindon, Guiseley (L), Solihull M									
Ibie	Sydney	22	Forward	Hemel Hempstead Town	7	6	7		
Hemel H									
Ibrahim	Deren	28	Goalkeeper	Dartford	15		1	15	1
Dartford, Maidstone (L)									
Ibrahim	Eze		Forward	Oxford City		4	5	4	
Oxford C									
Ighorae	Emmanuel	24	Midfielder	Dartford		8	2	8	
Wycombe, Havant & W (L), Concord R, Dartford									
Ijaha	David	29	Midfielder	Welling United	33	5	2	38	3
Harrow, Tonbridge A, Hayes & Y, Whitehawk, Plymouth, Wealdstone, Whitehawk, Welling									
Ikebuassi	Ezra		Defender	Sutton United			1		
Sutton U (Y)									
Ilesanmi	Femi	28	Defender	Boreham Wood	42	5	2	47	1
AFC Wimbledon, QPR, Ashford T (Kent), Dagenham & R, Histon (L), York, Boreham W, DoverBoreham W,									
Inman	Dean	28	Defender	Billericay Town	13	6	3	19	2
Hampton & R, Hayes & Yeading, Maidenhead, Billericay									
Ironside	Joe	25	Forward	Kidderminster Harriers	30	7		37	19
				York City (L)	4	6	1	10	
Sheff Utd (Y), Halifax (L), Harrogate (L), Alfreton (L), Hartlepool (L), Alfreton, Nuneaton, Kidderminster, York (L),									
Isaac	Chez	26	Midfielder	Dartford	10	2	3	12	
				Chelmsford City	22	4	2	26	2
Watford, Tamworth (L), Boreham W, Braintree, Woking, Dartford, Chelmsford									
Iyayi	Columbus		Forward	Braintree Town			1		
Braintree (Y)									
Jackman	Josh		Defender	Slough Town	37	3	6	40	2
Slough									
Jackson	Alex		Midfielder	Stockport County		1			
Stockport									
Jackson	Ashley		Defender	Boston United	36	4		40	
Leek Town, Ossett T, Boston U									
Jackson	Ben	18	Midfielder	Darlington	6	1	1	7	1
Darlington									

Key: X - Started; SX - Sub on; S - Non-playing Sub; Ap - Total Appearances; Gls - Total goals.

SURNAME	FIRSTNAME	AGE	POSITION	CLUB	APPEARANCES			Ap	Gls
Jackson	Bradley	22	Forward	Ashton United	15	2		17	6
				Chester	19	1	1	20	
Burnley (Y), Bangor (L), Southport (L), Ashton U, Chester									
Jackson	Cieran		Midfielder	Spennymoor Town		2			
Shildon, Spennymoor									
Jackson	Jake		Forward	Gloucester City	22	5	5	27	9
Chippenham, Gloucester									
Jackson	Marlon	28	Forward	Hereford FC	3	3	4	6	1
				Weston-super-Mare	24	1		25	10
Bristol C (Y), Hereford (L), Aldershot (L), Aldershot (L), Northampton (L), Cheltenham (L), Telford (L), Hereford, Bury, Lincoln (L), Halifax, Oxford C, Tranmere, Oxford C, Newport Co, Hereford, Weston									
Jackson	Oran	20	Defender	Brackley Town (L)	3		15	3	
MK Dons (Y), Hemel H (L), Brackley (L)									
Jacobs	Kyle	32	Defender	Ashton United	3	1	1	4	
Mansfield, Macclesfield, Bangor, Porthmadog, Welshpool, FC United, Stockport, Chorley, Glossop NE, Colwyn, Ashton U, Ramsbottom									
Jahraldo-Martin	Calaum	26	Midfielder	Hemel Hempstead Town	2	1	1	3	
				Billericay Town	2	5	6	7	
Corby, Dulwich H, Hull, Tranmere (L), Alloa (L), Leyton O (L), Oldham, Newport, Boreham W, Hemel H, Billericay									
Jalal	Shawn	35	Goalkeeper	Chesterfield	27		2	27	
Tottenham, Woking (L), Woking, Sheff Wed (L), Peterborough, Morecambe (L), Bounremouth, Oxford U (L), Leyton Orient (L), Bury, Northampton, Macclesfield, Wrexham, Macclesfield, Chesterfield									
Jalloh	Hassan	20	Forward	Havant & Waterlooville	3	11	4	14	2
Marconi Stallions (Aus), Hayes & Y, Havant & W									
Jallow	Salou	20	Midfielder	FC United of Manchester	1	4	1	5	
Crusaders, Glentoran, FC United									
James	Cameron	21	Defender	Braintree Town (L)	34			34	2
Colchester (Y), Chelmsford (L), Braintree (L)									
James	Jack	19	Defender	Havant & Waterlooville (L)	6	1		7	
Luton (Y), Havant & W (L)									
James	Kingsley	27	Midfielder	Guiseley	42	2	2	44	10
Sheffield Utd, Port Vale, Hereford (L), Hereford, Chester, Halifax, Macclesfield, Chester, Barrow (L), Guiseley									
James	Luke	24	Forward	Hartlepool United	44	6		50	5
Hartlepool, Peterborough (L), Bradford (L), Hartlepool (L), Bristol (L), Forest Green, Barrow (L)Hartlepool									
James	Owen	18	Forward	Oxford City (L)	2	5	3	7	
Oxford U (Y), Oxford C									
James	Tom	30	Defender	Leamington			14		
Watford (Y), Nuneaton, Daventry, Tamworth, Hednesford, Leamington									
James-Taylor	Douglas		Forward	Salford City		1		1	
Salford (Y)									
Jameson	Kyle	20	Defender	Barrow (L)	21	4	14	25	1
Southport (Y), Chelsea (Y), West Brom (Y), Barrow (L)									
Jameson	Pete	26	Goalkeeper	Blyth Spartans	50			50	
South Shields, Darlington, Blyth S									
Janata	Arthur		Goalkeeper	Leyton Orient			3		
Leyton Orient									
Janneh	Saikou		Forward	Torquay United (L)	31	3		34	19
Bristol C (Y), Torquay (L)									
Jarvis	Nathaniel	27	Forward	Chippenham Town	46	2		48	19
Cardiff (Y), Southend (L), Newport Co (L), Forest GR (L), Kidderminster (L), Brackley, Bath, Gloucester, Hungerford, Bath, Chippenham									
Jay	Chris		Goalkeeper	Leamington			1		
Leamington									
Jebb	Jack	23	Midfielder	Welling United	15			15	4
Arsenal (Y), Stevenage (L), Newport Co, Sutton U, Welling									
Jeffers	Shaun	27	Forward	Boreham Wood			1		
				Brackley Town	9	8	15	17	3
Coventry, Cheltenham (L), Cambridge U (L), Tamworth (L), Peterborough, Newport Co, Yeovil, Woking (L), Chelmsford, Boreham W, Hampton & R (L), Brackley									
Jefford	Ben	24	Defender	Oxford City	26	2	1	28	
Reading (Y), Boreham W (L), Basingstoke (L), Port Vale, Southport (L), Welling, Ebbsfleet (L), Forest GR, Woking (L), Sutton U, Welling, Oxford C									
Jeffrey	Anthony	24	Midfielder	Dover Athletic	17	19	2	36	4
Arsenal, Stevenage (L), Boreham W (L), Wycombe (L), Boreham W, Welling, Concord R, Boreham W (L), Boreham W, Forest Green, Boreham W (L), Boreham W (L),Sutton, Dover (L), Dover									
Jennings	James	31	Defender	Wrexham	40	4	2	44	2
Macclesfield, Altrincham (L), Kettering, Cambridge U, Mansfield (L), Mansfield, Forest Green, Cheltenham (L), Morecambe (L), Wrexham (L), Wrexham									

2018-19 NATIONAL. NORTH & SOUTH PLAYERS **APPEARANCES**

SURNAME	FIRSTNAME	AGE	POSITION	CLUB PLAYED FOR				Ap	Gls
Jennings	Ryan	23	Forward	Nuneaton Borough	1	3	1	4	
				Ashton United	7	1		8	
Wigan (Y), Cheltenham (L), Grimsby (L), AFC Fylde, Warrington, Curzon A, Alfreton, Nuneaton, Ashton U									
Jennings	Steve	34	Midfielder	Barrow	6	8	15	14	
Tranmere (Y), Hereford U (L), Motherwell, Coventry, Tranmere, Port Vale, Tranmere (L), Tranmere, Southport, Warrington, Barrow									
Johnson	Andre		Forward	Boston United	3	13	12	16	2
Worksop, Heanor, Corby, Alfreton, Boston U Hednesford (dual)									
Johnson	Andrew		Midfielder	Spennymoor Town	27	12		39	7
Ashington, Spennymoor									
Johnson	Archie	21	Forward	Welling United			1		
Welling									
Johnson	Bobby		Midfielder	Alfreton Town	26	3	1	29	6
AFC Goole, North Ferriby, Alfreton									
Johnson	Dan	23	Defender	Bromley	3	3	7	6	1
				Dartford	29	1		30	
Maidstone, Herne Bay, Bromley, Dartford									
Johnson	Elliott	24	Defender	Barnet	48	1		49	2
Barnet (Y)									
Johnson	Oli	31	Forward	Bradford Park Avenue	28	11	2	39	11
Nostell Miners, Stockport, Norwich, Yeovil (L), Yeovil (L), Oxford U, York, Guiseley, Bradford PA (L), Bradford PA									
Johnson	Reda	31	Defender	Eastleigh	35			35	2
Amiens, Plymouth, Sheffield Wed, Coventry, Eastleigh									
Johnson	Roger	36	Defender	Bromley	28	7	6	35	2
Wycombe, Cardiff, Birmingham, Wolves, Sheffield Wed (L), West Ham (L), Charlton, Bromley									
Johnson	Ryan	22	Defender	Kidderminster Harriers	35	1	2	36	1
Stevenage Borough, St Albans City (L), Boreham Wood (L), Nuneaton Town (L), Kidderminster (L), Kidderminster									
Johnson	Sam	26	Goalkeeper	FC Halifax Town	54			54	
Stoke, Port Vale, Stafford (L), Alfreton (L), Halifax (L), Gateshead (L), Halifax (L), Halifax									
Johnson-Schuster	Marcus		Defender	Hungerford Town	38			38	2
Basingstoke, Wealdstone, Hungerford									
Johnston	John	24	Midfielder	Altrincham	44	2		46	15
Kidsgrove, Leek, Crewe, Leek (L), Alfreton (L), Alfreton, Salford (L), Salford, Nantwich (L), Altrincham									
Jolley	Christian	31	Forward	Woking	21	2	3	23	1
Wimbledon, Newport Co (L), Newport Co, Forest GR (L), Grimsby, Margate, Hampton & R, Woking									
Jones	Ashlee	31	Goalkeeper	Braintree Town	3			3	
Rushden & D (Y), Basingstoke, Harrow B, Potters B, Crawley, Fisher A, Kingstonian, Darlington, Billericay, Boreham W, Braintree, Wealdstone (L)Canvey Is, Lowestoft, Leiston, Chesham, Staines, Canvey Is, East Thurrock, Braintree									
Jones	Curtis	25	Defender	Ashton United	1	1	2	2	
Stockport (Y), Celtic (Y), Bristol C, Livingston, New Saints, Southport, Ashton U									
Jones	Dan	24	Defender	Barrow	43			43	1
Hartlepool, Grimsby, Gateshead (L), AFC Fylde (L), Barrow									
Jones	Dion		Defender	Chester			1		
Chester (Y)									
Jones	Eddie	28	Midfielder	Oxford City	39	6	3	45	
Solihull, Telford, Oxford C									
Jones	James	20	Defender	Salford City	3		6	3	
				Boston United (L)	5			5	
				Ashton United (L)	7			7	1
Chester, Salford, Boston U (L)Ashton U (L)									
Jones	James	22	Defender	Altrincham	43	1	3	44	4
New Saints, Gresford (L), Altrincham									
Jones	Joey	25	Defender	Eastleigh	30	5	2	35	2
Arsenal (Y), Leicester (Y), Yeovil (Y), Woking (L), Woking, Eastleigh									
Jones	Matthew	23	Defender	Hungerford Town	31	1	1	32	1
Swindon (Y), Farnborough (L), Chippenham, Hungerford									
Jones	Mike	20	Midfielder	FC United of Manchester	6	1	1	7	
FC United (Y)									
Jones	Mike	24	Midfielder	Chippenham Town	13	6	15	19	1
				Hungerford Town	9			9	
Fisher FC, Greenwich, Bromley, Canvey Isle, Hungerford, Chippenham, Hungerford									
Jordan	Corey	20	Defender	Eastbourne Borough (L)	11			11	1
Bournemouth (Y), Eastbourne B (L)									
Jordan	Luke	20	Forward	Chester	1	9	2	10	
Morecambe (Y), Kendal (L), Ramsbottom, Chester, Lancaster C (dual)									

Key: X - Started; SX - Sub on; S - Non-playing Sub; Ap - Total Appearances; Gls - Total goals.

SURNAME	FIRSTNAME	AGE	POSITION	CLUB	APPEARANCES			Ap	Gls
Jordan	Stephen	37	Defender	Chorley	14	7	13	21	
Man City (Y), Cambridge U (L), Burnley, Sheff Utd, Huddersfield (L), Rochdale, Dunfermline, Fleetwood, Chorley									
Jörgensen	Simon	26	Goalkeeper	Dulwich Hamlet	2			2	
Accrington, Whitehawk, Dulwich H									
Joseph	Harold	23	Defender	St Albans City	6		1	6	
Stevenage, Kings Langley, Tamworth, Enfield T, Oxford C, Hayes & Y, Enfield T, St Albans									
Joseph	Zak	26	Forward	Hampton & Richmond Borough	27	9	3	36	5
Egham, Hendon, Hampton & R									
Joyce-Dwarika	Luke	24	Forward	St Albans City		5	1	5	
St Albans									
Judd	Myles	19	Midfielder	Leyton Orient	22		1	22	
Leyton Orient									
Jules	Zak	21	Defender	Barnet (L)	5			5	
Reading (Yth), Braintree (L), Motherwell (L), Shrewsbury, Chesterfield (L), Port Vale (L), Barnet (L)									
Julian	Alan	36	Goalkeeper	Billericay Town	44		5	44	
Gillingham, Stevenage, Newport, Dartford, Sutton U, Bromley, Billericay									
Justham	Elliot	28	Goalkeeper	Dagenham & Redbridge	48		1	48	
Waltham F, Leyton, Redbridge, Brentwood, East Thurrock, Luton, Dagenham & R									
Kaba	Abadoulaye	18	Defender	Darlington			1		
Darlington									
Kabamba	Nicke	26	Forward	Havant & Waterlooville	27	5		32	6
				Hartlepool United (L)	17			17	7
Hayes, Uxbridge, AFC Hayes, Burnham, Hemel H (L), Hampton & R (L), Hampton & R, Portsmouth, Colchester (L), Aldershot (L), Havant & W, Hartlepool (L)									
Kalala	Kalvin	21	Midfielder	Torquay United	32	3		35	10
Cheltenham, Torquay									
Kaloczi	James	24	Defender	Hemel Hempstead Town	24	4	7	28	1
				St Albans City	7			7	1
St Albans, Hemel H, St Albans									
Kamara	Michael	30	Midfielder	Dulwich Hamlet	3			3	
				Woking			2		
Woking, Staines, Boreham W, Carshalton, Dover, Dulwich H, Hampton & R, Dulwich H, Woking									
Kamdjo	Clovis	28	Defender	St Albans City	21	4	5	25	6
Barnet, Salisbury, Forest GR, Boreham W (L), York, St Albans									
Kandi	Chike	23	Forward	Dagenham & Redbridge	16	27	1	43	6
Birmingham, Chelsea, West Brom, Brighton, Bognor Regis (Lx2), Woking, Leatherhead, Dagenham & R									
Kane	Danny	22	Defender	AFC Fylde (L)	6		3	6	
Huddersfield (Yth), Cork, AFC Fylde (L)									
Kanu	Idris	19	Forward	Boreham Wood (L)	13	6		19	4
West Ham (Y), Aldershot, Peterborough, Port Vale (L), Boreham W (L)									
Kargbo	Ibrahim	37	Defender	Dulwich Hamlet	18		3	18	
Malatyaspor (Tur), RWDM Brussels, Willem, Baki (Azerb), RWDM Brussels, Atletico CP (Por), Welling, Dulwich H									
Kari	Sven	21	Defender	Braintree Town (L)	5			5	
Derby, Braintree (L)									
Kavanagh	Rhys	20	Forward	Hungerford Town (L)	12	3		15	4
Bristol R (Y), Bath (L), Gloucester (L), Hungerford (L)									
Kay	Josh	22	Midfielder	Barrow	29	13	3	42	3
AFC Fylde, Barnsley, AFC Fylde (L), Tranmere (L), Chesterfield (L), Chesterfield, Barrow									
Kay	Scott	29	Midfielder	FC United of Manchester	7			7	
				Ashton United	24		4	24	
Man City (Y), Macclesfield, Huddersfield, Southport (L), Macclesfield, Southport, Mossley, FC United, Ashton U									
Kayode	Joshua	19	Forward	Chesterfield (L)		3	2	3	
Rotherham (Y), Chesterfield (L)									
Keane	Cieron	22	Defender	Boston United		2		2	
Wolves (Y), Notts Co, Nuneaton, Worcester, Kidderminster, Alfreton, Boston U & Basford (dual)									
Keane	Jordan	25	Midfielder	Stockport County	47	4	1	51	4
Stoke (Y), Tamworth (L), Alfreton, Lincoln (L), Nuneaton, Worcester, Boston U, Stockport									
Kearney	Dylan	21	Forward	Sutton United	5	6		11	2
Hayes & Y, Wealdstone, Uxbridge (L), Harrow B, Sutton U									
Keating	Ruairi	23	Forward	Torquay United	23	17		40	6
Sligo Rovers, Galway, Finn Harps, Torquay									
Keats	Noah	27	Midfielder	Truro City	12	9	7	21	1
Exeter, Bath, OKC Energy (US), Truro									

2018-19 NATIONAL. NORTH & SOUTH PLAYERS

SURNAME	FIRSTNAME	AGE	POSITION	CLUB PLAYED FOR	X	SX	S	Ap	Gls
Kedwell	Danny	35	Forward	Ebbsfleet United	35	11	4	46	13
Herne Bay, Welling, Grays, Wimbledon, Gillingham, Ebbsfleet									
Keetch	Bradley	18	Midfielder	Maidenhead United	1	2	1		
Maidenhead (Y)									
Kellerman	Jim	21	Midfielder	St Mirren	1	3	1	4	1
				AFC Fylde (L)	11	3	2	14	
Wolves (Yth), Aldershot, St Mirren, AFC Fylde (L)									
Kellum	Gabe	24	Forward	East Thurrock United	3	4	3		
East Thurrock, Canvey I (DR), Romford (DR)									
Kelly	Isaac		Defender	Gloucester City	5	1	6	6	
Gloucester									
Kelly	Josh	20	Forward	Maidenhead United	25	18	3	43	6
Maidenhead (Y)									
Kelly	Nathaniel	23	Defender	Nuneaton Borough	5	1		6	
Birmingham (Y), Kidderminster (Lx2)Solihull, Leamington (L), Nuneaton									
Kelly	Sam	25	Midfielder	Braintree Town	6			6	1
				Billericay Town	3		1	3	
Port Vale, Grimsby, Hamilton, Braintree, Billericay									
Kelly-Evans	Devon	22	Midfielder	Nuneaton Borough	25	8	3	33	
Coventry (Y), Nuneaton (L), Nuneaton									
Kempster	Alex	23	Forward	York City	18	3	1	21	5
				Spennymoor Town (L)	7		7	1	
York, Spennymoor (L)									
Kennedy	Callum	30	Defender	Billericay Town	25	1	3	26	1
Swindon (Y), Gillingham (L), Rotherham (L), Scunthorpe, Wimbledon, Leyton O, Wimbledon, Billericay									
Kennedy	Kieran	25	Defender	Wrexham	11	2		13	2
Man City (Y), Leicester, Motherwell, AFC Fylde, Macclesfield, Shrewsbury, Wrexham									
Kennedy	Mikhail	22	Forward	Chelmsford City (L)	1	6		7	1
				Concord Rangers (L)	1	2	3	3	
Charlton (Y), Derry (L), Chelmsford (L), Concord R (L)									
Kennedy	Terry	25	Defender	Guiseley	3	1	2	4	
Sheff Utd (Y), Cambridge U (L), Alfreton, Harrogate T, Guiseley									
Kerr	Fraser	26	Defender	Gateshead	38			38	3
				Hartlepool United (L)	9		1	9	
Birmingham, Motherwell, Cowdenbeath, Stenhousemuir, Gateshead, Hartlepool									
Kerry	Lloyd	30	Midfielder	Harrogate Town	30	7	12	37	1
Sheffield U (Y), Torquay (L), Chesterfield, Alfreton (L), Kidderminster (L), Hinckley U, Tamworth, Harrogate									
Khinda	Kiran	23	Defender	Woking	6	3	5	9	
				Chelmsford City	4		8	4	
Eastbourne B, Woking, Chelmsford									
Khoury	Louis	18	Forward	Curzon Ashton	1	9	5	10	
Man City (Y), Blackburn (Y), Curzon A									
Kiangebeni	Percy	22	Defender	St Albans City	18	6	9	24	1
St Albans									
Kiernan	Brendan	26	Midfielder	Welling United	36	8	1	44	15
Wimbledon, Braintree (L), Bromley, Staines, Ebbsfleet, Hayes & Y, Bromley, Hampton & R, Welling									
Kilgour	Alfie	21	Defender	Maidenhead United (L)	18			18	2
Bristol R (Y), Hungerford (L), Maidenhead (L)									
Killip	Ben	23	Goalkeeper	Braintree Town	40			40	
Chelsea (Y), Norwich, Lowestoft (L), Grimsby, Braintree									
Killock	Shane	30	Defender	Bradford Park Avenue	37	1	3	38	6
Huddersfield (Y), Hyde U (L), Harrogate T (L), Oxford U (L), Telford, Harrogate T, Guiseley (L), Hyde U, Scarborough, Bradford PA, Boston U (L)									
Kilman	Max	22	Defender	Maidenhead United	1		1	1	
Maidenhead									
King	Connor	20	Goalkeeper	Chester			6		
Chester (Y)									
King	Craig	28	Forward	Alfreton Town	5		3	5	
Leicester (Y), Hereford (L), Northampton (L), Telford, Worksop, Buxton, Bradford PA, Salford, Gainsborough, Alfreton, Matlock									
King	Craig	22	Goalkeeper	Oxford City	53			53	
Luton (Y), Bishop's S (L), Southport (L), Oxford C									
King	Dan		Midfielder	Gloucester City			1		
Gloucester									
King	Jack		Defender	Ebbsfleet United	35	2	3	37	2
Stevenage, Ebbsfleet									

Key: X - Started; SX - Sub on; S - Non-playing Sub; Ap - Total Appearances; Gls - Total goals.

SURNAME	FIRSTNAME	AGE	POSITION	CLUB	APPEARANCES			Ap	Gls
King	Lewis		Defender	Spennymoor Town	1		3	1	
Spennymoor									
King	Liam	31	Midfielder	FC Halifax Town	21	15	7	36	2
Rotherham, Altrincham (L), North Ferriby, Halifax, Gainsborough (L)									
King	Tom		Goalkeeper	Gloucester City	5		2	5	
Shortwood, Gloucester									
Kingston	Liam	19	Goalkeeper	Weston-super-Mare	2		12	2	
Weston									
Kinsella	Lewis	24	Defender	Aldershot Town	36	1		37	
Arsenal, Aston Villa, Luton (L), Kidderminster (L), Colchester, Aldershot									
Kinsella	Mike		Goalkeeper	Southport			4		
Southport									
Kioso	Peter	20	Defender	Hartlepool United	37	4	3	41	1
MK Dons (Y), Dunstable, Hartlepool									
Kirby	Jake	25	Midfielder	Stockport County	13	9	6	22	4
Tranmere, Stockport (L), Stockport, Warrington (L)									
Kissock	John	29	Midfielder	Welling United	15	5	2	20	
Everton, Hamilton, Southport, Luton, Macclesfield, Oldham (L), Whitehawk, Ebbsfleet, Telford (L), Southport, Welling									
Kitching	Liam	19	Defender	Harrogate Town (L)	39		6	39	4
Leeds (Y)Harrogate (L)									
Kitching	Mark	23	Defender	Hartlepool United	39	6	4	45	2
Middlesbrough (Y), York (L), Rochdale, Hartlepool									
Kiwomya	Alex	23	Forward	Chesterfield (L)	12	7	4	19	5
Chelsea (Y), Barnsley (L), Fleetwood (L), Crewe (L), Doncaster, Chesterfield (L)									
Kizzi	Joseph	25	Defender	Billericay Town	47	1		48	7
Billericay									
Klukowski	Yan	32	Midfielder	Chippenham Town	6	3	10	9	
Forest Green, Newport Co, York, Torquay, Kidderminster (L), Chippenham									
Kneeshaw	Wilson	25	Forward	Darlington	8	3	1	11	1
Middlesbrough (Y), Poli Timisoara (Rom), Darlington, Blyth S, Sacramento, Darlington									
Knight	Lewis		Forward	Bradford Park Avenue	34	2	5	36	6
Bradford PA									
Knight	Lewis	26	Defender	East Thurrock United	2	5	2		
				St Albans City	39		1	39	1
Concord R, East Thurrock, St Albans									
Knights	Darryl	31	Forward	AFC Telford United	38	6	4	44	5
Ipswich (Y), Yeovil, Cambridge U (L), Kidderminster, Newport Co, Solihull, Kidderminster, Tamworth, Telford									
Knott	Billy	26	Midfielder	Concord Rangers	13		2	13	1
				Chelmsford City	6	1		7	
Sunderland (Y), Wimbledon (L), Wycombe (L), Bradford, Gillingham, Lincoln C (L), Lincoln, Rochdale (L), Concord R, Chelmsford									
Knott	Sammy		Defender	East Thurrock United		2			
				Concord Rangers	1	3	2	4	
East Thurrock, Concord R									
Knowles	Chris		Midfielder	Gloucester City	24	5	3	29	1
Gloucester									
Knowles	Dominic	27	Forward	Harrogate Town	18	7	2	25	6
Burnley (Y), Gainsborough, Harrogate, Burton, Kidderminster (L), Harrogate									
Knowles	Tom		Forward	Dartford (L)	3			3	
				Hemel Hempstead Town (L)	5	1	3	6	2
Cambridge U (Y), Dartford (L), Hemel H (L)									
Kokolo	Williams	18	Defender	Darlington (L)	6	2	5	8	
Sunderland (Y), Darlington (L)									
Konchesky	Paul	38	Defender	East Thurrock United	5			5	
Charlton (Y), Tottenham (L), West Ham, Fulham, Liverpool, Nottingham F (L), Leicester, QPR (L), Gillingham, Billericay, East Thurrock									
Koroma	Josh	20	Forward	Leyton Orient	38	7		45	11
Leyton Orient									
Kosylo	Matt	26	Midfielder	FC Halifax Town	46	2		48	7
Stockport, Ashton, Hyde, Nantwich, Halifax									
Koszela	Olaf		Forward	Torquay United	1	9	9	10	1
Torquay (Y)									
Kotwica	Zack	24	Midfielder	Gloucester City	12	4	1	16	
Cheltenham (Y), Gloucester (L), Cirencester, Gloucester, Tamworth, Salisbury, Gloucester									
Koue Niate	Jean-Yves	26	Defender	Torquay United	32	4	4	36	3
Solihull M, Oxford C, Guiseley, Torquay									

2018-19 NATIONAL. NORTH & SOUTH PLAYERS

APPEARANCES

SURNAME	FIRSTNAME	AGE	POSITION	CLUB PLAYED FOR	X	SX	S	Ap	Gls
Kowalkowski	Pawel		Forward	Wealdstone	1	3		4	
Wealdstone									
Kpekawa	Cole	23	Defender	Billericay Town	7			7	
QPR (Y), Colchester (L), Portsmouth (L), Leyton O (L), Barnsley, Colchester, St Mirren, Billericay									
Kpohomouh	Jacques	22	Midfielder	Hemel Hempstead Town	15		1	15	
Bangor, Radcliffe B, Southport, Droylsden, Hemel H									
Krasniqi	Arti	22	Midfielder	Oxford City	1	2	7	3	
Oxford C									
Kretzschmar	Max	25	Midfielder	Woking	39	3	1	42	15
Wycombe, Woking, Hampton & R, Woking									
Kyei	Nana	21	Midfielder	Barnet	1	3		4	
				Concord Rangers (L)	3			3	1
				Hampton & Richmond Borough (L)	4			4	
Barnet (Y), Concord R (L), Hampton & R (L)									
Kyprianou	Hector	18	Midfielder	Hampton & Richmond Borough	1			1	
Hampton & R (Y)									
L'Ghoul	Nassim	21	Midfielder	Welling United	20	8	3	28	3
St Neots, Whitehawk (L), Welling									
Lacey	Patrick	26	Midfielder	Southport	5	5	5	10	
Bradford (Y), Vauxhall M (L), Droylsden (L), Altrincham, Barrow, Accrington, Southport									
Lafayette	Ross	33	Forward	Sutton United	11	2	2	13	4
				Billericay Town	20	7	2	27	5
Wealdstone, Welling, Luton, Woking (L), Welling (L), Eastleigh, Aldershot (L), Dover, Sutton U, Maidstone (L), Billericay									
Laing	Louis	26	Defender	Hartlepool United	1	4	1		
				Blyth Spartans	18	2	2	20	1
Sunderland, Wycombe (L), Nottingham F, Notts Co (L), Motherwell (L), Motherwell, Notts Co (L), Inverness CT, Hartlepool, Blyth S									
Lainton	Rob	29	Goalkeeper	Wrexham (L)	50		2	50	
Bolton (Y), Bury, Burton (L), Cheltenham (L), Port Vale, Wrexham (L)									
Lam	Jordan	24	Forward	Hereford FC	3	3	2	6	
Cardiff MU, Hereford									
Lamb	Joel		Defender	Braintree Town			1		
Braintree (Y)									
Lane	Jack	26	Defender	Alfreton Town	3			3	
				Leamington	23	5	9	28	
Macclesfield (Y), Newcastle T (L), Stockport S (L), Hinckley U, Ventura County (US), Sacramento, Ilkeston, Nuneaton, Tamworth, Alfreton, Leamington									
Langley	Josh	26	Defender	Southport	9		8	9	
				Altrincham (L)	1		5	1	
				Guiseley (L)	13			13	
Wigan, AFC Fylde (L), AFC Fylde, Southport, Altrincham (L), Guiseley (L)									
Langmead	Kelvin	34	Defender	Harrogate Town	37	2	3	39	3
Preston (Y), Tamworth (L), Carlisle (L), Kidderminster (L), Shrewsbury, Peterborough, Northampton, Ebbsfleet, Kidderminster (L), Nuneaton, Harrogate									
Langstaff	Macaulay	22	Forward	York City	23	12	4	35	10
				Bradford Park Avenue (L)	4	1		5	1
Gateshead, Blyth (L), York, Bradford PA (L)									
Lapworth	Freddie		Goalkeeper	Gloucester City (L)		3			
Cheltenham (Y), Gloucester (L)									
Lavelle-Moore	Malachi	24	Forward	Nuneaton Borough	4	1	4		
Notts Co (Y), Macclesfield, Torquay, Rushall, Boston U, Alfreton, Nuneaton									
Law	Josh	29	Defender	York City	25	6	8	31	
Alfreton, Motherwell, Oldham, York									
Law	Ryan	19	Defender	Gloucester City (L)	2		2		
Plymouth (Y), Gloucester (L)									
Lawless	Alex	34	Midfielder	Leyton Orient	12	10	4	22	
Fulham, Torquay, Forest Green, York, Luton (L), Luton, Yeovil, Leyton Orient									
Lawlor	Jake	28	Midfielder	Wrexham	40			40	
Guiseley, AFC Fylde (L), Salford, Wrexham									
Lawrence	Byron	23	Midfielder	Dulwich Hamlet	1	1	2	2	
Ipswich (Y), Colchester, Bishop's S, Leiston, Billericay, Dulwich H									
Lawrence	Jamal	22	Midfielder	Gloucester City	2	7	6	9	
Cheltenham, Oxford C (L), Hungerford, Gloucester									
Lea	Harrison		Midfielder	Chippenham Town		1			
Chippenham									

Key: X - Started; SX - Sub on; S - Non-playing Sub; Ap - Total Appearances; Gls - Total goals.

SURNAME	FIRSTNAME	AGE	POSITION	CLUB				Ap	Gls
Leacock-McLeod	Mekhi	22	Forward	FC Halifax Town	3	5	16	8	
				Welling United	1	1		2	
Fulham (Y), Wolves (Y), Rangers (Y), Ware, VCD Ath, Eastleigh, Accrington, FC Halifax, Welling									
Leather	Scott	26	Defender	Chorley	35	1	2	36	2
PNE (Y), Altrincham, Chorley									
Lee	Brandon	19	Midfielder	Chorley			3		
Chorley									
Lee	Charlie	32	Midfielder	Leyton Orient	29	9	3	38	2
Tottenham, Millwall (L), Peterborough, Gillingham (L), Gillingham, Stevenage, Leyton Orient									
Lee	Harry	24	Midfielder	East Thurrock United	28	6	4	34	
Leyton O (Y), Farnborough (Lx2), Welling (Lx2), Welling, Braintree, Concord R, East Thurrock									
Lee	Jake	27	Forward	Weston-super-Mare	33	3	4	36	3
Cheltenham, Thurrock (L), Shortwood, Weston									
Leek	Reece		Midfielder	Nuneaton Borough	2	6	1	8	
Nuneaton									
Lees	Mark	30	Defender	Ashton United	19	4	3	23	
New Mills, Buxton, Ashton U, Hyde, Altrincham, Stalybridge, Stockport, Ashton U									
Lees	Toby	22	Defender	Harrogate Town	1		1	1	
				Boston United (L)	2	3	3	5	
Harrogate Harrogate RW (L), Boston (L), Whitby (L)									
Leesley	Joe	25	Midfielder	Harrogate Town	32	8	2	40	2
Matlock, Alfreton, Harrogate									
Legg	George	23	Goalkeeper	Aldershot Town (L)	2		2	2	
				Braintree Town (L)	5			5	
				Boreham Wood (L)	8			8	
Reading (Yth), Chesham (L), Hungerford (L), Barnet (L), Aldershot (L), Braintree (L), Boreham W (L)									
Leigh-Gilchrist	Lewis	20	Midfielder	Truro City (L)	5	4		9	1
				Hungerford Town (L)	3	4		7	1
Bristol R (Y), Hungerford (L), Truro (L), Hungerford (L)									
Leighton	Noel	20	Forward	Dagenham & Redbridge	3	2	1	5	
				Woking (L)	2	3	1	5	
Millwall (Y), Dagenham & R, Woking (L)									
Lelan	Josh	24	Defender	Aldershot Town	20	7	9	27	
Derby, Gateshead (L), Swindon (L), Swindon (L), Northampton, Crawley, Aldershot									
Lema	Crossley	20	Defender	Sutton United	1		11	1	
Sutton U									
Lemonheigh-Evans	Connor	22	Midfielder	Torquay United (L)	33	2		35	5
Bristol C, Bath (L), Torquay (L), Torquay (L)									
Lench	Matt		Midfielder	Wealdstone	5	9	4	14	1
				Slough Town	14	3	1	17	3
Hitchin, Slough, Wealdstone, Slough									
Lenehan	Jack		Midfielder	Chorley			1		
Chorley									
Lenighan	Simon	25	Midfielder	FC Halifax Town	12	1	6	13	
Leeds, Bradford PA (L), Halifax (L), Harrogate T, Alfreton (L), Frickley A, Rotherham, Warrington T, Altrincham, Shaw Lane, Glossop NE, Guiseley, FC Halifax									
Leveson	Elliot		Midfielder	Dartford			6		
Dartford (Y)									
Levett	Albert			East Thurrock United	2			2	
East Thurrock									
Lewington	Chris	30	Goalkeeper	Dover Athletic			1		
				Maidstone United	11	1	4	12	
Charlton, Dulwich, Fisher Ath, Sittingbourne, Leatherhead, Dagenham & R, Colchester, Margate, Welling, Dover, Maidstone									
Lewington	Jared		Forward	Truro City	32	7	2	39	5
Buckland, Tiverton, Truro									
Lewis	Danny	36	Goalkeeper	Brackley Town	50			50	
Alvechurch, Studley, Kidderminster, Moor Green, Redditch, Kidderminster, Solihull, Brackley									
Lewis	Dennon	22	Forward	Bromley		4	2	4	
Watford (Y), Woking (L), Crawley (L), Falkirk, Bromley									
Lewis	Stuart	31	Midfielder	Maidstone United	13			13	
				Dover Athletic	35			35	2
Tottenham (Y), Barnet, Stevenage, Gillingham, Dagenham & R, Wycombe (L), Wycombe, Ebbsfleet, Maidstone (L), Maidstone, Dover									
Lewis	Theo	27	Midfielder	Havant & Waterlooville	32	6	5	38	4
Cheltenham (Y), Gloucester (L), Salisbury, Woking, Ebbsfleet, Havant & W									

2018-19 NATIONAL. NORTH & SOUTH PLAYERS

SURNAME	FIRSTNAME	AGE	POSITION	CLUB PLAYED FOR	APPEARANCES				
								Ap	Gls
Lewis-Potter	Keane	18	Forward	Bradford Park Avenue (L)	1	4	1	5	
Hull (Y), Bradford PA (L)									
Liburd	Rowan	26	Forward	Guiseley	29	2	1	31	12
				Hereford FC	7			7	2
Billericay, Reading, Wycombe (L), Stevenage, Leyton Orient (L), Hemel H (L), Guiseley (L), Guiseley, Hereford									
Liddiard	Matt	26	Midfielder	Gloucester City	20	2	1	22	2
Gloucester, Cirencester, Gloucester, Cirencester, Evesham, Gloucester									
Liddle	Adam		Midfielder	Eastbourne Borough (L)	5	3	1	8	
Reading (Y), Eastbourne B (L)									
Liddle	Michael	29	Defender	Blyth Spartans	39		1	39	
Sunderland (Y), Carlisle (L), Leyton O (L), Gateshead (L), Accrington (L), Accrington, Dunston UTS, Blyth S									
Lilly	Zak		Defender	AFC Telford United	3		8	3	
Telford (Y), Tamworth (L)									
Limpitshi-Bongwanga	Henry		Forward	FC United of Manchester	2	2	2		
FC United, Clitheroe									
Lindfield	Craig	30	Forward	Curzon Ashton			4		
Liverpool (Y), Notts Co (L), Chester (L), Bournemouth (L), Accrington (L), Macclesfield, Accrington, Kidderminster (L), Chester, FC United, Trafford, FC United, Curzon A									
Ling	Sam	22	Defender	Leyton Orient	24	3	5	27	1
Leyton O, Dagenham & R, Leyton O									
Linganzi	Amine	29	Midfielder	Salford City	4	1	2	5	
Saint-Etienne (Y), Blackburn, PNE (L), Accrington, Gillingham, Frejus-St-Ralph (Fra), Portsmouth, Swindon, Salford									
Lingthep	Sanny	17	Midfielder	Darlington		2	4	2	
Darlington									
Litchfield	Brodie	21	Forward	FC United of Manchester	3	4	5	7	1
Stocksbridge, FC United									
Little	Armani	22	Midfielder	Woking (L)	30	1		31	66
Southampton (Y), Oxford U, Woking (Lx3)									
Littlejohn	Zack		Defender	Concord Rangers		3			
Concord R									
Livesey	Danny	34	Defender	Chester (L)	35		2	35	4
Carlisle, Wrexham (L), Barrow, Salford, Chester (L)									
Ljubicic	Stefan	19	Midfielder	Eastbourne Borough (L)	10	1		11	1
Keflavik (Ice), Brighton (Y), Bognor R (L), Eastbourne B (L)									
Llewellyn	Tom	18	Midfielder	Weston-super-Mare	9	16	13	25	3
Weston (Y)									
Lloyd	George	19	Forward	Hereford FC (L)	19	2		21	4
Gloucester, Cheltenham, Hereford (Lx2)									
Lloyd-McGoldrick	Danny	27	Midfielder	Salford City	33	2	8	35	3
Southport (Y), Chorley (L), Skelmersdale (L), Colwyn, Lincoln C, Colwyn, Tamworth, AFC Fylde, Stockport, Peterborough, Salford									
Lluka	Ray		Forward	Aldershot Town		1		1	
Aldershot (Y)									
Loach	Scott	31	Goalkeeper	Hartlepool United	51			51	
Ipswich, Lincoln C, Watford, Stafford (L), Morecambe (L), Bradford (L), Ipswich, Rotherham, Bury (L), Peterborough (L), Yeovil (L), Notts Co, York (L), Hartlepool									
Lobjoit	Leon	24	Forward	Brackley Town			1		
				Oxford City		2		2	
				Hemel Hempstead Town	6	3	1	9	
MK Dons (Y), Coventry (Y), Hemel H, Buckingham T, Northhampton, Nuneaton (L), Brackley, Oxford C, Hemel H									
Lockett	Brandon		Midfielder	Salford City			3		
Salford City (Y)									
Loft	Doug	32	Midfielder	Dagenham & Redbridge (L)	12		1	12	
Brighton, Dag & Red (L), Port Vale, Gillingham, Colchester, Shrewsbury, Dag & Red (L)									
Logan	Joel	24	Midfielder	FC United of Manchester	4	5	4	9	
Rochdale, Southport (L), Stalybridge (L), Wrexham (L), Hednesford, Guiseley, Halifax (L), FC United									
Lokko	Kevin	23	Defender	Dover Athletic	41	1	2	42	6
Colchester, Welling, Maidstone, Stevenage, Dagenham & R (L), Dover (L), Dover									
Lonsdale	Cole	19	Defender	FC United of Manchester	1		3	1	
Bolton, FC United, Lancaster (DR)									
Lovelock	Tom	26	Goalkeeper	Hampton & Richmond Borough	40		2	40	
Leyton O, Welling (L), Bromley (L), Farnborough (L), Sutton U, Chelmsford, Bishop's S, Hendon, Hampton & R									
Lowe	Daniel	35	Defender	Bradford Park Avenue	30	2	4	32	1
Northampton, Halifax, Guiseley, Bradford PA									

Key: X - Started; SX - Sub on; S - Non-playing Sub; Ap - Total Appearances; Gls - Total goals.

2018-19 NATIONAL. NORTH & SOUTH PLAYERS

APPEARANCES

SURNAME	FIRSTNAME	AGE	POSITION	CLUB				Ap	Gls
Lowe	Matt	23	Midfielder	Brackley Town	47	3		50	5
Cambridge U (Y), Wealdstone (Lx2), Brackley (L), Brackley									
Lowe	Nathan	23	Midfielder	Southport	5		1	5	
FC United, Southport, Spennymoor (L)									
Lowth	Shane	21	Defender	Kidderminster Harriers		1			
Cobh Ramblers, Kidderminster									
Loza	Jamar	25	Forward	Maidstone United	7	4	1	11	
				Woking (L)	13	1		14	7
				Billericay Town	11	2	2	13	1
Norwich, Coventry (L), Leyton Orient (L), Southend (L), Yeovil (L), Stevenage (L), Southend (L), Maidstone, Woking (L), Billericay									
Lucas	Jamie	23	Forward	Weston-super-Mare	19	16	11	35	5
Bristol R, Weston (L), Boreham W (Lx2), Woking (L), Bath, Brackley, Weston									
Luer	Greg	24	Forward	Woking	29	12	7	41	9
Hull, Port Vale (L), Scunthorpe (L), Stevenage (L), Maidstone (L), Woking									
Lumeka	Levi	20	Midfielder	Leyton Orient (L)		1	1	1	
Crystal P (Y), Leyton Orient (L)									
Lumsden	Ryan	19	Goalkeeper	Gateshead			3		
Gateshead (Y)									
Lundstram	Josh	20	Midfielder	Nuneaton Borough (L)	15			15	
Crewe (Y), Nuneaton (L)									
Luque	Joan	26	Forward	Bromley (L)	2	2	1	4	
				Concord Rangers	11	2		13	5
Cornella (Y), Gramenet B, Montanesa, Vilassar de Mar, FC Santboia, CE Sabadell B, San Rafael, CD Llosetense, Heybridge S, Lincoln C, Bromley (L), Concord R									
Lussey	Jordan	24	Midfielder	Chorley			3		
				Nuneaton Borough	13			13	1
Liverpool (Y), Bolton (L), Bolton, York (L), Southport, Telford, Chorley, Witton (DR), Nuneaton									
Luyambula	Ngemba	20	Goalkeeper	Hungerford Town (L)	20			20	
Borussia Dort (Y), Birmingham (Y), Hungerford (L)									
Lycett	Thomas		Midfielder	Darlington			3		
Darlington									
Lynch	Chris	34	Defender	FC United of Manchester	34	1	2	35	1
Hyde, Altrincham, Ashton U, Salford, Murray Utd, Salford, Altrincham, FC United									
Lynch	Conor		Forward	Hungerford Town	8	15	5	23	3
Hungerford									
Lynch	David	26	Midfielder	Southport	12	2		14	
				Alfreton Town	21	1	4	22	
Burnley (Y), Droylsden (L), Stalybridge (L), Nantwich (L), Burscough, Workington, Clitheroe, Altrincham, Halifax, Southport, Alfreton									
Lynch	Jay	26	Goalkeeper	AFC Fylde	54		1	54	
Man Utd, Bolton, Accrington, Salford, AFC Fylde									
Lyne	Joe		Midfielder	Nuneaton Borough	6	1	2	7	
Nuneaton									
Lyons-Foster	Kodi		Defender	Braintree Town	41			41	1
Aldershot, Whitehawk (L), Whitehawk, Braintree									
MacDonald	Shaun	22	Goalkeeper	Torquay United	40		8	40	
Gateshead, Blyth, Torquay									
Mace	James	34	Defender	Leamington	42			42	1
Hinckley U, Leamington									
MacLaren	Casey	32	Midfielder	Hampton & Richmond Borough	22	4	4	26	2
HendonHampton & R									
Maddison	Jonny	24	Goalkeeper	Darlington	29		11	29	
Sunderland (Y), Crawley (L), Crawley, Leicester, Yeovil, Darlington									
Mafuta	Gus	23	Midfielder	Salford City	21	4	3	25	
Colchester (Y), Bristol C (Y), Weston (L), Nuneaton (L), Gateshead, Salford City									
Magnay	Carl	30	Defender	Hartlepool United	34			34	1
Leeds, Chelsea, MK Dons (L), Northampton (L), Gateshead, Grimsby, Hartlepool									
Magri	Sam	25	Defender	Ebbsfleet United	44	3	2	47	2
Portsmouth, QPR, Nuneaton (L), Dover (L), Dover, Ebbsfleet									
Maguire	Dan	26	Forward	Blyth Spartans	49	1		50	26
Blyth S, Halifax, Blyth S									
Maguire	Laurence	22	Defender	Chesterfield	25	4	5	29	2
Chesterfield (Y), AFC Fylde (L)									

2018-19 NATIONAL. NORTH & SOUTH PLAYERS

SURNAME	FIRSTNAME	AGE	POSITION	CLUB PLAYED FOR	X	SX	S	Ap	Gls
Maguire-Drew	Jordan	21	Forward	Wrexham (L)	14	5	5	19	3
				Leyton Orient	8	7	2	15	3
Brighton (Y), Dagenham & R (L), Lincoln C (L), Coventry (L), Wrexham (L), Leyton Orient									
Magunda	Joe	30	Midfielder	Leamington	2	6	4	8	
Brackley, Leamington									
Maher	Niall	23	Defender	FC Halifax Town	42	3	1	45	1
Bolton, Blackpool (L), Bury, Galway, Telford, Halifax									
Mahon	Craig	29	Midfielder	Chester	37	5	2	42	4
Wigan, Accrington (L), Salford, Vauxhall M, Chester									
Makoma	Donovan	20	Midfielder	Stevenage B					
				Woking (L)	2		1	2	
FC Lens, Barrow, Stevenage, Woking (L), Biggleswade (L)									
Malkowski	Sebastian	32	Goalkeeper	Boston United	3	1	7	4	
Lechia Gda sk (Pol), Bytovia, Zawisza, Boston U									
Maloney	Lewis	24	Midfielder	Gateshead	3	8	13	11	
Middlesbrough (Y), Gateshead									
Maloney	Taylor	20	Midfielder	Concord Rangers (L)	9			9	
Charlton (Y), Concord R (L)									
Mambo	Yado	27	Defender	Wealdstone	1		7	1	
				Hampton & Richmond Borough	6	1	2	7	
Charlton, Welling (L), Eastbourne (L), Ebbsfleet (L), Wimbledon (L), Shrewsbury (L), Ebbsfleet (L), Dover, Chelmsford, Hayes & Y, Margate, Bishop's S, Ebbsfleet, Wealdstone, Hampton & R									
Manesio	Sergio	24	Midfielder	Hampton & Richmond Borough	1		1		
Ottawa Fury, Hampton & R									
Mann	Adam	27	Forward	Bath City	37	3		40	7
Gloucester, Shortwood, Gloucester, Evesham, Bath									
Mannion	Will	21	Goalkeeper	Aldershot Town	26		6	26	
Wimbledon (Yth), Hull (Yth), Plymouth (L), Aldershot (L)									
Mansell	Lewis	21	Forward	FC United of Manchester (L)	5	3		8	1
Blackburn (Y), FC United (L), Partick (L)									
Mantack	Kallum	21	Defender	Stockport County	7	4	7	1	
				Altrincham	4	2	6	6	1
				Ashton United	11	4		15	3
Oldham (Y), Alfreton (L), FC United (L), Stockport (L), Stockport, Altrincham, Ashton U									
Mapmosa	Nkosilile		Forward	Southport	1			1	
Southport									
Margetts	Jonny	25	Forward	Boston United	3	3	5	6	
Hull (Y), Gainsborough (L), Harrogate (L), Gainsborough (L), Cambridge U (L), Tranmere, Stockport (L), Altrincham (L), Southport (L), Lincoln, Scunthorpe, Lincoln (L), Boston U, Gainsborough (L)									
Marlow	Ben	23	Midfielder	East Thurrock United	32	1	4	33	3
West Ham (Y), Canvey I (L), Bishop's S (L), Bishop's S, Chelmsford, East Thurrock, Leicester U23									
Marriott	Adam	28	Forward	Boston United	7	1	4	8	1
Cambridge U (Y), Cambridge C (L), Bishop's S (L), Cambridge C (L), Stevenage, Lincoln C, Royston T, Boston U, King's Lynn									
Marsh-Brown	Kyjoun	22	Midfielder	Welling United		2	2	2	
Whitehawk, Welling									
Marsh-Brown	Ronayne	34	Defender	East Thurrock United	5	1	1	6	
Harrow, East Thurrock									
Marsh-Hughes	Lloyd	18	Forward	Chester	1	12	10	13	
Chester									
Marshall	Paul	29	Midfielder	Curzon Ashton	9	2		11	
Man City (Y), Blackpool (L), Port Vale (L), Aberdeen (L), Walsall, Rochdale, Droylsden (L), Port Vale, Halifax, Stockport, Halifax, Bradford PA, Alfreton, Curzon A									
Marston	Jack		Midfielder	Hereford FC			1		
Hereford (Y), Ludlow T (DR)									
Martin	Dave	34	Midfielder	Eastbourne Borough	14	7	4	21	2
Millwall, Derby, Notts Co (L), Walsall (L), Southend, Luton, Dartford (L), Bristol R (L), Stevenage, Whitehawk, Bromley, Margate (L), Eastbourne B									
Martin	Josh	20	Defender	Hungerford Town	22			22	2
Hungerford									
Martin	Liam	25	Forward	Ashton United	11	6	3	17	2
Sligo Rovers (Y), Ballinamallard (L), Ballinamallard, Sligo R, Southport, Ashton U									
Martinez	Sheridan	26	Goalkeeper	AFC Telford United	2		6	2	
Khalsa, Telford, Solihull, Telford									
Mascoll	Jamie	22	Midfielder	Dulwich Hamlet (L)	11			11	1
Dulwich H, Charlton, Dulwich H (L)									

Key: X - Started; SX - Sub on; S - Non-playing Sub; Ap - Total Appearances; Gls - Total goals.

SURNAME	FIRSTNAME	AGE	POSITION	CLUB				Ap	Gls
Mason	Cameron	23	Goalkeeper	Curzon Ashton	43			43	
Chesterfield (Y), Southport (L), Curzon A									
Mason	Dean	30	Midfielder	Maidenhead United		1			
Barnet, Welwyn GC (L), AFC Wimbledon, Northwood (L), Maindenhead, Leyton (L), Bishop's S, Hayes (L), Chesham, Haringey B, Canvey Island, Wingate, Wealdstone, Arlesey, Lowestoft, Concord R, Cambridge C, Billericay, Ware, Enfield Town, Maidenhead									
Mason	Jude		Defender	Sutton United	1	1	11	2	
Sutton U (Y)									
Mason	Sam	18	Goalkeeper	Woking		1	19	1	
Woking									
Mason-Clarke	Ephron	19	Forward	Barnet	31	15	9	46	5
Barnet (Yth), Met Police (L),									
Massanka	Ntumba	22	Midfielder	Dover Athletic (L)	1	2	4	3	
Burnley (Y), York (L), Morecambe (L), Wrexham (L), Wrexham (L), Dover (L)									
Massey	Alan	30	Defender	Maidenhead United	46			46	1
Wealdstone, Braintree (L), Braintree, Maidenhead									
Matrevics	Rihards	20	Goalkeeper	Barnet		1	45	1	
West Ham (Yth), Barnet									
Matsuzaka	Daniel	20	Defender	Braintree Town	9	3	4	12	
Southend (Y), Harlow (L), Kataller Toyama (Jap), Braintree									
Matthews	Jason	44	Goalkeeper	Bath City			1		
Bristol R (Y), Welton R, Salisbury, Nuneaton, Exeter, Aberystwyth, Clevedon, Weymouth, Eastleigh, Bath, Dorchester, Weymouth, Chippenham (Coach), Bath (Coach)									
Matthews	Sam	22	Midfielder	Eastleigh (L)	6	4		10	
Bournemouth, Braintree (L), Eastleigh (L), Eastleigh (L), Bristol R, Eastleigh (L)									
Mavila	Nathan	25	Defender	Hampton & Richmond Borough	17	6		23	
				Dulwich Hamlet	5		1	5	
West Ham, Wealdstone (L), Aldershot (L), Wealdstone (L), Maidstone, Wealdstone, Wingate, Leyton O, Hampton & R, Dulwich H, Cavalry (Can)									
Mawford	Jake	26	Midfielder	Gloucester City	30	5	4	35	1
Weston-s-Mare (Y), Paulton (L), Gloucester									
Maxwell	Luke	21	Midfielder	Solihull Moors	17	23	10	40	3
Kidderminster, Birmingham, Kidderminster (L), Grimsby (L), Gateshead (L)Solihull (L), Solihull									
May	Adam	21	Midfielder	Portsmouth	1	1		2	
				Aldershot Town (L)	11	1		12	3
Portsmouth (Yth), Sutton (L), Aldershot (L)									
May	Jay	35	Forward	Dulwich Hamlet	6	4	7	10	
Billericay, Bromley, Maidstone, Hythe, Margate, Dulwich H									
Mayebi	Joslain	32	Goalkeeper	Hereford FC			5		
KSA Yaounde (Cam), FC Metz, AEK Larnaca (Cyp), Hapoel Ramet (Isr), B. Jerusalem (L), M Ahi Nazareth (L), Dinamo II (Rom), Wrexham, Kidderminster, TB Tvoroyri (F Isles), Royal Eagles (SA), Nuneaton, Hereford									
Maynard	Lois	30	Midfielder	Salford City	24	10	2	34	2
Winsford, Halifax, Tranmere, Salford									
Maynard-Brewer	Ashley	19	Goalkeeper	Chelmsford City (L)	6			6	
				Hampton & Richmond Borough (L)	6			6	
Charlton (Y), Chelmsford (L), Hampton & R (L)									
Mbeta	Christian		Goalkeeper	Sutton United			1		
Sutton U (Y)									
McAlinden	Liam		Forward	Brackley Town (L)	4	2	1	6	1
				Kidderminster Harriers (L)	14	1		15	
Wolves (Y), Shrewsbury (L), Fleetwood (Lx2), Shrewsbury (L), Crawley (L), Exeter, Cheltenham, Brackley (L), Kidderminster (L)									
McAllister	Craig	38	Forward	Gosport Borough					
Basingstoke,Stevenage, Ebbsfleet (L), Woking, Grays, Rushden (L), Oxford U, Exeter, Barnet (L), Rotherham (L), Crawley, Newport Co, Luton (L), Eastleigh, Sutton, Eastbourne (L), Eastleigh, Gosport									
McAllister	Sean	31	Midfielder	Chester	8	2	2	10	
Bolton (Y), Sheffield Wed (Y), Mansfield (L), Bury (L), Shrewsbury, Port Vale, Cowdenbeath, Scunthorpe, Grimsby, Chester									
McAnuff	Jobi	37	Midfielder	Leyton Orient	42	1		43	5
Wimbledon, West Ham, Cardiff, Crystal Palace, Watford, Reading, Leyton Orient, Stevenage, Leyton Orient									
McAtee	John	19	Forward	Ashton United (L)	3	6		9	1
				AFC Telford United (L)	3			3	1
				Curzon Ashton (L)	8	10	2	18	
Shrewsbury (Y), Halesowen (L), Telford (L), Ashton U (L), Telford (L), Curzon A (L)									
McAughtrie	Fergus	19	Defender	York City	2	1		3	
Sunderland (Y), York, Pickering, Selby									
McCall	Spencer	23	Midfielder	Hemel Hempstead Town	7	2	5	9	2
Bishop's S, Hendon, Wingate & F, Hemel H									

2018-19 NATIONAL. NORTH & SOUTH PLAYERS — APPEARANCES

SURNAME	FIRSTNAME	AGE	POSITION	CLUB PLAYED FOR				Ap	Gls
McCallum	Gavin	31	Defender	Welling United	24	10	5	34	5
Hereford, Lincoln C, Barnet (L), Woking, Sutton U, Tonbridge A (L), Eastbourne B, Welling									
McCallum	Paul	25	Forward	Eastleigh	42	3		45	27
Dulwich H, West Ham, Rochdale (L), AFC Wimbledon (L), Aldershot (L), Torquay (L), Hearts (L), Portsmouth (L), Leyton Orient, Eastleigh									
McClennon	George	23	Defender	Maidstone United	20	2	11	22	1
Ashford United, Maidstone									
McClure	Matt	27	Forward	Aldershot Town	21	10	4	31	4
Wycombe, Hayes & Y Utd (L), Dagenham & R, Aldershot									
McCombe	John	34	Defender	Boston United			1		
Huddersfield, Torquay (L), Hereford, Port Vale, Mansfield, York, Macclesfield, Chester, Harrogate T, Boston, Hyde									
McCootie	Nick	30	Forward	Chippenham Town	28	8	8	36	11
Bath, Chippenham									
McCorkell	Andrew	21	Goalkeeper	St Albans City			1		
MK Dons (Y), Chesham, Hendon, Northwood, Maidstone, Hendon, St Albans, Hayes & Y									
McCoy	Mark		Goalkeeper	Curzon Ashton			6		
Curzon A									
McCoy	Marvin	30	Defender	Aldershot Town	18	1	7	19	
Arsenal, Watford, Wealdstone, Wycombe, York, Ebbsfleet, Aldershot									
McCready	Charlie		Goalkeeper	Hungerford Town			3		
Hungerford									
McDonagh	Gerry	21	Forward	Aldershot Town (L)	7	6	2	13	1
Nottingham F, Wrexham (L), Cambridge U (L), Tranmere (L), Barnsley, Aldershot (L)									
McDonald	Cody	33	Forward	Ebbsfleet United	5	7	1	12	3
Witham (Y), Maldon&Tiptree, Dartford, Norwich, Gillingham (L), Coventry, Gillingham (L), Gillingham, AFC Wimbledon, Ebbsfleet									
McDonald	Curtis	31	Midfielder	Chippenham Town	23		1	23	3
Newport Co, Forest GR, Brackley, Chippenham									
McDonald	Dean	33	Forward	Welling United		1	1	1	
Rushden & D, Northwich V, Farnborough, Carshalton, Billericay, Macclesfield, Sutton U, Margate, Whitehawk, Welling									
McDonald	Nathan	28	Goalkeeper	Chelmsford City	31			31	
Braintree, Billericay (L), Enfield T (L), Enfield T (L), Enfield T, Braintree, Chelmsford									
McDonnell	Adam	22	Midfielder	Aldershot Town	39	5	2	44	7
Ipswich, Aldershot (L), Aldershot									
McEachran	Zac		Forward	Oxford City	30	5		35	9
Oxford CBanbury, Oxford C									
McFarlane	Kyle	22	Forward	Barrow (L)	1			1	
Birmingham (Y), Nuneaton (L), Nuneaton (L), Barrow (L)									
McGeoch	Lewis	19	Forward	Gateshead		4	6	4	
Gateshead (Y)									
McGiveron	Dominic	23	Midfielder	FC United of Manchester	3	1	3		
Kitsap Pumas (US), SJK Akatemia, FC United									
McGlashan	Jermaine	31	Midfielder	Wrexham (L)	3	5	1	8	1
Tooting & M, Staines, Bracknell (L), Kingstonian, Merstham, Ashford T, Aldershot, Cheltenham, Gillingham, Southend, Swindon, Wrexham (L)									
McGory	Louis	22	Forward	Weston-super-Mare	17	4	6	21	
Forest GR (Y), Aldershot (L), Hungerford (L), Gloucester (L), Telford, Weston									
McGrath	Michael	33	Midfielder	Hereford FC	18	1	1	19	3
Redditch, Kidderminster, Worcester (L), Galway Utd, Sligo R, Rushall, Stratford T, Hednesford, Hereford, Bromsgrove Sp, Redditch									
McGurk	Adam	30	Forward	Nuneaton Borough	14	1		15	2
				Chorley	1	9	3	10	
Aston Villa (Y), Hednesford, Tranmere, Burton, Portsmouth, Cambridge U, Morecambe, Nuneaton, Chorley									
McHale	Dom	23	Midfielder	Ashton United	6	4	2	10	1
				Southport	1			1	
				FC United of Manchester	4			4	1
Man City (Y), Barnsley, Northwich V (dual), Ramsbottom, Northwich V, Northwich MV, Achyronas L (Cyp), Salford, Trafford (L), Hyde (L), Ashton U, Southport, FC United									
McJannett	Cameron	20	Defender	Curzon Ashton (L)	36		1	36	3
Stoke (Y), Curzon A (L)									
McKay	John	22	Forward	Chesterfield (L)	2	2	5	4	
Doncaster (Y), Ilkeston (L), Leeds, Airdrieonians (L), Cardiff, Chesterfield (L)									
McKenna	Ben	26	Midfielder	Bradford Park Avenue	13	9	2	22	5
				Chester	6	2	4	8	1
Burnley (Y), Carlisle (Y), Annan Ath (L), Workington, Stalybridge, Bradford PA, Southport, Stockport, Curzon A, Bradford PA, Chester									
McKenna	Daniel	19	Midfielder	AFC Telford United (L)		1			
Belvedere (Eire), Wolves (Y), Bray W (L), Telford (L)									

Key: X - Started; SX - Sub on; S - Non-playing Sub; Ap - Total Appearances; Gls - Total goals.

APPEARANCES

SURNAME	FIRSTNAME	AGE	POSITION	CLUB				Ap	Gls
McKenzie	Tyrell	20	Midfielder	Curzon Ashton		2	1	2	
Curzon A									
McKeown	Eion	20	Forward	Wealdstone	2	8	2	10	2
Colchester, Wealdstone									
McKnight	Jack		Midfielder	Eastleigh	3	14	7	17	1
Beaconsfield, Eastleigh									
McLaughlin	Patrick	28	Midfielder	Hartlepool United	17	12	3	29	2
				York City (L)	15			15	3
Newcastle, York, Grimsby, Harrogate T (L), Gateshead, Hartlepool, York (L)									
McLeod	Matt		Forward	Hereford FC			1		
Hereford (Y)									
McLeod-Urquhart	Josh	28	Defender	Hampton & Richmond Borough	2			2	
				East Thurrock United	8			8	
				St Albans	10		5	10	
St Albans, Harlow, Wealdstone, Billericay, Hampton & R, Biggleswade, East Thurrock, St Albans									
McMahon	George	18	Goalkeeper	Ashton United	15			15	
Rotherham (Y), Ashton U									
McManus	Marc	21	Defender	Gateshead			1		
C C Mariners (Y) (Aus)Hercules CF B (Esp), Manly Utd (Aus), Gateshead, North Shields (L)									
McMillan	Anthony	37	Goalkeeper	Chorley	3			3	
Burscough, Southport, Altrincham, Barrow, Stalybridge, Warrington, Chorley (DR)									
McNamara	Dan	20	Midfielder	Welling United (L)	9		1	9	
				Dover Athletic (L)	8		1	8	1
				Havant & Waterlooville (L)	4			4	1
Millwall (Y), Welling (L), Dover (L), Havant & W (L)									
McQueen	Alex	24	Defender	Dagenham & Redbridge	33	5	5	38	5
Tottenham (Y), Carlisle, VPS, Dagenham & R									
McQueen	Darren	24	Forward	Ebbsfleet United	4	10	6	14	2
				Sutton United	2	7	4	9	
				Dartford (L)	10	2		12	3
Tottenham, Ipswich, Maldon & Tiptree, Ebbsfleet, Sutton U, Dartford (L)									
McQuilkin	James	30	Midfielder	AFC Telford United	38	6	4	44	2
FC Zlin (Czech), Tescoma Zlin, Hereford, Walsall, Hednesford, Torquay, Kidderminster, Telford									
Meaker	Michael	47	Midfielder	Truro City			4		
QPR (Y), Plymouth (L), Reading, Bristol R, Swindon (L), Plymouth, Northwich V, Southall, Henley T, Mangotsfield, Hounslow B, Mangotsfield, Hounslow B, Bitton, Paulton (L), Mangotsfield, Yate, Taunton, Truro									
Medford-Smith	Ramarni	20	Defender	Wealdstone (L)	10		1	10	
Reading (Y), Wealdstone (L)									
Mekki	Adam	27	Midfielder	Bromley	14	7	1	21	1
Aldershot Town, Barnet, Dover Athletic, Tranmere Rovers, Bromley									
Mellish	Jon	21	Defender	Gateshead	47	1		48	2
Gateshead									
Menayese	Rollin	21	Midfielder	Aldershot Town (L)	16			16	
Cardiff (Y), Weston, Bristol R, Swindon (L), Aldershot (L)									
Mendes	Joao	27	Goalkeeper	Ashton United	2		3	2	
Ashton U									
Mendes	Regan	25	Defender	Welling United	1		1	1	
Welling									
Mendy	Arnaud	29	Midfielder	Welling United	29	6	6	35	
Derby, Grimsby (L), Tranmere (L), Macclesfield, Luton (L), Whitehawk, Hemel H, Naxxar (Malta), Whitehawk, Welling									
Mendy	Matteo	20	Midfielder	Hemel Hempstead Town	8	6	8	1	
Quevilly (Fra), Hemel H									
Mensah	Bernard	24	Forward	Aldershot Town (L)	16			16	4
Watford, Braintree (L), V Guimaraes (L), V Guimaraes (L), Barnet (L), Braintree (L), Aldershot, Bristol R, Lincoln C (L), Aldershot (L)									
Mensah	Simon	27	Midfielder	Dartford	2	1	6	3	
				Wealdstone	19	9	5	28	3
Whitehawk, Dartford, Wealdstone									
Meppen-Walters	Courtney	24	Defender	Chorley	40	3	2	43	5
Man City (Y), Carlisle, Ashton U, Chorley, Stockport, Glossop, Chorley									
Meredith	Dan	19	Defender	Maidstone United (L)	4	2	5	6	
WBA (Y), Maidstone (L)									
Merrill	Luke	18	Midfielder	Curzon Ashton	3	1	8	4	
Blackburn (Y), Curzon A									

2018-19 NATIONAL. NORTH & SOUTH PLAYERS

SURNAME	FIRSTNAME	AGE	POSITION	CLUB PLAYED FOR	APPEARANCES				
					X	SX	S	Ap	Gls
Merson	Sam	24	Forward	St Albans City	21	15	7	36	9
Redditch, St Albans									
Merzouk	Lounisse	23	Defender	East Thurrock United	1		1	1	
Monaco, Le Pontet GA, East Thurrock									
Michael-Percil	Roman	24	Defender	St Albans City		2	5	2	
				East Thurrock United	9	5	1	14	2
Tottenham (Y), Ipswich (L), Concord R, Billericay, Farnborough, Grays, Dulwich H, Braintree, St Albans, East Thurrock									
Middleton	Ben	24	Defender	Boston United	20	1	4	21	
Scarborough A, North Ferriby, Harrogate, Boston U (Lx2), Boston U									
Middleton	Harry	24	Midfielder	Alfreton Town		6	3	6	
Doncaster (Y), Port Vale, Halifax (L), Alfreton									
MIdson	Jack	35	Forward	Concord Rangers	44	1	1	45	18
Histon, Oxford U, Wimbledon, Eastleigh, Braintree, Leatherhead, Concord R									
Miles	Jonathan	26	Goalkeeper	Ebbsfleet United	1		31	1	
Tottenham, Dagenham & R (L), Whitehawk (L), Brentwood (L), Ebbsfleet, Concord (L), Gosport (L), Margate (L), Welling (L),									
Miles	Taylor	23	Midfielder	Chelmsford City	3	13	1	16	
West Ham (Y), Concord R (L), Concord R, Braintree, Lincoln C, Boston U (L), Concord R (L), Hemel H, Chelmsford									
Miley	Cavanagh	24	Midfielder	Eastleigh	34	11	3	45	1
Jersey, Eastleigh									
Miller	Ashley	29	Defender	East Thurrock United	8	3	1	11	
Bishop's S, Chelmsford, East Thurrock, Bishop's S, Chelmsford, East Thurrock									
Miller	Brook	18	Defender	Hartlepool United		2			
Hartlepool (Y)									
Miller	Sean	24	Forward	Chester		1		1	
				Curzon Ashton	7	7	2	14	3
Chester (Y), Connah's Q, Altrincham, Chester, Droylsden (DR), Curzon A									
Miller	Tommy	40	Midfielder	Spennymoor Town		1			
Hartlepool, Ipswich, Sunderland, PNE (L), Ipswich, Sheff Wed, Huddersfield, Swindon, Bury, Hartlepool, Halifax, Spennymoor									
Miller-Rodney	Tyrell	25	Midfielder	Hampton & Richmond Borough	33	2	6	35	2
Brentford (Y), Maidenhead (L), Boreham W (L), Maidenhead (L), Hayes & Y, Hampton & R									
Milligan	Jamie	39	Midfielder	FC United of Manchester	2	7	2		
Everton (Y), Blackpool, Fleetwood, Hyde (L), Southport, Stockport, Harrogate T, Bamber Bridge, FC United									
Milloy	Ross		Goalkeeper	Chippenham Town		1			
Chippenham									
Mills	Danny	27	Forward	Welling United (L)	35	7	2	42	9
Crawley, Peterborough, Torquay (L), Rushden (L), Histon (L), Kettering (L), Tamworth (L), Kettering (L), Carshalton, Whitehawk, Ebbsfleet, Dartford (L)Welling (L)									
Mills	John	29	Forward	Bath City	3	9	3	12	
Hereford, Bath									
Ming	Sanchez	29	Forward	Dulwich Hamlet	17	8	4	25	
				Welling United	5			5	
Fisher, Welling, Bishop's S, Bromley, Staines, Dulwich H, Welling									
Minhas	Nathan		Forward	Billericay Town		2	1	2	
Beaconsfield, Billericay									
Minihan	Sam	25	Defender	Stockport County	39	8	7	47	1
Rochdale, Droylsden (L), Loughborough U, Worcester, Stockport									
Minshull	Lee	33	Midfielder	Concord Rangers	29	8	2	37	3
Wimbledon, Newport Co (L), Newport Co, Bromley, Leatherhead, Concord R									
Mirfin	David	34	Defender	York City (L)	7			7	
Huddersfield, Scunthorpe, Watford, Scunthorpe, Hartlepool (L), Mansfield, York (L)									
Mitchell	Kairo	21	Forward	Nuneaton Borough (L)	7	5	1	12	2
Leicester (Y), Nuneaton (L)									
Mitchell	Reece	23	Forward	Wealdstone	2	8	3	10	
Chelsea (Y), Chesterfield, Torquay, Wealdstone									
Modeste	Ricky	31	Forward	Billericay Town	8	5	2	13	
				Dover Athletic	5	7	2	12	1
Chelmsford, Dover, Billericay, Dover									
Mohammed	Zehn	21	Defender	Southport (L)	1		5	1	
				FC United of Manchester (L)	15		2	15	
Accrington, Southport (L), FC United (L)									
Moke	Adriano	29	Midfielder	York City	34	5	2	39	3
York (Y), Cambridge U, Tamworth (L), Halifax, Stockport, Macclesfield, Wrexham, Boreham, York									
Molyneaux	Lee	36	Defender	Havant & Waterlooville		4			
Gloucester, Gosport B, Havant & W									

Key: X - Started; SX - Sub on; S - Non-playing Sub; Ap - Total Appearances; Gls - Total goals.

SURNAME	FIRSTNAME	AGE	POSITION	CLUB	APPEARANCES			Ap	Gls
Molyneux	Lee	30	Defender	Barrow	11	5	17	16	
Everton, Southampton, Port Vale (L), Plymouth, Accrington, Crewe, Rochdale (L), Accrington (L), Accrington (L), Tranmere, Morecambe, Guiseley, Chorley (L), Barrow									
Molyneux	Luke	21	Midfielder	Gateshead (L)	12	6	2	18	3
				Hartlepool United (L)	12	4		16	2
Sunderland (Y), Gateshead (L), Hartlepool (L)									
Monakana	Jeffrey	25	Midfielder	Wealdstone	16	13	12	29	3
Arsenal, PNE, Colchester (L), Brighton, Crawley (L), Aberdeen (L), Mansfield (L), Carlisle (L), Bristol R (L), Voluntari (Rom), Sutton U, Margate (L), Welling (L), Wealdstone (L), Welling, Wealdstone									
Moncrieffe	Kamar		Forward	Salford City	1	2	4	3	
Salford (Y)									
Moncur	Freddy	22	Midfielder	East Thurrock United	5	6	6	11	2
				Ebbsfleet United	1	3	13	4	
Leyton Orient, Bishop's St. (L), Wingate, Kingstonian, East Thurrock, Ebbsfleet									
Monga Ebwa	Yannick	27		East Thurrock United	1	4	1		
Luckenwalde (Ger), East Thurrock									
Monlouis	Kieran	23	Midfielder	Hemel Hempstead Town	11	1		12	1
AFC Sudbury, St Albans, Hamilton, Hemel H									
Montague	Liam		Forward	Aldershot Town		1		1	
Aldershot (Y)									
Montrose	Lewis	30	Midfielder	AFC Fylde	5	2	1	7	
Man City, Wigan, Rochdale (L), Cheltenham (L), Cheltenham (L), Chesterfield (L), Wycombe, Gillingham, Oxford U (L), York , Stockport, AFC Fylde									
Moon	Jasper	18	Midfielder	York City (L)	3		2	3	
Leicester (Y), Barnsley, York (L)									
Mooney	Daniel	19	Forward	Chester (L)	32	5	2	37	8
Fleetwood (Y), Chorley (L), Chester (L)									
Moore	Deon	20	Defender	Bath City (L)		4	1	4	
Peterborough (Y), Bristol R, Bath (L)									
Moore	Lewis	22	Goalkeeper	Dagenham & Redbridge	2		48	2	
Swansea, Dagenham & R									
Moore	Sammy	31	Midfielder	Concord Rangers	1	3	13	4	
Charlton (Y), Chelsea (Y), Ipswich (Y), Brentford (L), Stevenage, Dover, Wimbledon, Leyton O, Dover (L), Leatherhead, Concord R									
Moore-Azille	Tarik	23	Defender	St Albans City	2		3	2	
				Hungerford Town	7		3	7	
				Oxford City	15			15	
Bishop's S, Margate, St Albans, Hungerford, Oxford C									
Moran	Jon	21	Defender	Chester	16	4	5	20	1
Nantwich, Forest GR, Altrincham (L), Weston (L), Chester									
Morford	Will	33	Forward	Gloucester City			6		
Gloucester, Shortwood, Gloucester									
Morgan	Adam	25	Forward	Curzon Ashton	6	4	2	10	3
LiverpoolRotherham (L), Yeovil (L), Yeovil, St Johnstone (L), Accrington, Hemel H, Curzon A, Halifax, Sligo Rovers, Curzon A									
Morgan	Alex	20	Forward	Boreham Wood			2		
Boreham W (Y), Northwood (L)									
Morgan	Ben	20	Defender	Brackley Town (L)	1		5	1	
Swansea (Y), Bristol R, Brackley (L)									
Morgan	David	24	Midfielder	Southport	46	1	1	47	6
Nottm Forest (Y), Lincoln C (L), Dundee (L), Tamworth (L), Ilkeston, Nuneaton, AFC Fylde, Harrogate, Southport									
Morgan-Smith	Amari	30	Forward	AFC Telford United	28	11	5	39	10
Crewe (Y), Stockport, Ilkeston T, Luton, Macclesfield, Kidderminster (L), Kidderminster, Oldham, Cheltenham, York (L), York, Telford									
Morley	Stephan	32	Defender	AFC Telford United	25	5	5	30	3
Hinckley U, Leamington, Corby, Brackley, Tamworth, Telford									
Morris	Kieran	23	Defender	Leamington		1	7	1	
Stourbridge (Y), Brentford (Y), Stourbridge (L), Maidenhead (L), Worcester, Stafford R, Leamington									
Morris-Edwards	George	20	Defender	Weston-super-Mare	1	19	1		
Weston									
Morrison	Brandon		Midfielder	Darlington			6		
Darlington									
Morrison	Curtis	21	Forward	Guiseley	9	15	12	24	1
Chesterfield, Matlock (L), Matlock (L), Guiseley									
Morrison-Derbyshire	Luis	24	Defender	Nuneaton Borough	11	4	8	15	
YPA (Fin), Farnborough, Maidenhead, Hampton & R, Grays, Concord, Altrincham, Alfreton, Nuneaton									
Morton	Callum	19	Forward	Braintree Town (L)	15			15	5
Yeovil (Y), WBA (Y), Braintree (L)									

2018-19 NATIONAL. NORTH & SOUTH PLAYERS

SURNAME	FIRSTNAME	AGE	POSITION	CLUB PLAYED FOR	APPEARANCES				
								Ap	Gls
Morton	Dan	26	Defender	Curzon Ashton	19			19	1
				FC United of Manchester	12			12	
Clitheroe, Stockport, Colne, Stalybridge, Curzon A, FC United									
Morton	James	20	Midfielder	Bath City (L)	36	1		37	1
Bristol C (Y), Chippenham (L), Bath (L), Bath (L)									
Mottley-Henry	Dylan	21	Midfielder	Harrogate Town (L)	4		4		
Bradford, Altrincham (L), Bradford PA (L), Barnsley, Tranmere (L), Chesterfield (L), Tranmere (L), Harrogate (L)									
Moult	Jake	30	Midfielder	Altrincham	49			49	5
Plymouth (Y), Kidderminster, Leek, Stafford R, Alfreton, Altrincham									
Moyo	Cliff	26	Defender	Guiseley	44	1	1	45	1
Alfreton, Barrow, Northwich, Drolsden, Trafford, Halifax, Guiseley									
Moyo	David	24	Forward	St Albans City	39	6	1	45	15
Northampton (Y), Stamford (L), Brackley (L), Brackley, Hemel H, St Albans									
Mudd	Reuben	18	Forward	East Thurrock United	2		2		
East Thurrock									
Mueller	Stefan	23	Defender	Southport	4	3	18	7	
Temple Owls (US), TB Uphusen (Ger), Southport									
Muggleton	Sam	23	Defender	Chesterfield	11	9	9	20	
				Darlington (L)	2			2	
Gillingham (Y), Barnet (L), Barnet, Eastleigh, York, Boston U (L), Chesterfield, Darlington (L)									
Muir	Adam	17	Defender	Curzon Ashton			6		
Curzon A									
Muir	Niko	26	Forward	Hartlepool United	29	11	11	40	6
Grays, Northwood, Hendon, Northwood, Wingate, Northwood, VCD Ath, Northwood, Hendon, Leiston, Hendon, Hartlepool									
Muldoon	Jack	30	Forward	Harrogate Town	44	6	2	50	17
Worksop, Rochdale, FC Halifax, Lincoln, AFC Fylde, Harrogate									
Muldoon	Oliver	24	Midfielder	Maidstone United	30	8	5	38	
Charlton, Gillingham (L), Dagenham & R (L), Braintree (L), Gillingham, Maidstone									
Muleba	Joanthan	23	Defender	Braintree Town	22	1		23	
Chelsea (Y), Bournemouth, Poole (L), Gosport (L), Bishop's S (L), Folkstone Inv, Enfield T, Braintree									
Mulhern	Euan (Frank)	22	Forward	Stockport County	36	15		51	16
Leeds, Southport (L), Huddersfield, Guiseley, Stockport									
Mulholland	Astley	31	Forward	Barrow	1	3		4	
Abbey Hey, Ashton U, Altrincham, FC United, Ashton U, FC United, Chorley, Glossop NE, Colwyn, Barrow									
Mullen	Damen	30	Defender	Blyth Spartans	25	4	10	29	
Ashington, Blyth S									
Mulley	James	30	Midfielder	Maidenhead United	7	7	5	14	
Hayes & Yeading, Chelmsford (L), AFC Wimbledon, Hayes & Yeading (L), Braintree, Maidenhead, Wingate & F (L), Hampton & R, Maidenhead, Enfield Town									
Mullings	Shamir	25	Forward	Maidstone United	8	3	2	11	2
				Dagenham & Redbridge (L)	5	5	2	10	1
Southend (Y), Thurrock (L), Tilbury (L), Harlow (L), Bromley, Thamesmead (L), Havant & W, Chelsmford, Forest Green, Macclesfield (L), Maidstone, Dagenham & R (L)									
Munns	Jack	25	Midfielder	Dagenham & Redbridge	24	6	3	30	2
Leyton O, Tottenham, Aldershot, Charlton, Cheltenham, Hartlepool, Dagenham & R									
Murombedzi	Shepherd	24	Midfielder	Brackley Town	27	7	8	34	2
Reading, Torquay, Nuneaton, Hayes & Y, Solihull M, Chester, Brackley									
Murphy	Billy	23	Forward	Hereford FC	15	1	3	16	
				Leamington		1		1	
Hereford, Bristol C, Bath (L), Bath, Hereford, Halesowen, Leamington									
Murphy	Jordan	23	Forward	Solihull Moors	2	7	13	9	1
				Leamington (L)	19		1	19	2
Stourbridge, Walsall, Worcester (L), Kidderminster (L), Worcester (L), Worcester, Telford U, Solihull, Leamington (L)									
Murphy	Luca	17	Defender	Hartlepool United		3			
Hartlepool (Y)									
Murphy	Rhys	28	Forward	Chelmsford City	39	1		40	24
Arsenal, Brentford (L), Preston (L), Dagenham & R, Oldham, Crawley (L), AFC Wimbledon (L), Forest Green, York (L), Crawley (L), Torquay (L), Gillingham, Chelmsford									
Murphy	Sam	29	Midfielder	Hemel Hempstead Town	3		1	3	
Hendon, Hemel H									
Murphy	Tom	27	Forward	Dartford	10	17	5	27	3
Lewes, Thurrock, Farnborough, Margate, Dover, Maidstone, Eastbourne B (L), Dartford									
Murray	Iwan	18	Forward	Chester	7	6	11	13	2
Rhyl, Chester									

Key: X - Started; SX - Sub on; S - Non-playing Sub; Ap - Total Appearances; Gls - Total goals.

SURNAME	FIRSTNAME	AGE	POSITION	CLUB				Ap	Gls
Murrell-Williamson	Rhys	25	Midfielder	Hampton & Richmond Borough	18	5	4	23	4
				Billericay Town		3		3	
				Woking	2		1	2	
Sutton U, Harrow, Hayes & Y, Dulwich, Boreham W, Dulwich, Welling (L), St Albans, Hampton & R, Billericay, Woking									
Murtagh	Keiran	30	Midfielder	Boreham Wood	48			48	8
Charlton, Fisher, Yeovil, Wycombe, Cambridge U, Macclesfield, Mansfield, Woking (L), Woking, Boreham W									
Muscatt	Joe	21	Defender	Salford City (L)	4		1	4	
Tottenham (Y), Bolton (Y), Salford (L)									
Musonda	Frankie	21	Midfielder	Oxford City (L)	6	1		7	1
				Hemel Hempstead Town (L)	13			13	2
Luton (Y), Braintree (L), Oxford C (L), Oxford C (L), Hemel H (L)									
Muyembe	Magloire		Forward	Hemel Hempstead Town		4			
Hemel H									
Myers	Louis		Forward	FC United of Manchester	7	3		10	1
Fleetwood, ChorleyRamsbottom, Radcliffe B, FC United									
Myles	Ellis	26	Defender	Brackley Town	29	11	10	40	1
Brackley, Rugby T, Stamford, Corby, Brackley									
Myles-Meekums	Reece	20	Forward	Bromley	3	7	9	10	
				Eastbourne Borough (L)	2	1	2	3	
Brighton (Y), Bromley, Worthing (L), Eastbourne B (L)									
Myrie-Williams	Jennison	31	Midfielder	Hereford FC	5	2		7	
				Weston-super-Mare	20			20	2
Bristol C, Cheltenham (L), Tranmere (L), Cheltenham (L), Carlisle (L), Hereford (L), Dundee Utd, St Johnstone, Stevenage, Port Vale (L), Port Vale, Scunthorpe, Tranmere (L), Sligo Rovers, Newport Co, Torquay, Hereford, Weston									
Nabay	Foday	20	Midfielder	Nuneaton Borough	3	1	3		
Birmingham (Y), Fulham (Y), Nuneaton									
Nabi	Samir	22	Midfielder	Torquay United	5	6	5	11	
WBA (Y), Delhi Dynamos, Carlisle, Torquay									
Najia	Tarek	17	Goalkeeper	Bromley (L)			1		
				Dagenham & Redbridge		1			
Dagenham & R (Y), Bromley (L)									
Nakov	Luka	19	Goalkeeper	Bromley			4		
Slavia Sofia (Bul), Bromley									
Nash	Liam	23	Forward	Dulwich Hamlet (L)	2		1	2	
				Concord Rangers (L)	12	1		13	5
Gillingham, Leatherhead (L), Dulwich (L), Concord R (L), Cork									
Nasha	Amos	23	Midfielder	Chelmsford City	10	2	5	12	2
				East Thurrock United	14	2		16	2
West Ham (Y), Dover, Concord R, Chelmsford, East Thurrock									
Naylor	Martyn	41	Defender	Leamington			4		
TNS, Telford, Rhyl, Telford, Stafford R, Worcester, Rushall, Leamington									
Ndiaye	Iliman		Midfielder	Boreham Wood			9		
Boreham W (Y)									
Ndlovu	Lee		Forward	Brackley Town	45	2	1	47	17
Holbeach U, Grantham, Ilkeston, Brackley									
Neal	Chris	33	Goalkeeper	Salford City	51		3	51	
PNE (Y), Tamworth (L), Shrewsbury (L), Shrewsbury, Port Vale, Doncaster (L), Bury (L), Fleetwood, Salford									
Neave	George		Goalkeeper	Salford City			1		
Salford (Y)									
Nelson	Andrew	21	Forward	Darlington (L)	5			5	6
Sunderland (Y), Darlington (L)									
Nelson	Michael	39	Defender	Chesterfield	13		9	13	
Leek, Spennymoor, Bishop A, Bury, Hartlepool, Norwich, Scunthorpe, Kilmarnock, Bradford, Hibernian, Cambridge U, Barnet, Chesterfield									
Nesbeth	Aaron		Defender	Gloucester City			2		
Gloucester									
Newall	Nathan	17	Defender	Guiseley			3		
Guiseley (Y)									
Newby	Alex	23	Forward	Chorley	33	3	4	36	11
Barrow (Y), Kendal (L), Clitheroe, Chorley									
Newby	Elliott	23	Midfielder	Chorley	46			46	8
Bolton (Y), Barrow, Burscough (L), Altrincham (L), Telford, Chorley									
Newey	Ben		Goalkeeper	Leamington			11		
Leamington (Y)									

2018-19 NATIONAL. NORTH & SOUTH PLAYERS

APPEARANCES

SURNAME	FIRSTNAME	AGE	POSITION	CLUB PLAYED FOR				Ap	Gls
Newton	Conor	27	Midfielder	Hartlepool United	3	12	10	15	
Newcastle, St Mirren (L), Rotherham, Cambridge U, Hartlepool									
Newton	Sean	30	Defender	York City	35	2	1	37	6
Droylsden, Barrow, Telford, Stockport (L), Stockport, Lincoln C, Notts Co (L), Wrexham, York (L), York									
Newton	Zack		Midfielder	Welling United	2	7	6	9	
Welling									
Nicholls	Ryan		Goalkeeper	Dartford			6		
Dartford									
Nicholson	Alex	25	Defender	Blyth Spartans	33	1	8	34	2
PNE (Y), Chorley (L), Blyth S, South Shields, Blyth S									
Nicholson	Jodan	25	Midfielder	Darlington	35	7	1	42	11
Histon, Peterborough, Nuneaton (L), Nuneaton (L), Barnet, Brackley (L), Darlington									
Nicholson	Shay		Forward	Leamington			2		
Leamington (Y)									
Nicholson	Tom	31	Goalkeeper	Alfreton Town	2		41	2	
Scarborough, Garforth, Hull City, North Ferriby,Halifax, Alfreton									
Nieskens	Dave	25	Defender	Braintree Town	9		2	9	
Barrow, Braintree									
Nisbet	Mark	32	Defender	Slough Town	40	2	7	42	2
Maidenhead, Slough									
Nketia	Joel		Defender	Hemel Hempstead Town		1			
Hemel H (Y)									
Noble	Cain		Midfielder	Chester	4	4	10	8	1
Chester									
Noble	David	37	Midfielder	St Albans City	21		4	21	1
Bristol C, Yeovil (L), Exeter, Rotherham, Cheltenham (L), Oldham, Exeter (L), Exeter, St Albans									
Noble	Lee	30	Midfielder	Dartford	35			35	3
Dartford									
Noble	Liam	28	Midfielder	Hartlepool United	40	5		45	13
Sunderland (Y), Carlisle (L), Carlisle (L), Carlisle, Notts Co, Forest GR, Notts Co, Hartlepool									
Noble-Lazarus	Reuben	25	Forward	Chorley		1	1	1	
Barnsley (Y), Scunthorpe (L), Rochdale (L), Rochdale, Chorley									
Noel-Williams	Dejon	20	Forward	Slough Town	3	4		7	
				Gloucester City	6	1	1	7	2
Slough, Gloucester									
Nolan	George		Defender	Hemel Hempstead Town		5			
Hemel H									
Nolan	Liam	24	Midfielder	Salford City (L)	7	2	2	9	
Crewe (Y), Southport, Accrington, Salford (L)									
Nombe	Sam	20	Forward	Oxford City (L)	13	1		14	3
				Maidenhead United (L)	12	1	4	13	
MK Dons (Y), Oxford C (L), Oxford C (L), Maidenhead (L)									
Noon	Mark	35	Midfielder	Brackley Town			15		
Coventry (Y), Tamworth, Nuneaton, Brackley									
Norrington-Davies	Rhys	20	Defender	Barrow (L)	29			29	
Swansea (Y), Sheffield U (Y), Barrow (L)									
Norris	David	38	Midfielder	Boston United	4	2	3	6	
Boston U (Y), Bolton, Boston U (L), Hull (L), Plymouth, Ipswich, Portsmouth, Leeds, Peterborough, Yeovil, Blackpool, Leatherhead, Salford, Shaw Lane, Boston U									
Nortey	Nortei	24	Midfielder	Dover Athletic	23	17	8	40	1
Chelsea, Welling, Wrexham, Solihull M, Dover									
North	Jonathan	28	Goalkeeper	Wealdstone	46			46	
Wealdstone									
Nowakowski	Adam	31	Midfielder	Bradford Park Avenue	6	24	12	30	1
Harrogate T, Darlington, Bradford PA (L), Bradford PA									
Nti	Daniel	25	Forward	Brackley Town	6	31	11	37	5
Worcester, York, Halifax (L), Kidderminster, Nuneaton, Brackley									
Nunn	Ben	29	Defender	Dagenham & Redbridge	22		1	22	1
Boston, Chelmsford, Boreham W (L), Boreham W, St Albans (L), Dagenham & R									
Nurse	George	20	Midfielder	Weston-super-Mare (L)	46	1		47	4
Bristol C, Weston (L)									
Nzengo	Jonathan	21	Defender	East Thurrock United	15	6	8	21	1
Ware, Maldon & T, Romford, East Thurrock									

Key: X - Started; SX - Sub on; S - Non-playing Sub; Ap - Total Appearances; Gls - Total goals.

SURNAME	FIRSTNAME	AGE	POSITION	CLUB	APPEARANCES				
								Ap	Gls
O'Brien	Danny	23	Midfielder	Alfreton Town	2	7	10	9	1
Aston Villa (Y), Wigan, Wrexham (L), Chester (L), Chester (L), Narpes Kraft (Fin), SJK II, Alfreton									
O'Brien	Jake		Midfielder	Chorley			1		
Chorley									
O'Connor	James	34	Defender	Kidderminster Harriers	22		2	22	3
Aston Villa (Y), Port Vale (L), Bournemouth, Doncaster, Derby, Bristol C (L), Walsall, Kidderminster									
O'Donnell	Jonathan	27	Midfielder	Gateshead	16	9	12	25	
Luton, Hyde (L), Gateshead (L), Gateshead									
O'Donoghue	John		Midfielder	Oxford City	1	1	15	2	
Oxford C									
O'Halloran	Stephen	31	Defender	FC United of Manchester	44			44	
Aston Villa (Y), Wycombe (L), Leeds (L), Southampton (L), Swansea (L), Coventry, Carlisle, Nuneaton, Stockport, Salford, Stockport, FC United									
O'Hanlon	Ben	23	Defender	Darlington	16	5	3	21	
Wolves (Y), Corby (L), Nuneaton (L), Telford (L), Nuneaton (L), Harrogate T, Darlington									
O'Hara	Jamie	32	Midfielder	Billericay Town	14	10	5	24	
Tottenham (Y), Chesterfield (L), Millwall (L), Portsmouth (L), Wolves (L), Wolves, Blackpool, Fulham, Gillingham, Billericay									
O'Keefe	Corey	21	Defender	Solihull Moors (L)	9	7	6	16	
Birmingham (Y), Solihull (L)									
O'Keefe	Josh	30	Midfielder	Chorley	37	5		42	9
Walsall, Lincoln C, Southport, Hereford, Kidderminster, Telford (L), Chester (L), Altrincham, Chorley									
O'Leary	Jack	21	Defender	Curzon Ashton	7		7	7	
Curzon A									
O'Neill	Tyrone	19	Forward	Hartlepool United (L)	2	4	3	6	1
Middlesbrough (Y), Hartlepool (L)									
O'Reilly	Luke	23	Goalkeeper	Chelmsford City	1		1	1	
Nike Acad, Cardiff (Y), Redditch (L), Tottenham U23, Carlisle, Chelmsford									
O'Sullivan	Tommy	24	Midfielder	Hereford FC	21	11	1	32	1
Cardiff, Port Vale (L), Newport Co (Lx2), Colchester,Torquay (L), Hereford									
Oastler	Joe	28	Defender	Oxford City	45			45	5
QPR (Y), Torquay (L), Torquay, Aldershot, Gosport B, Oxford C									
Oates	James	28	Defender	Hereford FC (L)	7			7	1
Manly Utd (Aus), Central Coast Mariners, Manly Utd (L), Manly Utd, Hereford, Exeter, Hereford (L)									
Obeng	Ahmed	27	Forward	Leamington	20	17	6	37	3
Rushall, Kidderminster, Hednesford, Stafford, Leamington									
Obeng	Curtis	30	Defender	Nuneaton Borough	34	1	1	35	
Wrexham, Swansea, Fleetwood (L), York (L), Stevenage (L), Newport Co (L), Witton, Macclesfield, Altrincham, Solihull, Nuneaton									
Obi	Ogo	21	Forward	Hampton & Richmond Borough	6	3	6		
				Wealdstone	1	2	2	3	
Watford (Y), Hemel H (L), Hemel H (L), Cardiff, Hampton & R, Wealdstone									
Obileye	Ayo	24	Defender	Maidenhead United	39	1	2	40	4
Sheffield Wed, Dagenham & Red (L), Dagenham & Red (L), Eastleigh, Dover (L), Maidenhead									
Ochieng	Henry	20	Midfielder	Braintree Town	4	2	6	6	
West Ham (Y), Leyton O, Braintree									
Odametey	Harold	26	Midfielder	Maidenhead United	41	6		47	1
Hampton & R, Maidenhead									
Odejayi	Kayode	37	Forward	Guiseley	27	7	7	34	7
Bristol C, Forest Green (L), Forest Green, Cheltenham, Barnsley, Scunthorpe (L), Colchester, Rotherham, Accrington (L), Accrington (L), Tranmere, Stockport, Guiseley									
Odelusi	Sanmi	25	Forward	FC Halifax Town	11	8	13	19	
Bolton (Y), MK Dons (L), Coventry (L), Wigan, Rochdale (L), Blackpool (L), Colchester, Cheltenham, FC Halifax									
Odubade	Yemi	31	Forward	Eastbourne Borough	5	14	2	19	4
Oxford U, Stevenage, Newport Co, Gateshead, Forest GR (L), Eastleigh, Woking (L), Maidstone, Eastbourne B, Weymouth									
Odusina	Oluwarotimi Mark	19	Defender	AFC Fylde (L)	7	6	7	13	
Norwich (Y), AFC Fylde (L)									
Ofoegbu	Ify	19	Forward	Chesterfield		3	1	3	
Hudderfield (Y), Chesterfield (Y)									
OFori-Acheampong	Duane	26	Forward	Woking	4	10	4	14	1
Torquay, Dover, Dartford, Woking									
Ofori-Twumasi	Nathan	29	Defender	Maidstone United	13	1	5	14	
				Maidenhead United	23	1	2	24	
Chelsea, Dagenham & R (L), Peterborough, Northampton (L), Northampton, Yeovil, Newport Co, Maidstone, Maidenhead									
Ogedi-Uzokwe	Junior	25	Forward	Bromley (L)	17	9	3	26	6
Carlton T, Enfield T, Hayes & Y, Barkingside, Lewes, Turk Ocagi, Maldon & T, Colchester, Bromley (L)									

2018-19 NATIONAL. NORTH & SOUTH PLAYERS

APPEARANCES

SURNAME	FIRSTNAME	AGE	POSITION	CLUB PLAYED FOR	X	SX	S	Ap	Gls
Ogie	Shadrach		Defender	Leyton Orient		1	1	1	
Leyton Orient (Y)									
Ogle	Reagan	20	Defender	Southport (L)	42			42	
Accrington (Y), Stoke U23 (L), Wealdstone (L), Southport (L)									
Ogunmekan	Prince		Midfielder	Bromley			2		
Bromley (Y)									
Ogunrinde	Emmanuel		Midfielder	Salford City		1		1	
Salford (Y)									
Öhman	Patrik		Goalkeeper	Chelmsford City			1		
Upsala (Swe), Chelmsford, Carshalton									
Ojemen	Briggs		Midfielder	Bromley		1		1	
Bromley (Y)									
Okimo	Jerome	31	Defender	Wealdstone	47			47	2
Stevenage, Braintree, Wealdstone									
Okoh	Stephen	24	Forward	Bromley			1		
Maidstone, VCD Athletic, Gazieh, Hastings U, Leatherhead, Lewes, Stranraer, Margate, Bromley									
Okosieme	Ejiro	26	Defender	Dover Athletic	4	4	8	8	
				Braintree Town	4	2		6	
Bishop's St, Macclesfield, Dover, Braintree,									
Okoye	Marc-Anthony		Defender	Bromley	27	11	2	38	2
Bromley, Merstham, Dulwich, Erith & Bel, Braintree, Bromley									
OkuonghAe	Magnus	33	Defender	Dulwich Hamlet	30	1		31	1
Aldershot, St Albans, Crawley, Dagenham & R, Weymouth, Dagenham & R, Colchester, Luton, Hartlepool (L), Dagenham & R, Maidstone, Welling (L), Dulwich									
Olaniran	Daniel		Defender	East Thurrock United		1			
East Thurrock									
Oliver	Connor	25	Midfielder	Blyth Spartans	30	11	5	41	1
Sunderland (Y), Hartlepool (L), Blackpool, Morecambe (L), North Ferriby, Halifax, Blyth S									
Oliyide	Karl	24	Midfielder	Hemel Hempstead Town	12	6	4	18	8
				Hampton & Richmond Borough	3	3	7	6	
Leiknir Reykjavik, Hendon, Braintree, Hemel H, Hampton & R									
Ollerenshaw	Josh	28	Goalkeeper	Ashton United	7			7	
Oldham (Y), Mossley (L), Northwich (L), Colwyn, Fleetwood, Colwyn, Ashton U									
Olley	Greg	23	Midfielder	Gateshead	39	2		41	8
Newcastle (Y), Hull (Y), Gateshead									
Ollis	James		Forward	Bath City		3	1	3	
Bath (Y)Mangotsfield (L)									
Omar	Arif	17	Midfielder	Ebbsfleet United	1	1	4	2	
Ebbsfleet (Y)									
Omotayo	Gold	25	Forward	Maidstone United (L)	1	4		5	1
FC Zurich (Y), FC Schlieren, FC Wettswil, Whitehawk, Bury, Maidstone (L)									
Omozusi	Elliot Junior	30	Defender	Chelmsford City	37			37	
Fulham (Y), Norwich (L), Charlton (L), Leyton O, Cambridge U, Whitehawk, Chelmsford									
Omrore	Manny	20	Defender	East Thurrock United	1	3	1		
East Thurrock									
Onariase	Emmanuel	22	Defender	Dagenham & Redbridge (L)	31			31	
West Ham (Y), Brentford, Cheltenham (L), Rotherham, Cheltenham (L), Dagenham & R (L)									
Onovwigun	Michael	23	Midfielder	Dulwich Hamlet	5	3	8	8	
Chesterfield (Y), Stalybridge (L), Gateshead (L), Southport, Dulwich H, Carshalton (L)									
Onyeaka	Jonathan	23	Defender	Nuneaton Borough	2		2	2	
Jersey Express (US), Nuneaton									
Onyemah	Mark	23	Defender	Dartford	27	1	5	28	
Luton, Dartford (L), Concord R, Dartford									
Orlu	Richard	30	Defender	Welling United	10	2	7	12	
				Hampton & Richmond Borough (L)	5			5	
Staines, Farnborough, Canvey I, Dover, Woking, Welling, Hampton & R (L)									
Ormson	Ian	25	Goalkeeper	Stockport County		55			
Stockport (Y)									
Orsi-Dadamo	Danilo		Forward	East Thurrock United	4	4	2	8	2
				Hungerford Town	28	3		31	9
East Thurrock, Hungerford									

Key: X - Started; SX - Sub on; S - Non-playing Sub; Ap - Total Appearances; Gls - Total goals.

SURNAME	FIRSTNAME	AGE	POSITION	CLUB	APPEARANCES			Ap	Gls
Osborn	Alex	25	Forward	Hemel Hempstead Town	9	7	8	16	1
				East Thurrock United	17	1	1	18	
Grays, Dag & Red, Thurrock (L), Chelmsford (L), Billericay, Ebbsfleet, Hayes & Y (L), Maidstone (L), Concord R (L), Whitehawk (L), Margate, Whitehawk, Hemel H, East Thurrock									
Osborne	Elliot	23	Midfielder	Southport	6	2	2	8	1
				Stockport County	22	16	7	38	2
Nantwich, Fleetwood, Tranmere (L), Stockport (L), Southport, Stockport (L), Stockport									
Osborne	Jamey	27	Midfielder	Solihull Moors	45	3	3	48	5
Hednesford, Ringmer (L), Redditch, Solihull M, Grimsby, Solihull M (L), Solihull M									
Osborne	Karleigh	31	Defender	Aldershot Town	6	2	2	8	
				Braintree Town	1		1	1	
Brentford (Yth),Hayes (L), Oxford U (L), Eastbourne (L), Millwall, Bristol C (L), Bristol C, Colchester (L), Wimbledon (L), Plymouth, Kilmarnock, Grimsby, Aldershot, Braintree									
Osho	Gabriel	20	Defender	Aldershot Town (L)	11			11	
Reading (Yth), Maidenhead (L), Aldershot (L)									
Ossai	Tariq	19	Defender	Chippenham Town	18			18	1
Chippenham									
Oswell	Jason	26	Forward	Wrexham	8	8	1	16	1
Crewe (Y), Rhyl (L), Inverness, Nantwich, APIA Leichhardt (Aus), Rhyl, Airbus, Newtown, Stockport, Morecambe, Wrexham									
Otudeko	Kunle	22	Forward	Oxford City	5	7	7	12	1
Bristol R (Y), Wealdstone (L), Poole (L), Oxford C									
Oualah	Zaki	24	Goalkeeper	Aldershot Town			2		
Uxbridge, Godalming, Hampton & R, Bedford T, Burham, Aylesbury U, Farnborough, US Biskra, Leatherhead, Hayes & Y, Aldershot									
Ouldridge	Tom	20	Midfielder	Hungerford Town	3	6	12	9	
Swindon (Y), Chippenham (L), Hungerford									
Owen-Evans	Tom	22	Midfielder	Hereford FC	31	1		32	11
Newport Co (Y), Gloucester (L), Truro (L), Falkirk, Hereford									
Owens	Kris	20	Defender	Southport	1			1	
Liverpool (Y), Stoke U23, Southport									
Owusu	Nana	23	Defender	Maidenhead United	12	14	18	26	2
Tranmere, Maidenhead									
Oyebanjo	Olanrewaju	29	Defender	Welling United		1	1	1	
Histon, York, Crawley, York, Welling									
Oyenuga	Olalekan	26	Midfielder	Dartford	7	12	7	19	1
Tottenham (Y), MYPA (Fin) (L), Bury (L), St Johnstone, Hayes & Y, Dundee U, Boreham W (L), Cowdenbeath (L), Hartlepool, Morton, Chelmsford, Dartford									
Ozono	Will	19	Forward	FC United of Manchester	1	1	1	2	
Crystal Palace (Y), FC United									
Page	Adam	22	Midfielder	Gloucester City	6	5	2	11	
Cheltenham, Gloucester (L), Hereford (L), Gloucester									
Palfrey	Billy	21	Defender	Truro City	6	7	15	13	
Plymouth (Y), Torquay (L), Truro									
Palinkas	Jan		Defender	FC United of Manchester	3	2	10	5	
FC United (Y)									
Palmer	Ashley	26	Defender	Stockport County	53			53	5
Scunthorpe, Southport (L), Droylsden, Buxton, North Ferriby, Guiseley, Stockport									
Palmer	Ed	27	Defender	Truro City	12		1	12	1
Torquay, Truro (L), Weymouth, Truro, Taunton, Truro									
Palmer	Romal	20	Midfielder	Darlington	15	2	1	17	
Darlington									
Palmer	Tom	19	Goalkeeper	Kidderminster Harriers	4	1	15	5	
Kidderminster (Y)									
Panayiotou	Harrison (Harry)	24	Forward	Nuneaton Borough	15	3	4	18	
Leicester, Port Vale (L),Raith (L), Barrow, Salford City (L), Nuneaton									
Pappoe	Daniel	25	Defender	Dulwich Hamlet	6		1	6	
Chelsea (Y), Colchester (L), Hemel H, BAK'07 (Ger), Hemel H, Crawley, Foresta Suceava (Rom), Dulwich H, Carshalton (L), Carshalton									
Parker	Ben	31	Defender	Harrogate Town			10		
Leeds (Y), Bradford (L), Darlington (L), Carlisle (L), Guiseley, Harrogate									
Parker	Dylan		Forward	Leamington (L)		2	3	2	
Walsall (Y), Rushall (L), Leamington (L)									
Parker	Joe	24	Forward	Gloucester City	32	6	1	38	2
Gloucester, Newport Co, Gloucester (L), Gloucester (Lx2), Gloucester									
Parkes	Jordan	29	Midfielder	Hemel Hempstead Town	47	3	1	50	15
Brentford, Barnet, Farnborough (L), Chelmsford, Hemel H, Ebbsfleet, Hemel H									

2018-19 NATIONAL. NORTH & SOUTH PLAYERS

SURNAME	FIRSTNAME	AGE	POSITION	CLUB PLAYED FOR	APPEARANCES			Ap	Gls
Parkhouse	David	19	Forward	Boston United (L)		3	1	3	
Maiden City (NI), Sheff Utd (Y), Boston U (L), Derry City (L)									
Parkin	Dylan	19	Goalkeeper	Boston United			7		
Chesterfield (Y), Boston U, Cleethorpes (L)									
Parkin	Jon	37	Forward	York City	5	19	9	24	3
Barnsley (Y), Hartlepool (L), York (L), York, Macclesfield, Hull, Stoke (L), Stoke, PNE, Cardiff, Doncaster (L), Huddersfield (L), Scunthorpe (L), Fleetwood, Forest GR, Newport Co, York (L), York									
Parkinson-Harvey	Sam	18	Midfielder	Weston-super-Mare		2			
Weston (Y)									
Parry	Andrew	27	Defender	Southport	17	6	11	23	
Kettering, Radcliffe, Southport, Luton, Telford (L), Southport (L), Altrincham (L), Barrow (L), Barrow, Southport									
Parry	Immanuel (Manny)	25	Defender	Boreham Wood	23	7	20	30	
Millwall, Stoke, Maidenhead (L), Nuneaton T (L), Weston-S-M (L), Worcester (L), Grays Ath, Maidstone, Margate, Braintree, Dover, Boreham W									
Parselle	Kieran	22	Defender	Chippenham Town	46	1	1	47	1
Newport Co, Salisbury (L), Gloucester, Chippenham									
Parslow	Danny	33	Defender	York City	3	1	4	4	
York, Grimsby (Lx2), Cheltenham, York (L), York									
Parsons	Aaron	20	Defender	Weston-super-Mare (L)	18			18	
Bristol C (Y), Weston (L), Weston (L)									
Passley	Josh	24	Defender	Dover Athletic	32	3	2	35	1
Fulham, Shrewsbury (L), Portsmouth (L), Dagenham & R, Whitehawk, Dover									
Paterson	Dylan	27	Goalkeeper	Wealdstone		1	13	1	
Wealdstone									
Paterson	Matt	29	Forward	Oxford City	11			11	7
				Welling United	9	1	1	10	2
				Havant & Waterlooville	6	6	2	12	4
Bournemouth (Y), Southampton (Y), Southend, Stockport (L), Hamilton A (L), Forest GR (L), Burton, Aldershot, Havant & W (L), Gosport, Havant & W, Oxford C, Welling, Havant & W									
Patterson	Christie	22	Midfielder	Braintree Town	10	7	5	17	
Welling, Carshalton, Braintree									
Paul	Christopher	21	Midfielder	Havant & Waterlooville	13	6	4	19	1
Tottenham (Y), QPR (Y), Havant & W									
Paulin	George		Goalkeeper	Hemel Hempstead Town		29			
Hemel H (Y)									
Pavey	Alfie	23	Forward	Havant & Waterlooville	14	6	1	20	4
				Dover Athletic	16	11	1	27	8
Maidstone, Millwall (Y), Barnet (L), Aldershot (L), Bromley (L), Hampton & R (L), Dartford (L), Welling, Dartford, Havant & W, Dover									
Paxman	Jack	25	Midfielder	Maidstone United	32	8	4	40	2
				Billericay Town	6			6	
Maidstone, East Thurrock (L), Billericay									
Payne	Jack	27	Midfielder	Ebbsfleet United	34	2	1	36	
				Eastleigh (L)	5		1	5	
Gillingham, Peterborough (L), Peterborough, Leyton Orient (L), Blackpool, Ebbsfleet, Eastleigh (L)									
Payne	Joe	20	Defender	Barnet	1	3	11	4	
				Wealdstone (L)	5		2	5	
Barnet, Solihull M (L), Wealdstone (L)									
Pearce	Bradley		Defender	Sutton United	9	2	1	11	1
Sutton U (Y)									
Pearce	Isaac	20	Forward	Gloucester City (L)	3	1		4	
Fulham (Y), Bath (L), Forest GR, Gloucester (L)									
Pears	Aynsley	21	Goalkeeper	Gateshead (L)	46		1	46	
Middlesbrough (Y), Darlington (L), Gateshead (L)									
Pearson	Sam	17	Midfielder	Bath City (L)			1		
Bristol C (Y), Bath (L)									
Pearson	Shaun	30	Defender	Wrexham	46			46	6
Grimsby, Wrexham									
Pearson	Tyler		Forward	Eastbourne Borough		1			
Eastbourne B									
Peck	William		Defender	Gloucester City		1	5	1	
Gloucester									
Peers	Tom	23	Forward	Altrincham	3	9	3	12	3
				FC United of Manchester	15	7	2	22	5
Chester (Y), Salford (L), Hednesford (L), Hednesford, Telford, Nantwich, Altrincham, FC United									

Key: X - Started; SX - Sub on; S - Non-playing Sub; Ap - Total Appearances; Gls - Total goals.

SURNAME	FIRSTNAME	AGE	POSITION	CLUB	APPEARANCES			Ap	Gls
Peniket	Richard	26	Forward	Alfreton Town	40	4		44	7
Fulham, Hereford (L), Kidderminster (L), Telford (L), Tamworth, Halifax, Telford (L), Gateshead, Alfreton									
Penn	Russell	33	Midfielder	York City	11	4	1	15	
				Kidderminster Harriers	18	6	1	24	
Scunthorpe, Kidderminster, Alvechurch (L), Burton, Cheltenham, York, Carlisle, Gateshead (L), Wrexham (L), Gateshead, York, Kidderminster									
Pennell	Luke	23	Defender	Dagenham & Redbridge	20		1	20	1
MK Dons, Rushden, Banbury United, Wolverton, Dunstable, Dagenham & R									
Pentney	Carl	29	Goalkeeper	Maidenhead United	48			48	
Leicester, York (Lx2)Ilkeston (L), Woking (L), Colchester, Bath (L), Hayes & Yeading (L), Chelmsford, Braintree, Maidenhead									
Perrin	Jordan	19	Goalkeeper	FC United of Manchester (L)	1	1	2	2	
Wigan (Y), FC United (L)									
Peters	Ryan	31	Midfielder	Maidenhead United		10			
Brentford, Ebbsfleet (L), Crawley (L), Margate, Braintree, Maidenhead									
Phenix	Mike	30	Midfielder	Southport	3	3	6	6	
Droylsden, Skelmersdale, Telford, Barnsley, Macclesfield (L), Southport (L), Salford, Southport									
Phillips	Aaron	25	Midfielder	Kidderminster Harriers	2	2	3	4	1
Coventry (Y), Nuneaton (L), Northampton, Kidderminster									
Phillips	Michael	21	Midfielder	Maidstone United	40	11	5	51	4
Crystal Palace, Maidstone									
Phillips	Trent		Goalkeeper	Slough Town			13		
Staines, Slough									
Philliskirk	Danny	28	Midfielder	AFC Fylde	41	7	6	48	4
Chelsea, Oxford U (L), Sheffield U (L), Sheffield U, Oxford U (L), Coventry, Oldham, Blackpool, AFC Fylde									
Philpot	Jamie	22	Forward	Dartford	16	5	2	21	5
				Maidstone United	1		1		
				Bromley		3	3	3	
				Barrow	7			7	
Millwall, Bromley (L), Woking (L)Welling (L), Dartford, Maidstone, Bromley, Barrow									
Phipps	Eli	21	Forward	Weston-super-Mare	11	15	7	26	4
Cardiff (Y), Gloucester (L), Colchester, Welling (L), Weston									
Phipps	Harry	20	Midfielder	Dagenham & Redbridge	16	7	3	23	1
Margate, Maidstone, Welling (L), East Thurrock (L), Dagenham & R									
Piergianni	Carl	27	Defender	Salford City	53			53	11
Peterborough (Y), Spalding (L), Altrincham (L), Stockport, Corby, Boston U, South Melbourne, Salford									
Pierson	Matte		Goalkeeper	Slough Town			2		
Slough									
PiggotT	Joe	19	Forward	Altrincham (L)	6			6	4
Rochdale (Y), Dundee Utd, Warrington, Wigan, Morecambe (L), Altrincham (L)									
Pilling	Luke	21	Goalkeeper	Ashton United (L)	20			20	
Tranmere, Glossop NE (L), Trafford (L), Ashton U (L)									
Pinney	Nathaniel	27	Midfielder	Welling United		1	9	1	
Crystal P (Y), Woking (L), Dag & Red (L), Braintree (L), Ebbsfleet, Tonbridge A, Eastbourne B, St Albans, Whitehawk, Welling									
Pittman	Jon-Paul	32	Midfielder	Truro City (L)	11	7	4	18	4
Nottingham F, Hartlepool (L), Bury (L), Doncaster, Crawley, Wycombe, Oxford U, Crawley (L), Wycombe, Grimsby, Harrogate T, TorquayTruro (L)									
Platt	Matthew	21	Defender	Southport (L)	14	1		15	2
Blackburn (Y), Barrow (L), Accrington (L), Southport (L)									
PLatt	Nick	31	Midfielder	Ashton United	3	1		4	
Liverpool (Y), Burnley (Y), FC United (L), FC United, Mandurah (Aus), FC United, Nantwich (L), Witton, Stockport, Salford, Nantwich, Ashton U									
Platt	Tom	25	Midfielder	Alfreton Town	30	5	8	35	3
York (Y), Halifax (L), Harrogate, Alfreton									
Plummer	Tristan	29	Forward	Weston-super-Mare	3	6		9	
Bristol C (Y), Luton (L), Torquay (L), Hereford (L), Gillingham (L), Bristol C, Portimonense (Por), Hereford, Weston, Aldershot, Weymouth (L), Weston (L), Weston, Hereford, Weston, Frome									
Poku	Godfrey	28	Midfielder	Wealdstone	48			48	
Luton (Y), St Albans (L), Southport (L), Mansfield, Southport (L), Alfreton (L), Telford, Woking, Havant & W (L), Oxford C, Wealdstone									
Politic	Dennis	19	Midfielder	Salford City (L)	8	5	1	13	2
Bolton (Y), Salford (L)									
Pollard	Harry		Defender	Eastbourne Borough	2	1	13	3	
Eastbourne B									
Pollard	Jim		Goalkeeper	Barrow			2		
Swallownest, Barrow									
Pollock	Aron	21	Defender	Concord Rangers	18	16	9	34	2
Leyton Orient, Wingate (L), Wealdstone (L), Leatherhead (L), LeatherheadConcord R									

2018-19 NATIONAL. NORTH & SOUTH PLAYERS — APPEARANCES

SURNAME	FIRSTNAME	AGE	POSITION	CLUB PLAYED FOR				Ap	Gls
Pond	Nathan	34	Defender	Salford City	45		3	45	2
Lancaster, Fleetwood, Kendal (L), Grimsby (L), Salford									
Poole	James	29	Forward	Altrincham	3	14	3	17	1
Man City (Y), Bury (L), Hartlepool (L), Hartlepool, Bury, Dover (L), Salford, Altrincham									
Pope	Jason	23	Midfielder	Weston-super-Mare	40		3	40	
Exeter (Y), Weston (L), Weston									
Popo Ebigbeyi	Tosan	26	Forward	Concord Rangers	34	2	2	36	
Charlton, Chelmsford (L), San Roque Lepe (Sp), San Roque Lepe, Concord R									
Porter	George	26	Forward	Bromley	45	2		47	8
Leyton O, Burnley, Colchester (L), AFC Wimbledon (L), Rochdale, Dagenham & R, Welling, Bromley									
Porter	Max	31	Midfielder	Chelmsford City	21	8	10	29	
Barnet, Rushden & D, Wimbledon, Newport Co (L), Newport Co, Bromley, Chelmsford									
Potter	Alfie	30	Forward	Billericay Town	18	16	2	34	
Peterborough, Kettering (L), Oxford U, Wimbledon, Northampton, Mansfield, Billericay									
Potts	Michael	27	Midfielder	FC United of Manchester	17	1	1	18	2
York, Guiseley, AFC Fylde, Stalybridge (L), Bradford PA, Curzon A, FC United									
Powell	Jack	25	Midfielder	Ebbsfleet United	7	5	2	12	1
				Maidstone United	37	1	2	38	4
West Ham, Millwall, Concord R (L), Braintree (L), Ebbsfleet, Maidstone									
Pratt	David	31	Forward	Wealdstone	40	5		45	12
Basingstoke, Maidenhead, Bath, Chippenham, Wealdstone									
Prestedge	Reece	33	Midfielder	Hemel Hempstead Town	4	1	3	5	
				East Thurrock United	16	9	5	25	
Bishop's St, Bromley, Chelmsford (L), MaidstoneHemel H, East Thurrock									
Preston	Jordan	23	Forward	FC Halifax Town	27	15	7	42	4
Blackburn, Ayr (L), Ayr, Guiseley, Gateshead, FC Halifax									
Priestley	Billy	30	Defender	Southport	4		6	4	
				FC United of Manchester (L)	5			5	
Bradford PA, Salford, Alfreton, Southport, FC United (L)									
Prior	Cody	19	Midfielder	Nuneaton Borough (L)	3			3	
Doncaster (Y), Nuneaton (L)									
Pritchard	John	23	Defender	Chester	6	8	4	14	4
Oldham (Y), FC United, Trafford, Ashton U, Chester									
Prosser	Alexander	20	Midfielder	Brackley Town (L)	3	4	3		
Aston Villa (Y), Brackley (L)									
Pryce	Sol	19	Midfielder	Dulwich Hamlet (L)	2	2	2		
				Bath City (L)	1	7		8	1
Swindon (Y), Dulwich H (L), Bath (L)									
Przybek	Adam	19	Goalkeeper	Gloucester City (L)	4			4	
WBA (Y), Gloucester (L)									
Puddy	Willem	31	Goalkeeper	Chippenham Town	17		8	17	
Swindon Sup, Chippenham, Salisbury, Bristol R, Braintree (L), Sutton U (L), Hereford, Chippenham									
Pugh	Andy	30	Forward	Dartford		2	1	2	
Gillingham (Y), Welling (L), Maidstone (L), Folkestone I (L), Grays (L), Dover (L), Welling (L), Histon (L), Welling, Cambridge U, Ebbsfleet (L), Dartford (L), Dartford									
Purdham	Ben	21	Goalkeeper	Curzon Ashton	1	1	1	2	
Curzon A									
Purnell	Luke	29	Goalkeeper	Weston-super-Mare	47			47	
Weston									
Purver	Alex	23	Midfielder	Guiseley	42	6		48	4
Leeds, Guiseley (L), Guiseley									
Pybus	Daniel	21	Midfielder	Blyth Spartans			1		
Sunderland (Y), Derby U23, Bradford, Bradford PA (L), Blyth S, Tønsberg									
Pyke	Rekeil	21	Forward	Wrexham (L)	15	12		27	5
Huddersfield (Y), Wrexham (L), Colchester (L), Port Vale (L), Wrexham (L), Rochdale (L)									
Qualter	Ryan	27	Defender	Boston United	42		1	42	1
Ossett T, Bradford PA, Scarborough A (L), Shaw Lane, Boston U									
Quebe	Tigana	25	Midfielder	Welling United		1	6	1	
Ninense (Por), Operario, Sacavenense, Almancilence, Estrela, Welling									
Quigley	Joe	22	Forward	Maidstone United	4	7		11	
				Bromley	4	4	1	8	1
				Havant & Waterlooville (L)	10	5		15	2
Bournemouth, Torquay (L), Wrexham (L), Woking (L), Woking (L), Gillingham (L), Gillingham (L), Newport Co (L), Boreham W (L), Maidstone, Bromley, Eastbourne B (L)Havant & W (L)									

Key: X - Started; SX - Sub on; S - Non-playing Sub; Ap - Total Appearances; Gls - Total goals.

2018-19 NATIONAL. NORTH & SOUTH PLAYERS

SURNAME	FIRSTNAME	AGE	POSITION	CLUB	APPEARANCES			Ap	Gls
Quigley	Scott	26	Forward	FC Halifax Town	11	6	2	17	2
The New Saints, Blackpool, Wrexham (L), Port Vale (L), FC Halifax (L)									
Quintyne	Jermaine		Forward	Aldershot Town	1			1	
Aldershot (Y)									
Rabbetts	Joe		Defender	Aldershot Town	1			1	
Aldershot (Y)									
Racchi	Danny	30	Midfielder	FC United of Manchester	4			4	
				Curzon Ashton	3	2		5	
Huddersfield (Y), Bury, Wrexham, York, Kilmarnock, Valur (Ice), Hyde, Halifax, Tamworth, Torquay, FC United, Curzon A									
Radovanovic	Marko	29	Goalkeeper	Hereford FC			1		
Liverton, Hereford									
Ramsbottom	Sam	23	Goalkeeper	Alfreton Town	46			46	
Tranmere, Galway FC, Barrow, Macclesfield, Alfreton									
Ramshaw	Rob	25	Midfielder	Spennymoor Town	45		1	45	7
Darlington, Gateshead, Spennymoor									
Rance	Dean	27	Midfielder	Ebbsfleet United	24	6	4	30	
Gillingham, Maidstone (L), Bishop's S (L), Dover (L), Dover, Ebbsfleet									
Randall	Dylan		Forward	Hampton & Richmond Borough	2	5	2		
Hampton & R									
Randall	Mark	29	Midfielder	Hemel Hempstead Town	4	2		6	
Arsenal (Y), Rotherham (L), Chesterfield, Ascoli, MK Dons, Barnet, Newport Co, Crawley, Hemel H									
Ransom	Harry	19	Forward	Eastbourne Borough	39	3	3	42	1
Eastbourne B (Y)									
Rawson	Luke	18	Forward	Chesterfield		2	1	2	
Chesterfield (Y)									
Raymond	Frankie	26	Midfielder	Bromley	43	2		45	3
Reading, Dagenham & R, Bromley									
Raynes	Joe	23	Midfielder	Bath City	44	1	1	45	3
Bath (Y), Odd Down, Larkhall Ath, Frome, Bath									
Raynes	Michael	31	Defender	Hartlepool United (L)	3			3	
Stockport (Y), Scunthorpe, Rotherham, Oxford U, Mansfield, Carlisle, Crewe, Hartlepool (L)									
Read	Arthur	20	Forward	Hemel Hempstead Town	2	2	1	4	
Luton (Y), Hemel H (L)									
Reason	Jai	29	Midfielder	Chelmsford City	5	4	4	9	
				Dover Athletic	25	5	1	30	6
Ipswich, Cambridge U (L), Cambridge U, Crawley, Braintree, Eastleigh, Boreham W, Maidstone, Chelmsford, Dover									
Reckord	Jamie	27	Defender	Solihull Moors	49		1	49	
Wolves, Northampton (L), Scunthorpe (L), Coventry (L), Plymouth (L), Swindon (L), Ross Co, Oldham, Solihull M									
Redmond	Devonte	22	Midfielder	Salford City	13	2		15	2
Man United (Y), Scunthorpe (L), Salford									
Reed	Jamie	31	Forward	Ashton United	2	12	1	14	1
Rhyl, Bangor, York, Cambridge U (L), Chester, New Saints, Aberystwyth (L), Llandudno, Bangor, Llandydno, Newtown, Ashton U									
Rees	Ricardo	19	Forward	Bath City (L)		1	3	1	
Bristol C (Y), Bath (L)									
Rees	Tommy		Goalkeeper	Hungerford Town			14		
Hungerford									
Reffell	Keyon	28	Midfielder	Hereford FC	1	6		7	
Caerau, Afan Lido, Carmarthen, Port Talbort, Kidderminster, Merthyr, Hereford									
Regan	Matt	25	Midfielder	Ashton United	42		1	42	3
Stalybridge, Curzon A, Ashton U									
Regis	Chris	22	Midfielder	Torquay United	8	1	3	9	1
				Wealdstone	1		3	1	
				Truro City	3	2	1	5	
Arsenal (Y), Southampton (Y), Colchester, Sittingbourne, Farnborough, Port Vale, Torquay, Wealdstone, Truro									
Reid	Alex	23	Forward	AFC Fylde (L)	12	9	1	21	3
Fleetwood, Wrexham (L), Solihull M (L), Stevenage, AFC Fylde (L)									
Reid	Jamie	24	Forward	Torquay United	46		2	46	32
Exeter (Y), Dorchester (L), Torquay (L), Truro (L), Torquay (L), Torquay									
Reid	Kyel	31	Forward	Chesterfield	13	17	7	30	
West Ham (Y), Barnsley (L), Crystal P (L), Blackpool (L), Wolves (L), Sheffield U, Charlton, Bradford, PNE, Bradford (L), Coventry, Colchester (L), Chesterfield									
Reid	Nathan		Forward	Barrow	3	2		5	
Barrow (Y)									

2018-19 NATIONAL. NORTH & SOUTH PLAYERS

SURNAME	FIRSTNAME	AGE	POSITION	CLUB PLAYED FOR	APPEARANCES				
								Ap	Gls
Reid	Sean	27	Midfielder	Blyth Spartans	38	7		45	15
Ryton & Crawcrook A, West Allotment C, Blyth S									
Reilly	Lewis	19	Forward	Curzon Ashton (L)	15			15	6
Crewe (Y), Curzon A (L)									
Rendell	Scott	32	Forward	Aldershot Town	27	5		32	8
Aldershot, Forest Green, Crawley, Cambridge U, Peterborough (L), Peterborough, Yeovil (L), Cambridge U (L), Torquay (L), Wycombe, Bristol R (L), Oxford U (L), Luton, Woking, Aldershot									
Render	Alex	18	Defender	Chesterfield			1		
Sheffield W (Y), Chesterfield (Y)									
Rents	Sam	31	Defender	Eastbourne Borough	2			2	
Crawley, Hayes & Y (L), Gateshead, Sutton U, Margate, Whitehawk, Worthing, Eastbourne B									
Reynolds	Callum	29	Defender	Barnet	35	2		37	
Rushden, Portsmouth, Luton (L), Tamworth, Corby (L), Boreham W, Aldershot, Barnet									
Reynolds	Lamar	23	Midfielder	Dagenham & Redbridge	9	16	1	25	1
				Chelmsford City (L)	2	7		9	1
Newport Co, Leyton Orient (L), Dag & Red, Chelmsford (L)									
Richards	Caleb	20	Defender	FC United of Manchester (L)	7			7	
Marine, Blackpool, Southport (L), Norwich, FC United (L), Tampa Bay									
Richards	Courtney	25	Midfielder	Nuneaton Borough	19	1		20	
				Braintree Town	23	1	3	24	1
Brighton, Torquay, Macclesfield, Solihull M (L)Nuneaton B, Braintree									
Richards	Eliot	27	Forward	Hereford FC	29	7	2	36	3
Bristol R (Y), Exeter (L), Tranmere, Cheltenham, Bath (L), Weston, Merthyr, Hereford									
Richards	Jack	20	Forward	Maidstone United	3	4	13	7	1
Maidstone, Welling (L), Eastbourne (L)									
Richards	Jamie	24	Defender	Truro City	42			42	5
Plymouth (Y), Linfield (L), Dartford (L), Torquay, Truro									
Richards	Jordan	26	Defender	Southport	39	2	7	41	2
Hartlepool, Alfreton (L), Darlington, AFC Fylde, Southport									
Richards	Kane	24	Forward	Kidderminster Harriers	8	29	5	37	4
Derby, Ilkeston, Chester, Dover, AFC Telford (L), Kidderminster									
Richards	Matt	34	Midfielder	Bath City	1	4	18	5	
Ipswich (Y), Brighton (L), Walsall, Shrewsbury, Cheltenham, Dag & Red, Bath									
Richards	Tom	20	Midfielder	Truro City	13	2	4	15	
Bristol C, Truro (L)									
Richards	Will	27	Midfielder	Chippenham Town	42		4	42	3
Stourbridge, Redditch, Solihull, Stourbridge, Redditch, Chippenham									
Richardson	Kenton	19	Defender	Hartlepool United	15	5	10	20	
Hartlepool									
Richman	Simon	29	Midfielder	Altrincham	19	17	6	36	1
Port Vale (Y), Worcester, Altrincham									
Ricketts	Mark	34	Midfielder	Boreham Wood	45		1	45	
Charlton, MK Dons (L), Ebbsfleet, WokingBoreham W									
Ridge	Marley	21	Midfielder	Havant & Waterlooville	2			2	
Moneyfields, Havant & W									
Ridley	Steve	36	Midfielder	Alfreton Town			1		
Barrow, Buxton, Ossett T, Lincoln U, Alfreton,									
Rigg	George	25	Midfielder	Chippenham Town	41	1		42	2
Weymouth, Bath, Chippenham									
Rigg	Sean	30	Midfielder	Bath City	25	4	1	29	7
Bristol R (Y), Forest GR (L), Port Vale (L), Port Vale, Oxford U, Wimbledon, Newport Co, Bath									
Rigg	Steven	26	Forward	Gateshead	39	8		47	10
Penrith (Y), Carlisle, Queen OTS, Carlisle, Chorley, Workington (L), Gateshead									
Riley	Martin	32	Defender	Alfreton Town	25	2	5	27	
Wolves, Shrewsbury (L), Kidderminster, Cheltenham, Mansfield, Wrexham, Mansfield, Tranmere, Wrexham, Halifax, Alfreton									
Riley-Lowe	Connor	23	Midfielder	Truro City	44			44	5
Exeter (Y), Truro (L), Truro (L), Truro									
Rivers	Harvey	23	Goalkeeper	Truro City	20	1	3	21	
Cheltenham, Gloucester, Truro									
Rivers	Jarrett	25	Midfielder	Blyth Spartans	33	8	3	41	6
Middlesbrough (Y), Sunderland RCA (L), Whitley B, Blyth S, Blackpool, Blyth S									
Roache	Rowan	19	Midfielder	FC United of Manchester (L)	1	1		2	
Blackpool (Y), Southport (L), FC United (L), Derby U23 (L)									

Key: X - Started; SX - Sub on; S - Non-playing Sub; Ap - Total Appearances; Gls - Total goals.

SURNAME	FIRSTNAME	AGE	POSITION	CLUB				Ap	Gls
					APPEARANCES				
Roast	Billy	24	Defender	Dartford	4	3	2	7	
Colchester, Maldon, Concord R, Dartford									
Robbins	Adam		Defender	Gloucester City	3		6	3	
Gloucester									
Robert	Fabien	30	Midfielder	Gloucester City (L)	21	1		22	8
Lorient, Boulogne (L), Doncaster (L), Swindon, Forest Green, Aldershot (L)Gloucester (Lx2)									
Roberts	Dan		Forward	Slough Town	2	5	2	7	1
Slough									
Roberts	Gary	32	Midfielder	Chester	36		1	36	4
Crewe, Yeovil, Rotherham, Port Vale, Mansfield, Connah's Q, Bangor, Southport, Chester									
Roberts	Grant	27	Midfielder	Boston United	1	3	2	4	
Histon, Gainsborough, Boston U, Hyde									
Roberts	James	22	Forward	Hereford FC	11	9	4	20	5
Wycombe (Y), Oxford U (Y), Chester (L), Oxford C (L), Barnet (L), Oxford C (L), Chelmsford (L), Guiseley (L)Hereford									
Roberts	John	20	Midfielder	Ashton United	2	3	22	5	
Accrington (Y), Macclesfield, Ashton U (L), Ashton U									
Roberts	Kevin	29	Defender	Wrexham	37	2	4	39	
Chester, Cambridge U, Halifax, Wrexham									
Roberts	Myles	17	Goalkeeper	Wealdstone (L)	1			1	
Reading (Y), Wealdstone (L)									
Roberts	Phil	25	Forward	Hemel Hempstead Town	8	5	2	13	5
				Dartford	16	1	2	17	8
Arsenal (Y), Inverness (L), Falkirk, Dundee, Alloa (L), Sligo, Chelmsford, Braintree, Chelmsford, Hemel H, Dartford									
Roberts	Taurean			Hampton & Richmond Borough	3	1	3		
Hampton & R									
Roberts	Theo	20	Goalkeeper	Chester			1		
Wigan (Y), Chester									
Robertson	Chris	32	Defender	Havant & Waterlooville (L)	2			2	
Sheffield U (Y), Chester (L), Torquay, PNE, Port Vale, Ross Co, AFC Wimbledon, Swindon, Havant & W (L)									
Robins	Jordy	22	Midfielder	Maidstone United		2			
Maidstone (Y), Niagara (US), MO State Bears, Maidstone, Margate (L)									
Robinson	Andy	26	Midfielder	Havant & Waterlooville	34	2	1	36	5
Southampton (Y), Bolton (L), Bolton, Dorchester, Gosport, Havant & W									
Robinson	Jake	32	Forward	Billericay Town	18	1	1	19	16
				Maidstone United	8	3	1	11	1
				Billericay Town	6			6	1
Brighton, Aldershot, Shrewsbury (L), Northampton, Luton (L), Whitehawk, Hempstead, Billericay, Maidstone, Billericay									
Robinson	Josh		Defender	Stockport County		1			
Stockport									
Robinson	Matt	25	Midfielder	Dagenham & Redbridge	40	1		41	1
Leicester, Luton, Kidderminster (L), Grimsby (L), Woking (L), Dagenham & R									
Robinson	Paul	37	Defender	Havant & Waterlooville	16	2	2	18	
Millwall (Y), Fisher Ath (L), Torquay (L), Portsmouth (L), Portsmouth, AFC Wimbledon, Havant & W									
Robson	Craig	27	Defender	Barnet	48	5	2	53	3
Havant & W, Sorrento FC (W.Aus), Bognor Regis, Dagenham & R, Barnet									
Rodgers	Harvey	22	Defender	Hartlepool United (L)	6			6	
Hull (Y), Accrington (L), Fleetwood, Accrington, Hartlepool (L)									
Rodney	Devante	21	Forward	Salford City	2	21	6	23	4
				FC Halifax Town (L)	12			12	7
Man City (Y), Sheff Wed (Y), Hartlepool, Salford, FC Halifax (L)									
Rollings	Callum		Midfielder	Maidstone United		1			
Maidstone (Y)									
Rollins	Jay		Midfielder	Boston United	19	5	1	24	4
Armthorpe, Boston U									
Rollinson	Joel	20	Midfielder	Eastbourne Borough (L)	9	2		11	1
Reading (Y), Eastbourne B (L)									
Romain	Elliott	27	Forward	Dagenham & Redbridge	15	1		16	4
				Maidstone United	22	12	1	34	2
Brighton, Millwall, Three Bridges, Lewes, Horsham YMCA (L), Eastbourne B, Dagenham & R, Welling (L), Torquay (L), Maidstone									
Romanski	Joe	19	Defender	Bath City (L)	8		4	8	
Swindon (Y), Bath (L)									
Rooney	Adam	31	Forward	Salford City	40	4	2	44	23
Crumlin Utd (Eire), Stoke (Y), Yeovil (L), Chesterfield (L), Bury (L), Inverness, Birmingham, Swindon (L), Oldham, Aberdeen, Salford									

2018-19 NATIONAL. NORTH & SOUTH PLAYERS

APPEARANCES

SURNAME	FIRSTNAME	AGE	POSITION	CLUB PLAYED FOR				Ap	Gls
Rooney	Daniel	20	Midfielder	Truro City (L)	26	3	1	29	7
Plymouth (Y), Truro (L)									
Rooney	John	28	Midfielder	Barrow	46	2		48	10
Macclesfield, Barnsley, Bury, Chester, Wrexham, Guiseley, Barrow									
Rooney	Louis	22	Forward	Truro City	15	15	4	30	1
Plymouth (Y), Truro (L), Hartlepool (L), Linfield, Truro									
Rooney	Luke	28	Midfielder	Welling United	3	3	1	6	
Gillingham, Swindon, Burton (L), Rotherham (L), Crawley (L), Maidstone, Luton, Ebbsfleet, Crawley, Phoenix Rising, Billericay, Welling									
Rooney	Paul	22	Defender	Bromley (L)	6		4	6	
				Billericay Town (L)	15	3	5	18	
St Pats, Bohemians, Millwall, Torquay (L), Colchester, Bromley (L), Billericay (L)									
Rose	Ahkeem	20	Forward	Boston United (L)	3	1		4	2
Heather St John, Grimsby, Boston U (L)									
Rose	Jordan	29	Defender	Havant & Waterlooville	19	6	5	25	1
SM Caen (Fra) (Y), Bournemouth (Y), Bashley, Weymouth, Paulton, Stockport, Eastleigh, Hereford Utd, Hayes & Y, Stockport, Telford, Alfreton, Tamworth, Whitehawk, Havant & W, Weymouth (L)									
Rose	Romone	29	Midfielder	Hungerford Town	13	4	4	17	2
Torquay, Wimbledon, QPR, Histon (L), Northampton (L), Cheltenham (L), Torquay (L), Newport Co, Maidenhead, Eastleigh, Staines, Gosport B, Whitehawk, Hungerford									
Ross	Craig	29	Goalkeeper	Woking	42			42	
Hampton & R, Cambridge U, Eastbourne B (L), Eastbourne B, Farnborough, Whitehawk, Macclesfield, Barnet, Boreham W, Woking									
Ross	Ethan	22	Goalkeeper	Maidstone United (L)	5			5	
Arsenal (Y), WBA (Y), Worcester (L), Worcester (L), Redditch (L), Colchester, Maidstone (L)									
Ross	Mark	29	Defender	Bradford Park Avenue	41	1	3	42	
Leigh Gen, Chorley, Stockport, Bradford PA									
Rowe	Danny	22	Forward	Braintree Town	6	7	4	13	
				Boston United	1	2	1	3	
				Hemel Hempstead Town	4	1		5	1
Leicester (Y), QPR (Y), Braintree, Boston U, Hemel H									
Rowe	Danny M	27	Forward	AFC Fylde	57		1	57	33
Stockport, Barrow, Macclesfield, AFC Fylde									
Rowe	James	27	Midfielder	Aldershot Town	6	7	2	13	1
Forest Green, Tranmere, Cheltenham, Aldershot									
Rowley	Joe	20	Midfielder	Chesterfield	25	7	2	32	1
Chesterfield (Y)									
Rowley	Shaun	22	Goalkeeper	FC Halifax Town			54		
Shrewsbury (Y), Watford (Y) (L), Halesowen (L), Chorley (L), Tamworth (L), FC Halifax									
Rowney	Chris	28	Midfielder	Curzon Ashton	40	2		42	
Oldham (Y), Mossley, Curzon A									
Rowthorn	Ben	20	Defender	Truro City (L)	8	2	3	10	
Southampton (Y), Truro (L)									
Royle	Jonathan	24	Midfielder	AFC Telford United	29	10	10	39	2
Wrexham (Y), Colwyn (L), Hednesford (L), Southport, Telford (L), Telford									
Rrapaj	Irdi	25	Forward	Braintree Town	1	2	1	3	
Weston-s-Mare, Wingate, Braintree									
Ruddick	Luke	29	Defender	Oxford City	9	2	6	11	
				Hampton & Richmond Borough	23		1	23	
Salisbury, Bath, Salisbury, Sutton U, Oxford C, Hampton & R									
Rusby	James		Defender	Hungerford Town	36	5		41	2
Hungerford									
Russe	Luke	19	Midfielder	Gloucester City (L)	9			9	1
Bristol R, Gloucester (L)									
Russell	Alex		Midfielder	Southport		1		1	
Southport									
Rutherford	Alfie		Forward	Havant & Waterlooville	26	10	7	36	16
				Eastbourne Borough (L)	5			5	6
Moneyfields, Bognor, Havant & W, Eastbourne B (L)									
Rutherford	Paul	31	Midfielder	Wrexham	38	14		52	2
Chester, Barrow, Southport, Wrexham									
Rutty	Harry	19	Defender	Chippenham Town	5		9	5	
Chippenham									
Sagaf	Mohammed	21	Midfielder	Braintree Town	22	7	11	29	4
North Greenford, Ternana (Y), Leatherhead, Waltham F, Braintree									

Key: X - Started; SX - Sub on; S - Non-playing Sub; Ap - Total Appearances; Gls - Total goals.

SURNAME	FIRSTNAME	AGE	POSITION	CLUB	APPEARANCES			Ap	Gls
Sage	James	24	Defender	St Albans City	3		3	3	
St Albans									
Sainty	Callum	23	Midfielder	Hereford FC	2	1	3	3	1
Barry, Hereford, Mangotsfield (DR)									
Salkeld	Cameron	20	Forward	Gateshead	13	15	9	28	1
Carlisle (Y), Whitby (L), Annan Ath (L), Gateshead									
Saltmer	Jonathan	20	Goalkeeper	Barrow			4		
Barrow (Y)									
Sam-Yorke	Delano	30	Forward	Dartford	5	7	4	12	1
Woking, AFC Wimbledon, Basingstoke, Cambridge U, Lincoln (L), Lincoln (L), Forest Green, Boreham W (L), Woking, Maidstone (L)Maidstone, Dartford									
Sambou	Solomon	23	Midfielder	St Albans City	42	7	3	49	4
Hayes & Y, Wealdstone (L), St Albans									
Samizadeh	Alex	20	Forward	Curzon Ashton	5	3	1	8	
				Wealdstone	1	1		2	
Bolton (Y), Chorley (L), Kilmarnock, Curzon A, Wealdstone, Burgess Hill,									
Sampson	Jack	26	Forward	Southport	40	5	2	45	14
Bolton (Y), Southend (L), Accrington (L), Morecambe, Macclesfield (L), Macclesfield, Chorley (L), Southport									
Sandell	Andy	35	Midfielder	Chippenham Town	1	3	2	4	
Salisbury, Aldershot, Wycombe, Forest GR (L), Newport Co, Chippenham									
Sanderson	Jordan	25	Midfielder	St Albans City	2	4	4	6	
Colchester (Y), Chelmsford (L), Ebbsfleet, Chania, Braintree, Concord R, St Albans									
Sang	Chris	19	Forward	Altrincham (L)	1	3	1	4	
Wigan (Y), Bury, Southport (L), Marine (L), Altrincham (L),									
Sang	Tom	19	Defender	AFC Fylde (L)	1		2	1	
Man Utd (Y), AFC Fylde (L)									
Sangha	Jordon	21	Midfielder	Ashton United (L)	6	1	1	7	
Walsall (Y), Telford (L), Rushall (L), Leamington (L), Ashton U (L)									
Santos	Brad			Eastbourne Borough	2	5	2		
Eastbourne B									
Saraiva	Fabio	25	Forward	Woking	1	1	2	2	
Merstham, Maidstone, Merstham, Woking									
Sardinha	Steven		Midfielder	Dulwich Hamlet			4		
Dulwich H									
Sargeant	Sam	21	Goalkeeper	Leyton Orient			51		
Leyton Orient									
Sargent	Matthew		Forward	Wrexham	1	1	1	2	
Wrexham (Y)									
Sarkic	Matija	21	Goalkeeper	Havant & Waterlooville (L)	1			1	
Aston Villa, Wigan (L), Havant & W (L)									
Sarpong Wiredu	Brendan	19	Midfielder	Bromley (L)	6	5	3	11	
Charlton (Y), Bromley (L)									
Sass-Davies	Billy	19	Defender	FC United of Manchester (L)	8			8	
				Altrincham (L)		2		2	
Crewe (Y), Colwyn B (L), Leek (L), FC United (L), Altrincham (L)									
Saunders	Harvey	21	Forward	Darlington	28	14	2	42	8
Durham City, Darlington, Fleetwood, Darlington (L)									
Sbarra	Joe	20	Midfielder	Solihull Moor (L)	1	5	2	6	
Burton, Solihull (L)									
Schmoll	Tim	26	Defender	Dover Athletic	14		3	14	1
Terre Sainte (Y), Servette (Y), Harvard, NY RB Academy, NY Red Bulls, Aldershot, Dover									
Schotterl	Herbert	24	Goalkeeper	Woking	11		18	11	
Seligenporten (Ger), Dartford, Woking									
Scory	Ben		Midfielder	Eastleigh		1	3	1	
Eastleigh (Y)									
Scott	Charlie	21	Midfielder	Altrincham			3		
Man Utd (Y), Hamilton (L), Altrincham, Newcastle T									
Scott	Josh	17	Forward	Hartlepool United		3			
Hartlepool (Y)									
Scott	Mark	28	Goalkeeper	Slough Town			1		
				Wealdstone	1			1	
Swindon, Salisbury (L), Salisbury, Oxford C, Slough, Wealdstone									
Scott	Ryan	24	Defender	East Thurrock United	42			42	2
East Thurrock									

2018-19 NATIONAL. NORTH & SOUTH PLAYERS

SURNAME	FIRSTNAME	AGE	POSITION	CLUB PLAYED FOR	X	SX	S	Ap	Gls
Sears	Ryan	20	Defender	AFC Telford United (L)	5	1		6	
Shrewsbury (Y), Newtown (L), Telford (L)									
Sefil	Sonhy	24	Defender	Ashton United (L)	2			2	
CS Sedan B, AJ Auxerre B, AJ Auxerre, Asteras Tripoli (Gre), AS Lyon-Duchere, Oldham, Ashton U (L)									
Sekajja	Ibra	26	Forward	Havant & Waterlooville	5	11	8	16	
Crystal P (Y), Kettering (L), MK Dons (L), Barnet (L), Inverness C, Livingston, Braintree, Hemel, Dulwich, Bognor, Havant & W									
Self	Jack		Midfielder	Oxford City	22	4	1	26	1
Didcot, Oxford C									
Sellers	Ryan	24	Defender	FC Halifax Town	29	1	2	30	
Bolton, Wycombe, Wingate, Wealdstone, FC Halifax									
Sendles-White	Jamie	25	Defender	Torquay United	17	8	5	25	
QPR, Colchester (L), Mansfield (L), Hamilton, Swindon, Leyton Orient, St Albans, Torquay									
Senior	Jack	22	Defender	Harrogate Town (L)	4	2	4	6	
Huddersfield (Y), Luton, Harrogate (L)									
Senior	Joel	20	Defender	FC United of Manchester	18	3	4	21	
				Curzon Ashton	10			10	
FC United, Curzon A									
Sephton	Scott	28	Midfielder	Ashton United	8	1	2	9	
Leigh Genesis, Congleton, Trafford, Ashton U									
Sesay	Alhaji	20	Goalkeeper	Gloucester City	2			2	
Bristol C (Y), Gloucester (L)									
Seymour	Ben	20	Forward	Gloucester City (L)	9	3		12	1
Weston-s-Mare, Exeter, Gloucester (L), Dorchester (L)									
Shabani	Brendan		Defender	Leyton Orient			1		
Leyton O									
Shaibu	Justin	21	Forward	Boreham Wood (L)	26	18	1	44	13
HB Koge (Y), Brentford, Walsall (L), Boreham W (L)									
Shakes	Ricky	34	Midfielder	Boreham Wood	44	7		51	2
Bolton, Bristol R (L), Bury (L), Swindon, Brentford, Ebbsfleet, Kidderminster, Boreham W									
Sharman	Jamie		Defender	Chesterfield	2	2		4	
Chesterfield (Y)									
Sharp	Chris	32	Forward	Curzon Ashton	2			2	
				FC United of Manchester	12	6	5	18	3
Rhyl (Y), Bangor, New Saints, Telford, Hereford, Lincoln (L), Stockport, Colwyn, Salford, Marine, Bradford PA, Alfreton, Curzon A, FC United									
Sharpe	Rhys	24	Defender	Nuneaton Borough	18			18	
Derby (Y), Shrewsbury (L), Notts Co, Swindon, Matlock, Tamworth, Nuneaton									
Shaw	Danny	34	Defender	Curzon Ashton	23	4	8	27	1
Curzon A									
Shaw	Frazer	24	Defender	Concord Rangers	33			33	1
Dulwich H, Leyton Orient, Accrington, Woking, Eastleigh, Leatherhead, Concord R									
Shaw	Gregor		Goalkeeper	Eastbourne Borough		7			
Eastbourne B									
Shaw	Lee		Forward	Chesterfield	30	14	6	44	2
Grantham, Chesterfield									
Sheckleford	Ryheem	22	Defender	Maidenhead United	1	1		2	
Fulham (Y), Wealdstone (L), Maidenhead									
Sheehan	Steve		Defender	East Thurrock United	31			31	1
East Thurrock, Billericay,Canvey I, East Thurrock									
Shelton	Mak	22	Midfielder	Salford City	13	1	3	14	2
Burton (Y), Ilkeston, Alfreton, Salford									
Shenton	Grant	28	Goalkeeper	Chester	45			45	
FC UnitedRamsbottom, Ashton U, Stalybridge, Trafford, Chester									
Shenton	Ryan	19	Midfielder	Curzon Ashton	3	11	6	14	1
Curzon A									
Shepherd	William		Midfielder	Salford City			1		
Salford (Y)									
Sheppard	Jake	22	Defender	Wealdstone	28	4	4	32	3
Reading (Y), Hayes & Y (L), Eastbourne B (L), Dag & Red (L), Guiseley (L), Wealdstone (L), Wealdstone									
Sheridan	Sam	29	Midfielder	Ashton United	37	2		39	5
Bolton (Y), Altrincham (L), Stockport, Southport (L), Barrow, Chorley, FC United, Altrincham, Ashton U									
Sheriff	Decarrey	21	Midfielder	Dulwich Hamlet	2	6	2	8	3
Dulwich H									

Key: X - Started; SX - Sub on; S - Non-playing Sub; Ap - Total Appearances; Gls - Total goals.

SURNAME	FIRSTNAME	AGE	POSITION	CLUB	APPEARANCES			Ap	Gls
Sheringham	Charlie	31	Forward	Hemel Hempstead Town	2	2		4	
				Dartford	21	4	1	25	10
Bishop's S, Histon, Dartford, Bournemouth, Dartford (L), Wimbledon, Salisbury (L), Ebbsfleet, Bishop's S (L), Hemel H (L), Hemel H, Saif (Bangl), Hemel H, Dartford									
Shields	Sean	27	Midfielder	Ebbsfleet United	11	8	4	19	3
				Maidstone United (L)	5	1		6	1
				Boreham Wood (L)	7	3	2	10	1
Tottenham, Potters Bar, St Albans, Dagenham & R, St Albans (L), Ebbsfleet (L), Ebbsfleet, Chelmsford (L), Margate (L), Hemel (L), Maidstone (L), Boreham W (L)									
Shiels	Luke	29	Defender	Alfreton Town	41		1	41	2
Worksop, Harrogate, Alfreton									
Sho-Silva	Richard	26	Defender	St Albans City	6	1		7	2
Kidderminster, Dartford, St Albans									
Sho-Silva	Tobi	24	Forward	Dover Athletic	6	3	4	9	
				Chelmsford City (L)	1	3		4	
CharltonWelling (L), Welling (L), Inverness CT (L), Bromley, Dover, Chelmsford (L)									
Shokunbi	Ademola	20	Defender	Billericay Town (L)	5	8	8	13	1
Reading (Y), Billericay (L)									
Shomotun	Fumnaya	22	Midfielder	Wealdstone (L)	8	4	1	12	2
Barnet (Y), Margate (L), Wealdstone (L)									
Short	Lewis	28	Defender	Chorley	2	3	3	5	
Crewe (Y), Nantwich (L), Northwich V, Airbus UK, Nantwich, Connah's Q, Bala T, Chorley									
Shulton	Scott	29	Midfielder	Hemel Hempstead Town	21	1	1	22	1
				St Albans City	5		1	5	
Ebbsfleet, Bishop's S, Braintree, Bishop's S, Enfield T, Braintree, Hemel H, St Albans									
Silverman	Asher		Defender	Chelmsford City		1		1	
Chelmsford City									
Simm	Matt		Midfielder	Eastleigh			1		
Eastleigh (Y)									
Simmons	Jack	24	Forward	East Thurrock United	6	3	2	9	1
Colchester, Canvey I, Dartford, East Thurrock									
Simões Inácio	Elliot Jorge	19	Forward	FC United of Manchester	12	4	2	16	
FC United, Barnsley									
Simpemba	Ian	36	Defender	Eastbourne Borough	4	4	4		
Havant & W, Ebbsfleet, Dover, Eastbourne B									
Simpson	Jay	30	Forward	Leyton Orient	7	1	6	8	1
Arsenal (Y), Millwall (L), WBA (L), QPR (L), Hull, Millwall (L), Buriram Utd (Thialand), Leyton Orient, Philadelphia, Leyton O									
Simpson	Jordan	20	Midfielder	Havant & Waterlooville (L)	2	2	2		
				Hampton & Richmond Borough (L)	2	2	2	4	
Swindon (Y), Forest GR, Havant & W (L), Hampton & R (L)									
Simpson	Luke	24	Goalkeeper	Wrexham			2		
Oldham (Y), Workington (L), Leicester (L), Accrington, Watford, York, Macclesfield, Tamworth, Wrexham									
Sinclair	Robert	29	Forward	Oxford City	12			12	4
				Hemel Hempstead Town	13	3		16	4
Salisbury, Stevenage, Aldershot (L), Salisbury, Forest GR, Oxford C, Hemel H									
Sinfield	Patrick		Goalkeeper	St Albans City			1		
St Albans									
Sinnott	Jordan	25	Defender	Alfreton Town	21	8	6	29	8
Huddersfield (Y), Altrincham (L), Bury (L), Altrincham, Halifax, Chesterfield, Alfreton									
Skarz	Joe	29	Defender	FC Halifax Town (L)	27	1	3	28	
Huddersfield (Y), Shrewsbury (L), Bury, Rotherham (L), Rotherham, Oxford U, Bury, FC Halifax (L)									
Skirpan	Bradley	17	Goalkeeper	Blyth Spartans			17		
Blyth Spartans									
Slater	Brandon		Defender	Gateshead			2		
Gateshead (Y)									
Slew	Jerome	21	Forward	Wealdstone		2	4	2	1
				Ashton United		1		1	
Sheff Utd (Y), Goole, Chester, North Ferriby, Wealdstone, Ashton U, Ramsbottom									
Slew	Jordan	26	Forward	Boston United	4	10	7	14	2
Sheff Utd (Y), Blackburn, Stevenage (L), Oldham (L), Rotherham (L), Ross Co (L), Port Vale (L), Cambridge U, Chesterfield, Plymouth, Rochdale, Radcliffe B, Boston U									
Sloan	Christian		Midfielder	Barrow		1	8	1	
Barrow (Y)									

2018-19 NATIONAL. NORTH & SOUTH PLAYERS

APPEARANCES

SURNAME	FIRSTNAME	AGE	POSITION	CLUB PLAYED FOR	X	SX	S	Ap	Gls
Smallcombe	Max	20	Midfielder	Truro City (L)	4	1	5	5	
Exeter (Y), Truro (L)									
Smalley	Chris		Defender	Stockport County	6	1	4	7	
Northwich V, Kendal, Stockport									
Smalley	Deane	30	Forward	Chester	4	15	4	19	2
Oldham (Y), Rochdale (L), Chesterfield (L), Oxford U, Bradford (L), Plymouth, Newport Co (L). Chester									
Smalley	Dominic	29	Defender	Chester	10	1	4	11	
Ashton U, Chester, Hyde U (L)									
Smart	Nathan	26	Midfielder	Slough Town			7		
Basingstoke, Slough									
Smerdon	Noah	18	Midfielder	Gloucester City	25	6	1	31	2
WBA (Y), Gloucester (Y)									
Smile	Josh	22	Midfielder	Chippenham Town	39	3	2	42	2
Fulham (Y), Chippenham									
Smith	Chris	21	Defender	Aldershot Town (L)	3	2	4	5	
Ipswich (Yth), Chelmsford (L), Aldershot (L)									
Smith	Christian	31	Midfielder	Maidenhead United	9	3	7	12	1
				Wealdstone	21	3	4	24	5
Port Vale, Cambridge U (L), Northwich (L), Clyde, Wrexham, York, Wrexham, Newport Co (L), Barrow (L), Tamworth (L), Telford, Chelmsford, Hayes & Yeading, Bishop's St, Maidenhead, Wealdstone									
Smith	Connor	26	Midfielder	Boreham Wood	9	2	16	11	
				Billericay Town	3	2	2	5	1
Watford (Y), Wealdstone (L), Gillingham (L), Stevenage (L), AFC Wimbledon, Plymouth, Yeovil, Boreham W, Billericay									
Smith	Darnell	20	Defender	Barnet			1		
Barnet (Y), Hungerford (L)									
Smith	David	20	Forward	Dover Athletic	1	2	3	3	
Sittingbourne, Dover									
Smith	Dominic	23	Defender	AFC Telford United	11	4	12	15	
				Alfreton Town (L)	9			9	
Shrewsbury (Y), Tamworth (L), Barrow (L), Southport (L), Telford, Alfreton (L)									
Smith	Emanuel	30	Defender	Wrexham	8		2	8	1
Walsall, Notts Co, Wrexham, Barrow, Gateshead, Wrexham									
Smith	George	22	Defender	Chesterfield	1	1	1	2	
				Dover Athletic (L)	7			7	
				Boston United (L)	8			8	
Barnsley (Y), Crawley (L), Gateshead, Northampton, Chesterfield, Dover (L), Boston U (L)									
Smith	Grant	25	Goalkeeper	Maidstone United (L)	7			7	
Fulham, Brighton, Hayes & Y (L), Bognor (L), Bognor, Boreham WLincoln C, Maidstone (L)									
Smith	Gregg	29	Forward	Brackley Town	1	6	3	7	2
				Boston United	5	1	1	6	1
Corby T, Grantham, King's Lynn, Spalding, Stamford, Grantham (L), Boston U, Brackley, Boston U, Tamworth, Stamford									
Smith	Harvey	20	Defender	Hereford FC (L)	20	2	8	22	
Bristol C (Y), Weston (L), Hereford (L)									
Smith	Jack		Defender	Dover Athletic	1		1	1	
Dover (Y)									
Smith	Jed		Defender	Concord Rangers	11	11	8	22	
Concord R									
Smith	Jedd		Defender	Dartford		1	6	1	
Dartford (Y)									
Smith	Jonathan	32	Midfielder	Chesterfield (L)	37	1		38	5
Morecambe (Y), Fleetwood (L), Forest Green, York, Swindon, York, Luton (L), Luton, Stevenage, Chesterfield (L)									
Smith	Kane	23	Defender	Boreham Wood	2		2	2	
Hitchin, Boreham W									
Smith	Kieran		Midfielder	Braintree Town		2	2	2	
Braintree (Y)									
Smith	Lance	27	Forward	Hereford FC	10	6	1	16	2
Evesham, Hereford									
Smith	Mark	23	Goalkeeper	Eastbourne Borough	28			28	
				Billericay Town	7		5	7	
				Eastbourne Borough (L)	4			4	
Brentford (Y), Lowestoft (L), Aldershot, Eastbourne B (L), Eastbourne B, Billericay, Eastbourne B (L)									
Smith	Matt		Midfielder	Chippenham Town	19	4	6	23	1
Chippenham									

Key: X - Started; SX - Sub on; S - Non-playing Sub; Ap - Total Appearances; Gls - Total goals.

SURNAME	FIRSTNAME	AGE	POSITION	CLUB	APPEARANCES				
								Ap	Gls
Smith	Mitchell		Defender	Aldershot Town	1			1	
Aldershot (Y)									
Smith	Nathan	32	Defender	Dagenham & Redbridge	12		6	12	1
Enfield T, Waltham F, Potters Bar, Yeovil, Chesterfield, Yeovil, Dagenham & R									
Smith	Scott	20	Midfielder	Guiseley	13	5	9	18	3
Guiseley									
Smith	Tom	21	Midfielder	Bath City (L)	24	9	3	33	5
Swindon (Y), Waterford (L), Bath (Lx3), Cheltenham, Bath (L)									
Smith	Tyler	20	Forward	Barrow (L)	24			24	11
Sheffield Utd (Y), Barrow (L)									
Smith	William	20	Defender	Darlington (L)	14			14	1
Barnsley (Y), Darlington (L)									
Smoker	Luke		Defender	Dartford			1		
Dartford (Y)									
Snedker	Dean	24	Goalkeeper	St Albans City	47			47	
Northampton, Brackley (Lx2), Brackley, Kidderminster, Nuneaton, Hempstead, Kettering, Cambridge C, St Albans									
Snelus	Jack	19	Midfielder	Hemel Hempstead Town	13	4	8	17	1
Luton (Y), Hemel H									
Soares	Louie	34	Midfielder	Slough Town	13	18	19	31	2
Aldershot, Southend, Hayes & Y, Grimsby, Ebbsfleet (L), Alfreton (L), Hayes & Y, Basingstoke, Oxford C, Hungerford, Slough									
Sokolik	Jakub	25	Defender	Torquay United	2		2	2	
Liverpool, Southend (L), Yeovil, Southend (L), Southend, Plymouth, Torquay									
Sole	Liam	19	Forward	Hampton & Richmond Borough (L)	3	2	1	5	
				St Albans (L)	3	10	2	13	1
MK Dons (Y), Hampton & R (L), St Albans (L)									
Sotiriou	Ruel	17	Forward	Leyton Orient		2	4	2	
				Chelmsford City (L)	1	2	1		
				Hampton & Richmond Borough (L)	7	2		9	6
Leyton O, Chelmsford (L), Hampton & R (L)									
Sousa	Erico	24	Forward	Barrow (L)	5	1	1	6	1
Vinhense (Y), Fabril Barreiro (Y), Barnsley (Y), Hyde (L), NK Celje, Tadcaster, Accrington, Tranmere, Accrington, Barrow (L)									
Southam	Glen	38	Midfielder	East Thurrock United	1			1	
Dag & Red, Hereford, Bishop's S (L), Histon (L), Barnet, Dover, Eastleigh, Chelmsford, Sutton U, Basingstoke, Whitehawk, East Thurrock									
Southwell	Dayle	25	Forward	FC Halifax Town	39			39	8
Grimsby, Harrogate (L), Boston U, Wycombe, Guiseley, FC Halifax									
Southwood	Luke	21	Goalkeeper	Eastleigh (L)	22		1	22	
Reading (Y), Bath (L), Eastleigh (L)									
Spark	Jack	18	Defender	Gloucester City	1	1	3	2	
Gloucester (Y)									
Sparkes	Daniel	27	Midfielder	Barnet	15	9	11	24	2
Histon, Braintree, Torquay, Dagenham & R, Barnet									
Sparkes	Jack	18	Forward	Chippenham Town (L)	2	4	2		
Exeter (Y), Chippenham (L), Salisbury (L)									
Spence	Daniel	29	Defender	Woking	8	1	17	9	
Reading, Salisbury (L), Salisbury, Hayes & Y, Eastleigh, Sutton U, Hemel H (L), Woking, Kingstonian (L)									
Spencer	Jamie	21	Midfielder	Bradford Park Avenue	26	15	3	41	4
Bradford PA									
Spillane	Michael	30		Chelmsford City	36	1	1	37	3
Norwich, Luton (L), Brentford, Dag & Red (L), Dag & Red, Southend, Cambridge U, Sutton U, Lowestoft, Chelmsford									
Splatt	Jamie		Defender	Dulwich Hamlet			1		
Dulwich H									
Sprague	Oliver	24	Midfielder	Hampton & Richmond Borough	23	4	4	27	1
Hendon, Welling, Billericay, Hampton & R									
Spyrou	Anthony	19	Midfielder	Wrexham (L)	2	1		3	
Norwich (Y), Wrexham (L)									
Stack	Graham	37	Goalkeeper	Eastleigh	10			10	
Arsenal, Beveren (L), Millwall (L), Reading (L), Reading, Leeds (L), Wolves (L), Plymouth, Blackpool (L), Wolves (L), Hibernian, Barnet, Eastleigh									
Staff	David	39	Midfielder	Brackley Town			2		
Rushden & Dia, Stamford, King's Lynn, Boston U, King's Lynn (L), King's Lynn, Nuneaton, Cambridge C (L), Rugby T (L), Rugby T, Brackley, Rugby T, Stamford, Brackley									
Stanley	James		Midfielder	AFC Fylde			1		
AFC Fylde (Y)									
Stansfield	Harry		Midfielder	Darlington		1	3	1	
Darlington									

2018-19 NATIONAL. NORTH & SOUTH PLAYERS

APPEARANCES

SURNAME	FIRSTNAME	AGE	POSITION	CLUB PLAYED FOR				Ap	Gls
Starcenko	Aleksandrs	18	Midfielder	Guiseley		1	2	1	
Frickley Ath (Y), Guiseley									
Staunton	Joshua	23	Defender	FC Halifax Town	20	4	13	24	2
Gillingham, St Albans (L), Dagenham & R, Woking, FC Halifax									
Stead	Tom	19	Defender	Ashton United (L)	2		1	2	
PNE (Y), Ashton U (L)									
Stearn	Ross	28	Midfielder	Bath City	38	8		46	14
Forest Green, Sutton U, Eastleigh, Sutton U, Bath (L), Bath									
Steele	Chekaine		Forward	Leamington		1	3	1	
Worcester, Telford, Leamington, Stourbridge									
Steer	Rene	29	Defender	Maidenhead United	38		2	38	
Arsenal, Gillingham (L), Oldham, Boston Utd, Maidenhead									
Stenson	Matty		Forward	Leamington	13			13	8
				Solihull Moors	7	14	5	21	1
Barwell, Leamington, Solihull									
Stephen	Tom	26	Defender	East Thurrock United	10	1	2	11	
East Thurrock, Concord R, East Thurrock									
Stephens	Dave	27	Defender	Boreham Wood	37	1	1	38	2
Norwich , Lincoln (L), Hibernian, Barnet, Boreham W									
Stephens	Sam		Goalkeeper	Barrow			1		
Barrow (Y)									
Stephenson	Darren	26	Forward	Stockport County	34	14	2	48	8
Bradford (Y), Hinckley U (L), Woodley Sp (L), Stocksbridge (L), Southport (L), Southport, Chorley, Tranmere, AFC Fylde (L), Stockport									
Sterling	Tyrone	31	Defender	Concord Rangers	43			43	1
Cray W, Dartford, Dover, Bromley, Concord R									
Sterling-James	Omari	25	Forward	Brackley Town (L)	2	6	6	8	
Birmingham (Y), Cheltenham, Oxford C (L), Gloucester (L), Solihull M, Mansfield, Solihull M (L), Brackley (L)									
Stevens	Connor	21	Defender	Wealdstone	41			41	5
Watford (Y), Oxford C (L), Wealdstone									
Stevens	Mathew	21	Forward	Slough Town (L)	17	1		18	8
Barnet, Peterborough, Sligo (L), Kettering (L), Slough (L)									
Stewart	Carl	22	Midfielder	Oxford City	2	1	2	3	
Watford (Y), Oxford C, Wingate & F									
Stewart	Ethan	19	Defender	Billericay Town (L)	2	1	1	3	
Nottm Forest (Y), Billericay (L)									
Stock	Brian	37	Midfielder	Havant & Waterlooville	23	1		24	
Bournemouth (Y), PNE, Doncaster, Burnley, Havant & W,									
Stockton	Cole	25	Forward	Wrexham (L)	2	7	2	9	1
Tranmere (Y), Vauxhall M (L), Southport (L), Morecambe (L), Morecambe (L), Hearts, Carlisle, Tranmere, Wrexham (L)									
Stopforth	Gary	32	Midfielder	Chester	22			22	1
Ramsbottom, Salford, Stockport, Colne, Chester									
Storer	Kyle	32	Midfielder	Solihull Moors	49		1	49	2
Leicester (Y), Bedworth U, Tamworth, Hinckley U, Atherstone, Nuneaton, Kidderminster, Wrexham, Cheltenham, Solihull									
Stott	Jamie	21	Defender	Stockport County (L)	32	2		34	3
Oldham, Curzon A (L), AFC Fylde (L), Curzon A (L), Stockport (L)Stockport (Lx2)									
Straker	Anthony	30	Midfielder	Bath City	47			47	7
Aldershot (Y), Southend, York, Motherwell (L), Grimsby, Aldershot, Bath									
Stratford	Harry		Midfielder	Kidderminster Harriers	1	7	1		
Kidderminster (Y), Stourport S (L)									
Streete	Theo	31	Defender	AFC Telford United	42	4	1	46	1
Derby (Y), Doncaster (L), Rotherham, Solihull, Alfreton, Nuneaton, Solihull, Brackley, Telford									
Strevens	Ben	39	Forward	Eastleigh			1		
BarnetSlough (L), St Albans (L), Crawley, Dagenham & R, Brentford, Wycombe, Gillingham, Dagenham & R, Eastleigh, Whitehawk (L)									
Strizovic	Josh	19	Goalkeeper	Maidstone United		20			
Braintree (Y), Waltham F (L), Burnham R, Billericay, Maidstone									
Strugnell	Dan	26	Defender	Havant & Waterlooville	29	7	1	36	1
Bournemouth (Y), Wimborne (L), Havant & W (L), Havant & W									
Stryjek	Max	22	Goalkeeper	Eastleigh (L)	14			14	
Polonia (Y), Sunderland (Y), Boston U (L), Accrington (L), Eastleigh (L)									
Styche	Reece	30	Forward	Darlington	11			11	5
				Alfreton Town	18	5	1	23	11
Hednesford, Bromsgrove (L), Grantham, Coalville T, Shepshed D, Chasetown, Forest GR, Wycombe (L), Kidderminster, Tamworth (Lx2), Macclesfield (L), Macclesfield, Gateshead, Nuneaton (L), Tamworth, Darlington, Alfreton									

Key: X - Started; SX - Sub on; S - Non-playing Sub; Ap - Total Appearances; Gls - Total goals.

SURNAME	FIRSTNAME	AGE	POSITION	CLUB	APPEARANCES			Ap	Gls
Sullivan	Charlie		Midfielder	Concord Rangers		2			
Concord R									
Summerfield	Luke	31	Midfielder	Wrexham	38	2		40	2
Plymouth (Y), Bournemouth (L), Leyton O (L), Cheltenham, Shrewsbury, York, Grimsby, Macclesfield (L), Wrexham									
Sutherland	Frankie	25	Forward	Bromley	41	3		44	10
QPR, Portsmouth (L), Leyton O (L), AFC Wimbledon (L), Dagenham & R (L), Crawley Town (L), Woking, Whitehawk, Bromley									
Sutton	Levi	23	Defender	Harrogate Town (L)	3	3	3		
Scunthorpe (Y), North Ferriby (L), Harrogate (L)									
Sutton	Shane	30	Defender	AFC Telford United	48		1	48	5
Newtown, Telford									
Swaby-Neavin	Javid		Defender	Ashton United (L)	5	4	3	9	
Oldham (Y), Ashton U (L)									
Swain	Ollie		Defender	Hemel Hempstead Town	7	4	12	11	
Hemel H									
Swaine	Rob	31	Defender	Chelmsford City	9			9	1
				Maidstone United	16	4	5	20	1
Chelmsford, Billericay, Bromley, Billericay, Chelmsford, Maidstone									
Swallow	Ben	29	Midfielder	Weston-super-Mare	16	7	10	23	
Bristol R (Y), York, Newport Co, Bromley, Dartford, Havant & W, Margate (L), Bognor R, Weston									
Sweeney	Dan	25	Midfielder	Barnet	53		1	53	1
Wimbledon (Yth), Kingstonian, Dulwich Hamlet, Maidstone, Barnet, Hampton & R (L)									
Sweeney	Dan	21	Midfielder	Solihull Moors	1	6	5	7	1
				Leamington (L)	1		1	1	
Kidderminster (Y), Halesowen (L), Stourport (L), Rushall (L), Sutton C (L), Stourport (L), Stourport, Solihull, Hednesford (L), Leamington (L)									
Sweeney	Jayden		Defender	Leyton Orient		1		1	
Leyton O (Y)									
Syers	David	31	Midfielder	Darlington	7	7	5	14	1
Farsley C, Harrogate T, Guiseley, Bradford, Doncaster, Scunthorpe (L), Scunthorpe, Rochdale, Guiseley, Darlington									
Syla	Roy	18	Midfielder	Hampton & Richmond Borough (L)	5			5	
Barnet (Y), Hampton & R (L)									
Symons	Michael	32	Forward	Hereford FC	24	4		28	4
Gloucester, Worcester, Oxford C, Worcester, Gloucester, Hereford									
Tait	Joe	29	Defender	York City	26		5	26	2
Dayton Dutch Lions (US), Philadelphia Union, Gateshead, Spennymoor, York									
Tajbakhsh	Aryan	28	Midfielder	Dover Athletic	7			7	
				Maidstone United	8	11	2	19	
				Dulwich Hamlet	10	1		11	2
Northwood, Barnet, Maidenhead, Antalyaspor, Yalovaspor (L), Braintree, Billericay, Harrow B, Farnborough, Maidenhead, St Albans, Cheshunt, Enfield, Hendon, Cray W, Crawley, Wealdstone (L), Dover, Maidstone, Dulwich H									
Talbot	Drew	32	Defender	Chesterfield	13			13	
Sheffield W (Y), Scunthorpe (L), Luton, Chesterfield (L), Chesterfield, Plymouth (L), Portsmouth, Chesterfield									
Tangara	Amadou		Goalkeeper	Dulwich Hamlet			1		
Dulwich H									
Tarbuck	Bradley	23	Forward	Havant & Waterlooville	20	6	5	26	
Portsmouth (Y), Dartford (L), Dorchester (L), Dorchester, Havant & W									
Tarpey	Dave	30	Forward	Barnet	8	7	2	15	1
				Maidenhead United (L)	1	2	1	3	
				Woking	7			7	3
Henley Town, Basingstoke, Hampton & R, Walton & H (L), Chertsey (L), Farnborough, Hampton & R, Maidenhead, Barnet, Maidenhead (L), Woking (L)									
Tasdemir	Serhat		Midfielder	AFC Fylde	11	23	14	34	9
AFC Fylde									
Tattum	Samuel	22	Defender	FC United of Manchester	9	2	1	11	
Man City (Y), Stalybridge, FC United									
Taylor	Bobby-Joe	24	Midfielder	Bromley	2	11	3	13	
Chelsea (Y), Cambridge, Bishop's St (L), Maidstone, Aldershot, Bromley, Dover (L), Dover									
Taylor	Bobby-Joe	24	Midfielder	Dover Athletic	25	3	1	28	
Taylor	Connor	26	Forward	Leamington	18	10	13	28	
Aston Villa (Y), Tamworth (L), Walsall, Nuneaton (L), Nuneaton, Tamworth, Leamington									
Taylor	Glen	29	Forward	Spennymoor Town	49			49	32
Blyth Spartans, Spennymoor									
Taylor	Harry	22	Defender	Woking (L)	7			7	
Chelsea (Y), Barnet (Y), Woking (L)									

2018-19 NATIONAL. NORTH & SOUTH PLAYERS

APPEARANCES

SURNAME	FIRSTNAME	AGE	POSITION	CLUB PLAYED FOR				Ap	Gls
Taylor	Harry		Midfielder	Aldershot Town			1		
Aldershot (Y)									
Taylor	Harry	22	Defender	Woking (L)	7			7	
				Barnet	19	2		21	
Chelsea (Y), Barnet (Y), Woking (L)									
Taylor	Jack	20	Midfielder	Barnet	35	4		39	4
Cheslea (Y), Barnet (Y), Hampton & R (L)									
Taylor	Jason	32	Midfielder	Barrow	44			44	1
Oldham , Stockport (L), Stockport, Rotherham, Rochdale (L), Cheltenham, Northampton, EastleighAFC Fylde, Barrow									
Taylor	Joel	23	Defender	Kidderminster Harriers	25	2	6	27	2
Stoke (Y), Rochdale (L), Kidderminster									
Taylor	Josh	24	Forward	Sutton United	16	8	5	24	1
				Maidstone United (L)	13	2		15	
Halifax, Sutton U, Hampton & R (L), Maidstone (L)									
Taylor	Michael	31	Forward	Leamington		3	1	3	
Worcester, Solihull, Worcester, Stratford T, Tamworth, Leamington, Stratford T									
Taylor	Quade	25	Defender	Dulwich Hamlet	31	1	6	32	
Dulwich H, Crystal P (U23), Welling (L), Bolton, Dag & Red (L), Braintree, Dulwich H									
Taylor-Randle	Reiss		Midfielder	Kidderminster Harriers	2	1	2		
Kidderminster (Y)Stourport S (L)									
Teague	Andrew	33	Defender	Chorley	45			45	7
Macclesfield, Hyde U (L), Leigh Gen, Lancaster C, Chorley									
Temple	Shane		Midfielder	Braintree Town		1	5	1	
Braintree (Y)									
Ten-Grotenhuis	Charlie	0	Midfielder	Hungerford Town	16	7	9	23	3
Hampton & R, Tooting & M (L), Bristol R, Gloucester (L), Hungerford									
Thackray	Kris	31	Defender	Spennymoor Town	23	4	19	27	
Reggina, Monopoli (L), Ancona (L), Andria, Cosenza, QFC (Malta), Alem Aachen (Ger), KFC Uerduingen, Gzira Utd (Malta), Spennymoor									
Thanoj	Andi	26	Midfielder	Boston United	40	2		42	
Grimsby (Y), Alfreton, Harrogate, Redditch, Boston U									
Tharme	Douglas		Defender	Wrexham	3	2	9	5	
Wrexham									
Theobalds	D'Sean		Midfielder	Concord Rangers	1	5	2	6	1
Leatherhead, Concord R, Leatherhead									
Thewlis	Jordan	26	Forward	Harrogate Town	7	3	2	10	1
				Boston United (L)		1		1	
Scunthorpe (Y), Gainsborough, Harrogate, Boston (L)									
Thomas	Adam	25	Midfielder	Stockport County	46	3		49	8
Stoke (Y), Macclesfield (L), Hednesford (L), Hednesford, Stockport									
Thomas	Aswad	29	Defender	Sutton United	33	3	2	36	2
Charlton, Accrington (L), Barnet (L), Woking, Braintree, Grimsby, Woking, Dover (L), Dover, Sutton U									
Thomas	Josh	20	Midfielder	Gloucester City	13	3	3	16	1
Cheltenham (Y), Gloucester									
Thomas	Kieran		Defender	Hereford FC	43			43	2
Cinderford, Gloucester, Hereford									
Thomas	Kwame	23	Forward	Solihull Moors	8	11	4	19	
				Kidderminster Harriers (L)	1	4		5	
Derby, Notts Co (L), Blackpool (L), Coventry, Sutton U (L), Solihull (L), Solihull, Kidderminster (L)									
Thomas	Sorba		Midfielder	Boreham Wood	16	20	4	36	
Boreham W									
Thomas-Asante	Brandon	20	Forward	Sutton United (L)	5	2	1	7	
				Oxford City (L)	15			15	3
MK Dons (Y), Sutton U (L), Oxford C (L)									
Thomas-Barker	Cory	19	Midfielder	Weston-super-Mare	3	9	3		
Weston (Y)									
Thompson	Conor	24	Goalkeeper	Chippenham Town	1		1	1	
Swindon (Y), Gloucester, Chippenham, Torquay, Newport Co, Gloucester, Chippenham									
Thompson	Dan	24	Forward	Braintree Town	6	4	1	10	
Hampton & R, Portsmouth, Havant & W (L), Dorchester (L), Bognor (L), Hampton & R, Hayes & Y, Bognor, Burgess H, Tonbridge A, Braintree									
Thompson	Dereece		Forward	Dulwich Hamlet	14	1	4	15	4
Dulwich H									
Thompson	Joe	19	Forward	Altrincham			2		
Crewe (Y), Altrincham, Winsford (dual)									

Key: X - Started; SX - Sub on; S - Non-playing Sub; Ap - Total Appearances; Gls - Total goals.

2018-19 NATIONAL. NORTH & SOUTH PLAYERS — APPEARANCES

SURNAME	FIRSTNAME	AGE	POSITION	CLUB				Ap	Gls
Thompson	Lewis	19	Defender	FC United of Manchester (L)	13			13	
Blackburn (Y), FC United									
Thompson	Niall	25	Midfielder	Truro City	42	1		43	3
Torquay, Worcester (L), Hucknall, Truro									
Thompson	Reece	25	Forward	Guiseley	5	1	1	6	
York, North Ferriby, Guiseley, Boston Utd (L)									
Thompson	Stephen	30	Forward	Darlington	39	4		43	10
Middlesbrough (Y), Port Vale, Stafford R (L), Telford, Durham C, Darlington									
Thompson	Tony	24	Goalkeeper	Altrincham	37		10	37	
Rotherham (Y), Southport (L), Morecambe, Chester, AFC Fylde, Altrincham									
Thomson	Connor	23	Defender	Gateshead	18	7	15	25	1
Carlisle (Y), Blackburn (Y), Barrow (L), FC Halifax, Gateshead									
Thomson	George	27	Midfielder	Harrogate Town	44	5	3	49	9
Histon, King's Lynn (L), King's Lynn, Chester, FC United (L), FC United, Harrogate									
Thomson	Matthew		Defender	Chester	9	3	14	12	
Chester									
Thorn	Jack		Midfielder	Wrexham		1	2	1	
Wrexham (Y)									
Thornley	Oliver	20	Defender	Curzon Ashton	19			19	
Curzon A									
Thornton	William	21	Defender	Guiseley	22	7	12	29	2
Guiseley									
Tibbetts	Josh	20	Goalkeeper	Solihull Moors (L)			3		
				Southport	1		24	1	
Birmingham (Y), Peterborough, Royston (L), Solihull (L), Southport									
Tindle	Greg		Defender	Chippenham Town	11			11	
Chippenham									
Tingley	James		Midfielder	Maidstone United		2			
Maidstone (Y)									
Tinkler	Robbie	22	Defender	Gateshead	48		1	48	2
Middlesbrough (Y), North Ferriby (L), Gateshead (L)Gateshead									
Togwell	Lee		Midfielder	Slough Town	47	3		50	5
Slough									
Togwell	Sam	34	Midfielder	Slough Town	46		1	46	3
Crystal Palace, Oxford U (L), Northampton (L), Port Vale (L), Barnsley, Scunthorpe, Chesterfield, Wycombe (L), Barnet, Eastleigh, Slough									
Tollitt	Ben	24	Midfielder	Wrexham (L)	8	6		14	4
Skelmersdale, Portsmouth, Tranmere, Wrexham (L)									
Tomlin	Gavin	36	Forward	Dulwich Hamlet	12	9	5	21	1
Yeovil, Dag & Red, Torquay (L), Gillingham (L), Southend, Port Vale, Crawley, Dulwich H									
Tomlinson	Ben	29	Forward	FC Halifax Town	12	6	1	18	1
Worksop, Macclesfield, Alfreton, Lincoln, Barnet, Grimsby (L), Tranmere (L), Barrow (L), Carlisle, Halifax									
Tomlinson	Connor	18	Forward	Hemel Hempstead Town (L)	2	2	3	4	
Luton (Y), Hemel H (L)									
Tomsett	Liam	26	Midfielder	Ashton United	31	8	2	39	5
Blackpool (Y), Altrincham (L), Ayr (L), Hyde (L), AFC Fylde, Curzon A, Ashton U									
Topley	Adam		Midfielder	Concord Rangers	4	9	3	13	1
Concord R									
Torres	Sergio	35	Midfielder	Eastbourne Borough	31	5	2	36	1
Wycombe, Peterborough, Lincoln, Crawley, Whitehawk, Eastbourne B									
Toulson	Ryan	33	Defender	Bradford Park Avenue	12	5	20	17	
Halifax, Harrogate T, Guiseley, Halifax, Guiseley, Bradford PA									
Touray	Ibou	24	Defender	Salford City	51			51	3
Everton (Y), Chester, Rhyl, Nantwich, Salford									
Toure	Cheick	26	Defender	Dulwich Hamlet	11		4	11	
Aviron Bayonnais, Lorient, Bourg-en-Bresse (L), Burgess H, Vyskov (Czech R), Dulwich H									
Toure	Gime	25	Forward	AFC Fylde	6	14		20	4
				Sutton United	18	4		22	3
BrestViry-Chatillon, West Brom, La Roche Vendee, Fontenay-Foot-Vendee, Macclesfield, Unattached, AFC Fylde, Sutton U									
Townsend	Michael	33	Defender	Nuneaton Borough	5	2		7	2
Cheltenham, Barnet (L), Hereford, Tamworth, Nuneaton									
Trotman	Luke	22	Defender	Darlington	43			43	
Luton (Y), Nuneaton, Darlington									
Truslove	Liam	23	Midfielder	Kidderminster Harriers	1	2	1		
Birmingham (Y), , Leamington (L), Kidderminster									

2018-19 NATIONAL. NORTH & SOUTH PLAYERS

SURNAME	FIRSTNAME	AGE	POSITION	CLUB PLAYED FOR	X	SX	S	Ap	Gls
Tshimanga	Kabongo	23	Forward	Oxford City	49	2		51	34
MK Dons, Aldershot (L), Chelmsford (L), Corby (L), Nuneaton (L), Throttur Reykjavik, MK Dons, Yeovil (L), Boston U, Oxford C									
Tudur-Jones	Owain	34	Midfielder	Nuneaton Borough	2	1	1	3	
Swansea (Y), Swindon (L), Norwich, Yeovil (L), Brentford (L), Inverness, Hibernian, Falkirk, Nuneaton									
Tunnicliffe	Jordan	25	Defender	AFC Fylde	47	4	3	51	6
West Brom, Barnsley, Kidderminster, Hednesford (L), AFC Fylde									
Turgott	Blair	25	Midfielder	Maidstone United	33	1		34	16
West Ham, Bradford (L), Colchester (L), Rotherham(L), Dagenham & R (L), Coventry, Leyton Orient, Bromley, Stevenage, Boreham Wood, Maidstone (L)Maidstone									
Turley	Jamie	29	Defender	Leyton Orient (L)	11	3	2	14	1
Wycombe (Y), Salisbury, Forest GR, Eastleigh, Newport Co, Boreham (L), Notts Co, Leyton Orient (L)									
Turnbull	Paul	30	Midfielder	Stockport County	25	9	7	34	2
Stockport, Altrincham (L), Northampton, Stockport (L), Stockport (L), Lincoln (L), Macclesfield, Barrow, Chester, Stockport									
Turner	Henry		Goalkeeper	Ashton United			3		
Ashton U									
Turner	Jack	26	Goalkeeper	Slough Town	51			51	
Wimbledon, Staines, Slough									
Turner	Jake	20	Goalkeeper	Darlington (L)	11			11	
Bolton (Y), Darlington (L)									
Turner	Rhys	23	Forward	Barrow	9	3	1	12	1
Stockport (Y), Oldham, York (L), Macclesfield (L), Morecambe, Stockport (L), Barrow									
Tuson-Firth	George		Midfielder	Aldershot Town	1			1	
Aldershot (Y)									
Tuton	Shaun	27	Forward	Chester	2			2	
				Spennymoor Town	17	12	3	29	2
				Chorley (L)	1	5		6	
Halifax, Barnsley, Grimsby (L), Barrow (L), Halifax (L), Chester (NC), Spennymoor, Chorley (L)									
Tutonda	David	23	Defender	Barnet	23	5	9	28	2
Cardiff (Yth), Newport Co (L), York (L), Barnet									
Tweed	Michael	20	Midfielder	Nuneaton Borough	1	5	6	6	
Nuneaton									
Tyler	Rhys	26	Defender	Wealdstone	29	1	2	30	
Hungerford, Wealdstone									
Uchechi	Danny	29	Forward	Hampton & Richmond Borough	10	11	5	21	
Dender (Bel), Leicester (L), Sheff Wed (L), Aberdeen (L), AFC Eskilstuna (Swe), Dalkurd, Boreham W, Hendon, Hampton & R									
Udoh	Daniel	22	Forward	AFC Telford United	44	2	1	46	26
Crewe Alexandra (Y), Solihull Moors (L), Chester (L), Leamington (L), Telford									
Ugwu	Gozie	26	Forward	Chesterfield	6	1		7	
				Boreham Wood (L)	21	3	2	24	4
				Ebbsfleet United (L)	8			8	2
Reading (Y), Ebbsfleet (L), Yeovil (L), Plymouth (L), Shrewsbury (L), Dunfermline, Yeovil, Wycombe, Woking, Chesterfield, Boreham W (L), Ebbsfleet (L)									
Umerah	Josh	21	Forward	Boreham Wood (L)	19	4		23	7
Charlton (Y), Kilmarnock (L), Wycombe (L), Boreham W (L)									
Unwin	James		Defender	Gloucester City		3	9	3	
Gloucester									
Upward	Ryan	27	Midfielder	Maidenhead United	24	3	2	27	5
Maidenhead									
Urwin	Matthew	25	Goalkeeper	Chorley (L)	41			41	
Blackburn (Y), Stalybridge (L), Bradford, AFC Fylde, Fleetwood, Telford (L), Chorley (L), Chorley (L)									
Vasiliou	Antonis	18	Midfielder	Barnet		2		2	
Barnet (Y)									
Vaughan	Lee	32	Defender	Kidderminster Harriers	31			31	2
				Solihull Moors	10		3	10	
Walsall (Y), Telford U, Kidderminster, Cheltenham, Tranmere, Kidderminster, Solihull									
Vaulks	Jack	19	Defender	Darlington			4		
Darlington									
Vilhete	Mauro	26	Midfielder	Barnet		1		1	1
Barnet, Boreham W (L), Boreham W (L), Boreham W (L)									
Vincent	Frank		Midfielder	Torquay United (L)	4	9	2	13	
Bournemouth (Y), Torquay (L)									
Vine	Chinedu		Forward	Oxford City		2	1	2	
Hayes & Y, Oxford C									

Key: X - Started; SX - Sub on; S - Non-playing Sub; Ap - Total Appearances; Gls - Total goals.

2018-19 NATIONAL. NORTH & SOUTH PLAYERS

SURNAME	FIRSTNAME	AGE	POSITION	CLUB	APPEARANCES				
								Ap	Gls
Vint	Ronnie	22	Defender	Dartford	38		3	38	3
Dartford									
Vose	Bailey	21	Goalkeeper	Dartford (L)	26		2	26	
Brighton (Y), Dartford (L), Concord R (L), Eastbourne B (L), Welling (L), Colchester, Dartford (L)									
Vose	Dominic	25	Forward	Dulwich Hamlet	30	10		40	1
Braintree, Barnet, Colchester, Welling, Wrexham, Scunthorpe, Grimsby (L), Whitehawk, Bromley, Chester, Dulwich H									
Wabo	Norman	21	Forward	Maidstone United (L)	2	1	2		
				Braintree Town (L)	5		5		
Southend, Cambridge C (L), Ebbsfleet (L), Maidstone (L), Braintree (L)									
Wade	Bradley	18	Goalkeeper	Barrow (L)			1		
Rochdale (Y), Barrow (L)									
Wafula	Jonathan	24	Midfielder	Boston United	20	7	6	27	1
Chesterfield, Worksop, Gainsborough, Boston U									
Wagner	Ed		Defender	Kidderminster Harriers		4			
				Alfreton Town			1		
USA, Alfreton, Kidderminster, Redditch (L), Alfreton									
Waite	James	20	Forward	Hereford FC	5	4	2	9	2
Hereford (Y)									
Wakefield	Charlie	19	Midfielder	Chesterfield			2		
Chesterfield (Y)									
Waldren	Darren	30	Midfielder	Billericay Town	34	8	5	42	1
Bromley, Dulwich H, Welling, Billericay									
Walker	Adam	28	Midfielder	Brackley Town	48	1	1	49	2
Coventry (Y), Nuneaton (L), Nuneaton, Solihull, Brackley									
Walker	Bradley	24	Midfielder	Wrexham (L)	31	1	1	32	4
Hartlepool (Y), Crewe, Wrexham (L), Shrewsbury, Wrexham (L)									
Walker	Charlie	29	Forward	Eastbourne Borough	28	10	3	38	11
Luton, Boreham W (L), Aldershot, St Albans, Eastbourne B									
Walker	Glenn	32	Midfielder	Brackley Town	39	4	1	43	2
Banbury, Corby, Brackley, Hednesford, Brackley									
Walker	Josh	21	Forward	Barnet	12	10	1	22	2
Tottenham (Yth), Fulham (Yth), Hendon, Barnet									
Walker	Laurie	29	Goalkeeper	Hemel Hempstead Town	51			51	
Cambridge U, Morecambe, Kettering, Brackley, Leamington, Hemel H, Oxford C, Brackley, Hemel H									
Walker	Mitch	27	Goalkeeper	Dover Athletic	39			39	
Brighton, Eastbourne B (L), Dover									
Walker	Nicky	24	Midfielder	Boston United	26	11	1	37	9
Rotherham (Y), Barrow (L), Wycombe (L), Boston U, Bradford PA, Boston U, Clipstone (L), Buxton, Shaw Lane, Gainsborough, Boston U									
Walker	Sam	32	Midfielder	Stockport County	43	6	1	49	10
Curzon Ashton, Halifax, Salford, Stockport, Curzon Ashton (L)									
Walker	Tom	23	Midfielder	Salford City	32	11	5	43	5
Bolton (Y), Bury (L), FC United, Salford City									
Wall	Alex	28	Forward	Concord Rangers	34	3	1	37	22
Maidenhead, Luton (L), Luton, Dartford (L), Bristol R (L), Bromley, Hungerford, Concord R									
Wall	Luke	22	Forward	Curzon Ashton	21	2	6	23	1
Blackburn (Y), Skelmersdale (L), Accrington, Bangor, Curzon A									
Wallen	Joshua	22	Midfielder	FC United of Manchester	21	3	2	24	3
QPR, Chelmsford (L), FC United									
Walsh	Louis	18	Midfielder	Guiseley (L)	5	4	1	9	
Barnsley (Y), Guiseley (L)									
Walsh	Max		Defender	Dartford			2		
Dartford (Y)									
Walters	Lewis	24	Forward	Guiseley	7	10	4	17	1
Leeds (Y), Nottingham F, Barrow (L)Guiseley, AFC Fylde									
Walters	Lewis	24	Forward	AFC Fylde	3	7	1	10	1
Walton	Simon	31	Midfielder	Billericay Town	3	3	2	6	1
				Maidstone United	31	3	4	34	1
Leeds, Charlton, Ipswich (L), Cardiff (L), QPR, Hull (L), Plymouth, Blackpool (L), Crewe (L), Sheff U (L), Hartlepool, Stevenage, Crawley, Guiseley, Sutton U, Billericay, Maidstone (L), Maidstone									
Wanadio	Luke	26	Midfielder	Aldershot Town	17	12	4	29	1
				Dulwich Hamlet (L)	4	5	2	9	1
Staines, Welling, Dartford, Bromley, Aldershot, Dulwich H (L)									
Warburton	Matthew		Forward	Stockport County	42	11	1	53	27
Curzon Ashton, Salford, Curzon Ashton, Stockport									

2018-19 NATIONAL. NORTH & SOUTH PLAYERS

APPEARANCES

SURNAME	FIRSTNAME	AGE	POSITION	CLUB PLAYED FOR				Ap	Gls
Ward	Darren	40	Defender	Hemel Hempstead Town	37	1	3	38	2
Wolves, Watford (L), Charlton (L), Millwall, Swindon (L), Swindon, Crawley (L), Yeovil, Hemel H,									
Ward	Ty		Midfielder	Hemel Hempstead Town	3			3	
Colney H, Chesham, Dunstable, AFC Rushden, Hemel H, St Ives									
Wardle	Louis	20	Defender	Curzon Ashton (L)	3	3	1	6	
Barnsley (Y), Curzon A (L)									
Waring	George	24	Forward	Kidderminster (L)	2	4		6	
				Chester	9	6		15	5
Stoke (Y), Barnsley (L), Oxford U (L), Shrewsbury (L), Carlisle (L), Tranmere, Halifax (L), Kidderminster (L), Kidderminster (L), Chester									
Warwick	Harry		Forward	Gloucester City (L)	1	5	1	6	
				Truro City (L)	1	2	2	3	
Bristol R (Y), Gloucester (L), Truro (L)									
Wassall	Ethan	21	Defender	Hereford FC (L)	5		1	5	
Derby (Y), Hereford (L)									
Wassmer	Charlie	28	Defender	Woking		1		1	
				Maidstone United (L)	6		2	6	
				Billericay Town	12			12	1
Hayes (Y), Harrow B (L), Crawley, Fleetwood (L), Dagenham & R (L), Cambridge U, Hayes & Y, Margate, Maidenhead, Hampton & R, Woking, Met Police (L), Leatherhead (L), Maidstone (L), Billericay									
Waters	George			Hemel Hempstead Town		2			
Hemel H (Y)									
Waters	Matty	21	Midfielder	Chester	16	3	4	19	
Chester									
Waterston	Nathan	22	Forward	Barrow	4	2	1	6	
				Altrincham (L)		2		2	
Barrow (Y), Penrith, Barrow, Altrincham (L)									
Watkins	Andy	34	Forward	Bath City	15	9	4	24	1
Truro, Bath									
Watson	Ian	33	Defender	Blyth Spartans	8	2	17	10	
Whitley B, Blyth S, Darlington, Spennymoor, Blyth S, Gateshead (Asst Man)									
Watson	Jordan	26	Defender	Blyth Spartans	32	3	6	35	
Sunderland (Y), Blyth S, Darlington, Blyth S									
Watson	Ryan		Midfielder	Ashton United		1		1	
Curzon A, Farsley, Ashton U, Scarborough									
Watt	Sanchez	28	Midfielder	Hemel Hempstead Town	26	5	1	31	8
Arsenal (Y), Southend (L), Leeds (L), Sheff Wed (L), Crawley (L), Colchester (L), Colchester, Kerala Blasters (India), Crawley, Billericay, Hemel H (L), Hemel H									
Weaver	Jake	22	Goalkeeper	Hungerford Town (L)	12			12	
				Kidderminster Harriers (L)	1		2	1	
Birmingham (Y), Hungerford (L), Kidderminster (L)									
Webb	David		Midfielder	Spennymoor Town	1	1	1		
Spennymoor									
Webb	Tom	35	Midfielder	Gloucester City			1		
Gloucester									
Webber	Patrick	20	Defender	Braintree Town (L)	6	1	6	7	
Worthing, Ipswich, Braintree (L), Braintree (L)									
Wedgbury	Samuel	30	Midfielder	Chesterfield	1	2	1	3	
Sheff Utd, Mansfield (L), Macclesfield, Altrincham (L), Stevenage, Forest Green, Wrexham, Chesterfield									
Weeks	Declan	23	Midfielder	Kidderminster Harriers	31	3		34	4
Southport, Kidderminster									
Weir	Robbie	30	Midfielder	Chesterfield	25	8	3	33	
Aye United (Y), Larne, Sunderland, York (L), Tranmere (L), Tranmere, Burton, Leyton O, Chesterfield									
Weir	Tyler	28	Midfielder	Gloucester City	6		1	6	
Hereford, Gloucester (L), Gloucester (L), Worcester (L), Gloucester, Worcester, Gloucester									
Welch	Jarrard	20	Midfielder	Weston-super-Mare	23	8	3	31	4
Weston									
Wellard	Ricky	31	Midfielder	Hampton & Richmond Borough	30	5	9	35	1
Wimbledon, Cambridge U (L), Cambridge U, Salisbury (L), Salisbury, Sutton U, Welling, Hemel H, Wealdstone, Hampton & R									
Wells	George	23	Midfielder	Slough Town	46		4	46	2
Slough									
Wells	Louis	37	Goalkeeper	Billericay Town	4		8	4	
				Dartford	3		3	3	
Staines, Dartford, Leatherhead (L), Hayes & Y (L), Basingstoke, Concord R, Billericay, Dartford									

Key: X - Started; SX - Sub on; S - Non-playing Sub; Ap - Total Appearances; Gls - Total goals.

SURNAME	FIRSTNAME	AGE	POSITION	CLUB				Ap	Gls
Wesolowski	James	31	Midfielder	Nuneaton Borough	9	1	2	10	
				Hereford FC	3	1	6	4	
Leicester, Cheltenham (L), Dundee Utd (L), Hamilton (L), Peterborough, Oldham, Shrewsbury, Guiseley, Nuneaton, Hereford									
West	Mark		Midfielder	FC United of Manchester	2			2	
FC United									
West	Michael	28	Midfielder	Eastbourne Borough	18	13	6	31	3
Ebbsfleet, Crewe, Hereford (L), Ebbsfleet, Whitehawk (L), Whitehawk, Chelmsford, Eastbourne B									
Westcarr	Craig	34	Forward	Boston United	1	5		6	
Nottingham F (Y), Lincoln C (L), MK Dons (L), Bedford T, Kettering, Notts Co, Chesterfield, Walsall (L), Walsall, Portsmouth, Mansfield, Southport (L), Alfreton, Boston U, Matlock									
Weston	Curtis	32	Midfielder	Chesterfield	48	1	1	49	2
Millwall (Y), Swindon, Leeds, Scunthorpe (L), Gillingham, Barnet, Chesterfield									
Weston	Myles	31	Midfielder	Ebbsfleet United	35	7	2	42	
Charlton, Notts Co (L), Notts Co, Brentford, Gillingham, Southend, Wycombe, Ebbsfleet									
Wharton	Theo	24	Midfielder	Nuneaton Borough	7	1	8	8	
				Hereford FC	6	7	10	13	
Cardiff (Y), Weston (L), York, Tamworth (L), Nuneaton, Hereford									
Wheatley	Josef	22	Midfielder	Darlington	26	3	1	29	1
Middlesbrough (Y), Darlington									
Wheeler	Nick	28	Midfielder	Woking	16	12	7	28	
Charlton, Lewis, Burgess Hill, Lewes, Tonbirdge A, Dagenham & R, Billericay, Woking									
Wheeler	Sonny		Goalkeeper	Wealdstone			3		
Wealdstone									
Whelpdale	Chris	30	Midfielder	Chelmsford City	35	6		41	10
Peterborough, Gillingham (L), Gillingham, Stevenage, Wimbledon, Stevenage, Chelmsford									
Whichelow	Matt	27	Midfielder	Hampton & Richmond Borough	10	11	9	21	4
Watford (Y), Exeter (L), Wycombe (L), Accrington (L), Boreham W, Chelmsford (L), Oxford C (L), Wealdstone, Hampton & R									
White	Andy	26	Defender	Altrincham	37		1	37	3
Crewe (Y), Nantwich, Southport, Altrincham									
White	Harry	24	Forward	Hereford	14	4	3	18	4
Gloucester, Barnsley, Kidderminster (L), Boreham W (L), Solihull M, Chester, Hereford, Oakleigh Cannons (Aus)									
White	Jaiden		Forward	Kidderminster Harriers	1	3	5	4	
Kidderminster (Y)									
White	Joe	20	Forward	Wealdstone (L)	5	1	1	6	1
Dagenham & R, Wealdstone (L), Stevenage, Wealdstone (L), Biggleswade (L)									
White	Lewis	20	Midfielder	Concord Rangers (L)	1	3		4	
Millwall (Y), Concord R (L)									
White	Nicholas (Ross)	22	Defender	AFC Telford United	49	1		50	
Wrexham (Y), Southport, Telford									
White	Ryan	20	Midfielder	FC United of Manchester	2	5	1	7	
Bolton, Bamber Bridge, AFC Blackpool, FC United									
White	Tom	22	Midfielder	Gateshead	44	2		46	3
Gateshead (Y), Spennymoor (L), West Auckland (L), Ashington (L), Scarborough (L)									
Whitehead	Danny	25	Midfielder	Salford City	38	6	2	44	5
Stockport, West Ham, Accrington, Macclesfield (L), Wigan, Macclesfield (L), Cheltenham (L), Macclesfield (L), Macclesfield, Salford									
Whitely	Corey	27	Forward	Ebbsfleet United	35	13	1	48	8
Tottenham, Waltham F, Cheshunt, Enfield T, Dagenham & R, Ebbsfleet United									
Whitham	Dale	27	Midfielder	Chorley	2	12	11	14	
				FC United (L)	9	1		10	3
Maine Road, Leigh Gen, Chorley, FC United (L)									
Whitley	Ryan	19	Goalkeeper	York City	5		28	5	
York									
Whittingham	Alfy	20	Midfielder	Hungerford Town	30	8	4	38	4
Havant & W (Y), Hungerford									
Whittingham	Richard	28	Midfielder	Hungerford Town	23	6	4	29	
Gosport B, Whitehawk, Hungerford (L), Hungerford									
Whittle	Billy	20	Midfielder	Southport	1			1	
Southport (Y)									
Widdowson	Joe	30	Defender	Leyton Orient	46			46	
West Ham, Rotherham (L), Grimsby (L), Grimsby, Rochdale, Northampton, Bury, Morecambe (L), Dagenham & R (L), Dagenham & R, Leyton Orient									
Wilde	Josh	27	Defender	Alfreton Town	41			41	3
Sheffield U, Buxton, Gainsborough, North Ferriby, Halifax, Alfreton									
Wilding	Samuel	19	Midfielder	Leamington (L)	6	6	3	12	
WBA (Y), Leamington (L)									

2018-19 NATIONAL. NORTH & SOUTH PLAYERS — APPEARANCES

SURNAME	FIRSTNAME	AGE	POSITION	CLUB PLAYED FOR				Ap	Gls
Wiles-Richards	Harvey	17	Goalkeeper	Bath City	1		30	1	
Bath (Y)									
Wilkinson	Conor	24	Forward	Dagenham & Redbridge (L)	23	1		24	11
Millwall (Y), Bolton, Chester (L), Torquay (L), Oldham (Lx2), Barnsley (L), Newport Co (L), Portsmouth (L), Chesterfield (L), Gillingham, Dagenham & R (L)									
Wilks	Daniel	23	Goalkeeper	Welling United	47			47	
Watford (Y), St Mirren, Maldon, Whitehawk (L), Whitehawk, Welling									
Williams	Aaron	25	Forward	Harrogate Town	9	29	8	38	5
Walsall (Y), Redditch (L), Romulus (L), Telford (L), Worcester, Rushall, Nuneaton, Peterborough, Nuneaton (L), Newport C, Brackley (L), Brackley, Harrogate									
Williams	Brett	31	Forward	Torquay United	7	12	4	19	2
				Sutton United (L)	19	3	1	22	3
Reading, Rotherham (L), Northampton, Woking (L), Aldershot, Stevenage, Forest Green, Torquay, Bromley, Torquay, Sutton U (L)									
Williams	Callum	22	Defender	Spennymoor Town (L)	28	4	8	32	
Newcastle, Gateshead (L), Spennymoor									
Williams	Cameron		Midfielder	Maidstone United		4			
Maidstone (Y)									
Williams	Danny	31	Midfielder	Accrington Stanley		1			
				AFC Fylde (L)	3	4	4	7	2
Daisy Hill, FC United, Clitheroe, Kendal, Chester (L), Inverness, Dundee, Unattached, Accrington, AFC Fylde (L)									
Williams	Ed	23	Midfielder	Kidderminster Harriers	32	4	1	36	13
Cheltenham (Y), Gloucester (L), Gloucester, Kidderminster									
Williams	Harry	23	Forward	Gloucester City	8	12	6	20	2
Cheltenham, Farnborough (L), Evesham (L), Gloucester (L), Gloucester (L), Sacramento, Gloucester									
Williams	Jason	23	Forward	Hemel Hempstead Town	3	4		7	1
Southend, Chelmsford (L), Welling (L), Chelmsford (L), Boreham W (L), Concord R, Hemel H									
williams	Manny	37	Forward	Slough Town	16	14	14	30	1
Weston-s-Mare, Havant & W, Maidenhead, Hayes & Y, Basingstoke, Hampton & R, Hungerford, Slough									
Williams	Matt	25	Defender	Gloucester City	5		7	5	
Bishops Cleeve, Gloucester, Evesham, Hungerford, Gloucester									
Williams	Rory		Defender	Havant & Waterlooville	39	1		40	3
Gosport, Havant & W									
Williams	Sean	27	Midfielder	Altrincham	30	5	4	35	1
Stockport, Vauxhall M, Hyde, Vauxhall M, Colwyn, Halifax, Colwyn, Altrincham, Hinckley U, Hednesford, Telford, Warrington, Altrincham									
Williams	Tyrone	24	Defender	Solihull Moors	45	3	5	48	2
Kidderminster, Hednesford (L), Solihull M									
Williamson	Ben	30	Forward	Eastleigh	31	9		40	7
Worthing, Jerez Ind., Bournemouth, Hyde, Port Vale (L), Port Vale, Gillingham, Cambridge U (L), Cambridge U, Eastleigh									
Williamson	Mike	35	Defender	Gateshead	34		2	34	
Torquay (Y), Southampton, Torquay (L), Doncaster (L), Wycombe, Watford, Portsmouth, Newcastle, Wolves (L), Wolves, Oxford U, Gateshead									
Willis	George	23	Goalkeeper	Boston United	41			41	
Sheff Utd (Y), Bradford PA (L), Alfreton (L), Matlock (L), Stalybridge, Gainsborough, Boston U									
Willmoth	Callum	28	Midfielder	Hungerford Town	2	3	6	5	
Hungerford									
Willock	Marshall	19	Defender	Solihull Moors		1	3	1	
Solihull (Y), Chesterfield (Y), Solihull									
Willoughby	Kurt	21	Forward	FC United of Manchester	41	1		42	19
Fleetwood (Y), Clitheroe, FC United									
Wills	Kane	29	Midfielder	Eastbourne Borough	47			47	4
Ebbsfleet, Eastbourne B (L), Lewes (L), Margate, Worthing, Eastbourne B									
Wilson	Brian	36	Defender	Barrow	11	1	1	12	
Stoke (Y), Cheltenham, Bristol C, Colchester, Oldham, Barrow									
Wilson	Glenn	33	Defender	Wealdstone	9		15	9	
Crawley, Fleetwood (L), Woking (L), Gateshead, Salisbury (L), Salisbury, Aldershot, Margate, Wealdstone									
Wilson	Josh	30	Forward	Chorley	30	10	2	40	
Northwich V, Leigh Gen, Burscough, Vauxhall M, Guiseley, Halifax, AFC Fylde, Telford, Chorley									
Wilson	Josh	30	Forward	Chorley	1	1		2	14
Burscough, Vauxhall M, Halifax, Guiseley (L), AFC Fylde (L), AFC Fylde, Telford, Chorley									
Wilson	Lawrie		Defender	Ebbsfleet United	25	4	7	29	
				Maidstone United (L)	3	1	1	4	
Charlton, Colchester, Stevenage, Charlton, Rotherham (L), Bolton, Peterborough (L), Port Vale, Ebbsfleet									
Wiltshire	Kyran		Midfielder	Oxford City	41	7		48	7
Maidenhead, Bishop's S (L), Oxford C									
Winfield	Dave	31	Defender	Ebbsfleet United	24	1	1	25	1
Aldershot, Salisbury (L), Wycombe, Shrewsbury, York, Wimbledon (L), Ebbsfleet									

Key: X - Started; SX - Sub on; S - Non-playing Sub; Ap - Total Appearances; Gls - Total goals.

SURNAME	FIRSTNAME	AGE	POSITION	CLUB	APPEARANCES				
								Ap	Gls
Winnard	Dean	29	Defender	Southport	27	2	2	29	4
Accrington (Y), Morecambe, Southport									
Winter	Harry	29	Midfielder	FC United of Manchester	20	3	1	23	1
Halifax, Hyde, AFC Fylde, Chorley, FC United, Stockport, FC United									
Wiseman	Scott	33	Defender	Salford City	51		2	51	1
Hull (Y), Boston U (L), Rotherham (L), Darlington (L), Darlington, Rochdale, Barnsley, PNE, Scunthorpe, Chesterfield, Rochdale (L), Salford									
Wishart	Dan	27	Defender	Sutton United	11	5	6	16	
				Maidstone United	24	1		25	
Hayes & Y, Alfreton, Hayes & Y (L), Margate (L), Eastleigh (L), Hayes & Y, Sutton U, Forest GR, Sutton U, Maidstone									
Wollacott	Jojo	22	Goalkeeper	Truro City (L)	10			10	
				Gloucester City (L)	13			13	
Bristol C, Bath (L), Woking (L), Truro (L), Truro (L), Gloucester (L)									
Wollerton	Alex	19	Forward	Darlington (L)	1	2	2	3	
Leeds (Y), Darlington (L)									
Wood	Marcus	21	Midfielder	Southport (L)	31			31	1
Man City (Y), Bolton, Southport (L)									
Wood	Sam	32	Midfielder	Eastleigh		1	2	1	
				Bromley	44			44	
Brentford, Rotherham (L), Wycombe, Eastleigh, Bromley									
Wood	Tommy	20	Forward	Slough Town (L)		4		4	
Wimbledon, Slough (L)									
Wood	William	22	Defender	Havant & Waterlooville (L)	8	1		9	
Southampton (Y), Accrington, Havant & W (L)									
Woodards	Danny	35	Defender	Boreham Wood	26	5	9	31	
Exeter, Crewe, MK Dons, Bristol R, Tranmere, Boreham W									
Woodford	Ryan	27	Defender	Havant & Waterlooville	23	7	18	30	1
Havant & W									
Woodford	Simon		Defender	Ashton United			4		
Curzon A, Glossop NE, Ashton U									
Woods	Michael	29	Midfielder	Hartlepool United	9	4	5	13	1
				Harrogate Town	6	12	9	18	2
Leeds, Chelsea, Notts Co (L), Yeovil, Doncaster, Harrogate T, Hartlepool, Harrogate									
Woodward	Harry		Defender	Aldershot Town	1			1	
Aldershot (Y)									
Wootton	Kyle	22	Forward	FC Halifax Town (L)	2	1		3	
Scunthorpe (Y), North Ferriby (L), Cheltenham (L), Stevenage (L), FC Halifax (L)									
Worgan	Lee	35	Goalkeeper	Maidstone United	18			18	
				Dover Athletic	12		15	12	
MK Dons, Wycombe (L), Rushden, Cardiff, Merthyr T (L), Eastbourne, Hastings, Tonbridge A, Maidstone, Dover									
Worner	Ross	29	Goalkeeper	Sutton United	20	1	8	21	
				Chelmsford City	4			4	
				Maidstone United (L)	7			7	
Woking (Y), Charlton, Aldershot, Eastbourne B (L), AFC Wimbledon, Woking (L), Sutton U, Chelmsford (L), Maidstone (L)									
Worsfold	Max	26	Midfielder	Maidenhead United	21	7	2	28	
Aldershot (Y), Maidenhead (L), Dorchester (L), Staines, Hayes & Y, Staines, Maidenhead									
Worsnop	John	36	Goalkeeper	Guiseley	6		11	6	
Droylsden, Worksop, FC United, Guiseley, Alfreton, Chester, Bradford PA, York, Southport, Guiseley									
Wraight	Tom	24	Forward	Chelmsford City	37	4		41	10
East Thurrock, Maidstone, Chelmsford									
Wratten	Marshall		Forward	Dover Athletic		1		1	
Dover (Y)									
Wray	Marvin		Midfielder	Braintree Town			1		
Braintree (Y)									
Wright	Akil	23	Defender	Wrexham	43	8	3	51	6
Fleetwood, AFC Fylde (L), Barrow (L), Wrexham									
Wright	Andre	22	Forward	Torquay United		5	6	5	
				Gloucester City	10	3		13	
WBA (Y), Kidderminster (L), Torquay (L), Coventry (L), Brighton U23, Kidderminster, Nuneaton, Torquay, Gloucester									
Wright	Danny	34	Forward	Solihull Moors	47	2	3	49	13
Dereham, Histon, Cambridge U, Wrexham, Forest GR, Gateshead, Kidderminster, Cheltenham, Solihull									
Wright	Harry	20	Goalkeeper	Chelmsford City (L)	3			3	
Ipswich (Y), East Thurrock (Lx2), Chelmsford (L)									

SURNAME	FIRSTNAME	AGE	POSITION	CLUB PLAYED FOR	X	SX	S	Ap	Gls
Wright	Jake	22	Forward	York City	18	10	7	28	5
				Boston United (L)	4			4	2
Sheff Utd (Y), York (L), Southport (L), Gateshead (L), Harrogate (L), Harrogate, York, Boston U (L)									
Wright	Max	21	Midfielder	Boston United (L)	24	8	2	32	4
Grimsby (Y), Scarborough A (L), Boston U (L)									
Wright	Tommy	22	Forward	Sutton United	9	5	1	14	3
Sutton U, Salisbury (L)									
Wright	Will	21	Midfielder	Dagenham & Redbridge (L)	32	6	5	38	1
Hitchen, Colchester, Dagenham & R (L)									
Wrightson	Adam	22	Forward	Blyth Spartans	7	28	9	35	3
Gateshead (Y), South Shields (L), Blyth S (L), Blyth S									
Wroe	Nicky	33	Midfielder	Bradford Park Avenue	24	4	1	28	1
				Boston United	12	3	1	15	1
Barnsley (Y), Bury (L), Hamilton, York, Torquay, Shrewsbury, PNE, Shrewsbury (L), Oxford U (L), Notts Co, Halifax (L), Halifax, Bradford PA, Boston U									
Wyatt	Ben	23	Defender	St Albans City	43	1	1	44	2
Ipswich (Y), Colchester, Concord R (L), Braintree, St Albans									
Wycherley	Andrew	21	Goalkeeper	AFC Telford United	19	1	11	20	
New Saints (Y), Telford									
Wylie	Reece		Midfielder	Aldershot Town	1			1	
Aldershot (Y)									
Wynne	Elliot	21	Goalkeeper	Altrincham	9		24	9	
Oldham (Y), Rochdale, AFC Fylde, Fleetwood, Lancaster (L), Glossop NE (L), Abbey Hey, Altrincham, Trafford (L)Trafford (L)									
Wynter	Alex	25	Defender	Eastleigh	45	1		46	4
Crystal Palace, Colchester (L), Portsmouth (L), Colchester, Maidstone, Eastleigh									
Wynter	Ben	21	Defender	Torquay United	42	3	1	45	2
Crystal Palace, BromleyHampton & R (L), Hampton & R, Torquay									
Wynter	Jordan	25	Midfielder	Maidstone United	5	3	3	8	
				Dartford (L)	27	1	1	28	1
Arsenal, Bristol C, Cheltenham (L), Cheltenham, Telford (Lx2), Bromley, Woking, Maidstone, Dartford (L)									
Yakubu	Ismail	34	Defender	Hemel Hempstead Town	28	3	1	31	1
Barnet, Wimbledon, Newport Co, Cambridge U (L), Woking, Hemel H									
Yao	Kenneth	20	Defender	Dartford (L)	2		1	2	
Charlton (Y), Dartford (L)									
Yarney	Josef	21	Defender	Chesterfield (L)	16			16	
Everton (Y), Newcastle (Y), Morecambe (L), Chesterfield (L)									
Yasar	Oguz	22	Midfielder	East Thurrock United		1			
Heidenheim (Y) (Ger), SSV Ulm, FC Gundelfingen, East Thurrock, Romford (DR)									
Yates	Matthew	20	Goalkeeper	Gloucester City (L)	14			14	
				Hereford FC (L)	34			34	
Derby (Y), Gloucester (L), Hereford (L)									
Yeates	Mark	34	Midfielder	Eastleigh	46	2	1	48	4
Tottenham, Brighton (L), Swindon (L), Colchester (L), Hull (L), Leicester (L), Colchester, Middlesbrough, Sheffield U, Watford, Bradford, Oldham, Blackpool, Notts Co, Eastleigh									
York	Wesley	26	Forward	York City	18	15	4	33	4
Nuneaton, Wrexham, Gateshead, York									
Young	Jake		Midfielder	Guiseley			3		
Shelley Juniors, Guiseley, Sheff Utd									
Young	Luke	26	Midfielder	Wrexham	34	14		48	4
Plymouth, Torquay, Wrexham									
Young	Matt	25	Defender	Chelmsford City	16	3	11	19	
Sheff Wed, Carlisle (L), Dover, Kidderminster, Chelmsford, Welling, Woking, Chelmsford									
Young	Reggie		Midfielder	Woking	2	9	3	11	
Woking									
Young	Ryan	39	Goalkeeper	Havant & Waterlooville	11			11	
Kettering, Telford, Havant & W, AFC Porchester									
Yussuf	Adi	27	Forward	Solihull Moors	36	19		55	21
Tamworth, Burton Albion, Lincoln City, Oxford City, Mansfield Town, Crawley Town (L), Grimsby Town (L), Barrow, Solihull Moors									
Zebroski	Chris	32	Forward	Eastleigh	18	21	4	39	2
Cirencester, Plymouth, Millwall, Oxford U (L), Torquay (L), Wycombe, Torquay (L), Torquay, Bristol R, Cheltenham, Eastleigh, Newport Co, Eastleigh									
Ziboth	Steven	20	Midfielder	Truro City		5	7	5	
Troyes (Fra), Mousehole, Truro									
Ziger	Karlo	18	Goalkeeper	Sutton United (L)	1			1	
Cheslea (Y), Sutton U (L)									

Key: X - Started; SX - Sub on; S - Non-playing Sub; Ap - Total Appearances; Gls - Total goals.

ISTHMIAN LEAGUE
PREMIER DIVISION TABLE 2018-19

		P	W	D	L	F	A	GD	Pts
1	Dorking Wanderers	42	28	9	5	87	31	56	93
2	Carshalton Athletic	42	21	8	13	70	49	21	71
3	Haringey Borough	42	21	8	13	73	54	19	71
4	Tonbridge Angels (PO Winners)	42	21	7	14	59	46	13	70
5	Merstham	42	20	10	12	60	50	10	70
6	Folkestone Invicta	42	21	6	15	77	58	19	69
7	Bishop's Stortford	42	20	7	15	70	57	13	67
8	Leatherhead	42	19	8	15	56	42	14	65
9	Worthing	42	18	11	13	72	63	9	65
10	Enfield Town	42	17	10	15	76	56	20	61
11	Lewes	42	16	12	14	61	53	8	60
12	Margate	42	16	11	15	45	48	-3	59
13	Brightlingsea Regent	42	16	11	15	49	54	-5	59
14	Bognor Regis Town	42	14	15	13	71	62	9	56*
15	Hornchurch	42	12	14	16	57	59	-2	50
16	Potters Bar Town	42	13	10	19	51	56	-5	49
17	Corinthian-Casuals	42	13	8	21	48	74	-26	47
18	Kingstonian	42	13	6	23	60	78	-18	45
19	Wingate & Finchley	42	12	7	23	57	86	-29	43
20	Whitehawk	42	10	11	21	50	72	-22	41
21	Burgess Hill Town	42	9	10	23	44	91	-47	37
22	Harlow Town	42	9	7	26	53	107	-54	34

PREMIER DIVISION		1	2	3	4	5	6	7	8	9	10	11	12	13	14	15	16	17	18	19	20	21	22
1	Hornchurch		0-1	1-1	1-2	2-0	1-1	3-0	1-1	2-0	4-1	2-2	3-0	2-2	3-0	1-5	1-2	1-1	0-1	0-2	1-2	3-0	1-1
2	Bishop's Stortford	1-0		0-0	3-2	2-2	3-1	3-0	1-1	2-1	0-1	2-0	1-0	0-3	1-1	1-2	2-1	2-0	1-2	3-4	4-2	3-2	3-0
3	Bognor Regis Town	2-0	3-0		1-2	8-0	2-0	0-1	0-1	1-2	2-4	0-4	1-1	3-1	0-4	2-2	0-0	3-1	2-2	2-3	0-0	4-2	2-2
4	Brightlingsea Regent	1-1	1-0	3-0		3-2	0-2	4-3	0-2	1-0	2-0	0-2	1-1	2-0	1-0	0-0	0-3	1-1	0-1	0-2	3-0	0-1	0-2
5	Burgess Hill Town	0-3	0-3	0-2	1-1		3-2	2-1	0-0	1-6	0-0	3-1	1-3	0-1	0-3	1-1	0-2	3-0	0-1	0-4	2-4	0-1	2-1
6	Carshalton Athletic	2-1	2-1	1-1	3-0	2-0		2-3	0-0	1-0	4-2	3-1	2-0	1-1	2-1	2-1	1-2	1-2	1-0	3-0	2-0	5-1	1-2
7	Corinthian-Casuals	1-0	1-1	1-3	1-1	3-0	1-0		0-0	1-6	1-3	3-1	0-0	1-2	2-1	0-2	0-3	1-1	1-2	2-1	2-0	3-1	1-1
8	Dorking Wanderers	3-3	1-0	2-0	2-1	6-0	2-3	2-0		1-0	6-0	2-0	5-3	7-1	2-0	1-2	2-0	2-2	4-1	0-1	2-1	3-0	3-0
9	Enfield Town	2-2	2-1	3-3	0-0	3-1	0-3	0-2	1-1		2-0	2-2	4-1	0-1	0-1	1-1	4-0	0-0	3-1	0-0	6-0	4-1	1-4
10	Folkestone Invicta	5-0	2-0	1-0	2-3	1-1	2-3	2-1	0-1	2-3		4-0	3-2	2-0	2-0	4-0	1-0	6-2	2-0	0-1	2-1	2-2	0-1
11	Haringey Borough	3-1	3-1	2-2	2-1	4-4	3-1	2-2	3-2	3-1	1-0		0-2	2-0	0-3	2-1	1-0	2-2	1-0	4-0	3-0	1-2	1-2
12	Harlow Town	2-4	1-3	1-1	0-1	1-1	0-4	1-2	0-1	1-3	2-4	2-1		3-1	2-2	2-1	3-4	1-4	2-5	1-0	0-3	2-7	0-2
13	Kingstonian	2-3	3-2	4-1	2-3	2-3	1-1	1-0	0-1	2-1	4-1	0-4	7-0		0-4	2-1	2-1	0-0	1-2	1-1	1-3	1-2	2-3
14	Leatherhead	1-2	1-0	2-2	0-1	3-0	1-0	1-2	0-3	4-1	0-0	2-1	1-3	2-1		1-1	0-1	0-1	2-1	1-0	1-1	2-1	2-1
15	Lewes	0-0	1-3	3-3	5-0	0-3	0-1	3-0	0-2	2-2	2-0	0-1	2-1	3-0	1-0		0-0	2-1	0-0	0-0	1-3	4-2	3-4
16	Margate	0-0	1-4	1-0	1-0	2-3	1-1	5-2	0-1	2-1	0-3	0-1	0-0	1-0	1-1	0-1		1-0	0-2	0-2	1-3	2-2	1-1
17	Merstham	3-0	1-1	1-2	1-0	0-2	2-0	2-1	4-1	1-0	1-3	0-0	5-1	2-0	0-2	3-2	1-1		3-1	0-3	1-0	3-0	1-0
18	Potters Bar Town	0-1	4-2	2-2	0-2	0-0	0-1	2-2	0-2	1-2	2-2	0-0	1-2	3-0	0-1	1-0	1-2	0-1		2-1	1-1	4-0	1-1
19	Tonbridge Angels	1-0	2-3	1-2	2-2	1-0	1-0	2-0	0-2	1-2	1-3	1-0	3-1	3-2	0-2	0-0	1-1	0-1	2-1		2-0	2-1	1-2
20	Whitehawk	1-1	0-2	1-4	1-1	4-1	2-2	4-0	1-1	1-3	0-0	1-3	4-2	1-1	0-2	0-1	0-0	0-1	1-0	0-4		2-3	1-2
21	Wingate & Finchley	1-1	2-2	0-2	2-2	4-2	2-0	2-0	1-2	1-1	0-3	0-4	0-2	0-4	1-0	0-1	0-1	2-0	4-2	1-2	1-1		1-2
22	Worthing	3-1	1-2	0-2	1-1	0-0	3-3	2-0	1-4	0-3	3-2	0-2	9-1	3-1	1-1	3-4	0-1	2-4	1-1	1-1	2-0	2-1	

ISTHMIAN LEAGUE
NORTH DIVISION TABLE 2018-19

		P	W	D	L	F	A	GD	Pts
1	Bowers & Pitsea	38	29	5	4	96	25	71	92
2	Aveley	38	24	8	6	84	49	35	80
3	Maldon & Tiptree	38	24	7	7	86	46	40	79
4	Coggeshall Town	38	22	8	8	79	43	36	74
5	Heybridge Swifts (PO winners)	38	23	5	10	70	51	19	74
6	Bury Town	38	17	8	13	72	63	9	59
7	Grays Athletic	38	14	11	13	65	64	1	53
8	AFC Sudbury	38	16	4	18	71	72	-1	52
9	Canvey Island	38	15	6	17	51	50	1	51
10	Felixstowe & Walton United	38	14	8	16	56	66	-10	50
11	Tilbury	38	13	11	14	64	64	0	49*
12	Barking	38	13	8	17	49	63	-14	47
13	Brentwood Town	38	12	9	17	71	77	-6	45
14	Dereham Town	38	14	5	19	71	82	-11	44*
15	Great Wakering Rovers	38	11	8	19	55	72	-17	41
16	Soham Town Rangers	38	12	4	22	44	64	-20	40
17	Basildon United	38	11	6	21	37	71	-34	39
18	Witham Town	38	9	7	22	38	68	-30	34
19	Romford	38	10	4	24	48	82	-34	34
20	Mildenhall Town	38	5	12	21	47	82	-35	27

	NORTH DIVISION	1	2	3	4	5	6	7	8	9	10	11	12	13	14	15	16	17	18	19	20
1	AFC Sudbury		0-2	1-1	0-0	0-1	5-3	3-4	3-0	0-1	8-2	4-2	2-3	2-1	0-1	1-5	3-1	1-3	0-3	4-3	3-1
2	Aveley	6-0		1-1	2-1	0-1	5-3	2-2	2-0	1-1	6-0	3-2	3-1	2-2	3-2	1-3	3-0	2-0	4-0	1-3	3-1
3	Barking	2-1	0-2		5-1	0-1	3-0	0-2	1-3	0-3	1-0	2-4	2-1	2-0	4-1	1-2	1-1	3-0	2-1	0-1	2-3
4	Basildon United	0-4	0-0	0-1		0-4	2-1	0-0	1-4	0-1	0-4	0-1	1-2	1-0	2-1	1-2	2-1	3-1	1-0	0-3	0-2
5	Bowers & Pitsea	3-0	3-3	9-0	4-0		6-0	2-2	2-0	3-2	4-0	4-0	1-0	4-1	1-3	0-0	3-0	2-0	3-1	3-1	3-0
6	Brentwood Town	5-2	4-4	1-0	1-1	3-0		1-1	1-3	1-1	1-2	3-1	0-1	3-2	1-3	0-1	2-2	2-0	4-1	2-2	3-1
7	Bury Town	2-3	1-2	2-1	4-2	1-5	2-1		1-1	2-3	3-3	2-0	4-2	3-2	1-2	1-4	3-0	1-1	1-0	3-0	5-2
8	Canvey Island	0-2	1-2	1-0	4-0	1-2	2-2	2-0		0-2	1-4	0-1	2-0	0-1	1-2	2-2	2-1	2-0	0-1	1-1	0-1
9	Coggeshall Town	0-1	1-2	1-0	3-0	0-0	2-3	2-1	3-3		0-0	2-1	4-0	3-0	0-1	2-3	3-0	3-1	3-0	1-1	2-0
10	Dereham Town	3-0	1-1	5-2	0-3	1-3	1-2	3-2	0-1	4-2		0-1	2-2	6-1	1-3	2-3	5-2	1-0	0-1	2-3	2-0
11	Felixstowe & Walton United	0-1	2-0	1-1	1-0	0-4	3-0	3-1	0-4	3-0	2-2		1-2	1-0	3-0	3-2	0-3	2-1	1-3	1-1	2-2
12	Grays Athletic	3-2	3-4	2-2	2-2	1-1	3-1	3-2	1-1	0-1	5-1	2-2		4-3	0-1	0-5	1-1	1-1	4-0	3-2	0-1
13	Great Wakering Rovers	1-1	2-3	0-3	4-1	1-0	1-1	1-2	2-1	2-2	2-1	2-0	2-2		3-2	2-4	1-1	2-1	1-1	2-3	2-1
14	Heybridge Swifts	2-0	1-2	2-0	3-2	1-0	3-1	2-0	2-1	2-3	0-3	4-2	2-1	0-0		1-1	1-1	3-1	2-0	2-1	1-0
15	Maldon & Tiptree	0-4	0-1	7-1	1-0	1-2	1-0	3-0	1-2	1-4	3-0	2-1	2-2	3-1	3-2		5-1	4-1	1-0	0-0	0-1
16	Mildenhall Town	3-3	1-2	1-2	0-1	1-2	0-6	0-0	2-3	2-4	3-0	3-3	0-3	0-3	3-4	1-1		2-1	1-1	2-2	2-0
17	Romford	3-1	2-0	0-0	0-0	1-4	1-4	0-4	0-1	3-5	3-4	3-1	1-0	3-0	1-5	2-4	2-1		5-2	2-1	3-1
18	Soham Town Rangers	0-2	0-1	1-2	1-2	0-1	3-3	0-3	1-0	0-3	2-1	0-2	1-2	3-1	3-1	0-2	1-3	4-0		2-2	3-0
19	Tilbury	0-4	3-0	0-0	1-2	0-3	4-1	1-2	3-0	1-5	4-2	2-2	1-1	0-3	1-1	2-3	2-0	4-1	0-3		3-0
20	Witham Town	2-0	1-3	1-1	3-5	0-2	2-1	1-2	0-1	1-1	2-3	1-1	0-2	2-1	1-1	1-1	1-1	2-0	0-1	0-2	

ISTHMIAN LEAGUE
SOUTH CENTRAL DIVISION TABLE 2018-19

		P	W	D	L	F	A	GD	Pts
1	Hayes & Yeading United	38	29	6	3	129	36	93	93
2	Bracknell Town	38	23	8	7	102	49	53	77
3	Cheshunt (PO winners)	38	22	10	6	79	43	36	76
4	Marlow	38	21	10	7	66	37	29	73
5	Westfield	38	21	7	10	77	54	23	70
6	Tooting & Mitcham United	38	18	11	9	66	52	14	65
7	Ware	38	18	9	11	90	59	31	63
8	Hanwell Town	38	16	12	10	71	65	6	60
9	Waltham Abbey	38	18	2	18	63	68	-5	56
10	Northwood	38	16	6	16	65	71	-6	54
11	Ashford Town (Middx)	38	15	5	18	55	70	-15	50
12	Bedfont Sports	38	13	9	16	75	76	-1	48
13	Chipstead	38	13	6	19	54	63	-9	45
14	Chalfont St Peter	38	10	13	15	52	60	-8	43
15	Uxbridge	38	11	9	18	50	71	-21	42
16	FC Romania	38	11	3	24	46	86	-40	36
17	South Park	38	9	6	23	47	92	-45	33
18	Hertford Town	38	6	13	19	55	85	-30	31
19	Molesey	38	7	7	24	36	76	-40	28
20	Egham Town	38	4	6	28	29	94	-65	18

SOUTH CENTRAL DIVISION		1	2	3	4	5	6	7	8	9	10	11	12	13	14	15	16	17	18	19	20
1	Ashford Town (Middx)		2-1	0-5	2-0	1-1	0-0	2-1	2-1	1-4	2-2	1-1	0-3	2-3	2-1	1-2	1-2	0-1	2-1	1-3	3-0
2	Bedfont Sports	4-0		1-1	2-3	2-2	1-0	4-1	1-2	3-3	2-6	3-3	0-1	1-1	3-0	4-0	0-1	5-1	4-1	3-2	3-0
3	Bracknell Town	6-0	1-1		2-0	1-1	1-0	7-1	6-0	2-2	3-3	2-0	3-3	4-0	2-1	4-3	3-1	4-0	1-0	3-2	3-1
4	Chalfont St Peter	2-1	3-0	2-2		0-2	0-2	3-0	1-0	2-2	1-5	1-1	4-1	1-1	1-2	1-2	0-2	1-1	4-3	0-1	2-2
5	Cheshunt	1-0	2-2	2-0	1-1		3-3	3-0	2-3	4-2	3-3	2-2	0-0	2-0	3-0	3-1	3-0	1-1	2-1	4-0	3-0
6	Chipstead	2-4	3-4	0-3	3-2	0-1		5-0	2-1	0-1	1-2	0-0	1-0	0-0	2-3	1-4	1-3	3-2	2-0	1-3	0-3
7	Egham Town	1-2	1-1	2-1	1-1	2-1	1-4		0-2	0-2	1-1	1-1	0-0	0-2	1-3	0-3	3-4	2-2	0-1	0-3	2-1
8	FC Romania	0-2	4-2	1-6	1-2	0-2	0-5	3-1		1-0	0-2	2-0	0-2	2-0	1-3	3-0	1-4	2-2	1-2	0-6	0-1
9	Hanwell Town	1-0	3-1	2-1	2-1	3-1	0-0	3-1	6-2		1-9	0-0	0-6	3-1	3-1	4-0	1-2	2-4	2-3	3-0	1-4
10	Hayes & Yeading United	7-1	6-0	1-0	4-0	1-0	1-0	4-0	5-1	1-1		8-1	0-2	2-0	6-0	5-2	3-0	5-0	4-2	1-0	5-1
11	Hertford Town	0-1	5-4	1-3	2-1	1-5	5-2	3-1	0-2	2-2	0-3		2-2	1-4	3-4	4-1	1-2	2-2	1-2	0-3	1-3
12	Marlow	1-0	1-0	0-1	0-0	4-0	4-0	2-0	2-0	4-1	2-1	1-1		3-0	3-0	1-1	1-1	1-0	1-3	0-4	0-1
13	Molesey	0-2	2-2	1-2	1-0	0-1	0-1	2-0	2-2	0-0	2-3	1-0	3-4		0-1	1-2	2-3	0-5	2-0	0-3	0-4
14	Northwood	3-0	3-2	0-3	0-1	1-2	2-0	0-2	4-1	2-2	1-2	1-1	1-2	6-1		2-2	4-3	1-1	0-2	2-2	1-3
15	South Park	2-5	0-1	0-3	0-5	1-4	0-1	2-0	1-1	0-3	1-6	3-2	1-2	3-1	1-4		1-1	0-1	1-2	1-6	0-3
16	Tooting & Mitcham United	2-3	1-2	2-2	1-1	1-2	3-1	3-0	2-1	0-0	1-3	3-1	0-0	2-0	1-1	1-1		4-2	2-1	1-1	1-1
17	Uxbridge	0-5	2-3	3-2	0-0	0-2	1-2	3-1	2-0	0-1	2-2	0-2	1-2	1-0	4-1	1-0	0-1		0-2	2-1	2-2
18	Waltham Abbey	2-1	2-1	1-5	2-2	5-3	0-3	2-1	1-2	3-2	1-0	3-2	3-3	3-0	0-1	2-3	0-2	3-0		1-2	0-3
19	Ware	2-2	4-2	7-2	4-1	0-1	3-3	3-1	3-2	2-2	1-3	1-1	3-0	2-2	2-3	2-1	2-2	2-1	2-3		1-1
20	Westfield	2-1	3-0	4-2	2-2	1-4	2-0	5-0	2-1	1-1	0-4	5-2	1-2	3-1	1-2	1-1	2-1	4-0	1-0	3-2	

ISTHMIAN SOUTH EAST LEAGUE TABLE 2018-19

		P	W	D	L	F	A	GD	Pts
1	Cray Wanderers	36	25	7	4	79	35	44	82
2	Horsham (PO winners)	36	23	5	8	73	38	35	74
3	Hastings United	36	21	7	8	78	45	33	70
4	Ashford United	36	21	5	10	74	36	38	68
5	Haywards Heath Town	36	18	9	9	65	52	13	63
6	VCD Athletic	36	20	2	14	74	66	8	62
7	Hythe Town	36	14	10	12	66	59	7	52
8	Whyteleafe	36	14	7	15	59	51	8	49
9	Phoenix Sports	36	13	10	13	65	65	0	49
10	Sevenoaks Town	36	13	8	15	49	54	-5	47
11	Ramsgate	36	11	12	13	54	53	1	45
12	Whitstable Town	36	11	10	15	36	55	-19	43
13	East Grinstead Town	36	11	8	17	65	72	-7	41
14	Three Bridges	36	12	5	19	51	69	-18	41
15	Herne Bay	36	11	5	20	65	85	-20	38
16	Sittingbourne	36	11	4	21	49	72	-23	37
17	Faversham Town	36	10	7	19	55	85	-30	37
18	Guernsey	36	7	9	20	50	77	-27	30
19	Greenwich Borough	36	8	6	22	40	78	-38	27*

Thamesmead Town resigned - record expunged.

SOUTH EAST DIVISION		1	2	3	4	5	6	7	8	9	10	11	12	13	14	15	16	17	18	19
1	Ashford United		1-3	1-0	2-0	7-0	3-0	0-2	5-0	4-1	2-3	3-1	0-2	3-0	2-1	1-1	2-4	3-1	2-0	0-0
2	Cray Wanderers	3-1		2-0	7-2	1-1	3-0	2-1	2-2	6-0	2-0	4-3	1-1	0-0	3-4	2-1	1-0	3-1	2-0	1-1
3	East Grinstead Town	1-2	0-2		1-2	1-3	3-0	2-1	3-3	1-1	0-0	5-2	1-3	1-0	1-1	2-1	4-4	3-1	4-0	1-3
4	Faversham Town	0-4	1-1	1-1		4-1	2-1	2-2	2-4	1-1	0-2	2-1	0-0	1-3	3-1	3-1	3-0	3-4	1-2	1-0
5	Greenwich Borough	0-3	0-3	2-0	4-1		4-0	1-3	1-4	2-7	0-2	2-0	0-1	1-2	0-1	2-1	2-2	1-2	0-0	0-0
6	Guernsey	0-3	1-2	2-5	2-2	1-1		0-1	3-1	2-1	1-2	0-2	3-5	2-1	1-2	1-2	0-3	3-4	1-1	1-3
7	Hastings United	2-2	3-2	2-3	2-1	4-0	1-1		2-4	5-0	2-0	1-1	3-0	3-0	1-0	5-0	2-1	2-1	3-1	3-0
8	Haywards Heath Town	1-1	0-1	3-1	2-0	0-0	1-2	2-1		2-1	2-0	0-1	2-2	2-3	0-1	2-0	2-0	0-1	2-1	3-1
9	Herne Bay	2-1	1-2	2-5	3-1	1-2	2-2	4-1	0-1		2-3	3-1	2-4	1-5	1-2	1-1	0-3	1-7	3-1	0-1
10	Horsham	0-0	4-2	3-1	4-0	2-0	1-1	1-1	4-5	1-0		2-1	3-2	1-0	3-1	1-2	2-0	4-0	4-0	1-0
11	Hythe Town	3-1	1-3	3-0	5-4	1-2	1-1	3-1	0-0	2-2	2-4		5-1	2-2	0-0	3-2	1-0	3-0	2-0	1-0
12	Phoenix Sports	1-2	0-1	5-1	2-2	3-2	3-2	3-3	2-4	5-2	1-0	3-3		1-1	1-0	3-4	5-2	0-2	0-2	2-2
13	Ramsgate	1-3	2-2	3-2	1-0	3-1	2-2	2-3	0-0	4-5	0-0	1-1	0-0		1-3	4-0	1-1	1-2	4-1	2-1
14	Sevenoaks Town	1-0	0-1	3-3	4-1	2-1	0-2	2-3	2-2	2-1	1-2	2-0	1-2	1-1		0-1	0-0	1-3	1-1	1-3
15	Sittingbourne	0-2	0-2	2-1	3-1	4-2	2-2	0-3	1-2	2-3	1-6	0-3	1-1	0-1	4-1		0-1	1-2	1-2	2-1
16	Three Bridges	0-1	0-2	0-2	2-4	2-0	0-5	1-3	3-4	1-5	2-1	2-3	2-0	3-1	2-0	0-5		1-2	2-1	3-2
17	VCD Athletic	0-4	1-2	5-4	5-2	4-1	2-3	0-2	3-0	2-0	1-3	2-2	2-0	2-1	1-3	1-2	2-1		3-1	0-0
18	Whitstable Town	1-0	1-0	1-1	1-2	2-0	3-1	1-1	0-0	0-4	0-3	0-0	2-1	1-0	1-1	2-1	1-1	4-1		0-2
19	Whyteleafe	1-3	1-3	3-1	6-0	4-1	3-1	2-0	2-3	0-2	3-1	4-3	2-0	1-1	2-3	3-0	0-2	1-4	1-1	

ALAN TURVEY TROPHY 2018-19

HOLDERS: BILLERICAY TOWN

PRELIMINARY ROUND

Aveley	v	Hanwell Town	2-0
Bowers & Pitsea	v	Waltham Abbey	5-0
Bracknell Town	v	Kingstonian	3-3, 5-4p,
Corinthian-Casuals	v	Westfield	5-1
Haywards Heath Town	v	Horsham	2-5
Mildenhall Town	v	Heybridge Swifts	1-0
Soham Town Rangers	v	Uxbridge	2-3
Ware	v	Romford	3-3, 5-4p
Whitehawk	v	Three Bridges	2-1
Whyteleafe	v	Bedfont Sports	2-0
FC Romania	v	AFC Sudbury	2-3
Sittingbourne	v	Phoenix Sports	2-0
Tonbridge Angels	v	VCD Athletic	1-0

ROUND ONE

Ashford Town	v	Hayes & Yeading United	0-1
Canvey Island	v	Enfield Town	0-1
Harlow Town	v	Potters Bar Town	1-2
Bracknell Town	v	Horsham	3-1
Chalfont St Peter	v	Ware	0-2
Chipstead	v	Dorking Wanderers	1-0
Faversham Town	v	Burgess Hill Town	1-2
Maldon & Tiptree	v	Uxbridge	3-2
Witham Town	v	Grays Athletic	0-0, 5-3p
Mildenhall Town	v	Wingate & Finchley	1-2
Leatherhead	v	Worthing	0-1
Carshalton Athletic	v	Corinthian-Casuals	0-3
Ashford United	v	Folkestone Invicta	0-4
Barking	v	Brentwood Town	2-2, 4-5p
Basildon United	v	Hornchurch	0-1
Bognor Regis Town	v	Whitehawk	8-0
Coggeshall Town	v	Great Wakering Rovers	2-2, 3-2p
East Grinstead Town	v	Hastings United	2-9
Felixstowe & Walton United	v	AFC Sudbury	0-0, 4-3p
Herne Bay	v	Hythe Town	0-6
Hertford Town	v	Bishop's Stortford	1-2
Molesey	v	Greenwich Borough	0-1
Northwood	v	Bury Town	2-0
Tilbury	v	Marlow	1-0
Tooting & Mitcham United	v	Margate	2-0
Thamesmead Town	v	Merstham	2-4
South Park	v	Sittingbourne	1-2
Aveley	v	Cheshunt	0-4
Bowers & Pitsea	v	Haringey Borough	3-1
Egham Town	v	Whyteleafe	2-1
Ramsgate	v	Whitstable Town	0-2
Tonbridge Angels	v	Sevenoaks Town	3-0

ROUND TWO

Enfield Town	v	Ware	2-1
Hornchurch	v	Coggeshall Town	0-2

Coggeshall Town were expelled for fielding ineligible players.

Hornchurch were reinstated.

Bishop's Stortford	v	Tilbury	1-1, 8-7p
Burgess Hill Town	v	Tooting & Mitcham United	2-0
Hayes & Yeading United	v	Potters Bar Town	2-2, 5-4p
Maldon & Tiptree	v	Witham Town	1-0
Felixstowe & Walton United	v	Northwood	3-1
Hythe Town	v	Bognor Regis Town	2-1
Cheshunt	v	Brentwood Town	2-1
Corinthian-Casuals	v	Chipstead	0-0, 3-4p
Folkestone Invicta	v	Sittingbourne	3-1
Egham Town	v	Bracknell Town	0-1
Whitstable Town	v	Greenwich Borough	4-3
Hastings United	v	Merstham	1-2
Worthing	v	Tonbridge Angels	0-0, 3-2p
Bowers & Pitsea	v	Wingate & Finchley	3-3, 4-5p

ROUND THREE

Whitstable Town	v	Cheshunt	4-3
Folkestone Invicta	v	Hayes & Yeading United	2-0
Hornchurch	v	Chipstead	3-0
Hythe Town	v	Burgess Hill Town	0-2
Maldon & Tiptree	v	Enfield Town	1-2
Bracknell Town	v	Felixstowe & Walton United	3-1
Worthing	v	Merstham	1-3
Wingate & Finchley	v	Bishop's Stortford	1-5

QUARTER-FINALS

Hornchurch	v	Whitstable Town	4-1
Bracknell Town	v	Folkestone Invicta	4-1
Enfield Town	v	Burgess Hill Town	4-1
Merstham	v	Bishop's Stortford	1-1, 2-3p

SEMI-FINALS

Hornchurch	v	Bracknell Town	3-2
Enfield Town	v	Bishop's Stortford	3-3, 4-2p

FINAL

Hornchurch	v	Enfield Town	0-2

BISHOP'S STORTFORD MATCH RESULTS 2018-19

Date	Comp	H/A	Opponents	Att:	Result		Goalscorers	Pos	No.
Aug 11	Isth Prem	H	Dorking Wanderers	274	D	1 - 1	Cureton 70	12	1
14	Isth Prem	A	Enfield	459	L	1 - 2	Dark 79	16	2
18	Isth Prem	A	Bognor Regis Town	482	L	0 - 3		19	3
25	Isth Prem	H	Leatherhead	260	D	1 - 1	Cass 89	18	4
27	Isth Prem	A	Harlow Town	725	W	3 - 1	Olutoyosi 44 Cass 56 Mason 63	14	5
Sept 1	Isth Prem	H	Folkstone Invicta	323	L	0 - 1		15	6
8	**FAC 1Q**	**A**	**St Neots Town**	**209**	**L**	**1 - 2**	**Cass 76**		7
15	Isth Prem	A	Kingstonian	244	L	2 - 3	Cureton 54 79	18	8
22	Isth Prem	H	Carshalton Athletic	222	W	3 - 1	Mason 52 Charles 65 Cureton 90	15	9
29	Isth Prem	A	Tonbridge Angels	517	W	3 - 2	Charles 6 Cass 45 60	10	10
Oct 2	Isth Prem	H	Wingate & Finchley	236	W	3 - 2	Cureton 8 24 Mason 90	9	11
6	Isth Prem	H	Burgess Hill Town	302	D	2 - 2	Cureton 43 90	9	12
13	Isth Prem	A	Merstham	180	D	1 - 1	Nkosi 80	8	13
20	Isth Prem	H	Corinthian-Casuals	331	W	3 - 0	Mason 13 Cureton 49 Cass 87	6	14
23	Isth Prem	A	Potters Bar Town	256	L:	2 - 4	N.Brown 17 Charles 23	8	15
27	**FAT 1Q**	**A**	**Hythe Town**	**242**	**W**	**2 - 1**	**Cureton Mason**		16
Nov 3	Isth Prem	H	Hornchurch	332	W	1 - 0	Charles 43	8	17
10	**FAT 2Q**	**A**	**Greenwich Borough**	**104**	**L**	**0 - 1**			18
17	Isth Prem	H	Whitehawk	556	W	4 - 2	CURETON 3 (12 32 70) Callander 56	6	19
24	Isth Prem	A	Margate	458	W	4 - 1	Callender 30 Charles 34 Cureton 48 87	5	20
Dec 1	Isth Prem	A	Worthing	645	W	2 - 1	Richens 65 N.Brown 79	5	21
8	Isth Prem	H	Lewes	322	L	1 - 2	Charles 3	6	22
10	Isth Prem	A	Haringey Borough	296	L	1 - 3	Callander 52	6	23
15	Isth Prem	A	Folkestone Invicta	333	L	0 - 2		8	24
26	Isth Prem	H	Harlow Town	687	W	1 - 0	Henshaw 10	8	25
29	Isth Prem	A	Brightlingsea Regent	252	L	0 - 1		9	26
Jan 5	Isth Prem	H	Kingstonian	326	L	0 - 3		10	27
19	Isth Prem	H	Tonbridge Angels	260	L	3 - 4	Worman 17 Cureton 29 Renee 84	14	28
26	Isth Prem	A	Burgess Hill Town	325	W	3 - 0	Charles 7 51 Worman 63	13	29
Feb 2	Isth Prem	H	Merstham	223	W	2 - 0	Worman 77 Miles 90	12	30
5	Isth Prem	H	Enfield Town	340	W	2 - 1	Worman 7 Cureton 90	10	31
9	Isth Prem	A	Leatherhead	337	L	0 - 1		11	32
16	Isth Prem	H	Bognor Regis Town	347	D	0 - 0		11	33
19	Isth Prem	A	Wingate & Finchley	139	D	2 - 2	Calander 2 40	11	34
23	Isth Prem	A	Dorking Wanderers	513	L	0 - 1		12	35
Mar 2	Isth Prem	H	Potters Bar Town	274	L	1 - 2	Worman 26	13	36
9	Isth Prem	A	Corinthian-Casuals	232	D	1 - 1	Renee 45	13	37
16	Isth Prem	H	Haringey Borough	347	W	2 - 0	Worman 41 73	13	38
23	Isth Prem	A	Hornchurch	344	W	1 - 0	Cureton 13	11	39
30	Isth Prem	A	Whitehawk	357	W	2 - 0	Mason 72 Miles 88	10	40
Apr 6	Isth Prem	H	Margate	344	W	2 - 1	Worman 34 Cureton 88	10	41
13	Isth Prem	H	Worthing	308	W	3 - 0	Cureton 26 (pen) 81 Ogie 79	8	42
20	Isth Prem	A	Lewes	691	W	3 - 1	Henshaw 4 Callander 31 Renee 66	7	43
22	Isth Prem	H	Brightlingsea Regent	640	W	3 - 2	Cureton 14 17 Callander 72	5	44
27	Isth Prem	A	Carshalton Athletic	663	L	1 - 2	Robbins 30	7	45

GOALSCORERS	SG	CSG	Pens	Hat tricks	Total
Cureton	13	2	1	1	23
Charles	7				8
Worman	7	4			8
Calender	7	2			7
Cass	5	2			6
Mason	5				6
Renee	3				3
Brown N	2				2
Henshaw	2				2
Miles	2				2
Dark	1				1
Nkosi	1				1
Ogie	1				1
Olutoyosi	1				1
Richens	1				1
Robbins	1				1

BOGNOR REGIS TOWN MATCH RESULTS 2018-19

Date	Comp	H/A	Opponents	Att:	Result		Goalscorers	Pos	No.
Aug 11	Isth Prem	A	Haringey Borough	246	D	2 - 2	Muitt 46 Olufemi 72 (og)	12	1
14	Isth Prem	H	Merstham	502	**W**	3 - 1	Lethbridge 14 Field 30 Smith 36	6	2
18	Isth Prem	H	Bishop's Stortford	482	**W**	3 - 0	Lethbridge 72 Smith 76 82 (pen)	2	3
25	Isth Prem	A	Hornchurch	231	D	1 - 1	Lethbridge 37	5	4
27	Isth Prem	A	Lewes	873	D	3 - 3	Muitt 19 45 (pen) Lethbridge 81	4	5
Sept 1	Isth Prem	H	Kingstonian	539	**W**	3 - 1	Smith 15 66 Lethbridge 90	3	6
8	**FAC 1Q**	**A**	**Whitstable Town**	**297**	**W**	**5 - 0**	**Muitt 6 22 Lethbridge 34 Smith 55 Walsh 73**		7
15	Isth Prem	A	Carshalton Athletic	409	D	1 - 1	Muitt 45	3	8
22	**FAC 2Q**	**H**	**AFC Sudbury**	**431**	**D**	**1 - 1**	**Whyte 33**		9
25	**FAC 2Qr**	**A**	**AFC Sudbury**	**210**	**L**	**2 - 3**	**Muitt 53 Whyte 58**		10
29	Isth Prem	A	Potters Bar Town	218	D	2 - 2	Smith 48 Whyte 77	4	11
Oct 2	Isth Prem	H	Burgess Hill Town	433	**W**	8 - 0	Whyte 35 Tuck 36 Walsh 59 SCUTT 3 (64 72 85) Lethbridge 76 Muitt 83	3	12
13	Isth Prem	A	Tonbridge Angels	814	**W**	2 - 1	Lethbridge 51 Walsh 90	3	13
16	Isth Prem	H	Folkestone Invicta	508	L	2 - 4	Muitt 21 Scutt 81	4	14
20	Isth Prem	H	Margate	551	D	0 - 0		4	15
27	**FAT 1Q**	**A**	**Bracknell Town**	**339**	**D**	**2 - 2**	**Mills 35 Lethbridge 90**		16
30	**FAT 1Qr**	**H**	**Bracknell Town**	**306**	**D**	**2 - 2**	**Davies 37 Wild 88 (won 3-2 on pens)**		17
Nov 3	Isth Prem	A	Leatherhead	481	D	2 - 2	Scutt 56 Lethbridge 90	6	18
10	**FAT 2Qr**	**A**	**Walton Casuals**	**197**	**L**	**0 - 2**			19
13	Isth Prem	H	Corinthian-Casuals	402	L	0 - 1		6	20
17	Isth Prem	H	Wingate & Finchley	556	**W**	4 - 2	Smith 15 Muitt 55 Walsh 67 Scutt 81	4	21
Dec 1	Isth Prem	A	Harlow Town	195	D	1 - 1	Muitt 9 (pen)	9	22
4	Isth Prem	H	Enfield Town	376	L	1 - 2	Walsh 43	9	23
8	Isth Prem	H	Dorking	398	L	0 - 1		10	24
15	Isth Prem	A	Kingstonian	310	L	1 - 4	Smith 4	11	25
22	Isth Prem	A	Worthing	1852	**W**	2 - 0	Smith 53 Walsh 80	10	26
26	Isth Prem	H	Lewes 721	731	D	2 - 2	Tomlinson 66 74	10	27
Jan 1	Isth Prem	A	Whitehawk	400	**W**	4 - 1	Muitt 12 16 (pen) Whyte 55 Smith 60	8	28
5	Isth Prem	H	Carshalton Athletic	401	**W**	2 - 0	Walsh 10 Muitt 55	6	29
8	Isth Prem	A	Brightlingsea Regent	216	L	0 - 3		6	30
12	Isth Prem	A	Burgess Hill Town	508	**W**	2 - 0	Muitt 56 (pen) 90	5	31
19	Isth Prem	H	Potters Bar Town	520	D	2 - 2	Muitt 33 50 (pen)	6	32
26	Isth Prem	A	Corinthian Casuals	434	**W**	3 - 1	Scutt 55 Muitt 60 (pen) 90	5	33
Feb 2	Isth Prem	H	Tonbridge Angels	559	L	2 - 3	Lethbridge 15 Muitt 17	8	34
6	Isth Prem	A	Merstham	196	**W**	2 - 1	Lethbridge 14 Smith 49	3	35
9	Isth Prem	H	Hornchurch	475	**W**	2 - 0	Widdrington 41 (pen) Gilot 50	3	36
16	Isth Prem	A	Bishop's Stortford	347	D	0 - 0		5	37
23	Isth Prem	H	Haringey Borough	517	L	0 - 4		7	38
Mar 2	Isth Prem	H	Worthing	1137	D	2 - 2	Walsh 9 Tomlinson 22	7	39
9	Isth Prem	A	Margate	503	L	0 - 1		9	40
16	Isth Prem	A	Enfield Town	418	D	3 - 3	Widdrington 14 Lethbridge 74 Walsh 82	9	41
23	Isth Prem	H	Leatherhead	549	L	0 - 4		11	42
30	Isth Prem	A	Wingate & Finchley	126	**W**	2 - 0	Walsh 70 75	11	43
Apr 6	Isth Prem	H	Brightlingsea Regent	403	L	1 - 2	Widdrington 66 (pen)	12	44
13	Isth Prem	H	Harlow Town	308	D	1 - 1	Wild 90	11	45
20	Isth Prem	A	Dorking Wanderers	659	L	0 - 2		12	46
22	Isth Prem	H	Whitehawk	467	D	0 - 0		11	47
27	Isth Prem	A	Folkestone Invicta	707	L	0 - 1		14	48

GOALSCORERS	SG	CSG	Pens	Hat tricks	Total
Muitt	15	6	6		21
Lethbridge	13	6			13
Smith	10	2	1		12
Walsh	7			1	11
Whyte	5	4			7
Scutt	8				5
Tomlinson	2				3
Widdrington	3		2		3
Wild	2				2
Davies	1				1

	SG	CSG	Pens	Hat tricks	Total
Field	1				1
Gilot	1				1
Mills	1				1
Opponents	1				1
Tuck	1				1

BRIGHTLINGSEA REGENT MATCH RESULTS 2018-19

Date	Comp	H/A	Opponents	Att:	Result		Goalscorers	Pos	No.
Aug 11	Isth Prem	A	Kingstonian	255	W	3 - 2	Hodd 14 24 Hunt 54	5	1
14	Isth Prem	H	Haringey Borough	156	L	0 - 2		13	2
18	Isth Prem	H	Margate	206	L	0 - 3		15	3
25	Isth Prem	A	Merstham	106	L	0 - 1		16	4
27	Isth Prem	H	Hornchurch	212	D	1 - 1	Turner 4	17	5
Sept 1	Isth Prem	A	Corinthian Casuals	168	D	1 - 1	Baxter 47	18	6
8	**FAC 1Q**	**H**	**Cambridge City**	**187**	**W**	**4 - 3**	**Baxter 23 Clowsley 51 Hunt 62 81 (pen)**		7
15	Isth Prem	H	Tonbridge Angels	198	L	0 - 2		20	8
22	**FAC 2Q**	**A**	**Egham Town**	**140**	**D**	**3 - 3**	**Baxter 7 Gould 16 53**		9
25	**FAC 2Qr**	**H**	**Egham Town**	**190**	**W**	**2 - 1**	**Hunt 45 Turner 67**		10
29	Isth Prem	A	Folkestone Invicta	416	W	3 - 2	Hodd 23 44 Lewis 54	18	11
Oct 2	Isth Prem	H	Potters Bar Town	88	L	0 - 1		20	12
6	**FAC 3Q**	**H**	**Torquay United**	**470**	**L**	**0 - 3**			13
13	Isth Prem	A	Whitehawk	565	L	0 - 1		20	14
16	Isth Prem	A	Enfield	311	D	0 - 0		19	15
23	Isth Prem	A	Harlow Town	133	W	1 - 0	Baxter 76	17	16
27	**FAT 1Q**	**A**	**Canvey Island**	**183**	**W**	**1 - 0**	**Hunt 81 (pen)**		17
Nov 3	Isth Prem	H	Carshalton Athletic	140	L	0 - 2		18	18
10	**FAT 2Q**	**H**	**Hornchurch**	**181**	**W**	**2 - 1**	**Hunt 2 83**		19
13	Isth Prem	H	Wingate & Finchley	112	L	0 - 1			20
17	Isth Prem	A	Dorking Wanderers	407	L	1 - 2	Hunt 43	20	21
24	**FAT 3Q**	**A**	**Hayes & Yeading**	**144**	**D**	**0 - 0**			22
27	**FAT 3Qr**	**H**	**Hayes & Yeading**	**108**	**L**	**1 - 2**	**Clowsley 40**	**19**	23
Dec 1	Isth Prem	H	Burgess Hill Town	102	W	3 - 2	Gould 23 Condon 57 79	19	24
8	Isth Prem	A	Leatherhead	276	W	1 - 0	Hunt 60		25
12	Isth Prem	A	Lewes	354	L	0 - 5			26
15	Isth Prem	H	Corinthian Casuals	100	W	4 - 3	Barnett 2 Hunt 6 Condon 28 31	17	27
22	Isth Prem	A	Hornchurch	215	W	2 - 1	Condon 56 71	17	28
29	Isth Prem	H	Bishop's Stortford	252	W	1 - 0	Condon 90	15	29
Jan 5	Isth Prem	A	Tonbridge Angels	356	D	2 - 2	Hodd 25 Hunt 48	15	30
8	Isth Prem	H	Bognor Regis Town	216	W	3 - 0	Hodd 25 Barnett 50 Hunt 90	12	31
12	Isth Prem	A	Potters Bar Town	160	W	2 - 0	Hunt 47 (pen) 90	11	32
19	Isth Prem	H	Fokestone Invicta	202	W	2 - 0	Barnett 1 Condon 5	11	33
22	Isth Prem	H	Worthing	189	L	0 - 2		11	34
26	Isth Prem	A	Wingate & Finchley	112	D	2 - 2	Condon 18 Jones 60	11	35
Feb 2	Isth Prem	H	Whitehawk	159	W	3 - 0	Jones 48 Hunt 77 88	10	36
4	Isth Prem	A	Haringey Borough	341	L	1 - 2	Hunt 8	11	37
9	Isth Prem	H	Merstham	231	D	1 - 1	Turner 61	12	38
16	Isth Prem	A	Margate	563	L	0 - 1		12	39
23	Isth Prem	H	Kingstonian	177	W	2 - 0	Gould 54 Brothers 85	11	40
Mar 2	Isth Prem	H	Harlow Town	192	D	1 - 1	Simms 44 (og)	12	41
9	Isth Prem	A	Worthing	788	D	1 - 1	Clarke 6 (og)	12	42
16	Isth Prem	H	Lewes	163	D	0 - 0		13	43
23	Isth Prem	A	Carshalton Athletic	482	L	0 - 3		14	44
30	Isth Prem	H	Dorking Wanderers	208	L	0 - 2		14	45
Apr 6	Isth Prem	A	Bognor Regis Town	403	W	2 - 1	Cripps 6 Turner 83	14	46
13	Isth Prem	A	Burgess Hill Town	364	D	1 - 1	Wood 90	14	47
20	Isth Prem	H	Leatherhead	233	W	1 - 0	Condon 89	13	48
22	Isth Prem	A	Bishop's Stortford	640	L	2 - 3	Condon 76 Gould 90	13	49
27	Isth Prem	H	Enfield Town	222	W	1 - 0	Boyland 83	13	50

GOALSCORERS	SG	CSG	Pens	Hat tricks	Total
Hunt	13	3	3		17
Condon	8	3			11
Hodd	4				6
Gould	5				5
Baxter	4				4
Turner	4				4
Barnett	2				3
Clowsley	2				2
Jones	2				2
Opponents	2				2
Boyland	1				1
Brothers	1				1
Cripps	1				1
Lewis	1				1
Wood	1				1

BURGESS HILL TOWN MATCH RESULTS 2018-19

Date	Comp	H/A	Opponents	Att:	Result		Goalscorers	Pos	No.
Aug 11	Isth Prem	H	Potters Bar Town	383	L	0 - 1		17	1
14	Isth Prem	A	Harlow Town	180	D	1 - 1	Tighe 23	16	2
18	Isth Prem	A	Tonbridge	409	L	0 - 1		16	3
25	Isth Prem	H	Enfield	423	L	1 - 6	Harding 75	19	4
27	Isth Prem	A	Worthing	1189	D	0 - 0		20	5
Sept 1	Isth Prem	H	Whitehawk	428	L	2 - 4	McCollin 35 Pope 42	22	6
8	**FAC 1Q**	**H**	**Folkestone Invicta**	**337**	**W**	**1 - 0**	**Pope 52**		7
15	Isth Prem	A	Folkestone Invicta	414	D	1 - 1	Beck 70	22	8
22	**FAC 2Q**	**A**	**Hampton & Richmond**	**422**	**L**	**0 - 3**			9
29	Isth Prem	H	Hornchurch	368	L	0 - 3		22	10
Oct 2	Isth Prem	A	Bognor Regis Town	433	L	0 - 8		22	11
6	Isth Prem	H	Bishop's Stortford	302	D	2 - 2	Harding 25 Pope 79	22	12
13	Isth Prem	A	Haringey Borough	651	W	3 - 1	Pamment 31 Franzen-Jones 49 Harding 90	22	13
16	Isth Prem	H	Wingate & Finchley	405	L	0 - 1		22	14
23	Isth Prem	H	Dorking Wanderers	321	D	0 - 0		22	15
27	**FAT 1Q**	**H**	**Worthing**	**459**	**D**	**1 - 1**	**Pamment 85**		16
30	**FAT 1Qr**	**A**	**Worthing**	**408**	**L**	**1 - 2**	**McCollin 25**		17
Nov 3	Isth Prem	A	Margate	481	W	3 - 2	Harding 24 Cadman 67 McCollin 88	20	18
10	Isth Prem	H	Kingstonian	358	L	0 - 1		20	19
17	Isth Prem	H	Merstham	399	W	3 - 0	Richmond 29 Pope 89 Dixon 90	19	20
21	Isth Prem	A	Leatherhead	287	L	0 - 3		20	21
24	Isth Prem	A	Corinthian-Casuals	272	L	0 - 3		21	22
Dec 1	Isth Prem	A	Brightlingsea Regent	102	L	2 - 3	Pope 20 90	21	23
8	Isth Prem	H	Carshalton Athletic	327	W	3 - 2	Harding 6 Smith-Joseph 31 39	21	24
26	Isth Prem	H	Worthing	539	W	2 - 1	Elphick 38 Smith-Joseph 41	20	25
Jan 1	Isth Prem	A	Lewes	1100	W	3 - 0	Elphick 51 Pope 59 Harding 72	20	26
5	Isth Prem	H	Folkestone Invicta	445	D	0 - 0		19	27
12	Isth Prem	A	Bognor Regis Town	508	L	0 - 2		19	28
19	Isth Prem	H	Hornchurch	226	L	0 - 2		19	29
26	Isth Prem	H	Bishop Stortford	325	L	0 - 3		21	30
Feb 2	Isth Prem	A	Haringey Borough	354	D	4 - 4	Rance 48 Smith-Joseph 52 Pope56 (p) Sargent 63	20	31
6	Isth Prem	A	Harlow Town	297	L	1 - 3	Richmond 69	21	32
9	Isth Prem	A	Enfield	421	L	1 - 3	Rance 32	21	33
16	Isth Prem	A	Tonbridge Angels	417	L	0 - 4		22	34
19	Isth Prem	A	Whitehawk	301	L	1 - 4	Beck 58	22	35
23	Isth Prem	A	Potters Bar Town	188	D	0 - 0		22	36
Mar 2	Isth Prem	H	Dorking Wanderers	607	L	0 - 6		22	37
9	Isth Prem	A	Leatherhead	407	L	0 - 3		22	38
16	Isth Prem	A	Kingstonian	248	W	3 - 2	Murdoch 43 59 Wood 82	22	39
23	Isth Prem	H	Margate	408	L	0 - 2		22	40
30	Isth Prem	A	Mersthem	210	W	2 - 0	Wood 59 85	22	41
Apr 6	Isth Prem	H	Corinthian Casuals	354	W	2 - 1	Kipeye-Bonno 87 Wood 90 (pen)	20	42
13	Isth Prem	H	Brightlingsea Regent	364	D	1 - 1	Wood 90	20	43
19	Isth Prem	A	Carshalton Athletic	691	L	0 - 2		20	44
22	Isth Prem	H	Lewes	798	D	1 - 1	Beck 78	20	45
27	Isth Prem	A	Wingate & Finchley	177	L	2 - 4	Beck 54 68	21	46

GOALSCORERS	SG	CSG	Pens	Hat tricks	Total
Pope	6		1		8
Harding	5	2			6
Beck	4				5
Wood	4				5
Smith-Joseph	3				4
McCollin	3				3
Elphick	2				2
Murdoch	1				2
Pamment	2				2
Rance	2				2
Richmond	2				2
Cadman	1				1
Dixon	1				1
Franzen-Jones	1				1
Kipeye-Bonno	1				1
Sergent	1				1
Tighe	1				1

CARSHALTON ATHLETIC MATCH RESULTS 2018-19

Date	Comp	H/A	Opponents	Att:	Result		Goalscorers	Pos	No.
Aug 11	Isth Prem	A	Lewes	613	W	1 - 0	Sagbanmu 59	8	1
13	Isth Prem	H	Worthing	341	L	1 - 2	Korboa 21	12	2
18	Isth Prem	H	Kingstonian	419	D	1 - 1	Korboa 34	12	3
25	**FAC P**	**H**	**Horsham**	**274**	**L**	**0 - 1**			4
27	Isth Prem	A	Leatherhead	403	W	2 - 1	Dixon 64 Korboa 67	10	5
Sept 1	Isth Prem	A	Hornchurch	211	D	1 - 1	Dos Santos 83	10	6
15	Isth Prem	H	Bognor Regis Town	409	D	1 - 1	Cheadle 28	11	7
22	Isth Prem	A	Bishop's Stortford	222	L	1 - 3	Dixon 55	13	8
29	Isth Prem	A	Merstham	251	L	0 - 2		15	9
Oct 1	Isth Prem	H	Margate	254	L	1 - 2	Cheadle 62 (pen)	16	10
13	Isth Prem	A	Harlow Town	211	W	4 - 0	Onovwigun 21 Price 45 Dixon 84 Mendy 86	12	11
20	Isth Prem	H	Potters Bar Town	342	W	1 - 0	Bradford 62	11	12
23	Isth Prem	A	Folkestone Invicta	352	W	3 - 2	Dos Santos 37 Pappoe 84 Parker 90	10	13
27	**FAT 1Q**	**A**	**Metropolitan Police**	**129**	**D**	**2 - 2**	**Cheadle 35 Koroma 43**		14
30	**FAT1Qr**	**H**	**Metropolitan Police**	**128**	**W**	**2 - 1**	**Dos Santos 45 47**		15
Nov 3	Isth Prem	A	Brightlingsea Regent	140	W	2 - 0	Mendy 20 Dos Santos 51	9	16
10	**FAT 2Q**	**H**	**Harlow Town**	**358**	**W**	**3 - 1**	**Koroma 16 Dudley 42 Cheadle 55**		17
12	Isth Prem	H	Whitehawk	176	W	2 - 0	Koroma 6 Morath-Gibbs 13	8	18
17	Isth Prem	H	Corinthian-Casuals	392	L	2 - 3	Korboa 50 Karoma 66 (pen)	9	19
24	**FAT 3Q**	**H**	**Walton Casuals**	**238**	**W**	**2 - 0**	**Mendy 66 74**		20
26	Isth Prem	H	Dorking Wanderers	307	D	0 - 0			21
Dec 1	Isth Prem	H	Enfield Town	310	W	1 - 0	Dixon 45	6	22
8	Isth Prem	H	Burgess Hill Town	327	L	2 - 3	Adeniyi 53 Mendy 61	8	23
15	**FAT 1P**	**H**	**Dorking Wanderers**	**291**	**W**	**1 - 0**	**Hamilton-Downes 60**	**8**	24
17	Isth Prem	A	Haringey Borough	365	L	1 - 3	Sogbanmu 70	9	25
22	Isth Prem	A	Wingate & Finchley	89	L	0 - 2		10	26
26	Isth Prem	H	Leatherhead	436	L	0 - 1		11	27
29	Isth Prem	A	Tonbridge Angels	410	W	3 - 0	Bradford 20 Pattisson 50 Lee 59 (og)	9	28
Jan 5	Isth Prem	H	Bognor Regis Town	401	L	0 - 2		13	29
12	**FAT 2P**	**H**	**Salisbury**	**514**	**W**	**4 - 1**	**Bradford 20 Dixon 37 Wright (og) 45 Hamilton-Downes13**		30
19	Isth Prem	H	Merstham	408	L	1 - 2	Dixon 7	15	31
21	Isth Prem	H	Hornchurch	249	W	2 - 1	Olomowewe 11 Dixon 44	15	32
26	Isth Prem	A	Whitehawk	184	D	2 - 2	Mendy 3 Bradford 51	15	33
Feb 1	**FAT 3P**	**H**	**Barnet**	**938**	**D**	**3 - 3**	**Sagbanmu 69 Price 90 (pen) Harrison (og) 78**		34
5	Isth Prem	A	Worthing	385	D	3 - 3	Bradford 12 79 Pattisson 80	15	35
9	Isth Prem	A	Haringey Borough	378	W	3 - 1	Korboa 16 35 Ottaway 57	14	36
12	**FAT 3Pr**	**A**	**Barnet**	**606**	**L**	**1 - 2**	**Mendy 19**	**14**	37
16	Isth Prem	H	Kingstonian	348	D	1 - 1	Ottaway 27	12	38
23	Isth Prem	H	Lewes	427	W	2 - 1	Korboa 77 80	11	39
26	Isth Prem	A	Margate	399	D	1 - 1	Korboa 4		40
Mar 2	Isth Prem	H	Folkeston Town	354	W	4 - 2	OTTAWAY 3 (3 75 80) Mendy 58	11	41
4	Isth Prem	H	Harlow Town	240	W	2 - 0	Robert 42 Mendy 67	8	42
9	Isth Prem	A	Potters Bar Town	181	W	1 - 0	Dixon 54	7	43
16	Isth Prem	H	Dorking Wanderers	812	W	3 - 2	Price 50 Bradford 57 79	6	44
23	Isth Prem	A	Brighlingsea Rovers	482	W	3 - 0	Bradford 42 Koroma 81 87	6	45
30	Isth Prem	A	Corinthian-Casuals	410	L	0 - 1		6	46
Apr 6	Isth Prem	H	Wingate & Finchley	497	W	5 - 1	Ottaway 25 Njie 63 (og) KORBOA 3 (63 68 86)	4	47
13	Isth Prem	H	Enfield Town	378	W	3 - 0	Ottaway 48 Koroma 50 Adenijyi 57	4	48
19	Isth Prem	A	Burgess Hill Town	691	W	2 - 0	Korboa 41 63	3	49
22	Isth Prem	H	Tonbridge Angels	861	L	0 - 1		3	50
27	Isth Prem	A	Bishops Stortford	663	W	2 - 1	Ottaway 2 Korboa 24	2	51
May 2	**PO SF**	**H**	**Merstham**	**1151**	**L**	**1 - 2**	**Adeniyi 17**		52

GOALSCORERS	SG	CSG	Pens	Hat tricks	Total		SG	CSG	Pens	Hat tricks	Total
Korboa	9	2		1	15	Price	3		1		3
Bradford	7				9	Sagbanmu	3				3
Mendy	8				9	H-Downes	2				2
Dixon	8	3			8	Onovwigun	3				2
Ottaway	7				8	Pattisson	2				2
Koroma	6		1		7	Dudley	1				1
Dos Santos	4	2			5	M-Gibbs	1				1
Cheadle	4		1		4	Pappoe	1				1
Opponents	4				4	Parker	1				1
Adeniyi	3				3	Robert	1				1

CORINTHIAN-CASUALS MATCH RESULTS 2018-19

Date	Comp	H/A	Opponents	Att:	Result		Goalscorers	Pos	No.
Aug 11	Isth Prem	A	Margate	510	L	2 - 5	Mfula 69 Carvalho 88	20	1
14	Isth Prem	H	Folkeston Invicta	226	L	1 - 3	Antonio 15	21	2
18	Isth Prem	H	Merstham	201	D	1 - 1	Cunningham 18	21	3
25	**FAC P**	**H**	**Croydon**	**162**	**W**	**6 - 0**	**Mfula (2) Cunningham (2) Strange Morgan**	**21**	4
27	Isth Prem	A	Kingstonian	462	L	0 - 1		21	5
Sept 1	Isth Prem	H	Brightlingsea Regent	168	D	1 - 1	Strange 30	21	6
8	**FAC 1Q**	**H**	**Whyteleafe**	**260**	**D**	**0 - 0**			7
11	**FAC 1Qr**	**A**	**Whyteleafe (Disqualified)**	**183**	**L**	**1 - 2**	**Cunningham 43 (pen)**		8
15	Isth Prem	A	Harlow Town	191	W	2 - 1	Ekim 63 Cunningham 90	19	9
29	Isth Prem	H	Enfield Town	278	L	1 - 6	Odunaike 62	20	10
Oct 2	**FAC 2Q**	**H**	**St Albans City**	**403**	**D**	**1 - 1**	**Uzun**		11
6	**FAC 2Qr**	**H**	**St Albans City**	**112**	**L**	**0 - 3**			12
9	Isth Prem	H	Whitehawk	183	W	2 - 0	Mfula 54 Odunaike 68	20	13
13	Isth Prem	A	Hornchurch	321	W	1 - 0	Odunaike 79	18	14
20	Isth Prem	A	Bishop's Stortford	331	L	0 - 3		18	15
23	Isth Prem	H	Haringey Borough	203	W	3 - 1	Mfula 28 Spencer 45 Maan 66	15	16
27	**FAT 1Q**	**A**	**Horsham**	**137**	**L**	**0 - 3**			17
Nov 3	Isth Prem	A	Dorking Wanderers	368	L	0 - 2		15	18
13	Isth Prem	A	Bognor Regis Town	402	W	1 - 0	Odunaike	13	19
17	Isth Prem	A	Carshalton Athletic	392	W	3 - 2	Clarke 6 Mfula 57 Maan 76	12	20
24	Isth Prem	H	Burgess Hill Town	272	W	3 - 0	Mfula 7 Antonio 41 Strange 85		21
28	Isth Prem	A	Leatherhead	271	W	2 - 1	Mfula 45 Oldham 80		22
Dec 1	Isth Prem	A	Wingate & Finchley	133	L	0 - 2		10	23
4	Isth Prem	A	Lewes	252	L	0 - 3		11	24
8	Isth Prem	H	Potters Bar Town	228	L	1 - 2	Mfula 53	11	25
11	Isth Prem	H	Tonbridge Angels	173	W	2 - 1	Hannigan 31 Mfula 73	11	26
15	Isth Prem	A	Brightlingsea Regent	100	L	3 - 4	Odunaike 28 Oldham 54 Adelakun 88	11	27
22	Isth Prem	H	Kingstonian	631	L	1 - 2	Odunaike 83	12	28
29	Isth Prem	A	Worthing	745	L	0 - 2		13	29
Jan 5	Isth Prem	H	Harlow Town	244	D	0 - 0		14	30
12	Isth Prem	H	Leatherhead	404	W	2 - 1	Odunaike 2	13	31
19	Isth Prem	A	Enfield Town	364	W	2 - 0	Odunaike 82 Mtula 90	12	32
26	Isth Prem	H	Bognor Regis Town	434	L	1 - 3	Antonio 10	14	33
Feb 2	Isth Prem	H	Hornchurch	225	L	0 - 3		15	34
5	Isth Prem	A	Folkeston Invicta	331	L	1 - 2	Mfula 27	15	35
16	Isth Prem	A	Merstham	236	L	1 - 2	Mfula 84	15	36
23	Isth Prem	H	Margate	337	L	0 - 3		17	37
Mar 2	Isth Prem	H	Haringey Borough	394	D	2 - 2	Odunaike 11 Osman 64	17	38
5	Isth Prem	H	Lewes	201	L	0 - 2		17	39
9	Isth Prem	H	Bishops Stortford	232	D	1 - 1	Mfula 38	18	40
16	Isth Prem	H	Dorking Wanderers	461	D	0 - 0		18	41
23	Isth Prem	A	Tonbridge Angels	391	L	0 - 2		17	42
30	Isth Prem	H	Carshalton Athletic	410	W	1 - 0	Mfula 46	17	43
Apr 6	Isth Prem	A	Burgess Hill Town	354	L	1 - 2	Mfula 44	17	44
13	Isth Prem	H	Wingate & Finchley	240	W	3 - 1	Osman 14 74 Mfula 44	17	45
20	Isth Prem	A	Potters Bar Town	221	D	2 - 2	Dillon 2 Strange 7	17	46
22	Isth Prem	H	Worthing	466	D	1 - 1	Mfula 64	17	47
27	Isth Prem	A	Whitehawk	401	L	0 - 4		17	48

GOALSCORERS	SG	CSG	Pens	Hat tricks	Total
Mfula	17	3			18
Odunaike	8	2	1		8
Cunningham	4		1		5
Strange	4				4
Antonio	3				3
Osman	2				3
Maan	2				2
Oldham	2				2
Adelakun	1				1
Carvalho	1				1
Clarke	1				1
Dillon	1				1
Ekim	1				1
Hall	1				1
Hannigan	1				1
Morgan	1				1
Opponents	1				1
Spencer	1				1
Uzun	1				1

DORKING WANDERERS MATCH RESULTS 2018-19

Date	Comp	H/A	Opponents	Att:	Result		Goalscorers	Pos	No.
Aug 11	Isth Prem	A	Bishop's Stortford	274	D	1 - 1	Prior 3	13	1
14	Isth Prem	H	Margate	475	W	2 - 0	Richards 5 Prior 47 (pen)	9	2
18	Isth Prem	H	Lewes	453	L	1 - 2	Prior 79	11	3
24	Isth Prem	A	Kingstonian	322	W	1 - 0	Briggs 61	7	4
27	Isth Prem	H	Merstham	527	D	2 - 2	Richards 7 Prior 90 (pen)	8	5
Sept 1	Isth Prem	A	Enfield	467	D	1 - 1	Briggs 67	7	6
8	**FAC 1Q**	**H**	**Hartley Wintney**	**331**	**W**	**2 - 0**	**Briggs 45 Richards 78**		7
15	Isth Prem	H	Hornchurch	334	D	3 - 3	Lavery 49 Prior 67 McManus 81	6	8
22	**FAC 2Q**	**A**	**Leverstock**	**130**	**W**	**4 - 2**	**Prior 26 (pen) McManus 45 Tolfrey 63 Lavery 86**		9
29	Isth Prem	A	Harlow Town	170	W	1 - 0	Moore 16	5	10
Oct 2	Isth Prem	H	Whitehawk	305	W	2 - 1	Tolfrey 30 McShane 38	5	11
6	**FAC 3Q**	**A**	**Gloucester City**	**333**	**D**	**3 - 3**	**Prior 52 66 (pen) Lavery 80**		12
9	**FAC 3Qr**	**H**	**Gloucester City**	**563**	**L**	**0 - 3**			13
13	Isth Prem	A	Folkestone Invicta	443	W	1 - 0	Richards 13	4	14
20	Isth Prem	H	Wingate & Finchley	429	W	3 - 0	Sole 49 O'Sullivan 51 Prior 82	2	15
23	Isth Prem	A	Burgess Hill Town	321	D	0 - 0		3	16
27	**FAT 1Q**	**H**	**Sevenoaks**	**259**	**W**	**2 - 1**	**Prior 34 68 (pen)**		17
Nov 3	Isth Prem	H	Corinthian Casuals	368	W	2 - 0	Richards 14 Prior 18	1	18
6	Isth Prem	H	Potters Bar Town	230	W	4 - 1	PRIOR 3 (2 13 35) Moore 20		19
10	**FAT 2Q**	**H**	**Tonbridge Angels**	**330**	**W**	**1 - 0**	**Prior 36**		20
17	Isth Prem	H	Brightlingsea Regent	407	W	2 - 1	O'Sullivan 11 31	1	21
19	Isth Prem	A	Haringey Borough	247	L	2 - 3	McManus 19 McShane 21	1	22
24	**FAT 3Q**	**A**	**Poole Town**	**285**	**W**	**3 - 2**	**O'Sullivan Sole El Abd**		23
26	Isth Prem	A	Carshalton Athletic	307	D	0 - 0		1	24
Dec 1	Isth Prem	H	Tonbridge Angels	526	L	0 - 1		1	25
8	Isth Prem	A	Bognor Regis Town	398	W	1 - 0	Taylor 45	1	26
15	**FAT 1P**	**A**	**Carshalton Athletic**	**291**	**L**	**0 - 1**		**2**	27
22	Isth Prem	A	Merstham	181	L	1 - 4	Prior 80	2	28
29	Isth Prem	H	Leatherhead	1529	W	2 - 0	Sole 48 McShane 81	2	29
Jan 5	Isth Prem	A	Hornchurch	203	D	1 - 1	Lavery 68	3	30
12	Isth Prem	A	Whitehawk	221	D	1 - 1	McManus 67	4	31
15	Isth Prem	A	Worthing	603	W	4 1	Sole 9 Taylor 65 McManus 70 Hall 89	2	32
19	Isth Prem	H	Harlow Town	386	W	5 - 3	Richards 5 Roy 56 79 Briggs 90 Moore 90	2	33
22	Isth Prem	H	Enfield Town	404	W	1 - 0	Moore 78	1	34
26	Isth Prem	A	Potters Bar Town	187	W	2 - 0	Taylor 54 McShana 63	1	35
Feb 2	Isth Prem	H	Folkeston Invicta	518	W	6 - 0	Jason 41 Prior 58 (pen) McShane 59 90 Richards 61 Taylor 86	1	36
5	Isth Prem	A	Margate	312	W	1 - 0	Prior 66	1	37
9	Isth Prem	H	Kingstonian	713	W	7 - 1	El-Abd 15 Taylor 28 Richards 54 78 Prior 66 McShane 80 Tolfrey 90	1	38
16	Isth Prem	A	Lewes	689	W	2 - 0	Freeman 7 (og) McShane 56	1	39
23	Isth Prem	H	Bishop's Stortford	513	W	1 - 0	Briggs 53	1	40
Mar 2	Isth Prem	H	Burgess Hill Town	607	W	6 - 0	Buchanan 4 19 Prior 35 Briggs 71 McShane 72 Ray 88	1	41
9	Isth Prem	A	Wingate & Finchley	151	W	2 - 1	Prior 41 Buchanan 57	1	42
16	Isth Prem	H	Carshalton Athletic	812	L	2 - 3	Moore 14 Buchanan 86	1	43
23	Isth Prem	A	Corinthian Casuals	481	D	0 - 0		1	44
30	Isth Prem	A	Brightlingsea Regent	208	W	2 - 0	Prior 38 pen) Richards 76	1	45
Apr 6	Isth Prem	H	Worthing	1023	W	3 - 0	Prior 37 (pen) Moore 65 Taylor 68	1	46
13	Isth Prem	A	Tonbridge Angels	825	W	2 - 0	Prior 13 Hall 44	1	47
20	Isth Prem	H	Bognor Regis Town	659	W	2 - 0	Moore 3 Buchanan 23	1	48
22	Isth Prem	A	Leatherhead	816	W	3 - 0	Prior 16 Briggs 55 McShane 58	1	49
27	Isth Prem	H	Haringey Borough	746	W	2 - 0	Prior 6 Buchanan 38	1	50

GOALSCORERS	SG	CSG	Pens	Hat tricks	Total
Prior	23	4	8		27
McShane	8	2			10
Richards	9				10
Briggs	6				7
Moore	7				7
Buchanan	6	2			6
Taylor	6				6
McManus	4				5
Lavery	4				4
O'Sullivan	4				4
Sole	4				4
Tolfrey	2				3
El-Abd	2				2
Hall	2				2
Roy	1				2
Jason	1				1
Opponents	1				1
Ray	1				1

ENFIELD TOWN MATCH RESULTS 2018-19

Date	Comp	H/A	Opponents	Att:	Result		Goalscorers	Pos	No.
Aug 11	Isth Prem	A	Folkestone Invicta	449	W	3 - 2	Banks 12 (og) Adams 78 79	6	1
14	Isth Prem	H	Bishop's Stortford	459	W	2 - 1	Cheney 12 Youngs 26	2	2
18	Isth Prem	H	Hornchurch	443	D	2 - 2	Olomowewe 17 Hope 52	5	3
25	Isth Prem	A	Burgess Hill Town	423	W	6 - 1	Hope 14 Olomowewe 27 Youngs 33 85 Johnson 49 Blackman 88	1	4
27	Isth Prem	A	Wingate & Finchley	320	D	1 - 1	Greene 71	2	5
Sept 1	Isth Prem	H	Dorking Wanderers	467	D	1 - 1	Hatton 16	4	6
8	**FAC 1Q**	**H**	**Bedford Town**	**393**	**L**	**0 - 3**			7
15	Isth Prem	A	Lewes	648	D	2 - 2	Bricknell 81 82	2	8
29	Isth Prem	A	Corinthian Casuals	278	W	6 - 1	Sayoud 26 Rumens 44 Bricknell 57 70 (pen) Youngs 67 Cheney 73	2	9
Oct 6	Isth Prem	H	Merstham	312	D	0 - 0			10
13	Isth Prem	A	Margate	658	L	1 - 2	Bricknell 33	5	11
16	Isth Prem	H	Brightlingsea Regent	311	D	0 - 0			12
20	Isth Prem	H	Whitehawk	403	W	6 - 0	Percell 4 Bricknell 23 32 Johnson 58 Adams 77 Hope 82	3	13
23	Isth Prem	A	Tonbridge Angels	490	W	2 - 1	Blackman 44 Olomowewe	2	14
27	**FAT 1Q**	**A**	**Lowestoft Town**	**289**	**W**	**1 - 0**	**Hope 88**		15
Nov 3	Isth Prem	H	Haringey Borough	571	D	2 - 2	Bricknell 10 Youngs 43	3	16
10	**FAT 2Q**	**A**	**Bassingstoke Town**	**310**	**L**	**1 - 2**	**Taafle 17**		17
13	Isth Prem	H	Worthing	333	L	1 - 4	Bricknell 72 (pen)	4	18
17	Isth Prem	H	Leatherhead	467	L	1 - 4	Sayoud 79	5	19
24	Isth Prem	H	Kingstonian	433	L	0 - 1			20
Dec 1	Isth Prem	A	Carshalton Athletic	319	L	0 - 1		11	21
4	Isth Prem	A	Bognor Regis Town	376	W	2 - 1	Bricknell 68 Blackman 83	7	22
8	Isth Prem	H	Harlow Town	342	W	4 - 1	Greene 8 Bricknell 44 (pen) 64 Weatherstone 77	6	23
26	Isth Prem	H	Wingate & Finchley	444	W	4 - 1	Faal 9 20 Bricknell 51 (pen) Mubiayi 82	5	24
29	Isth Prem	A	Potters Bar Town	504	W	2 - 1	Faal 8 Weatherstone 86	3	25
Jan 5	Isth Prem	H	Lewes	434	D	1 - 1	Youngs 36	4	26
12	Isth Prem	A	Merstham	228	L	0 - 1		7	27
19	Isth Prem	H	Corinthian-Casuals	364	L	0 - 2		9	28
22	Isth Prem	A	Dorking Wanderers	404	L	0 - 1			29
26	Isth Prem	A	Worthing	743	W	3 - 0	Bricknell 42 Johnson 47 48	8	30
Feb 2	Isth Prem	H	Margate	403	W	4 - 0	Bricknell 37 Parcell 52 Weatherstone 56 Oliyide 62	6	31
5	Isth Prem	A	Bishop's Stortford	340	L	1 - 2	Ibe 68	6	32
9	Isth Prem	H	Burgess Hill Town	421	W	3 - 1	Oliyide 29 Bricknell 49 63	6	33
16	Isth Prem	H	Hornchurch	355	L	0 - 2		6	34
23	Isth Prem	H	Folkestone Invicta	382	W	2 - 0	Johnson 59 Bricknell 80	6	35
Mar 2	Isth Prem	H	Tonbridge Angels	401	D	0 - 0		6	36
9	Isth Prem	A	Whitehawk	325	W	3 - 1	Ibe 2 Payne 74 Bricknell 81	6	37
16	Isth Prem	H	Bognor Regis Town	418	D	3 - 3	Taaffe 8 Cheney 78 Ibe 87	7	38
23	Isth Prem	A	Haringey Borough	875	L	1 - 3	Weatherstone 10	7	39
30	Isth Prem	H	Leatherhead	403	L	0 - 1		8	40
Apr 6	Isth Prem	A	Kingstonian	293	L	1 - 2	Rumens 75	9	41
13	Isth Prem	H	Carshalton Athletic	378	L	0 - 3		10	42
20	Isth Prem	A	Harlow Town	339	W	3 - 1	Ibe 37 Johnson 90 Davison 90	10	43
22	Isth Prem	H	Potters Bar Town	362	W	3 - 1	Ibe 4 Younge 13 Sayoud 90	10	44
27	Isth Prem	A	Brightlingsea Regent	222	L	0 - 1		10	45

GOALSCORERS	SG	CSG	Pens	Hat tricks	Total
Bricknell	14	3	4		19
Youngs	6	2			7
Johnson	5				6
Ibe	5				5
Hope	4				4
Weatherstone	4				4
Adams	2				3
Blackman	3				3
Cheney	3				3
Faal	2				3
Olomowewe	3				3
Sayoud	3				3
Greene	2				2
Oliyide	2				2
Parcell	2				2
Rumens	2				2
Taaffe	2				2
Davison	1				1
Hatton	1				1
Mubiayi	1				1
Opponents	1				1
Payne	1				1

FOLKSTONE INVICTA MATCH RESULTS 2018-19

Date	Comp	H/A	Opponents	Att:	Result		Goalscorers	Pos	No.
Aug 11	Isth Prem	H	Enfeld	449	L	2 - 3	McCann 7 Yusuff 35	14	1
14	Isth Prem	A	Corinthian Casuals	226	W	3 - 1	McCann 1 73 Ter Horst 13	10	2
18	Isth Prem	A	Wingate & Finchley	95	W	3 - 0	Ter Horst 10 Yusuff 50 Evans 57	6	3
25	Isth Prem	H	Harlow Town	374	W	3 - 2	Yussuf 22 McCann 54 Aboagye 64	3	4
27	Isth Prem	H	Tonbridge Angels	548	L	0 - 1		5	5
Sept 1	Isth Prem	A	Bishop's Stortford	323	W	1 - 0	Rowland 8	5	6
8	**FAC 1Q**	**A**	**Burgess Hill Town**	**337**	**L**	**0 - 1**			7
15	Isth Prem	H	Burgess Hill Town	414	D	1 - 1	Yussuf 60	4	8
29	Isth Prem	H	Brightlingsea Regent	416	L	2 - 3	Draycott 45 Rowland 90	6	9
Oct 2	Isth Prem	H	Hornchurch	203	L	1 - 4	Draycott 83	6	10
6	Isth Prem	H	Kingstonian	244	L	1 - 4	Evans 63	8	11
13	Isth Prem	H	Dorking Wanderers	443	L	0 - 1		10	12
16	Isth Prem	A	Bognor Regis Town	508	W	4 - 2	Yussuf 4 39 Rowland 37 Smith 89	9	13
20	Isth Prem	A	Lewes	708	L	0 - 2		10	14
23	Isth Prem	H	Carshalton Athletic	352	L	2 - 3	Dolan 48 Ter Horst 74	11	15
27	**FAT 1Q**	**H**	**Leatherhead**	**281**	**W**	**5 - 1**	**Ter Horst 7 25 Rowland 38 Yusuff 54 62**		16
Nov 3	Isth Prem	H	Worthing	951	L	2 - 3	Rowland 10 Dolan 58	14	17
10	**FAT 2Q**	**H**	**Didcot Town**	**275**	**W**	**3 - 0**	**Rowland 4 Learoyd 25 (og) Draycott 77 (pen)**		18
17	Isth Prem	H	Potters Bar Town	399	W	2 - 0	Starkey 89 Draycott 90	13	19
22	**FAT 3Q**	**A**	**Woking**	**805**	**L**	**0 - 2**			20
27	Isth Prem	A	Whitehawk	110	D	0 - 0		13	21
Dec 1	Isth Prem	A	Merstham	318	W	6 - 2	DRAYCOTT 3 (8 41 47) Paxman 10 90 McCann 15	13	22
8	Isth Prem	H	Haringey Borough	261	L	0 - 1		13	23
15	Isth Prem	A	Bishop's Stortford	333	W	2 - 0	Yussuf 65 Paxman 33	12	24
22	Isth Prem	H	Leatherhead	411	W	2 - 0	Draycott 13 (pen) 51	11	25
26	Isth Prem	A	Tonbridge Angels	606	W	3 - 1	Draycott 8 Heard 78 Paxman 90	10	26
Jan 1	Isth Prem	H	Margate	629	W	1 - 0	Ter Horst 9	8	27
5	Isth Prem	A	Burgess Hill Town	445	D	0 - 0		7	28
12	Isth Prem	H	Hornchurch	446	W	5 - 0	Paxman 2 58 Ter Horst 43 Draycott 45 (pen) Yussuf 47	6	29
19	Isth Prem	A	Brightlingsea Regent	202	L	0 - 2		7	30
26	Isth Prem	H	Kingstonian	524	W	2 - 0	Draycott 11 (pen) Ter Horst 36	6	31
Feb 2	Isth Prem	H	Dorking Wanderers	578	L	0 - 6		6	32
5	Isth Prem	H	Corinthian-Casuals	331	W	2 - 1	O'Mara 21 Everitt 90	5	33
9	Isth Prem	A	Harlow Town	254	W	4 - 2	Newman 12 Ujah 15 (og) Paxman 32 Yussuf 49	4	34
16	Isth Prem	H	Wingate & Finchley	537	D	2 - 2	Draycott 90 (pen) Yussuf 90	7	35
23	Isth Prem	A	Enfield	382	L	0 - 2		8	36
Mar 2	Isth Prem	A	Carshalton Athletic	354	L	2 - 4	Paxman 20 Jackson 24	9	37
9	Isth Prem	A	Lewes	441	W	4 - 0	JACKSON 3 (4 22 34) Heard 84	8	38
16	Isth Prem	A	Leatherhead	355	D	0 - 0		8	39
23	Isth Prem	H	Worthing	578	L	0 - 1		10	40
30	Isth Prem	A	Potters Bar Town	192	D	2 - 2	Jackson 86 Yusuff 87	10	41
Apr 6	Isth Prem	H	Whitehawk	415	W	2 - 1	Newman 8 Yussuf 26	9	42
13	Isth Prem	H	Merstham	215	W	3 - 1	Jackson 43 Everitt 32 Yussuf 90	9	43
20	Isth Prem	H	Haringay Borough	584	W	4 - 0	Yussuf 12 47 Draycott 74 Ter Horst 90	8	44
22	Isth Prem	H	Margate	644	W	3 - 0	Newman 34 O'Mara 56 Ter Horst 74	7	45
27	Isth Prem	H	Bognor Regis Town	707	W	1 - 0	Jackson 69	6	46

GOALSCORERS	SG	CSG	Pens	Hat tricks	Total
Yussuf	14	4			17
Draycott	10	2	5	1	14
Ter Horst	9				10
Paxman	6				8
Jackson	5			1	7
Rowland	5	3			6
McCann	5				5
Newman	3				3
Dolan	2				2
Evans	2				2

	SG	CSG	Pens	Hat tricks	Total
Everitt	2				2
Heard	2				2
O'Mara	2				2
Opponents	2				2
Aboagye	1				1
Smith	1				1
Starkey	1				1

HARINGEY BOROUGH MATCH RESULTS 2018-19

Date	Comp	H/A	Opponents	Att:	Result		Goalscorers	Pos	No.
Aug 11	Isth Prem	H	Bognor Regis Town	246	D	2 - 2	Nouble 50 Akinwande 58	11	1
14	Isth Prem	A	Brightlingsea Regent	156	W	2 - 0	Nouble 41 (pen) Ademiluyi 63	8	2
18	Isth Prem	A	Leatherhead	335	L	1 - 2	Nouble 47	10	3
25	**FAC P**	**H**	**Stanway Rovers**	**151**	**W**	**1 - 0**	**McKenzie 69**		4
27	Isth Prem	A	Potters Bar Town	267	D	0 - 0		12	5
Sept 1	Isth Prem	H	Worthing	290	L	1 - 2	McKenzie 27	14	6
8	**FAC 1Q**	**A**	**Brentwood Town**	**199**	**W**	**3 - 2**	**Aresti 5 McKenzie 89 Akinwande 90**		7
15	Isth Prem	A	Whitehawk	335	W	3 - 1	NOUBLE 3 (41 (pen) 45 (pen) 66	12	8
22	**FAC 2Q**	**H**	**Erith Town**	**187**	**W**	**2 - 0**	**Nouble 37 (pen) McKenzie 48**		9
29	Isth Prem	A	Margate	530	W	1 - 0	Aresti 58	9	10
Oct 1	Isth Prem	H	Harlow Town	250	L	0 - 2		10	11
6	**FAC 3Q**	**H**	**AFC Sudbury**	**209**	**W**	**2 - 1**	**McKenzie 37 56**		12
13	Isth Prem	A	Burgess Hill Town	651	L	1 - 3	Nouble 47	14	13
20	**FAC 4Q**	**H**	**Poole Town**	**402**	**W**	**2 - 1**	**Sambu 77 Nouble 83**		14
23	Isth Prem	A	Corinthian-Casuals	203	L	1 - 3	Kirby 10	18	15
27	**FAT 1Q**	**H**	**Chesham United**	**223**	**D**	**1 - 1**	**Stone 5**		16
30	**FAT 1Qr**	**A**	**Chesham United**	**163**	**D**	**2 - 2**	**McKenzie 29 Barker 82 (lost 1-3 on pens)**		17
Nov 3	Isth Prem	A	Enfield Town	571	D	2 - 2	Richards 4 51	18	18
9	**FAC 1P**	**H**	**AFC Wimbledon**	**2710**	**L**	**0 - 1**			19
12	Isth Prem	H	Tonbridge Angels	260	W	4 - 0	Richards 22 Rowe 60 84 Aresti 90	16	20
17	Isth Prem	A	Lewes	812	W	1 - 0	Nouble 50 (pen)	14	21
19	Isth Prem	H	Dorking Wanderers	247	W	3 - 2	Staunton 45 Rowe 78 82	12	22
24	Isth Prem	H	Hornchurch	260	W	3 - 1	Kirby 3 66 McDonald 87	9	23
Dec 1	Isth Prem	A	Kingstonian	312	W	4 - 0	Nouble 16 Akinwande 48 Rowe 56 McKenzie 79	7	24
8	Isth Prem	H	Folkestone Invicta	261	W	1 - 0	Akinwande 25	7	25
10	Isth Prem	H	Bishops Stortford	296	W	3 - 1	Barker 11 Nouble 49 (pen) Durojaiye 66	7	26
15	Isth Prem	A	Worthing	502	W	2 - 0	Nouble 31 Gabriel 75	4	27
17	Isth Prem	H	Carshalton Athletic	365	W	3 - 1	Gabriel 30 33 Kirby 61	2	28
22	Isth Prem	H	Potters Bar Town	320	W	1 - 0	Gabriel 51	2	29
29	Isth Prem	H	Merstham	333	D	2 - 2	Gabriel 10 McDonald 67	1	30
1 Jan	Isth Prem	A	Wingate & Finchley	266	W	4 - 0	Richards 29 McDonald 60 Durojaiye 67 Kirby 90	1	31
5	Isth Prem	H	Whitehawk	336	W	3 - 0	McDonald 13 Gabriel 37 Akinwande 68	1	32
12	Isth Prem	A	Harlow Town	261	L	1 - 2	Gabriel 56	1	33
19	Isth Prem	H	Margate	275	W	1 - 0	Gabriel 67	1	34
26	Isth Prem	A	Tonbridge Angels	520	L	0 - 1		2	35
Feb 2	Isth Prem	H	Burgess Hill Town	354	D	4 - 4	Richards 39 (pen) GABRIEL 3 (42 88 pen 90 pen)	2	36
4	Isth Prem	H	Brighlingsea Regent	341	W	2 - 1	Gabriel 71 Sappleton 90	2	37
9	Isth Prem	A	Carshalton Athletic	378	L	1 - 3	Rowe 42	2	38
16	Isth Prem	H	Leatherhead	400	L	0 - 3		2	39
23	Isth Prem	A	Bognor Regis Town	517	W	4 - 0	Oyenuga 26 Nouble 53 66 (pre) Olufami 89	2	40
Mar 2	Isth Prem	H	Corinthian Casuals	394	D	2 - 2	Aresti 29 Nouble 31 (pen)	2	41
9	Isth Prem	A	Merstham	267	D	0 - 0		2	42
16	Isth Prem	A	Bishop's Stortford	347	L	0 - 2		2	43
23	Isth Prem	H	Enfield Town	875	W	3 - 1	Nouble 22 62 (pen) Akinwande 54	2	44
30	Isth Prem	H	Lewes	523	W	2 - 1	Rowe 16 Froxylias 56	2	45
Apr 6	Isth Prem	A	Hornchurch	277	D	2 - 2	Clark 20 (og) Rowe 51	2	46
13	Isth Prem	H	Kingstonian	511	W	2 - 0	Delle-Verdi 2 50	2	47
20	Isth Prem	A	Folkestone Invicta	583	L	0 - 4		2	48
22	Isth Prem	H	Wingate & Finchley	614	L	1 - 2	Akinwande 40	2	49
27	Isth Prem	A	Dorking Wanderers	746	L	0 - 2		3	50
May 2	**PO SF**	**H**	**Tonbridge Angels**	**810**	**L**	**1 - 2**	**Oyenuga 56 (pen)**		51

GOALSCORERS	SG	CSG	Pens	Hat tricks	Total
Nouble	14	3	9	1	18
Gabriel	9	4	1	1	12
McKenzie	7	2			8
Rowe	8				8
Akinwande	7	2			7
Kirby	4				5
Richards	4				5
Aresti	4				4
McDonald	4				4
Barker	2				2
Delle-Verdi	1				2
Durojajye	2				2
Oyenuga	2		1		2
Ademiluyi	1				1
Froxylias	1				1
Olufami	1				1
Opponents	1				1
Sambu	1				1
Sapleton	1				1
Staunton	1				1
Stone	1				1

HARLOW TOWN MATCH RESULTS 2018-19

Date	Comp	H/A	Opponents	Att:	Result		Goalscorers	Pos	No.
Aug 11	Isth Prem	A	Whitehawk	300	L	2 - 4	McCollin 42 (pen) Read 61	19	1
14	Isth Prem	H	Burgess Hill Town	180	D	1 - 1	Da Cruz 70	18	2
18	Isth Prem	H	Worthing	220	L	0 - 2		17	3
25	Isth Prem	A	Folkestone Invicta	374	L	2 - 3	Read 34 Acquah 90	18	4
27	Isth Prem	H	Bishop's Stortford	725	L	1 - 3	Edwards 88 (pen)	20	5
Sept 1	Isth Prem	A	Leatherhead	324	W	3 - 1	Martin 19 Vaughan 34 Acquah 46	19	6
8	**FAC 1Q**	**A**	**Hendon**	**264**	**D**	**1 - 1**	**Gymafi 25**		7
10	**FAC 1Qr**	**H**	**Hendon**	**173**	**L**	**1 - 2**	**Da Cruz 90**		8
15	Isth Prem	H	Corinthian Casuals	191	L	1 - 2	Read 48	21	9
29	Isth Prem	H	Dorking Wanderers	170	L	0 - 1		21	10
Oct 1	Isth Prem	A	Haringey Borough	250	W	2 - 0	Edwards 73 (pen) Read 90	20	11
6	Isth Prem	A	Margate	450	D	0 - 0		20	12
13	Isth Prem	H	Carshalton Athletic	211	L	0 - 4		21	13
20	Isth Prem	A	Kingstonian	275	L	0 - 7		21	14
23	Isth Prem	H	Brightlingsea Regent	133	L	0 - 1		21	15
27	**FAT 1Q**	**A**	**Whitehawk**	**161**	**W**	**3 - 2**	**Hitchcock 66 Koranteng 70 Acquah 84**		16
31	Isth Prem	A	Lewes	430	L	1 - 2	Hitchcock 24	22	17
Nov 3	Isth Prem	H	Merstham	132	L	1 - 4	Koranteng 1	22	18
10	**FAT 2Q**	**A**	**Carshalton Athletic**	**353**	**L**	**1 - 3**	**Adaje**		19
17	Isth Prem	H	Tonbridge Angels	277	W	1 - 0	Vaughan 85	22	20
24	Isth Prem	A	Potters Bar Town	175	W	2 - 1	Da Cruz 16 (pen) Theobalds 43	20	21
Dec 1	Isth Prem	H	Bognor Regis Town	198	D	1 - 1	Acquah 26	20	22
8	Isth Prem	A	Enfield Town	342	L	1 - 4	Hitchcock 34	20	23
11	Isth Prem	A	Wingate & Finchley	88	W	2 - 0	Yuill 20 Acquah 29	20	24
15	Isth Prem	H	Leatherhead	167	D	2 - 2	Hancock 61 Koranteng 74	21	25
26	Isth Prem	A	Bishop's Stortford	687	L	0 - 1		21	26
29	Isth Prem	H	Hornchurch	291	L	2 - 4	Acquah 37 Foy 41	21	27
Jan 5	Isth Prem	A	Corinthian Casuals	244	D	0 - 0		21	28
12	Isth Prem	H	Haringey Borough	261	W	2 - 1	Hitchcock 1 Acquah 46	21	29
19	Isth Prem	A	Dorking Wanderers	388	L	3 - 5	Foy 21 Acquah 51 70	21	30
26	Isth Prem	H	Lewes	174	W	2 - 1	Koranteng 63 (pen) Richardson 76	19	31
Feb 5	Isth Prem	A	Burgess Hill Town	297	W	3 - 1	Foy 5 45 (pen) Hitchcock 9	19	32
9	Isth Prem	H	Folkestone Invicrtta	254	L	2 - 4	Foy 30 63	19	33
16	Isth Prem	A	Worthing	716	L	1 - 9	Price-Placid 20	19	34
23	Isth Prem	H	Whitehawk	308	L	0 - 3		20	35
Mar 2	Isth Prem	A	Brightlingsea Regent	192	D	1 - 1	Price-Placid 42	20	36
4	Isth Prem	A	Carshalton Athletic	240	L	0 - 2		21	37
9	Isth Prem	H	Kingstoni8an	167	W	3 - 1	Hitchcock 7 58 Foy 90	21	38
16	Isth Prem	H	Wingate & Finchley	152	L	2 - 7	Foy 47 (pen) Acquah 89	21	39
23	Isth Prem	A	Merstham	213	L	1 - 5	Foy 50	21	40
30	Isth Prem	A	Tonbridge Angels	632	L	1 - 3	Foy 85	22	41
Apr 6	Isth Prem	H	Potters Bar Town	224	L	2 - 5	Hitchcock 49 Foy 57	22	42
13	Isth Prem	A	Bognor Regis Town	401	D	1 - 1	Hitchcock 68	22	43
20	Isth Prem	H	Enfield Town	339	L	1 - 3	Foy 67	22	44
22	Isth Prem	A	Hornchurch	269	L	0 - 3		22	45
27	Isth Prem	H	Margate	166	L	3 - 4	Davies 27 Hitchciock 63 Foy 74	22	46

GOALSCORERS	SG	CSG	Pens	Hat tricks	Total
Foy	14	5	2		13
Acquah	9	2			10
Hitchcock	9	2			10
Koranteng	4		1		4
Read	4				4
De Cruz	3				3
Edwards	2		2		2
Price-Placid	2				2
Vaughan	2				2
Adaje	1				1

	SG	CSG	Pens	Hat tricks	Total
Davies	1				1
Gymafi	1				1
Hancock	1				1
Martin	1				1
McCollin	1		1		1
Richardson	1				1
Theobalds	1				1
Yuill	1				1

HORNCHURCH MATCH RESULTS 2018-19

Date	Comp	H/A	Opponents	Att:	Result		Goalscorers	Pos	No.
Aug 11	Isth Prem	H	Leatherhead	267	W	3 - 0	Warner 39 Porter 52 Marks 64	1	1
14	Isth Prem	A	Wingate & Finchley	142	D	1 - 1	Purcell 6	4	2
18	Isth Prem	A	Enfield Town	443	D	2 - 2	Warner 78 Marks 90	8	3
25	Isth Prem	H	Bognor Regis Town	231	D	1 - 1	Marks 50	7	4
27	Isth Prem	H	Brighlingsea Regent	212	D	1 - 1	Warner 68	8	5
Sept 1	Isth Prem	H	Carshalton Athletic	211	D	1 - 1	Purcell 41	8	6
8	**FAC 1Q**	**H**	**Harrow Borough**	**324**	**W**	**1 - 0**	**Warner 48**		7
15	Isth Prem	A	Dorking Wanderers	334	D	3 - 3	Spence 16 Coker 23 Cooper 29	8	8
22	**FAC 2Q**	**H**	**East Grinstead Town**	**227**	**W**	**2 - 1**	**Purcell Marks**		9
29	Isth Prem	A	Burgess Hill Town	368	W	3 - 0	Cooper 30 Marks 39 Spence 64	6	10
Oct 2	Isth Prem	H	Folkestone Invicta	203	W	4 - 1	Purcell 7 Hogan 34 Marks 47 McKenzie 73	6	11
6	**FAC 3Q**	**A**	**Hampton & Rchmond B**	**316**	**L**	**0 - 1**			12
13	Isth Prem	A	Corinthian-Casuals	321	L	0 - 1		9	13
16	Isth Prem	H	Lewes	187	L	1 - 5	Purcell 52	10	14
20	Isth Prem	H	Tonbridge Angels	279	L	0 - 2		11	15
27	**FAT 1Q**	**H**	**Ramsgate**	**162**	**W**	**6 - 0**	**Boakye-Yiadom 14 25 Clark 19 Marks 30 44 Purcell 64**		16
30	Isth Prem	H	Merstham	100	D	1 - 1	Purcell 78	11	17
Nov 3	Isth Prem	A	Bishop's Stortford	332	L	0 - 1		13	18
10	**FAT 2Q**	**A**	**Brightlingsea Regent**	**181**	**L**	**1 - 2**	**McKenzie**		19
17	Isth Prem	H	Worthing	235	D	1 - 1	Purcell 42	19	20
24	Isth Prem	H	Haringey Borough	260	L	1 - 3	Marks 88	21	21
Dec 1	Isth Prem	A	Whitehawk	197	D	1 - 1	Porter 75	22	22
8	Isth Prem	H	Kingstonian	204	D	2 - 2	Saunders 81 Purcell 86	18	23
11	Isth Prem	H	Potters Bar Town	124	L	0 - 1			24
15	Isth Prem	A	Margate	340	D	0 - 0			25
22	Isth Prem	H	Brightlingsea Regent	215	L	1 - 2	Bentley 64	19	26
29	Isth Prem	A	Harlow Town	291	W	4 - 2	MARKS 3 (45 65 78) Porter 64		27
Jan 5	Isth Prem	H	Dorking Wanderers	203	D	1 - 1	Saunders 88	18	28
12	Isth Prem	A	Folkestone Invicta	446	L	0 - 5		18	29
19	Isth Prem	H	Burgess Hill Town	228	W	2 - 0	Prescott 23 Purcell 33	18	30
21	Isth Prem	A	Carshalton Athletic	249	L	1 - 2	Marks 70		31
26	Isth Prem	A	Merstham	196	L	0 - 3		18	32
Feb 2	Isth Prem	H	Corinthian-Casuals	225	W	3 - 0	Saunders 45 Purcell 68 84	16	33
9	Isth Prem	A	Bognor Regis Town	475	L	0 - 2		18	34
16	Isth Prem	H	Enfield Town	355	W	2 - 0	Winn 29 Stimson 74	18	35
23	Isth Prem	A	Leatherhead	374	W	2 - 1	Stimson 23 Spence 67	17	36
Mar 2	Isth Prem	H	Margate	273	L	1 - 2	Marks 11	18	37
5	Isth Prem	H	Wingate & Finchley	141	W	3 - 0	Stimson 32 Christou 85 Winn 87	16	38
9	Isth Prem	A	Tonbridge Angels	509	L	0 - 1		16	39
16	Isth Prem	A	Potters Bar Town	212	W	1 - 0	Marks 79	15	40
23	Isth Prem	H	Bishop's Stortford	344	L	0 - 1		15	41
30	Isth Prem	A	Worthing	804	L	1 - 3	Christou 90	15	42
Apr 6	Isth Prem	H	Haringey Borough	277	D	2 - 2	Spence 62 Dutton 90	14	43
13	Isth Prem	H	Whitehawk	228	L	1 - 2	Christou 73	16	44
20	Isth Prem	A	Kingstonian	298	W	3 - 2	Spence 45 Winn 46 Richmond 48 (og)	16	45
22	Isth Prem	H	Harlow Town	269	W	3 - 0	Lee 41 61 Marks 65	15	46
27	Isth Prem	A	Lewes	611	D	0 - 0		15	47

GOALSCORERS	SG	CSG	Pens	Hat tricks	Total
Marks	13	3		1	16
Purcell	11	2			12
Spence	5				5
Warner	4				4
Christou	3				3
Porter	3				3
Saunders	3				3
Stimson	3	2			3
Winn	3				3
B-Yiadom	1				2
Cooper	2				2
Lee	1				2
McKenzie	2				2
Bentley	1				1
Clark	1				1
Coker	1				1
Dutton	1				1
Hogan	1				1
Opponents	1				1
Prescott	1				1

KINGSTONIAN MATCH RESULTS 2018-19

Date	Comp	H/A	Opponents	Att:	Result		Goalscorers	Pos	No.
Aug 11	Isth Prem	H	Brightlingsea Regent	255	L	2 - 3	Theophanous 16 Faal 84 (pen)	15	1
14	Isth Prem	A	Potters Bar Toiwn	204	L	0 - 3		20	2
18	Isth Prem	A	Carshalton Town	419	D	1 - 1	Theophanous 48	18	3
25	Isth Prem	H	Dorking Wanderers	322	L	0 - 1		20	4
27	Isth Prem	A	Corinthian-Casuals	462	W	1 - 0	Buchanan 78	19	5
Sept 1	Isth Prem	H	Bognor Regis Town	539	L	1 - 3	Buchanan 43	20	6
8	**FAC 1Q**	**A**	**Hastings United**	**602**	**L**	**1 - 2**	**Gogonas 19**		7
15	Isth Prem	H	Bishop's Stortford	244	W	3 - 2	Lucien 16 Cundle 45 Brewer 90	17	8
29	Isth Prem	A	Whitehawk	404	D	1 - 1	Buchanan 62	18	9
Oct 6	Isth Prem	H	Folkestone invicta	244	W	4 - 1	Theophanous 39 70 Buchanan 86 Daly 90	17	10
13	Isth Prem	A	Worthing	1320	L	1 - 3	Buchanan 41	17	11
20	Isth Prem	H	Harlow Town	275	W	7 - 0	Fitzpatrick 7 Theophanous 10 25 Bexon 36 (og) Doughty 50 65 Buchanan 84	13	12
27	**FAT 1Q**	**H**	**Bedford Town**	**257**	**D**	**1 - 1**	**Buchanan 90**		13
30	**FAT 1Qr**	**A**	**Bedford Town**	**218**	**L**	**2 - 3**	**Buchanan 17 Doughty 62**		14
Nov 3	Isth Prem	H	Lewes	306	W	2 - 1	Daly 14 Buchanan 84	11	15
7	Isth Prem	H	Tonbridge Angels	290	D	1 - 1	Theophanous 32		16
10	Isth Prem	A	Burgess Hill Town	358	W	1 - 0	Buchanan 83	10	17
14	Isth Prem	A	Leatherhead	361	L	1 - 2	Doughty 2		18
17	Isth Prem	H	Margate	334	W	2 - 1	Faal 53 Theophanous 78	9	19
20	Isth Prem	A	Wingate & Finchley	103	W	4 - 0	Daly 23 (pen) Sam-Yorke 60 80 Gogonas 75	8	20
24	Isth Prem	A	Enfield Town	433	W	1 - 0	Daly 57	4	21
Dec 1	Isth Prem	H	Haringey Borough	312	L	0 - 4		4	22
8	Isth Prem	A	Hornchurch	204	D	2 - 2	Theophanous 45 Daly 88	7	23
15	Isth Prem	H	Bognor Regis Town	310	W	4 - 1	Daly 7 McAuley 18 Theophanous 28 Buchanan 59	4	24
22	Isth Prem	A	Corinthian-Casuals	631	W	2 - 1	Daly 37 84	2	25
Jan 1	Isth Prem	H	Merstham	366	D	0 - 0		2	26
5	Isth Prem	A	Bishop's Stortford	326	W	3 - 0	Buchanan 38 Theophanous 48 McAuley 73	2	27
12	Isth Prem	A	Tonbridge Angels	433	L	2 - 3	Inman 45 McAuley 45	3	28
19	Isth Prem	H	Whitehawk	275	L	1 - 3	Buchanan 15	6	29
26	Isth Prem	A	Folkestone Invicta	524	L	0 - 2		9	30
Feb 2	Isth Prem	H	Worthing	279	L	2 - 3	Davies 77 Theophanous 88	11	31
6	Isth Prem	H	Potters Bar Town	236	L	1 - 2	Musungu 90	11	32
9	Isth Prem	A	Dorking Wanderers	713	L	1 - 7	Inman 73	13	33
16	Isth Prem	H	Carshalton Athletic	348	D	1 - 1	Murrell-Williamson 8	12	34
23	Isth Prem	A	Brightlingsea Regent	177	L	0 - 2		14	35
Mar 2	Isth Prem	H	Wingate & Finchley	303	L	1 - 2	Murrell-Williamson 40	14	36
9	Isth Prem	A	Harlow Town	167	L	1 - 3	Smith 50	14	37
16	Isth Prem	H	Burgess Hill Town	248	L	2 - 3	Minhas 39 Kalozi 45	15	38
23	Isth Prem	A	Lewes	812	L	0 - 3		15	39
30	Isth Prem	A	Margate	519	L	0 - 1		16	40
Apr 6	Isth Prem	H	Enfield Town	293	W	2 - 1	Lamont 30 Sam-Yorke 50	16	41
13	Isth Prem	A	Haringey Borough	511	L	0 - 2		16	42
20	Isth Prem	H	Hornchurch	298	L	2 - 3	Sam-Yorke 45 (pen) 80	16	43
22	Isth Prem	A	Merstham	276	L	0 - 2		18	44
27	Isth Prem	H	Leatherhead	350	L	0 - 4		18	45

GOALSCORERS	SG	CSG	Pens	Hat tricks	Total
Buchanan	13	7			13
Theophanous	10	2			12
Daly	7				8
Sam-Yorke	4		1		5
Doughty	3				4
McAuley	3				3
Faal	2		1		2
Gogonas	2				2
Inman	2				2
M-Williamson	2				2
Brewer	1				1
Cundle	1				1
Davies	1				1
Kalozi	1				1
Lamont	1				1
Lucien	1				1
Minhas	1				1
Musungu	1				1
Opponents	1				1
Parcell	1				1
Smith	1				1

LEATHERHEAD MATCH RESULTS 2018-19

Date	Comp	H/A	Opponents	Att:	Result	Goalscorers	Pos	No.
Aug 11	Isth Prem	A	Hornchurch	287	L 0 - 3		21	1
14	Isth Prem	H	Whitehawk	376	D 1 - 1	Okojie 40	19	2
18	Isth Prem	H	Haringey Borough	335	W 2 - 1	Okojie 18 Gregory 31	14	3
25	Isth Prem	A	Bishop's Stortford	260	D 1 - 1	Okojie 43	11	4
27	Isth Prem	A	Carshalton Athletic	403	L 1 - 2	Cullen 76	13	5
Sept 1	Isth Prem	H	Harlow Town	324	L 1 - 3	Cullen 14	17	6
8	**FAC 1Q**	**H**	**Herne Bay**	**227**	**W 2 - 0**	**Okojie 12 Deakin 80**		7
15	Isth Prem	A	Potters Bar	171	W 1 - 0	Cullen 24	16	8
22	**FAC 2Q**	**A**	**Haverhill Rovers**	**401**	**W 6 - 0**	**Okojie 8 Cullen 40 Benyon 53 57 Gregory 80 (pen) 90**		9
29	Isth Prem	A	Worthing	906	D 1 - 1	Gregory 35	16	10
Oct 6	**FAC 3Q**	**H**	**Hanwell Town**	**279**	**D 1 - 1**	**Cue 90**		11
9	**FAC 3Qr**	**A**	**Hanwell Town**	**366**	**D 0 - 0**	**(won 4-2 on pens)**		12
13	Isth Prem	A	Wingate & Finchley	225	L 0 - 1		19	13
20	**FAC 4Q**	**A**	**Hitchin Town**	**1278**	**D 1 - 1**	**Gregory 52**	**19**	14
23	**FAC 4Qr**	**H**	**Hitchin Town**	**637**	**L 1 - 2**	**Nnamani 25 (aet)**	**19**	15
27	**FAT 1Q**	**A**	**Folkestone Invicta**	**281**	**L 1 - 5**	**Okojie 79**	**20**	16
Nov 3	Isth Prem	H	Bognor Regis Town	391	D 2 - 2	Okojie 17 Olutade 67	20	17
10	Isth Prem	H	Margate	314	L 0 - 1		21	18
14	Isth Prem	H	Kingstonian	361	W 2 - 1	Gregory 6 Theobalds 51	19	19
17	Isth Prem	H	Enfield Town	407	W 4 - 1	Gregory 6 Wassmer 15 Okojie 17 18	18	20
21	Isth Prem	H	Burgess Hill Town	287	W 3 - 0	Amoo 19 84 Okojie 80	17	21
24	Isth Prem	A	Tonbridge Angels	407	W 2 - 0	Amoo 16 (pen) Theobalds 43	16	22
28	Isth Prem	H	Corinthian-Casuals	271	L 1 - 2	Amoo 19	28	23
Dec 1	Isth Prem	A	Lewes	562	L 0 - 1		14	24
8	Isth Prem	H	Brightlingsea Regent	276	L 0 - 1		15	25
11	Isth Prem	A	Merstham	138	W 2 - 0	Olutade 27 Okojie 77	14	26
15	Isth Prem	A	Harlow Town	167	D 2 - 2	Olutade 6 Okojie 52 (pen)	15	27
22	Isth Prem	H	Folkestone Invicta	431	L 0 - 2		16	28
26	Isth Prem	H	Carshalton Athletic	436	W 1 - 0	Olutade 89	15	29
29	Isth Prem	A	Dorking Wanderers	1529	L 0 - 2		15	30
5	Isth Prem	H	Potters Bar Town	311	W 2 - 1	Gregory 29 Olutade 47	13	31
12	Isth Prem	A	Corinthian-Casuals	404	L 1 - 2	Wallace 7	14	32
19	Isth Prem	H	Worthing	372	W 2 - 1	Olutade 55 Okojie 80	13	33
26	Isth Prem	A	Margate	520	D 1 - 1	Okojie 17	13	34
Feb 2	Isth Prem	H	Wingate & Finchley	271	W 2 - 1	Okoyie 15 Nije 71 (og)	13	35
5	Isth Prem	H	Whitehawk	141	W 2 - 0	Salmon 12 Olutade 54 (pen)	11	36
9	Isth Prem	A	Bishops Stortford	337	W 1 - 0	Olutade 35	10	37
16	Isth Prem	A	Haringay Borough	400	W 3 - 9	Gregory 33 Olutade 48 67	8	38
23	Isth Prem	H	Hornchurch	374	L 1 - 2	Gregory 20	9	39
Mar 2	Isth Prem	H	Merstham	356	L 0 - 1		9	40
9	Isth Prem	A	Burgess Hill Town	407	W 3 - 0	Okojie 48 51 Skinner 57	9	41
16	Isth Prem	H	Folkestone Invicta	355	D 0 - 0		8	42
23	Isth Prem	A	Bognor Rigis Town	549	W 4 - 0	Skinner 23 Hester-Cook 45 Olutade 77 Gregory 87	8	43
30	Isth Prem	A	Enfield Town	403	W 1 - 0	Olutade 23	7	44
Apr 6	Isth Prem	H	Tonbridge Angels	505	W 1 - 0	Gallagher 72	6	45
13	Isth Prem	H	Lewes	381	D 1 - 1	Nnamani 15	6	46
20	Isth Prem	A	Brightlingsea Regent	233	L 0 - 1		7	47
22	Isth Prem	H	Dorking Wanderers	816	L 0 - 3		9	48
27	Isth Prem	A	Kingstonian	350	W 4 - 0	Gregory 57 72 Gallagher 68 Olutade 68	8	49

GOALSCORERS	SG	CSG	Pens	Hat tricks	Total
Okojie	14	3	1		17
Gregory	11	2	1		13
Olutade	12	3	1		13
Amoo	3				4
Cullen	4				4
Benyon	1				2
Gallagher	2				2
Nnamani	2				2
Skinner	2				2
Theobalds	2				2
Cue	1				1
Deakin	1				1
Hester-Cook	1				1
Opponents	1				1
Salmon	1				1
Wallace	1				1
Wassmer	1				1

LEWES MATCH RESULTS 2018-19

Date	Comp	H/A	Opponents	Att:	Result	Goalscorers	Pos	No.
Aug 11	Isth Prem	H	Carshalton Athletic	613	L 0 - 1		15	1
14	Isth Prem	A	Tonbridge	552	D 0 - 0		17	2
18	Isth Prem	A	Dorking Wanderers	453	W 2 - 1	Blewden 39 Lawson 78	13	3
25	**FAC P**	**A**	**Molesey**	**92**	**D 0 - 0**			4
27	Isth Prem	H	Bognor Regis Town	873	D 3 - 3	Field 9 (og) Smith 41 68	13	5
Sept 1	Isth Prem	A	Margate	479	W 1 - 0	Hammond 24	11	6
5	**FAC Pr**	**H**	**Molesey**	**350**	**W 8 - 1**	**Reed 35 Hammond 15 Conlon 55 61 Medlock 44 68 Blewden 78 82**		7
8	**FAC 1Q**	**A**	**Farnborough**	**263**	**D 2 - 2**	**Cotton 49 63**		8
12	**FAC 1Qr**	**H**	**Farnborough**	**397**	**D 1 - 1**	**Smith 38 (won 4-1 on pens)**		9
15	Isth Prem	H	Enfield Town	648	D 2 - 2	Smith 42 Coppola 59	10	10
22	**FAC 2Q**	**A**	**Kings Langley**	**288**	**D 1 - 1**	**Smith 39**		11
26	**FAC 2Qr**	**H**	**Kings Langley**	**361**	**W 2 - 1**	**Lawson 52 Appau 64**		12
29	Isth Prem	A	Wingate & Finchley	151	W 1 - 0	Hammond 58	10	13
Oct 3	Isth Prem	H	Worthing	745	L 3 - 4	Hammond 33 Conlon 43 Day 74	11	14
6	**FAC 3Q**	**A**	**Bath City**	**628**	**L 0 - 3**			15
13	Isth Prem	A	Potters Bar Town	244	L 0 - 1		13	16
16	Isth Prem	A	Hornchurch	187	W 5 - 1	Redwood 3 Brinkhurst 18 Lawson 28 Conlon 71 Smith 8912		17
20	Isth Prem	H	Folkestone Invicta	708	W 2 - 0	Day 76 Darbyshire 81	12	18
23	Isth Prem	A	Whitehawk	612	W 1 - 0	Smith 37 (pen)	12	19
27	**FAT 1Q**	**A**	**Ashford Town**	**101**	**W 2 - 1**	**Lawson 62 Appau 84**		20
31	Isth Prem	H	Harlow Town	430	W 2 - 1	Dome-Bemwin 7 Conlon 48		21
Nov 3	Isth Prem	H	Kingstonian	306	L 1 - 2	Smith 46		22
14	**FAT 2Q**	**H**	**Merthyr Town**	**475**	**W 2 - 0**	**Hammond 13 Blewdon 40**		23
17	Isth Prem	H	Haringey Borough	812	L 0 - 1		7	24
24	**FAT 3Q**	**H**	**Hemel Hempstead Town**	**325**	**D 2 - 2**	**Wilder 78 Smith 89**	8	25
27	**FAT 3Qr**	**A**	**Hemel Hempstead Town**	**137**	**L 2 - 3**	**Karl 43 Kaloczi (og) 70**		26
Dec 1	Isth Prem	A	Leatherhead	502	W 1 - 0	Hammond 4	8	27
5	Isth Prem	H	Corinthian Casuals	252	W 3 - 0	Lawson 28 Pamment 72 Golding 77	4	28
8	Isth Prem	H	Bishop's Stortford	322	W 2 - 1	Hammond 14 Chappell 55	2	29
12	Isth Prem	H	Brightlingsea Regent	354	W 5 - 0	Blewden 14 23 Golding 15 Freeman 42 Smith 45	1	30
19	Isth Prem	A	Merstham	132	L 2 - 3	Hammond 16 Pamment 48	3	31
26	Isth Prem	H	Bognor Regis Town	731	D 2 - 2	Widdrington 11 (og) Pamment 78	4	32
Jan 1	Isth Prem	H	Burgess Hill Town	1100	L 0 - 3			33
5	Isth Prem	H	Enfield Town	434	D 1 - 1	Lawson 12	5	34
12	Isth Prem	A	Worthing	1124	W 4 - 3	Hammond Coppola Blewden Overton	4	35
19	Isth Prem	H	Wingate & Finchley	516	W 4 - 2	Chappell 60 Smith 67 (pen) Overton 82 90	3	36
23	Isth Prem	H	Margate	510	D 0 - 0			37
26	Isth Prem	A	Harlow Town	174	L 1 - 2	Golding 67	3	38
Feb 2	Isth Prem	H	Potters Bar Town	414	D 0 - 0		4	39
16	Isth Prem	H	Dorking Wanderers	689	L 0 - 2		10	40
23	Isth Prem	A	Carshalton Athletic	427	L 1 - 2	Freeman 54	10	41
27	Isth Prem	H	Tonbridge Angels	404	D 0 - 0		10	42
Mar 2	Isth Prem	H	Whitehawk	881	L 1 - 3	Page 10	10	43
5	Isth Prem	A	Corinthian-Casuals	201	W 2 - 0	Pamment 66 Blewden 90	9	44
9	Isth Prem	A	Folkestone Invicta	441	L 0 - 4		11	45
16	Isth Prem	H	Brightlingsea Regent	163	D 0 - 0		11	46
23	Isth Prem	A	Kingstonian	812	W 3 - 0	Coppola 18 Pope 30 67	9	47
30	Isth Prem	A	Haringey Borough	523	L 1 - 2	Pope 21	10	48
Apr 6	Isth Prem	H	Merstham	524	W 2 - 1	Coppola 46 Reid 63	10	49
13	Isth Prem	H	Leatherhead	381	D 1 - 1	Hammond 10	10	50
20	Isth Prem	H	Bishop's Stortford	691	L 1 - 3	Coppola 42	12	51
22	Isth Prem	H	Burgess HIll Town	798	D 1 - 1	Adeyemo 88	11	52
27	Isth Prem	A	Hornchurch	611	D 0 - 0		11	53

GOALSCORERS	SG	CSG	Pens	Hat tricks	Total
Hammond	10	2			11
Smith	10	3	2		11
Blewden	6				8
Coppola	5				6
Lawson	6				6
Conlon	4				5
Pamment	4	2			4
Pope	2				4
Golding	3				3
Opponents	3				3
Overton	2				3
Appau	2				2
Chappell	2				2
Cotton	1				2
Day	2				2
Freeman	2				2
Adeyemo	1				1
Bernwin D	1				1
Brinkhurst	1				1
Darbyshire	1				1
Karl	1				1
Redwood	1				1
Reed	1				1
Widdrington	1				1
Wilder	1				1

MARGATE MATCH RESULTS 2018-19

Date	Comp	H/A	Opponents	Att:	Result	Goalscorers	Pos	No.
Aug 11	Isth Prem	H	Corinthian-Casuals	510	**W** 5 - 2	Aristride 11 Wynter 19 Brown 31 43 Colin 45	1	1
14	Isth Prem	A	Dorking Wanderers	475	L 0 - 2		11	2
18	Isth Prem	A	Brightlingsea Regent	206	**W** 3 - 0	Taylor 12 Collin 30 41	7	3
25	Isth Prem	H	Tonbridge Angels	648	L 0 - 2		9	4
27	Isth Prem	A	Whitehawk	251	D 0 - 0		10	5
Sept 1	Isth Prem	H	Lewes	479	L 0 - 1		13	6
8	**FAC 1Q**	**H**	**Horndean**	**273**	**W 3 - 2**	**Collin 43 Taylor 60 77**		7
15	Isth Prem	A	Worthing	905	**W** 1 - 0	Taylor 67	7	8
22	**FAC 2Q**	**A**	**Concord Rangers**	**219**	**L 0 - 2**			9
29	Isth Prem	H	Haringey Borough	530	L 0 - 1		8	10
Oct 1	Isth Prem	A	Carshalton Athletic	254	**W** 2 - 1	Collin 52 Taylor 89	7	11
6	Isth Prem	H	Harlow Town	450	D 0 - 0		7	12
13	Isth Prem	H	Enfield Town	658	**W** 2 - 1	Taylor 21 75	6	13
20	Isth Prem	A	Bognor Regis Town	551	D 0 - 0		9	14
27	**FAT 1Q**	**H**	**Potters Bar Town**	**154**	**L 1 - 2**	**Taylor 42**	**10**	15
Nov 3	Isth Prem	H	Burgess Hill Town	481	L 2 - 3	Flisher 6 Jones 14 (og)	11	16
10	Isth Prem	A	Leatherhead	314	**W** 1 - 0	Collin 82 (pen)	11	17
14	Isth Prem	A	Merstham	131	D 1 - 1	Friend 70	11	18
17	Isth Prem	A	Kingstonian	334	L 1 - 2	Brown 71	11	19
24	Isth Prem	H	Bishop's Stortford	458	L 1 - 4	Brown 17	12	20
Dec 1	Isth Prem	A	Potters Bar Town	157	**W** 2 - 1	Brown 43 Paxman 59	12	21
8	Isth Prem	H	Wingate & Finchley	431	D 2 - 2	Murphy 25 Swift 59		22
15	Isth Prem	H	Hornchurch	340	D 0 - 0		14	23
22	Isth Prem	H	Whitehawk	617	L 1 - 3	Bentley 64	15	24
Jan 1	Isth Prem	A	Folkestone Invicta	629	L 0 - 1			25
5	Isth Prem	H	Worthing	369	D 1 - 1	Colin 87	17	26
19	Isth Prem	A	Haringey Borougth	275	L 0 - 1		17	27
23	Isth Prem	A	Margate	510	D 0 - 0			28
26	Isth Prem	H	Leatherhead	520	D 1 - 1	Martin 89 (pen)	17	29
Feb 2	Isth Prem	A	Enfield Town	403	L 0 - 4		18	30
5	Isth Prem	H	Dorking Wanderers	312	L 0 - 1		18	31
9	Isth Prem	A	Tonbridge Angels	530	D 1 - 1	Swift 85	17	32
16	Isth Prem	H	Brightlingsea Regent	563	**W** 1 - 0	Swift 18	17	33
23	Isth Prem	A	Corinthian Casuals	337	**W** 3 - 0	Daniel 34 Leighton 39 52	16	34
26	Isth Prem	H	Carshalton Athletic	399	D 1 - 1	Daniel 90	16	35
Mar 2	Isth Prem	A	Hornchurch	273	**W** 2 - 1	Daniel 12 Sho-Silva 60	15	36
9	Isth Prem	H	Bognor Regis Town	503	**W** 1 - 0	Daniel 86	14	37
16	Isth Prem	H	Merstham	430	**W** 1 - 0	Leighton 44	14	38
23	Isth Prem	A	Burgess Hill Town	408	**W** 2 - 0	Smith 12 Toure 55 og	13	39
30	Isth Prem	H	Kingstonian	519	**W** 1 - 0	Leighton 18	13	40
Apr 6	Isth Prem	A	Bishop's Stortford	344	L 1 - 2	Leighton 25	13	41
13	Isth Prem	H	Potters Bat Town	480	L 0 - 2		13	42
20	Isth Prem	A	Wingate & Finchley	158	**W** 1 - 0	Leighton 60	13	43
22	Isth Prem	H	Folkestone Invicta	644	L 0 - 3		13	44
27	Isth Prem	A	Harlow Town	166	**W** 4 - 3	Rogers 33 (pen) SHO-SILVER 3 (47 66 77)	12	45

GOALSCORERS	SG	CSG	Pens	Hat tricks	Total
Taylor	6				8
Collin	6		1		7
Leighton	5				6
Brown	3	3			5
Daniel	4	4			4
Sho-Silva	2			1	4
Swift	3	2			3
Opponents	2				2
Anstride	1				1
Bentley	1				1
Flisher	1				1
Friend	1				1
Martin	1		1		1
Murphy	1				1
Paxman	1				1
Rogers	1		1		1
Smith	1				1
Wynter	1				1

MERSTHAM MATCH RESULTS 2018-19

Date	Comp	H/A	Opponents	Att:	Result	Goalscorers	Pos	No.
Aug 11	Isth Prem	H	Tonbridge	209	L 0 - 3		22	1
14	Isth Prem	A	Bognor Regis Town	502	L 1 - 3	Sow 12	22	2
18	Isth Prem	A	Corinthian-Casuals	201	D 1 - 1	Hall 18	22	3
25	Isth Prem	H	Brightlingsea Regent	106	**W** 1 - 0	Maynard-Abnett 63	16	4
27	Isth Prem	A	Dorking Wanderers	527	D 2 - 2	Saraiva 11 Hall 32	17	5
Sept 1	Isth Prem	H	Potters Bar Town	113	**W** 3 - 1	Kavanagh 59 Bird 88 Samuels 90	12	6
8	**FAC 1Q**	**H**	**Cray Valley**	**125**	**D 0 - 0**			7
12	**FAC 1Qr**	**A**	**Cray Valley**	**148**	**D 3 - 3**	**Davies 15 34 Antonio 88 (Lost 1-4 on pens)**		8
15	Isth Prem	A	Wingate & Finchley	96	L 0 - 2		15	9
29	Isth Prem	H	Carshalton Athletic	251	**W** 2 - 0	Saraiva 86 Figueira 89	12	10
Oct 6	Isth Prem	A	Enfield Town	312	D 0 - 0		10	11
13	Isth Prem	H	Bishop's Stortford	180	D 1 - 1	Figueira 43	10	12
27	**FAT 1Q**	**H**	**East Grinstead Town**	**121**	**W 2 - 0**	**Hutchings 75 Samuels 84**		13
30	Isth Prem	A	Hornchurch	100	D 1 - 1	Smith 87 (og)		14
Nov 3	Isth Prem	A	Harlow Town	132	**W** 4 - 0	Hayden-Smith 12 Figueira 51 Kavanagh 90 (pen) Bird 90		15
10	**FAT 2Q**	**A**	**Salisbury**	**422**	**L 0 - 2**		**10**	16
14	Isth Prem	H	Margate	131	D 1 - 1	Hayden-Smith 35	13	17
17	Isth Prem	A	Burgess Hill Town	399	L 0 - 3		15	18
Dec 1	Isth Prem	A	Folkestone Invicta	318	L 2 - 6	Bird 24 Sow 30	16	19
8	Isth Prem	H	Whitehawk	117	**W** 1 - 0	Beaney 80	14	20
11	Isth Prem	A	Leatherhead	138	L 0 - 2		14	21
15	Isth Prem	H	Potters Bar Town	111	**W** 1 - 0	Figueira 62	12	22
19	Isth Prem	H	Lewes	132	**W** 3 - 2	Cooper 27 Figueira 33 67	11	23
22	Isth Prem	H	Dorking Wanderers	181	**W** 4 - 1	Sow 28 Henriques 31 Figueira 32 Beaney 88	11	24
29	Isth Prem	A	Haringey Borough	333	D 2 - 2	Figueira 31 Beaney 32 (pen)	10	25
Jan 1	Isth Prem	A	Kingstonian	366	D 0 - 0		10	26
5	Isth Prem	A	Wingate & Finchley	152	**W** 3 - 0	Samuels 25 Figueira 36 Michael-Percil 90	9	27
12	Isth Prem	H	Enfield Town	228	**W** 1 - 0	Figueira 15	9	28
19	Isth Prem	A	Carshalton Athletic	403	**W** 2 - 1	Cook 20 Figueira 44	5	29
26	Isth Prem	H	Hornchurch	196	**W** 3 - 0	Osborne 40 Saralva 47 Michael-Percil 75	4	30
30	Isth Prem	H	Worthing	210	**W** 1 - 0	Kershaney 83	3	31
Feb 2	Isth Prem	H	Bishops Stortford	223	L 0 - 2		3	32
5	Isth Prem	H	Bognor Regis Town	196	L 1 - 2	Sow 40	3	33
9	Isth Prem	A	Brightlinsea Regent	231	D 1 - 1	Saraiva 44	5	34
16	Isth Prem	H	Corinthian-Casuals	236	**W** 2 - 1	Cooper 32 Sow 48	4	35
23	Isth Prem	A	Tonbridge Angels	552	**W** 1 - 0	Figueira 39	3	36
Mar 2	Isth Prem	H	Leatherhead	356	**W** 1 - 0	Michael-Percil 90	3	37
9	Isth Prem	A	Haringey Borough	267	D 0 - 0		3	38
16	Isth Prem	A	Marine	430	L 0 - 1		4	39
23	Isth Prem	H	Harlow Town	213	**W** 5 - 0	Sow 3 65 Figueira 29 Cooper 78 Hutchings 85	4	40
30	Isth Prem	H	Burgess Hill Town	210	L 0 - 2		5	41
Apr 6	Isth Prem	H	Lewes	524	L 1 - 2	Figueirs 50	6	42
13	Isth Prem	H	Folkestone Invicta	215	L 1 - 3	Samuels 28	8	43
20	Isth Prem	A	Whitehawk	380	**W** 1 - 0	Sow 6	7	44
22	Isth Prem	H	Kingstonian	276	**W** 2 - 0	Sow 29 Michaelo-Percil	7	45
27	Isth Prem	A	Worthing	932	**W** 4 - 2	Samuels 2 Figueira 3 6 Kavanagh 58 (pen)	5	46
May 2	**PO SF**	**A**	**Carshalton Athletic**	**1151**	**W 2 - 1**	**Figueira 2 Samuels 79**		47
6	**PO F**	**A**	**Tonbridge Angels**	**2268**	**L 0 - 2**			48

GOALSCORERS	SG	CSG	Pens	Hat tricks	Total
Figueira	14	4			17
Sow	8				9
Samuels	6	2			6
Saraiva	4				5
Michael-Percil	4				4
Beaney	3		1		3
Bird	3				3
Cooper	3				3
Kavanagh	3		2		3
Davies	1				2
Hall	2				2
Hayden-Smith	2				2
Hutchings	2				2
Antonio	1				1
Cook	1				1
Henriques	1				1
Kershaney	1				1
Maynard-Abnett	1				1
Opponents	1				1
Osborne	1				1

POTTERS BAR TOWN MATCH RESULTS 2018-19

Date	Comp	H/A	Opponents	Att:	Result		Goalscorers	Pos	No.
Aug 11	Isth Prem	A	Burgess Hill Town	383	W	1 - 0	Wynter 80	3	1
14	Isth Prem	H	Kingstonian	204	W	3 - 0	Cole 26 Casey 32 Nicholas 78	1	2
18	Isth Prem	H	Whitehawk	174	D	1 - 1	Brown 34	3	3
25	**FAC P**	**A**	**Aveley**	**154**	**W**	**2 - 0**	**Wynter 1 Sach 22**		4
27	Isth Prem	H	Haringey Borough	267	D	0 - 0		6	5
Sept 1	Isth Prem	A	Merstham	113	L	1 - 3	Wynter 36	9	6
8	**FAC 1Q**	**A**	**Hanwell Town**	**142**	**L**	**1 - 2**	**Wynter 48**		7
15	Isth Prem	H	Leatherhead	171	L	0 - 1		13	8
18	Isth Prem	H	Worthing	197	D	1 - 1	Sach 60		9
29	Isth Prem	H	Bognor Regis Town	218	D	2 - 2	Casey 11 Cole 44	14	10
Oct 2	Isth Prem	A	Brightlingsea Regent	88	W	1 - 0	Wynter 45	14	11
6	Isth Prem	A	Tonbridge Angels	393	L	1 - 2	Casey 49	12	12
13	Isth Prem	H	Lewes	244	W	1 - 0	Casey 81	7	13
20	Isth Prem	A	Carshalton Athletic	342	L	0 - 1		8	14
23	Isth Prem	H	Bishop Stortford	256	W	4 - 2	Brown 45 Cole 51 (pen) Sach 57 84	7	15
27	**FAT 1Q**	**A**	**Margate**	**154**	**W**	**2 - 1**	**Sach 11 16**		16
Nov 3	Isth Prem	H	Wingate & Finchley	184	W	4 - 0	WYNTER 3 (6 15 35 pen) Sach 88	7	17
6	Isth Prem	A	Dorking Wanderers	230	L	1 - 4	Cole 16	7	18
10	**FAT 2Q**	**A**	**Horsham**	**147**	**L**	**0 - 1**			19
17	Isth Prem	A	Folkestone iNvicta	399	L	0 - 2		10	20
24	Isth Prem	H	Harlow Town	175	L	1 - 2	Lomas 20	13	21
Dec 1	Isth Prem	H	Margate	157	L	1 - 2	Grace 69	15	22
8	Isth Prem	A	Corinthian-Casuals	228	W	2 - 1	A.Morgan-Cummins 69 Wynter 82	13	23
11	Isth Prem	A	Hornchurch	124	W	1 - 0	Sach 56	12	24
15	Isth Prem	H	Merstham	111	L	0 - 1		13	25
22	Isth Prem	A	Haringey Borough	320	L	0 - 1		14	26
29	Isth Prem	H	Enfield Town	504	L	1 - 2	Bonnett-Johnson 6	15	27
Jan 5	Isth Prem	A	Leatherhead	311	L	1 - 2	Wynter 13	16	28
12	Isth Prem	H	Brightlingsea Regent	160	L	0 - 2		17	29
19	Isth Prem	A	Bognor Regis Town	520	D	2 - 2	Ward-Cochrane 64 74	15	30
26	Isth Prem	H	Dorking Wanderers	187	L	0 - 2		17	31
Feb 2	Isth Prem	A	Lewes	414	D	0 - 0		17	32
6	Isth Prem	A	Kingstonian	236	W	2 - 1	Ward-Cochrane 30 57	16	33
9	Isth Prem	H	Worthing	657	D	1 - 1	Bonnett-Johnson 11	16	34
16	Isth Prem	A	Whitehawk	307	L	0 - 1		16	35
23	Isth Prem	H	Burgess Hill Town	185	D	0 - 0		16	36
Mar 2	Isth Prem	A	Bishop's Stortford	274	W	2 - 1	Grace 10 Hutchinson 52	16	37
9	Isth Prem	H	Carshalton Town	181	L	0 - 1		16	38
16	Isth Prem	H	Hornchurch	212	L	0 - 1		17	39
23	Isth Prem	A	Wingate & Finchley	152	L	2 - 4	Wynter 27 Sach 78	18	40
30	Isth Prem	H	Folkestone Invicta	192	D	2 - 2	Kyei 45 Sach 80	18	41
Apr 6	Isth Prem	A	Harlow Town	224	W	5 - 2	Wynter 13 72 (pen) Sach 18 22 Kyei 20	16	42
13	Isth Prem	A	Margate	480	W	2 - 0	Wynter 24 Hutchinson 84	15	43
20	Isth Prem	H	Corinthian Casuals	221	D	2 - 2	Wynter 47 Sach 50	15	44
22	Isth Prem	A	Enfield Town	362	L	1 - 3	Hutchinson 33	16	45
27	Isth Prem	H	Tonbridge Angels	315	W	2 - 1	M. Morgan 32 Kyei 52	16	46

GOALSCORERS	SG	CSG	Pens	Hat tricks	Total
Wynter	12	2	2	1	15
Sach	7				9
Casey	4				4
Cole	4		1		4
Sach	3				4
W-Cochrane	2				4
Hutchinson	3				3
Kyei	3				3
B-Johnson	2				2
Brown	2				2
Grace	2				2
Lomas	1				1
M-Cummins	1				1
Morgan	1				1
Nicholas	1				1

TONBRIDGE ANGELS MATCH RESULTS 2018-19

Date	Comp	H/A	Opponents	Att:	Result		Goalscorers	Pos	No.
Aug 11	Isth Prem	A	Merstham	209	W	3 - 0	Small 15 Jones 37 (og) Read 49	3	1
14	Isth Prem	H	Lewes	552	D	0 - 0		5	2
18	Isth Prem	H	Burgess Hill Town	409	W	1 - 0	Turner 26	4	3
25	Isth Prem	A	Margate	648	W	2 - 0	Beere 27 Read 49	2	4
27	Isth Prem	A	Folkeston Invicta	548	W	1 - 0	Read 14	1	5
Sept 1	Isth Prem	H	Wingate & Finchley	632	W	2 - 1	Parkinson 33 Miles 38	1	6
8	**FAC 1Q**	**A**	**Hythe Town**	**502**	**W**	**2 - 0**	**Read 7 81**		7
15	Isth Prem	A	Brighlingsea Regent	196	W	2 - 0	Read 32 Small 89	1	8
22	**FAC 2Q**	**A**	**Dulwich Hamlet**	**561**	**L**	**1 - 3**	**Miles 53**		9
29	Isth Prem	H	Bishop's Stortford	517	L	2 - 3	Ramadan 72 Lee 88	1	10
Oct 6	Isth Prem	H	Potters Bar Town	393	W	2 - 1	Parkinson 47 Turner 72	1	11
13	Isth Prem	H	Bognor Regis Town	814	L	1 - 2	Read 67	1	12
20	Isth Prem	A	Hornchurch	279	W	2 - 0	Read 45 (pen) 90	1	13
23	Isth Prem	H	Enfield Town	49	L	1 - 2	Turner 90	1	14
27	**FAT 1Q**	**H**	**Whyteleafe**	**380**	**W**	**2 - 1**	**Read 81 Turner 90 (pen)**		15
Nov 3	Isth Prem	H	Whitehawk	508	W	2 - 0	Turner 90 Drage 78 (og)	1	16
7	Isth Prem	A	Kingstonian	290	D	1 - 1	King 86	1	17
10	**FAT 2Q**	**A**	**Dorking Wanderers**	**330**	**L**	**0 - 1**			18
12	Isth Prem	A	Haringey Borough	260	L	0 - 4		2	19
17	Isth Prem	A	Harlow Town	277	L	0 - 1		2	20
24	Isth Prem	H	Leatherhead	407	L	0 - 2		2	21
Dec 1	Isth Prem	A	Dorking Wanderers	428	W	1 - 0	Read 90	2	22
8	Isth Prem	H	Worthing	440	L	1 - 2	Turner 43	3	23
11	Isth Prem	A	Corinthian-Casuals	173	L	1 - 2	Turner 49	3	24
26	Isth Prem	H	Folkestone Invicta	606	L	1 - 3	Murphy 45	5	25
29	Isth Prem	A	Carshalton Athletic	410	L	0 - 3		8	26
Jan 5	Isth Prem	H	Brightlingsea Regent	358	D	2 - 2	Parkinson 76 Read 64	11	27
12	Isth Prem	H	Kingstonian	433	W	3 - 2	Read 10 Turner 27 McKenzie 71	10	28
19	Isth Prem	A	Bishop's Stortford	280	W	4 - 3	Turner 9 50 McKenzie 47 69	8	29
26	Isth Prem	H	Haringey Borough	520	W	1 - 0	Ramadan 90	8	30
Feb 2	Isth Prem	A	Bognor Regis Town	559	W	3 - 2	Parter 1 Read 29 Turner 55 (pen)	8	31
9	Isth Prem	H	Margate	530	D	1 - 1	McKenzie 27 (pen)	9	32
13	Isth Prem	A	Wingate & Finchley	101	W	2 - 1	Turner 70 (pen) Small 86	4	33
16	Isth Prem	A	Burgess Hill Town	417	W	4 - 0	Turner 7 Derry 17 26 McKenzue 33	3	34
23	Isth Prem	H	Merstham	552	L	0 - 1		5	35
27	Isth Prem	A	Lewes	404	D	0 - 0		4	36
Mar 2	Isth Prem	A	Enfield Town	401	D	0 - 0		4	37
9	Isth Prem	H	Hornchurch	509	W	1 - 0	Derry 852	4	38
16	Isth Prem	H	Corinthian Casuals	391	W	2 - 0	McKenzie 10 Turner 85 (pen)	3	39
23	Isth Prem	A	Whitehawk	346	W	4 - 0	Miles 46 Mackenzie 66 Derry 77 90	3	40
30	Isth Prem	H	Harlow Town	632	W	3 - 1	McKENZIE 3 (12 54 79)	3	41
Apr 6	Isth Prem	A	Leatherhead	505	L	0 - 1		3	42
13	Isth Prem	H	Dorking Wanderers	825	L	0 - 2		3	43
19	Isth Prem	A	Worthing	1822	D	1 - 1	Turner 63	4	44
22	Isth Prem	H	Carshalton Athletic	861	W	1 - 0	Stone 79	4	45
27	Isth Prem	A	Potters Bar Town	3154	L	1 - 2	Miles 66	4	46
May 2	**PO SF**	**A**	**Haringey Borough**	**810**	**W**	**2 - 1**	**Ramadan 34 McKenzie 43**		47
6	**PO F**	**H**	**Merstham**	**2268**	**W**	**2 - 0**	**McKenzie 34 Turner 90 (pen)**		48
11	**PO F SPO**	**A**	**Metropolitan Police**	**1260**	**W**	**3 - 2**	**Lee 52 Theobalds 86 Derry 97 (aet)**		49

GOALSCORERS	SG	CSG	Pens	Hat tricks	Total
Turner	15	3	5		16
Read	12	2	1		14
McKenzie	9	3	1	1	12
Derry	5				6
Miles	4				4
Parkinson	3				3
Ramadan	3				3
Smith	2				3
Lee	2				2
Opponents					2
Beere	1				1
King	1				1
Murphy	1				1
Parter	1				1
Stone	1				1
Theobalds	1				1

WHITEHAWK MATCH RESULTS 2018-19

Date	Comp	H/A	Opponents	Att:	Result	Goalscorers	Pos	No.
Aug 11	Isth Prem	H	Harlow Town	300	W 4 - 2	Williams 4 Rodrigues 21 33 Marsh-Brown 39	4	1
15	Isth Prem	A	Leatherhead	376	D 1 - 1	O'Neill 16	7	2
18	Isth Prem	A	Potters Bar Town	174	D 1 - 1	Shooman 39	9	3
25	Isth Prem	H	Wingate & Finchley	277	L 2 - 3	Williams 28 Emberson 89	11	4
27	Isth Prem	H	Margate	251	D 0 - 0		11	5
Sept 1	Isth Prem	A	Burgess Hill Town	428	W 4 - 2	O'Neill 6 Rodrigues 45 Fraser 52 Muggeridge 59	6	6
8	**FAC 1Q**	**A**	**Pagham**	**212**	**W 2 - 0**	**Fraser 49 Mutongerwa 80**		7
15	Isth Prem	H	Haringey Borough	335	L 1 - 3	Fraser 9	9	8
22	**FAC 2Q**	**A**	**East Thurrock United**	**154**	**W 3 - 2**	**Williams 13 78 Muggeridge 67**		9
29	Isth Prem	H	Kingstonian	404	D 1 - 1	Hallard 85	12	10
Oct 2	Isth Prem	A	Dorking Wanderers	305	L 1 - 2	Hallard 19	13	11
6	**FAC 3Q**	**A**	**Billericay Town**	**609**	**L 1 - 9**	**Williams 89**		12
9	Isth Prem	A	Corinthian-Casuals	183	L 0 - 2			13
13	Isth Prem	H	Brightlingsea Regent	565	W 1 - 0	Marsh-Brown 34	15	14
20	Isth Prem	A	Enfield Town	403	L 0 - 6		17	15
23	Isth Prem	H	Lewes	612	L 0 - 1		19	16
27	**FAT 1Q**	**H**	**Harlow Town**	**161**	**L 2 - 3**	**Sisimayi Sanders**		17
Nov 3	Isth Prem	A	Tonbridge Angels	508	L 0 - 2		19	18
12	Isth Prem	A	Carshalton Athletic	176	L 0 - 2			19
17	Isth Prem	H	Bishop's Stortford	235	L 2 - 4	Pinney 81 83	21	20
24	Isth Prem	H	Folkestone Invicta	110	D 0 - 0		21	21
Dec 1	Isth Prem	H	Hornchurch	197	D 1 - 1	Rodrigues 24	22	22
8	Isth Prem	A	Merstham	112	L 0 - 1		22	23
22	Isth Prem	A	Margate	817	W 3 - 1	Goode 45 Williams 58 74	22	24
Jan 1	Isth Prem	H	Bognor Regis Town	400	L 1 - 4	Pinney 90	22	25
5	Isth Prem	A	Haringey Borough	336	L 0 - 3		22	26
8	Isth Prem	H	Worthing	273	L ! - 2	Williams	22	27
12	Isth Prem	H	Dorking Wanderers	221	D 1 - 1	Pinney 65	22	28
19	Isth Prem	A	Kingstonian	275	W 3 - 1	Rodrigues 27 Muggeridge 30 Christie 37	22	29
26	Isth Prem	H	Carshalton Athletic	184	D 2 - 2	Pinney 62 Christie 90	22	30
Feb 2	Isth Prem	A	Brightlingsea Regent	159	L 0 - 3		22	31
5	Isth Prem	H	Leatherhead	141	L 0 - 2		22	32
9	Isth Prem	A	Wingate & Finchley	151	D 1 - 1	Ovendon 51	22	33
16	Isth Prem	H	Potters Bar Town	307	W 1 - 0	Rodrigues 83	21	34
19	Isth Prem	H	Burgess Hill Town	301	W 4 - 1	Pinney 13 (pen) 25 Muggeridge 32 Rodrigues 51	21	35
23	Isth Prem	A	Harlow Town	308	W 3 - 0	Pinney 62 Tighe 70 74	19	36
Mar 2	Isth Prem	A	Lewes	881	W 3 - 1	Marsh -Brown20 Ofon-Acheampong 82 Muggeridge 90	19	37
9	Isth Prem	H	Enfield Town	325	L 1 - 3	Ofon-Acheampong 37	19	38
16	Isth Prem	A	Worthing	1030	L 0 - 2		20	39
23	Isth Prem	H	Tonbridge Angels	346	L 0 - 4		20	40
30	Isth Prem	A	Bishop's Stortford	357	L 0 - 1		20	41
Apr 6	Isth Prem	A	Folkeston Invicta	415	L 1 - 2	Ofon-Acheampong 48	20	42
13	Isth Prem	A	Hornchurch	228	W 2 - 1	Rodrigues 45 Walsh 60	20	43
20	Isth Prem	H	Merstham	380	L 0 - 1		20	44
22	Isth Prem	A	Bognor Regis Town	467	D 0 - 0		20	45
27	Isth Prem	H	Corinthian Casuals	401	W 4 - 0	MUGGERIDGE 3 (33 35 90 pen) Pinney 90	20	46

GOALSCORERS	SG	CSG	Pens	Hat tricks	Total
Muggeridge	6		1	1	8
Pinney	6		1		8
Rodrigues	6				8
Williams	6				8
Fraser	3	3			3
Marsh-Brown	3				3
Ofon-Acheampong	3				3
Christie	2	2			2
Hallard	2				2
O'Neill	2				2
Tighe	1				2
Dida	1				1
Emberson	1				1
Goode	1				1
Mutongerwa	1				1
Ovendon	1				1
Sanders	1				1
Shooman	1				1
Sismayi	1				1
Walsh	1				1

WINGATE & FINCHLEY MATCH RESULTS 2018-19

Date	Comp	H/A	Opponents	Att:	Result		Goalscorers	Pos	No.
Aug 11	Isth Prem	A	Worthing	755	L	1 - 2	Cronin 34 (pen)	16	1
14	Isth Prem	H	Hornchurch	142	D	1 - 1	Charles- Smith 53	15	2
18	Isth Prem	H	Folkeston Invicta	95	L	0 - 3		20	3
25	Isth Prem	A	Whitehawk	277	W	3 - 2	Weatherstone 37 (pen) 45 (pen) Charles-Smith 83	15	4
27	Isth Prem	H	Enfield	320	D	1 - 1	Charles-Smith 24	15	5
Sept 1	Isth Prem	A	Tonbridge Angels	632	L	1 - 2	Tejan-Sie 45	16	6
8	**FAC 1Q**	**H**	**Didcot Town**	**118**	**L**	**1 - 2**	**Cronin 88 (pen)**		7
15	Isth Prem	H	Merstham	96	W	2 - 0	Cronin 44 (pen) Weatherstone 68	14	8
29	Isth Prem	H	Lewes	151	L	0 - 1		16	9
Oct 2	Isth Prem	A	Bishop's Stortford	236	L	2 - 3	Weatherstone O'Neill	18	10
13	Isth Prem	H	Leatherhead	225	W	1 - 0	Charles-Smith 18	14	11
16	Isth Prem	A	Burgess Hill Town	405	W	1 - 0	Beckles-Richards 50	13	12
20	Isth Prem	A	Dorking Wanderers	429	L	0 - 3		14	13
27	**FAT 1Q**	**A**	**Sittingbourne**	**155**	**W**	**2 - 1**	**Beccles-Richards 35 65**		14
Nov 3	Isth Prem	A	Potters Bar Town	184	L	0 - 4		15	15
10	**FAT 2Q**	**A**	**Tiverton Town**	**162**	**W**	**3 - 2**	**Weatherstone Cole (o,g)**		16
13	Isth Prem	A	Brightlingsea Regent	112	W	1 - 0	Cole 45		17
17	Isth Prem	A	Bognor Regis Town	556	L	2 - 4	Cole 7 Laney 51	17	18
20	Isth Prem	H	Kingstonian	103	L	0 - 4		17	19
24	**FAT 3Q**	**A**	**Chippenham Town**	**280**	**D**	**1 - 1**	**Parselle 51**		20
27	**FAT 3Qr**	**H**	**Chippenham Town**	**350**	**W**	**3 - 2**	**Laney Beckles Ifil**		21
Dec 1	Isth Prem	H	Corinthian Casuals	133	W	2 - 0	Cronin 9 Mitchell 50	17	22
8	Isth Prem	A	Margate	431	D	2 - 2	Laney 8 Hermandez 90	18	23
11	Isth Prem	H	Harlow Town	88	L	0 - 2		19	24
15	**FAT 1**	**H**	**Dulwich Hamlet**	**202**	**W**	**2 - 0**	**Laney 27 60**		25
22	Isth Prem	H	Carshalton Athletic	89	W	2 - 0	Manu 38 62 (pen)	18	26
26	Isth Prem	A	Enfield	444	L	1 - 4	Manu 49	18	27
Jan 1st	Isth Prem	H	Haringey Borough	266	L	0 - 4		19	28
5	Isth Prem	A	Merstham	152	L	0 - 3		20	29
12	**FAT 2**	**A**	**Hemel Hempstead Town**	**454**	**L**	**2 - 4**	**Cronin 55 57 (pen)**	**20**	30
19	Isth Prem	A	Lewes	518	L	2 - 4	Rifat 11 Hammond 58 (og)	20	31
26	Isth Prem	H	Brightlingsea Regent	112	D	2 - 2	Cole 42 Cronin 90 (pen)	20	32
Feb 2	Isth Prem	A	Leatherhead	271	L	1 - 2	Cole 31	20	33
9	Isth Prem	H	Whitehawk	151	D	1 - 1	Njie 90	20	34
13	Isth Prem	H	Tonbridge Angels	101	L	1 - 2	Beckles-Richards 17	20	35
16	Isth Prem	A	Folkestone Invicta	537	D	2 - 2	Mendy 90 Njie 90	20	36
19	Isth Prem	H	Bishop's Stortford	139	D	2 - 2	Rapai 13 Cronon 20 (pen)	20	37
23	Isth Prem	H	Worthing	191	L	1 - 2	Rapai 63	21	38
Mar 2	Isth Prem	A	Kingstonian	303	W	2 - 1	Cole 12 Abrahams 75	20	39
5	Isth Prem	A	Hornchurch	141	L	0 - 3		21	40
9	Isth Prem	H	Dorking Wanderers	151	L	1 - 2	Abrahams 42	21	41
16	Isth Prem	A	Harlow Town	149	W	7 - 2	CRONIN 3 (7 17 87) Mendy19 21Beckles 33 Cole 67	20	42
23	Isth Prem	H	Potters Bar Town	152	W	4 - 2	Makoma 8 Cronin 14 (pen) Mendy 78 Ruff 85	19	43
30	Isth Prem	H	Bognor Regis Town	126	L	0 - 2		19	44
Apr 6	Isth Prem	A	Carshalton Athletic	497	L	1 - 5	Mendy 65	20	45
13	Isth Prem	A	Corinthian-Casuals	240	L	1 - 3	Mendy 72	20	46
20	Isth Prem	H	Margate	158	L	0 - 1		20	47
22	Isth Prem	A	Haringey Borough	614	W	2 - 1	Njie 52 Mendy 63	20	48
27	Isth Prem	H	Burgess Hill Town	177	W	4 - 2	Mendy 14 45 Ruff 81 Ifil 85	19	49

GOALSCORERS	SG	CSG	Pens	Hat tricks	Total
Cronin	9	2	6	1	12
Mendy	8	2			9
Cole	8				8
Beckles-Richards	4				5
Laney	4				5
Charles-Smith	4				4
Weatherstone	3		2		4
Manu	2		1		3
Njie	3				3
Abrahams	2				2
Ifil	2				2
Opponents	2				2
Rapai	2				2
Ruff	2				2
Beckles	1				1
Hernandez	1				1
Makoma	1				1
Mitchell	1				1
O'Neill	1				1
Parselle	1				1
Rifat	1				1
Tejan-Sie	1				1

WORTHING MATCH RESULTS 2018-19

Date	Comp	H/A	Opponents	Att:	Result	Goalscorers	Pos	No.
Aug 11	Isth Prem	H	Wingate & Finchley	755	W 2 - 1	Kealy 39 56	7	1
13	Isth Prem	A	Carshalton Athletic	341	W 2 - 1	Ajiboye 70 71	3	2
18	Isth Prem	A	Harlow Town	220	W 2 - 0	Aguiar 24 Ajiboye 90	1	3
27	Isth Prem	H	Burgess Hill Town	1189	D 0 - 0		4	4
Sept 1	Isth Prem	A	Haringey Borough	290	W 2 - 1	Parsons 28 Ajiboye 48	2	5
8	**FAC 1Q**	**A**	**Faversham Town**	**264**	**W 3 - 1**	**Budd 26 Ajiboye 52 Crane 71**		**6**
15	Isth Prem	A	Margate	905	L 0 - 1		5	7
18	Isth Prem	A	Potters Bar Town	197	D 1 - 1	Colbran 74	5	8
22	**FAC 2Q**	**A**	**Chelmsford City**	**563**	**W 2 - 1**	**Crane 20 76**		**9**
29	Isth Prem	H	Leatherhead	906	D 1 - 1	Kealy 88	3	10
Oct 3	Isth Prem	A	Lewes	745	W 4 - 3	Crane 21 Parsons 57 Pearce 85 Clarke 90	2	11
6	**FAC 3Q**	**A**	**Moneyfields**	**256**	**W 3 - 2**	**Racine 33 Ajiboye 63 (pen) Pearce 66**		**12**
13	Isth Prem	H	Kingstonian	1320	W 3 - 1	Kealy 31 Ajiboye 76 Parsons 90	5	13
20	**FAC 4Q**	**A**	**Ebbsfleet United**	**1011**	**L 0 - 4**		6	**14**
27	**FAT 1Q**	**A**	**Burgess Hill Town**	**459**	**D 1 - 1**	**Pearce 36**		**15**
30	**FAT 1Qr**	**H**	**Burgess Hill Town**	**408**	**W 2 - 1**	**Rents 3 Pearce 33**		**16**
Nov 3	Isth Prem	H	Folkestone Invicta	951	W 3 - 2	Rents 24 Davies 84 (og) Myles-Meekums 88	4	17
10	**FAT 2Q**	**H**	**Chesham United**	**802**	**W 1 - 0**	**Ajiboye 18**		**18**
13	Isth Prem	A	Enfield	333	W 4 - 1	Starkey 39 Ajiboye 62 81 Newton 77	3	19
17	Isth Prem	H	Hornchurch	235	D 1 - 1	Kealy 81	3	20
24	**FAT 3Q**	**A**	**Bedford Town**	**306**	**L `1 - 2**	**Rance 25**		**21**
Dec 1	Isth Prem	A	Bishop's Stortford	848	L 1 - 2	Rents 85	5	22
8	Isth Prem	H	Tonbridge Angels	440	W 2 - 1	Crane 11 (pen) Kealy 72	5	23
15	Isth Prem	A	Haringey Borough	502	L 0 - 3		6	24
22 Dec	Isth Prem	H	Bognor Regis Town	1852	L 0 - 2			25
26	Isth Prem	A	Burgess Hill Town	539	L 1 - 2	Ajiboye 31	7	26
29	Isth Prem	A	Corinthian-Casuals	745	W 2 - 0	Pearce 60 Strabange (og) 85	7	27
Jan 5	Isth Prem	H	Margate	369	D 1 - 1	Ajiboye 55	8	28
8	Isth Prem	A	Whitehawk	273	W 2 - 1	Jones 43 Pearce 82	5	29
12	Isth Prem	A	Lewes	1124	L 3 - 4	Pearce 34 90 (pen) Jones 71	8	30
15	Isth Prem	H	Dorking	603	L 1 - 4	Kealy 25	8	31
19	Isth Prem	H	Leatherhead	372	L 1 - 2	Newton 22	9	32
22	Isth Prem	A	Brightlingsea Regent	189	W 2 - 0	Pearce 9 Jones 66		33
26	Isth Prem	A	Enfield	143	L 0 - 3		9	34
30	Isth Prem	A	Merstham	210	L 0 - 1			35
Feb 2	Isth Prem	A	Kingstonian	279	W 3 - 2	Clarke 52 Newton 57 Pearce 68	7	36
5	Isth Prem	H	Carshalton Athletic	385	D 3 - 3	Aguiar 45 Gould 62 Jones 90	8	37
9	Isth Prem	H	Potters Bar Town	557	D 1 - 1	Jones 90	8	38
16	Isth Prem	H	Harlow Town	716	W 9 - 1	PEARCE 4 (36 43 54 81) Starkey 29 Clarke 57 Adubofour-Poku 66 Pattenden 85 Kealy 90	6	39
23	Isth Prem	A	Wingate & Finchley	191	W 2 - 1	Ajiboye 66 83	5	40
Mar 2	Isth Prem	A	Bognor Regis Town	1137	D 2 - 2	Crane 74 (pen) Starkey 90	5	41
9	Isth Prem	A	Brightlingsea Regent	788	D 1 - 1	Ajiboye 34 (pen)	6	42
16	Isth Prem	H	Whitehawk	1030	W 2 - 0	Ajiboye 5 (pen) Kealy 50	5	43
23	Isth Prem	A	Folkestone Invicta	578	W 1 - 0	Kealy 88	5	44
30	Isth Prem	H	Hornchurch	804	W 3 - 1	Adubofour-Poku 1 Ajiboye 17 (pen) Kealy 84	4	45
Apr 6	Isth Prem	A	Dorking Wanderers	1023	L 0 - 3		5	46
13	Isth Prem	A	Bishop's Stortford	308	L 0 - 3		5	47
19	Isth Prem	H	Tonbridge Angels	1322	D 1 - 1	Ajiboye 80	6	48
22	Isth Prem	H	Corinthian-Casuals	466	D 1 - 1	Clarke 87	7	49
27	Isth Prem	H	Merstham	932	L 2 - 4	Pearce 35 Starkey 68	9	50

GOALSCORERS	SG	CSG	Pens	Hat tricks	Total
Ajiboye	15	2	3		18
Pearce	11	2	1	1	15
Kealy	11	2			11
Crane	5				6
Jones	5				5
Clarke	4				4
Starkey	4				4
Newton	3				3
Parsons	3				3
Rents	3				3

	SG	CSG	Pens	Hat tricks	Total
Adubofour-Poku	2				2
Aguiar	2				2
Opponents	2				2
Budd	1				1
Colbran	1				1
Gould	1				1
Myles-Meekums	1				1
Pattenden	1				1
Racine	1				1
Rance	1				1

ISTHMIAN PREMIER STATISTICS 2018-19

CLUB	SG	CSG	FS	CFS	CS	CCS	PS	PC	TGC	TG
AFC Hornchurch	35	12	12	2	12	2	0	5	63	67
Bishop's Stortford	36	11	9	2	11	2	3	5	61	73
Bognor Regis Town	36	14	12	3	10	2	9	4	72	83
Brightlingsea Rovers	33	7	17	4	14	3	3	6	67	61
Burgess Hill Town	25	4	21	4	8	2	2	6	97	47
Carshalton Athletic	43	16	8	2	15	3	3	1	60	88
Corinthian-Casuals	32	5	16	2	10	2	2	7	62	56
Dorking Wanderers	44	16	6	2	26	7	8	0	43	102
Enfield Town	32	7	12	3	8	2	4	1	61	78
Folkestone Invicta	33	6	13	2	16	3*	5	1	62	85
Haringey Borough	41	15	9	2	17	2	12	4	62	86
Harlow Town	35	10	11	4	5	2	6	6	115	59
Kingstonian	34	17	11	2	7	2	3	1	84	64
Leatherhead	37	10	12	2	16	5	4	3	60	68
Lewes	39	10	14	2	17	2	2	4	68	83
Margate	29	10	16	3	15	4	3	3	54	49
Merstham	34	12	12	2	19	3	3	2	53	65
Potters Bar Town	32	7*	14	2	4	2	0	3	60	56
Tonbridge Angels	35	15	11	4	18	5	6	2	51	64
Whitehawk	30	16	16	3	8	2	2	9	84	58
Wingate & Finchley	38	10	11	2	7	2	10	6	98	71
Worthing	41	10	9	2	7	2	7	5	76	85

SG - Scoring Games; CSG - Consec Scoring Games; FS - Failure to Score; CFS - Consec Failure to Score; CS - Clean Sheets
CCS - Consec Clean Sheets; PS - Penalties Scored; PC - Pens Conceded; TGC - Total Goals Conceded; TG - Total Goals

CLUB GOAL SCORERS IN SEASON 2018-2019

Brandon Goodship enjoyed a great season as the seven senior non-league competitions' top scorer, helping champions Weymouth to promotion, with 38 goals scored in their League, FA Cup and FA Trophy matches.
Weymouth only failed to score in two of their 52 fixtures and their leading marksman, having claimed a hat trick in the first match of the season, continued to register in 23 more fixtures and celebrated 4 more hat tricks during a wonderful season.
Goodship was backed up at Weymouth by Ben Thomson (15 goals) and Calvin Brooks (10) and the Southern League Premier Division South champions finished the season with 110 goals.

Our individual scoring records for players with at least 10 goals in the 2018-2019 season show:--

60 players scored	10 goals	with a total of 600
48	11	528
32	12	384
22	13	286
19	14	266
17	15	255
17	16	272
16	17	272
13	18	234
9	19	171
37	20-29	844
10	30+	326

300 players with 10 + totals have scored 4,638 goals within the seven senior football competitions below The Football League.

Go to page 260 to see a list of those that scored 20 or more during the 2018-19 season.

NORTHERN PREMIER LEAGUE
PREMIER DIVISION TABLE 2018-19

		P	W	D	L	F	A	GD	Pts
1	Farsley Celtic	40	28	6	6	82	40	42	90
2	South Shields	40	27	6	7	86	41	45	87
3	Warrington Town (PO winners)	40	25	9	6	69	33	36	84
4	Nantwich Town	40	19	12	9	70	59	11	69
5	Buxton	40	18	12	10	60	45	15	66
6	Gainsborough Trinity	40	19	8	13	53	41	12	65
7	Basford United	40	18	7	15	82	67	15	61
8	Scarborough Athletic	40	18	7	15	70	56	14	61
9	Witton Albion	40	16	10	14	45	41	4	58
10	Hyde United	40	15	8	17	58	53	5	53
11	Whitby Town	40	15	4	21	48	59	-11	49
12	Lancaster City	40	12	13	15	42	61	-19	49
13	Hednesford Town	40	13	9	18	51	63	-12	48
14	Stafford Rangers	40	11	14	15	62	70	-8	47
15	Matlock Town	40	12	8	20	58	79	-21	44
16	Bamber Bridge	40	10	12	18	62	67	-5	42
17	Stalybridge Celtic	40	11	9	20	46	62	-16	42
18	Grantham Town	40	12	6	22	39	72	-33	42
19	Mickleover Sports	40	10	11	19	37	61	-24	41
20	Marine	40	10	10	20	39	54	-15	40
21	Workington	40	8	5	27	38	73	-35	29

North Ferriby United folded - record expunged.

	PREMIER DIVISION	1	2	3	4	5	6	7	8	9	10	11	12	13	14	15	16	17	18	19	20	21
1	Bamber Bridge		0-4	2-2	0-3	1-2	3-1	1-1	5-2	2-2	1-2	4-2	1-2	2-2	2-4	0-2	6-1	3-0	0-0	1-3	2-0	3-2
2	Basford United	1-0		2-0	4-3	0-1	3-1	1-2	3-8	3-1	0-0	6-0	2-1	7-3	3-1	0-3	2-2	5-2	2-3	2-0	3-1	3-2
3	Buxton	0-1	1-0		1-2	1-0	1-0	1-2	1-0	1-2	0-3	2-2	5-0	2-1	1-0	2-0	4-1	1-1	2-2	2-0	0-5	3-2
4	Farsley Celtic	3-2	2-0	1-1		1-1	1-1	1-2	1-1	2-0	2-0	3-2	1-0	2-1	3-1	4-1	2-1	2-1	3-3	3-1	0-1	2-0
5	Gainsborough Trinity	2-1	3-2	1-2	0-5		2-3	0-0	1-0	3-1	0-1	4-2	2-0	0-0	0-1	0-1	1-1	1-0	1-4	4-1	1-1	4-1
6	Grantham Town	1-1	2-1	0-1	0-4	0-2		1-2	1-0	0-2	1-1	2-0	2-1	2-3	1-0	2-1	0-5	0-1	0-2	3-2	1-0	0-2
7	Hednesford Town	1-1	3-1	1-1	0-1	1-2	2-1		1-0	0-1	0-1	2-0	1-1	4-4	0-1	2-1	1-3	1-0	1-0	1-2	0-1	2-0
8	Hyde United	0-2	1-0	1-1	1-2	1-3	3-0	2-0		1-2	1-2	1-2	2-1	1-2	2-3	4-1	5-3	1-0	0-2	3-0	1-0	0-0
9	Lancaster City	1-1	1-1	1-3	2-0	0-1	1-1	2-2	2-1		0-1	1-0	2-2	0-2	0-6	1-1	0-0	1-0	1-3	2-1	1-0	0-2
10	Marine	0-2	1-4	1-1	1-2	1-1	0-2	3-1	0-0	3-1		1-3	3-0	0-1	1-2	1-3	1-0	1-1	0-2	0-0	2-3	0-2
11	Matlock Town	2-1	2-2	0-6	1-2	0-2	7-0	3-3	0-0	4-0	3-1		1-1	0-1	0-0	0-3	3-2	3-1	0-2	0-3	1-2	2-1
12	Mickleover Sports	2-2	0-1	1-3	1-2	0-1	1-3	1-0	0-2	1-1	1-0	0-0		0-0	1-1	1-3	3-2	2-1	1-4	0-1	0-0	1-0
13	Nantwich Town	2-0	3-2	0-0	2-1	1-0	1-1	2-1	1-1	5-2	3-2	1-4	2-3		1-1	0-0	0-1	4-2	2-1	4-1	0-1	0-0
14	Scarborough Athletic	0-0	3-1	4-0	1-3	0-2	2-0	5-3	0-2	1-1	2-0	2-2	0-2	2-3		1-3	4-1	1-2	1-0	1-1	2-0	5-1
15	South Shields	3-3	1-1	1-1	1-0	1-0	5-0	4-1	4-0	2-0	2-1	5-0	3-2	4-0	3-2		3-0	3-2	1-2	5-2	2-1	4-1
16	Stafford Rangers	1-0	3-1	0-1	1-3	1-1	1-1	4-1	1-3	1-1	0-0	4-1	1-1	1-4	1-3	1-1		2-0	1-1	3-3	3-1	1-1
17	Stalybridge Celtic	3-2	0-2	1-1	2-2	2-1	1-0	1-0	2-2	1-2	3-2	3-1	0-0	1-1	2-3	0-1	2-2		1-2	0-1	0-2	1-0
18	Warrington Town	2-0	1-1	2-1	0-2	2-1	3-0	3-1	2-1	1-1	1-0	0-1	1-0	3-3	2-0	3-0	2-3	0-0		1-0	0-0	2-0
19	Whitby Town	2-1	4-1	1-0	0-2	1-0	2-1	1-2	0-1	1-1	2-1	1-3	4-0	0-1	2-0	0-1	1-2	2-1	0-1		0-1	0-1
20	Witton Albion	2-2	2-2	0-3	2-3	0-0	1-0	1-1	1-1	1-0	0-0	1-0	1-2	2-0	2-1	0-1	1-1	1-3	1-2	2-0		2-0
21	Workington	2-1	0-3	1-1	0-1	0-2	1-4	4-2	1-2	0-2	1-1	3-1	0-1	2-4	2-3	0-2	1-0	1-2	0-2	1-2	0-2	

NORTHERN PREMIER LEAGUE
DIVISION EAST TABLE 2018-19

		P	W	D	L	F	A	GD	Pts
1	Morpeth Town	38	28	4	6	90	33	57	88
2	Pontefract Collieries	38	23	7	8	91	54	37	76
3	Brighouse Town (PO winners)	38	21	8	9	74	43	31	71
4	Sheffield FC	38	21	6	11	81	63	18	69
5	Ossett United	38	18	13	7	65	37	28	67
6	Tadcaster Albion	38	20	6	12	71	47	24	66
7	Cleethorpes Town	38	18	10	10	90	62	28	64
8	Loughborough Dynamo	38	19	5	14	82	67	15	62
9	Belper Town	38	16	11	11	66	60	6	59
10	Marske United	38	16	10	12	63	47	16	58
11	Stamford	38	13	11	14	55	57	-2	50
12	Frickley Athletic	38	13	9	16	54	60	-6	48
13	Stocksbridge Park Steels	38	12	7	19	41	70	-29	43
14	Lincoln United	38	12	7	19	53	83	-30	43
15	AFC Mansfield	38	11	9	18	55	73	-18	42
16	Pickering Town	38	8	11	19	45	72	-27	35
17	Wisbech Town	38	6	13	19	43	70	-27	31
18	Spalding United	38	6	13	19	38	67	-29	31
19	Carlton Town	38	7	6	25	46	84	-38	27
20	Gresley FC	38	7	4	27	37	91	-54	25

	EAST DIVISION	1	2	3	4	5	6	7	8	9	10	11	12	13	14	15	16	17	18	19	20
1	AFC Mansfield		2-3	0-1	4-3	0-3	2-1	2-1	1-4	3-0	0-0	3-1	1-1	2-1	0-1	2-3	1-2	0-4	1-2	0-0	2-2
2	Belper Town	2-0		1-3	2-1	1-5	1-1	2-3	2-2	2-1	2-2	1-0	3-2	1-2	3-2	1-1	0-0	1-1	4-1	1-3	1-1
3	Brighouse Town	3-0	2-0		4-0	2-2	1-0	2-0	4-1	3-1	1-0	2-3	2-2	3-3	0-1	1-2	3-1	3-3	1-0	3-0	0-0
4	Carlton Town	0-2	1-3	1-2		1-5	1-2	5-0	3-1	2-3	2-2	0-1	1-1	1-2	2-6	0-1	1-2	0-4	1-1	0-1	0-1
5	Cleethorpes Town	3-3	0-1	1-1	4-2		1-2	3-0	4-1	3-3	0-1	2-1	1-1	2-1	4-2	3-4	1-1	6-0	6-2	1-5	3-1
6	Frickley Athletic	2-3	0-2	0-3	6-0	1-1		1-1	1-1	3-2	2-1	0-2	1-3	1-1	2-3	2-3	2-1	4-1	2-0	1-3	1-1
7	Gresley FC	0-3	1-5	0-1	0-1	2-3	1-0		2-1	1-2	0-1	0-3	0-5	1-2	0-4	0-3	0-1	2-1	3-3	2-1	2-2
8	Lincoln United	1-3	5-2	0-4	1-1	1-4	1-0	1-0		2-2	3-2	0-4	0-1	1-2	2-1	1-1	2-1	2-2	2-1	0-2	4-1
9	Loughborough Dynamo	4-1	2-0	5-2	2-1	1-0	2-0	4-1	5-1		0-4	2-1	1-3	4-2	3-3	6-0	2-2	1-0	5-1	1-2	1-3
10	Marske United	3-1	2-2	0-3	4-0	3-1	0-1	4-1	5-0	1-2		1-4	0-0	2-0	1-1	4-0	1-1	2-1	1-0	2-1	2-1
11	Morpeth Town	8-3	1-1	2-1	4-0	2-4	1-2	5-1	1-0	4-1	3-1		1-0	4-1	3-1	2-0	3-0	1-0	2-1	1-0	5-2
12	Ossett United	1-1	3-3	4-0	1-1	4-0	4-3	1-0	0-1	1-1	4-0	0-1		2-2	1-1	1-0	1-1	1-0	3-0	2-1	4-0
13	Pickering Town	1-3	0-3	0-2	0-2	0-2	4-4	2-3	1-2	1-5	1-0	1-1	0-1		0-1	1-5	1-1	3-3	0-2	1-1	2-0
14	Pontefract Collieries	3-2	4-2	2-1	4-2	3-0	2-2	3-0	3-0	3-0	1-1	1-1	1-0	3-2		3-0	3-0	1-2	2-0	1-2	4-0
15	Sheffield FC	2-0	0-0	1-2	4-2	2-1	1-2	4-1	2-1	4-0	3-3	0-0	3-0	3-1	5-3		2-1	2-0	2-1	3-4	5-1
16	Spalding United	1-1	2-1	0-3	2-2	1-2	0-1	2-2	0-3	0-2	0-2	0-4	1-2	0-0	7-3	2-1		2-2	0-1	0-1	1-2
17	Stamford	2-0	1-2	3-2	0-2	4-4	0-0	2-1	2-0	1-0	0-3	1-2	0-2	0-0	1-1	2-2	4-0		1-0	2-0	0-0
18	Stocksbridge Park Steels	2-1	0-2	1-0	1-0	0-3	2-0	3-2	3-0	3-2	0-0	0-4	1-1	0-2	0-5	3-2	1-1	2-4		0-3	1-0
19	Tadcaster Albion	1-1	2-1	2-2	0-2	1-1	4-0	2-1	8-3	1-0	2-1	0-3	0-1	0-1	2-3	3-4	3-0	3-0	1-1		2-0
20	Wisbech Town	1-1	1-2	1-1	1-2	1-1	0-1	1-2	2-2	2-4	3-1	0-1	4-1	1-1	1-2	3-1	1-1	0-1	1-1	1-4	

NORTHERN PREMIER LEAGUE
DIVISION WEST TABLE 2018-19

		P	W	D	L	F	A	GD	Pts
1	Atherton Collieries	38	26	4	8	89	34	55	82
2	Radcliffe FC (PO winners)	38	23	6	9	73	34	39	75
3	Leek Town	38	22	8	8	78	34	44	74
4	Colne	38	22	7	9	71	44	27	73
5	Ramsbottom United	38	21	9	8	78	41	37	72
6	Runcorn Linnets	38	22	6	10	69	50	19	72
7	Prescot Cables	38	21	6	11	84	54	30	69
8	Mossley	38	19	8	11	66	51	15	65
9	Trafford	38	17	10	11	53	44	9	61
10	Kidsgrove Athletic	38	15	13	10	58	40	18	58
11	Colwyn Bay	38	15	7	16	73	66	7	52
12	Widnes	38	15	6	17	60	61	-1	51
13	Chasetown	38	12	10	16	61	63	-2	46
14	Droylsden	38	12	7	19	61	72	-11	43
15	Newcastle Town	38	10	10	18	52	74	-22	40
16	Market Drayton Town	38	11	7	20	55	94	-39	40
17	Glossop North End	38	7	10	21	41	74	-33	31
18	Clitheroe	38	7	7	24	45	88	-43	28
19	Kendal Town	38	5	4	29	32	94	-62	19
20	Skelmersdale United	38	2	7	29	24	111	-87	13

	WEST DIVISION	1	2	3	4	5	6	7	8	9	10	11	12	13	14	15	16	17	18	19	20
1	Atherton Collieries		2-0	4-0	1-2	2-4	2-0	2-1	8-0	2-1	2-1	1-2	6-2	4-1	4-1	0-1	1-3	3-2	9-1	0-0	0-1
2	Chasetown	0-1		1-1	1-1	3-0	1-0	2-2	5-0	2-2	1-1	0-2	1-3	5-0	1-4	2-0	2-2	1-2	2-2	0-2	3-1
3	Clitheroe	3-5	0-3		1-3	0-2	5-1	2-0	1-3	0-4	0-1	2-3	1-1	1-1	1-2	0-7	1-2	0-5	2-1	1-2	2-3
4	Colne	2-1	3-1	3-0		3-2	1-0	0-1	3-1	1-3	3-2	8-1	1-2	2-2	0-1	1-0	1-0	1-6	1-0	0-1	1-0
5	Colwyn Bay	1-2	4-2	1-1	2-5		1-2	2-1	1-0	1-2	0-1	4-1	1-5	3-3	2-2	1-2	0-1	0-1	9-0	2-1	2-4
6	Droylsden	0-0	2-4	1-0	1-1	1-2		1-1	2-1	0-3	2-3	0-2	0-3	3-1	2-3	0-2	2-3	4-2	3-1	1-2	6-2
7	Glossop North End	0-2	1-2	0-2	1-4	0-5	1-1		1-4	1-2	0-2	2-0	3-3	3-1	0-0	1-3	0-5	0-2	0-0	0-0	3-6
8	Kendal Town	0-4	0-1	2-2	1-4	1-3	1-4	1-3		1-2	2-3	3-2	0-1	0-1	0-3	0-4	2-2	1-2	1-0	0-2	1-5
9	Kidsgrove Athletic	0-1	1-1	3-0	0-1	0-2	3-3	1-1	0-0		2-1	2-2	4-0	1-0	0-4	0-1	0-2	5-0	4-0	1-0	1-1
10	Leek Town	0-1	1-1	1-2	0-0	2-2	1-1	3-1	3-0	1-2		4-0	3-1	4-1	4-0	2-1	4-0	1-1	6-0	1-3	4-1
11	Market Drayton Town	0-2	2-1	3-0	0-4	1-4	3-1	2-2	2-4	1-1	1-1		1-1	2-1	4-4	2-1	1-3	3-2	2-1	1-4	0-2
12	Mossley	0-2	3-1	2-0	0-0	3-2	1-0	1-3	2-0	0-0	0-2	5-1		1-0	2-1	1-1	1-1	1-2	1-0	1-0	2-1
13	Newcastle Town	0-2	3-1	2-1	1-2	3-4	1-3	1-0	5-0	1-1	0-1	6-2	1-0		2-3	1-1	0-6	1-2	1-1	3-3	2-1
14	Prescot Cables	1-1	6-1	4-1	3-1	1-2	4-2	3-1	1-1	2-1	0-1	3-0	2-1	4-0		1-1	0-4	2-1	5-0	2-0	2-1
15	Radcliffe FC	2-0	2-1	4-1	1-1	3-0	2-1	1-2	2-0	1-0	1-3	2-1	3-4	4-0	3-2		0-0	1-0	0-2	3-0	3-1
16	Ramsbottom United	0-3	2-2	3-3	1-3	1-0	4-0	2-0	1-0	2-2	1-1	2-1	2-1	1-2	2-0	2-1		2-3	6-0	0-1	0-1
17	Runcorn Linnets	0-3	2-1	2-1	2-0	4-0	0-4	2-2	3-0	2-1	1-0	4-1	2-2	1-1	2-1	0-0	1-2		2-1	2-1	0-2
18	Skelmersdale United	0-3	0-2	1-4	1-2	0-0	1-2	0-3	1-0	2-2	0-4	1-1	1-5	0-0	1-5	1-2	0-3	1-3		1-6	0-1
19	Trafford	1-1	3-0	1-1	0-0	0-0	3-4	2-0	2-0	0-0	0-3	3-2	1-0	0-2	2-1	0-5	0-4	0-0	5-1		1-1
20	Widnes	1-2	0-3	1-2	3-2	2-2	1-1	2-0	3-1	0-1	0-2	3-0	1-4	1-1	2-1	0-2	1-1	0-1	4-1	0-1	

NPL PREMIER DIVISION STATISTICS 2018-19

CLUB	SG	CSG	FS	CFS	CS	CCS	PS	PC	TGC	TG
Farsley Celtic	44	12	5	1	17	4	10	3	48	105
South Shields	38	25	4	2	19	3	11	4	53	109
Basford United	41	17	6	1	9	2	6	5	79	98
Warrington Town	41	15	9	2	21	8	8	3	43	95
Nantwich Town	35	12	11	2	11	2	5	4+1c	71	83
Scarborough Athletic	35	12	10	1	10	4	7	7	63	79
Hyde United	34	17	11	3	14	2	4	5	58	70
Gainsborough Trinity	35	8	13	4	17	4	2	3	49	71
Bamber Bridge	32	9	11	3	4	2	5+1c	3	79	65
Buxton	40	8	9	2	15	2	3	4	63	76
Matlock Town	28	4	16	5	7	2	3+1c	5	84	65
Stafford Rangers	38	12	7	2	6	1	3	6	80	69
Workington	33	9	19	4	12	2	2+1c	7	86	61
Witton Albion	37	13	12	2	20	3	10+2c	1	47	63
Hednesford Town	34	8	11	1	11	2	5	7	71	57
Whitby Town	29	5	15	2	9	2	8	5	62	55
Marine	33	7	15	3	13	2	2	3+1c	64	51
Stalybridge Celtic	32	9	14	3	8	2	1+1c	4 +1c	67	52
Mickleover Sports	32	9	14	3	11	2	4	5	66	51
Lancaster City	35	16	13	3	11	2	4+1c	2	70	51
Grantham Town	27	9	18	4	5	1	4	8	83	43
Resigned from NPL										
North Ferriby United	20	5	15	5*	15	1	1	12	99	29

SG - Scoring Games; CSG - Consec Scoring Games; FS - Failure to Score; CFS - Consec Failure to Score; CS - Clean Sheets
CCS - Consec Clean Sheets; PS - Penalties Scored; PC - Pens Conceded; TGC - Total Goals Conceded; TG - Total Goals

CLUB GOAL SCORERS IN SEASON 2018-2019

...continued from page 256

SCORERS OF 20 OR MORE GOALS

Leading Goalscorers	Club	Lge	Cup	SG	CSG	Pens	Hat Tricks	Total
Brandon Goodship	Weymouh	37	1	24	4	9	5	38
Toby Holmes	Wimborne Town	29	6	21	9		2	35
Kabongo Tshimanga	Oxford City	24	11	25	4	4	2	35
Andrew Neal	Taunton Town	29	4	22	5	4	2	33
Glen Taylor	Spennymoor Town	27	6	27	7	3	1	33
Jamie Reid	Torquay United	29	3	23	5	3	1	32
Danny Rowe	AFC Fylde	28	4	24	4	2		32
Levi Landricombe	Tiverton Town	25	6	25	5	1	1	31
Jack Mazzone	Metropolitan Police	24	6	24	6	5		30
James Walshaw	Scarborough Athletic	27	3	25	6	2		30
Paul McCallum	Eastleigh	27	P-o 1	20	3	1	1	28
Jason Prior	Dorking Wanderers	22	5	23	4	8	1	27
James Spencer	Farsley Celtic	24	3	21	3		1	27
Alistair Waddecar	Bamber Bridge	25	2	19	3	7	1	27
Macauley Bonne	Leyton Orient	25	1	21	5	2	1	26
Daniel Udoh	AFC Telford United	20	6	20	3		1	26
Mathew Warburton	Stockport County	16	10	16	3		3	26
James Ewington	Walton Casuals	25		13	2	1	5	25
Dan Maguire	Blyth Spartans	19	6	19	3		1	25
Adam Marriott	King's Lynn Town	24	1	20	2	2	1	25
Connor McDonagh	Swindon Supermarine	25		21	4 + 5			25

...continued on page 288

LEAGUE CUP 2018-19

HOLDERS: ATHERTON COLLIERIES

ROUND ONE

Atherton Collieries	v	Droylsden	1–2
Brighouse Town	v	Ossett United	1–0
Bamber Bridge	v	Mossley	2–1
Buxton	v	Colwyn Bay	1–0
Colne	v	Kendal Town	2–0
Farsley Celtic	v	Pontefract Collieries	4–0
Frickley Athletic	v	Cleethorpes Town	5–4
Grantham Town	v	Glossop North End	0–6
Gresley	v	Gainsborough Trinity	4–1
Hyde United	v	Stalybridge Celtic	4–2
Lancaster City	v	Radcliffe	2–2, 4–3p
Loughborough Dynamo	v	Basford United	1–3
Marske United	v	North Ferriby United	3–1
Nantwich Town	v	Chasetown	1–1, 1-4p
Pickering Town	v	Whitby Town	1–2
Runcorn Linnets	v	Warrington Town	1–1, 5-4p
Scarborough Athletic	v	Tadcaster Albion	3–2
Sheffield	v	Stocksbridge Park Steels	3–1
Skelmersdale United	v	Trafford	3–3, 2-4p
South Shields	v	Morpeth Town	1–4
Spalding United	v	Belper Town	1–1, 2-4p
Stafford Rangers	v	Market Drayton Town	1–1, 5-3p
Stamford	v	Mickleover Sports	0–3
Wisbech Town	v	AFC Mansfield	1–3
Witton Albion	v	Widnes	2–1
Workington	v	Prescot Cables	1–2
Kidsgrove Athletic	v	Hednesford Town	3–1
Lincoln United	v	Carlton Town	1–2
Ramsbottom United	v	Clitheroe	1–1, 6-7p
Leek Town	v	Newcastle Town	5–3

ROUND TWO

Basford United	v	Matlock Town	1–0
Bamber Bridge	v	Colne	3–1
Chasetown	v	Stafford Rangers	1–2
Frickley Athletic	v	Farsley Celtic	1–1, 4-5p
Marine	v	Lancaster City	2–0
Morpeth Town	v	Brighouse Town	2–0
Prescot Cables	v	Hyde United	1–2
Scarborough Athletic	v	Whitby Town	1–1, 4-1p
Sheffield	v	Marske United	1–3
Trafford	v	Clitheroe	0–0, 5-4p
Witton Albion	v	Kidsgrove Athletic	1–2
Carlton Town	v	Gresley	0–2
Belper Town	v	AFC Mansfield	2–1
Glossop North End	v	Droylsden	2–4
Leek Town	v	Runcorn Linnets	1–4
Mickleover Sports	v	Buxton	0–3

ROUND THREE

Basford United	v	Buxton	2–3
Droylsden	v	Trafford	2–2, 7-8p
Farsley Celtic	v	Scarborough Athletic	2–1
Hyde United	v	Runcorn Linnets	1–1, 1-4p
Marske United	v	Morpeth Town	0–0, 4-3p
Stafford Rangers	v	Marine	1–1, 4-2p
Belper Town	v	Gresley	2–0
Kidsgrove Athletic	v	Bamber Bridge	1–3

QUARTER-FINALS

Bamber Bridge	v	Belper Town	2–3
Stafford Rangers	v	Farsley Celtic	0–5
Buxton	v	Marske United	3–3, 4-2p
Runcorn Linnets	v	Trafford	1–3

SEMI-FINALS

Farsley Celtic	v	Belper Town	3–1
Trafford	v	Buxton	1–0

FINAL

Farsley Celtic	v	Trafford	1–2

BAMBER BRIDGE MATCH RESULTS 2018-19

Date	Comp	H/A	Opponents	Att:	Result		Goalscorers	Pos	No.
Aug 18	NPL Prem	A	Grantham Town	259	D	1 - 1	White 47		1
21	NPL Prem	H	Workington	291	**W**	3 - 2	Waddecar 33 Lawlor 37 49	4	2
25	**FAC P**	**A**	**Stocksbridge Park Steels**	**144**	**W**	**3 - 1**	**Milligan 6 75 Waddecar 88**	**9**	3
27	NPL Prem	H	Warrington Town	407	D	0 - 0		10	4
Sept 1	NPL Prem	H	Witton Albion	366	**W**	2 - 0	Dudley 11 Waddecar 19	9	5
4	NPL Prem	A	Lancaster City	296	D	1 - 1	Forbes 86	10	6
8	**FAC 1Q**	**H**	**Tadcaster Albion**	**294**	**W**	**3 - 1**	**Waddecar 4 Carsley 20 Dudley 43**	**9**	7
11	NPL Prem	H	Buxton	330	D	2 - 2	White 83 Marlow 90	10	8
15	NPL Prem	A	Stalybridge Celtic	305	L	2 - 3	Charnock 7 White 67	14	9
22	**FAC 2Q**	**A**	**Cleethorps Town**	**302**	**D**	**3 - 3**	**CARSLEY 3 (32 75 81)**		10
25	**FAC 2Qr**	**H**	**Cleethorps Town**	**315**	**L**	**0 - 5**			11
29	NPL Prem	H	Stafford Rangers	383	**W**	6 - 1	WADDECAR 4 (13 60 87 89) Haworth 27 Darr 70	11	12
Oct	NPL Prem	A	Whitby Town	264	L	1 - 2	Waddecar 22	14	13
9	*Void*	*H*	*North Ferriby United*	*355*	***W***	*3 - 1*	*Carsley 31 79 Milligan 76 (pen)*	*12*	14
13	NPL Prem	A	Scarborough Athletic	1160	D	0 - 0		13	15
16	NPL Prem	A	Farsley Celtic	190	L	2 - 3	Carsley 9 18	14	16
20	NPL Prem	H	Basford United	329	L	0 - 4		14	17
27	**FAT 1Q**	**A**	**Hyde United**	**315**	**L**	**0 - 3**		**15**	18
Nov 3	NPL Prem	A	Hednesford Town	244	D	1 - 1	Argent-Barnes 55	14	19
10	NPL Prem	A	Matlock Town	338	L	1 - 2	Waddecar 61	14	20
17	NPL Prem	H	Nantwich Town	456	D	2 - 2	Waddecar 70 81	15	21
20	NPL Prem	H	Gainsborough Trinity	242	L	1 - 2	Argent-Barnes 80	15	22
24	NPL Prem	A	Buxton	314	**W**	1 - 0	Dudley 9	14	23
Dec 1	NPL Prem	H	Stalybridge Celtic	315	**W**	3 - 1	Marlow 53 Waddecar 73 Dawson 90	12	24
8	NPL Prem	A	Witton Albion	279	D	2 - 2	Waddecar 59 Charnock 90	12	25
22	NPL Prem	A	Mickleover Sports	174	D	2 - 2	Forbes 18 Waddecar 42 (pen)	13	26
26	NPL Prem	H	Marine	414	L	1 - 2	Dawson 54	15	27
Jan 1	NPL Prem	A	Warrington Town	460	L	0 - 2		15	28
5	NPL Prem	H	Grantham Town	381	**W**	3 - 1	Dawson 78 Waddecar 79 Navarro 90	14	29
12	NPL Prem	H	Hyde United	431	**W**	5 - 2	DAWSON 3 (19 59 69) Marlow 32 Dudley 45	12	30
19	NPL Prem	A	Workington	401	L	1 - 2	Harries 16	13	31
25	NPL Prem	H	Hednesford Town	375	D	1 - 1	Waddecar 88 (pen)	13	32
Feb 9	NPL Prem	A	South Shields	1582	D	3 - 3	Waddecar 63 (pen) Marlow 80 Lawlor 84	13	33
12	NPL Prem	H	Lancaster City	438	D	2 - 2	Dudley 15 Waddecar 90 (pen)	12	34
16	NPL Prem	A	Stafford Rangers	552	L	0 - 1		15	35
23	NPL Prem	H	South Shields	502	L	0 - 2		16	36
26	NPL Prem	A	Nantwich Town	301	L	0 - 2		16	37
Mar 2	NPL Prem	A	Gainsborough Trinity	527	L	1 - 3	McGiveron 90	18	38
9	NPL Prem	H	Whitby Town	314	L	1 - 3	Waddecar 4	19	39
23	NPL Prem	H	Farsley Celtic	418	L	0 - 3		19	40
30	NPL Prem	A	Basford United	207	L	0 - 1		19	41
Apr 6	NPL Prem	H	Scarborough Athletic	346	L	2 - 4	Waddecar 65 (pen) 70	20	42
13	NPL Prem	A	Hyde United	351	**W**	2 - 0	Charnock 49 Waddecar 68 (pen)	20	43
20	NPL Prem	H	Matlock Town	396	**W**	4 - 2	Harries 5 Dudley 30 Waddecar 62 90 (pen)	18	44
22	NPL Prem	A	Marine	544	**W**	2 - 0	Waddecar 32 48	16	45
27	NPL Prem	H	Mickleover Sports	300	L	1 - 2	Forbes 42	16	46

GOALSCORERS	SG	CSG	Pens	Hat tricks	Total
Waddecar	19	4	7	1	27
Carsley	4			1	8
Dawson	4	2		1	6
Dudley	5				6
Marlow	4				4
Charnock	3				3
Forbes	3				3
Lawlor	2				3
Milligan	3		1		3
White	3				3
Argent-Barnes	2				2
Harries	2				2
Darr	1				1
Haworth	1				1
McGiveron	1				1
Navarro	1				1

BASFORD UNITED MATCH RESULTS 2018-19

Date	Comp	H/A	Opponents	Att:	Result		Goalscorers	Pos	No.
Aug 18	NPL Prem	A	Hyde United	416	L	0 - 1			1
20	NPL Prem	H	Hednesford Town	312	L	1 - 2	Fenton 65	21	2
25	NPL Prem	A	Marine	311	W	4 - 1	Fenton 6 Watson 62 67 Grantham77	16	3
27	NPL Prem	H	Grantham Town	355	W	3 - 1	Thomas 7 Reid 15 Thornhill 64	12	4
Sept 1	NPL Prem	H	Farsley Celtic	195	W	4 - 3	WATSON 3 (3 61 pen 63) Thornhill 80	6	5
4	NPL Prem	A	Buxton	402	L	0 - 1		8	6
7 Sept	**FAC 1Q**	**H**	**Staveley Miners Welfare**	**379**	**L**	**1 - 3**	**Hakeem 71**		7
10	NPL Prem	H	Matlock Town	342	W	6 - 0	Thomas 38 Grantham 59 Thornhill 74 Watson 86 (p) Lambert 89 90	7	8
15	NPL Prem	A	Scarborough Athletic	1068	L	1 - 3	Watson 75	8	9
22	NPL Prem	H	Lancaster City	160	W	3 - 1	Meikle 62 82 Lambert 90	4	10
25	NPL Prem	A	Stafford Rangers	411	L	1 - 3	Hearn 17	4	11
29	NPL Prem	H	Workington	211	W	3 - 2	Hearn 35 Lambert 55 Roma 70	2	12
Oct 1	NPL Prem	H	Whitby Town	270	W	2 - 0	Hearn 27 Reid 35	1	13
6	NPL Prem	A	Lancaster City	216	D	1 - 1	Watson 26	3	14
9	NPL Prem	A	Gainsborough Trinity	368	L	2 - 3	Thornhill 51 Watson 80	2	15
13	NPL Prem	H	Stalybridge Celtic	415	W	5 - 2	REID 3 (11 42 57) Thornhill 45 Carr 73	3	16
20	NPL Prem	A	Bamber Bridge	329	W	4 - 0	Watson 28 Thomas 38 Grantham 49 Thornhill 83	2	17
27	**FAT 1Q**	**A**	**Cambridge City**	**164**	**W**	**2 - 1**	**Reid 8 Watson 29**		18
Nov 3	*Void*	*H*	*North Ferriby United*	*232*	*W*	*4 - 2*	*WATSON 3 (35 78 80) Hearn 78*	*3*	19
10	**FAT 2Q**	**H**	**Stafford Rangers**	**246**	**W**	**4 - 0**	**Goodson 6 17 Fenton 19 Hearn 90 (pen)**		20
17	NPL Prem	A	Warrington Town	638	D	1 - 1	Galinski 54	6	21
24	**FAT 3Q**	**H**	**Curzon Ashton**	**266**	**W**	**2 - 1**	**Hearn 4 Thomas 17**	**5**	22
Dec 1	NPL Prem	H	Scarborough Athletic	459	W	3 - 1	Tempest 14 Watson 28 88	5	23
8	NPL Prem	A	Farsley Celtic	226	L	0 - 2		6	24
15	**FAT 1P**	**A**	**Chesterfield**	**1276**	**L**	**1 - 5**	**Goodson 74**	**7**	25
22	NPL Prem	A	Nantwich Town	486	L	2 - 3	Thornhill 2 Goodson 86	8	26
26	NPL Prem	H	Mickleover Sports	286	W	2 - 1	Mills 12 (og) Watson 17	6	27
29	NPL Prem	H	Warington Town	280	L	2 - 3	Thornhill 8 Reid 39 (pen)	7	28
Jan 1	NPL Prem	A	Grantham Town	270	L	1 - 2	Meikle 56	8	29
5	NPL Prem	H	Hyde United	237	L	3 - 8	Goodson 50 83 Carr 90	8	30
12	NPL Prem	H	South Shields	401	L	0 - 3		8	31
19	NPL Prem	A	Hednesford Town	289	L	1 - 2	Reid 8	9	32
26	*Void*	*A*	*North Ferriby United*	*186*	*W*	*2 - 1*	*Carr 6 Watson 62*	*7*	33
Feb 11	NPL Prem	H	Witton Albion	264	W	3 - 1	Watson 30 88 Carr 80	7	34
16	NPL Prem	A	Workington	511	W	3 - 0	Harrad 13 (pen) Goodson 66 Taylor 68	7	35
23	NPL Prem	H	Stafford Rangers	308	D	2 - 2	Thomas 65 Harrod 69	7	36
Mar 2	NPL Prem	A	Whitby Town	293	L	1 - 4	Watson 15	9	37
9	NPL Prem	H	Buxton	239	W	2 - 0	Thomas 17 Roscoe 90 (og)	7	38
16	NPL Prem	H	Gainsborough Trinity	355	L	0 - 1		8	39
23	NPL Prem	A	Witton Albion	316	D	2 - 2	Reid 34 (pen) Watson 90	8	40
30	NPL Prem	H	Bamber Bridge	207	W	1 - 0	Gascoigne 20	8	41
Apr 2	NPL Prem	A	Matlock Town	311	D	2 - 2	Carr 13 Watson 49	8	42
6	NPL Prem	A	Stalybridge Celtic	274	W	2 - 0	Galinski 45 Nash 66	8	43
13	NPL Prem	A	South Shields	1509	D	1 - 1	Carr 60	8	44
20	NPL Prem	H	Marine	230	D	0 - 0		8	45
22	NPL Prem	A	Mickleover Sports	316	W	1 - 0	Wilder 57	7	46
27	NPL Prem	H	Nantwich Town	201	W	7 - 3	Watson 2 HEARN 4 (14 25 43 45) Goodson 71 Bourne 86 (og)	7	47

GOALSCORERS	SG	CSG	Pens	Hat tricks	Total
Watson	15	3	2	2	24
Hearn	7	3	1	1	10
Reid	9		2	1	9
Thornhill	7	3			9
Goodson	6	2			8
Carr	6				6
Thomas	5	2			5
Lambert	3				4
Fenton	3				3
Grantham	2				3
Meikle	3				3
Opponents	3				3
Galinski	2				2
Harrad	2		1		2
Gascoigne	1				1
Hakeem	1				1
Nash	1				1
Roma	1				1
Taylor	1				1
Tempest	1				1
Wilder	1				1

BUXTON MATCH RESULTS 2018-19

Date	Comp	H/A	Opponents	Att:	Result		Goalscorers	Pos	No.
Aug 18	NPL Prem	A	Whitby Town	282	L	0 - 1			1
21	NPL Prem	A	Nantwich Town	279	D	0 - 0		19	2
25	NPL Prem	A	Workington	326	D	1 - 1	Oyibo 58	18	3
27	NPL Prem	H	Hyde United	712	**W**	1 - 0	Hardy 55	10	4
Sept 1	NPL Prem	H	Mickleover Sports	262	**W**	3 - 1	Roscoe 51 DeGirolamo 75 Oyibo 90	7	5
4	NPL Prem	A	Basford United	402	**W**	1 - 0	Wilson 61	5	6
8	**FAC 1Q**	**A**	**Barwell**	**172**	**W**	**5 - 2**	**Hardy 39 44 Coppin 59 De Girolamo 63 69**		7
11	NPL Prem	H	Bamber Bridge	330	D	2 - 2	Roscoe 6 Chippendale 20	4	8
15	NPL Prem	H	Stafford Rangers	501	**W**	4 - 1	Oyibo 21 De Girolamo 31 39 Brown 42	3	9
22	**FAC 2Q**	**H**	**Coalville Town**	**322**	**D**	**0 - 0**			10
25	**FAC 2Qr**	**A**	**Coalvillle Town**	**198**	**L**	**1 - 4**	**Grayson 68**		11
29	NPL Prem	H	Lancaster City	403	L	1 - 2	De Girolamo 5	8	12
Oct 2	NPL Prem	H	South Shields	266	**W**	2 - 0	Hardy 7 Young 78	6	13
9	NPL Prem	H	Grantham Town	311	**W**	1 - 0	Young 39	6	14
13	NPL Prem	A	Farsley Celtic	265	D	1 - 1	Roscoe 37	5	15
16	NPL Prem	A	Scarborough Athletic	1005	L	0 - 4		7	16
20	*Void*	*H*	*North Ferriiby United*	*373*	*D*	*2 - 2*	*Omotola 17 Hardy 74 (pen)*	*8*	17
23	NPL Prem	A	Hednesford Town	236	D	1 - 1	De Girolamo 36	7	18
27	**FAT 1Q**	**H**	**Kings Lynn Town**	**285**	**D**	**3 - 3**	**Young 39 75 Chippendale 80**		19
30	**FAT1Qr**	**A**	**KIngs Lynn Town**	**277**	**W**	**2 - 1**	**Hardy 37 Oyibo 113 (aet)**		20
Nov 3	NPL Prem	A	Stalybridge Celtic	445	D	1 - 1	Clarke 52 (og)	7	21
10	**FAT 2Q**	**A**	**Stalybridge Celtic**	**409**	**D**	**0 - 0**		**10**	22
13	**FAT 2Qr**	**H**	**Stalybridge Celtic**	**283**	**L**	**1 - 2**	**DeGirolamo 34**		23
17	NPL Prem	H	Witton Albion	427	L	0 - 5		10	24
24	NPL Prem	H	Bamber Bridge	314	L	0 - 1		10	25
Dec 1	NPL Prem	A	Stafford Rangers	481	**W**	1 - 0	Young 49	9	26
8	NPL Prem	H	Mickleover Sports	273	**W**	5 - 0	Hardy 32 44 Grayson 48 Dean 52 Roscoe 67	9	27
15	NPL Prem	A	Gainsborough Trinity	416	**W**	2 - 1	Chippendale 20 78 (pen)	8	28
22	NPL Prem	A	Warrington Town	368	L	1 - 2	Brown 14	9	29
26	NPL Prem	H	Matlock Town	880	D	2 - 2	Pritchard 32 Grayson 36	9	30
Jan 1	NPL Prem	A	Hyde United	551	D	1 - 1	Dean 45	9	31
5	NPL Prem	H	Whitby Town	321	**W**	2 - 0	Hardy 16 (pen) Pritchard 50	7	32
12	NPL Prem	H	Marine	410	L	0 - 3		8	33
26	NPL Prem	H	Stalybridge Celtic	536	D	1 - 1	Grayson 90	9	34
Feb 9	NPL Prem	H	Gainsborough Trinity	453	**W**	1 - 0	Pritchard 22	7	35
16	NPL Prem	A	Lancaster City	258	**W**	3 - 1	Grayson 28 50 Dean 31	8	36
23	NPL Prem	H	Hednesford Town	453	L	1 - 2	Dean 86	8	37
26	NPL Prem	A	Witton Albion	244	**W**	3 - 0	Hardy 32 Chippendale 66 Grayson 73	7	38
Mar 2	NPL Prem	A	South Shields	1428	D	1 - 1	De Girolamo 20		39
5	NPL Prem	H	Nantwich Town	327	**W**	2 - 1	De Girolamo 27 Hardy 48	7	40
9	NPL Prem	A	Basford United	239	L	0 - 2		7	41
16	NPL Prem	A	Grantham Town	217	**W**	1 - 0	Hardy 59	7	42
23	NPL Prem	H	Scarborough Athletic	683	**W**	1 - 0	Chippendale 41	6	43
Apr 6	NPL Prem	H	Farsley Celtic	562	L	1 - 2	Hardy 61	6	44
13	NPL Prem	A	Marine	446	D	1 - 1	Pritchard 68	6	45
20	NPL Prem	H	Workington	436	**W**	3 - 2	De Girolamo 6 Hardy 7 Young 54	6	46
22	NPL Prem	A	Matlock Town	575	**W**	6 - 0	HARDY 4 (5 56 (p) 80 82) Brown 19 De Girolamo 34	6	47
27	NPL Prem	H	Warrington Town	943	D	2 - 2	Oyibo 9 Hardy 45	5	48
30	**PO SF**	**A**	**South Shields**	**1978**	**L**	**2 - 4**	**De Girolamo 29 Young 65**		49

GOALSCORERS	SG	CSG	Pens	Hat tricks	Total
Hardy	14	3	3		18
DeGirolamo	11	2			13
Grayson	6				7
Young	6	2			7
Chippendale	5		1		6
Oyibo	5				5
Pritchard	5				5
Dean	4				4
Roscoe	4				4
Brown	3				3
Coppin	1				1
Omootola	1				1
Opponents					1
Wilson	1				1

FARSLEY CELTIC MATCH RESULTS 2018-19

Date	Comp	H/A	Opponents	Att:	Result		Goalscorers	Pos	No.
Aug 18	NPL Prem	A	Warrington Town	312	W	2 - 0	Turner 13 Hayhurst 37		1
21	NPL Prem	H	South Shields	350	W	4 - 1	Cartman 57 Spencer 76 C.Atkinson 84 B. Atkinson 88	1	2
27	NPL Prem	H	Hednesford Town	345	L	1 - 2	Hayhurst 78 (pen)	12	3
Sept 1	NPL Prem	A	Basford United	195	L	3 - 4	Walker 30 Hayhurst 38 (pen) 45 (pen)	14	4
4	NPL Prem	H	Gainsborough Trinity	262	D	1 - 1	Turner 53	15	5
15	NPL Prem	H	Mickleover Sports	196	W	1 - 0	Turner 33	13	6
22	**FAC 2Q**	**H**	**Southport**	**306**	**L**	**0 - 3**			7
29	NPL Prem	H	Matlock Town	224	W	3 - 2	Spencer 38 40 Higgins 68	12	8
Oct 2	NPL Prem	H	Lancaster City	142	W	2 - 0	Walker 64 Higgins 65	9	9
6	NPL Prem	A	Nantwich Town	335	L	1 - 2	Spencer 45	10	10
9	NPL Prem	A	Stafford Rangers	382	W	3 - 1	Parkin 68 B.Atkinson 72 Spencer 90	9	11
13	NPL Prem	H	Buxton	265	D	1 - 1	Higgins 27	9	12
16	NPL Prem	H	Bamber Bridge	190	W	3 - 2	Clayton 13 Hayhurst 45 55	6	13
20	NPL Prem	A	Stalybridge Celtic	354	D	2 - 2	Hayhurst 19 Spencer 54	5	14
23	NPL Prem	A	Workington	254	W	1 - 0	Spencer 66	4	15
26	**FAT1Q**	**H**	**Brighouse Town**	**173**	**W**	**4 - 1**	**Hornshaw 37 Spencer 48 Cartman 66 Brito 81**		16
Nov 3	NPL Prem	H	Scarborough Athletic	727	W	3 - 1	Cartman 23 Hayhurst 68 (pen) Clayton 73	4	17
10	**FAT 2Q**	**H**	**Carlton Town**	**167**	**D**	**0 - 0**			18
14	**FAT 2Qr**	**A**	**Carlton Town**	**115**	**W**	**4 - 0**	**Spencer 11 Clayton 15 Ellis 44 Parkin 78**		19
17	*Void*	*A*	*North Ferriby United*	*321*	*W*	*6 - 0*	*B.Atkinson 14 (pen) Hayhurst 47 Spencer 63 67 - Smith 72 (og) Parkin 90*	*3*	20
24	**FAT 3Q**	**H**	**Alfreton Town**	**214**	**W**	**2 - 0**	**Cartman 25 Spencer 43**	3	21
Dec 1	NPL Prem	A	Mickleover Sports	127	W	2 - 1	Hayhurst 57 B.Atkinson 76 (pen)	3	22
8	NPL Prem	H	Basford United	226	W	2 - 0	Higgins 62 Cartman 76	3	23
15	**FAT1**	**A**	**AFC Telford United**	**452**	**L**	**3 - 4**	**Cartman 45 Dyche 77 87**		24
22	NPL Prem	A	Marine	295	W	2 - 1	B.Atkinson 18 (pen) Syers 39	3	25
26	NPL Prem	H	Whitby Town	324	W	3 - 1	Syers 31 Spencer 67 B Atkinson 74 (pen)	2	26
29	NPL Prem	A	Witton Albion	325	W	3 - 2	Higgins 42 Syers 67 Cartman 87	2	27
Jan 1	NPL Prem	A	Hednesfield Town	439	W	1 - 0	Cartman 35	2	28
5	NPL Prem	H	Warrington Town	471	D	3 - 3	Walker 45 Syers 57 Roberts 69 (og)	2	29
12	NPL Prem	H	Grantham Town	371	D	1 - 1	Spencer 7	1	30
19	NPL Prem	A	South Shields	2013	L	0 - 1		3	31
26	NPL Prem	A	Scarborough Athletic	1186	W	3 - 1	Spencer 4 41 Syers 66	3	32
Feb 9	NPL Prem	H	Nantwich Town	349	W	2 - 1	Clayton 18 B.Atkinson 86 (pen)	3	33
12	NPL Prem	A	Gainsborough Trinity	312	W	5 - 0	Spencer 21 Syers 26 Parkin 29 Hayjurst 41 Cartman 55	3	34
16	NPL Prem	A	Matlock Town	258	W	2 - 1	Hayhurst 21 Higgins 85	1	35
23	NPL Prem	H	Witton Albion	343	L	0 - 1		2	36
26	*Void*	*H*	*North Ferriby United*	*184*	*W*	*4 - 0*	*B.Atkinson 17 (pen) Spencer 19 78 Cartman 79*	*2*	37
Mar 2	NPL Prem	A	Lancaster City	259	L	0 - 2		2	38
5	NPL Prem	H	Workington	173	W	2 - 0	Walker 7 Spencer 40	2	39
9	NPL Prem	A	Hyde United	393	W	2 - 1	Cartman 31 Clayton 83	1	40
23	NPL Prem	A	Bamber Bridge	418	W	3 - 0	Cartman 17 78 Spencer 55	1	41
30	NPL Prem	H	Stalybridge Celtic	348	W	2 - 1	Syers 1 Spencer 27	1	42
Apr 6	NPL Prem	A	Buxton	562	W	2 - 1	Cartman 18 Spencer 81	1	43
9	NPL Prem	H	Stafford Rangers	206	W	2 - 1	Syers 45 Cartman 64	1	44
13	NPL Prem	A	Grantham Town	229	W	4 - 0	SPENCER 3(26 47 50) Atkinson 80	1	45
20	NPL Prem	H	Hyde United	518	D	1 - 1	Cartman 20	1	46
22	NPL Prem	A	Whitby Town	438	W	2 - 0	Carsley 25 34	1	47
27	NPL Prem	H	Marine	1527	W	2 - 0	Hayhurst 41 Spencer 75	1	48

GOALSCORERS	SG	CSG	Pens	Hat tricks	Total
Spencer	21	3			27
Cartman	14	2			17
Hayhurst	11	2	4		13
Atkinson B	9	2	6		9
Syers	8	3			8
Higgins	6				6
Clayton	4				4
Parkin	4				4
Walker	4				4
Turner	3				3

	SG	CSG	Pens	Hat tricks	Total
Carsley	1				2
Dyche	2				2
Opponents	2				2
Atkinson C	1				1
Brito	1				1
Ellis	1				1
Hornshaw	1				1

GAINSBOROUGH TRINITY MATCH RESULTS 2018-19

Date	Comp	H/A	Opponents	Att:	Result		Goalscorers	Pos	No.
Aug 18	NPL Prem	A	Nantwich Town	307	L	0 - 1			1
21	NPL Prem	H	Mickleover Sports	461	W	2 - 0	King 54 Byrne 69	9	2
25	NPL Prem	A	Hednesford Town	344	W	2 - 1	Worsfold 38 Simmons 90	3	3
27	NPL Prem	H	Matlock Town	626	W	4 - 2	Reeves 25 Hannah 36 Clarke 76 King 79	1	4
Sept 1	NPL Prem	H	Lancaster City	527	W	3 - 1	Worsfold 24 Hannah 37 64	1	5
4	NPL Prem	A	Farsley Celtic	262	D	1 - 1	Byrne 22	1	6
8	**FAC 1Q**	**A**	**Chasetown**	**350?**	**D**	**1 - 1**	**Byrne**		7
11	**FAC 1Qr**	**H**	**Chasetown**	**412**	**W**	**8 - 2**	**Hannah 4 Worsfold 9 50 Clarke 21 Russell 59 Byrne 70 King 77 O'Neill 89 (og)**		8
15	NPL Prem	A	Witton Albion	241	D	0 - 0		5	9
22	**FAC 2Q**	**A**	**Halesowen Town**	**338**	**W**	**3 - 0**	**Clarke 24 Worsfold 55 Simmons 74**		10
25	*Void*	*H*	*North Ferriby United*	*482*	*W*	*1 - 0*	*Reeves 45*	*4*	11
29	NPL Prem	A	Stalybridge Celtic	330	L	1 - 2	Hannah 90	6	12
Oct 6	**FAC 3Q**	**H**	**Blyth Spartans**	**428**	**L**	**1 - 2**	**Clarke 15**		13
9	NPL Prem	H	Basford United	368	W	3 - 2	Byrne 12 Worsfold 24 43	6	14
13	NPL Prem	A	Hyde United	467	W	3 - 1	Hannah 15 Simmons 53 Byrne 90	4	15
20	NPL Prem	A	South Shields	1163	L	0 - 1		7	16
23	NPL Prem	H	Scarborough Athletic	527	L	0 - 1		8	17
27	**FAT 1Q**	**H**	**Tamworth**	**620**	**D**	**0 - 0**			18
30	**FAT 1Qr**	**A**	**Tamworth**	**276**	**L**	**0 - 3**			19
Nov 4	NPL Prem	A	Stafford Rangers	457	D	1 - 1	Worsfold 81	8	20
10	NPL Prem	A	Marine	352	D	1 1	Russell 76	8	21
17	NPL Prem	H	Whitby Town	659	W	4 - 1	Worsfold 52 Simmons 54 78 Clarke 88	7	22
20	NPL Prem	A	Bamber Bridge	242	W	2 1	Simmons 66 Worsfold 81	5	23
24	NPL Prem	A	Scarborough Athletic	1096	W	2 - 0	Russell 72 Worsfold 77	3	24
Dec 1	NPL Prem	H	Witton Albion	506	D	1 - 1	Worsfold 70	6	25
8	NPL Prem	A	Lancaster City	194	W	1 - 0	Hannah 66	5	26
15	NPL Prem	H	Buxton	416	L	1 2	Margetts 90	5	27
22	NPL Prem	A	Whitby Town	243	L	0 - 1		6	28
26	NPL Prem	H	Grantham Town	709	L	2 - 3	Worsfold 48 Hannah 59	6	29
Jan 1	NPL Prem	A	Matlock Town	665	W	2 - 0	Margetts 44 Russell 90	6	30
5	NPL Prem	H	Nantwich Town	589	D	0 - 0		6	31
12	NPL Prem	H	Workington	572	W	4 - 1	Worsfold 19 74 Gordon 52 Russell 68	6	32
19	NPL Prem	A	Mickleover Sports	210	W	1 - 0	Watters 57	6	33
26	NPL Prem	H	Stafford Rangers	487	D	1 - 1	Worsfold 40	6	34
Feb 2	NPL Prem	H	Warrington	412	L	1 - 4	Reeves 85	6	35
9	NPL Prem	A	Buxton	453	L	0 - 1		6	36
12	NPL Prem	H	Farsley Celtic	312	L	0 - 5		6	37
16	NPL Prem	H	Stalybridge Celtic	509	W	1 - 0	Worsfold 81	6	38
23	*Void*	*A*	*North Ferriby United*	*314*	*W*	*4 - 0*	*Worsfold 18 43 (pen) Wilson 47 Reeves 90*	*5*	39
Mar 2	NPL Prem	H	Bamber Bridge	527	W	2 - 1	Stanfield 37 Russell 69	5	40
16	NPL Prem	A	Basford United	355	W	1 - 0	Simmons 90	5	41
23	NPL Prem	H	Marine	539	L	0 - 1		5	42
30	NPL Prem	A	Warrington Town	445	L	1 - 2	Worsfold 41	5	43
Apr 6	NPL Prem	H	Hyde United	523	W	1 - 0	Byrne 27	5	44
13	NPL Prem	A	Workington	373	W	2 - 0	Worsfield 40 Wilson 57	5	45
19	NPL Prem	H	Hednesford Town	812	D	0 - 0		6	46
22	NPL Prem	A	Grantham Town	422	W	2 - 0	Hannah 44 (pen) Hughes 48	6	47
27	NPL Prem	H	South Shields	1312	L	0 - 1		6	48

GOALSCORERS	SG	CSG	Pens	Hat tricks	Total
Worsfold	18	4	1		21
Hannah	8	2	1		9
Byrne	7	2			7
Simmons	6	2			7
Clarke	5				5
Russell	5				5
King	4				4
Reeves	4				4
Margetts	2				2
Wilson	2				2
Gordon	1				1
Hughes	1				1
Opponents	1				1
Stanfield	1				1
Watters	1				1

GRANTHAM TOWN MATCH RESULTS 2018-19

Date	Comp	H/A	Opponents	Att:	Result		Goalscorers	Pos
Aug 18	NPL Prem	H	Bamber Bridge	259	D	1 - 1	Acar 57	
21	NPL Prem	A	Stafford Rangers	562	D	1 - 1	Watters 65	14
25	NPL Prem	H	Scarborough Athletic	388	**W**	1 - 0	McGovern 82	6
27	NPL Prem	A	Basford United	355	L	1 - 3	Oliver 8	8
Sept 1	NPL Prem	H	Marine	294	**W**	2 - 0	Barrows 20 Hollingsworth 62 (pen)	7
4	NPL Prem	H	Mickleover Sports	311	**W**	2 - 1	Hollingsworth 26 (pen) 71	6
11	*Void*	*A*	*North Ferriby United*	*247*	*D*	*2 - 2*	*Barrows 50 Watters 60*	*6*
15	NPL Prem	H	Hyde United	275	**W**	1 - 0	McGovern 87 (pen)	4
22	**FAC 2Q**	**A**	**St Ives Town**	**293**	**D**	**1 - 1**	**Bastos 83**	
25	**FAC 2Qr**	**H**	**St Ives Town**	**294**	**L**	**0 - 2**		
29	NPL Prem	H	Whitby Town	272	**W**	3 - 2	Oliver 31 35 Siddons 90	5
Oct 2	NPL Prem	H	Hednesford Town	211	L	1 - 2	McGovern 58 (pen)	7
6	NPL Prem	A	South Shields	1382	L	0 - 5		8
9	NPL Prem	A	Buxton	311	L	0 - 1		8
13	NPL Prem	H	Lancaster City	316	L	0 - 2		11
16	NPL Prem	H	Nantwich Town	171	L	2 - 3	Oliver 2 Fletcher 9	13
23	NPL Prem	A	Matlock Town	345	L	0 - 7		14
27	**FAT 1Q**	**H**	**Halesowen Town**	**158**	**L**	**0 - 4**		
Nov 3	NPL Prem	H	Warrington Town	219	L	0 - 2		16
17	NPL Prem	A	Workington	352	**W**	4 - 1	Watters 33 64 Durkin 51 54	14
24	*Void*	*H*	*North Ferriby United*	*328*	*L*	*1 - 2*	*Durkin 6*	*15*
Dec 1	NPL Prem	A	Hyde United	350	L	0 - 3		16
8	NPL Prem	H	Marine	163	D	1 - 1	Durkin 16	16
15	NPL Prem	A	Mickleover Sports	137	**W**	3 - 1	Harrad 25 Fortnam-Tomlinson 80 Barrows 85	15
22	NPL Prem	H	Stalybridge Celtic	195	L	0 - 1		15
26	NPL Prem	A	Gainsborough Trinity	709	**W**	3 - 2	Durkin 57 Thompson 74 Maguire (og) 88	14
Jan 1	NPL Prem	H	Basford United	270	**W**	2 - 1	Fortnam-Tomlinson 22 Harrad 54	13
5	NPL Prem	A	Bamber Bridgde	381	L	1 - 3	Harrad 6	13
12	NPL Prem	A	Farsley Celtic	371	D	1 - 1	Ward 64	15
19	NPL Prem	H	Stafford Rangers	247	L	0 - 5		16
26	NPL Prem	A	Warrington Town	365	L	0 - 3		17
Feb 2	NPL Prem	H	Workington	266	L	0 - 2		17
9	NPL Prem	H	South Shields	312	**W**	2 - 1	Adebayo - Smith 36 76	15
16	NPL Prem	A	Whitby Town	287	L	1 - 2	Barrows 55	16
23	NPL Prem	H	Matlock Town	348	**W**	2 - 0	Dawson 68 Adebayo-Snith 89	17
Mar 2	NPL Prem	A	Hednesford Town	365	L	1 - 2	Dawson 90	17
9	NPL Prem	A	Witton Albion	288	L	0 - 1		18
16	NPL Prem	H	Buxton	217	L	0 - 1		18
23	NPL Prem	A	Nantwich Town	587	D	1 - 1	Benjamin 65	16
30	NPL Prem	H	Witton Albion	205	**W**	1 - 0	McGovern 82	14
Apr 6	NPL Prem	A	Lancaster City	213	D	1 - 1	Adebayo - Smith 3	14
13	NPL Prem	H	Farsley Celtic	229	L	0 - 4		15
20	NPL Prem	A	Scarborough United	911	L	0 - 2		16
22	NPL Prem	H	Gainsborough Trinity	422	L	0 - 2		17
27	NPL Prem	A	Stalybridge Celtic	439	L	0 - 1		18

No. 1 2 3 4 5 6 7 8 9 10 11 12 13 14 15 16 17 18 19 20 21 22 23 24 25 26 27 28 29 30 31 32 33 34 35 36 37 38 39 40 41 42 43 44 45 46 47 48 49 50 51 52

GOALSCORERS	SG	CSG	Pens	Hat tricks	Total
Durkin	4	2			5
Adebayo-Smith	3				4
Barrows	3				4
McGovern	4		2		4
Oliver	3				4
Watters	4				4
Harrad	3				3
Hollingsworth	2		2		3
Dawson	2				2
Fortnam-Tomlinson	2				2
Acar	1				1
Bastos	1				1
Benjamin	1				1
Fletcher	1				1
Opponents	1				1
Siddons	1				1
Thompson	1				1
Ward	1				1

HEDNESFORD TOWN MATCH RESULTS 2018-19

Date	Comp	H/A	Opponents	Att:	Result	Goalscorers	Pos	No.
Aug 18	NPL Prem	H	Scarborough Athletic	494	L 0 - 1			1
20	NPL Prem	A	Basford United	312	**W** 2 - 1	Howard 22 Gatter 32	12	2
25	NPL Prem	H	Gainsborough Trinity	344	L 1 - 2	Nelson 90	17	3
27	NPL Prem	A	Farsley Celtic	345	**W** 2 - 1	Davies 46 Hollis 86	14	4
Sept 1	NPL Prem	A	Whitby Town	318	**W** 2 - 1	Cockerline 28 Archer 76	10	5
4	NPL Prem	H	Stafford Rangers	916	L 1 - 3	Howard 20	9	6
11	NPL Prem	A	Mickleover Sports	172	L 0 - 1		9	7
15	NPL Prem	H	Workington	301	**W** 2 - 0	Archer 54 Davies 65 (pen)	9	8
22	**FAC 2Q**	**A**	**Rugby Town**	**328**	**W 3 - 1**	**Archer 23 34 Cockerline 31**		9
29	NPL Prem	A	Marine	379	L 1 - 3	King 36	15	10
Oct 2	NPL Prem	A	Grantham Town	211	**W** 2 - 1	Fitzpatrick 25 Howard 89	10	11
6	**FAC 3Q**	**A**	**Kettering Town**	**502**	**L 0 - 4**			12
9	NPL Prem	A	Nantwich Town	305	L 1 - 2	Sweeney 29	10	13
13	NPL Prem	H	South Shields	537	**W** 2 - 1	Sweeney 5 18	7	14
16	NPL Prem	H	Lancaster City	324	L 0 - 1		10	15
20	NPL Prem	A	Matlock Town	434	D 3 - 3	SWEENEY 3 (11pen 36 pen 47)	12	16
23	NPL Prem	H	Buxton	236	D 1 - 1	Howard 90	11	17
27	**FAT 1Q**	**A**	**AFC Mansfield**	**106**	**D 1 - 1**	**Griffiths 5**		18
30	**FAT 1Qr**	**H**	**AFC Mansfield**	**174**	**L 0 - 1**			19
Nov 3	NPL Prem	H	Bamber Bridge	244	D 1 - 1	Sweeney 81	12	20
10	NPL Prem	H	Warrington Town	264	**W** 1 - 0	Cockerline 70	11	21
17	NPL Prem	A	Hyde United	462	L 0 - 2		11	22
24	NPL Prem	H	Mickleover Sports	282	D 1 - 1	Howard 39	11	23
Dec 1	NPL Prem	A	Workington	301	L 2 - 4	Curley 36 Griffiths 45	13	24
8	NPL Prem	H	Whitby Town	265	L 1 - 2	Cockerline 22	13	25
15	NPL Prem	A	Stafford Rangers	668	L 1 - 4	Howard 6	14	26
22	NPL Prem	H	Witton Albion	303	L 0 - 1		15	27
26	*Void*	*A*	*North Ferriby United*	*273*	***W** 2 - 1*	*Cockerline 45 Cooper 90*	*15*	28
Jan 1	NPL Prem	H	Farsley Celtic	439	L 0 - 1		16	29
5	NPL Prem	A	Scarborough Athletic	959	L 3 - 5	King 55 73 Dodd 90	16	30
12	NPL Prem	A	Stalybridge Celtic	384	L 0 - 1		18	31
19	NPL Prem	H	Basford United	289	**W** 3 - 1	Benjamin 5 Ellis 49 64	16	32
26	NPL Prem	A	Bamber Bridge	375	D 1 - 1	Wells 32	16	33
Feb 9	NPL Prem	A	Warrington Town	348	L 1 - 3	Benjamin 23	17	34
16	NPL Prem	H	Marine	343	L 0 - 1		19	35
23	NPL Prem	A	Buxton	453	**W** 2 - 1	Wells 9 Grantham 55	17	36
26	NPL Prem	H	Hyde United	273	**W** 1 - 0	Wells 8	15	37
Mar 2	NPL Prem	H	Grantham Town	365	**W** 2 - 1	Hallahan 20 Grantham 33	13	38
16	NPL Prem	H	Nantwich Town	807	D 4 - 4	Wells 37 Sweeney 50 (pen) 57 O'Hanlon 86	14	39
23	NPL Prem	A	Lancaster City	259	D 2 - 2	Wells 28 Sweeney 35	14	40
30	NPL Prem	H	Matlock Town	391	**W** 2 - 0	Wells 6 58	13	41
Apr 6	NPL Prem	A	South Shields	1214	L 1 - 4	Wells 67	12	42
13	NPL Prem	H	Stalybridge Celtic	376	**W** 1 - 0	KIng 15	12	43
19	NPL Prem	A	Gainsborough Trinity	812	D 0 - 0		12	44
27	NPL Prem	A	Witton Albion	362	D 1 - 1	Wells 88	13	45

GOALSCORERS	SG	CSG	Pens	Hat tricks	Total
Sweeney	5	2	2		9
Wells	8	4			9
Howard	6				6
Archer	3				5
Cockerline	5		3	1	5
King	3				4
Benjamin	2				2
Davies	2				2
Ellis	1				2
Grantham	2				2
Griffiths	2				2
Cooper	1				1
Curley	1				1
Dodd	1				1
Fitzpatrick	1				1
Gatter	1				1
Hallahan	1				1
Hollis	1				1
Nelson	1				1
O'Hanlon	1				1

HYDE UNITED MATCH RESULTS 2018-19

Date	Comp	H/A	Opponents	Att:	Result		Goalscorers	Pos	No.
Aug 18	NPL Prem	H	Basford United	416	W	1 - 0	Chilaka 52		1
21	NPL Prem	A	Witton Albion	360	D	1 - 1	McCombe 48	7	2
25	**FAC P**	**H**	**Sheffield**	**381**	**W**	**5 - 1**	**JONES 3 (71 87 90) Chilaka14 Boyle 79**	**10**	3
27	NPL Prem	A	Buxton	712	L	0 - 1		14	4
Sept 1	NPL Prem	H	Scarborough Athletic	577	L	2 - 3	Jones 76 McCombe 83	17	5
4	NPL Prem	A	Nantwich Town	288	D	1 - 1	Greaves 50	17	6
8	**FAC 1Q**	**A**	**Colne**	**345**	**L**	**0 - 2**			7
11	NPL Prem	H	Warrington Town	306	L	0 - 2		18	8
15	NPL Prem	A	Grantham Town	275	L	0 - 1		19	9
22	NPL Prem	A	Whitby Town	251	W	1 - 0	Hughes 15	17	10
29	NPL Prem	H	Mickleover Sports	402	W	2 - 1	Porritt 21 Greaves 45	16	11
Oct 2	NPL Prem	H	Workington	227	D	0 - 0		15	12
6	NPL Prem	A	Matlock Town	448	D	0 - 0		15	13
13	NPL Prem	H	Gainsborough Trinity	467	L	1 - 3	Daly 59	16	14
16	NPL Prem	H	South Shields	371	W	4 - 1	Pratt 26 (pen) Simpson 42 McCombe 78 Platt 90	15	15
20	NPL Prem	A	Stafford Rangers	548	W	3 - 1	McCombe 72 Simpson 81 Pratt 90	11	16
27	**FAT 1Q**	**H**	**Bamber Bridge**	**315**	**W**	**3 - 0**	**Simpson 18 Platt 69 80**		17
Nov 3	NPL Prem	A	Marine	366	D	0 - 0		13	18
10	**FAT 2Q**	**A**	**South Shields**	**1095**	**L**	**1 - 2**	**Fagbola 24**		19
13	NPL Prem	A	Lancaster City	230	L	1 - 2	Simpson 20	13	20
17	NPL Prem	H	Hednesford Town	462	W	2 - 0	Simpson 84 Chilaka 89	12	21
24	NPL Prem	A	Warrington Town	322	L	1 - 2	Platt 42	13	22
Dec 1	NPL Prem	H	Grantham Town	350	W	3 - 0	Pratt 3 (pen) 23 Chilaka 88	10	23
8	NPL Prem	A	Scarborough Athletic	954	W	2 - 0	Simpson 18 Platt 22	10	24
15	NPL Prem	H	Nantwich Town	331	L	1 - 2	Roberts 19	11	25
22	*Void*	*H*	*North Ferriby United*	*307*	*W*	*3 - 0*	*Simpson 19 Pratt 67 Chilaka 90*	*10*	26
26	NPL Prem	A	Stalybridge Celtic	838	D	2 - 2	Chilaka 72 Pratt 75	10	27
Jan 1	NPL Prem	H	Buxton	551	D	1 - 1	Chilaka 64	10	28
5	NPL Prem	A	Basford United	237	W	8 - 3	CHILAKA 4 (10 25 41 70) Pratt 10 (pen) Platt 51 Lipka 86 McCombe 37	10	29
12	NPL Prem	A	Bamber Bridge	433	L	2 - 5	Fagbola 9 Chilaka 86	10	30
19	NPL Prem	H	Witton Albion	418	W	1 - 0	Smalley 77	7	31
26	NPL Prem	H	Marine	420	L	1 - 2	Chilaka 56		32
Feb 9	NPL Prem	H	Matlock Town	381	L	1 - 2	Platt 46	10	33
16	NPL Prem	A	Mickleover Sports	284	W	2 - 0	Smalley 45 Daly 72	9	34
23	NPL Prem	H	Whitby Town	351	W	3 - 0	Pratt 12 87 McCombe 73	8	35
26	NPL Prem	A	Hednesford Town	273	L	0 1		8	36
Mar 2	NPL Prem	A	Workington	424	W	2 - 1	Lane 40 Platt 45 (pen)	8	37
9	NPL Prem	H	Farsley Celtic	393	L	1 - 2	Smalley 63	9	38
16	NPL Prem	H	Lancaster City	398	L	1 2	Lane 70	10	39
23	NPL Prem	A	South Shields	1857	L	0 - 4		10	40
30	NPL Prem	H	Stafford Rangers	418	W	5 - 3	Hill 12 (og) Roberts 22 Pratt 44 Platt 72 O'Reilly 90	9	41
Apr 6	NPL Prem	A	Gainsborough Trinity	523	L	0 - 1		9	42
13	NPL Prem	H	Bamber Bridge	352	L	0 - 2		10	43
20	NPL Prem	A	Farsley Celtic	518	D	1 - 1	Smalley 23	10	44
22	NPL Prem	H	Stalybridge Celtic	787	W	1 - 0	Smalley 24	10	45

GOALSCORERS	SG	CSG	Pens	Hat tricks	Total
Chilaka	10	4		1	13
Pratt	7	2	3		10
Platt	7		1		9
Simpson	7	3			7
McCombe	6				6
Smalley	5			1	5
Jones	2				4
Daly	2				2
Fagbola	2				2
Greaves	2				2
Lane	2				2
Roberts	2				2
Boyle	1				1
Hughes	1				1
Lipka	1				1
O'Reilly	1				1
Opponents	1				1
Porritt	1				1

LANCASTER CITY MATCH RESULTS 2018-19

Date	Comp	H/A	Opponents	Att:	Result		Goalscorers	Pos	No.
Aug 18	NPL Prem	A	Matlock Town	407	L	0 - 4			1
21	NPL Prem	H	Warrington Town	236	L	1 - 3	Wills 11	22	2
25	NPL Prem	A	Nantwich Town	283	L	2 - 5	Wilson 59 Bailey 63	22	3
27	NPL Prem	H	Marine	265	L	0 - 1		22	4
Sept 1	NPL Prem	A	Gainsborough Trinity	527	L	1 - 3	Blinkhorn	22	5
4	NPL Prem	H	Bamber Bridge	296	D	1 - 1	Kilifin 76	22	6
8	**FAC 1Q**	**H**	**Trafford**	**234**	**L**	**0 - 2**			7
11	NPL Prem	A	South Shields	1151	L	0 - 2		22	8
15	*Void*	*H*	*North Ferriby United*	*228*	*D*	*0 - 0*		*22*	9
22	NPL Prem	A	Basford United	160	L	1 - 3	Blinkhorn 12	22	10
29	NPL Prem	A	Buxton	403	**W**	2 - 1	Fensome 56 Steel 89	21	11
Oct 2	NPL Prem	A	Farsley Celtic	142	L	0 - 2		22	12
6	NPL Prem	H	Basford United	216	D	1 - 1	Russell 10	22	13
13	NPL Prem	A	Grantham Town	316	**W**	2 - 0	Blinkhorn 32 Wilson 36	21	14
16	NPL Prem	A	Hednesford Town	321	**W**	1 - 0	Wilson 27	20	15
20	NPL Prem	H	Scarborough Athletic	324	L	0 - 6		20	16
23	NPL Prem	H	Stalybridge Celtic	195	**W**	1 - 0	Winder 67	17	17
27	**FAT 1Q**	**A**	**Marine**	**286**	**W**	**2 - 0**	**Wilson 73 (pen) Steel 87**		18
Nov 3	NPL Prem	A	Witton Albion	262	L	0 - 1		19	19
10	**FAT 2Q**	**H**	**Ossett United**	**262**	**W**	**1 - 0**	**Bailey 90**		20
13	NPL Prem	H	Hyde United	230	**W**	2 - 1	Wilson 57 (pen) 77	17	21
17	NPL Prem	H	Stafford Rangers	278	D	0 - 0		17	22
24	**FAT 3Q**	**H**	**Guiseley**	**259**	**D**	**2 - 2**	**Stanley 13 Wilson 75**	**16**	23
Dec 1	*Void*	*A*	*North Ferriby United*	*138*	***W***	*2 - 1*	*Williams 8 Norris 19*	*16*	24
8	NPL Prem	H	Gainsborough Trinity	194	L	0 - 1		16	25
11	**FAT 3Qr**	**A**	**Guiseley**	**283**	**W**	**2 - 1**	**Binkhorn 21 Williams 71**	**17**	26
15	**FAT 1P**	**H**	**Blyth Spartans**	**149**	**L**	**0 - 3**		**17**	27
22	NPL Prem	H	South Shields	254	D	1 - 1	Hudson 87	17	28
26	NPL Prem	H	Workington	320	L	0 - 2		18	29
Jan 1	NPL Prem	A	Marine	481	L	1 - 3	Steel 21	18	30
5	NPL Prem	H	Matlock Town	216	**W**	1 - 0	Wilson 5 (pen)	18	31
12	NPL Prem	H	Mickleover Sports	190	D	2 - 2	Berry (og) 30 Carsley 90	19	32
19	NPL Prem	A	Warington Town	375	D	1 - 1	Carsley 83	20	33
26	NPL Prem	H	Witton Albion	267	**W**	1 - 0	Dawson 90	18	34
Feb 2	NPL Prem	A	Stafford Rangers	532	D	1 - 1	Wilson 34 (pen)	18	35
9	NPL Prem	A	Whitby Town	248	D	1 - 1	Blinkhorn 42	16	36
12	NPL Prem	A	Bamber Bridge	438	D	2 - 2	Carsley 75 Steel 81	16	37
16	NPL Prem	H	Buxton	256	L	1 - 3	White 90	16	38
23	NPL Prem	A	Stalybridge Celtic	317	**W**	2 - 1	Bailey 8 $2	16	39
Mar 2	NPL Prem	H	Farsley Celtic	259	**W**	2 - 0	Bailey 43 Blinkhorn 65	14	40
16	NPL Prem	A	Hyde United	398	**W**	2 - 1	Bailey 62 Fensome 72	14	41
23	NPL Prem	H	Hednesford Town	259	D	2 - 2	Norris 53 Dawson 90	13	42
30	NPL Prem	A	Scarborough Athletic	969	D	1 - 1	Dawson 87 (pen)	13	43
Apr 6	NPL Prem	H	Grantham Town	213	D	1 - 1	Bailey 86	13	44
13	NPL Prem	A	Mickleover Sports	201	D	1 - 1	Dugdale 47	14	45
20	NPL Prem	H	Nantwich Town	321	L	0 - 2		14	46
22	NPL Prem	A	Workington	689	**W**	2 - 0	Carsley 25 34	13	47
27	NPL Prem	H	Whitby Town	255	**W**	2 - 1	Steel 72 Norris 84	12	48

GOALSCORERS	SG	CSG	Pens	Hat tricks	Total
Wilson	7	2	4		9
Bailey	6	3			7
Blinkhorn	6				6
Carsley	4				5
Steel	5				5
Dawson	2		1		3
Fensome	3				3
Norris	3				2
Williams	2				2
Dugdale	1				1
Hudson	1				1
Kilifin	1				1
Opponents	1				1
Russell	1				1
Stanley	1				1
White	1				1
Wills	1				1
Winder	1				1

MARINE MATCH RESULTS 2018-19

Date	Comp	H/A	Opponents	Att:	Result		Goalscorers	Pos	No.
Aug 18	NPL Prem	H	North Ferriby United	359	D	1 - 1	Carney 79		1
21	NPL Prem	A	Stalybridge Celtic	312	L	2 - 3	Hine 42 Mitchley 85 (pen)	15	2
25	NPL Prem	H	Basford United	311	L	1 - 4	Carney 37	20	3
27	NPL Prem	A	Lancaster City	265	W	1 - 0	Doyle 2	18	4
Sept 1	NPL Prem	H	Grantham Town	294	L	0 - 2		19	5
4	NPL Prem	A	Witton Albion	241	D	0 - 0		19	6
8	**FAC 1Q**	**H**	**Scarborough Athletic**	**496**	**D**	**1 - 1**	**Hine 55**		7
11	**FAC 1Qr**	**A**	**Scarborough Athletic**	**975**	**W**	**3 - 2**	**Mitchley 6 Reid 6 Carney 60**	9	8
15	NPL Prem	A	Warrington Town	363	L	0 - 1		20	9
22	**FAC 2Q**	**H**	**Frickley Athletic**	**401**	**W**	**1 - 0**	**Mitchley 46**		10
25	NPL Prem	A	Workington	317	D	1 - 1	Mitchley 24	20	11
29	NPL Prem	H	Hednesford Town	379	W	3 - 1	Carney 15 Doyle 57 Murray 87	17	12
Oct 2	NPL Prem	H	Stafford Rangers	289	W	1 - 0	Carney 7 (pen)	16	13
6	**FAC 3Q**	**A**	**Brackley Town**	**371**	**W**	**3 - 2**	**Snclair-Smith 7 39 Murray 32**		14
9	NPL Prem	A	Matlock Town	310	L	1 - 3	Yates 5 (og)	17	15
13	NPL Prem	H	Whitby Town	469	D	0 - 0		17	16
20	**FAC 4Q**	**H**	**Salford City**	**1709**	**L**	**1 - 2**	**Mitchley 49**		17
23	NPL Prem	H	Nantwich Town	321	L	0 - 1		19	18
27	**FAT 1Q**	**H**	**Lancaster City**	**286**	**L**	**0 - 2**			19
Nov 3	NPL Prem	H	Hyde United	366	D	0 - 0		20	20
10	NPL Prem	H	Gainsborough Trinity	352	D	1 - 1	Joyce 60	19	21
17	NPL Prem	A	Scarborough Athletic	1202	L	0 - 2		20	22
24	NPL Prem	A	Nantwich Town	402	L	2 - 3	Murray 66 Irwin 68	20	23
Dec 1	NPL Prem	H	Warington Town	521	L	0 - 2		20	24
8	NPL Prem	A	Grantham Town	163	D	1 - 1	Hynes 75	20	25
15	NPL Prem	H	Witton Albion	360	L	2 - 3	Carney 2 Doyle 41	20	26
22	NPL Prem	H	Farsley Celtic	395	L	1 - 2	Cummins 69	20	27
26	NPL Prem	A	Bamber Bridge	414	W	2 - 1	Cummins 11 Elstone 25	20	28
29	NPL Prem	A	Mickleover Sports	220	L	0 - 1		20	29
Jan 1	NPL Prem	H	Lancaster City	481	W	3 - 1	Steel 45 (og) Edge 75 Cummins 88	19	30
5	*Void*	*A*	*North Ferriby United*	*181*	*W*	*2 - 0*	*Doyle 46 Hynes 90*	*19*	31
12	NPL Prem	A	Buxton	401	W	3 - 0	Hynes 42 Irwin 74 Mitchley 77	17	32
19	NPL Prem	H	Stalybridge Celtic	430	D	1 - 1	Shaw 80	17	33
26	NPL Prem	A	Hyde United	420	W	2 - 1	Mitchley 15 Barnes 76	16	34
Feb 9	NPL Prem	H	Mickleover Sports	338	W	3 - 0	Carney 56 Cummins 78 Turner 84 (og)	15	35
16	NPL Prem	A	Hednesford Town	343	W	1 - 0	Irwin 28	14	36
23	NPL Prem	H	Workington	671	L	0 - 2		14	37
Mar 2	NPL Prem	A	Stafford Rangers	683	D	0 - 0		15	38
9	NPL Prem	H	Scarborough Athletic	495	L	1 - 2	Doyle 84	15	39
12	NPL Prem	A	South Shields	909	L	1 - 2	Brown 65	15	40
23	NPL Prem	A	Gainsborough Trinity	539	W	1 - 0	Muray 61	15	41
30	NPL Prem	H	South Shields	641	L	1 - 3	Mitchley 80	16	42
Apr 6	NPL Prem	A	Whitby Town	307	L	1 - 2	Mbalanda 36	17	43
9	NPL Prem	H	Matlock Town	2536	L	1 - 3	Doyle 52	17	44
13	NPL Prem	H	Buxton	446	D	1 - 1	Mbalanda 73	17	45
20	NPL Prem	A	Basford United	230	D	0 - 0		17	46
22	NPL Prem	H	Bamber Bridge	544	L	0 - 2		18	47
27	NPL Prem	A	Farsley Celtic	1527	L	0 - 2		20	48

GOALSCORERS	SG	CSG	Pens	Hat tricks	Total		SG	CSG	Pens	Hat tricks	Total
Mitchley	8	2	1		8	Sinclair-Smith	1				2
Carney	7		1		7	Barnes	1				1
Doyle	5				6	Brown	1				1
Cummins	4				4	Edge	1				1
Murray	4				4	Elstone	1				1
Hynes	3				3	Joyce	1				1
Irwin	3				3	Reid	1				1
Opponents	3				3	Shaw	1				1
Hine	2				2						
Mbalanda	2				2						

MATLOCK TOWN MATCH RESULTS 2018-19

Date	Comp	H/A	Opponents	Att:	Result		Goalscorers	Pos	No.
Aug 18	NPL Prem	H	Lancaster City	407	**W**	4 - 0	Harrod 30 (pen) 58 Watson 79 Jackson 85		1
21	NPL Prem	A	Scarborough Athletic	1280	D	2 - 2	Williams 76 Phillips 90	3	2
27	NPL Prem	A	Gainsborough Trinity	626	L	2 - 4	Green 27 Harrad 67	15	3
Sept 1	NPL Prem	A	Workington	422	L	1 - 3	Williams 76 Phillips 90	18	4
4	NPL Prem	H	Whitby Town	405	L	0 - 3		20	5
9	**FAC 1Q**	**H**	**Halesowen Town**	**403**	**L**	**1 - 2**	**Harrod 59 (pen)**		6
10	NPL Prem	A	Basford United	342	L	0 - 6		20	7
15	NPL Prem	H	South Shields	530	L	0 - 3		21	8
22	NPL Prem	A	Stalybridge Celtic	271	L	1 - 3	Westcarr 89	22	9
29	NPL Prem	A	Farsley Celtic	224	L	2 - 3	Marshall 13 65	22	10
Oct 2	*Void*	*A*	*North Ferriby United*	*144*	***W***	*5 - 2*	*WESTCARR 3 (11 19 84 pen) Marshall 58 Taylor 67*	*20*	11
6	NPL Prem	H	Hyde United	448	D	0 - 0		20	12
9	NPL Prem	H	Marine	310	**W**	3 - 1	Marshall 12 81 Westcarr 32 (pen)	18	13
13	NPL Prem	A	Warrington Town	303	**W**	1 - 0	King 21	15	14
16	NPL Prem	A	Mickleover Sports	330	D	0 - 0		16	15
20	NPL Prem	H	Hednesford Town	434	D	3 - 3	Westcarr 42 (pen) 69 Jackson 61	16	16
23	NPL Prem	H	Grantham Town	345	**W**	7 - 0	WESTCARR 3 (31 38 70) HINSLEY 3 (48 70 79) Whitehead 86	13	17
27	**FAT 1Q**	**A**	**St Neots Town**	**249**	**L**	**0 - 1**			18
Nov 3	NPL Prem	A	Nantwich Town	344	**W**	4 - 1	King 55 79 Taylor 68 Beatson 90	11	19
10	NPL Prem	H	Bamber Bridge	338	**W**	2 - 1	King 12 Whitehead 19	10	20
17	NPL Prem	H	Stalybridge Celtic	521	**W**	3 - 1	Marshall 13 65 Jackson 90 Green 90	8	21
Dec 1	NPL Prem	A	South Shields	1119	L	0 - 5		9	22
8	NPL Prem	H	Workington	346	**W**	2 - 1	Hinsley 27 Wafula 79	9	23
15	NPL Prem	A	Whitby Town	258	**W**	3 - 1	Marshall 32 79 Hinsley 68	8	24
22	NPL Prem	H	Stafford Rangers	493	**W**	3 - 2	Westcarr 16 69 Yates 74	8	25
26	NPL Prem	A	Buxton	880	D	2 - 2	Marshall 41 Westcarr 44	8	26
Jan 1	NPL Prem	H	Gainsborough Trinity	665	L	0 - 2		9	27
5	NPL Prem	A	Lancaster City	216	L	0 - 1		9	28
12	NPL Prem	A	Witton Albion	305	L	0 - 1		9	29
19	NPL Prem	H	Scarborough Athletic	549	D	0 - 0		9	30
26	NPL Prem	H	Nantwich Town	450	L	0 - 1		9	31
Feb 9	NPL Prem	A	Hyde United	391	**W**	2 - 1	Westcarr 34 79	8	32
16	NPL Prem	H	Farsley Celtic	454	L	1 - 2	Morpeth 12	10	33
23	NPL Prem	A	Grantham Town	348	L	0 - 2		11	34
Mar 2	*Void*	*H*	*North Ferriby United*	*405*	***W***	*1 - 0*	*Margetts 28*	*11*	35
23	NPL Prem	H	Mickleover Sports	580	D	1 - 1	Margetts 70	12	36
30	NPL Prem	A	Hednesford Town	391	L	0 - 2		12	37
Apr 2	NPL Prem	H	Basford United	311	D	2 - 2	Westcarr 79 Williams 82	15	38
6	NPL Prem	H	Warrington Town	419	L	0 - 2		15	39
9	NPL Prem	A	Marine	253	**W**	3 - 1	Williams 11 Chettle 28 68	13	40
13	NPL Prem	H	Witton Albion	346	L	1 - 2	Blake 77	13	41
20	NPL Prem	A	Bamber Bridge	396	L	2 - 4	Chapel 20 Westcarr 59	13	42
22	NPL Prem	H	Buxton	575	L	0 - 6		15	43
27	NPL Prem	A	Stafford Rangers	606	L	1 - 4	Marshall 34	15	44

GOALSCORERS	SG	CSG	Pens	Hat tricks	Total
Westcarr	10	2	2	2	17
Marshall	7	2			11
Hinsley	4			1	5
Harrod	4		2		4
King	2				4
Williams	4				4
Jackson	3				3
Chettle	1				2
Margetts	2				2
Taylor	2				2
Whitehead	2				2
Beatson	1				1
Blake	1				1
Chapel	1				1
Green	1				1
Morpeth	1				1
Phillips	1				1
Wafula	1				1
Watson	1				1
Yates	1				1

MICKLEOVER SPORTS MATCH RESULTS 2018-19

Date	Comp	H/A	Opponents	Att:	Result	Goalscorers	Pos	No.
Aug 18	NPL Prem	A	Stalybridge Celtic	379	D 0 - 0			1
21	NPL Prem	H	Gainsborough Trinity	461	L 0 - 2		20	2
25	*Void*	*H*	*North Ferriby United*	*208*	*W 3 - 2*	*Mills 34 42 Garnett 54*	*15*	3
27	NPL Prem	A	Stafford Rangers	618	D 1 - 1	Banks 58 (og)	16	4
Sept 1	NPL Prem	H	Buxton	262	L 1 - 3	Garnett 71	17	5
4	NPL Prem	A	Grantham Town	311	L 1 - 2	Garnett 89 (pen)	18	6
11	NPL Prem	H	Hednesford Town	172	W 1 - 0	Jarman 37	17	7
15	NPL Prem	A	Farsley Celtic	196	W 1 - 0	Turner 33	16	8
22	**FAC 2Q**	**A**	**Anstey Nomads**	**283**	**W 7 - 1**	**Roberts 10 Jarman 20 79 MARSELLA 3 (62 75 80) Phillips 83**		9
25	NPL Prem	H	Scarborough Athletic	221	D 1 - 1	Marsella 45	17	10
29	NPL Prem	A	Hyde United	402	L 1 - 2	Turner 59	18	11
Oct 2	NPL Prem	A	Warrington Town	211	L 0 - 1		19	12
6	**FAC 3Q**	**H**	**Alfreton Town**	**505**	**L 1 - 2**	**Marsella 82**		13
9	NPL Prem	A	Witton Albion	234	W 2 - 1	McGrath 10 Jarman 17	19	14
13	NPL Prem	H	Nantwich Town	210	D 0 - 0		18	15
16	NPL Prem	H	Matlock Town	330	D 0 - 0		17	16
20	NPL Prem	A	Whitby Town	288	L 0 - 4		17	17
27	**FAT 1Q**	**H**	**Redditch United**	**157**	**W 1 - 0**	**Garnett 90**		18
Nov 3	NPL Prem	H	Workington	151	W 1 - 0	Jarman 64	17	19
10	**FAT 2Q**	**A**	**Stratford Town**	**183**	**D 1 - 1**	**Norcross 85**		20
13	**FAT 2Qr**	**H**	**Stratford Town**	**157**	**L 0 - 1**			21
17	NPL Prem	A	South Shields	1749	L 2 - 3	Garnett 9 90	19	22
24	NPL Prem	A	Hednesford Town	282	D 1 - 1	Jarman 90 (pen)	19	23
Dec 1	NPL Prem	H	Farsley Celtic	127	L 1 - 2	Prusa 45	19	24
8	NPL Prem	A	Buxton	273	L 0 - 5		19	25
15	NPL Prem	H	Grantham Town	137	L 1 - 3	Mills 71	19	26
22	NPL Prem	H	Bamber Bridge	174	D 2 - 2	Mills 56 Jarman 79	19	27
26	NPL Prem	A	Basford United	286	L 1 - 2	McDonald 65	19	28
29	NPL Prem	H	Marine	220	W 1 - 0	Jarman 13	18	29
Jan 1	NPL Prem	H	Stafford Rangers	304	W 3 - 2	McDonald 61 77 Jarman 85 (pen)	17	30
5	NPL Prem	H	Stalybridge Celtic	184	W 2 - 1	McDonald 10 49	17	31
12	NPL Prem	A	Lancaster City	190	D 2 - 2	Mills 54 Berry 67	16	32
19	NPL Prem	H	Gainsborough Trinity	210	L: 0 - 1		18	33
Feb 9	NPL Prem	A	Marine	328	L 0 - 3		20	34
16	NPL Prem	H	Hyde United	284	L 0 - 2		20	35
23	NPL Prem	A	Scarborough Athletic	945	W 2 - 0	Amantchi 67 (pen) 69	19	36
Mar 2	NPL Prem	H	Warington Town	328	L 1 - 4	Garnett 53	20	37
9	NPL Prem	H	South Shields	294	L 1 - 2	Junek 81	20	38
23	NPL Prem	A	Matlock Town	580	D 1 - 1	Warren 72	20	39
30	NPL Prem	H	Whitby Town	212	L 0 - 1		20	40
Apr 2	NPL Prem	A	Workington	504	W 1 - 0	Storer 33	20	41
6	NPL Prem	A	Nantwich Town	410	W 3 - 2	Storer 20 Garnett 41 Boula 45	19	42
9	NPL Prem	H	Witton Albion	173	D 0 - 0		19	43
13	NPL Prem	H	Lancaster City	201	D 1 - 1	Storer 61	19	44
22	NPL Prem	H	Basford United	316	L 0 - 1		20	45
27	NPL Prem	A	Bamber Bridge	300	W 2 - 1	McDonald 74 (pen) Garnett 85	19	46

GOALSCORERS	SG	CSG	Pens	Hat tricks	Total
Garnett	8	2	1		9
Jarman	8	2	2		9
McDonald	4		1		6
Marsella	3			1	5
Mills	4				5
Storer	3				3
Amantchi	1		1		2
Turner	2				2
Berry	1				1
Bouyla	1				1
Junek	1				1
McGrath	1				1
Norcross	1				1
Opponents	1				1
Phillips	1				1
Prusa	1				1
Roberts	1				1
Warren	1				1

NANTWICH TOWN MATCH RESULTS 2018-19

Date	Comp	H/A	Opponents	Att:	Result		Goalscorers	Pos	No.
Aug 18	NPL Prem	H	Gainsborough Trinity	307	W	1 - 0	Jones 90		1
21	NPL Prem	A	Buxton	279	D	0 - 0		8	2
25	NPL Prem	H	Lancaster City	283	W	5 - 2	SAUNDERS 3 (8 41 90) Glover 45 83	1	3
27	NPL Prem	A	Witton Albion	357	L	0 - 2		9	4
Sept 1	NPL Prem	A	South Shields	1444	L	0 - 4		13	5
4	NPL Prem	H	Hyde United	288	D	1 - 1	Lawrie 90	14	6
8	**FAC 1Q**	**H**	**Worksop Town**	**374**	**W**	**5 - 2**	**Knight 16 60 Saunders 52 Lawrie 54 Jones 87**	**12**	7
15	NPL Prem	H	Whitby Town	272	W	4 - 1	Lawrie 23 51 Mwasile 71 Cotterill 88	10	8
22	**FAC 2Q**	**H**	**Blyth Spartans**	**371**	**D**	**3 - 3**	**Lawrie 13 85 Hughes 57**		9
25	**FAC 2Qr**	**A**	**Blyth Spartans**	**491**	**L**	**0 - 1**			10
29	NPL Prem	A	Scarborough Athletic	1055	W	3 - 2	GLOVER 3 (39 83 85)	9	11
Oct 2	NPL Prem	A	Stalybridge Celtic	211	D	1 - 1	Cooke 37	10	12
6	NPL Prem	H	Farsley Celtic	335	W	2 - 1	Lawrie 23 Stair 43	7	13
9	NPL Prem	H	Hednesford Town	305	W	2 - 1	Lindfield 10 49	7	14
13	NPL Prem	A	Mickleover Sports	210	D	0 - 0		7	15
16	NPL Prem	A	Grantham Town	171	W	3 - 2	Cooke 37 Lindfield 57 Saunders 81	4	16
20	NPL Prem	H	Workington	378	D	0 - 0		4	17
23	NPL Prem	A	Marine	321	W	1 - 0	Lindfield 45	4	18
27	**FAT 1Q**	**A**	**Stalybridge Celtic**	**247**	**L**	**0 - 1**			19
30	NPL Prem	H	Warrington Town	296	W	2 - 1	Cooke 5 Mwasile 3	2	20
Nov 3	NPL Prem	H	Matlock Town	344	L	1 - 4	Jones 25	2	21
10	*Void*	*A*	*North Ferriby United*	*219*	*W*	*4 - 1*	*Saunders 12 Glover 21 (pen) 67 Stair 33*	*2*	22
17	NPL Prem	A	Bamber Bridge	456	D	2 - 2	Cooke 20 Mwasile 75	2	23
24	NPL Prem	H	Marine	402	W	3 - 2	Cooke 3 Mwasile 8 Jones 90	2	24
Dec 1	NPL Prem	A	Whitby Town	212	W	1 - 0	Malkin 52	1	25
8	NPL Prem	H	South Shields	422	D	0 - 0		1	26
15	NPL Prem	A	Hyde United	331	W	2 - 1	Cooke 52 (pen) Brownhill 60 (og)	1	27
22	NPL Prem	H	Basford United	458	W	3 - 2	Malkin 10 75 Morgan 22	1	28
26	NPL Prem	A	Stafford Rangers	807	W	4 - 1	Cooke 32 Malkin 55 72 Mullarkey 80	1	29
Jan 1	NPL Prem	H	Witton Albion	956	L	0 - 1		2	30
5	NPL Prem	H	Gainsborough Trinity	589	D	0 - 0		4	31
26	NPL Prem	A	Matlock Town	460	W	1 - 0	Malkin 72	4	32
Feb 9	NPL Prem	A	Farsley Celtic	349	L	1 - 2	Lawrie 78	4	33
16	NPL Prem	H	Scarborough Athletic	729	D	1 - 1	Bell 90	4	34
23	NPL Prem	A	Warrington Town	647	D	3 - 3	Cooke 9 Glover 30 (pen) 34	4	35
26	NPL Prem	H	Bamber Bridge	301	W	2 - 0	Saunders 45 Malkin 82	4	36
Mar 2	NPL Prem	H	Stalybridge Celtic	426	W	4 - 2	Mullarkey 56 Malkin 57 88 Fuller 70	4	37
5	NPL Prem	A	Buxton	327	L	1 - 2	Glover 14	4	38
16	NPL Prem	A	Hednesford Town	907	D	4 - 4	Morgan 52 83 Glover 65 Malkin 75	4	39
23	NPL Prem	H	Grantham Town	587	D	1 - 1	Cooke 45 (pen)	4	40
30	NPL Prem	A	Workington	476	W	4 - 2	Glover 8 Cooke 18 (pen) 67 (pen) Saunders 90	4	41
Apr 6	NPL Prem	H	Mickleover Sports	410	L	2 - 3	Saunders 16 31	4	42
20	NPL Prem	A	Lancaster City	321	W	2 - 0	Stair 5 Cooke 9	4	43
22	NPL Prem	H	Stafford Rangers	605	L	0 - 1		4	44
27	NPL Prem	A	Basford United	201	L	3 - 7	Saunders 19 90 Morgan 87	4	45
30	**PO SF**	**A**	**Warrington Town**	**1424**	**L**	**1 - 4**	**Saunders 28**		46

GOALSCORERS	SG	CSG	Pens	Hat tricks	Total
Saunders	9	2		1	13
Cooke	11	2	4		12
Glover	8	2	2	1	12
Malkin	7	2			10
Lawrie	6	4			8
Jones	3				4
Lindfield	4				4
Morgan	4				4
Mwasile	3				4
Stair	3				3
Knight	1				2
Mullarkey	2				2
Bell	1				1
Cotterill	1				1
Fuller	1				1
Hughes	1				1
Opponents	1				1

NORTH FERRIBY UNITED MATCH RESULTS 2018-19

Date	Comp	H/A	Opponents	Att:	Result	Goalscorers	Pos	No.
Aug 11	Isth Prem	A	AFC Hornchurch	287	L 0 - 3		21	1
Aug 18	NPL Prem	A	Marine	359	D 1 - 1	Lofts 42		2
21	NPL Prem	H	Whitby Town	283	L 0 - 1		17	3
24	NPL Prem	A	Mickleover Sports	208	L 2 - 3	Norton 69 Williamson 82	19	4
27	NPL Prem	H	South Shields	452	**W** 3 - 0	Hinsley 6 89 Harrison 45	18	5
Sept 1	NPL Prem	H	Warrington Town	217	L 0 - 5		20	6
4	NPL Prem	A	Scarborough Athletic	1117	L 1 - 3	Lofts 16 (pen)	21	7
8	**FAC 1Q**	**A**	**Dunston UTS**	**303**	**L 1 - 4**	**Forrester 84**		8
11	NPL Prem	H	Grantham Town	247	D 2 - 2	Mail 85 Lofts 90	20	9
15	NPL Prem	A	Lancaster City	228	D 0 - 0		18	10
22	NPL Prem	H	Scarborough Athletic	605	L 1 - 3	Harrison 54	19	11
25	NPL Prem	A	Gainsborough Trinity	482	L 0 - 1		19	12
29	NPL Prem	H	Witton Albion	195	L 0 - 4		20	13
Oct 2	NPL Prem	H	Matlock Town	144	L 2 - 5	Harrison 39 HInsley 45	21	14
6	NPL Prem	A	Stalybridge Celtic	155	L 1 - 2	Mail 30	21	15
9	NPL Prem	A	Bamber Bridge	355	L 1 - 3	Hinsley 60	21	16
13	NPL Prem	H	Stafford Rangers	360	L 1 - 2	Hinsley 35	22	17
20	NPL Prem	A	Buxton	373	D 2 - 2	Hinsley 67 Lofts 77	22	18
27	**FAT 1Q**	**A**	**South Shields**	**714**	**L 0 - 4**			19
Nov 3	NPL Prem	A	Basford United	232	L 2 - 4	Nicholls 30 Harrison 45	22	20
10	NPL Prem	H	Nantwich Town	219	L 1 - 4	Waudby 35	22	21
17	NPL Prem	H	Farsley Celtic	321	L 0 - 6		22	22
24	NPL Prem	A	Grantham Town	328	**W** 2 - 1	Martindale 3 Bradshaw 55	22	23
Dec 1	NPL Prem	H	Lancaster City	138	L 1 - 2	Martindale 11	22	24
8	NPL Prem	A	Warrington Town	164	L 0 - 4		22	25
22	NPL Prem	A	Hyde United	307	L 0 - 3		22	26
26	NPL Prem	H	Hednesford Town	273	L 1 - 2	Waudby 35	22	27
Jan 1	NPL Prem	A	South Shields	1437	L 2 - 6	Vickers 69 78	22	28
5	NPL Prem	H	Marine	181	L 0 - 2		22	29
19	NPL Prem	A	Whitby Town	227	L 1 - 6	Hutchinson 88	22	30
26	NPL Prem	H	Basford United	186	L 1 - 2	Windass 37	22	31
Feb 9	NPL Prem	H	Workington	155	L 0 - 2		22	32
16	NPL Prem	A	Witton Albion	306	L 0 - 1		22	33
23	NPL Prem	H	Gainsborough Trinity	314	L 0 - 4		22	34
26	NPL Prem	A	Farsley Celtic	184	L 0 - 4		22	35
Mar 2	NPL Prem	A	Matlock Town	405	L 0 - 1		22	36
Club resign from Northern Premier League - record expunged.								37
16	NPL Prem	A	Bamber Bridge					38
23	NPL Prem	H	Gainsborough Trinity					39
30	NPL Prem	H	Buxton					40
Apr 6	NPL Prem	A	Stafford Rangers					41
13	NPL Prem	A	Northwich Town					42
20	NPL Prem	H	Bamber Bridge					43
22	NPL Prem	A	Hednesford Town					44
27	NPL Prem	H	Hyde United					45

GOALSCORERS	SG	CSG	Pens	Hat tricks	Total
Hinsley	5	3			6
Harrison	4				4
Lofts	4		1		4
Mail	2				2
Martindale	2				2
Vickers	1				2
Waudby	2				2
Bradshaw	1				1
Forrester	1				1
Hutchinson	1				1
Nicholls	1				1
Norton	1				1
Williamson	1				1
Windass	1				1

SCARBOROUGH ATHLETIC MATCH RESULTS 2018-19

Date	Comp	H/A	Opponents	Att:	Result		Goalscorers	Pos	No.
Aug 18	NPL Prem	A	Hednesford Town	494	**W**	1 - 0	Brooksby 9		1
21	NPL Prem	H	Matlock Town	1280	D	2 - 2	Brooksby 2 Walshaw 46	5	2
25	NPL Prem	A	Grantham Town	388	L	0 - 1		12	3
27	NPL Prem	H	Whitby Town	1976	D	1 - 1	Coulson 8	8	4
Sept 1	NPL Prem	A	Hyde United	577	**W**	3 - 2	Coulson 11 Walshaw 20 Cadman 47	6	5
4	*Void*	*H*	*North Ferriby United*	*1117*	***W***	*3 - 1*	*Burgess 67 Brooksby 76 90*	*4*	6
9	**FAC 1Q**	**A**	**Marine**	**496**	**D**	**1 - 1**	**Walshaw 57**		7
11	**FAC 1Qr**	**H**	**Marine**	**975**	**L**	**2 - 3**	**Walshaw 41 81**		8
15	NPL Prem	H	Basford United	1068	**W**	3 - 1	Gooda 26 Coulson 50 78 (pen)	6	9
22	*Void*	*A*	*North Ferriby United*	*605*	***W***	*3 - 1*	*Coulson 69 Walshaw 82 87*	*3*	10
25	NPL Prem	A	Mickleover Sports	221	D	1 - 1	Walshaw 46		11
29	NPL Prem	H	Nantwich Town	1055	L	2 - 3	Brooksby 27 Walshaw 45	3	12
Oct 2	NPL Prem	H	Witton Albion	807	**W**	2 - 0	Gooda 49 Walshaw 69	3	13
6	NPL Prem	A	Stafford Rangers	601	**W**	3 - 1	Brooksby 30 Walshaw 41 Burgess 54	1	14
9	NPL Prem	A	Stalybridge Celtic	408	**W**	3 - 2	Walshaw 44 Valentine 58 Coulson 90 (pen)	1	15
13	NPL Prem	H	Bamber Bridge	1160	D	0 - 0		1	16
16	NPL Prem	H	Buxton	1005	**W**	4 - 0	Gooda 35 Coulson 39 (pen) Walshaw 77 85	1	17
20	NPL Prem	A	Lancaster City	324	**W**	6 - 0	Fensome (og) Gooda 37 Coulson 42 (pen) Walshaw 55 Valentine 90 Johnson 90	1	18
23	NPL Prem	A	Gainsborough Trinity	627	**W**	1 - 0	Walshaw 59	1	19
27	**FAT 1Q**	**A**	**Workington**	**363**	**L**	**0 - 1**			20
Nov 3	NPL Prem	A	Farsley Celtic	727	L	1 - 3	Coulson 55	1	21
17	NPL Prem	H	Marine	1202	**W**	2 - 0	Killock 57 Coulson 82	1	22
24	NPL Prem	H	Gainsborough Trinity	1096	L	0 - 2		1	23
Dec 1	NPL Prem	A	Basford United	459	L	1 - 3	Coulson 45	2	24
8	NPL Prem	H	Hyde United	964	L	0 - 2		2	25
22	NPL Prem	A	Workington	390	**W**	3 - 2	Coulson 18 (pen) 90 Gooda 87	2	26
26	NPL Prem	H	South Shields	1608	L	1 - 3	Walshaw 15	3	27
Jan 1	NPL Prem	A	Whitby Town	1318	L	0 - 2		4	28
5	NPL Prem	H	Hednesford Town	959	**W**	5 - 3	Coulson 18 Walshaw 40 Watson 45 65 Lofts 75	5	29
12	NPL Prem	H	Warrington Town	1054	**W**	1 - 0	Walshaw 51	5	30
19	NPL Prem	A	Matlock Town	549	D	0 - 0		5	31
26	NPL Prem	H	Farsley Celtic	1186	L	1 - 3	Coulson 71	5	32
Feb 9	NPL Prem	H	Stafford Rangers	947	**W**	4 - 1	Williamson 10 Lofts 20 Thandi 55 (og) Walshaw 90 (pen)	5	33
16	NPL Prem	A	Nantwich Town	729	D	1 - 1	Lofts 4	5	34
23	NPL Prem	H	Mickleover Sports	945	L	0 - 2		6	35
Mar 2	NPL Prem	A	Witton Albion	348	L	1 - 2	Walshaw 19	6	36
9	NPL Prem	A	Marine	495	**W**	2 - 1	Walshaw 5 Coulson 78	6	37
16	NPL Prem	A	Stalybridge Celtic	801	L	1 - 2	Walshaw 30	6	38
23	NPL Prem	A	Buxton	683	L	0 - 1		7	39
30	NPL Prem	A	Lancaster City	969	D	1 - 1	Walshaw 44	7	40
Apr 6	NPL Prem	A	Bamber Bridge	346	**W**	4 - 2	Watson 30 Coulson 49 Walshaw 68 77	7	41
13	NPL Prem	H	Warrington Town	554	L	0 - 2		7	42
20	NPL Prem	A	Grantham Town	911	**W**	2 - 0	Walshaw 71 Coulson 78	7	43
22	NPL Prem	A	South Shields	2061	L	2 - 3	Walshaw 51 77 (pen)	8	44
27	NPL Prem	H	Workington	819	**W**	5 - 1	Coulson 24 Brooksby 37 McNaughton 61 Lofts 75 Walshaw 88	8	45

GOALSCORERS	SG	CSG	Pens	Hat tricks	Total
Walshaw	25	6	2		30
Coulson	17	2	4		19
Brooksby	6	2			7
Gooda	5				5
Lofts	4				4
Watson	2				3
Burgess	2				2
Opponents	2				2
Valentine	2				2
Cadman	1				1
Johnson	1				1
Killock	1				1
McNaughton	1				1
Williamson	1				1

SOUTH SHIELDS MATCH RESULTS 2018-19

Date	Comp	H/A	Opponents	Att:	Result		Goalscorers	Pos	No.
Aug 18	NPL Prem	H	Witton Albion	1677	W	2 - 1	Finnigan 45 82		1
21	NPL Prem	A	Farsley Celtic	350	L	1 - 4	Hunter 82		2
25	NPL Prem	H	Stafford Rangers	1363	W	3 - 0	Cogdon 33 Briggs 68 (pen) Finnigan 87	4	3
27	*Void*	*A*	*North Ferriby United*	*452*	*L*	*0 - 3*		*6*	4
Sept 1	NPL Prem	H	Nantwich Town	1444	W	4 - 0	Briggs 53 Gillies 61 Harmison 78 Adams 81	4	5
4	NPL Prem	A	Stalybridge Celtic	326	W	1 - 0	Cogdon 74	2	6
8	**FAC 1Q**	**H**	**Garforth Town**	**1148**	**W**	**5 - 1**	**Cogden 34 ADAMS 3 (41 42 47) Pattison 63**		7
11	NPL Prem	H	Lancaster City	1151	W	2 - 0	Gillies 66 Morse 71	1	8
15	NPL Prem	A	Matlock Town	530	W	3 - 0	Cogdon 30 Gillies 42 Foley 56	1	9
22	**FAC 2Q**	**H**	**Stockport County**	**1708**	**L**	**1 - 2**	**Finnigan 31**		10
29	NPL Prem	A	Warrington Town	505	L	0 - 3		4	11
Oct 2	NPL Prem	A	Buxton	266	L	0 - 2		6	12
6	NPL Prem	H	Grantham Town	1382	W	5 - 0	Briggs 13 Foley 47 Brown 59 Finnigan 82 Harmison 85	4	13
13	NPL Prem	A	Hednesford Town	537	L	1 - 2	Mason 67	7	14
16	NPL Prem	A	Hyde United	371	L	1 - 4	Briggs 49 (pen)	8	15
20	NPL Prem	H	Gainsborough Trinity	1163	W	1 - 0	Foley 45	6	16
27	**FAT 1Q**	**H**	**North Ferriby United**	**714**	**W**	**4 - 0**	**Shaw 14 FOLEY 3 (52 65 75)**		17
Nov 3	NPL Prem	A	Whitby Town	776	W	1 - 0	Baxter 81	6	18
10	**FAT 2Q**	**H**	**Hyde United**	**1095**	**W**	**2 - 1**	**Finnigan 12 Morse 32**		19
17	NPL Prem	H	Mickleover Sports	1749	W	3 - 2	Morse 33 Briggs 65 (pen) Gillies 90	6	20
24	**FAT 3Q**	**A**	**Stratford Town**	**378**	**L**	**1 - 2**	**Finnigan 18**		21
Dec 1	NPL Prem	H	Matlock Town	1119	W	5 - 0	Finnigan 11 Cogden 21 27 Shaw 52 Foley 84	7	22
8	NPL Prem	A	Nantwich Town	422	D	0 - 0		7	23
15	NPL Prem	H	Stalybridge Celtic	1152	W	3 - 2	Mason 35 61 Gillies 90	6	24
22	NPL Prem	A	Lancaster City	254	D	1 - 1	Foley 90	5	25
26	NPL Prem	A	Scarborough Athletic	1608	W	3 - 1	Mason 45 79 Harmison 90	4	26
29	NPL Prem	H	Workington	1501	W	4 - 1	Mason 12 Lowe 57 Briggs 68 (pen) Gillies 78	4	27
Jan 1	*Void*	*H*	*North Ferriby United*	*1437*	*W*	*6 - 2*	*Brown 6 Mason 35 37 Finnigan 59 Briggs 66 Lowe 90*	*4*	28
5	NPL Prem	A	Witton Albion	380	W	1 - 0	Mason 32	4	29
12	NPL Prem	A	Basford United	401	W	3 - 0	Foley 2 Morse 28 Cogdon 90	2	30
19	NPL Prem	H	Farsley Celtic	2013	W	1 - 0	Morse 90	1	31
26	NPL Prem	H	Whitby Town	1830	W	5 - 2	Foley 10 54 Briggs 25 (pen) Morse 87 Adams 89	2	32
Feb 9	NPL Prem	H	Bamber Bridge	1582	D	3 - 3	Low 2 Shaw 45 Briggs 73 (pen)	2	33
12	NPL Prem	A	Grantham Town	312	L	1 - 2	Daly 73	3	34
16	NPL Prem	H	Warrington Town	1998	L	1 - 2	Lowe 36	3	35
23	NPL Prem	A	Bamber Bridge	502	W	2 - 0	Foley 11 Briggs 17	3	36
Mar 2	NPL Prem	H	Buxton	1428	W	1 - 0	Mason 12 Lowe 57 Briggs 68 (pen) Gillies 78	3	37
9	NPL Prem	A	Mickleover Sports	294	W	3 - 1	Baxter 7 Harrison 27 58	3	38
12	NPL Prem	H	Marine	909	W	2 - 1	Mason 7 Briggs 35	3	39
23	NPL Prem	H	Hyde United	1857	W	4 - 0	Mason 24 Baxter 48 Lowe 55 Morse 89	3	40
30	NPL Prem	A	Marine	641	W	3 - 1	Lowe 29 77 Mason 60	3	41
Apr 6	NPL Prem	H	Hednesford Town	1214	W	4 - 1	Lowe 10 Bell 52 Briggs 58 77 (pen)	2	42
9	NPL Prem	A	Workington	413	W	2 - 0	Briggs 41 (pen) Lowe 81	2	43
13	NPL Prem	H	Basford United	1509	D	1 - 1	Briggs 90 (pen)	2	44
20	NPL Prem	A	Stafford Rangers	801	D	1 - 1	Briggs 90 (pen)	3	45
22	NPL Prem	H	Scarborough Athletic	2061	W	3 - 2	Mason 22 30 Daly 90	3	46
27	NPL Prem	A	Gainsborough Trinity	1312	W	1 - 0	Finnigan 62	2	47
30	**PO SF**	**H**	**Buxton**	**1878**	**W**	**4 - 2**	**Shaw 46 Finnigan 47 71 Giles 89**		48
May 4	**PO F**	**H**	**Warrington Town**	**2337**	**L**	**1 - 2**	**Gillies 30**		49

GOALSCORERS	SG	CSG	Pens	Hat tricks	Total		SG	CSG	Pens	Hat tricks	Total
Briggs	14	4	11		17	Shaw	4				4
Mason	10	4			15	Baxter	3				3
Finnigan	9	2			12	Brown	2				2
Foley	9	2		1	12	Daly	2				2
Lowe	8				9	Bell	1				1
Gillies	8				8	Hunter	1				1
Cogdon	6				7						
Morse	7				7						
Adams	3			1	5						
Harmison	4				5						

STAFFORD RANGERS MATCH RESULTS 2018-19

Date	Comp	H/A	Opponents	Att:	Result		Goalscorers	Pos	No.
Aug 18	NPL Prem	A	Workington	421	L	0 - 1			1
21	NPL Prem	H	Grantham Town	562	D	1 - 1	Briscoe 61	18	2
25	NPL Prem	A	South Shields	1363	L	0 - 3		21	3
27	NPL Prem	H	Mickleover Sports	618	D	1 - 1	Perry 21	17	4
Sept 1	NPL Prem	H	Stalybridge Celtic	564	W	2 - 0	Cuff 66 Reid 83 (pen)	14	5
4	NPL Prem	A	Hednesford Town	916	W	3 - 1	Reid 37 Briscoe 42 Sherratt 70	11	6
8	**FAC 1Q**	**A**	**Grimsby Borough**	**169**	**W**	**2 - 1**	**Perry 32 Benn 36**		7
11	NPL Prem	H	Witton Albion	483	W	3 - 1	Bailey-Jones 10 Wilson 60 (og) Banks 86	9	8
15	NPL Prem	A	Buxton	501	L	1 - 4	Green 64	11	9
22	**FAC 2Q**	**A**	**Kings Lynn Town**	**601**	**L**	**1 - 3**	**Cuff 86**		10
25	NPL Prem	H	Basford United	411	W	3 - 1	Jones 23 Coulson 25 Perry 45	9	11
29	NPL Prem	A	Bamber Bridge	383	L	`1 - 6	Coulson 25	10	12
Oct 2	NPL Prem	A	Marine	289	L	0 - 1		11	13
6	NPL Prem	H	Scarborough Trinity	601	L	1 - 3	Thorley 38	12	14
9	NPL Prem	H	Farsley Celtic	382	L	1 - 3	Charles 86	13	15
13	*Void*	*A*	*North Ferriby United*	*360*	*W*	*2 - 1*	*Coulson 20 Charles 82*	*13*	16
20	NPL Prem	H	Hyde United	548	L	1 - 3	Burns 86	15	17
27	**FAT 1Q**	**H**	**Rushall Olympic**	**371**	**W**	**2 - 1**	**Burns Stanton**		18
Nov 3	NPL Prem	H	Gainsborough Trinity	457	D	1 - 1	Reid 12	15	19
10	**FAT 2Q**	**A**	**Basford United**	**246**	**L**	**0 - 4**			20
17	NPL Prem	A	Lancaster City	276	D	0 - 0		16	21
24	NPL Prem	A	Witton Albion	375	D	3 - 3	Thorley 38 Cuff 41 80	16	22
Dec 1	NPL Prem	H	Buxton	481	L	0 - 1		17	23
8	NPL Prem	A	Stalybridge Celtic	347	D	2 - 2	Bailey-Jones 12 Jones 57		24
15	NPL Prem	H	Hedfnesford Town	668	W	4 - 1	CHARLES 3 (3 57 67) Cuff 40	17	25
22	NPL Prem	A	Matlock Town	493	L	2 - 3	Cuff 13 Charles 34	18	26
26	NPL Prem	H	Nantwich Town	807	L	1 - 4	Stair (og)	18	27
Jan 1	NPL Prem	A	Mickleover Sports	304	L	2 - 3	Bailey-Jones 16 Cuff 22	19	28
5	NPL Prem	H	Workington	526	D	1 - 1	Bailey-Jones 5	20	29
19	NPL Prem	A	Grantham Town	247	W	5 - 0	Jones 11Thorley 20 Bailey-Jones 29 Banks 65 Charles 70	19	30
26	NPL Prem	H	Gainsborough Trinity	487	D	1 - 1	Green 45 (pen)	19	31
Feb 2	NPL Prem	H	Lancaster City	532	D	1 - 1	Thorley 90	19	32
9	NPL Prem	A	Scarborough Athletic	647	L	1 - 4	Charles 42	19	33
16	NPL Prem	H	Bamber Bridge	552	W	1 - 0	Charles 11	18	34
23	NPL Prem	A	Basford United	308	D	2 - 2	Bailey-Jones 33 Roma 90 (og)	18	35
Mar 2	NPL Prem	H	Marine	683	D	0 - 0		19	36
9	NPL Prem	A	Warrington Town	553	W	3 - 2	Jones 45 64 Bailey-Jones 60	17	37
19	NPL Prem	A	Witton Albion	307	D	1 - 1	Bignot 90	17	38
23	NPL Prem	H	Warrington Town	759	D	1 - 1	Jones 45	17	39
30	NPL Prem	A	Hyde United	418	L	3 - 5	Mills 64 Charles 75 (pen) Thandi 71	18	40
Apr 9	NPL Prem	A	Farsley Celtic	206	L	1 - 2	Bailey-Jones 31	18	41
13	NPL Prem	A	Whitby Town	367	W	2 - 1	Thorley 2 Briscoe 45	16	42
20	NPL Prem	H	South Shields	801	D	1 - 1	Bailey-Jones 25	16	43
22	NPL Prem	A	Nantwich Town	605	W	1 - 0	Charles 57	14	44
27	NPL Prem	H	Matlock Town	606	W	4 - 1	Mills 36 Haworth 39 86 Coulson 48	14	45

GOALSCORERS	SG	CSG	Pens	Hat tricks	Total		SG	CSG	Pens	Hat tricks	Total
Charles	9	2	1	1	11	Bamks	2		1		2
Bailey-Jones	9	3			9	Burns	2				2
Cuff	6	2			7	Coulson	1				2
Jones	5				6	Green	2				2
Thorley	5				5	Mills	2				2
Coulson	4	2			4	Benn	1				1
Briscoe	3				3	Bignot	1				1
Opponents	3				3	Sherratt	1				1
Perry	3		1		3	Stanton	1				1
Reid	3				3	Thandi	1				1

STALYBRIDGE CELTIC MATCH RESULTS 2018-19

Date	Comp	H/A	Opponents	Att:	Result		Goalscorers	Pos	No.
Aug 18	NPL Prem	H	Mickleover Sports	379	D	0 - 0			1
21	NPL Prem	H	Marine	312	**W**	3 - 2	Brown 4 77 Tongue 9	6	2
25	NPL Prem	A	Warrington Town	217	D	0 - 0		7	3
27	NPL Prem	H	Workington	340	**W**	1 - 0	Kengni 67	6	4
Sept 1	NPL Prem	A	Stafford Rangers	564	L	0 - 2		10	5
4	NPL Prem	H	South Shields	326	L	0 - 1		13	6
8	**FAC 1Q**	**A**	**Radcliffe Borough**	**388**	**L**	**0 - 1**			7
11	NPL Prem	A	Whitby Town	287	L	1 - 2	Dent 11	14	8
15	NPL Prem	H	Bamber Bridge	305	**W**	3 - 2	Wolfendon 2 Bakkor 45 Kengni 65	12	9
22	NPL Prem	H	Matlock	271	**W**	3 - 1	Wolfendon 38 Bakkor 74 Kengni 78	9	10
29	NPL Prem	H	Gainsborough Trinity	330	**W**	2 - 1	Bakkor 8 Wolfendon 86	7	11
Oct 2	NPL Prem	H	Nantwich Town	211	D	1 - 1	Dent 42	6	12
6	*Void*	*A*	*North Ferriby United*	*155*	***W***	*2 - 1*	*Dent 62 Wolfendon 90*	*4*	13
9	NPL Prem	H	Scarborough Athletic	408	L	2 - 3	Wilson 20 Wolfendon 79	6	14
13	NPL Prem	A	Basford United	415	L	2 - 5	Bakkor 28 (pen) Wolfenden 49	8	15
20	NPL Prem	H	Farsley Celtic	354	D	2 - 2	Dent 40 64	10	16
23	NPL Prem	A	Lancaster City	195	L	0 - 1		10	17
27	**FAT 1Q**	**H**	**Nantwich Town**	**247**	**W**	**1 - 0**	**Bakkor 77 (pen)**		18
Nov 3	NPL Prem	H	Buxton	445	D	1 - 1	Kengni 90	10	19
6	NPL Prem	A	Witton Albion	220	**W**	3 - 1	Wolfenden 24 42 Tongue 56	7	20
10	**FAT 2Q**	**A**	**Buxton**	**283**	**D**	**0 - 0**			21
13	**FAT 2Qr**	**H**	**Buxton**	**409**	**W**	**2 - 1**	**Tongue 42 Sharp 76**		22
17	NPL Prem	H	Matlock Town	521	L	1 - 3	Tongue 64	9	23
24	**FAT 3Q**	**H**	**Workington**	**344**	**L**	**1 - 2**	**Sharp 16**		24
Dec 1	NPL Prem	A	Bamber Bridge	315	L	0 - 3		11	25
8	NPL Prem	H	Stafford Rangers	347	D	2 - 2	Scott 72 Kengni 90	12	26
15	NPL Prem	A	South Shields	1152	L	2 - 3	Kengni 18 47	12	27
22	NPL Prem	A	Grantham Town	195	**W**	1 - 0	Scott 7	11	28
26	NPL Prem	H	Hyde United	838	D	2 - 2	Kengni 43 56	11	29
Jan 1	NPL Prem	A	Workington	453	**W**	2 - 1	Scott 37 49	11	30
5	NPL Prem	A	Mickleover Sports	184	L	1 - 2	Cooke 83	11	31
12	NPL Prem	H	Hednesford Town	384	**W**	1 - 0	Bakkor 66	11	32
19	NPL Prem	A	Marine	430	D	1 - 1	Cockerline 66	11	33
26	NPL Prem	A	Buxton	536	D	1 - 1	Bakkor 74	11	34
Feb 9	NPL Prem	H	Witton Albion	301	L	0 - 2		11	35
16	NPL Prem	A	Guisborough Town	509	L	0 - 1		12	36
23	NPL Prem	H	Lancaster City	317	L	1 - 2	Kengni 12	13	37
Mar 2	NPL Prem	A	Nantwich Town	426	L	2 - 4	Kengni 43 Cockerline 84	16	38
16	NPL Prem	A	Scarboorough Athletic	801	**W**	2 - 1	Bakkor 87 Soloman-Davies 89	16	39
30	NPL Prem	A	Farsley Celtic	348	L	1 - 2	Howard 64	16	40
Apr 2	NPL Prem	H	Whitby Town	147	L	0 - 1		16	41
6	NPL Prem	H	Basford United	274	L	0 - 2		16	42
13	NPL Prem	A	Hednesford Town	376	L	0 - 1		18	43
20	NPL Prem	H	Warrington	386	L	1 - 2	Kengni 66	18	44
22	NPL Prem	A	Hyde United	787	L	0 - 1		19	45
27	NPL Prem	H	Grantham Town	439	**W**	1 - 0	Scott 45	17	46

GOALSCORERS	SG	CSG	Pens	Hat tricks	Total
Kengni	9	2			12
Bakkor	7	3	2		8
Wolfendon	7	3x2			8
Scott	5				6
Dent	4				5
Tongue	3				3
Brown	1				2
Cockerline	2				2
Sharp	2				2
Cooke	1				1
Kengni	1				1
Soloman-Davies	1				1
Wilson	1				1

WARRINGTON TOWN MATCH RESULTS 2018-19

Date	Comp	H/A	Opponents	Att:	Result		Goalscorers	Pos	No.
Aug 18	NPL Prem	H	Farsley Celtic	312	L	0 - 2			1
21	NPL Prem	A	Lancaster City	236	W	3 - 1	Gray 29 Amis 40 Caton 58	10	2
25	NPL Prem	H	Stalybridge Celtic	217	D	0 - 0		13	3
27	NPL Prem	A	Bamber Bridge	407	D	0 - 0		9	4
Sept 1	*Void*	*A*	*North Ferriby United*	*217*	**W**	*5 - 0*	*Gray 12 Brodie 19 (pen) Vassallo 42 Amis 78 Dixon 82*	*6*	5
4	NPL Prem	H	Workington	239	W	2 - 0	Gray 23 Mackreth 27	3	6
8	**FAC1 Q**	**H**	**Burscough**	**240**	**W**	**4 - 0**	**Gray 27 57 Mackreth 73 Brodie 90**		7
11	NPL Prem	A	Hyde United	306	W	2 - 0	Hughes 8 Mackreth 11	2	8
15	NPL Prem	H	Marine	383	W	1 - 0	Mackreth 16 (pen)	2	9
22	**FAC 2Q**	**A**	**Consett**	**451**	**D**	**3 - 3**	**Dixon 22 Vassallo 45 Gray 63**		10
25	**FAC 2Qr**	**H**	**Consett**	**312**	**W**	**2 - 0**	**Gray 7 Dixon 12**		11
29	NPL Prem	H	South Shields	505	W	3 - 0	Dixon 37 Kirby 80 Amis 90	1	12
Oct 2	NPL Prem	H	Mickleover Sports	211	W	1 - 0	Vassallo 6	1	13
6	**FAC 3Q**	**A**	**AFC Telford United**	**543**	**W**	**2 - 1**	**Dixon 45 Garrity 64**		14
9	NPL Prem	A	Whitby Town	267	W	1 - 0	Mackreth 60	2	15
13	NPL Prem	H	Matlock Town	303	L	0 - 1		2	16
20	**FAC 4Q**	**H**	**FC Halifax Town**	**929**	**D**	**2 - 2**	**Garrity 40 Gray 55**		17
23	**FAC 4Qr**	**A**	**FC Halifax Town**	**844**	**L**	**0 - 2**			18
27	**FAT 1Q**	**H**	**Prescot Cables**	**316**	**L**	**0 - 1**			19
30	NPL Prem	A	Nantwich Town	296	L	1 - 2	Hughes 74	5	20
Nov 3	NPL Prem	A	Grantham Town	219	W	2 - 0	Dixon 82 Mackreth 90 (pen)	5	21
10	NPL Prem	A	Hednesford Town	284	L	0 - 1		5	22
17	NPL Prem	H	Basford United	638	D	1 - 1	Mackreth 25	5	23
24	NPL Prem	H	Hyde United	322	W	2 - 1	Gray 20 Kirby 85	5	24
Dec 1	NPL Prem	A	Marine	521	W	2 - 0	Dixon 33 Gray 69	4	25
8	*Void*	*H*	*North Ferriby United*	*164*	**W**	*4 - 0*	*Mackreth 25 (pen) Hughes 29 Kirby 42 Dunn 90*	*4*	26
22	NPL Prem	H	Buxton	368	W	2 - 1	Dunn 86 (pen) Reid 90	4	27
26	NPL Prem	A	Witton Albion	507	W	2 - 1	Dunn 8 Mackreth 90	3	28
29	NPL Prem	A	Basford United	280	W	3 - 2	Garrity 9 62 Gray 35	3	29
Jan 1	NPL Prem	H	Bamber Bridge	460	W	2 - 0	McCarthy 48 61	3	30
5	NPL Prem	A	Farsley Celtic	471	D	3 - 3	Dixon 30 (pen) Amis 72 87	3	31
12	NPL Prem	A	Scarborough Athletic	1054	L	0 - 1		4	32
19	NPL Prem	H	Lancaster City	375	D	1 - 1	Cassley 83	3	33
26	NPL Prem	H	Grantham Town	365	W	3 - 0	AMIS 3 (47 50 69)	2	34
Feb 2	NPL Prem	A	Gainsborough Trinity	412	W	4 - 1	Gray 19 Dunn 22 Amis 49 Vassallo 69	1	35
9	NPL Prem	H	Hednesford Town	348	W	3 - 1	Vassalio 14 Amis 41 73	1	36
16	NPL Prem	A	South Shields	1928	W	2 - 1	Amis 27 Dunn 32	1	37
23	NPL Prem	H	Nantwich Town	647	D	3 - 3	Roberts 27 Amis 43 Gray 90	1	38
26	NPL Prem	A	Workington	379	W	2 - 0	Vassallo 77 86	1	39
Mar 2	NPL Prem	A	Mickleover Sports	328	W	4 - 1	Gray 3 Vassallo 42 Mackreth 57 (pen) Evans 69	1	40
9	NPL Prem	H	Stafford Rangers	553	L	2 - 3	Dixon 21 Cusani 87	2	41
23	NPL Prem	A	Stafford Rangers	759	D	1 - 1	Dunn 62	2	42
30	NPL Prem	H	Gainsborough Trinity	445	W	2 - 1	Mackreth 9 Allison 80 (pen)	2	43
Apr 6	NPL Prem	A	Matlock Town	419	W	2 - 0	Dunn 62 Gray 73	3	44
9	NPL Prem	H	Whitby Town	355	W	1 - 0	Cusani 80	3	45
13	NPL Prem	H	Scarborough Athletic	554	W	2 - 0	Gray 23 Dunn 90	3	46
20	NPL Prem	A	Stalybridge Celtic	386	W	2 - 1	Gray 25 Vassallo 54	2	47
22	NPL Prem	H	Witton Albion	733	D	0 - 0		3	48
27	NPL Prem	A	Buxton Town	943	D	2 - 2	Dixon 41 Roberts 79	3	49
30	**PO SF**	**H**	**Nantwich Town**	**1424**	**W**	**4 - 1**	**Garrity 57 80 Allinson 89 (og) Gray 90**		50
May 4	**PO F**	**A**	**South Shields**	**2337**	**W**	**2 - 1**	**Vassallo 67 Amis 87**		51
11	**Su PO F**	**H**	**King's Lynn Town**	**2200**	**L**	**2 - 3**	**Garrity 17 59**		52

GOALSCORERS	SG	CSG	Pens	Hat tricks	Total
Gray	17	3			18
Amis	10	4		1	14
Mackreth	12	4	3		11
Dixon	10	3	1		10
Vassallo	9				10
Dunn	8	3	1		8
Garrity	5				8
Hughes	3				3
Kirby	3				3
Brodie	2		1		2
Cusani	2				2
McCarthy	1				2
Roberts	2				2
Allison	1		1		1
Cassley	1				1
Caton	1				1
Evans	1				1
Opponents	1				1
Reid	1				1

WHITBY TOWN MATCH RESULTS 2018-19

Date	Comp	H/A	Opponents	Att:	Result	Goalscorers	Pos	No.
Aug 18	NPL Prem	H	Buxton	282	**W** 1 - 0	Gell 23		1
21	*Void*	*A*	*North Ferriby United*	*293*	*W 1 - 0*	*Hopson 90*	*2*	2
25	NPL Prem	H	Witton Albion	333	L 0 - 1		5	3
27	NPL Prem	A	Scarborough Athletic	1976	D 1 - 1	Mondal 26	6	4
Sept 1	NPL Prem	H	Hednesford Town	318	L 1 - 2	Parnaby 83	9	5
4	NPL Prem	A	Matlock Town	405	**W** 3 - 0	Tymon 44 Hopson 86 (pen) Mondal 90	7	6
8	**FAC 1Q**	**A**	**Whitley Bay**	**680**	**L 0 - 1**			7
11	NPL Prem	H	Stalybridge Celtic	287	**W** 2 - 1	Smyth 3 Wells 10	7	8
15	NPL Prem	A	Nantwich Town	272	L 1 - 4	Mondal 58 (pen)	7	9
22	NPL Prem	H	Hyde United	251	L 0 - 1		10	10
29	NPL Prem	A	Grantham Town	272	L 2 - 3	Hopson 18 (pen) Gell 23	13	11
Oct 1	NPL Prem	A	Basford United	270	L 0 - 2		14	12
6	NPL Prem	H	Bamber Bridge	264	**W** 2 - 1	Mondal 4 Hopson 79 (pen)	13	13
9	NPL Prem	H	Warrington Town	267	L 0 - 1		14	14
13	NPL Prem	A	Marine	469	D 0 - 0		13	15
16	NPL Prem	A	Workington	202	**W** 2 - 1	Monkhouse 61 Maloney 62	10	16
20	NPL Prem	H	Mickleover Sports	288	**W** 4 - 0	Hopson 8 68 McWilliams 84 Sukar 87	9	17
27	**FAT 1Q**	**H**	**Witton Albion**	**181**	**L 0 - 1**			18
Nov 3	NPL Prem	H	South Shields	776	L 0 - 1		9	19
17	NPL Prem	A	Gainsborough Trinity	659	L 1 - 4	Tymon 3	13	20
24	NPL Prem	A	Stafford Rangers	375	D 3 - 3	Hopson 35 (pen) Maloney 40 Patton 70	12	21
Dec 1	NPL Prem	H	Nantwich Town	212	L 0 - 1		14	22
8	NPL Prem	A	Hednesford Town	265	**W** 2 - 1	Patton 54 59	12	23
15	NPL Prem	H	Matlock Town	258	L 1 - 3	Tyman 6	11	24
22	NPL Prem	H	Gainsborough Trinity	368	**W** 1 - 0	Patton 43	11	25
26	NPL Prem	A	Farsley Celtic	324	L 1 - 3	Patton 45	12	26
Jan 1	NPL Prem	H	Scarborough Athletic	1318	**W** 2 - 0	Gell 25 Hopson 73 (pen)	12	27
5	NPL Prem	A	Buxton	321	L 0 - 2		13	28
19	*Void*	*H*	*North Ferriby United*	*227*	***W** 6 - 1*	*COFFEY 3 (15 38 45) Rutherford 43 (p) Patton 57 Hopson 62 (p)*	*12*	29
26	NPL Prem	A	South Shields	1830	L 2 - 5	Scott 3 Tymon 68	12	30
Feb 9	NPL Prem	H	Lancaster City	248	D 1 - 1	Scott 45	12	31
16	NPL Prem	H	Grantham Town	287	**W** 2 - 1	Rowe 11 Coffey 38	11	32
23	NPL Prem	A	Hyde United	351	L 0 - 3		12	33
Mar 2	NPL Prem	H	Basford United	293	**W** 4 - 1	Tymon 30 62 Fewster 46 66	12	34
9	NPL Prem	A	Bamber Bridge	314	**W** 3 - 1	Fewster 39 83 Gell 76	11	35
23	NPL Prem	H	Workington	321	L 0 - 1		11	36
30	NPL Prem	A	Mickleover Sports	212	**W** 1 - 0	Fewster 90	11	37
Apr 2	NPL Prem	A	Stalybridge Celtic	147	**W** 1 - 0	Tymon 88	11	38
6	NPL Prem	H	Marine	307	**W** 2 - 1	Hopson 39 Gell 84	11	39
9	NPL Prem	A	Warrington Town	355	L 0 - 1		11	40
13	NPL Prem	H	Stafford Rangers	367	L 1 - 2	Fewster 86	11	41
20	NPL Prem.	A	Witton Albion	263	L 0 - 2		11	42
22	NPL Prem	H	Farsley Celtic	438	L 0 - 2		11	43
27	NPL Prem	A	Lancaster City	255	L 1`- 2	Fewster 56	11	44
								45
								46

GOALSCORERS	SG	CSG	Pens	Hat tricks	Total
Hopson	8	1	6		10
Fewster	5				7
Tymon	5				7
Patton	5	2			6
Gell	5				5
Coffey	3			1	4
Mondal	4		1		4
Maloney	2				2
Scott	2				2
McWilliams	1				1
Monkhouse	1				1
Parnaby	1				1
Rowe	1				1
Rutherford	1		1		1
Smyth	1				1
Sukar	1				1
Wells	1				1

WITTON ALBION MATCH RESULTS 2018-19

Date	Comp	H/A	Opponents	Att:	Result		Goalscorers	Pos	No.
Aug 18	NPL Prem	A	South Shields	1677	L	1 - 2	Foley 47 (pen)		1
21	NPL Prem	H	Hyde United	360	D	1 - 1	Humphreys 71	16	2
25	NPL Prem	A	Whitby Town	333	**W**	1 - 0	Owens 87	14	3
27	NPL Prem	H	Nantwich Town	357	**W**	2 - 0	Hopley 27 50	10	4
Sept 1	NPL Prem	A	Bamber Bridge	366	L	0 - 2		13	5
4	NPL Prem	H	Marine	241	D	0 - 0		12	6
8	**FAC 1Q**	**H**	**Bottesford Town**	**248**	**W**	**5 - 0**	**Wilson 23 Hopley 29 Devine 81 Foley 76 (pen) Jones 85 (pen)**		7
11	NPL Prem	A	Stafford Rangers	483	L	1 - 3	Foley 66	15	8
15	NPL Prem	H	Gainsborough Trinity	241	D	0 - 0		15	9
22	**FAC 2Q**	**H**	**Spennymoor Town**	**322**	**W**	**2 - 1**	**Foley 50 Hopley 87**		10
29	*Void*	*A*	*North Ferriby United*	*195*	***W***	*4 - 0*	*Foley 16 (pen) 33 Smart 26 57*	*14*	11
Oct 2	NPL Prem	A	Scarborough Athletic	807	L	0 - 2		16	12
6	**FAC 3Q**	**A**	**FC United of Manchester**	**1234**	**W**	**2 - 1**	**Foley 10 Hopley 64**		13
9	NPL Prem	H	Mickleover Sports	234	L	1 - 2	Hopley 70	16	14
20	**FAC 4Q**	**H**	**Solihull Moors**	**683**	**L**	**0 - 2**			15
27	**FAT 1Q**	**A**	**Whitby Town**	**181**	**W**	**1 - 0**	**Smart 59**		16
Nov 3	NPL Prem	H	Lancaster City	262	**W**	1 - 0	Hopley 16	18	17
6	NPL Prem	H	Stalybridge Celtic	220	L	1 - 3	Foley 5 (pen)	18	18
10	**FAT 2Q**	**H**	**Rushden & Diamonds**	**300**	**W**	**2 - 0**	**Lingubar 20 Reynolds 72 (og)**	**10**	19
17	NPL Prem	A	Buxton	427	**W**	5 - 0	Jones 20 Foley 43 (pen) 63 McKenna 77 Meade 90 (og)	18	20
24	**FAT 3Q**	**A**	**Leamington**	**332**	**L**	**1 - 2**	**Foley 9**	**18**	21
Dec 1	NPL Prem	A	Gainsborough Trinity	506	D	1 - 1	Maguire 44 (og)	18	22
8	NPL Prem	H	Bamber Bridge	279	D	2 - 2	Wilson 75 (pen) Owens 77	18	23
15	NPL Prem	A	Marine	360	**W**	3 - 2	Hopley 18 78 Owens 72	17	24
22	NPL Prem	A	Hednesford Town	303	**W**	1 - 0	Foley 69 (pen)	14	25
26	NPL Prem	H	Warrington Town	507	L	1 - 2	Foley 45 (pen)	15	26
29	NPL Prem	H	Farsley Celtic	325	L	2 - 3	Owens 32 Foley 66 (pen)	15	27
Jan 1	NPL Prem	A	Nantwich Town	956	**W**	1 - 0	Jones 69	14	28
5	NPL Prem	H	South Shields	380	L	0 - 1		15	29
12	NPL Prem	H	Matlock Town	305	**W**	1 - 0	Beevers 51 (og)	14	30
19	NPL Prem	A	Hyde United	418	L	0 - 1		14	31
26	NPL Prem	A	Lancaster City	267	L	0 - 1		14	32
Feb 9	NPL Prem	A	Stalybridge Celtic	301	**W**	2 - 0	Hopley 16 Owens 65	14	33
11	NPL Prem	A	Basford United	264	L	1 - 3	Jones 9	13	34
16	*Void*	*H*	*North Ferriby United*	*306*	***W***	*1 - 0*	*Jones 21*	*13*	35
19	NPL Prem	A	Workington	289	**W**	2 - 0	Jones 71 Gardner 79	13	36
23	NPL Prem	A	Farsley Celtic	343	**W**	1 - 0	Hopley 48	12	37
26	NPL Prem	H	Buxton	244	L	0 - 3		12	38
Mar 2	NPL Prem	H	Scarborough Athletic	348	**W**	2 - 1	Foley 62 (pen) McKenna 85	10	39
9	NPL Prem	H	Grantham Town	288	**W**	1 - 0	Jones 82	9	40
19	NPL Prem	H	Stafford Rangers	307	D	1 - 1	Harrison 43	9	41
23	NPL Prem	H	Basford United	316	D	2 - 2	Hopley 9 Jones 18	9	42
30	NPL Prem	A	Grantham Town	205	L	0 - 1		10	43
Apr 6	NPL Prem	H	Workington	246	**W**	2 - 0	Harrison 8 62	10	44
9	NPL Prem	A	Mickleover Sports	173	D	0 - 0		10	45
13	NPL Prem	A	Matlock Town	346	**W**	2 - 1	Harrison 10 Hopley 47	9	46
20	NPL Prem	H	Whitby Town	263	**W**	2 - 0	Foley 10 (pen) Hopley 68	9	47
22	NPL Prem	A	Warrington Town	733	D	0 - 0		9	48
27	NPL Prem	H	Hednesford Town	362	D	1 - 1	Gardner 9	9	49

GOALSCORERS	SG	CSG	Pens	Hat tricks	Total
Foley	15	3	10		16
Hopley	12	2			14
Jones	8		1		8
Owens	5	2			5
Harrison	3				4
Opponents	4				4
Smart	2				3
Gardner	2				2
McKenna	2				2
Wilson	2		1		2
Devine	1				1
Humphreys	1				1
Lingubar	1				1

WORKINGTON MATCH RESULTS 2018-19

Date	Comp	H/A	Opponents	Att:	Result		Goalscorers	Pos	No.
Aug 18	NPL Prem	H	Stafford Rangers	421	W	1 - 0	Walker 50		1
21	NPL Prem	A	Bamber Briudge	291	L	2 - 3	Waker 58 90		2
25	NPL Prem	H	Buxton	326	D	1 - 1	Joel 80	11	3
27	NPL Prem	A	Stalybridge Celtic	340	L	0 - 1		14	4
Sept 1	NPL Prem	H	Matlock Town	422	W	3 - 1	Walker 5 84 Tinnion 81	13	5
4	NPL Prem	A	Warrington Town	239	L	0 - 2		16	6
8	**FAC 1Qr**	**A**	**Newcastle Benfield**	**294**	**D**	**1 - 1**	**Cowperthwaite 57**		7
11	**FAC 1Qr**	**A**	**Newcastle Benfield**	**372**	**W**	**5 - 3**	**Allison 4 Brown 10 Joel 49 Evans (og) 89 Mossop 90**		8
15	NPL Prem	A	Hednesford Town	301	L	0 - 2		17	9
22	**FAC 2Q**	**A**	**Knaresborough**	**507**	**W**	**4 - 1**	**Tinnion 15 Allison 68 Walker 78 Joel 85**		10
25	NPL Prem	H	Marine	317	D	1 - 1	Joel 22	17	11
29	NPL Prem	A	Basford United	211	L	2 - 3	Tinnion 2 Douglas 29	19	12
Oct 2	NPL Prem	A	Hyde United	227	D	0 - 0		18	13
6	**FAC 3Q**	**H**	**Kidsgrove Athletic**	**558**	**D**	**0 - 0**		**18**	14
10	**FAC 3Qr**	**A**	**Kidsgrove Athletic**	**423**	**L**	**1 - 2**	**Joel 60**		15
16	NPL Prem	H	Whitby Town	202	L	1 - 2	Tinnion 27	21	16
20	NPL Prem	H	Nantwich Town	378	D	0 - 0		21	17
23	NPL Prem	H	Farsley Celtic	254	L	0 - 1		21	18
27	**FAT 1Q**	**H**	**Scarborough Athletic**	**363**	**W**	**1 - 0**	**Allison 27**		19
Nov 3	NPL Prem	A	Mickleover Sports	151	L	0 - 1		21	20
10	**FAT 2Q**	**A**	**Newcastle Town**	**160**	**D**	**2 - 2**	**Tinnion 11 Roundtree 42**	**10**	21
13	**FAT 2Qr**	**H**	**Newcastle Town**	**219**	**W**	**5 0**	**Hubbold 10 Walker 22 Joel 36 Wordsworth 49 Allison7613**		22
17	NPL Prem	H	Grantham Town	352	L	1 - 4	Allison 74 (pen)	21	23
24	**FAT 3Q**	**A**	**Stalybridge Celtic**	**344**	**W**	**2 - 1**	**Allison 9 24 (pen)**		24
Dec 1	NPL Prem	H	Hednesford Town	301	W	4 - 2	Tinnion 21 Rowntree 55 Allison 59 Holt 85	21	25
8	NPL Prem	A	Matlock Town	346	L	1 - 2	Cowperthwaite 34	21	26
15	**FAT 1P**	**H**	**Ramsbottom United**	**298**	**D**	**0 - 0**			27
18	**FAT 1Pr**	**A**	**Ramsbottom United**	**170**	**L**	**0 - 2**			28
22	NPL Prem	H	Scarborough athletic	390	L	2 - 3	Tinnion 16 Paterson 90	21	29
26	NPL Prem	A	Lancaster City	320	W	2 - 0	Walker 47 Allison 90	21	30
29	NPL Prem	A	South Shields	1501	L	1 - 4	Tinnion 85	21	31
Jan 1	NPL Prem	H	Stalybridge Celtic	453	L	1 - 2	Carroll 16	21	32
5	NPL Prem	A	Stafford Rangers	526	D	1 - 1	Wordsworth 80	21	33
12	NPL Prem	A	Gainsborough Trinity	572	L	1 - 4	Walker 83	21	34
19	NPL Prem	H	Bamber Bridge	401	W	2 - 1	Joel 13 Smith 70	21	35
Feb 2	NPL Prem	A	Grantham Town	266	W	2 - 0	Cowperthwaite 58 Douglas 88	21	36
9	*Void*	*A*	*North Ferriby United*	*155*	*W*	*2 - 0*	*Thompson 42 Walker 53*	*21*	37
16	NPL Prem	H	Basford United	511	L	0 - 3		21	38
19	NPL Prem	H	Witton Albion	289	L	0 - 2		21	39
23	NPL Prem	A	Marine	671	W	2 - 0	Carroll 62 Joel 85	21	40
26	NPL Prem	H	Warrington Town	379	L	0 - 2		21	41
Mar 2	NPL Prem	H	Hyde United	424	L	1 - 2	Calvert 33	21	42
5	NPL Prem	A	Farsley Celtic	173	L	0 2		21	43
23	NPL Prem	A	Whitby Town	321	W	1 - 0	Tinnion 60	21	44
30	NPL Prem	H	Nantwich Town	476	L	2 - 4	Walker 9 Allison 80 (pen)	21	45
Apr 2	NPL Prem	H	Mickleover Sports	504	L	0 - 2		21	46
6	NPL Prem	A	Witton Albion	246	L	0 2		21	47
9	NPL Prem	H	South Shields	413	L	0 2		21	48
13	NPL Prem	H	Gainsborough Trinity	373	L	0 2		21	49
20	NPL Prem	A	Buxton	436	L	2 - 3	Walker 25 (pen) 77 (pen)	21	50
22	NPL Prem	H	Lancaster City	689	L	0 - 2		21	51
27	NPL Prem	A	Scarborough Athletic	819	L	1 5	Maguire 90	21	52

GOALSCORERS	SG	CSG	Pens	Hat tricks	Total		SG	CSG	Pens	Hat tricks	Total
Walker	10	2	2		13	Calvert	1				1
Allison	9	4	3		10	Holt	1				1
Tinnion	9				9	Hubbold	1				1
Joel	8				8	Maguire	1				1
Cowperthwaite	3				3	Mossop	1				1
Carroll	2				2	Opponents					1
Douglas	2				2	Paterson	1				1
Roundtree	2				2	Smith	1				1
Wordsworth	2				2	Thompson	1				1
Brown	1				1						

SOUTHERN LEAGUE
PREMIER DIVISION CENTRAL TABLE 2018-19

		P	W	D	L	F	A	GD	Pts
1	Kettering Town	42	30	4	8	84	41	43	94
2	King's Lynn Town (PO winners)	42	23	11	8	80	41	39	80
3	Stourbridge	42	22	12	8	79	40	39	78
4	Alvechurch	42	21	10	11	66	53	13	73
5	Stratford Town	42	21	9	12	55	49	6	69*
6	Coalville Town	42	20	7	15	78	66	12	67
7	Biggleswade Town	42	18	12	12	67	54	13	66
8	Rushall Olympic	42	17	11	14	56	49	7	62
9	AFC Rushden & Diamonds	42	15	16	11	60	49	11	61
10	Royston Town	42	18	7	17	59	53	6	60*
11	Needham Market	42	17	9	16	68	65	3	60
12	Tamworth	42	15	13	14	64	46	18	58
13	St Ives Town	42	14	13	15	36	43	-7	55
14	Lowestoft Town	42	14	9	19	55	60	-5	51
15	Redditch United	42	14	8	20	63	79	-16	50
16	Barwell	42	12	13	17	55	55	0	49
17	Banbury United	42	13	14	15	53	55	-2	49*
181	Hitchin Town	42	14	6	22	50	71	-21	48
19	Leiston	42	12	11	19	54	73	-19	47
20	St Neots	42	9	9	24	32	73	-41	36
21	Halesowen Town	42	6	14	22	26	66	-40	32
22	Bedworth United	42	3	10	29	32	91	-59	19

PREMIER DIVISION		1	2	3	4	5	6	7	8	9	10	11	12	13	14	15	16	17	18	19	20	21	22
1	AFC Rushden & Diamonds		1-1	1-1	1-1	3-1	3-3	3-1	2-0	2-1	0-1	1-0	1-1	1-1	2-1	5-2	0-0	0-2	0-0	2-0	1-2	2-0	2-2
2	Alvechurch	0-0		1-1	1-5	3-0	2-1	5-0	1-0	3-1	1-3	0-3	2-1	4-2	3-0	3-0	0-0	1-0	2-1	3-2	0-0	2-2	0-3
3	Banbury United	1-0	3-1		6-1	1-1	1-2	4-2	2-1	1-2	4-1	2-0	1-0	0-0	2-1	1-1	0-1	2-1	1-2	1-3	0-0	1-1	0-0
4	Barwell	1-1	1-2	2-1		1-1	0-0	2-3	1-1	0-1	0-1	1-3	3-0	1-1	0-2	4-0	1-2	1-3	1-1	6-1	1-1	0-0	0-1
5	Bedworth United	1-3	0-2	1-3	0-1		1-4	0-1	0-1	2-2	1-2	0-3	2-2	1-1	0-4	0-2	1-2	1-3	0-2	1-0	0-3	0-2	1-4
6	Biggleswade Town	1-0	4-2	0-0	1-1	1-1		3-0	1-0	1-1	1-0	1-2	1-2	3-1	2-0	2-0	1-4	0-1	1-0	1-0	1-2	0-0	3-0
7	Coalville Town	2-2	2-0	1-1	1-0	1-0	2-0		3-0	4-1	2-2	3-3	2-2	1-0	1-2	1-2	2-3	2-2	0-1	1-1	6-4	1-2	1-2
8	Halesowen Town	0-1	1-1	2-0	0-2	1-3	1-1	1-3		0-0	0-1	2-2	0-0	1-0	1-1	1-0	1-0	2-0	1-1	1-1	0-3	0-2	0-1
9	Hitchin Town	3-4	1-1	0-1	2-0	4-1	0-2	1-0	5-1		0-1	3-0	2-2	1-3	1-2	1-0	0-2	0-1	1-0	0-2	2-1	2-0	1-0
10	Kettering Town	2-1	1-2	3-0	0-1	5-1	2-3	2-3	2-0	5-0		2-1	1-2	3-0	3-2	4-4	1-0	2-1	0-3	2-0	4-2	5-1	2-1
11	King's Lynn Town	1-1	1-0	3-1	3-2	1-1	2-4	4-1	3-0	3-2	0-0		1-1	4-0	1-1	2-0	4-2	3-0	2-0	0-0	0-1	0-0	2-1
12	Leiston	1-4	2-0	0-0	0-1	1-1	3-0	2-0	4-0	1-2	0-1	1-5		0-4	2-1	4-3	1-1	0-1	0-2	2-0	0-3	1-2	2-2
13	Lowestoft Town	1-1	1-2	1-0	0-0	3-0	2-1	1-2	5-1	3-2	0-1	1-0	1-2		0-2	0-0	2-0	2-4	0-1	1-2	1-0	3-2	1-3
14	Needham Market	1-5	1-0	3-3	0-2	4-1	1-0	1-1	1-1	8-1	0-3	1-4	2-2	1-0		3-1	0-2	1-1	4-1	0-1	0-0	2-1	1-3
15	Redditch United	2-2	4-2	2-0	2-4	0-1	3-3	1-5	3-0	3-1	1-4	1-1	3-1	4-2	4-1		1-2	2-1	2-0	1-1	0-4	0-1	0-0
16	Royston Town	2-1	0-1	3-0	1-0	2-0	4-6	2-0	0-0	1-0	0-1	0-2	2-5	1-1	2-4	0-1		1-3	1-2	5-0	3-2	2-2	0-2
17	Rushall Olympic	2-1	1-2	1:1	1-1	0-0	2-2	0-2	0-0	1-2	0-1	2-1	2-0	3-1	0-1	1-3	0-3		4-1	3-2	0-0	2-2	1-1
18	St Ives Town	0-0	0-2	2-2	1-2	2-1	0-1	0-1	2-0	2-1	1-2	1-1	0-2	0-0	1-1	1-0	0-0	0-3		0-0	0-0	0-2	1-0
19	St Neots Town	0-1	0-3	0-3	1-0	2-1	2-2	1-4	1-1	0-0	0-3	0-5	2-0	1-3	0-3	3-1	1-0	0-1	0-1		1-2	1-2	0-0
20	Stourbridge	2-1	3-3	2-0	3-0	4-1	2-0	4-2	1-1	3-0	1-2	1-2	4-0	3-1	3-1	4-1	2-1	1-1	1-1	1-0		3-0	1-1
21	Stratford Town	1-0	0-1	2-1	2-1	3-1	3-2	0-2	2-1	2-0	1-3	0-2	3-2	1-3	3-1	2-0	2-0	0-1	0-0	1-0	0-0		2-1
22	Tamworth	1-1	1-1	4-0	3-3	2-2	1-1	1-3	4-1	2-0	0-0	0-1	5-0	0-2	1-2	1-3	1-2	2-0	1-2	5-0	1-0	0-1	

SOUTHERN LEAGUE
PREMIER DIVISION SOUTH TABLE 2018-19

		P	W	D	L	F	A	GD	Pts
1	Weymouth	42	25	11	6	96	51	45	86
2	Taunton Town	42	26	7	9	89	56	33	85
3	Metropolitan Police (PO winners)	42	22	12	8	91	64	27	78
4	Salisbury	42	22	11	9	97	69	28	77
5	Poole Town	42	20	10	12	84	59	25	70
6	Kings Langley	42	21	6	15	65	61	4	69
7	Harrow Borough	42	18	9	15	97	77	20	63
8	Hartley Wintney	42	17	12	13	82	70	12	63
9	Farnborough	42	18	8	16	72	72	0	62
10	Chesham United	42	15	14	13	54	55	-1	59
11	Swindon Supermarine	42	16	10	16	70	59	11	58
12	Beaconsfield Town	42	15	13	14	65	65	0	58
13	Merthyr Town	42	15	9	18	68	67	1	54
14	Wimborne Town	42	15	7	20	72	75	-3	52
15	Dorchester Town	42	14	10	18	67	75	-8	52
16	Hendon	42	14	10	18	64	74	-10	52
17	Walton Casuals	42	14	9	19	69	78	-9	51
18	Tiverton Town	42	13	12	17	65	75	-10	51
19	Gosport Borough	42	15	5	22	63	70	-7	50
20	Basingstoke Town	42	14	7	21	81	82	-1	49
21	Frome Town	42	11	4	27	45	74	-29	37
22	Staines Town	42	4	0	38	40	168	-128	12

	PREMIER DIVISION	1	2	3	4	5	6	7	8	9	10	11	12	13	14	15	16	17	18	19	20	21	22
1	Basingstoke Town		2-1	2-3	1-2	1-1	4-1	2-1	2-2	1-3	2-1	3-0	0-3	2-2	1-2	0-2	10-3	2-0	1-2	3-3	2-1	1-2	3-2
2	Beaconsfield Town	3-2		7-0	2-2	2-6	2-2	4-3	4-1	3-3	0-0	4-2	1-1	0-1	1-1	2-2	3-2	1-0	1-2	0-2	1-1	1-0	2-0
3	Chesham United	2-1	0-0		0-0	0-1	2-1	1-0	0-4	2-2	2-2	3-0	0-3	1-1	5-1	1-4	7-0	0-0	0-1	1-1	0-2	0-5	1-1
4	Dorchester Town	4-1	1-3	0-5		0-6	0-1	0-0	3-2	2-1	0-3	2-2	0-0	0-1	0-2	1-4	6-1	0-3	1-2	6-0	1-1	0-1	1-1
5	Farnborough	2-1	2-0	0-1	2-2		3-2	2-1	4-1	1-1	3-0	0-1	0-1	0-0	1-2	0-3	1-0	2-1	1-4	3-2	1-0	4-3	3-1
6	Frome Town	1-4	0-1	0-2	0-1	2-3		2-0	1-3	0-1	1-1	1-0	2-3	0-3	1-1	0-0	2-0	1-2	2-0	1-3	3-0	0-2	1-0
7	Gosport Borough	3-2	2-3	0-0	1-4	0-2	3-1		0-1	1-0	3-1	3-2	0-3	6-3	3-2	1-4	2-1	2-1	1-2	0-1	0-0	0-2	1-0
8	Harrow Borough	2-1	2-1	0-2	4-1	5-0	1-2	0-1		2-2	3-1	3-4	3-0	4-3	4-0	1-1	9-1	1-3	1-0	2-2	1-1	2-3	0-2
9	Hartley Wintney	0-2	2-0	1-2	3-1	2-2	2-1	1-0	3-0		2-3	0-0	1-1	1-4	4-3	3-4	7-0	2-2	3-1	1-0	3-4	0-3	3-0
10	Hendon	1-0	2-2	0-1	0-0	2-1	0-1	0-4	2-4	0-2		1-2	3-0	1-3	1-0	2-2	5-1	1-0	2-3	2-2	3-0	2-3	3-2
11	Kings Langley	2-0	3-0	1-0	1-0	5-1	2-0	3-0	2-4	2-1	3-1		1-0	1-2	0-3	1-1	3-1	1-2	1-2	2-2	1-0	2-1	1-0
12	Merthyr Town	1-0	0-1	1-0	1-7	0-0	1-3	4-2	1-1	1-2	0-2	1-1		2-2	0-2	1-2	9-0	2-2	3-1	5-1	1-2	2-1	2-0
13	Metropolitan Police	4-4	3-1	1-0	2-1	4-3	2-1	2-2	1-0	5-1	3-0	1-0	2-0		1-2	2-2	2-0	0-2	4-1	3-2	2-2	4-4	4-2
14	Poole Town	3-2	2-1	0-0	0-1	6-0	3-0	1-1	3-3	1-3	0-2	3-0	3-1	2-2		2-2	0-2	2-5	1-0	3-0	3-1	1-1	2-5
15	Salisbury	2-1	2-1	1-1	3-0	3-2	1-0	0-2	0-6	4-2	3-1	1-2	2-0	1-1	1-2		3-2	2-2	3-2	3-1	4-2	3-4	4-3
16	Staines Town	0-3	0-1	3-1	1-6	0-3	1-0	0-5	1-5	3-5	2-5	0-2	2-6	0-5	0-7	1-7		2-1	1-3	2-4	1-4	1-4	2-4
17	Swindon Supermarine	5-2	4-0	0-0	2-0	4-2	0-4	2-1	1-2	1-1	0-1	3-4	3-0	1-0	1-1	2-2	3-0		0-1	0-1	2-1	1-1	3-2
18	Taunton Town	0-0	2-1	4-0	1-1	2-1	3-0	3-2	7-0	2-2	3-3	2-1	3-2	1-3	1-0	4-3	4-0	1-1		2-1	4-0	3-3	4-2
19	Tiverton Town	4-1	1-1	0-2	2-3	1-1	3-1	1-0	1-1	1-1	0-0	1-2	2-2	2-1	0-2	2-0	3-2	2-2	1-3		5-1	1-2	0-3
20	Walton Casuals	3-3	1-1	2-2	2-3	2-1	4-1	3-1	3-2	1-2	5-1	1-0	1-3	2-2	0-4	3-1	3-1	3-1	0-1	1-2		1-2	3-0
21	Weymouth	1-2	1-1	1-1	5-0	3-0	4-0	1-3	2-2	2-2	3-0	2-2	2-1	4-0	2-2	2-1	4-0	2-1	2-1	2-1	3-2		1-0
22	Wimborne Town	2-4	0-1	0-0	2-4	1-1	3-2	3-2	5-3	2-1	3-3	5-0	4-0	3-0	0-4	1-4	1-0	1-0	1-1	2-1	3-0	0-0	

SOUTHERN LEAGUE
DIVISION ONE CENTRAL TABLE 2018-19

		P	W	D	L	F	A	GD	Pts
1	Peterborough Sports	38	30	5	3	109	28	81	95
2	Bromsgrove Sporting (PO winners)	38	27	6	5	108	44	64	87
3	Corby Town	38	24	5	9	106	60	46	77
4	Bedford Town FC	38	21	2	15	84	52	32	65
5	Sutton Coldfield Town	38	17	11	10	65	49	16	62
6	Berkhamsted	38	17	8	13	68	53	15	59
7	Didcot Town	38	16	10	12	69	61	8	58
8	Thame United	38	17	6	15	60	61	-1	57
9	Coleshill Town	38	16	8	14	60	58	2	56
10	AFC Dunstable	38	16	7	15	58	71	-13	55
11	Yaxley	38	15	4	19	72	92	-20	49
12	Cambridge City	38	12	11	15	58	54	4	47
13	Kempston Rovers	38	11	10	17	58	75	-17	43
14	Welwyn Garden City	38	11	10	17	52	64	-12	42*
15	Aylesbury United	38	12	6	20	62	86	-24	42
16	Barton Rovers	38	10	11	17	45	68	-23	41
17	North Leigh	38	9	7	22	67	106	-39	34
18	Kidlington	38	9	7	22	43	82	-39	34
19	Aylesbury	38	8	7	23	42	79	-37	31
20	Dunstable Town	38	8	7	23	49	92	-43	31

DIVISION ONE CENTRAL		1	2	3	4	5	6	7	8	9	10	11	12	13	14	15	16	17	18	19	20
1	AFC Dunstable		4-3	1-1	2-2	3-1	0-1	1-4	1-1	0-3	2-1	0-0	2-3	3-4	1-1	3-2	0-5	2-0	3-0	1-1	3-4
2	Aylesbury	0-2		3-1	2-2	1-0	0-3	0-0	3-0	1-1	1-4	2-4	3-2	1-2	0-1	0-3	1-0	0-2	0-3	0-0	0-1
3	Aylesbury United	1-2	2-0		3-1	1-4	2-4	0-3	1-1	3-4	1-2	1-4	3-0	3-1	2-1	1-4	0-4	1-2	0-1	3-1	2-1
4	Barton Rovers	0-2	1-1	1-1		0-8	1-2	0-3	3-1	2-4	5-2	1-2	1-1	0-3	2-3	2-1	1-1	1-3	2-4	1-0	0-0
5	Bedford Town	4-1	1-0	3-0	1-0		1-4	5-1	1-2	1-1	1-1	3-2	3-1	0-1	2-0	2-1	1-3	1-3	3-1	0-1	3-0
6	Berkhamsted	1-1	1-1	3-0	0-2	1-2		3-1	1-0	0-1	1-2	5-1	3-0	3-3	2-0	3-1	0-1	0-0	3-2	2-2	1-2
7	Bromsgrove Sporting	4-1	5-0	5-1	2-2	1-0	3-3		1-0	2-0	2-1	3-1	1-0	5-0	11-0	5-0	4-3	2-1	5-0	2-0	2-1
8	Cambridge City	0-1	2-3	3-4	0-0	3-2	0-2	1-1		2-0	1-1	2-0	3-3	1-0	0-0	6-1	1-3	0-2	1-1	4-1	6-2
9	Coleshill Town	1-2	2-0	0-1	1-1	2-3	2-2	3-0	0-2		0-2	2-1	3-1	1-2	2-0	0-4	2-3	2-1	2-2	2-1	1-1
10	Corby Town	2-1	5-2	3-2	3-0	4-1	3-1	6-0	4-1	3-0		3-2	1-2	5-1	3-1	5-2	1-3	1-0	1-3	1-4	3-2
11	Didcot Town	2-0	1-1	4-0	0-1	4-3	3-4	1-2	2-1	1-0	3-2		2-1	2-1	2-2	2-2	1-1	1-1	2-1	3-3	2-0
12	Dunstable Town	2-4	1-6	1-2	0-1	0-5	2-4	3-2	1-1	3-3	3-3	0-3		0-0	0-3	4-0	0-7	0-1	2-1	1-3	1-2
13	Kempston Rovers	1-2	3-0	2-2	1-3	1-3	3-0	0-4	1-1	2-5	1-3	1-1	1-3		3-2	3-2	1-2	1-1	1-1	2-3	2-2
14	Kidlington	0-0	3-2	2-4	1-2	0-5	1-0	0-4	2-0	0-1	1-2	1-2	1-5	0-3		3-3	0-2	0-4	0-1	0-0	6-1
15	North Leigh	1-2	3-1	4-2	4-0	2-3	1-1	1-5	2-4	1-2	1-8	2-0	3-1	3-1	0-3		3-3	2-5	1-2	3-3	3-3
16	Peterborough Sports	7-0	5-0	3-1	4-0	1-0	3-0	1-2	2-1	4-2	2-1	0-0	1-1	3-0	4-0	5-1		3-0	5-0	2-0	3-0
17	Sutton Coldfield Town	1-0	2-0	2-3	1-0	3-2	1-1	1-1	1-1	0-1	4-4	3-3	3-0	1-1	4-2	3-0	1-3		1-4	1-1	3-1
18	Thame United	3-1	4-1	2-1	0-2	2-1	2-1	1-1	1-0	0-2	1-1	0-1	5-0	1-3	0-0	3-2	0-1	0-3		4-2	2-1
19	Welwyn Garden City	0-1	2-0	0-0	1-0	0-3	0-1	0-3	0-1	2-2	2-5	2-1	0-1	1-2	2-1	3-0	1-3	1-1	3-1		3-2
20	Yaxley	4-2	1-3	3-7	4-1	1-2	2-1	3-6	0-4	2-0	0-4	4-3	2-0	3-2	1-2	6-2	1-3	3-0	2-1	4-3	

SOUTHERN LEAGUE
DIVISION ONE SOUTH TABLE 2018-19

		P	W	D	L	F	A	GD	Pts
1	Blackfield & Langley	38	26	4	8	75	34	41	82
2	Cirencester Town	38	23	6	9	110	52	58	75
3	Yate Town (PO winners)	38	23	6	9	74	51	23	75
4	Moneyfields	38	21	8	9	73	43	30	71
5	Cinderford Town	38	21	8	9	64	39	25	71
6	Winchester City	38	21	7	10	84	46	38	70
7	Evesham United	38	19	6	13	66	53	13	63
8	Street (Resigned)	38	17	10	11	58	51	7	61
9	Bideford	38	18	4	16	66	68	-2	58
10	AFC Totton	38	17	5	16	72	55	17	56
11	Thatcham Town	38	17	5	16	57	58	-1	56
12	Melksham Town	38	17	5	16	59	70	-11	56
13	Larkhall Athletic	38	16	7	15	52	51	1	55
14	Highworth Town	38	13	9	16	63	71	-8	48
15	Bristol Manor Farm	38	13	7	18	65	77	-12	46
16	Mangotsfield United	38	11	4	23	64	78	-14	37
17	Paulton Rovers	38	10	3	25	49	79	-30	33
18	Slimbridge	38	8	6	24	43	87	-44	30
19	Barnstaple Town	38	6	5	27	42	100	-58	23
20	Fleet Town	38	5	1	32	48	121	-73	16

	DIVISION ONE SOUTH	1	2	3	4	5	6	7	8	9	10	11	12	13	14	15	16	17	18	19	20
1	AFC Totton		5-0	4-0	0-1	2-1	1-2	0-2	1-3	5-3	3-1	1-2	2-1	5-0	1-0	5-2	2-1	2-0	0-3	1-1	1-1
2	Barnstaple Town	0-4		1-4	0-3	1-2	0-2	0-5	1-3	4-1	1-3	0-2	2-2	0-1	1-3	3-0	1-2	2-4	1-2	3-2	2-1
3	Bideford	3-2	1-0		0-1	3-1	0-1	4-0	3-1	2-1	1-0	1-1	0-0	1-1	1-3	3-2	2-0	0-1	0-1	1-0	3-1
4	Blackfield & Langley	1-1	3-1	4-1		3-0	1-0	2-0	4-0	4-1	3-0	4-1	3-0	3-2	1-2	0-0	1-0	2-1	3-0	0-4	1-2
5	Bristol Manor Farm	1-2	4-1	4-3	1-0		1-3	1-4	2-1	4-1	1-2	3-3	1-2	2-3	2-1	1-2	3-0	1-1	3-2	3-1	2-4
6	Cinderford Town	0-1	6-0	4-2	2-1	4-2		1-1	0-1	1-2	3-1	2-0	0-1	1-0	1-1	3-1	1-0	1-0	1-1	0-0	5-1
7	Cirencester Town	1-1	4-1	8-2	2-3	5-0	0-1		2-0	4-0	3-2	4-1	6-1	4-0	2-2	3-5	3-3	5-0	6-2	4-2	1-2
8	Evesham United	4-3	1-0	1-3	2-1	2-2	2-1	0-2		4-0	4-4	1-1	3-2	3-0	3-1	1-0	2-0	1-1	1-2	0-2	1-2
9	Fleet Town	2-5	4-3	3-2	0-2	2-2	0-2	1-4	1-4		3-4	1-2	1-2	0-3	1-5	2-3	0-3	1-3	1-2	1-2	2-1
10	Highworth Town	1-0	1-1	3-4	2-2	4-0	0-1	0-3	1-7	4-2		0-2	1-1	3-1	1-1	1-0	4-0	1-0	5-0	1-4	1-4
11	Larkhall Athletic	1-0	0-0	2-3	0-2	2-0	2-3	1-2	0-1	3-1	1-0		3-2	0-1	1-2	3-1	2-1	0-2	2-0	0-1	2-1
12	Mangotsfield United	3-0	4-0	0-2	1-2	0-2	5-0	1-5	0-0	5-3	0-1	3-1		1-2	0-4	4-1	2-3	1-2	1-2	1-2	1-3
13	Melksham Town	0-3	3-0	2-1	2-3	2-2	3-2	0-1	1-0	2-1	3-2	1-1	2-1		1-3	0-4	1-0	5-3	1-2	1-4	0-2
14	Moneyfields	2-0	3-1	2-1	0-1	1-0	1-0	2-1	1-0	4-1	2-1	0-1	3-1	3-3		5-1	1-0	2-2	0-0	0-2	1-2
15	Paulton Rovers	1-4	1-4	1-2	1-2	1-2	0-1	0-3	0-2	4-1	2-2	1-3	4-2	0-1	1-0		2-1	2-4	0-1	0-1	1-0
16	Slimbridge	4-3	2-2	3-2	0-4	3-3	1-3	2-2	0-1	1-3	0-0	1-1	1-8	1-3	2-4	1-0		1-2	1-0	1-3	1-4
17	Street	1-0	1-1	4-1	0-0	0-0	0-0	2-1	1-1	3-0	2-2	1-4	2-0	3-1	2-0	2-2	3-1		1-2	0-2	3-0
18	Thatcham Town	3-0	3-2	1-2	1-0	2-1	3-3	1-2	4-2	6-0	2-3	3-1	1-2	0-3	0-2	1-0	0-1	0-1		1-1	0-1
19	Winchester City	2-1	7-0	2-2	3-0	1-3	2-2	3-2	1-2	3-0	1-1	1-0	4-0	2-2	0-3	2-3	6-1	5-0	3-2		0-1
20	Yate Town	1-1	1-2	2-0	1-4	3-2	1-1	2-1	3-1	4-1	3-0	0-0	4-3	3-2	2-2	3-0	3-0	1-0	1-1	3-2	

SOUTHERN PREMIER CENTRAL & SOUTH STATISTICS 2018-19

CLUB	SG	CSG	FS	CFS	CS	CCS	PS	PC	TGC	TG
AFC Rushden & Diamonds		13	12	2	11	2	6+1c	0		
Alvechurch		8	11	2	15	3	2+2c	1		
Banbury United		9 (first games)	15	2	11	3	2+2c	6		
Barwell		11	13	3	11	2	3+1c	5		
Bedworth United		9	16	5	3	1	2	5		
Biggleswade Town		12	9	2	13	5	5	4		
Coalville Town		19	7	1	12	2	5	3		
Halesowen Town		5	20	3	11	2	3	5		
Hitchin Town		5	16	3	12	3	1+1c	1		
Kettering Town		12 first games	7	2	20	3	6+1c	1		
Kings Lynn Town		13	9	3	15	3	7	5		
Leiston		7	14	4	8	1	3	7		
Lowestoft Town		10	14	2	12	2	1	4		
Needham Market		10	6	1	13	3	5+3c	3		
Redditch United		8	14	3	7	2	2	4		
Royston Town		13	15	3	15	4	4	3		
Rushall Olympic		7	12	2	12	2	4	4		
St Ives Town		5	19	2	18	3	1+1c	4		
St Neots Town		4	21	3	9	2	1+1c	7		
Stourbridge		8	9	2	18	3	8+1c	2		
Stratford Town		14	13	3	18	3	3+2c	1		
Tamworth		12	13	2	16	5	1	0		
Basingstoke Town		11	6	1	6	1	4+1c	2		
Beaconsfield Town		19	9	2	13	3	3	2+1c		
Chesham United		4	18	2	14	3	2	8		
Dorchester Town		6	17	3	11	2	2	3		
Farnborough		11	9	2	9	3	4+1c	5		
Frome Town		10	10	4	9	2	2	5		
Gosport Borough		12	13	4	13	4	3+1c	3		
Harrow Borough		9	5	2	5	2	3	8		
Hartley Wintney		11	5	1	9	3	3+1c	3		
Hendon		19	10	2	13	2	9	6		
Kings Langley		8	11	4	13	2	4	2		
Merthyr Town		11	14	3	8	1	1	4+1c		
Metropolitan Police		15	6	1	12	2	5	4		
Poole Town		21	7	2	14	3	7+1c	2		
Salisbury		45	4	2	9	2	5+1c	3		
Staines Town		5	18	3	2	1	1	5		
Swindon Supermarine		14*	8	3	6	2	3	3		
TauntonTown		22	5	1	11	2	6	4		
TivertonTown		11	8	2	8	2	1	6		
Walton Casuals		7	13	3	8	2	5	1		
Weymouth		42	1	0	11	3	10	3		
Wimborne Town		8	14	2	11	2	1	2		

SG - Scoring Games; CSG - Consec Scoring Games; FS - Failure to Score; CFS - Consec Failure to Score; CS - Clean Sheets
CCS - Consec Clean Sheets; PS - Penalties Scored; PC - Pens Conceded; TGC - Total Goals Conceded; TG - Total Goals

CLUB GOAL SCORERS IN SEASON 2018-2019

...continued from page 260

SCORERS OF 20 OR MORE GOALS

Leading Goalscorers	Club	Lge	Cup	SG	CSG	Pens	Hat Tricks	Total
Ian Traylor	Merthyr Town	24	1	18	3	1	2	25
Max Blackmore	Metropolitan Police	20	4	18	2			24
Moses Emmanuel	Billericay Town	17	7	17	3		2	24
Nathan Watson	Basford United	23	1	16	3	2	2	24
Jamie Cureton	Bishops Stortford	22	1	13	2	1		23
Tyler Harvey	Truro City	22	1	17	3	2	1	23
Brady Hickey	Barwell	17	6	21	5	3		23
Greg Mills	Stourbridge	23		19	5	7		23
Joe White	Biggleswade Town	19	4	17	3	2	1	23
Colby Bishop	Leamington	21	1	16	3	2	1	22
Rhys Murphy	Chelmsford City	22		18	5			22
Adam Rooney	Salford City	20	2?	16	4	1	2	22
Alex Wall	Concord Rangers	21	1	19	3			22
Luke Benbow	Stourbridge	20	1	17	3	2	1	21
Nat Jarvis	Chippenham Town	16	5	18	3			21
Joseph Marsden	Needham Market	19	2	16	5	6	1	21
James Muitt	Bognor Regis Town	18	3	15	6	6		21
Adam Rooney	Salford City	20	1	15	4	1		21
Ashley Worsfold	Gainsborough Trinity	18	3	18	4		1	21
Addillahie Yussuf	Solihull Moors	16	5	16	2	3		21
Jake Beesley	Bradford PA	19	1	13	2	3	1	20
Ricardo German	Hendon	16	4	15	4	5	1	20
Joshua Hancock	Altrincham	18	2	15	2			20
Tyler Harvey	Truro City	18	2	12	3	3	1	20
Ryan Moss	Harrow Borough	19	1	15	3	2	1	20
Lee Ndlovu	Brackley Town	12	8	18	3	1	1	20
Ryan Pennery	Gosport Borough	18	2	17	5	4	1	20

THE LEAGUE CUP 2018-19

HOLDERS: HITCHIN TOWN

PRELIMINARY ROUND

Coleshill Town	v	Sutton Coldfield Town	1-1, 3-1p
Alvechurch	v	Bromsgrove Sporting	1-0
Fleet Town	v	Farnborough	1-3
Kings Langley	v	Welwyn Garden City	0-1
Leiston	v	Cambridge City	1-0
Mangotsfield United	v	Larkhall Athletic	1-2
North Leigh	v	Banbury United	1-5
Redditch United	v	Rushall Olympic	4-3
St Neots Town	v	Bedford Town	2-2, 4-1p
Tamworth	v	Coalville Town	6-0
Taunton Town	v	Street	2-5
Walton Casuals	v	Beaconsfield Town	2-1
Winchester City	v	Gosport Borough	1-1, 2-4p
Yaxley	v	St Ives Town	2-2, 2-0p
Hitchin Town	v	Harrow Borough	2-2, 4-2p
Chesham United	v	Dunstable Town	5-3
Didcot Town	v	Thame United	5-3
Corby Town	v	Peterborough Sports	2-3
Kempston Rovers	v	AFC Dunstable	3-1
Swindon Supermarine	v	Yate Town	4-1

ROUND ONE

AFC Totton	v	Moneyfields	3-1
Aylesbury	v	Berkhamsted	0-3
Aylesbury United	v	Chesham United	3-1
Banbury United	v	Kettering Town	2-3
Bedworth United	v	Barwell	0-0, 5-6p
Bristol Manor Farm	v	Cinderford Town	2-4
Didcot Town	v	Kidlington	1-0
Dorchester Town	v	Poole Town	1-1, 2-4p
Frome Town	v	Paulton Rovers	0-2
Gosport Borough	v	Blackfield & Langley	3-4
Kempston Rovers	v	AFC Rushden & Diamonds	2-2, 3-1p
King's Lynn Town	v	Peterborough Sports	4-1
Leiston	v	Needham Market	1-1, 4-2p
Lowestoft Town	v	St Neots Town	3-1
Royston Town	v	Hitchin Town	1-2
(R) Royston Town	v	Hitchin Town	4-3
Swindon Supermarine	v	Cirencester Town	1-3
Tamworth	v	Coleshill Town	1-1, 5-6p
Tiverton Town	v	Barnstaple Town	2-1
Walton Casuals	v	Staines Town	6-0
Welwyn Garden City	v	Barton Rovers	2-1
Wimborne Town	v	Weymouth	2-0
Yaxley	v	Biggleswade Town	0-9
Evesham United	v	Stourbridge	2-3
Highworth Town	v	Salisbury	0-0, 4-5p
Larkhall Athletic	v	Melksham Town	0-2
Redditch United	v	Halesowen Town	2-1
Slimbridge	v	Merthyr Town	5-1
Alvechurch	v	Stratford Town	2-4
Metropolitan Police	v	Hendon	1-0
Street	v	Bideford	1-2
Thatcham Town	v	Hartley Wintney	0-0, 8-9p
Basingstoke Town	v	Farnborough	HWO

ROUND TWO

Coleshill Town	v	Barwell	0-0, 3-4p
Stourbridge	v	Cinderford Town	2-3
Berkhamsted	v	Aylesbury United	2-0
Blackfield & Langley	v	AFC Totton	4-0
Didcot Town	v	Cirencester Town	3-0
Kettering Town	v	King's Lynn Town	5-1
Leiston	v	Lowestoft Town	0-1
Melksham Town	v	Slimbridge	0-4
Salisbury	v	Paulton Rovers	2-0
Stratford Town	v	Redditch United	2-1
Tiverton Town	v	Bideford	2-5
Metropolitan Police	v	Hartley Wintney	1-5
Welwyn Garden City	v	Kempston Rovers	8-0
Wimborne Town	v	Poole Town	3-0
Basingstoke Town	v	Walton Casuals	2-1
Royston Town	v	Biggleswade Town	4-1

ROUND THREE

Berkhamsted	v	Welwyn Garden City	0-0, 4-2p
Cinderford Town	v	Slimbridge	4-2
Didcot Town	v	Stratford Town	1-1, 2-4p
Kettering Town	v	Barwell	1-1, 4-2p
Wimborne Town	v	Bideford	1-2
Basingstoke Town	v	Hartley Wintney	1-4
Salisbury	v	Blackfield & Langley	1-3
Royston Town	v	Lowestoft Town	4-4, 3-1p

Royston Town were expelled for fielding an ineligible player.

Lowestoft Town were reinstated.

QUARTER-FINALS

Cinderford Town	v	Bideford	2-2, 4-3p
Stratford Town	v	Kettering Town	3-3, 4-1p
Hartley Wintney	v	Blackfield & Langley	0-1
Lowestoft Town	v	Berkhamsted	1-0

SEMI-FINALS

Cinderford Town	v	Blackfield & Langley	3-2
Stratford Town	v	Lowestoft Town	3-2

FINAL

Stratford Town	v	Cinderford Town	1-0

AFC RUSHDEN & DIAMONDS MATCH RESULTS 2018-19

Date	Comp	H/A	Opponents	Att:	Result		Goalscorers	Pos	No.
Aug 11	Sth Prem C	H	Redditch United	592	W	5 - 2	Bowen 3 Farrell 8 Diamond 42 57 Lorraine 61		1
14	Sth Prem C	A	Biggleswade Town	402	L	0 - 1			2
18	Sth Prem C	A	Stourbridge	560	L	1 - 2	Dean 10	12	3
25	**FAC P**	**A**	**Deeping Rangers**	**347**	**D**	**1 - 1**	**Bowen 37**		4
27	Sth Prem C	A	St Neots Town	609	W	1 - 0	Farrell 7 (pen)	11	5
31	Sth Prem C	H	Tamworth	683	D	2 - 2	Lorraine 22 90	11	6
Sept 4	**FAC Pr**	**H**	**Deeping Rangers**	**396**	**W**	**3 - 0**	**Lorraine 17 81 Westwood 50**		7
8	**FAC 1Qr**	**A**	**Hayes & Yeading**	**286**	**L**	**1 - 2**	**Farrell (pen) 90**		8
15	Sth Prem C	A	Royston Town	384	L	1 - 2	Bowen 60	12	9
29	Sth Prem C	H	St Ives Town	586	D	0 - 0		17	10
Oct 6	Sth Prem C	A	Needham Market	275	W	5 - 1	Diamond 26 Bowen 45 Rogers 69 Lorraine 80 Hopkins 90	12	11
13	Sth Prem C	H	Barwell	694	D	1 - 1	Hopkins 41	11	12
20	Sth Prem C	A	King's Lynn Town	816	D	1 - 1	Rogers 57	10	13
23	Sth Prem C	H	Coalville Town	407	W	3 - 1	Farrell 7 Rogers 14 Lorraine 70	8	14
27	**FAT 1Q**	**H**	**St Ives Town**	**386**	**W**	**2 - 1**	**Lorraine 45 Bowen 52**		15
Nov 3	Sth Prem C	H	Rushall Olympic	478	L	0 - 2		11	16
10	**FAT 2Q**	**A**	**Witton Albion**	**300**	**L**	**0 - 2**			17
13	Sth Prem C	H	Hitchin Town	366	W	2 - 1	Diamond 24 Bowen 53	9	18
17	Sth Prem C	H	Bedworth United	508	W	3 - 1	Bowen 24 Lorraine 70 Farrell 85 (pen)	7	19
20	Sth Prem C	A	Banbury United	340	L	0 - 1		7	20
24	Sth Prem C	A	Lowestoft Town	457	D	1 - 1	Farrell 90 (pen)	5	21
27	Sth Prem C	H	Halesowen Town	280	W	2 - 0	Farrell Lorraine	3	22
Dec 1	Sth Prem C	A	Leiston	277	W	4 - 1	Hopkins 2 Lorraine 31 Diamond 79 Farrell 85 (pen)	3	23
8	Sth Prem C	A	Alvechurch	241	D	0 - 0		4	24
22	Sth Prem C.	A	Redditch United	295	D	2 - 2	Rogers 45 Diamond 80	6	25
26	Sth Prem C	H	St Neots Town	644	W	2 - 0	Lorraine 39 69	4	26
29	Sth Prem C	H	Biggleswade Town	547	D	3 - 3	Hopkins 67 Farrell 89 (pen) 90	4	27
Jan 1	Sth Prem C	A	Kettering Town	2147	L	1 - 2	Hicks 53	5	28
5	Sth Prem C	A	Hitchin Town	530	W	4 - 3	Lorraine 7 19 Bowen 86 Berry-Hargreaves 90	5	29
12	Sth Prem C	H	Lowestoft Town	575	D	1 - 1	Farrell 45 (pen)	8	30
19	Sth Prem C	A	Bedworth United	284	W	3 - 1	Rogers 40 Lorraine 57 83	6	31
26	Sth Prem C	H	Banbury United	553	D	1 - 1	Diamond 57	7	32
Feb 9	Sth Prem C	H	Kings Lynn Town	614	W	1 - 0	Lorraine 39 69	7	33
16	Sth Prem C	H	Leiston	620	D	1 - 1	Ashton 23	8	34
19	Sth Prem C	H	Stratford Town	399	W	2 - 0	Dolman 59 Johnson 69	7	35
23	Sth Prem C	A	Halesowen Town	428	W	1 - 0	Diamond 60	4	36
Mar 2	Sth Prem C	H	Alvechurch	556	D	1 - 1	Johnson 2	4	37
9	Sth Prem C	A	Stratford Town	449	L	0 - 1		4	38
11	Sth Prem C	A	Rushall Olympic	221	L	0 - 2		5	39
16	Sth Prem C	H	Needham Market	410	W	2 - 1	Rogers 22 Bowen 42	4	40
23	Sth Prem C	A	Barwell	346	D	1 - 1	Diamond 50	5	41
30	Sth Prem C	H	Royston Town	634	D	0 - 0		6	42
Apr 6	Sth Prem C	A	St Ives Town	372	D	0 - 0		7	43
13	Sth Prem C	H	Stourbridge	519	L	1 - 2	Hicks 18	8	44
20	Sth Prem C	A	Coalville Town	265	L	0 - 5		8	45
22	Sth Prem C	H	Kettering Town	1165	L	0 - 1		8	46
27	Sth Prem C	A	Tamworth	705	D	1 - 1	Hicks 69	9	47

GOALSCORERS	SG	CSG	Pens	Hat tricks	Total		SG	CSG	Pens	Hat tricks	Total
Lorraine	12	2			18	Dean	1				1
Farrell	10	3	7		11	Dolman	1				1
Bowen	9				9	Westwood	1				1
Diamond	8				9						
Rogers	6				6						
Hopkins	4	2			4						
Hicks	3				3						
Johnson	2				2						
Ashton	1				1						
Berry-H	1				1						

ALVECHURCH MATCH RESULTS 2018-19

Date	Comp	H/A	Opponents	Att:	Result	Goalscorers	Pos	No.
Aug 11	Sth Prem C	H	Royston Town	177	D 0 - 0			1
14	Sth Prem C	A	Tamworth	592	D 1 - 1	Cook 22		2
18	Sth Prem C	A	Coalville Town	182	L 0 - 2		18	3
25	**FAC P**	**H**	**Bromsgrove Sporting**	**729**	**W 4 - 3**	**March 8 Yates 12 Turton 62 (pen) 75 (pen)**		4
27	Sth Prem C	H	Redditch United	420	W 3 - 0	Bellis 1 Ezewele 11 Mills 20 (og)	12	5
Sept 1	Sth Prem C	H	Needham Market	183	W 3 - 0	Yates 20 Ezewele 45 Turton 76 (pen)	11	6
8	**FAC 1Q**	**A**	**Stratford Town**	**238**	**W 1 - 0**	**Lloyd 78**		7
15	Sth Prem C	A	Hitchiin Town	361	D 1 - 1	March51	11	8
18	Sth Prem C	H	Stourbridge	347	D 0 - 0			9
22	**FAC 2Q**	**A**	**Corby Town**	**256**	**L 1 - 4**	**Cook 17**		10
29	Sth Prem C	H	Kettering Town	359	L 1 - 3	O'Callaghan 16	11	11
Oct 6	Sth Prem C	A	Barwell	172	W 2 - 1	March 35 Lloyd 53	8	12
13	Sth Prem C	H	St Ives Town	254	W 2 - 1	Botfield 27 Willets 62	7	13
20	Sth Prem C	A	Bedworth United	217	W 2 - 0	Bellis 23 Botfield 25	6	14
27	**FAT 1Q**	**H**	**Stratford Town**	**199**	**D 1 - 1**	**March26**	**6**	15
30	**FAT 1Qr**	**A**	**Stratford Town**	**172**	**L 0 - 3**		**7**	16
Nov 3	Sth Prem C	H	Kings Lynn Town	167	L 0 - 3		7	17
10	Sth Prem C	A	Rushall Olympic	226	W 2 - 1	Botfield 45 Cook 88	7	18
17	Sth Prem C	H	St Neots Town	239	W 3 - 2	Cook 6 47 Morrison 68	3	19
Dec 1	Sth Prem C	A	Biggleswade Town	150	L 2 - 4	March 46 Carvalho-Landell 90	6	20
4	Sth Prem C	A	Halesowen Town	406	D 1 - 1	March90	6	21
8	Sth Prem C	H	AFC Rushden & Diamonds	241	D 0 - 0		5	22
15	Sth Prem C	A	Lowestoft Town	291	W 2 - 1	Willetts 70 Carvalho-Landell 89	4	23
22	Sth Prem C.	A	Royston Town	243	W 1 - 0	Chilton 11	3	24
26	Sth Prem C	A	Redditch United	556	L 2 - 4	Carvalho-Landell 38 Chilton 44	6	25
29	Sth Prem C	H	Tamworth	324	L 0 - 3		8	26
Jan 1	Sth Prem C	A	Banbury United	462	L 1 - 3	Botfield 38	10	27
5	Sth Prem C	A	Stratford Town	246	W 1 - 0	March90	9	28
12	Sth Prem C	H	Halesowen Town	294	W 1 - 0	Nabi 45	9	29
19	Sth Prem C	A	St Neots Town	198	W 3 - 0	Cook 12 Chilton 67 84	7	30
22	Sth Prem C	H	Stratford Town	160	D 2 - 2	Nabi 41 Chilton 71	7	31
26	Sth Prem C	H	Rushall Olympic	179	W 1 - 0	Lloyd 90+4	5	32
9	Sth Prem C	H	Bedworth United	209	W 3 - 0	Turton 30 (pen) Cook 35 Morrison 71	5	33
16	Sth Prem C	H	Biggleswade Town	170	W 2 - 1	March 38 54	5	34
23	Sth Prem C	A	Leiston	236	L 0 - 2		5	35
Mar 2	Sth Prem C	A	AFC Rushden & Diamonds	556	D 1 - 1	Cook 64	8	36
9	Sth Prem C	H	Lowestoft Town	214	W 4 - 2	Cook 29 Carter 36 March 53 65	7	37
19	Sth Prem C	A	Kings Lynn Town	755	L 0 - 1		7	38
23	Sth Prem C	A	St Ives Town	270	W 2 - 0	Morrison 6 Tonks 48	6	39
26	Sth Prem C	H	Barwell	206	L 1 - 5	Willets 66	6	40
30	Sth Prem C	H	Hitchin Town	201	W 3 - 1	Tonks 38 Lloyd 45 March 77	5	41
Apr 2	Sth Prem C	H	Leiston	175	W 2 1	Cook 40 Roberts 47	5	42
6	Sth Prem C	A	Kettering Town	1567	W 2 - 1	Willets 3 Botfield 88	4	43
13	Sth Prem C	H	Coalville Town	287	W 5 - 0	March 10 23 Willetts 37 Tonks 76 Roberts 90	4	44
20	Sth Prem C	A	Stourbridge	1062	D 3 - 3	Roberts 43 90 March 50	4	45
22	Sth Prem C	H	Banbury United	300	D 1 - 1	Roberts 15	4	46
27	Sth Prem C	A	Needham Market	285	L 0 - 1		4	47
May 4	**PO SF**	**H**	**Stourbridge**	**894**	**W 2 - 1**	**Winwood 56 Roberts 61**		48
6	**PO F**	**A**	**King's Lynn Town**	**1617**	**L 0 - 3**			49

GOALSCORERS	SG	CSG	Pens	Hat tricks	Total
March	11	2			15
Cook	9	2			10
Botfield	5				5
Roberts	5	3			6
Chilton	4				5
Willetts	5				5
Lloyd	4				4
Turton	3		3		4
Carvalho-Landell	3				3
Morrison	3				3
Tonks	3				3
Bellis	2				2
Ezewele	2				2
Nabi	2				2
Yates	2				2
Carter	1				1
O'Callaghan	1				1
Opponents	1				1
Winwood	1				1

BANBURY UNITED MATCH RESULTS 2018-19

Date	Comp	H/A	Opponents	Att:	Result		Goalscorers	Pos	No.
Aug 11	Sth Prem C	A	Rushall Olympic	271	D	1 - 1	Shamsi 22		1
14	Sth Prem C	H	Halesowen Town	395	**W**	2 - 1	Wise 5 Kaziboni 16		2
18	Sth Prem C	H	Leiston	405	**W**	1 - 0	Johnson 65	5	3
27	Sth Prem C	H	Stratford Town	630	D	1 - 1	Kaziboni 16	8	4
Sept 1	Sth Prem C	A	Hitchin Town	375	**W**	1 - 0	Self 55	7	5
8	**FAC 1Q**	**A**	**Weymouth**	**751**	**D**	**1 - 1**	**Rasulo 51 (pen)**		6
11	**FAC 1Qr**	**H**	**Weymouth**	**551**	**W**	**2 - 1**	**Awadh 38 Rasulo 89 (pen)**		7
15	Sth Prem C	H	St Neots Town	490	L	1 - 3	Shamsi 12	7	8
18	Sth Prem C	A	Bedworth United	192	**W**	3 - 1	SHAMSI 3 (6 22 87)	4	9
22	**FAC 2Q**	**H**	**Bath City**	**654**	**L**	**0 - 2**			10
29	Sth Prem C	A	Kings Lynn Town	575	L	1 - 3	Rasulo 72		11
Oct 6	Sth Prem C	H	Tamworth	362	D	0 - 0		5	12
13	Sth Prem C	A	Biggleswade Town	242	D	0 - 0		7	13
16	Sth Prem C	A	Barwell	157	L	1 - 2	Kaziboni 15	10	14
20	Sth Prem C	H	Royston Town	421	L	0 - 1		12	15
27	**FAT 1Q**	**A**	**Swindon Supermarine**	**215**	**D**	**1 - 1**	**Rasulo**		16
30	**FAT1Qr**	**H**	**Swindon Supermarine**	**218**	**W**	**3 - 0**	**Kaziboni 50 64 Johnson 78**		17
Nov 3	Sth Prem C	A	Redditch United	322	L	0 - 2		14	18
10	**FAT 2Q**	**H**	**Hayes & Yeading**	**387**	**L**	**0 - 2**			19
17	Sth Prem C	A	Coalville Town	223	D	1 - 1	Johnson 90	15	20
20	Sth Prem C	H	AFC Rushden & Diamonds	340	**W**	1 - 0	Diggin 2	13	21
24	Sth Prem C	A	St Ives Town	179	D	2 - 2	Rasulu 18 Johnson 84		22
Dec 1	Sth Prem C	H	Lowestoft Town	327	D	0 - 0		13	23
8	Sth Prem C	A	Needham Market	221	D	3 - 3	Diggin 21 45 Shamsi 53	13	24
11	Sth Prem C	H	Stourbridge	313	D	0 - 0		`14	25
15	Sth Prem C	H	Kettering Town	371	**W**	4 - 1	Wise 30 Shami 59 70 Kaziboni 63	12	26
22	Sth Prem C	H	Rushall Olympic	451	**W**	2 - 1	Diggin 31 (pen) Kaziboni 64	9	27
26	Sth Prem C	A	Stratford Town	406	L	1 - 2	Shamsi 53	10	28
29	Sth Prem C	A	Halesowen Town	402	L	0 - 2		11	29
Jan 1	Sth Prem C	H	Alvechurch	462	**W**	3 - 1	Kaziboni 20 Shamsi 89 Diggin 90	10	30
5	Sth Prem C	H	Barwell	372	**W**	6 - 1	Kaziboni 19 Shamsi 54 66 Taylor 58 Rasulo 63 Diggin 81	9	31
12	Sth Prem C	A	Stourbridge	701	L	0 - 2		10	32
19	Sth Prem C	H	Coalville Town	360	**W**	4 - 2	Rasulo 14 pen) Kaziboni 17 Shamsi 43 Henderson 64	10	33
26	Sth Prem C	A	AFC Rushden & Diamonds	557	D	1 - 1	Diggin 78	10	34
Feb 9	Sth Prem C	A	Royston Town	254	L	0 - 3		12	35
16	Sth Prem C	A	Lowestoft Town	407	L	0 - 1		13	36
23	Sth Prem C	H	St Ives Town	439	L	1 - 2	Shamsi 57	13	37
26	Sth Prem C	H	Redditch United	302	D	1 - 1	Shamsi 27	13	38
Mar 2	Sth Prem C	H	Needham Market	402	**W**	2 - 1	Iaciofano 5 Rasulo 84	14	39
9	Sth Prem C	A	Kettering Town	760	L	0 - 3		14	40
16	Sth Prem C	A	Tamworth	620	L	0 - 4		15	41
23	Sth Prem C	H	Biggleswade Town	400	L	1 - 2	Johnson 11	15	42
30	Sth Prem C	A	St Neots Town	260	**W**	3 - 0	Iacofano 6 Johnson 45 63	15	43
Apr 6	Sth Prem C	H	Kings Lynn Town	426	**W**	2 - 0	Kaziboni 44 Awadh 88	15	44
13	Sth Prem C	A	Leiston	208	D	0 - 0		14	45
20	Sth Prem C	H	Bedworth United	409	D	1 - 1	Shamsi 41	14	46
22	Sth Prem C	A	Alvechurch	300	D	1 - 1	Awadh 12	15	47
27	Sth Prem C	H	Hitchin Town	427	L	1 - 2	Awadh 14	17	48

GOALSCORERS	SG	CSG	Pens	Hat tricks	Total
Shamsi	12	2		1	16
Kaziboni	10	2			11
Rasulo	8		3		8
Diggin	5		1		7
Johnson	6				7
Awadi	4				4
Iaciofano	2				2
Wise	2				2
Henderson	1				1
Self	1				1
Taylor	1				1

BARNWELL MATCH RESULTS 2018-19

Date	Comp	H/A	Opponents	Att:	Result		Goalscorers	Pos	No.
Aug 11	Sth Prem C	H	Stourbridge	278	D	1 - 1	McDonald 40		1
14	Sth Prem C	A	Redditch United	175	**W**	4 - 2	Julien 8 HIckey 15 (pen) McDonald 30 78		2
18	Sth Prem C	A	Needham Market	266	**W**	2 - 0	Hickey 59 Tomkinson 72	2	3
25	Sth Prem C	H	Kettering Town	454	L	0 - 1		5	4
27	Sth Prem C	A	Coalville Town	276	L	0 - 1		9	5
Sept 1	Sth Prem C	H	Royston	152	L	1 - 2	Hickey 36	11	6
8	**FAC 1Q**	**H**	**Buxton**	**172**	**L**	**2 - 5**	**Hickey 40 61**		7
15	Sth Prem C	H	Biggleswade Town	171	D	0 - 0		13	8
29	Sth Prem C	A	Leiston	235	**W**	1 - 0	Hickey 37	12	9
Oct 6	Sth Prem C	H	Alvechurch	172	L	1 - 2	Putman 59	11	10
13	Sth Prem C	A	AFC Rushden & Diamonds	694	D	1 - 1	Davidson-Miller 18	11	11
16	Sth Prem C	H	Banbury United	157	**W**	2 - 1	Davidson-Miller 79 Wise (og) 82	10	12
20	Sth Prem C	A	Lowestoft Town	355	D	0 - 0		10	13
27	**FAT 1Q**	**H**	**Coalville**	**180**	**D**	**1 - 1**	**Hickey**		14
30	**FAT 1Qr**	**A**	**Coalville**	**172**	**W**	**3 - 2**	**Desrosiers 63 Hickey 93 105 (aet)**		15
Nov 3	Sth Prem C	H	Bedworth United	233	D	1 - 1	McDonald 35	12	16
10	**FAT 2Q**	**A**	**St Neots Town**	**216**	**W**	**1 - 0**	**Ebanks-Blake 77**		17
17	Sth Prem C	H	King's Lynn Town	246	L	1 - 3	Davidson-Miller 39	14	18
20	Sth Prem C	A	Halesowen Town	269	**W**	2 - 0	Putman 37 Ebanks -Blake 76	13	19
27	**FAT 3Q**	**H**	**Stamford**	**126**	**D**	**3 - 3**	**Tomkinson 30 Hickey 36 Hildreth 85 (pen) (won 7-6 on pens)**		20
Dec 1	Sth Prem C	A	Hitchin Town	330	L	0 - 2		15	21
8	Sth Prem C	A	Stratford Town	212	L	1 - 2	Tomkinson 15	15	22
15	**FAT 1P**	**A**	**Spennymoor United**	**295**	**L**	**0 - 4**		**16**	23
18	Sth Prem C	H	St Neots Town	63	**W**	6 - 1	Eze 3 McDonald 48 61 Towers 66 Parr 75 Morgan 78	16	24
22	Sth Prem C	A	Stourbridge	719	L	0 - 3		17	25
26	Sth Prem C	H	Coalville Town	272	L	2 - 3	HIckey 15 Rowe 90	19	26
29	Sth Prem C	H	Redditch United	189	**W**	4 - 0	Eze 15 Hickey 78 (pen) Davidson-Miller 81 McDonald 89	17	27
Jan 1	Sth Prem C	A	Tamworth	555	D	3 - 3	Hickey 40 Eze 51 Gascoigne 90	16	28
5	Sth Prem C	A	Banbury United	372	L	1 - 6	Dwyer 25	17	29
7	Sth Prem C	A	Rushall Olympic	123	D	1 - 1	Tomkinson 27	17	30
12	Sth Prem C	H	Rushall Olympic	149	L	1 - 2	Hickey 15	17	31
19	Sth Prem C	A	King's Lynn Town	709	L	2 - 3	Nisevic 71 Hickey 84	17	32
22	Sth Prem C	H	St Ives Town	136	D	1 - 1	Hickey 64	16	33
26	Sth Prem C	H	Halesowen Town	192	D	1 - 1	Hickey 66	16	34
Feb 2	Sth Prem C	A	Bedworth United	195	**W**	1 - 0	Hickey 75	14	35
9	Sth Prem C	H	Lowestoft Town	181	D	1 - 1	Rowe 79	15	36
16	Sth Prem C	H	Hitchin Town	219	L	0 - 1		16	37
23	Sth Prem C	A	St Neots Town	171	L	0 - 1		17	38
Mar 2	Sth Prem C	H	Stratford Town	203	D	0 - 0		17	39
9	Sth Prem C	A	St Ives Town	168	**W**	2 - 1	Hickey 51 (pen) Eze 90	16	40
23	Sth Prem C	H	AFC Rushden & Diamonds	346	D	1 - 1	Davidson-Miller 18	18	41
26	Sth Prem C	A	Alvechurch	206	**W**	5 - 1	HIckey 15 75 Julien 49 Rowe 59 Hollis 81	18	42
30	Sth Prem C	A	Biggleswade Town	166	D	1 - 1	Perry 90 (og)	18	43
Apr 6	Sth Prem C	H	Leiston	138	**W**	3 - 0	Rowe 13 16 Hickey 82	16	44
13	Sth Prem C	H	Needham Markewt	159	L	0 - 2		16	45
20	Sth Prem C	A	Kettering Town	1039	**W**	1 - 0	Hickey 79	14	46
22	Sth Prem C	H	Tamworth	302	L	0 - 1		14	47
27	Sth Prem C	A	Royston Town	259	L	0 - 1		16	48

GOALSCORERS	SG	CSG	Pens	Hat tricks	Total
Hickey	20	5	3		23
McDonald	6	2			7
Davidson-Miller	5				5
Rowe	4				5
Eze	4				4
Tomkinson	4				4
Ebanks-Blake	2				2
Julien	2				2
Opponents	2				2
Putman	2				2
Desrosiers	1				1
Dwyer	1				1
Gascoigne	1				1
Hildreth	1		1		1
Hollis	1				1
Morgan	1				1
Nisevic	1				1
Parr	1				1
Towers	1				1

BEDWORTH UNITED MATCH RESULTS 2018-19

Date	Comp	H/A	Opponents	Att:	Result		Goalscorers	Pos	No.
Aug 11	Sth Prem C	H	Needham Market	171	L	0 - 4			1
14	Sth Prem C	A	St Neots Town	192	L	1 - 2	Troke 43		2
18	Sth Prem C	A	Biggleswade Town	172	D	1 - 1	Baldwin 1	21	3
25	**FAC P**	**H**	**Atherstone Town**	**326**	**L**	**1 - 3**	**Baldwin 59**		4
27	Sth Prem C	A	Kettering Town	845	L	1 - 5	Dubidat 4	22	5
Sept 1	Sth Prem C	H	Lowestoft Town	151	D	1 - 1	Gordon 18	22	6
15	Sth Prem C	A	Stratford Town	255	L	1 - 3	Tonge 49	22	7
18	Sth Prem C	H	Banbury United	192	L	1 - 3	Christie 10	22	8
29	Sth Prem C	H	Halesowen Town	239	L	0 - 1		22	9
Oct 6	Sth Prem C	A	Royston Town	170	L	0 - 2		22	10
13	Sth Prem C	H	Hitchin Town	203	D	2 - 2	Rowe 23 39	22	11
15	Sth Prem C	A	Stourbridge	405	L	1 - 4	Christie 90	22	12
20	Sth Prem C	H	Alvechurch	217	L	0 - 2		22	13
27	**FAT 1Q**	**A**	**Carlton Town**	**73**	**L**	**0 - 1**			14
Nov 3	Sth Prem C	H	Barwell	233	D	1 - 1	Rowe 90 (pen)	22	15
10	Sth Prem C	A	Redditch United	139	L	0 - 2		22	16
17	Sth Prem C	H	AFC Rushden & Diamonds	508	L	1 - 3	Troke 27	22	17
20	Sth Prem C	H	Tamworth	209	L	1 - 4	Diggin 2	22	18
24	Sth Prem C	A	King's Lynn Town	758	D	1 - 1	Story 57	22	19
Dec 1	Sth Prem C	H	Rushall Olympic	147	L	1 - 3	Maslen-Jones 45	22	20
8	Sth Prem C	A	St Ives Town	150	L	1 - 2	Rowe 17	22	21
15	Sth Prem C	H	Leiston	116	D	2 - 2	Gibson 1 Atkins 45 (og)	22	22
22	Sth Prem C	A	Needham Market	252	L	1 - 4	Abraham 49	22	23
26	Sth Prem C	H	Kettering Town	404	L	1 - 2	Hancocks 85	22	24
29	Sth Prem C	H	St Neots Town	164	**W**	1 - 0	Christie 90	22	25
Jan 1	Sth Prem C	A	Coalville Town	220	L	0 - 1		22	26
5	Sth Prem C	H	Stourbridge	257	L	0 - 3		22	27
12	Sth Prem C	A	Redditch United	230	**W**	1 - 0	Troke 42	22	28
19	Sth Prem C	H	AFC Rushden & Diamonds	284	L	1 - 3	Gibson 45	22	29
26	Sth Prem C	A	Tamworth	640	D	2 - 2	Rowe 20 Rowley 45	22	30
Feb 2	Sth Prem C	H	Barwell	195	L	0 - 1		22	31
9	Sth Prem C	A	Alvechurch	209	L	0 - 3		22	32
16	Sth Prem C	A	Rushall Olympic	198	D	0 - 0		22	33
23	Sth Prem C	H	King's Lynn Town	203	L	0 - 3		22	34
Mar 2	Sth Prem C	H	St Ives Town	143	L	0 - 2		22	35
9	Sth Prem C	A	Leiston	223	D	1 - 1	Christie 53	22	36
16	Sth Prem C	H	Royston Town	139	L	1 - 2	Christie 55	22	37
23	Sth Prem C	A	Hitchin Town	416	L	1 - 4	Troke 49	22	38
30	Sth Prem C	H	Stratford Town	151	L	0 - 2		22	39
Apr 6	Sth Prem C	A	Halesowen Town	503	**W**	3 - 1	Troke 37 74 (pen) Steele 90	22	40
13	Sth Prem C	H	Biggleswade Town	117	L	1 - 4	Rowley 45	22	41
20	Sth Prem C	A	Banbury United	409	D	1 - 1	Troke 17	22	42
22	Sth Prem C	H	Coalville Town	194	L	0 - 1		22	43
27	Sth Prem C	A	Lowestoft Town	461	L	0 - 3		22	44

GOALSCORERS	SG	CSG	Pens	Hat tricks	Total
Troke	7		1		8
Christie	5				5
Rowe	4		1		5
Baldwin	2				2
Gibson	2				2
Rowley	2				2
Abraham	1				1
Diggin	1				1
Dubidat	1				1
Gordon	1				1
Hancocks	1				1
Maslen-Jones	1				1
Opponents	1				1
Steel	1				1
Story	1				1

BIGGLESWADE TOWN MATCH RESULTS 2018-19

Date	Comp	H/A	Opponents	Att:	Result		Goalscorers	Pos	No.
Aug 11	Sth Prem C	A	Kings Lynn Town	726	W	4 - 2	McNamara 13 Dubois 65 Brooks 86 Vincent 90		1
14	Sth Prem C	H	AFC Rushden & Diamonds	402	W	1 - 0	Dudley		2
18	Sth Prem C	H	Bedworth United	172	D	1 - 1	Clark 84	4	3
25	Sth Prem C	A	HalesowenTown	463	D	1 - 1	Clark 66	4	4
27	Sth Prem C	H	Hitchin Town	532	D	1 - 1	McLeod-Urquhart 77	4	5
Sept 1	Sth Prem C	A	Rushall Olympic	165	D	2 - 2	Ball 26 Smith 47	4	6
8	**FAC 1Q**	**H**	**Chesham United**	**138**	**L**	**1 - 2**	**Vincent 86**		7
15	Sth Prem C	A	Barwell	171	D	0 - 0		5	8
29	Sth Prem C	A	Redditch United	202	W	2 - 0	White 29 Bradshaw 90	5	9
Oct 13	Sth Prem C	H	Banbury United	242	D	0 - 0		8	10
16	Sth Prem C	A	St Ives Town	267	W	1 - 0	White 58	6	11
20	Sth Prem C	H	Coalville Town	172	W	3 - 0	Ball 12 McNamara 31 White 85	4	12
27	**FAT 1Q**	**H**	**Harrow Borough**	**152**	**W**	**2 - 1**	**McNamara 77 Clark 84**	4	13
Nov 3	Sth Prem C	A	Leiston	252	L	0 - 3		6	14
10	**FAT 2Q**	**A**	**Hendon**	**223**	**W**	**2 - 1**	**Smith 47 White 87**		15
17	Sth Prem C	A	Tamworth	563	D	1 - 1	Smith 88	8	16
25	**FAT 3Q**	**A**	**Gloucester City**	**236**	**W**	**3 - 1**	**White 48 90 Clark 39**		17
27	Sth Prem C	H	Stourbridge	123	L	1 - 2	Pierpoint (og)	8	18
Dec 1	Sth Prem C	A	Alvechurch	150	W	4 - 2	White 3 Ball 31 79 Bell 65	4	19
4	Sth Prem C	H	Needham Market	151	W	2 - 0	Bell 51 83	4	20
8	Sth Prem C	A	Royston Town	209	W	6 - 4	B.Bell 13 Longe-King 22 Ball 50 (pen) Gent 55 White 68 90	3	21
15	**FAT 1P**	**H**	**Wealdstone**	**258**	**W**	**2 - 1**	**White 30 Ball 86**		22
18	Sth Prem C	A	Lowestoft Town	190	L	1 - 2	Ball 8	5	23
22	Sth Prem C	H	Kings Lynn Town	157	L	1 - 2	White 54	7	24
26	Sth Prem C	A	Hitchin Town	693	W	2 - 0	Brooks 51 White 86 (pen)	5	25
29	Sth Prem C	A	AFC Rushden & Diamonds	547	D	3 - 3	White 54 75 McNamara 79	5	26
Jan 1	Sth Prem C	H	Stratford Town	221	D	0 - 0		8	27
5	Sth Prem C	H	St Ives Town	202	W	1 - 0	Brooks 52	8	28
12	**FAT 2P**	**A**	**AFC Fylde**	**594**	**L**	**0 - 1**			29
15	Sth Prem C	A	Kettering Town	617	W	3 - 2	Ball 26 Walster 63 White 66	4	30
19	Sth Prem C	H	Tamworth	160	W	3 - 0	WHITE 3 (14 50 90)	4	31
26	Sth Prem C	A	Coalville Town	183	L	0 - 2		6	32
29	Sth Prem C	A	Needham Market	214	L	0 - 1		6	33
Feb 5	Sth Prem C	H	St Neots Town	188	W	1 - 0	Donnelly 82	6	34
9	Sth Prem C	A	Stourbridge	633	L	0 - 2		6	35
16	Sth Prem C	H	Alvechurch	170	L	1 - 2	White 88 (pen)	7	36
23	Sth Prem C	H	Lowestoft Town	203	W	3 - 1	White 8 32 Bell 65	6	37
Mar 2	Sth Prem C	H	Royston Town	189	L	1 - 4	Bradshaw 85	7	38
5	Sth Prem C	H	Leiston	130	L	1 - 2	Gent 19	7	39
9	Sth Prem C	A	St Neots Town	284	D	2 - 2	White 14 Gent 90	7	40
16	Sth Prem C	H	Kettering Toswn	443	W	1 - 9	White 41	7	41
23	Sth Prem C	A	Banbury United	400	W	2 - 1	Ball 4 Brooks 90	7	42
30	Sth Prem C	H	Barwell	166	D	1 - 1	Brooks 90 (pen)	7	43
Apr 6	Sth Prem C	H	Redditch United	200	D	3 - 3	Brooks 42 75 Lucien 85	8	44
13	Sth Prem C	A	Bedworth United	117	W	4 - 1	Brooks 17 Forbes 20 Nwabuoke 34 Draper 65	8	45
20	Sth Prem C	H	Halesowen Town	203	W	1 - 0	Nwabuoke 25	7	46
22	Sth Prem C	A	Stratford Town	415	L	2 - 3	Lucien 41 Ball 90 (pen)	7	47
27	Sth Prem C	H	Rushall Olympic	155	L	0 - 1		7	48

GOALSCORERS	SG	CSG	Pens	Hat tricks	Total
White	17	3	2	1	23
Ball	9	3	1		10
Brooks	7		1		8
Bell	4				5
Clark	4				4
McNamara	4				4
Gent	3				3
Smith	3				3
Bradshaw	2				2
Lucien	2				2
Nwabuoke	2				2
Vincent	2				2
Donnelly	1				1
Draper	1				1
Dubois	1				1
Dudley	1				1
Forbes	1				1
Longe-King	1				1
M-Urquhart	1				1
Opponents	1				1
Walstar	1				1

COALVILLE TOWN MATCH RESULTS 2018-19

Date	Comp	H/A	Opponents	Att:	Result		Goalscorers	Pos	No.
Aug 11	Sth Prem C	A	Leiston	316	L	0 - 2			1
14	Sth Prem C	H	Rushall Olympic	141	D	2 - 2	Omotola 30 (pen) McGlinchey 45		2
18	Sth Prem C	H	Alvechurch	182	W	2 - 0	Wright 51 (pen) Omotola 76	10	3
25	Sth Prem C	H	Stourbridge	233	W	6 - 4	Dean 17 Wright 38 (pen) McManus 56 Omotola 6 McGlinchey 68 Berridge 88		4
27	Sth Prem C	H	Barwell	276	W	1 - 0	Dean 41	2	5
Sept 1	Sth Prem C	A	St Ives Town	262	W	1 - 0	Berridge 65	2	6
8	**FAC 1Q**	**H**	**Racing Club Warwick**	**220**	**W**	**2 - 1**	**Otomola 11 McGlinchey 56**		7
15	Sth Prem C	A	Redditch United	211	W	5 - 1	McGlinchey 12 Wright 37 75 Berridge 69 81	2	8
22	**FAC 2Q**	**A**	**Buxton**	**322**	**D**	**0 - 0**			9
25	**FAC 2Qr**	**H**	**Buxton**	**198**	**W**	**4 - 1**	**Dean 6 McGlinchey 41 Creaney 76 Berridge 90**		10
29	Sth Prem C	H	Lowestoft Town	229	W	1 - 0	McGlinchey 29	2	11
Oct 6	**FAC 3Q**	**A**	**St Neots Town**	**518**	**D**	**2 - 2**	**Berridge 36 65**		12
9	**FAC 3Qr**	**H**	**St Neots Town**	**409**	**D**	**3 - 3**	**Doyle-Charles 45 Dean 60 Berridge 62 (lost 3-5 on pens)**		13
13	Sth Prem C	H	Needham Market	298	L	1 - 2	Berridge 65	5	14
20	Sth Prem C	A	Biggleswade Town	172	L	0 - 3		6	15
23	Sth Prem C	A	AFC Rushden & Diamonds	407	L	1 - 3	Jenno 15	7	16
27	**FAT 1Q**	**A**	**Barwell**	**180**	**D**	**1 - 1**	**McGinchley 83**		17
30	**FAT 1Qr**	**H**	**Barwell**	**172**	**L**	**2 - 3**	**McGlinchey 8 Dean 47**		18
Nov 3	Sth Prem C	H	St Neots Town	138	D	1 - 1	Mitchell 81	6	19
17	Sth Prem C	H	Banbury United	223	D	1 - 1	Doyle-Charles 70	10	20
Dec 1	Sth Prem C	A	Tamworth	502	W	3 - 1	McGlinchey 32 47 Berridge 90	9	21
8	Sth Prem C	H	King's Lynn Town	224	D	3 - 3	Towers 16 Mitchell 24 (pen) Wright 63	9	22
15	Sth Prem C	A	Stourbridge	451	L	2 - 4	Wright 2 Shaw 51	11	23
22	Sth Prem C	H	Leiston	125	D	2 - 2	Berridge 35 Shaw 66	11	24
26	Sth Prem C	A	Barwell	272	W	3 - 2	Wright 13 Mitchell 29 80 (pen)	11	25
29	Sth Prem C	A	Rushall Olympic	255	W	2 - 0	Wright 40 76	9	26
Jan 1	Sth Prem C	H	Bedworth United	220	W	1 - 0	Shaw 90	7	27
5	Sth Prem C	A	Halesowen Town	358	W	3 - 1	Wright 7 Dean 27 Mitchell 32	6	28
12	Sth Prem C	H	Kettering Town	432	D	2 - 2	Perry 60 69	7	29
19	Sth Prem C	A	Banbury United	360	L	2 - 4	Dean 79 Burrows 90	9	30
26	Sth Prem C	H	Biggleswade Town	183	W	2 - 0	Mitchell 59 McGlinchey 68	8	31
Feb 9	Sth Prem C	H	Hitchin Town	202	W	4 - 1	Ryan (og) 26 McManus 45 McGlinchey 78 Perry 80	8	32
12	Sth Prem C	A	Stratford Town	221	W	2 - 0	Towers 59 Wright 85	6	33
16	Sth Prem C	H	Tamworth	452	L	1 - 2	McGlinchey 13	8	34
23	Sth Prem C	A	Royston Town	258	L	0 - 2		9	35
26	Sth Prem C	H	Halesowen Town	127	W	3 - 0	Morris (og) 23 Wright 43 Shaw 62	8	36
Mar 2	Sth Prem C	A	King's Lynn Town	733	L	1 - 4	Wright 31	8	37
5	Sth Prem C	A	Kettering Town	663	W	3 - 2	Mitchell 29 Berrridge 80 Perry 90	8	38
16	Sth Prem C	H	Stratford Town	195	L	1 - 2	McGlinchey 42	8	39
20	Sth Prem C	A	Hitchin Town	275	L	0 - 1		8	40
23	Sth Prem C	A	Needham Market	270	D	1 - 1	McManus 90	8	41
26	Sth Prem C	A	St Neots Town	139	W	4 - 1	Wright 12 (pen) Fenton 50 Berridge 53 Mitchell 90	8	42
30	Sth Prem C	H	Redditch United	149	L	1 - 2	Wright 90	9	43
Apr 2	Sth Prem C	H	Royston Town	129	L	2 - 3	Mitchell 35 Wright 74	9	44
6	Sth Prem C	A	Lowestoft Town	367	W	2 - 1	McGlinchey 52 76	6	45
13	Sth Prem C	A	Alvechurch	287	L	0 - 5		7	46
20	Sth Prem C	H	AFC Rushden & Diamonds	265	W	5 - 0	BERRIDGE 3 (29 37 70) McManus 61 Omotale79	6	47
22	Sth Prem C	A	Bedworth United	194	W	1 - 0	Mitchell 64	6	48
27	Sth Prem C	H	St Ives Town	165	L	0 - 1		6	49

GOALSCORERS	SG	CSG	Pens	Hat tricks	Total
Berridge	11	2		1	16
McGlinchey	14	2			16
Wright	12	2	2		16
Mitchell	8		2		10
Dean	6				7
Omotola	5	3	1		5
McManus	4				4
Perry	3				4
Shaw	4				4
Doyle-Charles	2				2

	SG	CSG	Pens	Hat tricks	Total
Opponents	2				2
Towers	2				2
Burrows	1				1
Creaney	1				1
Fenton	1				1
Jenno	1				1

HALESOWEN TOWN MATCH RESULTS 2018-19

Date	Comp	H/A	Opponents	Att:	Result		Goalscorers	Pos	No.
Aug 11	Sth Prem C	H	Lowestoft Town	533	W	1 - 0	Hughes 88		1
14	Sth Prem C	A	Banbury United	395	L	1 - 2	Roberts 10 (pen)		2
18	Sth Prem C	A	Kettering Town	628	L	0 - 2		16	3
25	Sth Prem C	H	Biggleswade Town	463	D	1 - 1	Ali 37	18	4
28	Sth Prem C	A	Stourbridge	1733	D	1 - 1	Benbow 20 ??	16	5
Sept 1	Sth Prem C	H	St Neots Town	358	D	1 - 1	Charlton 90	15	6
8	**FAC 1Q**	**A**	**Matlock Town**	**403**	**W**	**2 - 1**	**Roberts 6 Hughes 70**		7
15	Sth Prem C	H	Kings Lynn Town	511	D	2 - 2	Roberts 5 Hughes 45 (pen)	17	8
22	**FAC 2Q**	**H**	**Gainsborough Trinity**	**338**	**L**	**0 - 3**			9
29	Sth Prem C	A	Bedworth United	239	W	1 - 0	Charlton 88	13	10
Oct 6	Sth Prem C	H	Rushall Olympic	406	W	2 - 0	Roberts 54 68	12	11
13	Sth Prem C	A	Leiston	302	L	0 - 4		13	12
20	Sth Prem C	H	Needham Market	502	D	1 - 1	Hughes 58	13	13
27	**FAT 1Q**	**A**	**Grantham Town**	**158**	**W**	**4 - 0**	**Hughes 43 65 Morris 53 Shamshi 86**		14
Nov 3	Sth Prem C	A	Royston Town	259	D	0 - 0		15	15
17	Sth Prem C	A	St Ives Town	178	L	0 - 2		17	16
20	Sth Prem C	H	Barwell	269	L	0 - 2		18	17
24	**FAT 2Q**	**A**	**Spennymoor Town**	**502**	**L**	**2 - 8**	**Bragoli Reilly**		18
27	Sth Prem C	A	AFC Rushden & Diamonds	260	L	0 - 2			19
Dec 1	Sth Prem C	H	Stratford Town	412	L	0 - 2		19	20
4	Sth Prem C	H	Alvechurch	406	D	1 - 1	Reilly 10	19	21
8	Sth Prem C	H	Tamworth	505	L	0 - 1		20	22
15	Sth Prem C	A	Hitchin Town	207	L	1 - 5	Coyle 7	18	23
26	Sth Prem C	H	Stourbridge	1994	L	0 - 3		21	24
29	Sth Prem C	H	Banbury United	402	W	2 - 0	Sweeney 48 Hughes 52	20	25
Jan 1	Sth Prem C	A	Redditch United	420	L	0 - 3		21	26
5	Sth Prem C	H	Coalville Town	358	L	1 - 3	Hughes 53	21	27
12	Sth Prem C	A	Alvechurch	294	L	0 - 1		21	28
19	Sth Prem C	H	St Ives Town	363	D	1 - 1	Hughes 95 (pen)	21	29
26	Sth Prem C	A	Barwell	192	D	1 - 1	Sweeney 59	21	30
Feb 2	Sth Prem C	H	Royston Town	405	W	1 - 0	Morris 85	21	31
9	Sth Prem C	A	Needham Market	305	D	1 - 1	Curley 12	21	32
16	Sth Prem C	A	Stratford Town	428	L	1 - 2	Mendez-Jones 64	21	33
23	Sth Prem C	H	AFC Rushden & Diamonds	428	L	0 - 1		21	34
26	Sth Prem C	A	Coalville Town	127	L	0 - 3		21	35
Mar 2	Sth Prem C	A	Tamworth	736	L	1 - 4	Fitzpatrick 90	21	36
9	Sth Prem C	H	Hitchin Town	517	D	0 - 0		21	37
16	Sth Prem C	A	Rushall Olympic	334	D	0 - 0		21	38
19	Sth Prem C	A	Lowestoft Town	389	L	1 - 5	Hughes 31	21	39
23	Sth Prem C	H	Leiston	442	D	0 - 0		21	40
30	Sth Prem C	A	Kings Lynn Town	790	L	0 - 3		21	41
Apr 6	Sth Prem C	H	Bedworth United	502	L	1 - 3	Molyneux 1	21	42
13	Sth Prem C	H	Kettering Town	938	L	0 - 1		21	43
20	Sth Prem C	A	Biggleswade Town	203	L	0 - 1		21	44
22	Sth Prem C	H	Redditch United	354	W	1 - 0	Marselia 19	21	45
27	Sth Prem C	A	St Neots Town	132	D	1 - 1	Hood 52 (og)	21	46

GOALSCORERS	SG	CSG	Pens	Hat tricks	Total
Hughes	9	2	2		10
Roberts	4				5
Charlton	2				2
Morris	2				2
Reilly	2				2
Sweeney	2				2
Ali	1				1
Benbow	1				1
Bragoli	1				1
Coyle	1				1
Curley	1				1
Fitzpatrick	1				1
Mendez-Jones	1				1
Marsella	1				1
Molyneux	1				1
Opponents	1				1
Shamshi	1				1

HITCHIN TOWN MATCH RESULTS 2018-19

Date	Comp	H/A	Opponents	Att:	Result	Goalscorers	Pos	No.
Aug 11	Sth Prem C	H	Kettering Town	471	L 0 - 1			1
14	Sth Prem C	A	Needham Market	320	L 1 - 8	Bickerstafff 23		2
18	Sth Prem C	A	Lowestoft Town	451	L 2 - 3	Spring 53 Forde 84	22	3
25	Sth Prem C	H	Redditch United	306	W 1 - 0	Webb 19		4
27	Sth Prem C	A	Biggleswade Town	532	D 1 - 1	Bickerstaff 32	20	5
Sept 1	Sth Prem C	H	Banbury United	375	L 0 - 1		20	6
8	**FAC 1Q**	**H**	**Godmanchester Rovers**	**25**	**W 3 - 1**	**Belgrove 86 88 Thake 90**		7
15	Sth Prem C	H	Alvechurch	361	D 1 - 1	Smith 11	20	8
22	**FAC 2Q**	**H**	**Didcot Town**	**298**	**D 1 - 1**	**Gardner 34**		9
25	**FAC 2Qr**	**A**	**Didcot Town**	**151**	**D 0 - 0**	**(won 4-2 on pens)**		10
29	Sth Prem C	A	St Neots Town	376	D 0 - 0		19	11
Oct 6	**FAC 3Q**	**H**	**Hastings United**	**425**	**W 2 - 0**	**Ferrell 24 Bickerstaff 49 (pen)**		12
13	Sth Prem C	A	Bedworth United	203	D 2 - 2	Ferrell 44 Galliford 58	20	13
20	**FAC 4Q**	**H**	**Leatherhead**	**1278**	**D 1 - 1**	**Bickerstaff 57**		14
23	**FAC 4Qr**	**A**	**Leatherhead**	**637**	**W 2 - 1**	**Webb 71 Green 100 (aet)**		15
27	**FAT 1Q**	**H**	**Hayes & Yeading United**	**317**	**L 0 - 1**			16
Nov 3	Sth Prem C	A	Tamworth	474	L 0 - 2		21	17
11	**FAC 1P**	**H**	**Solihull Moors**	**3148**	**L 0 - 2**			18
13	Sth Prem C	A	AFC Rushden & Diamonds	362	L 1 - 2	Forde 60		19
17	Sth Prem C	A	Stourbridge	667	L 0 - 3		21	20
21	Sth Prem C	H	Leiston	229	D 2 - 2	Galliford 11 Forde 90	21	21
Dec 1	Sth Prem C	H	Barwell	330	W 2 - 0	Cain 11 Bickerstaff 29	21	22
8	Sth Prem C	A	Rushall Olympic	218	W 2 - 1	Galliford 19 39	21	23
15	Sth Prem C	H	Halesowen Town	207	W 5 - 1	Forde 28 66 Cain 35 Galliford 60 Morris 78 (og)	18	24
19	Sth Prem C	H	St Ives Town	241	W 1 - 0	Cain 6	18	25
22	Sth Prem C	A	Kettering Town	650	L 0 - 5		19	26
26	Sth Prem C	H	Biggleswade Town	693	L 0 - 2		19	27
29	Sth Prem C	H	Needham Market	378	L 1 - 2	Ferrell 90	20	28
Jan 1	Sth Prem C	A	Royston Town	423	L 0 - 1		20	29
5	Sth Prem C	H	AFC Rushden & Diamonds	530	L 3 - 4	Galliford 24 63 Nolan 73	20	30
12	Sth Prem C	A	St Ives Town	228	L 1 - 2	Galliford 11 Forde 90	20	31
15	Sth Prem C	A	Stratford Town	192	L 0 - 2		20	32
19	Sth Prem C	H	Stourbridge	354	W 2 - 1	Galliford 34 Draper 71	18	33
23	Sth Prem C	H	Kings Lynn Town	301	W 3 - 0	Belgrove 20 Draper 6 Dowie 80 (pen)	18	34
26	Sth Prem C	A	Leiston	246	W 2 - 1	Belgrove 12 Galliford 60	17	35
Feb 9	Sth Prem C	A	Coalville Town	202	L 1 - 4	Galliford 83	18	36
16	Sth Prem C	A	Barwell	219	W 1 - 0	Chesmain 14	17	37
23	Sth Prem C	H	Stratford Town	467	D 0 - 0		16	38
Mar 2	Sth Prem C	H	Rushall Olympic	381	L 0 - 1	Maye 35	18	39
6	Sth Prem C	H	Tamworth	286	W 1 - 0	Cue 52	18	40
9	Sth Prem C	A	Halesowen Town	517	D 0 - 0		18	41
16	Sth Prem C	A	Kings Lynn Town	656	L 2 - 3	Forde 41 Bird 70	16	42
20	Sth Prem C	H	Coalville Town	275	W 1 - 0	Cain 67	15	43
23	Sth Prem C	H	Bedworth United	416	W 4 - 1	Draper 29 81 Ryan 51 Galliford 76	14	44
30	Sth Prem C	A	Alvechurch	201	L 1 - 3	Belgrove 74	15	45
Apr 6	Sth Prem C	H	St Neots Town	472	L 0 - 2		17	46
13	Sth Prem C	H	Lowestoft Town	401	L 1 - 3	Thake 27	17	47
20	Sth Prem C	A	Redditch United	195	L 1 - 3	Francis 20 (og)	18	48
22	Sth Prem C	H	Royston Town	436	L 0 - 2		19	49
27	Sth Prem C	A	Banbury United	427	W 2 - 1	Thake 35 Forde 83	18	50

GOALSCORERS	SG	CSG	Pens	Hat tricks	Total
Galliford	10	2			12
Forde	7		1		8
Belgrove	4	2			5
Bickenstaff	5				4
Cain	4				4
Draper	3				4
Thake	3				3
Ferrell	2	2			2
Opponents	2				2
Webb	2				2
Bird	1				1
Chesmain	1				1
Cue	1				1
Dowie	1		1		1
Gardner	1				1
Green	1				1
Maye	1				1
Nolan	1				1
Ryan	1				1
Smith	1				1
Spring	1				1

KETTERING TOWN MATCH RESULTS 2018-19

Date	Comp	H/A	Opponents	Att:	Result	Goalscorers	Pos	No.
Aug 11	Sth Prem C	A	Hitchin Town	470	W 1 - 0	Hoenes 22		1
14	Sth Prem C	H	King's Lynn Town	876	W 2 - 1	Hoenes 4 (pen) 44		2
18	Sth Prem C	H	Halesowen Town	628	W 2 - 0	Kelly 39 90	1	3
25	Sth Prem C	A	Barwell	454	W 1 - 0	Kelly 35	1	4
27	Sth Prem C	H	Bedworth United	845	W 5 - 1	Kelly-Evans 17 Milnes 49 Kelly 6 73 Hoenes 61	1	5
Sept 1	Sth Prem C	A	Stratford Town	396	W 3 - 1	Milnes 16 Stohrer 45 Kelly-Evans 54	1	6
8	**FAC 1Q**	**A**	**Romford**	**271**	**W 4 - 1**	**Sokhon 46 55 Hoenes 65 67**		**7**
15	Sth Prem C	H	Leiston	749	L 1 - 2	Solkon 34 (pen)	1	8
25	**FAC 2Q**	**H**	**AFC Mansfield**	**504**	**W 2 - 1**	**Stohrer 23 Milnes 56**		**9**
29	Sth Prem C	A	Alvechurch	359	W 3 - 1	Hughes 2 (pen) 60 Towera 45	1	10
Oct 6	**FAC 3Q**	**H**	**Hednesford Town**	**502**	**W 4 - 0**	**SOLKON 3 (14 73 pen) Borge 80**		**11**
13	Sth Prem C	A	St Neots Town	693	W 3 - 0	Solkon 57 (pen) Hoenes 81 (pen) Kelly 86	1	12
16	Sth Prem C	A	Tamworth	587	D 0 - 0		1	13
20	**FAC 4Q**	**A**	**Aldershot Town**	**1634**	**L 0 - 2**			**14**
27	**FAT 1Q**	**H**	**Stourbridge**	**409**	**W 2 - 0**	**Toseland 14 Hoenes 45**		**15**
Nov 3	Sth Prem C	A	Needham Market	406	W 3 - 0	Meikle 55 70 Hoenes 64	1	16
10	**FAT 2Q**	**H**	**Stamford**	**566**	**L 0 - 1**			**17**
17	Sth Prem C	H	Royston Town	559	W 1 - 0	Holman 42	1	18
20	Sth Prem C	H	Stourbridge	701	W 4 - 2	Meikle 38 Richens 42 Holman 71 Kelly 89	1	19
24	Sth Prem C	A	Rushall Olympic	317	W 1 - 0	Richens 26	1	20
27	Sth Prem C	H	Redditch United	453	D 4 - 4	O'Connor 14 Kelly-Evans 30 Holman 75 81	1	21
Dec 1	Sth Prem C	A	St Ives Town	653	L 0 - 3		1	22
8	Sth Prem C	H	Lowestoft Town	586	W 3 - 0	O'Connor 39 Towers 66 Kelly 67	1	23
15	Sth Prem C	A	Banbury United	371	L 1 - 4	Holman 54 (pen)	2	24
22	Sth Prem C	H	Hitchin Town	650	W 5 - 0	Meikke 27 Richens 45 Holman 65 Shamalo 83 87	2	25
26	Sth Prem C	A	Bedworth United	404	W 2 - 1	Cunnington 5 Hoenes 57	2	26
29	Sth Prem C	A	Kings Lynn Town	1286	D 0 - 0		2	27
Jan 1	Sth Prem C	H	AFC Rushden & Diamonds	2147	W 2 - 1	Meikle 73 Solkhon 90	2	28
5	Sth Prem C	H	Tamworth	805	W 2 - 1	Meikle 29 Holman 55	2	29
12	Sth Prem C	A	Coalville Town	432	D 2 - 2	Holman 64 O'Connor 90	2	30
15	Sth Prem C	H	Biggleswade Town	617	L 2 - 3	Holman 26 Kelly 90	2	31
19	Sth Prem C	H	Royston Town	661	W 1 - 0	O'Connor 70	2	32
26	Sth Prem C	A	Stourbridge	1734	W 2 - 1	Solkhon 85 Knowles 90	1	33
Feb 2	Sth Prem C	H	Needham Market	762	W 3 - 2	O'Connor 25 72 Meikle 90	1	34
9	Sth Prem C	A	Redditch United	379	W 4 - 1	Meikle 14 Hoenes 30 89 Holman 89	1	35
16	Sth Prem C	A	St Ives Town	639	W 2 - 1	O'Connor 55 Wright 85	1	36
23	Sth Prem C	H	Rushall Olympic	882	W 2 - 1	O'Connor 3 Solkhon 90	1	37
Mar 2	Sth Prem C	A	Lowestoft Town	233	W 1 - 0	Kelly-Evans 5	1	38
5	Sth Prem C	H	Coalville Town	663	L 2 - 3	Holman 38 Kelly 65	1	39
9	Sth Prem C	H	Banbury United	760	W 3 - 0	Hoenes 21 Stohrer 26 Solkhon 35	1	40
16	Sth Prem C	A	Biggleswade Town	443	L 0 - 1		1	41
23	Sth Prem C	H	St Neots Town	894	W 2 - 0	Hoenes 17 Towers 35	1	42
30	Sth Prem C	A	Leiston	328	W 1 - 0	O'Connor 90	1	43
Apr 6	Sth Prem C	H	Alvechurch	1567	L 1 - 2	Stanley 53	1	44
13	Sth Prem C	A	Halesowen Town	938	W 1 - 0	Hoenes 19	1	45
20	Sth Prem C	H	Barwell	1039	L 0 - 1		1	46
22	Sth Prem C	A	AFC Rushden & Diamonds	1165	W 1 - 0	Rowe-Turner 44	1	47
27	Sth Prem C	H	Stratford Town	660	W 5 - 1	Hoenes 16 58 Solkhon 37 Stanley 50 O'Connor 59	1	48

GOALSCORERS	SG	CSG	Pens	Hat tricks	Total		SG	CSG	Pens	Hat tricks	Total
Hoenes	14	2	2		17	Towers	3				3
Solkhon	9		3		12	Hughes	1				2
Holman	10	3	1		11	Shamalo	1				2
Kelly	8	3			10	Stanley	2				2
O'Connor	9	2			10	Borge	1				1
Meikle	7				8	Cunnington	1				1
Kelly-Evans	4				4	Knowles	1				1
Milnes	3				3	Rowe-Turner	1				1
Richens	3				3	Toseland	1				1
Stohrer	3				3	Wright	1				1

KING'S LYNN TOWN MATCH RESULTS 2018-19

Date	Comp	H/A	Opponents	Att:	Result		Goalscorers	Pos	No.
Aug 11	Sth Prem C	H	Biggleswade Town	726	L	2 - 4	Clunan 49 (pen) Fryatt 55		1
14	Sth Prem C	A	Kettering Town	568	L	1 - 2	Clunan 48		2
18	Sth Prem C	A	Tamworth	595	W	1 - 0	Clunan 30	15	3
25	Sth Prem C	H	St Neots Town	568	D	0 - 0			4
27	Sth Prem C	A	Lowestoft Town	750	L	0 - 1		19	5
Sept 1	Sth Prem C	H	Stourbridge	535	L	0 - 1		19	6
8	**FAC 1Q**	**H**	**Histon**	**491**	**D**	**2 - 2**	**Stewart Blake-Tracy**		7
11	**FAC 1Qr**	**A**	**Histon**	**388**	**W**	**7 - 0**	**HAWKINS 3 Hilliard 2 Parker Stewart**		8
15	Sth Prem C	A	Halesowen Town	51	D	2 - 2	Parker 2 Limb 83	19	9
22	**FAC 2Q**	**H**	**Stafford Rangers**	**601**	**W**	**3 - 1**	**Hawkins 3 Holgate (og) 65 Parker 70**		10
29	Sth Prem C	H	Banbury United	575	W	3 - 1	Gash 6 Clunan 57 (pen) Limb 61	18	11
Oct 6	**FAC 3Q**	**H**	**Ashton United**	**622**	**L**	**0 - 1**			12
13	Sth Prem C	H	Stratford Town	681	D	0 - 0		18	13
16	Sth Prem C	A	Leiston	303	W	5 - 1	Hawkins 31Marriott 14 Henderson 14 Gash 39 Clunan 81(P)	16	14
20	Sth Prem C	H	AFC Rushden & Diamonds	816	D	1 - 1	McAuley 90	15	15
27	**FAT 1Q**	**A**	**Buxton**	**285**	**D**	**3 - 3**	**Gash 43 Parker 60 Frohawk**		16
30	**FAT 1Qr**	**H**	**Buxton**	**277**	**L**	**1 - 2**	**Marriott**		17
Nov 3	Sth Prem C	A	Alvechurch	167	W	3 - 0	Marriott 6 Hawkins 14 35	12	18
10	Sth Prem C	H	St Ives Town	714	W	2 - 0	Parker 54 Henderson 62	8	19
17	Sth Prem C	A	Barwell	246	W	3 - 1	Gash 2 75 Marriott 41 (pen)	6	20
24	Sth Prem C	H	Bedworth United	758	D	1 - 1	McAuley 5	6	21
Dec 1	Sth Prem C	A	Redditch United	302	D	1 - 1	Clunan 31	7	22
8	Sth Prem C	H	Coalville Town	224	D	3 - 3	Henderson 45 Clunan 61 Marriott 87	7	23
15	Sth Prem C	A	Rushall Olympic	550	W	3 - 0	Hawkins 13 Clunan 43 (pen) McAuley 74	6	24
22	Sth Prem C	A	Biggleswade Town	157	W	2 - 1	Henderson 52 Marriott 77	5	25
26	Sth Prem C	H	Lowestoft Town	696	W	4 - 0	MARRIOTT 3 (5 9 67) Gash 67		26
29	Sth Prem C	A	Kettering Town	1286	D	0 - 0		3	27
1 Jan	Sth Prem C	A	Needham Market	417	W	4 - 1	Parker 12 Marriott 14 McAuley 33 Parker 37	3	28
5	Sth Prem C	H	Leiston	704	D	1 - 1	Marriott 71	3	29
12	Sth Prem C	A	Royston Town	370	W	1 - 0	Blake-Tracy 90	3	30
19	Sth Prem C	H	Barwell	709	W	3 - 2	Marriott 17 Clunan 31 73	3	31
23	Sth Prem C	A	Hitchin Town	301	L	0 - 3		4	32
26	Sth Prem C	A	St Ives Town	322	D	1 - 1	Marriott 62	4	33
29	Sth Prem C	H	Royston Town	389	W	4 - 2	Marriott 26 Fryatt 31 Gash 40 Brathwaite (og) 85	3	34
Feb 9	Sth Prem C	A	AFC Rushden & Diamonds	614	L	0 - 1		4	35
16	Sth Prem C	H	Redditch United	621	W	2 - 1	Fryatt 26 Mariott 76	4	36
23	Sth Prem C	A	Bedworth United	203	W	3 - 0	Marriott 10 Henderson 41 Hawkins 74	3	37
Mar 2	Sth Prem C	H	Coalville Town	733	W	4 - 1	Henderson 26 46 Gash 43 Marriott 88 (pen)	3	38
9	Sth Prem C	A	Rushall Olympic	211	L	1 - 2	Henderson 39	3	39
16	Sth Prem C	H	Hitchin Town	656	W	3 - 2	Marriott 5 Richards 12 Green (og) 62	3	40
19	Sth Prem C	H	Kings Lynn Town	755	W	1 - 0	Henderson 63	3	41
23	Sth Prem C	A	Stratford Town	402	W	2 - 0	Marriott 3 Gash 87	3	42
30	Sth Prem C	H	Halesowen Town	790	W	3 - 0	Marriott 9 14 (pen) Henderson 46	3	43
Apr 6	Sth Prem C	A	Banbury United	426	L	0 - 2		3	44
13	Sth Prem C	H	Tamworth	820	W	2 - 1	Barrows 11 Henderson 85	3	45
20	Sth Prem C	A	St Neots Town	320	W	5 - 0	Marriott 5 20 Hughes 53 (og) McAuley 56 Mellors-Blair 90	3	46
22	Sth Prem C	H	Needham Market	863	D	1 - 1	McAuley 90	3	47
27	Sth Prem C	A	Stourbridge	791	W	2 - 1	Marriott 41 63	2	48
May 4	**PO SF**	**H**	**Stratford Town**	**1253**	**W**	**3 - 1**	**Hawkins 61 Clunan 77 McAuley 77**		49
6	**PO F**	**H**	**Alvechurch**	**1617**	**W**	**3 - 0**	**Marriott 10 (pen) 49 Gash 87**		50
11	**Su PO F**	**A**	**Warrington Town**	**2200**	**W**	**3 - 2**	**Richards 15 Marriott 85 (pen) Gash 115**		51

GOALSCORERS	SG	CSG	Pens	Hat tricks	Total
Marriott	22	2	4	1	28
Clunan	10	3	4		11
Gash	10	3			11
Henderson	10	3			11
Hawkins	9				10
Parker	7	3			8
McAuley	7				7
Opponents	4				4
Fryatt	3				3
Blake-Tracy	2				2
Limb	2				2
Richards	2				2
Stewart	2				2
Barows	1				1
Frohawk	1				1
Hilliard	1				1
Mellors-Blair	1				1

LEISTON MATCH RESULTS 2018-19

Date	Comp	H/A	Opponents	Att:	Result		Goalscorers	Pos	No.
Aug 11	Sth Prem C	H	Coalville Town	316	W	2 - 0	Finch 38 Henderson 90		1
14	Sth Prem C	A	Royston Town	226	W	5 - 2	Brothers 5 Finch (p) 27 Dunbar 50 Reed 70 Blake 90		2
18	Sth Prem C	A	Banbury United	405?	L	0 - 1		7	3
25	Sth Prem C	H	Tamworth	329	D	2 - 2	Finch 38 Reed 7	7	4
27	Sth Prem C	A	Needham Market	657	D	2 - 2	Ramadan 10 Henderson 65	7	5
Sept 1	Sth Prem C	H	Redditch United	267	W	4 - 3	Henderson 18 Atkins 20 Reed 23 Lawrence 73	5	6
8	**FAC 1Q**	**A**	**Cheshunt**	**164**	**D**	**2 - 2**	**Docherty 72 Ramadan 84**		7
11	**FAC 1Qr**	**H**	**Cheshunt**	**179**	**W**	**4 - 2**	**Cheetham 2 90 Eagle 67 Blake 87**		8
15	Sth Prem C	A	Kettering Town	749	W	2 - 1	Docherty 13 Brothers 86	3	9
22	**FAC 2Q**	**H**	**Hastings United**	**263**	**L**	**3 - 4**	**Jefford 8 Blake 12 68**		10
29	Sth Prem C	H	Barwell	235	L	0 - 1		4	11
Oct 13	Sth Prem C	H	Halesowen Town	302	W	4 - 0	Reed 1 Lawrence 42 Blake 76 (pen) Finch 87 (pen)	4	12
16	Sth Prem C	H	Kings Lynn Town	303	L	1 - 5	Blake 5	6	13
20	Sth Prem C	A	Stratford Town	227	L	2 - 3	Finch 1 Reed 36	6	14
23	Sth Prem C	A	St Ives Town	111	W	2 - 0	Finch 14 Ramadan 87	5	15
27	**FAT 1Q**	**A**	**VCD Athletic**	**98**	**W**	**3 - 1**	**Finch 10 77 Reed 44**		16
Nov 3	Sth Prem C	H	Biggleswade Town	252	W	3 - 0	Reed 26 65 Blake 82	4	17
10	**FAT 2Q**	**H**	**Melksham Town**	**172**	**W**	**2 - 1**	**Lawrence 55 Blake 85**		18
17	Sth Prem C	H	Rushall Olympic	316	L	0 - 1		5	19
21	Sth Prem C	A	Hitchin Town	229	D	2 - 2	Jefford 67 Lawrence71		20
24	**FAT 3Q**	**A**	**Beaconsfield Town**	**89**	**L**	**1 - 3**	**Jefford 55**		21
Dec 1	Sth Prem C	A	Rushden & Diamonds	277	L	1 - 4	Finch 45	8	22
8	Sth Prem C	H	Stourbridge	197	L	0 - 3		10	23
15	Sth Prem C	A	Bedworth United	125	D	2 - 2	Blake 49 51	12	24
22	Sth Prem C	A	Coalville Town	125	D	2 - 2	Blake 49 51		25
26	Sth Prem C	H	Needham Market	440	W	2 - 1	Lawrence 6 Nicholls 79		26
29	Sth Prem C	A	Royston Town	249	D	1 - 1	Aitkins 75	10	27
Jan 1	Sth Prem C	A	Loweatoft Town	435	W	2 - 1	Reed 37 Blake 49	10	28
5	Sth Prem C	A	Kings Lynn Town	704	D	1 - 1	Blake 60	10	29
8	Sth Prem C	A	St Neots Town	128	L	0 - 2		11	30
12	Sth Prem C	H	St Neots Town	208	W	2 - 0	Brothers 30 Aitkens 57	10	31
19	Sth Prem C	H	Rushall Olympic	201	L	0 - 2		11	32
26	Sth Prem C	H	Hitchin Town	246	L	1 - 2	Davies 67	11	33
Feb 16	Sth Prem C	H	Rushdan & Diamonds	620	D	1 - 1	Rutherford 55	11	34
23	Sth Prem C	A	Alvechurch	236	W	2 - 0	Keys 73 Finch 90	11	35
Mar 2	Sth Prem C	H	Stourbridge	613	L	0 - 4		13	36
5	Sth Prem C	A	Biggleswade Town	130	W	2 - 1	Eagle 79 Davies 90	13	37
9	Sth Prem C	A	Bedworth United	223	D	1 - 1	Blake 84	13	38
16	Sth Prem C	H	St Ives Town	216	L	0 - 2		13	39
19	Sth Prem C	H	Stratford Town	182	L	1 - 2	Blake 26	13	40
23	Sth Prem C	A	Halesowen Town	442	D	0 - 0		13	41
30	Sth Prem C	A	Kettering Town	328	L	0 - 1		13	42
Apr 2	Sth Prem C	H	Alvechurch	175	L	1 - 2	Blake 25	13	43
6	Sth Prem C	A	Barwell	138	L	0 - 3		16	44
13	Sth Prem C	H	Banbury United	208	D	0 - 0		15	45
20	Sth Prem C	A	Tamworth	545	L	0 - 5		16	46
22	Sth Prem C	H	Lowestoft Town	431	L	0 - 4		17	47
27	Sth Prem C	A	Redditch United	210	L	1 - 3	Hood 52 (og)	19	48

GOALSCORERS	SG	CSG	Pens	Hat tricks	Total
Blake	13	2	1		15
Finch	9	3	2		10
Reed	8				9
Lawrence	5				5
Jefford	4				4
Atkins	3				3
Brothers	3				3
Henderson	3				3
Ramadan	3				3
Cheetham	1				2
Davies	2				2
Docherty	2				2
Eagle	2				2
Bullard	1				1
Dunbar	1				1
Keys	1				1
Nicholls	1				1
Opponents	1				1
Rutherford	1				1

LOWESTOFT TOWN MATCH RESULTS 2018-19

Date	Comp	H/A	Opponents	Att:	Result		Goalscorers	Pos	No.
Aug 11	Sth Prem C	A	Halesowen Town	533	L	0 - 1			1
14	Sth Prem C	H	St Ives Town	393	L	0 - 1			2
18	Sth Prem C	H	Hitchin Town	461	W	3 - 2	Zielonka 73 Smith 86 Bammant 88	13	3
25	Sth Prem C	A	Stratford Town	238	W	3 - 1	Bammant 4 Fowkes 83 Zielonka 89		4
27	Sth Prem C	H	Kings Lynn Town	750	W	1 - 0	Fowkes 14	5	5
Sept 1	Sth Prem C	A	Bedworth United	151	D	1 - 1	Fisk 83	7	6
8	**FAC 1Q**	**A**	**Ware**	**173**	**W**	**1 - 0**	**Bammant 65**		7
15	Sth Prem C	H	Tamworth	408	L	1 - 3	Higgs 64	9	8
22	**FAC 2Q**	**A**	**Hanwell Town**	**155**	**L**	**0 - 1**			9
29	Sth Prem C	A	Coalville Town	229	L	0 - 1			10
Oct 13	Sth Prem C	A	Rushall Olympic	281	L	1 - 3	McKendry 71	15	11
16	Sth Prem C	A	Needham Market	360	L	0 - 1		16	12
20	Sth Prem C	H	Barwell	355	D	0 - 0		15	13
23	Sth Prem C	H	St Neots Town	238	L	1 - 2	Schaar 80	16	14
27	**FAT 1Q**	**H**	**Enfield**	**289**	**L**	**0 - 1**			15
Nov 3	Sth Prem C	A	Stourbridge	594	L	1 - 3	Deeks 56	19	16
17	Sth Prem C	H	Redditch United	262	L	2 - 4	Brown 15 Bammant 89	20	17
20	Sth Prem C	H	Royston Town	215	W	2 - 0	Schaar 73 Deeks 80	19	18
24	Sth Prem C	H	AFC Rushden & Diamonds	457	D	1 - 1	Higgs 18	18	19
Dec 1	Sth Prem C	A	Banbury United	327	D	0 - 0		18	20
8	Sth Prem C	H	Kettering Town	586	L	0 - 3		19	21
15	Sth Prem C	A	Alvechurch	291	L	1 - 2	Higgs 9	20	22
18	Sth Prem C	H	Biggleswade Town	190	W	2 - 1	Deeks 53 69	20	23
26	Sth Prem C	A	King's Lynn Town	696	L	0 - 4		19	24
29	Sth Prem C	A	St Ives Town	221	D	0 - 0		18	25
Jan 1	Sth Prem C	H	Leiston	435	L	1 - 2	Bammant 22	18	26
5	Sth Prem C	H	Needham Market	335	L	0 - 2		19	27
12	Sth Prem C	A	AFC Rushden & Diamonds	575	D	1 - 1	Fowkes 23	19	28
19	Sth Prem C	H	Redditch United	332	D	0 - 0		20	29
26	Sth Prem C	A	Royston Town	281	D	1 - 1	Bammant 78	20	30
Feb 2	Sth Prem C	H	Stourbridge	334	W	1 - 0	Reed 32	19	31
9	Sth Prem C	A	Barwell	181	D	1 - 1	Fowkes 31	19	32
16	Sth Prem C	H	Banbury United	407	W	1 - 0	Deeks 19	19	33
23	Sth Prem C	A	Biggleswade Town	303	L	1 - 3	Cole 28	19	34
Mar 2	Sth Prem C	H	Kettering Town	233	L	0 - 1		19	35
9	Sth Prem C	A	Alvechurch	214	L	2 - 4	Tann 33 Barker 70	20	36
16	Sth Prem C	A	St Neots Town	293	W	3 - 1	REED 3 (2 21 48)	19	37
19	Sth Prem C	H	Haleswen Town	389	W	5 - 1	Griffiths (og) 1 Deeks 12 REED 3 (8 68 87)	19	38
23	Sth Prem C	H	Rushall Olympic	487	L	2 - 4	Reed 16 Smith 32	19	39
30	Sth Prem C	A	Tamworth	632	W	2 - 0	Curry 15 Reed 58	19	40
Apr 6	Sth Prem C	H	Coalville Town	367	L	1 - 2	Curry 67	19	41
13	Sth Prem C	A	Hittchin Town	401	W	3 - 1	Williams 12 Reed 23 74	19	42
20	Sth Prem C	H	Stratford Town	461	W	3 - 2	REED 3 (27 35 85)	18	43
22	Sth Prem C	A	Leiston	431	W	4 - 0	Schaar 17 Tann 29 Deeks 77 (pen) Zielonka 90	16	44
27	Sth Prem C	H	Bedworth United	461	W	3 - 0	Bammant 16 Pollock 83 Zielonka 90	14	45

GOALSCORERS	SG	CSG	Pens	Hat tricks	Total		SG	CSG	Pens	Hat tricks	Total
Reed	7	4		3	14	Barker	1				1
Bammant	7				7	Brown	1				1
Deeks	6		1		7	Cole	1				1
Fowkes	4				4	Fisk	1				1
Zielonka	4				4	McKendry	1				1
Higgs	3				3	Opponents	1				1
Schaar	3				3	Pollock	1				1
Curry	2	2			2	Williams	1				1
Smith	2				2						
Tann	2				2						

NEEDHAM MARKET MATCH RESULTS 2018-19

Date	Comp	H/A	Opponents	Att:	Result		Goalscorers	Pos	No.
Aug 11	Sth Prem C	A	Bedworth Town	171	W	4 - 0	Morphew 8 Marsden 22 83 Gordon (og) 42		1
14	Sth Prem C	H	Hitchin Town	320	W	8 - 1	INGRAM 3 (7 14 75) MARSDEN 3 (35 39 44) Griffiths 24 Mills 90	1	2
18	Sth Prem C	H	Barwell	266	L	0 - 2		6	3
25	Sth Prem C	A	St Ives Town	243	D	1 - 1	Kamanzi 50	6	4
27	Sth Prem C	H	Leiston	657	D	2 - 2	Marsden 15 (pen) Mills 24	6	5
Sept 1	Sth Prem C	A	Alvechurch	183	L	0 - 3		8	6
8	**FAC 1Q**	**A**	**Barton Rovers**	**154**	**W**	**4 - 0**	**Kamanzi 17 Dobson 65 Morphew 85 (pen) Mills 90**		7
15	Sth Prem C	A	Rushall Olympic	283	D	1 - 1	Ingram 33	10	8
22	**FAC 2Q**	**A**	**Metropolitan Police**	**100**	**D**	**2 - 2**	**Morphew 17 (pen) Mills 59**		9
25	**FAC 2Qr**	**H**	**Metropolitan Police**	**208**	**L**	**2 - 3**	**Ingram 9 Dobson 27**		10
29	Sth Prem C	A	Stourbridge	621	L	1 - 3	Issa 44	14	11
Oct 6	Sth Prem C	H	AFC Rushden & Diamonds	275	L	1 - 4	Morphew 48	16	12
13	Sth Prem C	A	Coalville Town	298	W	2 - 1	Dobson 14 Marsden 88	12	13
16	Sth Prem C	H	Lowestoft Town	360	W	1 - 0	Issa 90	9	14
20	Sth Prem C	A	Halesowen Town	502	D	1 - 1	Dobson 76	8	15
27	**FAT 1Q**	**A**	**Kings Langley**	**122**	**W**	**2 - 0**	**Mills 81 Marsden 87 (pen)**		16
Nov 3	Sth Prem C	H	Kettering Town	406	L	0 - 3		10	17
10	**FAT 2Q**	**A**	**Herne Bay**	**206**	**W**	**1 - 0**	**Dobson 71**		18
17	Sth Prem C	H	Stratford Town	288	W	2 - 1	Heath 22 Ingram 40	11	19
20	Sth Prem C	A	St Neots Town	139	W	3 - 0	Baker 10 Issa 58 Morphew 67	9	20
24	**FAT 3Q**	**A**	**Royston Town**	**202**	**D**	**1 - 1**	**Marsden 46 (pen)**	**7**	21
27	**FAT 3Qr**	**A**	**Royston Town**	**153**	**W**	**2 - 0**	**Baker 12 Mills 41**		22
Dec 1	Sth Prem C	A	Royston Town	222	W	4 - 2	Mills 7 48 Dobson 40 50	5	23
4	Sth Prem C	A	Biggleswade Town	151	L	0 - 2		5	24
8	Sth Prem C	H	Banbury United	221	D	3 - 3	Marsden 5 Mills 30 Dobson 63	6	25
18	Sth Prem C	H	Redditch United	206	W	3 - 1	Baker 44 86 Mills 75	5	26
22	Sth Prem C	H	Bedworth United	252	W	4 - 2	Marsden 37 90 Mills 47 Baker 75	4	27
26	Sth Prem C	A	Leiston	440	L	1 - 2	Mills 18	5	28
29	Sth Prem C	A	Hitchihn Town	378	W	2 - 1	Heath 31 Marsden 63	4	29
Jan 1	Sth Prem C	H	King's Lynn Town	417	L	1 - 4	Mills 26	4	30
5	Sth Prem C	A	Lowestoft Town	335	W	2 - 0	Marsden 10 Dobson 28	4	31
8	Sth Prem C	A	Tamworth	481	W	2 - 1	Heath 48 Dobson 85	5	32
19	Sth Prem C	A	Stratford Town	201	L	1 - 3	Marsden 78	8	33
26	Sth Prem C	H	St Neots Town	299	L	0 - 1		9	34
29	Sth Prem C	H	Biggleswade Town	214	W	1 - 0	Griffiths 90	9	35
Feb 2	Sth Prem C	A	Kettering Town	762	L	2 - 3	Marsden 44 80	9	36
9	Sth Prem C	A	Halesowen Town	305	D	1 - 1	Marsden 25 (pen)	9	37
16	Sth Prem C	H	Royston Town	299	L	1 - 4	Marsden 6 (pen)	9	38
23	Sth Prem C	A	Redditch United	293	L	1 - 4	Marsden 5	9	39
Mar 2	Sth Prem C	A	Banbury United	402	L	1 - 2	Marsden 45 (pen)	10	40
9	Sth Prem C	H	Tamworth	265	L	1 - 3	Morphew 59	11	41
16	Sth Prem C	A	AFC Rushden & Diamonds	410	L	1 - 2	Griffiths 20	13	42
23	Sth Prem C	H	Coalville Town	270	D	1 - 1	Griffiths 12	13	43
30	Sth Prem C	A	Rushall Olympic	192	W	1 - 0	Griffiths 40	12	44
Apr 6	Sth Prem C	H	Stourbridge	255	D	0 - 0		12	45
13	Sth Prem C	A	Barwell	159	W	2 - 0	Heath 12 Griffiths 29	11	46
20	Sth Prem C	H	St Ives Town	337	W	4 - 1	Heath 53 MILLS 3 (9 65 81)	10	47
22	Sth Prem C	A	King's Lynn Town	863	D	1 - 1	Mills 35	12	48
27	Sth Prem C	H	Alvechurch	285	W	1 - 0	Sheriff 45	8	49

GOALSCORERS	SG	CSG	Pens	Hat tricks	Total
Marsden	16	5	6	1	21
Mills	14	4		1	17
Dobson	9	2			10
Griffiths	6	3			6
Ingram	4			1	6
Morphew	6		2		6
Baker	4				5
Heath	5				5
Issa	3				3
Kamanzi	2				2

	SG	CSG	Pens	Hat tricks	Total
Opponents	1				1
Sheriff	1				1

REDDITCH UNITED MATCH RESULTS 2018-19

Date	Comp	H/A	Opponents	Att:	Result		Goalscorers	Pos	No.
Aug 11	Sth Prem C	A	AFC Rushden & Diamonds	592	L	2 - 5	Stokes Howards		1
14	Sth Prem C	H	Barwell	179	L	2 - 4	Gibson 40 Winters 55		2
18	Sth Prem C	H	St Ives Town	202	**W**	2 - 0	Moore Francis	17	3
25	Sth Prem C	A	Hitchin Town	306	L	0 - 1			4
27	Sth Prem C	A	Alvechurch	420	L	0 - 3		21	5
Sept 1	Sth Prem C	A	Leiston	267	L	3 - 4	Howards 3 52 Francis 72		6
8	**FAC 1Q**	**H**	**Rugby Town**	**242**	**L**	**2 - 4**	**Howards 7 Sinclair 57**		7
15	Sth Prem C	H	Coalville Town	211	L	1 - 5	Gibson 54	21	8
22	Sth Prem C	A	Stratford Town	225	L	0 - 2		21	9
29	Sth Prem C	A	Biggleswade Town	202	L	0 - 2		21	10
Oct 13	Sth Prem C	A	Tamworth	621	**W**	3 - 1	Loveridge 51 Parsons 67 Nelson 88	21	11
16	Sth Prem C	H	Rushall Olympic	215	**W**	2 - 1	Ali 4 Nelson 83	20	12
27	**FAT 1Q**	**A**	**Mickleover Sports**	**157**	**L**	**0 - 1**			13
Nov 3	Sth Prem C	H	Banbury United	322	**W**	2 - 0	Bunn 52 Leachman-Whittingham 61	19	14
10	Sth Prem C	A	Bedworth United	139	**W**	2 - 0	Howards 11 Leachman-Whittingham 27	17	15
13	Sth Prem C	H	Stourbridge	432	L	0 - 4			16
17	Sth Prem C	H	Lowestoft Town	262	**W**	4 - 2	Franklin 40 Ali 50 90 Howards 61	13	17
27	Sth Prem C	A	Kettering Town	453	D	4 - 4	Reynolds 19 Batchlor 22 Bunn 45 Franklin 90		18
Dec 1	Sth Prem C	H	King's Lynn Town	302	D	1 - 1	Piggon 90	16	19
8	Sth Prem C	A	St Neots Town	179	L	1 - 3	Batchelor 7	17	20
15	Sth Prem C	H	Royston Town	151	L	1 - 2	Washbourne 1		21
18	Sth Prem C	A	Needham Market	206	L	1 - 3	Evans 29		22
22	Sth Prem C	H	AFC Rushden & Diamonds	295	D	2 - 2	Franklin 27 Parsons 57	17	23
26	Sth Prem C	H	Alvechurch	556	**W**	4 - 2	White 12 34 Batchalor 53 Bunn 84		24
29	Sth Prem C	A	Barwell	189	L	0 - 4		17	25
Jan 1	Sth Prem C	H	Halesowen Town	420	**W**	3 - 0	Leachman-Whittingham 19 (p) Ali 45 Evans 57	16	26
5	Sth Prem C	A	Rushall Olympic	202	**W**	3 - 1	Leachman-Whittingham 11 45 (p) Reynolds 70	14	27
12	Sth Prem C	H	Bedworth United	230	L	0 - 1		14	28
19	Sth Prem C	A	Lowestoft Town	332	D	0 - 0		15	29
26	Sth Prem C	H	Stratford Town	356	L	0 - 1		16	30
Feb 9	Sth Prem C	H	Kettering Town	379	L	1 - 4	Johnson 62	17	31
16	Sth Prem C	A	Kings Lynn Town	621	L	0 - 2		17	32
23	Sth Prem C	H	Needham Market	299	**W**	4 - 1	Leachman-Whittingham 7 51 Bunn 43 Johnson 54	16	33
26	Sth Prem C	A	Banbury United	302	D	1 - 1	Evans 90	16	34
Mar 2	Sth Prem C	H	St Neots Town	221	D	1 - 1	Bunn 90	16	35
9	Sth Prem C	A	Royston Town	230	**W**	1 - 0	Leachman-Whittingham 90	16	36
16	Sth Prem C	H	Stourbridge	508	L	1 - 4	Bunn 23	17	37
23	Sth Prem C	A	Tamworth	413	D	0 - 0		17	38
30	Sth Prem C	A	Coalville Town	149	**W**	2 - 1	Parsons 73 Towers 86 (og)	16	39
Apr 6	Sth Prem C	H	Biggleswade Town	200	D	3 - 3	Gent (og) 25 Hawker 52 Franklin 90	17	40
13	Sth Prem C	A	St Ives Town	179	L	0 - 1		18	41
20	Sth Prem C	H	Hitchin Town	195	**W**	3 - 1	Howards 16 Hawker 66 Yates 77	17	42
22	Sth Prem C	A	Halesowen Town	354	L	0 - 1		18	43
27	Sth Prem C	H	Leiston	210	**W**	3 - 1	Nelson 6 Howards 27 Downing 83	15	44

GOALSCORERS	SG	CSG	Pens	Hat tricks	Total
Howards	6		2		8
Leachman-Whittingham	8				8
Bunn	5				6
Ali	4				4
Franklin	4				4
Batchelor	3				3
Evans	3				3
Nelson	3				3
Parsons	3				3
Francis	2				2
Gibson	2				2
Hawker	2				2
Johnson	2				2

	SG	CSG	Pens	Hat tricks	Total
Opponents	2				2
Reynolds	2				2
White	1				2
Downing	1				1
Loveridge	1				1
Moore	1				1
Piggon	1				1
Sinclair	1				1
Stokes	1				1
Washbourne	1				1
Winters	1				1
Yates	1				1

ROYSTON TOWN MATCH RESULTS 2018-19

Date	Comp	H/A	Opponents	Att:	Result	Goalscorers	Pos	No.
Aug 11	Sth Prem C	A	Alvechurch	177	D 0 - 0			1
14	Sth Prem C	H	Leiston	226	L 2 - 5	Potton 10 Murray 20		2
18	Sth Prem C	H	Stratford Town	202	D 2 - 2	Potton 50 Assombalonga 56	19	3
25	Sth Prem C	A	Rushall Olympic	151	W 3 - 0	Bola 71 79 Gordon 86		4
27	Sth Prem C	H	St Ives Tiown	361	L 1 - 2	Martin 26	14	5
Sept 1	Sth Prem C	A	Barwell	152	W 2 - 1	Bell 75 Ellesley 77	12	6
8	**FAC 2Q**	**A**	**AFC Sudbury**	**208**	**L 2 - 3**	**Assombalonga 35 Bola 55**		7
15	Sth Prem C	H	AFC Rushden & Diamonds	384	W 2 - 1	Murray 15 Corcoran 61	9	8
29	Sth Prem C	A	Tamworth	636	W 2 - 1	Castiglone 12 Martin 88	6	9
Oct 6	Sth Prem C	H	Bedworth United	170	W 2 - 0	Scott-Morriss 68 Castiglone 77	3	10
13	Sth Prem C	A	Stourbridge	651	L 1 - 2	Assombalonga 53	4	11
16	Sth Prem C	H	St Neots Twn	243	W 5 - 0	Wood 18 (og) Bola 37 Gordon 53 (p) 81 (p) Mooney 90	4	12
20	Sth Prem C	A	Banbury United	421	W 1 - 0	Potton 90	2	13
27	**FAT 1Q**	**A**	**Malden & Tiptree**	**88**	**W 3 - 0**	**Potton Bola Murray**		14
Nov 3	Sth Prem C	H	Halesowen Town	259	D 0 - 0		3	15
10	**FAT 2Q**	**H**	**Thame United**	**170**	**W 5 - 2**	**MOONEY 3 (16 35 41) Potton Spyros 80**		16
17	Sth Prem C	H	Kettering Town	559	L 0 - 1		5	17
20	Sth Prem C	A	Lowestoft Town	216	L 0 - 2			18
24	**FAT 3Q**	**H**	**Needham Market**	**202**	**D 1 - 1**			19
27	**FAT 3Qr**	**A**	**Needham Market**	**153**	**L 0 - 2**			20
Dec 1	Sth Prem C	H	Needham Market	222	L 2 - 4	Bola 27 45	8	21
8	Sth Prem C	H	Biggleswade Town	209	L 4 - 6	Potton 12 20 Castiglione 44 Brathwaite 87	10	22
15	Sth Prem C	A	Redditch United	151	W 2 - 1	Gordon 45 Murray 78	8	23
22	Sth Prem C	H	Alvechurch	243	L 0 - 1		9	24
26	Sth Prem C	A	St Ives Town	287	D 0 - 0		10	25
29	Sth Prem C	A	Leiston	249	D 1 - 1	Joseph 81	11	26
Jan 1	Sth Prem C	H	Hitchin Town	423	W 1 - 0	Mentis 87	10	27
5	Sth Prem C	A	St Neots Town	268	L 0 - 1		11	28
12	Sth Prem C	H	Kings Lynn Town	370	L 0 - 1		13	29
19	Sth Prem C	A	Kettering Town	661	L 0 - 1		13	30
26	Sth Prem C	H	Lowestoft Town	281	D 1 - 1	Newman 90	13	31
29	Sth Prem C	A	King's Lynn Town	398	L 2 - 4	Gordon 22 (pen) Neal 37	13	32
Feb 2	Sth Prem C	A	Halesowen Town	405	L 0 - 1		14	33
9	Sth Prem C	H	Banbury United	254	W 3 - 0	Bola 53 Newman 59 Kinali 82	13	34
16	Sth Prem C	A	Needham Market	252	W 2 - 0	Bola 2 67	12	35
23	Sth Prem C	H	Coalville Town	252	W 2 - 0	Bola 2 67	11	36
Mar 2	Sth Prem C	A	Biggleswade Town	189	W 4 - 1	MURRAY 3 (39 46 48) Knowles 88	9	37
9	Sth Prem C	H	Redditch United	230	L 0 - 1		9	38
16	Sth Prem C	A	Bedworth United	139	W 2 - 1	Knowles 12 Murray 78	9	39
23	Sth Prem C	H	Stourbridge	300	W 3 - 2	Kinali 24 Murray 45 Knowles 88 (pen)	8	40
30	Sth Prem C	A	AFC Rushden & Diamonds	634	D 0 - 0		9	41
Apr 2	Sth Prem C	A	Coalville Town	129	W 3 - 2	Kinali 22 Murray 45 Stanley 90	9	42
6	Sth Prem C	H	Tamworth	273	L 0 - 2		9	43
13	Sth Prem C	A	Stratford Town	245	L 0 - 2		9	44
20	Sth Prem C	H	Rushall Olympic	258	L 1 - 3	Joseph 13	11	45
22	Sth Prem C	A	Hitchin Town	436	W 2 - 0	Castiglone 70 Bola 90	11	46
27	Sth Prem C	H	Barwell	259	W 1 - 0	Corcoran 90	10	47

GOALSCORERS	SG	CSG	Pens	Hat tricks	Total
Bola	9	2			12
Murray	8	2		1	10
Potton	7				7
Gordon	4		3		5
Castiglone	4				4
Mooney	2			1	4
Assombalonga	3				3
Kinali	3				3
Knowles	3		3		3
Bola	2				2
Corcoran	2				2
Martin	2				2
Newman	2				2
Bell	1				1
Brathwaite	1				1
Ellesley	1				1
Joseph	1				1
Mentis	1				1
Neal	1				1
Opponents	1				1
Scott-Morriss	1				1
Spyros	1				1
Stanley	1				1

RUSHALL OLYMPIC MATCH RESULTS 2018-19

Date	Comp	H/A	Opponents	Att:	Result		Goalscorers	Pos	No.
Aug 11	Sth Prem C	H	Banbury United	271	D	1 - 1	Waldron 83		1
14	Sth Prem C	A	Coalville Town	141	D	2 - 2	Hull 40 Waldron 90		2
18	Sth Prem C	A	St Neots Town	202	W	1 - 0	Waldron 53	15	3
25	Sth Prem C	H	Royston Town	151	L	0 - 3			4
27	Sth Prem C	A	Tamworth	580	L	0 - 2		9	5
Sept 1	Sth Prem C	H	Biggleswade Town	165	D	2 - 2	Waldron 2 Singh 43	9	6
8	**FAC 1Q**	**A**	**Sutton Coldfield Town**	**249**	**D**	**2 - 2**	**Lund 43 Sammons 65**		7
12	**FAC 1Qr**	**H**	**Sutton Coldfield Town**	**236**	**L**	**0 - 1**			8
15	Sth Prem C	A	Needham Market	283	D	1 - 1	Waldron 25 (pen)	18	9
29	Sth Prem C	H	Stratford Town	182	D	2 - 2	Waldron 8 Sammons 71	19	10
Oct 6	Sth Prem C	A	Halesowen Town	406	L	0 - 2		19	11
13	Sth Prem C	H	Lowestoft Town	281	W	3 - 1	Whittall 22 (pen) Waldron 67 Lund 71	16	12
16	Sth Prem C	A	Redditch United	215	L	1 - 2	Hull 11	16	13
20	Sth Prem C	H	St Ives Town	202	W	4 - 1	Hull 42 Lund 45 Whittall 65 Richards 80 (pen)	13	14
27	**FAT 1Q**	**A**	**Stafford Rangers**	**371**	**L**	**1 - 2**	**Lund**		15
Nov 3	Sth Prem C	A	AFC Rushden & Diamonds	478	W	2 - 0	Pendley 45 Sammons 60	10	16
10	Sth Prem C	H	Alvechurch	226	L	1 - 2	Sammons 71	11	17
17	Sth Prem C	A	Leiston	316	W	1 - 0	Berry 90	10	18
24	Sth Prem C	H	Kettering Town	317	L	0 - 1		14	19
Dec 1	Sth Prem C	A	Bedworth United	147	W	3 - 1	Whittall 9 Waldron 79 O'Callaghan 90	11	20
8	Sth Prem C	H	Hitchin Town	218	L	1 - 2	Singh 76	13	21
15	Sth Prem C	A	Kings Lynn Town	550	L	0 - 3		14	22
22	Sth Prem C	A	Banbury United	451	L	1 - 2	Hull 58	16	23
26	Sth Prem C	H	Tamworth	437	D	1 - 1	O'Callaghan 10		24
29	Sth Prem C	H	Coalville Town	255	L	0 - 2		16	25
Jan 1	Sth Prem C	A	Stourbridge	913	D	1 - 1	Charlton 9	16	26
5	Sth Prem C	H	Redditch United	202	L	1 - 3	O'Callaghan 31	16	27
7	Sth Prem C	H	Barwell	123	D	1 - 1	Page 8	16	28
12	Sth Prem C	A	Barwell	149	W	3 - 1	Lyttle 5 82 Maye 790	15	29
19	Sth Prem C	H	Leiston	201	W	2 - 0	Parker 30 Lund 31	14	30
26	Sth Prem C	A	Alvechurch	179	L	0 - 1		14	31
Feb 9	Sth Prem C	A	St Ives Town	180	W	3 - 0	Parker (og) 12 Maye 55 Hull 67	14	32
16	Sth Prem C	H	Bedworth United	198	D	0 - 0		14	33
23	Sth Prem C	A	Kettering Town	882	L	1 - 2	Waldron 31	15	34
Mar 2	Sth Prem C	A	Hitchin Town	381	W	1 - 0	Maye 35	15	35
9	Sth Prem C	H	Kings Lynn Town	211	W	2 - 1	Hull 72 Lyttle 81	15	36
11	Sth Prem C	H	AFC Rushden & Diamonds	221	W	2 - 0	Hull 10 Parker 42	15	37
16	Sth Prem C	H	Halesowen Town	334	D	0 - 0		11	38
23	Sth Prem C	A	Lowestoft Town	487	W	4 - 2	Soleman 6 Hull 50 Waldron 72 90	10	39
30	Sth Prem C	H	Needham Market	192	L	0 - 1		11	40
Apr 6	Sth Prem C	A	Stratford Town	295	W	1 - 0	Maye 22	10	41
13	Sth Prem C	H	St Neots Town	203	W	3 - 2	Maye 55 Waldron 82 Whittall 85 (pen)	10	42
20	Sth Prem C	A	Royston Town	258	W	3 - 1	O'Callaghan 43 48 Pendley 67	9	43
22	Sth Prem C	H	Stourbridge	452	D	0 - 0		9	44
27	Sth Prem C	A	Biggleswade Town	155	W	1 - 0	Whittall 72	8	45

GOALSCORERS	SG	CSG	Pens	Hat tricks	Total
Waldron	11	3	1		12
Hull	10	2			8
Lund	5	2			5
Maye	5				5
O'Callaghan	4		2		5
Whittall	5		1		5
Sammons	4				4
Lyttle	2				3
Parker	2				2
Pendley	2				2
Singh	2				2
Berry	1				1
Charlton	1				1
Opponents	1				1
Page	1				1
Richards	1				1
Soleman	1				1

ST IVES TOWN MATCH RESULTS 2018-19

Date	Comp	H/A	Opponents	Att:	Result		Goalscorers	Pos	No.
Aug 11	Sth Prem C	H	Tamworth	306	W	1 - 0	Sundire 47		1
14	Sth Prem C	A	Lowestoft Town	393	W	1 - 0	Wilson 90		2
18	Sth Prem C	A	Redditch United	202	L	0 - 2		3	3
25	Sth Prem C	H	Needham Market	243	D	1 - 1	Parker 88 (pen)	4	4
27	Sth Prem C	A	Royston Town	361	W	2 - 1	Seymore-Shove 45 75	3	5
Sept 1	Sth Prem C	H	Coalville Town	262	L	0 - 1		6	6
8	**FAC 1Q**	**A**	**Saffron Walden Town**	**521**	**D**	**0 - 0**			7
11	**FAC 1Qr**	**H**	**Saffron Walden Town**	**258**	**W**	**3 - 1**	**McGowan 17 Wilson 57 Cartwright 84**		8
15	Sth Prem C	H	Stourbridge	268	D	0 - 0		8	9
22	**FAC 2Q**	**H**	**Grantham Town**	**293**	**D**	**1 - 1**	**Parker 43 (pen)**		10
25	**FAC 2Qr**	**A**	**Grantham Town**	**294**	**W**	**2 - 0**	**Cartwright 66 Snaith 71**		11
27	Sth Prem C	A	AFC Rushden & Diamonds	586	D	0 - 0		8	12
Oct 6	**FAC 3Q**	**A**	**York City**	**1243**	**L**	**0 - 3**		**10**	13
13	Sth Prem C	A	Alvechurch	254	L	1 - 2	Coulson 90	12	14
16	Sth Prem C	H	Biggleswade Town	267	L	0 - 1		15	15
20	Sth Prem C	A	Rushall Olympic	202	L	1 - 4	Wilson 85	16	16
23	Sth Prem C	H	Leiston	111	L	0 - 2		17	17
27	**FAT 1Q**	**A**	**Rushden & Diamonds**	**386**	**L**	**1 - 2**	**Snaith 87**		18
Nov 3	Sth Prem C	H	Stratford Town	259	L	0 - 2		18	19
10	Sth Prem C	A	Kings Lynn Town	714	L	0 - 2		19	20
17	Sth Prem C	H	Halesowen Town	178	W	2 - 0	Baker 19 Seymore-Shove 90	18	21
24	Sth Prem C	H	Banbury United	179	D	2 - 2	Newman 1 Kelly 5	18	22
Dec 1	Sth Prem C	A	Kettering Town	653	W	3 - 0	Snaith 22 Cartwrighht 33 Kelly 40	17	23
8	Sth Prem C	H	Bedworth United	150	W	2 - 1	Fitzharris (og) 89 Jackson 90	15	24
19	Sth Prem C	A	Hitchin Town	141	L	0 - 1		15	25
22	Sth Prem C	A	Tamworth	593	W	2 - 1	Newman 10 Ford 49	13	26
26	Sth Prem C	H	Royston Town	287	D	0 - 0			27
29	Sth Prem C	H	Lowestoft Town	221	D	0 - 0		14	28
Jan 1	Sth Prem C	A	St Neots Town	428	W	1 - 0	Newman 12	12	29
5	Sth Prem C	A	Biggleswade Town	202	L	0 - 1		13	30
12	Sth Prem C	H	Hitchin Town	228	W	2 - 1	Jackson 48 Death 60	12	31
19	Sth Prem C	A	Halesowen Town	363	D	1 - 1	Newman 42	12	32
22	Sth Prem C	A	Barwell	136	D	1 - 1	Osie-Bonsu 45	12	33
26	Sth Prem C	H	King's Lynn Town	322	D	1 - 1	Snaith 19	12	34
Feb 2	Sth Prem C	A	Stratford Town	285	D	0 - 0		11	35
9	Sth Prem C	H	Rushall Olympic	180	L	0 - 3		11	36
16	Sth Prem C	H	Kettering Town	639	L	1 - 2	Parker 29	12	37
23	Sth Prem C	A	Banbury United	439	W	2 - 1	Osie-Bonsu 14 Seymour-Shove 39	12	38
Mar 2	Sth Prem C	A	Bedworth United	143	W	2 - 0	Seymore-Shove 19 Coulson 33	11	39
9	Sth Prem C	H	Barwell	168	L	1 - 2	Seymore-Shove 20	12	40
16	Sth Prem C	A	Leiston	216	W	2 - 0	Newman 64 Parker 90	12	41
23	Sth Prem C	H	Alvechurch	270	L	0 - 2		12	42
30	Sth Prem C	A	Stourbridge	621	D	1 - 1	Sundire 87	12	43
Apr 6	Sth Prem C	H	AFC Rushden & Diamonds	372	D	0 - 0		13	44
13	Sth Prem C	H	Redditch United	179	W	1 - 0	Osie-Bonsu 45	13	45
20	Sth Prem C	A	Needham Market	337	L	1 - 4	Newman 3	13	46
22	Sth Prem C	H	St Neots Town	351	D	0 - 0		13	47
27	Sth Prem C	A	Coalville Town	165	W	1 - 0	Seymore-Shove 29	13	48

GOALSCORERS	SG	CSG	Pens	Hat tricks	Total
Seymore-Shove	6				7
Newman	6				6
Parker	4		1		4
Snaith	4				4
Cartwright	3				3
Osie-Bonsu	3				3
Wilson	3				3
Coulson	2				2
Jackson	2				2
Kelly	2				2
Sundire	2				2
Baker	1				1
Death	1				1
Ford	1				1
McGowan	1				1
Opponents	1				1

ST NEOTS TOWN MATCH RESULTS 2018-19

Date	Comp	H/A	Opponents	Att:	Result		Goalscorers	Pos	No.
Aug 11	Sth Prem C	A	Stratford Town	292	L	0 - 1			1
14	Sth Prem C	H	Bedworth Town	192	W	2 - 1	Ofuso 8 Parr 53		2
18	Sth Prem C	H	Rushall Olympic	202	L	0 - 1		14	3
25	Sth Prem C	A	Kings Lynn Town	568	D	0 - 0			4
27	Sth Prem C	H	Rushden & Diamonds	609	L	0 - 1		17	5
Sept 1	Sth Prem C	A	Halesowen Town	358	D	1 - 1	Ofuso 58	17	6
8	**FAC 1Q**	**H**	**Bishop's Stortford**	**209**	**W**	**2 - 1**	**Williams 37 (pen) Douglas 83**		7
15	Sth Prem C	A	Banbury United	490	W	3 - 1	Stout 31 37 Williams 59	14	8
22	**FAC 2Q**	**H**	**Romulus**	**325**	**W**	**4 - 3**	**Wood 40 Semble-Ferris 77 89 Herd 85**		9
29	Sth Prem C	H	Hitchin Town	376	D	0 - 0		12	10
Oct 6	**FAC 3Q**	**H**	**Coalville Town**	**518**	**D**	**2 - 2**	**Knight 86 Shariff 90**		11
9	**FAC 3Qr**	**A**	**Coalville Town**	**409**	**D**	**3 - 3**	**Ofosu 49 Wharton 88 92 (won 5-3 on pens)**		12
13	Sth Prem C	A	Kettering Town	693	L	0 - 3		17	13
16	Sth Prem C	A	Royston Town	243	L	0 - 5		18	14
20	**FAC 4Q**	**A**	**Alfreton Town**	**645**	**L**	**0 - 4**		**19**	15
23	Sth Prem C	A	Lowestoft Town	238	W	2 - 1	Short 11 58		16
27	**FAT 1Q**	**H**	**Matlock Town**	**249**	**W**	**1 - 0**	**Shariff 75**		17
Nov 3	Sth Prem C	H	Coalville Town	138	D	1 - 1	Semble-Ferris 25	17	18
6	Sth Prem C	H	Tamworth	181	D	0 - 0		17	19
10	**FAT 2Q**	**H**	**Barwell**	**714**	**L**	**0 - 1**			20
17	Sth Prem C	A	Alvechurch	239	L	2 - 3	Wood 30 Wharton 40	19	21
20	Sth Prem C	H	Needham Market	139	L	0 - 3		20	22
Dec 1	Sth Prem C	A	Stourbridge	188	L	1 - 2	Williams 14	20	23
8	Sth Prem C	H	Redditch United	179	W	3 - 1	Shariff 32 83 Williams 60	18	24
15	Sth Prem C	A	Barwell	63	L	1 - 6	Wharton 90	19	25
22	Sth Prem C	H	Stratford Town	258	L	1 - 2	Parr 90	20	26
26	Sth Prem C	A	AFC Rushden & Diamonds	244	L	0 - 2			27
29	Sth Prem C	A	Bedworth United	154	L	0 - 1		21	28
Jan 1	Sth Prem C	H	St Ives Town	428	L	0 - 1		20	29
5	Sth Prem C	A	Royston Town	268	W	1 - 0	Parr 82	18	30
8	Sth Prem C	H	Leiston	128	W	2 - 0	Norville-Williams 2 Williams 90		31
12	Sth Prem C	H	Leiston	208	L	0 - 2		18	32
19	Sth Prem C	H	Alvechurch	198	L	0 - 3		19	33
26	Sth Prem C	A	Needham Market	299	W	1 - 0	Short 54	19	34
Feb 5	Sth Prem C	A	Biggleswade Town	188	L	0 - 1		20	35
9	Sth Prem C	A	Tamworth	512	L	0 - 5		20	36
16	Sth Prem C	H	Stourbridge	596	L	0 - 1		20	37
23	Sth Prem C	H	Barwell	171	W	1 - 0	Wharton 60	20	38
Mar 2	Sth Prem C	H	Redditch United	221	D	1 - 1	Wharton 4	20	39
9	Sth Prem C	A	Biggleswade Town	284	D	2 - 2	Donkin 8 (og) Mutswunguma 36	20	40
16	Sth Prem C	H	Lowestoft Town	293	L	1 - 3	Wharton 71 (pen)	20	41
23	Sth Prem C	A	Kettering Town	894	L	0 - 2		20	42
26	Sth Prem C	H	Coalville Town	139	L	1 - 4	Walton 57 (og)	20	43
30	Sth Prem C	H	Banbury United	260	L	0 - 3		20	44
Apr 6	Sth Prem C	H	Hitchin Town	472	W	2 - 0	Trendall 37 51	20	45
13	Sth Prem C	H	Rushall Olympic	203	L	2 - 3	Bradley 39 Rhiney 57	20	46
20	Sth Prem C	A	Kings Lynn Town	320	L	0 - 5		20	47
22	Sth Prem C	H	St Ives Town	351	D	0 - 0		20	48
27	Sth Prem C	A	Halesowen Town	132	D	1 - 1	Trendall 4	20	49

GOALSCORERS	SG	CSG	Pens	Hat tricks	Total
Wharton	6		1		7
Williams	5		1		5
Shariff	3				4
Ofuso	3				3
Parr	3				3
Semble-Ferris	3				3
Short	2				3
Stout	2				3
Trendall	2				3
Opponents	2				2
Bradley	1				1
Douglas	1				1
Herd	1				1
Knight	1				1
Mutswunguma	1				1
N-Williams	1				1
Rhiney	1				1
Wood	1				1

STOURBRIDGE MATCH RESULTS 2018-19

Date	Comp	H/A	Opponents	Att:	Result	Goalscorers	Pos	No.
Aug 11	Sth Prem C	A	Barwell	278	D 1 - 1	Benbow 85 (pen)		1
13	Sth Prem C	H	Stratford Town	733	W 3 - 0	Hayden 10 Broadhurst 18 Mills 32		2
18	Sth Prem C	H	AFC Rushden & Diamonds	560	W 2 - 1	Mills 30 Broadhurst 90		3
25	Sth Prem C	A	Coalville Town	233	L 4 - 6	Bryant 23 (og) Mills 30 Benbow 32 Broadhurst 60		4
28	Sth Prem C	H	Halesowen Town	1733	D 1 - 1	Benbow 20		5
Sept 1	Sth Prem C	A	Kings Lynn Town	535	W 1 - 0	Forde 43		6
8	**FAC 1Q**	**A**	**Highgate United**	**320**	**W 2 - 1**	**Anderson 25 Hayden 55**		7
15	Sth Prem C	A	St Ives Town	266	D 0 - 0			8
18	Sth Prem C	A	Alvechurch	347	D 0 - 0			9
22	**FAC 2Q**	**H**	**Leamington**	**467**	**W 3 - 2**	**Lane (og) 48 Broadhurst 53 Anderson 90**		10
29	Sth Prem C	H	Needham Market	621	W 3 - 1	Powell 28 45 Anderson 34		11
Oct 6	**FAC 3Q**	**H**	**Kidderminster Harriers**	**1527**	**W 3 - 2**	**Anderson 62 70 Forde 77 (pen)**		12
13	Sth Prem C	H	Royston	651	W 2 - 1	Thompson-Brown 45 Powell 88		13
15	Sth Prem C	H	Bedworth United	405	W 4 - 1	Mills 39 (pen) 60 (pen) Steele 52 66		14
20	**FAC 4Q**	**A**	**Guiseley**	**633**	**L 1 - 3**	**Benbow 24**		15
27	**FAT 1Q**	**A**	**Kettering Town**	**409**	**L 0 - 2**			16
Nov 3	Sth Prem C	H	Lowestoft Town	594	W 3 - 1	Mills 40 59 Hayden 65		17
13	Sth Prem C	A	Redditch United	432	W 4 - 0	Powell 36 Mills 45 (pen) 73 Benbow 64		18
17	Sth Prem C	H	Hitchin Town	667	W 3 - 0	Mills 49 90 Broadhurst 90		19
20	Sth Prem C	A	Kettering Town	701	L 2 - 4	Mills 28 60		20
24	Sth Prem C	H	Tamwor4th	643	D 1 - 1	MIlls 16		21
27	Sth Prem C	A	Biggleswade Town	123	W 2 - 1	Mills 58 Thompson -Brown 89		22
Dec 1	Sth Prem C	A	At Neots Town	186	W 2 - 1	Benbow 57 McCone 62		23
8	Sth Prem C	A	Leiston	197	W 3 - 0	Forde 20 Benbow 51 Anderson 90		24
11	Sth Prem C	A	Banbury United	313	D 0 - 0			25
15	Sth Prem C	H	Coalville Town	451	W 4 - 2	Mills 29 (pen) Broadhurst 48 75 Benbow 65		26
22	Sth Prem C	H	Barwell	716	W 3 - 0	Hayden 9 Benbow 16 40		27
26	Sth Prem C	A	Helsowen Town	1994	W 3 - 0	Benbow 1 75 Anderson 90		28
29	Sth Prem C	A	Stratford Town	620	D 0 - 0			29
Jan 1	Sth Prem C	H	Rushall Olympic	913	D 1 - 1	Benbow 16		30
5	Sth Prem C	A	Bedworth United	257	W 3 - 0	Anderson 32 Mills 43 (pen) Benbow 75		31
12	Sth Prem C	H	Banbury United	701	W 2 - 0	Benbow 53 Mills 90		32
19	Sth Prem C	A	HItchin Town	354	L 1 - 2	Benbow 11		33
26	Sth Prem C	H	Kettering Town	1734	L 1 - 2	Broadhurst 75		34
Feb 2	Sth Prem C	A	Lowestoft Town	334	L 0 - 1			35
9	Sth Prem C	H	Biggleswade Town	856	W 2 - 0	Hayden 7 Benbow 70	2	36
16	Sth Prem C	H	St Neots Town	596	W 1 - 0	Mills 1	2	37
23	Sth Prem C	A	Tamworth	703	L 0 - 1		2	38
Mar 2	Sth Prem C	H	Leiston	613	W 4 - 0	BENBOW 3 (54 61 pen 64) MIlls 90	2	39
16	Sth Prem C	H	Redditch United	508	W 4 - 1	Forde 20 60 McCone 26 54	2	40
23	Sth Prem C	A	Royston Town	300	L 2 - 3	Birch 65 Mills 78	2	41
30	Sth Prem C	H	St Ives Town	621	D 1 - 1	Mills 2 (pen)	2	42
Apr 6	Sth Prem C	A	Needham Market	255	D 0 - 0		2	43
13	Sth Prem C	A	Rushden & Damonds	519	W 2 - 1	Thonpson-Brown 35 Benbow 75	2	44
19	Sth Prem C	H	Alvechurch	1062	D 3 - 3	McCone 52 Anderson 61 Hayden 72	2	45
22	Sth Prem C	A	Rushall Olympic	452	D 0 - 0		2	46
27	Sth Prem C	H	Kings Lynn Town	791	L 1 - 2	Mills 68	3	47
May 4	**PO SF**	**A**	**Alvechurch**	**894**	**L 1 - 2**	**Mills 45+3 (pen)**		48

GOALSCORERS	SG	CSG	Pens	Hat tricks	Total
Mills	20	5	7		24
Benbow	17	4	3	1	21
Anderson	8	3			9
Broadhurst	8	3			8
Hayden	6		1		6
Forde	5				5
McCone	3				4
Powell	4				4
Thompson-Brown	3				3
Opponents					2

	SG	CSG	Pens	Hat tricks	Total
Steele	1				2
Birch	1				1

STRATFORD TOWN MATCH RESULTS 2018-19

Date	Comp	H/A	Opponents	Att:	Result		Goalscorers	Pos	No.
Aug 11	Sth Prem C	H	St Neots Town	292	W	1 - 0	Grocott 50		1
13	Sth Prem C	A	Stourbridge	733	L	0 - 3			2
18	Sth Prem C	A	Royston Town	201	D	2 - 2	Maslen-Jones 39 Taylor 82	11	3
25	Sth Prem C	H	Lowestoft Town	238	L	1 - 3	Dias 40	14	4
27	Sth Prem C	A	Banbury United	630	D	1 - 1	Shariff 75 (pen)	16	5
Sept 1	Sth Prem C	H	Kettering Town	396	L	1 - 3	Taylor 18	18	6
8	**FAC 1Q**	**H**	**Alvechurch**	**238**	**L**	**0 - 1**			7
15	Sth Prem C	H	Bedworth United	255	W	3 - 1	Taylor 16 79 Wilson 55	15	8
22	Sth Prem C	H	Redditch United	225	W	2 - 0	Taylor 33 Williams 38	9	9
29	Sth Prem C	A	Rushall Olympic	182	D	2 - 2	Taylor 2 Wilson 47	9	10
Oct 13	Sth Prem C	A	King's Lynn Town	681	D	0 - 0		11	11
20	Sth Prem C	H	Leiston	227	W	3 - 2	Carvello 7 68 Skendi 23	9	12
27	**FAT 1Q**	**A**	**Alvechurch**	**199**	**D**	**1 - 1**	**Taylor 18**		13
30	**FAT 1Qr**	**H**	**Alvechurch**	**152**	**W**	**3 - 0**	**Carvalho 7 (pen) Taylor 37 42**		14
Nov 3	Sth Prem C	A	St Ives Town	181	W	2 - 0	Cox 1 Taylor 23		15
10	**FAT 2Q**	**H**	**Mickleove Sports**	**183**	**D**	**1 - 1**	**Williams 26**		16
13	**FAT 2Qr**	**A**	**Mickleover Sports**	**183**	**W**	**1 - 0**	**Taylor 88**		17
17	Sth Prem C	A	Needham Market	284	L	1 - 2	Morrison 85	12	18
24	**FAT 3Q**	**H**	**South Shields**	**378**	**W**	**2 - 1**	**Carvalho 58 (pen) Taylor 90**		19
Dec 1	Sth Prem C	A	Halesowen Town	412	W	2 - 0	Carvalho 58 Grocott 71	12	20
8	Sth Prem C	H	Barwell	212	W	2 - 1	Taylor 67 McAteer 90	10	21
11	Sth Prem C	A	Banbury United	243	W	2 - 1	Richards 25 Cox 65	9	22
15	**FAT 1P**	**A**	**AFC Fylde**	**491**	**L**	**1 - 5**	**Williams 90**		23
22	Sth Prem C	A	St Neots Town	258	W	2 - 1	Carvalho 68 Richards 83	8	24
26	Sth Prem C	H	Banbury United	406	W	2 - 1	Cox 3 Carvalho 66		25
29	Sth Prem C	H	Stourbridge	620	D	0 - 0		7	26
Jan 1	Sth Prem C	A	Biggleswade Town	221	D	0 - 0		7	27
5	Sth Prem C	H	Alvechurc	246	L	0 - 1		8	28
12	Sth Prem C	A	Tamworth	537	W	1 - 0	Carvalho 49	6	29
15	Sth Prem C	H	Hitchin Town	192	W	2 - 0	Carvalho 18 Wilson 24	5	30
19	Sth Prem C	H	Needham Market	201	W	3 - 1	Shariff 40 56 Williams 45	5	31
22	Sth Prem C	A	Alvechurch	160	D	2 - 2	Cox 68 Fry 82	4	32
26	Sth Prem C	A	Redditch United	356	W	1 - 0	Carvello71	3	33
Feb 2	Sth Prem C	H	St Ives Town	285	D	0 - 0		3	34
12	Sth Prem C	H	Coalville Town	221	L	0 - 2		3	35
16	Sth Prem C	H	Halesowen Town	450	W	2 - 1	Creaney 18 Cox 77	3	36
19	Sth Prem C	A	AFC Rushden & Diamonds	399	L	0 - 2		3	37
23	Sth Prem C	A	Hitchin Town	457	D	0 - 0		3	38
Mar 2	Sth Prem C	A	Barwell	203	D	0 - 0		4	39
9	Sth Prem C	H	AFC Rushden & Diamonds	449	W	1 - 0	Fry 75	6	40
16	Sth Prem C	A	Coalville Town	195	W	2 - 1	Grocott 50 Taylor 66	5	41
19	Sth Prem C	A	Leiston	182	W	2 - 1	Carvalho 45 (pen) Taylor 46	4	42
23	Sth Prem C	H	King's Lynn Town	402	L	0 - 2		4	43
30	Sth Prem C	A	Bedworth Town	151	W	2 - 0	Creaney 48 Wilson 65	4	44
Apr 6	Sth Prem C	H	Rushall Olympic	295	L	0 - 1		4	45
13	Sth Prem C	H	Royston Town	245	W	2 - 0	Wilson 13 Taylor 53	5	46
20	Sth Prem C	A	Lowestoft Town	461	L	2 - 3	Shariff 39 Creaney 47	5	47
22	Sth Prem C	H	Biggleswade Town	425	W	3 - 2	Taylor 68 Carvalho 73 (pen)	5	48
27	Sth Prem C	A	Kettering Town	660	L	1 - 5	Williams 47	5	49
May 4	**PO SF**	**A**	**King's Lynn Town**	**1253**	**L**	**1 - 3**	**Taylor 35**		50

GOALSCORERS	SG	CSG	Pens	Hat tricks	Total
Taylor	17	3			18
Carvello	12	2	3		12
Cox	6				6
Williams	5				5
Wilson	5				5
Shariff	3		1		4
Creaney	3				3
Grocutt	3				3
Fry	2				2
Richards	2				2
Dias	1				1
Maslen-Jones	1				1
McAteer	1				1
Morrison	1				1
Skendi	1				1

TAMWORTH MATCH RESULTS 2018-19

Date	Comp	H/A	Opponents	Att:	Result	Goalscorers	Pos	No.
Aug 11	Sth Prem C	A	St Ives Town	306	L 0 - 1			1
14	Sth Prem C	H	Alvechurch	592	D 1 - 1	Finn 1		2
18	Sth Prem C	H	Kings Lynn Town	595	L 0 - 1		20	3
25	Sth Prem C	A	Leiston	329	D 2 - 2	Lait 61 Asante 80	20	4
27	Sth Prem C	H	Rushall Olympic	580	W 2 - 0	Lait 12 Dunkley 90	15	5
31	Sth Prem C	A	AFC Rushden & Diamonds	683	D 2 - 2	Asante 12 Waite 25	12	6
Sept 8	**FAC 1Q**	**A**	**Hednesford Town**	**602**	**L 0 - 2**			7
15	Sth Prem C	A	Lowestoft Town	408	W 3 - 1	Finn 75 Lait 81 Waite 83	12	8
29	Sth Prem C	H	Royston Town	636	L 1 - 2	Waite 14	15	9
Oct 6	Sth Prem C	A	Banbury United	362	D 0 - 0		14	10
13	Sth Prem C	H	Redditch United	621	L 1 - 3	Beswick 22	17	11
16	Sth Prem C	H	Kettering Town	587	D 0 - 0		18	12
27	**FAT 1Q**	**A**	**Gainsborough Trinity**	**620**	**D 0 - 0**			13
30	**FAT 1Qr**	**H**	**Gainsborough Trinity**	**276**	**W 3 - 0**	**Lait 5 Waite 38**		14
Nov 3	Sth Prem C	H	Hitchin Town	474	W 2 - 0	Lait 15 90 Dunkley 73	16	15
6	Sth Prem C	A	St Neots Town	181	D 0 - 0		15	16
10	**FAT 2Q**	**A**	**Marske United**	**290**	**L 0 - 2**		**18**	17
17	Sth Prem C	H	Biggleswade Town	563	D 1 - 1	Johnson 4	17	18
20	Sth Prem C	A	Bedworth United	209	W 4 - 1	Waite 38 Smith 47 Johnson 50 61	16	19
24	Sth Prem C	A	Stourbridge	643	D 1 - 1	Johnson 55	12	20
Dec 1	Sth Prem C	H	Coalville Town	502	L 1 - 3	Smith 79	14	21
8	Sth Prem C	A	Halesowen Town	505	W 1 - 0	Lait 80	13	22
11	Sth Prem C	A	Stratford Town	243	L 1 - 2	Lilly 36	12	23
22	Sth Prem C	H	St Ives Town	593	L 1 - 2	Smith 22	15	24
26	Sth Prem C	A	Rushall Olympic	437	D 1 - 1	Maphosa 69	14	25
29	Sth Prem C	A	Alvechurch	324	W 3 - 0	Smith 68 Lait 73 Taylor 78	13	26
Jan 1	Sth Prem C	H	Barwell	555	D 3 - 3	Lait 6 Maphosa 44 Taylor 54	13	27
5	Sth Prem C	A	Kettering Town	805	L 1 - 2	Maphosa 58 (pen)	15	28
8	Sth Prem C	H	Needham Market	481	L 1 - 2	Verma 76	15	29
12	Sth Prem C	H	Stratford Town	537	L 0 - 1		16	30
19	Sth Prem C	A	Biggleswade Town	160	L 0 - 3		16	31
26	Sth Prem C	H	Bedworth United	640	D 2 - 2	Hayden 11 Clement 75	17	32
Feb 8	Sth Prem C	H	St Neots Town	512	W 5 - 0	Concannon 4 Lait 45 55 Smith 67 69	17	33
16	Sth Prem C	A	Coalville Town	452	W 2 - 1	Concannon 77 Waite 85	15	34
23	Sth Prem C	H	Stourbridge	703	W 1 - 0	Waite 90	14	35
Mar 2	Sth Prem C	H	Halesowen Town	736	W 4 - 1	Lait 38 53 Waite 72 Gordon 90	12	36
6	Sth Prem C	A	Hitchin Town	286	L 0 - 1		12	37
9	Sth Prem C	A	Needham Market	265	W 3 - 1	Beswick 38 Concannon 44 Lait 54	11	38
16	Sth Prem C	H	Banbury United	620	W 4 - 0	Waite 12 24 Lait 27 Dwyer 87	10	39
23	Sth Prem C	A	Redditch United	413	D 0 - 0		10	40
30	Sth Prem C	H	Lowestoft Town	632	L 0 - 2		11	41
Apr 6	Sth Prem C	A	Royston Town	273	W 2 - 0	Kettle 2 Waite 38	11	42
13	Sth Prem C	A	Kings Lynn Town	820	L 1 - 2	Waite 82	12	43
20	Sth Prem C	H	Leiston	545	W 5 - 0	Gordon 25 Maphosa 47 Concannon 72 Lait 73 85	11	44
22	Sth Prem C	A	Barwell	302	W 1 - 0	James 73	10	45
27	Sth Prem C	H	AFC Rushden & Diamonds	705	D 1 - 1	Gough 66	12	46

GOALSCORERS	SG	CSG	Pens	Hat tricks	Total
Lait	13	2			17
Waite	12	3			12
Smith	5				6
Concannon	4				4
Johnson	3	3			4
Maphosa	4		1		4
Asante	2				2
Beswick	2				2
Dunckley	2				2
Finn	2				2
Gordon	2				2
Taylor	2				2
Clement	1				1
Dwyer	1				1
Gough	1				1
Hayden	1				1
James	1				1
Kettle	1				1
Lilly	1				1
Verma	1				1

BASINGSTOKE TOWN MATCH RESULTS 2018-19

Date	Comp	H/A	Opponents	Att:	Result		Goalscorers	Pos	No.
Aug 11	Sth Prem S	A	Walton Casuals	218	D	3 - 3	Stow 43 Deadfield 47 Bunting 70		1
14	Sth Prem S	H	Beaconsfield Town	371	W	2 - 1	Smart 25 Akers 54		2
18	Sth Prem S	H	Poole Town	395	L	1 - 2	Stow 80	12	3
25	Sth Prem S	A	Frome Town	224	W	4 - 1	Argent 8 Hollamby 18 Stow 45 (pen) Akers 60	7	4
27	Sth Prem S	H	Gosport Borough	340	W	2 - 1	Argent 5 Deadfield 25	5	5
Sept 1	Sth Prem S	A	Taunton Town	562	D	0 - 0		5	6
8	**FAC 1Q**	**A**	**Paulton Rovers**	**282**	**D**	**1 - 1**	**Bennett 20**		7
11	**FAC 1Qr**	**H**	**Paulton Rovers**	**320**	**W**	**2 - 0**	**Akers 64 Deadfield 80**		8
15	Sth Prem S	H	Wimborne Town	385	W	3 - 2	Akers 44 Bunting 89 (pen) Collier 90	5	9
22	**FAC 2Q**	**A**	**Bristol Manor Farm**	**217**	**L**	**2 - 5**	**McKnight 12 40**		10
29	Sth Prem S	A	Tiverton Town	253	L	1 - 4	Stow 27 (pen)	7	11
Oct 6	Sth Prem S	H	Dorchester Town	331	L	1 - 2	McKnight 66	9	12
13	Sth Prem S	A	Metropolitan Police	195	D	4 - 4	Argent 16 McKnight 45 Stow 51 (pen) Wright 52	11	13
20	Sth Prem S	A	Staines Town	202	W	3 - 0	Argent 17 54 McKnight 48	9	14
27	**FAT 1Q**	**H**	**Wimborne Town**	**272**	**W**	**4 - 2**	**Argent 26 43 Wright 38 McKnight 66**		15
Nov 3	Sth Prem S	H	Weymouth	518	L	1 - 2	Argent 22	10	16
10	**FAT 2Q**	**H**	**Enfield**	**310**	**W**	**2 - 1**	**Smart 86 90**		17
17	Sth Prem S	H	Merthyr Town	382	L	0 - 3		12	18
20	Sth Prem S	A	Harrow Borough	141	L	! - 2	McNight 14	15	19
24	**FAT 3Q**	**H**	**Torquay United**	**472**	**D**	**1 - 1**	**Stow (pen) (lost 3-5 on pens)**	**18**	20
27	Sth Prem S	A	Hartley Wintney	342	L	1 - 3	Deadfield 30	19	21
Dec 8	Sth Prem S	H	Hendon	283	W	2 - 1	Bayliss 17 Deadfield 21	18	22
15	Sth Prem S	A	Swindon Supermarine	193	L	2 - 5	Argent 10 Thompson 53 (og)	18	23
22	Sth Prem S	H	Walton Casuals	287	W	2 - 1	Pearse 24 Smart 35	15	24
26	Sth Prem S	A	Gosport Borough	351	L	2 - 3	Stow 25 Deadfield 68	16	25
29	Sth Prem S	A	Beaconsfield Town	148	L	2 - 3	Stow 41 Collier 62	16	26
Jan 1	Sth Prem S	H	Farnborough	478	D	1 - 1	Stow 57	15	27
5	Sth Prem S	A	Hartley Wintney	451	W	2 - 0	Smart 62 Pearse 65	15	28
12	Sth Prem S	H	Chesham United	331	L	2 - 3	Argent 35 Wright 45	17	29
19	Sth Prem S	A	Merthyr Town	427	L	0 - 1		20	30
26	Sth Prem S	A	Harrow Borough	349	D	2 - 2	Wright 51 Stow 90	19	31
29	Sth Prem S	A	Kings Langley	101	L	0 - 2		19	32
Feb 2	Sth Prem S	A	Weymouth	795	W	2 - 1	Pearse 18 Smart 59	17	33
5	Sth Prem S	H	Salisbury	473	L	0 - 2		17	34
9	Sth Prem S	H	Staines Town	371	W	10- 3	Williams 41 53 Argent 43 61 Akers 5 Kokurinkov (og) 67 Deadfield 70 Harris 76 84 Smart 87	13	35
16	Sth Prem S	H	Kings Langley	365	W	3 - 0	Argent 19 Pearse 40 Smart 83	13	36
19	Sth Prem S	A	Chesham United	252	L	1 - 2	Argent 59	13	37
23	Sth Prem S	A	Salisbury	779	L	1 - 2	Akers 85	16	38
Mar 2	Sth Prem S	A	Hendon	259	L	0 - 1		19	39
9	Sth Prem S	H	Swindon Supermarine	357	W	2 - 0	Wright 15 Pearse 85	19	40
16	Sth Prem S	A	Dorchester Town	432	L	1 - 4	Smart 31	18	41
23	Sth Prem S	A	Metropolitan Police	436	D	2 - 2	Bayliss 33 Wright 85	18	42
30	Sth Prem S	A	Wimborne Town	417	W	4 - 2	Jordan 47 Wright 50 Maybury 70 (og) Argent 73	16	43
Apr 6	Sth Prem S	H	Tiverton Town	402	D	3 - 3	Smart 22 Pearse 45 Daedfield 64	16	44
13	Sth Prem S	A	Poole Town	452	L	2 - 3	Rusher 56 Argent 73	18	45
20	Sth Prem S	A	Frome Town	416	W	4 - 1	Jourden 21 Deadfield 57 Argent 69 81	16	46
22	Sth Prem S	H	Farnborough	546	L	1 - 2	Argent 58	17	47
27	Sth Prem S	H	TauntonTown	1011	L	1 - 2	Wright 68	20	48

GOALSCORERS	SG	CSG	Pens	Hat tricks	Total
Argent	15	4			19
Smart	10	2			11
Stow	10	3			10
Deadfield	9	2			9
Wright	8	2			8
McKnight	4	4			6
Akers	6	2			5
Pearse	5				5
Opponents	3				3
Bayliss	2				2
Bunting	2		1		2
Collier	2				2
Harris	1				2
Jordan	2				2
Williams	1				2
Bennett	1				1
Hollamby	1				1
McKnight	1				1
Rusher	1				1

BEACONSFIELD TOWN MATCH RESULTS 2018-19

Date	Comp	H/A	Opponents	Att:	Result		Goalscorers	Pos	No.
Aug 11	Sth Prem S	H	Salisbury	208	D	2 - 2	Eccleston 71 Losasso 80 (pen)		1
14	Sth Prem S	A	Basingstoke Town	371	L	1 - 2	Stead 22		2
18	Sth Prem S	A	Weymouth	631	D	1 - 1	Matthew 48	18	3
25	**FAC 1Q**	**H**	**Uxbridge**	**97**	**W**	**2 - 0**	**Stead 29 Losasso 42**		4
27	Sth Prem S	A	Staines Town	161	W	1 - 0	Stead 8	16	5
Sept 1	Sth Prem S	H	Tiverton Town	76	L	0 - 2		18	6
8	**FAC 2Q**	**A**	**Walthamstow Aveue**	**114**	**W**	**2 - 0**	**Stead 55 Cathline 66**		7
11	Sth Prem S	H	Hartley Wintney	85	D	3 - 3	Cathline 8 Lossaso 15 pen) Matthew 26	18	8
15	Sth Prem S	H	Dorchester Town	90	D	2 - 2	Mendy 10 58	18	9
22	**FAC 2Q**	**A**	**FC Romania**	**104**	**W**	**2 - 0**	**Mitford Ajanlekoko**		10
29	Sth Prem S	A	Wimborne Town	227	W	1 - 0	Ajanlekoko 50	16	11
Oct 6	**FAC 3Q**	**A**	**Concord Rangers**	**184**	**L**	**1 - 2**	**Balogun**		12
13	Sth Prem S	A	Gosport Borough	248	W	3 - 2	Cathline 12 Mendy 48 Losasso 82	12	13
16	Sth Prem S	H	Chesham United	194	W	7 - 0	MENDY 3 (15 24 26) Losasso 62 85 Pashaj 64 Matthew 88 (pen)	9	14
20	Sth Prem S	A	Merthyr Town	360	W	1 - 0	Matthew 78	6	15
27	**FAT 1Q**	**A**	**Kempston Rovers**	**102**	**D**	**1 - 1**	**Brown 11**		16
30	**FAT 1Qr**	**H**	**Kempston Rovers**	**59**	**W**	**3 - 1**	**Collard 15 (og) Matthew 35 O'Regan 90**		17
Nov 3	Sth Prem S	H	Frome Town	62	D	2 - 2	Mendy 12 Matthew 64	6	18
6	Sth Prem S	H	Swindon Supermarine	101	W	1 - 0	Matthew 67	4	19
10	**FAT 2Q**	**A**	**Aveley**	**147**	**W**	**2 - 1**	**Stead Pashaj**		20
17	Sth Prem S	H	Farnborough	143	L	2 - 6	Yorke 53 Pashaj 84	6	21
20	Sth Prem S	A	Hendon	161	D	2 - 2	Ajanlekoko 30 Matthew 48	8	22
24	**FAT 3Q**	**H**	**Leiston**	**89**	**W**	**3 - 1**	**Lossasso 3 Ajaniekoko 26 Morgan 77**		23
Dec 4	Sth Prem S	H	Kings Langley	112	W	4 - 2	Stead 6 Matthew 32 Pasha 36 51	6	24
8	Sth Prem S	H	Poole Town	93	D	1 - 1	Matthew 41	7	25
15	**FAT 1P**	**A**	**Leyton Orient**	**1177**	**L**	**0 - 4**			26
18	Sth Prem S	A	Harrow Borough	127	L	1 - 2	Morgan 4	8	27
22	Sth Prem S	A	Salisbury	654	L	1 - 2	Matthew 90	8	28
26	Sth Prem S	H	Staines Town	141	W	3 - 2	Morgan 26 Pashaj 38 Matthew 75	7	29
29	Sth Prem S	H	Basingstoke Town	148	W	3 - 2	Matthew 12 Morgan 26 Bates 84	7	30
Jan 2	Sth Prem S	A	Metropolitan Police	136	L	1 - 3	Bates 18	7	31
5	Sth Prem S	A	Chesham United	370	D	0 - 0		8	32
9	Sth Prem S	A	Taunton Town	410	L	1 - 2	Losasso 46		33
12	Sth Prem S	H	Harrow Borough	145	W	4 - 1	Morgan 13 80 Pashaj 42 Yorke 63	6	34
15	Sth Prem S	A	Walton Casuals	215	D	1 - 1	Lossasso 3	6	35
19	Sth Prem S	A	Farnborough	267	L	0 - 2		8	36
26	Sth Prem S	H	Hendon	161	D	0 - 0		9	37
Feb 16	Sth Prem S	H	Taunton Town	133	L	1 - 2	Matthew 51	11	38
23	Sth Prem S	A	Kings Langley	234	L	0 - 3		12	39
Mar 2	Sth Prem S	A	Poole Town	332	L	1 - 2	Matthew 57	15	40
9	Sth Prem S	H	Walton Casuals	131	D	1 - 1	Minhas 14	15	41
16	Sth Prem S	A	Swindon Supermarine	182	L	0 - 4		19	42
23	Sth Prem S	H	Gosport Borough	137	W	4 - 3	Ecleston 28 Neville 34 Matthew 70 Losasso 72	18	43
30	Sth Prem S	A	Dorchester Town	368	W	3 - 1	Minhas 37 71 Matthew 66	14	44
Apr 2	Sth Prem S	A	Frome Town	162	W	1 - 0	Matthew 21	14	45
6	Sth Prem S	H	Wimborne Town	101	W	2 - 0	Stead 48 50	11	46
13	Sth Prem S	H	Weymouth	297	W	1 - 0	Losasso 69	11	47
16	Sth Prem S	H	Merthyr Town	117	D	1 - 1	Stead 55	11	48
20	Sth Prem S	A	Hartley Wintney	203	L	0 - 2		12	49
22	Sth Prem S	H	Metropolitan Police	108	L	0 - 1		12	50
27	Sth Prem S	A	Tiverton Town	206	D	1 - 1	Bates 62		51

GOALSCORERS	SG	CSG	Pens	Hat tricks	Total
Matthew	18	3	1		18
Losasso	10		2		11
Stead	8	2			9
Mendy	5			1	7
Pashaj	6				7
Morgan	5	2			6
Ajanlekoko	4	2			4
Bates	3				3
Cathline	3				3
Minhas	3				3
Eccleston	2				2
Yorke	2				2
Balogun	1				1
Brown	1				1
Mitford	1				1
Neville	1				1
O'Regan	1				1
Opponents	1				1

CHESHAM UNITED MATCH RESULTS 2018-19

Date	Comp	H/A	Opponents	Att:	Result	Goalscorers	Pos	No.
Aug 11	Sth Prem S	H	Merthyr Town	278	L 0 - 3			1
14	Sth Prem S	A	Metropolitan Police	95	L 0 - 1			2
18	Sth Prem S	A	Staines Town	214	L 1 - 3	Locke 75	22	3
25	Sth Prem S	H	Weymouth	318	L 0 - 5		22	4
27	Sth Prem S	A	Kings Langley	333	L 0 - 1		22	5
Sept 1	Sth Prem S	H	Wimborne	234	D 1 - 1	Crilley 60	22	6
8	**FAC 1Q**	**H**	**Biggleswade**	**201**	**W 2 - 1**	**Noel-Williams 5 Donkin 74**		7
15	Sth Prem S	A	Taunton Town	566	L 0 4		22	8
22	**FAC 2Q**	**A**	**Welling United**	**435**	**L 1 - 2**	**Louis 30**		9
29	Sth Prem S	H	Harrow Borough	281	L 0 - 4		22	10
Oct 6	Sth Prem S	A	Farnborough	225	W 1 - 0	Swales 28	22	11
13	Sth Prem S	H	Salisbury	652	L 1 - 5	Louis 35	22	12
16	Sth Prem S	H	Beaconsfield	194	L 0 - 7		22	13
20	Sth Prem S	H	Tiverton Town	271	D 1 - 1	Louis 36	22	14
27	**FAT 1Q**	**A**	**Haringey Borough**	**223**	**D 1 - 1**	**Pearce 66**		15
30	**FAT 1Qr**	**H**	**Haringey Borough**	**163**	**D 2 - 2**	**McKenzie 29 Barker 82 (won 3-1 on pens)**		16
Nov 3	Sth Prem S	A	Gosport Borough	150	D 0 - 0		22	17
10	**FAT 2Q**	**A**	**Worthing**	**802**	**L 0 - 1**			18
17	Sth Prem S	A	Dorchester Town	398	W 5 - 0	Henegan 28 83 Louis 49 Maja 74 Bates 80	21	19
20	Sth Prem S	H	Walton Casuals	192	L 0 - 2		22	20
24	Sth Prem S	H	Frome Town	205	W 2 - 1	Louis 23 Pearce 87	21	21
Dec 1	Sth Prem S	A	Hartley Wintney	237	W 2 - 1	Louis 38 Patrick 45	21	22
8	Sth Prem S	H	Swindon Supermarine	228	W 3 - 1	Louis 25 Murphy 64 Casey 75		23
22	Sth Prem S	A	Merthyr Town	352	L 0 - 1		21	24
26	Sth Prem S	H	Kings Langley	405	W 3 - 0	Clayton 68 83 Blake 81	20	25
29	Sth Prem S	H	Metropolitan Police	301	D 1 - 1	Clayton 47	20	26
1 Jan	Sth Prem S	A	Hendon	303	W 1 - 0	Clayton 90	19	27
5	Sth Prem S	H	Beaconsfield	370	D 0 - 0		20	28
12	Sth Prem S	A	Basingstoke Town	331	W 3 - 2	Casey 33 Brown 56 Mfinda 62	18	29
19	Sth Prem S	H	Dorchester Town	290	D 0 - 0		17	30
26	Sth Prem S	A	Walton Casuals	212	D 2 - 2	Louis 41 Prosper 67	17	31
29	Sth Prem S	A	Poole Town	211	D 0 - 0		17	32
Feb 16	Sth Prem S	H	Hartley Wintney	343	D 2 - 2	Parker 34 Campbell 32	20	33
19	Sth Prem S	H	Basingstoke Town	252	W 2 - 1	Pearce 10 Casey 75	17	34
23	Sth Prem S	A	Frome Town	176	W 2 - 0	Pearce 49 Casey 90	15	35
26	Sth Prem S	H	Gosport Borough	229	W 1 - 0	Clayton 81	13	36
Mar 2	Sth Prem S	A	Swindon Supermarine	233	D 0 - 0		13	37
9	Sth Prem S	H	Poole Town	350	W 5 - 1	Pearce 13 65 Blake 52 Warner-Eley 72 Louis 89	12	38
16	Sth Prem S	H	Farnborough	295	L 0 - 1		12	39
23	Sth Prem S	A	Salisbury	676	D 1 - 1	Clayton 31	13	40
26	Sth Prem S	A	Tiverton Town	156	W 2 - 0	Rolfe 35 Martin 90 (pen)	12	41
30	Sth Prem S	H	Taunton Town	335	L 0 - 1		13	42
Apr 6	Sth Prem S	A	Harrow Borough	182	W 2 - 0	Sinclair 29 Rolfe 45	12	43
13	Sth Prem S	H	Staines Town	304	W 7 - 0	Heneghan 10 Casey 15 26 Rolfe 20 Louis 6 33	12	44
20	Sth Prem S	A	Weymouth	1545	D 1 - 1	Clayton 56	12	45
22	Sth Prem S	H	Hendon	442	D 2 - 2	Pearce 51 90 (pen)	11	46
27	Sth Prem S	A	Wimborne Town	437	D 0 - 0		10	47

GOALSCORERS	SG	CSG	Pens	Hat tricks	Total
Louis	11	3			12
Pearce	6	2			8
Clayton	6	3	1		7
Casey	5	2			6
Heneghan	2				3
Rolfe	3				3
Blake	2				2
Barker	1				1
Bates	1				1
Brown	1				1
Campbell	1				1
Crilley	1				1
Donkin	1				1
Locke	1				1
Maja	1				1
Martin	1		1		1
McKenzie	1				1
Mfinda	1				1
Murphy	1				1
Noel-Williams	1				1
Parker	1				1
Patrick	1				1
Prosper	1				1
Sinclair	1				1
Swales	1				1
Warner-Eley	1				1

DORCHESTER TOWN MATCH RESULTS 2018-19

Date	Comp	H/A	Opponents	Att:	Result		Goalscorers	Pos	No.
Aug 11	Sth Prem S	H	Metropolitan Police	375	L	0 - 1			1
14	Sth Prem S	A	Wimborne	535	W	4 - 2	Murray 2 Winsper 12 30 Lowes 42		2
18	Sth Prem S	A	Salisbury	659	L	0 - 3		16	3
25	Sth Prem S	H	Kings Langley	358	D	2 - 2	Murray 30 78	15	4
27	Sth Prem S	A	Weymouth	1832	L	0 - 5		16	5
Sept 1	Sth Prem S	H	Hartley Wintney	306	W	2 - 1	Kite 27 Pope 44	14	6
8	**FAC 1Q**	**A**	**Wimborne**	**523**	**D**	**1 - 1**	**Rose 90**		7
11	**FAC 1Qr**	**H**	**Wimborne**	**476**	**W**	**3 - 0**	**Lowes 51 Rodriguez 65 Winsper 80**		8
15	Sth Prem S	A	Beaconsfield Town	90	D	2 - 2	Rodriquez 18 83	14	9
22	**FAC 2Q**	**A**	**Tiverton Town**	**307**	**L**	**0 - 2**			10
29	Sth Prem S	H	Hendon	443	L	0 - 3		15	11
Oct 6	Sth Prem S	A	Basingstoke Town	331	W	2 - 1	Rodriquez 68 Murray 90	15	12
13	Sth Prem S	A	Walton Casuals	367	D	1 - 1	Winsper 38	16	13
16	Sth Prem S	H	Taunton Town	334	L	1 - 2	Winsper 32		14
20	Sth Prem S	A	Harrow Borough	132	L	1 - 4	Winsper 49	17	15
27	**FAT 1 Q**	**A**	**Yate Town**	**175**	**D**	**1 - 1**	**Winsper 49**	**17**	16
30	**FAT 1Q**	**H**	**Yate Town**	**207**	**W**	**2 - 0**	**Seymour 47 Kite 86**		17
Nov 3	Sth Prem S	H	Merthyr Town	459	D	0 - 0		17	18
10	**FAT 2Q**	**H**	**AFC Totton**	**285**	**W**	**3 - 1**	**Kite 20 Seymour 28 30**		19
17	Sth Prem S	H	Chesham United	398	L	0 - 5		19	20
24	**FAT 3Q**	**H**	**Hungerford Town**	**258**	**W**	**1 - 0**	**Seymour 57**		21
27	Sth Prem S	A	Frome Town	148	W	1 - 0	Seymour 63 (pen)	18	22
Dec 8	Sth Prem S	H	Gosport Borough	181	W	4 - 1	Seymour 13 80 Bailey 61 Kite 74	18	23
11	Sth Prem S	A	Staines Town	107	W	6 - 1	Carmichael 18 Blair 35 57 Diaz 37 68 Murray 72	17	24
15	**FAT 1P**	**A**	**Eastbourne Borough**	**215**	**W**	**4 - 0**	**BLAIR 3 (10 60 66) Diaz 46**	**16**	25
18	Sth Prem S	H	Swindon Supermarine	275	L	0 - 3		17	26
22	Sth Prem S	A	Metropolitan Police	115	L	1 - 2	Diaz 30	18	27
26	Sth Prem S	H	Weymouth	2217	L	0 - 1		19	28
29	Sth Prem S	H	Wimborne	594	D	1 - 1	Blair 8	19	29
Jsn 1	Sth Prem S	A	Tiverton Town	314	W	3 - 2	Seymour 18 34 Rodriquez 84	17	30
5	Sth Prem S	A	Taunton Town	732	D	1 - 1	Camp 38	17	31
8	Sth Prem S	A	Poole Town	472	W	1 - 0	Seymour	15	32
12	**FAT 2P**	**A**	**Barnet**	**878**	**L**	**1 - 2**	**Seymour 72**		33
15	Sth Prem S	H	Farnborough	253	L	0 - 6		17	34
19	Sth Prem S	A	Chesham United	597	D	0 - 0		17	35
26	Sth Prem S	H	Poole Town	597	L	0 - 2		18	36
Feb 9	Sth Prem S	H	Harrow Borough	263	W	3 - 2	Seymour 17 51 Winsper 46	15	37
12	Sth Prem S	H	Frome Town	232	L	0 - 1		16	38
16	Sth Prem S	H	Staines Town	339	W	6 - 1	DIAZ 3 (22 49 73) Seymour 13 Gillespie 76 Morris 81	15	39
23	Sth Prem S	A	Swindon Supermarine	301	L	0 - 2		16	40
Mar 2	Sth Prem S	H	Gosport Borough	478	D	0 - 0		20	41
9	Sth Prem S	A	Farnborough	333	D	2 - 2	Seymour 19 Blair 27	19	42
12	Sth Prem S	A	Merthyr Town	294	W	7 - 1	Winsper 8 Blair 45 Diaz 65 83 Keats 80 86 Seymour 90	18	43
16	Sth Prem S	H	Basingstoke Town	432	W	4 - 1	Rodriquez 14 55 Seymour 66 (pen) 89	15	44
23	Sth Prem S	A	Walton Casuals	243	W	3 - 2	Kite 11 Diaz 32 90	14	45
30	Sth Prem S	A	Beaconsfield Town	368	L	1 - 3	Blair 90	14	46
Apr 6	Sth Prem S	A	Dorchester Town	271	D	0 - 0		14	47
13	Sth Prem S	H	Salisbury	607	L	1 - 4	Lowes 82	15	48
20	Sth Prem S	A	Kings Langley	292	L	0 - 1		17	49
22	Sth Prem S	H	Tiverton Town	422	W	6 - 0	Blair 3 Winsper 17 Seymour 68 Walker 73 Jackson 90 Panesar-Dower 90	16	50
27	Sth Prem S	A	Hartley Wintley	288	L	1 - 3	Diaz 54	16	51

GOALSCORERS	SG	CSG	Pens	Hat tricks	Total
Seymour	14	2	2		19
Blair	7	2		1	11
Diaz	7	2		1	11
Winsper	8	4			10
Rodriguez	5				7
Kite	5				5
Mureray	4				5
Lowes	3				3
Keats	1				2
Bailey	1				1
Camp	1				1
Carmichael	1				1
Gillespie	1				1
Jackson	1				1
Morris	1				1
P-Dover	1				1
Pope	1				1
Rose	1				1
Walker	1				1

FARNBOROUGH MATCH RESULTS 2018-19

Date	Comp	H/A	Opponents	Att:	Result		Goalscorers	Pos	No.
Aug 11	Sth Prem S	H	Wimborne Town	327	W	3 - 1	Cumberbatch 54 Robertson 66 Elias-Fernandez 71		1
14	Sth Prem S	A	Staines Town	233	W	3 - 0	Louis 32 54 Cumberbatch 88		2
18	Sth Prem S	A	Hendon	278	L	1 - 2	Cullen 80	6	3
25	Sth Prem S	H	Merthyr Town	357	L	0 - 1		10	4
27	Sth Prem S	A	Hartley Wintney	492	D	2 - 2	King 25 Murphy-McVey 51	11	5
Sept 1	Sth Prem S	H	Weymouth	336	W	4 - 3	Calcutt 30 83 Robertson 69 79	9	6
8	**FAC 1Q**	**H**	**Lewes**	**263**	**D**	**1 - 1**	**Calcutt 60**		7
12	**FAC 1Qr**	**A**	**Lewes**	**397**	**D**	**1 - 1**	**Cumberbatch 70 (lost 1-4 on pens)**		8
15	Sth Prem S	H	Frome Town	316	W	3 - 2	Elias-Fernandez 30 52 Murphy-McVey 75	7	9
29	Sth Prem S	A	Poole Town	432	L	0 - 6		9	10
Oct 6	Sth Prem S	H	Chesham United	225	L	0 - 1		9	11
13	Sth Prem S	A	Tiverton Town	232	D	1 - 1	Sealy 28	13	12
16	Sth Prem S	A	Swindon Supermarine	209	L	2 - 4	Cullen 10 Elias-Fernandes 79	14	13
20	Sth Prem S	H	Salisbury	416	L	0 - 3		15	14
27	**FAT 1Q**	**H**	**Merthyr Town**	**203**	**L**	**2 - 3**	**Murphy-McVey 21 Cumberbatch 81 (pen)**		15
Nov 3	Sth Prem S	A	Metropolitan Police	96	L	3 - 4	Udoji 46 Musungu 47 Cullen 70	16	16
10	Sth Prem S	H	Kings Langley	246	L	0 - 1		16	17
17	Sth Prem S	A	Beaconsfield Town	143	W	6 - 2	Sealoy 9 YOUNG 3 (38 40 85) Cullen 49 Francis 57	15	18
21	Sth Prem S	H	Gosport Borough	203	W	2 - 1	Cullen 9 Charles-Smith 89	14	19
24	Sth Prem S	H	TauntonTown	242	L	1 - 4	Young 20		20
Dec 1	Sth Prem S	A	Harrow Borougth	170	L	0 - 5		14	21
8	Sth Prem S	H	Walton Casuals	288	W	1 - 0	Hylton-Bartley 4	14	22
15	Sth Prem S	A	Kings Langley	110	L	1 - 5	Cullen 41	16	23
22	Sth Prem S	A	Wimborne Town	290	D	1 - 1	Charles-Smith 4	16	24
26	Sth Prem S	H	Hartley Wintney	549	D	1 - 1	Coles 20	15	25
29	Sth Prem S	H	Staines Town	301	W	1 - 0	Owens 4	12	26
Jan 1	Sth Prem S.	A	Basingstoke Town	478	D	1 - 1	Coles 90	11	27
5	Sth Prem S	H	Swindon Supermarine	232	W	2 - 1	Cumberbatch 26 Bevans 72	9	28
15	Sth Prem S	A	Dorchester Town	253	W	6 - 0	Charles-Smith 10 Owens 30 Cumberbatch 53 Cullen 73 Young 79 Bonds 90	9	29
19	Sth Prem S	H	Beaconsfield Town	267	W	2 - 0	Cumberbatch 49 58	9	30
26	Sth Prem S	A	Gosport Boorough	230	W	2 - 0	Leggett 31 Cumberbatxh 73	9	31
Feb 16	Sth Prem S	H	Harrow Borough	348	W	4 - 1	Cumberbatch (pen) 41 (pen) 56 Cullen 52 Oyenuga 71	8	32
20	Sth Prem S	H	Metropolitan Police	316	D	0 - 0		8	33
23	Sth Prem S	A	Taunton Town	751	L	1 - 2	Elias-Fernandes 90	9	34
Mar 2	Sth Prem S	A	Walton Casuals	306	L	1 - 2	Young 15	10	35
9	Sth Prem S	H	Dorchester Town	333	D	2 - 2	Coles 7 55	9	36
12	Sth Prem S	A	Salisbury	424	L	2 - 3	Young 11 Coles 24	10	37
16	Sth Prem S	A	Chesham United	295	W	1 - 0	Cooksley 70 (pen)	8	38
23	Sth Prem S	H	Tiverton Town	331	W	3 - 2	Cumberbatch 22 Oyenuga 42 Fearn 56	8	39
30	Sth Prem S	A	Frome Town	237	W	3 - 2	Oakley 2 Cullen 65 Cumberbatch 88 (pen)	8	40
Apr 6	Sth Prem S	H	Poole Town	353	L	1 - 2	Young 26	8	41
13	Sth Prem S	H	Hendon	314	W	3 - 1	Cullen 45 Hylton-Bartley 59 Cumberbatch 68	7	42
20	Sth Prem S	A	Merthyr Town	421	D	0 - 0		7	43
22	Sth Prem S	H	Basingstoke Town	546	W	2 - 1	Young 40 Coles 88	7	44
27	Sth Prem S	A	Weymouth	2676	L	0 - 3		9	45

GOALSCORERS	SG	CSG	Pens	Hat tricks	Total
Cumberbatch	12	5	4		14
Cullen	10	2			10
Young	7			1	9
Coles	5				6
E-Ferdinand	3				4
Calcutt	2				3
Charles-Smith	3				3
M-McVey	3				3
Robertson	3				3
Hylton-Bartley	2				2
Louis	2				2
Owens	2				2
Oyanunga	2				2
Sealy	2				2
Bevans	1				1
Bonds	1				1
Cooksley	1		1		1
Elias-Fernandes	1				1
Fearn	1				1
Francis	1				1
King	1				1
Leggett	1				1
Musungu	1				1
Oakley	1				1
Udoji	1				1

FROME TOWN MATCH RESULTS 2018-19

Date	Comp	H/A	Opponents	Att:	Result		Goalscorers	Pos	No.
Aug 11	Sth Prem S	H	Hendon	245	D	1 - 1	Tingey 85 (og)		1
14	Sth Prem S	A	Tiverton Town	251	L	1 - 3	Simpson 2		2
18	Sth Prem S	A	Hartley Wintney	221	L	1 - 2	Morris 12	13	3
25	Sth Prem S	H	Basingstoke Town	224	L	1 - 4	Cottle 59	20	4
27	Sth Prem S	A	Merthyr Town	554	W	3 - 1	Knowles 65 Baker 68 88	16	5
Sept 1	Sth Prem S	H	Kings Langley	231	W	1 - 0	Davies 85	13	6
8	**FAC 1Q**	**A**	**Winchester City**	**165**	**D**	**1 - 1**	**Simpson 73**		7
12	**FAC 1Qr**	**H**	**Winchester City**	**151**	**L**	**1 - 2**	**Simpson 25 (aet)**		8
15	Sth Prem S	A	Farnborough	316	L	2 - 3	Mapstone 49 Bath 78	17	9
29	Sth Prem S	H	Walton Casuals	178	W	3 - 0	Bath 75 79 Baker 77	14	10
Oct 6	Sth Prem S	A	Taunton Town	587	L	0 - 3		17	11
13	Sth Prem S	H	Harrow Borough	247	L	1 - 3	Simpson 62	17	12
16	Sth Prem S	A	Wimborne Town	314	L	2 - 3	Bath 35 Scott 57	17	13
20	Sth Prem S	H	Gosport Borough	236	W	2 - 0	Simpson 40 Scott 53 (pen)	16	14
27	**FAT 1Q**	**A**	**Poole Town**	**271**	**L**	**1 - 2**	**Spetch (og) 45**		15
Nov 3	Sth Prem S	A	Beaconsfield Town	62	D	2 - 2	Simpson 14 Fletcher 62	15	16
17	Sth Prem S	A	Metropolitan Police	84	L	1 - 2	Webb 73 (og)	16	17
20	Sth Prem S	H	Swindon Supermarine	147	L	1 - 2	Miller 20	18	18
24	Sth Prem S	A	Chesham United	205	L	1 - 2	Scott 62 (pen)	19	19
27	Sth Prem S	H	Dorchester Town	148	L	0 - 1			20
Dec 1	Sth Prem S	A	Poole Town	290	D	1 - 1	Simpson 62	20	21
8	Sth Prem S	H	Weymouth	592	L	0 - 4		21	22
15	Sth Prem S	H	Staines Town	158	W	2 - 0	Rogers 33 German 71	20	23
22	Sth Prem S	A	Hendon	223	W	1 - 0	Bath 80	20	24
26	Sth Prem S	H	Merthyr Town	302	L	2 - 3	Rogers 32 Bath 52	21	25
29	Sth Prem S	H	Tiverton Town	215	L	1 - 3	Scott 88	21	26
Jan 1	Sth Prem S	A	Salisbury	768	L	0 - 1	Shepherd 38	21	27
5	Sth Prem S	A	Wimborne	198	W	1 - 0	Penny 83 (og)	21	28
19	Sth Prem S	H	Metropolitan Police	174	L	0 - 3		21	29
26	Sth Prem S	A	Swindon Supermarine	182	W	4 - 0	Bath 14 Mehew 61 Knowles 72 Mapstone 85	21	30
Feb 9	Sth Prem S	A	Gosport Borough	263	L	1 - 3	Morgan-Williams 86	21	31
12	Sth Prem S	A	Dorchester Town	232	W	1 - 0	Mannings 26	21	32
16	Sth Prem S	A	Poole Town	474	L	0 - 3		21	33
23	Sth Prem S	H	Chesham United	176	L	0 - 2		21	34
Mar 2	Sth Prem S	A	Weymouth	403	L	0 - 2		21	35
9	Sth Prem S	H	Staines Town	169	L	0 - 1		21	36
16	Sth Prem S	H	Taunton Town	261	W	2 - 0	Simpson 1 Mehew 8	20	37
23	Sth Prem S	A	Harrow Borough	132	W	2 - 1	Simpson 55 84	19	38
30	Sth Prem S	A	Farnborough	237	L	2 - 3	Low 22 Mannings 63	21	39
Apr 2	Sth Prem S	H	Beaconsfield Town	162	L	0 - 1		21	40
6	Sth Prem S	H	Walton Casuals	231	L	1 - 4	Mannings 75	21	41
13	Sth Prem S	H	Hartley Wintney	219	L	0 - 1		21	42
20	Sth Prem S	A	Basingstoke Town	416	L	1 - 4	Bath 49	21	43
22	Sth Prem S	A	Salisbury	467	D	0 - 0		21	44
27	Sth Prem S	A	Kings Langley	195	L	0 - 2		21	45

GOALSCORERS	SG	CSG	Pens	Hat tricks	Total
Simpson	8				10
Bath	8				8
Opponents	4				4
Scott	4		2		4
Baker	2				3
Mannings	3				3
Knowles	2				2
Mapstone	2				2
Mehew	2				2
Rogers	2				2
Cottle	1				1
Davies	1				1
Fletcher	1				1
German	1				1
Low	1				1
Miller	1				1
Morgan-Williams	1				1
Morris	1				1

GOSPORT BOROUGH MATCH RESULTS 2018-19

Date	Comp	H/A	Opponents	Att:	Result		Goalscorers	Pos	No.
Aug 11	Sth Prem S	H	Kings Langley	224	W	3 - 2	Pennery 23 Suraci 36 83		1
14	Sth Prem S	A	Hartley Wintney	225	L	0 - 1			2
18	Sth Prem S	A	Merthyr Town	401	L	2 - 4	Lee 23 Leggett 78	15	3
25	Sth Prem S	H	Staines Town	301	W	2 - 1	McAllister 7 Suraci 15	14	4
27	Sth Prem S	A	Basingstoke Town	394	L	1 - 2	Pennery 43	15	
Sept 1	Sth Prem S	H	Metropolitan Police	223	W	6 - 3	Suraci 15 42 PENNERY 3 (27 39 pen 57 pen) Tubbs 7	11	5
8	**FAC 1Q**	**A**	**Sittingbourne**	**154**	**W**	**1 - 0**	**Pennery 52 (pen)**		6
15	Sth Prem S	A	Harrow Borough	130	W	1 - 0	Pennery 64	9	7
22	**FAC 2Q**	**H**	**Ramsgate**	**157**	**L**	**2 - 3**			8
29	Sth Prem S	H	Salisbury	261	L	1 - 4	Pennery 51	12	9
Oct 6	Sth Prem S	A	Walton Casuals	84	L	1 - 3	Tubbs 85	13	10
13	Sth Prem S	H	Beaconsfield Town	248	L	2 - 3	Suraci 22 Lee 74	14	11
16	Sth Prem S	H	Poole Town	268	W	3 - 2	Suraci 27 78 Medway 37	14	12
20	Sth Prem S	A	Frome Town	236	L	0 - 2		14	13
27	**FAT 1Q**	**H**	**AFC Totton**	**191**	**L**	**1 - 2**	**Pennery 23**		14
Nov 3	Sth Prem S	H	Chesham United	220	D	0 - 0		14	15
17	Sth Prem S	H	Taunton Town	310	L	1 - 2	Pennery 90	15	16
21	Sth Prem S	A	Farnborough	203	L	1 - 2	Lee 75	15	17
24	Sth Prem S	H	Hendon	201	W	3 - 1	McAllister 40 Lee 61 Suraci 87	16	18
Dec 1	Sth Prem S	A	Swindon Supermarine	187	L	1 - 2	Lee 26	16	19
8	Sth Prem S	H	Dorchester Town	181	L	1 - 4	Lee 28	17	20
11	Sth Prem S	A	Weymouth	552	W	3 - 1	McAllister 8 Lanahan 57 Pennery 81	17	21
22	Sth Prem S	A	Kings Langley	165	L	0 - 3		17	22
26	Sth Prem S	H	Basingstoke Town	351	W	3 - 2	Pennery 34 Barker 65 Suraci 73	16	23
29	Sth Prem S	H	Hartley Wintney	285	W	1 - 0	Barker 45	15	24 25
Jan 1	Sth Prem S	A	Wimborne Town	451	L	2 - 3	Jerrard 73 Pennery 78	15	26
5	Sth Prem S	A	Poole Town	383	D	1 - 1	Pennery 37	15	27
8	Sth Prem S	A	Tiverton Town	162	L	0 - 1		15	28
19	Sth Prem S	A	Taunton Town	614	L	2 - 3	Lanahan 1 Pennery 90 (pen)	18	29
26	Sth Prem S	H	Farnborough	230	L	0 - 2		20	30
29	Sth Prem S	H	Weymouth	178	L	0 - 2		20	31
Feb 9	Sth Prem S	H	Frome Town	263	W	3 - 1	Pennary 65 70 Suraci 75	19	32
16	Sth Prem S	H	Swindon Supermarine	287	W	2 - 1	Davis 29 Lee 69	18	33
23	Sth Prem S	A	Hendon	226	W	4 - 0	Lee 18 54 Barker 41 Pennery 71	17	34
26	Sth Prem S	A	Chesham United	229	L	0 - 1		18	35
Mar 2	Sth Prem S	H	Dorchester Town	478	D	0 - 0		18	36
9	Sth Prem S	H	Tiverton Town	261	L	0 - 1		18	37
16	Sth Prem S	H	Walton Casuals	216	D	0 - 0		20	38
23	Sth Prem S	A	Beaconsfield Town	137	L	3 - 4	Lee 44 84 Pennery 52	20	39
30	Sth Prem S	H	Harrow Borough	302	L	0 - 1		20	40
Apr 6	Sth Prem S	A	Salisbury	714	W	2 - 0	Davis 65 Lanahan 90	20	41
13	Sth Prem S	H	Merthyr Town	267	L	0 - 3		20	42
20	Sth Prem S	A	Staines Town	180	W	5 - 0	Barker 27 60 Sekajja 46 McAllister 53 Davis 55	19	43
22	Sth Prem S	H	Wimborne Town	622	W	1 - 0	Davis 83	18	44
27	Sth Prem S	A	Metropolitan Police	268	D	2 - 2	Pennery 45 Sekajie 56	19	45

GOALSCORERS	SG	CSG	Pens	Hat tricks	Total
Pennery	17	5	4	1	20
Lee	9	4			11
Suraci	8	2			11
Barker	4				5
Davis	4				4
McAllister	4				4
Lanahan	3				3
Sekajie	2				2
Tubbs	2				2
Jerrard	1				1
Leggett	1				1
Medway	1				1

HARROW BOROUGH MATCH RESULTS 2018-19

Date	Comp	H/A	Opponents	Att:	Result	Goalscorers	Pos	No.
Aug 11	Sth Prem S	H	Weymouth	260	L 2 - 3	Moss 4 65		1
14	Sth Prem S	A	Kings Langley	235	W 4 - 2	Moore 9 48 Brown 16 51		2
18	Sth Prem S	A	Wimborne Town	341	L 3 - 5	Moss 14 Bryan 34 Moore 87	13	3
25	Sth Prem S	H	Tiverton Town	150	D 2 - 2	O'Connor 57 Moore 78	14	4
27	Sth Prem S	A	Hendon	381	W 4 - 2	O'Connor 19 Keita 42 Cole 49 Rush 90	12	5
Sept 1	Sth Prem S	H	Salisbury	223	D 1 - 1	Haugh 90	11	6
8	**FAC 1Q**	**A**	**AFC Hornchurch**	**324**	**L 0 - 1**			7
15	Sth Prem S	H	Gosport Borough	130	L 0 - 1		13	8
29	Sth Prem S	A	Chesham United	133	W 4 - 0	Kearney 13 42 O'Connor 83 Cole 90	13	9
Oct 6	Sth Prem S	H	Hartley Wintney	153	D 2 - 2	Moss 10 O'Connor 64	10	10
13	Sth Prem S	A	Frome Town	247	W 3 - 1	McCormack 60 (og) Haugh 50 Moore 54	9	11
20	Sth Prem S	H	Dorchester Town	132	W 4 - 1	Moss 13 O'Connor 17 Martoon (og) 24 Kearney 90	7	12
27	**FAT 1Q**	**A**	**Biggleswade Town**	**152**	**L 1 - 2**	**Moss 1**		13
Nov 3	Sth Prem S	A	Walton Casuals	172	L 2 - 3	Kearney 3 Moss 7	8	14
17	Sth Prem S	A	Swindon Supermarine	252	L 1 - 2	Moore 25 Kearney 34	8	15
20	Sth Prem S	H	Basingstoke Town	141	W 2 - 1	Moss 47 65	7	16
Dec 1	Sth Prem S	H	Farnborough	170	W 5 - 0	Moss 25 72 Preddie 5 Gough 59 O'Connor 89	6	17
8	Sth Prem S	A	TauntonTown	561	L 0 - 7		6	18
15	Sth Prem S	H	Merthyr Town	202	W 3 - 0	Keita 60 Kearney 70 Ismajli 84	6	19
18	Sth Prem S.	H	Beaconsfield Town	127	W 2 - 1	Kearney 11 86		20
22	Sth Prem S	A	Weymouth	674	D 2 - 2	Kearney 77 83	5	21
26	Sth Prem S	H	Hendon	248	W 3 - 1	Moss 14 Ireland 6 Kearney 78	4	22
29	Sth Prem S	H	Kings Langley	184	L 3 - 4	Cole 23 Moss 48 Haugh 57	4	23
Jan 1	Sth Prem S	H	Staines Town	155	W 5 - 1	Moss 11 Kearney 28 Bryan 38 Ireland 70 O'Connor 77	4	24
5	Sth Prem S	H	Metropolitan Police	145	W 4 - 3	KEARNEY 3 (10 47 90) O'Connor 83	4	25
8	Sth Prem S	A	Metropolitan Police	130	L 0 - 1		5	26
12	Sth Prem S	A	Beaconsfield Town	145	L 1 - 4	Neville 35 (og)	5	27
19	Sth Prem S	H	Swindon Supermarine	137	L 1 - 3	Keita 65	5	28
22	Sth Prem S	A	Poole Town	277	D 3 - 3	Kearney 67 90 Holland 90	5	29
26	Sth Prem S	A	Basingstoke Town	349	D 2 - 2	Kearney 44 Moss 70	5	30
Feb 9	Sth Prem S	A	Dorchester Town	338	L 2 - 3	O'Connor 68 84	6	31
16	Sth Prem S	A	Farnborough	348	L 1 - 4	Moss 73 (pen)	6	32
23	Sth Prem S	H	Poole Town	202	W 4 - 0	Keita 27 54 O'Connor 50 65	6	33
26	Sth Prem S	H	Walton Casuals	146	D 1 - 1	Preddie 36	6	34
Mar 2	Sth Prem S	H	Taunton Town	186	W 1 - 0	Moss 27 (pen)	6	35
9	Sth Prem S	A	Merthyr Town	287	D 1 - 1	Pepera 32	6	36
16	Sth Prem S	A	Hartley Wintney	230	L 0 - 3		7	37
23	Sth Prem S	H	Frome Town	132	L 1 - 2	Bitmead 44	7	38
30	Sth Prem S	A	Gosport Borough	302	W 1 - 0	Keita 90	7	39
Apr 6	Sth Prem S	H	Chesham United	182	L 0 - 2		7	40
13	Sth Prem S	H	Wimborne Town	138	L 0 - 2		9	41
20	Sth Prem S	A	Tiverton Town	242	D 1 - 1	Keita 83	9	42
22	Sth Prem S	H	Staines Town	166	W 9 - 1	MOORE 3 (4 15 63) KEITA 3 (24 49 87) Holland 82 Cole 85 O'Connor 90 (pen)	8	43
27	Sth Prem S	A	Salisbury	750	W 6 - 0	MOORE 3 (32 72 82) MOSS 3 (59 70 90)	7	44

GOALSCORERS	SG	CSG	Pens	Hat tricks	Total
Moss	15	3	2	1	20
Kearney	12	4		1	18
O'Connor	11	2	1		13
Moore	7	3		2	12
Keita	9				10
Cole	4				4
Haugh	3				3
Brown	1				2
Bryan	2				2
Holland	2				2

	SG	CSG	Pens	Hat tricks	Total
Ireland	2				2
Opponents	2				2
Preddie	2				2
Bitmead	1				1
Gough	1				1
Ismajli	1				1
Pepera	1				1
Rush	1				1

HARTLEY WINTNEY MATCH RESULTS 2018-19

Date	Comp	H/A	Opponents	Att:	Result		Goalscorers	Pos	No.
Aug 11	Sth Prem S	A	Poole Town	341	W	3 - 1	Eagle 25 Baxter 31 (pen) Ciardini 81	4	1
14	Sth Prem S	H	Gosport Borough	225	W	1 - 0	Eagle 40	2	2
18	Sth Prem S	H	Frome Town	221	W	2 - 1	Cardini 85 Smart 90	2	3
25	**FAC P**	**A**	**Baffins M.R.**	**181**	**W**	**4 - 1**	**French 41 Campbell 58 90 Ball 65**		4
27	Sth Prem S	H	Farnborough	492	D	2 - 2	Campbell 10 78		5
Sept 1	Sth Prem S	A	Dorchester Town	306	L	1 - 2	Herbert 2	7	6
8	**FAC 1Q**	**A**	**Dorking Wanderers**	**331**	**L**	**0 - 2**			7
11	Sth Prem S	A	Beaconsfield Town	85	D	3 - 3	Webb 68 Smith 85 (pen) Cook 88		8
15	Sth Prem S	A	Weymouth	744	D	2 - 2	Kpohomouh 41 Campbell 76		9
22	Sth Prem S	A	Staines Town	177	W	5 - 3	Eagle 27 Ciardini 34 Strudley 80 Smith 85 (pen) Cook 88	1	10
29	Sth Prem S	A	Merthyr Town	275	D	1 - 1	Smith 90 (pen)	4	11
Oct 6	Sth Prem S	A	Harrow Borough	153	D	2 - 2	Ciardini 3 Smart 52	5	12
13	Sth Prem S	H	Hendon	313	L	2 - 3	Campbell 11 Ball 56	6	13
20	Sth Prem S	H	Kings Langley	242	D	0 - 0		6	14
27	**FAT 1Q**	**H**	**Tiverton Town**	**162**	**D**	**1 - 1**	**Campbell 64**		15
30	**FAT 1Qr**	**A**	**Tiverton Town**	**148**	**L**	**1 - 5**	**Campbell 32**		16
Nov 3	Sth Prem S	A	Wimborne Town	326	L	1 - 2	Cook 51	8	17
17	Sth Prem S	A	Salisbury	689	L	2 - 4	Vine 32 74	9	18
20	Sth Prem S	H	Metropolitan Police	166	L	1 - 4	Eagle 90	9	19
24	Sth Prem S	A	Tiverton Town	211	D	1 - 1	Ball 63	10	20
27	Sth Prem S	A	Basingstoke Town	342	W	3 - 1	Hart 6 Cook 58 Paget 71	10	21
Dec 1	Sth Prem S	H	Chesham United	227	L	1 - 2	Ridge 5	11	22
15	Sth Prem S	H	Taunton Town	184	W	3 - 1	French 58 Platt 68 Webb 90	10	23
22	Sth Prem S	A	Poole Town	255	W	4 - 3	Felix 3 Ball 37 Stewart 40 83	9	24
26	Sth Prem S	A	Farnborough	549	D	1 - 1	Ball 89	9	25
29	Sth Prem S	A	Gosport Borough	285	L	0 - 1		11	26
Jan 1	Sth Prem S	H	Swindon Supermarine	247	D	2 - 2	Ridge 22 Parker 23	12	27
5	Sth Prem S	H	Basingstoke Town	451	L	0 - 2		15	28
12	Sth Prem S	A	Walton Casuals	252	W	2 - 1	Parker 5 Abubaker 65	12	29
19	Sth Prem S	H	Salisbury	378	L	3 - 4	Ball 25 Parker 34 Platt 50	12	30
26	Sth Prem S	A	Metropolitan Police	130	L	1 - 5	Ridge 15	15	31
Feb 16	Sth Prem S	A	Chesham United	343	D	2 - 2	Despors (og) 24 Brown 52	15	32
19	Sth Prem S	H	Walton Casuals	194	L	3 - 4	Duff 28 Marley-Ridge 35 Parker 70	17	33
23	Sth Prem S	H	Tiverton Town	244	W	1 - 0	Drage 75	16	34
26	Sth Prem S	H	Wimborne Town	180	W	3 - 0	Campbell 13 Duff 32 Parker 59	13	35
Mar 2	Sth Prem S	H	Staines Town	232	W	7 - 0	Ridge 14 Webb 18 PARKER 3 (38 40 85) Campbell 59 Duff 65	12	36
9	Sth Prem S	A	Taunton Town	686	D	2 - 2	Parker 11 Duff 69	12	37
16	Sth Prem S	H	Harrow Borough	230	W	3 - 0	Abubaker 32 Cambpell 35 Ball 47	10	38
23	Sth Prem S	A	Hendon	275	W	2 - 0	Parker 17 Campbell 52	10	39
26	Sth Prem S	A	Kings Langley	247	L	1 - 2	Campbell 35		40
30	Sth Prem S	H	Weymouth	437	L	0 - 3		11	41
Apr 6	Sth Prem S	A	Merthyr Town	343	W	2 - 1	Abubaker 87 Albert 90	10	42
13	Sth Prem S	A	Frome Town	219	W	1 - 0	Duff 70	9	43
20	Sth Prem S	H	Beaconsfield Town	203	W	2 - 0	Smart 11 Parker 55	8	44
22	Sth Prem S	A	Swindon Supermarine	269	D	1 - 1	Ball 2	8	45
27	Sth Prem S	H	Dorchester Town	288	W	3 - 1	Duff 61 Drage 75 Ball 89		46

GOALSCORERS	SG	CSG	Pens	Hat tricks	Total
Campbell	10	3			13
Parker	9	3		1	11
Ball	9	2			9
Duff	6	2			6
Ridge	5				5
Ciardini	4				4
Cook	4				4
Eagle	4				4
Abubaker	3				3
Smith	3		3		3
Webb	3				3
Drage	2				2
French	2				2
Platt	2				2
Smart	2				2
Stewart	1				2
Vine	1				2
Albert	1				1
Baxter	1		1		1
Bradshaw	1				1
Brown	1				1
Felix	1				1
Hart	1				1
Herbert	1				1
Kpohomouth	1				1
Marley-Ridge	1				1
Opponents	1				1
Paget	1				1
Strudley	1				1

HENDON MATCH RESULTS 2018-19

Date	Comp	H/A	Opponents	Att:	Result	Goalscorers	Pos	No.
Aug 11	Sth Prem S	A	Frome Town	245	D 1 - 1	German		1
14	Sth Prem S	H	Walton Casuals	236	W 3 - 0	Tingey 17 German 28 Hunte		2
18	Sth Prem S	H	Farnborough	278	W 2 - 1	Brown 35 Dombaxe 66	4	3
25	Sth Prem S	A	Taunton Town	523	D 3 - 3	GERMAN 3 (7 34 56)	5	4
27	Sth Prem S	H	Harrow Borough	381	L 2 - 4	German 77 (pen) 90	7	5
Sept 1	Sth Prem S	A	Swindon Spermarine	268	W 1 - 0	Crichlow 7	6	6
8	**FAC 1Q**	**H**	**Harlow Town**	**264**	**D 1 - 1**	**German**		7
11	**FAC 1Qr**	**A**	**Harlow Town**	**173**	**W 2 - 1**	**Jonas German (aet)**		8
15	Sth Prem S	H	Poole Town	263	W 1 - 0	German 9 (pen)	6	9
29	Sth Prem S	A	Dorchester Town	443	W 3 - 0	German 54 (pen) 84 Hyppolyte-Patrick 66	3	10
Oct 2	**FAC 2Q**	**H**	**Lancing**	**177**	**D 1 - 1**	**Hippolyte-Patrick**		11
7	**FAC 2Qr**	**A**	**Lancing**	**307**	**W 4 - 0**	**Ngamvoulou German Critchlow Hippolyte-Patrick**		12
Oct 10	**FAC 3Q**	**A**	**Chippenham Town**	**402**	**L 1 - 4**	**German 68**		13
13	Sth Prem S	H	Hartley Wintney	313	W 3 - 2	Ngamvoulou 28 Hippolye-Patrick 63 Dombaxe 71	2	14
20	Sth Prem S	H	Wimborne Town	215	W 3 - 2	German 35 Jonas 4 Hippolyte-Patrick 44	2	15
27	**FAT 1Q**	**H**	**Staines Town**	**169**	**W 2 - 1**	**Calcutt Brown**		16
Nov 3	Sth Prem S	A	Salisbury	731	L 1 - 3	Calcutt 9	4	17
10	**FAT 2Q**	**H**	**Biggleswade Town**	**223**	**L 1 - 2**	**Hippolyte-Patrick 47**		18
13	Sth Prem S	H	Staines Town	188	W 5 - 1	Calcutt 23 47 HYPPOLYTE-PATRICK 3 (54 63 81)	4	19
17	Sth Prem S	A	Tiverton Town	275	D 0 - 0		4	20
20	Sth Prem S	H	Beaconsfield Town	161	D 2 - 2	German 18 84	5	21
24	Sth Prem S	A	Gosport Borough	201	L 1 - 3	Hippolyte-Patrick 38	5	22
27	Sth Prem S	A	Kings Langley	168	L 1 - 3	Brown	5	23
Dec 1	Sth Prem S	H	Merthyr Town	249	W 3 - 0	Brown 15 32 Hippolyte-Patrick 73	4	24
8	Sth Prem S	A	Basingstoke Town	283	L 1 - 2	German 39 (pen)	4	25
11	Sth Prem S	H	Metropolitan Police	151	L 1 - 3	German 49	5	26
15	Sth Prem S	A	Walton Casuals	163	L 1 - 5	Harriott 43	5	27
22	Sth Prem S	H	Frome Town	223	L 0 - 1		6	28
26	Sth Prem S	A	Harrow Borough	248	L 1 - 3	German 6 (pen)	8	29
Jan 1	Sth Prem S	H	Chesham United	303	L 0 - 1		9	30
5	Sth Prem S	H	Kings Langley	236	L 1 - 2	Charles 21	10	31
12	Sth Prem S	A	Metropolitan Police	145	L 0 - 3		10	32
19	Sth Prem S	H	Tiverton Town	252	D 2 - 2	Brown 11 Hyppolyte-Patrick 21	15	33
26	Sth Prem S	A	Beaconsfield Town	161	D 0 - 0		14	34
Feb 2	Sth Prem S	H	Salisbury	283	D 2 - 2	Hyppolyte-Patrick 7 Calcutt 90	13	35
9	Sth Prem S	A	Wimborne Town	388	D 3 - 3	Hope 23 Hyppolyte-Patrick (pen) 43 Locke 66	14	36
16	Sth Prem S	A	Merthyr Town	511	W 2 - 0	Obi 40 (pen) Calcutt 69	14	37
23	Sth Prem S	H	Gosport Borough	226	L 0 - 4		15	38
26	Sth Prem S	H	Weymouth	251	L 2 - 3	Harriott 23 Obi 88	15	39
Mar 2	Sth Prem S	H	Basingstoke Town	259	W 1 - 0	Smith 31	14	40
9	Sth Prem S	A	Weymouth	759	L 0 - 3		16	41
16	Sth Prem S	A	Staines Town	149	W 5 - 2	Calcutt 10 40 Tingey 25 Hyppolyte-Patrick 34 Harriott 55	16	42
23	Sth Prem S	H	Gosport Borough	275	L 0 - 2		16	43
30	Sth Prem S	A	Poole Town	595	W 2 - 0	Hope 78 Obi 90	15	44
Apr 6	Sth Prem S	H	Dorchester Town	271	D 0 - 0		15	45
13	Sth Prem S	A	Farnborough	314	L 0 - 3		17	46
20	Sth Prem S	H	Taunton Town	263	L 2 - 3	Hyppolyte-Patrick 26 Obi 90	17	47
22	Sth Prem S	A	Chesham United	442	D 2 - 2	Hippolyte-Patrick 15 (pen) 74 (pen)	19	48
27	Sth Prem S	H	Swindon Supermarine	302	W 1 - 0	Hippolyte-Patrick 4		49

GOALSCORERS	SG	CSG	Pens	Hat tricks	Total
German	15	4	5	1	20
Hyppolyte-Patrick	16	3	3	1	19
Calcutt	7				8
Brown	5				6
Obi	4		1		4
Harriott	3				3
Critchlow	2				2
Dombaxe	2				2
Hope	2				2
Jonas	2				2
Ngamvoulou	2				2
Tingey	2				2
Charles	1				1
Hunte	1				1
Locke	1				1
Smith	1				1

KINGS LANGLEY MATCH RESULTS 2018-19

Date	Comp	H/A	Opponents	Att:	Result		Goalscorers	Pos	No.
Aug 11	Sth Prem S	A	Gosport Borough	224	L	2 - 3	Weiss 40 Adebiyi 90		1
14	Sth Prem S	H	Harrow Borough	235	L	2 - 4	Moss 79 (og) Cook 86		2
18	Sth Prem S	H	Taunton Town	171	L	1 - 2	Weiss 52	21	3
25	Sth Prem S	A	Dorchester Town	358	D	2 - 2	Pobbe 47 Connelly 77	19	4
27	Sth Prem S	H	Chesham United	333	**W**	1 - 0	Howe 43	18	5
Sept 1	Sth Prem S	A	Frome Town	231	L	0 - 1		19	6
8	**FAC 1Q**	**A**	**Northwood**	**229**	**D**	**0 - 0**			7
11	**FAC 1Qr**	**H**	**Northwood**	**230**	**W**	**3 - 1**	**Ryan Weiss (2)**		8
15	Sth Prem S	A	Tiverton Town	155	D	2 - 2	Weiss 61 66	19	9
22	**FAC 2Q**	**H**	**Lewes**	**28**	**D**	**1 - 1**	**Weiss 59**	**20**	10
26	**FAC 2Qr**	**A**	**Lewes**	**342**	**L**	**1 - 2**	**Adebiyi 50**		11
29	Sth Prem S	A	Swindon Supermarine	149	**W**	4 - 3	Ward 19 77 (pen) Adebiyi 45 Howe 81	18	12
Oct 13	Sth Prem S	A	Weymouth	334	L	0 - 5		18	13
20	Sth Prem S	H	Hartley Wintmey	242	D	0 - 0		18	14
27	**FAT 1Q**	**H**	**Needham Market**	**122**	**L**	**0 - 2**			15
Nov 3	Sth Prem S	H	Poole Town	228	L	0 - 3		20	16
10	Sth Prem S	A	Farnborough	246	**W**	1 - 0	Wade-Slater 61	16	17
17	Sth Prem S	H	Weymouth	309	**W**	2 - 1	Ward 5 Wade-Slater 58	14	18
20	Sth Prem S	A	Staines Town	132	**W**	2 - 0	Wade-Slater 72 Howe 90	12	19
27	Sth Prem S	H	Hendon	168	**W**	3 - 1	Weiss 25 Ward 38 (pen) Wade-Slater 72		20
Dec 4	Sth Prem S	A	Beaconsfield Town	112	L	2 - 4	Wade-Slater 45 Weiss 67	12	21
8	Sth Prem S	H	Merthyr Town	311	D	1 - 1	Adebiyi 26	12	22
15	Sth Prem S	A	Farnborough	119	**W**	5 - 1	Howe 27 Weiss 43 54 Collier 70 80	11	23
22	Sth Prem S	H	Gosport Borough	165	**W**	3 - 0	WEISS 3 (17 19 90)	11	24
26	Sth Prem S	A	Chesham United	405	L	0 - 3		12	25
29	Sth Prem S	A	Harrow Borough	184	**W**	4 - 3	Coldicott-Stevens 7 Ward 13 (pen) 21 Collier 39	10	26
Jan 1	Sth Prem S	H	Walton Casuals	204	**W**	1 - 0	Collier 5	9	27
5	Sth Prem S	A	Hendon	236	**W**	2 - 1	Adebiyi 54 Howe 71	8	28
19	Sth Prem S	A	Weymouth	727	D	2 - 2	Howe 19 Georgio 90 (pen)	7	29
26	Sth Prem S	H	Staines Town	1072	**W**	3 - 1	Georgiou 60 Howe 63 Weiss 85	6	30
29	Sth Prem S	H	Basingstoke Town	101	**W**	2 - 0	Georgiou 8 Howe 72	6	31
Feb 2	Sth Prem S	A	Poole Town	129	L	0 - 2		6	32
16	Sth Prem S	H	Basingstoke Town	365	L	0 - 3		6	33
19	Sth Prem S	H	Salisbury City	365	D	1 - 1	Ward 63	9	34
23	Sth Prem S	A	Beaconsfield Town	234	**W**	3 - 0	Weiss 3 Johnson 16 Switters 76	8	35
Mar 2	Sth Prem S	H	Merthyr Town	233	**W**	1 - 0	Weiss 55	7	36
5	Sth Prem S	H	Metropolitan Police	158	L	1 - 2	Weiss 6	7	37
9	Sth Prem S	A	Salisbury City	631	**W**	2 - 1	Howe 19 Coldicott-Stevens 89	6	38
16	Sth Prem S	A	Metropolitan Police	132	L	0 - 1		6	39
23	Sth Prem S	A	Wimborne Town	297	**W**	1 - 0	Howe 54	6	40
26	Sth Prem S	H	Hartley Wintney	247	**W**	2 - 1	Georgiou 50 Ward 85	5	41
30	Sth Prem S	A	Tiverton Town	209	**W**	2 - 1	Howe 18 Ward 79	5	42
Apr 6	Sth Prem S	H	Swindon Supermarine	313	L	1 - 2	Cook 83	5	43
13	Sth Prem S	H	Taunton Town	564	L	1 - 2	Ward 63	6	44
20	Sth Prem S	H	Dorchester Town	292	**W**	1 - 0	Connolly 90	5	45
22	Sth Prem S	H	Walton Casuals	346	L	0 - 1		6	46
27	Sth Prem S	A	Frome Town	195	**W**	2 - 0	Ward 5 Weiss 80	6	47

GOALSCORERS	SG	CSG	Pens	Hat tricks	Total
Weiss	14	3		1	19
Howe	11	4			11
Ward	10	2	3		11
Adebiyi	5	2			5
W-Slater	5	5			5
Collier	3				4
Georgio	4	3	1		4
C-Stevens	2				2
Connolly	2				2
Cook	2				2
Johnson	1				1
Opponents	1				1
Pobbe	1				1
Ryan	1				1
Switters	1				1

MERTHYR TOWN MATCH RESULTS 2018-19

Date	Comp	H/A	Opponents	Att:	Result		Goalscorers	Pos	No.
Aug 11	Sth Prem S	A	Chesham United	278	W	3 - 0	Traylor 25 42 Locke (og) 60		1
14	Sth Prem S	H	Swindon Supermarine	431	D	2 - 2	Meechan 17 Traylor 65 (pen)		2
18	Sth Prem S	H	Gosport Borough	401	W	4 - 2	Jenkins 10 Traylor 17 Morgan 21 Meechan 65	3	3
25	Sth Prem S	H	Farnborough	357	W	1 - 0	Meechan 55	3	4
27	Sth Prem S	A	Frome Town	554	L	1 - 3	Hunt 71	5	5
Sept 1	Sth Prem S	H	Walton Casuals	198	W	3 - 1	Davies 6 Meechan 73 Traylor 90	3	6
8	**FAC 1Q**	**A**	**Melksham**	**304**	**W**	**4 - 1**	**Morgan 76 Meechan 77 Jones 80 Jenkins 86**		7
15	Sth Prem S	A	Metropolitan Police	391	D	2 - 2	Evans 11 Traylor 18	3	8
22	**FAC 2Q**	**H**	**Winchester City**	**291**	**L**	**1 - 4**	**Lucas 58**		9
29	Sth Prem S	H	Hartley Wintney	275	D	1 - 1	Meechan 10	3	10
Oct 13	Sth Prem S	A	Staines Town	256	W	6 - 2	MEECHAN 4 (12 16 80 90) McDonald 21 Traylor 83	3	11
16	Sth Prem S	A	Salisbury	548	L	0 - 2		3	12
20	Sth Prem S	H	Beaconsfield Town	360	L	0 - 1		6	13
27	**FAT 1Q**	**A**	**Farnborough**	**203**	**W**	**3 - 2**	**Young 28 Lewis 31 Traylor 79**		14
Nov 3	Sth Prem S	A	Dorchester Town	459	D	0 - 0		8	15
10	**FAT 2Q**	**A**	**Lewes**	**475**	**L**	**0 - 2**			16
17	Sth Prem S	A	Basingstoke Town	382	L	0 - 3		9	17
20	Sth Prem S	H	Tiverton Town	425	W	5 - 1	Prosser 22 Lucas 28 TRAYLOR 3 (41 56 69)	7	18
24	Sth Prem S	A	Wimborne Town	377	W	2 - 0	Traylor 69 Morgan 90	6	19
Dec 1	Sth Prem S	A	Hendon	240	L	0 - 3		5	20
8	Sth Prem S	H	Kings Langley	311	D	1 1	Prosser 83	5	21
11	Sth Prem S	H	Poole Town	279	L	0 - 2		6	22
15	Sth Prem S	H	Harrow Borough	202	L	0 - 3		7	23
22	Sth Prem S	H	Chesham United	352	W	1 - 0	Morgan 67	6	24
26	Sth Prem S	A	Frome Town	302	W	3 - 2	Meechan 16 Prosser 51 Traylor 86	6	25
29	Sth Prem S	H	Swindon Supermarine	297	L	0 - 3		6	26
Jan 1	Sth Prem S	A	Taunton Town	502	W	3 - 1	Traylor 33 Jones 45 61	6	27
5	Sth Prem S	A	Salisbury	521	L	1 - 2	Lucas 90	7	28
12	Sth Prem S	H	Wimborne Town	433	L	0 - 4		7	29
19	Sth Prem S	H	Basingstoke Town	427	W	1 - 0	Meechan 76	7	30
Feb 2	Sth Prem S	H	Tivierton Town	218	D	2 - 2	Traylor 6 23	7	31
12	Sth Prem S	H	Weymouth	327	W	2 - 1	Traylor 19 Jones 70	6	32
16	Sth Prem S	A	Hendon	511	L	0 - 2		7	33
23	Sth Prem S	A	Weymouth	715	L	1 - 2	Prosser 56	8	34
Mar 2	Sth Prem S	H	Kings Langley	233	L	0 - 1		9	35
9	Sth Prem S	A	Harrow Borough	287	D	1 - 1	Traylor 49	9	36
12	Sth Prem S	H	Dorchester Town	294	L	1 - 7	Jackson (og) 61	9	37
16	Sth Prem S	H	Poole Town	314	L	1 - 3	Lewis 7	11	38
23	Sth Prem S	H	Staines Town	433	W	9 - 1	TRAYLOR 4 (1 3 10 12) Meecham 18 24 Jones 29 38 Young 50	10	39
30	Sth Prem S	A	Metropolitan Police	146	L	0 - 2		11	40
Apr 6	Sth Prem S	H	Hartley Whitney	343	L	1 - 2	Cook 83	13	41
13	Sth Prem S	A	Gosport Borough	267	W	3 - 0	Prosser 12 Traylor 51 Lewis 86	13	42
16	Sth Prem S	A	Beaconsfield Town	117	D	1 - 1	Traylor 42	13	43
20	Sth Prem S	H	Farnborough	421	D	0 - 0		13	44
22	Sth Prem S	A	Taunton Town	801	L	2 - 3	Traylor 59 Veale 68	13	45
27	Sth Prem S	A	Walton Casuals	355	L	1 - 2	Foulston 90		46

GOALSCORERS	SG	CSG	Pens	Hat tricks	Total
Traylor	17	3	1	2	25
Meechan	10	3		1	14
Jones	4				6
Prosser	5				5
Morgan	4				4
Lewis	3				3
Lucas	3				3
Jenkins	2				2
Opponents	2				2
Young	2				2
Cook	1				1
Davies	1				1
Evans	1				1
Foulston	1				1
Hunt	1				1
McDonald	1				1
Veale	1				1

METROPOLITAN POLICE MATCH RESULTS 2018-19

Date	Comp	H/A	Opponents	Att:	Result		Goalscorers	Pos	No.
Aug 11	Sth Prem S	A	Dorchester Town	375	W	1 - 0	Mazzone 6		1
14	Sth Prem S	H	Chesham United	95	W	1 - 0	Blackmore 32		2
18	Sth Prem S	H	Swindon Supermarine	100	L	0 - 2		9	3
25	Sth Prem S	A	Poole Town	299	D	2 - 2	Mazzone 16 88	10	4
27	Sth Prem S	H	Walton Casuals	240	D	2 - 2	Mitchel 39 Knight 48	10	5
Sept 1	Sth Prem S	A	Gosport Borough	242	L	3 - 6	Gilbert 5 60 Blackmore 27	12	6
8	**FAC 1Q**	**H**	**Cray Wanderers**	**96**	**W**	**3 - 2**	**Wright 1 Mazzone 67 Chislett 73**		7
15	Sth Prem S	A	Merthyr Town	391	D	2 - 2	Gilbert 45 Mazzone 86	12	8
22	**FAC 2Q**	**H**	**Needham Market**	**100**	**D**	**2 - 2**	**Mazzone 25 Gilbert 71**		9
25	**FAC 2Qr**	**A**	**Needham Market**	**208**	**W**	**3 - 2**	**Chislett 30 Mazzone 69 Hypolyte 90**		10
29	Sth Prem S	H	Taunton Town	140	W	4 - 1	Chislett 17 69 Blackmore 42 Mazzone 64	11	11
Oct 6	**FAC 3Q**	**A**	**Tiverton Town**	**399**	**D**	**3 - 3**	**Blackmore 5 63 Mazzone 86**		12
9	**FAC 3Qr**	**H**	**TivertonTown**	**217**	**W**	**1 - 0**	**Chislett 90**		13
13	Sth Prem S	H	Basingstoke Town	195	D	4 - 4	Blackmore 22 Mazzone 36 51 Hypolyte 72	11	14
20	**FAC 4Q**	**H**	**Havant & Waterlooville**	**335**	**W**	**1 - 0**	**Mazzone 39**		15
27	**FAT 1Q**	**H**	**Carshalton Athletic**	**129**	**D**	**2 - 2**	**Blackmore 29 40**		16
30	**FAT 1Qr**	**A**	**Carshalton Athletic**	**128**	**L**	**1 - 2**	**Mazzone 33**		17
Nov 3	Sth Prem S	H	Farnborough	96	W	4 - 3	McLaughlin 17 Blackmore 53 56 Glbert 72	13	18
10	**FAC 1**	**H**	**Newport County**	**1137**	**L**	**0 - 2**			19
17	Sth Prem S	H	Frome Town	84	W	2 - 1	Blackmore 39 75	10	20
20	Sth Prem S	A	Hartley Wintney	166	W	4 - 1	Blackmore 19 Mazzone 22 Chislett 45 Robertson 83	8	21
24	Sth Prem S	H	Staines Town	109	W	2 - 0	Mazzone 32 Knight 82	8	22
Dec 1	Sth Prem S	A	Salisbury	552	D	1 - 1	Chislett 5	7	23
8	Sth Prem S	H	Tiverton Town	96	W	3 - 2	Mummery 64 Mazzone 76 (pen) Gilbert 90	6	24
11	Sth Prem S	A	Hendon	151	W	3 - 1	Mazzone 18 (pen) Blackmore 45 Mummery 74	5	25
22	Sth Prem S	H	Dorchester Town	115	W	2 - 1	Knight 61 Hippolyte 80	4	26
26	Sth Prem S	A	Walton Casuals	327	D	2 - 2	Mazzone 22 Robinson 36	4	27
29	Sth Prem S	A	Chesham United	301	D	1 - 1	Blackmore 78	4	28
Jan 2	Sth Prem S	H	Beaconsfield Town	136	W	3 - 1	Gilbert 61 Mazzone 63 (pen) Blackmore 86	4	29
5	Sth Prem S	A	Harrow Borough	145	L	3 - 4	Mazzone 20 51 Hippolyte 24	5	30
8	Sth Prem S	H	Harrow Borough	130	W	1 - 0	Blackmore 70	4	31
12	Sth Prem S	H	Hendon	145	W	3 - 0	Mazzone 9 Blackmore 55 Hippolyte 78	2	32
19	Sth Prem S	A	Frome Town	174	W	3 - 1	Robinson 45 Mazzone 51 (pen) Blackmore 88	2	33
26	Sth Prem S	H	Hartley Wintney	130	W	5 - 1	Mazzone 22 Blackmore 49 64 Robinson 52 Murdoch 84	2	34
29	Sth Prem S	A	Wimborne Town	242	L	0 - 3		2	35
Feb 9	Sth Prem S	H	Weymouth	270	D	4 - 4	Robinson 45 ROBERTSON 3 (56 67 90)	4	36
16	Sth Prem S	H	Salisbury	300	D	2 - 2	MAZZONE 40 67 (pen)	4	37
20	Sth Prem S	A	Farnborough	316	D	0 - 0		4	38
23	Sth Prem S	H	Staines Town	163	W	5 - 0	Blackmore 20 27 Chislett 48 Hippolyte 78 Gilbert 88	4	39
Mar 2	Sth Prem S	A	Tiverton Town	206	L	1 - 2	Arthur 44	4	40
5	Sth Prem S	A	Kings Langley	158	W	2 - 1	Gilbert 16 Robertson 35	4	41
9	Sth Prem S	H	Wimborne Town	136	W	4 - 2	Robertson 4 83 Guiness-Walker 7 Eldstal 21	4	42
16	Sth Prem S	H	Kings Langley	182	W	1 - 0	Robertson 38	3	43
23	Sth Prem S	A	Basingstoke Town	436	D	2 - 2	Birch 11 Mazzone 69	3	44
30	Sth Prem S	H	Merthyr Town	146	W	2 - 0	Mazzone 45 Blackmore 90	3	45
Apr 2	Sth Prem S	A	Weymouth	1153	L	0 - 4		3	46
6	Sth Prem S	A	Taunton Town	771	W	3 - 1	Mazzone 26 54 Chislett 27	2	47
13	Sth Prem S	A	Swindon Supermarine	337	L	0 - 2		3	48
20	Sth Prem S	H	Poole Town	217	L	1 - 2	Chislett 60	4	49
22	Sth Prem S	A	Beaconsfield Town	108	W	1 - 0	Robinson 26	4	50
27	Sth Prem S	H	Gosport Borough	268	D	2 - 2	Gilbert 17 Hyppolyte	3	51
May 1	**PO SF**	**H**	**Salisbury**	**448**	**W**	**3 - 2**	**Mazzone 8 44 (pen) Blackmore 61**		52
6	**PO F**	**H**	**Poole Town**	**1025**	**W**	**1 - 0**	**Mazzone 73**		53
11	**Su PO F**	**H**	**Tonbridge Angels**	**1260**	**L**	**2 - 3**	**Chislett 18 Robinson 57**		54

GOALSCORERS	SG	CSG	Pens	Hat tricks	Total
Mazzone	27	6	6	1	33
Blackmore	19	4			25
Chislett	11	2	2		11
Gilbert	9	2			10
Robertson	5			1	8
Hyppolyte	7				7
Robinson	6				6
Knight	3				3
Mummery	2				2
Arthur	1				1
Birch	1				1
Eldstal	1				1
G-Walker	1				1
McLaughlin	1				1
Mitchel	1				1
Murdoch	1				1
Wright	1				1

POOLE TOWN MATCH RESULTS 2018-19

Date	Comp	H/A	Opponents	Att:	Result	Goalscorers	Pos	No.
Aug 11	Sth Prem S	H	Hartney Wintney	341	L 1 - 3	Clarke 46		1
14	Sth Prem S	A	Salisbury	885	W 2 - 1	Griffin 10 Clarke 48		2
18	Sth Prem S	A	Basingstoke Town	395	W 2 - 1	Spetch 45 Brooks 67	8	3
25	Sth Prem S	H	Metropolitan Police	299	D 2 - 2	Whisken 21 Brooks 55	9	4
27	Sth Prem S	A	Wimborne Town	918	W 4 - 0	Bedford 23 Brooks 59 Gillespie 75 90	8	5
Sept 1	Sth Prem S	H	Staines Town	362	L 0 - 1		8	6
8	**FAC 1Q**	**A**	**Shaftesbury**	**439**	**W 1 - 0**	**Roberts 34**		7
15	Sth Prem S	A	Hendon	263	L 0 - 1		10	8
22	**FAC 2Q**	**H**	**Cinderford Town**	**298**	**W 3 - 0**	**Baker 58 Bath 60 64**		9
29	Sth Prem S	H	Farnborough	422	W 6 - 0	HENRY 3 (20 pen 38 54 pen) Roberts 61 Bedford 42 Mazzone 64	8	10
Oct 6	**FAC 3Q**	**H**	**Horsham**	**355**	**D 1 - 1**	**Gillespie 2**		11
9	**FAC 3Qr**	**A**	**Horsham**	**381**	**W 2 - 1**	**Whisken 43 Moore 49**		12
13	Sth Prem S	H	Taunton Town	406	W 1 - 0	Brooks 27	7	13
16	Sth Prem S	A	Gosport Borough	268	L 2 - 3	Brooks 47 Devlin 55	7	14
20	**FAC 4Q**	**A**	**Haringey Borough**	**402**	**L 1 - 2**	**Devlin 31 (pen)**		15
27	**FAT 1Q**	**H**	**Frome Town**	**271**	**W 2 - 1**	**Bedford 45 Brooks 89**		16
Nov 3	Sth Prem S	A	Kings Langley	228	W 3 - 0	Bedford 5 Devlin 87 Griffin 89	7	17
10	**FAT 2Q**	**A**	**Brentwood**	**159**	**D 2 - 2**	**Brooks 42 Spetch 90**		18
13	**FAT 2Qr**	**H**	**Brentwood**	**276**	**W 4 - 1**	**Gillespie 6 Griffin 66 House 77 Scrimshaw 85**		19
17	Sth Prem S	A	Walton Casuals	206	W 4 - 0	Gillespie 7 (pen) Grange 79 Bedford 86 Davis 90	7	20
24	**FAT 3Q**	**H**	**Dorking Wanderers**	**285**	**L 2 - 3**	**Gillespie 2 Brooks**		21
Dec 1	Sth Prem S	A	Frome Town	290	D 1 - 1	Spetch 5	10	22
8	Sth Prem S	A	Beaconsfield Town	93	D 1 - 1	Roberts 4	10	23
11	Sth Prem S	A	Merthyr Town	279	W 2 - 0	Constable 62 Griffin 76	10	24
22	Sth Prem S	A	Hartley Wintney	255	L 3 - 4	Constable 22 (pen) Roberts 53 Felix 90 (og)	11	25
26	Sth Prem S	A	Wimborne Town	818	L 2 - 5	Constable 34 Roberts 39	12	26
29	Sth Prem S	H	Salisbury	523	D 2 - 2	Roberts 45 House 90	12	27
Jan 1	Sth Prem S	A	Weymouth	1270	D 2 - 2	Moore 17 Scrimshaw 71	12	28
5	Sth Prem S	H	Gosport Borough	383	D 1 - 1	Roberts 34	12	29
8	Sth Prem S	H	Dorchester Town	472	L 0 - 1		12	30
12	Sth Prem S	A	Tiverton Town	223	W 2 - 0	Constable 45 Roberts 55	10	31
15	Sth Prem S	H	Swindon Supermarine	294	L 2 - 5	Roberts 14 71	10	32
22	Sth Prem S	H	Harrow Borough	277	D 3 - 3	Brooks 30 Constable 32 Scrimshaw 79	11	33
26	Sth Prem S	A	Dorchester Town	507	W 2 - 0	Brooks 5 Constable 11 (pen)	11	34
29	Sth Prem S	H	Chesham United	211	D 0 - 0		11	35
Feb 2	Sth Prem S	H	Kings Langley	629	W 3 - 0	Brooks 9 Moore 62 Constable 73	8	36
5	Sth Prem S	H	Kings Langley	629	W 3 - 0	Brooks 9 Moore 62 Constable 73	5	37
9	Sth Prem S	A	Swindon Supermarine	242	D 1 - 1	Scrimshaw 84	5	38
12	Sth Prem S	H	Tiverton Town	301	W 3 - 0	Moore 22 Griffin 42 Scrimshaw 75	5	39
16	Sth Prem S	H	Frome Town	474	W 3 - 0	Scrimshaw 8 42 House 72	5	40
23	Sth Prem S	A	Harrow Borough	202	L 0 - 4		5	41
Mar 2	Sth Prem S	H	Beaconsfield Town	332	W 2 - 1	Spetch 6 Constable 57 (pen)	5	42
9	Sth Prem S	A	Chesham United	350	L 1 - 5	Constable 72 (pen)	5	43
16	Sth Prem S	H	Merthyr Town	314	W 3 - 1	Bedford 21 Smeeton 25 Constable 87	5	44
23	Sth Prem S	A	Taunton Town	801	L 0 - 1		5	45
30	Sth Prem S	H	Hendon	595	L 0 - 2		6	46
Apr 6	Sth Prem S	A	Farnborough	353	W 2 - 1	Constable 50 (pen) Scrimshaw 90	6	47
13	Sth Prem S	H	Basingstoke Town	452	W 3 - 2	Roberts 30 Constable 40 Boote 78	5	48
20	Sth Prem S	A	Metropolitan Police	217	W 2 - 1	Brooks 49 Scrimshaw 65	5	49
22	Sth Prem S	H	Weymouth	1596	D 1 - 1	Moore 21	5	50
27	Sth Prem S	A	Staines Town	202	W 7 - 0	Brooks 10 28 Constable 34 Bedford 38 Griffin 43 Grange 46 61	5	51
May 1	**PO SF**	**A**	**Taunton Town**	**1053**	**D 1 - 1**	**Dickson 43 (won 4-3 on pens)**		52
6	**PO F**	**A**	**Metropolitan Police**	**1025**	**L 0 - 1**			53

GOALSCORERS	SG	CSG	Pens	Hat tricks	Total
Brooks	14	3			15
Constable	13	3	4		14
Roberts	10	3			11
Scrimshaw	8				9
Bedford	7				7
Gillespie	5		1		6
Griffin	6				6
Moore	6				6
Spetch	4				4
Devlin	3		1		3
Grange	2				3
Henry	1		2	1	3

	SG	CSG	Pens	Hat tricks	Total
House	3				3
Bath	1				2
Clarke	2				2
Whisken	2				2
Baker	1				1
Boote	1				1
Davis	1				1
Dickson	1				1
Mazzone	1				1
Opponents	1				1
Smeeton	1				1

SALISBURY MATCH RESULTS 2018-19

Date	Comp	H/A	Opponents	Att:	Result	Goalscorers	Pos	No.
Aug 11	Sth Prem S	A	Beaconsfield Town	208	D 2 - 2	Hopper 28 Benson 40		1
14	Sth Prem S	H	Poole Town	885	L 1 - 2	Fitchett		2
18	Sth Prem S	H	Dorchester Town	669	W 3 - 0	Fitchett Wannell Hopper	10	3
25	**FAC P**	**H**	**Hamble Club**	**542**	**W 6 - 0**	**Whelan Colson Haysham-Membrillers Stanley Kotwica (2)**		4
27	Sth Prem S	H	Swindon Supermarine	658	D 2 - 2	Fitchett 45 Young 49	12	5
Sept 1	Sth Prem S	A	Harrow Borough	223	D 1 - 1	Wannell 77	15	6
8	**FAC 1Q**	**H**	**Yate**	**548**	**D 1 - 1**	**Young**		7
11	**FAC 1Qr**	**A**	**Yate**	**252**	**W 3 - 1**	**Shephard Wannell Benson**		8
15	Sth Prem S	H	Staines Town	565	W 3 - 2	Downing 2 Kotwica 28 65	11	9
18	Sth Prem S	A	Walton Casuals	178	L 1 - 3	Downing 61	11	10
22	**FAC 2Q**	**A**	**Weston-s-Mare**	**315**	**D 2 - 2**	**Partridge 76 Lucas (og) 84**		11
25	**FAC 2Qr**	**H**	**Weston-s-Mare**	**551**	**L 2 - 3**	**Downing Kotwicka (aet)**		12
29	Sth Prem S	A	Gosport Borough	423	W 4 - 1	HOPPER 3 (36 pen 61 pen 53) Whelan 75	10	13
Oct 13	Sth Prem S	A	Chesham United	652	W 4 - 1	Fitchett 15 33 Hopper 54 Whelan 88	8	14
16	Sth Prem S	H	Merthyr Town	548	W 2 - 0	Benson 5 Fitchett 86 (pen)	8	15
20	Sth Prem S	A	Farnborough	416	W 3 - 0	Hopper 30 Colson 45 Kotwica 90	6	16
23	Sth Prem S	H	Tiverton Town	624	W 3 - 1	Young 30 Whelan 71 Mullings 90	4	17
27	**FAT 1Q**	**A**	**Fleet Town**	**267**	**W 3 - 0**	**Benson Hopper (pen) Haysham-Membrillers**		18
Nov 3	Sth Prem S	H	Hendon	731	W 3 - 1	Wheelan 38 Benson 42 Kotwica 79	2	19
10	**FAT 2Q**	**H**	**Merstham**	**422**	**W 2 - 0**	**Benson Whelan**		20
17	Sth Prem S	H	Hartley Wintney	689	W 4 - 2	Benson 26 Whelan 35 Hopper 63 Fitchett 84	2	21
20	Sth Prem S	A	Weymouth	1006	L 1 - 2	Haysham-Membrillera 22	3	22
24	**FAT 3Q**	**H**	**East Thurrock United**	**465**	**W 2 - 1**	**Downing Whelan**		23
28	Sth Prem S	A	Taunton Town	602	L 3 - 4	Haysham-Membrillera 21 Norris (og) 50 Hopper 84 (pen)	3	24
Dec 1	Sth Prem S	H	Metropolitan Police	552	D 1 - 1	Kotwica 10	3	25
8	Sth Prem S	H	Wimbourne Town	122	W 4 - 3	Haysham-Membrillera20 Partridge 33 Hopper 48 Whelan49		26
22	Sth Prem S	H	Beaconsfield Town	654	W 2 - 1	Whelan 23 Hopper 41	3	27
26	Sth Prem S	A	Swindon Supermarine	366	D 2 - 2	Whelan 60 Fitchett 83	4	28
29	Sth Prem S	A	Poole Town	623	D 2 - 2	Benson 48 Partridge 54	5	29
Jan 1	Sth Prem S	H	Frome Town	768	W 1 - 0	Shephard 49	4	30
5	Sth Prem S	A	Merthyr Town	521	W 2 - 1	Whelan 48 Sparkes 85	4	31
8	**FAT 1P**	**H**	**Braintree Town**	**502**	**W 2 - 1**	**Mullings (2)**	**4**	32
12	**FAT 2P**	**A**	**Carshalton Athletic**	**514**	**L 1 - 4**	**Dawson 4**	**4**	33
19	Sth Prem S	A	Hartley Wintney	378	W 4 - 3	Benson 11 37 Bosma 15 Fitchett 78	4	34
26	Sth Prem S	H	Weymouth	1224	L 3 - 4	Hopper 71 (pen) Dawson 78 81	4	35
29	Sth Prem S	H	Taunton Town	542	W 3 - 2	Hopper 30 Dawson 74 Bosma 90	4	36
Feb 2	Sth Prem S	A	Hendon	283	D 2 - 2	Fitchett 45 64	3	37
5	Sth Prem S	A	Basingstoke Town	473	W 2 0	Whelan 24 Dawson 66	2	38
16	Sth Prem S	A	Metropolitan Police	300	D 2 - 2	Sparkes 49 Dawson 90	2	39
19	Sth Prem S	A	Kings Langley	219	D 1 - 1	Shephard 90	3	40
23	Sth Prem S	H	Basingstoke Town	779	W 2 - 1	Shepherd 58 Fitchett 90	3	41
Mar 2	Sth Prem S	A	Wimborne Town	624	W 4 - 1	Benson 6 O'Keefe 30 Partridge 66 Fitchett 70	3	42
9	Sth Prem S	H	Kings Langley	631	L 1 - 2	Benson 58	3	43
12	Sth Prem S	H	Farnborough	424	W 3 - 2	Hopper 41 Mullings 55 90	2	44
16	Sth Prem S	A	Tiverton Town	335	L 0 - 2		4	45
23	Sth Prem S	H	Chesham United	676	D 1 - 1	Flood 75	4	46
30	Sth Prem S	A	Staines Town	210	W 7 - 1	Young 12 Fitchett 49 Partridge 69 Shephard 74 78 Hopper 81 86	4	47
Apr 6	Sth Prem S	H	Gosport Borough	714	L 0 - 2		4	48
13	Sth Prem S	A	Dorchester Town	607	W 4 - 1	Whelan 21 Herbert 29 Shaphard 47 59	4	49
20	Sth Prem S	H	Walton Casuals	670	W 4 - 2	SHEPHARD 3 (5 16 43) Dawson 48	3	50
22	Sth Prem S	A	Frome Town	467	D 0 - 0		3	51
27	Sth Prem S	H	Harow Borough	750	L 0 - 6		4	52
May 1	**PO SF**	**A**	**Metropolitan Police**	**448**	**L 2 - 3**	**Downing 13 Benson 68**		53

GOALSCORERS	SG	CSG	Pens	Hat tricks	Total
Hopper	14	2	4	1	17
Fitchett	12	2	1		14
Whelan	13	2			13
Benson	8	2			12
Shephard	6	2		1	9
Kotwica	7	2			8
Dawson	6	3			7
Haysham-Membrillera	5				5
Partridge	5				5
Downing	3				4
Mullings	4				4
Wannell	3				3
Wannell	3				3
Bosma	2				2
Colson	2				2
Opponents	2				2
Sparkes	2				2
Flood	1				1
O'Keefe	1				1
Stanley	1				1

STAINES TOWN MATCH RESULTS 2018-19

Date	Comp	H/A	Opponents	Att:	Result	Goalscorers	Pos	No.
Aug 11	Sth Prem S	A	Taunton Town	571	L 0 - 4			1
14	Sth Prem S	H	Farnborough	233	L 0 - 3			2
18	Sth Prem S	A	Chesham	214	W 3 - 1	Clarke 55 87 Stow 85	16	3
25	Sth Prem S	A	Gosport Borough	301	L 1 - 2	Stow 90	18	4
27	Sth Prem S	H	Beaconsfield Town	161	L 0 - 1		18	5
Sept 1	Sth Prem S	A	Poole Town	362	W 2 - 0	Odetola 63 Ali 91	15	6
8	**FAC 1Q**	**A**	**Egham**	**384**	**L 0 - 1**			7
15	Sth Prem S	A	Salisbury	565	L 2 - 3	Khanye 32 Hamilton74	17	8
22	Sth Prem S	H	Hartley Wintney	177	L 3 - 5	Handelaar 58 Barker 63 69	18	9
29	Sth Prem S	H	Weymouth	282	L 1 - 4	Barker 8 (pen)	19	10
Oct 13	Sth Prem S	H	Merthyr Town	258	L 2 - 6	Gogo 27 Ali 79	21	11
16	Sth Prem S	A	Walton Casuals	192	L 1 - 3	Barker 56	21	12
20	Sth Prem S	H	Basingstoke Town	202	L 0 - 3		21	13
27	**FAT 1Q**	**A**	**Hendon**	**169**	**L 1 - 2**	**Ali 8**		14
Nov 3	Sth Prem S	A	Tiverton Town	261	L 2 - 3	Chingoka 5 19	21	15
10	Sth Prem S	H	Swindon Supermarine	168	W 2 - 1	Abraams 24 Ali 31	21	16
13	Sth Prem S	A	Hendon	188	L 1 - 5	Khanye 81	22	17
17	Sth Prem S	A	Wimborne	347	L 0 - 1		22	18
20	Sth Prem S	H	Kings Langley	132	L 0 - 2			19
24	Sth Prem S	A	Metropolitan Police	109	L 0 - 2		22	20
Dec 11	Sth Prem S	H	Dorchester Town	107	L 1 - 6	Gogo 88	22	21
15	Sth Prem S	A	Frome Town	158	L 0 - 2		22	22
22	Sth Prem S	H	Taunton Town	177	L 1 - 3	Tapp 90	22	23
26	Sth Prem S	H	Beaconsfield Town	141	L 2 - 3	Miskin 1 Tapp 4	22	24
29	Sth Prem S	A	Farnborough	301	L 0 - 1		22	25
Jan 1	Sth Prem S	H	Harrow Borough	155	L 1 - 5	Ali 74	22	26
5	Sth Prem S	H	Walton Casuals	202	L 1 - 4	Chabane 78	22	27
12	Sth Prem S	A	Swindon Supermarine	217	L 0 - 3		22	28
19	Sth Prem S	H	Wimborne	197	L 2 - 4	Charles-Valentine 37 Milenge 58	22	29
26	Sth Prem S	A	Kings Langley	1072	L 1 - 3	Wright 81	22	30
Feb 9	Sth Prem S	A	Basingstoke Town	371	L 3 -10	Deadfield (og) Torbett 28 Ali 58	22	31
16	Sth Prem S	A	Dorchester Town	339	L 1 - 6	Krabbendam 55	22	32
19	Sth Prem S	H	Tiverton Town	118	L 2 - 4	Constantinou 23 32	22	33
23	Sth Prem S	H	Metropolitan Police	163	L 0 - 5		22	34
Mar 2	Sth Prem S	A	Hartley Whitney	232	L 0 - 7		22	35
9	Sth Prem S	H	Frome Town	169	W 1 - 0	Juett 33	22	36
16	Sth Prem S	H	Hendon	149	L 2 - 5	Juett 66 Lavender 84	22	37
23	Sth Prem S	A	Merthyr Town	433	L 0 - 9		22	38
30	Sth Prem S	H	Salisbury	210	L 1 - 7	Bremford 29	22	39
Apr 6	Sth Prem S	A	Weymouth	996	L 0 - 4		22	40
13	Sth Prem S	A	Chesham United	304	L 0 - 7		22	41
20	Sth Prem S	H	Gosport Borough	180	L 0 - 5		22	42
22	Sth Prem S	A	Harrow Borough	166	L 1 - 9	Barreto 83	22	43
27	Sth Prem S	H	Poole Town	202	L 0 - 7		22	44

GOALSCORERS	SG	CSG	Pens	Hat tricks	Total
Ali	6				6
Barker	3	2	1		4
Chingoka	1				2
Clarke	1				2
Constantiou	1				2
Gogo	2				2
Juett	2				2
Khanye	2				2
Stow	2				2
Tapp	2				2
Abrahams	1				1
Barreto	1				1
Bremford	1				1
Charles-Valentine	1				1
Chabane	1				1
Hamilton	1				1
Handelaar	1				1
Krabbendam	1				1
Lavender	1				1
Milenge	1				1
Miskin	1				1
Odetola	1				1
Opponents	1				1
Torbett	1				1
Wright	1				1

SWINDON SUPERMARINE MATCH RESULTS 2018-19

Date	Comp	H/A	Opponents	Att:	Result	Goalscorers	Pos	No.
Aug 11	Sth Prem S	H	Tiverton Town	247	L 0 - 1			1
14	Sth Prem S	A	Merthyr Town	431	D 2 - 2	Hooper 10 Westlake 39		2
18	Sth Prem S	A	Metropolitan Police	100	**W** 2 - 0	McDonagh 52 Fleetwood 67	11	3
25	**FAC P**	**A**	**AFC Dunstable**	**81**	**D 0 - 0**			4
27	Sth Prem S	A	Salisbury	658	D 2 - 2	McDonagh 15 54	15	5
Sept 1	Sth Prem S	H	Hendon	268	L 0 - 1			6
4	**FAC Pr**	**H**	**AFC Dunstable**	**132**	**W 3 - 0**	**Parsons 50 90 Fleetwood 60**		7
8	**FAC 1Q**	**H**	**Woodbridge Town**	**204**	**W 7 - 1**	**Fleetwood 10 PARSONS 3 (25 47 55) Campbell 51 Westlake 78 Williams 80**		8
15	Sth Prem S	A	Walton Casuals	158	L 1 - 3	McDonagh 74	18	9
22	**FAC 2Q**	**A**	**Chippenham Town**	**384**	**D 2 - 2**	**Hooper 40 Fleetwood 86**		10
25	**FAC 2Qr**	**H**	**Chippenham Town**	**364**	**L 0 - 1**			11
29	Sth Prem S	H	KIngs Langley	149	L 3 - 4	Gray 11 Hooper 60 (pen) McDonagh 90	20	12
Oct 13	Sth Prem S	H	Weymouth	290	D 1 - 1	McDonagh 10		13
16	Sth Prem S	H	Farnborough	209	**W** 4 - 2	Ifil 25 McDonagh 40 Fleetwood 44 Gray 60	20	14
23	Sth Prem S	A	Wimborne	252	**W** 3 - 2	McDonagh 53 Gray 72 Fleetwood 83	18	15
27	**FAT 1Q**	**H**	**Banbury United**	**215**	**D 1 - 1**	**Gray 87**		16
30	**FAT 1Qr**	**A**	**Banbury United**	**218**	**L 0 - 3**			17
Nov 3	Sth Prem S	H	Taunton Town	281	L 0 - 1		19	18
6	Sth Prem S	A	Beaconsfield Town	101	L 0 - 1		19	19
10	Sth Prem S	A	Staines Town	168	L 1 - 2	McDonagh 28	19	20
17	Sth Prem S	H	Harrow Borough	252	L 1 - 2	Williams 5	20	21
24	Sth Prem S	A	Frome Town	147	**W** 2 - 1	Campbell 40 McDonagh 78	18	22
Dec 1	Sth Prem S	A	Gosport Borough	187	**W** 2 - 1	McDonagh 15 Campbell 23	17	23
8	Sth Prem S	A	Chesham United	228	L 1 - 3	Fleetwood 5	17	24
15	Sth Prem S	H	Basingstoke Town	193	**W** 5 - 2	Fleetwood 34 Spalding 46 McDonagh 59 80 Campbell 85	17	25
18	Sth Prem S	A	Dorchester Town	275	**W** 3 - 0	Martin 43 (og) McDonagh 55 Hooper 76 (pen)	17	26
22	Sth Prem S	A	Tiverton Town	217	D 2 - 2	Campbell 51 McDonagh 80	16	27
26	Sth Prem S	H	Salisbury City	366	D 2 - 2	McDonagh 62 69	15	28
29	Sth Prem S	A	Merthyr Town	297	**W** 3 - 0	McDonagh 36 55 Fleetwood 82	11	29
Jan 1	Sth Prem S	A	Hartley Wintney	247	D 2 - 2	Spalding 7 Ifil 46	9	30
5	Sth Prem S	A	Farnborough	232	L 1 - 2	Spalding 38	9	31
12	Sth Prem S	H	Staines Town	217	**W** 3 - 0	Ifil 72 Williams 75 Fleetwood 78		32
15	Sth Prem S	A	Poole Town	294	**W** 5 - 2	Campbell 20 McDonagh 28 63 Liddiard 33 Fleetwood 47 (p)	8	33
19	Sth Prem S	A	Harrow Borough	137	**W** 3 - 1	Spalding 9 Liddiard 20 McDonagh 57	8	34
26	Sth Prem S	H	Frome Town	182	L 0 - 4		9	35
Feb 9	Sth Prem S	A	Poole Town	242	D 1 - 1	McDonagh 18	10	36
16	Sth Prem S	H	Gosport Borough	287	L 1 - 2	Liddiard 54	11	37
23	Sth Prem S	H	Dorchester Town	301	**W** 2 - 0	Spalding 47 Fleetwood 80	9	38
27	Sth Prem S	A	Taunton Town	515	D 1 - 1	Liddiard 87	9	39
Mar 2	Sth Prem S	H	Chesham United	233	D 0 - 0		9	40
9	Sth Prem S	A	Basingstoke Town	357	L 0 - 2		11	41
16	Sth Prem S	H	Beaconsfield Town	182	**W** 4 - 0	Campbell 13 18 McDonagh 48 Fletwood 82	9	42
23	Sth Prem S	A	Weymouth	858	L 1 - 2	Fleetwood 58	11	43
30	Sth Prem S	A	Walton Casuals	317	**W** 2 - 1	Spalding 18 McDonagh 24	10	44
Apr 6	Sth Prem S	H	Kings Langley	313	**W** 2 - 1	Williams 19 Liddiard 57	9	45
13	Sth Prem S	H	Metropolitan Police	337	**W** 1 - 0	Williams 49	8	46
20	Sth Prem S	A	Wimborne	350	L 0 - 1		9	47
22	Sth Prem S	H	Hartley Wintney	269	D 1 - 1	Williams 10	10	48
27	Sth Prem S	A	Hendon	302	L 0 - 1		11	49

GOALSCORERS	SG	CSG	Pens	Hat tricks	Total
McDonagh	21	5			25
Fleetwood	14	2	1		15
Campbell	7	2			8
Spalding	6				6
Williams	6				6
Liddiard	5				5
Gray	4	3			4
Hooper	4		1		4
Parsons	2			1	4
Ifill	3				3
Westlake	2				2
Opponents					1

TAUNTON TOWN MATCH RESULTS 2018-19

Date	Comp	H/A	Opponents	Att:	Result		Goalscorers	Pos	No.
Aug 11	Sth Prem S	H	Staines Town	571	W	4 - 0	Neal, Chamberlain, Buse, Veal		1
14	Sth Prem S	A	Weymouth	879	L	1 - 2	Wright 4		2
18	Sth Prem S	A	Kings Langley	171	W	2 - 1	Adelsbury 25 Brett 86	3	3
25	Sth Prem S	H	Hendon	523	D	3 - 3	Wright 41 90 (pen) Sullivan 66	6	4
27	Sth Prem S	A	Tiverton Town	749	W	3 - 1	Wright 23 (pen) Chamberlain 58 Buse 90	4	5
Sept 1	Sth Prem S	A	Basingstoke Town	562	D	0 - 0		4	6
8	**FAC 1Q**	**H**	**Bemerton Heath**	**517**	**W**	**7 - 1**	**Neal 29 72 Sullivan 35 41 Chamberlain 38 Wright 42 60**		7
15	Sth Prem S	A	Chesham United	566	W	4 - 0	NEAL 3 (11 17 39) Wright 48	2	8
22	**FAC 2Q**	**H**	**Bitton**	**450**	**W**	**4 - 0**	**Neal 31 Sullivan 40 Buse 50 Nelmes 84**		9
29	Sth Prem S	A	Metropolitan Police	140	L	1 - 4	Adelsbury 52	3	10
Oct 6	Sth Prem S	H	Frome Town	587	W	3 - 0	Neal 23 90 Chamberlain 65	2	11
10	**FAC 3Q**	**A**	**St Albans City**	**595**	**W**	**5 - 2**	**Buse 21 90 Brett 26 Chamberlain 40 53**		12
13	Sth Prem S	A	Poole Town	406	L	0 - 1		5	13
16	Sth Prem S	A	Dorchester Town	334	W	2 - 1	Veal 29 Neal 46	4	14
20	**FAC 4Q**	**A**	**Billericay Town**	**976**	**D**	**2 - 2**	**Neal 22 Buse 44**		15
24	**FAC 4Qr**	**H**	**Billericay Town**	**1582**	**L**	**0 - 1**			16
27	**FAT 1Q**	**H**	**Weymouth**	**513**	**L**	**1 - 3**	**Wright 62**		17
Nov 3	Sth Prem S	H	Swindon Supermarine	281	W	1 - 0	Adelsbury 41	3	18
10	Sth Prem S	A	Wimborne Town	489	W	4 - 2	Brett 52 Sullivan 58 Veal 73 Wright 78	1	19
14	Sth Prem S	H	Walton Casuals	369	W	4 - 0	Wright 11 Mitchell 29 Veal 47 Sullivan 60	1	20
17	Sth Prem S	A	Gosport Borough	310	W	2 - 1	Hall 20 Sullivan 58		21
24	Sth Prem S	A	Farnborough	242	W	4 - 1	Sullivan 10 Neal 37 42 Veal 90	1	22
28	Sth Prem S	H	Salisbury	602	W	4 - 3	Hall 20 49 Nelmes 89 Buse 90	1	23
Dec 8	Sth Prem S	H	Harrow Borough	561	W	7 - 0	Neal 43 66 Palmer 45 Brett 50 85 Buse 55 Wright 71	1	24
15	Sth Prem S	A	Hartley Wintney	184	L	1 - 3	Debois (og) 50	1	25
22	Sth Prem S	A	Staines Town	177	W	3 - 1	Wright 12 Chamberlain 22 Veal 81		26
26	Sth Prem S	H	Tiverton Town	1377	W	2 - 1	Neal 23 (pen) Wright 35	1	27
29	Sth Prem S	A	Weymouth	1461	D	3 - 3	Buse 20 Neal 3 52	1	28
Jan 1	Sth Prem S	A	Merthyr Town	502	L	1 - 3	Palmer 81	1	29
5	Sth Prem S	H	Dorchester Town	732	D	1 - 1	Neal 10	1	30
9	Sth Prem S	H	Beaconsfield Town	410	W	2 - 1	Neal 20 39	1	31
19	Sth Prem S	H	Gosport Borough	614	W	`3 - 2	Hall 14 Brett 45 Chamberlain 65	1	32
26	Sth Prem S	A	Wimborne Town	485	D	1 - 1	Chamberlain 83	1	33
29	Sth Prem S	A	Salisbury	452	L	2 - 3	White 3 Brett 53	1	34
Feb 9	Sth Prem S	A	Walton Casuals	238	W	1 - 0	Brett 28	1	35
16	Sth Prem S	A	Beaconsfield Town	133	W	2 - 1	Sullivan 62 Palmer 86	1	36
23	Sth Prem S	H	Farnborough	751	W	2 - 1	White 14 Neal 76 (pen)	1	37
27	Sth Prem S	H	Swindon Supermatine	515	D	1 - 1	Neal 54	1	38
Mar 2	Sth Prem S	A	Harrow Borough	I86	L	0 - 1		1	39
9	Sth Prem S	H	Hartley Wintney	686	D	2 - 2	Sullivan 41 Neal 80 (pen)	2	40
16	Sth Prem S	H	Frome Town	261	L	0 - 2		2	41
23	Sth Prem S	H	Poole Town	801	W	1 - 0	Neal 10	2	42
30	Sth Prem S	A	Chesham United	335	W	1 - 0	Wright 43	2	43
Apr 6	Sth Prem S	H	Metropolitan Police	771	L	1 - 3	Neal 47	3	44
13	Sth Prem S	H	KIngs Langley	564	W	2 - 1	Neal 31 37	2	45
20	Sth Prem S	A	Hendon	263	W	3 - 2	NEAL 3 (6 27 87 pen)	2	46
22	Sth Prem S	H	Merthyr Town	801	W	3 - 2	Neal 70 Sullivan 74 Buse 90	2	47
27	Sth Prem S	A	Basingstoke Town	1011	W	2 - 1	Neal 18 Brett 51	2	48
May 1	**SO SF**	**H**	**Poole Town**	**1053**	**D**	**1 - 1**	**Brett 49 (lost 3-4 on pens)**		49

GOALSCORERS	SG	CSG	Pens	Hat tricks	Total
Neal	22	5	4	2	33
Wright	21	2	2		14
Buse	11	2			11
Sullivan	9	4			10
Brett	8	2			9
Chamberl;ain	8	4			9
Veal	6	2			6
Hall	3				4
Adelsbury	3				3
Palmer	3				3
Nelmes	2				2
White	2				2
Mitchell	1				1
Opposition	1				1
Sullivan	1				1

TIVERTON TOWN MATCH RESULTS 2018-19

Date	Comp	H/A	Opponents	Att:	Result		Goalscorers	Pos	No.
Aug 11	Sth Prem S	A	Swindon Supermarine	247	W	1 - 0	Landricombe 55		1
14	Sth Prem S	H	Frome Town	251	W	3 - 1	Landricombe 56 Evans 81 Rogers 83		2
18	Sth Prem S	H	Walton Casuals	203	W	5 - 1	Bath 1 3 Price 38 Landricombe 48 Allen 55	1	3
25	Sth Prem S	A	Harrow Borough	150	D	2 - 2	Landricombe 12 Hurst 90	1	4
27	Sth Prem S	H	Taunton Town	749	L	1 - 3	Allen 37	3	5
Sept 1	Sth Prem S	A	Beaconsfield Town	76	W	2 - 0	Bath 28 Landricombe 78	2	6
8	**FAC 1Q**	**A**	**Bridport**	**268**	**W**	**1 - 0**	**Landricombe 39**		7
15	Sth Prem S	A	Kings Langley	155	D	2 - 2	Landricombe 47 Allen 8	2	8
22	**FAC 2Q**	**H**	**Dorchester Town**	**307**	**W**	**2 - 0**	**Allen 16 Landricombe 69**		9
29	Sth Prem S	H	Basingstoke Town	253	W	4 - 1	Rogers 30 Ladricombe 55 74 Bath 69	2	10
Oct 6	**FAC 3Q**	**H**	**Metropolitan Police**	**338**	**D**	**3 - 3**	**Bath 4 Rogers 43 77**		11
9	**FAC 3Qr**	**A**	**Metropolitan Police**	**172**	**L**	**0 - 1**	**(aet)**		12
13	Sth Prem S	H	Farnborough	232	D	1 - 1	Rogers 39	4	13
16	Sth Prem S	H	Weymouth	378	L	1 - 2	Landricombe 22	4	14
20	Sth Prem S	A	Chesham United	271	D	1 - 1	Landricombe 60 (pen)	4	15
23	Sth Prem S	A	Salisbury	624	L	1 - 3	Rogers 4	5	16
27	**FAT 1Q**	**A**	**Hartley Wintney**	**162**	**D**	**1 - 1**	**Hurst 68**		17
30	**FAT 1Q**	**H**	**Hartley Wintney**	**148**	**W**	**5 - 1**	**LANDRICOMBE 3 (8 10 21) Bath 44 46**		18
Nov 3	Sth Prem S	H	Staines Town	261	W	3 - 2	Landricombe 9 Bath 35 Harris 45 (og)	5	19
10	**FAT 2Q**	**H**	**Wingate & Finchley**	**162**	**L**	**2 - 3**	**Landricombe 45 Smallcombe 48**		20
17	Sth Prem S	H	Hendon	275	D	0 - 0		5	21
20	Sth Prem S	A	Merthyr Town	425	L	1 - 5	Landricombe 51	6	22
24	Sth Prem S	H	Hartley Wintney	211	D	1 - 1	Price 31	7	23
Dec 1	Sth Prem S	A	Wimborne Town	299	L	1 - 2	Wadham 90	7	24
8	Sth Prem S	A	Metropolitan Police	96	L	2 - 3	Landricombe 52 Davis 66		25
22	Sth Prem S	H	Swindon Supermarine	217	D	2 - 2	Bath 3 Key 65	14	26
26	Sth Prem S	A	Taunton Town	1377	L	1 - 2	Colwell 69	15	27
29	Sth Prem S	A	Frome Town	215	W	3 - 1	Yetton 45 Landricombe 65 Hall 69	14	28
Jan 1	Sth Prem S	H	Dorchester Town	14	L	2 - 3	Landricombe 2 65	15	29
5	Sth Prem S	A	Weymouth	769	L	1 - 2	Price 80	16	30
8	Sth Prem S	H	Gosport Borough	162	W	1 - 0	Landricombe 6	14	31
12	Sth Prem S	H	Poole Town	223	L	0 - 2		14	32
19	Sth Prem S	A	Hendon	252	D	2 - 2	Landricombe 45 Bath 46	14	33
26	Sth Prem S	H	Merthyr Town	218	D	2 - 2	Smallcombe 40 Yetton 61	14	34
Feb 12	Sth Prem S	A	Poole Town	301	L	0 - 3		16	35
16	Sth Prem S	H	Wimborne Town	279	L	0 - 3		16	36
19	Sth Prem S	A	Staines Town	118	W	4 - 2	Yetton 28 67 Landricombe 45 Ball 59	15	37
23	Sth Prem S	A	Hartley Wintney	244	L	0 - 1		18	38
Mar 2	Sth Prem S	H	Metropolitan Police	206	W	2 - 1	Bath 42 Davis 90	17	39
9	Sth Prem S	A	Gosport Borough	261	W	1 - 0	Landricombe 46	15	40
16	Sth Prem S	H	Salisbury	335	W	2 - 0	Landricombe 50 75	14	41
23	Sth Prem S	A	Farnborough	331	L	2 - 3	Key 73 76	14	42
26	Sth Prem S	H	Chesham United	156	L	0 - 2		14	43
30	Sth Prem S	H	Kings Langley	209	L	1 - 2	Landricombe 21	15	44
Apr 6	Sth Prem S	A	Basingstoke Town	402	D	3 - 3	Yetton 63 75 Landricombe 72	15	45
13	Sth Prem S	A	Walton Casuals	264	W	2 - 1	Landriscombe 47 Key 63	14	46
20	Sth Prem S	H	Harrow Borough	242	D	1 - 1	Hall 55	14	47
22	Sth Prem S	A	Dorchester Town	422	L	0 - 6		16	48
27	Sth Prem S	H	Beaconsfield Town	206	D	1 - 1	Bath	18	49

GOALSCORERS	SG	CSG	Pens	Hat tricks	Total
Landricombe	26	5	1	1	31
Bath	10	2			11
Rogers	5				6
Yetton	4				6
Allen	3				4
Key	3				4
Price	3				3
Davis	2				2
Hall	2				2
Hurst	2				2
Smallcombe	2				2
Ball	1				1
Colwell	1				1
Colwell	1				1
Evans	1				1
Opponents	1				1
Wadham	1				1

WALTON CASUALS MATCH RESULTS 2018-19

Date	Comp	H/A	Opponents	Att:	Result		Goalscorers	Pos	No.
Aug 11	Sth Prem S	H	Basingstoke Town	218	D	3 - 3	Bamba 1 Hicks 52 82		1
14	Sth Prem S	A	Hendon	236	L	0 - 3			2
18	Sth Prem S	A	Tiverton Town	203	L	1 - 5	Newton 21	20	3
25	**FAC P**	**H**	**Shoreham**	**172**	**W**	**6 - 0**	**Hicks 45 47 Jayden 54 58 Yuseff 70 85**	**19**	4
27	Sth Prem S	A	Metropolitan Police	240	D	2 - 2	Bamba 29 Harper 86	20	5
Sept 1	Sth Prem S	H	Merthyr Town	198	L	1 - 3	Sarpong 61	21	6
8	**FAC 1Q**	**A**	**Beckenham Town**	**95**	**D**	**0 - 0**			7
11	**FAC 1Qr**	**H**	**Beckenham Town**	**118**	**W**	**3 - 0**	**Roberts 14 35 Sobowale 73**		8
15	Sth Prem S	A	Swindon Supermarine	158	W	3 - 1	Hicks 31 Hibbert 39 44	20	9
21	Sth Prem S	A	Frome Town	17	L	0 - 3		20	10
22	**FAC 2Q**	**A**	**Coggeshall Town**	**128**	**L**	**0 - 2**			11
29	Sth Prem S	A	Frome Town	178	L	0 - 3		17	12
Oct 6	Sth Prem S	H	Gosport Borough	84	W	3 - 1	Bennett 45 Roberts 52 Ewington 80	14	13
13	Sth Prem S	A	Dorchester Town	367	D	1 - 1	Kelly 79	15	14
16	Sth Prem S	H	Staines Town	192	W	3 - 1	EWINGTON 3 (41 88 90 pen)	15	15
20	Sth Prem S	H	Weymouth	808	L	2 - 3	Roberts 69 Battie 88	14	16
27	**FAT 1Q**	**A**	**Molesey**	**154**	**W**	**1 - 0**	**Mills 78**		17
Nov 3	Sth Prem S	H	Harrow Borough	172	W	3 - 2	Ewington 57 Ellison-Hustwick 75 Black 83	12	18
14	Sth Prem S	A	Taunton Town	369	L	0 - 4		12	19
17	Sth Prem S	H	Poole Town	206	L	0 - 4		13	20
20	Sth Prem S	A	Chesham United	192	W	2 - 0	Farrell 72 Roberts 98	12	21
24	**FAT 3P**	**A**	**Carshalton Athletic**	**192**	**L**	**0 - 2**		**13**	22
Dec 8	Sth Prem S	A	Farnborough	288	L	0 - 1		15	23
15	Sth Prem S	H	Hendon	163	W	5 - 1	EWINGTON 4 (9 29 35 67) Robins 90 (pen)	13	24
18	Sth Prem S	H	Wimborne	162	W	3 - 0	Ewington 37 Bennett 48 Roberts 65	11	25
22	Sth Prem S	H	Basingstoke Town	287	L	1 - 2	Black 31	11	26
26	Sth Prem S	A	Metropolitan Police	327	D	2 - 2	Bennett 31 Roberts 90	11	27
Jan 1	Sth Prem S	A	Kings Langley	204	L	0 - 1		11	28
5	Sth Prem S	A	Staines Town	202	W	4 - 1	EWINGTON 4 (36 56 60 76)	11	29
12	Sth Prem S	H	Hartley Wintney	252	L	1 - 2	Bennett 68	11	30
15	Sth Prem S	H	Beaconsfield Town	215	D	1 - 1	Ellison-Hustwick 5	11	31
26	Sth Prem S	A	Chesham United	212	D	2 - 2	Bennett 20 Sheckleford 85	13	32
Feb 5	Sth Prem S	H	Poole Town	257	L	1 - 3	Ewington 23	15	33
9	Sth Prem S	H	Taunton Town	238	L	0 - 1		18	34
16	Sth Prem S	H	Weymouth	319	L	1 - 2	Ewington 9	18	35
19	Sth Prem S	A	Hartley Wintney	194	W	4 - 3	EWINGTON 3 (22 53 56) Brown 35	19	36
23	Sth Prem S	A	Wimborne Town	343	L	0 - 3		20	37
26	Sth Prem S	A	Harrow Borough	146	D	1 - 1	Brown 51	19	38
Mar 2	Sth Prem S	H	Farnborough	306	W	2 - 1	Brown 57 (pen) Bettachie 75	16	39
9	Sth Prem S	A	Beaconsfield Town	131	D	1 - 1	Roberts 86	16	40
16	Sth Prem S	H	Gosport Borough	216	D	0 - 0		17	41
23	Sth Prem S	A	Dorchester Town	243	L	2 - 3	Ewington 17 Brown 45 (pen)	17	42
30	Sth Prem S	A	Swindon Supermarine	317	L	1 - 2	Bettache 81	18	43
Apr 6	Sth Prem S	H	Frome Town	231	W	4 - 1	EWINGTON 3 (10 57 77) Bettache 57	19	44
13	Sth Prem S	H	Tiverton Town	264	L	1 - 2	Brown 50 (pen)	19	45
20	Sth Prem S	A	Salisbury	670	L	2 - 4	Bamba 68 74	19	46
22	Sth Prem S	H	Kings Langley	346	W	1 - 0	Ewington 42	20	47
27	Sth Prem S	A	Merthyr Town	355	W	2 - 1	Brewer 26 Ewingrton 37	17	48

GOALSCORERS	SG	CSG	Pens	Hat tricks	Total
Ewington	13	2		5	25
Roberts	8				8
Bennett	5				5
Brown	5		3		5
Hicks	3				5
Bambs	3	3			4
Bettache	3				3
Black	2				2
Ellison-Hustwick	2				2
Hibbert	1				2
Jayden	1				2
Yusseff	1				2
Battie	1				1
Brewer	1				1
Farrell	1				1
Harper	1				1
Kelly	1				1
Mills	1				1
Newton	1				1
Robins	1		1		1
Sarpong	1				1
Sheckleford	1				1
Sobowale	1				1

WEYMOUTH MATCH RESULTS 2018-19

Date	Comp	H/A	Opponents	Att:	Result		Goalscorers	Pos	No.
Aug 11	Sth Prem S	A	Harrow Borough	150	W	3 - 2	GOODSHIP 3 (34 pen 52 71)		1
14	Sth Prem S	H	Taunton	879	W	2 - 1	Goodship 51 Baggie 90		2
18	Sth Prem S	H	Beaconsfield Town	831	D	1 - 1	Wakefield 88	5	3
25	Sth Prem S	A	Chesham United	318	W	5 - 0	GOODSHIP 3 (34 (pen) 52 71) Thomson 53 Zubar 90	1	4
27	Sth Prem S	H	Dorchester Town	1832	W	5 - 0	Goodship 7 Thomson 11 41 McQuoid 23 87	1	5
Sept 1	Sth Prem S	A	Farnborough	336	L	3 - 3	Thomson 6 Baggie 14 Zubar 37	1	6
8	**FAC 1Q**	**H**	**Banbury United**	**751**	**D**	**1 - 1**	**Wise 35**		**7**
11	**FAC 1Qr**	**A**	**Banbury United**	**550**	**L**	**1 - 2**	**Zubar 90**		**8**
15	Sth Prem S	H	Hartley Wintney	744	D	2 - 2	Baggie 81 Bentley 90	1	9
29	Sth Prem S	A	Staines Town	282	W	4 - 1	Goodship 14 Zubar 55 86 McCarthy 64	1	10
Oct 6	Sth Prem S	H	Wimborne Town	942	W	1 - 0	Baker 84	1	11
13	Sth Prem S	A	Swindon Supermarine	290	D	1 - 1	Brooks 39	1	12
16	Sth Prem S	A	Tiverton Town	378	W	2 - 1	McCarthy 66 Goodship 79	1	13
20	Sth Prem S	H	Walton Casuals	808	W	3 - 2	Baggie 16 Wakefield 34 Goodship 90	1	14
27	**FAT 1Q**	**A**	**Tiverton Town**	**513**	**W**	**3 - 1**	**Goodship 12 Zubar 49 Wakefield 79**	**1**	**15**
Nov 3	Sth Prem S	A	Basingstoke Town	518	W	2 - 1	Goodship 44 Thomson 74	1	16
10	**FAT 2Q**	**H**	**Street**	**629**	**D**	**2 - 2**	**Thomson 17 McCarthy 38**		**17**
13	**FAT 2Qr**	**A**	**Street**	**376**	**W**	**1 - 0**	**Baggie 81 Bentley 90**		**18**
17	Sth Prem S	A	Kings Langley	309	L	1 - 2	Brooks 46	2	19
20	Sth Prem S	H	Salisbury	1006	W	2 - 1	Goodship 49 (pen)	2	20
24	**FAT 3Qr**	**A**	**St Albans City**	**518**	**D**	**1 - 1**	**McCarthy 20**		**21**
27	**FAT 3Qr**	**H**	**St Albans City**	**174**	**W**	**2 - 0**	**Thomson 13 Glover 88**		**22**
Dec 4	Sth Prem S	H	Frome Town	492	W	4 - 0	GOODSHIP 3 (44 pen 68 80) Brooks 84	2	23
11	Sth Prem S	H	Gosport Borough	552	L	1 - 3	Odubade 43	2	24
15	**FAT 1P**		**Needham Market withdrew**						**25**
22	Sth Prem S	H	Harrow Borough	674	D	2 - 2	McCarthy 32 Goodship 71 (pen)	2	26
26	Sth Prem S	A	Dorchester Town	2217	W	1 - 0	Goodship 89	2	27
29	Sth Prem S	A	Taunton Town	1461	D	3 - 3	Odubade 12 59 (pen) Thomson 18	2	28
Jan 1	Sth Prem S	H	Poole Town	1270	D	2 - 2	Goodship 10 Brooks 58	2	29
5	Sth Prem S	H	Tiverton Town	769	W	2 - 1	Thomson 45 Wakefield 63	2	30
12	**FAT 2P**	**A**	**Ramsbottom United**	**457**	**D**	**2 - 2**	**McCarthy 37 Brooks 82**		**31**
15	**FAT 2Pr**	**H**	**Ramsbottom United**	**657**	**L**	**1 - 3**	**Thomson 34**		**32**
19	Sth Prem S	H	Kings Langley	727	D	2 - 2	Brooks 49 Goodship 67	3	33
26	Sth Prem S	A	Salisbury	1224	W	4 - 3	Goodship 15 Wakefield 26 Murray 75 Baker 84	3	34
29	Sth Prem S	A	Gosport Borough	17	W	2 - 0	Baker 45 54	2	35
Feb 2	Sth Prem S	H	Basingstoke Town	795	L	1 - 2	Brooks 90	3	36
9	Sth Prem S	A	Metropolitan Police	270	D	4 - 4	GOODSHIP 3 (5 45 pen 60) Murray 86	3	37
12	Sth Prem S	A	Merthyr Town	327	L	1 - 2	Thomson 90	4	38
16	Sth Prem S	A	Walton Casuals	319	W	2 - 1	Thomson 4 Goodship 69	3	39
23	Sth Prem S	H	Merthyr Town	715	W	2 - 1	Goodship 21 64 (pen)	2	40
26	Sth Prem S	A	Hendon	251	W	3 - 2	Ngalo 65 Goodship 76 McCarthy 80		41
Mar 2	Sth Prem S	A	Frome Town	403	W	2 - 0	Goodship 38 Wakefield 76	2	42
9	Sth Prem S	H	Hendon	759	W	3 - 0	Thomson 31 Odubade 62 Brooks 87	1	43
16	Sth Prem S	A	Wimborne Town	697	D	0 - 0		1	44
23	Sth Prem S	H	Swindon Supermarine	858	W	2 - 1	Odubade 42 Goodship 60 (pen)	1	45
30	Sth Prem S	A	Hartley Wintney	437	W	3 - 0	Odubade 19 Thomson 68 Murray 73	1	46
Apr 2	Sth Prem S	H	Metropolitan Police	1153	W	4 - 0	Goodship 30 90 Odubade 14 Thomson 68	1	47
6	Sth Prem S	H	Staines Town	996	W	4 - 0	GOODSHIP 4 (10 19 pen 52 82)	1	48
13	Sth Prem S	A	Beaconsfield Town	297	L	0 - 1		1	49
20	Sth Prem S	H	Chesham United	1545	D	1 - 1	Brooks 87	1	50
22	Sth Prem S	A	Poole Town	1596	D	1 - 1	Brooks 1	1	51
22	Sth Prem S	H	Farnborough	2675	W	3 - 0	Odubade 61 Goodship 64 Thomson 71	1	52

GOALSCORERS	SG	CSG	Pens	Hat tricks	Total
Goodship	25	4	9	5	38
Thomson	14	3			15
Brooks	10				10
McCarthy	7				7
Odubade	6		1		7
Wakefield	6				6
Zubar	3				6
Baggie	5	3			5
Murray	4				5
Baker	3				4
Bentley	2				2
McQuoid	1				2
Baggie	1				1
Ngalo	1				1
Wise	1				1

WIMBORNE TOWN MATCH RESULTS 2018-19

Date	Comp	H/A	Opponents	Att:	Result		Goalscorers	Pos	No.
Aug 11	Sth Prem S	A	Farnborough	327	L	1 - 3	T.Holmes 20		1
14	Sth Prem S	H	Dorchester Town	535	L	2 - 4	Davidson 47 Burbidge 90		2
18	Sth Prem S	H	Harrow Borough	341	W	5 - 3	T.Holmes 41 89 Lovell 55 (pen) Davidson 67 Young 83	15	3
25	**FAC P**	**H**	**Newport (I.o.W.)**	**214**	**W**	**6 - 0**	**T.HOLMES 4 (1 59 66 74) Burbidge 75 Francis 77**		4
27	Sth Prem S	H	Poole Town	918	L	0 - 4			5
Sept 1	Sth Prem S	A	Chesham United	234	D	1 - 1	Davidson 54	20	6
8	**FAC 1Q**	**A**	**Dorchester Town**	**476**	**L**	**0 - 3**			7
15	Sth Prem S	A	Basingstoke Town	385	L	2 - 3	Mendy 10 58	21	8
29	Sth Prem S	H	Beaconsfield Town	277	L	0 - 1		21	9
Oct 6	Sth Prem S	H	Weymouth	942	L	0 - 1		21	10
13	Sth Prem S	A	Kings Langley	334	W	5 - 0	Burbidge 44 T.Holmes 55 73 Clarke 86 Young 90	19	11
16	Sth Prem S	H	Frome Town	314	W	3 - 2	Oldring 16 Clarke 32 Burbidge 53	17	12
20	Sth Prem S	A	Hendon	215	L	2 - 3	T.Holmes 11 Clarke 61		13
23	Sth Prem S	A	Swindon Supermarine	252	L	2 - 3	Sawyer 36 (og) Penny 62	18	14
27	**FAT 1Q**	**A**	**Basingstoke Town**	**272**	**L**	**2 - 4**	**T.Holmes 20 ,39**		15
Nov 3	Sth Prem S	H	Hartley Wintney	326	W	2 - 1	Clarke 38 68	17	16
10	Sth Prem S	A	Taunton Town	489	L	2 - 4	Young 12 Lovell 83	18	17
17	Sth Prem S	H	Staines Town	347	W	1 - 0	Stokoe 45	16	18
24	Sth Prem S	A	Merthyr Town	377	L	0 - 2		16	19
Dec 1	Sth Prem S	H	Tiverton Town	299	W	2 - 1	T.Holmes 49 Burbidge 87	15	20
8	Sth Prem S	H	Salisbury	122	L	3 - 4	Burbidge 67 T. Holmes 74 Stokoe 90		21
18	Sth Prem S	A	Walton Casuals	162	L	0 - 3			22
22	Sth Prem S	H	Farnborough	290	D	1 - 1	T.Holmes 90	20	23
26	Sth Prem S	A	Poole Town	818	W	5 - 2	T.Holmes 9 90 Stokoe 72 Burbidge 73 Young 83	19	24
29	Sth Prem S	A	Dorchester Town	594	D	1 - 1	L. Holmes 49	18	25
Jan 1	Sth Prem S	H	Gosport Borough	451	W	3 - 2	T.Holmes 9 20 Young 62	16	26
5	Sth Prem S	A	Frome Town	198	L	0 - 1		16	27
12	Sth Prem S	H	Merthyr Town	433	W	4 - 0	T.HOLMES 3 (24 42 53) L.Holmes 73	12	28
19	Sth Prem S	A	Staines Town	197	W	4 - 2	Maybury 56 Oldring 66 Burbidge 70 T Holmes 87	11	29
26	Sth Prem S	A	Taumton	485	D	1 - 1	T.Holmes 72	10	30
29	Sth Prem S	H	Metropolitan Police	242	W	3 - 0	T.Holmes 45 89 Burbidge 53	10	31
Feb 9	Sth Prem S	A	Hendon	388	D	3 - 3	Burbidge 27 T. Holmes 53 64	9	32
16	Sth Prem S	H	Tiverton Town	279	W	3 - 0	T.Holmes 60 75 Young 90	10	33
23	Sth Prem S	H	Walton Casuals	343	W	3 - 0	T.Holmes 11 62 Penny 32	10	34
26	Sth Prem S	A	Hartley Wintney	180	L	0 - 3		11	35
Mar 2	Sth Prem S	H	Salisbury	624	L	1 - 4	T.Holmes 40	11	36
9	Sth Prem S	A	Metropolitan Police	136	L	2 - 4	Luke Holmes 48 Tobias Holmes 71	12	37
16	Sth Prem S	H	Weymouth	697	D	0 - 0		13	38
23	Sth Prem S	A	Kings Langley	297	L	0 - 1		14	39
30	Sth Prem S	A	Basingstoke Town	417	L	2 - 4	Clarke 25 T.Holmes 81	18	40
Apr 6	Sth Prem S	A	Beaconsfield Town	101	L	0 - 2		18	41
13	Sth Prem S	A	Harrow Borough	138	W	2 - 0		16	42
20	Sth Prem S	A	Swindon Supermarine	350	W	1 - 0	Clarke 70	14	43
22	Sth Prem S	H	Gosport Borough	622	L	0 - 1		15	44
27	Sth Prem S	H	Chesham United	437	D	0 - 0		14	45

GOALSCORERS	SG	CSG	Pens	Hat tricks	Total
Holmes T	21	9		2	35
Burbidge	9	2			10
Clarke	6	3			7
Young	7				6
Davidson	3				3
Holmes L	3				3
Oldring	3				3
Stokoe	3				3
Lovell	2		1		2
Mendy	1				2
Penny	2				2
Francis	1				1
Lee	1				1
Maybury	1				1
Opponents	1				1

COMBINED COUNTIES LEAGUE

RECENT CHAMPIONS

2016: Hartley Wintney **2017:** Hartley Wintney **2018:** Westfield

PREMIER DIVISION		P	W	D	L	F	A	GD	Pts
1	Chertsey Town	38	28	7	3	97	41	56	91
2	Sutton Common Rovers	38	23	9	6	85	48	37	78
3	Abbey Rangers	38	21	4	13	64	60	4	67
4	Southall	38	19	8	11	68	47	21	64*
5	Raynes Park Vale	38	17	9	12	47	48	-1	60
6	Spelthorne Sports	38	17	7	14	69	47	22	58
7	Guildford City	38	17	4	17	62	66	-4	55
8	Banstead Athletic	38	14	13	11	57	48	9	54*
9	Badshot Lea	38	14	8	16	52	69	-17	50
10	Horley Town	38	14	8	16	59	67	-8	49*
11	Knaphill	38	15	4	19	53	71	-18	49
12	Redhill	38	13	8	17	62	66	-4	47
13	Colliers Wood United	38	13	7	18	64	72	-8	46
14	Cobham	38	12	9	17	62	66	-4	45
15	Hanworth Villa	38	13	6	19	54	64	-10	45
16	Camberley Town	38	13	8	17	63	65	-2	44*
17	CB Hounslow United	38	13	6	19	59	69	-10	42*
18	Balham	38	11	7	20	55	69	-14	40
19	AFC Hayes	38	11	7	20	51	68	-17	40
20	Walton & Hersham	38	8	9	21	61	93	-32	33

DIVISION ONE		P	W	D	L	F	A	GD	Pts
1	Sheerwater	34	24	5	5	90	40	50	77
2	Frimley Green	34	23	7	4	75	41	34	76
3	Tooting Bec	34	21	7	6	85	39	46	70
4	Farnham Town	34	21	5	8	75	41	34	68
5	Bedfont & Feltham	34	18	8	8	100	55	45	62
6	Sandhurst Town	34	18	6	10	61	54	7	60
7	Ash United	34	17	7	10	82	66	16	58
8	Epsom & Ewell	34	17	4	13	77	67	10	55
9	Chessington & Hook United	34	14	6	14	69	67	2	48
10	British Airways	34	12	5	17	71	83	-12	41
11	Dorking Wanderers Res	34	12	6	16	63	77	-14	41*
12	Godalming Town	34	11	5	18	49	78	-29	38
13	Bagshot	34	10	5	19	39	93	-54	35
14	FC Deportivo Galicia	34	10	3	21	60	72	-12	33
15	Kensington Borough	34	7	10	17	45	74	-29	31
16	Eversley & California	34	8	3	23	66	88	-22	27
17	Fleet Spurs	34	7	5	22	55	86	-31	26
18	Cove	34	5	5	24	46	87	-41	20

PREMIER CHALLENGE CUP

HOLDERS: KNAPHILL

ROUND 1

Camberley Town	v	Cobham	1-3
Chessington & Hook United	v	AFC Hayes	2-4
FC Deportivo Galicia	v	Cove	4-1
Farnham Town	v	Southall	1-2
Hanworth Villa	v	Kensington Borough	3-1
Horley Town	v	Chertsey Town	0-1 (aet)
Badshot Lea	v	Walton & Hersham	3-1

ROUND 2

Eversley & California	v	Knaphill	1-5
Ash United	v	Fleet Spurs	2-3
Cobham	v	AFC Hayes	0-3
Bedfont & Feltham	v	Tooting Bec	2-0
FC Deportivo Galicia	v	AC London	5-0
Sutton Common Rovers	v	Southall	4-2
Spelthorne Sports	v	Raynes Park Vale	2-1
Hanworth Villa	v	Sandhurst Town	2-1
Chertsey Town	v	British Airways	3-2
Abbey Rangers	v	Redhill	3-0
Epsom & Ewell	v	Bagshot	1-0
Godalming Town	v	Dorking Wanderers Res	2-0
Frimley Green	v	Guildford City	0-2
CB Hounslow United	v	Badshot Lea	4-1
Sheerwater	v	Balham	1-0
Banstead Athletic	v	Colliers Wood United	4-3

ROUND 3

Knaphill	v	Fleet Spurs	3-1
AFC Hayes	v	Bedfont & Feltham	0-1
FC Deportivo Galicia	v	Sutton Common Rovers	0-2
Spelthorne Sports	v	Hanworth Villa	0-1
Chertsey Town	v	Abbey Rangers	1-2
Epsom & Ewell	v	Godalming Town	5-1
Guildford City	v	CB Hounslow United	0-2
Sheerwater	v	Banstead Athletic	0-3

QUARTER FINALS

Knaphill	v	Bedfont & Feltham	0-3
Sutton Common Rovers	v	Hanworth Villa	3-0
Abbey Rangers	v	Epsom & Ewell	3-1
CB Hounslow United	v	Banstead Athletic	2-1

SEMI-FINALS

Bedfont & Feltham	v	Sutton Common Rovers	0-1
Abbey Rangers	v	CB Hounslow United	0-4

FINAL

Sutton Common Rovers	v	CB Hounslow United	1-0

DIVISION ONE CHALLENGE CUP FINAL

Epsom & Ewell	v	Frimley Green	0-1

PREMIER DIVISION		1	2	3	4	5	6	7	8	9	10	11	12	13	14	15	16	17	18	19	20
1	Abbey Rangers		1-0	2-0	1-0	1-0	1-4	2-3	1-0	4-1	1-0	3-0	1-3	3-1	2-1	0-0	3-0	2-0	2-1	1-2	5-0
2	AFC Hayes	0-2		1-3	3-1	1-1	3-1	1-1	1-3	2-1	4-1	1-3	2-1	0-1	3-2	2-2	0-2	0-2	1-3	5-4	2-0
3	Badshot Lea	0-2	2-0		3-2	1-0	4-1	3-1	0-3	1-0	1-0	3-0	1-0	1-2	3-3	2-1	1-1	1-2	1-1	0-3	2-3
4	Balham	5-0	0-2	2-2		3-2	4-4	2-2	1-2	2-3	0-1	0-1	0-0	1-2	2-2	2-0	0-2	2-0	0-0	1-1	2-1
5	Banstead Athletic	3-1	3-1	3-0	3-2		2-1	1-0	1-2	3-3	1-3	2-0	1-2	0-2	1-1	1-1	3-1	1-1	1-0	2-3	1-1
6	Camberley Town	0-2	2-0	2-1	1-2	1-5		2-1	1-2	3-3	2-3	5-1	3-2	0-0	0-2	0-1	1-1	3-1	1-1	2-0	2-0
7	CB Hounslow United	6-1	2-2	1-2	1-2	2-2	0-2		0-4	0-2	3-1	2-1	2-1	3-0	3-1	4-0	3-1	1-5	0-2	0-1	4-1
8	Chertsey Town	3-1	3-1	2-1	4-1	3-3	1-0	4-2		2-1	3-0	2-2	1-0	3-1	5-1	4-1	2-1	5-1	1-3	2-2	6-0
9	Cobham	2-2	1-0	5-0	3-1	1-1	2-1	7-0	0-2		3-1	0-2	1-1	3-0	2-0	0-1	3-2	2-2	2-2	0-2	1-1
10	Colliers Wood United	4-0	2-1	6-2	1-0	0-1	2-1	1-1	3-3	3-2		2-2	5-0	4-3	1-2	1-1	3-3	3-2	2-3	0-0	1-1
11	Guildford City	4-2	1-4	4-2	4-0	1-2	1-0	4-3	0-1	2-1	1-0		3-0	0-1	0-2	0-2	0-1	1-1	2-1	2-2	3-4
12	Hanworth Villa	4-3	5-0	2-2	2-1	1-1	0-0	1-0	0-2	3-1	6-2	0-1		1-2	0-1	2-0	4-0	0-4	2-1	1-3	0-1
13	Horley Town	1-2	2-1	0-0	3-0	0-0	2-4	0-1	2-2	4-0	3-2	1-3	5-0		1-2	2-2	1-7	2-2	1-2	2-5	1-0
14	Knaphill	0-1	2-1	3-1	0-2	1-2	0-3	1-0	0-4	2-0	1-4	0-1	0-3	2-2		2-1	2-1	0-1	2-3	2-5	2-1
15	Raynes Park Vale	3-0	1-1	0-0	2-1	1-0	1-0	0-2	2-2	0-1	3-1	3-2	1-0	3-2	0-3		1-0	0-2	3-2	0-1	3-1
16	Redhill	0-1	2-2	1-2	2-3	0-0	2-2	2-3	1-4	2-1	2-0	2-1	3-2	2-0	2-1	1-2		1-4	2-1	2-2	3-3
17	Southall	1-1	1-1	0-1	3-1	3-1	4-3	2-0	0-1	1-1	2-0	4-1	2-0	1-2	6-0	1-0	1-0		1-1	0-1	4-3
18	Spelthorne Sports	1-2	0-2	3-0	1-2	0-1	4-0	2-1	1-2	5-1	4-0	3-1	0-1	2-2	1-3	1-2	1-0	2-0		0-0	3-0
19	Sutton Common Rovers	3-1	1-0	3-3	3-2	2-1	2-2	3-1	1-1	3-0	2-0	3-4	5-1	3-1	1-0	0-1	0-2	3-0	1-4		4-2
20	Walton & Hersham	4-4	3-0	4-0	2-3	1-1	2-3	0-0	4-1	3-2	2-1	1-3	3-3	0-2	2-4	2-2	3-5	0-1	2-4	0-5	

DIVISION ONE		1	2	3	4	5	6	7	8	9	10	11	12	13	14	15	16	17	18
1	Ash United		5-1	3-1	3-4	3-1	2-1	4-0	1-2	3-1	0-3	5-0	2-1	1-1	6-2	4-2	2-3	2-2	0-5
2	Bagshot	0-3		1-1	3-0	2-1	2-2	1-0	0-3	0-3	4-1	1-0	1-3	2-3	0-5	2-2	0-4	2-5	3-3
3	Bedfont & Feltham	3-3	11-0		5-0	2-0	4-1	4-0	4-6	2-1	2-4	1-0	7-1	0-0	5-0	4-0	5-0	3-2	1-1
4	British Airways	4-1	1-2	1-4		2-2	6-1	5-1	3-2	4-2	1-2	0-0	3-0	1-2	0-3	3-1	2-4	0-1	1-2
5	Chessington & Hook United	3-3	3-0	0-3	4-4		6-2	3-1	1-4	0-3	4-1	3-1	3-4	1-3	1-2	1-1	2-3	2-1	2-0
6	Cove	2-3	0-1	2-4	1-4	1-2		0-2	1-2	2-5	1-1	1-0	3-2	1-2	2-0	1-1	1-2	3-4	1-1
7	Dorking Wanderers Reserves	5-1	3-0	3-3	4-2	1-3	1-5		5-3	3-1	0-0	3-1	6-2	0-3	4-3	3-1	0-4	1-2	0-5
8	Epsom & Ewell	1-1	7-1	4-4	3-2	1-2	3-2	3-0		1-0	1-2	0-2	1-1	3-0	3-2	1-1	1-3	2-3	3-1
9	Eversley & California	1-2	0-1	1-5	1-3	3-4	2-2	2-2	2-1		1-2	5-6	3-0	2-4	5-1	3-0	2-3	1-3	0-3
10	Farnham Town	4-1	0-0	3-1	6-1	1-0	0-1	1-0	4-1	3-1		6-0	3-1	1-3	3-1	6-0	2-0	2-1	0-1
11	FC Deportivo Galicia	1-3	8-0	1-3	2-3	3-1	5-1	2-0	0-3	3-3	1-3		7-2	1-2	2-3	1-3	2-1	1-3	0-1
12	Fleet Spurs	1-4	2-3	0-0	1-2	1-2	2-1	1-2	2-3	4-5	5-1	3-4		4-0	1-2	0-0	2-2	0-2	1-1
13	Frimley Green	3-0	3-0	5-1	2-2	3-2	3-2	3-2	4-2	3-2	1-1	5-2	2-1		2-2	2-1	3-0	1-1	0-0
14	Godalming Town	0-4	2-0	0-2	1-1	1-3	1-0	2-5	1-3	2-1	1-1	0-0	1-3	0-2		2-2	2-1	0-3	1-5
15	Kensington Borough	1-1	1-4	3-3	3-2	0-1	3-1	1-1	5-1	3-1	0-3	0-3	0-1	1-3	1-0		3-3	0-3	1-0
16	Sandhurst Town	2-2	1-0	2-1	3-1	1-1	2-0	2-2	0-2	4-2	2-1	1-0	2-1	0-2	1-3	1-0		2-0	0-2
17	Sheerwater	3-1	4-2	4-1	7-0	3-2	2-0	1-1	3-0	5-0	2-4	1-0	4-2	1-0	5-1	4-1	1-1		4-2
18	Tooting Bec	2-3	3-0	3-0	4-3	3-3	7-1	3-2	4-1	4-1	2-0	2-1	4-0	1-0	1-2	5-3	4-1	0-0	

Borrowash Vics v Teversal. Photo: BIll Wheatcroft.

Graham Street Prims v Clifton All Whites. Photo: Bill Wheatcroft.

Graham Street Prims v Clifton All Whites - Clifton score the first goal. Photo: Bill Wheatcroft.

EAST MIDLANDS COUNTIES LEAGUE

RECENT CHAMPIONS

2016: St Andrews **2017:** West Bridgford **2018:** Dunkirk

		P	W	D	L	F	A	GD	Pts
1	Selston	38	29	7	2	120	36	84	94
2	Newark Flowserve	38	28	4	6	139	33	106	88
3	Sherwood Colliery	38	27	4	7	95	44	51	85
4	Heanor Town	38	24	2	12	95	45	50	71*
5	Radford	38	22	4	12	92	59	33	70
6	Eastwood C FC	38	21	5	12	91	60	31	68
7	Graham Street Prims	38	22	2	14	94	64	30	68
8	Barrow Town	38	21	3	14	77	71	6	66
9	Kimberley Miners Welfare	38	17	10	11	61	53	8	61
10	Belper United	38	17	8	13	80	55	25	59
11	Ingles	38	18	4	16	78	61	17	55*
12	Clifton All Whites	38	15	6	17	89	73	16	51
13	West Bridgford	38	16	3	19	66	104	-38	51
14	Ashby Ivanhoe	38	13	2	23	66	82	-16	41
15	Teversal	38	11	3	24	51	72	-21	36
16	Gedling Miners Welfare	38	10	6	22	56	83	-27	36
17	Rainworth Miners Welfare	38	10	4	24	49	90	-41	34
18	Clipstone	38	7	4	27	51	107	-56	25
19	Borrowash Victoria	38	5	3	30	31	170	-139	18
20	Arnold Town	38	3	4	31	35	154	-119	13

LEAGUE CUP

HOLDERS: RADFORD

ROUND 1

Heanor Town	v	Belper United	4 - 4, 3-4p
West Bridgford	v	Barrow Town	0 - 3
Kimberley Miners Welfare	v	Eastwood C FC	1 - 1, 5-6p
Graham Street Prims	v	Selston	4 - 3

ROUND 2

Borrowash Victoria	v	Rainworth Miners Welfare	1 - 2
Eastwood C FC	v	Arnold Town	3 - 0
Clipstone	v	Sherwood Colliery	1-4
Gedling Miners Welfare	v	Belper United	2 - 3
Newark Flowserve	v	Barrow Town	5 - 0
Radford	v	Ashby Ivanhoe	4 - 2
Graham Street Prims	v	Teversal	0 - 0, 3-0p
Ingles	v	Clifton All Whites	0 - 2

QUARTER FINALS

Radford	v	Graham Street Prims	5 - 0
Newark Flowserve	v	Rainworth Miners Welfare	5 - 0
Clifton All Whites	v	Sherwood Colliery	2 - 1
Eastwood C FC	v	Belper United	1 - 3

SEMI FINALS

Clifton All Whites	v	Belper United	2 - 1
Radford	v	Newark Flowserve	1 - 3

FINAL

Newark Flowserve	v	Clifton All Whites	0 - 0, 4-1p

		1	2	3	4	5	6	7	8	9	10	11	12	13	14	15	16	17	18	19	20
1	Arnold Town		4-2	0-3	0-5	1-2	2-2	3-2	1-2	2-2	1-6	0-2	1-11	0-3	0-7	1-4	0-1	2-6	0-3	3-1	3-5
2	Ashby Ivanhoe	3-1		1-2	0-2	2-0	2-3	7-1	2-0	4-2	0-5	0-4	2-4	1-2	0-4	1-6	2-0	0-2	3-4	1-2	5-2
3	Barrow Town	11-0	2-1		3-1	2-0	5-4	2-2	0-1	5-3	1-0	1-0	2-0	0-3	0-2	2-4	5-3	0-4	2-3	2-1	4-4
4	Belper United	2-2	2-2	1-2		6-0	4-0	2-0	3-3	4-1	1-2	0-4	2-0	0-0	0-2	0-1	4-1	1-2	0-2	2-1	4-0
5	Borrowash Victoria	3-1	0-6	0-2	1-0		2-0	1-9	0-2	0-5	1-2	0-11	1-6	2-2	0-4	0-1	0-2	0-6	0-3	0-2	1-2
6	Clifton All Whites	2-1	5-1	2-3	1-4	12-1		4-1	3-2	4-2	1-2	2-1	2-4	1-1	2-2	3-3	2-2	0-1	0-2	3-1	6-2
7	Clipstone	2-1	2-4	0-2	0-4	3-1	0-4		0-3	1-3	1-8	1-3	2-2	0-0	1-5	1-5	0-1	2-5	0-1	1-1	1-2
8	Eastwood Collieries	7-0	2-1	4-1	1-1	6-1	4-1	8-1		3-1	2-1	1-3	1-2	2-2	1-2	4-6	1-2	0-3	3-2	4-3	0-2
9	Gedling Miners Welfare	1-1	1-0	0-0	1-2	0-2	1-0	0-4	2-3		1-3	3-3	4-2	0-1	1-7	1-1	0-2	3-2	0-1	1-2	4-4
10	Graham Street Prims	7-0	2-1	2-3	2-1	10-0	0-3	1-0	1-2	1-3		3-0	0-6	4-1	3-3	2-1	0-2	0-2	2-3	4-0	3-0
11	Heanor Town	3-2	1-2	3-0	1-1	6-0	2-1	3-1	1-5	1-0	4-0		0-2	4-0	2-1	0-2	5-0	1-2	1-2	2-0	1-2
12	Ingles	5-0	2-1	1-2	1-3	2-2	3-2	0-1	1-0	2-1	2-0	0-1		0-1	1-0	0-4	3-1	1-3	2-0	3-2	1-1
13	Kimberley Miners Welfare	3-0	3-3	3-1	3-1	2-1	2-1	3-1	0-2	2-1	3-4	0-3	5-0		0-2	2-2	1-1	1-1	2-0	1-0	2-3
14	Newark Flowserve	8-0	0-1	6-0	6-0	13-0	2-0	7-2	4-1	3-1	4-2	4-1	3-0	3-1		0-1	3-1	2-2	1-1	4-0	4-1
15	Radford	4-0	2-1	0-1	3-1	7-0	3-1	2-1	0-2	3-1	2-3	1-4	3-2	2-2	0-1		2-1	2-3	4-1	1-2	2-3
16	Rainworth Miners Welfare	5-1	0-1	5-1	1-2	3-3	0-2	1-3	1-3	1-2	0-2	0-2	0-2	0-1	0-12	3-2		0-5	0-4	2-2	2-1
17	Selston	7-0	4-0	4-1	3-3	11-1	2-2	3-1	3-3	1-0	1-1	2-0	3-2	2-0	2-1	4-0	4-1		1-1	3-1	7-0
18	Sherwood Colliery	6-0	2-1	2-0	0-6	9-1	3-1	3-1	0-0	5-0	7-1	2-3	1-1	3-1	3-4	3-0	1-0	2-0		4-1	4-2
19	Teversal	4-1	1-2	1-0	1-1	5-1	0-3	0-1	0-2	0-2	0-1	2-3	2-1	0-1	0-2	1-2	2-1	1-3	0-1		6-1
20	West Bridgford	2-0	1-0	0-4	2-4	4-3	0-4	2-1	3-1	1-2	1-4	0-6	2-1	2-1	2-1	1-4	4-3	0-1	0-1	2-3	

EASTERN COUNTIES LEAGUE

RECENT CHAMPIONS

2016: Norwich United **2017:** Mildenhall Town **2018:** Coggeshall Town

PREMIER DIVISION	P	W	D	L	F	A	GD	Pts
1 Histon	38	30	5	3	91	34	57	95
2 Woodbridge Town	38	26	3	9	103	51	52	81
3 Godmanchester Rovers	38	21	10	7	89	56	33	73
4 Stowmarket Town	38	20	11	7	81	40	41	71
5 Kirkley & Pakefield	38	19	9	10	65	55	10	66
6 FC Clacton	38	19	6	13	76	74	2	63
7 Wroxham	38	19	5	14	70	54	16	62
8 Brantham Athletic	38	17	8	13	56	47	9	59
9 Walsham Le Willows	38	17	6	15	67	60	7	57
10 Newmarket Town	38	15	6	17	73	70	3	51
11 Norwich United	38	14	8	16	59	53	6	50
12 Haverhill Rovers	38	14	7	17	53	63	-10	49
13 Whitton United	38	13	5	20	53	66	-13	44
14 Thetford Town	38	13	4	21	62	76	-14	43
15 Gorleston	38	12	5	21	62	82	-20	41
16 Hadleigh United	38	12	4	22	64	92	-28	40
17 Long Melford	38	10	9	19	45	78	-33	39
18 Ely City	38	11	5	22	52	84	-32	38
19 Great Yarmouth Town	38	10	4	24	45	80	-35	34
20 Framlingham Town	38	6	4	28	47	98	-51	22

DIVISION ONE NORTH	P	W	D	L	F	A	GD	Pts
1 Swaffham Town	36	27	4	5	105	36	69	85
2 Harleston Town	36	27	3	6	123	44	79	84
3 Mulbarton Wanderers	36	23	5	8	84	42	42	74
4 March Town United	36	21	9	6	89	48	41	72
5 Lakenheath	36	22	4	10	104	53	51	70
6 Fakenham Town	36	21	7	8	72	49	23	70
7 Norwich CBS	36	20	7	9	92	54	38	67
8 Downham Town	36	18	6	12	64	58	6	60
9 Leiston Res	36	14	3	19	77	93	-16	45
10 Ipswich Wanderers	36	13	4	19	64	77	-13	43
11 Debenham LC	36	12	7	17	45	61	-16	43
12 Cornard United	36	11	9	16	68	82	-14	42
13 AFC Sudbury Res	36	11	6	19	73	81	-8	39
14 King's Lynn Town Res	36	11	5	20	65	96	-31	38
15 Diss Town	36	11	4	21	50	67	-17	37
16 Haverhill Borough	36	10	3	23	75	103	-28	33
17 Needham Market Res	36	9	6	21	62	94	-32	33
18 Wisbech St Mary	36	8	1	27	49	131	-82	25
19 Felixstowe & Walton Utd Res	36	6	1	29	43	135	-92	19

DIVISION ONE SOUTH	P	W	D	L	F	A	GD	Pts
1 Hashtag United	36	26	6	4	85	29	56	84
2 Coggeshall United	36	24	5	7	100	39	61	77
3 Halstead Town	36	24	4	8	92	52	40	76
4 White Ensign	36	22	5	9	87	53	34	71
5 Harwich & Parkeston	36	22	5	9	87	57	30	71
6 Hackney Wick	36	19	10	7	61	37	24	67
7 Little Oakley	36	19	7	10	73	63	10	64
8 May & Baker	36	18	4	14	70	64	6	58
9 Frenford	36	16	8	12	73	57	16	56
10 Wormley Rovers	36	15	7	14	70	50	20	52
11 Holland	36	16	3	17	67	68	-1	51
12 Benfleet	36	14	7	15	75	63	12	49
13 Burnham Ramblers	36	13	6	17	66	81	-15	45
14 Wivenhoe Town	36	10	7	19	48	82	-34	37
15 Braintree Town Res	36	6	10	20	41	87	-46	28
16 Lopes Tavares	36	6	8	22	52	89	-37	26
17 Newbury Forest	36	5	7	24	46	93	-47	22
18 Brightlingsea Regent Res	36	5	5	26	53	97	-44	20
19 Fire United	36	4	2	30	34	119	-85	14

CHALLENGE CUP

HOLDERS: BRANTHAM ATHLETIC

ROUND 1

Little Oakley	v	Brightlingsea Regent Res	2-3
White Ensign	v	Newbury Forest	2-1
Lopes Tavares	v	Hashtag United	4-0
May & Baker	v	Fire United	4-0
Benfleet	v	Hackney Wick	1-0
Holland	v	Felixstowe & Walton United	5-2
Halstead Town	v	Comard United	2-0
Braintree Town Res	v	Haverhill Borough	1-3
Whitton United	v	Leiston Res	0-2
Diss Town	v	Lakenheath	1-6
Wivenhoe Town	v	Needham Market Res	1-1, 2-4p
Burnham Ramblers	v	Ipswich Wanderers	4-3
Downham Town	v	Wisbech St Mary	1-2
Swaffam Town	v	King's Lynn Town Res	1-0

ROUND 2

Woodbridge Town	v	Long Melford	0-3
Hadleigh United	v	Brightlingsea Regent Res	5-2
Stowmarket Town	v	Haverhill Rovers	6-1
Godmanchester Rovers	v	Walsham le Willows	3-2
FC Clacton	v	Brantham Athletic	4-1
White Ensign	v	Lopes Tavares	6-2
May & Baker	v	Benfleet	1-6
Holland	v	Halstead Town	4-0
Ely City	v	Histon	3-0
Newmarket Town	v	Haverhill Borough	3-2
Gorleston	v	Leiston Res	7-3
Norwich United	v	Lakenheath	2-1
Kirkley & Pakefield	v	Wroxham	4-2
Needham Market Res	v	Burnham Ramblers	3-1
Wisbech St Mary	v	Fakenham Town	1-2
Thetford Town	v	Swaffham Town	2-2, 5-6p

ROUND 3

Long Melford	v	Hadleigh United	2-0
Stowmarket Town	v	Godmanchester Rovers	4-1
FC Clacton	v	White Ensign	1-1, 4-5p
Benfleet	v	Holland	3-2
Ely City	v	Newmarket Town	0-3
Gorleston	v	Norwich United	1-0
Kirkley & Pakefield	v	Needham Market Res	2-0
Fakenham Town	v	Swaffham Town	2-2, 8-7p

QUARTER FINALS

Long Melford	v	Stowmarket Town	3-1
White Ensign	v	Benfleet	2-2, 6-7p
Newmarket Town	v	Gorleston	3-0
Kirkley & Pakefield	v	Fakenham Town	0-0, 2-4p

SEMI FINALS

Long Melford	v	Benfleet	4-3
Newmarket Town	v	Fakenham Town	1-1, 2-4p

FINAL

Long Melford	v	Fakenham Town	1-0

DIVISION ONE CUP FINAL

Harleston Town	v	Holland	6-0

PREMIER DIVISION	1	2	3	4	5	6	7	8	9	10	11	12	13	14	15	16	17	18	19	20
1 Brantham Athletic		3-0	4-2	2-1	1-1	0-1	5-1	4-0	5-1	2-0	0-3	2-4	1-0	1-1	0-0	2-0	1-0	1-0	1-3	0-3
2 Ely City	2-2		1-1	3-1	2-1	1-0	3-2	2-1	1-3	1-2	2-1	4-0	2-0	1-6	3-3	1-2	0-3	2-5	0-2	0-3
3 FC Clacton	2-0	3-1		1-4	5-3	4-1	3-0	0-0	2-0	1-2	3-3	1-1	1-2	2-0	0-3	3-1	4-1	2-2	4-3	1-3
4 Framlingham Town	0-1	3-3	1-3		1-2	2-2	2-1	2-7	0-2	1-2	0-1	2-3	2-2	2-0	0-3	2-3	1-2	2-1	1-2	1-1
5 Godmanchester Rovers	2-2	3-1	4-3	5-0		4-3	1-1	5-0	4-1	1-3	2-2	2-2	3-0	2-3	3-2	1-1	2-2	1-1	3-0	5-0
6 Gorleston	3-0	3-2	0-2	4-1	2-4		1-1	0-1	2-0	2-4	0-1	2-1	2-1	4-2	0-2	2-4	0-3	4-1	0-4	1-2
7 Great Yarmouth Town	1-1	0-3	1-2	0-1	0-3	2-0		4-0	2-1	0-3	0-2	1-2	2-0	0-2	0-4	1-0	5-2	0-1	1-2	0-2
8 Hadleigh United	1-2	2-0	5-1	3-1	2-4	1-4	2-1		2-2	0-4	3-4	2-0	2-1	3-2	0-2	1-4	0-1	1-2	2-8	3-0
9 Haverhill Rovers	0-2	2-1	1-2	2-0	0-1	3-3	1-2	2-3		0-2	2-2	4-0	2-4	0-0	2-1	2-1	0-1	2-1	2-1	4-2
10 Histon	1-0	4-0	3-0	4-2	3-1	2-1	4-2	2-1	4-0		2-2	2-1	6-1	4-2	0-0	1-0	2-2	2-0	2-1	5-0
11 Kirkley & Pakefield	1-2	0-2	2-3	1-0	1-2	2-1	1-2	3-2	1-0	1-1		1-0	3-2	1-0	1-1	5-0	1-3	1-0	2-1	0-0
12 Long Melford	1-0	3-1	0-1	1-3	3-3	2-2	3-0	2-2	1-0	2-1	0-1		0-2	1-4	1-1	2-2	0-4	0-1	0-6	1-4
13 Newmarket Town	1-1	3-0	4-3	8-1	1-0	7-0	4-2	2-1	1-1	1-2	2-3	0-1		1-3	4-1	1-1	4-3	2-1	2-6	3-2
14 Norwich United	1-5	3-1	1-2	2-1	0-0	2-2	1-2	1-2	0-1	0-1	0-0	1-0	3-1		0-0	5-0	2-0	1-0	4-1	0-2
15 Stowmarket Town	2-0	2-2	5-1	3-0	1-2	4-3	3-0	1-1	4-1	1-1	5-0	5-0	2-0	1-1		2-1	2-3	1-0	4-2	1-2
16 Thetford Town	2-0	2-1	1-3	4-2	0-2	3-0	5-2	3-0	1-2	1-2	1-2	1-3	0-1	3-1	1-3		4-2	5-0	1-4	1-5
17 Walsham Le Willows	3-0	0-1	2-2	3-1	1-2	2-1	2-2	3-1	0-1	2-3	2-4	2-0	2-2	1-1	2-3	2-1		3-0	0-4	1-0
18 Whitton United	1-0	1-0	0-1	4-3	1-2	1-2	0-1	5-4	2-4	0-1	5-3	2-2	3-3	3-2	2-0	1-1	2-0		2-3	2-0
19 Woodbridge Town	1-1	4-1	4-2	4-0	3-0	3-1	5-2	5-1	2-2	2-1	3-2	4-0	1-0	1-0	1-1	3-1	0-2	1-0		2-3
20 Wroxham	1-2	5-1	5-0	3-0	2-3	1-3	3-1	3-2	0-0	0-3	1-1	2-2	1-0	1-2	0-2	4-0	1-0	3-0	0-1	

DIVISION ONE NORTH	1	2	3	4	5	6	7	8	9	10	11	12	13	14	15	16	17	18	19
1 AFC Sudbury Res		0-1	1-3	5-0	1-3	1-2	6-3	0-1	2-1	1-1	5-1	3-1	5-3	1-3	2-2	2-5	3-2	1-2	5-3
2 Cornard United	1-4		1-2	3-1	6-2	0-0	1-4	2-5	3-2	4-0	2-3	1-2	3-0	0-4	3-2	6-2	2-2	0-1	2-1
3 Debenham LC	2-0	2-2		1-1	1-3	0-0	2-2	1-3	1-0	1-0	0-1	2-3	0-1	1-1	0-2	3-2	0-1	1-2	2-0
4 Diss Town	1-0	0-0	1-2		0-1	2-3	5-0	0-1	5-0	1-2	3-2	0-6	3-2	1-2	3-1	1-0	1-2	1-1	1-4
5 Downham Town	2-0	2-1	3-1	1-0		1-1	1-0	1-1	3-0	0-3	1-2	4-2	0-4	2-2	0-2	3-1	0-0	2-2	1-0
6 Fakenham Town	1-0	3-3	4-0	4-0	2-3		4-2	1-4	2-0	1-2	2-1	0-5	5-2	3-1	0-3	0-0	1-2	2-1	2-0
7 Felixstowe & Walton United Res	0-6	0-3	1-3	0-4	1-6	1-2		1-5	1-2	3-2	1-2	3-2	1-4	0-4	1-5	1-0	1-5	0-3	2-3
8 Harleston Town	2-2	6-2	7-0	1-0	5-1	0-1	4-2		5-1	3-0	3-2	1-2	4-1	5-1	3-1	6-2	1-4	1-3	5-0
9 Haverhill Borough	4-2	6-0	3-3	4-0	2-5	1-3	7-1	0-6		3-4	3-3	1-0	2-6	1-3	2-3	0-0	2-3	1-6	7-1
10 Ipswich Wanderers	2-1	6-0	0-3	0-1	2-4	0-0	4-1	3-1	2-4		3-1	1-2	1-2	1-1	0-3	5-3	0-1	1-6	3-2
11 King's Lynn Town Res	5-1	1-4	2-1	0-0	3-3	3-5	6-2	1-6	2-5	4-1		0-3	1-1	1-3	1-3	1-1	0-4	0-2	4-0
12 Lakenheath	2-2	4-2	0-1	3-1	1-0	1-2	10-1	1-1	2-1	5-1	3-2		2-3	1-3	2-0	3-2	5-1	4-1	3-0
13 Leiston Res	2-2	3-1	3-0	2-5	1-2	0-2	6-1	0-8	3-2	2-1	10-3	2-3		1-2	0-4	2-2	1-2	1-5	3-1
14 March Town United	6-3	1-1	2-0	3-1	2-0	3-1	3-0	1-4	3-0	3-3	1-2	1-1	2-1		2-2	1-1	2-2	2-0	5-0
15 Mulbarton Wanderers	0-0	3-2	4-0	1-0	2-1	2-0	2-0	0-4	4-1	2-1	5-1	1-2	2-1	3-0		2-1	2-2	0-2	10-1
16 Needham Market Res	0-1	1-1	1-0	2-1	2-1	0-3	1-3	2-5	2-4	2-4	0-3	4-1	2-3	0-5	3-1		2-4	1-4	6-3
17 Norwich CBS	6-3	3-1	1-1	2-1	3-0	1-3	8-1	0-1	5-1	3-0	6-0	1-1	7-0	2-6	0-0	2-3		1-2	3-1
18 Swaffham Town	5-1	2-2	3-2	4-0	1-0	3-3	3-0	4-3	4-0	2-1	2-1	4-1	3-0	2-0	0-1	8-0	4-0		1-2
19 Wisbech St Mary	3-1	2-2	0-3	2-5	1-2	1-4	1-2	1-2	5-2	1-4	1-0	0-15	4-1	1-5	1-4	1-6	2-1	0-7	

DIVISION ONE SOUTH	1	2	3	4	5	6	7	8	9	10	11	12	13	14	15	16	17	18	19
1 Benfleet		0-0	1-0	6-1	1-5	6-3	1-2	1-1	0-1	1-0	1-1	0-1	2-3	5-3	0-1	3-0	1-3	1-1	3-1
2 Braintree Town Res	0-0		3-3	2-3	1-3	2-0	3-3	1-1	0-6	1-2	0-2	2-2	1-4	2-2	7-2	0-4	0-1	2-1	1-1
3 Brightlingsea Regent Res	2-2	8-0		1-6	0-3	3-0	2-3	1-2	0-3	2-3	0-3	2-3	1-3	3-0	1-2	2-5	1-3	0-3	0-0
4 Burnham Ramblers	0-7	5-1	3-0		0-1	4-2	3-1	1-0	1-5	2-3	0-4	3-2	2-2	2-2	2-0	2-0	2-2	0-0	0-1
5 Coggeshall United	4-1	1-2	4-1	5-1		9-0	3-1	0-3	1-1	4-1	2-3	0-2	1-1	0-1	2-3	2-0	3-0	5-2	3-1
6 Fire United	2-4	1-2	4-0	2-1	1-2		0-3	1-3	0-5	1-7	0-4	2-3	1-4	3-1	1-2	0-4	0-6	1-0	0-4
7 Frenford	2-2	1-1	5-2	2-1	2-2	4-0		1-2	0-1	1-3	0-3	3-2	7-0	1-3	4-2	2-2	1-1	1-2	2-3
8 Hackney Wick	3-0	1-0	6-1	2-0	2-2	2-2	0-0		1-4	1-1	1-1	3-0	2-0	2-2	3-0	2-1	0-2	0-1	1-0
9 Halstead Town	2-0	4-1	4-1	2-1	0-4	2-1	0-3	0-2		2-0	0-1	5-1	3-3	2-0	2-2	4-3	1-2	1-2	1-4
10 Harwich & Parkeston	2-1	5-1	4-2	4-3	0-4	4-3	1-1	3-2	2-3		2-1	1-1	1-2	4-1	1-0	3-0	3-3	2-0	1-2
11 Hashtag United	3-1	4-0	3-0	2-1	0-0	3-0	3-0	1-1	2-1	3-2		5-0	1-1	2-1	3-1	3-0	3-0	1-1	1-3
12 Holland	2-3	3-0	1-0	4-5	0-5	3-0	1-2	2-0	3-4	0-2	0-2		0-0	2-0	4-2	5-0	2-0	1-2	1-3
13 Little Oakley	0-5	2-1	5-0	1-0	2-3	2-0	2-3	2-2	1-3	0-2	3-2	3-1		4-0	4-0	4-1	1-2	2-1	2-4
14 Lopes Tavares	1-2	3-1	1-2	1-1	0-2	4-0	0-3	0-2	1-2	5-5	0-2	2-1	0-3		2-6	5-1	0-2	0-0	3-3
15 May & Baker	3-2	1-0	1-1	5-0	0-3	2-1	0-4	1-2	0-2	4-2	2-4	0-3	8-0	1-0		2-0	1-1	2-0	5-1
16 Newbury Forest	0-7	1-1	1-1	1-2	0-3	2-2	0-2	1-2	4-5	0-4	3-4	1-5	0-2	3-2	1-1		1-2	2-3	0-0
17 White Ensign	5-2	3-0	5-2	3-0	2-4	2-0	2-0	4-2	2-3	0-4	2-0	2-3	0-1	4-4	1-4	4-0		4-1	2-1
18 Wivenhoe Town	1-3	3-0	0-8	4-4	2-4	2-0	2-3	0-1	2-7	0-2	0-4	2-3	3-3	3-2	0-1	0-2	0-7		1-1
19 Wormley Rovers	4-0	1-2	2-0	1-4	2-1	8-0	2-0	0-1	1-1	0-1	0-1	2-0	0-1	8-0	0-3	2-2	2-3	2-3	

EMC - Graham Street Prims v Clifton All Whites. Photo: Bill Wheatcroft.

Graham Street Prims v Clifton All Whites. Photo: Bill Wheatcroft.

ESSEX SENIOR LEAGUE

Recent Champions

2016: Bowers & Pitsea **2017:** Barking **2018:** Great Wakering Rovers

PREMIER DIVISION	P	W	D	L	F	A	GD	PTS
1 Hullbridge Sports	38	27	6	5	79	33	46	87
2 Stansted	38	26	4	8	87	39	48	82
3 Walthamstow	38	24	8	6	85	38	47	80
4 Saffron Walden Town	38	23	7	8	106	53	53	76
5 Takeley	38	23	4	11	76	45	31	73
6 Woodford Town	38	19	7	12	88	54	34	64
7 St Margaretsbury	38	16	6	16	63	82	-19	54
8 Sporting Bengal United	38	15	8	15	79	76	3	53
9 Hoddesdon Town	38	13	13	12	55	45	10	52
10 Ilford	38	14	7	17	59	65	-6	49
11 Clapton	38	14	7	17	64	73	-9	49
12 Redbridge	38	13	8	17	71	78	-7	47
13 West Essex	38	13	8	17	61	69	-8	47
14 Enfield	38	12	10	16	56	79	-23	46
15 Stanway Rovers	38	12	6	20	53	80	-27	42
16 Tower Hamlets	38	11	7	20	51	64	-13	40
17 Southend Manor	38	11	6	21	49	66	-17	39
18 Sawbridgeworth Town	38	10	8	20	46	83	-37	38
19 Barkingside	38	6	7	25	39	92	-53	25
20 Leyton Athletic	38	4	11	23	36	89	-53	23

RESERVE DIVISION	P	W	D	L	F	A	GD	PTS
1 Aveley Res	22	18	2	2	85	27	58	56
2 Hullbridge Sports Res	22	14	4	4	58	30	28	46
3 Barkingside Res	22	13	3	6	63	40	23	42
4 Southend Manor Res	22	11	4	7	50	43	7	37
5 Waltham Abbey Res	22	11	1	10	50	37	13	34
6 Saffron Walden Town Res	22	10	1	11	48	53	-5	31
7 Takeley Res	22	9	3	10	39	47	-8	30
8 Redbridge Res	22	8	5	9	35	45	-10	29
9 Harlow Town Res	22	8	3	11	53	72	-19	27
10 Grays Athletic Res	22	7	4	11	37	42	-5	25
11 Sawbridgeworth Town Res	22	5	2	15	35	62	-27	17
12 Redbridge Development	22	2	0	20	31	86	-55	6

LEAGUE CHALLENGE CUP

HOLDERS: GREAT WAKERING ROVERS

ROUND 1

Southend Manor	v	Saffron Walden Town	2-3
Woodford Town	v	Hoddesdon Town	1-4
St Margaretsbury	v	Stanway Rovers	5-0
Sawbridgeworth Town	v	Tower Hamlets	2-3

ROUND 2

Walthamstow	v	Redbridge	5-0
Stansted	v	Takeley	2-0
Leyton Athletic	v	Barkingside	0-1
Ilford	v	Saffron Walden Town	1-3
Hullbridge Sports	v	Hoddesdon Town	1-5
Clapton	v	Enfield 1893	1-0
Sporting Bengal United	v	St Margaretsbury	1-0
Tower Hamlets	v	West Essex	3-3, 0-3p

QUARTER FINALS

Walthamstow	v	Stansted	0-2
Barkingside	v	Saffron Walden Town	0-4
Hoddesdon Town	v	Clapton	2-4
Sporting Bengal United	v	West Essex	2-2, 3-4p

SEMI FINALS

Stansted	v	Saffron Walden Town	5-0
Clpaton	v	West Essex	2-4

FINAL

Stansted	v	West Essex	1-0

GORDON BRASTED MEMORIAL TROPHY FINAL

Stansted	v	St Margaretsbury	1-0

PREMIER DIVISION	1	2	3	4	5	6	7	8	9	10	11	12	13	14	15	16	17	18	19	20
1 Barkingside		0-3	0-0	0-3	1-3	1-5	2-2	1-4	2-3	4-1	2-3	0-0	0-2	1-2	3-2	0-1	3-0	0-2	0-1	1-6
2 Clapton	2-1		3-0	1-1	1-0	0-2	2-2	1-4	0-3	3-0	1-1	7-1	0-0	2-5	2-2	1-2	1-0	1-3	3-1	3-4
3 Enfield 1893	1-3	4-2		3-2	2-5	1-3	6-1	2-2	1-3	2-1	3-1	2-2	2-3	1-0	3-1	1-0	2-4	0-4	0-1	1-3
4 Hoddesdon Town	1-1	3-0	0-0		1-2	1-1	1-0	2-2	1-3	2-0	1-2	2-0	1-4	0-1	3-0	1-2	1-1	2-2	0-2	4-1
5 Hullbridge Sports	0-0	4-2	6-1	1-0		2-2	2-2	1-2	2-0	6-1	0-2	4-3	3-1	2-1	2-1	3-1	2-0	1-1	2-0	2-1
6 Ilford	2-1	0-3	0-0	0-0	0-3		2-0	2-3	0-3	3-2	1-2	1-4	2-3	0-3	3-1	0-2	2-0	0-1	1-2	1-5
7 Leyton Athletic	5-0	2-4	0-0	0-2	0-4	0-0		2-2	0-5	1-0	2-3	2-6	1-1	1-0	1-2	0-3	0-0	0-5	2-2	0-1
8 Redbridge	3-0	1-1	2-2	2-2	0-1	1-4	1-0		1-1	4-1	4-1	1-2	1-2	0-4	3-3	0-1	1-4	0-3	0-2	1-3
9 Saffron Walden Town	2-2	4-0	5-2	1-1	0-1	5-1	7-0	3-1		5-1	3-2	4-4	5-2	3-5	4-0	0-1	5-0	3-3	2-3	1-2
10 Sawbridgeworth Town	1-0	1-1	1-1	0-3	2-1	2-2	0-3	3-1	1-1		2-1	2-1	1-3	2-2	2-0	1-3	0-3	0-2	4-2	1-0
11 Southend Manor	2-0	2-0	2-0	1-2	0-2	0-2	2-0	2-3	2-2	2-0		3-1	0-1	0-3	0-3	0-1	0-0	2-5	0-1	1-2
12 Sporting Bengal United	0-1	4-2	6-0	1-1	0-1	0-3	1-1	5-1	3-4	5-2	2-1		1-4	0-2	1-2	1-1	2-4	2-0	2-1	0-4
13 St Margaretsbury	1-3	1-0	1-2	0-1	1-2	0-3	3-1	0-10	0-4	0-0	1-1	1-4		0-4	2-1	2-2	6-0	2-2	2-6	3-1
14 Stansted	2-2	4-2	3-1	1-2	0-0	2-1	5-0	2-1	0-1	2-2	4-1	4-1	5-0		5-1	2-1	2-3	2-1	1-0	2-1
15 Stanway Rovers	4-1	0-2	1-2	2-1	2-1	4-2	1-0	1-2	0-3	2-0	2-1	2-2	0-5	1-2		1-5	2-1	1-2	0-0	1-1
16 Takeley	8-1	1-2	0-1	3-2	0-1	3-2	2-0	0-3	4-0	1-1	2-1	2-3	3-2	2-0	2-0		2-0	4-1	1-2	2-2
17 Tower Hamlets	4-0	5-0	0-2	1-0	1-1	2-1	2-1	1-3	0-1	2-3	1-0	2-3	1-2	1-2	2-3	2-3		0-2	2-2	1-2
18 Walthamstow	4-0	1-0	0-0	2-2	1-2	1-2	2-2	5-1	3-1	4-1	2-0	1-1	4-0	1-0	2-0	2-0	1-0		1-0	1-3
19 West Essex	3-1	2-3	5-2	2-2	0-2	1-2	4-1	2-0	1-4	2-3	1-1	1-4	0-2	0-1	3-3	2-5	1-1	1-5		0-2
20 Woodford Town	4-1	2-3	3-3	0-1	0-2	1-1	4-1	6-0	1-2	3-1	4-4	0-1	5-0	1-2	4-1	2-0	0-0	2-3	2-2	

HELLENIC LEAGUE

RECENT CHAMPIONS

2016: Kidlington **2017:** Thame United **2018:** Thatcham Town

PREMIER DIVISION	P	W	D	L	F	A	GD	Pts
1 Wantage Town	36	22	7	7	81	42	39	73
2 Brimscombe & Thrupp	36	22	5	9	74	47	27	71
3 Brackley Town Saints	36	22	4	10	71	47	24	70
4 Bishops Cleeve	36	20	9	7	80	47	33	69
5 Shrivenham	36	19	4	13	66	62	4	61
6 Windsor	36	18	6	12	67	46	21	60
7 Ascot United	36	15	12	9	72	49	23	57
8 Flackwell Heath	36	14	10	12	49	48	1	52
9 Binfield	36	14	8	14	59	62	-3	50
10 Royal Wootton Bassett Town	36	14	7	15	66	71	-5	49
11 Lydney Town	36	14	6	16	56	69	-13	48
12 Holmer Green	36	14	6	16	47	65	-18	48
13 Fairford Town	36	13	4	19	52	66	-14	43
14 Virginia Water	36	10	12	14	50	52	-2	42
15 Tuffley Rovers	36	9	10	17	57	68	-11	37
16 Longlevens	36	11	4	21	52	64	-12	37
17 Ardley United	36	10	7	19	59	77	-18	37
18 Reading City	36	10	1	25	50	82	-32	31
19 Abingdon United	36	8	4	24	36	80	-44	28

DIVISION ONE EAST	P	W	D	L	F	A	GD	Pts
1 Burnham	24	17	3	4	85	29	56	54
2 Thame Rangers	24	14	8	2	51	35	16	50
3 AFC Aldermaston	24	14	3	7	63	39	24	45
4 Holyport	24	13	5	6	53	22	31	44
5 Didcot Town Dev	24	13	2	9	47	33	14	41
6 Wokingham & Emmbrook	24	11	4	9	44	46	-2	37
7 Wallingford Town	24	10	5	9	47	49	-2	35
8 Chalvey Sports	24	10	4	10	56	44	12	34
9 Penn & Tylers Green	24	10	1	13	46	52	-6	31
10 Milton United	24	8	5	11	38	37	1	29
11 Woodley United	24	5	5	14	44	66	-22	20
12 Abingdon Town	24	5	2	17	37	112	-75	17
13 Chinnor	24	2	1	21	25	72	-47	7

Bicester Town resigned - record expunged.

DIVISION ONE WEST	P	W	D	L	F	A	GD	Pts
1 Easington Sports	22	17	1	4	61	13	48	52
2 Cheltenham Saracens	22	16	1	5	78	26	52	49
3 Thornbury Town	22	15	3	4	65	23	42	48
4 Malmesbury Victoria	22	15	1	6	83	25	58	46
5 Clanfield (85)	22	13	4	5	50	26	24	43
6 Kidlington Development	22	12	3	7	72	35	37	39
7 Almondsbury	22	11	4	7	58	30	28	37
8 Cirencester Town Dev	22	7	1	14	50	54	-4	22
9 Newent Town	22	6	4	12	32	56	-24	22
10 Pewsey Vale	22	5	4	13	37	62	-25	19
11 Tytherington Rocks	22	1	0	21	15	109	-94	3
12 New College Swindon	22	1	0	21	10	152	-142	3

Carterton resigned - record expunged.

North Leigh United resigned - record expunged.

LEAGUE CHALLENGE CUP

HOLDERS: BRACKNELL TOWN

PRELIMINARY ROUND

Risborough Rangers Res	v	Wallingford Town	1-1, 4-3p

ROUND 1

Newent Town	v	Abingdon United	2-4
Tuffley Rovers	v	Royal Wootton Bassett Town	4-0
Thame Rangers	v	Ascot United	1-2
Headington Amateurs	v	Adderbury Park	2-2, 3-1p
Ardley United	v	Lydney Town	2-0
Malmesbury Victoria	v	Chalvey Sports	3-1
Longlevens	v	Penn & Tylers Green	7-1
Thatcham Town Dev	v	Faringdon Town	3-2
Virginia Water	v	Easington Sports	1-4
Langley	v	Wantage Town	1-2
Wokingham & Emmbrook	v	New College Swindon	4-1
Reading City	v	Flackwell Heath	1-0
Pewsey Vale	v	Brimscombe & Thrupp	1-3
Abingdon Town	v	Holmer Green	1-0
Thornbury Town	v	Highworth Town Res	2-0
Binfield	v	Bourton Rovers	5-3
Bishops Cleeve	v	Brackley Town Saints	4-3 (aet)
Kidlington Dev	v	Tytherington Rocks	HW
Old Bradwell United	v	Clanfield (85)	1-7
Woodley United	v	Cirencester Town Dev	4-1
Chinnor	v	Taplow United	4-1
Chalfont Wasps	v	Risborough Rangers Res	1-3
Yately United	v	Burham	1-3
Stokenchurch	v	Almondsbury	2-4

ROUND 2

Abingdon United	v	Tuffley Rovers	4-1
Ascot United	v	Headington Amateurs	4-0
Ardley United	v	Malmesbury Victoria	3-2
Longlevens	v	Thatcham Town Dev	3-0
Easington Sports	v	Wantage Town	1-3
Wokingham & Emmbrook	v	Reading City	1-0
Brimscombe & Thrupp	v	Abingdon Town	7-0
Thornbury Town	v	Binfield	2-4
Bishops Cleeve	v	Kidlington Dev	6-2
Clanfield (85)	v	Woodley United	4-1
Chinnor (aet)	v	Risborough Rangers Res	1-2
Burnham	v	Almondsbury	0-2
Windsor	v	Holyport	2-0
Moreton Rangers	v	Shrivenham	2-0
Milton United	v	Cheltenham Saracens	1-4
Fairford Town	v	AFC Aldermaston	0-2

ROUND 3

Abingdon United	v	Ascot United	0-4
Ardley United	v	Longlevens	0-3
Wantage Town	v	Wokingham & Emmbrook	6-2
Brimscombe & Thrupp	v	Binfield	0-2
Bishops Cleeve	v	Clanfield (85)	5-0
Risborough Rangers Res	v	Almondsbury	2-4
Windsor	v	Moreton Rangers	2-1
Cheltenham Saracens	v	AFC Aldermaston	HW

QUARTER FINALS

Ascot United	v	Longlevens	3-2
Wantage Town	v	Binfield	3-0
Bishops Cleeve	v	Almondsbury	1-2
Windsor	v	Cheltenham Saracens	3-0

SEMI FINALS

Ascot United	v	Wantage Town	1-0
Almondsbury	v	Windsor	0-3

FINAL

Ascot United	v	Windsor	3-1

CHAIRMANS CHALLENGE CUP FINAL

Bourton Rovers	v	Penn & Tylers Green	4-1

DIVISION ONE SUBSIDARY CUP FINAL

Burham	v	Malmesbury Victoria	2-3

SUPPLEMENTARY CUP FINAL

Thornbury Town	v	Wallingford Town	2-1

PREMIER DIVISION		1	2	3	4	5	6	7	8	9	10	11	12	13	14	15	16	17	18	19	20
1	Abingdon United			0-2	2-4	4-0	1-2	1-3	1-2	2-3	2-0	0-0	0-3	0-1	3-0	2-0	0-3	2-2	0-2	0-4	0-1
2	Ardley United		4-1		2-3	1-4	2-2	3-4	4-2	4-5	2-1	0-0	3-3	1-4	3-0	2-0	0-1	2-1	1-0	1-3	1-1
3	Ascot United		2-2	4-1		0-0	1-0	1-1	1-3	3-0	1-3	4-0	2-0	4-1	5-0	1-1	2-3	1-1	1-0	1-1	4-2
4	Binfield		0-1	2-1	1-1		0-1	3-1	0-2	1-1	1-2	1-0	3-0	1-1	2-5	3-2	3-1	4-2	1-1	3-1	0-2
5	Bishops Cleeve		1-0	3-1	3-3	6-3		4-0	0-1	0-3	3-2	3-3	2-1	3-1	2-1	5-1	5-1	2-1	3-3	1-3	1-0
6	Brackley Town Saints		2-0	3-0	5-1	2-1	0-2		2-1	2-1	0-0	0-1	3-2	4-0	4-1	1-1	5-2	4-1	1-2	2-3	0-3
7	Brimscombe & Thrupp		4-0	6-4	3-1	3-3	0-2	2-3		1-2	2-1	3-0	0-2	3-2	3-1	2-0	2-0	2-1	2-1	0-0	3-1
8	Fairford Town		1-2	1-0	1-4	1-2	0-0	2-1	1-3		1-2	5-0	1-2	2-0	0-3	3-3	0-2	3-0	2-1	2-3	1-1
9	Flackwell Heath		0-0	2-0	1-0	1-2	1-1	1-3	2-0	1-2		0-0	0-0	1-2	4-1	3-3	1-2	2-1	1-1	2-1	0-0
10	Holmer Green		2-0	5-0	1-0	0-4	1-6	1-3	1-0	1-2	0-2		1-0	3-1	2-0	2-2	3-2	1-2	1-2	2-0	3-1
11	Longlevens		3-1	0-4	1-0	4-1	1-0	0-1	0-2	1-2	2-2	1-3		2-3	2-1	1-2	1-2	1-3	1-2	1-2	1-2
12 13	Lydney Town		3-0	3-3	3-3	0-2	0-5	1-2	2-2	1-0	2-0	3-1	3-2		0-3	0-2	1-3	0-0	1-0	1-0	2-0
14	Reading City		4-0	1-4	0-0	2-3	1-3	1-0	1-3	3-1	0-1	1-3	2-1	0-4		4-3	1-2	0-2	0-2	1-3	0-3
15	Royal Wootton Bassett Town		3-2	2-1	0-4	1-0	3-3	1-3	1-1	2-1	2-1	4-2	2-3	3-2	3-1		0-1	6-1	2-1	1-2	2-1
16	Shrivenham		1-2	3-0	2-2	4-1	1-3	0-2	3-5	3-0	0-1	2-0	4-1	3-3	1-5	2-0		2-1	1-1	2-1	1-3
17	Tuffley Rovers		1-3	4-0	2-2	2-1	1-1	1-2	1-0	3-0	1-1	3-3	1-2	4-1	1-3	1-3	0-3		6-1	0-0	3-6
18	Virginia Water		5-0	1-1	1-3	1-1	1-1	0-2	1-1	3-1	1-3	0-1	2-2	2-3	3-0	2-0	0-1	1-1		2-2	2-1
19	Wantage Town		7-1	0-0	2-1	4-1	3-1	0-0	1-2	4-1	3-4	6-0	2-1	4-1	4-2	3-2	1-1	2-1	3-1		2-0
20	Windsor		5-1	2-1	0-2	1-1	2-0	3-0	1-3	2-0	6-0	2-0	0-4	1-0	2-1	4-3	6-1	1-1	1-1	0-1	

DIVISION ONE EAST		1	2	3	4	5	6	7	8	9	10	11	12	13
1	Abingdon Town		2-3	0-9	2-1	4-1	0-1	0-7	3-2	1-2	1-2	3-3	6-1	6-4
2	AFC Aldermaston	5-0		3-3	1-1	3-0	1-5	2-4	2-3	4-0	1-2	6-1	1-2	3-2
3	Burnham	11-0	5-3		1-4	4-0	3-2	4-2	8-0	3-0	0-2	1-0	4-2	5-1
4	Chalvey Sports	15-1	0-2	3-3		3-2	5-2	0-1	1-3	4-0	3-3	0-4	2-1	0-2
5	Chinnor	7-0	0-5	0-3	1-0		2-3	1-4	1-1	2-3	0-4	1-3	0-1	1-3
6	Didcot Town Development	6-0	0-1	1-0	0-1	4-0		0-2	0-2	3-1	2-3	2-2	2-0	4-2
7	Holyport	7-0	3-2	2-1	4-1	5-0	0-1		1-1	2-1	3-0	2-0	0-0	0-0
8	Milton United	8-0	0-2	0-0	1-2	3-0	0-1	1-0		0-2	1-1	0-1	0-1	2-2
9	Penn & Tylers Green	5-0	1-3	1-4	2-3	3-0	4-2	2-1	1-2		2-3	5-2	1-3	4-3
10	Thame Rangers	3-1	1-1	1-4	2-1	2-1	2-1	1-1	3-0	0-0		4-4	4-4	1-1
11	Wallingford Town	2-2	1-3	0-3	1-0	4-3	0-1	1-0	2-1	5-2	1-2		0-3	3-0
12	Wokingham & Emmbrook	3-2	1-2	1-2	3-3	1-0	2-2	2-1	3-2	2-1	1-3	2-4		3-1
13	Woodley United	4-3	2-4	1-4	2-3	6-2	0-2	1-1	0-5	0-3	1-2	3-3	3-2	

DIVISION ONE WEST		1	2	3	4	5	6	7	8	9	10	11	12
1	Almondsbury		1-2	3-0	1-1	0-2	1-1	3-2	11-0	7-0	1-4	1-2	2-1
2	Cheltenham Saracens	3-0		5-0	1-2	2-0	3-1	2-3	7-1	3-0	6-0	1-1	5-1
3	Cirencester Town Development	2-3	2-6		0-4	0-4	4-0	1-3	5-1	1-2	3-1	0-1	14-0
4	Clanfield (85)	2-2	1-3	2-1		1-2	2-3	3-1	2-0	1-1	3-1	5-0	1-0
5	Easington Sports	2-1	1-0	1-0	1-3		4-1	0-1	11-0	2-0	4-0	0-0	11-0
6	Kidlington Development	0-2	6-1	4-1	3-1	0-1		2-2	16-0	5-1	3-3	0-4	9-0
7	Malmesbury Victoria	1-3	4-1	5-0	0-3	2-0	1-0		11-0	6-0	8-0	1-3	13-0
8	New College Swindon	0-6	0-7	0-8	1-6	1-4	0-7	0-8		0-4	0-10	1-5	3-1
9	Newent Town	0-3	0-1	2-5	1-1	1-3	1-5	0-2	5-1		3-1	2-6	5-1
10	Pewsey Vale	1-1	1-7	0-0	0-2	0-5	1-2	0-4	7-0	0-0		0-2	3-1
11	Thornbury Town	4-1	1-2	6-1	3-2	0-1	1-2	2-0	7-0	2-2	6-1		2-0
12	Tytherington Rocks	0-5	0-10	1-2	1-2	0-2	1-2	2-5	4-1	0-2	1-3	0-7	

	DIVISION TWO EAST	P	W	D	L	F	A	GD	Pts
1	Long Crendon	28	25	2	1	118	18	100	77
2	Langley	28	24	2	2	106	18	88	74
3	Penn & Tylers Green Dev	28	24	2	2	96	27	69	74
4	Thatcham Town Dev'	28	14	5	9	59	45	14	47
5	Yateley United	28	13	4	11	61	46	15	43
6	Stokenchurch	28	13	4	11	51	66	-15	43
7	Virginia Water Dev'	28	10	8	10	52	46	6	38
8	Risborough Rangers Res'	28	9	7	12	42	56	-14	34
9	Chalfont Wasps	28	8	5	15	37	62	-25	29
10	Chalvey Sports Res'	28	8	2	18	31	89	-58	26
11	Taplow United	28	6	6	16	42	88	-46	24
12	Chinnor Res'	28	7	3	18	34	81	-47	24
13	Wallingford Town Res'	28	5	8	15	38	67	-29	23
14	Aston Clinton Res'	28	6	4	18	50	72	-22	22
15	Old Bradwell United Dev'	28	5	4	19	34	70	-36	19

	DIVISION TWO WEST	P	W	D	L	F	A	GD	Pts
1	Moreton Rangers	24	19	1	4	89	23	66	58
2	Wantage Town Dev'	24	17	3	4	80	36	44	54
3	Abingdon United Dev'	24	17	2	5	68	27	41	53
4	Adderbury Park	24	14	3	7	71	35	36	45
5	Bourton Rovers	24	14	3	7	64	33	31	45
6	Highworth Town Res'	24	14	3	7	62	45	17	45
7	Headington Amateurs	24	13	4	7	53	35	18	43
8	Clanfield (85) Dev'	24	6	6	12	37	60	-23	24
9	Brimscombe & Thrupp Res'	24	6	4	14	44	75	-31	22
10	Shrivenham Dev	24	6	3	15	38	58	-20	21
11	Faringdon Town	24	5	2	17	38	74	-36	17
12	Newent Town Res	24	3	4	17	33	93	-60	13
13	Woodstock Town	24	2	2	20	32	115	-83	8

MIDLAND FOOTBALL LEAGUE

RECENT CHAMPIONS

2016: Hereford **2017:** Alvechurch **2018:** Bromsgrove Sporting

PREMIER DIVISION	P	W	D	L	F	A	GD	Pts
1 Ilkeston Town	38	25	4	9	93	50	43	79
2 Walsall Wood	38	24	7	7	67	32	35	79
3 Sporting Khalsa	38	20	7	11	61	44	17	67
4 Westfields	38	17	12	9	73	48	25	63
5 Boldmere St Michaels	38	17	8	13	65	66	-1	59
6 Quorn	38	16	10	12	74	61	13	58
7 Shepshed Dynamo	38	17	6	15	68	64	4	57
8 Coventry United	38	16	8	14	52	47	5	56
9 Coventry Sphinx	38	16	8	14	61	57	4	56
10 Lye Town	38	14	10	14	65	52	13	52
11 Worcester City	38	14	10	14	66	61	5	52
12 AFC Wulfrunians	38	14	9	15	53	54	-1	51
13 Stourport Swifts	38	14	9	15	53	55	-2	51
14 Highgate United	38	13	12	13	49	55	-6	51
15 Long Eaton United	38	14	8	16	59	61	-2	50
16 South Normanton Athletic	38	13	6	19	52	48	4	45
17 Romulus	38	12	8	18	53	68	-15	44
18 Loughborough University	38	10	9	19	58	79	-21	39
19 Dunkirk	38	6	7	25	40	102	-62	25
20 Wolverhampton Sporting Com	38	5	8	25	52	110	-58	23

DIVISION ONE	P	W	D	L	F	A	GD	Pts
1 Heather St Johns	36	30	3	3	135	43	92	93
2 Racing Club Warwick	36	27	4	5	119	46	73	85
3 Atherstone Town	36	26	5	5	98	33	65	83
4 Lichfield City	36	24	2	10	107	59	48	74
5 Leicester Road	35	23	3	9	91	32	59	72
6 NKF Burbage	36	18	7	11	71	56	15	61
7 Uttoxeter Town	36	17	5	14	68	56	12	56
8 Cadbury Athletic	36	15	9	12	53	50	3	54
9 Studley	35	14	9	12	63	46	17	51
10 Paget Rangers	36	14	7	15	61	66	-5	49
11 Brocton	36	14	6	16	73	79	-6	48
12 Chelmsley Town	36	11	6	19	59	67	-8	39
13 Stapenhill	36	10	7	19	49	96	-47	37
14 Rocester	36	10	5	21	49	79	-30	35
15 Coventry Copsewood	36	9	8	19	51	90	-39	35
16 Hinckley AFC	36	8	10	18	46	69	-23	34
17 Littleton	36	6	5	25	43	94	-51	23
18 Heath Hayes	36	6	4	26	30	111	-81	22
19 Nuneaton Griff	36	4	5	27	33	127	-94	17

DIVISION TWO	P	W	D	L	F	A	GD	Pts
1 Northfield Town	30	23	4	3	80	30	50	73
2 GNP Sports	30	22	4	4	97	34	63	70
3 Boldmere S&S Falcons	30	21	5	4	77	34	43	68
4 Moors Academy	30	20	5	5	105	40	65	65
5 Fairfield Villa	30	17	3	10	87	65	22	54
6 Coton Green	30	15	4	11	60	56	4	49
7 Coventry Alvis	30	13	6	11	68	68	0	45
8 Knowle	30	12	6	12	69	46	23	42
9 Barnt Green Spartak	30	11	3	16	52	89	-37	36
10 Lane Head	30	10	5	15	52	64	-12	35
11 Feckenham	30	9	5	16	54	69	-15	32
12 Redditch Borough	30	10	2	18	52	78	-26	32
13 Hampton	30	8	7	15	55	92	-37	31
14 FC Stratford	30	7	1	22	50	93	-43	22
15 Bolehall Swifts	30	5	2	23	32	88	-56	17
16 Earlswood Town	30	4	4	22	36	80	-44	16

DIVISION THREE	P	W	D	L	F	A	GD	Pts
1 Alcester Town	30	23	5	2	104	23	81	71 *
2 Continental Star	30	22	2	6	109	61	48	68
3 A F C Solihull	30	20	6	4	78	42	36	66
4 Coventry Plumbing	30	19	4	7	86	45	41	61
5 Inkberrow	30	19	4	7	64	35	29	61
6 Bartestree	30	15	7	8	76	32	44	52
7 Coventrians	30	14	5	11	70	65	5	47
8 Central Ajax	30	13	5	12	73	66	7	44
9 Enville Athletic	30	13	4	13	50	57	-7	43
10 W L V Sport	30	8	8	14	50	66	-16	32
11 F C Shush	30	8	4	18	66	91	-25	28
12 A F C Church	30	7	6	17	49	70	-21	27
13 Shipston Excelsior	30	5	6	19	41	89	-48	21
14 Castle Vale Town	30	6	6	18	54	127	-73	21*
15 Leamington Hibernian	30	4	5	21	33	81	-48	17
16 Birmingham Tigers	30	5	1	24	34	87	-53	16

LEAGUE CUP

HOLDERS: WALSALL WOOD

ROUND 1

Uttoxeter Town	v	Dunkirk	2-0
Stapenhill	v	South Normanton Athletic	1-5
Heather St Johns	v	NKF Burbage	0-1
Bolehall Swifts	v	Coventry Copsewood	3-2
Chelmsley Town	v	Paget Rangers	2-0
FC Stratford	v	Worcester City	1-3
Romulus	v	Atherstone Town	4-3
Westfields	v	Stourport Swifts	4-1
Heath Hayes	v	Brocton	0-2
Sporting Khalsa	v	Walsall Wood	5-2
Quorn	v	Loughborough University	1-0

ROUND 2

GNP Sports	v	Shepshed Dynamo	1-3
Long Eaton United	v	Uttoxeter Town	3-3, 3-2p
South Normanton Athletic	v	Lichfield City	3-3, 2-4p
NKF Burbage	v	Nuneaton Griff	5-0
Coventry Sphinx	v	Leicester Road	3-0
Coventry United	v	Bolehall Swifts	8-1
Chelmsley Town	v	Cadbury Athletic	1-1, 4-3p
Boldmere St Michaels	v	Lye Town	2-1
Highgate United	v	Worcester City	1-4
Littleton	v	Studley	0-4
Coton Green	v	Romulus	0-1
Racing Club Warwick	v	Westfields	2-6
Ilkeston Town	v	Rocester	6-0
Brocton	v	Sporting Khalsa	4-3
Quorn	v	Hinckley AFC	4-0
Wolverhampton Sporting Co	v	AFC Wulfrunians	1-2

ROUND 3

Shepshed Dynamo	v	Long Eaton United	0-0, 3-5p
Lichfield City	v	NKF Burbage	3-3, 3-4p
Coventry Sphinx	v	Coventry United	0-0, 4-3p
Chelmsley Town	v	Boldmere St Michaels	2-1
Worcester City	v	Studley	5-0
Romulus	v	Westfields	3-2
Ilkeston Town	v	Brocton	7-0
Quorn	v	AFC Wulfrunians	1-1, 7-6p

QUARTER FINALS

Long Eaton United	v	NKF Burbage	0-2
Coventry Sphinx	v	Chelmsley Town	2-1
Worcester City	v	Romulus	1-1, 7-6p
Ilkeston Town	v	Quorn	3-1

SEMI FINALS

NKF Burbage	v	Coventry Sphinx	1-0
Romulus	v	Ilkeston Town	2-0

FINAL

NKF Burbage	v	Romulus	1-2

CHALLENGE TROPHY FINAL

Gresley Res	v	Moors Academy Res	2-4

CHALLENGE VASE FINAL

Bartestree	v	Central Ajax	0-2

LES JAMES CHALLENGE CUP FINAL

Knowle	v	Redditch Borough	1-2

PRESIDENTS CUP FINAL

FC Stratford	v	GNP Sports	2-3

PREMIER DIVISION	1	2	3	4	5	6	7	8	9	10	11	12	13	14	15	16	17	18	19	20
1 AFC Wulfrunians		2-0	0-2	1-2	5-1	1-0	1-3	2-4	1-0	2-1	1-1	2-0	0-1	1-1	0-2	0-0	2-1	0-1	1-1	2-3
2 Boldmere St Michaels	1-1		0-0	4-3	2-3	1-1	1-1	2-1	3-2	2-2	1-1	3-1	5-2	2-2	0-2	2-4	0-1	0-6	4-1	3-2
3 Coventry Sphinx	0-1	2-1		4-1	2-0	4-1	2-2	5-2	3-0	1-0	0-4	1-1	2-1	0-0	0-2	2-3	1-2	3-5	2-3	0-1
4 Coventry United	1-0	0-1	0-1		1-0	0-1	0-0	2-1	1-0	1-2	1-1	1-0	1-0	1-2	0-2	3-1	1-0	2-1	3-1	0-2
5 Dunkirk	0-4	3-1	3-0	2-2		1-1	0-7	1-1	2-3	1-4	2-0	0-0	1-5	0-3	0-1	0-3	0-7	2-2	3-0	1-6
6 Highgate United	0-3	1-2	0-0	0-3	4-0		3-1	0-3	2-0	1-1	2-0	0-0	3-0	1-5	0-3	3-0	0-2	2-0	1-1	3-2
7 Ilkeston Town	3-1	2-0	0-4	3-1	3-1	4-1		2-0	4-1	2-3	2-1	3-0	4-1	4-1	3-0	3-2	0-4	2-0	6-1	2-1
8 Long Eaton United	3-1	2-1	4-0	1-1	2-1	0-0	2-4		2-3	3-0	3-1	5-1	2-2	0-6	1-1	2-0	0-2	1-1	1-2	1-2
9 Loughborough University	1-1	1-2	3-1	1-1	3-1	4-4	1-8	0-1		3-3	3-3	2-2	0-1	3-1	2-0	3-2	1-2	3-1	1-2	4-3
10 Lye Town	3-1	4-0	2-0	0-1	3-1	4-1	1-0	1-1	1-2		1-2	2-3	3-3	0-1	0-0	0-1	0-2	1-2	6-2	2-1
11 Quorn	1-1	0-1	3-4	3-1	4-1	4-0	2-0	4-2	3-2	1-3		5-2	1-2	1-0	2-1	1-1	1-2	2-2	3-1	2-5
12 Romulus	1-1	2-6	0-1	1-2	4-1	0-2	1-3	2-1	2-1	1-1	1-3		1-0	2-0	3-1	4-0	0-1	1-4	4-0	2-1
13 Shepshed Dynamo	1-3	4-0	1-0	0-0	2-1	2-1	2-3	2-0	3-1	3-3	1-3	1-0		2-0	2-1	0-2	1-2	2-0	4-1	1-2
14 South Normanton Athletic	1-2	1-2	0-1	0-1	0-1	0-0	3-0	2-1	2-1	1-4	1-2	4-0	4-1		0-0	2-1	0-2	0-1	3-0	0-0
15 Sporting Khalsa	4-1	0-2	1-1	3-2	5-2	0-2	1-0	0-2	2-0	1-0	3-1	4-2	2-0	4-2		0-0	1-1	0-4	4-1	2-2
16 Stourport Swifts	3-1	1-1	1-1	2-1	4-0	1-1	1-1	0-1	3-0	2-0	1-1	0-2	1-5	1-0	4-2		1-2	0-1	1-2	2-1
17 Walsall Wood	0-1	2-1	4-1	1-0	2-0	1-1	0-2	3-0	3-0	0-0	2-1	3-2	4-4	1-0	1-0	0-0		2-2	3-0	1-2
18 Westfields	2-2	1-2	1-1	2-2	2-2	0-0	1-2	3-1	1-1	1-0	1-2	2-2	4-1	2-0	0-1	3-1	1-0		2-0	1-1
19 Wolverhampton Sporting Community	3-4	1-4	1-5	1-7	2-2	2-3	2-4	1-1	1-1	1-3	2-2	1-1	2-4	1-3	1-4	1-2	4-0	3-4		2-3
20 Worcester City	2-0	1-2	3-4	2-2	2-0	0-3	3-0	0-1	1-1	1-1	2-2	0-2	1-1	2-1	0-1	3-1	1-1	1-6	1-1	

DIVISION ONE	1	2	3	4	5	6	7	8	9	10	11	12	13	14	15	16	17	18	19
1 Atherstone Town		3-0	2-1	3-0	3-0	2-0	1-3	3-0	1-2	3-1	3-2	1-1	7-1	2-0	1-0	0-1	8-2	2-1	2-2
2 Brocton	1-4		0-0	2-1	8-3	3-2	4-7	3-3	2-3	5-4	4-0	4-0	4-3	1-0	2-3	2-0	1-2	1-4	1-2
3 Cadbury Athletic	0-2	0-1		1-1	1-0	1-1	2-1	2-1	2-6	1-2	3-2	2-1	4-0	0-1	1-2	4-0	1-1	0-0	3-1
4 Chelmsley Town	1-6	2-2	2-2		2-5	5-1	1-2	1-2	1-1	0-4	6-0	0-0	1-1	0-1	0-1	4-0	6-0	1-3	0-1
5 Coventry Copsewood	0-4	2-1	0-1	3-1		1-1	2-4	1-1	0-2	0-4	1-1	2-7	4-2	1-1	2-3	1-4	0-3	0-3	1-3
6 Heath Hayes	0-5	4-2	0-3	0-1	1-2		0-4	0-1	0-7	1-2	2-2	1-5	1-0	0-6	2-5	2-3	2-0	0-0	2-0
7 Heather St Johns	6-3	6-4	2-0	3-0	7-1	7-0		2-2	1-0	6-1	3-1	3-1	6-1	5-0	3-0	4-1	6-1	1-1	2-1
8 Hinckley AFC	0-2	0-0	1-2	3-5	1-1	5-0	1-5		1-3	2-3	1-2	0-2	1-1	1-3	1-5	1-1	2-0	2-2	0-2
9 Leicester Road	0-2	1-2	3-0	2-0	4-1	6-0	4-0	1-0		6-1	5-1	1-2	4-0	0-1	0-1	5-0	0-0	A-A	2-4
10 Lichfield City	0-0	6-1	3-2	1-2	0-2	5-1	1-3	1-0	3-1		8-0	1-3	8-0	4-2	4-3	3-0	1-0	2-1	4-1
11 Littleton	0-2	1-0	0-3	2-0	1-4	5-0	0-5	0-2	0-1	1-3		2-2	4-1	2-2	0-4	2-2	0-1	2-3	0-1
12 NKF Burbage	0-5	2-0	3-0	2-4	1-0	1-2	1-1	3-2	2-0	0-1	2-1		6-0	3-1	1-1	1-1	4-3	0-4	0-2
13 Nuneaton Griff	2-6	1-1	1-2	0-2	1-1	2-0	0-10	1-2	1-4	0-2	2-0	1-2		0-4	0-5	1-0	5-3	0-0	1-5
14 Paget Rangers	1-0	2-3	1-1	1-2	0-3	6-0	2-3	3-0	0-3	0-5	1-3	3-1	3-2		1-4	2-2	3-0	1-1	1-4
15 Racing Club Warwick	2-4	2-4	2-2	4-2	5-0	8-0	2-1	5-1	1-1	3-3	6-2	3-1	6-0	5-0		2-1	7-0	4-2	3-1
16 Rocester	1-3	0-1	1-2	1-0	0-1	1-0	1-6	2-3	0-3	2-5	5-1	1-4	3-1	2-3	0-3		5-2	2-5	0-0
17 Stapenhill	0-0	3-2	4-0	0-1	2-2	2-1	1-2	2-2	0-6	2-9	2-1	1-1	1-0	2-2	1-5	1-3		5-2	2-1
18 Studley	1-2	0-0	2-2	3-2	4-1	1-0	1-2	0-1	0-1	2-1	2-1	1-3	7-1	0-0	1-2	0-3	2-0		4-0
19 Uttoxeter Town	1-1	3-1	0-2	4-2	3-3	2-3	1-3	0-0	2-3	3-1	2-1	1-3	8-0	1-3	1-2	1-0	3-0	1-0	

DIVISION TWO	1	2	3	4	5	6	7	8	9	10	11	12	13	14	15	16
1 Barnt Green Spartak		1-3	4-2	0-1	1-1	3-2	3-4	4-3	1-4	2-1	1-1	0-6	3-1	2-7	0-4	2-1
2 Boldmere Sports & Social Falcons	2-0		2-1	4-0	7-1	4-1	2-2	3-0	2-1	3-1	5-2	1-0	0-1	0-2	1-0	5-2
3 Bolehall Swifts	1-4	1-3		2-4	0-4	2-0	2-5	3-2	1-2	2-1	0-3	1-2	0-2	2-8	0-3	1-2
4 Coton Green	6-1	0-2	2-0		1-0	4-0	3-1	2-3	2-1	1-3	0-3	3-1	3-3	1-5	0-4	0-3
5 Coventry Alvis	2-1	4-3	2-2	1-6		4-2	2-1	3-3	4-1	1-2	8-1	2-1	2-2	3-2	1-2	1-1
6 Earlswood Town	2-3	1-1	0-1	4-2	2-2		1-4	3-2	4-3	0-4	0-2	0-2	5-3	1-2	1-4	1-2
7 Fairfield Villa	6-2	1-2	3-1	3-1	3-4	1-1		3-0	5-0	5-2	8-1	2-0	2-1	2-2	1-3	4-2
8 FC Stratford	1-3	0-5	3-1	0-2	2-5	4-2	2-4		3-4	0-8	5-1	3-2	2-3	1-3	1-3	4-2
9 Feckenham	0-3	3-3	1-1	2-3	4-0	4-0	1-2	3-0		1-6	2-2	3-3	1-0	1-2	1-4	5-3
10 GNP Sports	4-0	3-2	7-0	4-1	1-0	4-0	6-3	2-0	1-0		6-0	3-3	0-0	2-1	1-0	3-1
11 Hampton	2-2	1-3	4-1	0-1	3-1	1-1	1-6	3-2	2-2	2-5		2-1	2-4	1-5	1-3	2-3
12 Knowle	4-0	3-3	4-0	0-0	0-1	1-0	7-1	5-0	2-0	2-3	3-3		4-2	1-4	1-2	3-0
13 Lane Head	4-0	1-2	1-2	1-1	3-2	3-2	2-4	0-2	3-0	2-2	2-3	1-4		1-3	0-2	2-1
14 Moors Academy	8-0	0-1	4-0	2-3	5-0	3-0	2-1	7-1	5-1	2-2	5-1	2-2	6-1		2-2	3-0
15 Northfield Town	2-1	1-1	4-2	1-1	5-1	2-0	5-0	2-0	2-1	0-3	4-2	2-1	4-1	3-3		3-2
16 Redditch Borough	4-5	0-2	2-0	2-6	1-6	3-0	4-0	2-1	0-2	0-7	3-3	2-1	0-2	4-0	0-4	

NORTH WEST COUNTIES LEAGUE

RECENT CHAMPIONS

2016: Colne **2017:** Atherton Collieries **2018:** Runcorn Linnets

PREMIER DIVISION	P	W	D	L	F	A	GD	Pts
1 City of Liverpool	38	29	4	5	89	37	52	91
2 Bootle	38	28	5	5	98	36	62	89
3 Congleton Town	38	25	3	10	86	37	49	78
4 Northwich Victoria	38	20	7	11	85	49	36	67
5 Ashton Athletic	38	19	4	15	69	49	20	61
6 Charnock Richard	38	19	4	15	80	68	12	61
7 Runcorn Town	38	19	3	16	68	65	3	60
8 Squires Gate	38	17	7	14	79	62	17	57*
9 Silsden	38	17	6	15	59	65	-6	57
10 1874 Northwich	38	15	11	12	63	55	8	56
11 Barnoldswick Town	38	17	5	16	72	75	-3	56
12 Burscough	38	14	9	15	74	66	8	51
13 Irlam	38	13	10	15	57	62	-5	49
14 Whitchurch Alport	38	12	7	19	54	59	-5	43
15 Litherland REMYCA	38	11	7	20	51	78	-27	39*
16 Winsford United	38	10	8	20	55	86	-31	38
17 Hanley Town	38	11	5	22	53	85	-32	38
18 Padiham	38	10	7	21	55	85	-30	37
19 West Didsbury & Chorlton	38	10	4	24	55	89	-34	34
20 Abbey Hey	38	5	2	31	26	120	-94	17

DIVISION ONE NORTH	P	W	D	L	F	A	GD	Pts
1 Longridge Town	38	28	6	4	144	52	92	90
2 Avro	38	28	4	6	118	44	74	88
3 AFC Liverpool	38	25	4	9	97	67	30	79
4 Lower Breck	38	24	5	9	130	57	73	77
5 Prestwich Heys	38	22	3	13	82	52	30	69
6 Carlisle City	38	21	4	13	82	76	6	67
7 Garstang	38	18	6	14	87	68	19	60
8 Bacup Borough	38	18	6	14	84	71	13	59*
9 Ashton Town	38	16	7	15	82	88	-6	55
10 AFC Darwen	38	16	6	16	76	86	-10	54
11 Cleator Moor Celtic	38	15	6	17	78	87	-9	51
12 Shelley	38	13	9	16	59	76	-17	48
13 AFC Blackpool	38	13	8	17	57	79	-22	47
14 Nelson	38	12	9	17	60	66	-6	45
15 Steeton	38	11	11	16	80	93	-13	44
16 Chadderton	38	11	7	20	77	82	-5	40
17 St Helens Town	38	9	7	22	82	100	-18	34
18 Holker Old Boys	38	9	4	25	54	113	-59	31
19 Daisy Hill	38	6	7	25	58	124	-66	25
20 Atherton LR	38	3	5	30	30	136	-106	13*

DIVISION ONE SOUTH	P	W	D	L	F	A	GD	Pts
1 Rylands	38	28	4	6	111	27	84	85*
2 Vauxhall Motors	38	23	9	6	86	46	40	78
3 Stone Old Alleynians	38	21	9	8	92	56	36	72
4 Wythenshawe Amateurs	38	21	8	9	92	53	39	71
5 Wythenshawe Town	38	21	5	12	92	58	34	68
6 FC Oswestry Town	38	20	8	10	76	52	24	68
7 Sandbach United	38	19	10	9	88	54	34	67
8 Abbey Hulton United	38	20	4	14	71	65	6	64
9 Cheadle Heath Nomads	38	19	5	14	77	66	11	62
10 Stockport Town	38	16	5	17	76	62	14	53
11 St Martins	38	15	7	16	71	68	3	52
12 Barnton	38	15	5	18	71	72	-1	50
13 Eccleshall	38	14	4	20	65	91	-26	46
14 Maine Road	38	14	0	24	71	98	-27	42
15 Cammell Laird 1907	38	10	11	17	55	73	-18	41
16 Cheadle Town	38	11	10	17	61	67	-6	40*
17 Alsager Town	38	11	7	20	47	80	-33	40
18 New Mills	38	10	5	23	74	113	-39	35
19 Ellesmere Rangers	38	6	7	25	43	97	-54	25
20 Stone Dominoes	38	4	1	33	25	146	-121	13

THE MACRON CUP

HOLDERS: WIDNES

ROUND 1

Bootle	v	Vauxhall Motors	2-2, 4-2p
St Martins	v	Cammell Laird 1907	2-4
Stone Dominoes	v	Ashton Town	2-4
Abbey Hey	v	Daisy Hill	3-3, 6-5p
Backup Borough	v	Avro	2-3
Barnton	v	Congleton Town	0-4
Burscough	v	New Mills	5-1
Chadderton	v	1874 Northwich	3-4
Charnock Richard	v	Runcorn Town	0-0, 1-3p
Cheadle Heath Nomads	v	Litherland REMYCA	3-1
City of Liverpool	v	Ashton Athletic	3-1
Creator Moor Celtic	v	Winsford United	5-2
Eccleshall	v	AFC Darwen	3-2
FC Oswestry Town	v	West Didsbury & Chorlton	2-2, 5-4p
Holker Old Boys	v	Lower Breck	0-9
Irlam	v	Abbey Hulton United	1-3
Longridge Town	v	Squires Gate	1-3
Maine Road	v	Steeton	4-0
Nelson	v	Hanley Town	2-1
Padiham	v	Shelley	5-1
Rylands	v	Carlisle City	5-1
Sandbach United	v	AFC Liverpool	4-1
Silsden AFC	v	Garstang	0-2
St Helens Town	v	Cheadle Town	0-2
Stockport Town	v	Ellesmere Rangers	3-2
Stone Old Alleynians	v	AFC Blackpool	1-3
Whitchurch Alport	v	Prestwich Heys	1-1, 3-5p
Northwich Victoria	v	Alsager Town	5-1

ROUND 2

1874 Northwich	v	AFC Blackpool	5-0
Abbey Hey	v	Atherton LR	2-0
Avro	v	Wythenshawe Town	7-0
Barnoldswick Town	v	Wythenshawe Amateurs	3-0
Burscough	v	Sandbach United	3-1
Cammell Laird 1907	v	Lower Breck	0-0, 6-5p
Cheadle Town	v	Bootle	5-0
City of Liverpool	v	Squires Gate	1-0
Eccleshall	v	West Didsbury & Chorlton	1-2
Maine Road	v	Nelson	0-5
Prestwich Heys	v	Creator Moor Celtic	5-0
Rylands	v	Cheadle Heath Nomads	5-0
Stockport Town	v	Garstang	2-2, 3-5p
Stone Dominoes	v	Congleton Town	0-4
Northwich Victoria	v	Runcorn Town	3-1

ROUND 3

Abbey Hey	v	1874 Northwich	1-4
Abbey Hulton United	v	Congleton Town	0-1
Avro	v	Garstang	7-2
City of Liverpool	v	Burscough	6-2
Barnoldswick Town	v	Eccleshall	9-4
Nelson	v	Prestwich Heys	2-1
Northwich Victoria	v	Cheadle Town	5-2
Cammell Laird 1907	v	Rylands	3-1

QUARTER FINALS

1874 Northwich	v	Barnoldswick Town	3-2
Avro	v	Nelson	3-1
City of Liverpool	v	Northwich Victoria	2-1
Congleton Town	v	Cammell Laird 1907	6-0

SEMI FINALS

Avro	v	City of Liverpool	1-3
City of Liverpool	v	Avro	3-1
Congleton Town	v	1874 Northwich	0-5
1874 Northwich	v	Congleton Town	2-0

FINAL

1874 Northwich	v	City of Liverpool	1-0

FIRST DIVISION CUP FINAL

Avro	v	Sandbach United	2-4

THE REUSCH CHAMPIONS CUP FINAL

Runcorn Linnets	v	Widnes	0-3

PREMIER DIVISION	1	2	3	4	5	6	7	8	9	10	11	12	13	14	15	16	17	18	19	20
1 1874 Northwich		1-1	0-3	2-1	2-0	4-2	3-6	3-2	1-1	2-1	2-4	1-1	1-3	1-0	3-0	5-0	1-1	5-1	1-0	1-1
2 Abbey Hey	0-3		0-6	2-3	1-7	0-3	0-1	0-3	0-1	0-4	2-1	0-1	2-1	1-6	0-2	1-2	1-5	0-6	0-6	2-2
3 Ashton Athletic	2-2	3-0		2-0	0-3	1-2	0-4	0-3	0-1	1-0	3-2	2-0	8-0	3-0	3-0	1-0	0-1	5-0	2-1	4-1
4 Bootle	2-0	5-1	4-2		4-0	0-3	1-0	2-1	3-1	3-0	0-0	1-1	4-0	4-0	4-2	2-0	3-5	3-0	5-2	2-1
5 Barnoldswick Town	3-2	6-0	2-1	0-1		2-0	2-3	1-6	0-5	1-4	2-2	3-4	1-3	4-1	5-1	0-2	2-1	2-1	1-3	4-1
6 Burscough	1-1	5-0	2-4	0-3	5-0		0-1	0-1	1-1	1-2	1-2	5-3	3-3	1-1	4-0	3-2	1-1	3-0	2-3	4-0
7 City of Liverpool	1-1	3-0	2-1	0-2	2-0	3-0		2-1	5-3	3-2	2-2	2-1	3-0	4-0	4-0	1-2	3-2	4-0	1-0	5-2
8 Congleton Town	0-1	3-1	3-0	3-0	0-0	0-0	3-0		3-3	3-1	1-0	2-1	3-0	1-0	1-2	5-0	1-3	4-1	1-3	3-0
9 Charnock Richard	0-2	2-1	2-1	0-5	2-0	4-1	0-3	1-2		4-1	1-3	1-2	3-5	4-0	1-4	0-2	5-2	1-0	2-1	6-2
10 Hanley Town	2-2	2-0	1-2	0-3	0-3	1-2	2-4	0-4	1-5		4-2	0-3	0-1	1-3	3-2	1-0	2-1	1-1	1-6	2-0
11 Irlam	1-0	1-2	0-0	0-2	2-3	2-2	0-2	1-0	2-4	1-2		0-4	1-0	2-2	0-1	3-3	0-2	2-3	1-0	3-1
12 Northwich Victoria	3-2	3-1	0-0	2-3	0-1	2-2	1-2	1-3	2-0	3-1	0-1		2-2	2-1	5-1	2-0	2-1	6-0	2-0	4-1
13 Padiham	1-2	4-0	0-2	1-6	1-2	2-3	0-1	1-3	1-2	4-1	0-0	0-4		4-0	2-5	1-4	2-2	1-0	3-2	3-2
14 Litherhead REMYCA	2-1	3-1	2-0	1-1	3-3	2-0	1-2	0-3	3-2	1-3	5-1	0-5	2-2		2-1	0-2	1-2	0-4	1-3	1-1
15 Runcorn Town	2-1	5-1	1-0	0-2	2-2	2-3	2-1	3-1	4-0	2-0	1-1	1-1	3-2	1-0		0-2	2-3	5-0	2-1	3-0
16 Silsden	0-0	0-1	2-0	0-7	0-1	3-2	1-1	4-1	1-1	2-1	2-5	2-2	2-0	0-2	0-3		1-1	3-0	1-2	4-2
17 Squires Gate	3-0	4-1	6-2	0-1	5-2	6-1	0-3	0-1	0-3	1-1	2-5	0-3	1-0	3-0	2-0	3-4		0-1	4-0	0-2
18 West Didsbury & Chorlton	1-2	4-2	1-2	2-2	2-3	1-4	1-3	0-5	1-2	4-0	0-1	3-5	1-1	2-2	3-1	2-1	1-2		3-1	1-2
19 Whitchurch Alport	1-1	0-1	1-1	1-3	2-0	1-0	1-1	2-3	3-2	2-2	1-1	1-0	0-0	1-2	1-0	1-2	1-1	0-2		0-3
20 Winsford United	2-1	3-0	0-2	1-1	1-1	2-2	0-1	0-3	0-4	3-3	0-2	3-2	4-1	2-1	1-2	2-3	3-3	3-2	1-0	

DIVISION ONE NORTH	1	2	3	4	5	6	7	8	9	10	11	12	13	14	15	16	17	18	19	20
1 AFC Blackpool		3-1	0-2	1-0	4-0	0-4	2-3	3-0	0-0	0-0	2-2	3-1	2-2	1-1	2-8	2-1	1-0	1-2	1-0	1-1
2 AFC Darwen	2-3		0-1	1-0	1-1	1-4	2-1	2-2	5-1	3-0	1-3	2-1	2-1	2-6	3-2	2-1	2-3	2-0	7-1	2-4
3 AFC Liverpool	3-1	3-2		7-0	1-3	1-0	3-2	6-2	3-5	0-5	5-1	4-3	1-2	1-1	3-2	1-0	2-0	3-1	2-1	3-3
4 Atherton LR	3-2	4-4	1-3		0-6	0-2	0-5	0-3	2-2	0-3	1-4	0-5	0-1	0-6	1-7	1-1	1-2	0-2	0-3	0-3
5 Ashton Town	3-2	3-4	3-4	1-1		1-5	6-2	0-3	3-2	1-1	4-1	2-1	2-1	0-4	1-0	0-2	0-2	1-2	2-4	5-2
6 Avro	3-3	5-1	2-0	7-0	5-0		3-3	7-1	1-0	5-0	5-0	4-2	6-0	3-2	1-4	1-1	3-2	2-1	3-1	0-1
7 Bacup Borough	4-3	3-2	0-2	4-0	3-2	0-3		3-2	1-2	4-2	4-2	3-1	3-1	0-3	0-0	2-2	0-2	1-1	2-2	5-1
8 Carlisle City	1-2	1-3	4-0	3-0	5-4	4-2	2-1		1-0	3-0	6-3	1-3	2-1	0-2	0-3	2-2	2-1	4-0	4-5	4-3
9 Chadderton	3-0	4-0	1-2	6-2	2-3	1-1	3-3	1-2		6-1	1-1	4-2	5-0	1-2	1-7	0-1	1-2	3-4	3-2	1-0
10 Cleator Moor Celtic	4-1	7-1	0-4	2-0	1-1	1-2	1-2	2-0	4-1		5-0	0-3	1-0	3-6	1-4	5-1	0-3	4-4	2-1	5-4
11 Daisy Hill	0-1	2-3	0-6	2-2	1-4	1-4	1-2	1-2	3-2	3-1		2-0	0-3	3-3	4-1	1-4	3-3	1-2	0-5	2-2
12 Garstang	0-1	3-0	3-0	2-4	2-2	2-1	1-0	1-3	5-4	3-3	2-0		2-2	1-1	2-2	2-0	2-0	8-2	1-0	4-2
13 Holker Old Boys	5-0	0-3	3-3	5-0	0-2	0-3	2-1	3-5	3-0	0-4	3-3	0-4		2-11	6-2	0-4	0-4	0-2	2-1	1-2
14 Longridge Town	1-1	1-2	5-3	8-1	7-2	3-0	5-0	7-0	3-1	4-0	8-1	0-3	4-1		4-1	3-2	5-1	4-2	5-1	5-2
15 Lower Breck	3-1	5-0	4-2	8-2	6-1	2-3	3-1	2-2	4-2	8-1	2-1	5-1	7-1	3-0		1-0	3-0	6-0	1-2	5-1
16 Nelson	1-4	1-1	0-2	1-0	1-4	0-3	0-4	0-1	2-2	4-2	8-1	2-1	2-1	1-3	1-2		1-5	0-2	4-0	1-1
17 Prestwich Heys	8-1	1-0	1-2	6-0	2-4	2-6	1-0	1-0	1-0	2-0	3-1	4-1	6-0	1-2	2-1	1-1		0-2	2-2	3-1
18 Shelley	3-0	1-3	1-3	0-1	0-0	1-3	1-4	0-1	0-0	2-2	4-1	2-4	3-1	1-2	0-0	1-4	1-0		3-1	1-1
19 St Helens Town	3-2	2-2	3-3	3-0	1-2	0-2	2-6	0-2	2-4	1-3	4-2	1-3	9-0	4-4	3-5	2-2	1-2	2-2		4-6
20 Steeton	1-0	2-2	2-3	5-3	3-3	2-4	0-2	2-2	4-2	0-2	6-1	2-2	2-1	1-3	1-1	0-1	0-3	3-3	4-3	

DIVISION ONE SOUTH	1	2	3	4	5	6	7	8	9	10	11	12	13	14	15	16	17	18	19	20
1 Abbey Hutton United		2-1	2-1	3-1	4-0	1-1	1-0	1-0	2-1	3-5	4-1	2-0	2-2	2-1	1-2	5-0	3-1	0-1	2-2	HW
2 Alsager Town	2-0		1-1	3-3	4-1	2-0	1-1	0-1	0-5	2-0	3-1	2-1	1-2	1-3	1-1	3-1	0-2	1-2	1-0	1-4
3 Barnton	0-3	5-1		0-1	2-0	0-4	5-1	2-0	2-5	5-0	1-0	1-3	1-1	2-4	1-0	4-2	2-1	0-2	0-3	0-3
4 Cammell Laird 1907	2-3	1-1	2-6		1-0	1-1	1-0	1-1	2-0	1-0	1-1	0-0	1-1	3-3	1-0	8-1	1-1	1-4	1-3	1-3
5 Cheadle Heath Nomads	2-0	2-0	2-1	3-0		1-1	2-2	2-1	3-0	2-1	2-3	2-5	2-4	2-5	3-2	3-2	2-0	5-2	3-2	2-0
6 Cheadle Town	1-2	1-2	0-3	1-1	0-2		3-2	4-1	1-0	2-3	1-4	0-0	0-7	0-2	0-1	2-0	1-2	1-1	2-0	1-2
7 Eccleshall	2-4	3-1	5-2	0-4	1-4	0-0		2-4	2-0	4-2	3-2	0-3	1-4	1-3	3-0	0-1	4-3	2-1	1-3	3-11
8 Ellesmere Rangers	1-1	2-0	0-5	1-4	1-1	0-1	0-1		2-2	1-2	2-2	1-5	2-0	1-1	0-1	1-0	1-3	1-2	0-4	2-4
9 FC Oswestry Town	2-1	4-3	0-0	2-0	2-0	2-1	3-0	5-2		3-2	5-5	0-0	2-0	1-0	3-3	2-1	3-1	3-1	1-0	0-4
10 Maine Road	6-5	4-0	1-2	3-1	0-3	5-1	1-2	4-1	2-1		1-4	0-5	0-2	2-3	3-4	4-0	1-2	1-3	2-6	2-3
11 New Mills	2-0	2-3	2-5	5-2	2-4	1-3	1-5	3-2	1-3	1-2		1-6	1-2	3-1	2-3	4-2	1-1	1-4	3-2	0-4
12 Rylands	6-0	3-0	5-0	1-0	3-5	1-3	3-0	7-0	3-0	4-0	5-0		2-0	1-0	1-0	6-0	4-1	0-3	5-1	3-0
13 Sandbach United	1-2	0-0	3-3	6-2	3-0	2-2	4-2	3-1	1-3	5-1	2-2	1-3		0-1	5-3	3-0	1-2	1-1	2-2	2-2
14 Stone Old Alleynians	6-0	4-0	1-0	4-1	3-1	2-2	1-1	4-1	0-0	6-1	7-0	0-5	2-3		1-0	2-1	2-0	3-3	2-1	1-0
15 St Martins	1-4	3-2	4-1	3-1	1-1	3-1	1-2	1-1	3-2	1-2	2-6	2-0	1-3	2-2		9-1	0-2	0-0	0-4	1-1
16 Stone Dominoes	1-2	0-2	2-1	0-2	0-6	0-13	0-4	3-0	0-5	0-5	2-1	1-3	0-6	0-6	0-4		0-3	0-3	0-4	1-7
17 Stockport Town	2-0	2-2	1-2	0-0	2-1	3-1	5-1	4-0	3-0	3-0	4-1	0-4	1-2	8-0	1-2	1-1		1-2	2-3	3-4
18 Vauxhall Motors	2-1	5-0	3-2	5-1	3-1	2-2	3-1	3-2	0-0	3-0	4-1	0-1	0-1	2-1	4-3	5-0	3-2		1-1	1-1
19 Wythenshawe Amateurs	3-2	7-0	1-1	2-1	1-0	2-3	4-1	4-5	1-1	3-1	5-2	1-1	1-0	3-3	1-0	4-1	5-2	1-1		1-0
20 Wythenshawe Town	3-1	1-0	3-2	2-0	2-2	4-0	0-2	5-1	0-5	1-2	5-2	0-3	2-3	2-2	1-4	3-1	2-1	3-1	0-1	

NORTHERN COUNTIES EAST LEAGUE

RECENT CHAMPIONS

2016: Tadcaster Albion **2017:** Cleethorpes Town **2018:** Pontefract Collieries

PREMIER DIVISION	P	W	D	L	F	A	GD	Pts
1 Worksop Town	38	28	6	4	95	40	55	90
2 Penistone Church	38	26	4	8	112	49	63	82
3 Bridlington Town	38	24	5	9	98	51	47	77
4 Hemsworth Miners Welfare	38	24	3	11	89	51	38	75
5 Yorkshire Amateur	38	23	4	11	83	62	21	73
6 Maltby Main	38	19	11	8	66	37	29	68
7 Staveley Miners Welfare	38	19	10	9	77	45	32	67
8 Handsworth Parramore	38	19	6	13	70	67	3	63
9 Knaresborough Town	38	18	6	14	70	57	13	60
10 Eccleshill United	38	15	8	15	69	75	-6	53
11 Barton Town	38	15	7	16	56	53	3	52
12 Bottesford Town	38	14	10	14	61	65	-4	52
13 Liversedge	38	15	3	20	56	80	-24	48
14 Garforth Town	38	12	6	20	52	60	-8	42
15 Thackley	38	10	10	18	66	76	-10	40
16 Albion Sports	38	12	4	22	64	86	-22	40
17 Athersley Recreation	38	9	4	25	43	88	-45	31
18 Goole AFC	38	7	2	29	41	102	-61	23
19 Harrogate Railway Athletic	38	4	10	24	44	103	-59	22
20 Hall Road Rangers	38	5	5	28	50	115	-65	20

DIVISION ONE	P	W	D	L	F	A	GD	Pts
1 Grimsby Borough	38	26	6	6	108	44	64	84
2 Campion	38	25	7	6	99	50	49	82
3 Hallam	38	22	10	6	84	39	45	76
4 Winterton Rangers	38	23	6	9	76	38	38	75
5 Nostell Miners Welfare	38	22	8	8	78	39	39	74
6 Dronfield Town	38	20	7	11	64	47	17	67
7 Worsbrough Bridge Athletic	38	19	5	14	76	77	-1	62
8 Parkgate	38	19	4	15	64	56	8	61
9 Selby Town	38	18	3	17	82	76	6	57
10 Swallownest	38	15	7	16	57	62	-5	52
11 Glasshoughton Welfare	38	15	5	18	47	62	-15	50
12 AFC Emley	38	14	6	18	71	68	3	48
13 East Yorkshire Carnegie	38	13	5	20	73	79	-6	44
14 Rossington Main	38	12	6	20	49	77	-28	42
15 Skegness Town	38	12	4	22	43	72	-29	40
16 Ollerton Town	38	10	7	21	48	73	-25	37
17 Armthorpe Welfare	38	11	4	23	58	89	-31	37
18 Shirebrook Town	38	9	7	22	55	83	-28	34
19 FC Bolsover	38	9	4	25	49	110	-61	31
20 Harworth Colliery	38	8	5	25	47	87	-40	29

LEAGUE CUP

HOLDERS: NO FINAL WAS PLAYED.

ROUND 1

East Yorks Carnegie	v	Ollerton Town	1-2
Harworth Colliery	v	Winterton Rangers	1-4
Shirebrook Town	v	Rossington Main	3-0
Parkgate	v	Campion	1-5
Bridlington Town	v	Goole AFC	1-3 (aet)
Maltby Main	v	Glasshoughton Welfare	3-2
Penistone Church	v	Harrogate Railway Ath	6-0
Yorkshire Amateur	v	Handsworth Parramore	1-2

ROUND 2

Dronfield Town	v	Staveley MW	2-4
Garforth Town	v	Shirebrook Town	2-1
Hall Road Rangers	v	Grimsby Borough	5-0
Hallam	v	Knaresborough	2-0
Liversedge	v	Armthorpe Welfare	10-2
Albion Sports	v	Bottesford Town	3-1 (aet)
Athersley Recreation	v	Eccleshill United	1-3
Campion	v	AFC Emley	0-1
FC Bolsover	v	Penistone Church	2-3
Maltby Main	v	Thackley	3-2
Ollerton Town	v	Worsbrough Bridge	3-0
Worksop Town	v	Winterton Rangers	2-1
Barton Town	v	Hemsworth MW	2-4
Swallownest	v	Goole AFC	1-0
Nostell MW	v	Handsworth Parramore	3-4
Selby Town	v	Skegness Town	3-1

ROUND 3

Hall Road Rangers	v	Swallownest	1-2
Hemsworth MW	v	Ollerton Town	5-2
Liversedge	v	Penistone Church	4-1
AFC Emley	v	Hallam	0-1
Albion Sports	v	Handsworth Parramore	2-5
Maltby Main	v	Worksop Town	1-2 (aet)
Garforth Town	v	Staveley MW	1-1, 6-7p
Eccleshill United	v	Selby Town	1-3

QUARTER FINALS

Hemsworth MW	v	Handsworth Parramore	2-1
Liversedge	v	Hallam	3-2 (aet)
Selby Town	v	Swallownest	1-1, 2-4p
Staveley MW	v	Worksop Town	1-2

SEMI FINALS

Hemsworth MW	v	Worksop Town	0-2
Liversedge	v	Swallownest	1-0

FINAL

Liversedge	v	Worksop Town	1-3

PREMIER DIVISION		1	2	3	4	5	6	7	8	9	10	11	12	13	14	15	16	17	18	19	20
1	Albion Sports		1-0	1-2	1-1	2-2	2-3	3-0	1-4	2-1	2-4	2-1	0-2	1-2	2-4	0-4	0-1	1-4	1-3	0-4	0-4
2	Athersley Rec	0-3		1-0	2-1	2-4	1-2	0-4	1-0	2-0	2-2	2-2	0-8	1-3	1-3	0-1	1-4	1-2	3-2	1-6	0-3
3	Barton Town	5-1	1-2		1-1	1-0	2-0	2-0	3-1	3-0	3-1	5-0	0-2	4-6	4-0	0-3	2-1	1-3	1-3	0-0	4-3
4	Bottesford Town	2-5	2-1	1-0		0-1	2-0	1-0	4-0	3-2	7-2	0-4	0-2	0-3	2-3	1-0	2-2	1-2	2-1	2-3	5-2
5	Bridlington Town	4-1	1-2	5-1	1-1		7-0	2-1	3-0	4-1	2-0	1-1	3-0	1-0	10-0	6-3	2-2	1-2	0-4	3-1	3-0
6	Eccleshill United	0-3	3-1	0-1	4-1	2-3		0-0	5-0	3-2	2-3	1-1	1-1	0-3	2-1	0-0	3-7	2-2	1-1	0-1	2-1
7	Garforth Town	3-2	1-0	1-0	1-0	1-3	1-2		2-0	4-1	0-0	5-0	1-6	2-4	2-4	0-3	3-0	0-1	1-1	1-2	2-0
8	Goole AFC	1-0	0-3	2-1	1-1	0-3	2-4	1-4		2-1	1-3	2-2	0-2	1-4	0-2	0-3	2-5	0-3	1-5	1-2	1-2
9	Hall Road Rangers	2-5	4-1	1-2	2-2	1-4	1-2	2-0	2-4		1-3	1-1	2-5	2-1	4-1	0-0	0-5	2-2	3-4	2-4	1-5
10	Handsworth Parr	3-5	2-1	2-0	3-4	0-2	3-2	3-1	3-2	3-2		3-2	1-2	1-0	2-1	1-2	3-1	1-3	2-2	0-0	2-3
11	Harrogate RA	1-4	2-1	3-2	1-1	1-1	2-3	2-2	1-5	1-2	1-2		1-3	0-6	0-1	0-4	0-3	0-5	2-2	0-2	1-2
12	Hemsworth MW	4-1	0-0	0-1	3-3	1-0	5-1	3-2	5-1	2-0	1-0	4-2		2-3	4-3	1-2	2-3	1-0	4-2	1-2	4-1
13	Knaresborough	3-2	3-1	1-0	0-0	1-2	0-1	1-1	2-1	4-2	2-3	1-1	3-2		2-3	0-1	0-1	1-1	0-5	3-3	1-2
14	Liversedge	0-0	0-2	1-0	1-2	1-0	0-6	1-0	0-1	9-1	0-0	2-1	1-0	0-1		2-4	0-4	0-1	1-0	1-4	3-5
15	Maltby Main	0-0	4-1	0-0	1-2	4-1	2-2	1-1	4-0	1-0	1-1	2-0	1-0	0-1	4-2		0-1	2-1	4-1	0-2	1-1
16	Penistone Church	4-3	4-2	1-1	0-1	6-1	0-3	3-1	4-1	7-1	4-0	8-0	5-2	3-1	2-0	2-1		3-1	4-1	0-1	3-0
17	Staveley MW	1-0	1-1	1-1	1-0	1-3	3-3	3-1	4-1	8-0	0-2	1-2	3-0	1-1	2-2	2-2	4-1		2-0	0-1	3-1
18	Thackley	0-2	3-2	0-0	2-2	1-3	4-2	1-3	4-1	0-0	0-3	5-3	0-1	0-1	1-2	0-0	0-5	2-2		1-3	1-2
19	Worksop Town	3-0	4-1	2-2	3-1	2-3	2-1	1-0	2-0	3-1	2-3	4-1	2-3	4-1	2-1	1-1	2-1	2-1	5-2		7-0
20	Yorkshire Amateur	4-5	2-0	3-0	4-0	4-3	4-1	1-0	2-1	3-0	1-0	3-1	0-1	2-1	2-0	4-0	2-2	2-0	2-2	1-1	

DIVISION ONE		1	2	3	4	5	6	7	8	9	10	11	12	13	14	15	16	17	18	19	20
1	AFC Emley		3-0	2-3	0-2	2-1	4-0	0-2	2-2	1-2	3-2	2-3	1-4	2-1	1-2	4-4	5-0	3-0	3-1	2-1	4-3
2	Armthorpe Welfare	1-2		0-1	4-1	0-4	4-2	0-1	1-3	0-5	0-2	0-2	1-1	2-3	1-3	1-2	2-5	4-2	2-1	3-4	3-1
3	Campion	2-0	2-2		3-2	5-1	4-2	1-2	3-1	2-1	7-2	4-2	0-0	6-1	3-0	5-1	3-1	4-0	2-2	0-0	3-2
4	Dronfield Town	1-0	2-2	0-2		0-1	5-2	0-1	0-2	3-1	1-0	1-1	3-1	2-1	3-1	3-1	2-1	3-0	1-2	3-0	2-1
5	East Yorks Carnegie	2-2	1-2	2-3	2-1		2-1	4-1	2-3	0-0	7-0	0-5	2-1	0-3	2-1	2-3	2-2	3-4	5-2	2-2	2-3
6	FC Bolsover	0-6	3-2	3-0	1-2	2-4		3-2	1-3	0-7	1-1	1-5	2-0	2-3	1-4	1-4	2-2	2-3	2-2	1-0	0-2
7	Glasshoughton Welf	3-2	1-2	1-2	2-3	3-2	2-1		3-2	0-2	0-1	0-4	0-0	0-2	4-2	1-0	3-0	2-0	1-2	0-0	1-3
8	Grimsby Borough	0-0	3-0	4-2	1-0	1-4	10-0	4-0		3-3	3-0	3-2	2-4	2-1	2-0	4-0	0-0	1-0	2-2	3-0	5-0
9	Hallam	3-1	5-2	0-1	1-1	3-2	3-1	2-3	3-2		5-1	2-0	2-0	1-0	4-1	2-0	3-2	3-0	3-0	2-0	3-3
10	Harworth Colliery	1-2	1-2	2-2	1-2	5-2	1-2	2-0	1-7	0-0		0-4	0-1	1-3	4-3	2-1	3-1	0-2	1-4	1-2	1-2
11	Nostell MW	2-1	4-1	2-2	0-0	2-1	3-0	1-1	1-0	1-0	2-0		3-2	1-1	1-2	1-1	1-1	2-0	2-0	1-2	2-3
12	Ollerton Town	0-2	2-2	0-3	0-1	3-2	0-2	3-1	1-2	1-0	1-0	0-1		2-3	0-2	3-6	1-3	0-3	1-1	1-2	1-0
13	Parkgate	4-2	0-2	2-4	3-0	1-0	4-1	1-2	2-3	1-1	1-1	0-3	1-0		2-0	0-3	4-1	5-0	0-3	0-1	0-1
14	Rossington Main	2-2	2-1	0-4	1-1	3-1	1-0	1-1	0-3	0-0	1-0	0-1	1-1	0-1		1-0	0-4	2-2	2-1	1-8	1-2
15	Selby Town	3-2	2-1	2-0	3-2	5-1	3-1	3-0	2-2	2-3	2-3	2-5	4-2	0-3	5-3		7-0	4-0	1-0	1-3	1-3
16	Shirebrook Town	2-1	6-1	1-1	1-4	1-1	0-1	0-1	0-6	1-2	2-1	2-2	2-3	1-2	4-1	3-1		1-0	1-2	0-3	1-2
17	Skegness Town	3-0	3-1	1-4	1-1	1-0	4-0	1-1	2-4	1-1	2-1	0-3	0-3	1-2	1-0	1-0	2-1		0-2	1-2	1-2
18	Swallownest	1-0	0-3	2-4	0-2	1-2	0-2	2-1	1-3	1-1	4-3	2-0	2-2	0-1	1-3	2-0	4-1	1-0		3-1	1-1
19	Winterton Rangers	3-0	0-1	1-0	2-2	1-0	6-1	2-0	0-2	1-1	1-0	2-0	6-1	1-1	3-1	1-2	2-0	1-0	2-0		4-1
20	Worsbrough Bridge	2-2	4-2	3-2	1-2	1-2	2-2	2-0	1-5	1-4	2-2	0-3	5-2	4-1	2-1	5-1	2-1	3-1	1-2	0-6	

NCE1 - Dronfield Town v Hallam. Photo: Bill Wheatcroft.

NCE1 - Dronfield Town v Hallam. Photo: Bill Wheatcroft.

NORTHERN LEAGUE

RECENT CHAMPIONS

2016: Shildon **2017:** South Shields **2018:** Dunston UTS

DIVISION ONE	P	W	D	L	F	A	GD	Pts
1 Dunston UTS (C)	34	26	5	3	79	30	49	83
2 Hebburn Town	34	19	9	6	85	62	23	66
3 Bishop Auckland	34	18	8	8	84	53	31	62
4 Consett	34	18	7	9	80	58	22	61
5 Sunderland RCA	34	19	4	11	69	47	22	61
6 Shildon	34	16	8	10	62	46	16	56
7 Stockton Town	34	16	6	12	85	56	29	54
8 West Auckland Town	34	14	11	9	62	40	22	53
9 North Shields	34	16	4	14	58	55	3	52
10 Newcastle Benfield	34	15	6	13	59	65	-6	51
11 Ryhope CW	34	14	5	15	64	70	-6	47
12 Newton Aycliffe	34	9	9	16	49	66	-17	36
13 Whitley Bay	34	9	7	18	58	88	-30	34
14 Seaham Red Star	34	9	6	19	56	87	-31	33
15 Guisborough Town	34	8	7	19	56	69	-13	31
16 Ashington	34	7	8	19	44	65	-21	29
17 Whickham	34	6	7	21	54	86	-32	25
18 Penrith	34	5	7	22	39	100	-61	22

DIVISION TWO	P	W	D	L	F	A	GD	Pts
1 Billingham Town	38	29	6	3	106	37	69	93
2 Thornaby	38	29	4	5	98	37	61	91
3 Northallerton Town	38	23	6	9	86	55	31	75
4 Heaton Stannington	38	20	6	12	76	48	28	66
5 Chester-Le-Street	38	18	8	12	66	57	9	62
6 West Allotment Celtic	38	18	6	14	71	58	13	60
7 Redcar Athletic	38	15	11	12	86	66	20	56
8 Willington	38	15	11	12	70	57	13	56
9 Crook Town	38	16	8	14	82	70	12	56
10 Billingham Synthonia	38	15	10	13	65	52	13	55
11 Jarrow	38	14	10	14	63	71	-8	52
12 Ryton & Crawcrook Albion	38	14	9	15	57	61	-4	51
13 Birtley Town	38	13	9	16	62	73	-11	48
14 Bedlington Terriers	38	13	7	18	79	96	-17	46
15 Tow Law Town	38	11	10	17	62	72	-10	43
16 Easington Colliery	38	12	7	19	75	91	-16	43
17 Esh Winning	38	10	10	18	63	81	-18	40
18 Washington	38	9	2	27	46	86	-40	29
19 Brandon United	38	6	8	24	43	95	-52	26
20 Durham City	38	5	2	31	30	123	-93	17

BROOKS MILESON MEMORIAL LEAGUE CUP

HOLDERS: DUNSTON UTS

ROUND 1

Birtley Town	v	Seaham Red Star	2-0
Shildon	v	Willington	3-3, 1-4p
Ryton & Crawcrook Albion	v	Heaton Stannington	1-5
North Shields	v	Penrith	7-0
Guisborough Town	v	Redcar Athletic	1-1, 5-4p
Washington	v	Consett	2-4

ROUND 2

Durham City	v	Chester-Le-Street	0-1
West Auckland	v	Dunston UTS	2-0
Whitley Bay	v	North Shields	2-0
Newton Aycliffe	v	Bedlington Terriers	2-1
Hebburn Town	v	West Allotment Celtic	0-0, 1-4p
Ashington	v	Heaton Stannington	0-1
Consett	v	Northallerton Town	2-1
Willington	v	Esh Winning	1-0
Jarrow	v	Thornaby	1-4
Whickham	v	Tow Law Town	0-1
Newcastle Benfield	v	Birtley Town	2-0
Billingham Synthonia	v	Ryhope CW	1-1, 3-4p
Stockton Town	v	Brandon United	5-1
Guisborough Town	v	Billingham Town	4-0
Bishop Auckland	v	Easington Colliery	6-1
Crook Town	v	Sunderland RCA	1-6

ROUND 3

Thornaby	v	West Allotment Town	0-4
Chester-Le-Street	v	Heaton Stannington	2-2, 3-2p
Ryhope CW	v	Whitley Bay	1-3
Newton Aycliffe	v	Guisborough Town	1-0
Consett	v	Bishop Auckland	4-2
Sunderland RCA	v	Stockton Town	0-1
West Allotment Celtic	v	Newcastle Benfield	1-3
Tow Law Town	v	Willington	1-1, 6-5p

QUARTER FINALS

Chester-Le-Street	v	Newcastle Benfield	1-6
Newton Aycliffe	v	Whitley Bay	1-2
West Auckland	v	Tow Law Town	3-0
Stockton Town	v	Consett	2-1

SEMI FINALS

Newcastle Benfield	v	Whitley Bay	3-2
Stockton Town	v	West Auckland	2-3

FINAL

Newcastle Benfield	v	West Auckland	0-0, 3-4p

ERNEST ARMSTRONG MEMORIAL CUP FINAL

Chester-Le-Street	v	Northallerton Town	0-3

SOUTH WEST PENINSULA LEAGUE

RECENT CHAMPIONS

2016: Bodmin Town **2017:** Tavistock **2018:** Plymouth Parkway

PREMIER DIVISION	P	W	D	L	F	A	GD	Pts
1 Tavistock	36	29	4	3	120	41	79	91
2 Exmouth Town	36	28	5	3	91	28	63	89
3 Plymouth Argyle Res	36	25	3	8	123	45	78	78
4 Saltash United	36	24	4	8	87	42	45	76
5 St Austell	36	24	4	8	102	62	40	76
6 Falmouth Town	36	18	5	13	80	54	26	59
7 Torpoint Athletic	36	17	6	13	78	62	16	57
8 Cullompton Rangers	36	17	6	13	56	46	10	57
9 Bodmin Town	36	17	6	13	71	62	9	57
10 Millbrook	36	17	5	14	66	67	-1	56
11 Helston Athletic	36	14	8	14	58	52	6	50
12 Ivybridge Town	36	12	7	17	55	72	-17	43
13 Newquay	36	12	6	18	57	77	-20	42
14 Godolphin Atlantic	36	10	6	20	46	86	-40	36
15 Elburton Villa	36	8	9	19	53	81	-28	33
16 Launceston	36	7	4	25	52	111	-59	25
17 Callington Town	36	6	6	24	35	86	-51	24
18 Camelford	36	5	3	28	54	101	-47	18
19 Sticker	36	1	5	30	26	135	-109	8

DIVISION ONE EAST	P	W	D	L	F	A	GD	Pts
1 Stoke Gabriel	34	27	5	2	104	29	75	86
2 Bovey Tracey	34	24	6	4	120	50	70	78
3 Brixham	34	25	2	7	88	41	47	77
4 Torridgeside AFC	34	20	9	5	97	43	54	71*
5 Elmore	34	21	6	7	105	46	59	69
6 Axminster Town AFC	34	19	5	10	83	58	25	62
7 St Martins	34	16	7	11	76	48	28	55
8 IlfracombeTown	34	16	7	11	79	68	11	55
9 Sidmouth Town	34	14	6	14	76	68	8	48
10 Crediton United	34	14	4	16	62	68	-6	46
11 Teignmouth	34	13	6	15	84	70	14	45
12 Newton Abbot Spurs	34	12	6	16	71	78	-7	42
13 University of Exeter	34	12	3	19	97	97	0	39
14 Honiton Town	34	8	7	19	62	80	-18	31
15 Alphington AFC	34	8	5	21	56	93	-37	29
16 Waldon Athletic	34	8	5	21	59	103	-44	29
17 Budleigh Salterton	34	1	2	31	34	149	-115	5
18 Liverton United	34	2	1	31	31	195	-164	3*

Appledore resigned - record expunged.

DIVISION ONE WEST	P	W	D	L	F	A	GD	Pts
1 Liskeard Athletic	28	23	4	1	94	24	70	73
2 Mousehole	28	21	4	3	106	21	85	67
3 Porthleven	28	17	3	8	83	45	38	54
4 Wadebridge Town	28	15	6	7	68	57	11	51
5 St Dennis	28	14	6	8	78	59	19	48
6 Wendron United	28	13	4	11	66	45	21	43
7 Plymstock United	28	13	4	11	76	58	18	43
8 Holsworthy	28	13	4	11	46	43	3	43
9 Plymouth Marjons	28	10	6	12	62	53	9	36
10 Dobwalls	28	9	7	12	40	45	-5	34
11 St Blazey	28	10	4	14	52	62	-10	34
12 Penzance	28	10	3	15	52	61	-9	33
13 Bude Town AFC	28	7	1	20	54	77	-23	22
14 Bere Alston United	28	6	2	20	47	89	-42	20
15 Ludgvan	28	0	0	28	11	196	-185	-6*

WALTER C PARSON CUP

HOLDERS: FALMOUTH TOWN

ROUND 1

Liskeard Athletic	v	Porthleven	3-0
Ludgvan	v	St Dennis	AW
Plymstock United	v	Ivybridge Town	1-2
Witheridge	v	Cullompton Rangers	AW
St Martins	v	Honiton Town	3-2
Alphington AFC	v	Sidmouth Town	2-3
Crediton United	v	Axminster Town	1-2
Godolphin Atlantic	v	Callington Town	4-3
Liverton United	v	Waldon Athletic	AW
Galmpton & Roselands	v	Holsworthy	AW
Brixham	v	Stoke Gabriel	1-1, 4-3p
Ilfracombe Town	v	Budleigh Salterton	4-1
Appledore AFC	v	Teignmouth	0-1
Bude Town	v	Elburton Villa	0-4
Torpoint Athletic	v	Newton Abbot Spurs	9-0
Wadebridge Town	v	Sticker	0-3
Newquay	v	Mousehole	0-2
Elmore	v	Exmouth Town	4-2
Torridgeside AFC	v	University of Exeter	3-1
Bere Alston United	v	Plymouth Marjons	3-2
Bovey Tracey	v	Millbrook	2-1
Penzance	v	Wendron United	2-3
Dobwalls	v	St Blazey	2-1

Byes for: Bodmin Town, Camelford, Falmouth Town, Helston Athletic, Launceston, Plymouth Argyle Res, Saltash United, St Austell, Tavistock.

ROUND 2

Liskeard Athletic	v	St Dennis	5-2
Ivybridge Town	v	Camelford	4-0
Cullompton Rangers	v	St Martins	3-2
Sidmouth Town	v	Axminster Town	4-2
Godolphin Atlantic	v	St Austell	2-6
Waldon Athletic	v	Bodmin Town	1-4
Falmouth Town	v	Helston Athletic	3-2
Holsworthy	v	Brixham	1-5
Ilfracombe Town	v	Teignmouth	1-0
Elburton Villa	v	Torpoint Athletic	4-2
Sticker	v	Mousehole	0-4
Tavistock	v	Plymouth Argyle Res	1-3
Elmore	v	Torridgeside AFC	4-0
Bere Alston United	v	Saltash United	1-8
Bovey Tracey	v	Launceston	2-4
Wendron United	v	Dobwalls	0-1

ROUND 3

Liskeard Athletic	v	Ivybridge Town	2-3
Cullompton Rangers	v	Sidmouth Town	3-2
St Austell	v	Bodmin Town	5-1
Falmouth Town	v	Brixham	2-1
Ilfracombe Town	v	Elburton Villa	2-3
Mousehole	v	Plymouth Argyle Res	2-1
Elmore	v	Saltash United	1-2
Launceston	v	Dobwalls	4-3

QUARTER FINALS

Ivybridge Town	v	Cullompton Rangers	0-1
St Austell	v	Falmouth Town	0-1
Elburton Villa	v	Mousehole	1-0
Saltash United	v	Launceston	6-1

SEMI FINALS

Cullompton Rangers	v	Falmouth Town	0-1
Elburton Villa	v	Saltash United	1-5

FINAL

Falmouth Town	v	Saltash United	0-1

PREMIER DIVISION	1	2	3	4	5	6	7	8	9	10	11	12	13	14	15	16	17	18	19
1 Bodmin Town		1-1	2-1	0-2	2-2	2-2	0-1	4-2	1-5	6-1	3-2	1-1	2-0	2-1	0-2	1-0	2-0	7-2	0-1
2 Callington Town	0-1		4-1	0-3	1-1	0-2	0-2	2-0	1-4	1-5	3-2	0-2	0-5	0-7	0-3	1-3	1-1	2-3	1-2
3 Camelford	0-1	1-2		2-1	2-4	3-4	0-2	5-2	1-1	1-3	4-2	1-2	2-3	0-3	2-4	2-3	7-1	0-9	1-2
4 Cullompton Rangers	2-4	2-0	1-1		5-0	1-2	1-0	0-1	1-3	2-1	5-1	0-0	3-1	0-5	1-0	1-3	4-0	0-2	3-1
5 Elburton Villa	0-2	2-1	4-1	0-2		1-4	1-0	0-1	3-2	1-1	0-0	0-3	2-2	2-1	2-3	2-4	6-1	1-7	2-1
6 Exmouth Town	1-0	3-0	4-2	0-1	0-0		0-0	5-0	2-1	5-0	4-0	4-1	4-0	4-0	4-1	1-1	3-1	1-0	4-0
7 Falmouth Town	5-1	4-0	6-0	3-1	3-2	1-2		3-1	0-3	3-1	1-2	2-2	3-0	0-3	2-1	4-2	5-0	2-3	3-1
8 Godolphin Atlantic	2-2	1-3	1-0	1-3	4-3	0-3	0-5		0-2	0-4	1-0	2-1	2-1	1-1	0-2	0-4	3-1	2-2	0-2
9 Helston Athletic	1-0	0-0	2-1	1-1	1-1	0-1	1-0	1-1		1-1	4-1	3-2	2-2	1-3	0-2	0-1	2-1	2-2	2-1
10 Ivybridge Town	2-3	3-1	2-2	1-1	2-1	1-1	0-1	2-2	1-0		3-0	0-1	2-0	1-3	0-4	3-0	1-0	0-4	0-2
11 Launceston	2-4	0-2	2-1	2-2	3-0	1-5	3-4	1-4	0-4	5-3		1-5	1-1	1-5	1-4	1-3	2-1	0-5	1-6
12 Millbrook	3-1	3-1	3-0	0-1	2-1	2-5	2-1	2-0	2-1	2-3	2-5		1-0	2-2	1-4	2-1	4-0	0-3	1-3
13 Newquay	3-6	1-0	2-0	2-1	1-0	0-1	2-2	1-1	2-1	3-0	2-0	2-3		5-2	1-4	1-2	2-1	1-4	4-4
14 Plymouth Argyle Reserves	3-0	6-3	3-0	4-0	3-1	0-1	4-2	5-1	3-0	6-0	2-1	3-0	5-1		3-2	5-2	9-0	1-4	1-0
15 Saltash United	1-1	3-1	5-0	0-1	4-0	2-0	4-3	2-1	2-1	3-0	1-1	4-0	4-0	3-1		2-2	1-0	1-4	4-1
16 St Austell	2-1	3-1	2-0	4-2	5-2	3-4	4-1	5-3	3-2	2-2	6-2	5-2	3-2	3-3	2-1		4-1	5-0	4-0
17 Sticker	0-6	1-1	1-7	0-2	3-2	1-3	2-2	2-4	1-3	0-5	0-6	1-4	1-2	0-11	2-2	1-4		0-4	1-1
18 Tavistock	7-1	4-0	3-2	1-0	1-1	1-0	3-3	3-2	4-0	2-1	4-0	4-1	2-0	2-1	3-0	5-2	4-0		6-1
19 Torpoint Athletic	2-1	1-1	5-1	0-0	3-3	1-2	2-1	4-0	4-1	3-0	7-0	2-2	6-2	0-5	1-2	1-0	6-0	1-3	

DIVISION ONE EAST	1	2	3	4	5	6	7	8	9	10	11	12	13	14	15	16	17	18
1 Alphington AFC		0-2	3-3	1-2	3-1	0-4	1-5	1-2	0-3	5-2	2-3	2-0	1-2	1-4	1-9	2-4	3-2	2-2
2 Axminster Town AFC	2-2		1-6	3-2	4-0	3-1	1-3	2-0	2-2	10-0	5-2	1-0	3-1	3-0	1-1	1-3	4-3	3-1
3 Bovey Tracey	2-1	6-2		3-1	8-1	3-0	1-4	2-2	1-3	9-2	3-1	3-1	2-1	2-3	4-0	2-1	3-2	5-0
4 Brixham	4-2	1-0	0-2		2-1	4-1	1-0	3-0	6-0	5-1	5-1	2-1	1-3	0-1	2-2	1-2	3-2	2-1
5 Budleigh Salterton	1-5	2-4	0-10	0-6		2-3	0-8	1-4	1-2	3-1	1-2	1-2	0-1	1-7	0-2	3-3	2-2	1-4
6 Crediton United	2-1	2-1	3-4	0-2	1-0		0-2	3-0	1-3	4-2	2-2	3-1	0-1	0-7	5-1	1-2	2-2	4-1
7 Elmore	6-0	1-1	2-2	0-1	8-0	3-1		1-0	7-2	1-0	3-3	2-1	2-1	1-2	1-1	1-2	1-3	4-1
8 Honiton Town	1-1	7-2	1-4	2-3	2-1	2-2	3-2		2-2	6-1	1-2	0-1	2-5	0-2	3-0	0-5	3-3	0-1
9 IlfracombeTown	4-1	2-4	1-1	1-5	4-0	3-0	2-5	3-1		2-1	3-1	3-0	1-1	1-1	4-1	0-1	1-2	5-1
10 Liverton United	4-2	0-3	1-4	1-2	2-1	0-8	1-6	1-7	0-7		0-5	0-3	0-7	0-8	2-3	2-6	1-10	1-4
11 Newton Abbot Spurs	2-0	0-1	1-4	0-3	6-0	1-2	2-6	4-2	3-3	3-1		0-1	2-0	0-1	0-3	0-0	4-2	5-1
12 Sidmouth Town	1-2	1-3	3-3	3-4	4-2	2-1	2-3	1-0	4-2	12-2	5-1		1-1	3-3	3-1	1-1	5-1	3-3
13 St Martins	0-5	1-1	0-4	0-2	5-1	1-1	0-0	5-1	4-0	8-0	3-0	1-0		0-1	1-1	0-4	6-0	2-2
14 Stoke Gabriel	2-0	3-1	1-2	1-0	5-1	1-0	3-3	5-1	4-0	9-1	1-1	6-1	3-1		1-0	1-0	4-1	3-0
15 Teignmouth	4-2	1-2	2-3	2-3	7-1	2-0	2-5	3-3	1-2	9-0	7-4	2-2	1-3	1-2		4-2	3-0	3-0
16 Torridgeside AFC	6-0	3-2	3-3	1-1	11-0	8-0	0-1	2-2	2-2	0-0	3-1	5-1	2-5	2-2	2-0		4-2	2-1
17 University of Exeter	1-3	1-0	3-2	2-3	6-3	0-1	5-3	3-2	2-5	15-0	1-6	2-4	3-2	0-5	5-2	0-2		9-2
18 Waldon Athletic	1-1	0-5	0-4	1-6	5-2	1-4	1-5	3-0	2-1	8-1	3-3	2-3	1-4	1-2	1-3	1-3	3-2	

DIVISION ONE WEST	1	2	3	4	5	6	7	8	9	10	11	12	13	14	15
1 Bere Alston United		3-2	0-2	1-2	1-4	7-0	0-2	3-0	1-3	1-5	0-4	1-3	1-1	1-4	2-6
2 Bude Town AFC	3-0		2-3	0-3	1-3	14-0	0-2	3-2	1-2	1-0	3-1	0-2	1-3	2-3	1-3
3 Dobwalls	3-0	1-2		2-2	0-3	3-0	1-2	2-1	0-2	1-2	3-1	2-3	1-1	1-3	1-1
4 Holsworthy	6-0	1-1	3-0		0-1	H-W	2-3	2-1	3-0	2-1	1-1	0-2	0-3	1-3	1-2
5 Liskeard Athletic	5-0	3-1	2-0	2-0		20-1	1-1	3-0	1-1	2-1	1-0	7-2	4-0	1-1	5-1
6 Ludgvan	1-12	0-5	2-3	0-2	0-1		1-11	0-8	1-6	1-9	1-8	0-5	0-3	0-5	1-8
7 Mousehole	8-0	7-1	2-0	6-0	2-1	H-W		4-0	6-0	6-1	6-0	0-1	2-2	6-0	2-0
8 Penzance	1-2	2-1	1-2	1-1	1-1	5-0	2-1		4-1	2-1	2-3	5-2	3-4	0-0	3-2
9 Plymouth Marjons	2-4	3-0	1-1	2-0	1-2	11-0	1-5	5-0		5-1	3-4	2-2	2-3	1-2	1-0
10 Plymstock United	2-1	4-2	0-0	1-4	1-5	6-0	1-1	5-3	1-1		5-4	6-1	5-1	3-3	2-0
11 Porthleven	8-2	6-0	3-1	0-1	1-2	8-0	3-2	5-1	2-2	3-2		1-0	2-1	3-0	1-0
12 St Blazey	5-1	6-2	1-1	0-2	1-2	6-0	0-5	0-2	3-2	0-3	1-3		1-1	0-3	1-2
13 St Dennis	4-2	4-3	1-1	2-3	1-3	16-0	1-9	1-2	1-1	2-1	3-2	4-2		4-5	4-2
14 Wadebridge Town	1-1	7-1	1-5	5-3	3-4	3-2	2-2	2-0	2-1	3-5	0-4	4-1	1-4		1-1
15 Wendron United	2-0	3-1	3-0	3-1	2-5	11-0	0-3	5-0	3-0	3-2	2-2	1-1	0-3	0-1	

SOUTHERN COMBINATION FOOTBALL LEAGUE

RECENT CHAMPIONS

2016: Horsham **2017:** Shoreham **2018:** Haywards Heath Town

PREMIER DIVISION	P	W	D	L	F	A	GD	Pts
1 Chichester City	38	30	4	4	107	34	73	94
2 Horsham YMCA	38	27	4	7	95	45	50	85
3 Eastbourne Town	38	26	5	7	99	50	49	83
4 Newhaven	38	25	8	5	87	38	49	83
5 Saltdean United	38	21	8	9	77	54	23	71
6 Broadbridge Heath	38	19	9	10	78	46	32	66
7 AFC Uckfield Town	38	19	5	14	89	63	26	62
8 Lingfield	38	18	5	15	60	61	-1	59
9 Crawley Down Gatwick	38	16	9	13	70	62	8	57
10 Peacehaven & Telscombe	38	17	6	15	67	68	-1	57
11 Pagham	38	11	12	15	61	65	-4	45
12 Hassocks	38	12	8	18	63	85	-22	44
13 Lancing	38	12	7	19	58	77	-19	43
14 East Preston	38	11	8	19	50	64	-14	41
15 Langney Wanderers	38	9	10	19	47	77	-30	37
16 Little Common	38	9	8	21	52	82	-30	35
17 Loxwood	38	9	4	25	55	89	-34	31
18 Eastbourne United	38	8	3	27	37	88	-51	27
19 Arundel	38	6	9	23	50	104	-54	27
20 Shoreham	38	6	6	26	33	83	-50	24

DIVISION ONE	P	W	D	L	F	A	GD	Pts
1 Alfold	32	25	5	2	92	32	60	80
2 Steyning Town	32	24	5	3	78	24	54	77
3 AFC Varndeanians	32	22	5	5	82	38	44	71
4 Bexhill United	32	22	4	6	92	29	63	70
5 Selsey	32	20	6	6	63	25	38	66
6 Littlehampton Town	32	14	5	13	78	67	11	47
7 Mile Oak	32	14	4	14	59	53	6	46
8 Hailsham Town	32	10	10	12	62	61	1	40
9 Wick	32	12	4	16	55	78	-23	40
10 Sidlesham	32	11	4	17	40	57	-17	37
11 Seaford Town	32	10	6	16	54	74	-20	36
12 Billingshurst	32	10	5	17	58	88	-30	35
13 Southwick	32	10	1	21	40	72	-32	31
14 Storrington	32	8	5	19	47	82	-35	29
15 Oakwood	32	7	5	20	58	94	-36	26
16 Midhurst & Easebourne	32	7	4	21	47	81	-34	25
17 Worthing United	32	5	4	23	44	94	-50	19

St Francis Rangers resigned - record expunged.

DIVISION TWO	P	W	D	L	F	A	GD	Pts
1 Rustington	28	23	4	1	112	33	79	73
2 Copthorne	28	19	3	6	82	40	42	60
3 Roffey	28	18	5	5	110	45	65	59
4 Angmering Seniors	28	16	1	11	78	64	14	49
5 Rottingdean Village	28	14	4	10	68	44	24	46
6 Jarvis Brook	28	13	4	11	76	62	14	43
7 Montpelier Villa	28	13	3	12	76	64	12	42
8 Worthing Town	28	13	1	14	62	62	0	40
9 Westfield	28	12	2	14	49	59	-10	38
10 Bosham	28	11	3	14	50	67	-17	36
11 Upper Beeding	28	9	7	12	46	50	-4	34
12 Cowfold	28	11	1	16	49	74	-25	34
13 Littlehampton United	28	7	4	17	49	86	-37	25
14 Brighton Electricity	28	6	4	18	33	95	-62	22
15 Ferring	28	2	0	26	32	127	-95	6

LEAGUE CUP

HOLDERS: HAYWARDS HEATH TOWN

ROUND 1

AFC Vardeanians	v	Seaford Town	3–1
Alfold	v	Storrington	6–2
Oakwood	v	Midhurst & Easebourne	1–4
Selsey	v	Billingshurst	4–0
Southwick	v	St Franics Rangers	4–4, 3-4p
Steyning Town	v	Sidlesham	4–1

ROUND 2

Broadbridge Heath	v	Chichester City	1–2
Langney Wanderers	v	Peacehaven & Telscombe	2–3
Arundel	v	Midhurst & Easebourne	2–1
Eastbourne Town	v	Hailsham Town	4–2
Eastbourne United Association	v	AFC Uckfield Town	0–6
Hassocks	v	Bexhill United	3–2
Horsham YMCA	v	Lancing	4–1
Littlehampton Town	v	Wick	1–0
Newhaven	v	Little Common	7–0
Pagham	v	East Preston	6–3
Shoreham	v	Lingfield	1–2
Steyning Town	v	Worthing United	5–3
AFC Varndeanians	v	Mile Oak	3–1

AFC Varndeanians were expelled for fielding an ineligible player. Mile Oak were reinstated.

Loxwood	v	Alfold	0–0, 3-2p
St Francis Rangers	v	Saltdean United	0–7
Crawley Down Gatwick	v	Selsey	3–2

ROUND 3

Hassocks	v	Lingfield	0–3
AFC Uckfield Town	v	Loxwood	6–1
Arundel	v	Horsham YMCA	1–2
Newhaven	v	Crawley Down Gatwick	2–1
Pagham	v	Chichester City	0–0, 5-6p
Saltdean United	v	Eastbourne Town	2–1
Steyning Town	v	Peacehaven & Telscombe	0–3
Mile Oak	v	Littlehampton Town	4–2

QUARTER FINALS

Uckfield Town	v	Peacehaven & Telscombe	3–1
Chichester City	v	Mile Oak	6–0
Lingfield	v	Horsham YMCA	1–3
Newhaven	v	Saltdean United	2–2, 5-6p

SEMI FINALS

Saltdean United	v	Chichester City	2–1
Horsham YMCA	v	AFC Uckfield Town	2–3

FINAL

Saltdean United	v	AFC Uckfield Town	3–1

DIVISION ONE CHALLENGE CUP FINAL

Wick	v	Steyning Town	0–4

PREMIER DIVISION	1	2	3	4	5	6	7	8	9	10	11	12	13	14	15	16	17	18	19	20
1 AFC Uckfield Town		7-2	6-1	0-1	1-4	2-1	4-1	1-0	4-0	3-4	4-2	4-3	4-1	2-0	1-1	0-3	3-4	1-2	1-2	1-0
2 Arundel	0-5		0-6	2-5	0-0	2-3	3-2	1-2	1-3	2-5	3-1	0-0	0-3	1-4	1-3	1-3	0-0	5-2	2-3	3-0
3 Broadbridge Heath	2-3	1-1		1-2	5-4	2-2	2-0	2-1	6-0	0-3	0-1	6-0	5-4	3-0	5-0	1-3	0-0	3-1	0-1	4-0
4 Chichester City	1-0	6-1	0-0		3-0	1-2	1-0	3-2	3-3	2-1	4-1	2-0	7-0	5-1	4-2	2-0	5-0	6-1	1-1	2-0
5 Crawley Down Gatwick	3-1	3-2	1-1	1-5		2-1	2-0	1-1	2-5	0-3	1-2	3-0	0-0	3-3	3-0	0-2	1-1	5-0	4-4	3-2
6 Eastbourne Town	4-2	3-0	3-2	4-1	4-1		5-0	0-0	2-1	1-4	5-3	2-1	2-1	5-1	2-1	3-4	3-0	3-1	3-1	7-0
7 Eastbourne United Association	1-4	1-1	0-0	0-3	1-2	1-3		1-7	0-2	0-4	0-1	1-2	1-3	2-0	2-1	1-2	0-0	2-1	1-3	1-2
8 East Preston	3-3	1-3	1-2	0-4	0-1	1-1	2-3		2-2	0-3	2-2	2-1	0-1	1-0	4-1	0-5	2-2	2-0	1-0	3-0
9 Hassocks	1-2	0-2	1-1	0-6	1-2	0-2	3-0	1-0		5-3	3-1	2-2	3-2	1-1	3-3	1-2	4-0	0-4	1-4	0-5
10 Horsham YMCA	4-3	4-1	0-1	0-1	3-1	5-1	2-0	2-0	2-1		2-0	2-1	1-1	5-3	3-0	0-0	1-0	4-1	3-3	0-1
11 Lancing	0-3	4-3	0-4	0-1	0-1	1-3	3-1	1-1	2-2	2-4		4-1	1-3	8-4	1-0	1-3	0-4	1-1	2-0	1-0
12 Langney Wanderers	1-3	1-1	0-1	2-3	1-0	2-2	3-1	2-0	2-2	0-2	0-0		1-3	1-4	0-1	1-2	2-1	1-1	2-2	2-2
13 Lingfield	1-0	4-1	3-1	1-3	0-4	1-0	2-4	5-0	1-0	2-3	1-0	0-3		3-2	0-1	0-3	2-2	1-2	2-0	2-1
14 Little Common	1-0	0-0	0-3	0-2	1-0	0-1	4-0	1-0	4-2	2-3	1-3	0-0	1-1		1-4	1-1	4-1	2-5	0-2	2-2
15 Loxwood	1-3	7-3	1-2	0-2	1-1	1-3	5-1	0-1	0-4	2-3	0-2	2-3	0-1	3-0		2-1	1-7	1-3	2-3	2-3
16 Newhaven	1-1	6-0	0-0	3-2	4-3	1-2	3-1	2-4	0-1	1-1	1-0	4-0	0-0	3-0	3-1		2-2	4-2	2-1	4-1
17 Pagham	2-4	0-0	0-0	1-2	0-2	0-5	2-3	0-4	5-2	1-0	3-0	6-0	2-1	2-2	6-0	1-3		1-1	0-2	2-1
18 Peacehaven & Telscombe	3-1	2-1	1-2	1-1	2-1	2-2	H/W	4-0	3-1	0-2	3-2	1-2	0-2	1-0	1-0	1-1	2-3		1-3	4-1
19 Saltdean United	2-2	3-0	3-2	2-0	2-2	0-3	0-1	2-0	4-1	3-2	3-3	4-1	3-1	3-0	1-1	0-1	1-0	1-5		3-0
20 Shoreham	0-0	1-1	0-1	1-5	0-3	2-1	1-3	1-0	0-1	0-2	2-2	1-3	0-1	0-2	1-4	0-4	0-0	0-2	1-2	

DIVISION ONE	1	2	3	4	5	6	7	8	9	10	11	12	13	14	15	16	17
1 AFC Varndeanians		2-2	1-0	3-1	4-1	4-3	2-1	3-1	3-0	1-2	2-0	3-0	3-1	0-1	4-1	4-0	0-0
2 Alfold	2-0		1-0	6-0	0-0	4-3	10-0	1-1	4-0	2-1	2-0	2-0	3-1	2-1	3-0	5-3	4-1
3 Bexhill United	1-1	0-1		6-0	5-1	2-1	4-0	2-1	2-1	4-3	3-3	3-1	3-0	0-1	3-2	1-0	4-0
4 Billingshurst	4-4	2-3	1-2		3-1	4-2	1-5	2-1	4-2	2-1	0-2	1-2	4-2	2-5	6-1	3-1	1-3
5 Hailsham Town	5-4	1-3	0-2	0-0		0-3	H/W	6-0	4-2	2-2	2-2	1-1	2-0	1-2	4-4	1-1	4-2
6 Littlehampton Town	2-2	1-7	0-1	7-2	3-2		0-0	1-1	6-2	5-0	1-2	2-3	5-1	0-2	2-2	3-1	2-1
7 Midhurst & Easebourne	1-3	4-1	1-1	3-4	0-4	1-2		1-2	1-4	2-3	2-3	1-1	1-2	0-4	2-1	0-3	2-1
8 Mile Oak	1-5	1-4	2-1	3-0	1-0	7-0	4-1		2-3	5-3	0-1	2-2	1-0	1-2	0-1	4-1	0-2
9 Oakwood	2-3	1-1	1-6	2-3	2-1	3-1	6-5	2-6		2-2	1-3	5-2	0-1	0-3	2-2	3-5	7-4
10 Seaford Town	1-4	0-3	1-7	1-1	1-1	4-1	3-3	2-0	3-1		0-2	1-0	0-3	0-1	3-1	2-3	4-2
11 Selsey	0-1	1-2	1-0	6-0	2-2	1-1	0-1	3-0	2-0	0-0		3-0	0-2	0-0	4-0	3-1	3-0
12 Sidlesham	1-3	0-2	0-2	2-1	4-2	3-5	1-0	1-2	1-0	2-4	0-1		0-0	1-4	3-1	3-1	2-0
13 Southwick	0-4	0-2	0-4	4-1	0-3	2-4	2-1	0-1	3-2	1-2	0-2	0-1		1-2	4-5	2-0	3-2
14 Steyning Town	0-1	3-3	2-2	2-0	3-2	1-0	1-0	0-0	4-0	4-0	0-1	1-0	7-2		2-2	3-1	4-1
15 Storrington	0-2	1-2	1-7	1-0	1-3	1-4	1-3	2-0	6-1	2-1	0-3	1-0	1-2	0-4		1-2	3-1
16 Wick	3-2	4-3	0-6	2-2	1-3	1-7	5-2	1-3	0-0	3-1	1-3	3-1	2-1	1-5	1-1		3-0
17 Worthing United	1-4	0-2	1-8	3-3	3-3	0-1	2-3	0-6	1-1	4-3	1-6	0-2	4-0	0-4	4-1	0-1	

DIVISION TWO	1	2	3	4	5	6	7	8	9	10	11	12	13	14	15
1 Angmering Seniors		2-0	6-1	3-2	2-4	3-1	7-2	2-0	4-7	1-3	5-3	0-4	4-0	2-3	3-1
2 Bosham	2-1		3-1	1-3	1-4	5-3	5-3	5-2	2-1	1-2	1-0	1-5	1-1	1-2	2-3
3 Brighton Electricity	2-4	2-2		0-4	1-0	2-1	2-1	2-2	0-9	0-5	1-4	4-8	1-1	1-2	2-1
4 Copthorne	4-2	2-1	2-1		3-1	5-0	1-5	6-1	1-1	5-4	3-0	0-0	4-1	1-2	5-1
5 Cowfold	0-0	2-0	3-0	2-0		3-1	0-6	5-3	2-4	2-5	2-5	2-5	0-3	4-2	2-0
6 Ferring	1-10	2-3	3-1	1-4	1-2		0-2	0-4	0-6	2-4	0-5	0-7	1-6	2-5	1-5
7 Jarvis Brook	7-2	5-0	6-1	5-3	0-1	9-4		0-0	3-2	3-2	1-1	0-5	0-0	4-1	2-3
8 Littlehampton United	0-1	3-3	1-1	0-4	3-1	6-0	3-1		3-1	0-4	2-4	0-3	0-2	2-0	5-1
9 Montpelier Villa	0-3	0-2	6-0	0-4	7-1	3-1	2-3	4-3		1-6	2-2	2-7	3-0	3-0	3-5
10 Roffey	6-0	2-1	9-0	2-3	4-2	13-1	3-1	6-0	6-1		1-1	1-4	2-2	6-1	3-3
11 Rottingdean Village	2-3	2-1	6-0	4-2	3-1	1-3	H/W	11-1	0-1	2-2		2-4	0-3	0-1	2-0
12 Rustington	4-1	10-0	2-1	0-0	4-1	4-1	7-2	7-0	1-1	4-2	2-1		3-2	2-2	0-3
13 Upper Beeding	1-3	1-4	2-0	0-3	1-0	3-0	1-1	6-1	2-3	1-1	0-3	3-5		4-2	0-2
14 Westfield	1-2	2-0	1-3	2-5	4-0	1-0	1-3	3-2	2-1	1-3	1-2	1-3	0-0		5-1
15 Worthing Town	3-2	1-2	1-3	0-3	6-2	5-2	5-1	3-2	1-2	2-3	1-2	0-2	3-0	2-1	

SOUTHERN COUNTIES EAST LEAGUE

RECENT CHAMPIONS

2016: Greenwich Borough **2017:** Ashford United **2018:** Sevenoaks Town

PREMIER DIVISION	P	W	D	L	F	A	GD	Pts
1 Cray Valley (PM)	38	29	4	5	108	36	72	91
2 Corinthian	38	29	3	6	95	39	56	90
3 Fisher	38	27	4	7	77	31	46	85
4 Chatham Town	38	25	4	9	98	44	54	79
5 Beckenham Town	38	19	9	10	71	56	15	66
6 Erith Town	38	18	8	12	67	60	7	62
7 Sheppey United	38	19	3	16	77	69	8	60
8 Glebe	38	17	5	16	60	62	-2	56
9 Canterbury City	37	16	7	14	64	53	11	55
10 Lordswood	38	16	7	15	65	65	0	55
11 Deal Town	38	15	10	13	61	62	-1	55
12 K Sports	38	14	7	17	58	81	-23	49
13 Crowborough Athletic	38	14	6	18	53	81	-28	48
14 AFC Croydon Athletic	38	13	6	19	55	68	-13	45
15 Bearsted	37	13	5	19	57	76	-19	44
16 Tunbridge Wells	38	11	4	23	62	80	-18	37
17 Punjab United	38	8	11	19	55	71	-16	35
18 Hollands And Blair	38	9	5	24	52	78	-26	32
19 Rusthall	38	5	8	25	36	94	-58	23
20 Croydon	38	3	2	33	36	101	-65	11

DIVISION ONE	P	W	D	L	F	A	GD	Pts
1 Welling Town	34	24	6	4	88	41	47	78
2 Erith & Belvedere	34	24	5	5	103	46	57	77
3 Kennington	34	22	8	4	87	41	46	74
4 Bridon Ropes	34	21	6	7	94	52	42	69
5 Sutton Athletic	34	19	7	8	81	44	37	64
6 Holmesdale	34	17	2	15	66	52	14	53
7 Forest Hill Park	34	15	7	12	59	59	0	52
8 Stansfeld	34	14	6	14	69	63	6	48
9 Sporting Club Thamesmead	34	12	7	14	60	56	4	43*
10 Greenways	34	12	4	18	65	88	-23	40
11 Lewisham Borough (Com)	34	12	3	19	61	78	-17	39
12 Lydd Town	34	10	8	16	65	99	-34	38
13 FC Elmstead	34	9	10	15	49	58	-9	37
14 Kent Football United	34	9	9	16	67	67	0	36
15 Snodland Town	34	9	8	17	55	81	-26	35
16 Phoenix Sports Res	34	8	5	21	48	86	-38	29
17 Rochester United	34	7	4	22	48	89	-41	28*
18 Meridian VP	34	7	3	24	31	96	-65	24

LEAGUE CHALLENGE CUP

HOLDERS: WHITSTABLE TOWN

ROUND 1

Sheppey United	v	Bearsted	8-1
Phoenix Sports Res	v	Stansfeld	1-3
Lydd Town	v	Deal Town	0-4
Corinthian	v	Crowborough Athletic	6-0
Lewisham Borough	v	Welling Town	1-2
Croydon	v	Fisher	2-4

ROUND 2

FC Elmstead	v	Erith & Belvedere	3-1
Kennington	v	Sheppey United	0-2
Sporting Club Thamesmead	v	Meridan VP	4-1
Stansfeld	v	Beckenham Town	1-5
Kent Football United	v	Sutton Athletic	2-4
K Sports	v	Canterbury City	0-1
Hollands & Blair	v	Chatham Town	0-2
Forest Hill Park	v	Bridon Ropes	3-1
Cray Valley PM	v	Holmesdale	2-2, 3-1p
Lordswood	v	Greenways	4-1
Deal Town	v	Punjab United	3-1
Corinthian	v	AFC Croydon Athletic	2-1
Welling Town	v	Glebe	0-2
Tunbridge Wells	v	Erith Town	1-5
Fisher	v	Rusthall	4-1
Snodland Town	v	Rochester United	2-1

ROUND 3

FC Elmstead	v	Sheppey United	0-2
Sporting Club Thamesmead	v	Beckenham Town	2-1
Sutton Athletic	v	Canterbury City	0-1
Chatham Town	v	Forest Hill Park	4-2 (aet)
Cray Valley PM	v	Lordswood	3-2 (aet)
Deal Town	v	Corinthian	1-2 (aet)
Glebe	v	Erith Town	2-3
Fisher	v	Snodland Town	2-1

QUARTER FINALS

Sheppey United	v	Sporting Club Thamesmead	0-1
Canterbury City	v	Chatham Town	0-1 (aet)
Cray Valley PM	v	Corinthian	2-3 (aet)
Erith Town	v	Fisher	0-1

SEMI FINALS (Over two legs)

Sporting Club Thamesmead	v	Chatham Town	1-4
Chatham Town	v	Sporting Club Thamesmead	3-0
Corinthian	v	Fisher	0-0
Fisher	v	Corinthian	2-3 (aet)

FINAL

Chatham Town	v	Corinthian	3-2

ROY VINTER CHARITY SHIELD FINAL

Phoenix Sports Res	v	Cray Valley PM	5-0

PREMIER DIVISION		1	2	3	4	5	6	7	8	9	10	11	12	13	14	15	16	17	18	19	20
1	AFC Croydon Athletic		4-2	3-0	2-2	2-1	1-2	1-0	3-3	2-1	2-2	0-2	1-2	0-4	0-1	1-2	0-3	1-2	2-0	2-0	3-3
2	Bearsted	1-3		2-3	P-P	0-1	0-4	0-1	0-0	2-1	4-2	2-1	2-4	2-1	1-0	4-2	0-1	5-1	4-2	1-3	3-2
3	Beckenham Town	3-1	1-1		2-3	3-3	0-1	0-2	7-1	3-1	2-1	3-1	2-3	1-1	1-1	2-1	1-1	1-0	3-0	2-1	2-1
4	Canterbury City	2-0	1-1	3-0		1-2	2-3	0-2	2-3	5-2	1-1	0-1	0-1	1-0	3-2	1-3	4-0	1-0	5-2	3-1	1-1
5	Chatham Town	1-2	3-0	3-4	5-2		3-1	1-2	1-2	2-0	4-0	7-2	0-1	2-0	3-1	9-0	2-0	4-1	0-0	0-1	1-0
6	Corinthian	2-1	5-0	1-0	1-0	1-4		1-2	7-1	4-2	5-1	3-0	1-0	2-1	4-0	1-1	3-1	2-1	3-0	5-0	1-2
7	Cray Valley (PM)	3-0	3-0	2-2	2-0	0-1	2-3		2-1	5-0	2-3	3-1	2-0	2-1	7-1	1-1	3-0	4-4	1-0	5-0	5-1
8	Crowborough Athletic	3-2	3-1	2-3	1-1	1-3	1-4	0-4		1-0	2-4	1-1	1-4	3-1	2-1	2-0	2-1	0-0	1-3	3-4	1-2
9	Croydon	1-4	0-1	0-2	1-2	1-1	0-6	0-2	1-0		1-3	1-3	0-5	2-1	2-3	2-3	1-2	0-3	0-2	0-1	2-3
10	Deal Town	3-1	1-2	2-2	1-0	0-1	0-1	0-2	2-0	2-0		3-0	1-1	1-1	2-1	2-1	2-2	2-2	3-0	1-2	1-3
11	Erith Town	2-1	3-1	2-1	4-0	1-2	2-2	1-3	1-1	3-1	0-1		2-1	1-1	1-1	3-2	4-0	1-1	1-0	4-1	4-2
12	Fisher	0-0	3-2	4-0	3-1	2-1	2-0	1-2	6-0	2-1	2-0	2-2		4-0	1-0	4-1	0-1	4-1	3-0	2-1	1-0
13	Glebe	2-1	1-0	0-2	0-3	2-3	1-1	3-5	0-4	1-4	3-0	1-0	1-0		4-2	2-3	3-2	1-0	3-2	2-3	3-1
14	Hollands And Blair	1-2	3-3	2-3	1-3	0-1	0-1	3-2	0-3	2-0	2-3	0-2	1-0	2-3		1-1	0-3	4-1	3-0	0-2	0-2
15	K Sports	1-1	2-1	4-4	2-1	2-5	3-4	0-5	0-1	4-1	0-1	4-2	1-1	0-3	2-1		2-0	1-0	2-0	1-4	1-1
16	Lordswood	4-2	3-4	0-2	1-2	1-3	1-0	3-5	1-0	2-1	3-3	3-1	2-3	1-1	3-1	3-0		2-2	1-1	1-0	3-4
17	Punjab United	0-1	3-1	1-1	1-1	2-2	0-1	0-2	3-0	1-1	0-0	1-2	1-2	0-1	3-1	3-1	0-2		5-1	2-3	3-6
18	Rusthall	3-2	1-1	0-2	0-3	0-7	1-3	1-9	0-1	4-3	2-2	1-1	0-1	0-1	2-2	0-1	0-4	2-2		0-2	1-3
19	Sheppey United	4-0	3-1	1-0	1-1	3-2	2-4	1-3	5-0	4-0	3-1	2-3	0-1	1-3	2-4	1-2	3-3	5-1	3-3		1-2
20	Tunbridge Wells	0-1	1-2	0-1	0-3	3-4	1-2	1-1	1-2	5-2	2-4	1-2	0-1	1-3	0-4	3-1	0-1	2-4	1-2	1-3	

DIVISION ONE		1	2	3	4	5	6	7	8	9	10	11	12	13	14	15	16	17	18
1	Bridon Ropes		3-1	3-2	6-2	4-0	0-2	2-2	2-1	6-0	3-4	5-0	2-1	4-1	4-4	2-2	1-2	0-0	4-2
2	Erith & Belvedere	4-0		3-0	2-2	2-1	2-1	0-0	3-2	4-1	6-0	5-1	2-1	4-1	6-2	3-3	4-1	3-1	1-5
3	FC Elmstead	1-2	1-3		0-0	2-3	2-1	1-1	2-3	3-0	4-0	5-1	2-2	1-1	0-0	2-2	1-2	1-2	1-1
4	Forest Hill Park	2-1	0-2	4-0		1-1	2-5	2-1	2-2	0-2	3-1	2-0	2-4	6-2	0-0	3-2	2-3	1-1	0-1
5	Greenways	1-4	1-6	1-1	1-2		2-4	2-2	0-5	2-4	7-2	1-0	4-1	3-1	5-3	1-3	1-0	0-6	1-2
6	Holmesdale	4-3	0-3	0-1	0-1	2-1		3-1	2-2	0-3	4-2	4-0	2-0	0-2	2-2	2-0	2-0	2-1	0-3
7	Kennington	1-4	3-1	2-1	4-0	2-1	3-2		3-1	3-3	3-3	6-0	5-1	1-0	1-2	3-0	2-0	3-1	3-0
8	Kent Football United	1-1	1-3	1-1	2-4	3-4	1-0	1-1		2-2	1-3	5-0	3-1	7-0	2-2	1-1	2-0	0-1	0-3
9	Lewisham Borough (Community)	0-1	1-6	5-0	3-1	2-3	0-1	1-2	3-2		0-1	0-1	1-2	2-0	3-0	1-4	4-3	0-5	1-3
10	Lydd Town	0-4	2-2	3-1	1-0	1-2	1-5	0-4	2-2	2-5		4-1	3-3	4-1	2-2	3-3	2-0	0-2	1-5
11	Meridian VP	1-2	1-4	2-5	0-1	2-0	0-2	2-4	2-1	1-1	2-1		2-1	2-3	2-4	0-0	1-0	1-7	1-1
12	Phoenix Sports Reserves	4-6	4-1	0-0	1-3	1-2	0-4	0-5	0-5	1-2	6-2	2-1		0-0	0-2	1-0	1-1	0-4	0-4
13	Rochester United	0-2	0-1	3-1	1-2	0-5	2-4	3-5	3-1	4-2	2-3	2-4	2-3		3-2	HW	1-3	2-2	3-6
14	Snodland Town	0-5	0-3	1-3	0-3	3-0	2-1	0-4	2-3	1-4	3-3	4-0	2-1	0-0		1-2	2-1	2-0	1-4
15	Sporting Club Thamesmead	0-2	0-4	0-1	1-2	6-2	2-1	1-2	6-1	2-1	4-1	1-0	3-1	0-3	4-3		5-2	1-2	0-1
16	Stansfeld	2-2	2-5	1-2	3-3	4-1	3-1	2-3	4-1	4-1	5-2	6-0	1-3	3-1	4-2	0-0		2-1	3-2
17	Sutton Athletic	5-1	1-1	2-0	4-1	3-3	3-2	1-2	2-1	3-2	0-2	3-0	3-1	5-1	4-1	2-1	2-2		1-1
18	Welling Town	0-3	4-3	3-1	2-0	4-3	2-1	0-0	2-1	5-1	4-4	4-0	5-1	1-0	2-0	2-1	0-0	4-1	

SPARTAN SOUTH MIDLANDS LEAGUE

RECENT CHAMPIONS

2016: AFC Dunstable **2017:** London Colney **2018:** Welwyn Garden City

PREMIER DIVISION	P	W	D	L	F	A	GD	Pts
1 Biggleswade FC	38	27	8	3	105	35	70	89
2 Tring Athletic	38	26	5	7	94	43	51	83
3 Hadley	38	26	5	7	73	35	38	83
4 Biggleswade United	38	24	5	9	88	46	42	77
5 Baldock Town	38	20	7	11	76	47	29	66*
6 Colney Heath	38	18	11	9	65	38	27	65
7 Potton United	38	19	5	14	75	58	17	62
8 Arlesey Town	38	16	7	15	64	70	-6	55
9 Oxhey Jets	38	15	10	13	60	66	-6	55
10 Crawley Green	38	15	7	16	75	79	-4	52
11 Leighton Town	38	12	14	12	52	49	3	50
12 Wembley	38	12	11	15	61	59	2	47
13 Edgware Town	38	11	13	14	44	53	-9	46
14 Harpenden Town	38	13	5	20	54	73	-19	44
15 London Colney	38	10	7	21	42	69	-27	37
16 North Greenford United	38	9	7	22	56	89	-33	34
17 Leverstock Green	38	8	7	23	40	78	-38	31
18 Cockfosters	38	7	8	23	46	91	-45	29
19 Stotfold	38	7	8	23	40	88	-48	29
20 London Tigers	38	7	6	25	41	85	-44	27

DIVISION ONE	P	W	D	L	F	A	GD	Pts
1 Harefield United	38	36	2	0	125	34	91	110
2 Broadfields United	38	30	4	4	95	37	58	94
3 Winslow United	38	22	8	8	113	66	47	74
4 Buckingham Athletic	38	21	6	11	96	63	33	69
5 Bedford	38	19	4	15	79	85	-6	61
6 London Lions	38	18	6	14	77	63	14	60
7 Risborough Rangers	38	18	6	14	78	74	4	60
8 FC Broxbourne Borough	38	17	9	12	84	83	1	60
9 Enfield Borough	38	17	6	15	95	84	11	57
10 Ampthill Town	38	17	4	17	82	67	15	55
11 Langford	38	16	4	18	70	75	-5	52
12 Rayners Lane	38	15	6	17	76	91	-15	51
13 Park View	38	13	7	18	79	90	-11	46
14 Milton Keynes Robins	38	12	5	21	74	88	-14	41
15 Wodson Park	38	10	5	23	49	74	-25	35
16 Hillingdon Borough	38	16	2	20	88	101	-13	34*
17 Amersham Town	38	10	4	24	56	95	-39	34
18 Brimsdown	38	10	3	25	61	104	-43	33
19 Codicote	38	7	6	25	64	104	-40	27
20 Hatfield Town	38	5	5	28	40	103	-63	20

DIVISION TWO	P	W	D	L	F	A	GD	Pts
1 Bovingdon	26	22	2	2	101	23	78	68
2 Old Bradwell United	26	20	4	2	73	19	54	64
3 Berkhamsted Raiders	26	17	3	6	65	38	27	54
4 Aston Clinton	26	14	5	7	60	37	23	47
5 Pitstone & Ivinghoe	26	14	2	10	63	46	17	44
6 Mursley United	26	11	6	9	69	51	18	39
7 Grendon Rangers	26	12	2	12	51	54	-3	38
8 MK Gallacticos	26	11	5	10	59	47	12	35*
9 Totternhoe	26	9	4	13	48	57	-9	31
10 Unite MK	26	9	4	13	51	63	-12	31
11 New Bradwell St Peter FC	26	6	6	14	48	75	-27	24
12 Sarratt	26	7	2	17	35	58	-23	23
13 The 61 FC (Luton)	26	5	3	18	36	91	-55	18
14 Clean Slate	26	1	0	25	18	118	-100	3

CHALLENGE TROPHY

HOLDERS: BROADFIELDS UNITED

ROUND 1

Wembley	v	Enfield Borough	1-2
Totternhoe	v	Cockfosters	1-4
London Lions	v	Harpenden Town	1-1, 4-2p
Tring Corinthians	v	Biggleswade United	2-4
FC Broxbourne Borough	v	Hadley	0-3
Risborough Rangers	v	Rayners Lane	1-4
Tring Athletic	v	London Colney	3-1
Hatfield Town	v	Leighton Town	1-3
Hillingdon Borough	v	Codicote	3-3, 3-2p
Park View	v	Mursley United	2-1
Aston Clinton	v	Potton United	0-4
Unite MK	v	Leverstock Green	2-1
Old Bradwell United	v	Bedford	3-0
Colney Heath	v	Broadfields United	1-0
Harefield United	v	Edgware Town	3-2
Winslow United	v	Brimsdown	2-2, 6-5p
Milton Keynes Robins	v	Berkhamsted Raiders CFC	4-1
Wodson Park	v	Langford	1-0
MK Gallacticos	v	Stotfold	5-2
Crawley Green	v	The 61 FC (Luton)	5-0
Amersham Town	v	Grendon Rangers	5-0
Pitstone & Ivinghoe	v	Clean Slate	7-2
Oxhey Jets	v	Baldock Town	1-2

Byes for: Ampthill Town, Arlesey Town, Biggleswade FC, Bovingdon, Buckingham Athletic, London Tigers, New Bradwell St Peter, North Greenford United, Sarratt.

ROUND 2

Enfield Borough	v	Arlesey Town	3-1
Cockfosters	v	Sarratt	0-1
Bovingdon	v	London Lions	2-2, 3-2p
Biggleswade United	v	Hadley	1-0
Rayners Lane	v	Tring Athletic	0-2
Leighton Town	v	Hillingdon Borough	4-1
Park View	v	Potton United	0-4
Buckingham Athletic	v	Unite MK	3-1
Ampthill Town	v	London Tigers	2-1
Old Bradwell United	v	Colney Heath	1-1, 4-5p
Harefield United	v	Winslow United	0-1
Milton Keynes Robins	v	North Greenford United	4-3
Biggleswade FC	v	New Bradwell St Peter	4-1
Wodson Park	v	MK Gallacticos	3-5
Crawley Green	v	Amersham Town	7-3
Pitstone & Ivinghoe	v	Baldock Town	1-5

ROUND 3

Enfield Borough	v	Sarratt	3-0
Bovingdon	v	Biggleswade United	1-1, 4-3p
Tring Athletic	v	Leighton Town	0-1
Potton United	v	Buckingham Athletic	2-2, 5-4p
Ampthill Town	v	Colney Heath	0-1
Winslow United	v	Milton Keynes Robins	4-0
Biggleswade FC	v	MK Gallacticos	2-3
Crawley Green	v	Baldock Town	0-1

QUARTER FINALS

Enfield Borough	v	Bovingdon	2-0
Leighton Town	v	Potton United	1-2
Colney Heath	v	Winslow United	2-1
MK Gallacticos	v	Baldock Town	0-3

SEMI FINALS

Enfield Borough	v	Potton United	2-2, 6-7p
Colney Heath	v	Baldock Town	2-3

FINAL

Potton United	v	Baldock Town	0-4

PREMIER DIVISION CUP FINAL

Biggleswade FC	v	Baldock Town	2-0

DIVISION ONE CUP FINAL

London Lions	v	Risborough Rangers	0-2

DIVISION TWO CUP FINAL

Old Bradwell United	v	Aston Clinton	0-0, 3-2p

PREMIER DIVISION		1	2	3	4	5	6	7	8	9	10	11	12	13	14	15	16	17	18	19	20
1	Arlesey Town		1-3	1-3	1-1	3-1	2-1	1-3	0-0	1-1	1-1	2-1	2-0	4-0	2-0	1-0	4-2	3-1	1-2	1-3	0-1
2	Baldock Town	0-1		3-2	2-3	2-1	2-1	4-1	2-0	0-2	4-0	2-1	4-0	3-4	2-1	3-2	1-1	0-1	7-0	0-1	2-1
3	Biggleswade FC	4-1	3-1		4-1	9-0	1-2	3-1	3-0	2-0	4-1	0-0	2-0	3-0	7-1	4-0	1-1	1-3	1-1	1-0	2-2
4	Biggleswade United	5-3	1-1	2-2		5-1	3-3	2-1	2-2	0-2	4-1	3-0	0-1	2-0	4-0	3-0	1-2	2-0	3-1	2-0	1-0
5	Cockfosters	1-3	0-2	1-4	0-4		0-1	5-5	1-2	0-1	1-3	2-1	2-1	2-2	1-1	3-1	1-3	1-4	1-1	2-2	1-2
6	Colney Heath	1-1	0-0	1-2	2-3	1-1		3-1	2-0	1-1	2-0	2-2	2-2	4-2	1-1	4-0	3-0	1-2	4-0	1-0	0-0
7	Crawley Green	4-1	1-1	1-5	0-3	2-3	1-2		1-2	2-1	2-1	3-1	5-0	1-0	2-3	2-1	3-4	3-1	3-2	3-4	4-2
8	Edgware Town	2-3	1-4	2-2	1-0	1-2	3-0	1-2		0-0	1-2	1-4	3-1	1-0	4-0	0-0	2-2	2-2	3-2	2-4	1-1
9	Hadley	4-3	2-1	0-4	2-1	2-0	0-1	2-1	3-0		3-0	1-0	3-0	3-0	5-0	2-3	3-0	1-1	3-1	1-3	2-1
10	Harpenden Town	0-0	2-1	0-3	2-4	3-2	1-3	3-3	1-0	0-1		2-1	1-0	2-2	3-0	4-1	0-1	7-0	0-2	2-5	1-2
11	Leighton Town	3-0	1-1	2-2	3-1	2-2	1-0	0-2	0-0	1-1	2-0		0-0	1-1	1-0	3-3	0-0	1-2	5-3	2-3	0-0
12	Leverstock Green	2-2	0-2	1-1	0-5	4-0	0-5	1-1	0-0	1-6	3-1	0-1		1-3	1-3	1-2	6-0	2-4	0-1	2-3	2-1
13	London Colney	1-2	0-2	0-2	0-4	3-1	0-2	2-0	0-0	3-0	1-2	1-2	2-0		1-1	2-1	0-1	1-4	1-1	0-3	2-0
14	London Tigers	0-4	1-4	0-1	0-1	2-3	0-1	1-1	1-2	1-3	1-2	0-0	2-0	3-0		1-3	2-3	1-3	2-1	0-4	1-2
15	North Greenford United FC	0-3	2-4	0-1	3-1	0-0	1-4	3-3	3-0	1-4	2-0	1-0	2-3	0-3	0-3		3-1	1-3	2-2	4-4	0-2
16	Oxhey Jets	2-1	1-1	4-6	1-4	H-W	1-2	2-3	0-0	1-2	0-1	0-1	1-0	3-0	5-0	4-4		1-0	2-0	0-2	1-1
17	Potton United	4-0	2-2	1-3	1-2	2-0	2-1	5-0	1-2	0-2	3-2	0-1	4-1	2-2	2-1	2-0	2-3		3-0	0-2	4-0
18	Stotfold	2-5	0-3	0-3	1-2	1-2	1-1	1-0	0-3	0-1	2-1	0-6	0-1	3-0	1-0	1-5	1-1	2-2		1-3	0-0
19	Tring Athletic	5-0	2-0	0-2	1-0	3-1	1-0	1-2	2-0	0-1	5-1	7-1	1-1	1-0	3-3	3-0	3-3	1-0	4-1		0-2
20	Wembley	6-0	4-0	1-2	2-3	3-1	0-0	2-2	0-0	1-2	1-1	1-1	1-2	2-3	2-4	5-2	2-3	3-2	4-2	1-5	

DIVISION ONE		1	2	3	4	5	6	7	8	9	10	11	12	13	14	15	16	17	18	19	20
1	Amersham Town		4-4	0-5	1-0	0-3	1-4	0-4	1-2	1-2	2-6	6-1	1-6	1-4	1-2	2-0	2-0	1-2	1-3	0-3	1-1
2	Ampthill Town	4-3		0-3	3-1	1-3	2-0	1-2	0-4	11-0	1-3	3-0	3-2	1-3	4-0	0-2	0-2	4-0	1-0	0-2	2-0
3	Bedford	1-0	2-2		3-1	0-1	2-3	2-1	3-2	1-4	0-3	3-2	1-2	3-2	5-2	2-4	4-2	2-1	0-5	2-2	2-1
4	Brimsdown	0-1	1-0	3-2		1-5	0-5	4-3	4-2	0-1	1-5	3-0	1-2	0-3	3-3	2-6	1-2	1-4	3-2	1-2	3-1
5	Broadfields United	5-2	2-1	3-0	3-1		3-0	3-1	2-1	2-3	1-1	3-1	3-2	4-2	1-0	2-1	3-1	3-2	1-2	4-1	3-0
6	Buckingham Athletic	2-0	3-1	3-2	6-0	0-4		2-1	4-1	4-1	2-4	4-1	14-2	2-1	0-0	2-2	4-1	0-0	2-3	3-2	3-1
7	Codicote	1-2	1-3	1-3	3-2	0-3	0-1		0-2	2-2	3-4	3-1	2-7	1-3	1-3	1-3	3-2	3-3	0-0	2-5	3-2
8	Enfield Borough	3-2	0-1	2-3	2-2	0-0	5-1	6-3		2-0	0-1	7-2	1-5	5-1	6-3	2-2	3-2	3-3	7-2	4-1	2-1
9	FC Broxbourne Borough	1-1	3-3	4-0	3-2	0-5	1-1	7-0	2-2		1-3	2-0	5-1	4-0	1-2	2-1	4-3	0-2	3-3	4-4	3-0
10	Harefield United	4-1	3-1	5-1	5-1	4-0	3-1	3-1	2-1	3-2		3-1	4-1	4-0	1-0	5-1	4-1	4-1	4-1	4-1	2-1
11	Hatfield Town	0-0	0-2	1-4	2-0	0-1	0-0	2-1	2-5	0-1	0-2		4-2	0-4	2-1	2-5	1-4	3-0	1-2	1-2	0-3
12	Hillingdon Borough	2-4	2-3	2-0	5-2	0-2	5-2	3-2	3-2	3-3	0-3	4-1		2-3	0-1	4-2	4-1	3-4	7-0	1-6	0-0
13	Langford	4-1	2-1	1-1	3-0	0-1	2-0	1-1	0-0	1-2	1-2	3-2	4-1		2-2	3-2	3-2	3-0	2-3	2-3	1-0
14	London Lions	1-0	3-2	4-3	4-2	0-2	1-0	2-2	3-1	2-2	1-1	7-1	7-0	3-0		4-2	1-2	1-4	1-3	3-0	1-0
15	Milton Keynes Robins	4-1	3-5	3-4	0-3	2-4	2-3	4-2	0-1	2-3	0-4	2-2	0-1	2-0	1-0		1-1	2-0	2-2	1-5	1-2
16	Park View	4-2	4-3	0-1	2-1	2-2	4-4	3-0	5-2	1-3	2-3	2-2	0-1	4-2	1-4	1-3		2-3	3-0	0-5	3-3
17	Rayners Lane	1-3	0-2	2-5	1-3	1-4	2-3	2-2	6-3	6-3	0-5	0-0	2-1	4-3	3-1	3-1	3-4		4-0	2-4	2-0
18	Risborough Rangers	0-3	1-1	1-2	4-2	1-0	0-4	0-6	4-0	1-0	0-3	4-0	3-1	5-1	3-1	0-1	2-2	8-1		3-3	1-0
19	Winslow United	5-2	3-1	9-1	3-3	2-2	1-3	4-0	7-1	4-2	1-2	3-1	1-0	5-0	1-0	5-3	2-2	1-1	1-0		1-2
20	Wodson Park	1-2	0-5	1-1	2-3	1-2	2-1	4-2	1-3	4-0	1-3	2-1	4-1	1-0	0-3	3-1	1-2	0-1	0-6	3-3	

DIVISION TWO		1	2	3	4	5	6	7	8	9	10	11	12	13	14
1	Aston Clinton		1-0	2-1	5-1	4-0	4-1	3-1	2-2	0-2	2-3	2-3	3-0	0-3	3-1
2	Berkhamsted Raiders	3-1		1-2	3-0	2-1	3-1	6-2	2-3	0-5	4-1	3-2	2-1	3-0	3-3
3	Bovingdon	2-0	4-2		13-0	4-0	3-3	3-2	3-1	4-0	4-1	3-0	8-0	2-1	5-1
4	Clean Slate	0-7	2-8	0-6		0-4	1-4	0-4	0-3	1-4	1-3	1-3	4-3	1-6	0-6
5	Grendon Rangers	1-1	1-1	1-7	4-0		1-2	4-3	0-4	0-1	3-1	3-2	5-1	4-2	2-3
6	MK Gallacticos	1-1	0-3	1-4	7-2	0-2		3-1	6-1	1-4	3-2	5-0	4-0	6-2	2-2
7	Mursley United	5-5	2-2	1-3	8-1	4-2	2-1		2-2	0-4	0-0	1-0	6-1	3-0	5-1
8	New Bradwell St Peter FC	0-1	3-6	1-2	2-0	1-3	0-0	0-4		0-5	2-5	5-5	5-0	1-5	1-3
9	Old Bradwell United	1-1	0-1	1-0	3-0	3-0	1-1	1-1	3-2		1-0	3-0	5-1	3-1	0-0
10	Pitstone & Ivinghoe	1-4	1-2	1-1	3-1	2-4	1-0	1-0	5-1	3-5		3-0	2-1	4-2	7-0
11	Sarratt	0-2	0-2	0-2	3-1	0-1	1-4	2-1	3-4	0-2	1-2		3-0	3-1	1-0
12	The 61 FC (Luton)	2-3	1-0	3-6	4-1	2-0	3-0	0-3	2-2	0-10	2-7	1-1		2-2	4-1
13	Totternhoe	1-0	0-1	0-5	1-0	1-3	2-1	3-3	2-2	1-3	2-0	3-1	4-1		2-2
14	Unite MK	2-3	1-2	0-4	1-0	3-2	1-2	3-5	6-0	1-3	0-4	3-1	4-1	3-1	

UNITED COUNTIES LEAGUE

RECENT CHAMPIONS

2016: AFC Kempton Rovers **2017:** Peterborough Sports **2018:** Yaxley

PREMIER DIVISION	P	W	D	L	F	A	GD	Pts
1 Daventry Town	38	29	7	2	91	29	62	94
2 Deeping Rangers	38	28	4	6	81	45	36	88
3 Rugby Town	38	25	5	8	86	42	44	80
4 Pinchbeck United	38	20	10	8	76	46	30	70
5 Holbeach United	38	21	6	11	77	38	39	69
6 Eynesbury Rovers	38	21	5	12	82	43	39	68
7 Cogenhoe United	38	20	8	10	81	50	31	68
8 Newport Pagnell Town	38	18	7	13	77	53	24	61
9 Desborough Town	38	17	9	12	64	50	14	60
10 Oadby Town	38	18	5	15	67	61	6	59
11 Harborough Town	38	18	3	17	74	60	14	57
12 Leicester Nirvana	38	12	9	17	72	75	-3	45
13 Sleaford Town	38	13	5	20	60	72	-12	44
14 Wellingborough Town	38	11	8	19	50	75	-25	41
15 Northampton ON Chenecks	38	12	4	22	49	75	-26	40
16 Peterborough Northern Star	38	11	5	22	44	64	-20	38
17 Boston Town	38	10	8	20	52	76	-24	38
18 Rothwell Corinthians	38	6	12	20	48	79	-31	30
19 Kirby Muxloe	38	6	1	31	35	108	-73	19
20 Wellingborough Whitworth	38	2	3	33	26	151	-125	9

DIVISION ONE	P	W	D	L	F	A	GD	Pts
1 Lutterworth Town	38	30	5	3	133	30	103	95
2 Anstey Nomads	38	30	4	4	133	34	99	94
3 Melton Town	38	28	4	6	105	33	72	88
4 Bugbrooke St.Michael	38	20	12	6	86	41	45	72
5 Blackstones	38	20	8	10	81	59	22	68
6 Lutterworth Athletic	38	17	6	15	74	57	17	57
7 Harrowby United	38	17	5	16	81	73	8	56
8 Aylestone Park	38	16	7	15	85	70	15	55
9 Northampton Sileby Rangers	38	16	6	16	67	84	-17	54
10 Irchester United	38	15	8	15	70	63	7	53
11 Rushden & Higham United	38	15	7	16	62	67	-5	52
12 Burton Park Wanderers	38	14	5	19	66	89	-23	47
13 Bourne Town	38	11	13	14	64	90	-26	46
14 Holwell Sports	38	11	5	22	70	109	-39	38
15 Long Buckby AFC	38	9	9	20	57	92	-35	36
16 St Andrews	38	9	8	21	74	93	-19	35
17 Birstall United Social	38	11	8	19	56	93	-37	35*
18 Huntingdon Town	38	10	2	26	54	121	-67	32
19 Raunds Town	38	9	4	25	44	117	-73	31
20 Thrapston Town	38	5	8	25	48	95	-47	23

LEAGUE CUP

HOLDERS: LEICESTER NIRVANA

PRELIMINARY ROUND

Holwell Sports	v	Sleaford Town	0-6
Irchester United	v	Burton Park Wanderers	3-2
St Andrews	v	Lutterworth Athletic	4-3
Harborough Town	v	Rugby Town	1-4
Long Buckby AFC	v	Kirby Muxloe	2-2, 7-8p

ROUND 1

Sleaford Town	v	Holbeach United	0-1
Blackstones	v	Melton Town	0-5
Irchester United	v	Wellingborough Town	1-3
St Andrews	v	Aylestone Park	0-0, 4-3p
Rugby Town	v	Leicester Nirvana	1-2
Anstey Nomads	v	Oadby Town	2-2, 4-5p
Kirby Muxloe	v	Lutterworth Athletic	2-1
Wellingborough Whitworth	v	Northampton Sileby Ranger	1-0
Birstall United Social	v	Rothwell Corinthians	2-2, 4-5p
Thrapston Town	v	Raunds Town	1-1, 7-6p
Bourne Town	v	Pinchbeck United	0-7
Huntingdon Town	v	Deeping Rangers	0-5
Eynesbury Rovers	v	Rushden & Higham United	1-1, 4-3p
Peterborough Norther Star	v	Boston Town	1-1, 3-5p
Northampton ON Chenecks	v	Newport Pagnell Town	0-5
Daventry Town	v	Desborough Town	3-0

ROUND 2

Holbeach United	v	Melton Town	3-0
Wellingborough Town	v	St Andrews	4-1
Leicester Nirvana	v	Oadby Town	1-0
Kirby Muxloe	v	Wellingborough Whitworth	4-2
Rothwell United	v	Deeping Rangers	0-1
Eynesbury Rovers	v	Boston Town	4-0
Newport Pagnell Town	v	Daventry Town	1-4

QUARTER FINALS

Holbeach United	v	Wellingborough Town	2-1
Leicester Nirvana	v	Kirby Muxloe	3-3, 5-4p
Rothwell Corinthians	v	Deeping Rangers	0-1
Eynesbury Rovers	v	Daventry Town	1-0

SEMI FINALS

Holbeach United	v	Leicester Nirvana	2-0
Deeping Rangers	v	Daventry Town	6-2

Deeping removed from the competition.

FINAL

Holbeach United	v	Daventry Town	1-3

PREMIER DIVISION	1	2	3	4	5	6	7	8	9	10	11	12	13	14	15	16	17	18	19	20
1 Boston Town		1-0	1-2	0-4	1-1	0-5	0-3	0-2	2-0	5-0	1-2	2-0	1-3	1-0	1-1	0-0	1-2	1-4	5-2	2-1
2 Cogenhoe United	2-2		2-4	3-4	1-0	0-2	2-1	3-2	3-0	6-0	2-1	1-0	1-1	3-1	0-1	2-1	2-3	1-1	4-1	6-1
3 Daventry Town	1-0	6-2		4-1	2-2	1-2	5-2	3-1	3-1	1-0	3-1	4-1	1-1	2-0	6-0	2-2	3-0	2-2	1-1	4-0
4 Deeping Rangers	4-1	2-1	1-0		2-1	0-3	3-2	1-0	3-0	2-0	1-0	2-0	0-4	1-1	1-4	4-1	0-3	2-1	2-1	7-0
5 Desborough Town	3-1	1-2	0-2	1-1		0-2	0-2	0-2	5-1	3-0	2-1	1-0	1-0	2-1	0-1	3-1	1-1	3-1	1-1	2-2
6 Eynesbury Rovers	1-1	1-1	0-1	0-2	1-1		3-0	1-2	1-2	2-4	0-2	2-0	4-1	4-0	2-2	2-1	0-1	2-0	6-0	5-0
7 Harborough Town	4-1	2-2	0-1	1-5	2-1	3-2		0-2	4-0	5-4	5-1	2-0	4-2	1-0	1-2	1-1	3-0	3-1	3-0	8-0
8 Holbeach United	1-1	2-2	1-2	2-3	1-0	0-2	1-0		6-0	4-0	0-3	2-0	2-1	2-1	1-0	1-1	0-2	2-1	2-1	9-0
9 Kirby Muxloe	3-1	1-2	1-3	0-1	0-3	1-4	1-2	0-5		0-4	1-5	0-1	2-3	0-2	1-1	1-3	1-4	3-7	2-0	3-1
10 Leicester Nirvana	0-0	2-1	1-1	0-2	0-3	3-3	0-2	0-0	4-1		4-4	2-2	5-2	1-2	1-3	2-2	2-0	3-1	2-0	6-0
11 Newport Pagnell Town	4-1	0-0	0-1	1-1	4-0	0-1	1-0	0-0	3-1	3-0		2-1	0-1	4-0	6-3	1-1	1-2	1-3	2-0	3-1
12 Northampton ON Chenecks	0-1	1-6	0-4	4-1	0-1	0-1	1-0	2-4	3-1	3-2	0-4		2-1	2-1	0-1	2-2	2-0	2-1	1-1	4-0
13 Oadby Town	2-3	0-0	1-2	0-2	1-1	0-3	2-1	3-1	0-1	4-3	5-4	2-0		3-1	2-0	0-0	2-1	1-2	4-2	4-1
14 Peterborough Northern Star	3-2	0-1	1-2	3-5	2-3	1-2	3-0	1-2	2-0	1-1	0-1	2-6	1-0		1-1	0-1	0-4	1-0	0-0	1-0
15 Pinchbeck United	1-1	2-1	1-1	0-1	3-3	3-0	4-1	0-0	4-0	1-0	1-2	7-0	1-2	2-0		2-1	0-3	2-0	1-0	6-0
16 Rothwell Corinthians	6-2	1-6	0-1	1-2	1-3	2-1	1-1	0-5	1-2	1-6	1-1	2-2	1-3	0-5	2-3		1-3	0-1	1-2	2-1
17 Rugby Town	5-2	0-1	0-2	1-1	2-1	3-4	2-1	2-0	4-1	2-1	4-0	4-0	3-0	2-2	1-1	2-1		4-0	7-1	4-1
18 Sleaford Town	2-1	1-2	0-3	0-1	1-5	3-2	0-1	0-2	4-2	2-3	3-1	5-0	3-1	0-1	1-4	3-0	1-1		2-1	3-3
19 Wellingborough Town	2-0	1-4	0-2	0-3	1-2	2-1	4-2	2-1	3-1	1-1	2-2	1-0	0-2	3-0	2-2	1-1	1-2	5-0		2-1
20 Wellingborough Whitworth	0-6	0-3	0-3	1-3	3-4	0-5	2-1	0-7	1-0	0-5	1-6	0-7	1-3	0-3	1-5	0-4	1-2	0-0	2-3	

DIVISION ONE	1	2	3	4	5	6	7	8	9	10	11	12	13	14	15	16	17	18	19	20
1 Anstey Nomads		4-2	4-0	5-0	5-2	1-1	4-4	6-1	3-0	12-1	1-1	8-1	4-2	3-1	2-0	3-0	1-2	1-0	3-1	3-0
2 Aylestone Park	1-3		4-0	1-1	4-1	1-2	2-3	0-0	5-1	2-1	4-2	1-2	2-2	1-1	1-6	0-1	8-0	3-8	5-2	4-0
3 Birstall United Social	0-7	0-4		2-2	0-0	0-2	3-0	2-2	3-1	1-2	0-4	4-3	0-3	1-5	0-4	1-2	2-0	1-1	2-2	3-2
4 Blackstones	2-3	3-2	3-2		2-3	0-1	1-0	0-0	5-2	2-1	3-0	2-0	3-2	2-3	1-3	1-1	4-1	3-2	3-2	5-1
5 Bourne Town	2-2	1-4	0-1	0-4		0-5	4-3	4-3	2-1	1-1	0-4	2-2	0-2	1-4	0-1	1-1	7-1	3-1	0-0	1-1
6 Bugbrooke St.Michael	2-1	1-1	3-1	3-0	1-1		2-0	1-1	4-2	3-0	0-2	6-1	1-0	3-3	3-4	9-0	3-0	1-1	0-0	1-1
7 Burton Park Wanderers	1-0	0-1	2-2	1-9	0-3	3-1		0-1	6-3	2-3	0-2	4-0	2-6	1-3	1-3	2-0	2-0	0-2	2-1	1-0
8 Harrowby United	1-4	1-2	0-2	4-1	2-2	0-4	2-0		3-2	0-3	2-3	0-5	4-1	2-1	0-2	4-1	7-0	3-0	4-0	1-2
9 Holwell Sports	0-5	5-5	3-2	1-4	5-1	2-0	1-4	6-1		3-1	0-2	2-5	5-3	0-5	2-4	0-1	2-1	1-2	3-3	4-2
10 Huntingdon Town	0-5	0-3	0-6	0-3	3-5	1-1	2-1	3-4	6-2		2-5	1-4	1-0	0-5	0-1	1-2	2-1	0-2	1-2	4-1
11 Irchester United	0-4	2-0	1-1	1-1	2-3	0-1	4-4	1-0	0-0	1-2		0-2	0-1	1-1	1-5	4-3	4-0	1-3	4-1	5-2
12 Long Buckby AFC	3-4	0-1	2-0	2-3	2-2	0-4	1-1	0-7	1-2	4-2	1-0		0-1	1-1	1-3	1-0	3-3	1-2	3-7	1-1
13 Lutterworth Athletic	0-1	3-0	4-2	1-2	1-1	3-1	0-0	3-0	2-0	6-0	3-3	4-1		0-3	0-4	2-2	0-1	1-1	2-0	3-1
14 Lutterworth Town	2-0	3-0	7-1	3-0	10-2	1-1	9-1	2-5	5-0	3-1	1-0	4-0	2-0		1-0	1-0	9-0	2-0	5-0	5-0
15 Melton Town	0-2	0-0	1-1	2-0	4-0	2-2	7-0	2-0	4-1	8-0	3-2	3-0	3-2	1-2		2-0	2-0	4-0	4-1	1-0
16 Northampton Sileby Rangers	0-6	3-2	0-4	1-2	2-1	2-2	2-4	3-1	4-1	6-0	3-3	3-1	2-1	0-5	2-1		4-1	1-3	3-7	4-1
17 Raunds Town	1-4	2-4	5-1	1-1	2-2	1-3	0-3	3-6	1-2	3-2	0-4	0-0	1-0	2-5	0-6	1-0		2-1	2-5	4-1
18 Rushden & Higham United	0-4	2-1	1-2	2-2	1-2	2-1	1-3	0-5	1-2	2-1	3-0	1-1	1-2	0-2	2-1	3-3	4-0		2-1	2-4
19 St Andrews	0-4	4-0	7-2	0-1	1-1	1-4	1-4	1-2	2-2	7-3	0-1	1-0	2-5	0-2	2-2	1-3	0-2	1-2		3-3
20 Thrapston Town	0-1	0-4	0-1	0-0	2-3	2-3	3-1	1-2	1-1	2-3	3-0	2-2	1-3	0-6	1-2	1-2	3-0	1-1	2-5	

RESERVE DIVISION	P	W	D	L	F	A	GD	Pts
1 Desborough Town Res	32	22	6	4	110	39	71	72
2 Yaxley Res	32	22	3	7	119	49	70	69
3 Bugbrooke St.Michael Res	32	20	5	7	85	44	41	65
4 Rothwell Corinthians Res	32	20	2	10	74	55	19	62
5 Newport Pagnell Town Res	32	18	6	8	80	46	34	60
6 Northampton ON Ch Res	32	17	7	8	85	52	33	58
7 Harborough Town Res	32	18	4	10	95	68	27	58
8 Cogenhoe United Res	32	17	6	9	85	42	43	57
9 Daventry Town Res	32	12	6	14	70	73	-3	42
10 Deeping Rangers Res	32	12	5	15	63	86	-23	41
11 Wellingborough Town Res	32	11	6	15	56	68	-12	39
12 Wellingborough Whitworth Res	32	9	9	14	58	81	-23	36
13 Bourne Town Res	32	9	3	20	63	106	-43	30
14 Peterborough N Star Res	32	7	7	18	42	68	-26	28
15 Irchester United Res	32	8	4	20	33	84	-51	28
16 Potton United Res	32	6	6	20	34	88	-54	24
17 Raunds Town Res	32	0	3	29	29	132	-103	3

WESSEX LEAGUE

RECENT CHAMPIONS

2016: Salisbury **2017:** Portland United **2018:** Blackfield & Langley

PREMIER DIVISION	P	W	D	L	F	A	GD	Pts
1 Sholing	38	34	3	1	117	24	93	105
2 Horndean	38	22	8	8	93	44	49	74
3 Bournemouth	38	19	10	9	85	64	21	67
4 Portland United	38	20	3	15	80	63	17	63
5 Baffins Milton Rovers	38	16	10	12	67	51	16	58
6 Hamworthy United	38	18	4	16	83	72	11	58
7 Hamble Club	38	17	7	14	60	52	8	58
8 Tadley Calleva	38	14	10	14	61	68	-7	52
9 Bashley	38	16	6	16	69	71	-2	51*
10 Lymington Town	38	14	9	15	68	72	-4	51
11 Team Solent	38	14	8	16	83	77	6	50
12 Alresford Town	38	15	5	18	70	71	-1	50
13 AFC Portchester	38	14	8	16	66	69	-3	50
14 Shaftesbury	38	14	6	18	57	59	-2	48
15 Brockenhurst	38	14	5	19	48	65	-17	47
16 Christchurch	38	12	10	16	52	63	-11	46
17 Fareham Town	38	12	10	16	51	78	-27	46
18 Cowes Sports	38	11	4	23	43	87	-44	37
19 Bemerton Heath Harlequins	38	7	10	21	45	81	-36	31
20 Andover New Street	38	7	4	27	36	103	-67	25

DIVISION ONE	P	W	D	L	F	A	GD	Pts
1 AFC Stoneham	36	26	6	4	124	42	82	84
2 Amesbury Town	36	26	6	4	107	46	61	84
3 Hythe & Dibden	36	25	8	3	105	42	63	83
4 Romsey Town	36	26	3	7	103	44	59	81
5 United Services Portsmouth	36	20	7	9	92	63	29	67
6 Newport (IOW)	36	16	5	15	64	60	4	53
7 Downton	36	14	9	13	67	68	-1	51
8 Verwood Town	36	13	9	14	47	64	-17	48
9 Laverstock & Ford	36	13	7	16	70	71	-1	46
10 East Cowes Victoria	36	11	12	13	60	77	-17	45
11 Fawley AFC	36	14	5	17	55	63	-8	44*
12 Ringwood Town	36	12	7	17	52	77	-25	43
13 Alton	36	13	5	18	72	81	-9	41*
14 Whitchurch United	36	12	5	19	53	80	-27	41
15 Petersfield Town	36	11	7	18	56	75	-19	40
16 Folland Sports	36	9	4	23	53	109	-56	31
17 New Milton Town	36	8	4	24	44	81	-37	28
18 Andover Town	36	8	2	26	51	100	-49	26
19 Totton & Eling	36	6	7	23	48	80	-32	25

LEAGUE CUP

HOLDERS: AFC PORCHESTER

ROUND 1

Bemerton Heath Harlequins	v	AFC Stoneham	3-4
Laverstock & Ford	v	United Services Portsmouth	3-4
Ringwood Town	v	Baffins Milton Rovers	1-2
New Milton Town	v	Team Solent	0-2
Folland Sports	v	Fareham Town	1-6
Newport (IOW)	v	Whitchurch United	4-0
Horndean	v	Amesbury Town	3-1

ROUND 2

Andover New Street	v	Downton	1-3
AFC Stoneham	v	Hamworthy United	1-4
United Services Portsmouth	v	Andover Town	5-2
Petersfield Town	v	Christchurch	1-1, 5-4p
Hythe & Dibden	v	Shaftesbury	4-1
Fawley AFC	v	Baffins Milton Rovers	0-3
Bashley	v	Brockenhurst	1-1, 3-2p
East Cowes Victoria	v	Alton	1-4
Tadley Calleva	v	Sholing	1-0
Team Solent	v	Portland United	2-4
Romsey Town	v	AFC Porchester	0-1
Fareham Town	v	Cowes Sports	0-9
Totton & Eling	v	Lymington Town	1-2
Alresford Town	v	Newport (IOW)	4-1
Verwood Town	v	Bournemouth	0-6
Horndean	v	Hamble Club	3-1

ROUND 3

Downton	v	Hamworthy United	1-4
United Services Portsmouth	v	Petersfield Town	7-1
Hythe & Dibden	v	Baffins Milton Rovers	1-3
Bashley	v	Alton	1-2
Tadley Calleva	v	Portland United	2-2, 3-4p
AFC Porchester	v	Cowes Sports	3-1
Lymington Town	v	Alresford Town	5-1
Bournemouth	v	Horndean	1-2

QUARTER FINALS

Hamworthy United	v	United Services Portsmouth	3-2
Baffins Milton Rovers	v	Alton	4-0
Portland United	v	AFC Porchester	5-3
Lymington Town	v	Horndean	1-2

SEMI FINALS

Hamworthy United	v	Baffins Milton Rovers	2-2, 3-4p
Portland United	v	Horndean	3-2

FINAL

Baffins Milton Rovers	v	Portland United	1-0

	PREMIER DIVISION	1	2	3	4	5	6	7	8	9	10	11	12	13	14	15	16	17	18	19	20
1	AFC Portchester		1-2	8-1	2-2	2-0	2-0	2-4	2-1	1-4	1-0	0-0	2-1	1-3	2-4	3-1	1-2	3-1	1-3	0-0	5-2
2	Alresford Town	4-3		2-0	3-1	6-3	1-4	2-3	3-1	1-2	6-0	0-0	0-2	3-3	1-2	2-2	0-2	2-0	1-3	1-2	2-5
3	Andover New Street	1-4	0-5		1-4	0-3	2-0	1-3	2-3	0-3	0-1	0-0	2-0	1-0	1-4	0-2	3-2	1-2	2-4	1-0	0-5
4	Baffins Milton Rovers	1-1	2-2	2-0		3-0	1-1	1-2	0-0	3-1	4-1	3-1	0-0	3-1	1-1	1-0	3-0	1-3	1-3	2-2	3-4
5	Bashley	2-1	0-3	2-0	2-0		2-1	2-2	1-0	1-0	7-1	1-2	1-1	2-1	1-1	2-2	2-6	2-1	0-0	4-0	6-5
6	Bemerton Heath Harlequins	1-3	1-1	4-0	0-1	1-1		1-1	0-2	2-1	2-1	0-5	1-1	4-2	3-3	5-0	2-4	3-2	0-4	0-2	1-1
7	Bournemouth	0-1	1-2	1-0	3-2	1-4	5-1		3-0	3-3	3-0	0-0	1-1	5-1	0-0	2-1	2-1	1-1	2-6	4-1	1-1
8	Brockenhurst	0-1	2-0	3-0	0-1	2-4	2-2	1-1		0-0	2-1	1-2	2-1	2-2	1-3	3-2	0-3	1-0	0-5	0-1	1-4
9	Christchurch	2-1	1-2	3-0	0-3	4-1	0-0	0-2	0-4		1-1	3-0	2-3	1-4	1-1	2-0	1-0	2-2	1-5	1-0	1-2
10	Cowes Sports	3-3	0-3	1-1	1-3	4-3	3-0	1-3	1-0	1-0		2-1	0-3	3-0	1-3	1-2	0-3	1-0	0-2	1-1	2-1
11	Fareham Town	2-2	5-3	2-2	1-1	2-1	3-0	2-1	0-2	2-2	1-2		1-0	3-1	1-4	1-1	1-0	2-0	0-4	1-3	2-2
12	Hamble Club	1-1	3-0	3-0	0-3	3-0	2-1	3-2	3-1	1-3	1-2	4-0		0-3	0-1	0-0	2-3	2-1	0-1	2-1	1-0
13	Hamworthy United	1-2	2-0	1-2	3-2	2-1	2-0	6-2	3-0	2-2	5-0	5-0	3-5		2-1	3-1	0-3	1-3	2-3	3-1	5-1
14	Horndean	6-0	4-1	5-0	2-0	1-0	3-0	0-2	3-0	0-2	6-1	6-1	4-1	0-1		4-2	1-2	3-0	0-0	4-1	3-2
15	Lymington Town	5-0	0-2	3-1	3-1	4-1	1-1	2-2	0-2	4-1	3-2	6-0	2-2	0-4	4-3		4-2	1-0	0-5	4-1	1-4
16	Portland United	1-0	1-0	2-2	2-4	2-1	6-2	2-6	4-0	5-1	3-1	2-1	1-2	3-0	2-3	1-2		1-2	0-3	1-1	2-1
17	Shaftesbury	1-0	6-2	4-2	0-0	1-0	2-0	2-3	0-1	0-0	3-1	5-2	1-2	1-1	3-1	1-1	0-3		0-3	3-1	2-0
18	Sholing	2-1	0-1	6-1	3-1	3-1	4-1	4-2	6-2	3-0	3-0	5-1	3-0	5-0	1-0	2-0	3-0	2-0		3-0	3-2
19	Tadley Calleva	3-1	2-0	2-4	2-1	2-3	3-0	3-2	1-3	1-1	2-1	3-1	2-1	2-4	1-1	4-1	2-2	2-1	1-1		1-1
20	Team Solent	2-2	2-1	4-2	0-2	1-2	2-0	3-4	0-3	2-0	2-1	1-2	1-3	4-1	2-2	1-1	4-1	5-3	0-1	4-4	

	DIVISION ONE	1	2	3	4	5	6	7	8	9	10	11	12	13	14	15	16	17	18	19
1	AFC Stoneham		4-0	3-2	2-1	6-1	1-1	1-0	5-1	1-0	3-0	5-1	4-3	5-0	4-0	4-0	6-1	3-0	4-1	2-1
2	Alton	1-3		1-0	1-4	1-2	4-2	3-1	8-2	1-2	1-0	0-2	2-2	5-1	2-0	2-6	3-2	1-4	3-1	2-3
3	Amesbury Town	4-2	3-1		5-2	2-0	3-0	4-0	7-0	1-1	5-4	6-2	4-2	5-2	3-0	4-3	4-0	2-2	1-0	4-0
4	Andover Town	1-10	0-2	2-4		0-4	1-1	2-1	2-1	0-4	1-2	3-1	0-2	4-5	1-3	0-1	4-3	0-4	0-3	5-0
5	Downton	2-2	2-2	0-0	2-0		4-0	1-5	6-1	2-3	0-0	2-0	1-0	1-1	5-0	0-3	2-1	0-2	0-3	4-2
6	East Cowes Victoria	1-0	6-2	1-6	2-1	1-4		2-2	1-1	3-3	2-2	3-0	0-2	2-2	1-0	2-3	2-1	1-1	1-1	3-0
7	Fawley AFC	1-5	1-2	2-0	2-2	3-2	2-1		0-2	1-1	1-0	4-0	0-2	1-1	3-1	1-6	2-1	2-0	0-2	2-3
8	Folland Sports	0-4	4-2	2-4	2-3	1-0	5-0	2-2		1-7	2-3	3-2	4-0	1-1	1-0	0-2	1-2	1-2	2-2	3-2
9	Hythe & Dibden	4-2	4-0	4-4	5-0	5-1	5-2	0-1	3-1		4-0	4-1	1-0	3-0	1-1	3-1	H-W	2-2	2-1	3-2
10	Laverstock & Ford	2-5	3-0	1-2	4-3	0-0	7-0	1-2	3-1	1-2		1-1	3-4	0-3	4-2	2-0	3-2	3-2	1-1	2-2
11	New Milton Town	1-2	2-2	0-2	2-5	1-1	0-2	0-2	6-0	0-4	2-3		0-2	0-0	3-1	3-1	3-1	3-1	1-2	3-1
12	Newport (IOW)	0-4	H-W	0-1	3-1	3-5	1-1	1-0	4-0	0-2	3-2	1-0		2-0	2-2	1-2	3-1	0-2	1-1	8-2
13	Petersfield Town	0-0	3-1	0-3	2-1	5-0	2-3	3-1	6-1	3-4	1-3	3-1	0-3		2-0	1-3	2-0	0-3	1-0	0-1
14	Ringwood Town	0-9	3-2	1-1	2-1	0-3	0-2	3-1	3-1	3-3	1-0	2-1	3-2	2-1		1-1	4-1	2-3	1-2	2-1
15	Romsey Town	3-3	4-0	1-3	7-0	4-1	4-1	1-0	9-0	3-1	3-2	2-0	4-0	3-1	1-1		2-1	2-3	3-0	3-2
16	Totton & Eling	3-3	2-2	1-1	3-0	3-4	0-4	1-3	1-3	1-1	4-5	0-1	2-2	2-0	2-1	0-5		1-2	2-0	2-0
17	United Services Portsmouth	3-2	2-2	3-4	3-1	4-1	3-2	1-2	4-3	2-6	2-1	4-0	3-2	6-2	3-3	1-3	1-1		5-1	0-1
18	Verwood Town	1-1	1-7	1-0	1-0	1-1	1-1	3-2	1-0	0-5	2-2	4-0	3-2	5-2	1-2	0-2	0-0	0-6		0-3
19	Whitchurch United	2-4	0-4	2-3	1-0	3-3	3-3	3-2	2-0	0-3	2-0	2-1	0-1	0-0	3-2	0-2	1-0	3-3	0-1	

Tipton Town v Sikh Hunters. Photo: Bill Wheatcroft.

Tipton Town v Sikh Hunters. Photo: Bill Wheatcroft.

WEST MIDLANDS (REGIONAL) LEAGUE

RECENT CHAMPIONS

2016: Shawbury United **2017:** Haughmond **2018:** Wolverhampton Sporting Community

PREMIER DIVISION		P	W	D	L	F	A	GD	Pts
1	Tividale	38	29	4	5	133	32	101	91
2	Haughmond	38	28	3	7	118	38	80	87
3	Wolverhampton Casuals	38	25	7	6	111	44	67	82
4	Malvern Town	38	26	4	8	103	36	67	82
5	Wednesfield	38	24	6	8	86	54	32	75
6	Bewdley Town	38	21	7	10	82	53	29	70
7	Hereford Lads Club	38	19	6	13	80	52	28	63
8	Black Country Rangers	38	18	6	14	88	79	9	60
9	Wellington	38	17	6	15	80	72	8	57
10	Dudley Town	38	15	9	14	72	70	2	54
11	Cradley Town	38	15	5	18	67	79	-12	50
12	AFC Bridgnorth	38	13	9	16	64	75	-11	48
13	Bilston Town	38	12	6	20	59	91	-32	42
14	Pershore Town	38	11	6	21	66	100	-34	39
15	Dudley Sports	38	9	10	19	50	91	-41	37
16	Shawbury United	38	10	6	22	63	111	-48	36
17	Smethwick Rangers	38	10	5	23	33	103	-70	35
18	Wem Town	38	9	2	27	38	101	-63	29
19	Shifnal Town	38	8	4	26	62	91	-29	28
20	Pegasus Juniors	38	4	3	31	26	109	-83	15

DIVISION ONE		P	W	D	L	F	A	GD	Pts
1	Worcester Raiders	32	24	7	1	98	37	61	79
2	Darlaston Town (1874)	32	25	3	4	100	34	66	78
3	Droitwich Spa	32	22	3	7	107	31	76	69
4	Sikh Hunters	32	20	4	8	99	47	52	64
5	Team Dudley	32	18	5	9	82	55	27	59
6	Wrens Nest	32	16	6	10	67	64	3	54
7	Wellington Amateurs	32	14	4	14	68	67	1	46
8	Old Wulfrunians	32	14	4	14	48	51	-3	46
9	Allscott	32	13	3	16	56	64	-8	42
10	Wyrley	32	12	4	16	41	57	-16	40
11	Bromyard Town	32	11	6	15	62	78	-16	39
12	Newport Town	32	11	4	17	62	68	-6	37
13	Gornal Athletic	32	11	3	18	53	79	-26	36
14	Tipton Town	32	7	9	16	55	66	-11	30
15	Bustleholme	32	8	2	22	52	107	-55	26
16	Willenhall Town	32	5	5	22	37	89	-52	20
17	Telford Juniors	32	3	4	25	35	128	-93	13

DIVISION TWO		P	W	D	L	F	A	GD	Pts
1	Gornal Colts	20	14	3	3	55	28	27	45
2	Church Stretton Town	19	12	3	4	62	26	36	42
3	FC Darlaston	19	11	5	3	56	29	27	41
4	AFC Bentley	20	10	3	7	48	55	-7	33
5	Hawkins Sports	20	9	4	7	66	43	23	31
6	Ludlow	20	9	3	8	57	42	15	30
7	AFC Bridgnorth Dev	20	9	2	9	42	48	-6	29
8	Warstones Wanderers	20	7	4	9	41	51	-10	25
9	Rock Rovers	19	6	1	12	43	56	-13	19
10	Wolverhampton United	19	4	5	10	41	72	-31	17
11	Tipton Town Reserves	20	0	1	19	24	85	-61	1

Oldbury United resigned - record expunged.

Premier Division League Cup Final

Bewdley Town v Wolverhampton Casuals 0-2

Tipton Town v Sikh Hunters. Photo: Bill Wheatcroft.

Tipton Town v Sikh Hunters. Photo: Bill Wheatcroft.

WESTERN LEAGUE

Founded: 1892 **Sponsored by:** Toolstation

Recent Champions: 2015: Melksham Town **2016:** Odd Down (Bath) **2017:** Bristol Manor Farm

PREMIER DIVISION	P	W	D	L	F	A	GD	Pts
1 Willand Rovers	38	30	5	3	116	31	85	95
2 Plymouth Parkway	38	30	3	5	110	37	73	93
3 Bitton	38	29	5	4	112	44	68	92
4 Bridgwater Town	38	24	9	5	94	43	51	81
5 Westbury United	38	23	5	10	76	50	26	74
6 Clevedon Town	38	21	1	16	78	62	16	64
7 Bradford Town	38	17	11	10	78	55	23	62
8 Cribbs	38	17	9	12	71	61	10	60
9 Buckland Athletic	38	17	7	14	81	66	15	58
10 Chipping Sodbury Town	38	14	7	17	59	84	-25	49
11 Shepton Mallet	38	15	3	20	74	83	-9	48
12 Hallen	38	14	5	19	55	69	-14	47
13 Bridport	38	13	5	20	64	76	-12	44
14 Cadbury Heath	38	11	9	18	53	88	-35	42
15 Odd Down (BATH)	38	12	5	21	53	76	-23	41
16 Wellington	38	12	3	23	55	80	-25	39
17 Roman Glass St George	38	8	8	22	55	85	-30	32
18 Brislington	38	9	4	25	55	84	-29	31
19 Hengrove Athletic	38	5	6	27	40	102	-62	21
20 Shortwood United	38	1	6	31	29	132	-103	9

DIVISION ONE	P	W	D	L	F	A	GD	Pts
1 Keynsham Town	38	30	3	5	94	28	66	93
2 Cheddar	38	26	6	6	92	38	54	84
3 Corsham Town	38	20	10	8	69	43	26	70
4 Ashton & Backwell United	38	20	5	13	62	51	11	65
5 Longwell Green Sports	38	19	7	12	79	67	12	64
6 Warminster Town	38	19	5	14	74	53	21	62
7 Chard Town	38	17	9	12	79	63	16	60
8 Calne Town	38	16	8	14	59	45	14	56
9 Welton Rovers	38	17	5	16	60	57	3	56
10 Wells City	38	16	7	15	68	61	7	55
11 Devizes Town	38	16	5	17	63	68	-5	53
12 Bishops Lydeard	38	14	6	18	73	68	5	48
13 Sherborne Town	38	14	5	19	49	59	-10	47
14 Wincanton Town	38	10	14	14	74	74	0	44
15 Radstock Town	38	12	6	20	61	70	-9	42
16 Portishead Town	38	12	4	22	59	98	-39	40
17 Bishop Sutton	38	10	9	19	42	79	-37	39
18 Oldland Abbotonians	38	9	8	21	50	83	-33	35
19 Chippenham Park	38	9	7	22	53	79	-26	34
20 Bristol Telephones	38	6	7	25	46	122	-76	24*

LES PHILLIPS CUP

HOLDERS: BUCKLAND ATHLETIC

PRELIMINARY ROUND

Brislington	v	Hengrove Athletic	3-1
Bridport	v	Bristol Telephones	10-0

ROUND 1

Brislington	v	Warminster Town	4-2
Buckland Athletic	v	Longwell Green Sports	3-0
Ashton & Backwell United	v	Portishead Town	2-1
Cadbury Heath	v	Devizes Town	4-3
Wells City	v	Bishops Lydeard	2-1
Plymouth Parkway	v	Cribbs	2-0
Bishop Sutton	v	Keynsham Town	0-2
Clevedon Town	v	Bridport	4-0
Chipping Sodbury Town	v	Shortwood United	5-0
Shepton Mallet	v	Sherborne Town	4-1
Wellington	v	Willand Rovers	0-2
Westbury United	v	Odd Down (Bath)	0-3
Chard Town	v	Calne Town	1-2
Wincanton Town	v	Corsham Town	3-1
Welton Rovers	v	Bridgwater Town	1-3
Cheddar	v	Roman Glass St George	0-5

ROUND 2

Brislington	v	Buckland Athletic	0-0, 2-4p
Ashton & Backwell United	v	Cadbury Heath	0-3
Wells City	v	Plymouth Parkway	0-4
Keynsham Town	v	Clevedon Town	3-2
Chipping Sodbury Town	v	Shepton Mallet	1-3
Willand Rovers	v	Odd Down (Bath)	7-1
Calne Town	v	Wincanton Town	2-1
Bridgwater Town	v	Roman Glass St George	2-0

QUARTER FINALS

Buckland Athletic	v	Cadbury Heath	1-4
Plymouth Parkway	v	Keynsham Town	2-1
Shepton Mallet	v	Willand Rovers	2-4
Calne Town	v	Bridgwater Town	1-2

SEMI FINALS

Cadbury Heath	v	Plymouth Parkway	1-4
Willand Rovers	v	Bridgwater Town	1-1, 3-2p

FINAL

Plymouth Parkway	v	Willand Rovers	2-1

PREMIER DIVISION		1	2	3	4	5	6	7	8	9	10	11	12	13	14	15	16	17	18	19	20
1	Bitton		2-2	1-1	3-1	3-0	3-0	4-2	2-3	2-0	2-1	3-2	5-0	1-0	1-1	2-0	5-2	7-1	4-1	3-1	1-1
2	Bradford Town	0-2		0-0	3-2	1-0	2-2	5-0	1-1	3-0	2-0	1-1	1-0	0-0	1-2	2-0	1-2	2-1	0-2	5-2	1-2
3	Bridgwater Town	2-2	6-2		1-0	6-0	2-0	1-1	4-0	3-2	1-1	1-0	2-1	2-1	0-1	4-4	4-1	2-1	4-1	2-1	1-4
4	Bridport	2-4	2-2	0-2		0-1	3-1	1-2	4-2	1-4	1-2	1-2	3-1	4-3	0-2	3-1	4-0	1-1	3-0	0-1	1-5
5	Brislington	0-4	1-4	0-1	1-4		2-3	0-1	6-0	1-5	2-3	2-3	1-2	2-3	2-3	1-0	0-2	3-0	4-0	0-4	2-3
6	Buckland Athletic	4-5	4-1	5-3	2-1	4-2		7-0	0-1	1-2	2-4	4-0	3-3	3-0	1-2	1-1	5-1	4-2	2-0	1-0	0-1
7	Cadbury Heath	1-3	1-4	2-4	4-0	1-1	1-1		1-1	0-1	2-0	1-2	2-2	1-1	1-4	3-0	4-1	1-0	1-4	0-2	1-3
8	Chipping Sodbury Town	1-4	2-1	0-8	0-2	2-2	1-3	3-2		1-3	1-1	1-2	2-0	1-3	3-3	1-0	2-1	0-0	3-0	1-4	2-4
9	Clevedon Town	1-2	0-2	1-0	1-1	4-3	1-3	4-1	0-4		5-2	1-2	3-0	3-2	1-2	1-0	2-0	3-0	4-0	3-5	0-4
10	Cribbs	0-3	2-1	0-0	3-3	2-1	2-3	4-0	0-3	0-2		1-1	2-1	1-2	0-2	5-1	1-0	5-0	5-1	3-1	2-0
11	Hallen	0-1	1-2	1-2	2-3	2-1	2-1	1-1	1-0	0-3	1-2		1-0	3-2	2-4	0-2	0-3	3-0	2-1	3-4	0-4
12	Hengrove Athletic	1-6	0-4	1-4	2-4	1-1	0-4	2-3	1-2	0-2	2-4	0-4		2-1	0-1	1-1	1-7	7-2	2-1	0-1	0-4
13	Odd Down (BATH)	1-4	1-1	0-3	1-0	2-3	0-2	1-3	0-2	2-1	1-3	1-0	2-1		0-2	0-2	4-2	2-2	2-1	1-4	1-1
14	Plymouth Parkway	3-0	4-2	1-1	2-1	2-3	5-1	5-0	2-3	3-4	5-1	4-2	1-0	2-1		2-0	4-0	4-1	5-0	0-1	2-0
15	Roman Glass St George	0-7	3-3	3-5	2-3	1-2	4-1	2-2	3-1	2-3	0-2	0-0	1-1	1-4	0-8		3-1	2-0	1-3	1-4	1-3
16	Shepton Mallet	1-3	4-4	1-5	3-0	2-0	7-2	1-1	4-0	2-1	2-0	2-1	1-1	4-1	0-2	0-4		5-0	2-0	1-3	1-5
17	Shortwood United	2-4	1-7	2-4	0-1	2-2	1-1	1-3	0-4	1-3	1-1	0-6	2-3	1-4	0-8	0-7	2-5		0-1	1-2	0-4
18	Wellington	1-2	1-3	1-1	4-2	0-2	0-0	1-2	7-2	2-1	3-3	3-0	5-0	1-3	0-3	2-1	2-1	5-0		0-2	0-2
19	Westbury United	2-1	0-1	0-2	1-1	3-1	0-0	2-1	1-1	2-1	2-2	1-1	5-0	1-0	0-4	3-0	4-2	0-1	3-1		3-1
20	Willand Rovers	3-1	1-1	1-0	5-1	1-0	1-0	9-0	4-2	3-2	1-1	6-1	4-1	6-0	4-0	1-1	2-0	6-0	3-0	4-1	

DIVISION ONE		1	2	3	4	5	6	7	8	9	10	11	12	13	14	15	16	17	18	19	20
1	Ashton & Backwell United		2-1	3-1	2-0	1-0	1-3	2-3	6-1	1-1	1-3	0-2	0-3	0-1	2-1	1-0	1-2	2-1	2-1	2-0	1-1
2	Bishop Sutton	2-2		0-4	3-2	0-2	0-0	1-1	1-2	1-3	1-2	0-2	1-8	1-0	0-0	0-3	1-0	3-2	1-4	1-5	3-3
3	Bishops Lydeard	1-2	3-0		2-1	1-1	2-3	1-1	4-1	0-5	6-1	0-1	1-2	2-3	4-2	2-1	3-1	1-2	3-0	2-0	2-4
4	Bristol Telephones	1-2	1-1	2-1		1-1	1-9	0-9	1-1	1-6	1-5	1-2	2-3	1-1	3-1	4-4	0-3	1-7	3-5	1-4	1-1
5	Calne Town	3-0	1-2	2-2	1-0		1-0	1-3	1-0	1-1	0-0	0-1	4-3	0-1	5-0	5-0	2-0	1-3	1-3	0-3	3-0
6	Chard Town	0-2	3-0	1-3	1-2	3-1		2-2	3-3	0-3	1-0	1-0	3-0	4-0	6-1	3-2	0-1	3-3	3-3	1-1	2-2
7	Cheddar	3-0	2-0	3-2	4-1	2-0	2-3		2-0	3-2	1-0	0-2	2-2	1-1	1-2	4-1	2-1	1-0	1-2	2-1	3-0
8	Chippenham Park	1-0	1-0	4-5	1-2	2-0	3-4	2-3		2-2	2-3	1-4	4-1	2-2	2-3	1-0	1-2	1-0	3-3	0-1	0-1
9	Corsham Town	2-0	3-2	2-1	2-1	1-1	1-0	1-1	1-0		2-0	2-3	0-2	2-1	2-1	0-0	0-0	1-2	2-3	1-0	2-0
10	Devizes Town	1-2	0-1	1-0	1-4	3-1	2-1	0-4	2-0	3-5		0-5	4-2	0-1	0-3	2-0	1-3	6-1	1-1	0-2	2-1
11	Keynsham Town	2-1	5-0	3-2	5-0	0-2	4-0	0-3	3-2	3-0	1-0		6-2	9-0	2-0	1-0	2-0	1-0	1-3	1-1	2-1
12	Longwell Green Sports	1-0	1-6	2-2	3-0	0-1	4-0	0-2	2-1	1-1	1-1	0-0		4-2	5-0	1-3	3-1	0-5	5-4	2-3	1-1
13	Oldland Abbotonians	1-3	1-1	0-2	2-2	1-1	1-3	0-8	2-0	2-0	1-2	0-2	2-3		9-2	0-0	1-1	0-1	2-4	2-4	4-1
14	Portishead Town	0-6	0-1	2-4	4-2	0-3	0-0	2-3	3-0	0-3	0-5	0-4	1-3	1-2		5-6	2-0	3-2	2-1	5-1	3-2
15	Radstock Town	1-2	1-1	3-2	3-1	2-1	1-2	0-1	1-2	2-2	1-3	1-1	1-2	5-2	1-2		4-2	4-3	1-2	1-2	1-2
16	Sherborne Town	0-1	2-0	2-0	3-1	1-3	1-0	0-2	2-2	1-0	2-2	0-5	2-4	1-0	1-1	3-0		1-3	4-1	1-2	1-0
17	Warminster Town	0-1	2-2	2-0	4-0	3-1	3-5	3-0	3-1	0-2	1-1	1-3	1-0	2-0	1-0	1-0	2-1		4-2	0-2	5-0
18	Wells City	1-2	0-1	0-0	5-0	0-2	2-0	3-0	0-1	2-3	2-1	1-3	0-1	2-1	3-1	0-3	3-1	0-0		0-2	2-0
19	Welton Rovers	3-3	0-2	3-0	0-1	1-5	2-3	0-3	4-1	0-1	5-1	2-1	0-2	1-0	0-3	0-1	2-1	0-0	0-0		2-3
20	Wincanton Town	3-3	6-1	2-2	10-0	1-1	3-3	0-4	2-2	2-2	2-4	1-2	0-0	5-1	3-3	2-3	2-1	3-1	0-0	4-1	

ANGLIAN COMBINATION

RECENT CHAMPIONS

2016: Acle United **2017:** Spixworth **2018:** Harleston Town

PREMIER DIVISION	P	W	D	L	F	A	GD	Pts
1 Sheringham	30	23	2	5	96	38	58	71
2 Caister	30	20	5	5	80	42	38	65
3 Long Stratton	30	20	4	6	65	30	35	64
4 Waveney	30	19	3	8	57	39	18	60
5 Norwich CEYMS	30	15	7	8	62	43	19	52
6 Beccles Town	30	13	6	11	64	61	3	45
7 Scole United	30	11	9	10	48	47	1	42
8 Mattishall	30	12	7	11	66	69	-3	42*
9 Wymondham Town	30	12	5	13	60	55	5	41
10 Acle United	30	10	7	13	54	60	-6	37
11 Wroxham Res	30	10	5	15	40	50	-10	35
12 Bradenham Wands	30	11	2	17	59	71	-12	35
13 Blofield United	30	10	4	16	64	79	-15	34
14 Hellesdon	30	8	7	15	49	63	-14	31
15 St Andrews	30	5	5	20	37	74	-37	20
16 Norwich United U21	30	1	2	27	26	106	-80	5

DIVISION ONE	P	W	D	L	F	A	GD	Pts
1 UEA	30	23	3	4	93	29	64	72
2 Mundford	30	20	4	6	89	32	57	64
3 Bungay Town	30	16	10	4	69	40	29	58
4 Stalham Town	30	17	5	8	77	54	23	56
5 Yelverton	30	17	4	9	57	39	18	55
6 Easton	30	16	6	8	70	45	25	54
7 Aylsham	30	16	5	9	72	47	25	53
8 East Harling	30	16	5	9	53	43	10	53
9 Attleborough Town	30	14	3	13	56	51	5	45
10 Fakenham Town Res	30	9	7	14	61	54	7	34
11 Kirkley & Pakefield Res	30	10	3	17	41	60	-19	33
12 Thetford Rovers	30	8	7	15	53	76	-23	31
13 Watton United	30	8	4	18	39	77	-38	28
14 Hindringham	30	5	5	20	47	91	-44	20
15 Reepham Town	30	5	3	22	33	86	-53	18
16 North Walsham Town	30	2	2	26	29	115	-86	4*

DIVISION TWO	P	W	D	L	F	A	GD	Pts
1 Gorleston Res	28	20	4	4	84	26	58	64
2 Sprowston Athletic	28	20	2	6	75	27	48	62
3 Loddon United	28	16	3	9	60	41	19	51
4 Hingham Athletic	28	15	5	8	76	45	31	49*
5 Holt United	28	13	9	6	53	44	9	48
6 Gayton United	28	14	5	9	82	63	19	47
7 Brandon Town	28	13	6	9	54	48	6	45
8 Caister Res	28	14	3	11	54	54	0	44*
9 Wells Town	28	10	7	11	51	53	-2	37
10 Martham	28	8	7	13	48	79	-31	31
11 Freethorpe	28	7	7	14	52	64	-12	28
12 Buxton	28	8	4	16	43	68	-25	28
13 Cromer Town	28	7	2	19	49	81	-32	20*
14 Poringland Wands	28	5	5	18	41	77	-36	20
15 Mattishall Res	28	4	3	21	24	76	-52	9*

DIVISION THREE	P	W	D	L	F	A	GD	Pts
1 Heacham	26	24	2	0	112	13	99	74
2 Beccles Caxton	26	21	2	3	80	24	56	65
3 Swaffham Town Res	26	16	2	8	76	41	35	50
4 Long Stratton Res	26	13	3	10	53	51	2	42
5 South Walsham	26	11	6	9	49	49	0	39
6 Horsford United	26	12	2	12	62	50	12	37*
7 Gt Yarmouth Town Res	26	11	3	12	52	71	-19	36
8 Earsham	26	10	5	11	60	45	15	35
9 Hempnall	26	10	4	12	52	65	-13	34
10 Bradenham Wands Res	26	9	6	11	52	81	-29	33
11 Aylsham Res	26	8	3	15	60	61	-1	27
12 Norwich CEYMS Res	26	8	4	14	65	61	4	26*
13 Acle United Res	26	5	1	20	38	106	-68	14*
14 Hemsby	26	1	3	22	28	121	-93	3*

DIVISION FOUR	P	W	D	L	F	A	GD	Pts
1 Castle Acre Swifts	28	22	4	2	90	30	60	70
2 Attleborough Town Res	28	19	4	5	76	32	44	61
3 Waveney Res	28	17	5	6	80	39	41	56
4 AC Mill Lane	28	17	4	7	92	43	49	55
5 Beccles Town Res	28	17	3	8	75	55	20	54
6 UEA Res	28	12	6	10	79	42	37	42
7 Downham Town Res	28	12	3	13	67	83	-16	39
8 Mundford Res	28	10	5	13	51	66	-15	35
9 Costessey Sports	28	11	2	15	57	98	-41	34*
10 Gayton United Res	28	9	6	13	58	68	-10	33
11 St Andrews Res	28	10	2	16	47	55	-8	32
12 Wymondham Town Res	28	9	5	14	52	67	-15	32
13 Mulbarton Wands Res	28	8	4	16	47	79	-32	28
14 Bungay Town Res	28	3	8	17	40	74	-34	17
15 Blofield United Res	28	3	1	24	43	123	-80	9*

DIVISION FIVE NORTH	P	W	D	L	F	A	GD	Pts
1 Dussindale Rovers	24	18	3	3	81	16	65	57
2 Hellesdon Res	24	16	4	4	75	38	37	52
3 Norwich Eagles	24	16	3	5	95	63	32	51
4 Holt United Res	24	15	2	7	68	45	23	47
5 AFC Lynn Napier	24	13	2	9	67	45	22	41
6 Narborough	24	12	2	10	51	53	-2	38
7 Hindringham Res	24	11	4	9	48	51	-3	37
8 Sheringham Res	24	11	3	10	64	42	22	34*
9 Stalham Town Res	24	11	1	12	51	55	-4	33*
10 Reepham Town Res	24	8	0	16	43	69	-26	23*
11 Wells Town Res	24	5	5	14	29	61	-32	18*
12 Necton	24	3	2	19	28	89	-61	10*
13 Thorpe Village	24	1	1	22	21	94	-73	1*

DIVISION FIVE SOUTH	P	W	D	L	F	A	GD	Pts
1 Belton	22	18	2	2	104	26	78	56
2 Harleston Town Res	22	17	2	3	131	30	101	53
3 Scole United Res	22	16	3	3	56	21	35	51
4 Tacolneston	22	13	4	5	87	38	49	43
5 Yelverton Res	22	13	2	7	68	30	38	41
6 East Harling Res	22	13	1	8	73	50	23	40
7 Easton Res	22	10	1	11	74	56	18	31
8 Martham Res	22	7	1	14	31	73	-42	22
9 Thetford Rovers Res	22	6	0	16	32	74	-42	18
10 Poringland Wands Res	22	5	0	17	31	118	-87	13*
11 Freethorpe Res	22	4	0	18	26	116	-90	12
12 South Walsham Res	22	2	0	20	15	96	-81	3*

	PREMIER DIVISION	1	2	3	4	5	6	7	8	9	10	11	12	13	14	15	16
1	Acle United		2-2	5-3	2-1	1-3	1-0	1-2	1-3	1-3	2-2	5-1	0-1	2-2	4-1	2-0	1-2
2	Beccles Town	5-1		3-2	2-6	4-1	2-3	1-0	8-2	2-2	3-1	1-1	0-2	5-2	1-3	0-2	4-2
3	Blofield United	3-1	4-1		3-3	1-4	2-1	2-3	0-1	1-2	1-0	1-1	6-7	2-4	4-6	5-0	3-1
4	Bradenham Wands	0-2	3-2	0-1		2-3	2-2	2-4	1-2	5-2	6-1	4-3	1-5	3-2	3-2	0-4	3-2
5	Caister	2-2	3-1	4-1	1-0		6-2	1-2	3-1	0-0	9-1	4-2	2-5	2-1	1-3	4-0	1-3
6	Hellesdon	4-2	1-2	1-1	3-1	1-3		1-7	2-2	1-2	4-0	1-1	3-2	0-2	1-3	2-2	4-3
7	Long Stratton	1-1	3-1	5-0	2-0	0-0	1-0		0-3	2-1	4-1	0-0	1-0	6-0	3-1	2-0	2-0
8	Mattishall	3-4	2-2	3-1	4-2	1-3	2-1	4-6		1-2	2-1	3-3	1-3	2-6	2-2	2-2	6-2
9	Norwich CEYMS	3-0	1-1	3-4	3-0	0-2	0-0	0-2	5-2		1-0	3-1	1-4	5-0	2-0	0-4	2-2
10	Norwich United U21	1-5	0-4	1-2	3-2	0-2	1-3	1-2	0-2	1-6		1-4	2-6	2-2	0-5	1-2	0-3
11	Scole United	1-0	4-0	3-2	2-1	0-1	1-1	1-1	2-2	1-4	2-1		2-0	4-1	0-3	1-0	5-2
12	Sheringham	7-1	6-1	4-0	5-1	1-1	4-0	2-1	4-2	0-2	5-1	3-1		4-1	1-0	4-2	3-4
13	St Andrews	0-0	1-3	1-1	1-3	1-6	0-3	1-0	2-4	1-3	3-1	0-0	1-2		0-1	0-1	1-2
14	Waveney	3-1	0-1	4-3	2-0	1-1	3-1	2-1	H-W	2-1	4-1	1-0	0-5	1-0		0-1	2-1
15	Wroxham Res	1-1	1-1	3-4	0-2	2-3	2-1	0-2	0-1	1-1	4-1	0-1	0-1	4-1	0-2		1-0
16	Wymondham Town	0-3	0-1	4-1	1-2	3-4	3-2	3-0	1-1	2-2	6-0	1-0	0-0	2-0	0-0	5-1	

LEAGUE CUPS

CS MORLEY CUP FINAL

Belton v UEA Res 2-6

DON FROST CUP FINAL

Norwich CEYMS v Sheringham 2-0

CYRIL BALLYN CUP FINAL

Loddon United v Heacham 1-4 (aet)

MUMMERY CUP FINAL

Long Stratton v UEA 2-4 (aet)

BEDFORDSHIRE COUNTY LEAGUE

RECENT CHAMPIONS

2016: AFC Oakley M&DH **2017:** Flitwick Town **2018:** Shefford Town & Campton

PREMIER DIVISION	P	W	D	L	F	A	GD	Pts
1 Shefford Town & Campton	26	19	5	2	76	22	54	62
2 Cranfield United	26	19	5	2	70	23	47	62
3 Marston Shelton Rovers	26	12	7	7	59	56	3	43
4 Stevington	26	12	5	9	67	48	19	41
5 Queens Park Crescents	26	12	5	9	62	51	11	41
6 Wootton Blue Cross	26	11	6	9	49	50	-1	39
7 Crawley Green Res	26	11	5	10	57	46	11	37*
8 Riseley Sports	26	9	5	12	46	59	-13	32
9 Wilstead	26	9	4	13	67	68	-1	31
10 Flitwick Town	26	9	4	13	53	61	-8	31
11 Ickwell & Old Warden	26	9	3	14	61	85	-24	30
12 AFC Oakley M&DH	26	8	5	13	59	63	-4	29
13 AFC Kempston Town & B C	26	5	4	17	43	77	-34	19
14 Caldecote	26	4	3	19	32	92	-60	15

Renhold United resigned - record expunged.
Sharnbrook resigned - record expunged.

DIVISION ONE	P	W	D	L	F	A	GD	Pts
1 Biggleswade Res	28	21	3	4	100	38	62	66
2 Bedford Albion FC	28	20	5	3	91	27	64	65
3 Cranfield United Res	28	18	6	4	94	47	47	60
4 Shefford Town & Campton Res	27	15	7	5	78	34	44	52
5 Wixams	28	15	2	11	71	55	16	46*
6 Henlow	28	14	3	11	56	46	10	45
7 Totternhoe Res	28	13	5	10	55	48	7	44
8 Cople & Bedford SA	28	13	3	12	63	56	7	42
9 Lea Sports PSG	28	11	6	11	60	66	-6	39
10 The 61 FC (Luton) Res	28	11	4	13	49	58	-9	37
11 Christians In Sport (Luton)	28	9	6	13	50	73	-23	33
12 Flitwick Town Reserves	28	7	3	18	51	75	-24	24
13 AFC Kempston Town & B C Res	28	6	2	20	41	93	-52	19*
14 Wilstead Reserves	27	5	3	19	43	93	-50	13*
15 Sandy	28	1	2	25	26	119	-93	2*

Farley Boys resigned - record expunged.

DIVISION TWO	P	W	D	L	F	A	GD	Pts
1 Elstow Abbey	32	23	6	3	115	44	71	75
2 Sporting Lewsey Park	32	24	3	5	140	57	83	72*
3 Kempston Athletic	32	17	9	6	80	46	34	60
4 Houghton Athletic	32	18	5	9	84	49	35	59
5 Atletico Europa	32	17	6	9	88	66	22	57
6 Meltis Albion	31	17	5	9	76	53	23	55*
7 St Josephs (Saturday)	32	15	5	12	74	70	4	49*
8 Sundon Park Rovers	32	14	4	14	69	69	0	46
9 Luton Leagrave AFC	31	13	6	12	69	57	12	45
10 Clifton	31	14	2	15	66	56	10	44
11 CS Rovers	32	12	4	16	74	89	-15	39*
12 AFC Oakley M&DH Res	32	11	4	17	82	110	-28	36*
13 Caldecote Reserves	32	12	1	19	69	90	-21	34*
14 Black Swan (Luton)	31	12	4	15	71	59	12	31*
15 Marston Shelton Rovers Res	32	8	2	22	47	112	-65	22*
16 M&DH Clapham Sports	32	6	2	24	46	141	-95	19*
17 Unite MK Res	32	1	4	27	34	116	-82	-6*

FC Kokan resigned - record expunged.

DIVISION THREE	P	W	D	L	F	A	GD	Pts
1 Pines (Luton)	28	26	0	2	151	27	124	78
2 Thurleigh	28	19	2	7	91	36	55	58 *
3 Bedford Albion FC Res	28	16	6	6	102	48	54	54
4 Shefford Town & Campton 'A'	28	17	2	9	70	51	19	53
5 Real Haynes	27	16	4	7	100	51	49	52
6 Stevington Reserves	28	15	1	12	66	53	13	45 *
7 Harlington Juniors	28	15	1	12	84	84	0	44 *
8 FC Polonia (Luton)	28	14	2	12	75	61	14	43 *
9 Lidlington United Sports Club	28	12	3	13	66	68	-2	39
10 Wixams Wanderers	28	13	1	14	83	91	-8	39 *
11 Wootton Village	28	11	3	14	39	62	-23	36
12 Square	28	8	0	20	41	91	-50	24
13 Flitwick Town 'A'	27	8	1	18	51	92	-41	23 *
14 Dinamo Flitwick	28	5	2	21	54	90	-36	17
15 Real Haynes Res	28	0	0	28	11	179	-168	-1 *

Sandy Res - resigned - record expunged.

PREMIER DIVISION	1	2	3	4	5	6	7	8	9	10	11	12	13	14
1 AFC Kempston Town & Bedford College		5-3	1-1	0-2	0-3	1-5	4-7	2-3	3-3	2-4	0-1	1-4	4-3	1-3
2 AFC Oakley M&DH (Sat)	6-0		5-0	2-4	2-1	6-2	1-4	4-5	0-4	3-2	2-4	3-1	2-3	2-1
3 Caldecote	5-4	2-2		2-3	1-5	3-1	0-3	2-4	1-10	2-1	1-3	0-3	2-4	2-4
4 Cranfield United	1-1	3-0	6-0		2-0	4-0	4-2	4-1	2-0	5-1	1-4	3-0	2-2	1-1
5 Crawley Green Reserves	1-3	1-0	4-2	AW		2-3	3-2	1-2	2-2	0-0	1-2	5-1	3-0	2-1
6 Flitwick Town	1-3	5-3	3-0	0-2	1-2		4-2	1-4	2-3	0-1	1-3	1-4	5-4	2-2
7 Ickwell & Old Warden	2-1	2-2	6-1	2-1	1-6	0-0		3-3	4-2	2-4	0-3	1-5	2-1	1-2
8 Marston Shelton Rovers	2-2	2-2	1-1	1-3	5-5	0-3	4-2		3-1	5-2	1-1	2-3	1-0	3-2
9 Queens Park Crescents	1-2	1-0	3-0	1-1	2-1	3-2	5-2	3-1		1-3	4-7	2-1	1-1	1-0
10 Riseley Sports	2-0	2-1	4-0	1-3	2-2	2-5	5-1	1-2	0-3		0-6	2-1	1-1	0-2
11 Shefford Town & Campton	3-0	0-1	1-0	1-1	3-0	2-2	6-0	2-0	5-1	0-0		2-0	7-2	7-1
12 Stevington	5-1	2-2	5-0	0-1	2-2	4-2	7-0	1-2	3-3	4-4	2-1		0-4	3-3
13 Wilstead	4-1	3-3	5-2	1-7	6-2	1-2	5-7	3-0	3-1	6-1	1-2	1-3		2-4
14 Wootton Blue Cross	2-1	4-2	1-2	0-4	1-3	0-0	6-3	2-2	2-1	2-1	0-0	0-3	3-1	

LEAGUE CUPS

JUBILEE CUP FINAL
Kempston Athletic v CS Rovers 5-1

BRITTANIA CUP FINAL
Shefford Town & Campton v Wilstead 1-0

CENTENARY CUP FINAL
Cople & Bedford SA v Biggleswade Res 1-7

CAMBRIDGESHIRE COUNTY LEAGUE

RECENT CHAMPIONS

2016: Great Shelford **2017:** Hardwick **2018:** West Wratting

PREMIER DIVISION	P	W	D	L	F	A	GD	Pts
1 Great Shelford	30	24	2	4	98	27	71	74
2 Linton Granta	30	23	3	4	92	37	55	72
3 Cambridge University Press	30	22	2	6	91	42	49	68
4 Eynesbury Rovers Res	30	17	3	10	87	64	23	54
5 West Wratting	30	16	4	10	67	60	7	52
6 Ely City Res	30	14	6	10	64	57	7	48
7 Cherry Hinton	30	14	3	13	64	60	4	45
8 Comberton United	30	14	3	13	57	62	-5	45
9 Fulbourn Institute	30	12	7	11	61	63	-2	43
10 Foxton	30	13	2	15	59	69	-10	41
11 Eaton Socon	30	11	3	16	46	65	-19	36
12 Bar Hill	30	8	7	15	61	71	-10	31
13 Brampton	30	9	4	17	52	62	-10	31
14 Hemingfords United	30	6	6	18	47	72	-25	24
15 Cambridge City Dev	30	4	3	23	37	93	-56	12*
16 St Neots Town Res	30	2	4	24	36	115	-79	10

SENIOR A	P	W	D	L	F	A	GD	Pts
1 Over Sports	24	19	1	4	76	21	55	58
2 Chatteris Town	24	19	1	4	65	32	33	58
3 Gamlingay United	24	17	5	2	84	40	44	56
4 Orwell	24	16	2	6	66	38	28	50
5 Whittlesford United	24	14	5	5	66	35	31	47
6 Huntingdon United	24	13	4	7	61	34	27	43
7 Hundon	24	11	2	11	55	52	3	35
8 Milton	24	8	4	12	55	61	-6	28
9 Somersham Town	24	7	6	11	38	44	-6	27
10 Soham United	24	7	1	16	46	68	-22	22
11 Cottenham United	24	3	4	17	30	67	-37	13
12 Fulbourn Institute Res	24	3	2	19	25	101	-76	11
13 Girton United	24	0	1	23	12	86	-74	-5*

SENIOR B	P	W	D	L	F	A	GD	Pts
1 AFC Barley Mow	28	22	3	3	110	38	72	69
2 March Town United Res	28	17	6	5	76	42	34	57
3 Bluntisham Rangers	28	17	6	5	59	39	20	57
4 Witchford 96	28	16	5	7	72	45	27	53
5 Needingworth United	28	14	6	8	63	34	29	48
6 Wisbech St Mary Res	28	12	7	9	60	59	1	43
7 Newmarket Town Res	28	11	8	9	78	84	-6	41
8 Thaxted Rangers	28	12	3	13	67	62	5	39
9 St Ives Rangers	28	12	3	13	68	69	-1	39
10 Great Chishill	28	10	4	14	50	60	-10	34
11 Sawston Rovers	28	10	3	15	57	64	-7	33
12 West Wratting Res	28	11	5	12	62	57	5	32*
13 Lakenheath Res	28	6	6	16	45	92	-47	24
14 Cambridge Uni Pr Res	28	5	4	19	44	85	-41	19
15 Royston Town A	28	0	1	27	15	96	-81	-2*

DIVISION 1A	P	W	D	L	F	A	GD	Pts
1 Linton Granta Res	24	21	1	2	101	27	74	64
2 Bassingbourn	24	20	0	4	88	23	65	60
3 Duxford United	24	15	2	7	57	51	6	47
4 Hardwick	24	14	4	6	55	42	13	46
5 Cambourne Rovers	23	10	8	5	62	54	8	38
6 Debden	24	11	4	9	62	61	1	37
7 Clare Town	24	9	6	9	47	51	-4	33
8 Steeple Morden	23	8	3	12	39	57	-18	27
9 Mott MacDonald	24	7	3	14	31	53	-22	24
10 Milton Res	24	6	5	13	39	65	-26	23
11 Cherry Hinton Res	24	6	4	14	35	62	-27	22
12 Balsham	24	4	5	15	26	52	-26	17
13 Exning United	24	1	1	22	22	66	-44	-8*

PREMIER DIVISION	1	2	3	4	5	6	7	8	9	10	11	12	13	14	15	16
1 Bar Hill SSC		1-1	4-1	3-1	1-3	3-3	3-2	1-2	1-1	5-0	3-3	0-1	2-1	1-1	4-3	1-2
2 Brampton	3-3		1-0	3-1	0-0	2-1	6-0	3-4	5-1	1-5	2-1	0-2	2-3	1-2	4-0	1-2
3 Cambridge City FC Res	3-1	4-0		4-6	2-4	2-4	2-1	2-3	1-6	1-2	1-4	1-7	2-2	0-6	4-1	0-1
4 Cambridge University Press	4-0	5-2	4-0		1-0	2-1	5-1	1-1	2-1	3-1	3-0	3-1	3-1	2-4	8-0	6-0
5 Cherry Hinton	7-2	4-1	2-0	0-2		3-1	3-2	3-1	2-4	0-1	5-1	1-3	4-2	0-4	4-3	1-2
6 Comberton United	5-4	2-0	2-0	0-2	2-1		3-2	2-3	1-2	5-0	0-2	3-2	2-1	4-2	1-2	1-3
7 Eaton Socon Team	2-1	1-0	4-0	2-2	1-3	1-1		1-0	1-2	4-2	0-2	0-4	1-1	0-3	4-3	1-0
8 Ely City Res	2-1	3-5	2-0	4-1	0-1	1-2	3-0		4-0	1-0	1-1	0-6	2-1	1-2	8-0	4-3
9 Eynesbury Rovers Res	3-2	2-3	5-0	2-6	6-1	6-2	2-3	4-4		5-1	4-1	2-5	2-0	1-2	3-1	3-2
10 Foxton	3-3	3-2	2-1	3-1	4-1	2-3	6-1	1-1	3-8		0-2	3-0	1-2	1-4	4-0	1-4
11 Fulbourn Institute	2-3	3-2	4-1	0-3	2-2	0-0	2-0	1-1	2-2	3-1		2-7	7-2	1-3	1-0	1-2
12 Great Shelford	1-0	2-0	0-0	4-1	1-0	2-0	0-1	6-2	2-0	2-0	3-3		7-1	4-2	12-0	2-0
13 Hemingfords United	2-1	2-0	6-1	2-4	1-1	1-2	0-1	0-2	2-3	2-3	2-4	0-1		1-2	3-1	2-2
14 Linton Granta	4-2	2-0	4-1	1-3	3-2	5-1	3-1	2-0	2-1	3-0	6-0	1-2	6-1		2-2	2-2
15 St Neots Town Res	2-4	1-1	3-1	1-3	2-4	1-2	0-6	2-2	2-3	0-1	0-6	0-7	0-0	2-6		2-4
16 West Wratting	3-1	2-1	2-2	0-3	5-2	5-1	3-2	5-2	1-3	1-5	4-0	1-2	3-3	0-3	3-2	

LEAGUE CUPS

PREMIER LEAGUE CUP FINAL
Bar Hill SSC v Cherry Hinton 0-3

WILLIAM COCKELL MEMORIAL CUP FINAL
Gamlingay United v Over Sports 0-5

PERCY OLDMAN MEMORIAL CUP FINAL
AFC Barley Mow v Needingworth United 4-1

CREAKE CHARITY SHIELD
Houghton & Wyton v Isleham United 3-2

JOHN ABLETT CUP FINAL
Fordham Res v Outwell Swifts 0-3

REG HAIGH & ARTHUR PECK CUP
Ely Crusaders Res v Orwell Res 2-3

DIVISION 1B	P	W	D	L	F	A	GD	Pts
1 Fordham	22	16	1	5	48	22	26	49
2 Eaton Socon Res	22	14	6	2	68	25	43	48
3 Isleham United	22	12	4	6	53	33	20	40
4 Houghton & Wyton	22	12	3	7	76	58	18	39
5 Tuddenham 08	22	10	2	10	44	56	-12	32
6 Bar Hill Res	22	8	5	9	40	52	-12	29
7 Hemingfords United Res	22	8	3	11	33	50	-17	27
8 Alconbury	22	7	5	10	47	52	-5	26
9 Fenstanton	22	7	4	11	42	47	-5	25
10 Chatteris Town Res	22	7	2	13	34	46	-12	23
11 Godmanchester Rovers Res	22	5	7	10	42	41	1	22
12 Mepal Sports	22	4	2	16	44	89	-45	14

DIVISION 2A	P	W	D	L	F	A	GD	Pts
1 Comberton United Res	24	17	3	4	98	40	58	54
2 Sawston United	24	17	3	4	83	31	52	54
3 Meldreth	24	15	3	6	55	35	20	48
4 Gamlingay United Res	24	13	3	8	59	47	12	42
5 Papworth	24	13	3	8	58	54	4	42
6 Great Shelford Res	23	13	2	8	65	26	39	41
7 Litlington Athletic	23	12	2	9	75	64	11	38
8 Foxton Res	24	9	1	14	44	84	-40	28
9 Over Sports Res	24	8	3	13	47	57	-10	27
10 Haverhill Rovers A	24	7	3	14	44	57	-13	21*
11 Steeple Morden Res	24	6	2	16	41	86	-45	20
12 Whittlesford United Res	24	4	6	14	36	62	-26	15*
13 Linton Granta A	24	2	4	18	40	102	-62	10

DIVISION 2B	P	W	D	L	F	A	GD	Pts
1 Ely City 'A'	22	16	4	2	72	29	43	52
2 Brampton Res	22	14	6	2	75	32	43	48
3 Swavesey Institute	22	14	2	6	64	37	27	44
4 Burwell Swifts	22	11	4	7	60	44	16	37
5 Wisbech Town Acorns	22	10	6	6	50	44	6	36
6 Wimblington	22	9	5	8	55	53	2	32
7 Burwell Tigers	22	9	3	10	43	45	-2	30
8 Ely Crusaders	22	7	4	11	34	37	-3	25
9 Soham United Res	22	6	5	11	39	43	-4	23
10 Wisbech St Mary A	22	7	2	13	37	60	-23	23
11 Great Paxton	22	4	3	15	30	82	-52	15
12 Manea United	22	1	4	17	25	78	-53	7

DIVISION 3A	P	W	D	L	F	A	GD	Pts
1 Barrington	24	18	3	3	88	31	57	57
2 Melbourn	24	15	6	3	78	33	45	51
3 Suffolk Punch Haverhill	23	16	2	5	58	31	27	50
4 Cherry Hinton A	24	13	5	6	73	49	24	44
5 Guilden Morden	24	14	2	8	81	45	36	41*
6 Hundon Res	24	10	3	11	49	57	-8	33
7 Harston	24	9	5	10	63	55	8	32
8 Oakington Vikings	24	10	2	12	43	50	-7	32
9 Abington United	24	9	4	11	58	66	-8	31
10 Fulbourn Institute A	23	8	2	13	49	66	-17	23*
11 Duxford United Res	24	5	4	15	34	80	-46	19
12 Eaton Socon A	24	5	3	16	35	64	-29	18
13 Milton A	24	2	1	21	21	103	-82	1*

DIVISION 3B	P	W	D	L	F	A	GD	Pts
1 Outwell Swifts	24	22	1	1	94	16	78	67
2 Buckden Res	24	20	1	3	88	29	59	61
3 Fordham Res	24	14	6	4	59	35	24	48
4 Benwick Athletic	24	9	9	6	48	38	10	36
5 The Eagle	24	10	6	8	49	40	9	36
6 March Academy	24	7	9	8	41	57	-16	30
7 Alconbury Res	24	8	3	13	34	53	-19	27
8 St Ives Rangers Res	24	6	6	12	33	53	-20	24
9 Cottenham United Res	24	6	5	13	30	50	-20	23
10 Houghton & Wyton Res	24	7	1	16	41	80	-39	22
11 Bluntisham Rangers Res	24	5	6	13	40	58	-18	21
12 Wisbech St Mary B	24	7	4	13	47	63	-16	19*
13 Somersham Town Res	24	4	5	15	34	66	-32	17

DIVISION 4A	P	W	D	L	F	A	GD	Pts
1 Wickhambrook	22	19	0	3	78	39	39	57
2 Clare Town Res	22	14	7	1	67	27	40	49
3 Orwell Res	22	13	5	4	89	38	51	44
4 Kedington	22	11	3	8	53	55	-2	36
5 Barton Mills	22	10	4	8	77	63	14	34
6 Papworth Res	22	11	1	10	49	56	-7	34
7 Bassingbourn Res	22	9	2	11	57	47	10	26*
8 Sawston Rovers Res	22	8	2	12	41	59	-18	26
9 Cambridge Ambassadors	22	9	1	12	48	58	-10	25*
10 Thaxted Rangers Res	22	6	3	13	29	45	-16	18*
11 Guilden Morden Res	22	4	2	16	30	77	-47	14
12 Harston Res	22	3	0	19	20	74	-54	9

DIVISION 4B	P	W	D	L	F	A	GD	Pts
1 Longstanton	22	17	2	3	96	21	75	53
2 Isleham United Res	22	15	3	4	82	27	55	48
3 Little Downham Swifts	22	14	3	5	91	46	45	45
4 Hardwick Res	22	13	4	5	67	42	25	43
5 Ely Crusaders Res	22	12	3	7	71	44	27	39
6 Histon Hornets	22	12	1	9	61	39	22	37
7 Needingworth United Res	22	11	2	9	52	48	4	35
8 Wicken	22	8	2	12	51	75	-24	26
9 Fenstanton Res	22	6	1	15	36	85	-49	19
10 Hemingfords United A	22	5	2	15	32	97	-65	17
11 Mott MacDonald Res	22	3	2	17	31	87	-56	11
12 Swavesey Institute Res	22	3	1	18	22	81	-59	7*

DIVISION 4C	P	W	D	L	F	A	GD	Pts
1 Wimblington Res	22	19	1	2	65	25	40	58
2 Guyhirn	21	16	3	2	70	26	44	51
3 The Isle	22	16	1	5	78	42	36	49
4 Littleport Town	21	14	2	5	48	20	28	44
5 Wisbech Town Acorns Res	22	11	4	7	50	32	18	37
6 Chatteris Town A	22	10	1	11	53	48	5	31
7 Chatteris Fen Tigers Res	22	10	4	8	52	67	-15	31*
8 Outwell Swifts Res	22	7	3	12	50	61	-11	24
9 AFC Christchurch	22	6	3	13	42	62	-20	21
10 Benwick Athletic Res	22	4	2	16	27	57	-30	11*
11 March Academy Res	22	2	2	18	24	76	-52	8
12 Coldham United	22	3	0	19	39	82	-43	6*

CENTRAL MIDLANDS LEAGUE

RECENT CHAMPIONS

2016: Glapwell (N) Selston (S) **2017:** FC Bolsover (N) Selston (S)
2018: Harworth Colliery (N) Eastwood Community (S)

NORTH DIVISION	P	W	D	L	F	A	GD	Pts
1 Retford	26	22	3	1	109	26	83	69
2 Clay Cross Town	26	21	1	4	117	31	86	64
3 Collingham	26	20	3	3	77	28	49	63
4 Retford United	26	16	4	6	68	31	37	52
5 Renishaw Rangers	26	14	1	11	60	57	3	43
6 AFC Bentley	26	12	4	10	71	56	15	40
7 Appleby Frodingham	26	12	3	11	49	50	-1	39
8 Staveley Miners Welfare Res	26	11	3	12	51	48	3	36
9 Newark Town	26	8	2	16	38	91	-53	26
10 Phoenix	26	7	1	18	37	73	-36	22
11 Dinnington Town	26	6	4	16	27	72	-45	22
12 Dronfield Town Reserves	26	6	3	17	34	72	-38	21
13 Askern	26	4	3	19	29	79	-50	15
14 Thorne Colliery	26	4	3	19	42	95	-53	15

SOUTH DIVISION	P	W	D	L	F	A	GD	Pts
1 Hucknall Town	26	22	3	1	112	24	88	69
2 Matlock Town Reserves	26	18	4	4	69	23	46	58
3 Pinxton	26	17	2	7	82	36	46	53
4 Mickleover RBL	26	15	6	5	62	36	26	53*
5 Swanwick Pentrich Road	26	14	3	9	68	46	22	45
6 Holbrook St Michaels	26	12	4	10	52	50	2	40
7 Blidworth Welfare	26	11	5	10	51	47	4	38
8 Holbrook Sports	26	11	2	13	54	76	-22	35
9 Hilton Harriers	26	9	5	12	45	59	-14	31*
10 Underwood Villa	26	7	3	16	35	79	-44	24
11 Ashland Rovers	26	7	2	17	45	79	-34	23
12 Linby Colliery Welfare	26	6	3	17	31	67	-36	21
13 Teversal Reserves	26	5	4	17	36	74	-38	19
14 Welbeck Lions	26	2	6	18	30	76	-46	12

AFC Kilburn resigned - record expunged.

NORTH DIVISION ONE	P	W	D	L	F	A	GD	Pts
1 Sutton Rovers 2007	20	17	1	2	75	20	55	52
2 Crowle Colts	20	17	1	2	66	20	46	52
3 Epworth Town Colts	20	14	0	6	57	28	29	42
4 Alfreton Town Res	20	13	0	7	74	34	40	39
5 Harworth Colliery Res	20	10	3	7	38	38	0	33
6 Retford United Dev	20	7	3	10	39	59	-20	24
7 Nottingham	20	7	4	9	38	46	-8	22*
8 Hucknall Town Res	20	6	3	11	34	61	-27	21
9 Linby Colliery Welfare Res	20	4	1	15	34	63	-29	13
10 Shirebrook Rangers & Juniors	20	5	1	14	20	51	-31	13*
11 Welbeck Lions Reserves	20	1	1	18	22	77	-55	4

SOUTH DIVISION ONE	P	W	D	L	F	A	GD	Pts
1 Sherwood Colliery Res	22	18	2	2	96	22	74	56
2 Rowsley '86	22	18	1	3	96	16	80	55
3 Bakewell Town	22	16	1	5	64	27	37	49
4 Long Eaton United Com	22	16	0	6	86	35	51	48
5 Mickleover Sports Res	22	14	1	7	73	34	39	43
6 Wirksworth Town	22	12	1	9	55	31	24	37
7 Wirksworth Ivanhoe	22	10	2	10	50	40	10	32
8 AFC Kilburn Dev	22	7	1	14	48	70	-22	22
9 Heanor Town Res	22	4	3	15	20	56	-36	15
10 Holbrook St Michaels Dev	22	3	6	13	31	74	-43	12*
11 Chesterfield Town	22	3	2	17	20	86	-66	11
12 Cromford	22	0	2	20	12	160	-148	2

LEAGUE CUPS

LEAGUE CHALLENGE CUP FINAL

Hucknall Town	v	Pinxton	4-4, 4-5p

DIVISION ONE CUP FINAL

Bakewell Town	v	Crowle Colts	2-1

FLOODLIT CUP FINAL

Collingham	v	Pinxton	0-2

DIVISION NORTH	1	2	3	4	5	6	7	8	9	10	11	12	13	14
1 AFC Bentley		3-0	4-0	2-3	0-0	9-0	3-2	5-0	2-3	0-2	1-6	2-1	1-3	2-2
2 Appleby Frodingham	1-9		4-3	0-3	2-2	2-0	4-0	5-2	3-0	2-4	0-2	2-2	1-1	2-0
3 Askern	2-3	0-1		1-8	0-4	2-0	2-2	3-3	3-1	0-2	2-2	1-2	2-4	1-3
4 Clay Cross Town	5-1	1-0	7-0		4-3	6-2	6-0	9-1	8-1	8-0	3-5	2-1	6-0	6-0
5 Collingham	4-1	4-3	3-0	1-3		3-0	7-3	5-0	3-1	2-1	0-2	1-0	3-0	5-1
6 Dinnington Town	2-3	0-4	0-1	0-2	0-0		1-1	4-1	2-0	2-1	1-2	0-5	3-2	3-2
7 Dronfield Town Reserves	0-6	2-3	1-0	0-2	0-2	4-1		0-3	0-1	1-3	1-7	0-2	2-0	4-2
8 Newark Town	3-3	0-2	1-0	2-7	1-3	1-0	2-3		2-0	3-0	1-8	0-4	0-1	2-1
9 Phoenix	1-4	0-2	5-0	1-8	2-4	4-2	1-3	0-2		2-1	0-5	2-5	2-2	3-2
10 Renishaw Rangers	3-2	2-1	5-1	2-0	0-6	1-2	3-2	11-0	2-1		0-3	1-1	2-0	5-4
11 Retford	2-2	4-0	4-2	4-1	0-3	10-0	3-1	4-2	4-1	5-2		5-0	3-1	6-0
12 Retford United	6-0	2-1	5-0	2-2	0-1	4-0	2-0	9-2	2-0	4-1	1-1		2-1	3-2
13 Staveley Miners Welfare Reserves	0-2	1-2	5-0	1-0	3-4	0-0	4-0	4-2	1-0	4-2	1-3	1-2		4-1
14 Thorne Colliery	5-1	3-2	0-3	1-7	1-4	2-2	2-2	0-2	1-5	1-4	0-9	3-1	3-7	

DIVISION SOUTH	1	2	3	4	5	6	7	8	9	10	11	12	13	14
1 Ashland Rovers		1-3	3-4	1-4	3-1	0-4	2-2	1-6	1-4	0-4	2-5	3-0	1-3	3-0
2 Blidworth Welfare	1-2		0-4	2-3	1-3	2-5	1-0	0-1	2-2	0-0	2-1	2-1	1-2	7-1
3 Hilton Harriers	3-2	0-1		3-0	1-1	0-2	3-0	0-4	1-1	2-3	2-3	6-2	2-3	3-2
4 Holbrook Sports	2-6	2-4	1-2		0-4	0-7	3-3	1-2	1-4	3-1	4-4	2-1	4-1	3-1
5 Holbrook St Michaels	1-0	2-2	3-1	4-6		2-1	2-0	1-1	1-0	1-2	3-1	3-3	1-2	3-2
6 Hucknall Town	7-0	3-0	7-1	5-2	5-1		2-1	2-2	2-2	3-1	1-0	9-0	4-2	3-0
7 Linby Colliery Welfare	5-2	2-3	2-2	0-1	1-3	0-4		1-2	2-3	1-10	0-3	2-1	1-3	0-2
8 Matlock Town Reserves	4-0	1-1	5-0	6-0	1-0	0-4	1-2		0-2	2-0	2-3	3-0	7-0	3-1
9 Mickleover RBL	4-0	1-3	1-1	4-1	3-0	2-6	3-0	0-4		2-1	2-0	4-1	2-0	2-2
10 Pinxton	2-2	3-1	7-1	7-2	5-1	0-3	1-0	0-1	3-2		3-4	6-1	7-1	5-1
11 Swanwick Pentrich Road	4-3	1-1	3-0	3-0	3-2	1-1	10-2	0-3	3-4	1-2		4-0	2-1	4-0
12 Teversal Reserves	2-4	3-2	1-1	0-3	3-2	2-3	0-2	1-2	0-1	1-2	2-1		2-2	3-1
13 Underwood Villa	2-0	0-4	1-2	1-3	2-4	3-11	0-1	1-4	0-6	0-4	2-1	1-3		0-0
14 Welbeck Lions	2 - 3	3 - 5	1 - 0	0 - 3	1 - 3	0 - 8	0 - 1	2 - 2	1-1	0-3	2 - 3	3 - 3	2 - 2	

CHESHIRE LEAGUE

RECENT CHAMPIONS

2016: Knutsford **2017:** Whaley Bridge **2018:** Knutsford

PREMIER DIVISION	P	W	D	L	F	A	GD	Pts
1 Pilkington	30	19	7	4	85	35	50	64
2 Altrincham Res	30	19	7	4	74	29	45	64
3 Eagle Sports	30	16	6	8	66	45	21	54
4 Middlewich Town	30	13	7	10	69	66	3	46
5 Poynton	30	13	6	11	59	47	12	45
6 Congleton VR	30	14	3	13	49	49	0	45
7 Crewe	30	12	8	10	74	63	11	44
8 Whaley Bridge Athletic	30	12	7	11	65	63	2	43
9 Knutsford	30	12	6	12	48	45	3	42
10 Billinge	30	12	5	13	62	64	-2	41
11 Daten	30	12	4	14	58	57	1	40
12 Greenalls Padgate St Oswalds	30	11	6	13	50	68	-18	39
13 Egerton	30	9	4	17	58	78	-20	31
14 F.C. St. Helens	30	9	4	17	51	71	-20	31
15 Malpas	30	7	5	18	50	78	-28	26
16 Denton Town	30	6	3	21	39	99	-60	21

DIVISION ONE	P	W	D	L	F	A	GD	Pts
1 Lostock Gralam	27	21	2	4	84	31	53	65
2 Blacon Youth Club	28	20	3	5	81	40	41	63
3 Broadheath Central	28	19	5	4	88	42	46	62
4 Winstanley Warriors	28	16	4	8	87	61	26	52
5 Vulcan	27	17	1	9	65	41	24	52
6 Styal	27	13	4	10	54	47	7	43
7 Grappenhall Sports	28	11	5	12	59	50	9	38
8 Orford	26	11	2	13	64	64	0	35
9 Ford Motors	28	10	5	13	64	77	-13	35
10 Windle Labour	27	10	4	13	53	61	-8	34
11 Garswood United	28	10	4	14	44	52	-8	34
12 Moore United	28	7	3	18	46	97	-51	24
13 Halebank	28	5	5	18	46	101	-55	20
14 Buxton Reserves	28	4	6	18	49	82	-33	18
15 Golborne Sports	28	4	5	19	55	93	-38	17

DIVISION TWO	P	W	D	L	F	A	GD	Pts
1 Ashton Athletic Res	24	20	1	3	84	41	43	61
2 Maine Road Res	24	17	1	6	75	45	30	52
3 Cheadle Heath Nomads Res	24	14	4	6	62	45	17	46
4 Cuddington	24	13	4	7	86	45	41	43
5 Cheadle Town Res	24	11	4	9	56	49	7	37
6 Winnington Avenue Y.C. 94	24	10	4	10	65	46	19	34
7 Ashton Town Res	24	9	4	11	52	62	-10	31
8 Club AZ	24	9	3	12	58	61	-3	30
9 Sandbach United Res	24	9	2	13	57	68	-11	29
10 Mersey Valley	24	9	0	15	42	86	-44	27
11 St Helens Town Res	24	8	1	15	56	71	-15	25
12 Holmes Chapel Hurricanes	24	6	2	16	57	91	-34	20
13 Rylands Res	24	4	4	16	43	83	-40	16

RESERVE DIVISION	P	W	D	L	F	A	GD	Pts
1 Styal Res	30	24	3	3	112	40	72	75
2 Eagle Sports Res	30	24	0	6	78	35	43	72
3 Broadheath Central Res	30	17	4	9	62	42	20	55
4 Garswood United A	30	17	2	11	79	62	17	53
5 Vulcan Football Club Res	30	16	3	11	56	52	4	51
6 Billinge Reserve	30	15	5	10	81	68	13	50
7 Daten Res	30	14	6	10	71	55	16	48
8 Pilkington Reserve	30	14	6	10	62	54	8	48
9 Poynton Res	30	12	10	8	72	55	17	46
10 F.C. St. Helens Res	30	14	2	14	64	48	16	44
11 Middlewich Town Res	30	12	6	12	69	57	12	42
12 Orford Reserve	30	12	3	15	59	65	-6	39
13 Winstanley Warriors Res	30	6	4	20	41	72	-31	22
14 Moore United Res	30	6	3	21	47	90	-43	21
15 Greenalls Padgate St Oswalds Res	30	6	1	23	49	110	-61	19
16 Golborne Sports Seniors Res	30	1	2	27	31	128	-97	5

LEAGUE CUPS

JB PARKER PREMIER DIVISION CUP FINAL

St Helens v Whaley Bridge Athletic 1-1, 2-4p

J A WALTON CHALLENGE CUP FINAL

Blacon Youth Club v Moore United 3-1

CFL PRESIDENT'S CUP FINAL

Greenalls Padgate St Oswall v Middlewich Town 1-0

CFL MEMORIAL CUP FINAL

Knutsford v Whaley Bridge Athletic 5-1

RESERVE DIVISION CHALLENGE CUP FINAL

Middlewich Town Res v Styal Res 2-5

PREMIER DIVISION	1	2	3	4	5	6	7	8	9	10	11	12	13	14	15	16
1 Altrincham Res		4-0	4-0	0-0	2-0	5-0	2-2	5-3	4-1	4-0	2-0	3-0	3-3	1-3	1-0	4-0
2 Billinge	1-3		3-4	2-2	2-3	3-0	2-7	1-0	3-1	3-1	4-2	9-2	1-4	1-1	3-1	3-0
3 Congleton VR	0-2	2-0		3-4	1-0	0-3	4-2	3-1	2-1	1-2	1-0	4-0	2-1	1-3	1-3	1-1
4 Crewe	0-0	5-0	0-2		0-0	2-0	1-3	8-1	5-1	7-2	4-4	0-1	3-4	1-8	3-3	2-1
5 Daten	0-1	1-4	4-1	5-1		4-0	0-3	1-2	4-3	1-4	1-1	0-2	3-2	2-2	1-5	1-2
6 Denton Town	0-3	2-1	2-1	0-6	4-3		2-2	0-5	1-1	0-1	0-2	3-5	2-5	0-7	2-3	2-6
7 Eagle Sports	1-2	4-0	0-0	2-3	1-2	3-3		4-0	2-0	0-3	3-1	3-1	3-2	1-0	2-1	3-2
8 Egerton	1-3	2-2	2-1	2-4	1-4	1-2	3-2		2-2	9-1	0-1	0-1	4-0	4-4	1-4	2-5
9 F.C. St. Helens	4-1	0-1	0-1	3-5	3-2	3-1	2-1	3-1		2-4	2-1	3-0	0-3	1-3	4-1	2-3
10 Greenalls Padgate St Oswalds	3-3	2-1	0-2	2-1	0-3	2-1	1-1	2-4	2-3		1-1	2-1	1-1	0-1	0-2	3-3
11 Knutsford	1-0	2-1	1-1	3-0	4-2	0-1	1-2	3-0	3-0	1-0		1-0	2-3	2-2	1-2	3-2
12 Malpas	3-3	0-2	2-4	4-1	1-5	7-1	2-3	3-4	2-2	5-1	0-3		1-1	1-3	1-1	3-3
13 Middlewich Town	1-1	3-3	4-2	3-3	0-3	7-1	1-3	1-0	2-1	0-6	1-0	8-2		1-1	3-2	3-4
14 Pilkington	0-4	2-2	1-0	2-0	4-0	3-1	0-0	6-0	7-1	4-0	4-1	1-0	6-1		0-4	2-1
15 Poynton	0-3	1-2	3-1	2-2	0-2	4-2	1-2	1-1	2-0	1-2	1-1	1-0	3-0	3-1		3-4
16 Whaley Bridge Athletic	2-1	3-2	0-3	0-1	1-1	4-3	3-1	1-2	2-2	2-2	5-2	3-0	0-1	1-4	1-1	

DORSET PREMIER LEAGUE

RECENT CHAMPIONS

2016: Shatesbury Town **2017:** Holt United **2018:** Hamworthy Recreation

		P	W	D	L	F	A	GD	Pts
1	Hamworthy Recreation	32	26	3	3	115	33	82	81
2	Westland Sports	32	24	4	4	103	38	65	76
3	Merley Cobham Sports	32	23	3	6	135	50	85	72
4	Balti Sports	32	18	7	7	71	54	17	61
5	Gillingham Town	32	16	8	8	70	40	30	56
6	Holt United	32	17	4	11	72	61	11	55
7	Blandford United	32	14	3	15	78	83	-5	45
8	Bridport Reserves	32	13	5	14	71	64	7	44
9	Dorchester Sports	32	12	6	14	68	83	-15	42
10	Swanage Town And Herston	32	9	11	12	58	78	-20	38
11	Portland United Res	32	11	5	16	56	86	-30	38
12	Parley Sports	32	11	9	12	67	69	-2	36*
13	Sherborne Town Res	32	9	5	18	49	79	-30	32
14	Shaftesbury Town Res	32	9	4	19	54	69	-15	31
15	Corfe Castle	32	8	4	20	70	109	-39	28
16	Sturminster Newton United	32	5	1	26	24	85	-61	16
17	Wareham Rangers	32	4	4	24	38	118	-80	16

LEAGUE CUP

PREMIER LEAGUE CUP FINAL

Westland Sports v Merley Cobham Sports 2-3

		1	2	3	4	5	6	7	8	9	10	11	12	13	14	15	16	17
1	Balti Sports		2-2	3-2	4-3	3-1	2-1	2-1	2-0	3-1	3-2	1-1	4-1	4-1	6-0	1-1	3-1	2-3
2	Blandford United	1-3		1-4	4-1	1-2	2-2	0-6	4-1	1-5	4-3	3-5	4-1	7-1	2-1	2-3	2-1	1-2
3	Bridport Reserves	2-2	9-0		3-2	1-2	1-0	0-1	1-3	1-4	3-2	3-1	3-0	0-2	2-3	3-3	5-2	1-2
4	Corfe Castle	3-3	1-4	2-3		4-2	0-3	1-7	4-5	3-6	2-2	5-3	4-3	4-6	1-0	0-2	1-2	3-3
5	Dorchester Sports	3-0	3-1	1-1	3-2		3-1	1-8	2-3	3-6	2-4	1-1	2-1	0-3	3-0	2-2	8-1	2-2
6	Gillingham Town	2-0	1-2	0-0	2-1	4-1		1-0	2-1	2-1	2-2	3-0	1-0	1-1	2-1	5-0	4-2	1-1
7	Hamworthy Recreation	4-2	2-1	7-1	4-2	5-1	1-1		1-0	5-6	2-2	9-0	1-0	4-0	2-0	2-0	4-1	3-0
8	Holt United	2-3	5-3	3-2	1-1	0-1	2-1	0-7		3-3	2-2	2-1	4-2	3-0	2-1	0-0	6-2	0-1
9	Merley Cobham Sports	2-0	3-3	3-0	5-1	8-2	5-1	0-3	1-5		5-0	3-0	7-1	1-2	7-2	11-0	9-1	1-1
10	Parley Sports	6-0	3-6	2-1	4-2	2-2	1-1	0-3	3-1	1-3		0-4	2-0	4-0	5-0	2-2	0-1	1-4
11	Portland United Reserves	0-0	2-1	1-0	4-3	3-1	2-3	4-6	4-1	1-4	0-0		0-4	5-1	3-1	3-5	1-2	0-7
12	Shaftesbury Town Reserves	1-1	2-3	0-2	2-3	4-4	2-2	1-4	3-1	1-3	1-2	0-3		3-1	2-0	2-0	5-1	1-2
13	Sherborne Town Reserves	2-3	0-2	3-4	2-3	2-3	2-1	0-3	2-3	0-8	3-3	6-0	0-0		2-0	1-1	1-1	0-1
14	Sturminster Newton United	0-1	0-2	1-4	1-2	2-1	0-5	0-2	0-4	0-8	1-2	2-0	0-2	2-1		0-1	5-2	0-4
15	Swanage Town And Herston	3-5	4-1	2-2	2-3	4-2	0-2	4-4	1-3	1-3	5-1	1-1	0-3	1-2	2-0		2-2	5-3
16	Wareham Rangers	1-3	1-6	2-5	4-2	1-3	1-12	1-2	1-4	0-2	0-4	0-3	0-3	0-2	1-1	1-1		1-2
17	Westland Sports	1-0	4-2	4-2	10-1	3-1	3-1	1-2	0-2	3-1	4-0	8-0	5-3	4-0	2-0	6-0	7-1	

ESSEX & SUFFOLK BORDER LEAGUE

RECENT CHAMPIONS

2016: Coggeshall Town **2017:** Little Oakley **2018:** Gas Recreation

PREMIER DIVISION	P	W	D	L	F	A	GD	Pts
1 Gas Recreation	29	23	1	5	95	40	55	70
2 Tiptree Heath	30	20	3	7	82	49	33	63
3 Alresford Colne Rangers	30	18	6	6	67	33	34	60
4 West Bergholt	30	16	3	11	85	46	39	51
5 White Notley	30	15	5	10	84	66	18	50
6 Great Bentley	30	14	6	10	59	47	12	48
7 Hatfield Peverel	30	14	6	10	71	62	9	48
8 Dedham Old Boys	30	14	3	13	66	67	-1	45
9 Little Oakley Res	30	13	6	11	56	69	-13	45
10 Kelvedon Social	30	11	8	11	42	56	-14	41
11 Lawford Lads	30	10	9	11	71	57	14	39
12 Earls Colne	30	10	6	14	54	55	-1	36
13 Hedinghams United	30	7	7	16	44	82	-38	28
14 Wormingford Wanderers	30	8	2	20	50	84	-34	26
15 Barnston	29	6	4	19	27	75	-48	22
16 Brantham Athletic Res	30	1	3	26	41	106	-65	6

DIVISION ONE	P	W	D	L	F	A	GD	Pts
1 Flitch United	24	17	4	3	87	32	55	55
2 Tiptree Engaine	24	17	2	5	84	28	56	53
3 Alresford Colne Rangers Res	24	17	2	5	82	44	38	53
4 Colne Athletic	24	13	2	9	68	44	24	41
5 Cressing United	24	12	3	9	75	54	21	39
6 Tiptree Jobserve	24	10	7	7	49	41	8	37
7 Bures United	24	11	3	10	45	55	-10	36
8 West Bergholt Res	24	9	5	10	38	49	-11	32
9 Boxted Lodgers	24	8	4	12	51	59	-8	28
10 Belle Vue Social Club	24	8	4	12	51	60	-9	28
11 Little Oakley A	24	6	2	16	56	80	-24	20
12 Gas Recreation Res	24	5	4	15	46	99	-53	19
13 Brantham Athletic 'A'	24	0	4	20	22	109	-87	4

DIVISION TWO	P	W	D	L	F	A	GD	Pts
1 Stanway Pegasus	26	25	0	1	104	25	79	75
2 AFC Sudbury 'A'	26	18	2	6	118	45	73	56
3 Long Melford Res	26	18	2	6	86	45	41	56
4 FC Clacton Res	26	17	1	8	70	50	20	52
5 Tollesbury	26	14	4	8	99	68	31	46
6 Cavendish	26	12	4	10	59	54	5	40
7 Mersea Island	26	12	3	11	71	66	5	39
8 Harwich Rangers	26	11	2	13	57	70	-13	35
9 Hatfield Peverel Res	26	8	5	13	53	70	-17	29
10 Rowhedge	26	8	2	16	45	63	-18	26
11 Wormingford Wanderers Res	26	6	7	13	53	64	-11	25
12 Ramsey & Mistley	26	7	0	19	40	94	-54	21
13 Lawford Lads Res	26	5	1	20	33	75	-42	16
14 Boxted Lodgers Res	26	4	1	21	27	126	-99	13

DIVISION THREE	P	W	D	L	F	A	GD	Pts
1 Gosfield United	26	21	1	4	94	26	68	64
2 Great Bentley Res	26	16	9	1	69	22	47	57
3 Dedham Old Boys Res	26	17	2	7	80	42	38	53
4 Tavern	26	15	1	10	72	40	32	46
5 Tiptree Engaine Res	26	14	2	10	50	45	5	44
6 Tiptree Jobserve A	26	13	4	9	74	49	25	43
7 Elmden Rovers	26	12	7	7	64	45	19	43
8 Shrub End United	26	14	1	11	71	62	9	43
9 Oyster	26	12	4	10	63	54	9	40
10 Harwich & Parkeston Res	26	10	3	13	47	59	-12	33
11 Barnston Res	26	9	4	13	57	71	-14	31
12 Bradfield Rovers	26	4	0	22	20	116	-96	12
13 Hedinghams United Res	26	3	2	21	29	95	-66	11
14 Tiptree Heath Res	26	1	2	23	19	83	-64	5

LEAGUE CUPS

ESSEX BORDER KNOCK OUT CUP FINAL

Gas Recreation	v	AFC Sudbury A	2-1

TOMMY THOMPSON CUP FINAL

Stanway Pegasus	v	AFC Sudbury A	1-2

PREMIER DIVISION	1	2	3	4	5	6	7	8	9	10	11	12	13	14	15	16
1 Alresford Colne Rangers		1-0	6-0	0-1	0-0	2-5	2-1	1-1	5-0	3-0	2-3	2-0	2-2	2-1	0-2	6-0
2 Barnston	0-1		4-2	1-3	0-2	0-3	0-0	4-0	1-1	1-1	2-2	1-2	2-3	0-8	1-4	2-3
3 Brantham Athletic F.C. Res	0-2	0-5		1-2	5-2	2-3	1-3	1-4	1-1	1-2	1-4	3-3	0-2	1-5	2-3	1-3
4 Dedham Old Boys	3-6	4-0	4-1		3-0	3-1	0-0	2-3	3-2	3-5	2-1	2-2	2-3	1-4	2-4	6-0
5 Earls Colne	0-3	0-1	3-0	3-0		1-1	1-2	2-1	1-1	7-1	4-2	3-2	1-2	1-2	1-1	3-1
6 Gas Recreation	0-1	V-V	5-1	3-2	2-1		3-1	4-0	9-1	1-2	5-2	6-1	4-0	2-1	5-2	AW
7 Great Bentley	1-1	0-1	3-1	3-5	2-0	5-1		4-1	2-1	2-4	3-2	6-0	1-6	3-1	1-1	4-0
8 Hatfield Peverel	1-3	1-0	7-2	5-2	3-2	1-5	2-0		1-5	1-1	1-2	8-1	3-5	1-2	4-3	3-1
9 Hedinghams United	2-1	3-0	5-3	0-3	4-3	1-2	1-1	0-2		1-4	2-2	1-2	2-4	0-6	1-4	4-3
10 Kelvedon Social	1-4	0-1	4-1	1-1	0-0	0-5	0-1	1-3	0-0		2-1	1-0	0-1	0-0	2-1	2-3
11 Lawford Lads	2-2	5-0	3-1	AW	2-2	2-5	3-0	0-0	2-2	2-2		3-0	3-1	0-1	2-5	6-1
12 Little Oakley Res	1-1	4-0	3-1	4-2	1-4	2-4	2-1	0-0	5-0	2-2	2-1		3-2	2-1	3-2	HW
13 Tiptree Heath	3-2	9-0	4-3	2-1	1-0	2-3	1-2	3-4	3-0	2-0	1-1	4-1		2-1	2-2	2-1
14 West Bergholt	1-2	7-0	6-1	4-1	5-1	2-4	4-2	2-2	5-0	1-2	1-4	0-0	0-4		5-0	4-1
15 White Notley	1-2	3-0	4-3	4-2	5-2	2-4	2-2	4-4	1-2	1-2	3-1	3-1	4-3	3-4		5-3
16 Wormingford Wanderers	1-2	3-0	1-1	0-1	2-4	AW	0-3	0-4	3-1	6-0	4-4	1-3	1-3	4-1	0-5	

ESSEX OLYMPIAN LEAGUE

RECENT CHAMPIONS

2016: Kelvedon Hatch **2017:** Springfield **2018:** Catholic United

PREMIER DIVISION	P	W	D	L	F	A	GD	Pts
1 Buckhurst Hill	26	24	0	2	83	18	65	72
2 Kelvedon Hatch	26	14	5	7	57	40	17	47
3 Harold Wood Athletic	26	14	4	8	58	41	17	46
4 Bishop's Stortford Swifts	26	14	4	8	39	43	-4	46
5 Catholic United	26	14	3	9	68	40	28	45
6 Rayleigh Town	26	13	4	9	45	39	6	43
7 Leigh Ramblers	26	11	4	11	48	54	-6	37
8 Hutton	26	11	3	12	47	55	-8	36
9 Sungate	26	9	5	12	40	56	-16	32
10 Springfield	26	9	4	13	47	62	-15	31
11 Old Southendian	26	8	5	13	48	54	-6	29
12 Canning Town	26	7	4	15	43	61	-18	25
13 Manford Way	26	4	4	18	25	62	-37	14*
14 Great Baddow	26	3	5	18	24	47	-23	8*

DIVISION ONE	P	W	D	L	F	A	GD	Pts
1 Shenfield A.F.C.	22	15	3	4	68	29	39	48
2 Basildon Town	22	15	2	5	71	35	36	47
3 FC Hamlets	22	13	6	3	72	26	46	45
4 Snaresbrook	22	13	3	6	35	24	11	42
5 Ramsden Scotia	22	13	0	9	46	40	6	39
6 Galleywood	22	11	3	8	56	28	28	36
7 Old Chelmsfordians	22	11	3	8	40	31	9	36
8 Herongate Athletic	22	9	0	13	39	57	-18	27
9 Ongar Town	22	8	2	12	48	48	0	24*
10 Frenford Reserves	22	5	3	14	35	64	-29	18
11 Rayleigh Town Res	22	4	4	14	35	61	-26	16
12 May & Baker E. C. Res	22	0	1	21	15	117	-102	-3*

DIVISION TWO	P	W	D	L	F	A	GD	Pts
1 Chingford Athletic	18	12	4	2	85	12	73	40
2 Toby	18	13	1	4	67	28	39	40
3 Runwell Sports	18	11	3	4	59	23	36	36
4 Shoebury Town	18	10	4	4	59	30	29	34
5 Lakeside	18	11	0	7	68	40	28	33
6 Beacon Hill Rovers	18	8	2	8	32	38	-6	26
7 Harold Wood Athletic Res	18	6	2	10	33	38	-5	20
8 Ryan	18	5	1	12	28	57	-29	16
9 Rochford Town	18	5	0	13	40	79	-39	13*
10 May & Baker E.C. 'A'	18	0	1	17	9	135	-126	-3*

DIVISION THREE	P	W	D	L	F	A	GD	Pts
1 Old Southendian Res	20	12	6	2	49	30	19	42
2 Westhamians	20	12	4	4	41	21	20	40
3 Laindon Orient	20	15	2	3	75	24	51	38*
4 Academy Soccer	20	11	5	4	56	24	32	38
5 Wakering Sports	20	11	1	8	42	40	2	37*
6 Leigh Town	20	9	5	6	46	31	15	35*
7 Hutton Res	20	7	1	12	33	42	-9	22
8 White Ensign Res	20	5	2	13	29	56	-27	20*
9 Basildon Town Res	20	6	1	13	39	69	-30	19
10 Roydon	20	4	3	13	36	52	-16	15
11 Old Chelmsfordians Res	20	3	0	17	24	81	-57	7*

DIVISION FOUR	P	W	D	L	F	A	GD	Pts
1 Corinthians	22	17	3	2	83	25	58	54
2 Epping Town	22	18	1	3	103	28	75	52*
3 Dagenham United	22	13	3	6	74	65	9	42
4 Lakeside Res	22	11	4	7	75	58	17	37
5 Toby Reserves	22	9	1	12	61	65	-4	28
6 Buckhurst Hill Res	22	8	2	12	46	72	-26	28*
7 Galleywood Res	22	6	6	10	32	49	-17	26*
8 Canning Town Res	22	8	3	11	43	57	-14	25*
9 Shenfield AFC Res	22	7	3	12	38	70	-32	24
10 Catholic United Res	22	6	6	10	63	59	4	22*
11 Leigh Ramblers Res	22	6	4	12	42	65	-23	20*
12 Old Barkabbeyans	22	3	4	15	36	83	-47	11*

DIVISION FIVE	P	W	D	L	F	A	GD	Pts
1 Corinthians Res	20	14	1	5	73	27	46	43
2 Collier Row	20	14	0	6	52	31	21	42
3 Laindon Orient Res	20	11	5	4	47	20	27	38
4 Academy Soccer Res	20	12	0	8	66	38	28	36
5 Runwell Sports Res	20	9	2	9	34	45	-11	29
6 Herongate Athletic Res	20	8	3	9	43	50	-7	27
7 Wakering Sports Res	20	10	0	10	44	48	-4	26*
8 Springfield Res	20	7	2	11	37	62	-25	23
9 Newbury Forest Res	20	6	4	10	32	39	-7	22
10 Roydon Res	20	5	4	11	22	55	-33	19
11 Bishop's Stortford Swifts Res	20	3	1	16	27	62	-35	8*

LEAGUE CUPS

SENIOR LEAGUE CUP FINAL
Bishop's Stortford Swifts v Catholic United 3-2
SENIOR CHALLENGE CUP FINAL
Catholic United v Frenford Reserves 7-1
RESERVE LEAGUE CUP FINAL
Basildon Town Res v Catholic United Res 2-1

PREMIER DIVISION	1	2	3	4	5	6	7	8	9	10	11	12	13	14
1 Bishop's Stortford Swifts		1-0	2-1	1-1	HW	3-2	1-0	1-0	3-2	HW	4-2	2-3	2-3	1-2
2 Buckhurst Hill	7-0		5-0	3-1	1-0	3-0	3-1	3-0	2-1	4-0	6-2	5-1	3-0	1-0
3 Canning Town	2-1	1-9		3-2	4-1	0-2	2-4	2-3	0-1	0-1	4-1	0-0	4-1	1-2
4 Catholic United	6-2	0-1	1-0		6-0	3-2	3-0	2-2	1-1	9-0	8-0	2-1	7-2	3-2
5 Great Baddow	2-2	A-W	3-3	AW		2-3	AW	0-2	3-2	0-0	2-0	AW	1-2	2-2
6 Harold Wood Athletic	1-1	0-4	4-1	3-0	5-0		3-3	1-0	0-2	3-1	2-2	2-1	3-0	2-2
7 Hutton	2-1	2-4	5-3	4-2	HW	2-5		1-5	1-1	4-1	3-3	0-1	2-0	3-1
8 Kelvedon Hatch	1-1	1-4	3-1	3-1	2-1	3-1	3-1		8-3	5-1	2-2	0-1	2-1	2-3
9 Leigh Ramblers	0-2	0-4	2-2	0-1	3-1	0-2	3-1	1-2		2-2	3-2	3-2	2-7	3-1
10 Manford Way	0-2	1-2	2-2	1-0	1-2	2-4	1-2	2-2	1-0		0-1	2-1	0-3	1-2
11 Old Southendian	1-2	0-1	3-1	4-0	HW	1-3	3-0	1-1	2-4	4-0		1-2	6-1	0-0
12 Rayleigh Town	1-2	2-3	3-2	3-1	4-1	2-4	2-0	2-0	0-1	3-2	2-1		2-2	2-2
13 Springfield	1-2	3-0	0-2	1-4	3-3	1-0	1-4	1-2	3-5	2-1	3-1	1-1		2-2
14 Sungate	3-0	1-5	0-2	1-4	2-0	2-1	3-2	2-3	1-3	3-2	0-5	0-3	1-3	

League Champions Lebeq United - From Left to Right - Amin Jones - GK, Dan Payne, Shah Bakherd, Tyler Edmund, Kevin Camargo, Edward Bamfo, Twaine Plummer - Captain, Nathan Hall, James Hall, Sheldon Sawyers, Jamie Viera.

Les James League Cup winners Little Stoke Football Club - Luke Sperring, Khalil Limur, Luke Meacham, Ollie Jones, Alex Hill, Kieron William's, Matt Price(captain), Reuben Nuevo-Draper, Danny Matthews, Ashley Coles (Manager), Mark Curtis (assistant manager), Dave Franklin (assistant manager)
Back Rows - Ethan Moore, Jazz Bright, Harry Goldspink, Reece Hedges, Lewis Hogg, Russ Church, Ethan Tucker,
Top 2 - Jack Burgess, Jordan Yeo.

GLOUCESTERSHIRE COUNTY LEAGUE

RECENT CHAMPIONS

2016: AEK Boco **2017:** Bristol Telephones **2018:** Thornbury Town

		P	W	D	L	F	A	GD	Pts
1	Lebeq United	28	23	2	3	85	28	57	65*
2	Frampton United	28	20	3	5	64	32	32	63
3	Stonehouse Town	28	17	3	8	52	27	25	54
4	Rockleaze Rangers	28	17	0	11	61	48	13	51
5	Ruardean Hill Rangers	28	16	2	9	53	40	13	50*
6	Wick	28	14	5	9	54	41	13	47
7	Hardwicke	28	12	6	10	59	55	4	42
8	Little Stoke	28	13	2	13	44	49	-5	41
9	Patchway Town	28	12	4	12	43	41	2	40
10	Broadwell Amateurs	28	10	3	15	42	59	-17	33
11	Henbury	28	7	8	13	32	38	-6	29
12	AEK Boco	28	7	6	15	39	54	-15	27
13	Hanham Athletic	28	6	5	17	27	61	-34	23
14	Gala Wilton	28	5	1	22	35	73	-38	13*
15	Southmead CS Athletic	28	3	4	20	29	73	-44	13*

LEAGUE CUP

LES JAMES LEAGUE CUP FINAL

AEK Boco v Little Stoke 0-0, 1-4p

		1	2	3	4	5	6	7	8	9	10	11	12	13	14	15
1	AEK Boco		1-2	0-4	1-0	5-0	2-3	2-2	0-3	1-0	1-2	3-0	0-4	1-1	1-1	0-1
2	Broadwell Amateurs	3-1		0-2	3-2	1-0	2-2	1-2	1-3	1-1	0-1	0-1	1-3	4-2	0-4	2-1
3	Frampton United	1-2	3-1		5-2	2-1	4-2	2-1	0-1	7-1	3-1	0-3	2-0	1-0	0-2	2-0
4	Gala Wilton	2-1	1-3	1-6		5-1	0-2	1-1	0-1	0-3	1-4	0-2	1-2	1-4	2-1	0-2
5	Hanham Athletic	1-1	3-1	1-2	3-1		0-2	1-0	1-0	0-2	0-3	2-4	2-0	2-1	0-3	1-1
6	Hardwicke	1-2	2-4	1-1	3-2	2-2		3-0	1-3	4-1	1-1	2-5	4-1	3-1	2-1	2-1
7	Henbury	2-1	4-2	1-2	4-0	1-1	1-1		0-2	0-1	2-1	0-1	1-2	2-0	2-0	2-2
8	Lebeq United	4-1	5-2	5-0	4-1	5-1	5-3	0-0		3-0	8-2	2-3	4-1	4-1	0-0	1-2
9	Little Stoke	2-1	3-1	1-2	0-2	3-0	4-3	3-2	1-2		1-0	2-3	2-3	0-2	0-3	0-0
10	Patchway Town	4-1	0-1	0-0	5-1	3-0	1-0	0-0	0-2	3-2		1-2	0-1	1-1	1-3	1-3
11	Rockleaze Rangers	1-4	2-3	2-3	5-3	2-1	3-1	2-0	3-5	3-4	3-4		0-2	1-0	1-2	5-1
12	Ruardean Hill Rangers	2-2	4-0	1-4	1-0	2-2	5-3	1-0	4-5	0-2	2-0	1-0		A	2-1	0-1
13	Southmead CS Athletic	3-3	1-1	0-3	0-3	1-0	1-3	3-1	0-4	1-3	2-3	1-3	1-7		1-7	1-5
14	Stonehouse Town	3-0	2-1	1-2	2-1	2-0	0-1	1-1	1-2	1-0	2-1	1-0	1-0	2-1		1-3
15	Wick	2-1	3-1	1-1	4-2	6-1	2-2	2-0	0-2	1-3	0-2	2-3	1-2	4-2	3-1	

HAMPSHIRE PREMIER LEAGUE

RECENT CHAMPIONS

2016: Baffins Milton Rovers **2017:** Bush Hill **2018:** Paulsgrove

SENIOR DIVISION		P	W	D	L	F	A	GD	Pts
1	Bush Hill	30	26	0	4	126	32	94	78
2	Infinity	30	24	3	3	117	36	81	75
3	Paulsgrove	30	24	0	6	120	47	73	72
4	Overton United	30	18	4	8	50	49	1	58
5	Fleetlands	30	18	3	9	79	50	29	57
6	Sway	30	16	4	10	82	71	11	52
7	Winchester Castle	30	15	1	14	57	51	6	46
8	Liphook United	30	12	8	10	66	53	13	44
9	Stockbridge	30	13	4	13	52	61	-9	43
10	Colden Common	30	11	6	13	62	73	-11	38*
11	Hayling United	30	10	3	17	48	74	-26	32*
12	Liss Athletic	30	6	6	18	67	86	-19	24
13	Locks Heath	30	6	5	19	46	81	-35	23
14	Clanfield	30	5	6	19	36	73	-37	21
15	QK Southampton	30	5	1	24	42	100	-58	16
16	Athletico Romsey	30	2	4	24	26	139	-113	10

DIVISION ONE		P	W	D	L	F	A	GD	Pts
1	Lyndhurst	21	15	2	4	73	30	43	47
2	South Wonston Swifts	21	14	1	6	44	27	17	43
3	Netley Central Sports	21	13	1	7	54	33	21	40
4	Michelmersh & Timsbury	21	10	4	7	43	53	-10	34
5	Headley United	21	10	1	10	56	41	15	31
6	Hedge End Rangers	21	8	2	11	36	41	-5	26
7	Upham	21	4	1	16	31	66	-35	13
8	AFC Petersfield	21	2	4	15	31	77	-46	10

COMBINATION		P	W	D	L	F	A	GD	Pts
1	Liphook United Res	16	14	2	0	67	10	57	44
2	Paulsgrove Res	16	11	2	3	50	29	21	35
3	Fleetlands Res	16	10	3	3	49	25	24	33
4	Headley United Res	16	7	2	7	37	47	-10	23
5	Overton United Res	16	5	3	8	29	30	-1	18
6	QK Southampton Res	16	5	0	11	24	47	-23	15
7	Hayling United Res	16	4	3	9	21	51	-30	15
8	Lyndhurst Res	16	4	1	11	28	47	-19	13
9	South Wonston Swifts Res	16	3	2	11	34	53	-19	11

LEAGUE CUPS

SENIOR CUP FINAL

Lynhurst	v	Infinity	2-4

COMBINATION CUP FINAL

Overton United Res	v	Paulsgrove Res	1-5

SENIOR DIVISION		1	2	3	4	5	6	7	8	9	10	11	12	13	14	15	16
1	Athletico Romsey		1-11	3-2	1-5	1-4	1-4	0-5	0-2	1-1	0-7	1-5	2-4	1-3	0-0	4-5	0-3
2	Bush Hill	11-1		6-0	5-0	2-1	5-2	4-0	4-1	5-1	4-0	3-0	4-2	6-0	5-0	6-1	2-0
3	Clanfield	2-0	0-6		1-1	0-2	3-2	0-2	0-2	1-1	1-1	1-3	0-4	4-1	1-2	2-2	0-1
4	Colden Common	4-0	0-4	4-2		3-4	0-3	2-2	2-2	1-4	0-0	1-1	2-3	2-5	3-1	1-1	0-4
5	Fleetlands	4-1	4-3	2-2	2-3		5-0	4-3	2-3	5-1	3-0	1-1	2-3	3-2	0-1	4-1	3-2
6	Hayling United	5-0	1-6	1-1	1-3	0-2		2-1	3-3	4-2	2-0	0-2	1-2	2-3	1-0	0-6	3-1
7	Infinity	14-1	3-2	3-2	2-1	1-0	5-1		4-0	5-0	7-0	7-0	5-3	6-0	3-1	6-0	2-0
8	Liphook United	2-2	1-2	3-2	9-1	1-3	0-0	3-3		1-1	3-1	1-3	1-3	6-0	2-1	1-2	1-0
9	Liss Athletic	8-0	2-4	1-3	5-3	2-3	4-1	2-2	1-3		4-4	1-2	1-5	7-4	3-4	2-3	2-3
10	Locks Heath	2-1	1-4	3-0	2-3	2-5	4-1	1-3	0-3	1-4		1-4	1-4	3-1	1-1	3-5	0-3
11	Overton United	2-0	2-1	1-0	0-3	1-1	2-0	0-5	2-1	2-1	2-2		0-7	4-1	2-1	1-0	3-1
12	Paulsgrove	13-2	4-1	4-0	2-3	4-3	7-0	3-4	2-1	5-2	4-0	0-2		3-1	3-1	11-0	4-2
13	QK Southampton	0-0	AW	3-4	1-2	2-1	1-3	0-5	1-4	4-1	1-4	1-3	1-2		0-2	2-12	2-3
14	Stockbridge	8-0	2-5	3-1	0-6	1-0	2-0	2-3	2-2	3-2	1-0	4-0	2-3	1-0		1-0	0-5
15	Sway	0-1	1-3	4-0	4-2	3-4	3-2	1-2	3-3	1-1	3-2	1-0	3-1	3-1	8-3		3-1
16	Winchester Castle	3-1	1-2	2-1	2-1	1-2	0-3	1-4	3-1	3-0	4-0	2-0	0-5	3-1	2-2	1-3	

HERTS SENIOR COUNTY LEAGUE

RECENT CHAMPIONS

2016: Standon & Puckeridge **2017:** London Lions **2018:** Bovington

PREMIER DIVISION	P	W	D	L	F	A	GD	Pts
1 Letchworth Garden City Eagles	26	24	1	1	95	15	80	73
2 New Salamis	26	21	2	3	101	36	65	65
3 Bushey Sports Club	26	18	2	6	97	35	62	56
4 Ware Sports FC	26	16	3	7	58	49	9	51
5 Chipperfield Corinthians	26	14	2	10	59	47	12	44
6 Cuffley	26	11	4	11	56	63	-7	37
7 Sandridge Rovers	26	11	3	12	46	48	-2	36
8 Colney Heath Dev	26	10	5	11	38	41	-3	35
9 Belstone	26	11	2	13	47	67	-20	35
10 Bedmond Sports FC	26	8	3	15	48	60	-12	27
11 Knebworth	26	6	5	15	32	69	-37	23
12 Weston FC	26	5	5	16	61	76	-15	20
13 Broadfields	26	5	0	21	35	104	-69	15
14 Evergreen FC (HSCL)	26	1	5	20	27	90	-63	8

DIVISION ONE	P	W	D	L	F	A	GD	Pts
1 Bush Hill Rangers FC	32	26	3	3	99	36	63	81
2 Oxhey Jets Res	32	24	5	3	96	28	68	77
3 Cockfosters Res	32	20	6	6	87	38	49	66
4 Hoddesdon Town Res	32	18	9	5	97	55	42	63
5 Hinton	32	18	6	8	65	45	20	60
6 Rayners Lane Res	32	17	3	12	71	58	13	54
7 Oxhey	31	15	5	11	62	50	12	50
8 Hadley Res	32	14	3	15	66	55	11	45
9 Bovingdon Res	32	12	8	12	57	56	1	44
10 Aldenham FC	32	11	5	16	56	74	-18	38
11 Hatfield United	32	9	7	16	44	61	-17	34
12 Buntingford Town	32	8	5	19	47	72	-25	29
13 St Margaretsbury Res	31	7	8	16	47	80	-33	29
14 Old Parmiterians	32	7	7	18	34	76	-42	28
15 Wodson Park Res	31	7	6	18	42	77	-35	27
16 Lemsford	31	6	3	22	36	89	-53	21
17 Welham Albion	32	4	5	23	39	95	-56	17

RESERVE & DEV DIV ONE	P	W	D	L	F	A	GD	Pts
1 Wheathampstead Wanderers	20	15	2	3	77	29	48	47
2 Letchworth Garden City Eagles Res	20	15	2	3	64	21	43	47
3 Welham Albion Blues	20	16	2	2	64	22	42	46*
4 Bengeo Trinity	20	14	3	3	61	26	35	45
5 Hinton Res	20	9	3	8	52	44	8	30
6 Stevenage Borough Community	20	8	5	7	46	47	-1	29
7 Hatfield Town U25	20	6	2	12	30	49	-19	20
8 Knebworth Res	20	4	3	13	40	73	-33	15
9 Harpenden Rovers	20	4	2	14	30	61	-31	14
10 Buntingford Town Res	20	4	1	15	23	66	-43	13
11 Baldock Town FC Res	20	1	3	16	23	72	-49	3*

RESERVE & DEV DIV TWO	P	W	D	L	F	A	GD	Pts
1 Bedmond Sports FC Res	14	9	2	3	28	18	10	29
2 Chipperfield Corinthians Res	14	8	2	4	36	26	10	26
3 Oxhey Jets Vets	14	8	2	4	35	26	9	26
4 Cuffley (Seniors) Res	14	7	1	6	27	19	8	22
5 Oxhey Res	14	6	1	7	23	18	5	19
6 Wormley Rovers Res	14	4	3	7	19	25	-6	15
7 Sarratt Res	14	4	3	7	20	28	-8	15
8 Evergreen FC U21	14	2	2	10	16	44	-28	8

LEAGUE CUPS

AUBREY CUP FINAL

Oxhey Jets Res v New Salamis 1-2

BINGHAM COX CUP FINAL

Bengeo Trinity v Hinton 3-1

CECIL HUDSON CUP FINAL

Hinton v Welham Albion Blues 1-2

GREG CUP FINAL

Chipperfield Corinthians v Sarratt Res 1-2

SENIOR DIVISION	1	2	3	4	5	6	7	8	9	10	11	12	13	14
1 Bedmond Sports FC		1-1	5-0	0-5	2-1	4-2	3-3	5-0	0-3	0-2	1-2	1-4	AW	2-2
2 Belstone	3-4		4-3	0-5	2-3	2-0	1-2	3-0	2-1	0-3	6-5	0-1	1-2	4-3
3 Broadfields	1-6	5-0		0-5	1-3	0-5	2-3	3-1	0-3	0-8	2-4	1-3	1-4	2-6
4 Bushey Sports Club	4-1	8-1	2-3		2-1	3-1	5-1	11-0	7-2	1-2	2-4	3-1	4-3	4-0
5 Chipperfield Corinthians	4-0	2-1	9-0	2-1		1-3	1-3	2-1	2-0	2-3	2-2	4-2	1-2	2-3
6 Colney Heath Development	4-1	1-2	HW	1-4	1-1		1-1	1-0	0-1	0-4	HW	1-0	2-2	7-1
7 Cuffley	5-1	3-1	AW	1-6	1-3	3-3		7-2	1-0	1-4	0-3	3-1	0-4	3-2
8 Evergreen FC	0-4	2-2	4-2	0-3	1-3	0-1	2-4		2-2	1-3	1-6	0-3	1-2	3-3
9 Knebworth	2-0	0-1	HW	3-6	2-3	0-3	1-1	1-1		1-6	0-3	2-2	1-4	1-1
10 Letchworth Garden City Eagles	HW	3-0	9-0	3-1	5-1	5-0	6-1	6-0	4-0		2-2	2-0	4-0	1-0
11 New Salamis	7-2	4-0	4-5	2-0	4-0	HW	4-2	4-1	9-1	3-1		3-1	11-1	4-2
12 Sandridge Rovers	2-1	0-2	5-4	1-1	1-2	2-0	2-1	3-1	4-0	0-2	0-2		1-1	4-2
13 Ware Sports FC	2-1	2-3	2-0	0-2	2-0	1-1	3-1	4-1	5-2	0-2	3-4	5-2		4-3
14 Weston FC	1-3	4-5	9-0	2-2	2-4	3-0	2-5	2-2	2-3	1-5	1-5	4-1	AW	

HUMBER PREMIER LEAGUE

RECENT CHAMPIONS

2016: Wawne United **2017:** Crown FC **2018:** Chalk Lane

PREMIER DIVISION	P	W	D	L	F	A	GD	Pts
1 Chalk Lane	28	23	4	1	101	31	70	73
2 Pocklington Town	28	22	2	4	78	29	49	68
3 Beverley Town	28	17	3	8	84	43	41	54
4 Reckitts AFC	28	14	3	11	70	54	16	45
5 Hull United	28	12	7	9	58	54	4	43
6 Hornsea Town	28	13	4	11	72	78	-6	43
7 Sculcoates Amateurs	28	10	10	8	61	59	2	40
8 LIV Supplies	28	11	5	12	70	77	-7	38
9 North Ferriby Athletic	28	11	2	15	56	85	-29	35
10 Westella & Willerby	28	9	7	12	52	54	-2	34
11 Hessle Rangers	28	10	3	15	42	60	-18	33
12 South Cave United	28	8	5	15	49	62	-13	29
13 Walkington AFC	28	6	5	17	52	75	-23	23
14 Hedon Rangers	28	4	8	16	47	88	-41	20
15 East Riding Rangers	28	5	2	21	44	87	-43	17

DIVISION ONE	P	W	D	L	F	A	GD	Pts
1 Beverley Town Res	24	18	4	2	93	48	45	58
2 Driffield Junior FC	24	16	5	3	80	33	47	53
3 Barton Town FC Res	24	16	1	7	77	36	41	49
4 Bridlington Town Res	24	15	1	8	67	40	27	46
5 Howden AFC	24	13	5	6	71	59	12	44
6 Brandesburton AFC	24	11	4	9	61	53	8	37
7 Goole United	24	11	1	12	44	55	-11	34
8 Easington United	24	10	3	11	51	60	-9	33
9 Driffield Evening Institute	24	10	2	12	63	52	11	32
10 North Cave AFC	24	8	4	12	50	55	-5	25*
11 Blackburn Athletic	24	7	4	13	47	51	-4	22*
12 Hessle Sporting United	24	0	5	19	38	102	-64	5
13 Hall Road Rangers Res	24	1	1	22	30	128	-98	4

LEAGUE CUP FINAL

Hull United	v	Chalk Lane	0-0, 4-3p

PREMIER DIVISION	1	2	3	4	5	6	7	8	9	10	11	12	13	14	15
1 Beverley Town		3-3	4-1	5-4	1-2	5-1	4-1	2-3	4-1	4-3	3-0	1-1	2-0	3-1	1-0
2 Chalk Lane	1-0		3-0	7-1	2-1	4-3	8-0	8-1	0-2	3-3	2-0	8-1	2-1	4-2	2-0
3 East Riding Rangers	1-6	0-3		2-3	2-5	4-4	3-2	1-4	1-2	0-3	1-3	0-3	2-3	1-6	0-4
4 Hedon Rangers FC	1-3	4-6	1-4		2-2	1-1	0-3	4-4	5-7	2-3	1-3	1-1	1-1	1-1	0-0
5 Hessle Rangers	1-7	0-0	1-2	1-2		0-4	0-1	2-2	2-1	0-3	1-4	0-1	0-2	4-2	3-0
6 Hornsea Town	0-3	2-6	4-3	5-2	2-1		3-3	3-4	3-4	2-1	4-3	4-4	4-0	3-2	3-1
7 Hull United	2-2	1-1	0-0	5-0	1-2	4-1		4-3	4-0	0-1	3-4	2-1	1-0	2-1	3-1
8 LIV Supplies	0-6	2-3	7-3	3-0	1-2	4-2	3-1		4-3	0-4	1-4	1-1	2-2	4-0	1-2
9 North Ferriby Athletic	2-1	0-8	2-3	3-1	2-4	2-3	3-3	3-1		1-3	0-4	1-8	4-3	4-2	2-4
10 Pocklington Town	2-0	1-2	3-1	3-0	2-1	3-0	2-0	4-1	6-0		0-0	1-2	1-0	4-1	3-2
11 Reckitts AFC	4-1	0-1	2-6	4-1	3-0	0-1	1-2	4-6	2-1	1-2		7-2	2-2	5-4	3-3
12 Sculcoates Amateurs	3-2	1-2	2-1	5-5	1-2	4-0	3-3	2-1	1-2	1-3	3-1		2-2	1-1	2-2
13 South Cave United	1-4	1-5	4-2	1-2	5-0	1-4	4-2	3-1	1-2	3-4	1-0	4-2		0-1	1-3
14 Walkington AFC	3-2	0-5	1-0	5-1	1-3	7-3	1-3	3-5	1-1	1-5	0-2	1-2	2-2		0-3
15 Westella & Willerby	1-5	1-2	2-0	0-1	4-2	2-3	2-2	1-1	3-1	1-5	2-4	1-1	5-1	2-2	

KENT COUNTY LEAGUE

RECENT CHAMPIONS

2016: Faversham Strike Force Seniors **2017:** Punjab United **2018:** Kennington

PREMIER DIVISION	P	W	D	L	F	A	GD	Pts
1 Staplehurst Monarchs United	30	20	6	4	69	33	36	66
2 Borden Village	30	18	5	7	61	45	16	59
3 Peckham Town	30	18	3	9	88	41	47	57
4 Bromleians	30	17		7	98	54	44	57
5 New Romney	30	17	4	9	57	41	16	55
6 Otford United	30	15	5	10	59	47	12	50
7 Tudor Sports	30	15	5	10	52	44	8	50
8 Faversham Strike Force Seniors	30	15	3	12	64	67	-3	48
9 Hawkinge Town	30	13	6	11	77	59	18	45
10 Fleetdown United	30	10	8	12	41	43	-2	38
11 Kings Hill	30	12	4	14	53	62	-9	34*
12 Farnborough O B Guild	30	8	8	14	47	60	-13	32
13 Crockenhill	30	7	3	20	57	106	-49	24
14 Stansfeld (O&B)	30	6	4	20	48	79	-31	22
15 Bexley	30	7	2	21	42	90	-48	22*
16 Metrogas	30	5	2	23	46	88	-42	17

DIVISION ONE CENTRAL AND EAST	P	W	D	L	F	A	GD	Pts
1 K Sports Reserves	20	16	3	1	67	21	46	51
2 Wateringbury	20	11	2	7	48	44	4	35
3 Hollands & Blair Reserves	20	10	4	6	42	29	13	34
4 Cuxton 1991	20	10	2	8	52	50	2	32
5 Lydd Town Reserves	20	9	3	8	52	61	-9	27*
6 Guru Nanak	20	8	4	8	40	51	-11	27*
7 Rochester City	20	8	2	10	39	37	2	26
8 Burgess Hodgson	20	6	5	9	42	47	-5	23
9 Lordswood Reserves	20	7	2	11	40	56	-16	20*
10 Margate Sports	20	4	5	11	37	50	-13	17
11 Ramsgate Reserves	20	4	2	14	37	50	-13	11*

DIVISION ONE WEST	P	W	D	L	F	A	GD	Pts
1 Ide Hill	20	15	3	2	58	27	31	48
2 Sydenham Sports	20	13	5	2	61	21	40	44
3 Chipstead	20	13	4	3	65	30	35	43
4 South East Athletic	20	9	6	5	72	37	35	33
5 Club Langley	20	9	3	8	34	30	4	30
6 Halls AFC	20	9	3	8	37	38	-1	30
7 Welling Park	19	7	5	7	37	38	-1	26
8 Sutton Athletic Reserves	20	5	4	11	32	44	-12	19
9 AFC Mottingham	20	4	2	14	28	66	-38	14
10 Long Lane	20	3	2	15	37	91	-54	10*
11 Stansfeld (O&B) Reserves	19	3	1	15	25	64	-39	9*

DIVISION TWO CENTRAL & EAST	P	W	D	L	F	A	GD	Pts
1 Ashford	18	14	1	3	68	24	44	42*
2 Rusthall Reserves	18	10	3	5	66	29	37	33
3 Snodland Town Reserves	18	9	6	3	44	20	24	33
4 Southborough	18	10	1	7	41	26	15	31
5 Faversham Town Reserves	18	9	2	7	54	31	23	29
6 West Farleigh	18	9	1	8	34	30	4	28
7 Bearsted Reserves	18	7	1	10	35	46	-11	22
8 Margate Sports Reserves	18	7	2	9	51	37	14	20*
9 Punjab United Reserves	18	5	3	10	38	41	-3	15*
10 Tonbridge Invicta	18	0	0	18	7	154	-147	0

AFC Ashford United Withdrawn - Record Expunged

DIVISION TWO WEST	P	W	D	L	F	A	GD	Pts
1 Red Velvet	22	17	3	2	91	27	64	54
2 HFSP & Ten-Em-Bee	22	16	4	2	61	19	42	52
3 Belvedere	22	12	2	8	67	40	27	38
4 Drummond Athletic	22	12	2	8	60	51	9	38
5 Orpington	20	12	1	7	55	46	9	37
6 Crayford Arrows	21	11	1	9	51	49	2	33*
7 Sporting Club Thamesmead Res	21	7	4	10	50	59	-9	25
8 Dulwich Village	22	6	5	11	33	66	-33	23
9 Johnson & Phillips	22	5	6	11	31	53	-22	20*
10 Fleetdown United Ress	22	6	3	13	27	44	-17	18*
11 Metrogas Reserves	21	3	4	14	19	54	-35	16*
12 Bexley Reserves	21	3	3	15	28	65	-37	11*

DIVISION THREE CENTRAL & EAST	P	W	D	L	F	A	GD	Pts
1 Sturry	18	16	0	2	102	17	85	48
2 Rochester City Reserves	18	14	1	3	83	31	52	43
3 Tenterden Town	18	12	1	5	80	34	46	37
4 Deal Town Rangers	18	12	1	5	63	41	22	37
5 Larkfield And New Hythe Wanderers	18	7	1	10	41	50	-9	22
6 Canterbury City University	18	5	5	8	29	43	-14	20
7 University Of Kent	18	7	2	9	50	65	-15	20*
8 Staplehurst Monarchs United Res	18	5	3	10	44	65	-21	18
9 New Romney Reserves	18	4	1	13 36		74	-38	10*
10 Paddock Wood	18	0	1	17	10	118	-108	0*

Bromley Green Withdrawn - Record Expunged

DIVISION THREE WEST	P	W	D	L	F	A	GD	Pts
1 Tudor Sports Reserves	26	17	6	3	53	26	27	57
2 Parkwood Rangers	26	17	5	4	68	40	28	56
3 Equinoccial	26	16	5	5	84	43	41	53
4 Danson Sports	26	14	7	5	55	30	25	49
5 Welling Town Reserves	26	14	4	8	65	49	16	46
6 Long Lane Reserves	26	11	6	9	54	46	8	39
7 Halstead United	26	12	3	11	51	50	1	38*
8 South East Athletic Res	26	12	1	13	55	80	-25	37
9 Farnborough OB Guild Res	26	8	10	8	55	46	9	34
10 Bridon Ropes Reserves	26	6	8	12	43	50	-7	26
11 Peckham Town Reserves	26	7	5	14	47	83	-36	25*
12 Greenways Aces	26	6	6	14	46	55	-9	24
13 Bromleians Reserves	26	4	3	19	49	74	-25	15
14 AFC Lewisham	26	2	3	21	27	80	-53	5*

LEAGUE CUPS

'BILL MANKLOW' INTER-REGIONAL CHALLENGE CUP FINAL

Chipstead v New Romney 5-2

'BARRY BUNDOCK' WEST KENT CHALLENGE SHIELD FINAL

Parkwood Rangers v Johnson & Phillips 5-1

EASTERN SECTION 'LES LECKIE' CUP FINAL

Sturry v Rochester City Reserves 1-0

PREMIER DIVISION	1	2	3	4	5	6	7	8	9	10	11	12	13	14	15	16
1 Bexley		1-2	0-9	2-3	2-6	0-4	0-1	2-1	9-2	3-2	2-2	1-4	4-2	3-0	0-3	0-3
2 BordenVillage	2-1		3-3	1-0	2-0	3-0	3-0	4-1	4-2	4-3	0-2	0-1	2-0	3-3	0-2	1-1
3 Bromleians	2-1	1-2		6-2	4-0	4-1	2-0	2-2	3-0	4-2	4-1	2-2	2-6	15-1	1-4	4-1
4 Crockenhill	2-2	4-2	2-5		3-1	6-2	1-5	0-5	1-1	4-2	0-3	2-3	2-5	4-4	5-6	0-1
5 Farnborough O B Guild	2-0	0-1	2-2	3-1		1-2	1-1	2-2	0-5	6-2	1-2	1-0	0-2	1-1	2-2	4-1
6 Faversham Strike Force Seniors	2-1	1-3	2-1	2-1	2-1		2-1	1-2	4-0	1-4	3-1	5-2	2-0	4-3	3-5	3-3
7 Fleetdown United	1-0	1-1	4-0	4-0	2-2	1-2		0-6	5-0	2-0	0-2	1-0	1-0	4-1	2-2	1-1
8 Hawkinge Town	8-1	0-3	7-1	7-1	0-3	7-4	2-2		1-2	5-3	0-2	2-1	4-2	2-0	0-1	2-3
9 Kings Hill	6-0	4-1	4-1	4-1	4-1	0-3	1-1	0-0		5-2	3-2	0-3	1-5	3-2	0-1	1-0
10 Metrogas	5-1	0-3	3-5	3-5	1-2	1-0	4-2	0-2	1-1		0-2	1-3	0-4	0-2	1-2	2-3
11 New Romney	2-1	3-1	7-0	7-0	5-3	1-2	1-0	1-1	HW	6-0		2-0	2-0	1-2	2-2	0-1
12 Otford United	2-0	2-4	2-1	2-1	1-1	3-0	2-1	3-3	0-2	3-1	5-0		0-5	4-2	0-1	0-0
13 Peckham Town	7-1	1-1	9-1	9-1	3-0	3-3	3-0	2-3	4-2	1-1	5-1	2-3		2-0	3-0	4-1
14 Stansfeld (O&B)	1-3	2-3	2-3	2-3	4-0	1-2	2-0	3-0	4-0	1-2	0-1	1-4	0-2		2-2	2-4
15 Staplehurst Monarchs United	4-0	1-2	5-1	5-1	3-1	5-1	0-1	3-0	1-0	3-1	1-1	2-2	3-1	2-0		0-1
16 Tudor Sports	0-1	5-0	2-1	2-1	0-0	1-0	1-0	5-3	1-3	4-1	0-1	2-3	1-4	2-1	0-1	

ANDREAS CARTER KENT COUNTY LEAGUE

SEASON 2018-2019

Staplehurst Monarchs United FC
Premier Division Champions

Mick Northwood - Long Lane FC
Personality of the Year

Chipstead FC
'Bill Manklow' Inter-Regional Challenge Cup Winners

Brian Smith
League Long Service Award

Martyn Staveley
Referee of the Year

Sturry FC
Division Three Central & East Winners
Eastern Section 'Les Leckie' Cup Winners

Parkwood Rangers FC
'Barry Bundock' West Kent Challenge Shield Winners

Ide Hill FC
Division One West Winners

Red Velvet FC
Division Two West Winners
Kent FA Junior Cup Group A Winners

South East Athletic FC
Kent FA Intermediate Challenge Shield Winners

Ashford FC
Division Two Central & East Winners

K Sports FC Reserves
Division One Central & East Winners

Tudor Sports FC Reserves
Division Three West Winners

Cyril Windiate with wife Wendy and Committee Members

ANDREAS CARTER KENT COUNTY LEAGUE

LEAGUE CONTACT

Philip Smith - Marketing & Communications Officer
Telephone: 07939 046182
Email: philip.smith@kentcountyfootballleague.co.uk

LEICESTERSHIRE SENIOR LEAGUE

RECENT CHAMPIONS

2016: Birstall United **2017:** Lutterworth Town **2018:** Ingles FC

PREMIER DIVISION	P	W	D	L	F	A	GD	Pts
1 Rugby Borough	30	24	1	5	114	28	86	73
2 Saffron Dynamo	30	22	3	5	71	27	44	69
3 GNG	30	21	5	4	70	33	37	68
4 Thurnby Rangers	30	18	4	8	95	55	40	58
5 Barlestone St Giles	30	15	3	12	67	63	4	48
6 Hathern	30	14	4	12	62	57	5	46
7 Cottesmore Amateurs	30	12	9	9	74	56	18	45
8 Sileby Town	30	12	7	11	68	50	18	43
9 Khalsa GAD	30	13	5	12	67	76	-9	43*
10 Blaby & Whetstone	30	11	7	12	47	57	-10	40
11 Desford	30	10	5	15	63	61	2	35
12 Ellistown	30	9	2	19	47	90	-43	29
13 Allexton & New Parks	30	9	4	17	42	86	-44	28*
14 Friar Lane & Epworth	30	5	5	20	51	92	-41	20
15 Asfordby	30	5	5	20	49	87	-38	14*
16 Kirby Muxloe Res	30	4	3	23	37	106	-69	14*

DIVISION ONE	P	W	D	L	F	A	GD	Pts
1 Wymeswold	24	20	3	1	82	20	62	63
2 Ashby Ivanhoe Knights	24	18	4	2	56	25	31	58
3 County Hall	24	15	4	5	59	28	31	49
4 Magna 73	24	12	4	8	56	40	16	40
5 Anstey Nomads Res	24	10	6	8	56	41	15	36
6 Lutterworth Town Res	24	10	6	8	49	36	13	36
7 Loughborough	24	10	2	12	44	55	-11	31*
8 Barrow Town Res	24	8	5	11	60	48	12	29
9 Birstall United Res	24	8	4	12	43	53	-10	28
10 Earl Shilton Albion	24	7	4	13	44	56	-12	25
11 Anstey Town	24	6	3	15	34	67	-33	21
12 Highfield Rangers	24	5	5	14	42	64	-22	20
13 Holwell Sports Res	24	1	2	21	21	113	-92	-1*

DIVISION TWO	P	W	D	L	F	A	GD	Pts
1 North Kilworth Sports	20	14	3	3	73	37	36	45
2 Saffron Dynamo Res	20	14	3	3	62	27	35	45
3 Allexton & New Parks Res	20	14	1	5	63	37	26	42*
4 Friar Lane & Epworth Res	20	13	2	5	58	38	20	38*
5 Ingles Res	20	12	2	6	54	34	20	38
6 Thringstone Miners Welfare	20	12	2	6	64	36	28	37*
7 Sileby Town Res	20	5	1	14	39	56	-17	16
8 Cottesmore Amateurs Res	20	4	2	14	29	58	-29	14
9 Blaby & Whetstone Res	20	4	1	15	34	74	-40	13
10 Desford Dev	20	4	1	15	25	69	-44	13
11 GNG Dev	20	4	2	14	28	63	-35	11*

LEAGUE CUPS

LEAGUE CUP FINAL

Hathern	v	Khalsa GAD	2-1

PRESIDENT'S TROPHY FINAL

Anstey Nomads Res	v	Barrow Town Res	3-1

PREMIER DIVISION	1	2	3	4	5	6	7	8	9	10	11	12	13	14	15	16
1 Allexton & New Parks		2-3	5-4	3-1	0-6	2-1	2-1	2-0	3-1	1-5	1-2	0-4	1-5	2-3	1-1	3-5
2 Asfordby	1-3		0-1	0-2	2-2	1-4	2-3	0-1	7-2	3-5	1-2	2-0	0-4	0-0	0-0	2-3
3 Barlestone St Giles	1-2	3-1		3-0	2-0	1-1	5-1	3-5	4-3	5-3	3-2	2-0	0-0	0-1	4-3	2-3
4 Blaby & Whetstone	3-0	1-1	3-2		1-8	1-1	2-0	1-4	2-2	1-0	1-1	1-1	0-2	0-1	2-1	2-1
5 Cottesmore Amateurs	1-1	6-2	3-0	3-3		0-3	1-0	0-1	3-2	2-2	2-2	7-1	0-4	3-2	1-0	2-2
6 Desford	1-1	4-4	3-1	0-2	5-2		3-0	0-1	2-3	3-1	0-4	8-0	0-4	2-3	3-4	1-0
7 Ellistown	2-2	5-1	1-5	1-0	3-2	4-2		0-3	3-1	0-4	2-3	2-2	2-3	0-4	1-2	1-4
8 GNG	3-1	2-1	3-4	3-2	1-1	4-0	4-0		2-1	2-2	4-0	1-1	2-0	1-2	6-0	2-1
9 Khalsa GAD	2-0	2-3	2-1	2-6	2-2	0-6	7-2	2-3		3-0	5-3	3-2	2-1	2-2	1-1	4-3
10 Friar Lane & Epworth	4-0	2-5	0-2	2-2	0-4	5-4	4-5	2-2	1-2		1-3	1-6	1-3	2-4	0-5	0-0
11 Hathern	1-0	5-3	2-1	1-2	4-3	1-1	5-0	0-2	0-3	5-2		2-1	1-3	1-3	2-2	5-1
12 Kirby Muxloe Res	1-3	5-2	1-2	1-3	0-2	2-3	2-3	1-3	1-4	2-0	1-3		0-7	0-3	2-10	0-4
13 Rugby Borough	12-0	4-1	5-3	5-2	4-1	2-0	7-1	3-0	7-0	8-1	3-0	5-0		3-2	6-1	1-2
14 Saffron Dynamo	1-0	5-0	2-2	2-0	1-3	2-0	1-0	1-2	3-0	3-0	2-1	3-0	1-2		3-1	5-0
15 Sileby Town	5-0	4-0	0-1	4-0	1-1	3-1	1-3	0-1	1-1	4-0	2-0	5-0	1-0	0-3		2-3
16 Thurnby Rangers	6-1	5-1	8-0	2-1	5-3	3-1	6-1	2-2	2-3	3-1	2-1	12-0	3-1	0-3	4-4	

LIVERPOOL COUNTY PREMIER LEAGUE

RECENT CHAMPIONS

2016: Aigburth Peoples Hall **2017:** Aigburth Peoples Hall **2018:** Lower Breck

PREMIER DIVISION	P	W	D	L	F	A	GD	Pts
1 Waterloo Dock	24	19	3	2	89	37	52	60
2 East Villa	24	19	0	5	108	45	63	54*
3 Liverpool NALGO	24	16	3	5	64	38	26	51
4 BRNESC	24	15	3	6	78	31	47	48
5 Alder	24	15	3	6	69	38	31	48
6 Waterloo Grammar School OB	24	12	1	11	60	61	-1	37
7 MSB Woolton	24	10	4	10	60	73	-13	34
8 Old Xaverians	24	6	6	12	32	45	-13	24
9 Dock FC	24	6	5	13	36	46	-10	23
10 Custy's	24	8	2	14	51	65	-14	23*
11 Alumni	24	3	6	15	38	93	-55	15
12 Bankfield Old Boys	24	3	5	16	44	87	-43	14
13 AFC Liverpool Res	24	2	3	19	27	97	-70	9

DIVISION ONE	P	W	D	L	F	A	GD	Pts
1 FC Pilchy	14	11	3	0	58	23	35	36
2 Liver Academy	14	8	3	3	53	33	20	27
3 Edge Hill BCOB	14	5	3	6	30	38	-8	18
4 City of Liverpool Res	14	4	5	5	38	37	1	17
5 HARES FC	14	4	4	6	30	35	-5	16
6 Lower Breck Res	14	4	5	5	37	37	0	14*
7 BRNESC Res	14	3	3	8	28	43	-15	12
8 ROMA	14	3	2	9	30	58	-28	11

DIVISION TWO	P	W	D	L	F	A	GD	Pts
1 Stoneycroft	20	18	1	1	78	26	52	55
2 Marshalls Roby	20	14	2	3	50	24	26	44*
3 Red Rum	20	12	2	6	65	31	34	38
4 MSB Woolton Res	20	11	2	7	48	37	11	32*
5 ACOL	20	10	1	9	63	58	5	31
6 Mersey Harps	20	8	4	8	41	45	-4	25*
7 Finn Harps	20	6	4	9	44	59	-15	22*
8 Botanic	20	6	2	12	33	69	-36	20
9 Old Xaverians Res	20	4	3	13	47	57	-10	15
10 Liverpool Hibernia	20	4	1	15	34	69	-35	13
11 AFC Kirkby	20	4	2	14	33	61	-28	11*

LEAGUE CUPS

CHALLENGE CUP FINAL

BRNESC v Waterloo Dock 2-3

GEORGE MAHON CUP FINAL

BRNESC v FC Pilchy 3-1

ROY WADE MEMORIAL TROPHY FINAL

FC Pilchy v Lower Beck Res 2-3

LORD WAVERTREE CUP FINAL

Marshalls Roby v Stoneycroft 1-0 (aet)

JOHN GREGSON MEMORIAL TROPHY FINAL

Marshalls Roby v Stoneycroft 2-3

PREMIER DIVISION	1	2	3	4	5	6	7	8	9	10	11	12	13
1 AFC Liverpool Reserves		0-6	2-3	2-2	0-4	2-1	0-4	0-5	2-3	2-5	2-2	0-5	0-6
2 Alder	9-1		3-1	2-1	0-1	3-0	0-2	4-0	1-1	3-4	3-0	2-2	5-2
3 Alumni	1-1	2-3		1-6	0-13	3-4	1-2	4-8	1-3	2-1	1-1	0-9	3-5
4 Bankfield Old Boys	4-1	1-5	3-3		0-6	2-3	1-1	1-12	1-4	2-3	1-3	2-7	1-3
5 BRNESC	3-1	5-0	1-1	6-2		4-0	3-0	1-3	1-4	5-2	2-0	0-2	8-0
6 Custy's	7-1	2-3	2-4	4-1	3-1		3-0	2-3	2-3	3-3	1-0	2-4	1-3
7 Dock FC	3-1	0-2	0-0	3-3	1-1	1-1		0-1	2-4	4-2	1-2	2-3	2-3
8 East Villa	8-1	6-2	6-3	6-1	0-1	6-1	3-2		4-5	5-2	7-0	6-2	2-5
9 Liverpool NALGO	HW	1-3	1-1	3-1	1-4	7-1	0-1	1-3		1-1	3-1	3-2	1-0
10 MSB Woolton	2-1	3-2	2-0	4-2	4-4	3-2	4-2	4-6	3-9		3-3	0-2	1-3
11 Old Xaverians	1-2	0-4	9-0	0-0	1-0	1-3	2-0	1-2	0-1	0-1		0-0	3-1
12 Waterloo Dock	5-3	1-1	5-1	3-2	4-1	4-2	4-2	2-1	3-2	7-1	6-1		4-2
13 Waterloo Grammar School Old Boys	8-2	2-3	3-2	2-4	2-3	3-1	2-1	0-5	0-3	3-2	1-1	1-3	

MANCHESTER LEAGUE

RECENT CHAMPIONS

2016: Prestwich Heys **2017:** Rochdale Sacred Heart **2018:** Avro

PREMIER DIVISION	P	W	D	L	F	A	GD	Pts
1 Hindsford	28	19	4	5	83	33	50	61
2 Manchester Central	28	17	6	5	80	46	34	57
3 Royton Town	28	17	1	10	69	48	21	52
4 Heyside	28	17	1	10	60	46	14	52
5 Rochdale Sacred Heart	28	16	3	9	87	60	27	51
6 Springhead	28	14	7	7	63	44	19	49
7 Manchester Gregorians	28	11	7	10	50	61	-11	40
8 Stockport Georgians	28	10	6	12	48	61	-13	36
9 Bolton County	28	9	7	12	49	60	-11	34
10 Dukinfield Town	28	9	5	14	59	77	-18	32
11 Chadderton Res	28	8	5	15	56	69	-13	29
12 Old Altrinchamians	28	7	5	16	28	56	-28	26
13 Walshaw Sports	28	6	7	15	42	62	-20	25
14 Beechfield United	28	7	4	17	51	73	-22	25
15 East Manchester	28	6	6	16	46	75	-29	24

AFC Monton resigned - record expunged.

DIVISION ONE	P	W	D	L	F	A	GD	Pts
1 Heywood St James	24	19	2	3	83	43	40	59
2 Pennington	24	17	3	4	80	37	43	54
3 Altrincham Hale	24	15	3	6	68	48	20	48
4 Boothstown	24	12	5	7	62	49	13	41
5 Elton Vale	24	12	5	7	55	49	6	41
6 Tintwistle Athletic	24	10	5	9	62	42	20	35
7 Atherton Town	24	10	4	10	62	50	12	34
8 Uppermill	24	9	4	11	53	55	-2	31
9 Radcliffe Juniors	24	6	5	13	38	59	-21	22*
10 Leigh Athletic	24	6	5	13	46	58	-12	21*
11 Govan Athletic	24	3	8	13	40	64	-24	17
12 Bolton Lads & Girls Club	24	3	7	14	43	88	-45	15*
13 Wilmslow Albion	24	3	6	15	28	78	-50	15

DIVISION TWO	P	W	D	L	F	A	GD	Pts
1 Middleton Colts	24	19	1	4	131	41	90	58
2 Moorside Rangers	24	16	3	5	69	38	31	51
3 Avro Res	24	15	3	6	96	38	58	48
4 Irlam Steel	24	15	3	6	77	46	31	48
5 Rochdale Sacred Heart Res	24	12	5	7	87	57	30	41
6 Wythenshawe Amateurs Res	24	11	4	9	68	44	24	37
7 Hindsford Res	24	11	2	11	61	60	1	34*
8 Manchester Gregorians Res	24	11	1	12	60	63	-3	34
9 Atherton Town Res	24	9	4	11	40	51	-11	31
10 Astley & Tyldesley	24	8	1	15	32	67	-35	25
11 Walshaw Sports Res	24	6	2	16	49	95	-46	19*
12 Hollinwood	24	7	2	15	70	93	-23	15*
13 Breightmet United	24	0	1	23	15	162	-147	-2*

DIVISION THREE	P	W	D	L	F	A	GD	Pts
1 Uppermill Res	24	17	4	3	87	41	46	55
2 Elton Vale Res	24	17	2	5	78	42	36	53
3 Dukinfield Town Res	24	16	2	6	76	31	45	50
4 Chadderton EDS	24	14	3	7	84	49	35	45
5 Rochdale Sacred Heart A	24	12	6	6	84	53	31	42
6 East Manchester Academy	24	11	4	9	75	64	11	37
7 Springhead Res	24	10	4	10	57	70	-13	34
8 Bolton County Res	24	8	2	14	55	74	-19	26
9 Stockport Georgians Res	24	7	5	12	49	69	-20	26
10 Pennington Res	24	8	1	15	48	70	-22	25
11 Leigh Athletic Res	24	8	1	15	54	65	-11	24*
12 Old Altrinchamians Res	24	5	3	16	30	80	-50	18
13 Wilmslow Albion Res	24	3	3	18	33	102	-69	12

DIVISION FOUR	P	W	D	L	F	A	GD	Pts
1 Heyside Res	24	19	0	5	93	29	64	57
2 Royton Town Res	24	17	2	5	85	49	36	53
3 Heywood St James Res	24	15	3	6	90	57	33	48
4 Boothstown Res	24	14	3	7	65	49	16	45
5 Moorside Rangers Res	24	13	2	9	65	47	18	40*
6 Altrincham Hale Res	24	10	3	11	93	82	11	33
7 Tintwistle Athletic Res	24	11	2	11	55	73	-18	32*
8 Dukinfield Town A	24	9	1	14	68	70	-2	28
9 Manchester Central Res	24	9	2	13	67	77	-10	28*
10 Atherton Town A	24	9	1	14	53	72	-19	28
11 Govan Athletic Res	24	7	2	15	51	58	-7	23
12 Astley & Tyldesley Res	24	6	1	17	44	126	-82	19
13 Bolton Lads & Girls Club Res	24	4	4	16	44	84	-40	16

LEAGUE CUPS

GILCRYST CUP FINAL

Beechfield United v Rochdale Sacred Heart 0-3

MURRAY TROPHY FINAL

Boothstown v Avro Res 1-1, 7-6p

OPEN TROPHY FINAL

Rochdale Sacred Heart A v Elton Vale Res 0-7

MANCHESTER LEAGUE CUP FINAL

Chadderton EDS v East Manchester Academy 4-2

PREMIER DIVISION	1	2	3	4	5	6	7	8	9	10	11	12	13	14	15	16
1 Beechfield United		3-1	1-5	5-1	5-2	1-3	0-4	2-1	3-1	0-0	2-4	2-3	1-1	2-3	2-2
2 Bolton County	1-3		7-1	3-5	1-2	2-1	2-2	2-4	1-1	2-1	0-4	2-1	4-0	1-1	1-0
3 Chadderton Res	2-5	0-4		2-4	0-1	2-4	3-4	2-2	4-1	0-1	7-1	1-2	3-3	5-0	0-6
4 Dukinfield Town	3-1	5-1	7-0		4-0	1-3	0-7	1-1	2-1	2-2	2-6	0-3	3-0	2-2	1-2
5 East Manchester	2-2	5-1	0-2	5-4		0-1	0-3	2-7	2-4	5-0	1-3	4-1	1-5	1-4	3-4
6 Heyside	4-1	4-1	2-0	2-2	1-0		2-0	4-5	0-2	1-0	2-1	1-3	1-3	3-0	3-1
7 Hindsford	6-0	3-1	3-2	4-1	5-0	4-1		3-2	2-2	1-1	4-0	0-1	1-0	5-0	3-0
8 Manchester Central	4-0	1-1	1-1	3-2	4-1	5-2	2-2		3-2	3-0	2-5	2-5	2-1	0-2	7-0
9 Manchester Gregorians	2-1	0-0	0-7	5-0	2-2	2-1	2-4	0-3		3-2	5-3	0-5	2-0	0-3	4-3
10 Old Altrinchamians	1-0	2-1	2-2	3-0	0-0	1-3	0-4	0-1	0-1		1-3	3-0	0-6	4-1	1-0
11 Rochdale Sacred Heart	4-1	2-3	1-2	6-0	2-2	4-1	4-2	2-5	4-1	3-0		2-3	2-2	5-3	5-0
12 Royton Town	5-3	6-1	AW	3-1	4-1	1-2	2-1	2-5	2-2	4-0	2-3		1-4	4-3	3-2
13 Springhead	4-3	0-0	2-0	2-2	3-1	3-2	2-3	0-1	2-2	2-0	3-2	2-1		5-1	3-2
14 Stockport Georgians	3-2	1-1	3-1	4-1	2-2	1-3	0-2	0-2	1-2	4-2	3-3	1-0	1-3		0-0
15 Walshaw Sports	1-0	2-4	2-2	1-3	1-1	0-3	3-1	2-2	1-1	4-1	1-3	0-2	2-2	0-1	

MID-SUSSEX LEAGUE

RECENT CHAMPIONS

2016: Jarvis Brook **2017:** Lindfield **2018:** Lindfield

PREMIER DIVISION	P	W	D	L	F	A	GD	PTS
1 Cuckfield Rangers	26	23	1	2	88	19	69	70
2 Hollington United	26	21	2	3	68	26	42	65
3 Balcombe	26	19	2	5	96	37	59	59
4 Lindfield	26	16	4	6	88	39	49	52
5 Forest Row	26	13	4	9	69	65	4	43
6 Willingdon Athletic	26	9	9	8	45	49	-4	36
7 Burgess Hill Albion	26	10	5	11	62	53	9	35
8 Rotherfield	26	8	7	11	51	56	-5	31
9 AFC Uckfield Town II	26	7	6	13	59	86	-27	27
10 AFC Ringmer	26	6	8	12	35	56	-21	26
11 Eastbourne Rangers	26	6	4	16	44	70	-26	22
12 Sporting Lindfield	26	6	3	17	36	66	-30	21
13 Peacehaven & Telscombe II	26	6	3	17	46	97	-51	21
14 Buxted	26	1	4	21	22	90	-68	7

CHAMPIONSHIP	P	W	D	L	F	A	GD	PTS
1 Charlwood	22	20	1	1	102	26	76	61
2 Copthorne II	22	12	6	4	50	37	13	42
3 Polegate Town	22	12	4	6	67	43	24	40
4 West Hoathly	22	12	4	6	44	33	11	40
5 Crawley Devils	22	12	3	7	53	37	16	39
6 Ashurst Wood	22	9	6	7	55	46	9	33
7 Mile Oak II	22	10	2	10	43	53	-10	32
8 AFC Varndeanians II	22	9	2	11	44	38	6	29
9 Sovereign Saints	22	8	2	12	54	46	8	26
10 Lancing United	22	5	1	16	40	95	-55	16
11 Nutley	22	2	5	15	42	87	-45	11
12 Roffey II	22	1	4	17	25	78	-53	7

DIVISION ONE	P	W	D	L	F	A	GD	PTS
1 Charlwood	22	20	1	1	102	26	76	61
2 Copthorne II	22	12	6	4	50	37	13	42
3 Polegate Town	22	12	4	6	67	43	24	40
4 West Hoathly	22	12	4	6	44	33	11	40
5 Crawley Devils	22	12	3	7	53	37	16	39
6 Ashurst Wood	22	9	6	7	55	46	9	33
7 Mile Oak II	22	10	2	10	43	53	-10	32
8 AFC Varndeanians II	22	9	2	11	44	38	6	29
9 Sovereign Saints	22	8	2	12	54	46	8	26
10 Lancing United	22	5	1	16	40	95	-55	16
11 Nutley	22	2	5	15	42	87	-45	11
12 Roffey II	22	1	4	17	25	78	-53	7

DIVISION TWO NORTH	P	W	D	L	F	A	GD	PTS
1 Godstone	16	12	1	3	64	27	37	37
2 Holland Sports	16	12	0	4	85	24	61	36
3 South Godstone	16	11	2	3	51	30	21	35
4 South Park FC A	16	7	3	6	34	29	5	23 *
5 Walton Heath	16	5	4	7	42	46	-4	19
6 Stones	16	5	2	9	29	62	-33	17
7 Jarvis Brook II	16	5	0	11	29	63	-34	15
8 Copthorne A	16	4	2	10	24	62	-38	14
9 Dormansland Rockets	16	3	2	11	24	39	-15	11

DIVISION TWO SOUTH	P	W	D	L	F	A	GD	PTS
1 Lindfield II	18	12	4	2	39	19	20	40
2 Bolney Rovers	18	9	7	2	62	35	27	34
3 Ditchling	18	8	5	5	52	39	13	29
4 Cuckfield Rangers II	18	9	2	7	39	31	8	29
5 AFC Hurst	18	8	2	8	44	37	7	26
6 Willingdon Athletic II	18	7	4	7	48	48	0	25
7 Cuckfield Town	18	6	6	6	39	39	0	24
8 Eastbourne Rangers II	18	6	3	9	43	54	-11	21
9 Plumpton Athletic	18	5	5	8	34	45	-11	20
10 Wivelsfield Green	18	1	0	17	23	76	-53	3

DIVISION THREE NORTH	P	W	D	L	F	A	GD	PTS
1 Galaxy Saturday	18	16	1	1	89	29	60	49
2 Crawley & Maidenbower Panthers	18	15	1	2	64	30	34	46
3 Horley A.F.C.	18	12	2	4	93	42	51	38
4 DCK Maidenbower	18	9	3	6	48	33	15	30
5 Roffey III	18	8	1	9	45	48	-3	25
6 Forest Row II	18	7	1	10	42	67	-25	22
7 Rotherfield II	18	6	2	10	35	47	-12	20
8 Handcross Village	18	4	3	11	33	62	-29	15
9 Ashurst Wood II	18	4	0	14	38	76	-38	12
10 Ifield Albion	18	2	0	16	23	76	-53	6

DIVISION THREE SOUTH	P	W	D	L	F	A	GD	PTS
1 Fletching	18	15	1	2	88	26	62	46
2 Burgess Hill Rhinos	18	11	2	5	54	31	23	35
3 FC Sporting	18	10	3	5	51	40	11	33
4 Ridgewood II	18	10	2	6	53	27	26	32
5 AFC Ringmer II	18	9	3	6	44	23	21	30
6 AFC Uckfield Town III	18	10	0	8	55	43	12	30
7 Peacehaven & Telscombe III	18	9	3	6	43	35	8	30
8 Montpelier Villa AFC III	18	2	4	12	23	80	-57	10
9 Wisdom Sports	18	2	2	14	27	78	-51	8
10 Buxted II	18	1	2	15	18	73	-55	5

DIVISION FOUR NORTH	P	W	D	L	F	A	GD	PTS
1 East Grinstead Town III	16	13	1	2	40	11	29	40
2 Crawley United	16	10	2	4	50	24	26	32
3 Scaynes Hill	16	9	3	4	39	21	18	30
4 AFC Acorns II	16	8	2	6	35	31	4	26
5 Ifield	16	8	1	7	43	35	8	25
6 Lindfield III	16	6	3	7	36	38	-2	21
7 Cuckfield Town II	16	4	2	10	21	42	-21	14
8 Oakwood II	16	5	0	11	24	33	-9	12*
9 Handcross Village II	16	2	0	14	18	71	-53	6

DIVISION FOUR SOUTH	P	W	D	L	F	A	GD	PTS
1 Burgess Hill Albion II	20	18	2	0	75	15	60	56
2 Polegate Town II	20	14	1	5	80	31	49	43
3 Newick	20	13	1	6	56	35	21	40
4 Barcombe	20	12	1	7	78	52	26	37
5 Eastbourne Athletic	20	10	5	5	48	34	14	35
6 Willingdon Athletic III	20	8	0	12	43	51	-8	24
7 Maresfield Village	20	7	1	12	37	68	-31	22
8 Hurstpierpoint II	20	6	3	11	34	55	-21	21
9 Ditchling II	20	6	1	13	27	75	-48	19
10 Ansty Sports & Social Club II	20	3	3	14	25	55	-30	12
11 Fairfield	20	4	0	16	34	66	-32	12

DIVISION FIVE NORTH	P	W	D	L	F	A	GD	PTS
1 Balcombe III	18	15	2	1	76	23	53	47
2 Ashurst Wood III	18	10	5	3	67	33	34	35
3 Stones II	18	10	4	4	71	32	39	34
4 West Hoathly II	18	9	3	6	37	26	11	30
5 Hartfield	18	7	6	5	52	36	16	27
6 Horley A.F.C. II	18	6	4	8	39	67	-28	22
7 Holland Sports II	18	6	1	11	33	43	-10	19
8 East Grinstead Meads	18	4	3	11	40	54	-14	15
9 Crawley United II	18	4	3	11	29	71	-42	15
10 Galaxy Saturday II	18	2	3	13	23	82	-59	9

DIVISION FIVE SOUTH	P	W	D	L	F	A	GD	PTS
1 Horsted Keynes	18	17	1	0	52	11	41	52
2 AFC Uckfield Town IV	18	15	0	3	57	10	47	45
3 AFC Ringmer III	18	11	2	5	37	23	14	35
4 FC Rangers	18	8	1	9	52	59	-7	25
5 Keymer & Hassocks	18	8	0	10	43	22	21	24
6 Fletching II	18	8	0	10	44	53	-9	24
7 AFC Hurst II	18	5	3	10	23	48	-25	18
8 Fairfield II	18	5	2	11	29	54	-25	14*
9 Scaynes Hill II	18	4	1	13	33	57	-24	13
10 Ardingly II	18	4	0	14	24	57	-33	12

MIDDLESEX COUNTY LEAGUE

RECENT CHAMPIONS

2016: West Essex **2017:** FC Deportivo Galicia **2018:** British Airways

PREMIER DIVISION		P	W	D	L	F	A	GD	Pts
1	St Panteleimon	24	20	3	1	84	28	56	63
2	PFC Victoria London	24	19	3	2	71	30	41	57
3	Pitshanger Dynamo	24	17	2	5	77	30	47	53
4	CB Hounslow United Res	24	13	6	5	56	44	12	45
5	Lampton Park	24	9	8	7	50	42	8	35
6	Indian Gymkhana	24	10	4	10	64	51	13	34
7	Brentham	24	10	4	10	52	40	12	34
8	Hillingdon	24	9	2	13	37	63	-26	29
9	Sporting Hackney	24	7	3	14	36	57	-21	24
10	Kensington Dragons	23	4	8	11	40	64	-24	23
11	Larkspur Rovers	24	3	6	15	19	49	-30	15
12	South Kilburn	24	3	4	17	29	83	-54	13
13	Cricklewood Wanderers	23	3	3	17	33	67	-34	12

FC Assyria resigned - record expunged.

Tottenham Hale Rangers resigned - Record expunged.

DIVISION ONE CENTRAL & EAST		P	W	D	L	F	A	GD	Pts
1	Clapton Community	20	12	3	5	66	45	21	42
2	Stonewall	20	12	2	6	51	29	22	41
3	NW London	20	11	4	5	72	47	25	37
4	London Samurai United	20	16	2	2	72	14	58	35
5	The Curve	20	11	1	8	68	40	28	34
6	FC Star London	20	9	2	9	52	45	7	29
7	The Wilberforce Wanderers	20	7	2	11	50	53	-3	26
8	FC Roast	20	6	4	10	46	56	-10	25
9	Eastfield	20	7	3	10	44	52	-8	24
10	Ealing Town	20	5	5	10	36	43	-7	11
11	Hereford Palace	20	0	0	20	15	148	-133	3

Sporting Club of London resigned - Record expunged.

DIVISION ONE WEST		P	W	D	L	F	A	GD	Pts
1	Hilltop	18	14	4	0	61	13	48	46
2	Yeading Town	18	14	3	1	51	18	33	45
3	Kodak (Harrow)	18	13	2	3	40	27	13	41
4	FC Deportivo Galicia Res	18	10	1	7	33	27	6	31
5	Western Athletic	18	9	1	8	42	36	6	28
6	New Hanford	18	6	1	10	36	30	6	19
7	FC IGK	18	5	0	13	29	70	-41	15
8	Eagles FC	18	4	1	12	28	43	-15	13
9	London Rangers	18	3	3	12	22	56	-34	12
10	Alpha & Omega	18	2	2	14	16	38	-22	8

DIVISION TWO		P	W	D	L	F	A	GD	Pts
1	AFC Hanwell & Hayes	18	14	2	2	61	27	34	44
2	Pitshanger Dynamo Res	18	12	4	2	54	25	29	40
3	Hillingdon Abbots	18	10	2	6	64	51	13	32
4	Harrow Bhoys	18	9	3	6	47	32	15	30
5	Brentham Res	18	8	4	5	33	23	10	28
6	Heston Bombers	18	6	4	7	23	26	-3	22
7	C.B. Hounslow United 3rds	18	6	1	11	30	47	-17	19
8	Sudbury Court	18	6	0	12	27	46	-19	18
9	LPOSSA	18	3	4	11	29	54	-25	13
10	Global Diplomats	18	2	2	14	26	63	-37	8

COMBINATION		P	W	D	L	F	A	GD	Pts
1	Speedy United	18	13	1	4	53	27	26	40
2	Ruislip Town	18	12	3	3	51	20	31	39
3	Centenary Park	18	9	3	6	27	29	-2	33*
4	Ruislip	18	9	4	5	40	32	8	28*
5	London Titans	18	7	2	9	46	42	4	23
6	LNER	18	6	5	6	30	39	-9	23
7	Kensington Dragons Res	18	6	6	6	40	50	-10	23*
8	Stonewall Res	18	6	2	10	24	28	-4	20
9	West SL Benfica	18	4	4	9	36	50	-14	19*
10	New Queens Park	18	1	2	15	19	49	-30	4*

LEAGUE CUPS

THE ALEC SMITH PREMIER DIVISION CUP FINAL

St Panteleimon v Cricklewood Wanderers 2-2, 4-1p

THE JIM ROGERS DIVISION ONE CUP FINAL

Clapton Community v Hilltop 2-2, 4-3p

THE H & D DIVISION TWO CHALLENGE CUP FINAL

Brentham Res v AFC Hanwell & Hayes 4-0

	PREMIER DIVISION	1	2	3	4	5	6	7	8	9	10	11	12	13
1	Brentham		0-2	1-2	4-2	2-3	2-4	2-1	1-1	1-3	2-0	3-1	HW	1-3
2	C.B. Hounslow United Res	1-1		2-0	2-1	4-2	2-1	1-2	6-1	2-6	1-5	4-2	2-1	1-6
3	Cricklewood Wanderers	2-4	0-2		4-1	4-6	V-V	3-3	0-1	1-3	2-5	2-3	0-5	3-6
4	Hillingdon	3-3	2-4	2-0		1-8	2-1	1-5	2-1	1-3	2-1	4-2	3-1	0-3
5	Indian Gymkhana Club	3-1	1-1	4-2	1-2		2-5	2-0	4-0	2-3	2-3	5-1	2-3	5-0
6	Kensington Dragons	1-3	2-2	2-2	1-1	2-3		2-2	1-1	0-3	2-5	4-4	4-4	0-2
7	Lampton Park	3-2	1-1	1-1	1-2	1-1	2-2		3-1	2-4	1-2	2-0	4-0	2-5
8	Larkspur Rovers	0-5	0-1	2-0	1-2	2-2	2-3	0-2		0-1	0-2	3-2	1-1	AW
9	PFC Victoria London	2-2	1-1	7-0	6-2	3-2	4-0	3-4	1-0		2-1	4-1	HW	1-2
10	Pitshanger Dynamo	1-0	3-3	1-0	4-0	3-0	4-1	3-1	4-0	3-4		6-1	6-1	1-1
11	South Kilburn	0-7	2-6	2-4	2-1	2-2	0-1	3-3	0-0	AW	0-9		HW	1-12
12	Sporting Hackney	1-5	1-4	1-0	2-0	2-1	5-0	0-3	1-1	1-5	1-4	1-0		1-4
13	St Panteleimon	1-0	3-1	3-1	3-0	4-1	7-1	1-1	5-1	2-2	3-1	HW	8-3	

NORTH RIDING LEAGUE

RECENT CHAMPIONS

2016: Boro Rangers **2017:** Boro Rangers **2018:** Boro Rangers

PREMIER DIVISION	P	W	D	L	F	A	GD	Pts
1 Boro Rangers	30	27	1	2	155	19	136	82
2 Stockton West End 'A'	30	25	2	3	121	45	76	77
3 Yarm & Eaglescliffe	30	18	4	8	79	41	38	58
4 Grangetown Boys Club	30	19	1	10	82	77	5	58
5 Thornaby Dubliners	30	16	4	10	78	59	19	52
6 Redcar Town	30	15	5	10	56	37	19	50
7 Bedale AFC	30	16	2	12	95	61	34	47*
8 Redcar Newmarket	30	14	1	15	75	90	-15	43
9 Fishburn Park	30	12	6	12	59	70	-11	42
10 Staithes Athletic	30	10	3	17	57	90	-33	33
11 Guisborough Town Res	30	10	6	14	66	83	-17	30*
12 St Marys 1947	30	9	3	18	55	80	-25	30
13 Kader Mens	30	9	3	18	61	104	-43	30
14 Beads	30	8	3	19	71	99	-28	24*
15 Stokesley Sports Club	30	5	4	21	45	106	-61	19
16 New Marske	30	2	2	26	31	125	-94	5*

DIVISION ONE	P	W	D	L	F	A	GD	Pts
1 Thirsk Falcons	20	16	2	2	102	35	67	50
2 Stokesley Sports Club Res	20	15	1	4	78	36	42	46
3 TS1 Tees Valley Tigers	20	13	3	4	67	34	33	42
4 Redcar Athletic Res	20	12	1	7	78	53	25	37
5 Whitby Fishermans Society	20	11	3	6	75	42	33	36
6 Lingdale Village	20	11	2	7	64	53	11	35
7 Great Ayton United Royals	20	11	1	8	74	52	22	34
8 Loftus Athletic	20	7	1	12	55	66	-11	22
9 Stokesley Sports Club AFC	20	4	0	16	44	97	-53	12
10 Middlesbrough Rovers	20	2	0	18	29	115	-86	6
11 Loftus	20	1	0	19	39	122	-83	3

LEAGUE CUPS

D&G TROPHY FINAL

Whitby Fishermans Society	v	Great Ayton United Royals	2-0

LOU MOORE TROPHY FINAL

Grangetown Boys Club	v	Bedale AFC	2-4

MACMILLAN BOWL FINAL

Thornaby Dubliners	v	Boro Rangers	0-2

PREMIER DIVISION	1	2	3	4	5	6	7	8	9	10	11	12	13	14	15	16
1 Beads		2-4	1-2	6-0	1-3	5-3	0-0	2-6	2-3	2-1	5-7	2-4	2-3	5-3	1-3	1-6
2 Bedale AFC	1-4		0-4	3-1	3-4	4-0	2-1	9-1	2-0	3-1	3-1	9-0	2-4	6-3	9-1	0-2
3 Boro Rangers	7-0	3-2		1-2	7-1	5-1	4-1	11-0	3-0	0-0	4-1	7-1	0-1	14-1	6-1	6-0
4 Fishburn Park	4-1	1-5	0-5		1-1	1-1	5-1	4-1	1-0	0-1	4-2	2-1	1-5	5-2	2-2	2-0
5 Grangetown Boys Club	3-2	3-1	0-8	3-1		6-2	4-0	3-0	3-2	3-1	5-1	6-1	1-5	2-3	1-4	0-4
6 Guisborough Town	3-2	4-2	0-7	2-2	3-1		4-0	2-1	13-1	1-3	2-2	1-1	2-7	4-0	1-6	2-5
7 Kader Mens	4-3	4-4	1-11	1-3	4-8	3-2		4-3	5-5	0-8	0-4	3-1	4-3	6-5	3-1	0-3
8 New Marske	1-5	0-3	0-6	0-1	3-5	1-1	0-6		0-3	1-6	1-3	0-4	1-2	1-1	0-6	1-6
9 Redcar Newmarket	4-2	3-5	1-8	3-2	1-4	2-3	4-1	8-3		1-0	5-4	1-3	6-1	2-0	2-3	1-2
10 Redcar Town	1-1	4-1	0-3	0-1	3-0	2-0	1-0	3-0	2-0		1-1	5-4	0-4	2-1	0-1	1-1
11 St Marys 1947	0-3	0-2	1-6	4-3	0-3	1-1	2-1	2-0	1-2	4-1		1-4	2-3	2-1	2-1	2-3
12 Staithes Athletic	0-0	4-1	0-1	3-1	0-3	1-4	3-4	3-2	5-2	1-2	3-0		2-2	2-1	0-4	1-4
13 Stockton West End 'A'	9-2	1-0	1-3	7-2	11-1	6-1	4-2	7-1	7-1	2-0	2-1	6-3		6-0	2-1	3-0
14 Stokesley Sports Club	2-3	1-8	0-6	3-3	0-1	2-1	2-1	0-1	2-6	0-4	3-2	5-0	1-3		1-2	1-1
15 Thornaby Dubliners	6-3	3-0	1-3	3-3	1-4	3-0	2-1	6-0	2-4	1-3	4-2	5-1	2-2	1-1		1-0
16 Yarm & Eaglescliffe	6-3	1-1	1-4	3-1	4-0	1-2	3-0	3-2	1-2	0-0	4-0	6-1	1-2	6-0	2-1	

NORTHAMPTONSHIRE COMBINATION

RECENT CHAMPIONS

2016: James King Blisworth **2017:** James King Blisworth **2018:** James King Blisworth

PREMIER DIVISION	P	W	D	L	F	A	GD	Pts
1 James King Blisworth	28	24	1	3	109	23	86	73
2 Kettering Nomads	28	22	2	4	74	32	42	68
3 Woodford United FC	28	21	3	4	74	27	47	66
4 Wootton St George	28	19	4	5	87	39	48	61
5 Harpole	28	15	4	9	61	40	21	49
6 Moulton	28	15	3	10	97	50	47	48
7 Wollaston Victoria	28	13	7	8	79	66	13	46
8 Roade FC Saturday	28	10	4	14	38	56	-18	34
9 Heyford Athletic	28	8	3	17	59	96	-37	27
10 Corby Pegasus	28	7	4	17	43	73	-30	25
11 Desborough & Rothwell United	28	6	5	17	48	90	-42	23
12 Earls Barton United	28	7	2	19	43	91	-48	23
13 Spratton	28	6	3	19	43	89	-46	21
14 Corby Stewart & Lloyds	28	5	5	18	36	77	-41	20
15 Burton United	28	4	6	18	35	77	-42	15

DIVISION ONE	P	W	D	L	F	A	GD	Pts
1 James King Blisworth Res	24	21	0	3	106	24	82	63
2 Weldon United F.C.	24	19	2	3	101	36	65	59
3 West Haddon Albion	24	15	4	5	74	38	36	49
4 Finedon Volta F.C.	24	12	6	6	65	48	17	42
5 Higham Town	24	13	3	8	55	59	-4	42
6 Moulton Spartak	24	12	5	7	51	42	9	41
7 AFC Houghton Magna	24	10	5	9	50	51	-1	35
8 Corby Strip Mills	24	7	5	12	56	68	-12	23*
9 Roade Juniors Res	24	7	3	14	33	70	-37	21*
10 Milton Milton	24	5	5	14	31	51	-20	17*
11 Woodford Wolves	24	5	3	16	39	68	-29	15*
12 Bugbrooke St.Michael A	24	5	3	16	46	85	-39	15*
13 Brixworth All Saints	24	2	2	20	28	95	-67	5

DIVISION TWO	P	W	D	L	F	A	GD	Pts
1 Wollaston Victoria Res	24	19	3	2	97	40	57	60
2 Corby White Hart Loco's	24	16	4	4	69	27	42	52
3 Yelvertoft Sat	24	15	3	6	73	41	32	48
4 Bugbrooke St.Michael B	24	14	6	4	67	36	31	48
5 Wilby	24	12	2	10	90	76	14	35*
6 Harpole Res	24	10	5	9	46	48	-2	35
7 Weldon United F.C. Res	24	10	3	11	77	61	16	33
8 Northampton FC Fotogold	24	9	3	12	58	67	-9	30
9 Moulton Res	24	8	2	14	60	84	-24	26
10 Kettering Nomads Res	24	6	6	12	54	73	-19	24
11 Desborough & Rothwell Utd Res	24	7	3	14	43	70	-27	24
12 Corby Pegasus Res	24	7	3	14	58	79	-21	21*
13 Kettering Orchard Park	24	1	1	22	24	114	-90	4

DIVISION THREE	P	W	D	L	F	A	GD	Pts
1 Corby Ravens	22	19	3	0	93	19	74	60
2 Stanwick Rovers	22	16	0	6	75	38	37	48
3 Thrapston Venturas Seniors	22	12	3	7	67	39	28	39
4 Weldon United F.C. A	22	12	4	6	52	37	15	37*
5 Woodford United FC Res	22	12	2	8	48	30	18	32*
6 Corby FC Siam	22	10	2	10	53	50	3	32
7 Finedon Volta F.C. Res	22	10	2	10	47	47	0	32
8 Irthlingborough Rangers	22	9	2	11	42	40	2	26*
9 Medbourne	22	6	2	14	50	75	-25	20
10 Grendon Sapphires	22	8	2	12	45	60	-15	17*
11 Heyford Athletic Res	22	5	2	15	40	67	-27	11*
12 Spratton Res	22	1	0	21	23	133	-110	0*

DIVISION FOUR	P	W	D	L	F	A	GD	Pts
1 Kettering All Stars	18	15	1	2	67	26	41	46
2 Corby FC Siam Res	18	14	3	1	79	26	53	45
3 Corby Ravens Res	18	11	0	7	62	34	28	33
4 Corby White Hart Loco's Res	18	11	0	7	54	45	9	33
5 West Haddon Albion Res	18	8	4	6	41	36	5	28
6 Higham Town Res	18	6	4	8	34	51	-17	22
7 Corby Rising Hope FC	18	6	3	9	49	52	-3	21
8 Corby Trades & Labour FC	18	4	3	11	34	45	-11	15
9 Great Doddington	18	4	1	13	17	62	-45	13
10 Wilby Res	18	1	1	16	18	78	-60	4

LEAGUE CUPS

PREMIER DIVISION CUP FINAL

Blisworth James King v Wootton St George 6-0

DIVISION ONE CUP FINAL

Weldon United v Blisworth James King Res 2-1

DIVISION TWO CUP FINAL

Wollaston Victoria Res v Yelvertoft 0-0, 2-4p

DIVISION THREE CUP FINAL

Grendon Sapphires v Corby Ravens 1-3

DIVISION FOUR CUP FINAL

Corby FC Siam Res v Corby White Hart Loco's Res 3-1

PREMIER DIVISION	1	2	3	4	5	6	7	8	9	10	11	12	13	14	15
1 James King Blisworth		8-0	5-0	5-0	6-1	6-1	3-0	HW	1-2	5-1	1-2	4-0	3-1	3-0	3-0
2 Burton United	0-0		1-2	1-3	1-3	2-2	0-8	1-4	AW	2-5	0-0	6-2	0-2	0-1	3-2
3 Corby Pegasus	0-6	1-7		2-1	1-2	6-2	1-2	9-1	3-4	1-1	1-0	1-1	1-4	0-3	0-7
4 Corby Stewart & Lloyds	1-2	0-0	1-1		3-2	2-1	1-5	3-4	0-1	1-1	2-3	3-1	1-1	1-3	0-4
5 Desborough and Rothwell United	0-9	0-5	1-4	2-2		1-2	1-3	5-1	0-0	1-7	3-3	4-4	7-4	1-2	1-3
6 Earls Barton United	1-2	5-0	1-0	4-2	3-0		2-8	2-3	0-4	2-8	1-1	0-3	0-2	0-3	0-4
7 Harpole	0-2	0-0	2-1	3-0	5-1	3-2		3-1	0-1	3-0	1-0	0-2	3-2	0-1	1-3
8 Heyford Athletic	2-10	1-1	6-2	4-1	4-2	0-2	1-1		1-4	1-2	1-3	3-2	3-5	1-3	0-6
9 Kettering Nomads	3-2	3-0	2-1	3-0	1-3	6-2	4-0	3-0		2-0	6-1	3-0	2-4	1-3	4-1
10 Moulton	3-5	7-1	6-0	5-1	3-0	8-1	5-1	4-3	1-3		7-0	5-1	1-1	2-3	3-4
11 Roade FC	1-2	2-1	1-1	2-1	0-1	2-0	0-3	1-4	1-2	0-2		5-2	5-1	0-1	1-5
12 Spratton	0-6	5-2	0-3	0-2	3-2	3-4	3-2	1-1	1-4	2-1	2-3		1-5	1-6	0-2
13 Wollaston Victoria	0-4	6-1	1-0	5-3	6-3	4-2	2-2	10-2	3-3	1-6	0-1	2-1		1-5	3-3
14 Woodford United FC	2-3	5-0	1-0	4-1	4-0	5-0	0-0	2-1	2-3	3-2	4-0	5-1	1-1		1-1
15 Wootton St George	2-3	HW	4-1	8-0	1-1	3-1	1-2	8-6	2-0	2-1	1-0	5-1	2-2	3-1	

NORTHERN ALLIANCE

RECENT CHAMPIONS

2016: Blyth Town **2017:** Killingworth Town **2018:** Newcastle University

PREMIER DIVISION	P	W	D	L	F	A	GD	Pts
1 AFC Killingworth	30	26	2	2	122	30	92	80
2 Newcastle University	30	24	3	3	131	29	102	75
3 Newcastle Blue Star	30	21	2	7	92	32	60	65
4 Wallington	30	15	6	9	62	56	6	51
5 Gateshead Rutherford AFC	30	15	4	11	62	58	4	49
6 Ponteland United	30	13	4	13	60	57	3	43
7 AFC New Fordley	30	13	3	14	53	70	-17	42
8 Newcastle Chemfica	30	12	5	13	68	71	-3	41
9 Alnwick Town	30	12	3	15	53	60	-7	39
10 Gateshead FC Res	30	10	4	16	72	82	-10	34
11 Percy Main Amateurs	30	9	4	17	41	70	-29	31
12 Shankhouse F C	30	10	1	19	37	68	-31	31
13 Seaton Delaval AFC	30	9	3	18	44	90	-46	30
14 North Shields Athletic F.C.	30	5	10	15	57	78	-21	25
15 Whitley Bay A	30	8	3	19	59	102	-43	24*
16 FC United of Newcastle	30	8	3	19	55	115	-60	21*

DIVISION TWO	P	W	D	L	F	A	GD	Pts
1 Rothbury FC	30	22	6	2	88	36	52	72
2 Whitley Bay Sporting Club	30	21	2	7	91	56	35	65
3 Whitburn & Cleadon FC	30	20	3	7	78	42	36	63
4 Cramlington United	30	18	4	8	94	52	42	58
5 Blyth FC	30	18	2	10	80	49	31	56
6 Willington Quay Saints	30	17	3	10	88	67	21	54
7 Coundon & Leeholme FC	30	15	4	11	71	61	10	49
8 Ellington FC	30	13	6	11	75	67	8	45
9 Spittal Rovers	30	13	4	13	69	56	13	43
10 Jesmond	30	11	1	18	72	71	1	34
11 Seaton Sluice FC	30	10	3	17	76	100	-24	33
12 Stobswood Welfare	30	10	3	17	52	83	-31	30 (-3)
13 Wideopen And District	30	7	5	18	58	107	-49	26
14 Gateshead Redheugh 1957	30	7	2	21	56	98	-42	23
15 Cramlington Town	30	7	2	21	48	108	-60	23
16 Burradon FC	30	6	0	24	39	82	-43	18

DIVISION ONE	P	W	D	L	F	A	GD	Pts
1 Blyth Town	30	26	2	2	95	16	79	80
2 Cullercoats	30	23	2	5	88	28	60	71
3 Winlaton Vulcans	30	23	1	6	91	45	46	70
4 Blyth Spartans Reserves	30	19	3	8	115	45	70	60
5 Bedlington FC	30	18	4	8	86	53	33	58
6 Hexham	30	15	5	10	67	53	14	50
7 Prudhoe Youth Club FC Seniors	30	15	4	11	75	53	22	49
8 Hebburn Town U23	30	15	2	13	79	68	11	47
9 Forest Hall	30	12	6	12	73	67	6	36*
10 Wallsend Boys Club	30	12	2	16	55	66	-11	35*
11 Felling Magpies	30	7	8	15	44	85	-41	29
12 Seaton Burn	30	7	4	19	44	76	-32	25
13 Gosforth Bohemians	30	6	5	19	54	93	-39	23
14 Red Row Welfare	30	6	2	22	49	95	-46	14*
15 Longbenton FC	30	4	2	24	42	132	-90	11*
16 Newcastle East End FC	30	4	4	22	41	123	-82	7*

LEAGUE CUPS

CHALLENGE CUP FINAL

AFC Killingworth	v	Newcastle Chemfica	2-1

LEAGUE CUP FINAL

Cullercoats	v	Newcastle University	3-4

BILL GARDNER CUP FINAL

AFC Killingworth	v	Gosforth Bohemians	4-1

AMATEUR CUP FINAL

Blyth	v	Stobswood Welfare	2-1

PREMIER DIVISION	1	2	3	4	5	6	7	8	9	10	11	12	13	14	15	16
1 AFC Killingworth		6-0	3-2	8-2	8-1	2-0	2-0	2-1	2-1	8-2	2-0	2-0	6-0	3-0	3-1	7-3
2 AFC New Fordley	1-4		1-0	3-2	1-2	1-3	1-4	3-2	1-4	1-0	2-0	1-6	2-0	7-2	1-0	4-3
3 Alnwick Town	0-3	2-1		1-0	3-2	3-1	0-3	2-4	0-5	2-3	0-1	2-2	3-0	4-3	2-2	1-3
4 FC United of Newcastle	0-4	4-3	1-3		0-9	2-2	2-9	0-5	0-8	3-3	1-6	6-3	0-5	1-4	1-1	4-5
5 Gateshead FC A Res	2-5	2-3	1-3	8-1		4-2	2-0	1-1	1-6	0-0	0-2	1-2	2-4	3-0	2-4	5-2
6 Gateshead Rutherford	1-0	2-3	2-1	3-1	2-1		1-1	4-0	2-4	2-2	2-1	0-3	5-0	3-2	1-0	3-3
7 Newcastle Blue Star	1-1	3-1	2-0	2-4	3-2	3-0		7-0	0-2	0-2	6-2	2-3	4-0	4-0	0-2	7-0
8 Newcastle Chemfica	2-9	2-2	2-2	4-2	2-3	6-1	1-3		1-3	2-2	6-2	4-0	3-0	4-0	2-3	3-2
9 Newcastle University	4-0	1-1	4-2	5-1	8-1	1-2	0-3	5-0		7-1	3-1	6-2	7-0	4-0	3-3	7-1
10 North Shields Athletic	3-3	4-1	1-4	2-3	1-1	0-2	2-4	2-3	0-6		2-2	2-2	4-5	1-4	1-2	6-1
11 Percy Main Amateurs	0-4	0-0	0-2	2-3	1-1	2-3	0-2	3-2	0-9	2-0		0-5	4-1	1-2	1-1	3-2
12 Ponteland United	1-3	1-3	2-0	3-2	3-4	4-3	2-3	2-0	0-2	0-0	0-1		0-1	4-2	1-4	1-1
13 Seaton Delaval AFC	0-7	4-3	1-4	1-3	0-4	1-2	0-4	4-1	3-3	1-6	2-1	0-1		1-1	2-2	1-3
14 Shankhouse	0-4	0-2	2-0	0-3	3-2	2-1	0-1	1-2	0-2	2-1	1-3	1-3	2-0		0-1	1-0
15 Wallington	1-6	3-0	2-3	2-0	6-2	4-3	0-4	1-1	0-7	3-2	2-0	1-0	1-4	2-0		5-0
16 Whitley Bay A	1-5	4-0	3-2	1-3	6-3	1-4	0-7	0-2	1-4	2-2	4-0	0-4	2-3	1-2	4-3	

NOTTINGHAMSHIRE SENIOR LEAGUE

RECENT CHAMPIONS

2016: Ruddington Village **2017:** Clifton All Whites **2018:** Newark Flowserve

PREMIER DIVISION	P	W	D	L	F	A	GD	Pts
1 Stapleford Town	34	28	2	4	104	32	72	86
2 Bingham Town	34	24	6	4	89	50	39	78
3 Southwell City	34	22	6	6	94	30	64	72
4 Awsworth Villa	34	20	3	11	104	63	41	63
5 Cotgrave	34	18	6	10	87	45	42	60
6 AFC Dunkirk	34	19	2	13	95	75	20	59
7 Aslockton & Orston	34	18	4	12	69	56	13	58
8 Sandiacre Town	34	18	2	14	82	63	19	56
9 FC Cavaliers	34	16	7	11	73	57	16	55
10 Keyworth United	34	16	4	14	97	82	15	52
11 Wollaton	34	14	5	15	77	79	-2	47
12 Eastwood CFC Dev	34	11	6	17	60	65	-5	39
13 Attenborough	34	9	6	19	62	103	-41	33
14 Magdala Amateurs	34	9	5	20	64	84	-20	32
15 Calverton Miners Welfare	34	9	4	21	57	83	-26	31
16 Bilborough Town	34	8	5	21	54	117	-63	29
17 Radcliffe Olympic	34	6	2	26	46	121	-75	20
18 Gedling Southbank	34	3	1	30	46	155	-109	10

DIVISION ONE	P	W	D	L	F	A	GD	Pts
1 Woodthorpe Park Rangers	32	27	4	1	121	32	89	85
2 Burton Joyce	32	23	4	5	117	39	78	73
3 Ravenshead	32	19	7	6	89	53	36	64
4 Basford United Community	32	19	4	9	102	44	58	61
5 Bridgford United	31	19	4	8	102	53	49	58*
6 Southwell City Res	32	16	5	11	59	56	3	53
7 Mansfield Hosiery Mills	32	15	6	11	67	54	13	51
8 Ruddington Village	32	13	5	14	73	77	-4	44
9 Bestwood Miners Welfare	32	13	4	15	76	73	3	43
10 AFC Bridgford	32	12	7	13	69	66	3	43
11 Beeston	32	12	6	14	81	75	6	42
12 Awsworth Villa Res	32	11	3	18	56	96	-40	36
13 Kirton Brickworks	32	10	5	17	53	84	-31	35
14 Selston Res	31	8	4	19	49	84	-35	28
15 Radford Res	32	7	6	19	57	105	-48	27
16 Wollaton Res	32	5	2	25	42	122	-80	17
17 Kimberley Miners Welfare Res	32	2	4	26	39	139	-100	10

DIVISION TWO	P	W	D	L	F	A	GD	Pts
1 Newark Flowserve Res	28	22	2	4	119	39	80	68
2 AFC Top Valley	28	21	3	4	126	41	85	66
3 Ruddington Village Res	28	21	2	5	89	40	49	65
4 Robin Hood Colts	28	20	3	5	113	41	72	63
5 Clifton All Whites Dev	28	17	2	9	90	63	27	53
6 Stapleford Town Res	28	15	3	10	70	47	23	48
7 Bingham Town Res	28	11	6	11	47	46	1	39
8 Keyworth United Dev	28	12	3	13	68	79	-11	39
9 AFC Clifton	28	11	5	12	72	61	11	38
10 Cotgrave Res	28	11	3	14	56	63	-7	36
11 Barrowby	28	9	5	14	51	68	-17	32
12 Ravenshead Res	28	6	3	19	34	87	-53	21
13 Elston United	28	6	2	20	34	87	-53	20
14 Nottingham Community	28	3	2	23	33	105	-72	11
15 Sneinton Town	28	3	0	25	18	153	-135	9

LEAGUE CUPS

SENIOR CUP FINAL

Stapleford Town	v	Southwell City	1-0

JUNIOR CUP FINAL

Cotgrove Res	v	Robin Hood Colts	0-3

PREMIER DIVISION	1	2	3	4	5	6	7	8	9	10	11	12	13	14	15	16	17	18
1 AFC Dunkirk		4-2	4-2	5-0	6-4	3-4	6-1	1-3	2-0	0-3	9-1	2-5	1-1	1-0	3-2	1-4	0-4	2-3
2 Aslockton & Orston	0-3		0-1	1-2	1-2	1-1	5-2	0-2	2-0	3-1	3-2	3-5	1-0	1-0	5-1	3-4	0-2	3-2
3 Attenborough	0-2	2-4		1-1	6-3	2-3	4-0	0-7	3-3	0-6	7-1	5-2	4-4	1-6	1-5	0-8	0-5	2-2
4 Awsworth Villa	8-2	4-0	6-0		1-2	2-2	3-1	3-1	4-1	2-4	6-0	4-3	5-1	4-0	5-1	3-0	2-3	5-2
5 Bilborough Town	1-4	1-3	4-3	0-5		1-1	3-3	1-5	HW	1-1	3-2	0-6	2-5	2-3	0-5	0-4	0-3	0-5
6 Bingham Town	2-4	2-2	4-0	4-1	6-2		4-3	2-1	3-1	3-1	6-2	2-2	3-1	2-0	2-3	3-1	1-0	2-0
7 Calverton Miners Welfare	2-1	1-2	2-2	0-2	3-0	1-4		3-1	3-2	0-2	5-3	0-1	1-2	3-0	2-3	1-1	2-4	1-2
8 Cotgrave	5-3	0-1	3-2	2-1	5-1	2-3	1-0		1-1	2-3	5-1	6-1	0-0	5-0	0-1	0-1	3-0	2-2
9 Eastwood CFC Development	0-2	0-0	5-0	2-1	2-2	1-2	3-1	4-4		0-1	5-1	0-2	3-2	3-3	3-5	0-1	1-6	5-1
10 FC Cavaliers	0-4	0-1	2-2	2-1	1-1	0-0	2-4	2-2	HW		3-1	6-1	3-2	8-1	5-2	0-6	1-7	1-2
11 Gedling Southbank	1-5	0-3	1-4	0-5	2-3	2-5	3-1	0-2	1-4	0-3		3-3	3-2	4-3	2-3	0-5	1-4	2-4
12 Keyworth United	4-2	2-4	3-0	4-4	4-3	4-1	1-2	4-3	2-3	1-5	3-1		5-1	6-1	2-3	1-1	1-3	7-0
13 Magdala Amateurs	4-5	0-4	2-3	8-1	1-2	0-3	4-3	1-4	2-3	2-1	2-0	2-0		2-2	0-4	1-0	2-4	1-2
14 Radcliffe Olympic	2-3	0-5	0-2	1-5	1-4	1-2	2-1	0-5	2-3	3-2	4-1	0-2	4-2		0-6	0-8	1-6	0-5
15 Sandiacre Town	1-3	4-0	2-0	4-0	3-1	1-2	0-1	0-1	0-2	0-1	7-1	4-6	2-2	3-2		0-0	1-3	3-2
16 Southwell City	2-0	3-4	2-0	0-2	8-1	0-1	6-2	1-1	3-0	1-1	7-1	2-1	4-2	3-0	3-0		1-0	1-0
17 Stapleford Town	1-1	2-1	HW	3-0	3-2	1-2	2-0	HW	2-0	HW	13-2	3-1	2-1	7-1	2-1	1-1		5-1
18 Wollaton	3-1	1-1	1-3	3-6	6-2	4-2	2-2	2-3	1-0	2-2	8-1	3-2	0-2	4-3	1-2	0-2	1-3	

OXFORDSHIRE SENIOR LEAGUE

RECENT CHAMPIONS

2016: OUP **2017:** Adderbury Park **2018:** Heyford Athletic

PREMIER DIVISION	P	W	D	L	F	A	GD	Pts
1 Freeland	26	20	2	4	71	22	49	62
2 Heyford Athletic	26	17	6	3	61	17	44	57
3 Kennington Athletic	26	16	4	6	60	35	25	52
4 Marston Saints	26	15	6	5	55	33	22	51
5 Cropredy s	26	15	3	8	58	35	23	48
6 Mansfield Road	26	13	6	7	52	40	12	45
7 Charlton United	26	8	7	11	44	52	-8	31
8 Yarnton	26	8	6	12	40	62	-22	30
9 Bicester Town Colts Bicester United	26	7	8	11	41	49	-8	29
10 Launton Sports	26	7	6	13	43	55	-12	27
11 Middleton Cheney	26	8	2	16	36	45	-9	26
12 Horspath	26	6	8	12	38	50	-12	26
13 Garsington	26	4	6	16	29	61	-32	18
14 Chalgrove Cavaliers	26	2	2	22	21	93	-72	8

DIVISION ONE	P	W	D	L	F	A	GD	Pts
1 Chesterton	20	17	0	3	102	29	73	51
2 Summertown Stars AFC	20	14	3	3	66	34	32	45
3 Hanborough	20	14	2	4	55	25	30	44
4 Long Crendon Res	20	12	1	7	56	43	13	37
5 Freeland Res	20	11	3	6	54	33	21	36
6 M.IN.I	20	7	2	11	37	63	-26	23
7 Adderbury Park Res	20	7	1	12	43	71	-28	22
8 Kennington Athletic Res	20	6	1	13	49	58	-9	19
9 Woodstock Town Dev	20	6	0	14	30	69	-39	18
10 Eynsham Association	20	5	1	14	31	65	-34	16
11 Lusitanos Oxford	20	3	2	15	38	71	-33	11

DIVISION TWO	P	W	D	L	F	A	GD	Pts
1 Marston Saints Res	20	17	1	2	73	21	52	52
2 Yarnton Res	20	15	1	4	61	38	23	46
3 Chesterton Res	20	12	2	6	40	20	20	38
4 Garsington Res	20	11	2	7	49	34	15	35
5 Heyford Athletic Res	20	10	4	6	42	27	15	34
6 Mansfield Road Res	20	10	1	9	41	48	-7	31
7 Launton Sports Res	20	9	3	8	53	51	2	30
8 Hanborough Res	20	5	4	11	25	50	-25	19
9 Charlton United Res	20	6	1	13	17	57	-40	19
10 Horspath Res	20	4	0	16	28	38	-10	12
11 Chinnor A	20	1	1	18	20	65	-45	4

LEAGUE CUPS

CHALLENGE CUP FINAL

AFC Killingworth v Newcastle Chemfica 2-1

LEAGUE CUP FINAL

Cullercoats v Newcastle University 3-4

BILL GARDNER CUP FINAL

AFC Killingworth v Gosforth Bohemians 4-1

AMATEUR CUP FINAL

Blyth v Stobswood Welfare 2-1

PREMIER DIVISION	1	2	3	4	5	6	7	8	9	10	11	12	13	14
1 Bicester Town Colts Bicester United		6-3	1-1	2-0	1-2	3-3	2-2	0-3	0-3	1-2	1-5	2-1	2-0	0-2
2 Chalgrove Cavaliers	0-5		1-4	0-4	1-2	4-2	0-1	1-0	A-W	0-3	2-2	1-3	0-1	1-2
3 Charlton United	2-2	5-2		0-1	1-0	3-2	1-4	1-1	1-1	1-0	0-2	5-4	0-2	1-2
4 Cropredy s	4-0	6-0	4-1		0-3	3-0	0-0	3-2	2-1	1-3	6-1	0-6	2-1	4-0
5 Freeland	2-1	7-0	4-1	2-4		3-0	1-1	5-1	0-2	2-1	0-4	3-1	3-0	3-1
6 Garsington	1-3	2-2	3-1	0-2	0-6		1-2	1-3	1-2	1-1	0-1	2-2	HW	3-0
7 Heyford Athletic	3-0	9-0	2-2	1-1	1-1	8-1		3-0	2-0	4-0	HW	2-0	HW	6-0
8 Horspath	1-1	3-0	0-0	3-1	0-5	1-1	1-0		0-3	1-2	0-2	1-1	2-3	1-3
9 Kennington Athletic	2-2	7-0	5-2	1-0	1-4	3-0	2-1	3-2		3-2	0-0	2-2	1-2	2-0
10 Launton Sports	1-1	5-0	2-4	1-3	0-4	2-2	0-1	2-2	1-0		2-2	2-5	0-3	1-2
11 Mansfield Road	2-1	6-2	0-3	2-1	0-4	1-0	0-2	3-1	3-6	5-3		0-0	3-1	1-1
12 Marston Saints	2-0	H-W	1-0	4-2	0-2	2-0	1-0	3-3	3-1	4-2	1-0		HW	3-0
13 Middleton Cheney	0-2	1-0	5-3	1-1	0-1	1-2	1-3	1-4	2-4	1-3	1-1	1-4		5-0
14 Yarnton	2-2	7-1	1-1	0-3	0-2	2-1	1-2	2-2	3-5	2-2	2-6	2-2	3-2	

PETERBOROUGH & DISTRICT LEAGUE

RECENT CHAMPIONS

2016: Moulton Harrox **2017:** Peterborough Sports Reserves **2018:** Netherton United

PREMIER DIVISION		P	W	D	L	F	A	GD	Pts
1	Moulton Harrox	30	24	4	2	110	38	72	76
2	Thorney	30	22	0	8	78	40	38	66
3	Peterborough Sports Dev	30	19	4	7	93	39	54	63*
4	Stamford Lions	30	17	8	4	72	36	36	62*
5	Whittlesey Athletic	30	17	9	4	70	32	38	60
6	Netherton United	30	18	5	7	90	48	42	59
7	Holbeach United Res	30	15	5	10	67	48	19	50
8	Oakham United	30	11	7	12	68	59	9	43*
9	Tydd	30	13	5	12	63	58	5	43*
10	Ketton	30	10	4	15	55	73	-18	37*
11	Leverington Sports	30	8	4	18	56	86	-30	28
12	ICA Sports	30	7	6	17	60	77	-17	27
13	Sutton Bridge United	30	7	2	21	48	102	-54	23
14	Long Sutton Athletic	30	7	6	17	41	83	-42	22*
15	Langtoft United	30	5	1	23	46	111	-65	15*
16	Peterborough Polonia	30	2	2	25	26	113	-87	7*

DIVISION ONE		P	W	D	L	F	A	GD	Pts
1	FC Parson Drove	26	21	2	1	113	16	97	71*
2	Uppingham Town	26	17	4	3	73	15	58	61*
3	Bretton North End	26	15	0	8	67	46	21	47*
4	Stamford Belvedere	26	12	4	8	45	40	5	46*
5	Eye United	26	12	3	10	58	58	0	45*
6	Crowland Town	26	11	5	10	73	58	15	38
7	Wittering Harriers	26	10	5	10	50	53	-3	37*
8	Oundle Town	26	10	4	12	58	61	-3	34
9	Whittlesey Athletic Res	26	10	2	13	54	62	-8	31*
10	Moulton Harrox Res	26	8	4	11	48	63	-15	28*
11	Spalding Town	26	9	2	12	55	60	-5	27*
12	Kings Cliffe	26	7	6	13	37	70	-33	24*
13	Peterborough	26	4	2	19	35	97	-62	11*
14	Oakham United Res	26	3	1	19	24	91	-67	11*

DIVISION TWO		P	W	D	L	F	A	GD	Pts
1	Stilton United	21	19	1	1	112	29	83	58
2	Premiair	22	14	3	5	104	31	73	45
3	Cardea	22	12	6	4	81	42	39	42
4	Rippingale & Folkingham	22	12	3	7	67	57	10	39
5	Eunice Huntingdon	21	12	1	7	58	47	11	37*
6	Netherton United Res	22	11	3	8	68	49	19	36
7	Ketton Res	22	8	1	12	28	52	-24	28*
8	Langtoft United Res	22	8	3	11	52	46	6	27
9	Warboys Town	22	8	2	12	55	68	-13	26
10	Whaplode Drove	22	5	3	13	45	102	-57	15*
11	Stamford Lions Res	22	3	3	16	20	82	-62	12
12	Spalding Athletic	22	1	3	17	17	102	-85	8*

DIVISION THREE		P	W	D	L	F	A	GD	Pts
1	Peterborough NECI	24	20	0	3	83	28	55	63*
2	Oundle Town Res	24	14	3	6	95	42	53	48*
3	Stamford Belvedere Res	24	15	3	6	69	44	25	48
4	Thorpe Wood Rangers	24	14	3	6	77	53	24	48*
5	Huntingdon Town Res	24	12	4	7	76	38	38	40*
6	Long Sutton Athletic Res	24	11	4	8	51	44	7	40*
7	Farcet United	24	11	6	7	86	41	45	39
8	Leverington Sports Res	24	10	3	9	76	63	13	39*
9	Whittlesey Athletic 'A'	24	7	6	9	45	51	-6	30*
10	Uppingham Town Res	24	6	6	11	55	66	-11	23*
11	Peterborough Res	24	1	3	20	28	112	-84	9*
12	Holbeach Bank	24	2	3	16	18	111	-93	6*
13	Stamford Lions 'A'	24	1	4	16	21	87	-66	4*

DIVISION FOUR		P	W	D	L	F	A	GD	Pts
1	Glinton & Northborough	26	19	1	5	81	35	46	61*
2	FC Parson Drove Res	26	16	2	7	92	45	47	53*
3	Holbeach United Sports	26	15	5	5	84	38	46	53*
4	Orton Rangers	26	16	2	7	78	51	27	53*
5	Ramsey Town First	26	16	4	6	85	52	33	52
6	Parkside	26	15	2	9	90	57	33	47
7	Hampton	26	10	6	9	67	57	10	39*
8	Huntingdon Rovers	26	10	3	11	75	63	12	35*
9	Premiair Res	26	10	1	15	70	81	-11	31
10	Wittering Harriers Res	26	9	2	14	52	75	-23	28*
11	Tydd Res	26	4	6	14	38	89	-51	24*
12	Whittlesey Athletic 'B'	26	9	0	11	54	64	-10	22*
13	Kings Cliffe Res	26	3	2	21	43	114	-71	11
14	Netherton United 'A'	26	3	2	21	48	136	-88	11

DIVISION FIVE		P	W	D	L	F	A	GD	Pts
1	Stanground Sports	10	7	2	1	44	15	29	26*
2	The Limetree	12	6	2	3	34	38	-4	26*
3	Thurlby Tigers	11	8	0	3	51	16	35	24
4	Casterton	12	10	1	0	69	9	60	22*
5	Cardea Res	12	6	1	5	35	29	6	19
6	Stilton United Res	11	6	1	4	26	21	5	19
7	Hampton Res	12	5	1	6	30	36	-6	19*
8	Leverington Sports 'A'	12	5	0	6	30	37	-7	17*
9	Gunthorpe Harriers	12	4	2	6	26	35	-9	17*
10	Peterborough City	11	3	4	4	23	18	5	16*
11	Orton Rangers Res	12	2	0	10	18	70	-52	6
12	Hampton 'A'	11	0	2	9	11	34	-23	5*
13	Eunice Huntingdon Res	10	2	0	7	17	56	-39	5*

LEAGUE CUPS

SENIOR CUP FINAL

Moulton Harrox	v	Whittlesey Athletic	3-4

CHALLENGE CUP FINAL

Uppingham Town	v	Eye United	2-1

JUNIOR CUP FINAL

Stilton United	v	Premiair	3-3, 2-4p

MINOR CUP FINAL

Stanground Sports	v	Premiair Res	1-2

PREMIER DIVISION		1	2	3	4	5	6	7	8	9	10	11	12	13	14	15	16
1	Holbeach United Res		3-3	6-0	2-2	2-0	6-0	1-1	0-3	2-1	5-2	2-1	2-2	3-1	0-1	4-0	1-3
2	ICA Sports	2-3		2-3	5-3	0-0	5-1	1-4	2-2	3-3	2-0	1-3	2-3	3-0	1-3	2-4	0-0
3	Ketton	3-1	4-1		2-3	2-2	2-3	0-2	4-3	2-2	1-1	3-2	0-4	4-1	1-4	1-3	1-1
4	Langtoft United	1-4	3-2	3-6		3-6	4-0	1-6	1-5	1-6	1-2	1-5	V-V	4-1	0-1	3-1	1-2
5	Leverington Sports	0-2	4-3	0-2	3-1		8-3	2-5	1-2	3-3	2-1	1-5	0-3	2-3	1-3	4-3	0-2
6	Long Sutton Athletic	1-3	1-0	2-3	4-1	1-1		0-3	0-1	3-2	3-3	0-3	2-4	3-0	1-3	0-2	1-1
7	Moulton Harrox	3-2	7-0	8-0	9-2	2-0	5-1		3-1	5-1	4-0	3-3	2-2	8-1	4-2	2-0	1-1
8	Netherton United	4-0	6-1	4-3	11-0	8-1	1-0	2-7		3-1	2-0	1-3	1-1	7-0	2-1	6-1	2-2
9	Oakham United	3-4	6-1	1-0	5-2	4-0	3-0	1-3	1-1		5-0	1-2	1-1	5-4	2-1	1-1	0-4
10	Peterborough Polonia	0-4	0-5	V-V	2-1	1-8	0-2	2-3	0-2	0-4		0-14	1-2	2-4	1-3	0-4	1-2
11	Peterborough Sports Development	0-0	2-2	0-1	2-0	3-0	7-1	0-4	5-1	4-1	3-0		4-3	8-0	1-4	2-1	2-1
12	Stamford Lions	4-2	0-1	2-1	4-0	4-0	0-2	5-0	1-1	1-1	6-0	3-2		2-1	2-1	2-1	2-1
13	Sutton Bridge United	0-2	1-5	4-3	3-2	2-3	1-1	1-2	0-3	3-1	5-3	1-2	2-5		0-2	2-1	3-3
14	Thorney	1-0	4-3	3-1	6-2	4-3	6-0	0-1	1-2	2-1	5-0	0-3	2-1	5-1		5-1	1-3
15	Tydd	2-1	3-2	2-1	2-0	5-1	2-2	2-3	4-2	0-1	6-1	1-1	1-1	5-3	2-3		1-1
16	Whittlesey Athletic	4-0	1-0	3-1	4-0	4-0	3-3	4-0	4-1	3-1	5-3	2-1	2-2	3-0	0-1	1-2	

SHEFFIELD COUNTY SENIOR LEAGUE

RECENT CHAMPIONS

2016: Frecheville CA **2017:** Swallownest FC **2018:** Swinton Athletic

PREMIER DIVISION	P	W	D	L	F	A	GD	Pts
1 North Gawber Colliery	28	21	5	2	80	31	49	68
2 Dodworth Miners Welfare	28	20	4	4	69	26	43	64
3 Swinton Athletic	28	17	5	6	79	39	40	56
4 Penistone Church Res	28	16	5	7	69	29	40	53
5 Stocksbridge Park Steels Res	28	14	6	8	53	48	5	48
6 Frecheville	28	13	4	11	68	57	11	43
7 Wombwell Main	28	14	0	14	69	43	26	42
8 Grimethorpe Sports	28	13	2	13	65	73	-8	41
9 Hepworth United	28	11	6	11	39	40	-1	39
10 High Green Villa	28	9	7	12	58	54	4	34
11 Jubilee Sports	28	8	7	13	44	49	-5	31
12 Oughtibridge W.M.S.C.	28	7	6	15	38	52	-14	27
13 Handsworth Parramore Res	28	4	6	18	34	62	-28	18
14 Denaby United	28	5	3	20	33	105	-72	18
15 South Kirkby Colliery	28	4	2	22	20	110	-90	14

DIVISION ONE	P	W	D	L	F	A	GD	Pts
1 Burngreave F.C. 1st	24	20	2	2	89	39	50	62
2 Ecclesfield Red Rose 1915	24	20	0	4	78	29	49	60
3 Houghton Main	24	17	3	4	61	33	28	54
4 AFC Dronfield	24	17	2	5	77	36	41	53
5 Denaby Main JFC	24	15	1	8	97	31	66	46
6 Kiveton Park	24	10	5	9	50	43	7	35
7 Hemsworth M W Res2	4	9	3	12	47	48	-1	27*
8 Wombwell Main Res	24	7	4	13	48	69	-21	25
9 Caribbean Sports	24	7	3	14	50	58	-8	24
10 Sheffield Medics F.C.	24	6	6	12	53	62	-9	24
11 Boynton Sports JFC	24	4	5	15	36	71	-35	20*
12 Sheffield Bankers	24	5	4	15	49	93	-44	19
13 Millmoor Juniors	24	0	0	24	22	145	-123	0

DIVISION TWO	P	W	D	L	F	A	GD	Pts
1 Wombwell Town	20	17	2	1	63	16	47	53
2 Stocksbridge Park Steels Dev	20	15	4	1	74	27	47	49
3 Sheffield Union SUFC1	20	11	5	4	58	30	28	38
4 New Bohemians	20	10	1	9	48	51	-3	31
5 Ardsley Athletico Junior	20	9	3	8	43	28	15	30
6 Dodworth M W Res	20	8	3	9	42	27	15	27
7 Swinton Athletic Res	20	7	3	10	38	47	-9	24
8 United Worksop	20	6	5	9	35	37	-2	23
9 AFC Dronfield Res	20	7	0	13	37	48	-11	21
10 Thurcroft Miners Institute	20	4	5	11	31	77	-46	17
11 Worsbrough Bridge Athletic Dev	20	0	1	19	14	95	-81	1

LEAGUE CUPS

LEAGUE CUP FINAL

North Gawber Colliery	v	Grimethorpe Sports	2-1

BRIAN BRADLEY MEMORIAL CUP FINAL

Burngrove	v	Hepworth United	0-2

PREMIER DIVISION	1	2	3	4	5	6	7	8	9	10	11	12	13	14	15
1 Denaby United		3-3	1-3	2-1	0-1	1-3	3-1	2-1	1-5	2-0	1-6	5-1	2-3	0-5	0-4
2 Dodworth Miners Welfare Senior	7-0		HW	1-0	2-0	2-1	2-0	2-0	2-2	HW	2-0	1-0	3-3	1-1	3-0
3 Frecheville	4-0	2-1		6-2	3-1	0-6	3-3	0-1	1-2	2-0	1-3	7-1	3-1	2-4	2-1
4 Grimethorpe Sports	7-0	2-1	6-4		1-1	2-0	5-1	1-3	3-9	3-2	2-2	HW	4-0	0-6	4-2
5 Handsworth Parramore Res Res	2-2	1-4	3-2	1-5		0-1	3-2	1-2	1-2	1-2	1-2	6-0	0-3	0-6	1-2
6 Hepworth United	H-W	0-3	0-5	3-0	2-2		2-1	1-1	0-4	2-1	2-0	2-0	0-3	0-1	1-2
7 High Green Villa	12-0	0-6	2-2	3-2	1-1	1-0		2-0	1-1	2-2	0-1	7-1	2-2	5-4	0-3
8 Jubilee Sports	3-2	0-2	1-4	1-2	2-2	2-2	2-2		2-3	2-3	1-1	2-0	2-2	3-4	2-1
9 North Gawber Colliery	4-2	4-1	3-0	7-1	2-1	2-1	1-0	1-1		4-0	1-3	4-0	0-0	3-1	4-1
10 Oughtibridge W.M.S.C.	4-1	3-1	1-1	4-5	1-0	2-2	2-4	1-2	1-2		2-0	0-1	0-2	0-1	2-6
11 Penistone Church Res	7-0	1-4	6-0	0-2	5-0	1-1	1-2	1-0	5-1	1-1		12-0	0-1	1-0	1-0
12 South Kirkby Colliery	2-2	1-7	2-5	2-1	HW	0-3	2-1	1-5	0-3	0-0	1-2		0-3	1-4	1-5
13 Stocksbridge Park Steels Res	3-0	2-5	2-2	4-1	2-1	1-2	1-0	3-2	0-3	2-0	1-1	4-2		0-3	3-2
14 Swinton Athletic	4-1	0-2	2-1	3-1	3-3	2-2	2-1	1-0	1-1	1-1	1-3	10-1	7-2		1-0
15 Wombwell Main	9-0	0-1	2-3	5-2	3-0	1-0	0-2	2-1	1-2	2-3	1-3	9-0	1-0	4-1	

SOMERSET COUNTY LEAGUE

RECENT CHAMPIONS

2016: Bishops Lydeard **2017:** Watchet Town **2018:** Chilcompton Sports

PREMIER DIVISION	P	W	D	L	F	A	GD	Pts
1 Chilcompton Sports	30	21	6	3	81	24	57	69
2 Nailsea & Tickenham	30	21	5	4	73	38	35	68
3 Fry Club	30	19	7	4	86	42	44	64
4 Middlezoy Rovers	30	18	5	7	64	27	37	59
5 Watchet Town	29	18	2	9	65	32	33	56
6 Shirehampton	30	17	1	12	83	56	27	52
7 Worle	30	15	6	9	70	64	6	51
8 Ilminster Town	30	14	4	12	46	49	-3	46
9 Stockwood Green	30	9	9	12	39	50	-11	36
10 Nailsea United	30	10	4	16	41	56	-15	34
11 Clevedon United	30	10	3	17	40	54	-14	33
12 Stockwood Wanderers	30	8	5	17	32	56	-24	29
13 Clutton	30	11	2	17	50	67	-17	28*
14 Westfield	30	7	2	21	42	80	-38	23
15 Wrington Redhill	30	2	9	19	23	74	-51	15
16 Odd Down (BATH) Res	29	1	6	22	20	86	-66	6*

DIVISION ONE	P	W	D	L	F	A	GD	Pts
1 Mendip Broadwalk	30	21	2	7	88	50	38	65
2 Keynsham Town Res	30	20	3	7	105	48	57	63
3 Uphill Castle	30	18	4	8	88	42	46	58
4 Bridgwater Town FC Res	30	17	5	8	74	51	23	56
5 Winscombe	30	16	3	11	74	46	28	51
6 Timsbury Athletic	30	15	4	11	76	45	31	49
7 Somerton Town	30	14	6	10	63	44	19	48
8 Saltford	30	13	9	8	57	46	11	48
9 Minehead AFC	30	14	3	13	47	60	-13	45
10 Staplegrove	30	12	4	14	76	78	-2	40
11 Nailsea & Tickenham Res	30	12	4	14	53	72	-19	40
12 Yatton & Cleeve United	30	10	7	13	86	89	-3	37
13 Burnham United	30	9	5	16	54	63	-9	32
14 Hengrove Athletic Res	30	7	6	17	52	71	-19	21*
15 Wells City Res	30	4	1	25	26	111	-85	13
16 Long Ashton	30	3	4	23	36	139	-103	13

DIVISION TWO	P	W	D	L	F	A	GD	Pts
1 Broad Plain House	28	19	7	2	64	33	31	64
2 Street Res	28	19	2	7	81	33	48	59
3 Glastonbury	28	16	2	10	45	49	-4	50
4 Castle Cary	28	15	3	10	75	46	29	48
5 Ashton & Backwell United Res	28	15	3	10	46	38	8	48
6 Radstock Town Res	28	13	6	9	62	44	18	45
7 Portishead Town Res	28	12	6	10	52	43	9	42
8 AFC Brislington	28	12	5	11	59	48	11	41
9 Imperial	28	10	5	13	48	63	-15	35
10 Welton Rovers Res	28	10	5	13	33	48	-15	35
11 Frome Town Sports	28	10	4	14	47	59	-12	34
12 Fry Club Res	28	8	6	14	46	53	-7	30
13 Peasedown Miners Welfare	28	7	5	16	28	48	-20	26
14 Brislington Res	28	7	3	18	56	75	-19	22*
15 Clevedon United Res	28	5	2	21	42	104	-62	14*

DIVISION THREE	P	W	D	L	F	A	GD	Pts
1 Middlezoy Rovers Res	30	22	5	3	89	41	48	71
2 Cheddar Res	30	21	7	2	72	26	46	70
3 Hutton	30	22	3	5	110	29	81	69
4 Draycott	30	18	5	7	75	38	37	59
5 Chew Magna	30	16	7	7	98	48	50	55
6 Nailsea United Res	30	14	9	7	76	40	36	51
7 Somerton Town Res	30	13	7	10	80	50	30	46
8 Winscombe Res	30	11	8	11	56	75	-19	41
9 Banwell	30	10	7	13	57	59	-2	37
10 Burnham United Res	30	11	4	15	52	78	-26	37
11 Combe St Nicholas	30	10	6	14	58	67	-9	36
12 Stockwood Green Res	30	9	4	17	50	87	-37	31
13 Yatton & Cleeve United Res	30	8	6	16	47	62	-15	25*
14 Tunley Athletic	30	7	2	21	26	94	-68	23
15 Congresbury	30	5	3	22	36	88	-52	18
16 Cutters Friday	30	1	1	28	21	121	-100	0*

LEAGUE CUPS

PREMIER & FIRST DIVISION CUP FINAL

Middlezoy Rovers v Minehead 2-0

DIVISION TWO & THREE CUP FINAL

Chew Magna v Broad Plain House 3-1

PREMIER DIVISION	1	2	3	4	5	6	7	8	9	10	11	12	13	14	15	16
1 Chilcompton Sports		4-0	2-1	2-2	3-0	1-1	1-1	4-1	5-0	3-1	4-1	2-2	1-0	5-0	6-2	7-1
2 Clevedon United	1-3		1-2	1-1	1-1	0-1	1-2	1-2	2-0	2-0	2-0	1-3	0-1	2-1	3-4	2-1
3 Clutton	0-1	2-3		1-4	1-2	1-4	1-7	3-0	2-1	1-3	2-2	3-1	0-6	2-0	1-2	0-2
4 Fry Club	2-2	3-2	6-3		0-1	2-2	0-2	4-0	7-2	2-1	5-0	3-1	2-1	8-2	5-1	7-1
5 Ilminster Town	1-0	3-1	0-3	1-1		0-3	1-2	3-2	3-0	1-2	2-0	1-0	2-4	3-1	2-3	2-1
6 Middlezoy Rovers	1-2	1-2	3-1	0-2	3-2		0-1	2-0	2-0	1-3	3-0	5-0	2-1	2-1	1-1	2-0
7 Nailsea & Tickenham	3-2	4-2	1-0	1-4	6-1	1-4		3-0	2-1	4-3	4-2	0-0	3-1	5-2	1-1	2-0
8 Nailsea United	0-2	3-1	3-1	0-2	1-2	2-2	0-2		2-2	1-2	1-1	3-1	1-2	3-1	0-3	3-1
9 Odd Down (BATH) Res	0-3	1-0	2-2	0-0	0-3	0-7	0-5	0-1		1-5	0-1	1-2	0-3	2-3	2-2	1-1
10 Shirehampton	1-2	2-3	1-2	6-2	1-1	0-4	2-1	2-1	11-1		3-1	3-0	0-3	4-2	3-2	3-1
11 Stockwood Green	2-0	3-0	1-3	3-0	3-2	1-1	1-1	0-0	2-0	0-3		1-2	1-3	4-4	2-0	1-1
12 Stockwood Wanderers	0-1	0-3	0-2	1-2	1-0	0-1	0-3	2-3	4-0	1-2	1-1		0-3	1-1	0-5	2-0
13 Watchet Town	0-0	3-0	2-3	1-2	1-2	1-0	5-1	1-0	P-P	3-0	1-0	3-1		5-1	2-3	0-0
14 Westfield	0-3	3-1	3-2	1-3	1-2	0-2	0-1	1-2	3-2	3-2	0-2	0-2	3-5		1-2	1-0
15 Worle	0-7	0-2	3-2	1-3	3-1	2-1	2-2	4-2	3-1	7-1	2-2	2-3	3-4	2-0		2-2
16 Wrington Redhill	0-3	0-0	1-3	2-2	1-1	0-3	1-2	1-4	0-0	0-13	0-1	1-1	1-0	1-3	2-3	

STAFFORDSHIRE COUNTY SENIOR LEAGUE

RECENT CHAMPIONS

2016: Leek CSOB **2017:** Abbey Hutton United **2018:** Wolstanton United

PREMIER DIVISION	P	W	D	L	F	A	GD	Pts
1 Silverdale Athletic	28	22	2	4	125	30	95	68
2 Leek CSOB	28	20	5	3	103	32	71	65
3 Tunstall Town	28	16	7	5	77	41	36	55
4 Foley Meir	28	17	3	8	99	42	57	54
5 Stafford Town	28	16	2	10	93	48	45	50
6 Alsager Town	28	13	7	8	64	32	32	46
7 Redgate Clayton	28	13	6	9	71	52	19	45
8 Wolstanton United	28	11	7	10	70	40	30	40
9 Brereton Social	28	11	4	13	75	53	22	37
10 Eastwood Hanley	28	10	6	12	76	55	21	36
11 Cheadle Town	28	10	1	17	42	65	-23	31
12 Hanley Town	28	9	2	17	54	68	-14	29
13 Ashbourne	28	7	3	18	49	72	-23	24
14 Walsall Phoenix	28	5	5	18	48	83	-35	20
15 Florence	28	0	0	28	12	345	-333	0

DIVISION TWO	P	W	D	L	F	A	GD	Pts
1 AFC Alsager	26	19	4	3	89	29	60	61
2 AFC Hawkins Sports	26	16	4	6	62	39	23	52
3 Lichfield City Casuals	26	16	3	7	92	46	46	51
4 Chesterton AFC	26	16	3	7	79	47	32	51
5 Hilton Harriers	26	14	5	7	53	50	3	47
6 Newport Town	26	15	1	10	75	62	13	46
7 Coven Athletic	26	15	1	10	75	67	8	46
8 Acorn Albion	26	10	3	13	56	63	-7	33
9 Cannock United	26	8	4	14	44	66	-22	28
10 Eastwood Hanley Res	26	8	4	14	40	67	-27	28
11 Featherstone	26	8	5	13	55	62	-7	26
12 Audley Res	26	6	5	15	26	50	-24	23
13 Cheadle Town Res	26	7	2	17	40	71	-31	23
14 Keele University Res	26	2	0	24	21	88	-67	6

DIVISION ONE	P	W	D	L	F	A	GD	Pts
1 Silverdale Athletic	28	22	2	4	125	30	95	68
2 Leek CSOB	28	20	5	3	103	32	71	65
3 Tunstall Town	28	16	7	5	77	41	36	55
4 Foley Meir	28	17	3	8	99	42	57	54
5 Stafford Town	28	16	2	10	93	48	45	50
6 Alsager Town	28	13	7	8	64	32	32	46
7 Redgate Clayton	28	13	6	9	71	52	19	45
8 Wolstanton United	28	11	7	10	70	40	30	40
9 Brereton Social	28	11	4	13	75	53	22	37
10 Eastwood Hanley	28	10	6	12	76	55	21	36
11 Cheadle Town	28	10	1	17	42	65	-23	31
12 Hanley Town	28	9	2	17	54	68	-14	29
13 Ashbourne	28	7	3	18	49	72	-23	24
14 Walsall Phoenix	28	5	5	18	48	83	-35	20
15 Florence	28	0	0	28	12	345	-333	0

LEAGUE CUPS

LEAGUE CHALLENGE CUP FINAL

Leek CSOB	v	Stafford Town	2-2, 4-5p

PRESIDENT'S TROPHY FINAL

Leek CSOB Res	v	Shenstone Pathfinder	0-4

DIVISION TWO LEAGUE CUP FINAL

AFC Alsager	v	Chesterton AFC	2-0

LEEK CUP FINAL

Alsager Town	v	Leek CSOB	0-2

PREMIER DIVISION	1	2	3	4	5	6	7	8	9	10	11	12	13	14	15
1 Alsager Town		3-0	2-1	0-1	5-0	11-0	1-0	2-2	0-2	3-0	0-3	0-0	0-0	2-0	1-1
2 Ashbourne	0-2		1-2	6-2	1-1	8-1	2-6	5-1	0-6	0-1	1-8	0-1	1-3	4-0	2-1
3 Brereton Social	0-3	2-0		1-2	2-3	25-0	1-4	3-1	0-0	4-2	1-5	2-1	5-6	2-1	0-0
4 Cheadle Town	1-3	1-1	1-3		1-2	10-2	0-6	1-0	1-5	0-2	0-4	0-3	0-2	4-2	2-0
5 Eastwood Hanley	1-4	2-1	1-2	6-0		21-0	1-2	3-2	1-3	5-3	4-4	1-3	0-1	2-2	1-1
6 Florence	1-9	0-3	1-10	2-3	0-8		0-16	0-11	0-11	0-7	0-14	1-15	0-6	1-4	0-11
7 Foley Meir	1-1	2-0	3-1	1-0	4-1	12-0		3-2	1-4	5-3	1-5	2-2	4-1	4-0	1-3
8 Hanley Town	0-4	2-1	2-0	1-5	2-0	7-0	2-1		2-4	1-0	2-0	2-5	2-3	0-0	1-2
9 Leek CSOB	2-0	2-0	1-1	3-0	4-0	23-0	0-5	2-1		2-2	2-4	4-2	2-1	2-2	4-2
10 Redgate Clayton	2-2	5-5	1-0	1-0	0-2	11-1	3-2	4-1	1-3		2-5	4-2	4-1	5-1	1-1
11 Silverdale Athletic	5-1	5-2	6-2	2-0	2-1	16-1	1-0	7-1	3-0	1-1		2-3	5-1	6-0	0-1
12 Stafford Town	2-1	2-0	3-1	3-4	3-1	20-0	4-2	4-0	1-3	1-2	0-3		2-5	5-1	1-3
13 Tunstall Town	0-0	7-1	1-1	1-0	1-1	15-0	1-1	4-1	1-1	2-1	3-1	2-1		3-0	4-3
14 Walsall Phoenix	5-3	1-3	1-3	1-0	0-5	19-0	1-7	0-5	0-5	1-2	0-4	2-3	2-2		1-0
15 Wolstanton United	2-1	3-1	1-0	2-3	2-2	19-1	2-3	5-0	1-3	1-1	0-4	0-1	2-0	1-1	

SUFFOLK & IPSWICH LEAGUE

RECENT CHAMPIONS

2016: Crane Sports **2017:** Henley Athletic **2018:** Achilles

SENIOR DIVISION	P	W	D	L	F	A	GD	Pts
1 Crane Sports	30	23	3	4	100	28	72	72
2 Henley Athletic	30	20	4	6	96	28	68	64
3 Achilles	30	20	3	7	106	44	62	63
4 Claydon	30	16	5	9	74	46	28	53
5 Coplestonians	30	15	7	8	82	54	28	52
6 Haughley United	30	15	6	9	70	49	21	51
7 Bourne Vale United	30	15	6	9	54	47	7	51
8 Benhall St Mary	30	12	9	9	55	40	15	45
9 East Bergholt United	30	13	5	12	67	62	5	44
10 Capel Plough	30	13	4	13	47	57	-10	43
11 Trimley Red Devils	30	11	7	12	45	55	-10	40
12 Westerfield United	30	9	9	12	48	63	-15	36
13 Leiston St Margarets	30	7	5	18	33	85	-52	26
14 Bramford United	30	7	1	22	38	103	-65	22
15 Grundisburgh	30	3	2	25	41	103	-62	11
16 Wenhaston United	30	2	2	26	21	113	-92	8

DIVISION ONE	P	W	D	L	F	A	GD	Pts
1 Old Newton United	24	17	5	2	71	18	53	56
2 Bildeston Rangers	24	16	3	5	66	37	29	51
3 Sporting 87	24	15	6	3	51	26	25	51
4 Bacton United 89	24	13	4	7	62	38	24	43
5 Ransomes Sports	24	11	5	8	51	44	7	38
6 Wickham Market	24	9	7	8	47	42	5	34
7 Stanton	24	9	5	10	39	40	-1	32
8 Stowupland Falcons	24	6	8	10	39	49	-10	26
9 Barham Athletic	24	8	2	14	42	62	-20	26
10 AFC Kesgrave	24	7	4	13	46	63	-17	25
11 Coddenham Athletic	24	5	7	12	36	59	-23	22
12 Mendlesham	24	4	6	14	37	61	-24	18
13 Saxmundham Sports	24	3	4	17	34	82	-48	13

DIVISION TWO	P	W	D	L	F	A	GD	Pts
1 Halesworth Town	23	20	3	0	102	16	86	63
2 Southwold Town	24	19	2	3	67	19	48	59
3 Shotley	24	16	1	7	67	41	26	49
4 Cockfield United	24	13	3	8	66	38	28	42
5 AFC YourShirts	24	13	4	7	66	46	20	41*
6 Ipswich Athletic	24	12	3	9	64	46	18	39
7 Kirton Athletic	24	11	5	8	53	43	10	38
8 Bramford Road Old Boys	24	9	2	13	57	62	-5	29
9 Stonham Aspal	24	8	1	15	42	56	-14	25
10 Tacket Street BBOB	24	8	0	16	51	61	-10	24
11 Somersham	24	7	0	17	37	78	-41	21
12 Kesgrave Kestrels	23	5	0	18	47	95	-48	15
13 Ipswich Valley Rangers	24	1	2	21	22	140	-118	5

DIVISION THREE	P	W	D	L	F	A	GD	Pts
1 Bedricks Worth	20	18	0	2	91	25	66	54
2 Tattingstone United	20	14	3	3	84	43	41	45
3 Ufford Sports	20	13	2	5	81	38	43	41
4 Thurston	19	11	0	8	66	51	15	33
5 Woolverstone United	20	10	1	9	65	52	13	31
6 Witnesham Wasps	20	9	3	8	42	36	6	30
7 Bardwell Sports	19	6	3	10	41	42	-1	21
8 Elmswell	20	6	3	11	44	73	-29	21
9 Felixstowe Rangers	20	6	3	11	50	71	-21	19*
10 Wortham	20	2	5	13	36	83	-47	11
11 Sutton Heath Saxons	18	1	1	16	19	105	-86	2*

DIVISION FOUR	P	W	D	L	F	A	GD	Pts
1 Whitton United 'A'	22	20	1	1	73	20	53	61
2 Saxmundham Sports Res	22	15	3	4	61	33	28	48
3 Claydon 'A'	22	15	2	5	75	40	35	47
4 Occold	22	15	3	4	75	34	41	42*
5 Hope Church	22	10	3	9	60	38	22	33
6 Bacton United 89 'A'	22	9	6	7	68	51	17	33
7 Elmswell Res	22	8	3	11	46	63	-17	27
8 Old Newton United 'A'	22	8	2	12	33	44	-11	26
9 AFC Kesgrave 'A'	22	6	1	15	41	51	-10	19
10 Tacket Street BBOB Res	22	4	6	12	35	65	-30	18
11 Woolverstone United Res	22	3	2	17	30	103	-73	11
12 Bramford Road Old Boys Res	22	3	0	19	27	82	-55	9

LEAGUE CUPS

BOB COLEMAN CUP FINAL

Henley Athletic v Crane Sports 1-0 (aet)

TRAVEL PLUS TOURS CUP FINAL

Achilles Res v Trimley Red Devils Res 1-4 (aet)

CLUB COLOURS CUP FINAL

Thurston v Framlingham Town A 5-3

PREMIER DIVISION	1	2	3	4	5	6	7	8	9	10	11	12	13	14	15	16
1 Achilles		2-0	4-0	12-0	2-0	0-1	3-1	1-2	3-1	12-2	3-2	0-3	3-1	6-1	5-1	4-0
2 Benhall St Mary	0-0		1-1	2-1	1-2	2-1	4-1	0-1	3-0	2-2	0-1	4-3	5-0	1-2	4-1	2-2
3 Bourne Vale United	2-0	1-1		2-0	3-2	2-1	2-3	2-1	3-0	4-0	3-4	0-1	2-0	1-1	2-1	1-2
4 Bramford United	2-7	1-3	0-2		1-3	1-2	1-4	2-6	0-4	3-2	0-6	1-3	4-2	1-0	4-2	1-4
5 Capel Plough	1-2	2-2	2-3	4-2		0-5	0-2	1-2	1-3	4-1	2-5	0-5	1-0	2-0	3-1	2-0
6 Claydon	3-3	2-1	1-2	3-1	3-4		2-2	0-3	2-1	7-3	4-2	0-0	6-0	4-1	5-0	4-1
7 Coplestonians	2-1	2-2	2-2	2-3	2-3	4-2		0-5	7-1	3-1	2-1	1-1	7-1	4-4	5-0	3-1
8 Crane Sports	1-3	0-0	4-2	9-0	2-0	3-0	2-1		3-1	3-0	1-1	0-3	9-0	3-0	4-1	4-1
9 East Bergholt United	5-2	0-1	3-2	3-0	3-1	2-1	2-2	3-5		3-3	3-1	0-0	4-1	2-3	5-0	2-2
10 Grundisburgh	2-3	1-5	1-2	1-2	0-2	1-4	3-6	1-7	1-5		0-1	0-3	0-2	0-1	8-2	0-1
11 Haughley United	1-3	0-3	4-0	2-1	0-1	1-1	2-1	1-1	4-1	4-2		0-4	2-2	3-3	4-0	3-3
12 Henley Athletic	5-1	6-0	4-2	6-1	4-0	1-2	1-2	0-2	2-3	1-2	3-2		2-0	2-2	9-0	5-1
13 Leiston St Margarets	0-7	0-4	2-2	0-1	1-1	2-2	1-4	2-1	2-1	4-1	0-5	0-4		1-2	2-0	2-0
14 Trimley Red Devils	1-2	2-0	0-0	3-2	0-1	2-1	2-1	1-5	2-3	6-1	0-1	0-3	2-2		1-0	1-1
15 Wenhaston United	1-9	0-0	1-2	3-1	1-1	0-3	0-5	1-5	4-2	0-2	0-3	0-8	0-2	0-2		1-3
16 Westerfield United	3-3	3-2	1-2	1-1	1-1	1-2	1-1	0-6	1-1	1-0	2-4	2-4	3-1	2-0	4-0	

SURREY ELITE INTERMEDIATE LEAGUE

RECENT CHAMPIONS

2016: Horsley **2017:** Virginia Water **2018:** Tooting Bec

		P	W	D	L	F	A	GD	Pts
1	AFC Cubo	28	19	4	5	86	34	52	61
2	Battersea Ironsides	28	17	5	6	83	45	38	56
3	Spartans Youth	28	17	7	4	75	36	39	55*
4	Westside	28	16	7	5	62	33	29	55
5	Chessington KC	28	15	3	10	72	64	8	51*
6	Horsley	28	14	3	11	83	68	15	45
7	Staines Lammas	28	13	5	10	68	46	22	44
8	Merrow	28	12	6	10	60	48	12	42
9	Royal Holloway Old Boys	28	12	5	11	60	43	17	41
10	NPL	28	10	7	11	60	58	2	37
11	Worcester Park	28	7	7	14	52	77	-25	28
12	Ripley Village	28	6	6	16	41	86	-45	24
13	AFC Spelthorne Sports	28	4	10	14	40	66	-26	22
14	Farleigh Rovers	28	7	1	20	39	89	-50	22
15	West End Village	28	2	2	24	39	127	-88	8

LEAGUE CUP

CHALLENGE CUP FINAL

NPL v Battersea Ironsides 2-1

		1	2	3	4	5	6	7	8	9	10	11	12	13	14	15
1	AFC Cubo		4-1	1-4	0-1	8-0	5-2	3-0	3-0	2-1	4-3	4-0	6-1	13-0	2-1	3-1
2	AFC Spelthorne Sports	2-5		0-1	1-2	2-6	2-4	1-1	2-2	1-1	1-1	2-1	1-2	3-3	2-2	2-3
3	Battersea Ironsides	3-1	1-1		3-4	1-0	4-5	1-0	3-3	6-0	4-1	0-0	3-6	5-0	0-3	5-1
4	Chessington KC	1-1	3-3	3-1		2-0	3-3	1-2	1-3	4-0	1-2	2-6	3-1	3-1	3-1	4-3
5	Farleigh Rovers	1-2	2-0	1-6	1-4		2-7	1-2	3-5	0-5	0-3	1-0	2-1	0-4	0-1	0-2
6	Horsley	1-3	2-0	5-8	4-3	1-4		3-2	2-2	7-3	2-1	0-1	1-0	7-2	0-1	2-2
7	Merrow	1-1	4-3	0-1	3-2	3-1	4-2		0-0	0-1	0-1	1-2	1-3	9-1	0-2	4-1
8	N P L	0-3	2-3	2-3	3-4	4-1	1-0	0-2		6-3	0-0	1-1	2-1	7-2	2-2	4-2
9	Ripley Village	2-0	0-0	3-5	0-9	2-4	2-1	1-3	3-0		0-6	1-1	0-2	2-1	1-3	1-1
10	Royal Holloway Old Boys	2-3	1-1	3-1	2-0	7-2	1-2	2-3	0-2	5-2		3-4	3-1	4-1	1-1	1-2
11	Spartans Youth	3-2	3-1	1-1	8-0	3-2	3-1	3-3	3-1	5-1	2-1		0-0	2-1	1-1	5-2
12	Staines Lammas	2-2	5-0	0-4	6-2	4-0	1-2	2-2	2-0	7-1	0-0	1-2		4-3	1-2	1-1
13	West End Village	0-2	3-1	0-5	2-3	0-4	2-8	2-4	2-5	2-2	0-3	0-7	0-7		0-5	3-4
14	Westside	0-0	1-2	0-3	4-1	10-1	4-2	3-2	3-2	3-3	2-0	3-1	0-1	2-1		1-1
15	Worcester Park	1-3	1-2	1-1	0-3	0-0	2-7	4-4	4-1	2-0	2-3	0-7	3-6	6-3	0-1	

THAMES VALLEY PREMIER LEAGUE

RECENT CHAMPIONS

2016: Reading YMCA **2017:** Reading YMCA **2018:** Reading YMCA

PREMIER DIVISION	P	W	D	L	F	A	GD	Pts
1 Marlow United	22	17	3	2	67	19	48	54
2 Cookham Dean	22	16	3	3	57	29	28	51
3 Woodcote Stoke Row	22	13	6	3	57	24	33	45
4 Mortimer	22	12	2	8	46	34	12	38
5 Berks County FC	22	10	5	7	46	36	10	35
6 Westwood United	22	9	4	9	32	39	-7	31
7 Burghfield FC	22	9	4	9	31	38	-7	31
8 Wraysbury Village	22	8	4	10	50	35	15	28
9 Richings Park	22	7	3	12	35	48	-13	24
10 Wokingham & Emmbrook Res	22	6	1	15	30	53	-23	19
11 Reading City U23	22	4	2	16	22	55	-33	14
12 Woodley United Royals	22	2	1	19	22	85	-63	7

DIVISION ONE	P	W	D	L	F	A	GD	Pts
1 Newbury FC	20	17	2	1	74	12	62	53
2 Maidenhead Town	20	12	2	6	64	39	25	41*
3 Westwood United Res	20	11	2	7	38	36	2	35
4 FC Imaan Lions	19	8	6	5	45	39	6	27*
5 Reading YMCA Rapids	20	9	4	7	43	37	6	27*
6 Finchampstead	19	7	5	7	40	32	8	26
7 Rotherfield United	20	6	4	10	31	44	-13	25*
8 Hurst	20	6	6	8	31	40	-9	24
9 Cookham Dean Res	19	5	5	9	28	35	-7	20
10 Eldon Celtic	17	5	2	10	28	43	-15	16*
11 White Eagles	20	2	0	18	21	86	-65	5*

DIVISION TWO	P	W	D	L	F	A	GD	Pts
1 Wargrave	20	15	1	4	80	28	52	46
2 Mortimer Res	20	13	5	2	65	29	36	44
3 Woodcote Stoke Row Res	20	10	5	5	59	43	16	35
4 Maidenhead Town Res	20	9	3	8	48	41	7	30
5 Hurst Res	20	7	6	7	47	53	-6	27
6 Richings Park Res	20	8	3	9	37	52	-15	27
7 Phoenix Old Boys	20	6	7	7	37	38	-1	25
8 Harchester Hawks	20	6	3	11	33	49	-16	21
9 AFC Corinthians	20	6	1	13	28	69	-41	19
10 Marlow United Res	20	5	3	12	36	57	-21	18
11 Goring United	20	4	5	11	35	46	-11	17

DIVISION THREE	P	W	D	L	F	A	GD	Pts
1 Henley Town	18	12	2	4	44	23	21	38
2 Woodley United 'A'	18	11	2	5	39	37	2	35
3 Twyford & Ruscombe	17	11	1	5	52	32	20	34
4 Hambleden	18	10	2	6	45	32	13	32
5 Berks County Res	18	10	0	8	47	37	10	26*
6 Taplow United 'A'	17	7	5	5	41	35	6	26
7 Maidenhead Town 'A'	18	7	1	10	38	56	-18	22
8 Pangbourne	18	6	3	9	31	33	-2	21
9 Cintra Park Rovers	18	3	3	12	12	18	-6	12
10 Goring United Res	18	1	3	14	17	63	-46	9*

DIVISION FOUR	P	W	D	L	F	A	GD	Pts
1 Datchet Village	16	13	2	1	77	22	55	41
2 Westwood United Dev	16	11	2	3	42	24	18	35
3 Berks County Rovers	16	9	2	5	50	34	16	29
4 Farnham Royal Mavericks	16	7	0	9	22	38	-16	21
5 AFC Corinthians 'A'	16	5	4	7	19	29	-10	19
6 Harchester Hawks Dev	16	5	2	9	33	38	-5	17
7 Phoenix Old Boys Res	16	5	2	9	23	39	-16	17
8 Taplow United Res	16	4	4	8	26	44	-18	16
9 Henley Town Dev	16	4	0	12	24	48	-24	12

LEAGUE CUPS

SENIOR CUP FINAL

Marlow United	v	Mortimer	2-1

INTERMEDIATE CUP FINAL

Wargrave	v	Westwood United Res	3-0

JUNIOR CUP FINAL

Harchester Hawks Dev	v	Datchet Village	2-4

PREMIER DIVISION	1	2	3	4	5	6	7	8	9	10	11	12
1 Berks County FC		1-1	1-2	2-2	1-0	3-2	7-1	3-1	3-1	H-W	3-0	1-4
2 Burghfield FC	2-1		0-4	0-2	0-3	1-1	1-0	1-1	2-3	0-4	2-2	1-5
3 Cookham Dean	1-1	2-1		1-1	4-2	2-1	2-1	1-3	4-1	3-6	1-0	2-0
4 Marlow United	4-1	2-0	1-2		0-2	3-0	6-1	3-2	H-W	0-0	4-2	2-0
5 Mortimer	2-3	1-4	1-4	1-3		3-0	1-0	2-1	3-0	3-3	7-1	HW
6 Reading City U23	3-1	0-2	0-5	0-7	1-3		0-1	0-1	0-2	1-5	4-1	2-2
7 Richings Park	3-1	0-2	2-6	0-4	2-1	1-3		0-2	4-1	0-1	8-3	0-5
8 Westwood United	1-7	0-2	0-2	0-3	2-2	4-2	0-0		2-0	0-0	3-0	HW
9 Wokingham & Emmbrook Res	1-1	0-2	2-6	1-3	1-4	2-0	0-4	2-3		1-3	3-1	3-0
10 Woodcote Stoke Row	1-1	4-3	4-1	2-5	2-3	4-1	0-0	4-1	3-0		3-0	1-0
11 Woodley United Royals	3-1	2-3	0-1	0-6	0-1	2-0	0-5	2-4	0-3	0-6		0-9
12 Wraysbury Village	1-3	0-1	1-1	2-6	2-1	0-1	2-2	3-1	5-3	1-1	8-3	

WEARSIDE LEAGUE

RECENT CHAMPIONS

2016: Stockton Town **2017:** Jarrow FC **2018:** Redcar Athletic

		P	W	D	L	F	A	GD	Pts
1	Hebburn Town Res	30	24	3	3	84	22	62	75
2	Sunderland West End	30	23	2	5	93	37	56	71
3	Wolviston	30	20	3	7	101	51	50	63
4	Richmond Town	30	18	3	9	71	41	30	57
5	Silksworth Colliery Welfare	30	17	5	8	73	49	24	56
6	Harton and Westoe CW	30	16	7	7	91	49	42	55
7	Hartlepool	30	16	4	10	79	49	30	52
8	Horden Community Welfare	30	16	1	13	76	53	23	49
9	Annfield Plain	30	11	3	16	58	74	-16	36
10	Gateshead Leam Rangers	30	10	2	18	61	83	-22	32
11	Boldon CA	30	9	4	17	49	80	-31	31
12	Darlington RA	30	9	3	18	57	87	-30	30
13	Darlington Town	30	9	2	19	64	77	-13	29
14	Windscale	30	8	2	20	49	89	-40	26
15	West Auckland Tunns	30	5	6	19	45	96	-51	21
16	Coxhoe Athletic	30	3	2	25	39	153	-114	11

LEAGUE CUPS

MONKWEARMOUTH CHARITY CUP FINAL
Silksworth Colliery Welfare v Richmond Town 1-0

SHIPOWNERS CHARITY CUP FINAL
Hebburn Town Res v Horden Community Welfare 1-2

ALAN HOOD CHARITY CUP FINAL
Gateshead Leam Rangers v Silksworth Colliery Welfare 1-1, 5-6p

		1	2	3	4	5	6	7	8	9	10	11	12	13	14	15	16
1	Annfield Plain		1-0	5-3	3-2	6-5	0-3	3-2	0-2	1-4	0-3	0-4	1-0	2-3	4-0	0-1	3-4
2	Boldon CA	1-3		4-2	2-3	2-2	2-0	1-2	1-6	0-2	1-2	0-1	2-2	0-9	3-1	3-2	1-6
3	Coxhoe Athletic	0-3	2-4		2-1	2-4	3-0	1-11	1-7	0-7	1-5	1-7	4-5	1-9	2-2	1-8	0-9
4	Darlington RA	0-6	2-6	3-4		2-1	1-2	1-1	2-5	1-3	0-1	3-2	3-3	0-3	1-0	3-4	1-7
5	Darlington Town	10-2	3-4	3-2	2-4		3-5	0-2	6-1	0-1	2-3	4-2	0-3	0-4	2-2	2-0	3-1
6	Gateshead Leam Rangers	0-5	3-0	3-1	0-3	5-2		1-2	3-3	2-4	0-6	1-3	2-5	1-5	2-1	9-0	0-8
7	Hartlepool	1-0	6-0	4-2	2-4	2-0	4-1		2-2	2-5	3-2	0-1	3-0	2-0	2-3	6-0	3-4
8	Harton and Westoe CW	2-1	3-3	6-0	2-2	3-2	5-1	4-0		2-3	4-3	1-2	0-1	3-0	6-1	5-0	2-2
9	Hebburn Town Reserves	2-2	2-1	4-0	2-0	1-0	1-0	1-1	1-0		4-1	5-0	1-2	3-1	9-1	5-0	2-1
10	Horden Community Welfare	4-0	0-2	7-0	7-3	4-1	1-5	1-4	3-2	0-1		3-4	0-2	1-4	8-1	4-0	0-2
11	Richmond Town	6-1	1-1	6-1	3-0	0-2	2-1	2-2	5-0	1-1	0-1		1-0	0-3	3-0	2-0	4-2
12	Silksworth Colliery Welfare	1-1	3-2	8-0	2-3	3-0	2-1	0-3	1-4	1-0	1-1	2-0		2-4	4-1	6-2	4-1
13	Sunderland West End	2-0	4-0	2-1	4-1	1-2	2-2	2-0	1-1	2-1	2-1	1-0	4-0		8-1	5-3	1-7
14	West Auckland Tunns	5-2	3-1	2-2	3-5	4-1	2-4	2-3	0-6	0-4	0-2	1-4	1-1	1-2		0-0	1-3
15	Windscale	1-1	1-2	7-0	2-1	1-0	4-3	3-2	0-2	0-3	0-1	2-4	3-5	1-2	1-5		1-3
16	Wolviston	3-2	3-0	3-2	3-2	5-2	3-1	3-2	2-2	0-2	4-1	2-1	1-4	0-3	1-1	4-2	

WEST CHESHIRE LEAGUE

RECENT CHAMPIONS

2016: South Liverpool **2017:** Newton **2018:** South Liverpool

DIVISION ONE	P	W	D	L	F	A	GD	Pts
1 Newton (Wirral)	30	23	4	3	98	44	54	73
2 Rainhill Town	30	18	7	5	76	51	25	61
3 Mossley Hill Athletic	30	18	4	8	65	34	31	58
4 Maghull	30	17	5	8	61	42	19	56
5 South Liverpool	30	16	3	11	81	57	24	51
6 Upton AA	30	15	3	12	69	61	8	48
7 Ellesmere Port Town	30	14	5	11	61	51	10	47
8 Vauxhall Motors FC Res	30	13	6	11	57	48	9	45
9 Ashville	30	14	3	13	71	64	7	45
10 Richmond Raith Rovers	30	12	7	11	72	72	0	43
11 Redgate Rovers	30	13	2	15	56	71	-15	41
12 Hale	30	11	5	14	57	66	-9	38
13 Neston Nomads	30	8	3	19	56	85	-29	27
14 Chester Nomads	30	7	5	18	44	76	-32	26
15 Marshalls	30	6	4	20	54	74	-20	22
16 West Kirby	30	1	2	27	22	104	-82	5

DIVISION TWO	P	W	D	L	F	A	GD	Pts
1 Page Celtic	26	20	3	3	67	28	39	63
2 Capenhurst Villa	26	19	2	5	63	29	34	59
3 Heswall	26	17	3	6	67	44	23	54
4 Cheshire Lines	26	14	4	8	51	45	6	46
5 South Liverpool Res	26	11	8	7	62	39	23	41
6 Mallaby	26	13	2	11	72	61	11	41
7 Maghull Reserve	26	9	7	10	55	52	3	34
8 Mossley Hill Athletic Res	26	10	4	12	48	55	-7	34
9 West Kirby Res	26	10	4	12	43	57	-14	34
10 Rainhill Town Reserve	26	9	5	12	53	57	-4	32
11 Litherland Remyca Dev	26	7	2	17	42	76	-34	23
12 Ashville Res	26	5	6	15	34	59	-25	21
13 Wirral SB FC Team	26	6	2	18	31	55	-24	20
14 Prescot Cables Reserve	26	5	2	19	33	64	-31	17

DIVISION THREE	P	W	D	L	F	A	GD	Pts
1 Aintree Villa	24	21	1	2	108	20	88	64
2 South Sefton Borough Res	24	19	1	4	102	43	59	58
3 Mersey Royal	24	16	4	4	80	33	47	52
4 Poulton Royal	24	12	8	4	62	37	25	44
5 Capenhurst Villa Res	24	12	4	8	57	57	0	40
6 Burscough Dynamo	24	11	2	11	62	62	0	35
7 Neston Nomads Res	24	11	1	12	50	62	-12	34
8 Chester Nomads Res	24	9	3	12	46	56	-10	30
9 Marshalls Reserve	24	8	2	14	59	63	-4	26
10 Heswall Res	24	7	1	16	42	71	-29	22
11 Wirral SB FC Res	24	6	1	17	36	57	-21	19
12 Redgate Rovers Res	24	6	0	18	33	60	-27	18
13 Ellesmere Port Town Res	24	3	2	19	22	138	-116	11

LEAGUE CUPS

HOWARTH & GALLAGHER BOWL FINAL

Capenhurst Villa v Page Celtic 0-1

PYKE CUP FINAL

Ellesmere Port Town v Redgate Rovers 0-1

SHIELD FINAL

Aintree Villa v Mersey Royal 2-0

PREMIER DIVISION	1	2	3	4	5	6	7	8	9	10	11	12	13	14	15	16
1 Ashville		3-2	3-1	4-1	0-2	3-1	0-1	3-2	2-3	2-2	6-1	3-4	3-6	6-1	2-1	6-0
2 Chester Nomads	1-1		1-2	2-0	0-3	2-1	0-1	2-1	2-5	1-2	0-3	2-1	0-5	1-2	3-1	7-1
3 Ellesmere Port Town	0-3	5-2		4-0	2-1	3-2	1-1	2-1	1-3	2-3	0-1	4-1	2-0	0-2	0-1	2-0
4 Hale	1-1	4-2	0-5		2-2	1-0	2-1	2-2	3-2	1-3	2-1	2-0	1-3	1-1	2-2	3-0
5 Maghull	4-1	1-0	1-1	3-1		2-0	1-2	6-2	0-0	2-1	5-1	3-1	1-3	2-6	1-0	4-0
6 Marshalls	1-3	0-0	1-2	6-2	2-1		6-2	1-2	0-3	4-4	8-1	4-1	2-3	1-5	0-6	3-2
7 Mossley Hill Athletic	2-3	5-0	1-0	5-0	3-1	2-1		4-2	1-1	1-2	2-1	2-0	3-0	2-3	1-2	4-0
8 Neston Nomads	1-3	5-0	0-5	0-7	3-4	2-1	1-3		0-3	4-3	1-3	2-2	3-1	0-1	0-5	7-1
9 Newton (Wirral)	3-1	3-3	3-1	3-2	4-0	4-1	2-1	3-0		1-2	1-0	4-0	6-2	5-4	4-2	5-1
10 Rainhill Town	4-2	5-2	3-3	HW	2-1	1-0	0-0	2-3	3-6		0-1	3-3	1-1	3-1	2-1	5-0
11 Redgate Rovers	3-0	2-2	1-3	3-6	1-3	6-1	3-2	2-1	3-3	1-4		1-3	0-5	4-1	4-1	3-1
12 Richmond Raith Rovers	2-1	4-2	6-1	2-1	2-2	3-2	AW	2-2	4-2	2-2	2-4		5-4	3-3	5-3	4-1
13 South Liverpool	5-2	1-2	5-3	2-1	0-2	2-2	0-2	7-0	3-5	1-2	2-0	3-1		3-0	0-3	4-1
14 Upton AA	6-0	5-1	1-1	3-1	0-1	5-3	1-3	3-2	0-4	2-3	1-0	3-4	1-3		1-0	5-1
15 Vauxhall Motors FC Res	3-2	2-0	1-1	1-2	2-2	0-0	1-1	4-3	2-3	0-5	4-0	3-2	2-2	2-0		1-0
16 West Kirby	0-2	2-2	3-4	1-3	A-W	1-0	0-7	0-4	0-4	0-2	1-2	3-3	1-5	1-2	0-1	

WEST LANCASHIRE LEAGUE

RECENT CHAMPIONS

2016: Blackpool Wren Rovers **2017:** Longridge Town **2018:** Garstang

PREMIER DIVISION	P	W	D	L	F	A	GD	Pts
1 Fulwood Amateurs	30	20	4	6	86	42	44	64
2 Slyne with Hest	30	19	7	4	79	47	32	64
3 Thornton Cleveleys	30	18	3	9	77	56	21	57
4 Poulton	30	17	4	9	82	61	21	55
5 Turton	30	16	3	11	46	44	2	51
6 Vickerstown	30	14	3	13	57	47	10	45
7 Tempest United	30	12	8	10	55	60	-5	44
8 Burscough Richmond	30	12	4	14	52	54	-2	40
9 Blackpool Wren Rovers	30	11	6	13	47	61	-14	39
10 Euxton Villa	30	11	5	14	59	55	4	38
11 Hurst Green	30	11	3	16	50	58	-8	36
12 Southport Hesketh	30	9	8	13	52	70	-18	35
13 Whitehaven	30	10	4	16	48	55	-7	34
14 Hesketh Bank	30	9	5	16	47	66	-19	32
15 Coppull United	30	9	3	18	55	78	-23	30
16 Haslingden St Marys	30	5	4	21	36	74	-38	13*

DIVISION ONE	P	W	D	L	F	A	GD	Pts
1 Lytham Town	24	15	3	6	62	37	25	48
2 CMB	24	14	5	5	70	41	29	47
3 Hawcoat Park	24	11	8	5	60	37	23	41
4 Lostock St Gerards	24	14	3	7	57	45	12	39*
5 Stoneclough	24	12	3	9	51	40	11	39
6 Millom	24	10	6	8	47	34	13	36
7 Eagley	24	11	3	10	60	60	0	36
8 Kendal County	24	9	4	11	49	52	-3	31
9 Crooklands Casuals	24	9	2	13	41	58	-17	29
10 Ulverston Rangers	24	8	7	9	45	47	-2	28*
11 Milnthorpe Corinthians	24	7	4	13	40	47	-7	25
12 Wyre Villa	24	6	3	15	33	75	-42	14*
13 Askam United	24	2	5	17	32	74	-42	11

DIVISION TWO	P	W	D	L	F	A	GD	Pts
1 Horwich St Mary's Victoria	22	15	6	1	65	27	38	51
2 Croston Sports	22	16	3	3	65	30	35	51
3 Walney Island	22	10	7	5	63	40	23	37
4 Dalton United	22	9	9	4	52	36	16	36
5 Furness Rovers	22	11	2	9	51	53	-2	35
6 Charnock Richard Res	22	9	3	10	44	40	4	30
7 Kendal United	22	7	5	10	41	45	-4	26
8 Garstang Res	22	6	7	9	47	56	-9	25
9 Furness Cavaliers	22	5	6	11	32	59	-27	21
10 Mill Hill St Peters	22	5	6	11	30	52	-22	18*
11 Longridge Town Res	22	4	3	15	27	67	-40	15
12 Galgate	22	5	3	14	42	54	-12	14*

RESERVE DIVISION ONE	P	W	D	L	F	A	GD	Pts
1 Tempest United Res	22	15	2	5	69	41	28	47
2 Lostock St Gerards Res	22	13	4	5	49	26	23	43
3 Turton Res	22	12	2	8	42	39	3	38
4 Fulwood Amateurs Res	22	11	3	8	61	44	17	36
5 Hurst Green Res	22	10	4	8	68	45	23	34
6 CMB Res	22	10	3	9	48	54	-6	33
7 Euxton Villa Res	22	8	8	6	49	44	5	32
8 Thornton Cleveleys Res	22	10	1	11	48	42	6	31
9 Poulton Res	22	8	6	8	44	50	-6	27*
10 Burscough Richmond Res	22	6	4	12	34	67	-33	22
11 Eagley Res	22	6	3	13	35	51	-16	18*
12 Haslingden St Marys Res	22	2	2	18	35	79	-44	8

RESERVE DIVISION TWO	P	W	D	L	F	A	GD	Pts
1 Blackpool Wren Rovers Res	20	15	4	1	85	34	51	49
2 Slyne with Hest Res	20	15	2	3	76	33	43	47
3 Lytham Town Res	20	15	2	3	67	24	43	47
4 Coppull United Res	20	10	3	7	54	42	12	33
5 Stoneclough Res	20	7	3	10	39	45	-6	24
6 Thornton Cleveleys A	20	7	3	10	34	51	-17	24
7 Croston Sports Res	20	7	2	11	48	59	-11	23
8 Horwich St Mary's Victoria Res	20	6	4	10	35	44	-9	22
9 Hesketh Bank Res	20	7	1	12	43	67	-24	22
10 Milnthorpe Corinthians Res	20	5	2	13	42	70	-28	17
11 Wyre Villa Res	20	3	0	17	26	80	-54	9

LEAGUE CUPS

RICHARDSON CUP FINAL

Turton v Coppull United 2-0

PRESIDENT'S CUP FINAL

Lostock St Gerards v CMB 1-4

CHALLENGE CUP FINAL

Furness Cavaliers v Walney Island 1-7

STEWART ROWE MEMORIAL CUP FINAL

Poulton Res v Thornton Cleveleys Res 2-1

PREMIER DIVISION	1	2	3	4	5	6	7	8	9	10	11	12	13	14	15	16
1 Blackpool Wren Rovers		3-3	1-2	1-1	0-2	3-1	2-0	1-0	1-2	2-2	1-0	3-1	2-1	2-3	1-1	0-1
2 Burscough Richmond	3-0		2-4	3-2	1-3	1-1	0-1	2-0	7-1	0-3	1-1	0-1	1-2	0-3	3-2	1-0
3 Coppull United	3-2	0-1		2-0	2-3	5-0	1-0	3-4	3-4	2-2	3-4	3-2	6-3	0-2	1-7	1-1
4 Euxton Villa	2-2	3-2	0-1		2-3	4-3	3-2	1-2	2-1	5-1	2-2	1-1	3-1	0-2	1-2	3-1
5 Fulwood Amateurs	2-3	2-1	5-0	3-2		4-1	2-1	3-1	4-1	2-2	2-2	2-0	4-1	5-2	2-0	3-0
6 Haslingden St Marys	2-0	1-3	4-0	3-6	0-4		2-4	2-1	0-2	1-2	0-0	1-1	0-2	0-1	3-0	1-1
7 Hesketh Bank	2-3	1-2	2-1	2-0	0-5	2-4		2-0	1-7	2-5	2-3	1-1	1-2	2-1	1-1	3-1
8 Hurst Green	1-2	3-1	5-1	2-1	3-3	4-0	0-0		0-5	1-4	3-1	2-2	0-3	1-2	2-0	3-5
9 Poulton	3-2	6-2	5-3	3-1	3-2	5-1	3-1	2-3		1-1	1-1	1-2	2-5	5-1	3-2	2-1
10 Slyne with Hest	7-0	2-0	3-2	3-1	4-3	2-0	4-3	2-0	2-2		7-2	4-2	1-1	2-0	1-1	2-1
11 Southport Hesketh	2-1	2-6	2-2	1-0	4-2	2-1	1-2	1-4	0-5	3-0		1-2	2-4	1-1	1-2	4-1
12 Tempest United	3-5	1-2	3-2	0-4	1-1	4-2	3-3	0-3	2-2	4-3	1-2		3-2	3-3	1-4	3-0
13 Thornton Cleveleys	2-2	2-1	3-2	3-1	0-5	3-1	4-0	2-1	4-0	6-1	4-4	2-3		4-1	3-1	1-0
14 Turton	0-1	0-0	2-0	1-3	2-1	2-1	1-3	2-0	4-1	0-3	3-1	0-1	2-1		2-1	1-0
15 Vickerstown	5-0	3-0	1-0	1-4	0-2	5-0	1-0	4-1	2-0	0-2	3-1	0-2	3-4	1-0		4-1
16 Whitehaven	4-1	1-3	5-0	1-1	3-2	1-0	3-3	1-0	1-4	0-2	4-1	1-2	3-2	1-2	5-0	

WEST YORKSHIRE LEAGUE

RECENT CHAMPIONS

2016: Beeston St Anthony's **2017:** Carlton Athletic **2018:** Carlton Athletic

PREMIER DIVISION	P	W	D	L	F	A	GD	Pts
1 Carlton Athletic	30	25	4	1	104	25	79	79
2 Leeds City	30	22	3	5	91	37	54	69
3 Beeston St Anthony	30	20	4	6	86	46	40	64
4 Ilkley Town	30	18	5	7	82	42	40	59
5 Hunslet Club	30	15	9	6	71	49	22	54
6 Whitkirk Wanderers	30	14	4	12	51	47	4	46
7 Huddersfield Amateur	30	12	5	13	63	62	1	41
8 Knaresborough Town	30	11	8	11	54	59	-5	41
9 Horbury Town	30	11	7	12	51	50	1	40
10 Field	29	12	4	13	56	64	-8	40
11 Robin Hood Athletic	30	10	7	13	59	64	-5	37
12 Sherburn White Rose	30	9	2	19	52	88	-36	29
13 Rawdon Old Boys	30	8	2	20	45	71	-26	26
14 Headingley	29	7	4	18	40	62	-22	25
15 Salts First	30	7	1	22	46	108	-62	22
16 Wyke Wanderers	30	2	3	25	25	102	-77	9

DIVISION ONE	P	W	D	L	F	A	GD	Pts
1 Boroughbridge	30	23	3	4	94	42	52	72
2 Hall Green United	30	20	5	5	91	40	51	65
3 Aberford Albion	30	19	4	7	72	46	26	61
4 Newsome	30	18	2	10	70	43	27	56
5 Kirk Deighton Rangers	30	16	5	9	80	61	19	53
6 Hartshead	30	14	3	13	87	65	22	45
7 Otley Town	30	11	11	8	82	66	16	44
8 Kippax	30	12	5	13	58	62	-4	41
9 East End Park	30	13	2	15	61	73	-12	41
10 Oxenhope Recreation	30	12	5	13	66	82	-16	41
11 Featherstone Colliery	30	12	3	15	67	76	-9	39
12 Wetherby Athletic	30	9	4	17	56	75	-19	31
13 Pool	30	9	4	17	49	70	-21	31
14 Leeds Modernians	30	8	4	18	37	76	-39	28
15 Rothwell	30	7	4	19	39	70	-31	25
16 Howden Clough	30	4	2	24	40	102	-62	14

DIVISION TWO	P	W	D	L	F	A	GD	Pts
1 Campion	26	22	2	2	90	25	65	68
2 Glasshoughton Rock	26	18	5	3	106	40	66	59
3 Shelley	26	19	1	6	79	30	49	58
4 Huddersfield YM	26	18	4	4	76	38	38	58
5 Swillington Saints	26	15	3	8	77	50	27	48
6 Altofts	26	11	4	11	71	60	11	37
7 Kellingley Welfare	26	11	4	11	60	64	-4	37
8 Old Centralians	26	10	5	11	68	77	-9	35
9 Ripon City	26	10	3	13	77	81	-4	33
10 Tingley Athletic	26	7	3	16	42	77	-35	24
11 Hunsworth	26	7	3	16	54	101	-47	24
12 Brighouse Old Boys	26	4	4	18	34	90	-56	16
13 Knaresborough Celtic	26	3	5	18	46	87	-41	14
14 Baildon Trinity Athletic	26	3	2	21	37	97	-60	11

ALLIANCE DIVISION ONE	P	W	D	L	F	A	GD	Pts
1 Field Res	26	20	2	4	104	35	69	62
2 Beeston St Anthony Res	26	19	1	6	111	38	73	58
3 Whitkirk Wanderers Res	26	18	3	5	105	52	53	57
4 Robin Hood Athletic Res	26	16	3	7	78	60	18	51
5 Leeds City Res	26	15	4	7	80	46	34	49
6 Hunslet Club Res	26	12	6	8	71	59	12	42
7 Huddersfield Amateur Res	26	10	8	8	67	61	6	38
8 Hall Green United Res	26	11	3	12	72	65	7	36
9 Headingley Res	26	9	2	15	52	78	-26	29
10 Hartshead FC Res	26	7	4	15	53	78	-25	25
11 Horbury Town Res	26	7	4	15	51	97	-46	25
12 Aberford Albion Res	26	6	3	17	48	110	-62	21
13 Oxenhope Recreation Res	26	5	3	18	56	95	-39	18
14 Leeds Modernians Res	26	2	4	20	32	106	-74	10

ALLIANCE DIVISION TWO	P	W	D	L	F	A	GD	Pts
1 Salts Res	26	21	2	3	83	36	47	65
2 Boroughbridge Res	26	19	2	5	83	36	47	59
3 Otley Town Res	26	18	4	4	93	34	59	58
4 Kirk Deighton Rangers Res	26	18	3	5	81	34	47	57
5 Ilkley Town Res	26	16	5	5	99	47	52	53
6 East End Park Res	26	12	3	11	76	59	17	39
7 Rothwell Res	26	11	4	11	59	58	1	37
8 Altofts Res	26	11	2	13	67	65	2	35
9 Kippax Reserves	26	10	4	12	71	58	13	34
10 Howden Clough Res	26	9	0	17	55	94	-39	27
11 Sherburn White Rose Res	26	8	2	16	59	75	-16	26
12 Wyke Wanderers Res	26	6	2	18	32	95	-63	20
13 Old Centralians Res	26	3	1	22	38	145	-107	10
14 Pool Res	26	1	4	21	37	97	-60	7

LEAGUE CUPS

WEST YORKSHIRE LEAGUE CUP FINAL

Leeds City v Shelley 4-0

WEST YORKSHIRE LEAGUE TROPHY FINAL

Hall Green United Res v Whitkirk Wanderers Res 2-2, 8-7p

PREMIER DIVISION	1	2	3	4	5	6	7	8	9	10	11	12	13	14	15	16
1 Beeston St Anthony		0-3	1-6	6-1	3-2	3-5	2-2	0-1	3-3	3-1	2-0	2-2	7-1	7-2	5-0	5-1
2 Carlton Athletic	2-2		4-1	3-0	2-0	5-2	2-0	5-1	3-0	2-1	4-0	4-1	8-2	3-0	2-1	9-0
3 Field	0-5	0-8		A-A	0-6	3-1	1-3	2-1	4-2	0-2	1-2	0-1	2-1	2-2	1-0	5-1
4 Headingley	1-2	1-3	3-2		3-3	0-2	2-2	1-5	1-1	0-3	0-2	1-2	2-0	6-0	1-2	3-1
5 Horbury Town	1-2	1-1	1-4	1-0		1-0	1-2	0-2	1-3	1-1	2-0	0-0	7-1	4-3	0-1	3-1
6 Huddersfield Amateur	0-2	1-3	1-1	4-1	1-2		1-4	2-2	1-1	2-2	2-2	2-0	5-0	5-1	1-2	4-0
7 Hunslet Club	1-2	1-1	1-0	1-3	5-1	1-3		0-2	3-3	1-5	4-1	2-2	2-0	3-1	1-1	6-0
8 Ilkley Town	0-2	2-2	4-1	1-0	4-1	1-2	3-3		6-1	3-4	3-1	2-0	4-0	3-2	9-0	2-4
9 Knaresborough Town	1-4	1-3	1-1	2-1	0-0	3-1	1-2	1-1		0-2	3-1	4-5	1-0	2-4	1-3	1-0
10 Leeds City	4-1	2-4	3-1	4-1	0-2	4-1	3-4	3-0	4-0		2-1	4-1	9-2	5-0	3-1	7-0
11 Rawdon Old Boys	2-3	0-2	1-5	2-0	2-0	2-3	1-2	0-4	3-3	2-3		1-6	6-0	2-1	0-1	2-1
12 Robin Hood Athletic	0-1	0-5	5-3	1-1	1-3	3-1	1-1	2-5	1-2	1-2	5-0		5-0	2-3	2-1	2-2
13 Salts First	1-4	1-3	2-3	2-1	4-1	4-5	3-3	1-2	0-3	1-3	4-3	4-3		0-3	2-1	3-2
14 Sherburn White Rose	2-4	1-4	0-3	1-2	3-3	2-1	1-5	1-5	0-6	0-2	2-0	2-3	4-1		2-0	3-0
15 Whitkirk Wanderers	1-0	3-1	1-1	2-1	1-1	5-1	1-3	1-1	1-2	1-2	2-0	5-1	5-2	4-0		4-0
16 Wyke Wanderers	0-3	0-3	0-3	1-3	2-3	0-2	2-3	1-3	0-3	0-2	1-1	1-6	1-1	1-4	1-6	

WILTSHIRE LEAGUE

RECENT CHAMPIONS

2016: Trowbridge Town **2017:** Wroughton FC **2018:** Kintbury Rangers

		P	W	D	L	F	A	GD	Pts
1	Wroughton FC	28	20	5	3	94	28	66	65
2	Kintbury Rangers	28	19	5	4	94	40	54	59*
3	Shrewton United	28	17	2	9	95	49	46	53
4	Melksham Town Res	28	15	6	7	82	43	39	51
5	Purton FC	28	15	6	7	70	43	27	51
6	Trowbridge Town	28	12	11	5	56	37	19	44*
7	Corsham Town Res	28	12	8	8	60	47	13	44
8	Cricklade Town	28	12	5	11	68	55	13	41
9	Ludgershall Sports	28	10	7	11	48	67	-19	37
10	Malmesbury Victoria Dev	28	9	5	14	53	89	-36	32
11	Royal Wootton Bassett Town Dev	28	9	2	17	57	76	-19	29
12	Marlborough Town	28	6	6	16	38	69	-31	24
13	Pewsey Vale Dev	28	3	6	19	28	89	-61	15
14	Devizes Town Res	28	4	3	21	23	104	-81	15
15	Football ID	28	6	5	17	43	73	-30	13*

LEAGUE CUPS

FOUNTAIN TROPHY SENIOR CUP FINAL

Kintbury Rangers v Wroughton FC 3-2

		1	2	3	4	5	6	7	8	9	10	11	12	13	14	15
1	Corsham Town Res		5-0	7-0	2-2	2-1	3-0	5-1	0-0	1-1	2-0	4-4	3-2	2-2	0-0	1-1
2	Cricklade Town	5-0		6-0	3-2	3-4	7-3	3-1	3-1	3-2	5-2	0-1	2-3	5-1	2-3	1-3
3	Devizes Town Res	1-2	2-1		0-1	2-2	1-3	1-4	0-3	0-1	0-1	0-3	2-2	1-3	1-5	0-6
4	Football ID	2-6	3-2	0-2		1-7	2-4	0-2	7-0	2-0	2-2	1-2	4-1	0-4	0-2	1-4
5	Kintbury Rangers	2-1	2-2	11-0	4-2		6-0	2-2	4-1	2-0	5-0	5-1	8-1	2-0	3-2	3-2
6	Ludgershall Sports	3-1	1-1	1-2	3-1	1-4		3-0	2-1	1-0	4-3	3-3	3-2	0-4	1-1	1-3
7	Malmesbury Victoria Dev	0-6	1-3	6-0	1-4	0-5	3-3		3-0	3-3	2-0	2-7	5-0	3-4	2-2	2-0
8	Marlborough Town	3-1	2-2	1-0	2-0	2-3	0-0	5-0		0-3	3-3	0-0	0-1	1-2	2-6	0-6
9	Melksham Town Res	2-0	3-3	6-1	4-0	2-1	8-3	9-0	2-2		9-2	2-0	2-1	4-3	5-1	3-5
10	Pewsey Vale Dev	0-0	3-0	0-0	2-0	1-1	1-1	0-4	0-4	0-4		0-2	2-5	1-5	1-3	0-7
11	Purton FC	0-1	1-1	6-1	2-2	5-1	5-1	1-2	3-2	5-0	6-0		2-1	2-4	0-1	0-5
12	Royal Wootton Bassett Town Dev	1-2	0-1	5-2	2-2	1-3	2-1	7-2	9-2	0-4	3-0	1-2		0-2	3-2	0-5
13	Shrewton United	6-2	1-3	10-0	6-1	1-2	0-1	9-0	5-1	3-2	4-1	2-3	6-2		2-1	1-3
14	Trowbridge Town	4-1	3-0	3-4	1-1	0-0	2-0	1-1	1-0	0-0	4-1	1-1	2-1	3-3		1-1
15	Wroughton FC	4-0	2-1	5-0	3-0	5-1	1-1	6-1	3-0	1-1	4-2	0-3	5-1	3-2	1-1	

YORK LEAGUE

RECENT CHAMPIONS

2016: Old Malton St. Mary's **2017:** Wigginton Grasshoppers **2018:** Wigginton Grasshoppers

PREMIER DIVISION	P	W	D	L	F	A	GD	Pts
1 Old Malton	28	23	3	2	105	19	86	72
2 Church Fenton FC	28	18	3	7	50	43	7	57
3 Wigginton GH	28	17	5	6	111	46	65	56
4 Dringhouses	28	17	4	7	94	53	41	55
5 Thorpe United	28	15	6	7	79	51	28	51
6 Huntington Rovers	28	15	5	8	75	46	29	50
7 Dunnington	28	15	2	11	71	59	12	47
8 F1 Racing	28	14	2	12	69	53	16	44
9 Kirkbymoorside	28	11	2	15	65	81	-16	35
10 Poppleton United	28	8	2	18	68	98	-30	26
11 Copmanthorpe	28	8	2	18	59	97	-38	26
12 Tadcaster Magnets	28	8	1	19	49	93	-44	25
13 Hemingbrough United	28	7	2	19	56	87	-31	23
14 Sporting Knavesmire	28	7	2	19	41	80	-39	23
15 Osbaldwick	28	5	3	20	44	130	-86	18

DIVISION ONE	P	W	D	L	F	A	GD	Pts
1 Pocklington Town 2nd	22	16	3	3	55	23	32	51
2 Easingwold Town	22	15	2	5	59	29	30	47
3 Rawcliffe	22	12	3	7	62	37	25	39
4 Tockwith AFC	22	11	5	6	55	32	23	38
5 Haxby Town	22	10	3	9	59	50	9	33
6 Strensall Tigers	22	8	8	6	57	51	6	32
7 Cliffe	22	8	2	12	47	73	-26	26
8 Malton & Norton	22	8	1	13	39	50	-11	25
9 Heworth AFC	22	6	4	12	44	50	-6	22
10 Harrison Signs F.C.	22	6	4	12	28	53	-25	22
11 Bishopthorpe United	22	6	3	13	48	69	-21	21
12 Riccall United	22	5	4	13	43	79	-36	19

DIVISION TWO	P	W	D	L	F	A	GD	Pts
1 Malt Shovel FC	22	16	3	3	77	23	54	53*
2 Stamford Bridge	22	14	6	2	74	39	35	48
3 The Beagle FC	22	14	3	5	55	41	14	45
4 Rufforth United	22	13	3	6	82	35	47	42
5 Civil Service	22	12	3	7	80	52	28	39
6 Pollington FC	22	9	6	7	49	48	1	33
7 Brooklyn FC	22	8	2	12	39	54	-15	26
8 Wilberfoss	22	7	1	14	53	97	-44	22
9 Cawood	22	6	1	15	43	81	-38	19
10 Bubwith White Swan FC	22	5	0	17	48	95	-47	18*
11 Clifford FC	22	7	3	12	45	54	-9	14*
12 Barmby Moor	22	3	5	14	40	66	-26	14

DIVISION THREE	P	W	D	L	F	A	GD	Pts
1 Wheldrake	22	17	0	5	65	29	36	51
2 Wombleton Wanderers	22	16	2	4	101	29	72	50
3 Heslington	22	16	0	6	92	42	50	48
4 Helperby United	22	14	3	5	95	41	54	45
5 Selby Olympia	22	13	2	7	64	51	13	41
6 Crayke United	22	11	2	9	58	66	-8	35
7 Walnut Tree	22	10	3	9	64	64	0	33
8 Fulford FC	22	8	4	10	70	55	15	28
9 LNER Builders	22	9	1	12	75	91	-16	28
10 Swinton AFC	22	3	3	16	37	86	-49	12
11 Elm Park	22	5	0	17	38	108	-70	12*
12 Stillington S&C	22	0	0	22	16	113	-97	0

RESERVE DIVISION A	P	W	D	L	F	A	GD	Pts
1 Thorpe United	20	16	1	3	70	26	44	49
2 Dunnington	20	16	1	3	45	27	18	49
3 Pocklington Town 3rd	20	13	2	5	54	29	25	41
4 Old Malton	20	13	1	6	79	41	38	40
5 Huntington Rovers	20	11	2	7	55	33	22	35
6 Church Fenton FC	20	8	2	10	40	46	-6	26
7 Wigginton Grasshoppers	20	7	4	9	49	58	-9	25
8 Poppleton United	20	7	2	11	36	58	-22	23
9 Easingwold Town	20	4	1	15	41	61	-20	13
10 Osbaldwick	20	4	1	15	42	85	-43	13
11 Hemingbrough Utd	20	2	1	17	33	80	-47	4*

RESERVE DIVISION B	P	W	D	L	F	A	GD	Pts
1 Dringhouses	20	19	0	1	103	23	80	57
2 Tockwith AFC	20	14	2	4	57	22	35	44
3 Haxby Town	20	13	2	5	61	39	22	41
4 Malt Shovel	20	12	2	6	64	45	19	38
5 Malton & Norton	20	10	1	9	47	38	9	31
6 Copmanthorpe	20	9	1	10	54	59	-5	28
7 Tadcaster Magnets	20	9	0	11	37	55	-18	27
8 Bishopthorpe United	20	6	2	12	43	70	-27	20
9 F1 Racing FC	20	5	4	11	50	68	-18	19
10 Stamford Bridge	20	4	2	14	31	67	-36	14
11 Wilberfoss	20	1	0	19	24	85	-61	3

RESERVE DIVISION C	P	W	D	L	F	A	GD	Pts
1 Rawcliffe Res	18	14	3	1	53	19	34	45
2 Rufforth United	18	14	2	2	66	14	52	44
3 Sporting Knavesmire Res	18	10	1	7	42	40	2	31
4 Cliffe	18	9	1	8	52	40	12	28
5 Heworth AFC	18	8	1	9	39	49	-10	25
6 Harrison Signs FC	18	7	2	9	33	47	-14	23
7 Fulford	18	6	4	8	31	31	0	22
8 Brooklyn	18	6	3	9	43	51	-8	21
9 Civil Service	18	5	3	10	36	57	-21	18
10 Wheldrake Res	18	1	0	17	16	63	-47	3

PREMIER DIVISION	1	2	3	4	5	6	7	8	9	10	11	12	13	14	15
1 Church Fenton FC		1-0	0-3	1-0	1-0	1-0	0-0	2-1	1-2	5-2	6-3	0-0	3-1	0-1	2-0
2 Copmanthorpe	3-1		0-5	1-5	2-3	7-2	0-8	1-1	0-4	2-1	5-2	4-2	0-4	1-6	2-2
3 Dringhouses	1-1	7-2		4-1	4-0	6-1	2-3	7-2	0-3	9-1	7-5	2-3	2-1	6-1	4-1
4 Dunnington	5-0	3-1	1-2		2-1	0-2	2-2	5-1	0-5	6-2	4-2	5-1	2-0	1-5	1-4
5 F1 Racing	0-2	6-0	0-2	4-0		7-2	3-1	3-1	2-4	3-1	5-6	2-0	6-1	1-1	1-3
6 Hemingbrough United	1-3	3-2	5-5	2-3	1-1		3-5	1-2	1-4	2-3	5-4	1-3	1-2	3-1	1-5
7 Huntington Rovers	3-2	1-3	5-1	1-2	1-3	3-2		2-1	1-0	3-4	3-1	1-2	4-1	2-3	4-3
8 Kirkbymoorside	3-4	4-3	3-1	1-5	5-1	3-1	1-5		1-4	7-1	2-4	5-2	6-3	4-2	3-5
9 Old Malton St Marys	9-2	6-2	3-0	2-1	0-2	3-1	1-1	8-0		5-0	2-0	3-0	6-0	0-0	4-1
10 Osbaldwick	0-1	0-4	1-1	4-6	2-5	1-7	1-7	2-2	0-8		2-6	3-2	0-2	2-2	1-12
11 Poppleton United	2-3	3-2	1-1	2-6	3-4	1-0	0-0	2-4	1-4	1-4		0-1	6-2	5-4	0-6
12 Sporting Knavesmire	0-1	2-1	1-6	0-3	1-4	0-4	0-2	3-0	1-7	2-4	6-2		1-6	2-3	2-2
13 Tadcaster Magnets	0-1	1-7	1-3	1-0	2-0	0-2	1-4	1-2	0-6	9-0	2-4	4-2		1-8	0-11
14 Thorpe United	1-2	5-2	6-0	2-2	2-0	2-1	2-1	1-0	0-1	5-2	4-1	4-2	3-3		2-3
15 Wigginton Grasshoppers	2-4	9-2	1-3	6-0	3-2	10-1	2-2	2-0	1-1	6-0	4-1	1-0	3-0	3-3	

ALDERSHOT & DISTRICT FOOTBALL LEAGUE

SENIOR DIVISION	P	W	D	L	F	A	GD	Pts
1 Hartley Wintney A	16	15	0	1	74	23	51	45
2 Frimley Select	16	10	0	6	51	43	8	30
3 Yateley United Res	16	9	1	6	39	27	12	28
4 Fleet Spurs A	16	8	2	6	46	49	-3	26
5 Wey Valley	16	6	3	7	53	60	-7	21
6 Traco Athletic	16	6	2	8	35	41	-6	20
7 Sandhurst Sports	16	5	1	10	32	42	-10	16
8 Four Marks	16	4	2	10	44	55	-11	14
9 Normandy	16	3	1	12	23	57	-34	10

DIVISION ONE	P	W	D	L	F	A	GD	Pts
1 Ropley	18	13	3	2	70	22	48	42
2 Headley United A	18	13	2	3	58	32	26	41
3 Yateley United A	18	11	1	6	57	40	17	34
4 Mytchett Athletic	18	9	4	5	55	30	25	31
5 AFC Fleet	18	10	1	7	64	41	23	31
6 Normandy Specials	18	6	5	7	53	54	-1	23
7 AFC Laffans	18	6	4	8	28	46	-18	22
8 Wey Valley Res	18	5	1	12	50	69	-19	16
9 Letef Select	18	3	0	15	45	72	-27	9
10 Farnborough North End	18	2	3	13	29	103	-74	9

BASINGSTOKE & DISTRICT FOOTBALL LEAGUE

DIVISION ONE	P	W	D	L	F	A	GD	Pts
1 Twentyten	14	10	3	1	67	10	57	33
2 Silchester	14	10	3	1	60	24	36	33
3 AFC Berg	14	11	0	3	54	28	26	33
4 Hook	14	8	2	4	37	23	14	26
5 Tadley Calleva A	14	4	2	8	33	46	-13	14
6 AFC Aldermaston Res	14	3	3	8	31	43	-12	12
7 Herriard Sports	14	1	2	11	16	61	-45	5
8 Overton Utd A	14	1	1	12	16	79	-63	4

DIVISION TWO	P	W	D	L	F	A	GD	Pts
1 Overton Utd B	16	12	0	4	64	27	37	36
2 Renegades	16	10	3	3	40	14	26	33
3 Twentyten Res	16	7	3	6	44	36	8	24
4 Oakridge	16	6	5	5	30	31	-1	23
5 AFC Aldermaston A	16	7	1	8	35	32	3	22
6 North Warnborough	16	6	4	6	30	33	-3	22
7 Basingstoke Athletic	16	6	1	9	29	57	-28	19
8 Chineham	16	4	2	10	26	41	-15	14
9 AFC Berg Res	16	3	3	10	27	54	-27	12

BRISTOL AND DISTRICT LEAGUE

SENIOR DIVISION	P	W	D	L	F	A	GD	Pts
1 Nicholas Wanderers	22	21	1	0	83	15	68	64
2 Hillfields Old Boys	22	15	3	4	88	46	42	48
3 Bradley Stoke Town	22	13	4	5	70	38	32	43
4 Made For Ever	22	11	4	7	59	56	3	37
5 St Nicholas Old Boys	22	10	3	9	47	29	18	33
6 AEK Boco A Team	22	9	3	10	48	57	-9	30
7 Cribbs A Team	22	7	5	10	48	58	-10	26
8 Patchway Town Res	22	8	0	14	33	68	-35	24
9 Wick (Saturday) Res	22	7	1	14	32	62	-30	22
10 Mendip Broadwalk Res	22	5	4	13	38	46	-8	19
11 Longwell Green Sports A	22	5	3	14	55	75	-20	18
12 Bristol Barcelona	22	4	3	15	42	93	-51	15

DIVISON ONE	P	W	D	L	F	A	GD	Pts
1 Fry Club A Team	20	14	4	2	53	25	28	46
2 Nicholas Wanderers Res	20	13	4	3	60	26	34	43
3 AFC Mangotsfield District	20	9	6	5	42	33	9	33
4 Henbury Res	20	10	3	7	40	31	9	33
5 Bendix	20	9	4	7	43	42	1	31
6 Hanham Athletic Res	20	10	1	9	34	41	-7	31
7 Stapleton AFC Res	20	9	2	9	43	34	9	26*
8 Seymour United Res	20	7	1	12	37	49	-12	22
9 Totterdown United Res	20	6	3	11	41	47	-6	21
10 Rangeworthy	20	4	1	15	28	54	-26	13
11 Greyfriars Athletic Res	20	3	3	14	28	67	-39	12

DIVISION TWO	P	W	D	L	F	A	GD	Pts
1 Highridge United Res	22	18	1	3	41	17	24	55
2 Lawrence Rovers	22	17	2	3	56	26	30	53
3 Tormarton FC	22	13	4	5	68	30	38	43
4 Hartcliffe	22	12	3	7	54	34	20	39
5 Chipping Sodbury Town A	22	12	1	9	65	45	20	37
6 Olveston United Res	22	11	3	8	57	47	10	36
7 Hambrook Res	22	10	3	9	40	32	8	33
8 Bradley Stoke Town Res	22	10	3	9	44	39	5	33
9 Iron Acton Res	22	7	2	13	47	64	-17	23
10 Sea Mills Park Res	22	7	1	14	31	43	-12	22
11 Rangeworthy Res	22	3	1	18	23	55	-32	10
12 Fishponds Athletic	22	0	0	22	26	120	-94	0

DIVISION THREE	P	W	D	L	F	A	GD	Pts
1 Hillfields Old Boys Res	20	15	3	2	70	34	36	48
2 Brimsham Green	20	13	3	4	53	30	23	42
3 Old Sodbury	20	12	1	7	56	27	29	37
4 Roman Glass St George A	20	11	2	7	51	37	14	35
5 Stokeside FC 1st	20	10	2	8	54	33	21	32
6 Real Thornbury Res	20	8	5	7	33	27	6	29
7 Mendip Broadwalk A	20	8	3	9	44	51	-7	27
8 Nicholas Wanderers A	20	7	2	11	33	39	-6	23
9 Westerleigh Sports	20	5	3	12	35	58	-23	18
10 Cutters SB	20	6	1	13	41	57	-16	16*
11 Greyfriars Athletic A	20	1	3	16	29	106	-77	6

DIVISION FOUR	P	W	D	L	F	A	GD	Pts
1 Fry Club B Team	20	14	5	1	53	23	30	47
2 Bradley Stoke Town A	20	12	5	3	52	25	27	41
3 Stoke Lane Athletic	20	12	4	4	62	37	25	40
4 Shaftesbury Crusade Res	20	10	6	4	62	24	38	36
5 Pucklechurch Sports Res	20	9	2	9	47	50	-3	29
6 Cribbs B Team	20	7	7	6	50	52	-2	28
7 Crosscourt United	20	7	1	12	30	66	-36	22
8 Iron Acton A	20	6	1	13	52	77	-25	19
9 AFC Mangotsfield District Res	20	4	6	10	35	41	-6	18
10 Yate Athletic	20	4	6	10	34	43	-9	18
11 DRG Frenchay Res	20	2	3	15	20	59	-39	9

DIVISION FIVE	P	W	D	L	F	A	GD	Pts
1 Winterbourne United Res	22	18	3	1	94	23	71	57
2 Highridge United A	22	16	3	3	60	22	38	51
3 Hanham Athletic A	22	15	1	6	77	49	28	46
4 Oldland Abbotonians Colts	22	13	2	7	71	38	33	41
5 Fry Club C Team	22	12	1	9	45	34	11	37
6 Hanham Abbotonians 1st	22	10	6	6	70	37	33	36
7 Seymour United A	22	9	5	8	49	40	9	32
8 Phoenix, The	22	7	4	11	45	61	-16	25
9 AFC Grace	22	4	6	12	45	78	-33	18
10 Made For Ever Res	22	5	3	14	32	80	-48	18
11 Westerleigh Sports Res	22	2	4	16	22	81	-59	10
12 Greyfriars Athletic B	22	0	4	18	31	98	-67	4

BRISTOL AND SUBURBAN LEAGUE

PREMIER ONE	P	W	D	L	F	A	GD	Pts
1 Bromley Heath United	22	15	6	1	65	21	44	51
2 Avonmouth	22	17	0	5	72	32	40	51
3 Filton Athletic	22	15	3	4	42	19	23	48
4 Old Cothamians	22	13	2	7	63	30	33	41
5 AFC Mangotsfield	22	12	3	7	61	54	7	39
6 St Aldhelms	22	11	1	10	53	54	-1	33*
7 Easton Cowboys	22	8	6	8	29	36	-7	30
8 Bristol Bilbao	22	7	5	10	44	53	-9	26
9 Rockleaze Rangers Res	22	7	3	12	42	63	-21	24
10 Lawrence Weston	22	5	3	14	25	59	-34	18
11 Old Georgians	22	3	3	16	23	49	-26	12
12 Ashton United	22	1	1	20	22	71	-49	4

PREMIER TWO	P	W	D	L	F	A	GD	Pts
1 Stoke Gifford United	20	14	4	2	82	30	52	46
2 Parson Street Old Boys	20	13	2	5	81	40	41	41
3 Bristol Spartak	20	12	3	5	46	27	19	39
4 Port of Bristol	20	11	4	5	63	46	17	37
5 MPK Lofts	20	10	3	7	62	51	11	33
6 North Bristol United	20	10	1	9	45	43	2	31
7 Fishponds Old Boys	20	8	4	8	40	45	-5	28
8 Almondsbury Res	20	7	4	9	33	38	-5	25
9 AFC Brislington Res	20	5	2	13	33	69	-36	17
10 Cadbury Heath Res	20	2	4	14	25	58	-33	9*
11 Ridings High	20	1	3	16	18	81	-63	6

DIVISION ONE	P	W	D	L	F	A	GD	Pts
1 Stoke Rangers	20	17	2	1	82	21	61	53
2 Wessex Wanderers	20	11	5	4	64	41	23	38
3 Rockleaze Rangers 'A'	20	11	3	6	62	41	21	36
4 Keynsham Town A	20	10	6	4	48	40	8	36
5 Wanderers	20	8	5	7	38	35	3	29
6 North Bristol Trust	20	9	0	11	50	40	10	27
7 Stockwood Wanderers Res	20	7	4	9	49	51	-2	25
8 Easton Cowboys Res	20	7	2	11	39	48	-9	22*
9 Bristol Telephones Res	20	7	1	12	37	40	-3	21*
10 AFC Mangotsfield Res	20	5	3	12	31	59	-28	18
11 St Aldhelms Res	20	2	1	17	19	103	-84	7

DIVISION TWO	P	W	D	L	F	A	GD	Pts
1 Cosmos	20	15	2	3	75	37	38	47
2 Park Knowle	20	11	7	2	57	31	26	40
3 Bedminster Cricketers	20	12	2	6	59	36	23	38
4 Stoke Gifford United Res	20	11	4	5	64	37	27	36*
5 Old Cothamians Res	20	11	2	7	54	40	14	35
6 Little Stoke Res	20	7	4	9	43	43	0	24*
7 Bromley Heath United Res	20	7	3	10	40	48	-8	24
8 Corinthian Sports	20	5	5	10	38	54	-16	20
9 Avonmouth Res	20	5	4	11	44	66	-22	19
10 Long Ashton Res	20	6	0	14	30	54	-24	18
11 Fishponds Old Boys Res	20	3	1	16	24	82	-58	10

DIVISION THREE	P	W	D	L	F	A	GD	Pts
1 AFC Mangotsfield A	18	14	2	2	64	22	42	44
2 Broad Plain Res	18	13	2	3	57	23	34	40*
3 Filton Athletic Res	18	11	2	5	49	20	29	35
4 Imperial Res	18	10	2	6	47	32	15	32
5 Port of Bristol Res	18	10	1	7	41	31	10	31
6 Rockleaze Rangers B	18	8	3	7	42	44	-2	27
7 Lockleaze Community	18	8	2	8	51	55	-4	26
8 Old Georgians Res	18	3	4	11	25	47	-22	13
9 Tytherington Rocks Res	18	2	2	14	34	61	-27	8
10 Brandon Sports	18	1	0	17	29	104	-75	3

DIVISION FOUR	P	W	D	L	F	A	GD	Pts
1 Bristol Phoenix	16	13	2	1	60	26	34	41
2 Cadbury Heath 'A'	16	12	0	4	67	32	35	36
3 Cosmos Res	16	10	1	5	66	42	24	31
4 AFC Whitchurch	16	10	1	5	52	35	17	31
5 Easton Cowboys A	16	7	1	8	72	46	26	22
6 Parson Street OB Res	16	6	2	8	40	53	-13	20
7 Lawrence Weston Res	16	4	3	9	33	60	-27	15
8 Wessex Wanderers Res	16	3	1	12	26	67	-41	10
9 TC Sports	16	0	3	13	23	78	-55	3

DIVISION FIVE	P	W	D	L	F	A	GD	Pts
1 Park Knowle Res	18	16	2	0	92	12	80	50
2 Ridings High Res	18	14	2	2	101	28	73	43*
3 Avonmouth 'A'	18	11	1	6	70	48	22	33*
4 Socius United	18	9	3	6	57	40	17	30
5 Cutters Friday Res	18	8	1	9	43	50	-7	25
6 Bristol Phoenix Res	18	7	1	10	44	87	-43	22
7 Stoke Gifford United A	18	5	3	10	34	56	-22	18
8 Cosmos A	18	4	5	9	28	50	-22	17
9 Kellaway Rangers	18	3	2	13	34	71	-37	10*
10 Hanham Abbotonians Res	18	3	0	15	21	82	-61	9

BRISTOL PREMIER COMBINATION LEAGUE

PREMIER DIVISION	P	W	D	L	F	A	GD	Pts
1 Cribbs Res	24	19	3	2	86	40	46	60
2 Sea Mills Park	24	15	7	2	71	28	43	52
3 Shaftesbury Crusade	24	16	3	5	61	40	21	51
4 Highridge United	24	13	5	6	70	50	20	44
5 Longwell Green Sports Res	24	11	4	9	54	46	8	37
6 Stapleton AFC	24	10	5	9	45	49	-4	35
7 Seymour United	24	9	7	8	45	44	1	34
8 Totterdown United	24	9	4	11	54	42	12	31
9 Olveston United	24	8	3	13	57	62	-5	27
10 Lebeq (Saturday)	24	7	3	14	38	63	-25	24
11 Chipping Sodbury Town Res	24	5	5	14	39	57	-18	20
12 AEK Boco Res	24	5	3	16	31	68	-37	18
13 Hallen Res	24	2	2	20	35	97	-62	8

DIVISION ONE	P	W	D	L	F	A	GD	Pts
1 Winterbourne United	24	21	0	3	95	28	67	63
2 Pucklechurch Sports	24	19	0	5	60	30	30	57
3 Iron Acton	24	15	1	8	74	50	24	46
4 De Veys	24	13	4	7	62	41	21	43
5 Shirehampton Res	23	12	3	8	45	46	-1	39
6 Roman Glass St George Res	24	11	3	10	52	44	8	36
7 Bitton Res	24	10	6	8	56	54	2	36
8 Bristol Manor Farm Res	24	9	5	10	60	49	11	32
9 Greyfriars Athletic	24	9	2	13	55	57	-2	29
10 Real Thornbury	24	8	5	11	38	50	-12	29
11 Hambrook	23	5	4	14	23	43	-20	19
12 DRG Frenchay	24	2	4	18	21	78	-57	10
13 Oldland Abbotonians Res	24	1	3	20	20	91	-71	3*

BROMLEY AND SOUTH LONDON FOOTBALL LEAGUE

PREMIER DIVISION	P	W	D	L	F	A	GD	Pts
1 Red Velvet 'A'	14	13	0	1	41	10	31	39
2 Meridian Sports	14	11	0	3	53	21	32	33
3 Wickham Park	14	10	1	3	47	28	19	31
4 Eltham Town	14	6	1	7	38	25	13	19
5 FC Greenwich	14	5	2	7	27	42	-15	17
6 West Bromley Albion	14	3	1	10	25	33	-8	10
7 Eden Park Rangers	14	2	2	10	25	59	-34	8
8 Kingsdale	14	2	1	11	21	59	-38	7

DIVISION ONE	P	W	D	L	F	A	GD	Pts
1 Cray Wanderers Community	18	15	1	2	56	19	37	46
2 Old Colfeians	18	13	1	4	87	40	47	40
3 Old Roan	18	12	3	3	73	34	39	39
4 Eltham Town Res	18	10	3	5	47	34	13	33
5 River Plate	18	9	1	8	45	50	-5	28
6 Lewisham Athletic	18	6	4	8	39	45	-6	22
7 Lewisham Lions FC	18	5	2	11	39	53	-14	17
8 Farnborough OBG 3rd	18	5	2	11	45	61	-16	17
9 Beckenham	18	3	1	14	31	80	-49	10
10 Erith & Belvedere FC Res	18	1	4	13	26	72	-46	7

DIVISION TWO	P	W	D	L	F	A	GD	Pts
1 Russellers	16	11	2	3	46	24	22	35
2 Farnborough OBG 4th	16	8	4	4	33	28	5	28
3 Ground Hoppers	16	7	4	5	56	37	19	25
4 New Russellers AFC	16	7	2	7	34	43	-9	23
5 South Dulwich FC	16	6	4	6	53	37	16	22
6 Crofton Albion	16	6	2	8	44	41	3	20
7 Eden Park FC	16	5	3	8	31	42	-11	18
8 Eltham Eagles	16	5	3	8	28	49	-21	18
9 Welling Town A	16	4	2	10	29	53	-24	14

DIVISION THREE	P	W	D	L	F	A	GD	Pts
1 Teviot Rangers	20	18	1	1	71	27	44	55
2 Welling Park Res	20	15	1	4	63	32	31	46
3 South East Athletic A	20	10	2	8	48	50	-2	32
4 Wickham Park Res	20	9	3	8	48	43	5	30
5 Seven Acre Sports	20	9	2	9	48	39	9	29
6 Charlton Athletic Deaf	20	9	2	9	50	51	-1	29
7 AWS	20	9	1	10	90	79	11	28
8 Slade Green Knights	20	9	0	11	57	66	-9	27
9 Latter Day Saints	20	7	3	10	63	68	-5	24
10 Dulwich Village Res	20	2	4	14	38	63	-25	10
11 Bosco FA FC Res	20	3	1	16	45	103	-58	10

CENTRAL & SOUTH NORFOLK LEAGUE

DIVISION ONE	P	W	D	L	F	A	GD	Pts
1 Briston F.C.	16	14	1	1	58	16	42	43
2 Longham	16	13	3	0	60	22	38	41*
3 UEA A	16	10	2	4	40	21	19	31*
4 Dereham Taverners	16	7	2	7	49	43	6	23
5 Castle Acre Swifts Res	16	5	1	10	31	53	-22	16
6 Norwich Medics	16	4	3	9	25	33	-8	15
7 Watton United Res	16	4	1	11	15	37	-22	13
8 Hethersett Ath	16	3	3	10	14	43	-29	12
9 Rockland United	16	3	2	11	23	47	-24	11

DIVISION TWO	P	W	D	L	F	A	GD	Pts
1 Redgrave Rangers	22	17	3	2	62	20	42	54
2 Briston F.C. Res	22	16	2	4	68	33	35	47*
3 Hockering	22	15	1	6	82	34	48	46
4 Dussindale Rovers Res	22	14	2	6	47	23	24	44
5 Mundford Exiles	22	12	1	9	65	53	12	37
6 Bridgham United F.C.	22	10	1	11	47	55	-8	31
7 Tacolneston Res	22	8	4	10	45	54	-9	28
8 Gressenhall	22	8	3	11	42	43	-1	27
9 Brandon Town F.C. Res	22	8	2	12	52	50	2	26
10 Yaxham	22	8	0	14	35	49	-14	24
11 Dereham Taverners Res	22	4	2	16	25	90	-65	14
12 Bar 33	22	1	1	20	25	91	-66	4

DIVISION THREE	P	W	D	L	F	A	GD	Pts
1 Longham Res	16	12	2	2	60	25	35	38
2 Feltwell United	16	11	2	3	59	18	41	35
3 Wensum Albion	16	9	3	4	56	41	15	30
4 Hingham Athletic Res	16	8	2	6	45	29	16	26
5 AFC Weeting	16	7	4	5	43	38	5	25
6 Cockers	16	7	3	6	29	27	2	24
7 Bowthorpe Rovers	16	4	3	9	27	45	-18	15
8 Bacton	16	3	1	12	36	79	-43	10
9 Home Care United	16	1	0	15	31	84	-53	0

DIVISION FOUR	P	W	D	L	F	A	GD	Pts
1 Sprowston Athletic Res	16	14	1	1	70	14	56	43
2 Hempnall Res	16	11	2	3	67	34	33	35
3 Rockland United Res	16	11	2	3	33	21	12	35
4 Litcham	16	10	4	2	77	22	55	34
5 Hockering Res	16	6	1	9	28	40	-12	19
6 Narborough Res	16	6	1	9	24	42	-18	19
7 Necton Res	16	4	1	11	35	56	-21	13
8 Bar 33 Res	16	3	0	13	14	56	-42	9
9 Colkirk	16	0	2	14	7	70	-63	2

CHELTENHAM ASSOCIATION FOOTBALL LEAGUE

DIVISION ONE	P	W	D	L	F	A	GD	Pts
1 Andoversford	22	16	4	2	83	18	65	52
2 Upton Town	22	14	4	4	88	27	61	46
3 Hanley Swan	22	13	3	6	73	48	25	42
4 Cheltenham Civil Service Res	22	13	3	6	58	36	22	42
5 Southside Star FC	22	12	3	7	54	42	12	39
6 Bishops Cleeve FC A	22	12	2	8	46	31	15	38
7 Tewkesbury Town	22	10	5	7	49	39	10	35
8 Kings	22	8	5	9	44	40	4	29
9 Shurdington Rovers	22	8	2	12	41	51	-10	26
10 Dowty Dynamos	22	3	3	16	19	75	-56	12
11 Newton	22	3	2	17	30	91	-61	10*
12 Fintan	22	2	0	20	25	112	-87	6

DIVISION TWO	P	W	D	L	F	A	GD	Pts
1 AFC Renegades	18	16	1	1	70	26	44	49
2 St Pauls United	18	12	2	4	60	25	35	38
3 Prestbury Rovers	18	12	1	5	74	29	45	37
4 Bredon Res	18	12	1	5	55	33	22	37
5 Brockworth Albion Res	18	7	5	6	40	44	-4	26
6 FC Barometrics Res	18	7	2	9	36	39	-3	23
7 Shurdington Rovers Res	18	5	3	10	30	54	-24	18
8 Gala Wilton Res	18	4	3	11	35	62	-27	15
9 Pittville United	18	4	2	12	26	55	-29	14
10 Charlton Rovers Res	18	0	2	16	16	75	-59	2

DIVISION THREE	P	W	D	L	F	A	GD	Pts
1 Malvern Vale FC	26	21	2	3	120	28	92	65
2 Leckhampton Rovers	26	19	3	4	109	36	73	60
3 Welland Res	26	17	2	7	81	54	27	53
4 Prestbury Rovers Res	26	16	0	10	63	54	9	47*
5 Kings Res	26	16	1	9	67	56	11	46*
6 Andoversford Res	26	12	4	10	79	68	11	40
7 Windyridge Rovers	26	11	6	9	55	57	-2	38*
8 Falcons Res	26	11	3	12	62	72	-10	36
9 Dowty Dynamos Res	26	9	1	16	50	72	-22	28
10 Smiths Athletic Res	26	8	3	15	61	77	-16	27
11 Cheltenham Civil Service 3rds	26	8	2	16	70	89	-19	26
12 Tewkesbury Town Res	26	7	2	17	49	90	-41	23
13 Southside Star FC Res	26	4	5	17	42	99	-57	17
14 Gala Wilton Thirds	26	4	4	18	34	90	-56	10*

DIVISION FOUR	P	W	D	L	F	A	GD	Pts
1 FC Lakeside Res	24	23	0	1	147	24	123	69
2 Malvern Cave FC	24	17	4	3	93	45	48	54*
3 Cheltenham United	24	17	1	6	94	53	41	52
4 Cheltenham Saracens Res	24	13	3	8	54	44	10	42
5 Woodmancote United	24	13	2	9	53	47	6	41
6 Malvern Vale FC Res	24	11	5	8	74	59	15	38
7 Pittville United Res	24	8	5	11	39	60	-21	29
8 Kempsey Corinthians FC	24	8	4	12	52	70	-18	28
9 Winchcombe Town Res	24	8	3	13	52	59	-7	27
10 Bishops Cleeve FC Dev	24	7	5	12	49	65	-16	25*
11 Andoversford Thirds	24	6	3	15	50	81	-31	21
12 Tewkesbury Athletic	24	4	2	18	28	91	-63	14
13 Charlton Rovers Thirds	24	2	1	21	29	116	-87	7

COLCHESTER & EAST ESSEX LEAGUE

PREMIER DIVISION	P	W	D	L	F	A	GD	Pts
1 Old Memorial Services	21	14	2	5	48	21	27	44
2 St Osyth	21	13	2	6	63	26	37	41
3 Langham Lodgers	21	13	2	6	42	30	12	41
4 Stanway Athletic	21	12	4	5	79	29	50	40
5 Sporting Rebels	21	9	4	8	36	36	0	33*
6 Abbey Fields	21	7	4	10	50	49	1	25
7 Ramsey & Mistley Res	21	3	2	16	18	72	-54	10*
8 Bradfield Rovers Res	21	3	0	18	33	106	-73	9

DIVISION ONE	P	W	D	L	F	A	GD	Pts
1 Oyster Res	21	18	1	2	99	32	67	55
2 Stoke by Nayland	21	15	2	4	89	40	49	47
3 Tollesbury Res	21	12	0	9	62	50	12	36
4 Tiptree Engaine A	21	10	0	11	46	44	2	30
5 Cavendish Res	21	9	3	9	57	58	-1	30
6 Mersea Island Res	21	7	1	13	52	52	0	22
7 Stanway Athletic Res	21	5	2	14	40	76	-36	17
8 Parkeston Welfare Park	21	3	1	17	22	115	-93	10

CORNWALL COMBINATION LEAGUE

	P	W	D	L	F	A	GD	Pts
1 Perranporth	36	27	4	5	109	40	69	87*
2 Penryn Athletic	36	25	6	5	129	31	98	85*
3 St Day	36	25	5	6	123	52	71	82*
4 St Ives Town	36	24	5	7	102	34	68	77
5 Helston Athletic Res	36	24	2	10	119	55	64	74
6 Illogan RBL	36	21	5	10	95	52	43	68
7 Falmouth Town Res	36	21	4	11	100	50	50	67
8 Perranwell	36	18	2	16	70	50	20	58*
9 Hayle	36	17	4	15	80	63	17	57*
10 Wendron United Res	36	10	13	13	67	74	-7	47*
11 St Just	36	12	9	15	70	84	-14	46*
12 Pendeen Rovers	36	13	7	16	70	74	-4	42*
13 Mullion	36	12	4	20	60	91	-31	40
14 Lizard Argyle	36	10	6	20	65	92	-27	36
15 RNAS Culdrose	36	11	3	22	61	93	-32	36
16 St Agnes	36	9	7	20	64	100	-36	34
17 Redruth United	36	8	3	25	53	121	-68	27
18 Portleven Res	36	5	4	27	54	158	-104	11*
19 Carharrack	36	0	7	29	23	200	-177	-13*

DEVON & EXETER LEAGUE

PREMIER DIVISION	P	W	D	L	F	A	GD	Pts
1 Exwick Villa	28	21	5	2	110	22	88	68
2 Newtown	28	21	5	2	97	27	70	68
3 Cronies	28	20	5	3	96	23	73	65
4 Colyton	28	18	3	7	99	46	53	57
5 Lyme Regis	28	15	4	9	68	49	19	49
6 Witheridge Res	28	15	2	11	79	56	23	47
7 Upottery	28	12	4	12	60	64	-4	40
8 Exmouth Town Res	28	12	4	12	43	63	-20	40
9 Heavitree United	28	12	2	14	55	66	-11	38
10 Clyst Valley	28	11	2	15	54	84	-30	35
11 Beer Albion	28	7	6	15	41	64	-23	27
12 Feniton	28	6	3	19	48	83	-35	21
13 Topsham Town	28	6	3	19	39	100	-61	21
14 Okehampton Argyle	28	5	1	22	38	120	-82	16
15 Seaton Town	28	4	1	23	42	102	-60	13

DIVISION ONE	P	W	D	L	F	A	GD	Pts
1 Lapford	20	16	2	2	69	18	51	50
2 Bampton	20	12	4	4	55	30	25	40
3 Kentisbeare	20	12	2	6	61	35	26	38
4 Chagford	20	11	3	6	49	39	10	36
5 Sidmouth Town Res	20	9	1	10	43	56	-13	28
6 Hatherleigh Town	20	7	3	10	39	47	-8	24
7 University of Exeter Res	20	7	2	11	62	70	-8	23
8 Wellington Res	20	6	4	10	34	44	-10	22
9 Chard Town Res	20	6	1	13	34	51	-17	18*
10 Alphington Res	20	4	5	11	31	52	-21	17
11 Heavitree United Res	20	5	3	12	28	63	-35	17*

DIVISION TWO	P	W	D	L	F	A	GD	Pts
1 Whipton & Pinhoe	26	22	3	1	96	29	67	69
2 Thorverton s	26	21	3	2	103	37	66	66
3 Royal Oak FC	26	16	3	7	95	53	42	51
4 Crediton United Res	26	14	4	8	82	51	31	45*
5 University of Exeter 3rd	26	13	4	9	80	44	36	43
6 Dawlish United	26	13	4	9	74	64	10	43
7 Axminster Town Res	26	12	3	11	74	68	6	39
8 Tipton St John	26	10	4	12	57	61	-4	34
9 Newtown Res	26	10	4	12	63	70	-7	34
10 Bow Amateur Athletic Club	26	9	3	14	70	79	-9	30
11 Halwill	26	8	2	16	46	74	-28	26
12 Uplowman Athletic	26	7	4	15	61	74	-13	25
13 Priory	26	3	1	22	40	148	-108	10
14 Honiton Town Res	26	3	0	23	43	132	-89	9

DIVISION THREE	P	W	D	L	F	A	GD	Pts
1 Lympstone	26	19	2	5	81	27	54	59
2 University of Exeter 4th	26	18	2	6	106	39	67	56
3 Winchester	26	17	3	6	78	50	28	54
4 Ottery St Mary AFC	26	17	0	9	105	53	52	51
5 East Budleigh	26	16	1	9	69	55	14	49
6 Newton St Cyres	26	14	3	9	77	63	14	45
7 Sandford	26	13	1	12	97	65	32	40
8 Beer Albion Res	26	11	5	10	63	60	3	38
9 Otterton	26	10	2	14	50	62	-12	32
10 Clyst Valley Res	26	8	6	12	47	57	-10	30
11 Tedburn St Mary	26	7	5	14	58	83	-25	26
12 Axmouth United	26	7	5	14	39	93	-54	26
13 Budleigh Salterton Res	26	5	3	18	42	88	-46	17*
14 North Tawton	26	1	0	25	19	136	-117	3

DIVISION FOUR	P	W	D	L	F	A	GD	Pts
1 Elmore Res	24	22	0	2	96	25	71	66
2 Halwill Res	24	17	2	5	96	51	45	53
3 Alphington 3rd	24	14	4	6	76	50	26	46
4 University of Exeter 5th	24	14	3	7	60	50	10	45
5 Lyme Regis Res	24	13	3	8	64	35	29	41*
6 Teignmouth Res	24	12	2	10	67	62	5	38
7 Winkleigh	24	10	4	10	51	56	-5	33*
8 Pinhoe	24	10	1	13	42	67	-25	31
9 Hemyock	24	9	3	12	54	61	-7	30
10 St Martins Res	24	7	1	16	48	81	-33	22
11 Feniton Res	24	4	5	15	32	72	-40	15*
12 Millwey Rise	24	3	4	17	39	70	-31	13
13 Sampford Peverell	24	3	4	17	29	74	-45	13

DIVISION FIVE	P	W	D	L	F	A	GD	Pts
1 Dunkeswell Rovers	24	17	4	3	69	28	41	55
2 Exmouth Spartans	24	18	0	6	82	44	38	54
3 Westexe Park Rangers	24	16	4	4	64	46	18	52
4 Upottery Res	24	14	3	7	75	46	29	45
5 Bampton Res	24	11	3	10	58	63	-5	36
6 Cranbrook	24	10	5	9	45	36	9	35
7 Central	24	10	4	10	61	54	7	34
8 Devon Yeoman	24	9	6	9	66	52	14	33
9 Sidmouth Town 3rd	24	8	5	11	64	57	7	29
10 Culm United	24	7	3	14	44	67	-23	24
11 Bravehearts	24	5	7	12	52	81	-29	19*
12 Starcross Generals	24	3	4	17	44	108	-64	13
13 Awliscombe	24	4	0	20	25	67	-42	12

DIVISION SIX	P	W	D	L	F	A	GD	Pts
1 Kentisbeare Res	26	24	2	0	115	24	91	74
2 Spreyton FC	26	21	5	0	114	22	92	66*
3 Cheriton Fitzpaine AFC	26	13	8	5	85	45	40	47
4 Colyton Res	26	13	5	8	72	62	10	44
5 Amory Green Rovers	26	11	5	10	63	70	-7	38
6 Witheridge 3rd	26	10	5	11	61	65	-4	35
7 Lapford Res	26	11	2	13	52	67	-15	35
8 Exeter United	26	8	8	10	54	41	13	30*
9 Seaton Town Res	26	9	4	13	59	82	-23	30*
10 Silverton	26	8	4	14	58	69	-11	28
11 Bradninch Town	26	5	10	11	47	83	-36	25
12 Willand XI	26	6	6	14	39	69	-30	24
13 Chagford Res	26	5	4	17	40	95	-55	19
14 Offwell Rangers FC	26	3	2	21	35	100	-65	11

DIVISION SEVEN	P	W	D	L	F	A	GD	Pts
1 Cowick Barton FC	26	23	1	2	110	34	76	70
2 East Budleigh Res	26	20	0	6	97	43	54	60
3 Broadclyst	26	18	3	5	104	45	59	57
4 The Village Inn FC	26	18	1	7	93	36	57	54*
5 Bickleigh	26	16	2	8	92	52	40	50
6 Thorverton Res	26	14	2	10	75	68	7	44
7 Otterton Res	26	12	1	13	68	72	-4	37
8 Okehampton Argyle Res	26	11	4	11	75	83	-8	37
9 Sidmouth Town 4ths	26	8	3	15	48	73	-25	27
10 Culm United Res	26	8	3	15	69	74	-5	25*
11 Pinhoe Res	26	6	5	15	37	71	-34	23
12 Cheriton Fitzpaine AFC Res	26	7	1	18	47	92	-45	22
13 HT Dons	26	5	4	17	44	104	-60	17*
14 Kenn Valley United	26	0	2	24	25	137	-112	2

DIVISION EIGHT	P	W	D	L	F	A	GD	Pts
1 Dawlish United Res	26	23	2	1	148	31	117	71
2 Elmore 3rd	26	20	3	3	111	45	66	63
3 Topsham Town Res	26	20	1	5	129	44	85	61
4 Devon Yeoman Res	26	17	1	8	82	37	45	52
5 Lympstone Res	26	12	7	7	66	50	16	43
6 Central Res	26	15	2	9	84	71	13	43*
7 Sandford Res	26	11	5	10	60	53	7	38
8 Priory Res	26	10	5	11	53	66	-13	35
9 Bradninch Villa	26	10	2	14	65	82	-17	32
10 Tedburn St Mary Res	26	6	4	16	41	76	-35	22
11 Millwey Rise Res	26	5	5	16	52	86	-34	20
12 Exmouth Town 3rd	26	3	4	19	49	110	-61	13
13 Honiton Town 3rd	26	4	2	20	49	128	-79	13*
14 Amory Green Rovers Res	26	2	5	19	43	153	-110	11

DORSET LEAGUE

SENIOR DIVISION	P	W	D	L	F	A	GD	Pts
1 Westland Sports Res	24	20	2	2	66	28	38	62
2 Mere Town FC	24	17	5	2	88	32	56	56
3 Tisbury United	24	16	4	4	74	30	44	52
4 Chickerell United	24	14	3	7	73	51	22	45
5 AFC Blandford	24	12	4	8	74	47	27	40
6 Cranborne	24	10	7	7	46	42	4	36*
7 Wincanton Town Res	24	7	3	14	51	73	-22	24
8 Beaminster	24	7	3	14	44	78	-34	24
9 Dorchester Sports Res	24	7	2	15	33	63	-30	23
10 Corfe Mullen United	24	5	7	12	52	58	-6	22
11 Poole Borough	24	5	6	13	47	79	-32	21
12 Broadstone FC Seniors	24	4	5	15	37	57	-20	17
13 Allendale	24	4	5	15	41	88	-47	17

DIVISION ONE	P	W	D	L	F	A	GD	Pts
1 Sturminster Marshall	26	24	1	1	126	22	104	73
2 Merley Cobham Sports Res	26	18	3	5	64	30	34	57
3 Stalbridge	26	16	5	5	77	41	36	53
4 Upwey and Broadwey	26	16	1	9	66	43	23	49
5 Balti Sports Res	26	12	6	8	69	47	22	42
6 Portland Town	26	13	3	10	50	48	2	42
7 Blandford United Res	26	10	7	9	55	49	6	37
8 Wool United Team	26	10	4	12	56	63	-7	34
9 Hamworthy Recreation A	26	10	3	13	82	72	10	33
10 Boscombe Polonia	26	9	3	14	74	92	-18	30
11 Portland United A Team	26	7	2	17	46	78	-32	20*
12 Swanage Town & Herston Res	26	5	4	17	38	97	-59	19
13 Wareham Rangers Res	26	5	4	17	34	93	-59	18*
14 Allendale Res	26	2	4	20	39	101	-62	6*

DIVISION TWO	P	W	D	L	F	A	GD	Pts
1 Gill Dons	24	18	5	1	115	25	90	59
2 Alderholt	24	18	4	2	86	30	56	58
3 Shaftesbury Town Colts	24	13	6	5	70	30	40	45
4 Bridport 3rd Team	24	14	1	9	71	43	28	43
5 Canford United	24	12	5	7	59	42	17	41
6 Parley Sports Res	24	11	2	11	63	57	6	35
7 Maiden Newton & Cattistock	24	7	6	11	46	75	-29	27
8 Portesham United	24	7	5	12	61	54	7	25*
9 Gillingham Town Phoenix	24	7	3	14	39	78	-39	24
10 Broadmayne	24	7	3	14	36	77	-41	24
11 Piddlehinton United	24	6	5	13	28	50	-22	23
12 Broadstone FC Seniors Res	24	6	3	15	37	105	-68	21
13 Sturminster Newton United Res	24	4	4	16	37	82	-45	16

DIVISION THREE	P	W	D	L	F	A	GD	Pts
1 Wool United Res	24	15	6	3	64	38	26	51
2 Donhead United	24	15	5	4	80	57	23	50
3 Verwood All Stars	24	16	1	7	70	34	36	49
4 Piddlehinton United Res	24	13	6	5	64	44	20	45
5 Bere Regis	24	12	3	9	59	55	4	39
6 Handley Sports	24	10	7	7	47	41	6	37
7 Okeford United	24	10	5	9	39	36	3	35
8 Poole Bay Team	24	9	4	11	50	41	9	31
9 Corfe Mullen United Res	24	7	3	14	42	64	-22	24
10 Marnhull	24	5	6	13	30	51	-21	21
11 Portland Town Res	24	6	3	15	48	80	-32	21
12 Corfe Castle Res	24	4	7	13	37	62	-25	19
13 South Cheriton United	24	4	4	16	37	64	-27	16

DIVISION FOUR	P	W	D	L	F	A	GD	Pts
1 Portland United Yth Panthers	24	17	4	3	79	36	43	55
2 Redlands Rebels	24	14	7	3	68	34	34	49
3 Puddletown FC	24	15	4	5	66	32	34	49
4 Chickerell United A	24	15	3	6	87	39	48	48
5 Alderholt Res	24	14	3	7	53	41	12	45
6 Poole Borough Res	24	13	4	7	77	40	37	42*
7 Crossways Spitfires	24	10	4	10	41	54	-13	34
8 Tisbury United Res	24	10	0	14	56	65	-9	30
9 Upton	24	8	5	11	52	65	-13	29
10 Shillingstone	24	7	1	16	31	64	-33	22
11 Verwood All Stars Dev	24	8	1	15	48	44	4	21*
12 Portland Town A Team	24	4	2	18	40	72	-32	14
13 Okeford United Res	24	2	0	22	16	128	-112	6

EAST CORNWALL PREMIER LEAGUE

PREMIER DIVISION	P	W	D	L	F	A	GD	Pts
1 AFC St Austell Res	24	18	4	2	72	20	52	58
2 Saltash United Res	24	18	2	4	69	28	41	56
3 Torpoint Athletic Res	24	17	2	5	66	28	38	53
4 Polperro	24	15	1	8	85	40	45	46
5 Tavistock Association 2nd	24	13	4	7	67	37	30	43
6 Plymstock United 2nd	24	11	3	10	59	68	-9	36
7 Callington Town Res	24	11	2	11	53	52	1	35
8 Millbrook Res	24	9	3	12	42	42	0	30
9 St Stephens Borough	24	9	2	13	46	55	-9	29
10 Liskeard Athletic Res	24	8	2	14	42	58	-16	26
11 Launceston Res	24	6	4	14	44	72	-28	22
12 Wadebridge Town Res	24	2	3	19	26	93	-67	9
13 Looe Town FC	24	3	0	21	22	100	-78	9

DIVISION ONE	P	W	D	L	F	A	GD	Pts
1 St Stephen	18	13	2	3	40	13	27	41
2 Morwenstow	18	12	1	5	65	31	34	37
3 St Minver 1sts	18	12	1	5	50	22	28	37
4 Mevagissey	17	9	2	6	49	24	25	29
5 Roche	18	7	5	6	28	25	3	26
6 Padstow United	18	7	3	8	38	47	-9	24
7 Lanreath	18	6	3	9	40	43	-3	21
8 St Blazey Res	18	6	2	10	37	50	-13	20
9 Newquay Res	17	3	3	11	20	70	-50	12
10 St Teath	18	2	2	14	20	62	-42	8

HALIFAX & DISTRICT LEAGUE

PREMIER DIVISION	P	W	D	L	F	A	GD	Pts
1 Shelf United	18	13	3	2	63	22	41	42
2 Shelf FC	18	13	2	3	74	37	37	41
3 Sowerby Bridge	18	12	4	2	58	29	29	40
4 Greetland	18	9	3	6	52	46	6	30
5 Hebden Royd Red Star	18	9	2	7	54	35	19	29
6 Midgley United	18	9	2	7	42	36	6	29
7 Sowerby United	18	7	1	10	40	53	-13	22
8 Denholme United	18	4	2	12	33	65	-32	14
9 Ryburn United	18	2	1	15	28	80	-52	7
10 Calder 76	18	1	2	15	27	68	-41	5

DIVISION ONE	P	W	D	L	F	A	GD	Pts
1 AFC Illingworth St Mary's	12	10	1	1	58	23	35	31
2 Northowram	12	8	1	3	49	26	23	25
3 St Columbas	12	8	1	3	32	18	14	25
4 Mixenden United	12	6	0	6	52	24	28	18
5 Brighouse Sports	12	4	2	6	25	22	3	14
6 Elland Allstars	12	1	2	9	18	65	-47	5
7 Salem	12	1	1	10	13	69	-56	4

DIVISION TWO	P	W	D	L	F	A	GD	Pts
1 AFC Crossleys	18	17	0	1	93	20	73	51
2 AFC Illingworth St Mary's Res	18	12	1	5	54	48	6	37
3 Midgley United Res	18	10	3	5	48	33	15	33
4 Shelf United Res	18	10	1	7	48	43	5	31
5 Northowram Res	18	6	4	8	42	44	-2	22
6 Greetland Res	18	6	2	10	40	48	-8	20
7 Sowerby United Res	18	6	2	10	24	39	-15	20
8 Calder 76 Res	18	6	1	11	24	40	-16	19
9 Sowerby Bridge Res	18	5	3	10	25	49	-24	18
10 Stainland United	18	2	3	13	24	58	-34	9

DIVISION THREE	P	W	D	L	F	A	GD	Pts
1 Elland United	20	18	1	1	103	21	82	55
2 Shelf FC Res	20	10	3	7	56	35	21	33
3 Flying Dutchman	20	10	2	8	62	48	14	32
4 Hebden Royd Red Star Res	20	7	3	10	47	53	-6	24
5 AFC Crossleys Res	20	8	0	12	50	80	-30	24
6 Warley Rangers	20	1	3	16	30	111	-81	6

HUDDERSFIELD AND DISTRICT ASSOCIATION FOOTBALL LEAGUE

DIVISION ONE	P	W	D	L	F	A	GD	Pts
1 Linthwaite Athletic	21	16	3	2	84	36	48	51
2 Holmbridge F.C.	21	14	4	3	61	19	42	46
3 Heywood Irish Centre FC	22	12	4	6	62	38	24	40
4 Berry Brow	22	12	2	8	67	38	29	38
5 Shepley F.C.	22	11	4	7	39	36	3	37
6 Honley	22	10	4	8	52	47	5	34
7 Skelmanthorpe A.F.C.	22	9	3	10	47	49	-2	30
8 Slaithwaite United	22	8	5	9	59	69	-10	29
9 Newsome	22	7	4	11	53	66	-13	25
10 Diggle	22	6	4	12	47	69	-22	22
11 Hepworth United	22	3	2	17	24	66	-42	11
12 Colne Valley	22	2	3	17	23	85	-62	9

DIVISION TWO	P	W	D	L	F	A	GD	Pts
1 Fothergill & Whittles	24	21	0	3	60	21	39	63
2 Scholes A.F.C.	24	19	2	3	58	30	28	59
3 Britannia Sports	24	14	6	4	66	37	29	48
4 Netherton	24	13	6	5	63	42	21	45
5 Dalton Dynamos	24	12	5	7	71	50	21	41
6 AFC Lindley	24	12	1	11	47	49	-2	37
7 Shelley	24	10	5	9	60	55	5	35
8 Marsden	24	8	1	15	58	66	-8	25
9 H.V.Academicals	24	7	4	13	44	56	-12	25
10 Almondbury Woolpack	24	7	4	13	43	61	-18	25
11 Kirkheaton Rovers	24	4	3	17	28	57	-29	15
12 Littleborough Cricket Club	24	4	3	17	37	80	-43	15
13 Lepton Highlanders	24	4	2	18	31	62	-31	14

DIVISION THREE	P	W	D	L	F	A	GD	Pts
1 Junction	20	15	0	5	69	38	31	45
2 3D Dynamos	20	13	2	5	66	35	31	41
3 Cumberworth	20	11	1	7	54	46	8	34*
4 Scissett	20	10	3	7	43	38	5	33
5 Dewsbury Town FC	20	9	5	6	52	46	6	32
6 Hade Edge A.F.C.	20	8	1	11	40	44	-4	25
7 AFC Dalton	20	7	3	9	41	38	3	24*
8 Uppermill FC	20	6	4	10	46	60	-14	22
9 Brook Motors	20	6	4	10	48	66	-18	22
10 Moorside FC	20	5	5	10	49	46	3	20
11 Golcar United	20	4	2	14	35	86	-51	14

DIVISION FOUR	P	W	D	L	F	A	GD	Pts
1 Huddersfield YM FC	22	20	2	0	93	22	71	62
2 Grange Moor Saints A.F.C.	22	16	1	5	67	39	28	49
3 Sporting C.A.V FC	22	13	4	5	60	45	15	43
4 Deighton FC	22	13	3	5	83	36	47	42*
5 Kirkburton	22	12	3	7	69	35	34	39
6 Meltham Athletic	22	11	3	8	54	58	-4	36
7 Wooldale Wanderers	22	8	3	11	54	53	1	27
8 Flockton FC	22	7	4	11	35	48	-13	25
9 Cleckheaton AFC	22	6	2	14	41	84	-43	20
10 Brighouse Athletic	22	5	2	15	41	66	-25	17
11 Mount	22	4	1	17	32	69	-37	13
12 Cartworth Moor A.F.C.	22	1	2	18	19	93	-74	5*

HARROGATE AND DISTRICT FOOTBALL LEAGUE

PREMIER DIVISION	P	W	D	L	F	A	GD	Pts
1 Harlow Hill First	18	13	5	0	69	22	47	44
2 Ventus Yeadon Celtic First	18	9	7	2	43	29	14	34
3 Pateley Bridge First	18	9	6	3	46	35	11	33
4 Bardsey FC	18	8	4	6	41	44	-3	28
5 Kirkby Malzeard First	18	7	6	5	52	41	11	27
6 Bramhope First	18	7	5	6	48	44	4	26
7 Hampsthwaite FC	18	5	3	10	31	54	-23	18
8 Pannal Sports First	18	5	3	10	36	46	-10	17*
9 Beckwithshaw Saints First	18	3	2	13	21	49	-28	10*
10 Burley Trojans First	18	3	1	14	25	48	-23	9*

DIVISION ONE	P	W	D	L	F	A	GD	Pts
1 Bedale AFC Res	18	13	1	4	77	32	45	40
2 Kirkstall Crusaders JFC	18	12	3	3	49	23	26	39
3 Harrogate Railway Athletic	18	12	0	6	67	26	41	36
4 Harrogate Old Boys	18	11	1	6	49	41	8	33*
5 Beckwithshaw Saints Res	18	9	1	8	41	53	-12	27*
6 Bardsey Res	18	8	0	10	57	57	0	21*
7 Ripon City Res	18	5	3	10	38	75	-37	18
8 Dalton Athletic	18	5	3	10	43	53	-10	12*
9 Harlow Hill Res	18	4	2	12	37	51	-14	11*
10 Kirkby Malzeard Res	18	3	2	13	21	68	-47	8*

LOWESTOFT & DISTRICT LEAGUE

DIVISION ONE	P	W	D	L	F	A	GD	Pts
1 Mutford & Wrentham	24	22	1	1	102	13	89	67
2 Norton Athletic	24	10	6	8	41	54	-13	36
3 & Last	24	10	2	12	32	57	-25	32
4 Oulton Broad	24	13	0	11	58	34	24	27*
5 Spexhall	24	7	3	14	45	75	-30	24
6 Kirkley & Pakefield U23	24	8	3	13	41	60	-19	18*
7 Beccles Caxton . Res	24	5	3	16	38	64	-26	18

DIVISION TWO	P	W	D	L	F	A	GD	Pts
1 Celt Rangers	20	20	0	0	114	10	104	60
2 Carlton Colville Town	20	17	1	2	72	14	58	52
3 Waveney A	20	12	1	7	46	22	24	34*
4 Mariners	20	9	2	9	41	70	-29	29
5 Norton Athletic Res	20	4	7	9	36	40	-4	19
6 Kirkley & Pakefield 'B'	20	6	4	10	27	45	-18	19*
7 Hearts of Oak	20	8	3	9	41	60	-19	18*
8 Crusaders	20	5	3	12	41	66	-25	18
9 Bungay Town 'A'	20	5	3	12	31	69	-38	18
10 Earsham Res	20	5	2	13	28	45	-17	17
11 Redwood United	20	4	4	12	29	65	-36	16

DIVISION THREE	P	W	D	L	F	A	GD	Pts
1 Loddon United Res	22	17	4	1	110	28	82	55
2 Shrublands	22	17	3	2	87	19	68	54
3 F.C. Whitehorse	22	16	3	3	89	30	59	51
4 A.F.C. Oulton	22	15	3	4	84	29	55	48
5 Mutford & Wrentham Res	22	12	3	7	89	42	47	36*
6 Art Eternal	22	10	5	7	68	38	30	32*
7 Carlton Colville Town Res	22	7	2	13	41	92	-51	23
8 Southwold Town . Res	22	5	5	12	38	54	-16	20
9 Spexhall Res	22	6	2	14	54	72	-18	20
10 Payton	22	6	1	15	51	82	-31	19
11 Roman Hill	22	3	1	18	37	106	-69	7*
12 Hawthorn United	22	1	2	19	12	168	-156	5

MIDLANDS REGIONAL ALLIANCE

PREMIER DIVISION	P	W	D	L	F	A	GD	Pts
1 Allestree	28	23	1	4	106	33	73	70
2 Melbourne Dynamo	28	23	1	4	105	32	73	70
3 Castle Donington	28	18	3	7	67	42	25	57
4 Derby Singh Brothers	28	17	3	8	78	59	19	54
5 Mayfield	28	15	1	12	59	57	2	46
6 Rolls-Royce Leisure	28	13	3	12	74	64	10	42
7 Tibshelf	28	13	3	12	69	75	-6	42
8 Moira United Saturday	28	13	1	14	64	66	-2	40
9 Little Eaton	28	10	6	12	64	78	-14	36
10 Ashbourne Res	28	9	4	15	50	67	-17	31
11 Rowsley '86 Res	28	9	3	16	60	79	-19	30
12 Ripley Town	28	8	4	16	49	66	-17	28
13 Wirksworth Town Res	28	8	3	17	46	64	-18	27
14 Willington	28	6	3	19	55	102	-47	21
15 Burton Town	28	5	1	22	38	100	-62	16

DIVISION ONE	P	W	D	L	F	A	GD	Pts
1 Melbourne Dynamo Res	26	21	4	1	102	35	67	67
2 Sherwin	26	19	3	4	78	39	39	60
3 Willington Res	26	19	0	7	104	41	63	57
4 Little Eaton Res	26	14	3	9	77	51	26	45
5 Netherseal St Peter's Sports	26	13	3	10	60	48	12	42
6 Castle Donington Res	26	11	5	10	65	72	-7	38
7 Derby Athletic	26	9	8	9	49	53	-4	35
8 Asha Seconds	26	10	3	13	41	54	-13	33
9 Holbrook St Michaels Juniors	26	10	2	14	65	82	-17	32
10 South Normanton United	26	8	6	12	58	79	-21	30
11 Wirksworth Ivanhoe Res	26	8	6	12	57	80	-23	30
12 Punjab United (Sat)	26	7	2	17	54	84	-30	20*
13 Bargate Rovers	26	4	3	19	50	90	-40	15
14 South Normanton Colts	26	4	2	20	32	84	-52	14

MID-SOMERSET LEAGUE

PREMIER DIVISION	P	W	D	L	F	A	GD	Pts
1 Frome Collegians	18	13	3	2	73	24	49	42
2 Peasedown Albion	18	13	3	2	76	33	43	42
3 Pilton United	18	11	4	3	75	27	48	37
4 Bath Villa	18	12	2	4	52	27	25	36*
5 Purnell Sports Res	18	10	0	8	43	47	-4	27*
6 Coleford Athletic	18	8	2	8	46	36	10	26
7 Westhill Sports	18	5	2	11	23	49	-26	17
8 Westfield Res	18	5	1	12	40	68	-28	16
9 Victoria Sports	18	3	0	15	23	100	-77	2*
10 Radstock Town A	18	1	1	16	21	61	-40	1*

DIVISION ONE	P	W	D	L	F	A	GD	Pts
1 Peasedown Albion Res	18	14	2	2	69	30	39	44
2 Evercreech Rovers	18	9	4	5	44	30	14	31
3 High Littleton	18	7	7	4	36	30	6	28
4 Chew Magna Res	18	9	2	7	41	40	1	28*
5 Chilcompton Sports Res	18	8	3	7	59	38	21	27
6 Wells City A	18	9	2	7	34	29	5	25*
7 Timsbury Athletic Res	18	6	6	6	49	45	4	24
8 Somer Valley Sports	18	5	4	9	40	53	-13	19
9 Clutton Res	18	3	4	11	29	45	-16	13
10 Meadow Rangers	18	2	2	14	21	82	-61	5*

DIVISION TWO	P	W	D	L	F	A	GD	Pts
1 Wessex	18	15	1	2	79	27	52	46
2 Belrose	18	12	3	3	64	35	29	39
3 Weston FC	18	13	1	4	75	24	51	37*
4 Coleford Athletic Res	18	12	1	5	60	31	29	37
5 Stoke Rovers	18	5	5	8	33	33	0	20
6 Saltford Res	18	8	2	8	33	48	-15	20*
7 Farrington Gurney	18	6	2	10	30	53	-23	20
8 Timsbury Athletic A	18	4	0	14	31	69	-38	12
9 Glastonbury Res	18	4	2	12	30	48	-18	11*
10 Westhill Sports Res	18	2	1	15	21	88	-67	3*

DIVISION THREE	P	W	D	L	F	A	GD	Pts
1 Mendip Rangers	16	12	3	1	62	18	44	39
2 Pilton United Res	16	11	3	2	62	29	33	36
3 Frome Collegians Res	16	11	1	4	79	25	54	34
4 Peasedown Albion A	16	10	2	4	55	23	32	32
5 Chilcompton United	16	6	3	7	33	40	-7	21
6 Chilcompton Sports A	16	5	2	9	35	50	-15	17
7 Westfield A	16	4	1	11	24	60	-36	13
8 Evercreech Rovers Res	16	2	2	12	25	55	-30	8
9 FC Lantokay	16	2	1	13	18	93	-75	4*

NORTH WEST NORFOLK LEAGUE

DIVISION ONE	P	W	D	L	F	A	GD	Pts
1 Dersingham Rovers	18	16	2	0	57	23	34	50
2 King's Lynn Town "A"	18	12	0	6	67	36	31	36
3 Snettisham	18	12	0	6	34	31	3	36
4 Birchwood	18	9	2	7	45	38	7	29
5 Heacham Res (Sat)	18	9	2	7	43	40	3	29
6 Terrington Tigers Youth	18	8	4	6	33	34	-1	28
7 AFC Walpole	18	7	1	10	38	35	3	22
8 Denver	18	7	0	11	43	44	-1	21
9 Hunstanton	18	3	1	14	19	35	-16	10
10 Ingoldisthorpe	18	1	0	17	13	76	-63	3

DIVISION TWO	P	W	D	L	F	A	GD	Pts
1 Dersingham Rovers Res	20	16	2	2	77	27	50	50
2 Gayton United 'A' Team	20	13	3	4	47	28	19	42
3 Ingoldisthorpe Res	20	12	2	6	53	56	-3	38
4 Reffley Youth	20	9	4	7	67	50	17	31
5 Woottons (The)	20	10	1	9	59	55	4	31
6 Docking Rangers	20	9	2	9	51	49	2	29
7 F.C. International	20	7	4	9	48	59	-11	25
8 West Lynn	20	7	2	11	41	69	-28	23
9 Marshland Saints	20	5	2	13	50	56	-6	17
10 Watlington S & S Club	20	4	5	11	47	53	-6	17
11 Clenchwarton	20	4	1	15	44	82	-38	13

DIVISION THREE	P	W	D	L	F	A	GD	Pts
1 West Winch	18	14	0	4	78	30	48	42
2 Woottons (The) Res	18	12	2	4	80	34	46	38
3 Terrington Tigers Youth Res	18	10	1	7	53	28	25	31
4 South Creake	18	9	4	5	45	40	5	31
5 Castle Rising	18	8	4	6	38	38	0	28
6 Heacham Social Club	18	8	3	7	46	39	7	27
7 River Lane Rangers	18	9	0	9	41	59	-18	27
8 Hunstanton Town	18	5	3	10	31	46	-15	18
9 Hungate Rovers Youth	18	3	1	14	30	84	-54	10
10 F.C. International Res	18	2	2	14	29	73	-44	8

PERRY STREET AND DISTRICT LEAGUE

PREMIER DIVISION	P	W	D	L	F	A	GD	Pts
1 South Petherton	20	17	1	2	76	19	57	52
2 Winsham United	20	14	3	3	72	22	50	45
3 Misterton	20	11	3	6	45	29	16	36
4 Farway United 1st	20	12	4	4	51	27	24	32*
5 Barrington	20	8	5	7	43	53	-10	29
6 West & Middle Chinnock	20	8	4	8	49	38	11	28
7 Merriott Rovers	20	7	2	11	45	52	-7	22*
8 Halstock	20	8	2	10	36	52	-16	20*
9 Chard United	20	4	5	11	39	56	-17	14*
10 Shepton Beauchamp	20	2	5	13	31	70	-39	11
11 Pymore	20	1	2	17	23	92	-69	4*

DIVISION ONE	P	W	D	L	F	A	GD	Pts
1 Thorncombe	20	14	4	2	70	23	47	46
2 Perry Street & Yonder Hill Res	20	14	2	4	76	25	51	44
3 Waytown Hounds	20	14	2	4	61	22	39	44
4 Forton Rangers	20	13	0	7	74	41	33	39
5 Ilminster Town Res	20	10	5	5	55	31	24	35
6 Hawkchurch 1st	20	7	8	5	46	33	13	29
7 Misterton Res	20	7	4	9	33	56	-23	25
8 Crewkerne Rangers	20	5	3	12	32	55	-23	18
9 Uplyme 1st	20	3	5	12	34	70	-36	14
10 Combe St Nicholas Res	20	3	1	16	21	69	-48	10
11 Netherbury	20	1	4	15	17	94	-77	7

DIVISION TWO	P	W	D	L	F	A	GD	Pts
1 South Petherton Res	20	15	4	1	65	14	51	49
2 Charmouth	20	14	2	4	75	35	40	44
3 Forton Rangers Res	20	12	2	6	63	38	25	38
4 Donyatt United	20	10	3	7	57	50	7	33
5 Dowlish Wake & Donyatt	20	8	3	9	46	43	3	27
6 Chard United Res	20	10	0	10	43	53	-10	26*
7 Chard Rangers	20	8	1	11	37	48	-11	25
8 Ilminster Town A Team	20	8	0	12	40	54	-14	24
9 Shepton Beauchamp Res	20	6	2	12	31	56	-25	20
10 Crewkerne Rangers Res	20	4	3	13	41	78	-37	15
11 Kingsbury Episcopi	20	4	2	14	33	62	-29	14

DIVISION THREE	P	W	D	L	F	A	GD	Pts
1 Lyme Regis Rovers	20	14	3	3	88	27	61	45
2 Winsham United Res	20	14	2	4	85	33	52	44
3 Ilminster Town B Team	20	11	5	4	55	37	18	38
4 Thorncombe Res	19	10	2	7	45	32	13	31*
5 Farway United 2nd	20	9	3	8	66	52	14	30
6 Merriott Dynamos	19	8	5	6	50	39	11	29
7 Combe St Nicholas A	20	8	2	10	52	63	-11	25*
8 Merriott Wildcats	20	7	4	9	43	57	-14	25
9 Netherbury Res	20	6	4	10	38	52	-14	21*
10 Chard Rangers Res	20	6	2	12	49	59	-10	20
11 Crewkerne Rangers A	20	0	0	20	26	146	-120	0

PLYMOUTH & WEST DEVON FOOTBALL LEAGUE

PREMEIR DIVISION	P	W	D	L	F	A	GD	Pts
1 Mount Gould FC	24	18	2	4	92	26	66	50*
2 Chaddlewood Miners O.B.	24	13	2	9	61	44	17	44*
3 The Windmill FC	24	13	2	9	58	40	18	41
4 Plympton Athletic	24	12	2	10	52	49	3	38
5 Signal Box Oak Villa	22	10	2	10	42	54	-12	32
6 Millbridge	24	9	3	12	40	58	-18	30
7 Lakeside Athletic	24	8	5	11	44	57	-13	26*
8 Morley Rangers	22	8	2	12	33	54	-21	26
9 Saltram Athletic	24	4	2	18	24	64	-40	11*

DIVISION ONE	P	W	D	L	F	A	GD	Pts
1 The Windmill FC Res	24	22	0	2	111	27	84	66
2 Plympton Athletic 2nd	24	15	1	8	91	64	27	46
3 Millbridge 2nd	24	13	3	8	62	53	9	42
4 Horrabridge Rangers	24	12	3	9	60	63	-3	36*
5 Pennycross SC	24	10	5	9	62	61	1	35
6 Cherry Tree	24	11	2	11	50	49	1	32*
7 Activate	24	9	3	12	60	67	-7	30
8 Plymouth Hope	24	8	5	11	54	64	-10	29
9 DC Auto Repairs	24	9	2	13	52	63	-11	29
10 Hooe Rovers	24	9	0	15	52	62	-10	27
11 Signal Box Oak Villa 2nd	24	8	3	13	50	61	-11	27
12 Plymouth Vaults	24	8	1	15	43	80	-37	25
13 Plymouth Marjon 2nd	24	7	2	15	53	86	-33	23

DIVISION TWO

	DIVISION TWO	P	W	D	L	F	A	GD	Pts
1	Lakeside Athletic 2nd	24	20	0	4	106	34	72	60
2	Team Carpy	24	17	2	5	113	42	71	53
3	Torpoint Athletic 4th Team	24	12	7	5	87	51	36	43
4	Tavistock Rovers	24	13	3	8	79	59	20	42
5	Morley Rangers 2nd	24	13	2	9	60	59	1	41
6	Plymouth United	24	11	4	9	74	60	14	37
7	Belgrave	24	10	1	13	63	78	-15	31
8	Elburton Villa 2nds	24	9	4	11	79	83	-4	28*
9	South Brent	24	10	2	12	74	52	22	26*
10	Princetown	24	9	3	12	78	80	-2	24*
11	Millbridge 3rd	24	8	1	15	53	111	-58	22*
12	Activate 2nd	24	7	0	17	43	123	-80	21
13	Plymouth Armada FC	24	2	1	21	36	113	-77	7

SOUTH DEVON LEAGUE

	PREMEIR DIVISION	P	W	D	L	F	A	GD	Pts
1	Buckland Athletic 2nd	22	19	2	1	91	25	66	59
2	Chudleigh Athletic	22	17	1	4	55	24	31	52
3	Dartmouth	22	16	1	5	54	32	22	49
4	Kingsteignton Athletic	22	14	3	5	86	32	54	45
5	Totnes & Dartington SC 2nd	22	12	3	7	35	38	-3	39
6	East Allington United	22	9	3	10	46	56	-10	30
7	Paignton Villa	22	6	3	13	37	55	-18	21
8	Roselands	22	4	5	13	39	75	-36	17
9	Ashburton Association	22	6	4	12	37	52	-15	16*
10	Brixham AFC 2nd	22	4	4	14	36	75	-39	16
11	Watcombe Wanderers	22	4	4	14	38	76	-38	10
12	Kingskerswell & Chelston	22	4	1	17	43	57	-14	7*

	DIVISION ONE	P	W	D	L	F	A	GD	Pts
1	Paignton Saints	22	18	2	2	70	27	43	56
2	Broadmeadow ST	22	11	6	5	56	45	11	39
3	Torbay Police	22	11	5	6	76	35	41	38
4	Ivybridge Town 2nd	22	11	2	9	62	43	19	35
5	Newton Abbot Spurs 2nd	22	10	5	7	47	48	-1	35
6	Buckland Athletic 3rd	22	10	4	8	46	43	3	34
7	Bovey Tracey 2nd	22	10	2	10	74	46	28	32
8	Newton Abbot 66	22	9	3	10	53	60	-7	30
9	Salcombe Town	22	8	4	10	54	53	1	28
10	Beesands Rovers	22	6	6	10	38	51	-13	24
11	Loddiswell Athletic	22	5	2	15	35	77	-42	17
12	Babbacombe Corinthians	22	2	1	19	34	117	-83	7

	DIVISION TWO	P	W	D	L	F	A	GD	Pts
1	Buckfastleigh Rangers	24	20	2	2	84	23	61	62
2	Ipplepen Athletic	24	19	1	4	89	27	62	58
3	Meadowbrook Athletic	24	15	3	6	67	39	28	48
4	Kingsteignton Athletic 2nd	24	13	0	11	86	59	27	39
5	Barton Athletic	24	12	3	9	71	78	-7	39
6	Riviera United	24	9	6	9	61	58	3	33
7	Stoke Gabriel 2nd	24	8	3	13	65	75	-10	27
8	Harbertonford 2nd	24	8	3	13	58	76	-18	27
9	Chudleigh Athletic 2nd	24	9	3	12	52	81	-29	24*
10	Waldon Athletic 2nd	24	8	0	16	40	76	-36	24
11	Abbotskerswell	24	5	6	13	49	90	-41	21
12	Dartmouth 2nd	24	8	5	11	45	44	1	17*
13	Roselands 2nd	24	3	3	18	30	71	-41	12

	DIVISION THREE	P	W	D	L	F	A	GD	Pts
1	Watts Blake Bearne	22	18	2	2	101	24	77	56
2	Buckfastleigh Rangers 2nd	22	13	3	6	71	44	27	42
3	Dittisham United	22	11	4	7	55	43	12	37
4	Paignton Villa 2nd	22	11	2	9	41	53	-12	35
5	Newton Rovers	22	10	2	10	50	52	-2	32
6	Torbay Police 2nd	22	9	3	10	58	54	4	30
7	Torquay Town	22	8	5	9	50	54	-4	29
8	Hookhills United	22	6	7	9	58	67	-9	25
9	Upton Athletic 2nd	22	6	5	11	41	74	-33	23
10	Riviera United 2nd	22	6	6	10	42	50	-8	21*
11	East Allington United 2nd	22	7	4	11	29	44	-15	19*
12	Bishopsteignton United 2nd	22	5	1	16	44	81	-37	7*

	DIVISION FOUR	P	W	D	L	F	A	GD	Pts
1	Galmpton United	26	22	2	2	102	30	72	68
2	Babbacombe Corinthians 2nd	26	22	2	2	98	37	61	68
3	Paignton Saints 2nd	26	17	2	7	104	45	59	53
4	Ilsington Villa	26	14	5	7	65	40	25	47
5	Ipplepen Athletic 2nd	26	15	1	10	82	52	30	46
6	Newton Abbot 66 2nd	26	14	2	10	66	64	2	44
7	Broadhempston United	26	13	2	11	74	75	-1	41
8	Kingsbridge & Kellaton United	26	10	3	13	44	62	-18	33
9	Stoke Fleming & Strete	26	11	4	11	53	45	8	28*
10	Watts Blake Bearne 2nds	26	6	5	15	41	68	-27	23
11	Teign Village	26	5	5	16	41	80	-39	20
12	Newton Rovers 2nd	26	5	1	20	38	92	-54	16
13	Chudleigh Athletic 3rds	26	5	1	20	35	84	-49	10*
14	Barton Athletic 2nd	26	5	1	20	41	110	-69	10*

SOUTHAMPTON FOOTBALL LEAGUE

	PREMIER DIVISION	P	W	D	L	F	A	GD	Pts
1	Chamberlayne AFC	16	12	3	1	51	18	33	39
2	Bishops Waltham	16	9	6	1	39	13	26	33
3	Compton	16	10	3	3	43	24	19	33
4	Alderbury	16	9	5	2	39	21	18	32
5	Montefiore Halls	16	6	2	8	29	42	-13	20
6	Priory Rovers	16	5	3	8	34	39	-5	18
7	Soton University	16	4	2	10	22	31	-9	14
8	Comrades Sports	16	3	3	10	24	40	-16	12
9	BTC Soton	16	0	1	15	8	61	-53	1

	SENIOR DIVISION	P	W	D	L	F	A	GD	Pts
1	FC Independence	16	12	1	3	49	19	30	37
2	Braishfield	16	11	2	3	73	18	55	35
3	Knightwood Utd	16	11	2	3	63	33	30	35
4	Durley	16	11	0	5	53	22	31	33
5	Hedge End Town	16	10	1	5	58	23	35	31
6	Warsash Wasps	16	5	2	9	41	45	-4	17
7	Comrades Sports Res	16	3	3	10	28	67	-39	12
8	BTC Soton Res	16	1	2	13	16	83	-67	5
9	Nursling	16	1	1	14	18	89	-71	4

STROUD & DISTRICT LEAGUE

	DIVISION ONE	P	W	D	L	F	A	GD	Pts
1	Kings Stanley	22	16	4	2	55	20	35	52
2	Charfield	22	16	1	5	53	26	27	49
3	Tredworth Tigers	22	10	4	8	52	43	9	34
4	Hardwicke Res	22	8	8	6	34	32	2	32
5	Randwick	22	9	4	9	39	36	3	31
6	Stonehouse Town Res	22	9	3	10	35	39	-4	30
7	Dursley Town	22	9	1	12	39	44	-5	28
8	Tetbury Town	22	5	10	7	37	38	-1	25
9	Old Richians	22	6	7	9	27	40	-13	25
10	Rodborough Old Boys	22	6	5	11	34	44	-10	23
11	Kingswood Res	22	6	5	11	26	37	-11	20*
12	Longlevens 3rds	22	5	2	15	22	54	-32	14*

	DIVISION TWO	P	W	D	L	F	A	GD	Pts
1	Didmarton	22	15	2	5	44	33	11	47
2	Quedgeley Wanderers Res	22	15	1	6	57	28	29	46
3	Chalford Res	22	13	5	4	63	40	23	44
4	Ramblers	22	13	4	5	54	40	14	43
5	Minchinhampton	22	11	2	9	60	44	16	35
6	Sharpness Res	22	9	1	12	45	47	-2	28
7	Wotton Rovers	22	8	3	11	58	57	1	27
8	Taverners Res	22	7	4	11	45	64	-19	25
9	Tibberton United	22	7	2	13	31	42	-11	23
10	Cam Bulldogs Res	22	7	1	14	27	51	-24	22
11	Eastcombe	22	6	3	13	47	59	-12	21
12	Trident	22	6	2	14	32	58	-26	20

	DIVISION THREE	P	W	D	L	F	A	GD	Pts
1	Kingsway Rovers	22	18	3	1	94	29	65	57
2	Upton St Leonards Res	22	16	3	3	79	22	57	51
3	Tuffley Rovers 3rds	22	14	0	8	71	50	21	42
4	Wickwar Wanderers	22	11	2	9	53	40	13	35
5	Uley	22	8	6	8	38	50	-12	30
6	Longford	22	8	5	9	56	50	6	29
7	Tredworth Tigers Res	22	9	2	11	49	66	-17	29
8	Tetbury Town Res	22	9	2	11	36	55	-19	29
9	Horsley United	21	8	3	10	36	63	-27	27
10	Thornbury Town Res	22	5	4	13	41	45	-4	16*
11	Barnwood United Res	21	3	5	13	37	67	-30	14
12	Quedgeley Wanderers 3rds	22	4	1	17	25	78	-53	10*

DIVISION FOUR	P	W	D	L	F	A	GD	Pts
1 Charfield Res	20	17	1	2	80	30	50	52
2 Hempsted	20	16	1	3	81	30	51	49
3 Avonvale United	20	13	4	3	52	17	35	43
4 Hardwicke 3rds	20	10	2	8	53	51	2	32
5 Cotswold Rangers	20	8	5	7	40	38	2	26*
6 Stonehouse Town 3rds	20	7	4	9	54	69	-15	25
7 Old Richians Res	20	7	6	7	49	42	7	24*
8 Frampton United 3rds	20	6	5	9	35	50	-15	23
9 Tuffley Rovers 4ths	20	4	3	13	34	71	-37	15
10 Saintbridge	20	1	1	18	33	85	-52	4
11 Alkerton Rangers	20	4	2	14	36	64	-28	-4*

DIVISION FIVE	P	W	D	L	F	A	GD	Pts
1 North Nibley	22	18	1	3	93	29	64	55
2 Abbeymead Rovers Res	21	15	3	3	79	41	38	48
3 Kingsway Rovers Res	22	14	2	6	98	54	44	44
4 Painswick	22	13	3	6	71	54	17	42
5 Rodborough Old Boys Res	22	10	1	11	43	59	-16	31
6 Chalford 3rds	22	8	6	8	62	51	11	30
7 Kings Stanley Res	22	9	2	11	57	79	-22	29
8 Berkeley Town Res	22	8	2	12	43	67	-24	26
9 Dursley Town Res	22	7	2	13	45	60	-15	23
10 Longlevens 4ths	22	7	2	13	39	67	-28	20*
11 Randwick Res	22	5	4	13	49	66	-17	19
12 Wotton Rovers Res	21	3	0	18	35	87	-52	3*

DIVISION SIX	P	W	D	L	F	A	GD	Pts
1 Cashes Green	24	16	4	4	72	23	49	52
2 Minchinhampton Res	24	17	0	7	72	40	32	51
3 Gloster Rovers	24	15	4	5	91	52	39	49
4 Tuffley Rovers 5ths	24	13	5	6	58	40	18	44
5 Cotswold Rangers Res	24	11	5	8	45	56	-11	38
6 Sharpness 3rds	24	11	4	9	42	63	-21	37
7 Eastcombe Res	24	9	1	14	48	60	-12	28
8 Abbeymead Rovers 3rds	24	6	9	9	51	58	-7	27
9 Cam Bulldogs 3rds	24	7	5	12	49	56	-7	26
10 Leonard Stanley Res	24	7	5	12	38	53	-15	26
11 Brockworth Albion 3rds	24	7	4	13	46	57	-11	25
12 Longford Res	24	7	2	15	35	53	-18	23
13 Uley Res	24	4	4	16	47	83	-36	16

DIVISION SEVEN	P	W	D	L	F	A	GD	Pts
1 Ramblers Res	22	16	3	3	88	38	50	51
2 Rodborough Old Boys 3rds	22	15	2	5	76	33	43	47
3 Chalford 4ths	22	13	3	6	112	38	74	42
4 Stonehouse Town 4ths	22	12	5	5	71	51	20	41
5 Stroud United	22	13	1	8	82	59	23	40
6 Horsley United Res	22	10	4	8	81	48	33	34
7 Tetbury Town 3rds	22	12	2	8	64	56	8	32*
8 Cam Everside Wanderers	22	10	4	8	68	45	23	30*
9 Randwick 3rds	22	6	3	13	44	75	-31	21
10 Woodchester	22	5	2	15	39	126	-87	16*
11 Cashes Green Res	22	2	3	17	37	94	-57	6*
12 Uley 3rds	22	1	2	19	21	120	-99	5

SURREY COUNTY INTERMEDIATE LEAGUE (WESTERN)

PREMIER DIVISION	P	W	D	L	F	A	GD	Pts
1 Lyne Seniors	12	7	4	1	31	16	15	25
2 Guildford United	12	6	4	2	36	21	15	22
3 Shottermill & Haslemere	12	5	3	4	31	27	4	18
4 Cranleigh	12	4	2	6	22	27	-5	14
5 Milford & Witley	12	4	1	7	20	31	-11	13
6 Chobham Burymead	12	5	1	6	29	30	-1	9*
7 University of Surrey	12	2	3	7	26	43	-17	8*

DIVISION ONE	P	W	D	L	F	A	GD	Pts
1 Knaphill Athletic	14	8	4	2	45	22	23	28
2 Lightwater United	14	7	3	4	28	27	1	24
3 Hambledon	14	7	2	5	43	30	13	23
4 Manorcroft United	14	6	3	5	30	28	2	21
5 Windlesham United	14	5	3	6	29	41	-12	18
6 Chiddingfold	14	5	1	8	25	28	-3	16
7 Keens Park Rangers	14	3	6	5	30	34	-4	15
8 Ottershaw	14	2	4	8	18	38	-20	10

SURREY SOUTH EASTERN COMBINATION

DIVISION ONE	P	W	D	L	F	A	GD	Pts
1 Old Rutlishians	26	20	3	3	90	25	65	63
2 Wandgas Sport	26	18	4	4	78	43	35	58
3 Frenches Athletic	26	15	6	5	62	33	29	51
4 Goldfingers	26	16	5	5	62	39	23	50*
5 Tooting Bec Reserves	26	15	4	7	63	40	23	49
6 A.M.Y	26	14	4	8	52	39	13	46
7 West Fulham	26	12	4	10	58	48	10	40
8 Hanworth Sports	26	12	2	12	50	37	13	38
9 Westminster Casuals	26	8	6	12	40	41	-1	30
10 Balham Reserves	26	8	2	16	45	49	-4	26
11 Reigate Priory	26	5	4	17	33	86	-53	19
12 Turkocagi Bermondsey	26	4	4	18	31	91	-60	19*
13 LDN South West	26	5	4	17	32	79	-47	17*
14 Forestdale	26	2	4	20	29	75	-46	10

DIVISION TWO	P	W	D	L	F	A	GD	Pts
1 Earlsfield United	24	17	4	3	67	41	26	57*
2 AFC Walcountians	24	16	5	3	103	38	65	53
3 Kew Park Rangers	24	14	6	4	77	37	40	48
4 AFC Ewell	24	15	3	6	68	42	26	48
5 Dover House Lions	24	13	5	6	76	39	37	44
6 Oxted & District	24	12	1	11	59	50	9	37
7 Sporting 50	24	11	3	10	47	51	-4	36
8 Claygate Royals	24	10	2	12	50	47	3	32
9 Merton Social	24	6	5	13	37	60	-23	23
10 Chelsea Rovers	24	6	2	16	42	75	-33	20
11 Rygas	24	6	2	16	29	42	-13	19*
12 AC Malden	24	6	0	18	24	107	-83	18
13 Ashtead	24	4	2	18	37	87	-50	14

SWINDON & DISTRICT FOOTBALL LEAGUE

PREMIER DIVISION	P	W	D	L	F	A	GD	Pts
1 Ruby Removals	16	14	0	2	59	26	33	42
2 Stratton Juniors	16	10	4	2	46	18	28	34
3 Bakers Arms FC	16	8	4	4	34	26	8	28
4 Wheatsheaf Stratton	16	9	1	6	38	41	-3	28
5 FC Dorcan	16	8	1	7	40	36	4	25
6 Ashton Keynes	16	7	1	8	47	41	6	22
7 Swindon Supermarine Dev	16	6	2	8	47	53	-6	20
8 Lower Stratton	16	2	2	12	30	61	-31	8
9 Marlborough Town Res	16	0	1	15	19	58	-39	1

DIVISON ONE	P	W	D	L	F	A	GD	Pts
1 Blunsdon FC	18	17	0	1	87	21	66	51
2 Kintbury Rangers Res	18	16	0	2	84	13	71	48
3 Wroughton Reserves	18	9	3	6	79	50	29	30
4 Highworth Town Dev	18	8	3	7	58	37	21	27
5 Sportz Central	18	8	2	8	46	48	-2	26
6 Chiseldon FC	18	8	1	9	41	40	1	25
7 Ramsbury	18	8	1	9	44	51	-7	25
8 North Swindon WMC FC	18	6	2	10	38	74	-36	20
9 Village Inn	18	3	0	15	30	52	-22	9
10 Swindon Centurians FC	18	1	0	17	27	148	-121	3

DIVISION TWO	P	W	D	L	F	A	GD	Pts
1 Redhouse FC	18	15	2	1	74	19	55	47
2 Spectrum	18	10	0	8	51	45	6	30
3 Cricklade Town Res	18	8	5	5	40	35	5	29
4 Swindon AFC	18	8	4	6	46	29	17	28
5 Priory Vale FC	18	8	3	7	34	34	0	27
6 Moredon FC	18	8	1	9	32	38	-6	25
7 Down Ampney	18	7	3	8	39	43	-4	24
8 FC Abbeymeads	18	6	2	10	25	57	-32	20
9 Bassett Bulldogs FC	18	5	4	9	40	41	-1	19
10 Brockhill United FC	18	1	4	13	21	61	-40	7

TAUNTON LEAGUE

DIVISION ONE	P	W	D	L	F	A	GD	Pts
1 Bishops Lydeard Res	22	19	3	0	74	17	57	60
2 Bridgwater Sports s	22	15	4	3	58	29	29	49
3 Wembdon	22	15	2	5	69	29	40	47
4 Westonzoyland	22	12	4	6	51	33	18	40
5 North Petherton	22	10	4	8	60	55	5	34
6 Redgate	22	9	4	9	56	46	10	31
7 Galmington Dragons	22	9	4	9	62	53	9	31
8 Creech Cougars	22	6	7	9	58	64	-6	25
9 Alcombe Rovers	22	6	6	10	41	55	-14	21*
10 Watchet Town Res	22	4	6	12	30	55	-25	18
11 Porlock	22	3	1	18	31	74	-43	10
12 Morganians	22	1	1	20	12	92	-80	1*

DIVISION TWO	P	W	D	L	F	A	GD	Pts
1 FC Castlemoat	20	18	1	1	123	32	91	55
2 Stogursey	20	18	1	1	99	25	74	55
3 North Curry (Sat)	20	11	3	6	60	30	30	36
4 Bridgwater Sports Res	20	11	2	7	50	55	-5	35
5 Minehead AFC Res	20	7	4	9	32	43	-11	25
6 Dulverton Town	20	7	2	11	46	59	-13	23
7 White Eagles (Taunton)	20	6	3	11	44	61	-17	18*
8 Middlezoy Rovers Athletic	20	5	3	12	23	67	-44	18
9 Bridgwater Grasshoppers	20	5	1	14	39	85	-46	16
10 Norton Fitzwarren	20	1	8	11	33	68	-35	11
11 Butlins	20	4	6	10	36	60	-24	9*

DIVISION THREE	P	W	D	L	F	A	GD	Pts
1 Wembdon Res	28	25	3	0	133	23	110	78
2 Staplegrove Crusaders	28	25	2	1	171	33	138	77
3 Wellington A	28	17	5	6	103	39	64	56
4 Wyvern United	28	18	2	8	104	55	49	56
5 FC Castlemoat Res	28	17	1	10	113	74	39	52
6 Nether Stowey	28	13	6	9	85	51	34	45
7 Galmington Dragons Res	28	11	4	13	53	97	-44	37
8 Porlock Res	28	9	2	17	79	84	-5	29
9 Hamilton Athletic Foxes	28	9	1	18	74	123	-49	28
10 Minehead AFC Colts	28	8	4	16	60	110	-50	28
11 North Petherton (Mens) Res	28	7	6	15	39	68	-29	27
12 Bridgwater Sports Colts	28	8	3	17	47	94	-47	27
13 Exmoor Rangers	28	8	1	19	38	106	-68	25
14 Morganians Res	28	9	2	17	61	119	-58	20 *
15 Norton Fitzwarren Res	28	4	2	22	40	124	-84	14

THE ST EDMUNDSBURY FOOTBALL LEAGUE

DIVISION ONE	P	W	D	L	F	A	GD	Pts
1 Walsham Le Willows B	17	15	0	2	92	21	71	45
2 St Edmunds 1965	17	15	0	2	81	11	70	45
3 Walsham Le Willows A	18	7	5	6	48	45	3	26
4 Vipers	18	7	3	8	37	43	-6	24
5 Stage	18	7	3	8	41	53	-12	24
6 Bury Town Rams	18	1	3	14	23	87	-64	5*
7 RF Saints	18	1	4	13	16	78	-62	4*

TROWBRIDGE & DISTRICT FOOTBALL LEAGUE

DIVISION ONE	P	W	D	L	F	A	GD	Pts
1 Holt	18	15	1	2	64	32	32	46
2 Freshford United	18	13	1	4	88	30	58	40
3 Hilperton United	18	12	0	6	69	39	30	36
4 Heytesbury	18	11	0	7	67	42	25	33
5 Three Daggers	18	11	0	7	57	44	13	33
6 Semington Magpies	18	7	3	8	38	37	1	24
7 Melksham Town 'A'	18	7	3	8	45	56	-11	24
8 Warminster Town Res	18	3	2	13	41	67	-26	14*
9 Calne Eagles	18	2	1	15	24	84	-60	7
10 Trowbridge Town Res	18	2	3	13	23	85	-62	7*

DIVISION TWO	P	W	D	L	F	A	GD	Pts
1 Warminster United	18	17	0	1	64	5	59	51
2 Marshfield	18	13	1	4	66	15	51	40
3 Calne Town Res	18	13	1	4	74	25	49	40
4 Westbury United Res	18	12	1	5	46	23	23	37
5 Aces	18	9	2	7	34	40	-6	29
6 Zeals	18	7	2	9	51	53	-2	23
7 Greyhound	18	5	2	11	28	62	-34	17
8 The Stiffs	18	3	2	13	15	61	-46	11
9 Seend United	18	3	0	14	25	62	-37	9*
10 Trowbridge Wanderers Dev	18	1	1	15	14	71	-57	4*

WAKEFIELD & DISTRICT LEAGUE

PREMIER DIVISION	P	W	D	L	F	A	GD	Pts
1 Crackenedge FC	16	16	0	0	74	21	53	48
2 Crofton Sports FC	16	10	1	5	43	40	3	31
3 Royston Cross FC	16	8	1	7	38	35	3	25
4 Snydale Athletic	16	8	1	7	37	38	-1	25
5 Beechwood Santos FC	15	6	1	8	41	47	-6	19
6 Overthorpe SC	16	5	3	8	41	53	-12	18
7 Durkar FC	16	6	0	10	27	44	-17	18
8 Ryhill FC	16	4	1	11	36	41	-5	12*
9 Fox & Hounds (Batley) FC	15	4	0	11	32	50	-18	12

DIVISION ONE	P	W	D	L	F	A	GD	Pts
1 Red Lion Alverthorpe FC	18	14	1	3	78	34	44	43
2 Nostell Miners Welfare	18	13	2	3	85	19	66	41
3 Fieldhead Hospital	18	12	2	4	71	46	25	38
4 Ossett Dynamos	18	10	3	5	67	37	30	33
5 Waterloo FC	18	7	6	5	54	40	14	27
6 Pontefract Sports & Social	18	7	5	6	43	39	4	26
7 West End Terriers FC	17	5	4	8	47	39	8	19
8 FC Thornes	18	4	4	10	35	74	-39	16
9 Thorn Tree United	17	3	1	13	35	98	-63	0*
10 AFC Sheaf	18	0	0	18	17	106	-89	0

DIVISION TWO	P	W	D	L	F	A	GD	Pts
1 Howden Clough	20	17	1	2	95	26	69	52
2 Great Preston FC	20	16	2	2	102	34	68	50
3 Dewsbury Westside	20	13	1	6	63	53	10	40
4 Thornhill United	20	12	1	7	56	36	20	37
5 Snydale Athletic Res	20	12	0	8	62	46	16	33*
6 Pontefract Town	20	11	2	7	60	44	16	32*
7 Garforth WMC FC	20	10	1	9	65	59	6	31
8 Crofton Sports FC Res	20	5	1	14	25	58	-33	16
9 New Carlton FC	20	5	1	14	33	82	-49	13*
10 FC Broadway	20	2	1	17	28	93	-65	7
11 Overthorpe SC Res	20	1	1	18	22	80	-58	4

WEST RIDING COUNTY AMATEUR LEAGUE

PREMIER DIVISION	P	W	D	L	F	A	GD	Pts
1 Golcar United	22	20	1	1	105	20	85	61
2 Littletown FC	22	17	3	2	79	37	42	54
3 Ryburn United	22	14	3	5	81	45	36	45
4 TVR United	22	15	0	7	75	52	23	45
5 Lower Hopton	22	14	1	7	63	45	18	43
6 Route One Rovers	22	11	3	8	47	47	0	36
7 Steeton Reserves	22	11	2	9	68	82	-14	35
8 Bradford Olympic	22	5	2	15	30	47	-17	17
9 Toller FC	21	5	2	14	54	86	-32	17
10 Ovenden West Riding	21	4	1	16	35	92	-57	13
11 PFC	22	3	1	18	39	78	-39	10
12 Lepton Highlanders	22	2	1	19	22	67	-45	7

DIVISION ONE	P	W	D	L	F	A	GD	Pts
1 Ovenden West Riding	18	17	1	0	113	24	89	52
2 Salts Res	18	11	2	5	56	36	20	35
3 Steeton Res	18	10	2	6	75	39	36	32
4 Golcar United Res	18	10	2	6	64	34	30	32
5 Overthorpe Sports Club	18	8	3	7	48	59	-11	27
6 West Horton	18	6	4	8	47	66	-19	22
7 Tingley Athletic	18	6	3	9	30	44	-14	21
8 T V R United	18	5	3	10	59	74	-15	18
9 Hunsworth	18	5	1	12	34	70	-36	16
10 Bradford FC	18	1	1	16	26	106	-80	4

WESTON SUPER MARE AND DISTRICT FOOTBALL LEAGUE

DIVISION ONE	P	W	D	L	F	A	GD	Pts
1 St George Easton In Gordano	18	12	2	4	53	29	24	38
2 Portishead Town A Team	18	11	3	4	61	32	29	36
3 K V	18	10	2	6	35	30	5	32
4 Locking Park	18	9	4	5	36	29	7	31
5 Nailsea United A Team	18	9	2	7	42	44	-2	29
6 Uphill Castle Res	18	7	1	10	33	41	-8	22
7 Sporting Weston	18	5	5	8	31	36	-5	20
8 Wedmore	18	6	2	10	26	48	-22	20
9 Clapton In Gordano	18	4	3	11	33	49	-16	15
10 Worle Res	18	4	2	12	24	36	-12	14

DIVISION TWO	P	W	D	L	F	A	GD	Pts
1 Portishead Town B Team	20	16	2	2	63	22	41	50
2 Churchill Club 70	20	12	6	2	56	24	32	42
3 Winscombe A	20	11	5	4	54	34	20	38
4 Congresbury Res	20	10	4	6	43	39	4	34
5 Nailsea United B Team	20	10	2	8	35	36	-1	32
6 Locking Park Res	20	9	1	10	48	60	-12	24*
7 Banwell Res	20	6	5	9	57	61	-4	23
8 Wrington Redhill Res	20	7	2	11	35	55	-20	23
9 Yatton & Cleeve United A	20	5	2	13	29	36	-7	17
10 Worle Rangers	20	4	4	12	41	48	-7	15*
11 South Park Rangers	20	3	1	16	28	74	-46	10

DIVISION THREE	P	W	D	L	F	A	GD	Pts
1 Shipham	24	18	0	6	82	39	43	54
2 Hutton Res	24	16	3	5	117	48	69	51
3 Selkirk United	24	16	0	8	97	41	56	48
4 Lodway	24	14	3	7	99	57	42	45
5 Cheddar A Team	24	12	3	9	49	44	5	39
6 St George Easton In Gordano Res	24	10	6	8	58	48	10	36
7 Burnham United A	24	11	3	10	59	57	2	36
8 Uphill Castle A	24	9	5	10	58	50	8	32
9 West Wick	24	9	3	12	54	77	-23	30
10 Sporting Weston Res	24	8	2	14	47	104	-57	26
11 Banwell A	24	7	0	17	30	86	-56	21
12 AFC Nailsea	24	5	5	14	32	67	-35	20
13 Congresbury A	24	4	1	19	22	86	-64	13

DIVISION FOUR	P	W	D	L	F	A	GD	Pts
1 Weston Town	22	21	1	0	134	17	117	64
2 Axbridge Town	22	17	3	2	74	34	40	54
3 Hutton A	22	14	2	6	98	47	51	44
4 Huntspill Crowns SAT	22	14	1	7	56	34	22	43
5 Weston Celtic s	22	12	1	9	92	73	19	37
6 Nailsea United C Team	22	12	0	10	70	51	19	36
7 Clevedon United A	22	10	2	10	56	51	5	32
8 Burnham United B	22	7	2	13	39	62	-23	23
9 Worle Rangers Res	22	7	0	15	51	105	-54	18*
10 Wedmore Res	22	5	2	15	40	105	-65	16*
11 "Wrington Redhill ""A"""	22	4	0	18	23	52	-29	12
12 AFC Nailsea Res	22	2	0	20	18	120	-102	6

WITNEY & DISTRICT LEAGUE

PREMIER DIVISION	P	W	D	L	F	A	GD	Pts
1 Charlbury Town	18	13	4	1	65	26	39	43
2 Hailey	18	10	5	3	47	28	19	35
3 FC Hollybush	18	10	4	4	37	23	14	34
4 Aston	18	7	5	6	33	39	-6	26
5 Tower Hill	18	5	6	7	28	26	2	24*
6 Kirtlington FC	17	7	3	7	35	41	-6	24
7 Minster Lovell	17	5	4	8	25	34	-9	19
8 Carterton Rangers	18	3	6	9	24	39	-15	15
9 Carterton Town A	18	6	0	12	27	43	-16	15*
10 Spartan Rangers	18	3	3	12	25	47	-22	12

DIVISION ONE	P	W	D	L	F	A	GD	Pts
1 Stonesfield	18	13	1	4	64	26	38	40
2 Milton-U-Wychwood	18	11	2	5	62	37	25	35
3 Chadlington	18	9	3	6	42	30	12	33*
4 Moreton Rangers	18	10	3	5	44	37	7	33
5 Middle Barton	18	7	4	7	43	43	0	25
6 Bampton United	18	7	2	9	45	43	2	23
7 Witney Royals	18	6	3	9	32	48	-16	21
8 Bourton Rovers	18	7	2	9	41	45	-4	20*
9 Combe	18	4	5	9	25	37	-12	17
10 Eynsham SSC	18	3	1	14	32	84	-52	10

DIVISION TWO	P	W	D	L	F	A	GD	Pts
1 Minster Lovell Res	16	10	2	4	47	23	24	32
2 Kingham All Blacks	16	10	1	5	45	24	21	31
3 Hailey Res	16	8	4	4	38	28	10	28
4 Siege	16	7	3	6	34	33	1	24
5 Ducklington	16	6	3	7	27	38	-11	21
6 Charlbury Town Res	16	5	4	7	34	40	-6	19
7 Witney Wanderers	16	6	0	10	28	39	-11	18
8 Brize Norton	16	4	4	8	32	39	-7	16
9 Aston Res	16	4	3	9	20	41	-21	15

DIVISION THREE	P	W	D	L	F	A	GD	Pts
1 Carterton Town B	18	14	4	0	58	15	43	46
2 Spartan Rangers Res	18	11	3	4	59	37	22	36
3 Hook Norton FC	18	11	1	6	75	44	31	34
4 Wootton Sports	18	11	1	6	61	41	20	34
5 Bletchington Res	18	8	2	8	42	30	12	26
6 FC Mills	18	8	2	8	49	49	0	26
7 Bourton Rovers Res	18	6	3	9	37	45	-8	21
8 Witney Royals Res	18	5	1	12	28	73	-45	16
9 Chipping Norton Town Res	18	4	1	13	25	58	-33	13
10 Tower Hill Res	18	2	2	14	24	66	-42	8

DIVISION FOUR	P	W	D	L	F	A	GD	Pts
1 Chadlington Res	20	14	3	3	56	18	38	47*
2 Kingham All Blacks Res	20	12	3	5	61	35	26	39
3 Stonesfield Res	20	12	3	5	59	59	0	39
4 Wootton Sports Res	20	10	3	7	47	31	16	33
5 Brize Norton Res	20	10	3	7	57	44	13	33
6 Milton-U-Wychwood Res	20	10	2	8	73	41	32	32
7 Bampton United Res	20	10	2	8	49	37	12	32
8 Eynsham SSC Res	20	8	1	11	46	58	-12	25
9 FC Ascott	20	6	4	10	49	53	-4	21*
10 Spartan Rangers A	20	3	1	16	37	100	-63	10
11 FC Ascott Rangers	20	2	1	17	18	76	-58	7

YEOVIL AND DISTRICT LEAGUE

PREMEIR DIVISION	P	W	D	L	F	A	GD	Pts
1 Ashcott	16	13	2	1	60	17	43	41
2 Templecombe Rovers	16	10	2	4	48	21	27	32
3 Stoke	16	10	1	5	43	31	12	31
4 Castle Cary Res	16	8	3	5	36	28	8	24*
5 Wagtail Athletic	16	7	3	6	37	36	1	24
6 Bradford Abbas	16	7	2	7	39	36	3	23
7 Pen Mill Athletic	16	4	3	9	28	53	-25	15
8 Keinton Park Rangers	16	2	2	12	24	54	-30	8
9 Martock United	16	1	2	13	16	55	-39	4*

DIVISION ONE	P	W	D	L	F	A	GD	Pts
1 Milborne Port	16	14	1	1	75	16	59	43
2 Odcombe	16	12	1	3	50	26	24	37
3 Manor Athletic	16	9	2	5	35	23	12	29
4 Barwick & Stoford	16	6	4	6	36	33	3	22
5 Huish AFC	16	5	4	7	33	46	-13	19
6 Langport & Huish Sports	16	5	3	8	38	37	1	17*
7 Bruton United	16	5	1	10	33	58	-25	16
8 Ashcott Res	16	4	2	10	29	46	-17	14
9 Pen Mill Athletic Res	16	3	0	13	23	67	-44	9

DIVISION TWO	P	W	D	L	F	A	GD	Pts
1 Queen Camel	16	16	0	0	86	10	76	48
2 AFC Strode	16	14	0	2	73	18	55	42
3 Ilchester	16	9	1	6	48	32	16	28
4 Wyndham Athletic	16	7	1	8	36	58	-22	22
5 Odcombe Res	16	5	2	9	33	54	-21	17
6 Keinton Park Rangers Res	16	5	1	10	30	43	-13	13*
7 Stoke Res	16	3	4	9	29	48	-19	13
8 Crewkerne Rangers Colts	16	4	4	8	27	50	-23	12*
9 Milborne Port Res	16	1	3	12	17	66	-49	6

YORKSHIRE AMATEUR LEAGUE

PREMEIR DIVISION	P	W	D	L	F	A	GD	Pts
1 Farsley Celtic Juniors	22	19	2	1	98	13	85	59
2 Leeds Medics & Dentists	22	15	5	2	50	24	26	50
3 Grangefield Old Boys	22	16	0	6	50	31	19	48
4 Drighlington	22	15	2	5	62	29	33	47
5 Stanley United	22	9	2	11	51	57	-6	29
6 Horsforth St. Margarets	22	8	3	11	40	48	-8	27
7 Athletico FC	22	8	2	12	63	61	2	26
8 Alwoodley	22	7	5	10	43	45	-2	26
9 Calverley United FC	22	6	4	12	42	70	-28	22
10 Wibsey	22	6	1	15	46	90	-44	19
11 Ealandians	22	5	2	15	40	85	-45	17
12 Stanningley Old Boys	22	3	2	17	42	74	-32	10*

CHAMPIONSHIP	P	W	D	L	F	A	GD	Pts
1 Wortley	22	18	2	2	80	28	52	56
2 Gildersome Spurs O.B.	22	17	2	3	107	38	69	53
3 Leeds City FC	22	14	2	6	65	41	24	44
4 Morley Town AFC	22	13	3	6	58	55	3	42
5 St Bedes	22	10	3	9	75	63	12	33
6 Shire Academics	22	10	2	10	53	53	0	32
7 Leeds Medics & Dentists Res	22	7	3	12	36	50	-14	24
8 Mount St Marys	22	4	8	10	31	60	-29	20
9 Ealandians Res	22	6	2	14	38	75	-37	20
10 Garforth Crusaders	22	6	3	13	45	65	-20	18*
11 Leeds Independent	22	5	2	15	33	62	-29	17
12 Beeston St Anthony	22	5	2	15	41	72	-31	16*

DIVISION ONE	P	W	D	L	F	A	GD	Pts
1 Amaranth Crossgates	24	20	1	3	109	41	68	61
2 Collegians	24	17	2	5	71	42	29	53
3 Idle FC	24	16	4	4	60	46	14	52
4 Woodkirk Valley	24	14	2	8	81	48	33	44*
5 Golcar United	24	12	5	7	70	55	15	41
6 Dewsbury Rangers	24	13	1	10	53	45	8	40
7 Beeston Juniors	24	11	2	11	71	57	14	35
8 Thornesians	24	10	1	13	61	68	-7	31
9 Farsley Celtic Juniors Res	24	9	2	13	62	74	-12	26*
10 Alwoodley Res	24	7	1	16	48	84	-36	19*
11 Collingham Juniors	24	6	0	18	57	98	-41	18
12 Whitkirk Wanderers	24	6	1	17	36	72	-36	13*
13 Leeds Medics & Dentists III	24	2	4	18	37	86	-49	7*

DIVISION TWO	P	W	D	L	F	A	GD	Pts
1 Colton Athletic	20	16	3	1	86	31	55	51
2 Shire Academics Res	20	13	2	5	69	40	29	41
3 Tyersal	20	12	4	4	71	44	27	40
4 Fairbank United	20	12	1	7	58	54	4	37
5 Leeds City FC Res	20	10	0	10	52	42	10	30
6 Horsforth St. Margarets Res	20	9	1	10	39	58	-19	28
7 Morley Town AFC Res	20	8	2	10	64	59	5	26
8 Trinity & All Saints Old Boys	20	6	2	12	46	79	-33	20
9 Sandal Wanderers	20	6	2	12	61	78	-17	17*
10 Littletown	20	5	3	12	41	59	-18	9*
11 Garforth Rangers	20	2	2	16	33	76	-43	5*

DIVISION THREE	P	W	D	L	F	A	GD	Pts
1 New Middleton	22	21	0	1	126	27	99	60*
2 Leeds City FC III	22	13	5	4	76	48	28	44
3 Norristhorpe	22	11	3	8	72	57	15	36
4 North Leeds	22	10	5	7	54	46	8	35
5 Huddersfield Amateur	22	11	2	9	53	47	6	35
6 Prospect FC	22	7	8	7	51	53	-2	29
7 Ealandians III	22	4	11	7	43	58	-15	23
8 Lepton Highlanders	22	7	4	11	42	56	-14	22*
9 Tingley Athletic FC	22	7	1	14	41	62	-21	22
10 Morley Town AFC III	22	6	3	13	47	81	-34	21
11 Farnley Sports FC	22	5	4	13	50	80	-30	19
12 Leeds Modernians	22	5	4	13	44	84	-40	19

DIVISION FOUR	P	W	D	L	F	A	GD	Pts
1 Middleton Park	24	22	2	0	80	18	62	68
2 Gildersome Spurs O.B. Res	24	17	5	2	90	26	64	56
3 Norristhorpe Res	24	13	4	7	72	54	18	43
4 Shire Academics III	24	13	4	7	66	51	15	43
5 Drighlington Res	24	14	0	10	78	40	38	42
6 Morley Amateur	24	13	3	8	71	49	22	42
7 Colton Athletic Res	24	10	3	11	66	51	15	33
8 Calverley United Reserves	24	8	6	10	46	57	-11	30
9 St Bedes Res	24	7	3	14	44	76	-32	24
10 North Leeds Res	24	5	3	16	36	72	-36	18
11 Dewsbury Rangers Res	24	5	4	15	41	88	-47	16*
12 Thornesians Res	24	3	4	17	43	92	-49	13
13 Beeston Juniors Old Boys Res	24	5	1	18	34	93	-59	7*

DIVISION FIVE	P	W	D	L	F	A	GD	Pts
1 Savile United FC	24	18	4	2	98	38	60	58
2 Morley Town AFC Dev	24	17	1	6	86	49	37	52
3 Middleton Park Under 21's	24	16	4	4	89	35	54	49*
4 Old Batelians	24	16	0	8	125	56	69	48
5 Tyersal Res	24	15	1	8	73	57	16	46
6 West End Park	24	11	2	11	75	74	1	35
7 Old Centralians	24	11	0	13	57	98	-41	33
8 Huddersfield Amateur Res	24	10	2	12	82	87	-5	32
9 Shire Academics IV	24	7	4	13	61	107	-46	25
10 St Bedes Academy	24	6	4	14	70	86	-16	22
11 Leeds Modernians Res	24	6	3	15	47	81	-34	18*
12 Thornesians III	24	4	4	16	48	100	-52	16
13 Leeds City FC IV	24	4	1	19	45	88	-43	10*

ISLAND FOOTBALL

ISLE OF MAN LEAGUE

PREMIER DIVISION	P	W	D	L	F	A	GD	Pts
1 St Marys First	22	19	2	1	109	19	90	59
2 St Georges First	22	16	4	2	97	28	69	52
3 Peel First	22	16	2	4	90	38	52	50
4 Corinthians First	22	13	5	4	95	37	58	44
5 Rushen United First	22	13	3	6	73	32	41	42
6 Douglas Athletic First	22	9	3	10	51	73	-22	30
7 DHSOB First	22	9	2	11	59	56	3	29
8 Marown First	22	6	1	15	38	87	-49	19
9 Laxey First	22	5	0	17	46	96	-50	15
10 Castletown First	22	5	0	17	32	114	-82	15
11 Douglas Royal First	22	4	2	16	37	107	-70	14
12 St Johns United First	22	4	2	16	30	70	-40	13*

DIVISION TWO	P	W	D	L	F	A	GD	Pts
1 Ramsey First	24	17	5	2	100	27	73	56
2 Pulrose United First	24	17	4	3	100	25	75	55
3 RYCOB First	24	16	6	2	88	35	53	54
4 Foxdale First	24	15	3	6	83	39	44	48
5 Malew First	24	15	3	6	76	45	31	48
6 Union Mills First	24	11	4	9	72	53	19	37
7 Onchan First	24	11	2	11	76	56	20	35
8 Colby First	24	11	1	12	62	60	2	34
9 Ayre United First	24	11	1	12	56	57	-1	34
10 Douglas & District First	24	7	0	17	57	97	-40	21
11 Gymnasium First	24	6	2	16	43	100	-57	20
12 Michael United First	24	1	2	21	27	127	-100	5
13 Governors Athletic First	24	1	1	22	30	149	-119	4

ISLE OF WIGHT LEAGUE

DIVISION ONE	P	W	D	L	F	A	GD	Pts
1 Whitecroft & Barton	21	16	5	0	69	10	59	53
2 Brading Town	21	12	4	5	58	32	26	40
3 Shanklin	22	12	4	6	53	36	17	40
4 Northwood St Johns	22	11	6	5	44	32	12	39
5 Pan Sports FC	22	10	4	8	48	54	-6	34
6 E.C.S.	22	8	6	8	44	43	1	30
7 West Wight	22	8	4	10	32	39	-7	28
8 Binstead & COB	22	8	3	11	39	48	-9	27
9 Cowes Sports	22	7	5	10	36	52	-16	26
10 Ventnor	22	6	5	11	53	55	-2	23
11 Sandown	22	4	6	12	42	60	-18	18
12 Osbourn Coburg	22	1	4	17	18	75	-57	7

DIVISION TWO	P	W	D	L	F	A	GD	Pts
1 Bembridge	24	21	1	2	124	28	96	64
2 Carisbrooke Utd	24	18	3	3	99	36	63	56*
3 Ryde Saints	24	18	1	5	94	34	60	55
4 AFC Wootton	24	14	3	7	50	35	15	45
5 Newchurch	24	14	2	8	66	46	20	44
6 Oakfield FC	24	12	3	9	74	56	18	39
7 Niton Community	24	12	2	10	71	67	4	38
8 Seaview	24	11	1	12	62	66	-4	34
9 Adgestone	24	9	1	14	61	73	-12	28
10 East Cowes Vics A	24	5	4	15	51	62	-11	21*
11 Wroxall	24	5	2	17	46	57	-11	17
12 Brighstone	24	4	3	17	36	77	-41	15
13 Yarmouth & Calb	24	0	0	24	22	219	-197	0

GUERNSEY LEAGUE

PRIAULX LEAGUE	P	W	D	L	F	A	GD	Pts
1 St Martins AC	24	17	5	2	66	18	48	56
2 Alderney	24	16	5	3	50	24	26	53
3 Rovers AC	24	15	6	3	74	23	51	51
4 Northerners AC	24	14	5	5	74	33	41	47
5 Rangers FAC	24	9	1	14	38	69	-31	28
6 Manzur	24	7	4	13	45	58	-13	25
7 Vale Recreation	24	5	6	13	42	54	-12	21
8 UCF Sylvans	24	6	3	15	28	63	-35	21
9 Belgrave Wanderers	24	1	1	22	25	100	-75	4

DIVISION ONE	P	W	D	L	F	A	GD	Pts
1 Vale Recreation Res	14	10	2	2	45	24	21	32
2 Rovers AC	14	10	0	4	54	19	35	30
3 St Martins AC	14	7	1	6	41	33	8	22
4 BW Rangers	14	7	1	6	41	39	2	22
5 Manzur Res	14	7	0	7	29	31	-2	21
6 UCF Sylvans	14	6	2	6	30	32	-2	20
7 Belgrave Wanderers	14	3	1	10	20	55	-35	10
8 Northerners AC Res	14	2	1	11	14	41	-27	7

DIVISION TWO	P	W	D	L	F	A	GD	Pts
1 Red Lion	16	14	0	2	77	16	61	42
2 UCF Sylvans Res	16	10	2	4	40	18	22	32
3 Rovers AC Res	16	10	1	5	48	33	15	31
4 St Martins AC Res	16	9	1	6	37	38	-1	28
5 London House Bels	16	8	1	7	46	45	1	25
6 Vale Recreation 3rds	16	7	1	8	38	44	-6	22
7 Manzur 3rds	16	6	1	9	24	36	-12	19
8 Northerners AC 3rds	16	4	1	11	43	61	-18	13
9 Centrals	16	0	0	16	14	76	-62	0

DIVISION THREE	P	W	D	L	F	A	GD	Pts
1 Manor Farm Saints	16	12	2	2	80	35	45	38
2 Rocquaine Pirates	16	10	2	4	51	25	26	32
3 Police	16	8	2	6	44	40	4	26
4 Vale Recreation 4ths	16	6	4	6	39	49	-10	22
5 CF Independant	16	7	1	8	36	49	-13	22
6 Thrive Physiotherapy	16	7	0	9	44	40	4	21
7 Rovers AC 3rds	16	6	3	7	46	44	2	21
8 Centrals Res	16	4	2	10	27	58	-31	14
9 Rangers FAC	16	3	2	11	23	50	-27	11

JERSEY FOOTBALL COMBINATION

PREMIERSHIP	P	W	D	L	F	A	GD	Pts
1 St Paul's	18	17	0	1	61	13	48	51
2 St Peter	18	14	1	3	61	24	37	43
3 JTC Jersey Wanderers	18	10	1	7	46	37	9	31
4 St Clement	18	5	4	9	28	39	-11	19
5 St Ouen	18	5	1	12	18	44	-26	16
6 Rozel Rovers	18	3	3	12	26	64	-38	12
7 Trinity	18	3	2	13	26	45	-19	11

CHAMPIONSHIP	P	W	D	L	F	A	GD	Pts
1 Grouville	15	12	2	1	56	17	39	38
2 St Lawrence	15	10	1	4	54	24	30	31
3 Sporting Academics	14	8	1	5	34	30	4	25
4 St Brelade	15	8	0	7	51	33	18	24
5 First Tower Utd	15	2	0	13	26	56	-30	6
6 St John	14	2	0	12	13	74	-61	6

AMATEUR FOOTBALL ASSOCIATION

AMATEUR FOOTBALL COMBINATION

PREMIER DIVISION	P	W	D	L	F	A	GD	Pts
1 Old Hamptonians	18	16	0	2	67	11	56	48
2 Old Meadonians	18	12	3	3	55	27	28	39
3 Dorkinians	18	10	3	5	48	41	7	33
4 Honourable Artillery Company	18	9	3	6	40	35	5	30
5 Old Suttonians	18	8	2	8	42	46	-4	26
6 Wandsworth Borough	18	7	2	9	32	33	-1	23
7 Old Wokingians	18	6	4	8	33	35	-2	22
8 Old Thorntonians	18	5	3	10	35	48	-13	18
9 UCL Academicals	18	4	1	13	30	71	-41	13
10 Old Parmiterians	18	2	1	15	21	56	-35	7

SENIOR ONE	P	W	D	L	F	A	GD	Pts
1 Fulham Compton Old Boys	20	13	3	4	49	27	22	42
2 Old Ignatian	20	12	1	7	45	42	3	37
3 Albanian	20	10	6	4	51	37	14	36
4 Fitzwilliam Old Boys	20	7	8	5	40	30	10	29
5 Bealonians	20	8	3	9	44	38	6	27
6 Queen Mary College Old Boys	20	7	6	7	47	49	-2	27
7 Old Meadonians II	20	8	3	9	41	44	-3	27
8 Old Manorians	20	8	2	10	43	39	4	26
9 Reigatians	20	8	4	8	37	43	-6	25*
10 Altis FC	20	5	3	12	49	59	-10	18
11 Clapham Old Xaverians	20	3	3	14	25	63	-38	12

SENIOR TWO NORTH	P	W	D	L	F	A	GD	Pts
1 Old Minchendenians	16	12	1	3	83	29	54	37
2 Latymer Old Boys	16	11	3	2	49	25	24	36
3 Old Aloysians	16	10	2	4	46	25	21	32
4 IB Albion	16	6	3	7	42	49	-7	21
5 Bealonians II	16	6	3	7	30	46	-16	21
6 Hale End Athletic	16	4	6	6	36	46	-10	18
7 Enfield Old Grammarians	16	4	4	8	27	36	-9	16
8 Old Salvatorians	16	4	2	10	19	44	-25	14
9 Southgate County	16	2	2	12	19	51	-32	8

SENIOR TWO SOUTH	P	W	D	L	F	A	GD	Pts
1 Old Tenisonians	18	11	2	5	40	28	12	35
2 Honourable Artillery Company II	18	10	3	5	41	22	19	33
3 Old Hamptonians II	18	10	2	6	52	34	18	32
4 Royal Bank of Scotland	18	9	2	7	45	36	9	29
5 Glyn Old Boys	18	6	6	6	34	32	2	24
6 Economicals	18	6	6	6	31	29	2	24
7 Old Thorntonians II	18	6	6	6	35	37	-2	24
8 Shene Old Grammarians	18	6	5	7	26	35	-9	23
9 Worcester College Old Boys	18	6	2	10	32	41	-9	20
10 Old Pauline	18	2	2	14	21	63	-42	8

THE NON-LEAGUE PAPER
ESSENTIAL READING FOR FOLLOWERS OF THE NATIONAL GAME

carpetking

LATICS AND BREWERS ON THE UP!
WE WERE ALL LAUGHING AS JIMMY GOT BEATEN UP
FOOTBALL
OING UP!

SENIOR THREE NORTH	P	W	D	L	F	A	GD	Pts
1 Albanian II	18	12	1	5	59	31	28	37
2 Old Manorians II	18	12	1	5	53	29	24	37
3 Globe Rangers	18	11	3	4	51	30	21	36
4 Old Salvatorians II	18	11	2	5	36	27	9	35
5 Spaniards	18	8	2	8	38	40	-2	26
6 Bealonians III	18	7	3	8	34	41	-7	24
7 Leyton County Old Boys	18	6	3	9	31	48	-17	21
8 Old Woodhouseians	18	6	2	10	39	44	-5	20
9 Old Ignatian II	18	5	3	10	27	50	-23	18
10 Old Uffingtonians	18	0	4	14	18	46	-28	4

SENIOR THREE SOUTH	P	W	D	L	F	A	GD	Pts
1 Old Sedcopians	16	11	2	3	47	26	21	35
2 Rob Roy Reds	16	9	4	3	42	26	16	31
3 Old Suttonians II	16	9	3	4	46	33	13	30
4 Dorkinians II	16	8	2	6	44	30	14	26
5 Mickleham Old Boxhillians	16	7	4	5	42	30	12	25
6 New-Magdalen AFC	16	6	3	7	39	50	-11	21
7 Old Strand Academicals	16	4	5	7	35	45	-10	17
8 Royal Bank of Scotland II	16	3	4	9	30	46	-16	13
9 Old Meadonians III	16	0	3	13	17	56	-39	3

ARTHURIAN LEAGUE

PREMIER DIVISION	P	W	D	L	F	A	GD	Pts
1 Old Carthusians	18	10	7	1	44	19	25	37
2 Kings College Wimbledon	18	9	4	5	33	24	9	31
3 Old Etonians	18	8	4	6	38	24	14	28
4 Old Salopians	18	8	0	10	26	37	-11	24
5 Old Chigwellians	18	7	2	9	28	33	-5	23
6 Old Tonbridgians	18	6	5	7	30	37	-7	23
7 Old Foresters	18	6	5	7	23	31	-8	23
8 Old Bradfieldians	18	5	7	6	42	39	3	22
9 Old Wykehamists	18	7	0	11	35	42	-7	21
10 Old Brentwoods	18	6	2	10	39	52	-13	20

DIVISION ONE	P	W	D	L	F	A	GD	Pts
1 Old Alleynians AFC	18	12	1	5	61	31	30	37
2 Old Harrovians	18	10	1	7	51	38	13	31
3 Lancing Old Boys	18	9	3	6	48	29	19	30
4 Old Cholmeleians	18	7	7	4	33	28	5	28
5 Old Malvernians	18	8	3	7	29	35	-6	27
6 Old Marlburians	18	8	2	8	31	34	-3	26
7 Old Berkhamstedians	18	7	3	8	39	35	4	24
8 Old Radleians	18	7	3	8	38	45	-7	24
9 Old Reptonians	18	7	1	10	46	43	3	22
10 Old Aldenhamians	18	2	2	14	15	73	-58	5*

DIVISION TWO	P	W	D	L	F	A	GD	Pts
1 Old Carthusians II	18	13	2	3	47	21	26	41
2 Old Westminsters	18	11	5	2	57	29	28	38
3 Old Etonians II	18	11	1	6	43	26	17	34
4 Old Citizens	18	11	2	5	45	30	15	34*
5 Old Foresters II	18	7	4	7	34	35	-1	25
6 Old Harrovians II	18	6	4	8	30	41	-11	22
7 Old Chigwellians II	18	6	3	9	19	30	-11	21
8 Old Merchant Taylors	18	5	0	13	26	46	-20	15
9 Lancing Old Boys II	18	5	0	13	23	44	-21	15
10 Kings College Wimbledon II	18	3	3	12	20	42	-22	9*

DIVISION THREE	P	W	D	L	F	A	GD	Pts
1 Old Sennockians	16	11	1	4	39	24	15	34
2 Old Rugbeians	16	9	4	3	45	27	18	31
3 Old Johnians FC	16	9	3	4	37	19	18	30
4 Old Tonbridgians II	16	7	5	4	42	31	11	26
5 Old Epsomians	16	8	2	6	32	30	2	19*
6 Old Carthusians III	16	5	4	7	28	38	-10	19
7 Old Wellingtonians	16	5	3	8	47	35	12	15*
8 Old Salopians II	16	4	1	11	25	53	-28	9*
9 Old Aldenhamians II	16	2	1	13	22	60	-38	-8*

DIVISION FOUR	P	W	D	L	F	A	GD	Pts
1 Old Suttonians SV	16	13	2	1	61	31	30	40*
2 Old Columbans	16	11	2	3	54	26	28	35
3 Old Harrovians III	16	9	5	2	52	23	29	32
4 Old Stoics	16	9	1	6	52	44	8	28
5 Old Alleynians AFC II	16	6	4	6	42	33	9	22
6 Old Bancroftians AFC	16	4	3	9	30	38	-8	15
7 Old Brentwoods II	16	3	5	8	31	43	-12	14
8 Old Eastbournians	16	3	1	12	28	58	-30	10
9 Old Haberdashers	16	2	1	13	34	88	-54	4*

DIVISION FIVE NORTH	P	W	D	L	F	A	GD	Pts
1 Old Kimboltonians	12	8	3	1	43	13	30	27
2 Old Albanians SA	12	8	1	3	29	26	3	25
3 Old Cholmeleians II	12	4	3	5	26	25	1	12*
4 Old Merchant Taylors II	12	5	3	4	24	28	-4	12*
5 Old Brentwoods III	12	2	5	5	24	35	-11	11
6 Old Foresters III	12	4	1	7	21	30	-9	7*
7 Old Chigwellians III	12	2	2	8	20	30	-10	5*

DIVISION FIVE SOUTH	P	W	D	L	F	A	GD	Pts
1 Old Shirburnians	12	9	2	1	45	21	24	29
2 Old King's Scholars	12	7	1	4	29	21	8	21*
3 Old Wykehamists II	12	6	2	4	29	31	-2	17*
4 Old Kingstonians KGS	12	5	2	5	34	39	-5	17
5 Old Westminsters II	12	4	1	7	29	34	-5	12*
6 Old Berkhamstedians II	12	3	3	6	24	31	-7	12
7 Old Amplefordians	12	1	3	8	21	34	-13	5*

SOUTHERN AMATEUR LEAGUE

SENIOR DIVISION ONE	P	W	D	L	F	A	GD	Pts
1 West Wickham	20	13	5	2	49	22	27	44
2 Polytechnic	20	12	4	4	49	26	23	40
3 Nottsborough	20	11	4	5	41	30	11	37
4 Old Owens	20	8	5	7	37	36	1	29
5 Alleyn Old Boys	20	7	6	7	33	29	4	27
6 Actonians Association	20	7	4	9	33	40	-7	25
7 Winchmore Hill	20	7	4	9	22	31	-9	25
8 Old Wilsonians	20	6	5	9	31	39	-8	23
9 Old Parkonians	20	6	4	10	27	38	-11	22
10 Old Garchonians	20	3	9	8	26	36	-10	18
11 Civil Service	20	2	6	12	17	38	-21	12

SENIOR DIVISION TWO	P	W	D	L	F	A	GD	Pts
1 Norsemen	18	15	3	0	56	19	37	48
2 East Barnet Old Grammarians	18	11	3	4	50	33	17	36
3 Bank of England	18	10	1	7	58	38	20	31
4 Old Finchleians	18	9	4	5	48	32	16	31
5 NUFC Oilers	18	7	5	6	40	36	4	26
6 Alexandra Park	18	7	4	7	40	35	5	25
7 Carshalton	18	5	5	8	37	42	-5	20
8 Merton	18	4	4	10	23	43	-20	16
9 HSBC	18	3	3	12	18	55	-37	12
10 Ibis Eagles	18	3	0	15	21	58	-37	9

SENIOR DIVISION THREE	P	W	D	L	F	A	GD	Pts
1 Crouch End Vampires	18	16	0	2	54	23	31	48
2 Old Stationers	18	12	2	4	40	29	11	38
3 South Bank Cuaco	18	12	0	6	51	30	21	36
4 Old Blues	18	10	1	7	41	30	11	31
5 Cambridge Heath	18	7	4	7	28	30	-2	25
6 Old Lyonians	18	7	2	9	39	38	1	23
7 Weirside Rangers	18	6	2	10	31	41	-10	20
8 The Warren	18	4	3	11	19	31	-12	15
9 Kew Association	18	4	3	11	29	52	-23	15
10 AFC Oldsmiths	18	3	1	14	23	51	-28	10

NORTHERN IRELAND TABLES 2018-19

NORTHERN IRELAND FOOTBALL LEAGUE

Premiership	P	W	D	L	F	A	GD	Pts
1 Linfield	38	26	7	5	77	27	50	85
2 Ballymena United	38	24	6	8	83	47	36	78
3 Glenavon	38	20	10	8	74	46	28	70
4 Crusaders	38	20	5	13	68	55	13	65
5 Cliftonville	38	19	4	15	70	66	4	61
6 Coleraine	38	15	11	12	59	55	4	56
7 Glentoran	38	13	10	15	58	53	5	49
8 Institute	38	13	5	20	50	72	-22	44
9 Dungannon Swifts	38	11	9	18	44	65	-21	42
10 Warrenpoint Town	38	10	9	19	51	79	-28	39
11 Ards	38	6	9	23	31	63	-32	27
12 Newry City	38	6	5	27	31	68	-37	23

Championship	P	W	D	L	F	A	GD	Pts
1 Larne	32	26	3	3	87	19	68	81
2 Carrick Rangers	32	20	4	8	59	42	17	64
3 Portadown	32	15	6	11	59	55	4	51
4 Dundela	32	13	7	12	67	60	7	46
5 Ballinamallard United	32	12	3	17	39	51	-12	39
6 HW Welders	32	11	2	19	45	68	-23	35
7 Loughgall	32	11	9	12	60	52	8	42
8 Dergview	32	13	3	16	51	51	0	42
9 Ballyclare Comrades	32	11	7	14	58	68	-10	40
10 Knockbreda	32	10	7	15	45	63	-18	37
11 PSNI	32	9	7	16	48	72	-24	34
12 Limavady Utd	32	8	8	16	45	62	-17	32

Premier Intermediate League	P	W	D	L	F	A	GD	Pts
1 Queens University	22	18	2	2	55	16	39	56
2 Annagh United	22	13	5	4	55	26	29	44
3 Tobermore United	22	13	2	7	48	32	16	41
4 Lisburn Distillery	22	10	6	6	41	37	4	36
5 Banbridge Town	22	9	6	7	37	27	10	33
6 Portstewart	22	9	5	8	28	28	0	32
7 Newington YC	22	8	5	9	31	35	-4	29
8 Moyola Park	22	8	3	11	36	39	-3	27
9 Dollingstown	22	5	5	12	35	48	-13	20
10 Armagh City	22	5	5	12	24	44	-20	20
11 Lurgan Celtic	22	5	4	13	23	48	-25	19
12 S&L Swifts	22	4	2	16	32	65	-33	14

BALLYMENA & PROVINCIAL LEAGUE

Intermediate Division	P	W	D	L	F	A	GD	Pts
1 Bangor FC	28	27	1	0	115	24	91	82
2 Glebe Rangers	28	22	1	5	66	30	36	67
3 St James Swifts	28	21	0	7	102	43	59	63
4 Coagh United	28	16	4	8	60	47	13	52
5 Brantwood	28	13	6	9	50	37	13	45
6 Ballymoney Utd	28	12	5	11	63	51	12	41
7 Newtowne	28	9	9	10	52	50	2	36
8 Dunloy FC	28	10	5	13	47	49	-2	35
9 Cookstown Youth	28	10	5	13	49	62	-13	35
10 Chimney Corner	28	10	4	14	53	71	-18	34
11 Wakehurst FC	28	9	5	14	46	55	-9	32
12 Ballynure OB	28	8	6	14	52	66	-14	30
13 Donegal Celtic	28	6	4	18	46	101	-55	22
14 Cookstown RBL	28	3	4	21	26	81	-55	13
15 Desertmartin	28	2	5	21	36	96	-60	11

Junior Division One	P	W	D	L	F	A	GD	Pts
1 Woodlands	18	15	2	1	84	21	63	47
2 Antrim Rovers	18	14	2	2	81	24	57	44
3 Rathcoole FC	18	14	1	3	68	27	41	43
4 Killymoon Rangers	18	6	4	8	37	50	-13	22
5 Cookstown Olympic	18	6	4	8	27	42	-15	22
6 Castle Star	18	6	3	9	43	44	-1	21
7 FC Whiteabbey	18	7	0	11	36	62	-26	21
8 Desertmartin Swifts	18	5	2	11	30	54	-24	17
9 Cookstown Youth Colts	18	4	4	10	27	61	-34	16
10 Brantwood Res	18	2	0	16	30	78	-48	6

Newington IIs withdrawn - record expunged.

Junior Division Two	P	W	D	L	F	A	GD	Pts
1 St James Swifts 2nds	18	15	2	1	82	18	64	47
2 Ballynure OB B	18	12	2	4	65	28	37	38
3 North Belfast Utd	18	10	4	4	49	36	13	34
4 Loughside FC	18	8	1	9	39	52	-13	25
5 Clough Rangers Athletic	18	7	1	10	45	74	-29	22
6 Cookstown RBL Res	18	4	0	14	39	61	-22	12
7 Mallusk Athletic	18	2	0	16	19	69	-50	6

Junior Division Three	P	W	D	L	F	A	GD	Pts
1 St James Swifts 3rds	20	17	0	3	70	22	48	51
2 Carrick Athletic	20	13	1	6	66	33	33	40
3 3rd Ballyclare OB	20	11	3	6	41	30	11	36
4 Ballyclare North End	20	11	2	7	57	41	16	35
5 68th Newtownabbey OB	20	11	1	8	51	37	14	34
6 North United	20	9	1	10	48	53	-5	28
7 Greenisland 3rds	20	8	1	11	62	55	7	25
8 Red Star	20	7	4	9	42	46	-4	25
9 Grange Rangers	20	5	2	13	27	62	-35	17
10 Newington Rangers Res	20	5	2	13	21	67	-46	17
11 Carniny Amateur and Youth FC Dev	20	3	3	14	31	70	-39	12

MID ULSTER LEAGUE (PART TABLES)

Intermediate A		P	W	D	L	F	A	GD	Pts
1	Hanover	26							64
2	Crewe United	26							56
3	Banbridge Rangers	26							52
4	Windmill Stars	26							49
5	Moneyslane	26							46
6	Valley Rangers	26							46
7	Fivemiletown United	26							41
8	Richhill AFC	26							34
9	Ballymacash Rangers	26							28
10	Bourneview Mill	26							26
11	Tandragee Rovers	26							25
12	Laurelvale	26							25
13	St Marys	26							24
14	AFC Silverwood	26							1

Intermediate B		P	W	D	L	F	A	GD	Pts
1	Oxford Sunnyside	22							51
2	Rectory Rangers	22							47
3	Lurgan Town	22							41
4	Markethill Swifts	22							40
5	Dromore Amateurs	22							33
6	Craigavon City	22							32
7	Seagoe	22							31
8	Lower Maze	22							30
9	Tullyvallen	22							26
10	Dungannon Tigers	22							24
11	Seapatrick	22							14
12	Broomhedge Maghaberry	22							3

Division One		P	W	D	L	F	A	GD	Pts
1	Coalisland Athletic	24							72
2	Hill Street	24							64
3	Ambassadors	24							49
4	Ballyoran	24							45
5	Caledon Rovers	24							38
6	Sandy Hill	24							36
7	Glenavy	24							31
8	Lurgan BBOB	24							27
9	Newmills	24							24
10	Portadown BBOB	24							21
11	Armagh Celtic	24							19
12	Red Star	24							15
13	Keady Celtic	24							11

Division Two		P	W	D	L	F	A	GD	Pts
1	Banbridge YCOB	20							45
2	Derryhirk United	20							44
3	Goodyear	20							32
4	West End Hibs	20							31
5	Ballymacash YM	20							30
6	Scarva Rangers	20							28
7	United LT	20							28
8	Hillsborough Boys	20							27
9	Knockmenagh Swifts	20							19
10	Donacloney	20							13
11	White City	20							13

Division Three		P	W	D	L	F	A	GD	Pts
1	Annalong	22							59
2	Ballyvea	22							50
3	Armagh Blues	22							50
4	Gilford Crusaders	22							44
5	Armagh Rovers	22							40
6	Glenavy Youth	22							36
7	Moira Albion	22							23
8	Dungannon Rovers	22							20
9	Tollymore United	22							17
10	Damolly	22							17
11	Magheralin Village	22							15
12	The Dons	22							6

NORTHERN AMATEUR LEAGUE

Premier Division		P	W	D	L	F	A	GD	Pts
1	Crumlin Star	26	22	4	0	88	12	76	70
2	East Belfast	26	17	5	4	89	26	63	56
3	Immaculata F.C.	26	17	3	6	53	25	28	54
4	Ballynahinch Olympic	26	17	2	7	75	38	37	53
5	Rathfriland Rangers	26	14	6	6	58	32	26	48
6	Islandmagee	26	13	3	10	62	50	12	42
7	Shankill United	26	10	8	8	53	47	6	38
8	Crumlin United	26	8	4	14	49	60	-11	28
9	Ards Rangers	26	8	4	14	38	58	-20	28
10	1st Bangor Old Boys	26	8	3	15	42	53	-11	27
11	Derriaghy C C	26	7	4	15	30	64	-34	25
12	Drumaness Mills	26	6	6	14	49	74	-25	21*
13	Albert Foundry F.C.	26	3	7	16	31	60	-29	16
14	Downpatrick F.C.	26	1	3	22	22	140	-118	6

Division One A		P	W	D	L	F	A	GD	Pts
1	Larne Tech O.B.	24	18	5	1	72	17	55	59
2	Killyleagh Y.C	24	17	5	2	83	25	58	56
3	Orangefield Old Boys	24	16	2	6	76	39	37	50
4	Sirocco Wks	24	10	10	4	51	36	15	40
5	Comber Rec F.C.	24	11	6	7	50	42	8	39
6	Abbey Villa	24	10	8	6	57	35	22	38
7	Kilmore Rec	24	12	2	10	51	38	13	38
8	Rosario Y.C.	24	8	4	12	41	51	-10	28
9	Malachians	24	6	6	12	51	70	-19	24
10	Newcastle	24	7	3	14	43	71	-28	24
11	Dunmurry Rec	24	6	1	17	35	59	-24	19
12	Lisburn Rangers	24	5	2	17	31	77	-46	17
13	St Patricks Y.M. F.C.	24	1	4	19	27	108	-81	7

Division One B	P	W	D	L	F	A	GD	Pts
1 Grove United	26	19	4	3	77	36	41	61
2 Dromara Village	26	14	6	6	81	55	26	48
3 Bryansburn Rangers	26	12	7	7	64	48	16	43
4 18th Newtownabbey O.B.	26	14	4	8	44	38	6	43*
5 St Lukes F.C.	26	11	9	6	45	38	7	42
6 Barn United	26	11	3	12	52	57	-5	36
7 Portaferry Rovers	26	10	4	12	37	44	-7	34
8 Mossley F.C.	26	8	7	11	60	52	8	31
9 Ballynahinch United	26	8	6	12	34	47	-13	30
10 Ballywalter Rec. F.C.	26	8	6	12	41	51	-10	29*
11 Colin Valley F.C.	26	7	8	11	47	60	-13	29
12 Downshire YM	26	8	4	14	36	51	-15	28
13 Dundonald	26	7	6	13	33	49	-16	27
14 Dunmurry Y. M.	26	7	2	17	45	70	-25	23

Division One C	P	W	D	L	F	A	GD	Pts
1 Aquinas FC	26	20	4	2	84	15	69	64
2 Bangor Amateurs F.C.	26	17	6	3	90	35	55	57
3 Shorts FC	26	17	3	6	87	43	44	54
4 Suffolk F.C.	26	15	8	3	66	33	33	53
5 Saintfield United	26	14	5	7	59	46	13	47
6 Rosemount Rec	26	13	7	6	82	39	43	46
7 Woodvale F.C.	26	13	3	10	54	52	2	42
8 Tullycarnet FC	26	10	2	14	71	64	7	32
9 Bloomfield F.C.	26	8	8	10	45	48	-3	32
10 Holywood F.C.	26	8	3	15	59	66	-7	27
11 Bangor Swifts	26	6	2	18	38	90	-52	20
12 Wellington Rec	26	6	2	18	42	86	-44	17*
13 Iveagh United	26	4	4	18	34	81	-47	13*
14 Groomsport	26	2	1	23	27	140	-113	7

Division Two A	P	W	D	L	F	A	GD	Pts
1 St Oliver Plunkett F.C.	22	18	4	0	70	18	52	58
2 Greenisland F.C.	22	16	3	3	70	20	50	51
3 Portavogie Rangers F.C.	22	14	4	4	61	33	28	46
4 Ballysillan Swifts	22	13	3	6	88	44	44	42
5 Donaghadee F.C.	22	10	5	7	55	37	18	35
6 Finaghy F.C.	22	10	5	7	45	37	8	35
7 Lower Shankill FC	22	8	4	10	55	62	-7	28
8 Queens Grads.	22	8	3	11	45	52	-7	27
9 Ford	22	7	3	12	44	58	-14	24
10 Newington Rangers	22	3	4	15	35	67	-32	13
11 University of Ulster at Jordanstown	22	3	1	18	39	96	-57	10
12 Kircubbin F.C.	22	1	3	18	16	99	-83	6

Division Two B	P	W	D	L	F	A	GD	Pts
1 Willowbank FC	20	19	0	1	138	16	122	57
2 Shamrock FC	20	17	1	2	91	34	57	52
3 Nortel	20	15	1	4	61	34	27	46
4 Kelvin Old Boys	20	10	2	8	45	42	3	32
5 St Teresas Y.C.	20	7	4	9	28	51	-23	25
6 Bangor Y.M.	20	7	4	9	42	68	-26	25
7 Bangor Rangers	20	5	3	12	46	58	-12	18
8 Newtownbreda F C	20	5	2	13	32	64	-32	17
9 Queens University 11's	20	5	1	14	45	65	-20	16
10 Civil Service	20	5	1	14	34	74	-40	16
11 Castlewellan Town FC	20	5	1	14	35	91	-56	16

Division Two C	P	W	D	L	F	A	GD	Pts
1 Beann Mhádagháin FC	22	20	2	0	101	15	86	62
2 St Matthews	22	16	2	4	101	35	66	50
3 Tullymore Swifts	22	13	6	3	75	38	37	45
4 Ravenhill YM FC	22	12	2	8	60	44	16	38
5 St Mary's	22	10	4	8	69	51	18	34
6 Carryduff Colts	22	10	1	11	49	51	-2	31
7 Suffolk Swifts	22	9	2	11	41	48	-7	29
8 4th Newtownabbey F.C.	22	8	4	10	50	54	-4	28
9 Whitehead Eagles	22	6	4	12	46	63	-17	22
10 22nd Old Boys	22	7	1	14	45	68	-23	22
11 Rooftop	22	5	1	16	28	114	-86	16
12 Agapé FC	22	1	1	20	15	99	-84	4

NORTHERN IRELAND INTERMEDIATE LEAGUE

	P	W	D	L	F	A	GD	Pts
1 Strabane Athletic	14	11	3	0	40	8	32	36
2 Maiden City	14	9	3	2	33	14	19	30
3 Newbuildings Utd	14	8	1	5	31	20	11	25
4 Magherafelt Sky Blues	14	8	1	5	33	28	5	25
5 Ardstraw	14	5	1	8	17	29	-12	16
6 Dungiven	14	4	1	9	19	31	-12	13
7 Trojans	14	3	3	8	16	34	-18	12
8 Oxford United Stars	14	1	1	12	7	32	-25	4

IRISH CUP

HOLDERS: COLERAINE

ROUND

Valley Rangers	v	Tandragee Rovers	3-2
Albert Foundry	v	Aquinas	4-3
Ardstraw	v	Dromore Amateurs	7-0
Ballymacash Rangers	v	Kilmore Recreation	1-3
Ballynahinch United	v	Groomsport	3-2
Banbridge Rangers	v	Sirocco Works	2-0
Bangor Amateurs	v	Newcastle	3-2
Brantwood	v	Orangefield Old Boys	4-2
Broomhedge Maghaberry	v	Ballynahinch Olympic	1-12
Comber Recreation	v	Immaculata	1-0
Cookstown Youth	v	Islandmagee	1-6
Crumlin United	v	Bangor Swifts	2-1
Desertmartin	v	Ballynure Old Boys	2-2, 7-6p
Dungiven Celtic	v	Iveagh United	5-2
Dunloy	v	Hanover	2-0
Dunmurry Young Men	v	Rathfriland Rangers	4-5
Fivemiletown United	v	Bloomfield	7-0
Glebe Rangers	v	Bangor	1-2
Grove United	v	Chimney Corner	5-2
Holywood	v	Newbuildings United	1-2
Killyleagh YC	v	Markethill Swifts	5-3
Lisburn Rangers	v	Dromara Village	2-1
Lower Maze	v	Trojans	2-3
Malachians	v	Maiden City	2-9
Mossley	v	Dunmurry Recreation	3-4
Newtowne	v	18th Newtownabbey OB	6-3
Oxford Sunnyside	v	Bryansburn Rangers	6-3
Oxford United Stars	v	Wakehurst	0-1
Rosario YC	v	Ballymoney United	1-2
Saintfield United	v	Laurelvale	1-3
Seapatrick	v	Coagh United	1-6

Silverwood	v	Shorts	1-8
St James' Swifts	v	Sofia Farmer	2-1
St Luke's	v	Larne Tech Old Boys	0-2
Strabane Athletic	v	Derriaghy Cricket Club	2-1
Suffolk	v	Colin Valley	1-1, 3-4p
Tullycarnet	v	Tullyvallen	4-3
Woodvale	v	St Patrick's Young Men	2-3

SECOND ROUND

Newington	v	Valley Rangers	3-1
Ballymoney United	v	Strabane Athletic	1-5
Banbridge Town	v	Rathfriland Rangers	3-1
Bangor	v	Banbridge Rangers	2-0
Bangor Amateurs	v	Tullycarnet	0-1
Brantwood	v	Laurelvale	2-1
Colin Valley	v	Shorts	3-4
Comber Rec	v	Lisburn Rangers	4-1
Crewe United	v	Moyola Park	2-1
Crumlin United	v	Moneyslane	5-1
Downshire Young Men	v	Drumaness Mills	0-4
Dundonald	v	Larne Tech Old Boys	0-3
Dunloy	v	Armagh City	2-0
Dunmurry Recreation	v	Dungiven Celtic	1-4
Grove United	v	Abbey Villa	3-4 aet
Islandmagee	v	Albert Foundry	2-1
Killyleagh YC	v	Crumlin Star	2-3
Kilmore Recreation	v	Sport & Leisure Swifts	1-2
Lisburn Distillery	v	Wellington Recreation	2-0
Lurgan Celtic	v	St Patrick's Young Men	HW
Lurgan Town	v	Desertmartin	4-1
Maiden City	v	Trojans	3-1
Newbuildings United	v	Ards Rangers	2-0
Newtowne	v	Ballynahinch Olympic	0-0, 5-3p
Oxford Sunnyside	v	Portstewart	AW
Queen's University	v	Dollingstown	4-3
Rosemount Recreation	v	Annagh United	2-1
Seagoe	v	Ballynahinch United	4-3
Shankill United	v	1st Bangor Old Boys	2-1
St. James' Swifts	v	Coagh United	4-2
Tobermore United	v	Ardstraw	5-3
Wakehurst	v	Fivemiletown United	2-3

THIRD ROUND

Crewe United	v	Sport & Leisure Swifts	1-0
Crumlin Star	v	Bangor	5-3
Crumlin United	v	Islandmagee	1-3
Drumaness Mills	v	Comber Recreation	1-2
Fivemiletown United	v	Tullycarnet	1-2
Larne Tech Old Boys	v	Dungiven Celtic	2-1
Lurgan Celtic	v	Portstewart	2-3
Lurgan Town	v	Dunloy	1-2
Newtowne	v	Rosemount Recreation	1-1, 3-5p
Queen's University	v	Tobermore United	6-3
Seagoe	v	Maiden City	1-4
Shankill United	v	Lisburn Distillery	2-4
Shorts	v	Abbey Villa	1-3
St James' Swifts	v	Newbuildings United	2-0
Strabane Athletic	v	Banbridge Town	2-0
Brantwood	v	Newington	2-3

FOURTH ROUND

Crewe United	v	Crumlin Star	1-2
Dunloy	v	Larne Tech Old Boys	0-2
Lisburn Distillery	v	Comber Recreation	4-3
Maiden City	v	Portstewart	1-0
Queen's University	v	Newington	4-1
Rosemount Recreation	v	Islandmagee	3-1
Strabane Athletic	v	St James' Swifts	2-0
Tullycarnet	v	Abbey Villa	3-4

FIFTH ROUND

Ards	v	Carrick Rangers	0-1
Ballinamallard United	v	PSNI	5-1
Cliftonville	v	Dungannon Swifts	0-1
Coleraine	v	Harland & Wolff Welders	2-0
Crusaders	v	Glentoran	4-1
Dergview	v	Maiden City	3-2
Dundela	v	Ballymena United	1-3
Glenavon	v	Rosemount Recreation	5-0
Institute	v	Warrenpoint Town	0-2
Knockbreda	v	Strabane Athletic	1-2
Larne	v	Newry City	2-1
Limavady United	v	Larne Tech Old Boys	0-2
Linfield	v	Ballyclare Comrades	1-0
Loughgall	v	Crumlin Star	1-4
Portadown	v	Abbey Villa	5-1
Queen's University	v	Lisburn Distillery	6-0

SIXTH ROUND

Ballinamallard United	v	Carrick Rangers	1-0
Ballymena United	v	Portadown	4-1
Coleraine	v	Dergview	3-0
Glenavon	v	Dungannon Swifts	0-1
Larne	v	Crumlin Star	3-1
Larne Tech Old Boys	v	Strabane Athletic	3-1
Linfield	v	Crusaders	1-2
Warrenpoint Town	v	Queen's University	2-0

QUARTER FINALS

Larne	v	Coleraine	3-5 aet
Crusaders	v	Ballymena United	3-0
Dungannon Swifts	v	Ballinamallard United	2-2, 2-3p
Warrenpoint Town	v	Larne Tech Old Boys	3-1

SEMI FINALS

Ballinamallard United	v	Warrenpoint Town	0-0, 5-4p
Coleraine	v	Crusaders	0-2

FINAL

Saturday 4th May 2018

Ballinamallard United	v	Crusaders	0-3

Megginson (Cove) shoots wide under pressure from Proctor (East Kilbride).

Reid (East Kilbride) Brown (Cove). Photos: Keith Clayton.

SCOTTISH TABLES 2018-19

HIGHLAND LEAGUE

		P	W	D	L	F	A	GD	Pts
1	Cove Rangers FC	34	30	3	1	100	12	88	93
2	Brora Rangers FC	34	27	4	3	99	12	87	85
3	Fraserburgh FC	34	26	1	7	125	37	88	79
4	Formartine United FC	34	22	6	6	97	37	60	72
5	Inverurie Loco Works FC	34	20	6	8	96	48	48	66
6	Forres Mechanics FC	34	21	3	10	79	40	39	66
7	Wick Academy FC	34	15	7	12	69	54	15	52
8	Buckie Thistle FC	34	14	7	13	72	54	18	49
9	Huntly FC	34	14	7	13	57	65	-8	49
10	Rothes FC	34	13	8	13	73	57	16	44*
11	Nairn County FC	34	13	3	18	61	67	-6	42
12	Deveronvale FC	34	13	2	19	55	65	-10	41
13	Keith FC	34	10	7	17	62	68	-6	37
14	Strathspey Thistle FC	34	10	3	21	47	90	-43	33
15	Turriff United FC	34	9	5	20	74	91	-17	32
16	Clachnacuddin FC	34	6	6	22	44	79	-35	24
17	Lossiemouth FC	34	2	2	30	29	139	-110	8
18	Fort William FC	34	0	2	32	21	245	-224	-7*

LOWLAND LEAGUE

		P	W	D	L	F	A	GD	Pts
1	East Kilbride	28	23	3	2	66	12	54	72
2	BSC Glasgow	28	18	7	3	67	29	38	61
3	Kelty Hearts	28	16	6	6	61	32	29	54
4	The Spartans	28	14	9	5	63	31	32	51
5	Civil Service Strollers	28	15	4	9	51	38	13	49
6	East Stirlingshire	28	11	6	11	57	47	10	39
7	Cumbernauld Colts	28	11	6	11	40	47	-7	39
8	Gala Fairydean Rovers	28	10	4	14	43	48	-5	34
9	Edusport Academy	28	9	6	13	43	52	-9	33
10	University of Stirling	28	7	10	11	43	50	-7	31
11	Edinburgh University	28	7	9	12	38	54	-16	30
12	Gretna 2008	28	9	2	17	42	67	-25	29
13	Vale of Leithen	28	8	5	15	43	74	-31	29
14	Dalbeattie Star	28	5	7	16	33	63	-30	22
15	Whitehill Welfare	28	2	6	20	24	70	-46	12

PLAY-OFF

1ST LEG

East Kilbride v Cove Rangers 1-2

2ND LEG

Cove Rangers v East Kilbride 3-0

FINAL 1ST LEG

Cove Rangers v Berwick Rangers 4-0

2ND LEG

Berwick Rangers v Cove Rangers 0-3

Cove Rangers win 7-0 on aggregate to claim a spot in the SPFL's League Two and in the process ended Berwick Rangers' 68-year membership.

EAST OF SCOTLAND LEAGUE

Conference A		P	W	D	L	F	A	GD	Pts
1	Penicuik Athletic	24	20	3	1	92	15	77	63
2	Hill of Beath Hawthorn	24	20	2	2	99	17	82	62
3	Musselburgh Athletic	24	17	3	4	74	31	43	54
4	Newtongrange Star	24	14	5	5	79	32	47	47
5	Dunbar United	24	13	4	7	62	34	28	43
6	Leith Athletic	24	10	4	10	41	51	-10	34
7	Coldstream	24	10	3	11	56	51	5	30*
8	Easthouses Lily Miners Welfare	24	9	1	14	41	67	-26	28
9	Oakley United	24	6	5	13	34	50	-16	23
10	Arniston Rangers	24	7	2	15	34	71	-37	23
11	Peebles Rovers	24	6	4	14	40	73	-33	22
12	Hawick Royal Albert	24	4	1	19	21	86	-65	13
13	Tweedmouth Rangers	24	1	1	22	20	115	-95	4

Conference B		P	W	D	L	F	A	GD	Pts
1	Bonnyrigg Rose Athletic	24	22	1	1	105	17	88	67
2	Bo'ness United	24	18	4	2	81	27	54	58
3	Tranent Juniors	24	16	2	6	81	37	44	50
4	Dundonald Bluebell	24	15	4	5	79	42	37	49
5	Crossgates Primrose	24	13	2	9	65	42	23	41
6	Sauchie Juniors	24	12	4	8	50	39	11	40
7	Lothian Thistle Hutchison Vale	24	10	3	11	43	47	-4	33
8	Dalkeith Thistle	24	9	5	10	41	45	-4	32
9	Haddington Athletic	24	9	4	11	72	54	18	31
10	Tynecastle	24	5	3	16	37	80	-43	18
11	Burntisland Shipyard	24	5	1	18	39	87	-48	16
12	Dunipace	24	4	3	17	32	66	-34	15
13	Eyemouth United	24	0	0	24	21	163	-142	-3*

Conference C		P	W	D	L	F	A	GD	Pts
1	Broxburn Athletic	24	22	0	2	83	21	62	66
2	Linlithgow Rose	24	20	1	3	106	24	82	61
3	Jeanfield Swifts	24	17	4	3	91	30	61	55
4	Camelon Juniors	24	17	3	4	87	33	54	54
5	Blackburn United	24	10	2	12	61	59	2	32
6	Preston Athletic	24	9	5	10	50	57	-7	32
7	Heriot-Watt University	24	9	3	12	42	53	-11	30
8	St Andrews United	24	8	5	11	41	46	-5	29
9	Stirling University Res	24	7	4	13	46	78	-32	25
10	Craigroyston	24	7	1	16	28	79	-51	22
11	Edinburgh United	24	5	2	17	34	69	-35	17
12	Inverkeithing Hillfield Swifts	24	5	1	18	35	85	-50	16
13	Ormiston	24	3	3	18	32	102	-70	12

Championship Play-off		P	W	D	L	F	A	GD	Pts
1	Bonnyrigg Rose Athletic	2	2	0	0	5	3	2	6
2	Penicuik Athletic	2	1	0	1	4	4	0	3
3	Broxburn Athletic	2	0	0	2	4	6	-2	0

Bonnyrigg Rose Athletic earn promotion to the Lowland League.

SOUTH OF SCOTLAND LEAGUE

		P	W	D	L	F	A	GD	Pts
1	Stranraer Res	30	29	1	0	131	24	107	88
2	Bonnyton Thistle	30	22	4	4	120	39	81	70
3	Nithsdale Wanderers	30	19	3	8	100	72	28	60
4	Abbey Vale	30	17	6	7	100	54	46	57
5	Upper Annandale	30	17	6	7	72	53	19	57
6	Mid Annandale	30	17	4	9	105	50	55	55
7	Lochar Thistle	30	16	5	9	71	47	24	53
8	Heston Rovers	30	15	3	12	66	48	18	48
9	Threave Rovers	30	14	3	13	79	54	25	45
10	St Cuthbert Wanderers	30	13	6	11	79	57	22	45
11	Lochmaben FC	30	8	5	17	59	87	-28	29
12	Wigtown & Bladnoch	30	8	3	19	48	94	-46	27
13	Newton Stewart	30	6	4	20	38	115	-77	22
14	Creetown FC	30	4	7	19	36	87	-51	19
15	Dumfries YMCA	30	3	2	25	29	125	-96	11
16	Annan Athletic	30	0	2	28	26	153	-127	2

NORTH CALEDONIAN LEAGUE

		P	W	D	L	F	A	GD	Pts
1	Golspie Sutherland (C)	16	11	3	2	38	15	23	36
2	Invergordon	16	11	1	4	44	19	25	34
3	Orkney	16	10	3	3	40	19	21	33
4	Alness United	16	8	2	6	42	31	11	26
5	Inverness Athletic	16	8	1	7	40	34	6	25
6	St Duthus	16	6	3	7	35	36	–1	21
7	Thurso	16	4	5	7	32	35	–3	17
8	Halkirk United	16	3	2	11	15	43	–28	11
9	Bunillidh Thistle	16	1	0	15	21	75	–54	3

SJFA EAST REGION

Superleague North		P	W	D	L	F	A	GD	Pts
1	Lochee United	22	20	2	0	71	11	60	62
2	Broughty Athletic	22	17	2	3	55	21	34	53
3	Thornton Hibs	22	12	2	8	51	37	14	38
4	Whitburn Juniors	22	11	3	8	58	53	5	36
5	Tayport	22	10	3	9	42	37	5	33
6	Forfar West End	22	8	5	9	37	36	1	29
7	Carnoustie Panmure	22	8	4	10	37	43	–6	28
8	Kennoway Star Hearts	22	8	2	12	38	39	–1	26
9	Kirriemuir Thistle	22	6	4	12	41	62	–21	22
10	Fauldhouse United	22	5	4	13	34	56	–22	19
11	Downfield	22	6	1	15	33	61	–28	19
12	Glenrothes	22	3	4	15	24	65	–41	13

Premier Division North		P	W	D	L	F	A	GD	Pts
1	Dundee North End	22	19	2	1	92	24	68	59
2	Luncarty	22	15	6	1	73	21	52	51
3	Kinnoull	22	15	2	5	69	23	46	47
4	Scone Thistle	22	14	2	6	65	29	36	44
5	Dundee East Craigie	22	12	4	6	57	28	29	40
6	Dundee Violet	22	11	1	10	48	40	8	34
7	Lochee Harp	22	10	3	9	64	47	17	33
8	Blairgowrie Juniors	22	10	1	11	60	45	15	31
9	Brechin Victoria	22	6	3	13	45	76	31	21
10	Arbroath Victoria	22	4	1	17	37	100	63	13
11	Forfar Albion	22	3	1	18	25	65	40	10
12	Coupar Angus	22	0	0	22	11	148	137	0

Premier Division South		P	W	D	L	F	A	GD	Pts
1	Pumpherston Juniors	22	18	2	2	75	31	44	56
2	Livingston United	22	11	7	4	43	29	14	40
3	Armadale Thistle	22	11	4	7	58	37	21	37
4	Bathgate Thistle	22	9	7	6	43	29	14	34
5	Lochore Welfare	22	8	10	4	47	44	3	34
6	Harthill Royal	22	8	7	7	43	39	4	31
7	Stoneyburn Juniors	22	8	2	12	49	66	-17	26
8	Newburgh Juniors	22	7	3	12	41	64	-23	24
9	West Calder United	22	5	8	9	47	50	-3	23
10	Rosyth	22	6	5	11	44	55	-11	23
11	Kirkcaldy YM	22	7	2	13	32	50	-18	23
12	Lochgelly Albert	22	3	5	14	36	64	-28	14

SJFA NORTH REGION

Superleague		P	W	D	L	F	A	GD	Pts
1	Banks O' Dee	26	23	2	1	113	20	93	71
2	Bridge of Don Thistle	26	17	2	7	72	37	35	53
3	Montrose Roselea	26	15	6	5	48	26	22	51
4	Hermes	26	14	3	9	49	42	7	45
5	Culter	26	13	5	8	58	41	17	44
6	Maud	26	11	2	13	49	64	–15	35
7	Nairn St. Ninian	26	10	3	13	51	64	–13	33
8	Dyce Juniors	26	8	8	10	45	44	1	32
9	Colony Park	26	9	4	13	39	55	–16	31
10	Hall Russell United	26	7	6	13	31	38	–7	27
11	East End	26	7	6	13	34	63	–29	27
12	Ellon United	26	7	3	16	41	67	–26	24
13	Dufftown	26	7	2	17	43	88	–45	23
14	Stonehaven	26	6	4	16	34	58	–24	22

Division One		P	W	D	L	F	A	GD	Pts
1	Banchory St Ternan	24	15	2	7	52	29	23	47
2	Deveronside	24	12	4	8	55	40	15	40
3	Fraserburgh United	24	11	5	8	43	36	7	38
4	Stoneywood Parkvale	24	11	3	10	52	45	7	36
5	Sunnybank	24	10	5	9	42	38	4	35
6	Longside	24	9	6	9	47	50	-3	33
7	Buckie Rovers	24	8	5	11	35	55	-20	29
8	Burghead Thistle	24	8	4	12	35	46	-11	28
9	Forres Thistle	24	4	6	14	34	56	-22	18

Division Two		P	W	D	L	F	A	GD	Pts
1	Buchanhaven Hearts	24	18	2	4	86	35	51	56
2	Aberdeen University	24	17	3	4	69	29	40	54
3	Islavale	24	15	2	7	74	36	38	47
4	Glentanar	24	12	2	10	70	52	18	38
5	Newmachar United	24	10	4	10	40	38	2	34
6	New Elgin	24	9	3	12	42	54	-12	30
7	Whitehills	24	9	3	12	43	61	-18	30
8	Spey Valley United	24	6	3	15	32	65	-33	21
9	Cruden Bay Juniors	24	0	2	22	15	101	-86	2

SJFA WEST REGION

Premiership		P	W	D	L	F	A	GD	Pts
1	Auchinleck Talbot	30	27	2	1	82	15	67	83
2	Hurlford United	30	22	3	5	79	37	42	69
3	Pollok	30	16	8	6	57	32	25	56
4	Beith Juniors	30	14	10	6	64	42	22	52
5	Glenafton Athletic	30	14	7	9	54	43	11	49
6	Irvine Meadow XI	30	14	5	11	47	48	-1	47
7	Largs Thistle	30	12	10	8	69	41	28	46
8	Clydebank	30	13	4	13	59	47	12	43
9	Kilwinning Rangers	30	12	3	15	41	46	-5	39
10	Cumnock Juniors	30	10	4	16	46	63	-17	34
11	Kirkintilloch Rob Roy	30	8	8	14	41	54	-13	32
12	Troon	30	9	5	16	39	53	-14	32
13	Kilbirnie Ladeside	30	10	2	18	38	57	-19	32
14	Renfrew	30	8	6	16	41	66	-25	30
15	Petershill	30	5	3	22	24	80	-56	15*
16	Cambuslang Rangers	30	5	2	23	35	92	-57	14*

Championship		P	W	D	L	F	A	GD	Pts
1	Rutherglen Glencairn	30	23	4	3	108	33	75	73
2	Benburb	30	23	4	3	102	42	60	73
3	Rossvale	30	19	6	5	61	23	38	63
4	Cumbernauld United	30	19	4	7	84	41	43	61
5	Arthurlie	30	17	5	8	78	40	38	56
6	Kilsyth Rangers	30	17	2	11	81	52	29	53
7	Darvel	30	12	11	7	57	44	13	47
8	Neilston Juniors	30	12	7	11	60	59	1	43
9	Whitletts Victoria	30	12	5	13	68	69	-1	41
10	St Roch's	30	12	3	15	67	64	3	39
11	Dalry Thistle	30	10	5	15	45	68	-23	35
12	Irvine Victoria	30	8	4	18	52	78	-26	28
13	Craigmark Burntonians	30	7	7	16	45	72	-27	28
14	Girvan	30	5	4	21	33	92	-59	19
15	Kello Rovers	30	3	4	23	30	89	-59	13
16	Larkhall Thistle	30	3	1	26	29	134	-105	10

League One		P	W	D	L	F	A	GD	Pts
1	Gartcairn Juniors	30	21	7	2	105	36	69	70
2	Shotts Bon Accord	30	21	5	4	85	30	55	68
3	Blantyre Victoria	30	19	4	7	87	42	45	61
4	Ardrossan Winton Rovers	30	17	6	7	67	42	25	57
5	Greenock Juniors	30	15	3	12	49	46	3	48
6	Port Glasgow Juniors	30	14	4	12	49	40	9	46
7	Bellshill Athletic	30	12	7	11	52	50	2	43
8	East Kilbride Thistle	30	11	8	11	49	54	-5	41
9	Glasgow Perthshire	30	11	7	12	60	77	-17	40
10	Royal Albert	30	11	6	13	59	57	2	39
11	Wishaw Juniors	30	10	8	12	50	58	-8	38
12	Maryhill	30	12	0	18	46	82	-36	36
13	Shettleston	30	8	8	14	44	52	-8	32
14	Yoker Athletic	30	7	5	18	47	70	-23	26
15	Maybole Juniors	30	4	5	21	43	92	-49	17
16	Lugar Boswell Thistle	30	4	3	23	43	107	-64	8*

League Two		P	W	D	L	F	A	GD	Pts
1	Lanark United	28	24	2	2	92	33	59	74
2	Lesmahagow Juniors	28	23	3	2	120	40	80	72
3	Carluke Rovers	28	15	5	8	65	44	21	50
4	Vale of Clyde	28	15	5	8	64	44	20	50
5	Ashfield	28	15	3	10	70	45	25	48
6	Vale of Leven	28	14	3	11	71	50	21	45
7	Thorniewood United	28	13	2	13	71	55	16	41
8	St Anthony's	28	13	2	13	53	53	0	41
9	Muirkirk Juniors	28	11	5	12	49	52	-3	38
10	Johnstone Burgh	28	10	4	14	51	61	-10	34
11	Annbank United	28	10	3	15	67	80	-13	33
12	Forth Wanderers	28	8	6	14	59	66	-7	30
13	Saltcoats Victoria	28	5	3	20	38	93	-55	18
14	Newmains United	28	5	3	20	41	104	-63	18
15	Ardeer Thistle	28	3	3	22	30	121	-91	12

C League		P	W	D	L	F	A	GD	Pts
1	Langlee Ams	20	17	3	0	111	24	87	54
2	Berwick Colts	20	15	0	5	52	42	10	45
3	Gala Fairydean Rovers	20	14	2	4	75	37	38	44
4	Ancrum	20	10	3	7	62	39	23	33
5	Selkirk Victoria	20	9	6	5	54	35	19	33
6	Highfields United	20	10	2	8	62	51	11	32
7	Melrose	20	7	2	11	48	73	-25	23
8	Hawick Legion Rovers	20	7	1	12	39	61	-22	22
9	Gala Thistle	20	4	2	14	43	82	-39	14
10	Tweeddale Rovers Colts	20	2	4	14	26	63	-37	10
11	Kelso Ams	20	1	3	16	23	88	-65	6

SCOTTISH JUNIOR CUP

HOLDERS: Auchinleck Talbot

ROUND 1

Colony Park	v	Kirriemuir Thistle	4-2

ROUND 2

Kinnoul	v	Saltcoats Victoria	2-0
Cambuslang Rangers	v	Fraserburgh United	5-0
Troon	v	Lochee Harp	5-1
Blantyre Victoria	v	Vale of Clyde	2-2
Auchinleck Talbot	v	Forfar West End	4-2
Cumnock Juniors	v	Coupar Angus	HW
Cumbernauld United	v	Glenafton Athletic	1-2
Ellon United	v	Forth Wanderers	3-2
Girvan	v	Culter	2-0
Bellshill Athletic	v	Burghead Thistle	4-0
Islavale	v	Vale of Leven	3-0
Lochore Welfare	v	Fauldhouse United	2-4
Pollok	v	Buchanhaven Hearts	9-0
Dundee Violet	v	Maryhill	4-2
East End	v	Lochgelly Albert	2-1
New Elgin	v	Whitehills	1-1
Rosyth	v	Newmains United	1-2
Carnoustie Panmure	v	Longside	3-0
Kirkcaldy YMCA	v	Renfrew	0-3
Muirkirk	v	Yoker Athletic	2-2
Gartcairn	v	Kilbirnie Ladeside	3-23
Arthurlie	v	Forres Thistle	3-0
Tayport	v	Port Glasgow	3-1
Rutherglen Glencairn	v	Deveronside	8-0
Bridge of Don Thistle	v	Ardrossan Winton Rovers	2-1
Maybole	v	Aberdeen University	2-2
Kilwinning Rangers	v	Beith	3-1
Benburb	v	Broughty Athletic	0-4

Banks O'Dee	v	Dyce Juniors	6-0
Scone Thistle	v	Neilston	0-1
Hurlford United	v	Dufftown	10-0
Spey Valley United	v	Harthill Royal	2-7
Livingston United	v	Kilsyth Rangers	0-2
Glenrothes	v	Brechin Victoria	3-0
Wishaw	v	West Calder United	2-0
Hermes	v	Newburgh	4-3
Lochee United	v	Dalry Thistle	6-2
Glasgow Perthshire	v	St. Roch's	1-6
St. Anthony's	v	Irvine Meadow XI	0-3
Irvine Victoria	v	Kirkintilloch Rob Roy	1-9
Petershill	v	Darvel	1-2
Royal Albert	v	Lugar Boswell Thistle	5-3
Annbank United	v	Ardeer Thistle	5-0
Hall Russell United	v	Kennoway Star Hearts	4-3
Glentanar	v	Carluke Rovers	1-3
Colony Park	v	Stonehaven	4-1
Ashfield	v	Banchory St Ternan	1-0
Nairn St Ninian	v	Buckie Rovers	3-0
Clydebank	v	Armadale Thistle	4-0
Thornton Hibs	v	Stoneywood Parkvale	7-1
East Kilbride Thistle	v	Montrose Roselea	1-0
Arbroath Victoria	v	Largs Thistle	0-9
Bathgate Thistle	v	Craigmark Burntonians	1-2
Newmachar United	v	Whitburn	1-3
Kello Rovers	v	Blairgowrie	2-1
Shettleston	v	Dundee North End	0-1
Whitletts Victoria	v	Lanark United	2-2
Thorniewood United	v	Dundee East Craigie	0-3
Shotts Bon Accord	v	Maud	3-2
Greenock	v	Rossvale	2-5
Stoneyburn	v	Luncarty	2-4
Sunnybank	v	Lesmahagow	0-3
Downfield	v	Larkhall Thistle	7-1
Pumpherston	v	Forfar Albion	3-1
REPLAYS			
Vale of Clyde	v	Blantyre Victoria	0-7
Whitehills	v	New Elgin	1-3
Yoker Athletic	v	Muirkirk	3-3, 4-5p
Aberdeen University	v	Maybole	1-0
Lanark United	v	Whitletts Victoria	2-0

ROUND 3

New Elgin	v	Luncarty	0-7
Pollok	v	Cumnock Juniors	0-0
Ashfield	v	Neilston	4-2
Renfrew	v	Fauldhouse United	2-1
Wishaw	v	Lanark United	1-1
Pumpherston	v	Blantyre Victoria	1-4
Kinnoull	v	Clydebank	0-3
St Roch's	v	Downfield	4-1
Hurlford United	v	Broughty Athletic	2-1
Tayport	v	Rossvale	1-0
Colony Park	v	Cambuslang Rangers	1-6
Gartcairn Juniors	v	Lochee United	0-2
Darvel	v	Whitburn	4-2
Muirkirk	v	Girvan	2-2
East End	v	Dundee North End	0-3
Largs Thistle	v	Shotts Bon Accord	4-0
Bridge of Don Thistle	v	Rosyth	3-5
Carnoustie Panmure	v	Aberdeen University	5-0
Troon	v	Nairn St. Ninian	4-2
Kilsyth Rangers	v	Irvine Meadow	2-0
Carluke Rovers	v	Hermes	1-0
Craigmark Burntonians	v	East Craigie	4-1
Ellon United	v	Glenafton Athletic	1-3
Royal Albert	v	Harthill Royal	2-2
Banks O' Dee	v	East Kilbride Thistle	5-1
Annbank United	v	Kello Rovers	2-1
Glenrothes	v	Hall Russell United	8-0
Kirkintilloch Rob Roy	v	Thornton Hibs	1-3
Arthurlie	v	Dundee Violet	1-3
Islavale	v	Rutherglen Glencairn	1-4
Kilwinning Rangers	v	Bellshill Athletic	2-0
Auchinleck Talbot	v	Lesmahagow	9-1
REPLAYS			
Cumnock Juniors	v	Pollok	1-3
Girvan	v	Muirkirk	4-4, 6-5p
Harthill Royal	v	Royal Albert	3-3, 3-5p
Lanark United	v	Wishaw	2-1

ROUND 4

Glenafton Athletic	v	Pollok	0-0
Craigmark Burntonians	v	Glenrothes	2-1
Carluke Rovers	v	Lochee United	1-3
Royal Albert	v	Clydebank	1-3
Kilsyth Rangers	v	Hurlford United	1-3
Darvel	v	Largs Thistle	1-2
Kilwinning Rangers	v	Banks O' Dee	3-1
St Roch's	v	Luncarty	3-0
Lanark United	v	Rossvale	1-1
Dundee North End	v	Cambuslang Rangers	0-4
Rutherglen Glencairn	v	Ashfield	7-1
Girvan	v	Dundee Violet	7-1
Rosyth	v	Annbank United	2-0
Carnoustie Panmure	v	Troon	1-3
Blantyre Victoria	v	Auchinleck Talbot	0-4
Thornton Hibs	v	Renfrew	2-0
REPLAYS			
Pollok	v	Glenafton Athletic	1-1, 3-0p
Rossvale	v	Lanark United	3-1

ROUND 5

Kilwinning Rangers	v	Thornton Hibs	6-2
Largs Thistle	v	St Roch's	1-1
Cambuslang Rangers	v	Troon	0-1
Rossvale	v	Hurlford United	1-1
Pollok	v	Rosyth	8-2
Auchinleck Talbot	v	Rutherglen Glencairn	4-1
Girvan	v	Clydebank	1-7
Craigmark Burntonians	v	Lochee United	0-4
REPLAYS			
St Roch's	v	Largs Thistle	2-5
Hurlford United	v	Rossvale	4-3

QUARTER FINALS

Largs Thistle	v	Kilwinning Rangers	5-0
Troon	v	Lochee United	0-2
Hurlford United	v	Clydebank	1-1
Pollok	v	Auchinleck Talbot	0-3
REPLAY			
Clydebank	v	Hurlford United	1-3

SEMI FINALS 1st LEG

Lochee United	v	Auchinleck Talbot	1-4
Largs Thistle	v	Hurlford United	2-2
SEMI FINALS 2nd LEG			
Hurlford United	v	Largs Thistle	1-2
Auchinleck Talbot	v	Lochee United	2-0

FINAL

Auchinleck Talbot	v	Largs Thistle	2-0	Att: 4629

McCracken 3 Samson 38

WELSH TABLES 2018-19

WELSH PREMIER

		P	W	D	L	F	A	GD	Pts
1	The New Saints (C)	32	23	5	4	99	16	83	74
2	Connah's Quay Nomads	32	19	5	8	76	33	43	62
3	Barry Town United	32	17	5	10	54	51	3	56
4	Caernarfon Town	32	13	7	12	45	47	–2	46
5	Newtown	32	13	7	12	53	56	–3	46
6	Bala Town	32	13	5	14	55	63	–8	44
7	Cardiff Metropolitan University	32	16	3	13	53	40	13	51
8	Aberystwyth Town	32	13	5	14	44	61	–17	44
9	Carmarthen Town	32	12	6	14	49	53	–4	39*
10	Cefn Druids	32	10	9	13	43	49	–6	39
11	Llandudno	32	5	7	20	33	65	–32	22
12	Llanelli Town	32	4	4	24	31	101	–70	16

After 22 games the League splits into two. The top six then play each other twice again and the bottom six do the same. However, once split, no team can climb back into the top six no matter what points they finish on.

Division Two

	Division Two	P	W	D	L	F	A	GD	Pts
1	STM Sports	30	22	4	4	108	41	67	70
2	Swansea University	30	20	4	6	100	35	65	64
3	Caerau (Ely)	30	17	3	10	69	43	26	54
4	Caldicot Town	30	17	2	11	72	42	30	53
5	Abergavenny Town	30	16	4	10	61	38	23	52
6	Monmouth Town	30	15	6	9	70	48	22	51
7	Aberbargoed Buds	30	15	5	10	50	34	16	50
8	Pontardawe Town	30	14	7	9	63	51	12	49
9	Croesyceiliog	30	12	6	12	54	59	-5	42
10	Garden Village	30	10	9	11	55	60	-5	39
11	Bridgend Street	30	11	6	13	68	76	-8	39
12	Dinas Powys	30	9	4	17	38	61	-23	31
13	Risca United	30	8	6	16	45	64	-19	30
14	AFC Llwydcoed	30	6	6	18	49	81	-32	24
15	West End	30	7	2	21	39	114	-75	23
16	Aberdare Town	30	3	2	25	34	128	-94	11

CYMRU ALLIANCE

		P	W	D	L	F	A	GD	Pts
1	Airbus UK Broughton	30	24	4	2	75	20	55	76
2	Flint Town United	30	17	7	6	52	31	21	58
3	Porthmadog	30	17	6	7	60	32	28	57
4	Bangor City	30	16	3	11	68	48	20	51
5	Rhyl	30	16	3	11	55	44	11	51
6	Guilsfield	30	13	6	11	43	45	-2	45
7	Ruthin Town	30	13	4	13	46	47	-1	43
8	Buckley Town	30	12	6	12	51	50	1	42
9	Prestatyn Town	30	11	6	13	52	49	3	39
10	Gresford Athletic	30	10	9	11	42	46	-4	39
11	Conwy Borough	30	9	9	12	46	42	4	36
12	Llanrhaeadr YM	30	10	2	18	34	71	-37	32
13	Penrhyncoch	30	7	9	14	35	44	-9	30
14	Holywell Town	30	8	6	16	38	58	-20	30
15	Denbigh Town	30	9	2	19	37	65	-28	29
16	Holyhead Hotspur	30	5	4	21	29	71	-42	19

Division Three

	Division Three	P	W	D	L	F	A	GD	Pts
1	Penydarren BGC	30	24	2	4	90	30	60	74
2	Trefelin Boys & Girls Club	30	23	4	3	97	33	64	73
3	Penrhiwceiber Rangers	30	22	5	3	89	23	66	71
4	Pontyclun	30	18	7	5	77	48	29	61
5	Trethomas Bluebirds	30	14	8	8	68	41	27	50
6	Tredegar Town	30	13	7	10	59	46	13	46
7	Treharris Athletic Western	30	14	4	12	54	49	5	46
8	Panteg	30	13	7	10	56	58	-2	46
9	Ynysygerwn	30	11	6	13	50	50	0	39
10	AFC Porth	30	7	9	14	31	59	-28	30
11	Treowen Stars	30	8	5	17	42	70	-28	29
12	Newport City	30	7	7	16	48	63	-15	28
13	Chepstow Town	30	7	4	19	36	91	-55	25
14	Albion Rovers	30	5	7	18	49	69	-20	22
15	Ely Rangers	30	7	1	22	50	91	-41	22
16	Caerau	30	3	5	22	30	105	-75	14

WELSH LEAGUE

	Division One	P	W	D	L	F	A	GD	Pts
1	Penybont	30	25	5	0	81	22	59	80
2	Cambrian & Clydach	30	18	6	6	58	32	26	60
3	Haverfordwest County	30	16	6	8	69	34	35	54
4	Afan Lido	30	15	6	9	68	59	9	51
5	Goytre United	30	15	5	10	52	39	13	50
6	Cwmamman United	30	14	8	8	55	55	0	50
7	Llantwit Major	30	14	6	10	46	37	9	48
8	Briton Ferry Llansawel	30	12	6	12	44	50	-6	42
9	Ammanford	30	10	6	14	51	57	-6	36
10	Cwmbran Celtic	30	10	6	14	49	57	-8	36
11	Pontypridd Town	30	9	6	15	52	66	-14	33
12	Undy Athletic	30	8	7	15	51	64	-13	31
13	Port Talbot Town	30	6	11	13	39	50	-11	29
14	Taffs Well	30	7	4	19	33	62	-29	25
15	Goytre	30	6	6	18	39	65	-26	24
16	Ton Pentre	30	6	4	20	38	76	-38	22

WELSH NATIONAL LEAGUE

	Premier	P	W	D	L	F	A	GD	Pts
1	Queens Park	28	20	3	5	88	24	64	63
2	Corwen	28	20	2	6	94	33	61	62
3	Brymbo	28	20	2	6	89	43	46	62
4	Mold Alexandra	28	15	9	4	85	38	47	54
5	FC Nomads of Connah's Quay	28	15	5	8	58	43	15	50
6	Saltney Town	28	14	7	7	66	46	20	49
7	Llay Welfare	28	12	4	12	47	58	-11	40
8	Chirk AAA	28	10	9	9	51	39	12	39
9	Cefn Albion	28	9	6	13	58	69	-11	30*
10	Rhos Aelwyd	28	7	8	13	32	42	-10	29
11	Brickfield Rangers	28	9	2	17	48	101	-53	26*
12	Penycae	28	7	3	18	42	87	-45	24
13	Rhostyllen	28	7	3	18	38	85	-47	24
14	Llanuwchllyn	28	4	9	15	29	73	-44	21
15	Hawarden Rangers	28	2	6	20	34	78	-44	12

Action from what turn out to be title decider in the Welsh Alliance Division One campaign between Llangefni Town and Bodedern Athletic.

The goal that brought the Championship home for Llangefni Town.

Llangefni Town celebrate their success. All photos: Bill Wheatcroft.

Division One	P	W	D	L	F	A	GD	Pts
1 Plas Madoc	22	20	2	0	106	26	80	62
2 Castell Alun Colts	22	13	4	5	51	38	13	43
3 Rhydymwyn	22	11	3	8	59	32	27	36
4 Llangollen Town	22	11	3	8	74	48	26	36
5 Rhosllanerchrugog	22	11	3	8	37	41	-4	36
6 Coedpoeth United	22	11	3	8	48	53	-5	36
7 Mynydd Isa Spartans	22	11	2	9	52	42	10	35
8 New Brighton Villa	22	11	3	8	62	36	26	33*
9 Offa Athletic	22	5	5	12	39	59	-20	20
10 Overton Recreational	22	4	7	11	28	59	-31	19
11 Cefn Mawr Rangers	22	3	3	16	35	65	-30	12
12 Johnstown Youth	22	1	2	19	16	108	-92	5

NORTH EAST WALES LEAGUE

Division One	P	W	D	L	F	A	GD	Pts
1 Flint Mountain	20	18	2	0	111	20	91	56
2 Acton	20	16	0	4	111	34	77	48
3 Mold Town United	20	14	2	4	58	29	29	44
4 Airbus UK Broughton Youth	20	11	2	7	60	49	11	35
5 Caerwys	20	10	2	8	58	51	7	32
6 Penyffordd Lions	20	10	1	9	90	59	31	31
7 Brymbo Victoria	20	9	0	11	71	51	20	27
8 Connah's Quay Nomads U18	20	7	3	10	72	59	13	24
9 Borras Park Albion	20	4	1	15	25	90	-65	13
10 Bradley Park	20	2	1	17	26	107	-81	7
11 Bellevue	20	2	0	18	29	162	-133	6

WELSH ALLIANCE

Division One	P	W	D	L	F	A	GD	Pts
1 Llangefni Town	28	21	4	3	74	16	58	67
2 Bodedern Athletic	28	20	1	7	72	31	41	61
3 Llandudno Albion	28	18	3	7	76	48	28	57
4 Greenfield	28	13	7	8	54	46	8	46
5 Llanrug United	28	12	9	7	57	40	17	45
6 Nantlle Vale	28	13	6	9	63	40	23	42*
7 Prestatyn Sports	28	12	3	13	53	56	-3	39
8 Penrhyndeudraeth	28	11	5	12	65	56	9	38
9 St Asaph City	28	11	5	12	54	61	-7	38
10 Llanberis	28	9	10	9	46	50	-4	37
11 Llanrwst United	28	11	3	14	52	52	0	36
12 Mynydd Llandegai	28	9	8	11	46	65	-19	35
13 Llandyrnog United	28	5	6	17	30	68	-38	21
14 Barmouth & Dyffryn United	28	4	5	19	34	68	-34	14*
15 Llandudno Junction	28	2	3	23	19	98	-79	9

Division Two	P	W	D	L	F	A	GD	Pts
1 Glan Conwy	28	20	4	4	92	32	60	64
2 Blaenau Amateurs	28	20	2	6	79	44	35	62
3 Llannefydd	28	19	3	6	79	34	45	60
4 Pwllheli	28	17	4	7	82	40	42	55
5 Aberffraw	28	15	5	8	73	59	14	50
6 Llannerchymedd	28	16	2	10	59	51	8	50
7 Kinmel Bay	28	13	6	9	72	56	16	45
8 Y Felinheli	27	12	7	8	75	52	23	43
9 Penmaenmawr Phoenix	28	9	8	11	53	48	5	35
10 Pentraeth	28	10	4	14	53	57	-4	34
11 Gaerwen	28	8	11	9	53	54	-1	32*
12 Holyhead Town	28	6	7	15	53	77	-24	22*
13 Meliden	27	6	2	19	31	92	-61	14*
14 Mochdre Sports	28	3	3	22	32	96	-64	12
15 Amlwch Town	28	0	2	26	26	120	-94	2

GWYNEDD LEAGUE

	P	W	D	L	F	A	GD	Pts
1 Menai Bridge Tigers	20	18	1	1	85	19	66	55
2 Gwalchmai	20	15	3	2	52	24	28	48
3 Bro Goronwy	20	12	1	7	56	33	23	37
4 Glantraeth	20	11	3	6	72	39	33	36
5 Nefyn United	20	11	2	7	50	39	11	35
6 Llangoed & District	20	9	2	9	52	47	5	29
7 Talysarn Celts	20	5	7	8	42	47	-5	22
8 Waunfawr	20	5	5	10	37	56	-19	17
9 Llanystumdwy	20	5	2	13	42	63	-21	17
10 Mynydd Tigers	20	4	1	15	26	74	-48	10
11 Bontnewydd	20	1	1	18	23	96	-73	4

ANGLESEY LEAGUE

	P	W	D	L	F	A	GD	Pts
1 Bryngwran Bulls	20	14	4	2	91	33	58	46
2 Caergybi	20	15	0	5	106	39	67	45
3 Arriva Bangor	20	13	2	5	78	42	36	41
4 Cefni	20	11	3	6	43	38	5	36
5 Holyhead Hotspur Res	20	11	2	7	68	36	32	35
6 Valley Athletic	20	7	6	7	63	63	0	27
7 Llanfairpwll	20	7	4	9	38	44	-6	25
8 Pentraeth Res	20	6	3	11	47	68	-21	21
9 Cemaes Bay	20	6	2	12	37	51	-14	20
10 Bodorgan	20	6	2	12	41	78	-37	20
11 Llandegfan	20	0	0	20	25	145	-120	0

MID WALES LEAGUE

Division One	P	W	D	L	F	A	GD	Pts
1 Llanfair United	28	20	6	2	70	24	46	66
2 Llanidloes Town	28	21	3	4	69	33	36	66
3 Berriew	28	19	4	5	85	37	48	61
4 Caersws	28	18	6	4	82	26	56	60
5 Welshpool Town	28	13	6	9	78	49	29	45
6 Builth Wells	28	13	6	9	66	47	19	45
7 Carno	28	12	4	12	51	57	-6	40
8 Llandrindod Wells	28	11	6	11	52	39	13	39
9 Aberaeron	28	11	3	14	57	58	-1	36
10 Radnor Valley	28	12	2	14	63	63	0	35*
11 Bow Street	28	8	6	14	40	46	-6	30
12 Tywyn Bryncrug	28	8	2	18	43	97	-54	26
13 Kerry	28	7	4	17	59	93	-34	25
14 Llansantffraid Village	28	4	7	17	38	81	-43	19
15 Churchstoke	28	0	1	27	19	122	-103	1

Division Two	P	W	D	L	F	A	GD	Pts
1 Montgomery Town	24	18	4	2	68	22	46	58
2 Four Crosses	24	19	2	3	86	30	56	56*
3 Hay St Mary's	24	17	1	6	90	39	51	52
4 Waterloo Rovers	24	10	7	7	53	46	7	37
5 Rhayader Town	24	10	5	9	51	39	12	35
6 Newbridge-on-Wye	24	11	2	11	59	67	-8	35
7 Abermule	24	9	5	10	50	54	-4	32
8 Dyffryn Banw	24	9	4	11	35	58	-23	31
9 Dolgellau Athletic	24	8	5	11	53	65	-12	26*
10 Borth United	24	6	6	12	57	66	-9	24
11 Machynlleth	24	5	8	11	48	70	-22	20*
12 Presteigne St. Andrews	24	4	4	16	45	84	-39	16
13 Aberystwyth University	24	2	3	19	29	84	-55	6*

VALE OF CLYWD & CONWY LEAGUE

Premier Division		P	W	D	L	F	A	GD	Pts
1	Llandudno Amateurs	16	12	0	4	69	35	34	36
2	Llandudno Athletic	16	11	2	3	59	32	27	35
3	Llansannan	16	11	2	3	42	27	15	35
4	Abergele	16	9	0	7	43	35	8	27
5	Bro Cernyw	16	6	2	8	28	29	-1	20
6	Rhuddlan Town	16	6	2	8	44	59	-15	20
7	Llanfairfechan Town	16	5	2	9	39	44	-5	17
8	Machno United	16	4	4	8	41	57	-16	16
9	Cerrig-y-Drudion	16	0	2	14	20	67	-47	2

Old Colwyn resigned - record expunged.

Division One		P	W	D	L	F	A	GD	PTS
1	Llanelwy Athletic	20	17	3	0	115	26	89	54
2	Y Glannau	20	13	5	2	68	33	35	44
3	Rhos United	20	13	1	6	62	42	20	40
4	Henllan	20	11	6	3	58	39	19	39
5	St Asaph City Res	20	9	5	6	66	43	23	32
6	Penrhyn Bay Dragons	20	8	4	8	70	56	14	28
7	Llysfaen	20	7	1	12	38	69	-31	22
8	Rhuddlan Town Res	20	5	4	11	41	57	-16	19
9	Llanfairfechan Town Res	20	5	2	13	46	76	-30	17
10	Betws-y-Coed	20	2	3	15	38	98	-60	9
11	Denbigh Development	20	2	2	16	24	87	-63	8

PEMBROKESHIRE LEAGUE

Division One		P	W	D	L	F	A	GD	Pts
1	Monkton Swifts	24	20	1	3	105	30	75	61
2	Merlins Bridge	24	19	3	2	98	40	58	60
3	Goodwick United	24	18	3	3	101	23	78	57
4	Carew	24	17	4	3	112	37	75	55
5	Hakin United	24	17	2	5	76	38	38	53
6	Pennar Robins	24	10	2	12	61	67	-6	32
7	St Clears	24	10	2	12	52	68	-16	32
8	Clarbeston Road	24	9	2	13	71	86	-15	29
9	Narberth	24	8	1	15	51	88	-37	25
10	Neyland	24	6	1	17	35	102	-67	19
11	Saundersfoot Sports	24	5	3	16	44	81	-37	18
12	Milford United	24	3	2	19	26	85	-59	11
13	Herbrandston	24	0	2	22	27	114	-87	2

Lamphey resigned - record expunged.

Division Two		P	W	D	L	F	A	GD	Pts
1	Fishguard Sports	24	20	1	3	97	24	73	61
2	Merlins Bridge II	24	18	2	4	80	35	45	56
3	Kilgetty	24	15	4	5	63	36	27	49
4	Hakin United II	24	15	3	6	72	22	50	48
5	Johnston	24	14	2	8	83	42	41	44
6	St Ishmaels	24	11	4	9	46	43	3	36
7	Broad Haven	24	10	4	10	69	59	10	34
8	Solva	24	7	6	11	49	71	-22	27
9	Hundleton	24	6	4	14	32	84	-52	22
10	Lawrenny	24	6	2	16	37	78	-41	20
11	Camrose	24	6	3	15	43	62	-19	18*
12	Llangwm Haverfordwest CC	24	3	6	15	32	88	-56	17
13	Letterston	24	4	1	19	31	90	-59	13

Prendergast Villa resigned - record expunged.

Division Three		P	W	D	L	F	A	GD	Pts
1	Pennar Robins II	26	23	1	2	134	23	111	70
2	Monkton Swifts II	26	22	0	4	161	55	106	66
3	Carew II	26	19	2	5	120	25	95	56
4	Goodwick United II	26	15	5	6	68	38	30	44 *
5	Pembroke Boro	26	13	2	11	83	55	28	41
6	Pendine	26	12	2	12	76	70	6	38
7	Clarbeston Road II	26	11	4	11	68	72	-4	37
8	Milford Athletic	26	10	4	12	63	57	6	34
9	Fishguard Sports II	26	9	5	12	38	48	-10	32
10	Narberth II	26	11	0	15	57	87	-30	30*
11	St Clears II	26	7	5	14	48	103	-55	26
12	Milford United II	26	6	4	16	47	85	-38	16*
13	St Florence	26	3	2	21	52	129	-77	14
14*	Solva II	26	2	2	22	24	192	-168	2*

Division Four		P	W	D	L	F	A	GD	Pts
1	Cosheston AFC	20	17	0	3	93	29	64	51
2	Pennar Robins III	20	17	0	3	73	28	45	51
3	Broad Haven II	20	13	1	6	84	40	44	40
4	Llangwm Haverfordwest CC II	20	11	0	9	72	49	23	30*
5	Neyland II	20	9	2	9	45	60	-15	29
6	Camrose II	20	9	1	10	55	48	7	28
7	St Ishmaels II	20	7	3	10	45	67	-22	21*
8	Pembroke Boro II	20	6	0	14	62	97	-35	18
9	Hundleton II	20	7	0	13	38	74	-36	18*
10	Herbrandston II	20	5	1	14	48	85	-37	13*
11	Kilgetty II	20	4	2	14	41	79	-38	8*

Division Five		P	W	D	L	F	A	GD	Pts
1	Tenby	14	13	1	0	85	21	64	40
2	Johnston II	14	11	2	1	64	18	46	35
3	Carew III	14	6	4	4	33	30	3	19
4	Saundersfoot Sports II	14	5	1	8	42	44	-2	16
5	Lawrenny II	14	3	2	9	22	55	-33	11
6	Milford Athletic II	14	4	1	9	24	48	-24	10
7	Newport Tigers	14	4	0	10	26	37	-11	9
8	Letterston II	14	4	1	9	27	70	-43	7

WELSH CUP - From the First Round

HOLDERS: CONNAH'S QUAY NOMADS

ROUND 1

Penlan Club	v	Goytre United	0-1
Cefn Albion	v	Dolgellau Athletic Amateur	7-1
Llandudno Albion	v	St. Asaph City	3-4 aet
Briton Ferry Llansawel AFC	v	Caerau Ely AFC	1-0
Cambrian & Clydach	v	Port Talbot Town	5-0
Cwmamman United	v	Dinas Powys	4-0
Cwmbran Celtic	v	Ammanford AFC	3-0
Cwmbran Town	v	Afan Lido FC	3-2
Garden Village	v	Blaenrhondda	1-2
Llandrindod Wells FC	v	Aberbargoed Buds	3-4
Llanidloes Town FC	v	Pontypridd Town	1-2
Panteg AFC	v	Penybont FC	1-3

Pontyclun FC	v	Llantwit Major FC	3-1
Radnor Valley	v	Goytre AFC	1-2
STM Sports	v	Haverfordwest County	1-2
Sully Sports	v	Brecon Corries	3-1
Ton Pentre FC	v	Pencoed Athletic AFC	3-1
Trefelin BGC	v	Swansea University	1-2
Treharris Athletic Western	v	Cornelly United	3-2
Undy Athletic	v	Monmouth Town	3-4
West End FC	v	Caldicot Town	0-6
Ynysddu Welfare	v	Taffs Well	2-1
Bangor City	v	Mold Alexandra	4-2
Berriew FC	v	Penrhyncoch FC	5-4
Buckley Town	v	Brymbo FC	3-1
Caersws FC	v	Holywell Town	3-2 aet
Coedpoeth United	v	Ruthin Town	2-3
Conwy Borough FC	v	Rhyl FC	1-2
Pwllheli FC	v	Porthmadog FC	0-3
Denbigh Town	v	Holyhead Town	9-3
Gresford Athletic	v	Brickfield Rangers	4-3 aet
Guilsfield FC	v	Rhostyllen FC	2-0
Hawarden Rangers	v	Llanfair United	2-3
Holyhead Hotspur	v	Corwen FC	4-2
Llangefni Town FC	v	Borth United	2-0
Llanrhaeadr-ym-Mochnant	v	Flint Town United	1-2
Llay Welfare	v	Rhydymwyn FC	2-0
Penycae FC	v	Airbus UK	0-4
Prestatyn Town	v	New Brighton Villa	5-1
Llandudno Amateurs	v	Dyffryn Nanttle Vale	2-4 aet

ROUND 2

Caldicot Town	v	Cambrian & Clydach	2-3
Sully Sports	v	Cwmbran Celtic	1-3
Airbus UK	v	Llay Welfare	9-1
Bangor City	v	Cefn Albion	6-1
Buckley Town	v	Denbigh Town	1-3
Flint Town United	v	Gresford Athletic	3-2
Guilsfield FC	v	Dyffryn Nanttle Vale	4-3
Holyhead Hotspur	v	Ruthin Town	3-1
Llanfair United	v	Porthmadog FC	1-4
Llangefni Town FC	v	St. Asaph City	5-1
Prestatyn Town	v	Berriew FC	6-3
Rhyl FC	v	Caersws FC	3-1
Cwmbran Town	v	Ton Pentre FC	1-2
Goytre United	v	Pontyclun FC	1-0
Haverfordwest County	v	Swansea University	4-3
Monmouth Town	v	Ynysddu Welfare	1-3
Pontypridd Town	v	Goytre AFC	6-3
Aberbargoed Buds	v	Penybont FC	0-2
Cwmamman United	v	Blaenrhondda	2-1
Treharris Athletic Western	v	Briton Ferry Llansawel AFC	3-4

ROUND 3

Barry Town United	v	Penybont FC	4-1 aet
Bangor City	v	Holyhead Hotspur	4-1
Prestatyn Town	v	Caernarfon Town	0-3
Cwmbran Celtic	v	The New Saints	0-3
Cwmamman United	v	Aberystwyth Town	3-4
Airbus UK	v	Porthmadog FC	4-2
Goytre United	v	Carmarthen Town	0-3
Denbigh Town	v	Cambrian & Clydach	1-2
Guilsfield FC	v	GAP Connah's Quay FC	2-4
Llangefni Town FC	v	Llanelli Town	1-0
Newtown AFC	v	Rhyl FC	1-2
Ton Pentre FC	v	Cardiff Metropolitan	1-4
Briton Ferry Llansawel AFC	v	Llandudno FC	2-3
Haverfordwest County	v	Pontypridd Town	3-0
Ynysddu Welfare	v	Cefn Druids	1-3
Flint Town United	v	Bala Town	0-3

ROUND 4

Carmarthen Town	v	GAP Connah's Quay FC	1-3
Haverfordwest County	v	Bala Town	0-4 aet
Barry Town United	v	Cefn Druids	3-2
Airbus UK	v	The New Saints	2-5
Cambrian & Clydach	v	Rhyl FC	3-1
Aberystwyth Town	v	Cardiff Metropolitan	1-3
Llangefni Town FC	v	Llandudno FC	1-3
Bangor City	v	Caernarfon Town	1-2

QUARTER-FINALS

Caernarfon Town	v	GAP Connah's Quay FC	1-2
Bala Town	v	Cardiff Metropolitan	0-1 aet
Llandudno FC	v	The New Saints	1-8
Barry Town United	v	Cambrian & Clydach	3-2

SEMI-FINALS

The New Saints	v	Barry Town United	2-0
Cardiff Metropolitan	v	GAP Connah's Quay FC	0-3

FINAL

GAP Connah's Quay FC	v	The New Saints	0-3

WELSH TROPHY

HOLDERS: CONWY BOROUGH

QUARTER-FINALS

Corwen	v	Cefn Albion	3-5
Penydarren BGC	v	STM Sports	1-2
Llangefni Town	v	Bodedern Athletic	0-1
Plas Madoc	v	Pontardawe Town	2-4

SEMI-FINALS

Cefn Albion	v	STM Sports	3-1 aet
Bodedern Athletic	v	Pontardawe Town	0-5

FINAL

Cefn Albion	v	Pontardawe Town	4-0

21 DAYS of Positivity

DAY 01
Enjoyment and Positivity
Try three things that make your session positive: Allow enjoyment, be positive and smile

DAY 02
How well do you know your Players?
Take some time to get to know your players better

DAY 03
This is a Safe Place
Think about how you react when a mistake is made, encourage creativity and experimentation

DAY 04
What do your Players want from Training
Fun, fitness or because they love it, consider the reasons your players are there

DAY 05
Make Matchday about Learning
Provide equal opportunities and focus on communication

DAY 06
How to deal with Winning and Losing
Look for opportunities to show how to deal with adversity and frustration with dignity and respect

DAY 07
Are You a Role Model
So much of young player's behaviour on matchday mimics that of the coach, refresh yourself with our code of conduct

DAY 08
Arrival Activities: Get Players Moving
Tag, small-sided games or movement activities are all fun, engaging and active ways to start your session

DAY 09
Routines and Boundaries
Having consistent coaching routines can help create a safe place for young players to learn

DAY 10
When are we Playing a Game
Small-sided games give players lots of touches of the ball and the chance to attack and defend

DAY 11
How to Include Goalkeeper in Coaching Sessions
What individual challenges can you give to your goalkeeper within a group practice?

DAY 12
Improving Strenghts
Write down the strengths of five players in your squad? How can you challenge them to improve their strengths?

DAY 13
What are You Looking For?
More specific observation will lead to more specific and relevant feedback.

DAY 14
'Drop Off' 'Squeeze' 'Get Tight'
Having a consistent way of talking about football is one way to link training and matchday

DAY 15
One Size Doesn't Fit All
To get the most out of each individual try tailoring your training tasks for specific players

DAY 16
How to Work as a Coaching Pair
Defining coaching roles is crucial. If one coach 'leads' the session, the other coach is free to focus on individuals

DAY 17
Effective Observation
Stand back and carefully watch two or three players, what did you learn about the group you didn't already know?

DAY 18
Communication Styles
Using a variety of communication methods is one way you can cater for the different needs in your group

DAY 19
Countdown to Kickoff
Before each game players should be given the chance to: spend time together, warm-up and think about the game

DAY 20
Half-Time
Let players have a drink, ask their thoughts, pick out positive moments for praise, finish with a positive message

DAY 21
Full-Time
Is a chance for you to help the players make sense of the matchday experience, highlight positive moments and provide constructive feedback

Visit TheFA.com/Respect to find out more

#WeOnlyDoPositive

RESPEC

ENGLAND C

RESULTS 2018-19

10 October 2018 - Friendly - Leyton Orient FC.

ENGLAND C	v	ESTONIA U23	1-0	Att: 635
Pavey 65 (pen)				

England: *Ben Killip (Ryan Huddart 51), Robbie Tinkler, Marvin Ekpiteta, Laurence Maguire (Luke Pennell 87), Jerome Binnom-Williams (Joe Millish 51), Ryan Croasdale, Alfie Pavey (Kurt Willoughby 75), Thomas Walker (Joshua Taylor 72), Wesley Fonguck, James Hardy, Ed Williams*

20 March 2019 - Friendly - Salford FC.

ENGLAND C	v	WALES C	2-2	Att: 709
Peate (og) Willoughby		*McLaggon Roscow*		

England: *Ben Killip (Ryan Huddart 83); Luke Trotman, Laurence Maguire, Jon Mellish. Dan Jones (Dan Happe 53); Josh Taylor; Luke James (Joe Rowley 70), Greg Olley, Ed Williams (Tom White 49), James Hardy; Kurt Willoughby (Brandon Goodship 81)*

5 June 2019 - Friendly - Kadrioru Stadium, Tallinn, Estonia.

ESTONIA U23	v	ENGLAND C	2-0
Poom 88 Usta 90+2			

England: *Ben Killip (Ryan Huddart 70); Luke Trotman, David Longe-King, Mitch Dickenson, Alex Brown; Ryan Croasdale, Tom White; James Hardy (Isaac Galliford 55); Ephron Mason-Clark (Matt Lowe 64), Kurt Willoughby, Joe Rowley (Wes Fonguck 59)*

GOALSCORERS 1979 - 2019

13 GOALS...
Carter, Mark

7 GOALS...
Cole, Mitchell

6 GOALS...
Ashford, Noel

5 GOALS...
Davison, Jon
Williams, Colin

4 GOALS...
Culpin, Paul
D'Sane, Roscoe
Johnson, Jeff
Mackhail-Smith, Craig
Norwood, James

3 GOALS...
Adamson, David
Guinan, Steve
Grayson,Neil
Hatch, Liam
Kirk, Jackson
Morison, Steve
Morrison, Michael
Okenabirhie, Fejiri (Hatrick)
Opponents
Taylor, Matt
Watkins, Dale

2 GOALS...
Alford, Carl
Barnes-Homer, Matthew
Barrett, Keith
Bishop, Andrew
Burgess, Andrew
Casey, Kim
Cordice, Neil
Elding, Anthony
Gray, Andre
Hayles, Barry
Hill, Kenny
Howell, David
John, Louis
McQueen, Darren
Mutrie, Les
Patmore, Warren
Pearson, Matty
Richards, Justin
Seddon, Gareth
Southam, Glen
Watson, John
Weatherstone, Simon
Whitbread, Barry
Yiadom, Andy

1 GOAL...
Agana, Tony
Anderson, Dale
Ashton, John
Beautyman, Harry
Benson, Paul
Berry
Blackburn, Chris
Boardman, Jon
Bogle, Omar
Bolton, Jimmy
Boyd, George
Bradshaw, Mark
Briscoe, Louis
Brown, Paul
Browne, Corey
Carey-Bertram, Daniel
Carr, Michael
Cavell, Paul
Charles, Lee
Charley, Ken
Charnock, Kieran
Constable, James
Crittenden, Nick
Davies, Paul
Day, Matt
Densmore, Shaun
Drummond, Stewart
Fleming, Andrew
Franks, Franks
Furlong, Paul
Grant, John
Guthrie, Kurtis
Harrad, Shaun
Hine, Mark
Holland, Jack
Holroyd, Chris
Humphreys, Delwyn
Howells, Jake
Jackson, Kayden
Jackson, Marlon
James, Kingsley
Jennings, Connor
Kennedy, John
Kerr, Scott
Kimmins,Ged
King, Simon
Leworthy, David
Lowe, Jamal
McDougald, Junior
McFadzean, Kyle
Mayes, Bobby
Moore, Neil
Moore, Luke
Newton, Sean
O'Keefe, Eamon
Oli, Dennis
Pavey, Alfie
Penn, Russell
Pennell, Luke
Pitcher, Geoff
Porter, Max
Ricketts, Sam
Robbins, Terry
Roberts, Jordan
Robinson, Mark
Roddis,Nick
Rodgers, Luke
Rodman, Alex
Rogers, Paul
Ryan, Tim
Sarcevic, Antoni
Sellars, Neil
Shaw, John
Sheldon, Gareth
Simpson, Josh
Sinclair, Dean
Smith, Ian
Smith, Ossie
Spencer, Scott
Stansfield, Adam
Stephens, Mickey
Stott, Steve
Taylor, Steve
Thurgood, Stuart
Tubbs, Matthew
Venables, David
Walker, Thomas
Watkins, Adam
Way, Darren
Webb, Paul
Whitehouse, Elliott
Wilcox, Russ
Willoughby, Kurt

ENGLAND'S RESULTS 1979 - 2019

BARBADOS

02.06.08	Bridgetown	2 - 0

BELGIUM

11.02.03	KV Ostend	1 - 3
04.11.03	Darlington	2 - 2
15.11.05	FC Racing Jets	2 - 0
19.05.09	Oxford United	0 - 1
09.02.11	Luton Town	1 - 0
12.09.12	Gemeentalijk Sportstadion	2 - 1

BERMUDA

04.06.13	Hamilton	6 - 1

BOSNIA & HERZEGOVINA

16.09.08	Grbavia Stadium	2 - 6

CYPRUS U21

17.02.15	Larnaca	1 - 2

CZECH REPUBLIC UNDER-21

19.11.13	Home	2 - 2

ESTONIA

12.10.10		1 - 0

UNDER-23

18.11.14	FC Halifax Town	4 - 2
15.11.16	A Le Coq Arena, Tallinn	2 - 1
10.10.18	Leyton Orient FC	1 - 0
05.06.19	Kadrioru Stadium	0 - 2

FINLAND UNDER-21

14.04.93	Woking	1 - 3
30.05.94	Aanekoski	0 - 2
01.06.07	FC Hakka	1 - 0
15.11.07	Helsinki	2 - 0

GIBRALTAR

27.04.82	Gibraltar	3 - 2
31.05.95	Gibraltar	3 - 2
21.05.08	Colwyn Bay	1 - 0
15.11.11	Gibraltar	1 - 3

GRENADA

31.05.08	St. George's	1 - 1

HOLLAND

03.06.79	Stafford	1 - 0
07.06.80	Zeist	2 - 1
09.06.81	Lucca	2 - 0
03.06.82	Aberdeen	1 - 0
02.06.83	Scarborough	6 - 0
05.06.84	Palma	3 - 3
13.06.85	Vleuten	3 - 0
20.05.87	Kirkaldy	4 - 0
11.04.95	Aalsmeer	0 - 0
02.04.96	Irthlingborough	3 - 1
18.04.97	Appingedam	0 - 0
03.03.98	Crawley	2 - 1
30.03.99	Genemuiden	1 - 1
21.03.00	Northwich	1 - 0
22.03.01	Wihemina FC	3 - 0
24.04.02	Yeovil Town	1 - 0
25.03.03	BV Sparta 25	0 - 0
16.02.05	Woking	3 - 0
29.11.06	Burton Albion	4 - 1

HUNGARY

15.09.09	Szekesfehervar	1 - 1
28.05.14	Budapest	2 - 4

IRAQ

27.05.04	Macclesfield	1 - 5

IRISH PREMIER LEAGUE XI

13.02.07	Glenavon FC	1 - 3

ITALY

03.06.80	Zeist	2 - 0
13.06.81	Montecatini	1 - 1
01.06.82	Aberdeen	0 - 0
31.05.83	Scarborough	2 - 0
09.06.84	Reggio Emilia	0 - 1
11.06.85	Houten	2 - 2
18.05.87	Dunfermline	1 - 2
29.01.89	La Spezia	1 - 1
25.02.90	Solerno	0 - 2
05.03.91	Kettering	0 - 0
01.03.99	Hayes	4 - 1
01.03.00	Padova	1 - 1
20.11.02	AC Cremonese	3 - 2
11.02.04	Shrewsbury	1 - 4
10.11.04	US Ivrea FC	1 - 0
15.02.06	Cambridge United	3 - 1
12.11.08	Benevento	2 - 2
28.02.12	Fleetwood Town	1 - 1

JORDAN UNDER-23

04.03.14	Jordan	1 - 0

LATVIA UNDER-23

10.09.13	Latvia	0 - 1

MALTA UNDER-21

17.02.09	Malta	4 - 0

NORWAY UNDER-21

01.06.94	Slemmestad	1 - 2

PANJAB

28.05.17	Solihull Moors	1 - 2

POLAND

17.11.09	Gradiszk Wielpolski	2 - 1

PORTUGAL

19.05.11	Sixfields Stadium	0 - 1

REPUBLIC OF IRELAND

24.05.86	Kidderminster	2 - 1
26.05.86	Nuneaton	2 - 1
25.05.90	Dublin	2 - 1
27.05.90	Cork	3 - 0
27.02.96	Kidderminster	4 - 0
25.02.97	Dublin	0 - 2
16.05.02	Boston	1 - 2
20.05.03	Merthyr Tydfil	4 - 0
18.05.04	Deverondale	2 - 3
24.05.05	Cork	1 - 0
23.05.06	Eastbourne Boro'	2 - 0
22.05.07	Clachnacuddin	5 - 0
26.05.10	Waterford United	2 - 1

UNDER-21

01.06.15	Galway	2 - 1

AMATEURS

27.05.18	Whitehall Stadium	2 - 4

RUSSIA

05.06.12	Russia	0 - 4

SCOTLAND

31.05.79	Stafford	5 - 1
05.06.80	Zeist	2 - 4
11.06.81	Empoli	0 - 0
05.06.82	Aberdeen	1 - 1
04.06.83	Scarborough	2 - 1
07.06.84	Modena	2 - 0
15.06.85	Harderwijk	1 - 3
23.05.87	Dunfermline	2 - 1
18.05.02	Kettering	2 - 0
24.05.03	Carmarthen Town	0 - 0
23.05.04	Deverondale	3 - 1
28.05.05	Cork	3 - 2
27.05.06	Eastbourne Boro'	2 - 0
25.05.07	Ross County	3 - 0
22.05.08	Colwyn Bay	1 - 0

SLOVAKIA UNDER-21/23

24.05.14	Slovakia	0 - 1
05.06.16	Sutton United	3 - 4
08.11.17	Ziar nad Hronon Stadium	0 - 4

SPARTA PRAGUE B

21.05.14	Prague	2 - 2

TURKEY U23

05.02.13	Dartford FC	0 - 1
14.10.14	Istanbul	0 - 2

UKRAINE

22.03.16	Kiev	2 - 0

USA

20.03.02	Stevenage Boro.	2 - 1
09.06.04	Charleston USA	0 - 0

WALES

27.03.84	Newtown	1 - 2
26.03.85	Telford	1 - 0
18.03.86	Merthyr Tydfil	1 - 3
17.03.87	Gloucester	2 - 2
15.03.88	Rhyl	2 - 0
21.03.89	Kidderminster	2 - 0
06.03.90	Merthyr Tydfil	0 - 0
17.05.91	Stafford	1 - 2
03.03.92	Aberystwyth	1 - 0
02.03.93	Cheltenham	2 - 1
22.02.94	Bangor	2 - 1
28.02.95	Yeovil Town	1 - 0
23.05.99	St Albans	2 - 1
16.05.00	Llanelli	1 - 1
13.02.01	Rushden & Dia.	0 - 0
14.05.02	Boston	1 - 1
22.05.03	Merthyr Tydfil	2 - 0
20.05.04	Keith FC	0 - 2
26.05.05	Cork	1 - 0
25.05.06	Eastbourne Boro'	1 - 1
27.05.07	Clachnacuddin	3 - 0
21.02.08	Exeter City	2 - 1
24.05.08	Rhyl	3 - 0
15.09.10	Newtown FC	2 - 2

WALES C

20.03.18	Barry FC	3 - 2
20.03.19	Salford City FC	2 - 2

RESULTS SUMMARY 1979 - 2019	P	W	D	L	F	A
Barbados	1	1	0	0	2	0
Belgium	6	3	1	2	8	7
Bermuda	1	1	0	0	6	1
Bosnia & Herzegovina	1	0	0	1	2	6
Cyprus U21	1	0	0	1	1	2
Czech Republic U21	1	0	2	0	2	2
Finland U21	4	2	0	2	4	5
Estonia	1	1	0	0	1	0
Estonia U23	4	3	0	1	7	5
Grenada	1	0	1	0	1	1
Gibraltar	4	3	0	1	8	7
Holland	19	14	5	0	40	8
Hungary	2	0	1	1	3	5
Iraq	1	0	0	1	1	5
Irish Premier League XI	1	0	0	1	1	3
Italy	18	5	8	4	24	22
Jordan U23	1	1	0	0	1	0
Latvia U23	1	0	0	1	0	1
Malta	1	1	0	0	4	0
Norway U21	1	0	0	1	1	2
Panjab	1	1	0	0	2	1
Poland	1	1	0	0	2	1
Portugal	1	0	0	1	0	1
Republic of Ireland	13	10	0	3	30	11
Republic of Ireland U21	1	1	0	0	2	1
Republic of Ireland Amateurs	1	0	0	1	2	4
Russia	1	0	0	1	0	4
Scotland	15	10	3	2	30	15
Slovakia U21/U23	3	0	0	3	3	9
Sparta Prague B	1	0	2	0	2	2
Turkey U23	2	0	0	2	0	3
Ukraine	1	1	0	0	2	0
USA	2	1	1	0	2	1
Wales	24	13	7	4	34	20
Wales C	2	1	1	0	5	4
TOTALS	**139**	**74**	**32**	**34**	**233**	**160**

MANAGERS 1979 - 2019

		P	W	D	L	F	A	*Win%
1979	Howard Wilkinson	2	2	0	0	6	1	-
1980 - 1984	Keith Wright	17	9	5	3	30	16	53
1985 - 1988	Kevin Verity	12	7	2	3	23	15	58
1989 - 1996	Tony Jennings	19	10	4	5	27	18	53
1997	Ron Reid	2	0	1	1	0	2	-
1998 - 2002	John Owens	14	8	5	1	22	10	57
2002 -	Paul Fairclough	74	39	13	22	125	95	53

*Calculated for those who managed for 10 games or more.

the
FOOTBALL ASSOCIATION COMPETITIONS

THE FA CUP 2018-19

There's still something special about an FA Cup tie...Woking fans before their Third Round tie against Watford.
Photo: Peter Barnes.

FA CUP ATTENDANCES

	2018/19		2017/18	
	Total Crowds	Total Games	Total Crowds	Total Games
EP	28718	222	31169	221
P	34229	191	35568	194
1Q	39223	146	36688	131
2Q	40787	101	40017	97
3Q	26175	48	32401	48
4Q	45370	39	44428	42
1P	147015	53	125980	45
2P	92930	25	84112	27
3P	655502	36	710011	39
4P	409836	19	370950	20
5P	146476	8	210328	10
QF	86030	4	206568	4
SF	151613	2	158063	2
F	85854	1	87647	1
Totals	**1989758**	**895**	**2173930**	**881**
Ave	2223		2468	
Ave (+/-)	-244			

EXTRA PRELIMINARY ROUND

SATURDAY 11 AUGUST 2018 - WINNERS RECEIVE £2,250 LOSERS RECEIVE £750

No	Home		Away	Score	Att
1	Consett	v	North Shields	2-1	292
2	Thackley	v	Whitley Bay	2-3	131
3	Hebburn Town	v	Dunston UTS	2-3	233
4	Ashington	v	Knaresborough Town	0-2	185
5	Goole	v	Morpeth Town	1-5	171
6	Glasshoughton Welfare	v	Blyth	1-2	106
7	Newcastle Benfield	v	Stockton Town	1-1	186
	Stockton Town	v	Newcastle Benfield (15/8)	0-3	269
8	Selby Town	v	Whickham	3-2	160
9	Seaham Red Star	v	Heaton Stannington	1-1	76
	Heaton Stannington	v	Seaham Red Star (15/8)	4-4aet	201
	(Seaham Red Star won 4-2 on kicks from the penalty mark)				
10	Team Northumbria	v	Shildon		
	(walkover for Shildon – Team Northumbria removed)				
11	Northallerton Town	v	Garforth Town	0-4	110
12	Guisborough Town	v	Newton Aycliffe	3-3	144
	Newton Aycliffe	v	Guisborough Town (14/8)	0-2	200
13	Barnoldswick Town	v	Billingham Synthonia	1-1	157
	Billingham Synthonia	v	Barnoldswick Town (15/8)	0-4	149
14	Washington	v	West Auckland Town	0-4	102
15	Sunderland RCA	v	Sunderland Ryhope CW	5-2	173
16	Bridlington Town	v	Harrogate Railway Athletic	3-0	221
17	Penrith	v	Albion Sports	0-3	106
18	Bishop Auckland	v	Pickering Town	0-2	321
19	AFC Darwen	v	Barnton	3-1	89
20	Liversedge	v	Padiham	5-2	120
21	City of Liverpool	v	Silsden	2-1	630
22	AFC Liverpool	v	Ashton Athletic	2-2	139
	Ashton Athletic	v	AFC Liverpool (14/8)	4-1	148
23	Widnes	v	Northwich Victoria	1-1	126
	Northwich Victoria	v	Widnes (15/8)	1-0	132
24	Burscough	v	1874 Northwich	2-2	150
	1874 Northwich Victoria	v	Burscough	3-3aet	213
	(Burscough won 4-2 on kicks from the penalty mark)				
25	Congleton Town	v	Eccleshill United	1-0	149
26	Prestwich Heys	v	Abbey Hey	2-1	188
27	West Didsbury & Chorlton	v	Squires Gate	2-3	214
28	Winsford United	v	Irlam	1-2	148
29	Penistone Church	v	Bootle	2-1	165
30	Hemsworth Miners Welfare	v	Runcorn Town	1-1	130
	Runcorn Town	v	Hemsworth Miners Welfare (15/8)	1-0	102
31	Hallam	v	Runcorn Linnets (12/8)	0-2	327
32	Maltby Main	v	Athersley Recreation	3-0	97
33	Parkgate	v	Sandbach United	2-0	89
34	Litherland Remyca	v	Charnock Richard	4-2	126
	(tie awarded to Charnock Richard – Litherland Remyca removed)				
35	Maine Road	v	Handsworth Parramore	0-1	105
36	Walsall Wood	v	Worcester City	1-1	187
	Worcester City	v	Walsall Wood (14/8)	1-1aet	350
	(Walsall Wood won 3-2 on kicks from the penalty mark)				
37	Highgate United	v	AFC Wulfrunians	1-0	74
38	Boldmere St Michaels	v	Malvern Town	2-2	133
	Malvern Town	v	Boldmere St Michaels (14/8)	3-2	203
39	Atherstone Town	v	Hanley Town	1-1	178
	Hanley Town	v	Atherstone Town (14/8)	1-4	175
40	Stourport Swifts	v	Shawbury United	2-1	124
41	Wednesfield	v	Rocester	2-1	45
42	Coventry United	v	Rugby Town (12/8)	1-2	258
43	Coventry Sphinx	v	Whitchurch Alport	0-1	157
44	Haughmond	v	Wolverhampton SC	2-0	66
45	Racing Club Warwick	v	Coleshill Town	4-3	219
46	Romulus	v	Westfields	6-1	71
47	Ellesmere Rangers	v	Leicester Road	0-1	73
48	Sporting Khalsa	v	Tividale	2-1	125
49	Long Eaton United	v	St Andrews	2-1	54
50	Sleaford Town	v	South Normanton Athletic	0-1	112
51	Heather St Johns	v	Kimberley Miners Welfare	3-6	73
52	Kirby Muxloe	v	AFC Mansfield	0-6	83
53	Clipstone	v	Barton Town	0-0	84
	Barton Town	v	Clipstone (14/8)	3-4	136
54	Lutterworth Town	v	Heanor Town	2-1	216
55	Hinckley	v	Anstey Nomads	1-1	218
	Anstey Nomads	v	Hinckley (14/8)	4-3aet	237
56	Worksop Town	v	Shepshed Dynamo	3-3	341
	Shepshed Dynamo	v	Worksop Town (14/8)	4-5aet	207
57	Rainworth MW	v	Dunkirk	2-1	78
58	Staveley MW	v	Boston Town	4-2	161
59	Teversal	v	Loughborough University	1-2	74
60	Oadby Town	v	Shirebrook Town	3-1	147
61	Bottesford Town	v	Radford	3-1	84
62	Quorn	v	Belper United	6-1	127
63	Leicester Nirvana	v	Grimsby Borough	0-3	63
64	Cogenhoe United	v	Wisbech Town	1-2	149
65	Wellingborough Whitworth	v	Harborough Town	0-1	31
66	Deeping Rangers	v	Holbeach United	3-2	182
67	Raunds Town	v	Eynesbury Rovers	1-2	67
68	Arlesey Town	v	Desborough Town	3-4	125
69	Thetford Town	v	Fakenham Town (10/8)	1-0	130
70	Northampton Sileby Rangers	v	Ely City	2-0	114
71	Godmanchester Rovers	v	Newport Pagnell Town	2-0	103
72	Biggleswade United	v	Wellingborough Town	1-1	88
	Wellingborough Town	v	Biggleswade United (14/8)	2-1	130
73	Histon	v	Peterborough Northern Star	6-1	156
74	Daventry Town	v	Potton United	9-2	61
75	Biggleswade	v	Northampton On Chenecks	2-0	91
76	Swaffham Town	v	Yaxley	1-3	95
77	Rothwell Corinthians	v	Pinchbeck United	3-0	70
78	Hullbridge Sports	v	Gorleston	2-1	113
79	Wroxham	v	Saffron Walden Town	1-1	126
	Saffron Walden Town	v	Wroxham (14/8)	3-2aet	272
80	Great Yarmouth Town	v	Hadleigh United	1-3	86
	(at Hadleigh United FC)				
81	Walthamstow	v	Walsham Le Willows	3-1	78
82	Kirkley & Pakefield	v	FC Clacton	2-2	94
	FC Clacton	v	Kirkley & Pakefield (21/8)	3-2	114
	(tie reversed – at Kirkley & Pakefield FC)				
83	Wodson Park	v	Hoddesdon Town	1-3	94
84	Tower Hamlets	v	Stanway Rovers (21/8)	0-2	85
	(at Stanway Rovers FC) (11/8 – tie abandoned after 81 minutes)				
85	Norwich United	v	Takeley	1-2	85
86	St Margaretsbury	v	Enfield 1893 (12/8)	2-0	148
87	Framlingham Town	v	Whitton United	1-1	87
	Whitton United	v	Framlingham Town (14/8)	3-1	73
88	Southend Manor	v	FC Romania	1-3	65
89	Wivenhoe Town	v	Brantham Athletic	0-5	93
90	Stowmarket Town	v	Basildon United	0-2	282
91	Sporting Bengal United	v	Ilford	4-3	55
92	Haverhill Rovers	v	Haverhill Borough	2-0	602
	(Live on BBC Sport)				
93	Ipswich Wanderers	v	Baldock Town	0-5	66
94	Barkingside	v	Leyton Athletic	0-0	50
	Leyton Athletic	v	Barkingside (15/8)	3-0	100
95	Cockfosters	v	Newmarket Town	0-2	77
96	Woodbridge Town	v	Clapton	2-2	117
	Clapton	v	Woodbridge Town (14/8)	1-1aet	66
	(Woodbridge Town won 5-4 on kicks from the penalty mark)				

EXTRA PRELIMINARY ROUND

97	Burnham Ramblers	v	West Essex	3-5	102
98	Stansted	v	Sawbridgeworth Town (12/8)	2-1	137
	(at Bishop's Stortford FC)				
99	Redbridge	v	Long Melford	1-3	52
100	Oxhey Jets	v	Wantage Town	3-4	77
101	Tuffley Rovers	v	Colney Heath	1-4	94
102	Winslow United	v	Easington Sports (10/8)	2-2	390
	Easington Sports	v	Winslow United (14/8)	2-0	123
103	Harpenden Town	v	Edgware Town	1-0	191
104	Hadley	v	Fairford Town	2-0	66
105	Brackley Town Saints	v	London Colney	1-0	31
	(at Oxford City FC)				
106	London Lions	v	Wembley	2-1	57
107	Windsor	v	Highworth Town	3-3	125
	Highworth Town	v	Windsor (15/8)	1-2	204
108	Bishops Cleeve	v	Stotfold	5-2	103
109	AFC Hayes	v	Lydney Town	1-2	35
110	Flackwell Heath	v	North Greenford United	0-2	70
111	Tring Athletic	v	Berkhamsted	0-2	202
112	Southall	v	Leverstock Green (12/8)	0-1	98
113	Holmer Green	v	Longlevens	0-1	54
114	Ardley United	v	Shortwood United	7-0	95
115	Holyport	v	Brimscombe & Thrupp	1-2	89
116	Abingdon United	v	Burnham	2-2	77
	Burnham	v	Abingdon United (14/8)	2-0	72
117	Crawley Green	v	Woodley United	7-1	56
118	Reading City	v	Chipping Sodbury Town	1-1	146
	Chipping Sodbury Town	v	Reading City (14/8)	2-1aet	92
119	Leighton Town	v	Royal Wootton Bassett Town	0-1	128
120	Arundel	v	Chertsey Town	4-1	75
121	Sutton Common Rovers	v	CB Hounslow United (12/8)	0-2	94
122	Broadbridge Heath	v	Shoreham	0-2	82
123	Langney Wanderers	v	Epsom & Ewell (12/8)	1-2	189
124	Bearsted	v	Chichester City	2-1	156
125	Redhill	v	Horley Town	1-3	128
126	AFC Croydon Athletic	v	Rochester United	5-0	58
127	Spelthorne Sports	v	Peacehaven & Telescombe	3-0	81
128	Hassocks	v	Erith Town	1-3	62
129	Worthing United	v	Littlehampton Town	1-1	55
	Littlehampton Town	v	Worthing United (15/8)	2-4aet	144
130	Little Common	v	Bedfont Sports (12/8)	2-2	102
	Bedfont Sports	v	Little Common (14/8)	2-1	61
131	Crowborough Athletic	v	Hanworth Villa	1-1	102
	Hanworth Villa	v	Crowborough Athletic (14/8)	2-0	76
132	Raynes Park Vale	v	Lingfield	3-0	86
133	AFC Uckfield Town	v	Glebe	1-0	53
134	Abbey Rangers	v	Newhaven	0-4	73
135	Cobham	v	Sheppey United	1-0	80
136	Fisher	v	Horsham YMCA	1-2	157
137	Loxwood	v	Hollands & Blair	2-1	80
138	Sevenoaks Town	v	Lordswood	6-1	131
139	Crawley Down Gatwick	v	Three Bridges	0-1	118
140	Eastbourne United	v	Hackney Wick	0-2	69
141	Cray Valley (PM)	v	Eastbourne Town (12/8)	3-2	145
142	Croydon	v	Tunbridge Wells	2-2	96
	Tunbridge Wells	v	Croydon (14/8)	2-3aet	162
143	Erith & Belvedere	v	Saltdean United	0-0	71
	Saltdean United	v	Erith & Belvedere (14/8)	2-0	89
144	Haywards Heath Town	v	Lancing	0-2	125
145	Rusthall	v	Wick (12/8)	3-0	185
	(at Tunbridge Wells FC)				
146	East Preston	v	Balham	0-2	108

147	K Sports	v	Pagham	2-2	101
	Pagham	v	K Sports (14/8)	2-0	116
148	Deal Town	v	Whitstable Town	2-2	187
	Whitstable Town	v	Deal Town (15/8)	4-3	236
149	Broadfields United	v	Banstead Athletic	3-0	53
150	Chatham Town	v	Walton & Hersham	3-1	195
151	Corinthian	v	Canterbury City	3-0	49
152	Beckenham Town	v	Colliers Wood United	1-1	238
	Colliers Wood United	v	Beckenham Town (14/8)	0-2	74
153	Hamworthy United	v	Team Solent	3-2	90
154	Melksham Town	v	Badshot Lea	4-0	238
155	AFC Stoneham	v	AFC Portchester	0-0	129
	AFC Portchester	v	AFC Stoneham (14/8)	0-3	78
156	Newport (IW)	v	Amesbury Town	3-1	140
157	Knaphill	v	Sholing	0-3	100
158	Guildford City	v	Petersfield Town	0-1	87
159	Tadley Calleva	v	Baffins Milton Rovers	1-3	187
160	Bemerton Heath Harlequins	v	Cowes Sports	1-0	51
161	Andover New Street	v	Romsey Town	4-0	121
162	United Services Portsmouth	v	Andover Town	5-2	42
	(at AFC Portchester)				
163	Horndean	v	Godalming Town	5-0	75
164	Hamble Club	v	Alresford Town	1-1	125
	Alresford Town	v	Hamble Club (14/8)	0-2	92
165	Farnham Town	v	Binfield	1-2	107
166	Brockenhurst	v	Christchurch	2-2	153
	Christchurch	v	Brockenhurst (14/8)	0-2	152
167	Bashley	v	Bournemouth	0-2	148
168	Fareham Town	v	Frimley Green	1-2	80
169	Ascot United	v	Camberley Town (10/8)	2-1	277
170	Sandhurst Town	v	Lymington Town	1-1	75
	Lymington Town	v	Sandhurst Town (15/8)	5-1	67
	(at New Milton Town FC)				
171	Clevedon Town	v	Portland United	1-2	102
172	Westbury United	v	Cribbs	3-0	58
173	Hallen	v	Longwell Green Sports	0-0	40
	Longwell Green Sports	v	Hallen (14/8)	0-1	40
174	Wells City	v	Shaftesbury	2-5	102
175	Bodmin Town	v	Keynsham Town	4-4	102
	Keynsham Town	v	Bodmin Town (14/8)	1-3	139
176	Cheddar	v	Bridgwater Town	3-2	120
177	Shepton Mallet	v	Willand Rovers	1-1	115
	Willand Rovers	v	Shepton Mallet (15/8)	3-0	157
178	Bitton	v	Tavistock	7-0	73
179	Buckland Athletic	v	Pewsey Vale	3-0	131
180	Bridport	v	Wellington AFC	0-0	166
	Wellington AFC	v	Bridport (15/8)	0-3	97
	(at Cullompton Rangers FC)				
181	Hengrove Athletic	v	Plymouth Parkway	1-5	62
182	Saltash United	v	Odd Down	1-0	92
183	Brislington	v	Cadbury Heath	1-2	57
184	Bradford Town	v	Roman Glass St George	5-2	109
	Total Attendance 28,718		**over 222 games**	**129 Ave**	
17/18	**Total Attandance 31,169**		**over 221 games**	**141 Ave**	

FAC - EP - Above and below, goalmouth action from the Bishop's Cleeve v Stotfold tie. Photo: Peter Barnes.

Stotfold's Tommy Carroll (4) scores in the first half @ Bishop's Cleeve

FAC - EP - Cray Valley PM v Eastbourne Town - Cray Valleys Jake Rose and Eastbourne Towns Dan Tear challenge for the ball. Photo: Alan Coomes.

PRELIMINARY ROUND

SATURDAY 25 AUGUST 2018 - WINNERS RECEIVE £2,890 LOSERS RECEIVE £960

No.	Home		Away	Score	Att
1	Knaresborough Town	v	Blyth	5-1	165
2	Bridlington Town	v	Garforth Town	1-2	231
3	Dunston UTS	v	Pontefract Collieries	4-2	241
4	Newcastle Benfield	v	West Auckland Town	1-0	191
5	Whitley Bay	v	Barnoldswick Town	6-1	305
6	Morpeth Town	v	Marske United	1-0	230
7	Consett	v	Seaham Red Star	5-2	251
8	Tadcaster Albion	v	Shildon	4-1	302
9	Clitheroe	v	Sunderland RCA	6-6	230
	Sunderland RCA	v	Clitheroe (4/9)	2-3	248
10	Kendal Town	v	Selby Town	1-1	125
	Selby Town	v	Kendal Town (4/9)	1-1aet	377
	(Kendal Town won 5-3 on kicks from the penalty mark)				
11	Pickering Town	v	Colne	0-4	123
12	Albion Sports	v	Guisborough Town	2-2	120
	Guisborough Town	v	Albion Sport (29/8)	4-0	213
13	Ashton Athletic	v	Skelmersdale United	2-1	135
14	Ossett United	v	Mossley	2-2	432
	Mossley	v	Ossett United (4/9)	1-1aet	246
	(Mossley won 4-2 on kicks from the penalty mark)				
15	Burscough	v	Northwich Victoria	2-0	95
16	Atherton Collieries	v	Colwyn Bay	2-1	184
17	Kidsgrove Athletic	v	Ramsbottom United	1-1	120
	Ramsbottom United	v	Kidsgrove Athletic (4/9)	0-0aet	168
	(Kidsgrove Athletic won 3-2 on kicks from the penalty mark)				
18	Stocksbridge Park Steels	v	Bamber Bridge	1-3	144
19	Prescot Cables	v	Irlam	1-2	303
20	Brighouse Town	v	Parkgate	0-2	121
21	Prestwich Heys	v	Radcliffe	0-2	513
	(Live on BBC Sport)				
22	Droylsden	v	Squires Gate	4-4	164
	Squires Gate	v	Droylsden (4/9)	1-0	157
23	Hyde United	v	Sheffield	5-1	381
24	Handsworth Parramore	v	Congleton Town	0-1	100
25	Frickley Athletic	v	Liversedge	10-1	165
26	Runcorn Linnets	v	Maltby Main	1-2	256
27	Penistone Church	v	Runcorn Town	1-3	187
28	Charnock Richard	v	Leek Town (4/9)	2-2	232
	Leek Town	v	Charnock Richard (8/9)	3-2	243
29	AFC Darwen	v	Trafford	1-4	174
30	City of Liverpool	v	Glossop North End	1-1	446
	Glossop North End	v	City of Liverpool (4/9)	2-3aet	348
31	Stourport Swifts	v	Sporting Khalsa	2-1	126
32	Sutton Coldfield Town	v	Gresley	3-0	122
33	Alvechurch	v	Bromsgrove Sporting	4-3	730
34	Malvern Town	v	Racing Club Warwick	1-2	230
35	Bedworth United	v	Atherstone Town	1-3	326
36	Romulus	v	Newcastle Town	4-0	82
37	Walsall Wood	v	Whitchurch Alport	2-1	101
38	Highgate United	v	Leicester Road	3-0	70
39	Wednesfield	v	Chasetown	2-2	105
	Chasetown	v	Wednesfield (4/9)	3-1	231
40	Rugby Town	v	Evesham United	1-0	225
41	Haughmond	v	Market Drayton Town	1-1	98
	Market Drayton Town	v	Haughmond (4/9)	0-1	149
42	Kimberley Miners Welfare	v	Oadby Town	0-2	83
43	Loughborough Dynamo	v	Bottesford Town	2-4	96
44	Staveley MW	v	Lutterworth Town	3-0	220
45	Belper Town	v	Lincoln United	2-1	266
46	Worksop Town	v	Carlton Town (26/8)	2-1	435
47	Loughborough University	v	Cleethorpes Town	3-3	147
	Cleethorpes Town	v	Loughborough University (4/9)	1-0	231
48	AFC Mansfield	v	Rainworth MW	1-0	157
49	Anstey Nomads	v	Clipstone	4-1	252
50	Grimsby Borough	v	Long Eaton United	1-0	97
51	Quorn	v	South Normanton Athletic	3-2	121
52	Stamford	v	Peterborough Sports	1-1	344
	Peterborough Sports	v	Stamford (4/9)	4-3	331
53	Northampton Sileby Rangers	v	Wisbech Town	1-1	109
	Wisbech Town	v	Northampton Sileby Rangers (4/9)	0-0aet	209
	(Wisbech Town won 5-3 on kicks from the penalty mark)				
54	Deeping Rangers	v	AFC Rushden & Diamonds	1-1	347
	AFC Rushden & Diamonds	v	Deeping Rangers (4/9)	3-0	396
55	Harborough Town	v	Cambridge City	1-2	254
56	Corby Town	v	Dunstable Town	3-3	372
	Dunstable Town	v	Corby Town (4/9)	0-4	146
57	Biggleswade	v	Soham Town Rangers (4/9)	3-5	138
	(25/8 – tie abandoned after 57 mins due to serious injury to player, 3-2)				
58	Thetford Town	v	Godmanchester Rovers (24/8)	0-5	121
59	Desborough Town	v	Kempston Rovers	0-3	123
60	Bedford Town	v	Dereham Town	4-1	252
61	Histon	v	Eynesbury Rovers	1-1	182
	Eynesbury Rovers	v	Histon (28/8)	1-3	238
62	Daventry Town	v	Yaxley	7-5	110
63	Barton Rovers	v	Rothwell Corinthians	3-2	82
64	Spalding United	v	Wellingborough Town	3-2	125
65	Waltham Abbey	v	Bury Town	0-2	128
66	Felixstowe & Walton United	v	Walthamstow	0-1	325
67	AFC Sudbury	v	Mildenhall Town	2-0	213
68	Heybridge Swifts	v	West Essex	3-0	206
69	Aveley	v	Potters Bar Town	0-2	154
70	Hertford Town	v	Tilbury	5-3	181
71	Stansted	v	Takeley (26/8)	0-1	71
	(at Bishop's Stortford FC)				
72	Long Melford	v	St Margaretsbury	3-0	107
73	Bowers & Pitsea	v	Barking (24/8)	1-0	191
	(at Aveley FC)				
74	Coggeshall Town	v	Witham Town (24/8)	0-0	309
	Witham Town	v	Coggeshall Town (4/9)	1-3	379
75	Haverhill Rovers	v	Maldon & Tiptree	2-1	170
76	Brantham Athletic	v	Welwyn Garden City	1-0	81
77	Haringey Borough	v	Stanway Rovers	1-0	151
78	Cheshunt	v	Canvey Island	1-0	151
79	FC Romania	v	Grays Athletic	2-0	146
	(at Aveley FC)				
80	Woodbridge Town	v	Hadleigh United	5-1	189

FAC - P - Karl Dent of Cray Wanderers and Rusthalls Ryan Waterman challenge for the ball. Photo: Alan Coomes.

FAC - P - A Brimscombe & Thrupp defender manages to get in the way of this spectacular effort from Hayes & Yeading's Lee Barney. Unfortunately for B&T they were unable to stop the visiting striker from notching five of his sides seven. Photo: Peter Barnes.

PRELIMINARY ROUND

SATURDAY 25 AUGUST 2018 - WINNERS RECEIVE £2,890 LOSERS RECEIVE £960

No.	Home		Away	Score	Att
81	Basildon United	v	Whitton United	2-1	105
82	Great Wakering Rovers	v	Leyton Athletic	4-1	122
83	FC Clacton	v	Ware	2-4	132
84	Newmarket Town	v	Hullbridge Sports	2-1	164
85	Saffron Walden Town	v	Hoddesdon Town	4-1	293
86	Brentwood Town	v	Sporting Bengal United	1-1	137
	Sporting Bengal United	v	Brentwood Town (29/8)	1-3	100
87	Romford	v	Baldock Town (26/8)	3-2	98
88	Easington Sports	v	Chipping Sodbury Town	1-2	191
89	Northwood	v	Longlevens	3-1	107
90	Ardley United	v	Burnham	2-4	86
91	AFC Dunstable	v	Swindon Supermarine	0-0	81
	Swindon Supermarine	v	AFC Dunstable (4/9)	3-0	132
92	Crawley Green	v	Aylesbury United	2-3	90
93	Kidlington	v	Marlow	0-1	68
94	Thame United	v	Berkhamsted	0-2	120
95	Bishop's Cleeve	v	North Greenford United	5-2	93
96	Didcot Town	v	Aylesbury	1-1	129
	Aylesbury	v	Didcot Town (4/9)	0-1	116
97	Brackley Town Saints	v	Hadley (27/8)	0-0	111
	Hadley	v	Brackley Town Saints (29/8)	1-0	70
	(at Potters Bar Town FC)				
98	Slimbridge	v	Wantage Town	1-1	65
	Wantage Town	v	Slimbridge (4/9)	1-0	133
99	Chalfont St Peter	v	London Lions	1-0	91
100	Beaconsfield Town	v	Uxbridge	2-0	97
101	Colney Heath	v	Cinderford Town	1-3	128
102	Harpenden Town	v	Leverstock Green	0-6	114
103	Brimscombe & Thrupp	v	Hayes & Yeading United	0-7	106
104	North Leigh	v	Hanwell Town	2-4	92
105	Cirencester Town	v	Windsor	5-0	128
106	Royal Wootton Bassett Town	v	Lydney Town	0-0	93
	Lydney Town	v	Royal Wootton Bassett Town (4/9)	5-3	167
107	Tooting & Mitcham United	v	Horley Town (24/8)	2-1	304
108	East Grinstead Town	v	South Park	1-0	116
109	Walton Casuals	v	Shoreham	6-0	172
110	Beckenham Town	v	Epsom & Ewell	2-2	92
	Epsom & Ewell	v	Beckenham Town (28/8)	0-3aet	95
111	Three Bridges	v	Phoenix Sports	2-3	86
112	Arundel	v	Herne Bay	1-7	144
113	Sittingbourne	v	Bearsted	2-0	204
114	Newhaven	v	Pagham	0-2	107
115	Cobham	v	Egham Town	1-3	69
116	Cray Valley (PM)	v	Ashford Town (Middx) (26/8)	4-1	87
117	Molesey	v	Lewes	0-0	112
	Lewes	v	Molesey (5/9)	8-1	350
118	AFC Croydon Athletic	v	Hanworth Villa	1-1	59
	Hanworth Villa	v	AFC Croydon Athletic (4/9)	0-1	74
119	Raynes Park Vale	v	Spelthorne Sports	1-1	101
	Spelthorne Sports	v	Raynes Park Vale (4/9)	4-3	107
120	Carshalton Athletic	v	Horsham	0-1	274
121	Ashford United	v	Horsham YMCA	0-2	266
122	AFC Uckfield Town	v	Broadfields United	4-1	92

No.	Home		Away	Score	Att
123	Greenwich Borough	v	Lancing	3-7	66
124	Chipstead	v	Corinthian	0-1	60
125	Loxwood	v	Erith Town	1-1	76
	Erith Town	v	Loxwood (3/9)	4-1	74
126	Hythe Town	v	Worthing United	3-0	191
127	Whyteleafe	v	Saltdean United	1-1	116
	Saltdean United	v	Whyteleafe (4/9)	1-2	109
128	Corinthian Casuals	v	Croydon	6-0	162
129	Ramsgate	v	Chatham Town	2-1	252
130	CB Hounslow United	v	Whitstable Town	0-2	143
131	Cray Wanderers	v	Rusthall	1-1	111
	Rusthall	v	Cray Wanderers (5/9)	1-1aet	274
	(Cray Wanderers won 4-3 on kicks from the penalty mark)				
132	Faversham Town	v	Hackney Wick	4-1	206
133	Balham	v	Thamesmead Town	0-2	117
134	Hastings United	v	VCD Athletic	3-2	428
135	Sevenoaks Town	v	Bedfont Sports	1-0	129
136	Thatcham Town	v	Bemerton Heath Harlequins	0-0	167
	Bemerton Heath Harlequins	v	Thatcham Town (4/9)	3-2	154
137	Salisbury	v	Hamble Club	6-0	542
138	Binfield	v	Brockenhurst	2-1	187
139	Moneyfields	v	Andover New Street	3-1	70
140	Hamworthy United	v	AFC Totton	1-0	109
141	Lymington Town	v	Frimley Green	2-0	68
	(at New Milton Town FC)				
142	Fleet Town	v	Petersfield Town	3-1	141
143	United Services Portsmouth	v	Sholing (24/8)	1-3	111
144	AFC Stoneham	v	Westfield	2-0	168
145	Baffins Milton Rovers	v	Hartley Wintney	1-4	181
146	Wimborne Town	v	Newport (IW)	6-0	214
147	Melksham Town	v	Blackfield & Langley	1-0	216
148	Ascot United	v	Horndean	1-2	158
149	Winchester City	v	Bournemouth	1-0	133
150	Bodmin Town	v	Cadbury Heath	2-2	123
	Cadbury Heath	v	Bodmin Town (29/8)	4-1	120
151	Bideford	v	Bristol Manor Farm	2-2	214
	Bristol Manor Farm	v	Bideford (4/9)	4-2aet	167
152	Bradford Town	v	Paulton Rovers	0-1	192
153	Hallen	v	Bridport	0-5	43
154	Barnstaple Town	v	Shaftesbury	0-1	110
155	Plymouth Parkway	v	Larkhall Athletic	1-0	177
156	Portland United	v	Bitton	0-2	265
157	Westbury United	v	Saltash United	3-0	55
158	Cheddar	v	Yate Town	0-3	238
159	Willand Rovers	v	Street	1-2	187
160	Buckland Athletic	v	Mangotsfield United	2-0	138

Total Attendance 34,229 **over 191 games** **174 Ave**

17/18 Total Attandance 35,568 **over 194 games** **183 Ave**

FAC - 1Q - Karkach (AFC Mansfield) gets the ball past Jeacock (Stourport Swifts) to equalise. Photo: Keith Clayton.

FAC - 1Q - Action from the Chipping Sodbury Town v Bristol Manor Farm match whiched ended 0-2. Photo: Peter Barnes.

FAC - 1Q - Corinthian v Horsham - Horshams Steven Metcalf goes between Corinthians Jamie Miller and Jordan Campbell (Right). Photo: Alan Coomes.

FAC - 1Q - Leverstock Green v Hadley - Alfie Bartram (3) shoots v Leverstock. Photo: Bill Wheatcroft.

FAC - 1Q - Hunt (Merthyr) and Lyons (Melksham) contest for the ball. Photo: Keith Clayton.

FIRST QUALIFYING ROUND

SATURDAY 8 SEPTEMBER 2018 - WINNERS RECEIVE £6,000

No	Home		Away	Score	Att
1	Radcliffe	v	Stalybridge Celtic	1-0	388
2	Squires Gate	v	City of Liverpool	1-5	201
3	Lancaster City	v	Trafford	0-2	212
4	South Shields	v	Garforth Town	5-1	1148
5	Warrington Town	v	Burscough	4-0	240
6	Runcorn Town	v	Irlam	2-3	162
7	Whitley Bay	v	Whitby Town	1-0	680
8	Marine	v	Scarborough Athletic	1-1	496
	Scarborough Athletic	v	Marine (11/9)	2-3	975
9	Colne	v	Hyde United	2-0	345
10	Newcastle Benfield	v	Workington	1-1	294
	Workington	v	Newcastle Benfield (11/9)	5-3	372
11	Dunston UTS	v	North Ferriby United	4-1	303
12	Knaresborough Town	v	Kendal Town	7-3	315
13	Atherton Collieries	v	Kidsgrove Athletic	1-2	161
14	Guisborough Town	v	Farsley Celtic	0-4	277
15	Congleton Town	v	Consett	0-1	276
16	Witton Albion	v	Bottesford Town	5-0	248
17	Clitheroe	v	Mossley	2-5	356
18	Ashton Athletic	v	Morpeth Town	1-1	132
	Morpeth Town	v	Ashton Athletic (11/9)	1-2	307
19	Maltby Main	v	Frickley Athletic	1-2	524
	(Live on BBC Sport)				
20	Parkgate	v	Leek Town (12/9)	2-2	180
	Leek Town	v	Parkgate (18/9)	3-0	214
21	Bamber Bridge	v	Tadcaster Albion	3-1	294
22	Basford United	v	Staveley MW (7/9)	1-3	379
23	Highgate United	v	Stourbridge	1-2	326
24	Cleethorpes Town	v	Walsall Wood	4-1	227
25	AFC Mansfield	v	Stourport Swifts (9/9)	2-1	213
26	Romulus	v	Belper Town	4-0	132
27	Nantwich Town	v	Worksop Town	5-2	374
28	Sutton Coldfield Town	v	Rushall Olympic	2-2	249
	Rushall Olympic	v	Sutton Coldfield Town (10/9)	0-1	236
29	Quorn	v	Atherstone Town	0-1	295
30	Coalville Town	v	Racing Club Warwick	2-1	220
31	Hednesford Town	v	Tamworth	2-0	602
32	Grimsby Borough	v	Stafford Rangers	1-2	169
33	Matlock Town	v	Halesowen Town	1-2	403
34	Barwell	v	Buxton	2-5	172
35	Daventry Town	v	Grantham Town	0-1	190
36	Mickleover Sports	v	Haughmond	6-0	170
37	Anstey Nomads	v	Oadby Town	2-1	418
38	Chasetown	v	Gainsborough Trinity	1-1	238
	Gainsborough Trinity	v	Chasetown (11/9)	8-2	412
39	Redditch United	v	Rugby Town	2-4	242
40	Stratford Town	v	Alvechurch	0-1	238
41	Leverstock Green	v	Hadley	0-0	94
	Hadley	v	Leverstock Green (12/9)	0-1	116
	(at Potters Bar Town FC)				
42	St Neots Town	v	Bishop's Stortford	2-1	209
43	Burnham	v	Bury Town	1-0	133
44	Cambridge City	v	Brightlingsea Regent	3-4	187
45	Aylesbury United	v	Marlow (9/9)	0-0	171
	Marlow	v	Aylesbury United (11/9)	2-1aet	170
46	Heybridge Swifts	v	Newmarket Town	2-0	226
47	Hanwell Town	v	Potters Bar Town	2-1	142
48	Brantham Athletic	v	Spalding United	1-0	169
49	Corby Town	v	Hertford Town	2-0	507
50	AFC Sudbury	v	Royston Town	3-2	208
51	Ware	v	Lowestoft Town	0-1	173
52	Hendon	v	Harlow Town	1-1	264
	Harlow Town	v	Hendon (11/9)	1-2aet	173
53	Brentwood Town	v	Haringey Borough	2-3	199
54	Haverhill Rovers	v	Long Melford	0-0	206
	Long Melford	v	Haverhill Rovers (12/9)	1-2	287
55	AFC Hornchurch	v	Harrow Borough	1-0	324
56	Swindon Supermarine	v	Woodbridge Town	7-1	204
57	FC Romania	v	Soham Town Rangers	4-0	62
	(at Bedfont Sports FC)				
58	Chesham United	v	Biggleswade Town	2-1	201
59	Chalfont St Peter	v	Kempston Rovers	1-1	106
	Kempston Rovers	v	Chalfont St Peter (11/9)	2-2aet	108
	(Kempston Rovers won 4-1 on kicks from the penalty mark)				
60	Great Wakering Rovers	v	Wisbech Town	3-1	112
61	Romford	v	Kettering Town (9/9)	1-4	271
62	King's Lynn Town	v	Histon	2-2	491
	Histon	v	King's Lynn Town (11/9)	0-7	388
63	Hayes & Yeading United	v	AFC Rushden & Diamonds	2-1	286
64	Northwood	v	Kings Langley	0-0	229
	Kings Langley	v	Northwood (11/9)	3-1	230
65	Coggeshall Town	v	Berkhamsted	1-1	208
	Berkhamsted	v	Coggeshall Town (11/9)	1-2	156
66	Saffron Walden Town	v	St Ives Town	0-0	507
	St Ives Town	v	Saffron Walden Town (11/9)	3-1	258
67	Walthamstow	v	Beaconsfield Town	0-2	114
68	Wingate & Finchley	v	Didcot Town	0-2	118
69	Cheshunt	v	Leiston	2-2	164
	Leiston	v	Cheshunt (11/9)	4-2	179
70	Hitchin Town	v	Godmanchester Rovers	3-1	256
71	Bowers & Pitsea	v	Takeley	5-1	105
	(at Aveley FC)				
72	Basildon United	v	Peterborough Sports	0-2	198
73	Barton Rovers	v	Needham Market	0-4	154
74	Enfield Town	v	Bedford Town	0-3	390
75	Ramsgate	v	Sevenoaks Town	1-1	242
	Sevenoaks Town	v	Ramsgate (11/9)	1-3	172
76	Hastings United	v	Kingstonian	2-1	602
77	Metropolitan Police	v	Cray Wanderers	3-2	89
78	Faversham Town	v	Worthing	1-3	244
79	Farnborough	v	Lewes	2-2	262
	Lewes	v	Farnborough (12/9)	1-1aet	395
	(Lewes won 4-1 on kicks from the penalty mark)				
80	AFC Uckfield Town	v	AFC Croydon Athletic	1-0	183
81	Fleet Town	v	East Grinstead Town	1-2	159
82	Phoenix Sports	v	Lancing	2-2	153
	Lancing	v	Phoenix Sports (11/9)	0-3	171
	(tie awarded to Lancing – Phoenix Sports removed)				
83	Merstham	v	Cray Valley (PM)	0-0	155
	Cray Valley (PM)	v	Merstham (12/9)	3-3aet	138
	(Cray Valley (PM) won 4-1 on kicks from the penalty mark)				
84	Spelthorne Sports	v	Erith Town	1-5	123
85	Hythe Town	v	Tonbridge Angels	0-2	503
86	Egham Town	v	Staines Town	1-0	384
87	Corinthian Casuals	v	Whyteleafe	0-0	260
	Whyteleafe	v	Corinthian Casuals (11/9)	2-1	183
	(tie awarded to Corinthian Casuals – Whyteleafe removed)				
88	Margate	v	Horndean	3-2	283
89	Moneyfields	v	Thamesmead Town	1-0	73
90	Whitstable Town	v	Bognor Regis Town	0-5	297
91	Horsham YMCA	v	Tooting & Mitcham United	1-2	191
92	Corinthian	v	Horsham	1-1	108
	Horsham	v	Corinthian (12/9)	5-0	124
93	Pagham	v	Whitehawk	0-2	212
94	Leatherhead	v	Herne Bay	2-0	227
95	Beckenham Town	v	Walton Casuals	0-0	98
	Walton Casuals	v	Beckenham Town (11/9)	3-0	118
96	Burgess Hill Town	v	Folkestone Invicta	1-0	337
97	Dorking Wanderers	v	Hartley Wintney	2-0	331
98	Sittingbourne	v	Gosport Borough	0-1	154
99	Weymouth	v	Banbury United	1-1	751
	Banbury United	v	Weymouth (11/9)	2-1	550
100	Melksham Town	v	Merthyr Town	1-4	304
101	Bitton	v	Westbury United	3-0	116
102	AFC Stoneham	v	Cirencester Town	0-7	253
103	Salisbury	v	Yate Town	1-1	548
	Yate Town	v	Salisbury (11/9)	1-3	252
104	Cadbury Heath	v	Cinderford Town	0-1	121
105	Binfield	v	Buckland Athletic	3-0	248
106	Frome Town	v	Winchester City	1-1	165
	Winchester City	v	Frome Town (11/9)	2-1aet	151
107	Wimborne Town	v	Dorchester Town	1-1	523
	Dorchester Town	v	Wimborne Town (11/9)	3-0	476
108	Shaftesbury	v	Poole Town	0-1	439
109	Sholing	v	Hamworthy United	0-0	230
	Hamworthy United	v	Sholing (11/9)	0-1	146
110	Plymouth Parkway	v	Street	0-0	203
	Street	v	Plymouth Parkway (11/9)	1-4	207
111	Taunton Town	v	Bemerton Heath Harlequins	7-1	517
112	Paulton Rovers	v	Basingstoke Town	1-1	282
	Basingstoke Town	v	Paulton Rovers (11/9)	2-0	330
113	Bridport	v	Tiverton Town	0-1	268
114	Bishop's Cleeve	v	Wantage Town	0-2	147
115	Chipping Sodbury Town	v	Bristol Manor Farm	0-2	133
116	Lymington Town	v	Lydney Town	2-2	97
	Lydney Town	v	Lymington Town (11/9)	1-2	337
	Total Attendance 39,223		**over 146 games**	**269 Ave**	
17/18	**Total Attendance 36,688**		**over 131 games**	**280 Ave**	

FAC - 2Q - Gloucester City v Plymouth Parkway. Photo: Peter Barnes.

FAC - 2Q - Kempston Rovers v Marlow - Harlem Sambu shoots past Marlow keeper Simon Grant to win the cup tie for Kempston. Photo: Bill Wheatcroft.

FAC - 2Q - Truro on the attack against Hereford. Photo: Peter Barnes.

SECOND QUALIFYING ROUND

SATURDAY 22 SEPTEMBER 2018 - WINNERS RECEIVE £9,000

1	Chester	v	City of Liverpool	4-0	1086
2	Ashton United	v	Trafford	3-0	240
3	Radcliffe	v	Curzon Ashton	1-2	450
4	Farsley Celtic	v	Southport	0-3	306
5	Mossley	v	Kidsgrove Athletic	1-2	439
6	Staveley MW	v	Guiseley	0-4	437
7	South Shields	v	Stockport County	1-2	1708
8	Knaresborough Town	v	Workington	1-4	507
9	Cleethorpes Town	v	Bamber Bridge	3-3	302
	Bamber Bridge	v	Cleethorpes Town (25/9)	0-5	315
10	York City	v	Ashton Athletic	5-0	1020
11	Marine	v	Frickley Athletic	1-0	401
12	Dunston UTS	v	Irlam	2-1	365
13	FC United of Manchester	v	Colne	2-0	1130
14	Nantwich Town	v	Blyth Spartans	3-3	371
	Blyth Spartans	v	Nantwich Town (25/9)	1-0	490
15	Darlington	v	Bradford (Park Avenue)	0-1	1037
16	Chorley	v	Leek Town	3-0	746
17	Witton Albion	v	Spennymoor Town	2-1	322
18	Altrincham	v	Whitley Bay	5-0	680
19	Consett	v	Warrington Town	3-3	451
	Warrington Town	v	Consett (25/9)	2-0	312
20	Sutton Coldfield Town	v	Alfreton Town	2-2	284
	Alfreton Town	v	Sutton Coldfield Town (25/9)	3-0	194
21	Boston United	v	Peterborough Sports	0-2	935
22	St Ives Town	v	Grantham Town	1-1	293
	Grantham Town	v	St Ives Town (25/9)	0-2	294
23	Kidderminster Harriers	v	Atherstone Town	5-0	1212
24	Stourbridge	v	Leamington	3-2	467
25	Rugby Town	v	Hednesford Town	1-3	328
26	St Neots Town	v	Romulus	4-3	325
27	Nuneaton Borough	v	Brackley Town	1-1	491
	Brackley Town	v	Nuneaton Borough (25/9)	2-0	325
28	Alvechurch	v	Corby Town	1-4	256
29	Kettering Town	v	AFC Mansfield	2-1	504
30	Anstey Nomads	v	Mickleover Sports	1-7	283
31	Halesowen Town	v	Gainsborough Trinity	0-3	338
32	King's Lynn Town	v	Stafford Rangers	3-1	601
33	AFC Telford United	v	Bedford Town	3-1	737
34	Buxton	v	Coalville Town	0-0	322
	Coalville Town	v	Buxton (25/9)	4-1	198
35	Hampton & Richmond Borough	v	Burgess Hill Town	3-0	422
36	Kings Langley	v	Lewes	1-1	288
	Lewes	v	Kings Langley (26/9)	2-1	342
37	Wealdstone	v	Great Wakering Rovers	2-0	402
38	Welling United	v	Chesham United	2-1	479
39	Hendon	v	Lancing (2/10)	1-1	177
	Lancing	v	Hendon (7/10)	0-4	307
40	Woking	v	Tooting & Mitcham United	4-0	1031
41	Hanwell Town	v	Lowestoft Town	1-0	155
42	Egham Town	v	Brightlingsea Regent	3-3	140
	Brightlingsea Regent	v	Egham Town (25/9)	2-1	190
43	Chelmsford City	v	Worthing	1-2	563
44	Concord Rangers	v	Margate	2-0	219
45	Leverstock Green	v	Dorking Wanderers	2-4	130
46	Haringey Borough	v	Erith Town	2-0	187
47	Leiston	v	Hastings United	3-4	263
48	Coggeshall Town	v	Walton Casuals	2-0	128
49	St Albans City	v	Corinthian Casuals (2/10)	1-1	403
	Corinthian Casuals	v	St Albans City (6/10)	0-3	112
	(at Metropolitan Police FC)				
50	Bowers & Pitsea	v	Hemel Hempstead Town	1-6	215
51	Billericay Town	v	Burnham	4-1	700
52	Kempston Rovers	v	Marlow	1-0	145
53	Hitchin Town	v	Didcot Town	1-1	298
	Didcot Town	v	Hitchin Town (25/9)	0-0aet	151
	(Hitchin Town won 4-2 on kicks from the penalty mark)				
54	Bognor Regis Town	v	AFC Sudbury	1-1	431
	AFC Sudbury	v	Bognor Regis Town (25/9)	3-2aet	210
55	Haverhill Rovers	v	Leatherhead	0-6	401
56	East Thurrock United	v	Whitehawk	2-3	154
57	Brantham Athletic	v	Eastbourne Borough	0-1	275
58	Oxford City	v	Cray Valley (PM)	5-0	142
59	Gosport Borough	v	Ramsgate	2-3	157
60	AFC Hornchurch	v	East Grinstead Town	2-1	227
61	AFC Uckfield Town	v	Dartford	1-3	500
62	Hayes & Yeading United	v	Moneyfields	0-1	177
63	FC Romania	v	Beaconsfield Town	0-2	104
64	Horsham	v	Heybridge Swifts	4-3	162
65	Dulwich Hamlet	v	Tonbridge Angels	3-1	569
66	Metropolitan Police	v	Needham Market	2-2	100
	Needham Market	v	Metropolitan Police (aet)	2-3aet	208
67	Merthyr Town	v	Winchester City	1-4	291
68	Lymington Town	v	Torquay United	0-7	639
	(Live on BBC Sport)				
69	Chippenham Town	v	Swindon Supermarine	2-2	384
	Swindon Supermarine	v	Chippenham Town (25/9)	0-1	364
70	Bristol Manor Farm	v	Basingstoke Town	5-2	217
71	Gloucester City	v	Plymouth Parkway (23/9)	3-1	349
72	Weston Super Mare	v	Salisbury	2-2	315
	Salisbury	v	Weston Super Mare (25/9)	2-3aet	551
73	Tiverton Town	v	Dorchester Town	2-0	307
74	Hereford	v	Truro City	0-0	1441
	Truro City	v	Hereford (26/9)	3-4aet	269
75	Poole Town	v	Cinderford Town	3-0	298
76	Taunton Town	v	Bitton	4-0	450
77	Banbury United	v	Bath City	0-2	654
78	Hungerford Town	v	Wantage Town (25/9)	1-1	166
	(22/9 – tie abandoned after 70 mins due to serious injury to player)				
	Wantage Town	v	Hungerford Town	2-2aet	330
	(Hungerford Town won 4-1 on kicks from the penalty mark)				
79	Binfield	v	Cirencester Town	0-3	204
80	Slough Town	v	Sholing	2-2	465
	Sholing	v	Slough Town (25/9)	0-3	327
	Total Attendance 40,787		**over 101 games**	**404 Ave**	
17/18	**Total Attendance 40,017**		**over 97 games**	**413 Ave**	

FAC - 1P - Alfreton Town v Fleetwood Town. Photo: Bill Wheatcroft.

FAC - 1P - Alfreton Town v Fleetwood Town. Photo: Bill Wheatcroft.

THIRD QUALIFYING ROUND

SATURDAY 6 OCTOBER 2018 - WINNERS RECEIVE £15,000

1	Workington	v	Kidsgrove Athletic	0-0	558
	Kidsgrove Athletic	v	Workington (10/10)	2-1aet	423
2	Stockport County	v	Corby Town	3-0	1935
3	Mickleover Sports	v	Alfreton Town	1-2	505
4	Kettering Town	v	Hednesford Town	4-0	502
5	Brackley Town	v	Marine	2-3	371
6	Peterborough Sports	v	Chorley	0-3	404
	(Live on BBC Sport)				
7	Altrincham	v	Bradford (Park Avenue)	4-2	780
8	Dunston UTS	v	Chester	4-3	873
9	Stourbridge	v	Kidderminster Harriers	3-2	1527
10	FC United of Manchester	v	Witton Albion	1-2	1234
11	Cleethorpes Town	v	Guiseley	2-2	255
	Guiseley	v	Cleethorpes Town (9/10)	2-1	384
12	St Neots Town	v	Coalville Town	2-2	518
	Coalville Town	v	St Neots Town (9/10)	3-3aet	409
	(St Neots Town won 5-3 on kicks from the penalty mark)				
13	King's Lynn Town	v	Ashton United	0-1	622
14	Curzon Ashton	v	Southport	1-2	408
15	Gainsborough Trinity	v	Blyth Spartans	1-2	428
16	York City	v	St Ives Town	3-0	1250
17	Warrington Town	v	AFC Telford United	2-1	543
18	Tiverton Town	v	Metropolitan Police	3-3	338
	Metropolitan Police	v	Tiverton Town (9/10)	1-0aet	172
19	Haringey Borough	v	AFC Sudbury	2-1	209
20	Gloucester City	v	Dorking Wanderers	3-3	333
	Dorking Wanderers	v	Gloucester City (9/10)	0-3	563
21	Leatherhead	v	Hanwell Town	1-1	279
	Hanwell Town	v	Leatherhead (9/10)	0-0aet	366
	(Leatherhead won 4-2 on kicks from the penalty mark)				
22	Eastbourne Borough	v	Dulwich Hamlet	4-3	570
23	Woking	v	Kempston Rovers	3-2	944
24	Taunton Town	v	St Albans City (10/10)	5-2	595
25	Billericay Town	v	Whitehawk	9-1	609
26	Hereford	v	Welling United	0-2	1330
27	Hitchin Town	v	Hastings United	2-0	425
28	Concord Rangers	v	Beaconsfield Town	2-1	184
29	Hemel Hempstead Town	v	Ramsgate	5-0	307
30	Moneyfields	v	Worthing	2-3	256
31	Bath City	v	Lewes	3-0	628
32	Slough Town	v	Bristol Manor Farm	2-2	486
	Bristol Manor Farm	v	Slough Town (9/10)	0-4	541
33	Hungerford Town	v	Wealdstone	1-2	306
34	Hampton & Richmond Borough	v	AFC Hornchurch	1-0	316
35	Chippenham Town	v	Hendon (10/10)	4-1	402
36	Brightlingsea Regent	v	Torquay United	0-3	470
37	Weston Super Mare	v	Coggeshall Town	1-0	267
38	Horsham	v	Poole Town	1-1	355
	Poole Town	v	Horsham (9/10)	2-1	381
39	Oxford City	v	Dartford	4-1	312
40	Winchester City	v	Cirencester Town	3-0	302
	Total Attendance 26,175		**over 48 games**	**545 Ave**	
17/18	**Total Attendance 32,401**		**over 48 games**	**675 Ave**	

FOURTH QUALIFYING ROUND

SATURDAY 20 OCTOBER 2018 - WINNERS RECEIVE £25,000

1	Guiseley	v	Stourbridge	3-1	633
2	Warrington Town	v	FC Halifax Town	2-2	929
	FC Halifax Town	v	Warrington Town (23/10)	2-0	844
3	Chorley	v	Barrow	3-2	1734
4	Hartlepool United	v	Kidsgrove Athletic	1-0	2703
5	AFC Fylde	v	Chesterfield	1-3	1092
6	Southport	v	Ashton United	2-1	770
7	Blyth Spartans	v	York City	0-1	1378
8	Harrogate Town	v	Wrexham	0-0	1540
	Wrexham	v	Harrogate Town (23/10)	2-0	2581
9	Dunston UTS	v	Gateshead	0-4	2520
	(Live on BBC Sport)				
10	Stockport County	v	Altrincham	2-0	2931
11	Marine	v	Salford City	1-2	1709
12	Witton Albion	v	Solihull Moors	0-2	681
13	Alfreton Town	v	St Neots Town	4-0	645
14	Woking	v	Welling United	1-0	1281
15	Hitchin Town	v	Leatherhead	1-1	1278
	Leatherhead	v	Hitchin Town (24/10)	1-2aet	637
16	Chippenham Town	v	Maidenhead United	1-1	706
	Maidenhead United	v	Chippenham Town (23/10)	1-0	738
17	Eastbourne Borough	v	Slough Town	1-2	802
18	Hemel Hempstead Town	v	Oxford City	1-1	762
	Oxford City	v	Hemel Hempstead Town (23/10)	5-0	405
19	Weston Super Mare	v	Bath City	1-0	963
20	Boreham Wood	v	Dagenham & Redbridge	2-2	408
	Dagenham & Redbridge	v	Boreham Wood (23/10)	0-1	792
21	Metropolitan Police	v	Havant & Waterlooville	1-0	335
22	Gloucester City	v	Bromley	0-1	615
23	Aldershot Town	v	Kettering Town	2-0	1634
24	Torquay United	v	Winchester City	4-1	2202
25	Billericay Town	v	Taunton Town	2-2	976
	Taunton Town	v	Billericay Town (24/10)	0-1	1502
26	Eastleigh	v	Hampton & Richmond Borough	0-1	740
27	Wealdstone	v	Sutton United	1-2	1082
28	Ebbsfleet United	v	Worthing	4-0	1011
29	Maidstone United	v	Leyton Orient	2-0	1906
30	Haringey Borough	v	Poole Town	2-1	402
31	Barnet	v	Braintree Town	4-2	1057
32	Concord Rangers	v	Dover Athletic	0-1	446
	Total Attendance 45,370		**over 39 games**	**1,163 Ave**	
17/18	**Total Attendance 44,428**		**over 42 games**	**1,057 Ave**	

FAC - 2P - Nottingham (Blackpool) and Wright (Solihull) challenge for the ball. Photo: Keith Clayton.

FAC - 2P - Reflex save from Hinchcliffe (Stockport) to deny Harrison (Barnet). Photo: Keith Clayton.

FAC - 1P - Rooney (Salford) gets the ball past Arnold (Shrewsbury) to equalise. Photo: Keith Clayton.

FIRST ROUND PROPER

SATURDAY 10 NOVEMBER 2018 - WINNERS RECEIVE £36,000

1	Haringey Borough	v	AFC Wimbledon (9/11)	0-1	2710
	(Live on BBC Two)				
2	Maidstone United	v	Macclesfield Town	2-1	2169
3	Ebbsfleet United	v	Cheltenham Town	0-0	1624
	Cheltenham Town	v	Ebbsfleet United (20/11)	2-0	1435
4	Hampton & Richmond Borough	v	Oldham Athletic (12/11)	1-2	2720
	(Live on BT Sport 1)				
5	Swindon Town	v	York City	2-1	3744
6	Mansfield Town	v	Charlton Athletic (11/11)	1-1	3240
	Charlton Athletic	v	Mansfield Town (20/11)	5-0	1910
7	Torquay United	v	Woking	0-1	2419
8	Scunthorpe United	v	Burton Albion	2-1	2260
9	Port Vale	v	Sunderland (11/11)	1-2	7238
	(Live on BT Sport 1)				
10	Aldershot Town	v	Bradford City	1-1	2455
	Bradford City	v	Aldershot Town (20/11)	1-1aet	2248
	(Bradford City won 4-1 on kicks from the penalty mark)				
11	Grimsby Town	v	Milton Keynes Dons	3-1	1991
12	Chorley	v	Doncaster Rovers (11/11)	2-2	3239
	Doncaster Rovers	v	Chorley (20/11)	7-0	3048
13	Alfreton Town	v	Fleetwood Town (11/11)	1-4	872
14	Bromley	v	Peterborough United	1-3	3107
15	Southport	v	Boreham Wood	2-0	1463
16	Plymouth Argyle	v	Stevenage	1-0	5719
17	Chesterfield	v	Billericay Town	1-1	2957
	Billericay Town	v	Chesterfield (20/11)	1-3	2493
18	Lincoln City	v	Northampton Town	3-2	6012
19	Barnet	v	Bristol Rovers (11/11)	1-1	1705
	Bristol Rovers	v	Barnet (21/11)	1-2	2740
20	Yeovil Town	v	Stockport County	1-3	2550
21	Bury	v	Dover Athletic	5-0	2355
22	Gillingham	v	Hartlepool United	0-0	2111
	Hartlepool United	v	Gillingham (21/11)	3-4aet	1873
23	Oxford United	v	Forest Green Rovers	0-0	3933
	Forest Green Rovers	v	Oxford United (20/11)	0-3	1614
24	Tranmere Rovers	v	Oxford City	3-3	4206
	Oxford City	v	Tranmere Rovers (20/11)	0-2	1303
	(Live on BT Sport 1)				
25	Accrington Stanley	v	Colchester United	1-0	1267
26	Barnsley	v	Notts County	4-0	5878
27	Shrewsbury Town	v	Salford City (11/11)	1-1	4351
	Salford City	v	Shrewsbury Town (21/11)	1-3	2432
	(Live on BT Sport 1)				
28	Metropolitan Police	v	Newport County	0-2	1031
29	Walsall	v	Coventry City	3-2	4760
30	Rochdale	v	Gateshead	2-1	2415
31	Hitchin Town	v	Solihull Moors (11/11)	0-2	3148
32	Sutton United	v	Slough Town	0-0	1830
	Slough Town	v	Sutton United (20/11)	1-1aet	1360
	(Slough Town won 8-7 on kicks from the penalty mark)				
33	Guiseley	v	Cambridge United (11/11)	4-3	1097
34	Exeter City	v	Blackpool	2-3	3188
35	Luton Town	v	Wycombe Wanderers	2-0	5343
36	Morecambe	v	FC Halifax Town	0-0	1736
	FC Halifax Town	v	Morecambe (20/11)	1-0	1218
37	Crewe Alexandra	v	Carlisle United	0-1	2468
38	Southend United	v	Crawley Town	1-1	3935
	Crawley Town	v	Southend United (20/11)	2-6aet	3120
39	Maidenhead United	v	Portsmouth	0-4	3205
	(Live on BT Sport 1)				
40	Weston Super Mare	v	Wrexham (11/11)	0-2	1770
	Total Attendance 147,015		**over 53 games**	**2,774 Ave**	
17/18	**Total Attendance 125,980**		**over 45 games**	**2,800 Ave**	

SECOND ROUND PROPER

SATURDAY 1 DECEMBER 2018 - WINNERS RECEIVE £54,000

1	Guiseley	v	Fleetwood Town (3/11)	1-2	2324
	(Live on BT Sport 1)				
2	Bury	v	Luton Town (2/12)	0-1	2977
3	Wrexham	v	Newport County	0-0	5295
	Newport County	v	Wrexham (11/12)	4-0	4143
4	Tranmere Rovers	v	Southport (2/12)	1-1	4701
	Southport	v	Tranmere Rovers (17/12)	0-2	5414
	(Live on BT Sport 1)				
5	Southend United	v	Barnsley	2-4	3616
6	Shrewsbury Town	v	Scunthorpe United (2/12)	1-0	3427
7	Solihull Moors	v	Blackpool (30/11)	0-0	3005
	Blackpool	v	Solihull Moors (18/12)	3-2aet	1441
	(Live on BT Sport 1)				
8	Chesterfield	v	Grimsby Town (2/12)	0-2	4537
9	Peterborough United	v	Bradford City	2-2	3750
	Bradford City	v	Peterborough United (11/12)	4-4aet	3486
	(Peterborough United won 3-2 on kicks from the penalty mark)				
10	Swindon Town	v	Woking (2/12)	0-1	3654
11	Maidstone United	v	Oldham Athletic	0-2	3560
12	Lincoln City	v	Carlisle United	2-0	6438
13	FC Halifax Town	v	AFC Wimbledon	1-3	2044
14	Plymouth Argyle	v	Oxford United	1-2	5984
15	Barnet	v	Stockport County (2/12)	1-0	2826
16	Rochdale	v	Portsmouth (2/12)	0-1	2555
17	Walsall	v	Sunderland	1-1	3142
	Sunderland	v	Walsall (11/12)	0-1	8212
18	Accrington Stanley	v	Cheltenham Town	3-1	1066
19	Charlton Athletic	v	Doncaster Rovers	0-2	3249
20	Slough Town	v	Gillingham (2/12)	0-1	2084
	Total Attendance 92,930		**over 25 games**	**3,717 Ave**	
17/18	**Total Attendance 84,112**		**over 27 games**	**3,115 Ave**	

THIRD ROUND PROPER

SATURDAY 5 JANUARY 2019 - WINNERS RECEIVE £135,000

1	Bolton Wanderers	v	Walsall	5-2	5506
2	Millwall	v	Hull City (6/1)	2-1	5307
3	Gillingham	v	Cardiff City	1-0	7090
4	Brentford	v	Oxford United	1-0	6106
5	Sheffield Wednesday	v	Luton Town	0-0	16974
	Luton Town	v	Sheffield Wednesday (15/1)	0-1	9259
6	Manchester United	v	Reading	2-0	73918
7	Everton	v	Lincoln City	2-1	37900
8	Tranmere Rovers	v	Tottenham Hotspur (4/1)	0-7	12553
9	Preston North End	v	Doncaster Rovers (6/1)	1-3	8101
10	Newcastle United	v	Blackburn Rovers	1-1	36440
	Blackburn Rovers	v	Newcastle United (15/1)	2-4aet	14228
	(Live on BT Sport 2)				
11	Chelsea	v	Nottingham Forest	2-0	40544
12	Crystal Palace	v	Grimsby Town	1-0	19967
13	Derby County	v	Southampton	2-2	17095
	Southampton	v	Derby County (16/1)	2-2aet	14651
	(Derby County won 5-3 on kicks from the penalty mark – Live on BBC1)				
14	Accrington Stanley	v	Ipswich Town	1-0	2869
15	Bristol City	v	Huddersfield Town	1-0	12179
16	Newport County	v	Leicester City (6/1)	2-1	6705
17	Fulham	v	Oldham Athletic (6/1)	1-2	16134
18	Shrewsbury Town	v	Stoke City	1-1	7512
	Stoke City	v	Shrewsbury Town (15/1)	2-3	10261
19	Blackpool	v	Arsenal	0-3	8955
20	Manchester City	v	Rotherham United (6/1)	7-0	52708
21	AFC Bournemouth	v	Brighton & Hove Albion	1-3	10522
22	West Ham United	v	Birmingham City	2-0	54840
23	Woking	v	Watford (6/1)	0-2	5717
24	Burnley	v	Barnsley	1-0	11053
25	Queens Park Rangers	v	Leeds United (6/1)	2-1	11637
26	Sheffield United	v	Barnet (6/1)	0-1	9906
27	Norwich City	v	Portsmouth	0-1	23201
28	Fleetwood Town	v	AFC Wimbledon	2-3	2131
29	West Bromwich Albion	v	Wigan Athletic	1-0	15465
30	Middlesbrough	v	Peterborough United	5-0	11647
31	Wolverhampton Wanderers	v	Liverpool (7/1)	2-1	25849
32	Aston Villa	v	Swansea City	0-3	30572
	Total Attendance 655,502		**over 36 games**	**18,208 Ave**	
17/18	**Total Attendance 710,011**		**over 39 games**	**18,205 Ave**	

FAC - 4Q - Weston, on the attack, went on to win this West Country derby over Bath City 1-0. Photo: Peter Barnes.

FAC - 1P - Gilmour (Tranmere) does enough to prevent Fleet (Oxford City) from scoring. Photo: Keith Clayton.

FOURTH ROUND PROPER

SATURDAY 26 JANUARY 2019 - WINNERS RECEIVE £180,000

	Home		Away	Score	Att
1	Swansea City	v	Gillingham	4-1	15080
2	AFC Wimbledon	v	West Ham United	4-2	4777
	(Live on BT Sport 2)				
3	Shrewsbury Town	v	Wolverhampton Wanderers	2-2	9503
	Wolverhampton Wanderers	v	Shrewsbury Town (5/2)	3-2	28844
4	Millwall	v	Everton	3-2	16354
	(Live on BBC One)				
5	Brighton & Hove Albion	v	West Bromwich Albion	0-0	27001
	West Bromwich Albion	v	Brighton & Hove Albion (6/2)	1-3aet	8645
	(Live on BBC One)				
6	Bristol City	v	Bolton Wanderers (25/1)	2-1	13747
7	Accrington Stanley	v	Derby County	0-1	5397
	(Live on BT Sport 2)				
8	Doncaster Rovers	v	Oldham Athletic	2-1	11260
9	Chelsea	v	Sheffield Wednesday (27/1)	3-0	37433
	(Live on BBC One)				
10	Newcastle United	v	Watford	0-2	34604
11	Middlesbrough	v	Newport County	1-1	15794
	Newport County	v	Middlesbrough (5/2)	2-0	6552
	(Live on BT Sport 2)				
12	Manchester City	v	Burnley	5-0	50121
13	**Barnet**	v	**Brentford (28/1)**	3-3	6215
	(Live on BT Sport 2)				
	Brentford	v	**Barnet (5/2)**	3-1	6954
14	Portsmouth	v	Queens Park Rangers	1-1	19378
	Queens Park Rangers	v	Portsmouth (5/2)	2-0	13115
15	Arsenal	v	Manchester United (25/1)	1-3	59571
	(Live on BBC One)				
16	Crystal Palace	v	Tottenham Hotspur (27/10	2-0	19491
	(Live on BT Sport 2)				
	Total Attendance 409,836		**over 19 games**		**21,570 Ave**
17/18	**Total Attendance 370,950**		**over 20 games**		**18,548 Ave**

FIFTH ROUND PROPER

SATURDAY 16 FEBRUARY 2019 - WINNERS RECEIVE £360,000

	Home		Away	Score	Att
1	Bristol City	v	Wolverhampton Wanderers (17/2)	0-1	24394
2	AFC Wimbledon	v	Millwall	0-1	4795
3	Doncaster Rovers	v	Crystal Palace (17/2)	0-2	14010
4	Newport County	v	Manchester City	1-4	9680
5	Chelsea	v	Manchester United (18/2)	0-2	40562
6	Swansea City	v	Brentford (17/2)	4-1	11261
7	Queens Park Rangers	v	Watford (15/2)	0-1	17212
8	Brighton & Hove Albion	v	Derby County	2-1	24562
	Total Attendance 146,476		**over 8 games**		**18,310 Ave**
17/18	**Total Attendance 210,328**		**over 10 games**		**21,033 Ave**

QUARTER FINALS

SATURDAY 16 MARCH 2019 - WINNERS RECEIVE £720,000

	Home		Away	Score	Att
1	Swansea City	v	Manchester City (5.20)	2-3	19785
2	Watford	v	Crystal Palace (12.15)	2-1	18104
3	Wolverhampton Wanderers	v	Manchester United (7.55)	2-1	31004
4	Millwall	v	Brighton & Hove Albion (2.00)	2-2aet	17137
	(Brighton & Hove Albion won 5-4 on penalties)				
	Total Attendance 86,030		**over 4 games**		**21,508 Ave**
17/18	**Total Attendance 208,568**		**over 4 games**		**52,142 Ave**

SEMI FINALS

WINNERS RECEIVE £1,800,000 LOSERS RECEIVE £900,000

SUNDAY 7 APRIL 9 - at Wembley Stadium

	Home		Away	Score	Att
1	Watford	v	Wolverhampton Wanderers	3-2aet	80092
17/18	**Total Attendance 158,083**		**over 2 games**		**79,042 Ave**

SATURDAY 6 APRIL 2019 - at Wembley Stadium

	Home		Away	Score	Att
2	Manchester City	v	Brighton & Hove Albion (5.30)	1-0	71521
	Total Attendance 151,613		**over 2 games**		**75,807 Ave**

THE FINAL

SATURDAY 18 MAY 2019 WINNERS RECEIVE £3.6m RUNNERS-UP £1.8m

MANCHESTER CITY	6	0	WATFORD
Silva D 26 Jesus 38 68 De Bruyne 61 Sterling 81 87			

AT WEMBLEY STADIUM ~ ATTENDANCE: 85,854 (17/18 - 87,647)

FAC - 3P - Watford 'keeper. Gomez, makes a good save to keep out Woking. Photo: Peter Barnes.

FAC - 1P - Swindon v York City. Photo: Peter Barnes.

FAC - 1P - Weston-super-Mare v Wrexham. Photo: Peter Barnes.

THE FA TROPHY 2018-19

EXTRA PRELIMINARY ROUND

SATURDAY 29 SEPTEMBER 2018 - WINNERS RECEIVE £2,000

1	Atherton Collieries	v	Runcorn Linnets	4-2	
2	Cleethorpes Town	v	Mossley	3-1	179
3	Sheffield	v	Prescot Cables	2-2	248
	Prescot Cables	v	Sheffield (2/10)	6-2	
4	Trafford	v	Colne	2-1	317
5	Glossop North End	v	Brighouse Town	0-2	201
6	Droylsden	v	Widnes	2-1	
7	Bromsgrove Sporting	v	Corby Town	1-3	954
8	Loughborough Dynamo	v	Market Drayton Town	5-2	
9	Peterborough Sports	v	Sutton Coldfield Town	2-1	
10	Coleshill Town	v	Kidsgrove Athletic	1-2	120
11	Witham Town	v	Coggeshall Town (28/9)	1-0	
12	Uxbridge	v	Chalfont St Peter	1-1	
	Chalfont St Peter	v	Uxbridge (2/10)	0-0 aet	
	(Chalfont St Peter won 5-4 on kicks from the penalty mark)				
13	Felixstowe & Walton United	v	Grays Athletic	1-3	250
14	Romford	v	Great Wakering Rovers (30/9)	2-3	115
15	Bedford Town	v	Cheshunt	1-1	
	Cheshunt	v	Bedford Town (2/10)	1-2	102
16	Bury Town	v	Horsham	1-2	
17	Aveley	v	Tooting & Mitcham United	3-1	106
18	Didcot Town	v	Thamesmead Town	3-1	
19	Ashford Town (Middx)	v	Heybridge Swifts	4-2	
20	Barton Rovers	v	Kempston Rovers	1-3	102
21	Whyteleafe	v	Bowers & Pitsea	4-1	
22	Waltham Abbey	v	Hastings United	1-3	191
23	AFC Sudbury	v	Egham Town	0-1	
24	Ashford United	v	Haywards Heath Town	4-4	
	Haywards Heath Town	v	Ashford United (2/10)	3-0	78
25	Blackfield & Langley	v	Highworth Town	3-0	65
26	Evesham United	v	Moneyfields (30/9)	1-5	149
27	Slimbridge	v	Winchester City	2-2	85
	Winchester City	v	Slimbridge (2/10)	3-3aet	93
	(Slimbridge won 6-5 on kicks from the penalty mark)				

PRELIMINARY ROUND

SATURDAY 13 OCTOBER 2018 - WINNERS RECEIVE £3,000

1	Prescot Cables	v	Kendal Town	5-1	
2	Pickering Town	v	Stocksbridge Park Steels (14/10)	3-0	138
3	Marske United	v	Atherton Collieries	3-3	292
	Atherton Collieries	v	Marske United (15/10)	0-1	
4	Radcliffe	v	Cleethorpes Town	2-3	
5	Droylsden	v	Tadcaster Albion	1-1	
	Tadcaster Albion	v	Droylsden (16/10)	0-2	220
6	Trafford	v	Ramsbottom United	1-2	272
7	Skelmersdale United (at Frickley Athletic FC)	v	Frickley Athletic	1-3	
8	Ossett United	v	Colwyn Bay	6-0	630
9	Morpeth Town	v	Brighouse Town	3-4	
10	Clitheroe	v	Pontefract Collieries	3-2	
11	Spalding United	v	Carlton Town	1-4	
12	Wisbech Town	v	Kidsgrove Athletic	1-2	
	(tie awarded to Wisbech Town – Kidsgrove Athletic removed)				
13	Peterborough Sports	v	Cambridge City	2-4	
14	Gresley	v	Newcastle Town	1-2	
15	Belper Town	v	Stamford	0-0	
	Stamford	v	Belper Town (16/10)	1-0	
16	Chasetown	v	Lincoln United	2-1	223
17	Soham Town Rangers	v	AFC Mansfield	0-0	
	AFC Mansfield	v	Soham Town Rangers (16/10)	2-1	103
18	Leek Town	v	Loughborough Dynamo	0-0	
	Loughborough Dynamo	v	Leek Town (16/10)	2-5	
19	Corby Town	v	Yaxley	2-3	445
20	Chipstead	v	Welwyn Garden City	2-1	125
21	Berkhamsted	v	South Park	5-1	149
22	Barking	v	Hayes & Yeading United	0-1	103
23	AFC Dunstable	v	Witham Town (12/10)	0-1	156
24	Hythe Town	v	FC Romania	2-0	
25	Grays Athletic	v	Sevenoaks Town	2-4	
26	Aylesbury United	v	Mildenhall Town (14/10)	2-3	
27	Didcot Town	v	Hertford Town	2-1	151
28	Greenwich Borough	v	Egham Town	4-1	
29	Dunstable Town	v	Northwood	2-0	
30	Haywards Heath Town	v	Bracknell Town	2-3	
31	Faversham Town	v	Sittingbourne	0-2	310
32	Phoenix Sports	v	Ramsgate	1-1	
	Ramsgate	v	Phoenix Sports	1-0	100
33	Bedfont Sports	v	Whitstable Town	1-4	61
34	Canvey Island	v	Cray Wanderers	2-0	
35	Tilbury	v	Bedford Town	1-4	120
36	Horsham	v	Ware	3-1	103
37	Great Wakering Rovers	v	East Grinstead Town	0-1	96
38	Dereham Town	v	Kempston Rovers	1-3	204
39	VCD Athletic	v	Hanwell Town	3-1	
40	Aylesbury	v	Herne Bay	1-2	158
41	Three Bridges	v	Molesey	0-1	
42	Hastings United	v	Whyteleafe	2-4	
43	Ashford Town (Middx)	v	Westfield	0-0	
	Westfield	v	Ashford Town (Middx) (16/10)	2-3	93
44	Chalfont St Peter	v	Maldon & Tiptree	0-2	
45	Brentwood Town	v	Marlow	4-1	
46	Aveley	v	Basildon United (12/10)	2-1	188
47	Slimbridge	v	Melksham Town	2-3	81
48	AFC Totton	v	North Leigh	1-1	254
	North Leigh	v	AFC Totton (16/10)	1-5	156
49	Yate Town	v	Blackfield & Langley	1-0	174
50	Cinderford Town	v	Moneyfields	5-0	104
51	Bideford	v	Street	2-3	
52	Thatcham Town	v	Cirencester Town	2-0	
53	Mangotsfield United	v	Kidlington	3-0	114
54	Larkhall Athletic	v	Thame United	0-0	
	Thame United	v	Larkhall Athletic (16/10)	1-0	59
55	Fleet Town	v	Barnstaple Town	2-1	104
56	Bristol Manor Farm	v	Paulton Rovers	1-0	188

FAT - 3Q - Action between Hereford and FC United. Photo: Peter Barnes.

FAT - 3Q - Breeden (Leamington) saves from Goulding (Witton).
Photo: Keith Clayton

FAT - 3Q - Bishop (Leamington) sends Hall (Witton) the wrong way from the penalty spot. Photo: Keith Clayton.

FIRST QUALIFYING ROUND

SATURDAY 27 OCTOBER 2018 - WINNERS RECEIVE £3,250

No.	Home		Away	Score	Att
1	Workington	v	Scarborough Athletic	1-0	363
2	Marine	v	Lancaster City	0-2	286
3	Warrington Town	v	Prescot Cables	0-1	316
4	Pickering Town	v	Droylsden	2-2	162
	Droylsden	v	Pickering Town (30/10)	2-3	109
5	Frickley Athletic	v	Ramsbottom United	0-3	127
6	Whitby Town	v	Witton Albion	0-1	181
7	Farsley Celtic	v	Brighouse Town	4-1	173
8	Ossett United	v	Clitheroe	2-1	
9	South Shields	v	North Ferriby United	4-0	714
10	Hyde United	v	Bamber Bridge	3-0	
11	Cleethorpes Town	v	Marske United	0-2	
12	Stalybridge Celtic	v	Nantwich Town	1-0	
13	Gainsborough Trinity	v	Tamworth	0-0	
	Tamworth	v	Gainsborough Trinity (30/10)	3-0	
14	Buxton	v	King's Lynn Town	3-3	285
	King's Lynn Town	v	Buxton (31/10)	1-2aet	
15	Kettering Town	v	Stourbridge	2-0	409
16	AFC Rushden & Diamonds	v	St Ives Town	2-1	
17	Stamford	v	Leek Town	0-0	
	Leek Town	v	Stamford (30/10)	0-1	
18	Cambridge City	v	Basford United	1-2	164
19	Carlton Town	v	Bedworth United	1-0	73
20	Newcastle Town	v	Chasetown	5-2	
21	Mickleover Sports	v	Redditch United	1-0	157
22	St Neots Town	v	Matlock Town	1-0	249
23	Wisbech Town	v	Yaxley (6/11)	1-1	
	Yaxley	v	Wisbech Town (10/11)	2-0	
24	Stafford Rangers	v	Rushall Olympic	2-1	371
25	AFC Mansfield	v	Hednesford Town	1-1	
	Hednesford Town	v	AFC Mansfield (30/10)	0-1	174
26	Grantham Town	v	Halesowen Town	0-4	159
27	Alvechurch	v	Stratford Town	1-1	199
	Stratford Town	v	Alvechurch (30/10)	3-0	172
28	Barwell	v	Coalville Town	1-1	172
	Coalville Town	v	Barwell (30/10)	2-3aet	172
29	Chipstead	v	Berkhamsted	2-1	
30	Sittingbourne	v	Wingate & Finchley	1-2	155
31	Brentwood Town	v	Whitstable Town	3-1	147
32	Hythe Town	v	Bishop's Stortford	1-2	
33	Molesey	v	Walton Casuals	0-1	
34	Kingstonian	v	Bedford Town	1-1	257
	Bedford Town	v	Kingstonian (30/10)	3-2	218
35	Margate	v	Potters Bar Town	1-2	
36	Horsham	v	Corinthian Casuals	3-0	137
37	Burgess Hill Town	v	Worthing	1-1	459
	Worthing	v	Burgess Hill Town (30/10)	2-1	408
38	Dorking Wanderers	v	Sevenoaks Town	2-1	
39	Biggleswade Town	v	Harrow Borough	2-1	
40	Hitchin Town	v	Hayes & Yeading United	0-1	317
41	Maldon & Tiptree	v	Royston Town	0-3	
42	Haringey Borough	v	Chesham United	1-1	
	Chesham United	v	Haringey Borough (30/10)	2-2aet	163
	(Chesham United won 3-1 on kicks from the penalty mark)				
43	Ashford Town (Middx)	v	Lewes	1-2	101
44	Lowestoft Town	v	Enfield Town	0-1	289
45	AFC Hornchurch	v	Ramsgate	6-0	162
46	Kempston Rovers	v	Beaconsfield Town	1-1	102
	Beaconsfield Town	v	Kempston Rovers (30/10)	3-1	
47	Folkestone Invicta	v	Leatherhead	5-1	121
48	Merstham	v	East Grinstead Town	2-0	
49	Tonbridge Angels	v	Whyteleafe	2-1	
50	Hendon	v	Staines Town	2-1	169
51	VCD Athletic	v	Leiston	1-3	
52	Mildenhall Town	v	Greenwich Borough	2-4aet	147
53	Metropolitan Police	v	Carshalton Athletic	2-2	129
	Carshalton Athletic	v	Metropolitan Police (29/10)	2-1	128
54	Canvey Island	v	Brightlingsea Regent	0-1	183
55	Bracknell Town	v	Bognor Regis Town	2-2	339
	Bognor Regis Town	v	Bracknell Town (30/10)	2-2aet	306
	(Bognor Regis Town won 3-2 on kicks from the penalty mark)				
56	Whitehawk	v	Harlow Town	2-3	161
57	Aveley	v	Dunstable Town	1-0	
58	Kings Langley	v	Needham Market	0-2	122
59	Herne Bay	v	Witham Town	2-1	210
60	Yate Town	v	Dorchester Town	1-1	175
	Dorchester Town	v	Yate Town (30/10)	2-0	207
61	Gosport Borough	v	AFC Totton	1-2	191
62	Cinderford Town	v	Street	2-2	
	Street	v	Cinderford Town (30/10)	4-1	101
63	Thame United	v	Bristol Manor Farm	4-2	83
64	Farnborough	v	Merthyr Town	2-3	
65	Fleet Town	v	Salisbury	0-3	267
66	Taunton Town	v	Weymouth	1-3	513
67	Thatcham Town	v	Melksham Town	1-2	286
68	Poole Town	v	Frome Town	2-1	271
69	Hartley Wintney	v	Tiverton Town	1-1	
	Tiverton Town	v	Hartley Wintney (30/10)	5-1	
70	Didcot Town	v	Mangotsfield United	1-1	121
	Mangotsfield United	v	Didcot Town (30/10)	2-4aet	
71	Basingstoke Town	v	Wimborne Town	4-2	272
72	Swindon Supermarine	v	Banbury United	1-1	
	Banbury United	v	Swindon Supermarine (30/10)	3-0	

FAT - 1P - Chesterfield v Basford United. The Basford attacker gets in a powerful header. Photo: Bill Wheatcroft.

FAT - 1P - Hereford v Billericay Town. Billericay clear the danger. Photo: Peter Barnes.

FAT - 1P - Yate Town v Dorchester Town. Photo: Peter Barnes.

SECOND QUALIFYING ROUND

SATURDAY 10 NOVEMBER 2018 - WINNERS RECEIVE £4,000

	Home		Away	Score	Att
1	Basford United	v	Stafford Rangers	4-0	246
2	Stamford	v	Kettering Town	1-0	
3	Stalybridge Celtic	v	Buxton	0-0	409
	Buxton	v	Stalybridge Celtic (13/11)	1-2	283
4	Yaxley	v	Ramsbottom United (13/11)	2-2	85
	Ramsbottom United	v	Yaxley (20/11)	5-1	
5	AFC Mansfield	v	Pickering Town	2-2	105
	Pickering Town	v	AFC Mansfield (13/11)	2-0	188
6	St Neots Town	v	Barwell	0-1	216
7	Lancaster City	v	Ossett United	1-0	262
8	Newcastle Town	v	Workington	2-2	160
	Workington	v	Newcastle Town (13/11)	5-0	219
9	Marske United	v	Tamworth	2-0	290
10	Halesowen Town	v	Prescot Cables	3-2	
11	Stratford Town	v	Mickleover Sports	1-1	183
	Mickleover Sports	v	Stratford Town (13/11)	0-1	
12	Witton Albion	v	AFC Rushden & Diamonds	2-0	300
13	Farsley Celtic	v	Carlton Town	0-0	167
	Carlton Town	v	Farsley Celtic (14/11)	0-4	115
14	South Shields	v	Hyde United	2-1	1095
15	Brightlingsea Regent	v	AFC Hornchurch	2-1	
16	Lewes	v	Merthyr Town	2-0	475
17	Chipstead	v	Bedford Town	2-2	98
	Bedford Town	v	Chipstead (13/11)	2-0	182
18	Dorking Wanderers	v	Tonbridge Angels	1-0	
19	Hendon	v	Biggleswade Town	1-2	223
20	Basingstoke Town	v	Enfield Town	2-1	310
21	Royston Town	v	Thame United	5-2	
22	Horsham	v	Potters Bar Town	1-0	
23	Brentwood Town	v	Poole Town	2-2	159
	Poole Town	v	Brentwood Town (13/11)	4-1	276
24	Herne Bay	v	Needham Market	0-1	207
25	Leiston	v	Melksham Town	2-1	172
26	Salisbury	v	Merstham	2-0	422
27	Banbury United	v	Hayes & Yeading United	0-2	387
28	Carshalton Athletic	v	Harlow Town	3-1	358
29	Weymouth	v	Street	2-2	629
	Street	v	Weymouth (13/11)	0-1	376
30	Dorchester Town	v	AFC Totton	3-1	285
31	Aveley	v	Beaconsfield Town	1-2	
32	Worthing	v	Chesham United	1-0	802
33	Walton Casuals	v	Bognor Regis Town	2-0	
34	Folkestone Invicta	v	Didcot Town	3-0	
35	Greenwich Borough	v	Bishop's Stortford	1-0	
36	Tiverton Town	v	Wingate & Finchley	2-3	162

THIRD QUALIFYING ROUND

SATURDAY 24 NOVEMBER 2018 - WINNERS RECEIVE £5,000

	Home		Away	Score	Att
1	Altrincham	v	Bradford (Park Avenue)	4-0	
2	Blyth Spartans	v	Marske United	4-1	642
3	Alfreton Town	v	Farsley Celtic	0-2	214
4	Spennymoor Town	v	Halesowen Town	8-2	502
5	Stamford	v	Barwell	1-1	
	Barwell	v	Stamford (27/11)	3-3aet	126
	(Barwell won 7-6 on kicks from the penalty mark)				
6	Hereford	v	FC United of Manchester	3-1	1067
7	Brackley Town	v	Nuneaton Borough	3-0	350
8	Stratford Town	v	South Shields	2-1	378
9	Kidderminster Harriers	v	York City	1-3	
10	Southport	v	Chester	0-0	914
	Chester	v	Southport (27/11)	0-2	
11	Leamington	v	Witton Albion	2-1	332
12	Darlington	v	AFC Telford United (23/11)	0-2	717
13	Ashton United	v	Boston United	0-5	
14	Pickering Town	v	Ramsbottom United	0-0	222
	Ramsbottom United	v	Pickering Town (27/11)	2-1	
15	Basford United	v	Curzon Ashton	2-1	
16	Lancaster City	v	Guiseley	2-2	259
	Guiseley	v	Lancaster City (11/12)	1-2	283
17	Stockport County	v	Chorley	3-0	1245
18	Stalybridge Celtic	v	Workington	1-2	344
19	Lewes	v	Hemel Hempstead Town	2-2	325
	Hemel Hempstead Town	v	Lewes (27/11)	3-2	137
20	Bedford Town	v	Worthing	2-1	
21	Salisbury	v	East Thurrock United	2-1	465
22	Dorchester Town	v	Hungerford Town	1-0	258
23	Slough Town	v	Weston Super Mare	2-3	
24	Poole Town	v	Dorking Wanderers	2-3	285
25	Weymouth	v	St Albans City	1-1	508
	St Albans City	v	Weymouth (27/11)	0-2	174
26	Concord Rangers	v	Wealdstone	2-3	
27	Truro City	v	Greenwich Borough	3-0	
28	Chippenham Town	v	Wingate & Finchley	1-1	280
	Wingate & Finchley	V	Chippenham Town (27/11)	3-2	90
29	Beaconsfield Town	v	Leiston	3-1	89
30	Hampton & Richmond Borough	v	Billericay Town	0-1	298
31	Eastbourne Borough	v	Dartford	1-1	340
	Dartford	v	Eastbourne Borough (27/11)	2-3	404
32	Welling United	v	Dulwich Hamlet	1-1	478
	Dulwich Hamlet	v	Welling United (28/11)	2-1	
33	Woking	v	Folkestone Invicta	2-0	
34	Basingstoke Town	v	Torquay United	1-1aet	
	(Torquay United won 5-4 on kicks from the penalty mark)				
35	Carshalton Athletic	v	Walton Casuals	2-0	
36	Royston Town	v	Needham Market	1-1	
	Needham Market	v	Royston Town (27/11)	2-0	153
37	Hayes & Yeading United	v	Brightlingsea Regent	0-0	144
	Brightlingsea Regent	v	Hayes & Yeading United (27/11)	1-2	
38	Gloucester City	v	Biggleswade Town (25/11)	1-3	
39	Horsham	v	Bath City (25/11)	1-2	328
40	Oxford City	v	Chelmsford City	4-0	220

FAT - 2P - The Hereford player gets in a shot before the incoming Brackley Town defender can get a block in. Photo: Peter Barnes.

FAT - QF - The Brackley Town No.9 heads back across the area against Leyton Orient.
Photo: Peter Barnes.

Danny Lewis saves a penalty kick from Leyton Orient striker Macauley Bonne in the second half

FAT - QF - More action between Brackley Town and Leyton Orient. Photo: Peter Barnes.

FIRST ROUND PROPER

SATURDAY 15 DECEMBER 2018 - WINNERS RECEIVE £6,000

1	Southport	v	Solihull Moors	0-1	767
2	Lancaster City	v	Blyth Spartans	0-3	149
3	AFC Fylde	v	Stratford Town	5-1	
4	Salford City	v	Gateshead (18/12)	3-1	380
5	Chesterfield	v	Basford United	5-1	1276
6	Wrexham	v	Boston United	3-0	1083
7	Barrow	v	FC Halifax Town	1-2	578
8	Harrogate Town	v	York City	2-1	1336
9	Leamington	v	Hartlepool United	0-1	344
10	Workington	v	Ramsbottom United	0-0	298
	Ramsbottom United	v	Workington (18/12)	2-0	170
11	Spennymoor Town	v	Barwell	4-0	295
12	Altrincham	v	Stockport County	0-1	
13	AFC Telford United	v	Farsley Celtic	4-3	
14	Wingate & Finchley	v	Dulwich Hamlet	2-0	202
15	Biggleswade Town	v	Wealdstone	2-1	
16	Maidenhead United	v	Oxford City (8/1)	1-2aet	
	(15/12 – tie abandoned after 64 mins due to waterlogged pitch, 0-1)				
17	Hereford	v	Billericay Town	2-1	1097
18	Aldershot Town	v	Bedford Town	3-3	
	Bedford Town	v	Aldershot Town (18/12)	7-0	485
19	Carshalton Athletic	v	Dorking Wanderers	1-0	
20	Hemel Hempstead Town	v	Eastleigh	2-1	234
21	Dover Athletic	v	Havant & Waterlooville	2-2	327
	Havant & Waterlooville	v	Dover Athletic (8/1)	0-1	229
22	Woking	v	Maidstone United	1-1	
	Maidstone United	v	Woking (18/12)	3-2aet	602
23	Ebbsfleet United	v	Dagenham & Redbridge	0-1	720
24	Barnet	v	Bath City	3-2	
25	Bromley	v	Sutton United	2-1	776
	(tie awarded to Sutton United – Bromley removed)				
26	Truro City	v	Weston Super Mare	4-0	255
	(at Treyew Road)				
27	Salisbury	v	Braintree Town (8/1)	2-1	502
28	Boreham Wood	v	Torquay United	3-1aet	207
29	Leyton Orient	v	Beaconsfield Town	4-0	1177
30	Brackley Town	v	Hayes & Yeading United	4-2	268
31	Weymouth	v	Needham Market		
	(walkover for Weymouth – Needham Market withdrawn)				
32	Eastbourne Borough	v	Dorchester Town	0-4	215

SECOND ROUND PROPER

SATURDAY 12 JANUARY 2019 - WINNERS RECEIVE £7,000

1	Ramsbottom United	v	Weymouth	2-2	457
	Weymouth	v	Ramsbottom United (15/1)	1-3	657
2	Hartlepool United	v	AFC Telford United	1-2	1920
3	Maidstone United	v	Oxford City	1-0	1156
4	Hemel Hempstead Town	v	Wingate & Finchley	4-2	454
5	Barnet	v	Dorchester Town	2-1	878
6	Hereford	v	Brackley Town	1-3	1569
7	Salford City	v	Dagenham & Redbridge	2-0	1061
8	Blyth Spartans	v	Boreham Wood	1-0	712
9	AFC Fylde	v	Biggleswade Town	1-0	594
10	Spennymoor Town	v	Sutton United	3-0	760
11	Stockport County	v	Truro City	5-0	1677
12	Dover Athletic	v	Harrogate Town	1-2	463
13	Chesterfield	v	Bedford Town	1-0	2213
14	Carshalton Athletic	v	Salisbury	4-1	514
15	FC Halifax Town	v	Solihull Moors	2-2	798
	Solihull Moors	v	FC Halifax Town (15/1)	1-0	355
16	Wrexham	v	Leyton Orient	0-1	1949

THIRD ROUND PROPER

SATURDAY 2 FEBRUARY 2019 - WINNERS RECEIVE £8,000

1	Ramsbottom United	v	AFC Fylde (5/2)	5-5	743
	AFC Fylde	v	Ramsbottom United (12/2)	4-1	
2	Spennymoor Town	v	AFC Telford United (5/2)	1-2	571
3	Carshalton Athletic	v	Barnet	3-3	
	Barnet	v	Carshalton Athletic (12/2)	2-1	
4	Chesterfield	v	Brackley Town	0-2	2054
5	Leyton Orient	v	Blyth Spartans	1-0	1842
6	Hemel Hempstead Town	v	Solihull Moors (5/2)	0-5	438
7	Salford City	v	Maidstone United (5/2)	1-1	706
	Maidstone United	v	Salford City (12/2)	3-0	880
8	Harrogate Town	v	Stockport County	2-4	1142

FOURTH ROUND PROPER

SATURDAY 23 FEBRUARY 2019 - WINNERS RECEIVE £10,000

1	Brackley Town	v	Leyton Orient	1-2	1563
2	AFC Fylde	v	Barnet	0-0aet	795
	(AFC Fylde won 4-1 on kicks from the penalty mark)				
3	Stockport County	v	Maidstone United	1-1	2585
	Maidstone United	v	Stockport County (26/2)	0-3	1140
4	Solihull Moors	v	AFC Telford United	1-2	1577

SEMI FINALS

1ST LEG SATURDAY 16 MARCH / 2ND LEG SATURDAY 23 MARCH 2019 - WINNERS RECEIVE £20,000

Leyton Orient	v	AFC Telford United	1-0	3622
AFC Telford United	v	Leyton Orient	1-2	3478
Leyton Orient through 3-1 on aggregate.				7100
AFC Fylde	v	Stockport County	0-0	2605
Stockport County	v	AFC Fylde	2-3	6064
AFC Fylde through 3-2 on aggregate.				8669

THE FINAL...

AFC FYLDE **1**
Rowe 60 (direct free-kick)
LEYTON ORIENT **0**

Wembley Stadium ~ Att: 42,962
**combined Trophy/Vase attendance*

THE SQUADS

AFC FYLDE	LEYTON ORIENT
Jay Lynch	Dean Brill
Arlen Birch (sub 90)	Jamie Turley (sub 46)
Neil Byrne (c) (sub 12)	Marvin Ekpiteta
Jordan Tunnicliffe	Josh Coulson
Zaine Francis-Angol	Daniel Happe (sub 68)
Danny Philliskirk	Joe Widdowson
Ryan Croasdale	Craig Clay
Nick Haughton (sub 74)	James Brophy
Alex Reid	John McAnuff (c) (sub 78)
Andy Bond	Josh Koroma
Danny Rowe	Macauley Bonne
Substitutes	**Substitutes**
Tom Brewitt (12)	Jordan Maguire-Drew (46)
Tim Odusina (74)	Matt Harrold (68)
Tom Crawford (90)	Charlie Lee (78)
Russell Griffiths	Sam Sargeant
James Hardy	Sam Ling

Referee Andrew Madley.
Assisted by Nick Hopton & Akil Howson.
Fourth official Matt Donohue.

It was ironic that eight days earlier AFC Fylde had, at this same stadium, missed out on promotion to the Football League by losing to Salford City in a play off. Yet now, in this Trophy Final, they found themselves facing the team which had avoided the play offs, their opponents, Leyton Orient, having been already crowned National League champions, thus gaining automatic promotion. It was estimated that Orient had sold in excess of 25,000 tickets so the bulk of the crowd was rooting for them although Fylde support was not insignificant.

Under their original name of Kirkham and Wesham, Fylde, from the north west, had been victorious in the FA Vase final of 2008 and had, at that time, bravely stated their aim of reaching the Football League. It seems not such an idle boast considering the progress made in the last decade, from Step Five to Step One, and victory here will have given further credibility to their intentions. They have become the first team to have both Trophy and Vase triumphs on their achievement board, after Forest Green and Tamworth had, in earlier years, been brought down at the Trophy hurdle.

It was an inauspicious start for The Coasters as, in the opening minutes, a head injury to their skipper Neil Byrne led to intense discussions between physios and management as to the wisdom of the evidently groggy Byrne remaining on the pitch. Eventually the medical evidence was heeded and Byrne was replaced by Tom Brewitt. Despite this unexpected early change Fylde had greater possession during the opening half hour, Orient keeper Dean Brill holding safely on to efforts by Fylde's top scorer Danny Rowe and parrying for a corner a left footed shot from Alex Reid. A tame free kick hit over from outside the box by John McAnuff was Orient's only response during this period. Nick Haughton was providing some moments of danger to the Orient goal and colleague Alex Reid, left with only Brill to beat, found the ball trapped under his foot and,

AFC Fylde's Rowe sends his free-kick over the wall...
Photo: Peter Barnes.

...where Brill (Leyton Orient) can only watch as it goes in.
Photo: Keith Clayton.

when well placed, was only able to roll the ball to O's relieved keeper. The half ended with Rowe breaking away dangerously down the right but his final ball left doubt as to whether his aim was a shot or a cross. Not a particularly inspiring half, most agreed.

On the restart the introduction of Jordan Maguire-Drew added much greater zip to Orient attacks, leading immediately to goalmouth pressure on Fylde with his forays forwards. He and Marvin Ekpiteta both hit the goal frame but in the 60th minute Fylde's top scorer Danny Rowe made the break through. Awarded a free kick just outside the area, he let rip, high into the top right corner, with Brill left absolutely stunned and motionless. It was Rowe's 33rd goal of the season. Little wonder there had been firm offers from higher ranked clubs for the services of this valued local boy, all resisted and laughed away by management.

Stung into retaliation Orient stormed to the other end where Joe Widdowson's fierce drive rebounded off the post to Maguire-Drew whose goalbound shot was prevented from hitting the net when it hit his colleague, Matt Harrold, whose embarrassment was lessened by his being adjudged offside. Harrold then headed a scoring attempt into the ground, the ball bouncing over in the next attack.

Zaine Francis-Angol and Rowe combined to make a chance for Ryan Croasdale who shot marginally wide of the post and, with the period of additional time ebbing away Alex Reid raced towards goal but failed to find a shot or a colleague and next minute sending another chance over the bar. The five additional minutes ended with Jay Lynch safely clutching Maguire-Drew's cross to begin the Coasters' celebrations.

Having previously suffered defeat at Wembley, both as player and manager, Fylde's Dave Challinor was delighted by the victory. "We've deserved to come out of the season with something and as it is this group have made history. It gives us some reward after a long hard season and hopefully this gives everyone a real boost." Opposition Head Coach, Justin Edinburgh, admitted his side had been "sluggish" in the first half but that their second session performance, with hitting the woodwork on so many occasions, had warranted the gaining of extra time. He also thought that his team's wait for the final, relaxing in the glow of their National League title and promotion, while Fylde had been actively engaged in the play offs, might have contributed to his team's early lethargy.

Fylde's hero, Danny Rowe, released by Manchester United as a 16 year old, though pleased to be on the winning side, had some consoling words for Orient in that he thought he and his team mates would willingly have swapped the Trophy victory for a win the previous week which would have enabled them to join Orient in achieving Football League status.

Arthur Evans

Photo: Peter Barnes.

PAST FINALS

1970 **MACCLESFIELD TOWN** **2 (Lyons, B Fidler)** — **TELFORD UNITED 0** — **Att: 28,000**
Northern Premier League — *Southern League*
Macclesfield: Cooke, Sievwright, Bennett, Beaumont, Collins, Roberts, Lyons, B Fidler,Young, Corfield, D Fidler.
Telford: Irvine, Harris, Croft, Flowers, Coton, Ray,Fudge, Hart, Bentley, Murray, Jagger. Ref: K Walker

1971 **TELFORD UTD** **3 (Owen, Bentley, Fudge)** — **HILLINGDON BORO. 2 (Reeve, Bishop)** — **Att: 29,500**
Southern League — *Southern League*
Telford: Irvine, Harris, Croft, Ray, Coton, Carr, Fudge, Owen, Bentley, Jagger ,Murray.
Hillingdon B.: Lowe, Batt, Langley, Higginson, Newcombe, Moore, Fairchild,Bishop, Reeve, Carter, Knox. Ref: D Smith

1972 **STAFFORD RANGERS** **3 (Williams 2, Cullerton)** — **BARNET 0** — **Att: 24,000**
Northern Premier League — *Southern League*
Stafford R.: Aleksic, Chadwick, Clayton, Sargeant, Aston, Machin, Cullerton, Chapman,Williams, Bayley, Jones.
Barnet: McClelland, Lye, Jenkins, Ward, Embrey, King, Powell, Ferry, Flatt, Easton, Plume . Ref: P Partridge

1973 **SCARBOROUGH** **2 (Leask, Thompson)** — **WIGAN ATHLETIC 1 (Rogers) aet** — **Att:23,000**
Northern Premier League — *Northern Premier League*
Scarborough: Garrow, Appleton, Shoulder, Dunn, Siddle, Fagan, Donoghue, Franks,Leask (Barmby), Thompson, Hewitt.
Wigan: Reeves, Morris, Sutherland, Taylor,Jackson, Gillibrand, Clements, Oats (McCunnell), Rogers, King, Worswick. Ref: H Hackney

1974 **MORECAMBE** **2 (Richmond, Sutton)** — **DARTFORD 1 (Cunningham)** — **Att: 19,000**
Northern Premier League — *Southern League*
Morecambe: Coates, Pearson, Bennett, Sutton, Street, Baldwin, Done, Webber,Roberts (Galley), Kershaw, Richmond.
Dartford: Morton, Read, Payne, Carr, Burns,Binks, Light, Glozier, Robinson (Hearne), Cunningham, Halleday. Ref: B Homewood

1975(1) **MATLOCK TOWN** **4 (Oxley, Dawson, T Fenoughty, N Fenoughy)** — **SCARBOROUGH 0** — **Att: 21,000**
Northern Premier League — *Northern Premier League*
Matlock: Fell, McKay, Smith, Stuart, Dawson, Swan, Oxley, N Fenoughy, Scott, T Fenoughty, M Fenoughty.
Scarborough: Williams, Hewitt, Rettitt, Dunn, Marshall, Todd, Houghton, Woodall, Davidson, Barnby, Aveyard. Ref: K Styles

1976 **SCARBOROUGH** **3 (Woodall, Abbey, Marshall(p))** — **STAFFORD R. 2 (Jones 2) aet** — **Att: 21,000**
Northern Premier League — *Northern Premier League*
Scarborough: Barnard, Jackson, Marshall, H Dunn, Ayre (Donoghue), HA Dunn, Dale,Barmby, Woodall, Abbey, Hilley.
Stafford: Arnold, Ritchie, Richards, Sargeant,Seddon, Morris, Chapman, Lowe, Jones, Hutchinson, Chadwick. Ref: R Challis

1977 **SCARBOROUGH** **2 (Dunn(p), Abbey)** — **DAGENHAM 1 (Harris)** — **Att: 21,500**
Northern Premier League — *Isthmian League*
Scarborough: Chapman, Smith, Marshall (Barmby), Dunn, Ayre, Deere, Aveyard,Donoghue, Woodall, Abbey, Dunn.
Dagenham: Hutley, Wellman, P Currie, Dunwell,Moore, W Currie, Harkins, Saul, Fox, Harris, Holder. Ref: G Courtney

1978 **ALTRINCHAM** **3 (King, Johnson, Rogers)** — **LEATHERHEAD 1 (Cook)** — **Att: 20,000**
Northern Premier League — *Isthmian League*
Altrincham: Eales, Allan, Crossley, Bailey, Owens, King, Morris, Heathcote,Johnson, Rogers, Davidson (Flaherty).
Leatherhead: Swannell, Cooper, Eaton, Davies,Reid, Malley, Cook, Salkeld, Baker, Boyle (Bailey). Ref: A Grey

1979 **STAFFORD RANGERS** **2 (A Wood 2)** — **KETTERING TOWN 0** — **Att: 32,000**
Northern Premier League — *Southern League*
Stafford: Arnold, F Wood, Willis, Sargeant, Seddon, Ritchie, Secker, Chapman, A Wood, Cullerton, Chadwick (Jones).
Kettering: Lane, Ashby, Lee, Eastell, Dixey,Suddards, Flannagan, Kellock, Phipps, Clayton, Evans (Hughes). Ref: D Richardson

1980(2) **DAGENHAM** **2 (Duck, Maycock)** — **MOSSLEY 1 (Smith)** — **Att: 26,000**
Isthmian League — *Northern Premier League*
Dagenham: Huttley, Wellman, Scales, Dunwell, Moore, Durrell, Maycock, Horan,Duck, Kidd, Jones (Holder).
Mossley: Fitton, Brown, Vaughan, Gorman, Salter, Polliot, Smith, Moore, Skeete, O'Connor, Keelan (Wilson). Ref: K Baker

1981(3) **BISHOP'S STORTFORD** **1 (Sullivan)** — **SUTTON UNITED 0** — **Att: 22,578**
Isthmian League — *Isthmian League*
Bishop's Stortford: Moore, Blackman, Brame, Smith (Worrell), Bradford, Abery, Sullivan,Knapman, Radford, Simmonds, Mitchell.
Sutton Utd.: Collyer, Rogers, Green, J Rains,T Rains, Stephens (Sunnucks), Waldon, Pritchard, Cornwell, Parsons, Dennis. Ref: J Worrall

1982 **ENFIELD** **1 (Taylor)** — **ALTRINCHAM 0** — **Att: 18,678**
Alliance Premier League — *Alliance Premier League*
Enfield: Jacobs, Barrett, Tone, Jennings, Waite, Ironton, Ashford, Taylor,Holmes, Oliver (Flint), King. Ref: B Stevens
Altrincham: Connaughton, Crossley, Davison, Bailey, Cuddy, King (Whitbread), Allan, Heathcote, Johnson, Rogers, Howard.

Notes:
1 The only occasion three members of the same family played in the same FA Trophy Final team.
2 The first of the Amateurs from the Isthmian League to win the FA Trophy.
3 Goalkeeper Terry Moore had also won an Amateur Cup Winners Medal with Bishop's Stortford in 1974.
All games played at Wembley (old & new) unless stated.

1983 **TELFORD UTD** 2 (Mather 2) — NORTHWICH VICTORIA 1 (Bennett) — Att: 22,071
Alliance Premier League — *Alliance Premier League*
Telford: Charlton, Lewis, Turner, Mayman (Joseph), Walker, Easton, Barnett,Williams, Mather, Hogan, Alcock.
Northwich: Ryan, Fretwell, Murphy, Jones, Forshaw, Ward, Anderson, Abel (Bennett), Reid, Chesters, Wilson. Ref: B Hill

1984 NORTHWICH VICTORIA 1 (Chester) — BANGOR CITY 1 (Whelan) — Att: 14,200
Replay **NORTHWICH VICTORIA** 2 (Chesters(p), Anderson) — BANGOR CITY 1 (Lunn) — Att: 5,805 (at Stoke)
Alliance Premier League — *Alliance Premier League*
Northwich: Ryan, Fretwell, Dean, Jones, Forshaw (Power 65), Bennett, Anderson,Abel, Reid, Chesters, Wilson. Ref: J Martin
Bangor: Letheren, Cavanagh, Gray, Whelan, Banks,Lunn, Urqhart, Morris, Carter, Howat, Sutcliffe (Westwood 105) . Same in replay.

1985 **WEALDSTONE** 2 (Graham, Holmes) — BOSTON UNITED 1 (Cook) — Att: 20,775
Alliance Premier League — *Alliance Premier League*
Wealdstone: Iles, Perkins, Bowgett, Byatt, Davies, Greenaway, Holmes, Wainwright,Donnellan, Graham (N Cordice 89), A Cordice.
Boston: Blackwell, Casey, Ladd,Creane, O'Brien, Thommson, Laverick (Mallender 78), Simpsom, Gilbert, Lee, Cook. Ref: J Bray

1986 **ALTRINCHAM** 1 (Farrelly) — RUNCORN 0 — Att: 15,700
Gola League — *Gola League*
Altrincham: Wealands, Gardner, Densmore, Johnson, Farrelly, Conning, Cuddy,Davison, Reid, Ellis, Anderson. Sub: Newton.
Runcorn: McBride, Lee, Roberts,Jones, Fraser, Smith, S Crompton (A Crompton), Imrie, Carter, Mather, Carrodus. Ref: A Ward

1987 KIDDERMINSTER HARRIERS 0 — BURTON ALBION 0 — Att: 23,617
Replay **KIDDERMINSTER HARRIERS** 2 (Davies 2) — BURTON ALBION 1 (Groves) — Att: 15,685 (at West Brom)
Conference — *Southern League*
Kidderminster: Arnold, Barton, Boxall, Brazier (sub Hazlewood in rep), Collins (sub Pearson 90 at Wembley), Woodall, McKenzie, O'Dowd, Tuohy, Casey, Davies. sub:Jones.
Burton: New, Essex, Kamara, Vaughan, Simms, Groves, Bancroft, Land, Dorsett, Redfern, (sub Wood in replay), Gauden. Sub: Patterson. Ref: D Shaw

1988 ENFIELD 0 — TELFORD UNITED 0 — Att: 20,161
Replay **ENFIELD** 3 (Furlong 2, Howell) — TELFORD UNITED 2 (Biggins, Norris(p)) — Att: 6,912 (at W Brom)
Conference — *Conference*
Enfield: Pape, Cottington, Howell, Keen (sub Edmonds in rep), Sparrow (sub Hayzleden at Wembley), Lewis (sub Edmonds at Wembley), Harding, Cooper, King,Furlong, Francis.
Telford: Charlton, McGinty, Storton, Nelson, Wiggins, Mayman (sub Cunningham in rep (sub Hancock)), Sankey, Joseph, Stringer (sub Griffiths at Wembley, Griffiths in replay), Biggins, Norris. Ref: L Dilkes

1989 **TELFORD UNITED** 1 (Crawley) — MACCLESFIELD TOWN 0 — Att: 18,102
Conference — *Conference*
Telford: Charlton, Lee, Brindley, Hancock, Wiggins, Mayman, Grainger, Joseph, Nelson, Lloyd, Stringer. Subs: Crawley, Griffiths.
Macclesfield: Zelem, Roberts, Tobin, Edwards, Hardman, Askey, Lake, Hanton, Imrie, Burr, Timmons. Subs: Devonshire, Kendall.

1990 **BARROW** 3 (Gordon 2, Cowperthwaite) — LEEK TOWN 0 — Att: 19,011
Conference — *Northern Premier League*
Barrow: McDonnell, Higgins, Chilton, Skivington, Gordon, Proctor, Doherty (Burgess), Farrell (Gilmore), Cowperthwaite, Lowe, Ferris.
Leek: Simpson, Elsby (Smith), Pearce, McMullen, Clowes, Coleman (Russell),Mellor, Somerville, Sutton, Millington, Norris Ref: T Simpson

1991 **WYCOMBE W.** 2 (Scott, West) — KIDDERMINSTER HARRIERS 1 (Hadley) — Att: 34,842
Conference — *Conference*
Wycombe: Granville, Crossley, Cash, Kerr, Creaser, Carroll, Ryan, Stapleton,West, Scott, Guppy (Hutchinson). Ref: J Watson
Kidderminster: Jones, Kurila, McGrath, Weir, Barnett, Forsyth, Joseph (Wilcox), Howell (Whitehouse), Hadley, Lilwall, Humphries

1992 **COLCHESTER UTD*** 3 (Masters, Smith, McGavin) — WITTON ALBION 1 (Lutkevitch) — Att: 27,806
Conference — *Conference*
Colchester: Barrett, Donald, Roberts, Knsella, English, Martin, Cook, Masters,McDonough (Bennett 65), McGavin, Smith. Ref: K P Barratt
Witton: Mason, Halliday, Coathup, McNeilis, Jim Connor, Anderson, Thomas, Rose, Alford, Grimshaw (Joe Connor), Lutkevitch (McCluskie)

1993 **WYCOMBE W*.** 4 (Cousins, Kerr, Thompson, Carroll) — RUNCORN 1 (Shaughnessy) — Att: 32,968
Conference — *Conference*
Wycombe: Hyde, Cousins, Cooper, Kerr, Crossley, Thompson (Hayrettin 65),Carroll, Ryan, Hutchinson, Scott, Guppy. Sub: Casey.
Runcorn: Williams, Bates, Robertson, Hill, Harold (Connor 62), Anderson, Brady (Parker 72), Brown, Shaughnessy, McKenna, Brabin

1994 **WOKING** 2 (D Brown, Hay) — RUNCORN 1 (Shaw (pen)) — Att: 15,818
Conference — *Conference*
Woking: Batty, Tucker, L Wye, Berry, Brown, Clement, Brown (Rattray 32), Fielder, Steele, Hay (Puckett 46), Walker. Ref: Paul Durkin
Runcorn: Williams, Bates, Robertson, Shaw, Lee, Anderson, Thomas, Connor, McInerney (Hill 71), McKenna, Brabin. Sub: Parker

1995 **WOKING** 2 (Steele, Fielder) — KIDDERMINSTER HARRIERS 1 aet (Davies) — Att: 17,815
Conference — *Conference*
Woking: Batty, Tucker, L Wye, Fielder, Brown, Crumplin (Rattray 42), S Wye, Ellis, Steele, Hay (Newberry 112), Walker. (Sub: Read(gk)
Kidderminster: Rose, Hodson, Bancroft, Webb, Brindley (Cartwright 94), Forsyth, Deakin, Yates, Humphreys (Hughes 105), Davies, Purdie. Sub: Dearlove (gk) Ref: D J Gallagher

1996 MACCLESFIELD TOWN 3 (Payne, OG, Hemmings) *Conference* — **NORTHWICH VICTORIA 1 (Williams)** *Conference* — **Att: 8,672**

Macclesfield: Price, Edey, Gardiner, Payne, Howarth(C), Sorvel, Lyons, Wood (Hulme 83), Coates, Power, Hemmings (Cavell 88).
Northwich: Greygoose, Ward, Duffy, Burgess (Simpson 87), Abel (Steele), Walters, Williams, Butler (C), Cooke, Humphries, Vicary.
Ref: M Reed

1997 WOKING 1 (Hay 112) *Conference* — **DAGENHAM & REDBRIDGE 0** *Isthmian League* — **Att: 24,376**

Woking: Batty, Brown, Howard, Foster, Taylor, S Wye, Thompson (sub Jones 115), Ellis, Steele (L Wye 108), Walker, Jackson (Hay 77).
Dagenham: Gothard, Culverhouse, Connor, Creaser, Jacques (sub Double 75), Davidson, Pratt (Naylor 81), Parratt, Broom, Rogers, Stimson (John 65).
Ref: J Winter

1998 CHELTENHAM TOWN 1 (Eaton 74) *Conference* — **SOUTHPORT 0** *Conference* — **Att: 26,387**

Cheltenham: Book, Duff, Freeman, Banks, Victory, Knight (Smith 78), Howells, Bloomer, Walker (sub Milton 78), Eaton, Watkins. Sub: Wright.
Southport: Stewart, Horner, Futcher, Ryan, Farley, Kielty, Butler, Gamble, Formby (sub Whittaker 80), Thompson (sub Bollard 88), Ross. Sub: Mitten.
Ref: G S Willard

1999 KINGSTONIAN 1 (Mustafa 49) *Conference* — **FOREST GREEN ROVERS 0** *Conference* — **Att: 20,037**

Kingstonian: Farrelly, Mustafa, Luckett, Crossley, Stewart, Harris, Patterson, Pitcher, Rattray, Leworthy (Francis 87), Akuamoah. Subs (not used): John, Corbett, Brown, Tranter
Forest Green Rovers: Shuttlewood, Hedges, Forbes, Bailey (Smart 76), Kilgour, Wigg (Cook 58), Honor (Winter 58), Drysdale, McGregor, Mehew, Sykes. Subs (not used): Perrin, Coupe
Ref: A B Wilkie

2000 KINGSTONIAN 3 (Akuamoah 40, 69, Simba 75) *Conference* — **KETTERING TOWN 2 (Vowden 55, Norman 64p)** *Conference* — **Att: 20,034**

Kingstonian: Farelly, Mustafa, Luckett, Crossley, Stewart (Saunders 77), Harris, Kadi (Leworthy 83), Pitcher, Green (Basford 86), Smiba, Akuamoah. Subs (not used): Hurst, Allan
Kettering Town: Sollit, McNamara, Adams, Perkins, Vowden, Norman (Duik 76), Fisher, Brown, Shutt, Watkins (Hudson 46), Setchell (Hopkins 81). Subs (not used): Ridgway, Wilson
Ref: S W Dunn

2001 CANVEY ISLAND 1 (Chenery) *Isthmian League* — **FOREST GREEN ROVERS 0** *Conference* — **Att: 10,007 at Villa Park**

Forest Green Rovers: Perrin, Cousins, Lockwood, Foster, Clark, Burns, Daley, Drysdale (Bennett 46), Foster (Hunt 75), Meecham, Slater. Subs (not used): Hedges, Prince, Ghent
Canvey Island: Harrison, Duffy, Chenery, Bodley, Ward, Tilson, Stimson (Tanner 83), Gregory, Vaughan (Jones 76), Parmenter. Subs (not used): Bennett, Miller, Thompson.
Ref: A G Wiley

2002 YEOVIL TOWN 2 (Alford, Stansfield) *Conference* — **STEVENAGE BOROUGH 0** *Conference* — **Att: 18,809 at Villa Park**

Yeovil Town: Weale, Lockwood, Tonkin, Skiverton, Pluck (White 51), Way, Stansfield, Johnson, Alford (Giles 86), Crittenden (Lindegaard 83), McIndoe. Subs (not used): O'Brien, Sheffield
Stevenage Borough: Wilkerson, Hamsher, Goodliffe, Trott, Fraser, Fisher, Wormull (Stirling 71), Evers (Williams 56), Jackson, Sigere (Campbell 74), Clarke. Subs (not used): Campbell, Greygoose
Ref: N S Barry

2003 BURSCOUGH 2 (Martindale 25, 55) *Northern Premier* — **TAMWORTH 1 (Cooper 78)** *Southern Premier* — **Att: 14,265 at Villa Park**

Burscough: Taylor, Teale, Taylor, Macauley (White 77), Lawless, Bowen, Wright, Norman, Martindale (McHale 80), Byrne (Bluck 84), Burns. Subs (not used): McGuire (g/k) Molyneux.
Tamworth: Acton, Warner, Follett, Robinson, Walsh, Cooper, Colley, Evans (Turner 64), Rickards (Hatton 88), McGorry, Sale (Hallam 54). Subs (not used): Grocutt, Barnes (g/k).
Ref: U D Rennie

2004 HEDNESFORD TOWN 3 (Maguire 28, Hines 53, Brindley 87) *Southern Premier* — **CANVEY ISLAND 2 (Boylan 46, Brindley 48 og)** *Isthmian Premier Champions* — **Att: 6,635 at Villa Park**

Hednesford Town: Young, Simkin, Hines, King, Brindley, Ryder (Barrow 59), Palmer, Anthrobus, Danks (Piearce 78), Maguire, Charie (Evans 55). Subs (not used): Evans (g/k) McGhee.
Canvey Island: Potter, Kennedy, Duffy, Chenery, Cowan, Gooden (Dobinson 89), Minton, Gregory (McDougald 80), Boylan, Midgley (Berquez 73), Ward. Subs (not used): Theobald, Harrison (g/k).
Ref: M L Dean

2005 GRAYS ATHLETIC 1 (Martin 65) Pens: 6 *Conference South* — **HUCKNALL TOWN 1 (Ricketts 75) Pens: 5** *Conference North* — **Att: 8,116 at Villa Park**

Grays Athletic: Bayes, Brennan, Nutter, Stuart, Matthews, Thurgood, Oli (Powell 80), Hopper (Carthy 120), Battersby (sub West 61), Martin, Cole. Subs (not used): Emberson, Bruce..
Hucknall Town: Smith, Asher, Barrick (Plummer 30), Hunter, Timons, Cooke, Smith (Ward 120), Palmer (Heathcote 94), Ricketts, Bacon, Todd. Subs (not used): Winder, Lindley.
Ref: P Dowd

2006 GRAYS ATHLETIC 2 (Oli, Poole) *Conference* — **WOKING 0** *Conference* — **Att: 13,997 at Upton Park**

Grays Athletic: Bayes, Sambrook, Nutter, Stuart, Hanson, Kightly (Williamson 90), Thurgood, Martin, Poole, Oli, McLean. Subs (not used): Eyre (g/k), Hooper, Olayinka, Mawer.
Woking: Jalal, Jackson, MacDonald, Nethercott (Watson 60), Hutchinson, Murray, Smith (Cockerill 60), Evans (Blackman 85), Ferguson, McAllister, Justin Richards. Subs (not used): Davis (g/k), El-Salahi.
Ref: Howard Webb (Sheffield)

2007 STEVENAGE BOROUGH 3 (Cole, Dobson, Morrison) **KIDDERMINSTER HARRIERS 2 (Constable 2)** **Att: 53,262**
Conference *Conference* **(New Trophy record)**
Stevenage Borough: Julian, Fuller, Nutter, Oliver, Gaia, Miller, Cole, Morrison, Guppy (Dobson 63), Henry, Beard.
Subs not used: Potter, Slabber, Nurse, McMahon.
Kidderminster Harriers: Bevan, Kenna, Hurren, Creighton, Whitehead, Blackwood, Russell, Penn, Smikle (Reynolds 90), Christie (White 75) , Constable.
Subs not used: Taylor, Sedgemore, McGrath. Ref: Chris Foy (Merseyside)

2008 EBBSFLEET UNITED 1 (McPhee) **TORQUAY UNITED 0** **Att: 40,186**
Blue Square Premier *Blue Square Premier*
Ebbsfleet United: Cronin, Hawkins, McCarthy, Smith, Opinel, McPhee, Barrett, Bostwick, Long (MacDonald 84), Moore, Akinde.
Subs not used: Eribenne, Purcell, Ricketts, Mott.
Torquay United: Rice, Mansell, Todd, Woods, Nicholson, D'Sane (Benyon 66), Hargreaves, Adams, Zebroski, Sills (Hill 88), Phillips (Stevens 46). Subs not used: Hockley and Robertson. Ref: Martin Atkinson (West Riding)

2009 STEVENAGE BOROUGH 2 (Morison, Boylan) **YORK CITY 0** **Att: 27,102**
Blue Square Premier *Blue Square Premier*
Stevenage Borough: Day, Henry, Bostwick, Roberts, Wilson, Mills, Murphy, Drury, Vincenti (Anaclet 86), Boylan, Morison.
Subs not used: Bayes, Albrighton, Maamria and Willock.
York City:Ingham, Purkiss, McGurk, Parslow, Pejic, Mackin, Greaves(McWilliams 74), Rusk (Russell 80), Brodie, McBreen (Sodje 60), Boyes. Subs not used – Mimms and Robinson. Referee: Michael Jones.

2010 BARROW 2 (McEvilly 79, Walker 117) **STEVENAGE BOROUGH 1 (Drury 10)** **Att: 21,223**
Blue Square Premier *Blue Square Premier*
Barrow: Stuart Tomlinson, Simon Spender, Paul Jones, Phil Bolland, Paul Edwards, Simon Wiles (sub Carlos Logan 63rd min), Robin Hulbert, Andy Bond, Paul Rutherford (sub Mark Boyd 109th min), Jason Walker, Gregg Blundell (sub Lee McEvilly 73rd min).
Subs not used – Tim Deasy and Mike Pearson.
Stevenage Borough: Chris Day (sub Ashley Bayes 90th min), Ronnie Henry, Jon Ashton, Mark Roberts, Scott Laird, Joel Byrom (sub Lawrie Wilson 58th min), David Bridges, Michael Bostwick, Andy Drury, Chris Beardsley (sub Charlie Griffin 64th min), Yemi Odubade. Subs not used – Stacey Long and Peter Vincenti.
Man of the match - Paul Rutherford. Referee Lee Probert.

2011 DARLINGTON 1 (Senior 120) **MANSFIELD TOWN 0** **Att: 24,668**
Blue Square Premier *Blue Square Premier*
Darlington: Sam Russell, Paul Arnison, Ian Miller, Liam Hatch, Aaron Brown, Jamie Chandler, Chris Moore, Marc Bridge-Wilkinson (sub Paul Terry 100th min), Gary Smith (sub Arman Verma 38th min), John Campbell (sub Chris Senior 75th min), Tommy Wright.
Subs not used – Danzelle St Louis-Hamilton (gk) and Phil Gray.
Mansfield Town: Alan Marriott, Gary Silk, Stephen Foster, Tom Naylor, Dan Spence, Louis Briscoe, Tyrone Thompson, Kyle Nix, Adam Smith (sub Ashley Cain 95th min), Adam Murray (sub Danny Mitchley 108th min), Paul Connor
Subs not used – Paul Stonehouse and Neil Collett (gk)
Man of the match - Jamie Chandler. Referee Stuart Atwell

2012 YORK CITY 2 (Blair 61, Oyebanjo 68) **NEWPORT COUNTY 0** **Att: 19,844**
Blue Square Premier *Blue Square Premier*
York City: Michael Ingham, Jon Challinor, Chris Smith, Daniel Parslow, Ben Gibson, Matty Blair, Lanre Oyebanjo, Patrick McLaughlan (sub Jamal Fyfield 82nd min), James Meredith, Ashley Chambers (Adriano Moke (89th min), Jason Walker (Jamie Reed 90th min).
Subs not used – Paul Musselwhite (g/k), Michael Potts.
Newport County: Glyn Thompson, David Pipe, Ismail Yakubu, Gary Warren, Andrew Hughes, Sam Foley, Lee Evans, Nat Jarvis (sub Jake Harris 68th min), Max Porter (sub Darryl Knights 79th min), Romone Rose (sub Elliott Buchanan 68th min), Lee Minshull.
Subs not used – Matthew Swan (g/k), Paul Rodgers.
Man of the match - Lanre Oyebanjo. Referee Anthony Taylor

2013 WREXHAM 1 (Thornton 82 (pen)) **GRIMSBY TOWN 1 (Cook 71)** **Att: 35,226**
Wrexham won 4-1 on kicks from the penalty mark after extra time.
Blue Square Premier *Blue Square Premier*
Wrexham: Chris Maxwell, Stephen Wright, Martin Riley, Jay Harris, Danny Wright, Brett Ormerod (Robert Ogleby 77 min), Andy Morrell (Adrian Cieslewicz 61 min), Dean Keates, Johnny Hunt, Chris Westwood, Kevin Thornton (Joe Clarke 89 min).
Subs not used - Andy Coughlin (gk) Glen Little.
Grimsby Town: Sam Hatton, Aswad Thomas, Shaun Pearson, Ian Miller, Joe Colbeck, Craig Disley, Frankie Artus, Andy Cook, James McKeown, Ross Hannah (Andi Thanoj 55 min), Marcus Marshall (Richard Brodie 87 min).
Subs not used - Jamie Devitt, Bradley Wood, Lenell John-Lewis. Referee Jonathan Moss

2014 CAMBRIDGE UNITED 4 (Bird 38, Donaldson 50,59, Berry 78 (pen)) **GOSPORT BOROUGH 0** **Att: 18,120**
Conference Premier *Conference South*
Cambridge United: Will Norris, Greg Taylor, Jock Coulson (Tom Bonner 87 min), Ian Miller, Ryan Donaldson, Tom Champion, Richard Tait, Liam Hughes (Nathan Arnold 73 min), Luke Berry, Ryan Bird, Josh Gillies (Andy Pugh 61 min).
Subs not used - Kevin Roberts, Mitch Austin.
Gosport Borough: Nathan Ashmore, Lee Molyneaux, Andy Forbes, Jamie Brown (Rory Williams 57 min), Brett Poate, Sam Pearce, Josh Carmichael, Danny Smith, Tim Sills (Dan Woodward 57 min), Justin Bennett, Michael Gosney (Dan Wooden 72 min).
Subs not used - Ryan Scott, Adam Wilde.
Referee Craig Pawson

2015 NORTH FERRIBY UNITED 3 (King 76 (pen), Kendall 86, 111) **WREXHAM** 3 (Moult 11, 118, Harris 59) **Att: 14,548**
Conference North *Conference National*
North Ferriby United: Adam Nicklin, Sam Topliss, Danny Hone, Matt Wilson, Josh Wilde (Nathan Peat 90), Liam King, Adam Bolder (Nathan Jarman 62), Russell Fry (Ryan Kendall 80), Danny Clarke, Tom Denton, Jason St Juste.
Subs not used - Tom Nicholson and Mark Gray.
Wrexham: Andy Coughlin, Steve Tomassen, Manny Smith, Blaine Hudson, Neil Ashton, Jay Harris, Dean Keates (Robbie Evans 73), Joe Clarke (Andy Bishop 102), Kieron Morris (Wes York 87), Louis Moult, Connor Jennings.
Subs not used - Mark Carrington and Luke Waterfall. Referee Michael Oliver

2016 FC HALIFAX TOWN 1 (McManus 48) **GRIMSBY TOWN** 0 **Att: 46,781** (Inaugural Non-League finals day)
Conference National *Conference National*
FC Halifax Town: Sam Johnson, Matty Brown, Hamza Bencherif, Kevin Roberts, James Bolton, Nicky Wroe, Jake Hibbs, Scott McManus (Kingsley James 73), Josh McDonald (Sam Walker 63), Jordan Burrow, Richard Peniket (Connor Hughes 86).
Subs not used - Jordan Porter and Shaquille McDonald.
Grimsby Town: James McKeown, Richard Tait (Danny East 81), Shaun Pearson, Aristote Nsiala, Gregor Robertson, Andy Monkhouse (Jon-Paul Pitman 68), Craig Disley, Craig Clay (Nathan Arnold 63), Jon Nolan, Omar Bogle, Padraig Amond.
Subs not used - Josh Gowling and Josh Venney. Referee Lee Mason

2017 YORK CITY 3 (Parkin 8, Oliver 22, Connolly 86) **MACCLESFIELD TOWN** 2 (Browne 13, Norburn 45+1)
Conference National *Conference National* **Att: 38,224** (Combined Trophy/Vase att.)
York City: Kyle Letheren, Asa Hall (Aidan Connolly 69), Yan Klukowski (Adriano Moke 46), Hamza Bencherif, Danny Holmes (Shaun Rooney 76) Amari Morgan-Smith, Simon Heslop, Sean Newton, Daniel Parslow, Jon Parkin, Vadaine Oliver.
Subs not used - Luke Simpson, Scott Fenwick.
Macclesfield Town: Scott Flinders, Andy Halls, David Fitzpatrick, Neill Byrne (John McCombe 68), George Pilkington, Rhys Browne, Chris Holroyd, Kingsley James, Ollie Norburn (Anthony Dudley 89), Mitch Hancox (Luke Summerfield 86), Danny Whitaker.
Subs not used - Craig Ross, Danny Whitehead. Referee Paul Tierney

2018 BRACKLEY TOWN 1, 5p (R Johnson 90+6 (og)) **BROMLEY** 1, 4p (Bugiel 19)
Conference National North *Conference National* **Att: 31,430** (Combined Trophy/Vase att.)
Brackley Town: Danny Lewis, Matt Lowe, Connor Franklin (Ellis Myles 77), Shane Byrne, Alex Gudger, Gareth Dean (c), Glenn Walker, James Armson, Lee Ndlovu (Andy Brown 53), Aaron Williams, Adam Walker..
Subs not used - Luke Graham, Theo Streete, Steve Diggin.
Bromley: David Gregory, Jack Holland (c), Raymond Raymond, Louis Dennis (Brandon Hanlan 68), Adam Mekki (Ben Chorley 72), Jordan Higgs, Tyrone Sterling, George Porter (Josh Rees 61), Roger Johnson, Frankie Sutherland, Omar Bugiel.
Subs not used - Alan Dunne, Dan Johnson. Referee Chris Kavanagh

All Finals at Wembley unless otherwise stated.

FAT - F - Croasdale (Fylde) fouls Brophy (Leyton Orient). Photo: Keith Clayton.

THE FA VASE 2018-19

FIRST QUALIFYING ROUND

SATURDAY 1 SEPTEMBER 2018 - WINNING CLUB TO RECEIVE £550 LOSING CLUB TO RECEIVE £175

1	Alnwick Town	v	Charnock Richard	1-2	113
2	Stokesley SC	v	Guisborough Town	0-9	
3	Holker Old Boys	v	Prestwich Heys	0-2	
4	Goole	v	Barnoldswick Town	1-2	100
5	Whickham	v	Jarrow (31/8)	1-0	
6	West Allotment Celtic	v	Yorkshire Amateur	3-0	
7	Darlington Railway Athletic	v	Bedlington Terriers	0-5	35
8	Chester-Le-Street Town	v	Sunderland Ryhope CW	1-5	
9	Esh Winning	v	Whitley Bay	0-6	130
10	Bishop Auckland	v	Newton Aycliffe	2-2aet	394
	Newton Aycliffe	v	Bishop Auckland (4/9)	0-2	220
11	North Shields	v	Consett	1-2	
12	Daisy Hill	v	Whitehaven	5-2	36
13	Harrogate Railway Athletic	v	Silsden	3-4	
14	Thackley	v	Thornaby	3-2	110
15	Dunston UTS	v	Heaton Stannington	2-0	220
16	Team Northumbria	v	Garforth Town		
	(walkover for Garforth Town – Team Northumbria removed)				
17	Billingham Town	v	Campion	2-0	188
18	Blyth	v	Crook Town		
	(walkover for Crook Town – Blyth removed)				
19	Billingham Synthonia	v	Knaresborough Town	3-1	85
20	Durham City	v	Seaham Red Star	0-5	
21	Eccleshill United	v	Hebburn Town	0-1	111
22	Northallerton Town	v	Willington	2-2aet	121
	Willington	v	Northallerton Town (5/9)	2-3	
23	Lower Breck	v	West Didsbury & Chorlton	3-1	101
24	Longridge Town	v	Vauxhall Motors	1-3	
25	Worksop Town	v	Grimsby Borough	2-1	374
26	Burscough	v	Alsager Town	5-1	68
27	Wythenshawe Town	v	Rylands		
	(Wythenshawe Town & Rylands not accepted into the Competition)				
28	Winsford United	v	Liversedge	2-1aet	92
29	Maltby Main	v	Ashton Athletic	5-1	
30	Ashton Town	v	St Helens Town	3-1	57
31	Barton Town	v	AFC Liverpool	3-1	139
32	AFC Blackpool	v	Nostell MW	3-1	
33	Sandbach United	v	Athersley Recreation	5-1	104
34	Shelley	v	Penistone Church	2-1	225
35	AFC Emley	v	Litherland Remyca (31/8)	3-4aet	199
36	Swallownest	v	Abbey Hey	1-0	128
37	Cammell Laird 1907	v	Harworth Colliery	2-1	
38	Armthorpe Welfare	v	Worsbrough Bridge Athletic	1-2	78
39	Parkgate	v	Chadderton	5-2aet	
40	Congleton Town	v	Bootle	1-2	150
41	Selby Town	v	Stavely MW	0-5	135
42	Kirby Muxloe	v	Brocton	1-2	42
43	Nuneaton Griff	v	Coton Green	3-1	
44	Littleton	v	Lichfield City	1-0	
45	Coventry Sphinx	v	Sporting Khalsa	2-2aet	92
	Sporting Khalsa	v	Coventry Sphinx (4/9)	3-0	
46	FC Stratford	v	Bewdley Town (2/9)	0-1	
47	Abbey Hulton United	v	Whitchurch Alport	2-3	159
48	AFC Bridgnorth	v	Wolverhampton Casuals	1-3	
49	Ellesmere Rangers	v	Birstall United Social	0-4	63
50	Rugby Borough	v	Malvern Town	3-2	
51	Stafford Town	v	Wednesfield	2-3	40
52	Droitwich Spa	v	Coventry United	2-4	
53	Boldmere St Michaels	v	GNP Sports	4-1	113
54	Heather St Johns	v	Rocester	4-1	40
55	Rugby Town	v	Team Dudley		
	(walkover for Rugby Town – Team Dudley not accepted into Competition)				
56	Racing Club Warwick	v	Pegasus Juniors	10-0	
57	Melton Town	v	Ingles	2-2aet	
	Ingles	v	Melton Town (12/9)	1-0	
58	Lutterworth Athletic	v	Cradley Town	1-3	59
59	Wellington FC	v	St Martins	3-2	50
60	Dudley Sports	v	Shawbury United	3-1	
61	Coventry Copsewood	v	Eccleshall	6-3aet	25
62	NKF Burbage	v	Lutterworth Town (2/9)	2-1	
63	Gornal Athletic	v	Stone Old Alleynians	1-2	
64	Wellington Amateurs	v	Ellistown		
	(walkover for Wellington Amateurs – Ellistown not accepted into Competition)				
65	Heath Hayes	v	Shifnal Town	3-1	
66	Dudley Town	v	Bardon Hill		
	(walkover for Dudley Town – Bardon Hill withdrawn)				
67	Pershore Town	v	Hanley Town	0-4	
68	Ashby Ivanhoe	v	Friar Lane & Epworth	2-0	74
69	Bolehall Swifts	v	Tipton Town	3-0	
70	Haughmond	v	Saffron Dynamo	2-4	56
71	Gedling MW	v	Ilkeston Town	0-4	
72	Rainworth MW	v	Teversal	0-3	
73	Newark Flowserve	v	Harrowby United		
	(walkover for Harrowby United – Newark Flowserve not accepted into the Competition)				
74	Leicester Road	v	Bottesford Town	1-1aet	
	Bottesford Town	v	Leicester Road (5/9)	2-1	55
75	Loughborough University	v	West Bridgford	6-0	
76	Ollerton Town	v	New Mills	1-0	72
77	Skegness Town	v	Clay Cross Town	4-1	158
78	Anstey Nomads	v	Eastwood Community	2-5	236
79	Borrowash Victoria	v	Hucknall Town	0-7	
80	Clifton All Whites	v	Belper United	4-4aet	54
	Belper United	v	Clifton All Whites (4/9)	3-0	
81	Blidworth Welfare	v	Blaby & Whetstone Athletic	5-3	36
82	Clipstone	v	Aylestone Park	1-2	51
83	South Normanton Athletic	v	St Andrews	3-0	
84	Oadby Town	v	Sherwood Colliery	1-7	
85	Dunkirk	v	Stapenhill	3-1aet	46
86	Quorn	v	Retford United	5-0	142
87	Holwell Sports	v	Pinxton	1-4	
88	Lincoln Moorlands Railway	v	Kimberley Miners Welfare	1-3	52
89	Radford	v	Selston	1-3	
90	Framlingham Town	v	Wisbech St Mary	3-2	
91	Deeping Rangers	v	Blackstones	7-1	109
92	Woodbridge Town	v	Eynesbury Rovers	3-1	154
93	Gorleston	v	Boston Town	5-1	101
94	Peterborough Northern Star	v	Fakenham Town	2-0	
95	Walsham Le Willows	v	Diss Town (31/8)	3-0	179
96	Newmarket Town	v	Downham Town	2-1	
97	Bourne Town	v	March Town United	3-4	
98	Huntingdon Town	v	Wroxham	0-4	
99	Ely City	v	Norwich United	4-3aet	
100	Stotfold	v	Leyton Athletic	4-0	34
101	St Margaretsbury	v	Hadleigh United (2/9)	0-3	84
102	Newbury Forest	v	Wivenhoe Town	2-1	30
103	Wormley Rovers	v	Biggleswade United (4/9)	1-2aet	59
	(at Biggleswade United FC)		(31/8 tie abandoned due to serious injury)		
104	Enfield Borough	v	Halstead Town	6-0	
105	Clapton	v	Woodford Town	1-1aet	
	Woodford Town	v	Clapton (4/9)	1-3	71

FAV - 1Q - South Normanton Ath v St Andrews. Photo: Bill Wheatcroft.

FAV - 1Q - Brimscombe & Thrupp 5 v 1 Ash United. Photo: Peter Barnes.

FAV - 1Q - Lewisham Borough v Broadbridge Heath - Lewisham Borough's Damarli Morrison gets in front of two Broadbridge defenders.
Photo: Alan Coomes.

FIRST QUALIFYING ROUND

No.	Home		Away	Score	Att
106	May & Baker Eastbrook Community	v	Burnham Ramblers	8-1	
107	Stanway Rovers	v	White Ensign (4/9)	4-2	
	(1/9 tie abandoned due to serious injury)				
108	Baldock Town	v	Long Melford	2-1	
109	Haverhill Rovers	v	Ilford	2-1	124
110	Holland	v	Cornard United	4-2	
111	Walthamstow	v	Takeley	1-3aet	
112	Langford	v	Tower Hamlets	3-2	42
113	Southend Manor	v	Ipswich Wanderers	3-0	40
114	Stansted	v	Brantham Athletic	1-3	38
115	London Colney	v	Cockfosters	2-1	
116	Whitton United	v	Hatfield Town	5-2	55
117	British Airways	v	Harefield United	1-3	
118	Rothwell Corinthians	v	CB Hounslow United	0-5	47
119	Spelthorne Sports	v	Northampton On Chenecks	5-3aet	
120	FC Deportivo Galicia	v	London Tigers	3-2	
121	Sandhurst Town	v	Kensington Borough	1-2	
122	Wellingborough Whitworth	v	Bugbrooke St Michaels	0-2	
123	Hanworth Villa	v	Bedford	5-1	38
124	Ampthill Town	v	Edgware Town	1-3	47
125	Broadfields United	v	Daventry Town	5-0	
126	AFC Hayes	v	Wembley	1-2	34
127	Rushden & Higham United	v	Winslow United	4-5aet	
128	Raunds Town	v	Cranfield United	2-1	
129	Bicester Town	v	AFC Spelthorne Sports Club (2/9)	3-2	
130	Southall	v	Reading City	3-2	
131	Leverstock Green	v	Unite MK	10-0	
132	Cricklewood Wanderers	v	Risborough Rangers	4-3	
133	Burnham	v	Hillingdon		
	(walkover for Burnham – Hillingdon not accepted into Competition)				
134	St Panteleimon	v	Holmer Green	3-1	
135	Shrivenham	v	Tytherington Rocks	9-0	34
136	Bashley	v	AFC Portchester	6-0	152
137	Binfield	v	Frimley Green	5-0	83
138	Tadley Calleva	v	Ascot United	3-1	95
139	Milton United	v	Clanfield 85	0-3	50
140	Chertsey Town	v	Woodley United	4-2	
141	Brimscombe & Thrupp	v	Ash United	5-1	60
142	Wallingford Town	v	Abingdon United	1-4	
143	Penn & Tylers Green	v	AFC Stoneham	1-3	37
144	Lydney Town	v	Abbey Rangers	1-3	82
145	Cove	v	Fleet Spurs	0-2	
146	Royal Wootton Bassett Town	v	Oxford City Nomads		
	(walkover for Royal Wootton Bassett Town – Oxford City Nomads withdrawn)				
147	Ardley United	v	Holyport	1-4	45
148	Fairford Town	v	Baffins Milton Rovers	2-3aet	25
149	Colliers Wood United	v	Stansfeld	3-1	
150	Bagshot	v	Sidlesham (31/8)	0-5	
151	Raynes Park Vale	v	Cobham	0-1	
152	Lingfield	v	Epsom & Ewell (31/8)	6-1	
	(at Whyteleafe FC)				
153	Croydon	v	Little Common	2-3	
154	Sutton Athletic	v	Cray Valley (PM)	1-2	60
155	Hassocks	v	K Sports	0-2	52
156	St Francis Rangers	v	FC Elmstead	3-1	
157	Knaphill	v	AFC Varndeanians	1-4	41
158	Wick	v	Godalming Town	2-1	44
159	Mile Oak	v	Selsey	2-2aet	34
	Selsey	v	Mile Oak (4/9)	3-0	107
160	Billingshurst	v	Tunbridge Wells	0-3	64
161	Lordswood	v	Fire United Christian	2-0	45
162	Sheerwater	v	Lancing (2/9)	2-1	
163	Meridian VP	v	Southwick	0-1	14

No.	Home		Away	Score	Att
164	Chessington & Hook United	v	Oakwood	7-0	35
165	Erith Town	v	Arundel	5-0	40
166	Lewisham Borough (Community)	v	Broadbridge Heath	1-2aet	103
167	Kent Football United	v	Steyning Town Community	2-3aet	
168	Sporting Club Thamesmead	v	Midhurst & Easebourne United	4-3	55
169	Westside	v	AC London (2/9)	2-4	
170	AFC Croydon Athletic	v	Worthing United	4-1	
171	AFC Uckfield Town	v	Hollands & Blair	2-0	51
172	Glebe	v	Loxwood	3-0	
173	Seaford Town	v	Tooting Bec	1-0	51
174	Lydd Town	v	Punjab United	1-2	35
175	Snodland Town	v	Newhaven	2-3	98
176	Erith & Belvedere	v	Rusthall (2/9)	1-3	
177	Fisher	v	Corinthian	4-4aet	
	Corinthian	v	Fisher (4/9)	3-2	63
178	East Preston	v	Eastbourne United	5-2	81
179	Bearsted	v	Bexhill United	4-1	
180	Sheppey United	v	Balham	3-1	233
181	Langney Wanderers	v	Canterbury City	0-2	
182	Saltdean United	v	Crawley Down Gatwick	2-1	
183	Redhill	v	Holmesdale	2-0	
184	Guildford City	v	Rochester United	4-0	65
	(at Godalming Town FC)				
185	Whitchurch United	v	Almondsbury	0-2	
186	Devizes Town	v	Warminster Town	0-2	102
187	Calne Town	v	Fawley	4-5	95
188	Christchurch	v	Folland Sports (31/8)	3-0	81
189	Cowes Sports	v	Westbury United	3-5aet	131
190	Chippenham Park	v	Bitton (2/9)	0-4	
191	Lymington Town	v	Portland United	4-2	61
	(at Brockenhurst FC)				
192	Oldland Abbotonians	v	Totton & Eling	2-3	
193	Hamworthy United	v	Amesbury Town	5-0	80
194	Romsey Town	v	Bridport	4-4aet	
	Bridport	v	Romsey Town (5/9)	4-2	
195	Ringwood Town	v	Alresford Town	1-2	55
196	Stockbridge	v	Roman Glass St George	1-3	
197	Hallen	v	Fareham Town	2-3	48
198	East Cowes Victoria Athletic	v	Pewsey Vale	4-3	25
199	Team Solent	v	Longwell Green Sports	2-3	
200	Eversley & California	v	Downton	1-0	
201	Bournemouth	v	Bristol Telephones	8-0	51
202	Hythe & Dibden	v	Bemerton Heath Harlequins	1-2aet	
203	Corsham Town	v	Laverstock & Ford	1-0	61
204	Exmouth Town	v	Callington Town	4-2	
205	Plymouth Parkway	v	Brislington	5-1	124
206	Tavistock	v	Helston Athletic	3-1	65
207	Keynsham Town	v	Sidmouth Town	2-3	112
208	Bishops Lydeard	v	Bishop Sutton	3-0aet	37
209	Godolphin Atlantic	v	Portishead Town	1-0	
210	Hengrove Athletic	v	Newquay	1-2aet	90
211	Wellington AFC	v	Saltash United	1-3	45
	(at Cullompton Rangers FC)				
212	Liskeard Athletic	v	Bovey Tracey	1-3	73
213	Crediton United	v	Clevedon Town	0-3	131
214	AFC St Austell	v	Ilfracombe Town	3-1	
215	Wincanton Town	v	Radstock Town	1-2	
216	Witheridge	v	Wells City		
	(walkover for Wells City – Witheridge withdrawn)				
217	Odd Down	v	Shepton Mallet	4-1	56
218	Elburton Villa	v	Launceston	3-1	

FAV - 2Q - Action from the Buckland Athetic and Newquay tie which was won with a 92nd minute penalty in favour of the visitors. Photo: Peter Barnes.

FAV - 2Q - Heanor Town v Dunkirk - Jamie Sleigh gives Heanor a 3-2 win with this penalty. Photo: Bill Wheatcroft.

SECOND QUALIFYING ROUND

SATURDAY 15 SEPTEMBER 2018 - WINNING CLUB TO RECEIVE £725 LOSING CLUB TO RECEIVE £250

1	Northallerton Town	v	Steeton	1-2	119
2	Ashington	v	Crook Town	6-2	111
3	Nelson	v	Tow Law Town	5-2	
4	Thackley	v	Carlisle City	5-2	57
5	Whickham	v	Whitley Bay	2-1aet	
6	Billingham Town	v	Birtley Town	3-1	206
7	Albion Sports	v	Silsden (16/9)	0-1	144
8	Sunderland Ryhope CW	v	Dunston UTS	0-2	104
9	Bishop Auckland	v	West Allotment Celtic	3-1aet	231
10	Brandon United	v	Washington	3-2aet	62
11	Penrith	v	Charnock Richard	1-4	123
12	Padiham	v	Prestwich Heys	2-2aet	129
	Prestwich Heys	v	Padiham (18/9)	5-2	89
13	Hebburn Town	v	Billingham Synthonia (14/9)	3-1	310
14	Ryton & Crawcrook Albion	v	Garforth Town	1-2	
15	Guisborough Town	v	Barnoldswick Town	4-2	177
16	Bedlington Terriers	v	Redcar Athletic	2-0	
17	Bridlington Town	v	Consett	1-0aet	329
18	Daisy Hill	v	Seaham Red Star	0-2	54
19	AFC Darwen	v	Garstang	1-2	99
20	Northwich Victoria	v	Maltby Main (16/9)	2-0	124
21	Swallownest	v	AFC Blackpool	4-1	
22	Avro	v	Barnton	3-0	
23	Irlam	v	Burscough	4-2	72
24	Bacup Borough	v	Litherland Remyca	1-4	
25	Cammell Laird 1907	v	Shelley	2-1	
26	Glasshoughton Welfare	v	Parkgate	3-1	82
27	Cheadle Town	v	Vauxhall Motors	2-2aet	60
	Vauxhall Motors	v	Cheadle Town (18/9)	6-0	67
28	Bootle	v	Hallam	0-1	111
29	Worsbrough Bridge Athletic	v	Squires Gate (16/9)	0-2	
30	Staveley MW	v	Maine Road	4-1	227
31	Wythenshawe Town or Rylands	v	Hemsworth Miners Welfare		
	(walkover for Hemsworth Miners Welfare – Wythenshawe Town & Rylands not accepted into the Competition)				
32	Barton Town	v	Ashton Town	4-0	
33	Atherton LR	v	Sandbach United	0-4	
34	Winsford United	v	Worksop Town	5-0	150
35	Winterton Rangers	v	Rossington Main	2-0	
36	Lower Breck	v	Stockport Town	1-0	
37	Chelmsley Town	v	Tividale	3-1	80
38	Dudley Sports	v	Hanley Town	0-4	
39	Rugby Borough	v	Bustleholme	0-2	
40	Whitchurch Alport	v	Shepshed Dynamo	2-3aet	182
41	Littleton	v	Smethwick	0-1	
42	Birstall United Social	v	Heather St Johns	0-4	
43	Coventry Copsewood	v	Hereford Lads Club	1-2	65
44	Boldmere St Michaels	v	Studley	3-0	89
45	Lye Town	v	Bolehall Swifts	2-0	65
46	Wednesfield	v	Bromyard Town	5-2	
47	Uttoxeter Town	v	Walsall Wood	2-2aet	
	Walsall Wood	v	Uttoxeter Town (18/9)	5-4aet	80
48	Wellington Amateurs	v	Racing Club Warwick	6-3	
49	NKF Burbage	v	Cradley Town (16/9)	2-1	
50	Brocton	v	Nuneaton Griff	4-0	63
51	Cadbury Athletic	v	Wem Town	2-0	42
52	Coventry United	v	Atherstone Town	2-1	
53	Paget Rangers	v	Kington Town		
	(walkover for Paget Rangers – Kington Town removed)				
54	Saffron Dynamo	v	Heath Hayes	4-0	
55	Ingles	v	Rugby Town	0-2	
56	Ashby Ivanhoe	v	Bewdley Town	0-1	77
57	Black Country Rangers	v	Dudley Town	4-0	
58	Wolverhampton Casuals	v	Romulus	0-1	55
59	AFC Wulfrunians	v	Wellington FC	1-2	
60	Stone Old Alleynians	v	Sporting Khalsa	3-7	47
61	Hucknall Town	v	Harrowby United	2-0	
62	Aylestone Park	v	Kimberley Miners Welfare	2-1	

63	Pinxton	v	Bottesford Town	1-1aet	
	Bottesford Town	v	Pinxton (19/9)	3-0	94
64	Holbrook Sports	v	Blidworth Welfare	3-5	
65	Belper United	v	Teversal (16/9)	1-0	
66	Quorn	v	Skegness Town	4-1	122
67	Barrow Town	v	Shirebrook Town	4-1	64
68	Heanor Town	v	Dunkirk	3-2	
69	South Normanton Athletic	v	Selston	1-3	
70	Ollerton Town	v	Long Eaton United	1-5aet	
71	Arnold Town	v	Loughborough University	0-5	
72	Sleaford Town	v	Sandiacre Town	2-0	
73	Eastwood Community	v	Sherwood Colliery	3-2	98
74	Graham St Prims	v	Ilkeston Town	0-2	
75	Dronfield Town	v	Harborough Town	3-1	75
76	FC Bolsover	v	Leicester Nirvana	1-2	40
77	Peterborough Northern Star	v	March Town United	1-0	
78	Histon	v	Team Bury		
	(walkover for Histon – Team Bury withdrawn)				
79	Walsham Le Willows	v	Deeping Rangers	1-4	63
80	Wroxham	v	Mulbarton Wanderers	3-0	132
81	Framlingham Town	v	Swaffham Town	0-0aet	
	Swaffham Town	v	Framlingham Town (18/9)	2-1	69
82	Woodbridge Town	v	Pinchbeck United	2-1	
83	Great Yarmouth Town	v	Thetford Town	3-1	66
84	Gorleston	v	Kirkley & Pakefield	0-2	118
85	Newmarket Town	v	Ely City	5-2	82
86	Saffron Walden Town	v	May & Baker Eastbrook Community	1-4	
87	Southend Manor	v	Haverhill Rovers	4-3	
88	Hoddesdon Town	v	FC Clacton	2-3	101
89	London Lions	v	Biggleswade United	0-3	47
90	Colney Heath	v	Langford	2-1	
91	Brantham Athletic	v	Takeley	3-4	62
92	Haverhill Borough	v	Whitton United	2-1	
93	Little Oakley	v	Hadleigh United	1-0	
94	Barkingside	v	Wodson Park	1-1aet	
	(Wodson Park won 4-2 on kicks from the penalty mark)				
95	London Colney	v	FC Broxbourne Borough	3-1	
96	Coggeshall United	v	Sawbridgeworth Town (16/9)	0-4	
97	Enfield Borough	v	Sporting Bengal United (16/9)	3-2	
98	Baldock Town	v	Stanway Rovers (16/9)	1-0	
99	Codicote	v	Holland	1-0	54
100	Clapton	v	Newbury Forest	0-2	
101	Hadley	v	Enfield 1893	0-1	32
102	Stotfold	v	West Essex	2-4	
103	Amersham Town	v	Hanworth Villa	0-1	
104	Southall	v	Wembley	5-0	
105	Brackley Town Saints	v	Crawley Green	0-1	42
106	Burton Park Wanderers	v	FC Deportivo Galicia (16/9)	0-5	
107	Brimsdown	v	Bicester Town		
	(walkover for Brimsdown – Bicester Town withdrawn)				
108	Leverstock Green	v	Raunds Town	4-0	34
109	Wellingborough Town	v	Burnham	3-2	89
110	Potton United	v	CB Hounslow United	2-3	64
111	St Panteleimon	v	Long Buckby	4-1	47
112	Cricklewood Wanderers	v	North Greenford United	3-6aet	
113	Arlesey Town	v	Irchester United	1-2aet	96
114	Kensington Borough	v	Northampton Sileby Rangers	4-2	
115	Broadfields United	v	Edgware Town (16/9)	2-0	
116	Bedfont & Feltham	v	Winslow United	2-0	
117	Bugbrooke St Michaels	v	Spelthorne Sports	3-3aet	37
	Spelthorne Sports	v	Bugbrooke St Michaels (18/9)	2-0	
118	Rayners Lane	v	Thrapston Town	3-2	
119	Harefield United	v	Oxhey Jets	4-1aet	
120	Easington Sports	v	Brimscombe & Thrupp	1-2	
121	Baffins Milton Rovers	v	New College Swindon	14-1	88
122	Royal Wootton Bassett Town	v	Bashley	0-4	52
123	Thame Rangers	v	Farnham Town (16/9)	1-0	

FAV - 2Q - Cray Valley PM v Hailsham Town - Hailshams Paul Richardson blocks this effort from Cray Valleys Anthony Edgar. Photo: Alan Coomes.

FAV - 3P - Erith Town v Windsor - Windsors Joe Crook heads clear from Erith Towns Adrian Stone. Alan Coomes.

SECOND QUALIFYING ROUND

No	Home		Away	Score	Att
124	Tadley Calleva	v	Chertsey Town	0-1	148
125	Abingdon United	v	Alton	3-0	46
126	AFC Stoneham	v	Binfield	3-2	
127	Chipping Sodbury Town	v	Abbey Rangers	1-3	50
128	Clanfield 85	v	Buckingham Athletic	2-5	32
129	Shrivenham	v	Badshot Lea	1-4	47
130	Malmesbury Victoria	v	Virginia Water	3-1	110
131	Cheltenham Saracens	v	Flackwell Heath	0-1	
132	Longlevens	v	Tuffley Rovers (14/9)	0-0aet	184
	Tuffley Rovers	v	Longlevens (18/9)	0-1	
133	Holyport	v	Fleet Spurs	2-1	
134	Redhill	v	Forest Hill Park	2-1aet	
135	Steyning Town Community	v	Punjab United	1-1aet	130
	(Steyning Town Community won 9-8 on kicks from the penalty mark)				
136	AFC Varndeanians	v	Canterbury City	0-2	43
137	Cray Valley (PM)	v	Hailsham Town (16/9)	2-0	106
138	Cobham	v	Gravesham Borough		
	(walkover for Cobham – Gravesham Borough withdrawn)				
139	St Francis Rangers	v	Lordswood	0-6	
140	Sporting Club Thamesmead	v	Banstead Athletic	0-1	
141	Tunbridge Wells	v	Bridon Ropes	1-1aet	
	Bridon Ropes	v	Tunbridge Wells (19/9)	0-1	
142	Guildford City	v	Rusthall	0-2	50
143	Wick	v	Hackney Wick	4-2	38
144	Peacehaven & Telscombe	v	Shoreham	3-1	
145	AFC Uckfield Town	v	Southwick	5-0	67
146	AC London	v	Erith Town	2-3	
147	Colliers Wood United	v	Sidlesham	0-1	
148	Saltdean United	v	Littlehampton Town	3-1	47
149	Selsey	v	Bearsted	0-2	
150	Chatham Town	v	Camberley Town	5-1	136
151	Corinthian	v	Glebe	3-0	38
152	Chessington & Hook United	v	Sheerwater	0-5	
153	Newhaven	v	Little Common	1-0	
154	Sheppey United	v	Seaford Town	5-3	204
155	K Sports	v	Deal Town	1-4	
156	East Preston	v	Broadbridge Heath	1-0	51
157	AFC Croydon Athletic	v	Lingfield	5-2aet	65
158	Hamworthy United	v	Fawley	3-1	82
159	Roman Glass St George	v	Bemerton Heath Harlequins	3-0	
160	Bournemouth	v	Christchurch	3-1	85
161	Verwood Town	v	Alresford Town	1-1aet	
	Alresford Town	v	Verwood Town (18/9)	1-0	50
162	Bridport	v	Warminster Town	5-0	145
163	Eversley & California	v	Lymington Town	2-1	
164	Shortwood United	v	Cribbs	1-5	97
165	Swanage Town & Herston	v	Longwell Green Sports	0-3	67
166	Fareham Town	v	Corsham Town	2-1aet	104
167	Bitton	v	Bishops Cleeve	3-1	45
168	Petersfield Town	v	Westbury United	1-3	70
169	New Milton Town	v	Cadbury Heath	1-2	
170	Totton & Eling	v	East Cowes Victoria Athletic	1-0	
171	Sherborne Town	v	Almondsbury	0-1	
172	Shaftesbury	v	Andover New Street	5-1	
173	United Services Portsmouth	v	Brockenhurst	0-2	
174	Buckland Athletic	v	Newquay	0-1	
175	Odd Down	v	Welton Rovers	2-1	104
176	Radstock Town	v	Plymouth Parkway	1-3	72
177	Cullompton Rangers	v	Ivybridge Town	0-4	73
178	Sidmouth Town	v	Godolphin Atlantic	4-1	
179	Saltash United	v	Axminster Town	6-0	84
180	Bovey Tracey	v	Tavistock	1-2aet	93
181	Falmouth Town	v	Clevedon Town	2-1	166
182	Bishops Lydeard	v	Elburton Villa	0-4	55
183	Exmouth Town	v	Bridgwater Town	3-0	185
184	Cheddar	v	Newton Abbot Spurs	2-0	
185	Camelford	v	Bodmin Town	3-3aet	69
	Bodmin Town	v	Camelford (19/9)	4-0	
186	Porthleven	v	Torpoint Athletic	3-6	
187	Wells City	v	AFC St Austell	2-3	

FIRST ROUND PROPER

SATURDAY 13 OCTOBER 2018 - WINNING CLUB TO RECEIVE £825 LOSING CLUB TO RECEIVE £275

No	Home		Away	Score	Att
1	Hallam	v	Charnock Richard	3-1	403
2	Northwich Victoria	v	Cammell Laird 1907	5-0	
3	Litherland Remyca	v	Thackley	1-4	
4	Prestwich Heys	v	Garforth Town	6-2	
5	Irlam	v	Handsworth Parramore	2-0	
6	Staveley MW	v	Silsden	2-2aet	271
	Silsden	v	Staveley MW (16/10)	2-0	179
7	Bedlington Terriers	v	Whickham	5-1	
8	Sunderland RCA	v	Bridlington Town	3-2aet	
9	Hebburn Town	v	City of Liverpool	4-0	
10	Vauxhall Motors	v	Seaham Red Star	4-0	86
11	Squires Gate	v	Sandbach United	2-1	57
12	Bishop Auckland	v	Hemsworth MW	2-3	327
13	Swallownest	v	Garstang	1-1aet	
	(Garstang won 4-3 on kicks from the penalty mark)				
14	Steeton	v	Avro	2-3	174
15	Runcorn Town	v	Guisborough Town	3-3aet	
	Guisborough Town	v	Runcorn Town (17/10)	2-4aet	244
16	Billingham Town	v	Dunston UTS	1-3	240
17	Winterton Rangers	v	Lower Breck	1-0	
18	Nelson	v	Ashington (16/10)	0-5	
19	Shildon	v	Glasshoughton Welfare	1-0	
20	Barton Town	v	Brandon United	8-0	187
21	Shepshed Dynamo	v	Bewdley Town	2-0	
22	Cadbury Athletic	v	Hanley Town	4-0	60
23	Aylestone Park	v	Blidworth Welfare	0-3	
24	Lye Town	v	Chelmsley Town	5-2	
25	Romulus	v	Wellington FC	3-3aet	60
	Wellington FC	v	Romulus (16/10)	1-3	89
26	Bustleholme	v	NKF Burbage	1-4	
27	Coventry United	v	Wednesfield (14/10)	5-0	109
28	Loughborough University	v	Heather St Johns	1-2	213
29	Wellington Amateurs	v	Leicester Nirvana	1-2	
30	Belper United	v	Quorn (14/10)	1-4	
31	Brocton	v	Highgate United	3-2aet	69
32	Heanor Town	v	Ilkeston Town	0-3	
33	Sporting Khalsa	v	Winsford United	1-0	
34	Saffron Dynamo	v	Bottesford Town	3-3aet	
	Bottesford Town	v	Saffron Dynamo (17/10)	2-3	85
35	Barrow Town	v	Dronfield Town	0-1	
36	Hereford Lads Club	v	Paget Rangers	2-0	
37	Eastwood Community	v	Selston	3-0	293
38	Boldmere St Michaels	v	Rugby Town	2-1	200
39	Hucknall Town	v	Black Country Rangers	3-2	181
40	Worcester City	v	Long Eaton United	2-1	424
41	Smethwick	v	Walsall Wood	0-3	
42	Baldock Town	v	Brimsdown	3-0	
43	Little Oakley	v	Enfield 1893	2-2aet	
	Enfield 1893	v	Little Oakley (16/10)	2-0	60
44	Newmarket Town	v	Deeping Rangers	0-1	
45	Great Yarmouth Town	v	Wroxham	3-1	228
46	Colney Heath	v	Histon	1-1aet	
	Histon	v	Colney Heath (16/10)	2-0	
47	FC Deportivo Galicia	v	Irchester United (14/10)	1-2	
48	Buckingham Athletic	v	FC Clacton	2-2aet	
	FC Clacton	v	Buckingham Athletic (16/10)	3-2	
49	Newbury Forest	v	Newport Pagnell Town	2-3	55
50	Biggleswade United	v	Holbeach United	2-3aet	
51	Haverhill Borough	v	Swaffham Town	3-4	
52	Enfield Borough	v	Kirkley & Pakefield (14/10)	2-3aet	

FAV - 1P - Joe Nwoko of AFC Croydon tries to shake off Fareham Towns Shawn Benjamin (stripes).
Photo: Alan Coomes.

FAV - 4P - Cribbs 0 v 2 Sholing. Photo: Peter Barnes.

FIRST ROUND PROPER

No	Home		Away	Score	Att
53	London Colney	v	Wellingborough Town	2-3aet	
54	Southend Manor	v	Redbridge	1-4	
55	May & Baker Eastbrook Community	v	North Greenford United	4-2aet	
56	Thame Rangers	v	Crawley Green	4-2	
57	West Essex	v	Godmanchester Rovers (14/10)	1-2	
58	Takeley	v	Wodson Park	0-2	93
59	Codicote	v	Wantage Town	1-7	
60	Harefield United	v	Woodbridge Town	0-2	
61	Stowmarket Town	v	Harpenden Town	5-0	
62	Sleaford Town	v	Peterborough Northern Star	2-2aet	
	Peterborough Northern Star	v	Sleaford Town (16/10)	2-0	
63	Leverstock Green	v	Sawbridgeworth Town	3-0	
64	Sidlesham	v	Chatham Town	0-2	
65	Redhill	v	Peacehaven & Telscombe	2-3	
66	Sheppey United	v	East Preston	4-0	279
67	Wick	v	Lordswood	0-3	28
68	Corinthian	v	Deal Town	3-2	66
69	Eversley & California	v	Horndean	0-1	
70	Southall	v	Sheerwater (12/10)	6-0	79
71	Spelthorne Sports	v	CB Hounslow United	2-1	73
72	Rayners Lane	v	Abbey Rangers	2-3	
73	Bearsted	v	Beckenham Town	3-0	
74	Canterbury City	v	Saltdean United (14/10)	2-1	
75	Broadfields United	v	Banstead Athletic (14/10)	1-7	
76	Hanworth Villa	v	Pagham	2-4	
77	Sutton Common Rovers	v	Cobham	2-1	75
78	Chertsey Town	v	Flackwell Heath	6-1	
79	AFC Croydon Athletic	v	Fareham Town	3-0	96
80	Horsham YMCA	v	Kensington Borough	0-2	110
81	St Panteleimon	v	Cray Valley (PM) (17/10)	1-3	56
	(12/10 – tie abandoned)				
82	Bedfont & Feltham	v	Erith Town	1-2	
83	Newhaven	v	Rusthall	2-1	
84	Tunbridge Wells	v	AFC Uckfield Town	0-2	
85	Steyning Town Community	v	Walton & Hersham	1-0	
86	Bashley	v	Baffins Milton Rovers	1-2	
87	Saltash United	v	Westbury United	2-1	105
88	Brimscombe & Thrupp	v	Cribbs	2-3	91
89	Longwell Green Sports	v	Brockenhurst	1-3	
90	Ivybridge Town	v	Holyport	0-0aet	165
	Holyport	v	Ivybridge Town (16/10)	0-3	92
91	Torpoint Athletic	v	Sholing	0-1	116
92	Exmouth Town	v	Elburton Villa	2-0	128
93	Cheddar	v	Totton & Eling	1-0aet	
94	Roman Glass St George	v	Malmesbury Victoria	0-2	
95	Andover Town	v	Badshot Lea	1-4	117
96	Odd Down	v	Willand Rovers	1-4	56
97	Alresford Town	v	Abingdon United	1-0	190
98	Bridport	v	Falmouth Town	0-6	179
99	Bodmin Town	v	AFC Stoneham	2-1	
100	Bournemouth	v	Newquay	6-0	72
101	Longlevens	v	Tavistock	1-3aet	89
102	Cadbury Heath	v	Sidmouth Town	5-0	71
103	AFC St Austell	v	Plymouth Parkway	6-1	
104	Almondsbury	v	Bitton	2-1	56
105	Shaftesbury	v	Hamworthy United	1-2	

SECOND ROUND PROPER

SATURDAY 3 NOVEMBER 2018 - WINNING CLUB TO RECEIVE £900 LOSING CLUB TO RECEIVE £300

No	Home		Away	Score	Att
1	Hallam	v	Hebburn Town	1-2	
2	Vauxhall Motors	v	Runcorn Town (2/11)	1-3	297
3	Silsden	v	Bedlington Terriers	3-1	
4	Newcastle Benfield	v	1874 Northwich	2-0	262
5	Avro	v	Squires Gate	2-1	
6	Winterton Rangers	v	Dunston UTS	2-1	162
7	Irlam	v	Hemsworth MW	3-1	
8	Barton Town	v	Shildon	0-2	307
9	Garstang	v	Sunderland RCA	2-6	
10	Thackley	v	West Auckland Town	0-1	148
11	Stockton Town	v	Ashington	4-1	343
12	Prestwich Heys	v	Northwich Victoria	0-0aet	
	Northwich Victoria	v	Prestwich Heys (7/11)	1-0	102
13	Westfields	v	Romulus	3-2	
14	Shepshed Dynamo	v	Blidworth Welfare	3-0	159
15	Worcester City	v	Desborough Town (4/11)	0-2	365
16	Cadbury Athletic	v	Heather St Johns	3-2	70
17	Coventry United	v	Boldmere St Michaels	3-0	105
18	Sporting Khalsa	v	Hucknall Town	3-2	
19	Quorn	v	Eastwood Community	1-2	165
20	Wolverhampton SC	v	Ilkeston Town	0-2	124
21	Walsall Wood	v	Dronfield Town	3-1	81
22	Lye Town	v	Brocton	4-1	92
23	Stourport Swifts	v	NKF Burbage	0-2	118
24	Hinckley	v	Hereford Lads Club	3-1	156
25	Leicester Nirvana	v	Saffron Dynamo	3-0	
26	Biggleswade	v	Norwich CBS	3-1	85
27	Cogenhoe United	v	Leighton Town	2-0	
	(tie awarded to Leighton Town - Cogenhoe United removed)				
28	FC Clacton	v	Kirkley & Pakefield	1-0	
29	Great Yarmouth Town	v	Godmanchester Rovers	1-3	112
30	Enfield 1893	v	Leverstock Green (13/11)	1-4	66
31	Redbridge	v	Peterborough Northern Star	1-0	
32	Hullbridge Sports	v	Irchester United	3-1	
33	Wellingborough Town	v	Tring Athletic	0-7	
34	May & Baker Eastbrook Community	v	Swaffham Town (4/11)	0-1	
35	Stowmarket Town	v	Baldock Town	3-1aet	
36	Histon	v	Woodbridge Town (2/11)	5-4	174
37	Wantage Town	v	Deeping Rangers	1-2	89
38	Wodson Park	v	Holbeach United	0-2	
39	Newport Pagnell Town	v	Thame Rangers	3-2	
40	Chertsey Town	v	Horndean	2-0	
41	Sutton Common Rovers	v	Horley Town (2/11)	6-1	63
42	Abbey Rangers	v	Lordswood	5-0	49
43	Chichester City	v	Windsor	0-2	
44	Kensington Borough	v	Erith Town (4/11)	0-3	
45	Steyning Town Community	v	Banstead Athletic	1-0	
46	AFC Croydon Athletic	v	AFC Uckfield Town	1-2	85
47	Spelthorne Sports	v	Sheppey United	1-2	95
48	Badshot Lea	v	Cray Valley (PM) (4/11)	0-7	
49	Crowborough Athletic	v	Eastbourne Town	0-4	251
50	Corinthian	v	Canterbury City	2-4aet	62
51	Pagham	v	Peacehaven & Telscombe	4-1	108
52	Bearsted	v	Newhaven	1-0	
53	Southall	v	Chatham Town	1-0aet	
54	Sholing	v	Malmesbury Victoria	5-1	
55	Exmouth Town	v	Cadbury Heath	3-4	
56	Almondsbury	v	Hamble Club	1-2	60
57	Bodmin Town	v	Alresford Town	1-0aet	
58	Cheddar	v	AFC St Austell	1-2	
59	Newport (IW)	v	Cribbs	0-2	
60	Baffins Milton Rovers	v	Bournemouth	3-2	
61	Brockenhurst	v	Bradford Town	0-4	138
62	Willand Rovers	v	Tavistock	2-1	
63	Ivybridge Town	v	Saltash United	1-3	
64	Hamworthy United	v	Falmouth Town	3-1aet	

FAV - SF1 - Canterbury's Adam Woolcott blocks this effort from Cray Valley's Danny Smith. Photo: Alan Coomes.

FAV - SF1 - Cray Valley keeper Andy Walker punches clear a Canterbury corner. Photo: Peter Barnes.

THIRD ROUND PROPER

SATURDAY 1 DECEMBER 2018 - WINNING CLUB TO RECEIVE £1,125 LOSING CLUB TO RECEIVE £375

1	Shildon	v	Sunderland RCA	2-3	212
2	Northwich Victoria	v	Silsden	3-0	
3	Stockton Town	v	Hebburn Town	3-5	427
4	Avro	v	West Auckland Town	0-2	
5	Irlam	v	Winterton Rangers (8/12)	2-0	
	(at Winterton Rangers FC) (1/12 – tie abandoned after 45 mins, 0-0)				
6	Newcastle Benfield	v	Runcorn Town	5-4	153
7	Ilkeston Town	v	Eastwood Community	1-2	
8	Coventry United	v	Hinckley	4-0	145
9	Cadbury Athletic	v	Desborough Town	3-2	91
10	Westfields	v	Leicester Nirvana	0-4	128
11	Shepshed Dynamo	v	NKF Burbage	3-0	241
12	Lye Town	v	Leighton Town	4-0aet	
13	Sporting Khalsa	v	Walsall Wood	3-1	
14	Histon	v	Leverstock Green (2/12)	5-1	212
15	Godmanchester Rovers	v	Holbeach United	2-0	
16	Swaffham Town	v	Stowmarket Town	0-0aet	
	Stowmarket Town	v	Swaffham Town (4/12)	2-1	
17	Tring Athletic	v	Biggleswade	1-1aet	239
	Biggleswade	v	Tring Athletic (8/12)	0-0aet	
	(Biggleswade won 5-3 on kicks from the penalty mark)				
18	Hullbridge Sports	v	Newport Pagnell (8/12)	0-2	
19	Deeping Rangers	v	FC Clacton	4-2	129
20	AFC Uckfield Town	v	Sutton Common Rovers (8/12)	5-2	38
21	Eastbourne Town	v	Abbey Rangers	0-1	
22	Redbridge	v	Chertsey Town (8/12)	0-5	
23	Bearsted	v	Steyning Town Community	3-2aet	
24	Sheppey United	v	Cray Valley (PM)	0-4	
25	Canterbury City	v	Southall	1-0aet	
26	Erith Town	v	Windsor	1-2	
27	Saltash United	v	Cribbs (8/12)	2-4	135
28	Bradford Town	v	Baffins Milton Rovers	1-3	158
29	Willand Rovers	v	Bodmin Town	3-0	
30	Cadbury Heath	v	AFC St Austell (8/12)	4-8	
31	Hamble Club	v	Hamworthy United	1-1aet	
	Hamworthy United	v	Hamble Club (4/12)	4-1	110
32	Sholing	v	Pagham	6-2	144

FOURTH ROUND PROPER

SATURDAY 5 JANUARY 2019 - WINNING CLUB TO RECEIVE £1,875 LOSING CLUB TO RECEIVE £625

1	Godmanchester Rovers	v	Sporting Khalsa	1-0	
	(tie awarded to Sporting Khalsa – Godmanchester Rovers removed)				
2	Irlam	v	Cadbury Athletic	4-0	320
3	Hebburn Town	v	Shepshed Dynamo	2-1	
4	Newcastle Benfield	v	Northwich Victoria	2-3	360
5	Sunderland RCA	v	West Auckland Town	0-1	
6	Coventry United	v	Leicester Nirvana	3-2	159
	(tie awarded to Leicester Nirvana – Coventry United removed)				
7	Deeping Rangers	v	Eastwood Community	4-0	
8	Histon	v	Lye Town	2-1	276
9	Willand Rovers	v	Hamworthy United	1-0	
10	Canterbury City	v	Newport Pagnell Town (6/1)	3-2	259
11	AFC Uckfield Town	v	Windsor	1-4	138
12	Cribbs	v	Sholing	0-2	155
13	Bearsted	v	Abbey Rangers	1-2aet	250
14	Chertsey Town	v	AFC St Austell	5-0	
15	Biggleswade	v	Stowmarket Town (6/1)	1-0	527
16	Cray Valley (PM)	v	Baffins Milton Rovers	3-1	139

FIFTH ROUND PROPER

SATURDAY 2 FEBRUARY 2019 - WINNING CLUB TO RECEIVE £2,250 LOSING CLUB TO RECEIVE £750

1	Irlam	v	Chertsey Town (9/2)	0-2	449
2	Cray Valley (PM)	v	Abbey Rangers	3-1	217
3	Histon	v	Northwich Victoria	1-3aet	643
4	Sholing	v	Sporting Khalsa	3-1	441
5	Hebburn Town	v	West Auckland Town (9/2)	0-2	1310
6	Biggleswade	v	Windsor (3/2)	6-1	557
7	Willand Rovers	v	Deeping Rangers	3-2	
8	Canterbury City	v	Leicester Nirvana	2-1	334

QUARTER FINALS

SATURDAY 23 FEBRUARY 2019 - WINNING CLUB TO RECEIVE £4,125 LOSING CLUB TO RECEIVE £1,375

1	West Auckland Town	v	Chertsey Town	0-2	735
2	Canterbury City	v	Biggleswade (24/2)	2-1	602
3	Willand Rovers	v	Cray Valley (PM)	1-3	768
4	Northwich Victoria	v	Sholing	3-1aet	719

SEMI FINALS

1ST LEG SATURDAY 16 MARCH / 2ND LEG SATURDAY 23 MARCH 2018 - WINNERS RECEIVE £5,500 LOSING CLUB TO RECEIVE £1,750

Cray Valley (PM)	v	Canterbury City	1-0	663
Canterbury City	v	Cray Valley (PM)	1-1	1274
Cray Valley (PM) through 2-1 on aggregate.				1937
Northwich Victoria	v	Chertsey Town	1-1	1288
Chertsey Town	v	Northwich Victoria	0-0	1847
Chertsey Town through after winning 5-3 on penalties.				3135

THE FINAL...

CHERTSEY TOWN 3

Flegg 39 Baxter 105 (pen) Rowe 117

CRAY VALLEY (PM) 1

Tomlin 36

Wembley Stadium ~ Att: 42,962*

**combined Trophy/Vase attendance*

Unusually, out of the 638 original entrants there was no northern team in this year's final, let alone a team from the Northern League which had provided the victors in seven of the previous nine finals. Not so unusually, both Chertsey, the Curlews, and Cray Valley, the Millers, each with over 100 years of history, were making their first visits to Wembley. Both had also finished the season atop their respective leagues. Thus both will start next season at Step 4, although they will not have any league clashes since Cray have been allocated to the south eastern division of the Isthmian, Chertsey to the south central section.

It was Chertsey who began in lively fashion, Dale Binns twice providing scoring opportunities for Lubomir Guentchev whose head and foot efforts left goalkeeper Andy Walker untroubled. Lewis Driver saw his shot blocked while Liam Hickey retaliated by hitting a thirty yarder well over. The Curlews' next attack ended with a Mason Welch-Turner cross looking as if it might be heading for the net but Walker showed good judgement in leaving it to drift over. Cray's Anthony Edgar's astute pass let in Paul Semakula but a defender quickly blocked his effort at goal, while the veteran Kevin Lisbie, ex Charlton and Leyton Orient with over 450 professional appearances behind him, set up an opportunity for the lively Gavin Tomlin to volley over. Edgar came close to putting the Millers ahead on the half hour only to see his shot cleared off the line. Chertsey's Guentchev, whose father played for the towns of Ipswich and Luton in his professional career, was responsible for Town's main set pieces and tested Walker on a couple of first half occasions before, in the 36th minute, a Liam Hickey pass set Tomlin free. Taking full advantage he accurately guided the ball past Nick Jupp to give Cray the lead. However, within two minutes Chertsey were level. Driver was brought down just outside the Cray penalty area. Sam Murphy's shot was blocked for a corner which Guentchev landed on the head of his centre back Michael Peacock. His header smacked against the post but fortuitously ricocheted to full back Sam Flegg who was able to turn the rebound home joyfully, leaving the teams on level terms at half time.
A Guentchev corner headed over by Driver opened the second half while Lisbie saw a header pass just over and a ground shot easily saved by Jupp. Ashley Sains was relieved to see his mistake not punished by Jake Baxter whose shot was off target. Denzel Gayle and Tomlin both threatened the Chertsey net in goalmouth scrambles as half chances were presented at both ends. Neither side was able to create a clear cut chance as the minutes ebbed away, Edgar going closest for Cray when he hit the bar, as the spectre of extra time loomed ever nearer.
Into that extra time the teams duly ventured with the anticipated spate of substitutions occurring as both managers sought to tilt the balance by introducing fresh legs and minds. Arriving at the last minute of the first 15 minute period there came the turning point. Guentchev was judged to have been fouled just inside the area by Cem Tumkaya. Without fuss Baxter calmly put the spot kick away and Chertsey were in front for the first time.

THE SQUADS

CHERTSEY TOWN	CRAY VALLEY (PM)
Nick Jupp	Andy Walker
Sam Flegg	Denzel Gayle
Michael Peacock	Cem Tumkaya (sub 106)
Quincy Rowe	Ashley Sains (sub 112)
Mason Welch-Turner	Liam Hickey
Kevin Maclaren (sub 79)	Danny Smith
Lubomir Guentchev	Ryan Flack (sub 72)
Sam Murphy	Paul Semakula
Lewis Driver (sub 83)	Anthony Edgar
Dale Binns (sub 97)	Gavin Tomlin
Jake Baxter (sub 118)	Kevin Lisbie (sub 100)
Substitutes	**Substitutes**
Dave Taylor (79)	Josh James (72)
Andy Crossley (83)	Francis Babalola (100)
Lewis Jackson (97)	min Brad Potter (106)
John Pomroy (118)	Calum Willock (112)
Lewis Gallifent	Deren Ibrahim
Michael Kinsella	Tyler Myers
Danny Bennell	Lea Dawson

Referee Ross Joyce
Assisted by Rob Smith and Matthew Lee
4th official, Thomas Bramall

Edgar (Cray) hits the Chertsey crossbar in the last minute. Photo: Keith Clayton.

Those final fifteen minutes were an endurance test rather than one of skill and artistry and the contest ended when some neat Chertsey interpassing led to Quincy Rowe shooting accurately home with just two minutes left on the clock. There was still time for Guentchev to hit the post with the keeper beaten before the blue and whites were able to collect the Vase and bring the curtain down on a very successful season.

Reflecting on the outcome later, Cray's manager Kevin Watson was upbeat, although naturally disappointed to have lost the lead so soon after acquiring it. He recalled the adage of being at your most vulnerable after scoring. He felt his team, in their centenary season, had acquitted themselves well. Stressing the positives he opined, "This was a high. It's fine margins. It has been a great experience. Many players who will play a lot higher will not experience a day like this."

Winning manager, former goalkeeper Dave Anderson, declaring his side's Wembley victory as "every schoolboy's dream", proceeded to announce his retirement to his victorious troops in the privacy of the dressing room. After over 1,000 games in the managerial role, with a variety of teams in the north west London area, and nearing the start of his seventh decade, having been persuaded to leave the golf course for a last stab at management, Anderson described the triumph to be the pinnacle of his career, adding, "How lucky am I to get that on the last day of my career."

Arthur Evans.

PAST FINALS

1975 HODDESDON TOWN 2 *(South Midlands)* **EPSOM & EWELL 1 *(Surrey Senior)*** **Att: 9,500**
Sedgwick 2 **Wales** **Ref: Mr R Toseland**
Hoddesdon: Galvin, Green, Hickey, Maybury, Stevenson, Wilson, Bishop, Picking, Sedgwick, Nathan, Schofield
Epsom & Ewell: Page, Bennett, Webb, Wales, Worby, Jones, O'Connell, Walker, Tuite, Eales, Lee

1976 BILLERICAY TOWN 1 *(Essex Senior)* **STAMFORD 0 (aet) *(United Counties)*** **Att: 11,848**
Aslett **Ref: Mr A Robinson**
Billericay: Griffiths, Payne, Foreman, Pullin, Bone, Coughlan, Geddes, Aslett, Clayden, Scott, Smith
Stamford: Johnson, Kwiatowski, Marchant, Crawford, Downs, Hird, Barnes, Walpole, Smith, Russell, Broadbent

1977 BILLERICAY TOWN 1 *(Essex Senior)* **SHEFFIELD 1 (aet) *(Yorkshire)*** **Att: 14,000**
Clayden **Coughlan og** **Ref: Mr J Worrall**
Billericay: Griffiths, Payne, Bone, Coughlan, Pullin, Scott, Wakefield, Aslett, Clayden,Woodhouse, McQueen. Sub: Whettell
Sheffield: Wing, Gilbody, Lodge, Hardisty, Watts, Skelton, Kay, Travis, Pugh, Thornhill,Haynes. Sub: Strutt
Replay BILLERICAY TOWN 2 **SHEFFIELD 1** **Att: 3,482**
Aslett, Woodhouse **Thornhill** **at Nottingham Forest**
Billericay: Griffiths, Payne, Pullin, Whettell, Bone, McQueen, Woodhouse, Aslett, Clayden, Scott, Wakefield
Sheffield: Wing, Gilbody, Lodge, Strutt, Watts, Skelton, Kay, Travis, Pugh, Thornhill, Haynes

1978 NEWCASTLE BLUE STAR 2 *(Wearside)* **BARTON ROVERS 1 *(South Midlands)*** **Att: 16,858**
Dunn, Crumplin **Smith** **Ref: Mr T Morris**
Newcastle: Halbert, Feenan, Thompson, Davidson, S Dixon, Beynon, Storey, P Dixon, Crumplin, Callaghan, Dunn. Sub: Diamond
Barton Rovers: Blackwell, Stephens, Crossley, Evans, Harris, Dollimore, Dunn, Harnaman, Fossey, Turner, Smith. Sub: Cox

1979 BILLERICAY TOWN 4 *(Athenian)* **ALMONDSBURY GREENWAY 1 *(Glos. Co)*** **Att: 17,500**
Young 3, Clayden **Price** **Ref: Mr C Steel**
Billericay: Norris, Blackaller, Bingham, Whettell, Bone, Reeves, Pullin, Scott, Clayden,Young, Groom. Sub: Carrigan
Almondsbury: Hamilton, Bowers, Scarrett, Sulllivan, Tudor, Wookey, Bowers, Shehean, Kerr, Butt, Price. Sub: Kilbaine

1980 STAMFORD 2 *(United Counties)* **GUISBOROUGH TOWN 0 *(Northern Alliance)*** **Att: 11,500**
Alexander, McGowan **Ref: Neil Midgeley**
Stamford: Johnson, Kwiatkowski, Ladd, McGowan, Bliszczak I, Mackin, Broadhurst, Hall,Czarnecki, Potter, Alexander. Sub: Bliszczak S
Guisborough: Cutter, Scott, Thornton, Angus, Maltby, Percy, Skelton, Coleman, McElvaney,Sills, Dilworth. Sub: Harrison

1981 WHICKHAM 3 *(Wearside)* **WILLENHALL 2 (aet) *(West Midlands)*** **Att: 12,000**
Scott, Williamson, Peck og **Smith, Stringer** **Ref: Mr R Lewis**
Whickham: Thompson, Scott, Knox, Williamson, Cook, Ward, Carroll, Diamond, Cawthra,Robertson, Turnbull. Sub: Alton
Willenhall: Newton, White, Darris, Woodall, Heath, Fox, Peck, Price, Matthews, Smith,Stringer. Sub: Trevor

1982 FOREST GREEN ROVERS 3 *(Hellenic)* **RAINWORTH M.W 0 *(Notts Alliance)*** **Att: 12,500**
Leitch 2, Norman **Ref: Mr K Walmsey**
Forest Green: Moss, Norman, Day, Turner, Higgins, Jenkins, Guest, Burns, Millard, Leitch, Doughty. Sub: Dangerfield
Rainworth M.W: Watson, Hallam, Hodgson, Slater, Sterland, Oliver, Knowles, Raine, Radzi, Reah, Comerford. Sub: Robinson

1983 V.S. RUGBY 1 *(West Midlands)* **HALESOWEN TOWN 0 *(West Midlands)*** **Att: 13,700**
Crawley **Ref: Mr B Daniels**
VS Rugby: Burton, McGinty, Harrison, Preston, Knox, Evans, ingram, Setchell, Owen,Beecham, Crawley. Sub: Haskins
Halesowen Town: Coldicott, Penn, Edmonds, Lacey, Randall, Shilvock, Hazelwood, Moss, Woodhouse,P Joinson, L Joinson. Sub: Smith

1984 STANSTED 3 *(Essex Senior)* **STAMFORD 2 *(United Counties)*** **Att: 8,125**
Holt, Gillard, Reading **Waddicore, Allen** **Ref: Mr T Bune**
Stanstead: Coe, Williams, Hilton, Simpson, Cooper, Reading, Callanan, Holt, Reevs,Doyle, Gillard. Sub: Williams
Stamford: Parslow, Smitheringate, Blades, McIlwain, Lyon, Mackin, Genovese, Waddicore,Allen, Robson, Beech. Sub: Chapman

1985 HALESOWEN TOWN 3 *(West Midlands)* **FLEETWOOD TOWN 1 *(N W Counties)*** **Att: 16,715**
L Joinson 2, Moss **Moran** **Ref: Mr C Downey**
Halesowen: Coldicott, Penn, Sherwood, Warner, Randle, Heath, Hazlewood, Moss (Smith),Woodhouse, P Joinson, L Joinson
Fleetwood Town: Dobson, Moran, Hadgraft, Strachan, Robinson, Milligan, Hall, Trainor, Taylor(Whitehouse), Cain, Kennerley

1986 HALESOWEN TOWN 3 *(West Midlands)* **SOUTHALL 0 *(Isthmian 2 South)*** **Att: 18,340**
Moss 2, L Joinson **Ref: Mr D Scott**
Halesowen: Pemberton, Moore, Lacey, Randle (Rhodes), Sherwood, Heath, Penn, Woodhouse, PJoinson, L Joinson, Moss
Southall: Mackenzie, James, McGovern, Croad, Holland, Powell (Richmond), Pierre,Richardson, Sweales, Ferdinand, Rowe

1987 **ST. HELENS** 3 *(N W Counties)* — **WARRINGTON TOWN 2** *(N W Counties)* — **Att: 4,254**
Layhe 2, Rigby — **Reid, Cook** — **Ref: Mr T Mills**
St Helens: Johnson, Benson, Lowe, Bendon, Wilson, McComb, Collins (Gledhill), O'Neill,Cummins, Lay, Rigby. Sub: Deakin
Warrington: O'Brien. Copeland, Hunter, Gratton, Whalley, Reid, Brownville (Woodyer), Cook,Kinsey, Looker (Hill), Hughes

1988 **COLNE DYNAMOES** 1 *(N W Counties)* — **EMLEY 0** *(Northern Counties East)* — **Att: 15,000**
Anderson — **Ref: Mr A Seville**
Colne Dynamoes: Mason, McFafyen, Westwell, Bentley, Dunn, Roscoe, Rodaway, Whitehead (Burke),Diamond, Anderson, Wood (Coates)
Emley: Dennis, Fielding, Mellor, Codd, Hirst (Burrows), Gartland (Cook), Carmody,Green, Bramald, Devine, Francis

1989 **TAMWORTH 1** *(West Midlands)* — **SUDBURY TOWN 1 (aet)** *(Eastern)* — **Att: 26,487**
Devaney — **Hubbick** — **Ref: Mr C Downey**
Tamworth: Bedford, Lockett, Atkins, Cartwright, McCormack, Myers, Finn, Devaney, Moores,Gordon, Stanton. Subs: Rathbone, Heaton
Sudbury Town: Garnham, Henry, G Barker, Boyland, Thorpe, Klug, D Barker, Barton, Oldfield,Smith, Hubbick. Subs: Money, Hunt
Replay **TAMWORTH** 3 — **SUDBURY TOWN 0** — **Att: 11,201**
Stanton 2, Moores — **at Peterborough**
Tamworth: Bedford, Lockett, Atkins, Cartwright, Finn, Myers, George, Devaney, Moores,Gordon, Stanton. Sub: Heaton
Sudbury Town: Garnham, Henry, G Barker, Boyland, Thorpe, Klug, D Barker, Barton, Oldfield,Smith, Hubbick. Subs: Money, Hunt

1990 **YEADING 0** *(Isthmian 2 South)* — **BRIDLINGTON TOWN 0 (aet)** *(N Co East)* — **Att: 7,932**
Ref: Mr R Groves
Yeading: Mackenzie, Wickens, Turner, Whiskey (McCarthy), Croad, Denton, Matthews, James(Charles), Sweates, Impey, Cordery
Bridlington: Taylor, Pugh, Freeman, McNeill, Warburton, Brentano, Wilkes (Hall), Noteman,Gauden, Whiteman, Brattan (Brown)
Replay **YEADING** 1 — **BRIDLINGTON TOWN 0** — **Att: 5,000**
Sweales — **at Leeds Utd FC**
Yeading: Mackenzie, Wickens, Turner, Whiskey, Croad (McCarthy), Schwartz, Matthews,James, Sweates, Impey (Welsh), Cordery
Bridlington: Taylor, Pugh, Freeman, McNeill, Warburton, Brentano, Wilkes (Brown), Noteman,Gauden (Downing), Whiteman, Brattan

1991 **GRESLEY ROVERS 4** *(West Midlands)* — **GUISELEY 4 (aet)** *(Northern Co East)* — **Att: 11,314**
Rathbone, Smith 2, Stokes — **Tennison 2, Walling, A Roberts** — **Ref: Mr C Trussell**
Gresley: Aston, Barry, Elliott (Adcock), Denby, Land, Astley, Stokes, K Smith, Acklam,Rathbone, Lovell (Weston)
Guiseley: Maxted, Bottomley, Hogarth, Tetley, Morgan, McKenzie, Atkinson (Annan),Tennison, Walling, A Roberts, B Roberts
Replay **GUISELEY** 3 — **GRESLEY ROVERS 1** — **Att: 7,585**
Tennison, Walling, Atkinson — **Astley** — **at Bramall Lane**
Guiseley: Maxted, Annan, Hogarth, Tetley, Morgan, McKenzie (Bottomley), Atkinson,Tennison (Noteman), Walling, A Roberts, B Roberts
Gresley: Aston, Barry, Elliott, Denby, Land, Astley, Stokes (Weston), K Smith, Acklam, Rathbone, Lovell (Adcock)

1992 **WIMBORNE TOWN** 5 *(Wessex)* — **GUISELEY 3** *(Northern Premier Div 1)* — **Att: 10,772**
Richardson, Sturgess 2, Killick 2 — **Noteman 2, Colville** — **Ref: Mr M J Bodenham**
Wimborne: Leonard, Langdown, Wilkins, Beacham, Allan, Taplin, Ames, Richardson, Bridle,Killick, Sturgess (Lovell), Lynn
Guiseley: Maxted, Atkinson, Hogarth, Tetley (Wilson), Morgan, Brockie, A Roberts,Tennison, Noteman (Colville), Annan, W Roberts

1993 **BRIDLINGTON TOWN** 1 *(NPL Div 1)* — **TIVERTON TOWN 0** *(Western)* — **Att: 9,061**
Radford — **Ref: Mr R A Hart**
Bridlington: Taylor, Brentano, McKenzie, Harvey, Bottomley, Woodcock, Grocock, A Roberts, Jones, Radford (Tyrell), Parkinson. Sub: Swailes
Tiverton Town: Nott, J Smith, N Saunders, M Saunders, Short (Scott), Steele, Annunziata, KSmith, Everett, Daly, Hynds (Rogers)

1994 **DISS TOWN** 2 *(Eastern)* — **TAUNTON TOWN 1** *(Western)* — **Att: 13,450**
Gibbs (p), Mendham — **Fowler** — **Ref: Mr K. Morton**
Diss Town: Woodcock, Carter, Wolsey (Musgrave), Casey (Bugg), Hartle, Smith, Barth, Mendham, Miles, Warne, Gibbs
Taunton Town: Maloy, Morris, Walsh, Ewens, Graddon, Palfrey, West (Hendry), Fowler, Durham, Perrett (Ward), Jarvis

1995 **ARLESEY TOWN** 2 *(South Midlands)* — **OXFORD CITY 1** *(Ryman 2)* — **Att: 13,670**
Palma, Gyalog — **S Fontaine** — **Ref: Mr G S Willard**
Arlesey: Young, Cardines, Bambrick, Palma (Ward), Hull, Gonsalves, Gyalog, Cox, Kane,O'Keefe, Marshall (Nicholls). Sub: Dodwell
Oxford: Fleet, Brown (Fisher), Hume, Shepherd, Muttock, Hamilton (Kemp), Thomas, Spittle, Sherwood, S Fontaine, C Fontaine. Sub: Torres

1996 **BRIGG TOWN** 3 *(N Co East)* — **CLITHEROE 0** *(N W Counties)* — **Att: 7,340**
Stead 2, Roach — **Ref: Mr S J Lodge**
Brigg: Gawthorpe, Thompson, Rogers, Greaves (Clay), Buckley (Mail), Elston, C Stead, McLean, N Stead (McNally), Flounders, Roach
Clitheroe: Nash, Lampkin, Rowbotham (Otley), Baron, Westwell, Rovine, Butcher, Taylor (Smith), Grimshaw, Darbyshire, Hill (Dunn)

1997 **WHITBY TOWN** 3 *(Northern)* — **NORTH FERRIBY UTD. 0** *(N Co East)* — **Att: 11,098**
Williams, Logan, Toman — **Ref: Graham Poll**
North Ferriby: Sharp, Deacey, Smith, Brentano, Walmsley, M Smith, Harrison (Horne), Phillips (Milner), France (Newman), Flounders, Tennison
Whitby Town: Campbell, Williams, Logan, Goodchild, Pearson, Cook, Goodrick (Borthwick), Hodgson, Robinson, Toman (Pyle), Pitman (Hall)

1998 **TIVERTON TOWN** 1 *(Western)* — TOW LAW TOWN 0 *(Northern Division 1)* — Att: 13,139
Varley — Ref: M A Riley

Tiverton Town: Edwards, Felton, Saunders, Tatterton, Smith J, Conning, Nancekivell (Rogers), Smith K (Varley), Everett, Daly, Leonard (Waters)
Tow Law Town: Dawson, Pickering, Darwent, Bailey, Hague, Moan, Johnson, Nelson, Suddick, Laidler (Bennett), Robinson.

1999 **TIVERTON TOWN** 1 *(Western)* — BEDLINGTON TERRIERS 0 *(Northern)* — Att: 13, 878
Rogers 88 — Ref: W. C. Burns

Bedlington Terriers: O'Connor, Bowes, Pike, Boon (Renforth), Melrose, Teasdale, Cross, Middleton (Ludlow), Gibb, Milner, Bond. Subs: Pearson, Cameron, Gowans
Tiverton Town: Edwards, Fallon, Saunders, Tatterton, Tallon, Conning (Rogers), Nancekivell (Pears), Varley, Everett, Daly, Leonard. Subs: Tucker, Hynds, Grimshaw

2000 **DEAL TOWN** 1 *(Kent)* — CHIPPENHAM TOWN 0 *(Western)* — Att: 20,000
Graham 87 — Ref: D Laws

Deal Town: Tucker, Kempster, Best, Ash, Martin, Seager, Monteith, Graham, Lovell, Marshall, Ribbens. Subs: Roberts, Warden, Turner
Chippenham Town: Jones, James, Andrews, Murphy, Burns, Woods, Brown, Charity, Tweddle, Collier, Godley. Subs: Tiley, Cutler

2001 **TAUNTON TOWN** 2 *(Western)* — BERKHAMPSTED TOWN 1 *(Isthmian 2)* — (at Villa Park) Att: 8,439
Fields 41, Laight 45 — Lowe 71 — Ref: E. K. Wolstenholme

Taunton Town: Draper, Down, Chapman, West, Hawkings, Kelly, Fields (Groves), Laight, Cann (Tallon), Bastow, Lynch (Hapgood). Subs: Ayres, Parker
Berkhampsted Town: O'Connor, Mullins, Lowe, Aldridge, Coleman, Brockett, Yates, Adebowale, Richardson, Smith, Nightingale. Subs: Ringsell, Hall, Knight, Franklin, Osborne

2002 **WHITLEY BAY** 1 *(Northern)* — TIPTREE UNITED 0 *(Eastern)* — (at Villa Park) Att: 4742
Chandler 97 — Ref: A Kaye

Whitley Bay: Caffrey, Sunderland, Walmsley, Dixon (Neil), Anderson, Locker, Middleton, Bowes (Carr), Chandler, Walton, Fenwick (Cuggy). Subs: Cook, Livermore
Tiptree United: Haygreen, Battell, Wall, Houghton, Fish, Streetley (Gillespie), Wareham (Snow), Daly, Barefield, Aransibia (Parnell), Brady. Subs: Powell, Ford.

2003 **BRIGG TOWN** 2 *(Northern Co.East)* — A.F.C SUDBURY 1 *(Eastern Counties)* — (at Upton Park) Att: 6,634
Housham 2, Carter 68 — Raynor 30 — Ref: M Fletcher

Brigg Town:- Steer, Raspin, Rowland, Thompson, Blanchard, Stones, Stead (Thompson 41), Housham, Borman (Drayton 87), Roach, Carter. Subs (not used) Nevis, Gawthorpe.
AFC Sudbury:- Greygoose, Head (Norfolk 63), Spearing, Tracey, Bishop, Anderson (Owen 73), Rayner, Gardiner (Banya 79), Bennett, Claydon, Betson. Subs (not used) Taylor, Hyde.

2004 **WINCHESTER CITY** 2 *(Wessex)* — A.F.C SUDBURY 0 *(Eastern Counties)* — (at St Andrews) Att: 5,080
Forbes 19, Smith 73 (pen) — Ref: P Crossley

Winchester City:- Arthur, Dyke (Tate 83), Bicknell, Redwood, Goss, Blake, Webber, Green, Mancey, Forbes (Rogers 70), Smith (Green 90). Subs (not used) - Lang and Rastall.
AFC Sudbury:- Greygoose, Head, Wardley, Girling, Tracey, Norfolk, Owen (Banya 62), Hyde (Calver 57), Bennett, Claydon, Betson (Francis 73n). Subs (not used) - Rayner, Nower.

2005 **DIDCOT TOWN** 3 *(Hellenic)* — A.F.C SUDBURY 2 *(Eastern Counties)* (at White Hart Lane) Att: 8,662
Beavon (2), Wardley (og) — Wardley, Calver (pen) — Ref: R Beeeby

Didcot Town:- Webb, Goodall, Heapy, Campbell, Green, Parrott, Hannigan, Ward, Concannon (Jones 88), Beavon (Bianchini 90), Powell. Subs (not used) – Cooper, Allen, Spurrett.
AFC Sudbury:- Greygoose, Girling, Wardley, Bennett, Hyde (Hayes 78), Owen (Norfolk 65), Claydon (Banya 59), Head, Calver, Betson, Terry Rayner. Subs (not used) – Howlett, Nower.

2006 **NANTWICH TOWN** 3 *(NWC 1)* — HILLINGDON BOROUGH 1 *(Spartan S.Mids P.)* (at St Andrews) Att: 3,286
Kinsey (2), Scheuber — Nelson

Nantwich Town:- Hackney, A.Taylor, T.Taylor, Smith, Davis, Donnelly, Beasley, Scheuber (Parkinson 69), Kinsey (Marrow 69), Blake (Scarlett 86) and Griggs. Subs (not used): O'Connor and Read.
Hillingdon Borough:- Brown, Rundell (Fenton 80),Kidson, Phillips, Croft, Lawrence, Duncan (Nelson 46), Tilbury, Hibbs, Wharton (Lyons 38). Subs (not used): O'Grady, White.

2007 **TRURO** 3 *(Western Division 1)* — AFC TOTTON 1 *(Wessex Division 1)* — Att: 27,754 (New Vase record)
Wills (2), Broad — Potter — Ref: P Joslin

AFC Totton: Brunnschweiler, Reacord, Troon (Stevens 60), Potter (Gregory 82), Bottomley, Austen, Roden, Gosney, Hamodu (Goss 89), Osman, Byres. Subs not used: Zammit, McCormack.
Truro City: Stevenson, Ash, Power, Smith, Martin (Pope 84), Broad, Wills, Gosling, Yetton, Watkins, Walker (Ludlam 90). Subs not used: Butcher, Routledge, Reski.

2008 **KIRKHAM & WESHAM** 2 *(North West Co. Div.2)* LOWESTOFT TOWN 1 *(Eastern Co. Premier)* **Att: 19,537**
Walwyn (2) **Thompson (og)** **Ref: A D'Urso**

Kirkham and Wesham: Summerfield, Jackson (Walwyn 79), Keefe (Allen 55), Thompson, Shaw, Eastwood, Clark, Blackwell, Wane, Paterson (Sheppard 90), Smith. Subs not used: Moffat and Abbott

Lowestoft Town: Reynolds, Poppy, Potter, Woodrow, Saunders, Plaskett (McGee 79), Godbold, Darren Cockrill (Dale Cockrill 46), Stock, Hough, King (Hunn 55). Subs not used: McKenna and Rix.

2009 **WHITLEY BAY** 2 *(Northern Division One)* GLOSSOP NORTH END 0 *(North West Co. Prem)* **Att: 12,212**
Kerr, Chow **Ref: K Friend**

Whitley Bay: Burke, Taylor, Picton, McFarlane (Fawcett 60), Coulson, Ryan, Moore, Robson, Kerr, Chow (Robinson 73), Johnston (Bell 60). Subs not used: McLean and Reay.

Glossop North End: Cooper, Young, Kay, Lugsden, Yates, Gorton, Bailey (Hind 57), Morris, Allen (Balfe 65), Hamilton (Bailey 72), Hodges. Subs not used: Whelan and Parker.

2010 **WHITLEY BAY** 6 *(Northern Division One)* WROXHAM 1 *(Eastern Counties Premier Division)* **Att: 8,920**
Chow 21(sec), Easthaugh 16 (og), Kerr, Johnston, Robinson, Gillies **Cook 12** **Ref: A Taylor**

Whitley Bay: Terry Burke, Craig McFarlane, Callum Anderson, Richard Hodgson, (sub Lee Picton 69th min), Darren Timmons, Leon Ryan, Adam Johnston (sub Joshua Gillies 77th min), Damon Robson, Lee Kerr, Paul Chow (sub Phillip Bell 61st min), Paul Robinson.
Subs not used – Tom Kindley and Chris Reid.

Wroxham: Scott Howie, Gavin Pauling (sub Ross Durrant 57th min), Shaun Howes, Graham Challen, Martin McNeil (sub Josh Carus 46th min), Andy Easthaugh (sub Owen Paynter 69th min), Steve Spriggs, Gavin Lemmon, Paul Cook, Danny White, Gary Gilmore.
Subs not used – Danny Self and Gareth Simpson.

2011 **WHITLEY BAY** 3 *(Northern Division One)* COALVILLE TOWN 2 *(Midland Alliance)* **Att: 8,778**
Chow 28, 90, Kerr 61 **Moore 58, Goodby 80** **Ref: S Mathieson**

Whitley Bay: Terry Burke, Craig McFarlane (sub Steve Gibson 90th min), Callum Anderson, Darren Timmons, Gareth Williams (sub David Coulson 68th min), Damon Robson, Lee Kerr, Paul Chow, Paul Robinson, David Pounder (sub Brian Smith 68th min), Gary Ormston.
Subs not used – Kyle Hayes (gk) and Brian Rowe. Coalville Town: Sean Bowles, Ashley Brown (sub Matthew Gardner 88th min), Cameron Stuart, Adam Goodby, Zach Costello, Lee Miveld,
Callum Woodward, Anthony Carney (sub Craig Attwood 90th min), Ryan Robbins (sub Ashley Wells 66th min), Matt Moore, Jerome Murdock.
Subs not used – Richard Williams (gk) and James Dodd.

2012 **DUNSTON UTS** 2 *(Northern Division One)* WEST AUCKLAND TOWN 0 *(Northern Division One)* **Att: 5,126**
Bulford 32, 79 **Ref: R East**

Dunston UTS: Liam Connell, Ben Cattenach, Terry Galbraith, Michael Robson, Chris Swailes, Kane Young, Steven Shaw, Michael Dixon, Stephen Goddard (sub Sreven Preen 84th min), Andrew Bulford (sub Danny Craggs 88th min), Lee McAndrew.
Subs not used – Andrew Clark (g/k), Ian Herron, Jack Burns.

West Auckland Town: Mark Bell, Neil Pattinson, Andrew Green, Jonny Gibson, John Parker, Mark Stephenson (sub Daniel Hindmarsh 76th min), Stuart Banks, Mark Hudson, Mattie Moffatt, Michael Rae, Adam Nicholls (sub Martin Young 60th min).
Subs not used – Daryll Hall, Ross Preston, Matthew Coad.

2013 **SPENNYMOOR TOWN** 2 *(Northern Division One)* TUNBRIDGE WELLS 1 *(Kent League)* **Att: 16,751**
Cogdon 18, Graydon 80 **Stanford 78** **Ref: M Naylor**

Spennymoor Town: Robert Dean, Kallum Griffiths, Leon Ryan, Chris Mason, Stephen Capper, Keith Graydon, Lewis Dodds, Wayne Phillips (Anthony Peacock 64 min), Joe Walton (Andrew Stephenson 73 min), Mark Davison, (Michael Rae 76 min), Gavin Congdon.
Subs not used - David Knight (g/k), Steven Richardson.

Tunbridge Wells: Chris Oladogba, Jason Bourne, Scott Whibley, Perry Spackman, Lewis Mingle, Jon Pilbeam (Richard Sinden 85 min), Andy McMath, Joe Fuller (Tom Davey 58 min), Andy Irvine, Carl Connell (Jack Harris 58 min), Josh Stanford.
Subs not used - Michael Czanner (gk), Andy Boyle.

2014 **SHOLING** 1 *(Wessex Premier Division - 1st)* WEST AUCKLAND TOWN 0 *(Northern Division One - 5th)* **Att: 5,432**
McLean 71 **Ref: D Coote**

Sholing: Matt Brown, Mike Carter, Marc Diaper, Peter Castle (Dan Miller 53 min), Lee Bright, Tyronne Bowers (Kevin Brewster 75 min), Barry Mason, Lewis Fennemore (Alex Sawyer 78 min), Lee Wort, Byron Mason, Marvin McLean.
Subs not used - Ashley Jarvis, Nick Watts.

West Auckland Town: Jordan Nixon, Neil Pattinson, Andrew Green (Jonathan Gibson 63 min), Daryll Hall, Lewis Galpin, Brian Close, Shaun Vipond (Stuart Banks 76 min), Robert Briggs, Mattie Moffat (Steven Richardson 74 min). John Campbell, Dennis Knight.
Subs not used - Paul Garthwaite, Adam Wilkinson..

2015 **NORTH SHIELDS** 2 *(Northern Division One - 4th)* GLOSSOP NORTH END 1 *(North West Co. Premier - 1st)* **Att: 9,674**
Bainbridge 80, Forster 96 **Bailey 55** **Ref: A Madley**

North Shields: Christopher Bannon, Stuart Donnison, John Parker, Kevin Hughes, John Grey, James Luccock (Ryan Carr 59), Ben Richardson, Mciahel McKeown, Dean Holmes (Adam Forster 69), Denver Morris, Gareth Bainbridge (Kieran Wrightson 107).
Subs not used - Curtis Coppen and Marc Lancaster.

Glossop North End: Greg Hall, Michael Bowler, Matthew Russell, Kevin Lugsden, Dave Young, Martin Parker, Lee Blackshaw (Samuel Grimshaw 69), Samuel Hare (Samuel Hind 82), Tom Bailey, Kieran Lugsden, Eddie Moran (Daniel White 60).
Subs not used - Benjamin Richardson and Richard Gresty.

2016 MORPETH TOWN 4 *(Northern Division One - 4th)* **HEREFORD 1** *(Midland League - 1st)* **Att: 46,781**
Swailes 34, Carr 47, Taylor 59, Bell 92 **Purdie 2** (Inaugural Non-League finals day)
Ref: S Atwelly

Morpeth Town: Karl Dryden, Stephen Forster, James Novak, Ben Sayer, Chris Swailes, Michael Hall, Sean Taylor (sub Damien Mullen 78), Keith Graydon, Luke Carr (sub Shaun Bell 88), Michael Chilton (sub Steven Anderson 69), Jordan Fry.
Subs not used - Dale Pearson and Niall Harrison.
Hereford: Martin Horsell, Jimmy Oates, Joel Edwards, Rob Purdie, Ryan Green, Aaron Birch, Pablo Haysham, Mike Symons, Jamie Willets (sub John Mills 70), Joe Tumelty (sub Mustapha Bundu 55), Sirdic Grant.
Subs not used - Nathan Summers, Dylan Bonella and Ross Staley.

2017 SOUTH SHIELDS 4 *(Northern Division One - 1st)* **CLEETHORPES TOWN 0** *(Northern Counties East Premier - 1st)* **Att: 38,224**
Finnigan 43 (pen), Morse 80, Foley 86, 89 (Combined FA trophy/Vase att.)
Ref: D England

South Shields: Liam Connell, Alex Nicholson, Darren Lough, Jon Shaw, Dillon Morse, Julio Arca, Andrew Stephenson (sub Robert Briggs 56), Wayne Phillips (sub Barrie Smith 82), Gavin Congdon, Carl Finnigan (sub Michael Richardson 71), David Foley.
Subs not used - Louis Storey and Darren Holden.
Cleethorpes Town: Liam Higton, Tim Lowe, Peter Winn, Liam Dickens, Matt Bloomer, Matty Coleman (sub Luke Mascall 70), Liam Davis (sub Jack Richardson 73), Alex Flett, Marc Cooper (Andy Taylor 61), Brody Richardson, Jon Oglesby.
Subs not used - Gary King and Kieran Wressell.

2018 THATCHAM TOWN 1 *(Hellenic Premier - 1st)* **STOCKTON TOWN 0** *(Northern League D1 - 6th)* **Att: 31,430**
Cooper-Clark 23 (pen) (Combined FA trophy/Vase att.)
Ref: J Brooks

Thatcham Town: Chris Rackley, Lewis Brownhill, Curtis Angell, Tom Melledew (c) (Ashliegh James 81), Baboucarr Jarra, Tom Moran, Harrison Bayley, Shane Cooper-Clark (Rose Cook 89), Gavin James, Ekow Elliott, Jordan Brown (Jemel Johnson 70).
Subs not used - Harry Grant, Gareth Thomas.
Stockton Town: Michael Arthur, Joe Carter (Matthew Garbutt 61), James Ward (Adam Nicholson 79), Nathan Mulligan, Dale Mulligan, Tom Coulthard (c), Kevin Hayes, Fred Woodhouse, Jamie Owens, James Risbrough, Chris Stockton (Sonni Coleman 67).
Subs not used - Alan Cossavella, Chris Dunwell.

All Finals at Wembley unless otherwise stated.

FAV - F - Chertsey's 'keeper, Jupp, keeps this Cray attack out. Photo: Peter Barnes.

FAV - F - Midfield action from the final. Photo: Peter Barnes.

FAV - F - The race is on to get to the ball first. Photo: Peter Barnes.

PRELIMINARY ROUND

No.	Home		Away	Score	Att
1	Chester-Le-Street Town	v	Ryton & Crawcrook Albion (4/9)	0-4	
2	Workington	v	Hebburn Town (3/9)	1-2	103
3	Stockton Town	v	South Shields (28/8)	3-4	
4	AFC Darwen	v	Hyde United (5/9)	0-6	
5	FC United of Manchester	v	Nantwich Town (5/9)	2-1	244
6	Prescot Cables	v	Abbey Hey (5/9)	4-0	
7	Curzon Ashton	v	Witton Albion (3/9)	10-4	127
8	Marine	v	Southport (3/9)	2-2aet	153
	(Marine won 7-6 on kicks from the penalty mark)				
9	Stockport County	v	Radcliffe (4/9)	5-2	187
10	Chester	v	Sandbach United (5/9)	5-1	
	(at Sandbach United FC)				
11	Ashton Town	v	Altrincham (4/9)	0-5	55
12	West Didsbury & Chorlton	v	City of Liverpool (12/9)	0-2	25
	(5/9 – match abandoned after 45 minutes due to floodlight failure)				
13	Litherland Remyca	v	Cheadle Town (5/9)	3-1	
14	Ashton Athletic	v	Mossley (6/9)	4-2aet	79
15	Bootle	v	Vauxhall Motors (5/9)	1-0	
16	Staveley MW	v	Bradford (Park Avenue) (3/9)	2-4	117
17	Handsworth Parramore	v	York City (5/9)	1-3	72
18	Steeton	v	Harrogate Railway Athletic (6/9)	2-4	34
	(at Harrogate Railway Athletic FC)				
19	Ossett United	v	Silsden (5/9)	4-2	
	(at Ossett Albion FC)				
20	Farsley Celtic	v	Tadcaster Albion (5/9)	0-8	
21	Selby Town	v	Frickley Athletic (7/9)	0-11	70
22	Rossington Main	v	Shelley (3/9)	2-1	
23	Pickering Town	v	Nostell MW		
	(walkover for Nostell MW – Pickering Town withdrawn)				
24	Deeping Rangers	v	Harrowby United (6/9)	7-1	
25	Heather St Johns	v	Lincoln United (5/9)	3-1aet	
26	Cleethorpes Town	v	Eastwood Community (6/9)	1-0	61
27	Dunkirk	v	Basford United (6/9)	0-7	113
28	Grantham Town	v	Harborough Town (6/9)	4-2	64
29	Bottesford Town	v	Sandiacre Town		
	(walkover for Bottesford Town – Sandiacre Town withdrawn)				
30	Buxton	v	Blaby & Whetstone Athletic (5/9)	3-0	
31	West Bridgford	v	Dronfield Town (6/9)	6-1	
32	Alfreton Town	v	Long Eaton United (4/9)	1-3	118
33	Anstey Nomads	v	Ashby Ivanhoe		
	(walkover for Anstey Nomads – Ashby Ivanhoe withdrawn)				
34	Mickleover Sports	v	Boston United (5/9)	1-1aet	
	(Mickleover Sports win 4-3 on kicks from the penalty mark)				
35	Hinckley	v	Aylestone Park	0-1	68
36	Spalding United	v	Bourne Town (4/9)	2-3	
37	Newcastle Town	v	Bedworth United (4/9)	2-1aet	42
38	Stafford Rangers	v	Stourbridge (6/9)	0-2	98
39	Halesowen Town	v	Nuneaton Griff		
	(walkover for Halesowen Town – Nuneaton Griff withdrawn)				
40	Alvechurch	v	Stratford Town (5/9)	1-4	41
41	Rushall Olympic	v	Leek Town (3/9)	4-2	
42	Bromsgrove Sporting	v	Haughmond (6/9)	1-3aet	40
43	Coventry Sphinx	v	Coton Green (6/9)	3-4	44
44	Ellesmere Rangers	v	Racing Club Warwick (6/9)	0-4	25
45	Coleshill Town	v	Walsall Wood (7/9)	3-1	48
46	Kidderminster Harriers	v	Dudley Town (4/9)	7-0	
47	AFC Telford United	v	Evesham United (6/9)	2-2aet	
	(AFC Telford United won 5-3 on kicks from the penalty mark)				
48	Leamington	v	Eccleshall		
	(walkover for Leamington – Eccleshall withdrawn)				
49	Lye Town	v	Lichfield City (6/9)	2-6	77
50	Nuneaton Borough	v	Hednesford Town (6/9)	6-2	45
51	Brackley Town	v	St Ives Town (5/9)	4-2	
52	Peterborough Sports	v	Biggleswade Town (6/9)	6-0	
53	Rothwell Corinthians	v	Cogenhoe United (6/9)	0-9	
54	Godmanchester Rovers	v	Potton United		
	(walkover for Godmanchester Rovers – Potton United withdrawn)				
55	AFC Rushden & Diamonds	v	Peterborough Northern Star (7/9)	3-0	44
56	Huntingdon Town	v	Bugbrooke St Michaels		
	(walkover for Bugbrooke St Michaels – Huntingdon Town withdrawn)				
57	Kettering Town	v	Desborough Town		
	(walkover for Kettering Town – Desborough Town withdrawn)				
58	Irchester United	v	AFC Dunstable		
	(walkover for AFC Dunstable – Irchester United withdrawn)				
59	Kempston Rovers	v	Corby Town (6/9)	0-6	105
60	Gorleston	v	March Town United (6/9)	6-0	54
61	Whitton United	v	Ipswich Wanderers (6/9)	1-5	66
62	Walsham Le Willows	v	Haverhill Rovers (6/9)	3-2	45
63	Mildenhall Town	v	Histon (6/9)	4-3	46
64	Dereham Town	v	Fakenham Town (6/9)	6-2	74
65	Framlingham Town	v	King's Lynn Town (6/9)	0-1	
66	Wisbech St Mary	v	Hadleigh United (4/9)	0-2	
67	Swaffham Town	v	Needham Market (6/9)	1-5	
68	Felixstowe & Walton United	v	Bury Town (6/9)	2-3aet	87
69	Norwich United	v	Woodbridge Town (3/9)	5-1	40
70	Hitchin Town	v	Barking (11/9)	1-0	
	(3/9 – match postponed)				
71	Cheshunt	v	Welwyn Garden City (5/9)	0-20	
72	Tower Hamlets	v	Heybridge Swifts (3/9)	3-0	
73	St Margaretsbury	v	Walthamstow (6/9)	0-2	
74	Redbridge	v	Hullbridge Sports (7/9)	0-1	
75	Clapton	v	Tring Athletic		
	(walkover for Tring Athletic – Clapton withdrawn)				
76	Woodford Town	v	Grays Athletic (14/9)	1-1aet	
	(Grays Athletic won 3-1 on kicks from the penalty mark – at Aveley FC)				
77	St Albans City	v	Ware (5/9)	1-2aet	
78	Aveley	v	Potters Bar Town (3/9)	3-1	
79	Royston Town	v	Chelmsford City (4/9)	1-3	
80	Great Wakering Rovers	v	Waltham Abbey		
	(walkover for Great Wakering Rovers – Waltham Abbey withdrawn)				
81	Witham Town	v	East Thurrock United		
	(walkover for Witham Town – East Thurrock United withdrawn)				
82	Concord Rangers	v	Saffron Walden Town (6/9)	0-1	109
83	Hertford Town	v	Barkingside (7/9)	1-5	60
84	Romford	v	Hoddesdon Town		
	(walkover for Romford – Hoddesdon Town withdrawn)				
85	Codicote	v	Takeley (6/9)	0-1	27
86	AFC Hornchurch	v	Ilford (4/9)	3-2	
87	Hanwell Town	v	Hendon (4/9)	2-3	32
88	Haringey Borough	v	Wingate & Finchley (3/9)	1-2	
89	Colney Heath	v	Ashford Town (Middx) (3/9)	16-0	
90	Staines Town	v	Flackwell Heath (3/9)	1-3	59
91	Burnham	v	Aylesbury (6/9)	1-1aet	33
	(Aylesbury won 5-3 on kicks from the penalty mark)				
92	North Greenford United	v	Harefield United (5/9)	0-1	64
93	Spelthorne Sports	v	Chalfont St Peter (5/9)	0-4	45
94	Uxbridge	v	Amersham Town		
	(walkover for Uxbridge – Amersham Town withdrawn)				
95	Leverstock Green	v	Cockfosters (6/9)	3-1	41
96	Chesham United	v	Sandhurst Town		
	(walkover for Sandhurst Town – Chesham United withdrawn)				
97	Harrow Borough	v	Hayes & Yeading United (3/9)	0-4	75
98	Enfield Town	v	Wallingford Town (6/9)	5-1	
99	CB Hounslow United	v	Abingdon United		
	(walkover for CB Hounslow United – Abingdon United withdrawn)				
100	Shrivenham	v	Buckingham Athletic (6/9)	0-4	58
101	Northwood	v	Brimsdown (6/9)	5-0	24
102	Glebe	v	Dartford (4/9)	2-3	
103	Phoenix Sports	v	Herne Bay (5/9)	6-0	
104	Cray Wanderers	v	Holmesdale (3/9)	4-2aet	
105	Sevenoaks Town	v	Tooting & Mitcham United		
	(walkover for Tooting & Mitcham United – Sevenoaks Town withdrawn)				
106	Dulwich Hamlet	v	Fisher (5/9)	3-1	
107	Croydon	v	Cray Valley (PM) (3/9)	3-0	
108	Lingfield	v	Lewisham Borough		
	(walkover for Lingfield – Lewisham Borough withdrawn)				
109	Welling United	v	Eastbourne Borough (6/9)	2-4	62
110	Eastbourne United	v	Chatham Town		
	(walkover for Chatham Town – Eastbourne United withdrawn)				
111	Hollands & Blair	v	Erith & Belvedere		
	(walkover for Hollands & Blair - Erith & Belvedere withdrawn)				
112	Ramsgate	v	Tonbridge Angels (6/9)	1-2	56
113	Bridon Ropes	v	VCD Athletic (6/9)	3-6	
114	Ashford United	v	Erith Town		
	(walkover for Ashford United – Erith Town withdrawn)				
115	South Park	v	Abbey Rangers (3/9)	4-2	42
116	Chichester City	v	Raynes Park Vale (5/9)	1-4	
117	Three Bridges	v	Steyning Town Community (3/9)	4-3	18
118	Crowborough Athletic	v	Mile Oak (6/9)	3-0	42
119	Burgess Hill Town	v	Whitehawk (3/9)	1-2	95
120	Hackney Wick	v	Sutton Common Rovers (7/9)	7-2	
	(at Haringey Borough FC)				

121	East Preston	v	Newhaven (6/9)	0-3	
122	Dorking Wanderers	v	Chertsey Town (6/9)	4-2	118
123	Leatherhead	v	Whyteleafe (3/9)	2-5	61
124	Haywards Heath Town	v	Lancing (6/9)	3-0	57
125	Knaphill	v	Shoreham (4/9)	6-1	
126	Horley Town	v	Loxwood (5/9)	0-10	49
127	Hastings United	v	Metropolitan Police (6/9)	1-3	
128	Camberley Town	v	Corinthian Casuals (6/9)	13-0	
129	Worthing United	v	Woking (6/9)	1-1aet	
	(Woking won 3-1 on kicks from the penalty mark)				
130	Clanfield 85	v	Hungerford Town (6/9)	2-4	
131	Thame United	v	Banbury United		
	(walkover for Banbury United – Thame United withdrawn)				
132	Fleet Spurs	v	Basingstoke Town (3/9)	6-0	
133	Fleet Town	v	Thatcham Town (3/9)	4-1	47
134	Alton	v	Bracknell Town (4/9)	1-9	65
135	Hartley Wintney	v	Ascot United (5/9)	4-5aet	
136	Windsor	v	Binfield (6/9)	5-1	53
137	Andover Town	v	Ardley United (6/9)	1-0aet	
138	Christchurch	v	Team Solent (6/9)	1-6	
139	Sholing	v	Salisbury (6/9)	4-0	115
140	Farnborough	v	Cove (3/9)	3-1	
141	Tuffley Rovers	v	Bitton (6/9)	6-1	73
142	Chippenham Town	v	Yate Town (6/9)	2-3	
143	Oldland Abbotonians	v	Cirencester Town (3/9)	0-2	
144	Bishops Cleeve	v	Almondsbury (6/9)	1-3	44
145	Portishead Town	v	Radstock Town (13/9)	4-2	
	(6/9 – match postponed)				
146	Wellington AFC	v	Odd Down (4/9)	1-7	46
147	Torquay United	v	Elburton Villa (11/9)	3-1	
148	Bath City	v	Street (5/9)	2-1	
149	Weston Super Mare	v	Helston Athletic (4/9)	2-5	
150	Frome Town	v	Wells City (5/9)	0-2	52
151	Welton Rovers	v	Keynsham Town (4/9)	1-0	45

FIRST ROUND QUALIFYING

1	Hebburn Town	v	Carlisle City (19/9)	2-1	
2	Ryton & Crawcrook Albion	v	North Shields (20/9)	1-7	109
3	Seaham Red Star	v	Consett (17/9)	6-2	43
4	South Shields	v	Spennymoor Town (17/9)	3-1	231
5	Bootle	v	Prescot Cables (19/9)	3-1aet	
6	Stockport Town	v	Litherland Remyca (17/9)	2-8	39
7	Stalybridge Celtic	v	Irlam (19/9)	3-4	
8	Curzon Ashton	v	Hyde United (26/9)	1-1aet	130
	(Hyde United won 3-1 on kicks from the penalty mark)				
9	Chorley	v	Stockport County (19/9)	4-0	192
10	Daisy Hill	v	Ashton Athletic (19/9)	4-3	61
11	Marine	v	Chester (17/9)	0-6	188
12	City of Liverpool	v	FC United of Manchester (19/9)	4-1	45
	(at Ashville FC)				
13	Lancaster City	v	Altrincham		
	(walkover for Altrincham – Lancaster City withdrawn)				
14	St Helens Town	v	Runcorn Town		
	(walkover for St Helens Town – Runcorn Town withdrawn)				
15	Bradford (Park Avenue)	v	Harworth Colliery (19/9)	2-4	128
16	Garforth Town	v	Harrogate Railway Athletic (20/9)	4-0	
17	AFC Emley	v	Sheffield (20/9)	1-6	45
18	Ossett United	v	Frickley Athletic (26/9)	3-1	57
	(at Ossett Albion FC)				
19	Nostell MW	v	Stocksbridge Park Steels (27/9)	2-5	62
20	Guiseley	v	Rossington Main (18/9)	11-0	125
21	Tadcaster Albion	v	York City (17/9)	3-1	
22	West Bridgford	v	Leicester Road (20/9)	5-1	35
23	Cleethorpes Town	v	Aylestone Park (20/9)	1-4	44
24	Leicester Nirvana	v	Long Eaton United (19/9)	1-3	
25	Heather St Johns	v	Anstey Nomads (20/9)	2-3	40
26	Deeping Rangers	v	Basford United (20/9)	1-2	
27	Stamford	v	Matlock Town (17/9)	1-6	
28	Bottesford Town	v	Lutterworth Athletic (27/9)	5-1	41
29	Buxton	v	Mickleover Sports (19/9)	1-2	60
30	Grantham Town	v	Bourne Town (20/9)	3-1	95
31	Hereford	v	Tipton Town (25/9)	11-3	154
32	Lichfield City	v	Stourbridge (17/9)	1-2	
33	Worcester City	v	Malvern Town (17/9)	0-2	91
34	Coleshill Town	v	Tamworth (17/9)	2-0	159
35	Romulus	v	Kidderminster Harriers (21/9)	0-2	
36	Newcastle Town	v	Halesowen Town (19/9)	3-5aet	44
37	Sutton Coldfield Town	v	Pegasus Juniors (17/9)	8-0	47
38	Rushall Olympic	v	Racing Club Warwick (17/9)	3-0	44
39	Boldmere St Michaels	v	AFC Telford United (18/9)	0-3	
40	Bustleholme	v	Nuneaton Borough (18/9)	0-2	
41	Rugby Town	v	Leamington (19/9)	11-2	76
42	Rugby Borough	v	Coton Green (17/9)	2-1	
43	Stratford Town	v	Haughmond (20/9)	4-1	41
44	Wellingborough Town	v	Biggleswade United		
	(walkover for Wellingborough Town – Biggleswade United withdrawn)				
45	St Neots Town	v	Peterborough Sports (17/9)	1-4	61
46	AFC Dunstable	v	AFC Rushden & Diamonds (20/9)	1-2	66
47	Kettering Town	v	Bugbrooke St Michaels (20/9)	1-0	59
48	Brackley Town	v	Godmanchester Rovers (17/9)	8-1	68
49	Corby Town	v	Cogenhoe United (17/9)	2-4	77
50	Ely City	v	Walsham Le Willows (20/9)	1-2aet	
51	AFC Sudbury	v	Norwich United (20/9)	3-1	69
52	Wroxham	v	Stowmarket Town (20/9)	4-1	
53	Mildenhall Town	v	Gorleston (20/9)	5-2	76
54	Brantham Athletic	v	King's Lynn Town (18/9)	1-5	
55	Cornard United	v	Cambridge City (20/9)	0-1	
56	Dereham Town	v	Hadleigh United (20/9)	3-1	62
57	Bury Town	v	Ipswich Wanderers (17/9)	5-0	85
58	Leiston	v	Needham Market (20/9)	2-1	64
59	Newmarket Town	v	Great Yarmouth Town (18/9)	3-1aet	
60	Great Wakering Rovers	v	FC Broxbourne Borough (20/9)	2-1aet	51
61	Walthamstow	v	Saffron Walden Town (20/9)	0-1aet	
62	Takeley	v	Brentwood Town (20/9)	3-7	
63	Hitchin Town	v	Grays Athletic (20/9)	0-1	
64	Tilbury	v	AFC Hornchurch (21/9)	0-3	54
65	Sawbridgeworth Town	v	Brightlingsea Regent (20/9)	5-5aet	
	(Sawbridgeworth Town won 5-4 on kicks from the penalty mark)				
66	Hullbridge Sports	v	Chelmsford City (19/9)	4-1	152
67	Bishop's Stortford	v	Barkingside (19/9)	4-3	77
68	Tower Hamlets	v	Romford (17/9)	0-1	
69	Welwyn Garden City	v	Ware (20/9)	4-2	
70	Tring Athletic	v	Hadley		
	(walkover for Tring Athletic – Hadley withdrawn)				
71	Aveley	v	Witham Town (17/9)	1-0	
72	Hayes & Yeading United	v	Bedfont Sports Club (19/9)	3-2	51
73	Flackwell Heath	v	CB Hounslow United (20/9)	9-0	50
74	Didcot Town	v	Winslow United (20/9)	4-1	46
75	Hendon	v	Chalfont St Peter (19/9)	4-2	54
	(tie awarded to Chalfont St Peter – Hendon removed)				
76	Kings Langley	v	Newport Pagnell Town (20/9)	4-1	38
77	Wealdstone	v	Hemel Hempstead Town (19/9)	0-1	76
78	Aylesbury	v	Sandhurst Town (20/9)	5-1	54
79	London Tigers	v	Buckingham Athletic (19/9)	0-3	
	(at Rayners Lane FC)				
80	Colney Heath	v	Northwood (17/9)	2-1aet	
81	Wingate & Finchley	v	Uxbridge (20/9)	2-0	96
82	Harefield United	v	Edgware Town		
	(walkover for Harefield United – Edgware Town withdrawn)				
83	Leverstock Green	v	Enfield Town (20/9)	3-0	32
84	VCD Athletic	v	Cray Wanderers (18/9)	0-6	
85	Folkestone Invicta	v	Hollands & Blair (18/9)	3-0	
86	Corinthian	v	East Grinstead Town (18/9)	6-0	38
87	Tooting & Mitcham United	v	Dartford (17/9)	0-3	
88	AFC Croydon Athletic	v	Croydon (19/9)	0-5	20
89	Thamesmead Town	v	Tonbridge Angels (17/9)	0-1	
	(at Rochester United FC)				
90	Dulwich Hamlet	v	Lingfield		
	(walkover for Dulwich Hamlet – Lingfield withdrawn)				
91	Chatham Town	v	Phoenix Sports (18/9)	1-4	114
92	Carshalton Athletic	v	Eastbourne Borough (21/9)	3-1	78
93	Chipstead	v	Ashford United (20/9)	3-4aet	30
94	Lewes	v	Hackney Wick (20/9)	6-2	31
95	Hampton & Richmond Borough	v	Knaphill (19/9)	5-1	
96	Three Bridges	v	Worthing (20/9)	0-4	36
97	Crowborough Athletic	v	Whitehawk (20/9)	2-8	40
98	Sidlesham	v	Arundel		
	(walkover for Arundel – Sidlesham withdrawn)				
99	Loxwood	v	Kingstonian (19/9)	1-2	52
100	Haywards Heath Town	v	Bognor Regis Town (20/9)	2-3aet	232
101	Redhill	v	Guildford City (20/9)	1-2	
102	Chessington & Hook United	v	Dorking Wanderers	3-3aet	80
	(Dorking Wanderers won 7-5 on kicks from the penalty mark)				

No.	Home		Away	Score	Att
103	Woking	v	South Park (20/9)	2-3	90
104	Raynes Park Vale	v	Walton & Hersham (20/9)	3-2	
105	Balham	v	Whyteleafe	1-1aet	
	(Whyteleafe won 4-1 on kicks from the penalty mark)				
106	Camberley Town	v	Westfield		
	(walkover for Camberley Town – Westfield withdrawn)				
107	Newhaven	v	Metropolitan Police (17/9)	1-3	72
108	Oxford City	v	Holmer Green (18/9)	2-2aet	51
	(Oxford City won 3-2 on kicks from the penalty mark)				
109	Kidlington	v	Banbury United (20/9)	3-0	45
110	Andover Town	v	Bracknell Town (17/9)	4-0	55
111	Windsor	v	Ascot United (20/9)	1-2	77
112	Hungerford Town	v	Fleet Town (19/9)	2-1	53
113	Reading City	v	Fleet Spurs (17/9)	4-3aet	
	(at Fleet Spurs FC)				
114	Winchester City	v	Moneyfields (20/9)	0-4	51
115	Totton & Eling	v	Sholing (20/9)	5-3	
116	AFC Totton	v	Wimborne Town (20/9)	4-2aet	102
117	AFC Stoneham	v	AFC Portchester (19/9)	1-0	
118	Team Solent	v	Poole Town (20/9)	5-4aet	
119	Brockenhurst	v	Farnborough (20/9)	8-2	
120	Longwell Green Sports	v	Cirencester Town (17/9)	1-7	
121	Pewsey Vale	v	Malmesbury Victoria (19/9)	1-9	40
122	Tuffley Rovers	v	Slimbridge (20/9)	1-4	121
123	New College Swindon	v	Almondsbury (17/9)	0-3	
124	Yate Town	v	Bristol Manor Farm (19/9)	4-0	46
125	Wells City	v	Torquay United (18/9)	0-6	30
126	Paulton Rovers	v	Bridgwater Town (20/9)	2-4	46
127	Portishead Town	v	Welton Rovers (20/9)	5-3	
128	Clevedon Town	v	Bath City (17/9)	1-0	81
129	Odd Down	v	Helston Athletic (18/9)	2-1	61

SECOND ROUND QUALIFYING

No.	Home		Away	Score	Att
1	North Shields	v	Seaham Red Star (1/10)	3-1	135
2	Hartlepool United	v	Hebburn Town (3/10)	5-1	188
3	South Shields	v	Gateshead (1/10)	3-1	218
4	Litherland Remyca	v	Irlam (2/10)	4-0	40
	(at Irlam FC)				
5	City of Liverpool	v	Hyde United (3/10)	1-3	37
	(at Ashville FC)				
6	St Helens Town	v	Chorley (7/10)	0-7	
7	Chester	v	Wrexham (3/10)	3-2	
8	Salford City	v	Bootle (4/10)	3-0aet	240
9	Daisy Hill	v	Altrincham (3/10)	3-4	
10	Barrow	v	AFC Fylde (3/10)	0-5	92
11	Harrogate Town	v	Guiseley (1/10)	1-5	105
12	Garforth Town	v	FC Halifax Town (4/10)	0-1	
13	Ossett United	v	Harworth Colliery (3/10)	5-3aet	42
14	Tadcaster Albion	v	Stocksbridge Park Steels (3/10)	5-2aet	114
15	Long Eaton United	v	Basford United (2/10)	4-1	120
16	West Bridgford	v	Aylestone Park (4/10)	0-2	42
17	Matlock Town	v	Mickleover Sports (3/10)	2-1	
18	Grantham Town	v	Bottesford Town (4/10)	2-1	75
19	Sheffield	v	Chesterfield (4/10)	1-6	164
20	Coleshill Town	v	Kidderminster Harriers (1/10)	0-3	76
21	Nuneaton Borough	v	Halesowen Town (4/10)	8-9	83
22	Stratford Town	v	Sutton Coldfield Town (4/10)	2-5	49
23	AFC Telford United	v	Stourbridge (4/10)	3-1	84
24	Hereford	v	Malvern Town (4/10)	4-0	142
25	Rushall Olympic	v	Rugby Borough (1/10)	1-5	77
26	Anstey Nomads	v	Solihull Moors (4/10)	2-3	76
27	Brackley Town	v	Cogenhoe United (1/10)	2-4	92
28	AFC Rushden & Diamonds	v	Kettering Town (3/10)	2-1	108
29	Rugby Town	v	Wellingborough Town (3/10)	2-1	
30	Mildenhall Town	v	Wroxham (4/10)	1-4	106
31	AFC Sudbury	v	Leiston (4/10)	10-0	59
32	King's Lynn Town	v	Cambridge City (3/10)	2-0aet	
33	Walsham Le Willows	v	Newmarket Town (4/10)	3-1aet	41
34	Sawbridgeworth Town	v	Peterborough Sports (4/10)	0-2	
35	Bury Town	v	Dereham Town (1/10)	1-2	
36	Saffron Walden Town	v	Great Wakering Rovers (4/10)	2-0	89
37	Leyton Orient	v	Romford (2/10)	2-1	192
38	Brentwood Town	v	Grays Athletic (3/10)	1-1aet	
	(Brentwood Town won 4-3 on kicks from the penalty mark)				
39	Dagenham & Redbridge	v	Aveley (3/10)	0-2	225
40	Bishop's Stortford	v	Braintree Town (4/10)	5-1	
41	Hullbridge Sports	v	AFC Hornchurch (2/10)	7-2	75
42	Chalfont St Peter	v	Kings Langley (9/10)	1-2	58
43	Harefield United	v	Hemel Hempstead Town (4/10)	0-3	50
44	Welwyn Garden City	v	Buckingham Athletic (4/10)	9-0	
45	Wingate & Finchley	v	Hayes & Yeading United (4/10)	5-1	96
46	Tring Athletic	v	Flackwell Heath (4/10)	2-1aet	24
47	Colney Heath	v	Leverstock Green (1/10)	2-5	
48	Barnet	v	Boreham Wood (2/10)	2-0	287
49	Folkestone Invicta	v	Cray Wanderers (4/10)	1-4	
50	Maidstone United	v	Phoenix Sports (4/10)	1-2	126
51	Corinthian	v	Dartford (2/10)	1-2	131
52	Dover Athletic	v	Lewes (2/10)	0-4	
53	Metropolitan Police	v	Bromley (4/10)	3-2aet	73
54	Dulwich Hamlet	v	Tonbridge Angels (4/10)	2-1	
55	Dorking Wanderers	v	Carshalton Athletic (4/10)	1-6	67
56	Bognor Regis Town	v	Guildford City (3/10)	3-1	35
57	Croydon	v	Camberley Town (3/10)	2-2aet	
	(Croydon won 4-3 on kicks from the penalty mark)				
58	Raynes Park Vale	v	Arundel (4/10)	5-1	
59	Kingstonian	v	Whitehawk (4/10)	1-2	30
	(at Colliers Wood United FC)				
60	Ashford United	v	Hampton & Richmond Borough (1/10)	1-5	
61	South Park	v	Worthing (1/10)	0-5	92
62	Sutton United	v	Whyteleafe (5/10)	3-1	
63	Ascot Untied	v	Hungerford Town (2/10)	2-1	
64	Kidlington	v	Andover Town (4/10)	0-4	35
65	Reading City	v	Aylesbury (3/10)	4-1	72
66	Malmesbury Victoria	v	Didcot Town (4/10)	1-3	
67	Oxford City	v	Maidenhead United (4/10)	0-5	99
68	Totton & Eling	v	AFC Totton (4/10)	3-1	
69	Havant & Waterlooville	v	Moneyfields (3/10)	1-3	93
70	AFC Stoneham	v	Brockenhurst (11/10)	1-4	
	(4/10 – tie abandoned after 37 mins due to floodlight failure, 0-1)				
71	Almondsbury	v	Team Solent (4/10)	0-1	
72	Eastleigh	v	Aldershot Town (3/10)	1-3	150
73	Torquay United	v	Slimbridge (2/10)	1-0	
74	Portishead Town	v	Yate Town (4/10)	3-4	28
75	Clevedon Town	v	Bridgwater Town (1/10)	3-0	71
76	Cirencester Town	v	Odd Down (2/10)	1-0	21

THIRD ROUND QUALIFYING

No.	Home		Away	Score	Att
1	South Shields	v	Chorley (17/10)	3-2	208
2	Guiseley	v	Ossett United (15/10)	13-0	155
3	Tadcaster Albion	v	Altrincham (15/10)	2-4	180
4	FC Halifax Town	v	Litherland Remyca (17/10)	5-0	122
5	Hartlepool United	v	Chester (16/10)	2-4	149
6	Hyde United	v	Salford City (19/10)	0-1	235
7	North Shields	v	AFC Fylde (18/10)	2-1	153
8	Matlock Town	v	Sutton Coldfield Town (17/10)	1-2	
9	Long Eaton United	v	Hereford (16/10)	3-1	
10	Kidderminster Harriers	v	Chesterfield (17/10)	1-0	
11	AFC Telford United	v	Rugby Town (18/10)	2-1	
12	Rugby Borough	v	Solihull Moors (15/10)	3-1aet	121
13	Cogenhoe United	v	Aylestone Park (18/10)	1-0	
14	Grantham Town	v	Halesowen Town (18/10)	4-2	89
15	AFC Sudbury	v	Wroxham (16/10)	11-1	77
16	Hullbridge Sports	v	Aveley (17/10)	3-2	163
17	Barnet	v	Bishop's Stortford (16/10)	3-1	214
18	Brentwood Town	v	Saffron Walden Town (18/10)	2-1	
19	King's Lynn Town	v	Dereham Town (17/10)	2-0	307
20	Peterborough Sports	v	Walsham Le Willows (18/10)	3-2	
21	AFC Rushden & Diamonds	v	Leyton Orient (17/10)	2-3	
22	Leverstock Green	v	Maidenhead United (18/10)	0-8	74
23	Ascot United	v	Wingate & Finchley (16/10)	1-2	107
24	Kings Langley	v	Tring Athletic (25/10)	9-1	
	(18/10 – tie abandoned)				
25	Reading City	v	Hemel Hempstead Town (17/10)	0-4	
26	Welwyn Garden City	v	Andover Town (18/10)	1-3aet	
27	Phoenix Sports	v	Hampton & Richmond Borough (17/10)	3-2	104
28	Croydon	v	Lewes (19/10)	2-3	
29	Metropolitan Police	v	Whitehawk (18/10)	2-3	120
30	Dartford	v	Dulwich Hamlet (16/10)	0-3	202
31	Cray Wanderers	v	Raynes Park Vale (17/10)	3-0	94
32	Bognor Regis Town	v	Sutton United (17/10)	2-3aet	
33	Carshalton Athletic	v	Worthing (15/10)	1-5	99
34	Team Solent	v	Moneyfields (18/10)	0-1	
35	Torquay United	v	Yate Town (16/10)	7-2	
36	Cirencester Town	v	Aldershot Town (15/10)	1-4aet	57
37	Clevedon Town	v	Brockenhurst (15/10)	8-1	63
38	Didcot Town	v	Totton & Eling (18/10)	1-3	

FIRST ROUND PROPER

1	North Shields	v	Bury (1/11)	0-7	256
2	Doncaster Rovers	v	Rochdale (30/10)	0-3	
3	Fleetwood Town	v	Carlisle United (1/11)	2-1	197
4	Morecambe	v	Crewe Alexandra (25/10)	0-2	170
5	Blackpool	v	Guiseley (29/10)	4-0	156
6	Tranmere Rovers	v	Accrington Stanley (31/10)	0-3	211
7	FC Halifax Town	v	Sunderland (31/10)	0-1	159
8	Salford City	v	Bradford City (31/10)	3-1	210
9	Chester	v	Barnsley (1/11)	2-1	
10	Altrincham	v	Oldham Athletic (1/11)	1-6	
11	South Shields	v	Macclesfield Town (29/10)	6-2	359
12	Scunthorpe United	v	AFC Telford United (31/10)	6-1	152
13	Rugby Borough	v	Sutton Coldfield Town (29/10)	2-6	172
14	Shrewsbury Town	v	Lincoln City (25/10)	0-1	258
15	Cogenhoe United	v	Grantham Town (1/11)	2-1	118
16	Grimsby Town	v	Mansfield Town (30/10)	2-3	146
17	Long Eaton United	v	Milton Keynes Dons (1/11)	1-2	173
18	Port Vale	v	Kidderminster Harriers (29/10)	6-1	
19	Walsall	v	Notts County (19/10)	1-2	286
20	Burton Albion	v	Coventry City (19/10)	1-2	
21	Stevenage	v	Colchester United (30/10)	3-2	330
22	Peterborough Sports	v	Barnet (1/11)	0-1	122
23	Cambridge United	v	AFC Sudbury (31/10)	2-1	215
24	Leyton Orient	v	Southend United (1/11)	3-4aet	336
25	Luton Town	v	Brentwood Town (26/10)	4-1	
26	Hullbridge Sports	v	Peterborough United (30/10)	0-2	278
27	Northampton Town	v	King's Lynn Town (30/10)	4-0	
28	Worthing	v	Cray Wanderers (1/11)	1-2	170
29	Wingate & Finchley	v	Kings Langley (1/11)	5-3	102
30	Phoenix Sports	v	Andover Town (31/10)	1-4	
31	Lewes	v	Sutton United (1/11)	2-3	105
32	Charlton Athletic	v	Whitehawk (7/11)	6-0	243
33	Hemel Hempstead Town	v	Oxford United (31/10)	0-3	120
34	AFC Wimbledon	v	Gillingham (25/10)	1-3	339
35	Maidenhead United	v	Dulwich Hamlet (1/11)	5-0	
36	Exeter City	v	Plymouth Argyle (31/10)	3-2	
37	Newport County	v	Yeovil Town (26/10)	1-2	
38	Portsmouth	v	Bristol Rovers (24/10)	5-2	591
39	Forest Green Rovers	v	Cheltenham Town (29/10)	1-3	
40	Aldershot Town	v	Clevedon Town (31/10)	1-4	
41	Torquay United	v	Totton & Eling (29/10)	4-1	
42	Swindon Town	v	Moneyfields (3/11)	7-0	151

SECOND ROUND PROPER

1	Lincoln City	v	South Shields (13/11)	4-2	442
2	Bury	v	Fleetwood Town (8/11)	3-2	277
3	Scunthorpe United	v	Blackpool (6/11)	1-2aet	202
4	Mansfield Town	v	Chester (21/11)	2-0	325
5	Sunderland (at Eppleton CW FC)	v	Oldham Athletic (15/11)	4-1	
6	Accrington Stanley	v	Notts County (12/11)	2-1	
7	Rochdale	v	Milton Keynes Dons (12/11)	2-0	301
8	Port Vale	v	Sutton Coldfield Town (13/11)	3-1	231
9	Salford City	v	Crewe Alexandra (9/11)	1-2	
10	Cogenhoe United	v	Coventry City (15/11)	3-2	238
11	Yeovil Town	v	Cambridge United (14/11)	1-4	231
12	Charlton Athletic (at Welling United FC)	v	Southend United (21/11)	2-0	166
13	Clevedon Town (tie awarded to Clevedon Town – Sutton United removed)	v	Sutton United (19/11)	1-2aet	226
14	Peterborough United	v	Luton Town (6/11)	3-0	429
15	Oxford United (at Oxford City FC)	v	Barnet (14/11)	1-0	266
16	Stevenage	v	Exeter City (10/11)	4-0	
17	Northampton Town	v	Swindon Town (14/11)	2-0	
18	Maidenhead United	v	Torquay United (12/11)	3-1	
19	Cray Wanderers	v	Portsmouth (21/11)	0-4	270
20	Cheltenham Town	v	Gillingham (14/11)	0-4	212
21	Wingate & Finchley (Andover Town won 8-7 on kicks from the penalty mark)	v	Andover Town (15/11)	2-2aet	135

THIRD ROUND PROPER

1	Sheffield Wednesday	v	Stoke City (13/12)	2-3	
2	Blackburn Rovers	v	Gillingham (5/12)	1-2	224
3	Everton	v	Sunderland (1/12)	4-1	132
4	Burnley (Oxford United won 3-2 on kicks from the penalty mark)	v	Oxford United (11/12)	1-1aet	363
5	Huddersfield Town	v	Peterborough United (5/12)	0-2	301
6	Watford (at Wingate & Finchley FC)	v	Birmingham City (13/12)	1-0	207
7	Preston North End (Preston North End won 3-1 on kicks from the penalty mark)	v	Charlton Athletic (4/12)	2-2aet	530
8	Leicester City	v	Fulham (11/12)	2-1aet	
9	Arsenal (at Boreham Wood FC)	v	Northampton Town (12/12)	2-0	527
10	Accrington Stanley	v	Leeds United (12/12)	4-2aet	
11	Wolverhampton Wanderers	v	Wigan Athletic (10/12)	1-2	
12	Hull City	v	Cardiff City (5/12)	2-1	250
13	Maidenhead United	v	Nottingham Forest (11/12)	1-5	454
14	Middlesbrough (at Bishop Auckland FC)	v	Sheffield United (12/12)	0-1	163
15	Bristol City	v	Crewe Alexandra (11/12)	1-2	
16	West Bromwich Albion	v	Lincoln City (11/12)	5-1	
17	Liverpool (at St Helens RFC)	v	Portsmouth (18/12)	3-2	254
18	Manchester United (at Leigh Sports Village)	v	Chelsea (17/12)	4-3	
19	West Ham United (Brighton & Hove Albion won 5-4 on kicks from the penalty mark)	v	Brighton & Hove Albion (3/12)	1-1aet	238
20	Southampton	v	Rotherham United (4/12)	2-0	266
21	Aston Villa	v	Swansea City (11/12)	4-2	407
22	Blackpool	v	Derby County (4/12)	1-2	
23	Ipswich Town	v	Andover Town (4/12)	4-0	
24	Bolton Wanderers	v	Newcastle United (5/12)	2-1	416
25	AFC Bournemouth	v	Mansfield Town (12/12)	2-1	
26	Stevenage	v	Bury (12/12)	2-4aet	
27	Cogenhoe United	v	Crystal Palace (6/12)	1-2	439
28	Millwall	v	Tottenham Hotspur (17/12)	1-2aet	752
29	Port Vale	v	Norwich City (12/12)	2-3	
30	Clevedon Town	v	Manchester City (19/12)	0-4	1591
31	Queens Park Rangers	v	Rochdale (3/12)	3-2aet	
32	Cambridge United	v	Reading (11/12)	1-3	233

FOURTH ROUND PROPER

1	Stoke City (Everton won 3-1 on kicks from the penalty mark)	v	Everton (10/1)	2-2aet	440
2	Gillingham	v	Ipswich Town (11/1)	1-2	
3	Derby County	v	Sheffield United (15/1)	3-0	
4	Hull City	v	Wigan Athletic (12/1)	2-6	397
5	Oxford United (at Oxford City FC)	v	AFC Bournemouth (16/1)	0-3	348
6	Leicester City	v	Crewe Alexandra (15/1)	4-0	
7	Arsenal (at Boreham Wood FC)	v	Tottenham Hotspur (17/1)	5-2aet	946
8	Crystal Palace	v	Bolton Wanderers (18/1)	2-4	984
9	West Bromwich Albion	v	Queens Park Rangers (17/1)	5-1	307
10	Manchester United (at Leigh Sports Village)	v	Brighton & Hove Albion (21/1)	1-3	
11	Preston North End	v	Norwich City (22/1)	3-0	620
12	Liverpool (at St Helens RFC)	v	Accrington Stanley (21/1)	4-0	706
13	Aston Villa	v	Reading (15/1)	4-1	
14	Peterborough United	v	Bury (17/1)	0-1	614
15	Watford (at Wingate & Finchley FC)	v	Southampton (17/1)	2-1	207
16	Manchester City (at Academy Arena)	v	Nottingham Forest (18/1)	4-1	663

FIFTH ROUND PROPER

1	Preston North End	v	Bury (8/2)	0-2	1024
2	AFC Bournemouth	v	Aston Villa (1/2)	2-0	356
3	Arsenal (at Boreham Wood FC)	v	West Bromwich Albion (9/2)	1-2	391
4	Everton	v	Brighton & Hove Albion (12/2)	2-0	178
5	Bolton Wanderers	v	Leicester City (30/1)	0-3	267
6	Liverpool (at Chester FC)	v	Wigan Athletic (13/2)	2-0	576
7	Derby County	v	Manchester City (31/1)	1-2	
8	Watford (at Wingate & Finchley FC)	v	Ipswich Town (12/2)	4-1	260

FIRST ROUND

1	Essex	v	Hertfordshire (7/10)	3-0	91
	(at Aveley FC)				
2	Bedfordshire	v	Cornwall (23/9)	0-5	
	(at Kempston Rovers FC)				

SECOND ROUND

1	Cheshire	v	Sheffield & Hallamshire (27/10)	7-2	
	(at Vauxhall Motors FC)				
2	Northumberland	v	Nottinghamshire (27/10)	0-3	
	(at Whitley Park)				
3	Lancashire	v	Staffordshire (20/10)	4-0	
	(at Lancashire FA County Ground)				
4	Shropshire	v	Isle of Man (14/10)	1-2	
	(at Market Drayton Town FC)				
5	Cumberland	v	Westmorland (20/10)	4-2	
	(at The Falcon Complex)				
6	Durham	v	Manchester (3/11)	1-4	
	(at Hetton Centre)				
7	West Riding	v	Liverpool (3/11)	2-6	
	(at West Riding County FA)				
8	Birmingham	v	North Riding (3/11)	6-1	
	(at Birmingham FA County Ground)				
9	Guernsey	v	Essex (3/11)	0-5	
	(at Track Cycling Ground)				
10	Cornwall	v	Norfolk (27/10)	3-4aet	130
	(at Helston Athletic FC)				
11	Amateur Football Alliance	v	London (27/10)	1-0	
	(at Enfield Town FC)				
12	Kent	v	Gloucestershire (4/11)	2-6	
	(at Maidstone United FC)				
13	Middlesex	v	Wiltshire (3/11)	14-0	45
	(at Harrow Borough FC)				
14	Northamptonshire	v	Devon (20/10)	4-2	
	(at Wellingborough Town FC)				
15	Sussex	v	Herefordshire		
	(walkover for Sussex FA – Herefordshire FA withdrawn)				
16	Berks & Bucks	v	Somerset (28/10)	3-2aet	86
	(at Slough Town FC)				

PREVIOUS TEN FINALS

2018	Norfolk	v	Staffordshire	2-0
2017	Middlesex	v	Cornwall	2-1
2016	Liverpool	v	Sussex	2-0
2015	Cheshire	v	Middlesex	3-2
2014	Lancashire	v	Suffolk	3-2 aet
2013	Bedfordshire	v	Manchester	4-4, 4-2p
2012	Essex	v	West Riding	4-2 aet
2011	Norfolk	v	Staffordshire	4-2
2010	Kent	v	Sheffield & Hallamshire	1-0
2009	Birmingham	v	Kent	2-1

THIRD ROUND

1	Berks & Bucks	v	Cumberland (6/1)	7-2	
	(at Slough Town FC)				
2	Lancashire	v	Cheshire (1/12)	1-2	
	(at Lancashire FA County Ground)				
3	Manchester	v	Essex (8/12)	4-1	
	(at Ashton United FC)				
4	Sussex	v	Northamptonshire (1/12)	5-0	
	(at Sussex County FA)				
5	Nottinghamshire	v	Amateur Football Alliance (1/12)	1-3	95
	(at RH Academy)				
6	Norfolk	v	Isle of Man (24/11)	3-1	
	(at FDC, Norwich)				
7	Liverpool	v	Middlesex (5/1)	2-1	
	(at Liverpool Soccer Centre)				
8	Gloucestershire	v	Birmingham (8/12)	3-2	60
	(at Oaklands Park)				

FOURTH ROUND

1	Liverpool	v	Amateur Football Alliance (19/1)	2-1	
	(at Liverpool Soccer Centre)				
2	Gloucestershire	v	Cheshire (12/1)	2-2aet	65
	(Cheshire won 4-2 on kicks from the penalty mark – at Oaklands Park)				
3	Sussex	v	Norfolk (6/1)	0-1	
	(at Sussex County FA)				
4	Manchester	v	Berks & Bucks (3/2)	4-2	68
	(at Hyde United FC)				

SEMI FINALS

1	Cheshire	v	Norfolk (23/2)	1-3
	(at Vauxhall Motors FC)			
2	Manchester	v	Liverpool (16/2)	5-0
	(at Hyde United FC)			

THE FINAL - Saturday 13 APRIL 2019

Manchester	v	Norfolk	3-0	402
(at Rochdale AFC)				

FA YOUTH CUP

SIXTH ROUND PROPER

1	Leicester City	v	Watford (27/2)	1-2aet	716
2	West Bromwich Albion	v	Everton (26/2)	4-3	613
3	AFC Bournemouth	v	Manchester City (26/2)	1-4	1136
4	Bury	v	Liverpool (6/3)	1-5	765

SEMI FINALS

1	Manchester City	v	West Bromwich Albion (1/4)	4-2	1703
2	Liverpool	v	Watford (17/3)	2-1	1279

THE FINAL

Manchester City	v	Liverpool (25/4)	1-1, 3-5p	860

PREVIOUS TEN FINALS

				Aggregate Score
2018	Chelsea	v	Arsenal	7-1
2017	Chelsea	v	Manchester City	6-2
2016	Chelsea	v	Manchester City	4-2
2015	Chelsea	v	Manchester City	5-2
2014	Chelsea	v	Fulham	7-6
2013	Norwich City	v	Chelsea	4-2
2012	Chelsea	v	Blackburn Rovers	4-1
2011	Manchester Utd	v	Sheffield United	4-1
2010	Chelsea	v	Aston Villa	3-2
2009	Arsenal	v	Liverpool	6-2

FIRST ROUND

	Home		Away	Score	Att
1	Newton Aycliffe Iron Horse	v	Dawdon Welfare Park	1-3	67
	(at Shildon AFC)				
2	Amble Tavern	v	Peterlee Catholic Club	0-2	
	(at Alnwick Town FC)				
3	Thornton United	v	Queens Park		
	(walkover for Queens Park – Thornton United withdrawn)				
4	Dock	v	Campfield	0-3	
	(at Ashville FC)				
5	Main Line Social	v	Melling Victoria	1-3	
	(at Beeston St Anthony's)				
6	Clay Brow	v	Mayfair (1.00)	0-4	
	(at JMO Playing Fields)				
7	Lobster	v	Bleak House (12.00)	2-1	
	(at St John Bosco School)				
8	Custys	v	FC Walkers Hounds	3-1	
	(at William Collins Playing Fields)				
9	Linthwaite	v	Leeds City Rovers	0-1	
	(at Campion AFC)				
10	Oakenshaw	v	Canada	5-3	38
	(at Liversedge FC)				
11	Mottram	v	Kirkdale	1-0	
	(at Litherland Sports Park)				
12	BRNESC	v	Garston		
	(walkover for BRNESC – Garston withdrawn)				
13	Eastwood	v	Callow End	2-0	
	(at Eastwood CFC)				
14	Birstall Stamford	v	Sporting Dynamo	8-2	
	(at Birstall United FC)				
15	AFC Jacks	v	Austin Ex Apprentices	6-4	
	(at Sporting Khalsa FC)				
16	Asianos	v	Borussia Martlesham	4-1aet	
	(at Tilbury FC)				
17	Global	v	Priory Sports	3-3aet	
	(Global won 5-4 on kicks from the penalty mark)				
	(at Clapton FC)				
18	Larkspur Rovers	v	St Josephs (Luton)	0-2	
	(at Rayners Lane FC)				
19	AC Sportsman	v	Club Lewsey	1-4	
	(at Shefford Town FC)				
20	Magpies 91	v	Old Southall	1-7	
	(at Spratleys Meadow)				
21	AFC 2015	v	Lambeth All Stars	2-5	
	(at Southwick FC)				
22	Rudgwick Panthers SX	v	Broadwater	3-5	
	(at Crawley Down Gatwick FC)				
23	Watersedge Park	v	Lebeqs Tavern Courage	1-5	
	(at AFC Portchester)				

SECOND ROUND

	Home		Away	Score	Att
1	Burradon & New Fordley	v	Mottram	5-1	
	(at AFC Killingworth)				
2	Joker	v	Pineapple	4-1	
	(at Maltby Main FC)				
3	Peterlee Catholic Club	v	Greenside	2-3	110
	(at Horden CW FC)				
4	Crossflatts Village	v	Dengo United	2-0	
	(at Silsden FC)				
5	Kensington Fields	v	Campfield	4-0	
	(at Jeffrey Humble Playing Fields)				
6	Home Bargains	v	Sunderland Southwick	0-1aet	
	(at Alder Sports Club)				
7	AFC Blackburn Leisure	v	Melling Victoria		
	(walkover for Melling Victoria – AFC Blackburn Leisure withdrawn)				
8	FC Dovecot	v	LIV Supplies	1-3	
	(at Lower Breck FC)				
9	Custys	v	Oyster Martyrs	1-3	
	(at William Collins Playing Fields)				
10	Allerton	v	Hope Inn Whites	4-2aet	
	(at North Field, Jericho Lane)				
11	Queens Park	v	Oakenshaw	7-0	
	(at Vauxhall Motors FC)				
12	Dawdon Welfare Park	v	Lobster	2-4	
	(at Dawdon Welfare Park, Green Drive)				
13	Leeds City Rovers	v	BRNESC	4-1	
	(at Adel Memorial Ground)				
14	Western Avenue	v	Mayfair	0-2	
	(at Litherland Sports Park)				
15	Blucher Blue Star	v	Huyton Cons	0-1	
	(at Heaton Stannington AFC)				
16	Billingham The Merlin	v	Rock Ferry Social		
	(tie awarded to Billingham The Merlin – Rock Ferry Social removed)				
17	Eastwood	v	OJM	0-6	
	(at Kimberley MW FC)				
18	Rolls Royce	v	Oadby Athletic	0-4	
	(at Rolls Royce Leisure)				
19	Attenborough Cavaliers	v	Falcons	3-3aet	20
	(Attenborough Cavaliers won 4-2 on kicks from the penalty mark)				
	(at Radford FC)				
20	Hampton	v	Leighton Madrid	2-3	
	(at Hampton Sports Ground)				
21	AFC Jacks	v	FC Topps	6-1	
	(at Sporting Khalsa FC)				
22	Black Horse (Redditch)	v	RHP Sports & Social	4-0	
	(at Studley Sports & Social Club)				
23	Newark Town	v	Birstall Stamford (18/11)	3-5aet	
	(at Grantham Town FC)				
24	Real Milan	v	Club Lewsey	3-7	
	(at Slough Town FC)				
25	St Josephs (Luton)	v	Global	5-3	21
	(at Arlesey Town FC)				
26	Flaunden	v	Old Southall	1-5	

(at Bovingdon FC)

27	Aylesbury Flooring	v	NLO (18/11)	4-2	
	(at Aylesbury FC)				
28	Asianos	v	Gym United (18/11)	1-4	
	(at Tilbury FC)				
29	East Christchurch SSC	v	Navy Inn	3-2aet	42
	(at Hurn Bridge Sports Club)				
30	Barnes AFC	v	Lambeth All Stars (18/11)	0-5	
	(at Hanworth Villa FC)				
31	Broadwater	v	Poplar		
	(walkover for Broadwater – Poplar withdrawn)				
32	Portland	v	Lebeqs Tavern Courage (18/11)	4-1	
	(at AFC Croydon Athletic)				

THIRD ROUND

1	Greenside	v	Crossflatts Village	3-0	137
	(at Dunston UTS FC)				
2	Queens Park	v	Mayfair	0-2	
	(at Vauxhall Sports Club)				
3	Leeds City Rovers	v	Sunderland Southwick	0-3	50
	(at Adel Memorial Ground)				
4	Lobster	v	Allerton (16/12)	5-3	
	(at St John Bosco School)				
5	Melling Victoria	v	Kensington Fields	2-3	
	(at Jeffrey Humble Playing Fields)				
6	Billingham The Merlin	v	Joker	0-2	
	(at Wolviston FC)				
7	Oyster Martyrs	v	Huyton Cons	4-2	
	(at JMO Sports Park)				
8	Burradon & New Fordley	v	LIV Supplies	6-2	40
	(at AFC Killingworth)				
9	AFC Jacks	v	OJM	4-1	
	(at Sporting Khalsa FC)				
10	Birstall Stamford	v	Oadby Athletic	4-1	52
	(at Birstall United FC)				
11	Black Horse (Redditch)	v	Attenborough Cavaliers (23/12)	2-1	30
	(tie reversed – at Radford FC)				
12	Old Southall	v	Club Lewsey	3-1	
	(at Brunel University Sports Park)				
13	Leighton Madrid	v	Aylesbury Flooring	0-7	
	(at Leighton Town FC)				
14	Gym United	v	St Josephs (Luton)	0-2	
	(at Bury Town FC)				
15	East Christchurch SSC	v	Portland	4-2	
	(at Hurn Bridge Sports Club)				
16	Lambeth All Stars	v	Broadwater (23/12)	2-1aet	
	(tie reversed –at Littlehampton Town FC)				
	(tie awarded to Broadwater – Lambeth All Stars removed)				

FOURTH ROUND

1	Burradon & New Fordley	v	Kensington Fields	4-0	
	(at AFC Killingworth)				
2	Sunderland Southwick	v	Greenside	3-0	
	(at Nissan Sports Complex)				
3	Mayfair	v	Lobster (2.00)	2-2aet	
	(Mayfair won 9-8 on kicks from the penalty mark - at Lower Breck FC)				
4	Joker	v	Oyster Martyrs	1-0aet	
	(at Maltby Main FC)				
5	Birstall Stamford	v	Old Southall	5-1	115
	(at Birstall United FC)				
6	Black Horse (Redditch)	v	St Josephs (Luton) (1.30)	2-2aet	
	(Black Horse Redditch won 3-2 on kicks from the penalty mark - at Studley Sports & Social)				
7	Broadwater	v	East Christchurch SSC	0-3	30
	(at Littlehampton Town FC)				
8	AFC Jacks	v	Aylesbury Flooring	3-4aet	
	(at Sporting Khalsa FC)				

FIFTH ROUND

1	Mayfair	v	Joker	2-2aet	
	(Joker won 5-3 on kicks from the penalty mark – at Lower Breck FC)				
2	Burradon & New Fordley	v	Sunderland Southwick	2-3	
	(at AFC Killingworth)				
3	East Christchurch SSC	v	Birstall Stamford	0-2	
	(at Christchurch FC)				
4	Black Horse (Redditch)	v	Aylesbury Flooring	3-5	
	(at Studley Sports & Social)				

SEMI FINALS

1	Sunderland Southwick	v	Aylesbury Flooring	0-2	203
	(at Gainsborough Trinity FC)				
2	Birstall Stamford	v	Joker	3-0	467
	(at Alfreton Town FC)				

THE FINAL - SUNDAY 29 APRIL 2018

Aylesbury Flooring	v	Birstall Stamford	3-1	860
(at Peterborough United FC)				

PREVIOUS TEN FINALS

2018	Hardwick Social	v Gym United	2-0 aet
2017	Hardwick Social	v New Salamis	1-1, 3-1p
2016	New Salamis	v Barnes	1-1, 4-3p
2015	Campfield	v OJM	2-0
2014	Humbledon Plains Farm	v Oyster Martyrs	5-2
2013	Oyster Martyrs	v Barnes Albion	4-3
2012	Hetton Lyons C.C.	v Canada	5-1
2011	Oyster Martyrs	v Paddock	1-0
2010	Hetton Lyons C.C.	v Magnet Tavern	4-2
2009	Scots Grey	v Oyster Martyrs	4-3 aet

FIRST QUALIFYING ROUND

No.	Home		Away	Score	Att
1	South Park Rangers	v	Redcar Town		
	(walkover for Redcar Town - South Park Rangers withdrawn)				
2	Durham Cestria	v	Alnwick Town	1-2	
	(at Graham Sports Centre)				
3	Boro Rangers	v	Cramlington United	8-1	
	(at Hurlingham Centre)				
4	Washington	v	Hartlepool United	2-4	
	(at Northumbria Centre)				
5	Carlisle United	v	Bishop Auckland	1-2	
	(at Creighton Rugby Club)				
6	Penrith	v	Wallsend Boys Club	5-1	
	(at Carlisle City FC)				
7	Wakefield	v	Sheffield Wednesday	0-4	
	(at Nostell MW FC)				
8	Ossett United	v	Farsley Celtic	1-2	103
	(at Dimplewells)				
9	Tingley Athletic	v	Harrogate Town	4-0	
	(at Tingley Athletic FC)				
10	Oughtibridge WM	v	Malet Lambert		
	(walkover for Oughtibridge WM - Malet Lambert withdrawn)				
11	Rotherham United	v	Bridlington Rovers	1-3	
	(at Parkgate FC)				
12	Chesterfield	v	Yorkshire Amateur	4-0	73
	(at Glapwell FC)				
13	Warrington Wolverines	v	Stockport County	1-4	
	(at Grappenhall Sports Club)				
14	Wythenshawe Amateurs	v	Accrington Girls & Ladies	1-3	
	(at Wythenshawe Amateurs FC)				
15	Manchester Stingers	v	West Didsbury & Chorlton	2-5	
	(at Whalley Range FC)				
16	Cammell Laird 1907	v	Burscough Dynamo	4-0	
	(at Cammell Laird 1907 FC)				
17	Tranmere Rovers	v	Bury	6-3	
	(at Ellesmere Port Sports Village)				
18	FC United of Manchester	v	Didsbury	6-0	110
	(at New Mills AFC)				
19	Leicester City Women Dev	v	Coalville Town Ravenettes	15-0	
	(at Riverside Pavillion)				
20	Oadby & Wigston	v	Mansfield Town	4-2	88
	(at Oadby & Wigston FC)				
21	Grimsby Borough	v	Boston United	1-4	
	(at Lucarlys, Wilton Road)				
22	Loughborough Students	v	Rise Park	5-1	
	(at Arnold Town FC)				
23	Leicester City	v	Lutterworth Athletic	2-5	45
	(at Linwood Playing Fields)				
24	Stockingford AA Pavilion	v	Lye Town	2-0	98
	(at Stockingford AA Pavilion FC)				
25	Stourbridge	v	Solihull United	1-2	100
	(at Stourbridge FC)				
26	St Johns	v	Sandwell	5-4aet	
	(at Holly Lane Sports)				
27	Shifnal Town	v	Leafield Athletic	0-7	
	(at Shifnal Town FC)				
28	Leek Town	v	Sutton Coldfield Town	1-2	
	(at Leek Town FC)				
29	Hereford Lads Club	v	Kidderminster Harriers (9/9)	0-9	
	(at Hereford County Ground)				
30	Rugby Town	v	Shenstone	5-1	
	(at Kilsby Lane Sports Centre)				
31	Redditch United	v	Kingfisher	0-3	
	(at Redditch United FC)				

No.	Home		Away	Score	Att
32	Crusaders	v	Solihull Sporting	5-0	
	(at Rowheath Pavilion)				
33	Peterborough Northern Star	v	Northampton Town	4-4aet	
	(Peterborough Northern Star won 3-1 on kicks from the penalty mark)				
	(at Peterborough Northern Star FC)				
34	St Ives Town	v	Peterborough United	1-2	
	(at St Ives Town FC)				
35	Wymondham Town	v	Roade		
	(walkover for Wymondham Town - Roade withdrawn)				
36	Kettering Town	v	Acle United	1-3	25
	(at Kettering Town FC)				
37	Cambridge City	v	Riverside	14-0	
	(at Trinity College Sports Ground)				
38	Histon	v	Thrapston Town	2-1	
	(at Histon FC)				
39	Leigh Ramblers	v	Bowers & Pitsea	2-0	
	(at Basildon Sports & Leisure Club)				
40	Corringham Cosmos	v	Bungay Town		
	(walkover for Corringham Cosmos - Bungay Town withdrawn)				
41	Brentwood Town	v	Harlow	1-2	
	(at Garon Park Cricket Ground)				
42	Chelmsford City	v	AFC Sudbury	0-1	55
	(at Chelmsford City FC)				
43	AFC Dunstable	v	Watford Ladies Dev	5-0	30
	(at AFC Dunstable)				
44	Bishop's Stortford	v	Royston Town	0-11	
	(at Bishop's Stortford FC)				
45	Colney Heath	v	Houghton Athletic	2-0	
	(at Colney Heath FC)				
46	Ashford Town (Middx)	v	Wargrave	15-0	
	(at Ashford Town (Middx) FC)				
47	New London Lionesses	v	Hampton & Richmond Borough	4-0	
	(at Hackney Marshes Centre)				
48	Queens Park Rangers Girls	v	Wealdstone		
	(walkover for Queens Park Rangers Girls – Wealdstone not accepted into Competition)				
49	Sandhurst Town	v	Newbury		
	(walkover for Newbury – Sandhurst Town withdrawn)				
50	Wycombe Wanderers	v	Ascot United	1-3	
	(at Spring Lane, Flackwell Heath)				
51	Abingdon United	v	Oxford City	1-3	
	(at Abingdon United FC)				
52	Newhaven	v	Ashford Ladies	2-1	
	(at Newhaven FC)				
53	London Kent Football United	v	Godalming Town	1-2	
	(at Dartford FC)				
54	Hassocks	v	Islington Borough	2-4	25
	(at Hassocks FC)				
55	Meridian	v	Worthing	1-4	20
	(at The Victory Academy School)				
56	Regents Park Rangers	v	Whyteleafe	3-4	
	(at Barns Elms Sports Trust)				
57	Kent Football United	v	Victoire	8-0	
	(at Glentworth Club, Dartford)				
58	Burgess Hill Town	v	Thamesview	9-2	
59	Abbey Rangers	v	Saltdean	2-1aet	
	(at Abbey Rangers FC)				
60	AFC Phoenix	v	Phoenix Sports	5-0	
	(at Coldharbour Leisure Centre)				
61	Aylesford	v	Fulham	1-3	
	(at Kings Hill Sports Park)				
62	Basingstoke Town	v	AFC Bournemouth	0-13	15
	(at Queen Mary's College)				

63 Swindon Spitfires v Southampton FC Women (9/9) 0-6
(at Watchfield Recreation Ground)
64 Shanklin v New Milton Town 0-3 38
(at Shanklin FC)
65 Warsash Wasps v Royal Wootton Bassett Town (9/9) 3-1
(at New Road)
66 Alton v Eastleigh 0-2
(at Anstey Road Enclosure)
67 Frampton Rangers v Feniton 4-3
(at Oaklands Park)
68 Exeter City v Frome Town 5-0 55
(at Exwick Sports Hub)
69 Ilminster Town v Middlezoy Rovers 4-0
(at Ilminster Town FC)
70 Marine Academy Plymouth v Exeter & Tedburn Rangers 13-1
(at Ivybridge FC)
71 Portishead Town v Downend Flyers 2-1
(at Portishead Town FC)
72 St Agnes v Keynsham Town Dev 1-3 121
(at Eynes Parc)
73 Torquay United v Weston Super Mare 1-2 50
(at Torquay United FC)

SECOND QUALIFYING ROUND

1 Steel City Wanderers v Chester Le Street Town 1-8
(at SGP Thorncliffe)
2 Cammell Laird 1907 v Crewe Alexandra 1-3
(at Cammell Laird 1907 FC)
3 Morecambe v Norton & Stockton Ancients 1-5
(at Lancaster & Morecambe College)
4 Redcar Town v Sheffield Wednesday 6-2 97
(at Redcar Town FC)
5 Bishop Auckland v Stockport County 0-8 110
(at St Johns College, Bishop Auckland)
6 Tingley Athletic v West Didsbury & Chorlton 0-5
(at Tingley Athletic FC)
7 Bridlington Rovers v Accrington Girls & Ladies 4-1
(at Bridlington Rovers FC)
8 Brighouse Town v Penrith 5-0
(at Brighouse Town FC)
9 Oughtibridge WM v FC United of Manchester 0-4
(at Oughtibridge WM Sports Ground)
10 Bolton Wanderers v Hartlepool United 3-0
(at Atherton Colliers FC)
11 Barnsley v Newcastle United 2-3aet
(at Dorothy Hyman Sports Centre)
12 Tranmere Rovers v Boro Rangers 0-1 60
(at Ellesmere Port Sports Village)
13 Burnley v Liverpool Feds 3-2
(at Padiham FC)
14 Alnwick Town v Leeds United 2-3
(at Alnwick Town FC)
15 Chorley v Farsley Celtic 5-0
(at Chorley FC)
16 Oadby & Wigston v Sutton Coldfield Town 2-0 64
(at Oadby & Wigston FC)
17 Crusaders v Sporting Khalsa 0-2
(at Rowheath Pavilion)
18 Rugby Town v West Bromwich Albion 0-10
(at Rugby Town JFC)
19 Long Eaton United v The New Saints 7-1
(at Long Eaton United FC)
20 Chesterfield v Burton Albion (30/9) 1-0
(at Glapwell FC)
21 Leicester City Women Dev v Solihull United 6-3
(at Riverside Pavillion)
22 St Johns v Kidderminster Harriers 1-4
(at Holly Lane Sports)
23 Wolverhampton Wanderers v Kingfisher 6-0 75
(at Bilston Town FC)
24 Bedworth United v Birmingham & West Midlands 0-2
(at Bedworth United FC)
25 Leafield Athletic v Lutterworth Athletic 0-0aet
(Leafield Athletic won 4-2 on kicks from the penalty mark)
(at Dickens Heath Sports Club)
26 Stockingford AA Pavilion v Nettleham 1-2 89
(at Stockingford AA Pavilion FC)
27 Solihull Moors v Loughborough Students 3-2
(at Tally Ho Sports)
28 Billericay Town v Colney Heath 9-1
(at Billericay Town FC)
29 Wymondham Town v Corringham Cosmos 17-1
(at Wymondham Town FC)
30 AFC Sudbury v Acle United 0-7
(at AFC Sudbury)
31 Chesham United v Peterborough United 5-0
(at Chesham United FC)
32 Histon v Leigh Ramblers 3-2
(at Histon FC)
33 Cambridge City v Leyton Orient 5-4
(at Trinity College Sports Ground)
34 Luton Town v AFC Dunstable 7-0 94
(at Stockwood Park)
35 Enfield Town v Actonians 2-1
(at Enfield Town FC)
36 Boston United v Norwich City 3-11
(at Boston United FC)
37 New London Lionesses v Ipswich Town 2-2aet
(New London Lionesses won 4-2 on kicks from the penalty mark)
(at Hackney Marshes Centre)
38 Peterborough Northern Star v Stevenage 1-5
(at Peterborough Northern Star FC)
39 Queens Park Rangers Girls v Royston Town (30/9) 5-1
(at QPR FC Training Ground)
40 Cambridge United v Harlow Town (30/9) 6-0
(at Mildenhall Town FC)
41 Worthing v Islington Borough 1-5
(at Worthing FC)
42 Denham United v Crawley Wasps (30/9) 1-3
(at The Den)
43 AFC Wimbledon v AFC Phoenix 1-0
(at Carshalton Athletic FC)
44 Oxford City v Fulham 4-3
(at Oxford City FC)
45 Newhaven v Newbury 3-1
(at Newhaven FC)
46 Kent Football United v Burgess Hill Town (30/9) 9-0
(at Glentworth Club, Dartford)
47 Godalming Town v Abbey Rangers 4-2
(at Godalming Town FC)
48 Whyteleafe v Maidenhead United 2-0
(at Whyteleafe FC)
49 Ashford Town (Middx) v Ascot United 11-2
(at Ashford Town (Middx) FC)

No.	Home		Away	Score	Att
50	Buckland Athletic (at Buckland Athletic FC)	v	Ilminster Town (26/9)	4-0	
51	Southampton FC Ladies (at AFC Totton)	v	New Milton Town	5-0	
52	Poole Town (at Dorset County FA Ground)	v	Frampton Rangers	3-1	44
53	St Nicholas (walkover for Eastleigh – St Nicholas withdrawn)	v	Eastleigh		
54	Larkhall Athletic (at Larkhall Athletic FC)	v	Weston Super Mare	7-2	
55	Swindon Town (at Fairford Town FC)	v	Keynsham Town	0-8	
56	Cheltenham Town (at Cheltenham Saracens FC)	v	Brislington	4-1	
57	Southampton Saints (at Sholing FC)	v	Warsash Wasps (30/9)	3-0	
58	AFC Bournemouth (at Verwood Town FC)	v	Portishead Town	4-1	
59	Southampton	v	Marine Academy Plymouth	1-2	

THIRD QUALIFYING ROUND

No.	Home		Away	Score	Att
1	West Didsbury & Chorlton (at West Didsbury & Chorlton FC)	v	Bolton Wanderers	0-4	
2	Leeds United (at Thorp Arch)	v	Boro Rangers	8-0	
3	Norton & Stockton Ancients (at Norton Sports Complex)	v	Redcar Town	3-1	80
4	FC United of Manchester (at FC United of Manchester)	v	Bridlington Rovers	13-0	147
5	Chorley (at Chorley FC)	v	Crewe Alexandra	2-1	88
6	Chesterfield (at Glapwell FC)	v	Stockport County	0-6	168
7	Brighouse Town (at Brighouse Town FC)	v	Burnley	3-1	
8	Newcastle United (at Druid Park)	v	Chester Le Street Town (4.00)	0-2	
9	Sporting Khalsa (at Long Eaton United FC)	v	Long Eaton United	1-6	
10	Kidderminster Harriers (at Kidderminster Harriers FC)	v	Solihull Moors	2-1	
11	Leicester City Women Dev (at Riverside Pavillion)	v	Oadby & Wigston	2-1	
12	Birmingham & West Midlands (at Castle Vale Stadium)	v	Wolverhampton Wanderers	0-2	
13	Leafield Athletic (at Dickens Heath Sports Club)	v	West Bromwich Albion	1-2	283
14	Nettleham (at Mulsanne Park)	v	Histon	9-0	
15	Norwich City (at Norwich United FC)	v	Enfield Town	4-0	
16	Acle United (at Great Yarmouth Town FC)	v	Cambridge City	0-1	84
17	Cambridge United (Cambridge United won 4-2 on kicks from the penalty mark) (at Mildenhall Town FC)	v	Stevenage	2-2aet	
18	Wymondham Town (at Wymondham Town FC)	v	Billericay Town	3-4	
19	Chesham United (at Chalfont St Peter FC)	v	Crawley Wasps	0-3	
20	Islington Borough (at St Aloysius College Playing Fields)	v	New London Lionesses	1-2aet	
21	Ashford Town (Middx) (at Ashford Town (Middx) FC)	v	Kent Football United	3-4	40
22	AFC Wimbledon (at Carshalton Athletic FC)	v	Godalming Town	4-0	70
23	Whyteleafe (at Whyteleafe FC)	v	Queens Park Rangers Girls	1-2	
24	Luton Town (at Stockwood Park Athletics Stadium)	v	Oxford City	5-2	44
25	Newhaven (at Newhaven FC)	v	AFC Bournemouth	0-8	
26	Buckland Athletic (at Buckland Athletic FC)	v	Marine Academy Plymouth	2-0	
27	Eastleigh (at Eastleigh FC)	v	Poole Town	1-2	
28	Keynsham Town (at Keynsham Town FC)	v	Southampton Saints	6-0	
29	Southampton FC Women (at AFC Totton)	v	Larkhall Athletic	4-1	
30	Cheltenham Town (at Cheltenham Saracens FC)	v	Exeter City	1-0	

FIRST ROUND

No.	Home		Away	Score	Att
1	FC United of Manchester (at Avro FC)	v	Chester-Le-Street Town	0-5	110
2	Chorley (at Barnoldswick Town FC)	v	Stockport County	1-2	77
3	Leeds United (at Garforth Town FC)	v	Brighouse Town	1-0	
4	Norton & Stockton Ancients (at Norton Sports Complex)	v	Bolton Wanderers	0-1	100
5	Nettleham (at Mulsanne Park)	v	Long Eaton United	2-3	
6	Kidderminster Harriers (at Kidderminster Harriers FC)	v	Wolverhampton Wanderers	1-6	
7	West Bromwich Albion (at Boldmere St Michaels FC)	v	Leicester City Women Dev	2-1	100
8	Cambridge City (at Mildenhall Town FC – 11/11 – tie ordered to be replayed)	v	Cambridge United (25/11)	0-2	
9	Norwich City (at Norwich United FC)	v	Billericay Town	2-3aet	
10	Luton Town (Luton Town won 3-1 on kicks from the penalty mark)	v	Kent Football United	1-1aet	
11	New London Lionesses (AFC Wimbledon won 4-3 on kicks from the penalty mark - at Northwood FC)	v	AFC Wimbledon (18/11)	3-3aet	
12	Crawley Wasps (at Oakwood FC)	v	Queens Park Rangers Girls	6-0	80
13	Buckland Athletic (at Buckland Athletic FC)	v	Cheltenham Town	2-0	74
14	Keynsham Town (at Keynsham Town FC)	v	AFC Bournemouth	8-1	100
15	Poole Town (at Milborne St Andrew FC)	v	Southampton FC Women	0-3	66

SECOND ROUND

No.	Home		Away	Score	Att
1	Sheffield FC (at Sheffield FC)	v	Nottingham Forest	2-3	
2	Long Eaton United (at Long Eaton United FC)	v	Hull City	0-5	60
3	Leeds United (at Thorpe Arch)	v	Doncaster Rovers Belles	4-3aet	200
4	Huddersfield Town (at Shelley FC)	v	Bradford City	7-1	105

5	Sunderland (at Eppleton CW FC)	v	Fylde	1-3	85
6	Chester-Le-Street Town (at Chester-Le-Street Town FC)	v	Stoke City	0-2	60
7	Middlesbrough (at Billingham Town FC)	v	Stockport County	1-0	83
8	Bolton Wanderers (Bolton Wanderers won 5-4 on kicks from the penalty mark - at Little Lever School)	v	West Bromwich Albion (9/12)	2-2aet	
9	Guiseley AFC Vixens (at Mickleover Sports FC)	v	Derby County	0-2	35
10	Wolverhampton Wanderers (at AFC Wulfrunians)	v	Blackburn Rovers	0-4	60
11	Keynsham Town (at Keynsham Town FC)	v	C&K Basildon	8-3	
12	Loughborough Foxes (at Loughborough University Stadium)	v	Gillingham	3-1aet	48
13	Billericay Town (at Billericay Town FC)	v	Luton Town	3-1aet	
14	MK Dons (at Milton Keynes Dons FC)	v	Southampton FC Women	4-0	
15	AFC Wimbledon (at Carshalton Athletic FC)	v	Portsmouth	2-0	95
16	Oxford United (at Oxford City FC)	v	Cambridge United	4-0	85
17	Watford (at Kings Langley FC)	v	Buckland Athletic (9/12)	1-0	70
18	Coventry United (at Daventry Town FC)	v	Plymouth Argyle	2-1	
19	Crawley Wasps (at Worthing FC)	v	Chichester City (9/12)	2-0	
20	Cardiff City (at CCB Centre of Sporting Excellence)	v	Queens Park Rangers Women	4-0	125

THIRD ROUND

1	Cardiff City (at Centre of Sporting Excellence)	v	Bolton Wanderers (2.00)	2-0	150
2	Derby County (at Mickleover Sports FC)	v	Stoke City	1-2	244
3	Huddersfield Town (at Shelley FC)	v	Leeds United	4-1	156
4	Middlesbrough (at Billingham Town FC)	v	Watford	2-7	98
5	Billericay Town (at Billericay Town FC)	v	Loughborough Foxes	3-4	
6	Hull City (at Hull University)	v	AFC Wimbledon	0-3	
7	Coventry United (at Daventry Town FC)	v	Crawley Wasps	1-2	70
8	Nottingham Forest (at Carlton Town FC)	v	MK Dons (2.00)	0-1	
9	Oxford United (at Oxford City FC)	v	Blackburn Rovers (2.00)	1-2	203
10	Keynsham Town (at Keynsham Town FC)	v	Fylde	2-1	85

FOURTH ROUND

1	Loughborough Foxes (at Loughborough University Stadium)	v	Sheffield United (10/2)	0-2	216
2	Charlton Athletic (Huddersfield Town won 5-4 on kicks from the penalty mark – at VCD Athletic FC)	v	Huddersfield Town	3-3aet	184
3	Brighton & Hove Albion (at Crawley Town FC)	v	Manchester United (12.30)	0-2	715
4	West Ham United (at Rush Green Stadium)	v	Blackburn Rovers (1.00)	3-1	
5	Stoke City (at Norton United FC)	v	Aston Villa (10/2)	1-2	
7	Yeovil Town (at Dorchester Town FC)	v	Birmingham City (3.00) (10/2)	1-3	523
8	AFC Wimbledon (at Carshalton Athletic FC)	v	Bristol City	0-3	410
9	Crystal Palace (at Bromley FC)	v	Tottenham Hotspur	0-3	282
10	Millwall Lionesses (at Dartford FC)	v	Lewes (10/2)	1-0	326
11	Durham (at New Ferens Park)	v	Cardiff City (12.00) (10/2)	5-1	
12	Everton (at Southport FC)	v	Chelsea (3.00)	0-2	560
13	Crawley Wasps (at Oakwood FC)	v	Arsenal (3.00)	0-4	1550
14	Leicester City (at Quorn FC)	v	London Bees	0-2	274
15	Reading (at venue Woking FC)	v	Keynsham Town (10/2)	13-0	272
16	Liverpool (at Tranmere Rovers FC)	v	MK Dons (10/2)	6-0	394

FIFTH ROUND

1	Liverpool (at Tranmere Rovers FC)	v	Millwall Lionesses	2-0	412
2	Bristol City (at Stoke Gifford Stadium)	v	Durham	0-2	
3	Reading (at Wycombe Wanderers FC)	v	Birmingham City	2-1	275
4	Chelsea (at AFC Wimbledon)	v	Arsenal	3-0	2232
5	Manchester United (at Hyde United FC)	v	London Bees	3-0	838
6	West Ham United (at Rush Green Stadium)	v	Huddersfield Town	8-1	865
7	Aston Villa (Aston Villa won 5-3 on kicks from the penalty mark – at Boldmere St Michaels FC)	v	Sheffield United (3.00)	3-3aet	252
8	Tottenham Hotspur (at Cheshunt FC)	v	Manchester City	0-3	1158

QUARTER FINALS

1	Reading (at Wycombe Wanderers FC)	v	Manchester United	3-2aet	951
2	Aston Villa (at Boldmere St Michaels FC)	v	West Ham United	0-1	609
3	Durham (at New Ferens Park)	v	Chelsea (12.00)	0-1	1629
4	Manchester City (at Academy Stadium)	v	Liverpool	3-0	1366

SEMI FINALS

1	Reading (West Ham United won 4-3 on kicks from the penalty mark - at Wycombe Wanderers FC – Live on BBC Red Button & iPlayer)	v	West Ham United (12.30)	1-1aet	2334
2	Manchester City (at Academy Stadium – Live on BBC Two)	v	Chelsea (3.30)	1-0	1726

THE FINAL - Saturday 4 May - @ Wembley Stadium

Manchester City	v	West Ham United (5.30)	3-0	43264

THE FA DISABILTY FINALS DAY

Saturday 15 and Sunday 16 June
At St. George's Park - Photos: Keith Clayton

Amputee Final
Everton Amputee FC 4-1 Portsmouth Amputee FC
Blind Final
West Bromwich Albion 0-2 Merseyside Blind
Cerebral Palsy Final
CP North West 8-1 North East & Yorkshire Disability
Partially Sighted Final
Birmingham Futsal 4-9 North West Scorpions
Powerchair Final
Aspire PFC 4-1 Northern Thunder PFC

Everton Amputee FC.

Merseyside Blind

CP North West

North West Scorpions

Aspire PFC

Everton's Tweed fires in a free kick.

Harris (WBA) gets away from Turnham and Mbuangi (Merseyside).

Fletcher (NW) slips the ball past Carr (NEY) for his first goal.

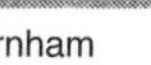

THE NON-LEAGUE CLUB DIRECTORY 2019-20

FA Constitutions for Steps 1 - 7

STEP 1

STEP 2

STEP 3 & 4

STEP 5/6

STEP 7+

AFC FYLDE

The Coasters **Club Colours** White

Founded 1988

Club Contact Details 01772 682 593 info@afcfylde.co.uk
Mill Farm, Coronation Way, Wesham, Preston PR4 3JZ

2018-19 SEASON
Nat 5
FAC 4Q
FAT F

Record
P 58 W 29 D 18 L 11

Top Goalscorer
Rowe (33)

Honours
FA Trophy

Previous Names: Wesham FC and Kirkham Town amalgamated in 1988 to form Kirkham & Wesham > 2008.

Previous Leagues: West Lancashire > 2007. North West Counties 2007-09. Northern Premier 2009-14.

Ground Capacity: 6,000 **Seats:** 6,000 **Covered:** Yes **Clubhouse:** Yes **Shop:** Yes
Previous Grounds: Coronation Road > 2006. Kellamergh Park 2006-2016.
Record Attendance: 3,858 v Chorley, National League North, 26/12/2016.

09-10		10-11		11-12		12-13		13-14		14-15		15-16		16-17		17-18	
NP1N	13	NP1N	5	NP1N	1	NP P	5	NP P	2	Conf N	2	Nat N	3	Nat N	1	Nat	7
FAC	2Q	FAC	P	FAC	2Qr	FAC	1P	FAC	2Q	FAC	1P	FAC	1P	FAC	2Q	FAC	2Pr
FAT	3Qr	FAT	P	FAT	1Q	FAT	3Q	FAT	3Q	FAT	3P	FAT	3P	FAT	1Pr	FAT	1P

League Honours: West Lancashire League 1999-2000, 00-01, 01-02, 03-04, 04-05, 05-06, 06-07.
North West Counties League 2008-09. Northern Premier Division One North 2011-12. National North 2016-17.

County FA Honours: Lancashire FA Challenge Trophy 2010-11, 12-13, 13-14. Lancashire Amateur Shield 2000-01, 03-04, 04-05, 05-06.
Northern Inter Counties Cup 2004-05, 05-06, 06-07.

FA Cup Second Round Proper 2017-18

FA Trophy Winners 2018-19

FA Vase Winners 2007-08

Victory: 8-1 v Oxford City, Conference North, 06/09/14. 9-2 v (H) Boston United, Conference North, 19/11/16.

Goalscorer: Danny Rowe - 132 - August 2014 - 01/12/2017 (still playing)

Access to the site via the A585 is less than 1 mile from the M55 Junction 3 to the north, which leads to Blackpool to the west and Preston and the M6 to the east. To the south, the A585 Fleetwood Road forms the Kirkham and Wesham Bypass and connects with the A583 Blackpool Road, a main route between Blackpool and Preston.

Nearest Railway Station Kirkham & Wesham half a mile away.
Bus Route No. 61

ALDERSHOT TOWN

The Shots **Club Colours** Red & blue

Founded 1992

Club Contact Details 01252 320 211 admin@theshots.co.uk
EBB Stadium, High street, Aldershot, GU11 1TW

2018-19 SEASON
Nat 21
FAC 1Pr
FAT 1Pr

Record
P 51 W 12 D 14 L 25

Top Goalscorer
Rendell (8)

Honours
-

Previous Names: None

Previous Leagues: Isthmian 1992-2003. Conference 2003-2008. Football League 2008-13.

Ground Capacity: 7,025 **Seats:** 2,676 **Covered:** 5,975 **Clubhouse:** Yes **Shop:** Yes
Previous Grounds: None
Record Attendance: 7,500 v Brighton & Hove Albion, FA Cup 1st Round, 18/11/2000

09-10		10-11		11-12		12-13		13-14		14-15		15-16		16-17		17-18	
FL 2	6	FL 2	14	FL 2	11	FL 2	24	Conf	19	Conf	18	Nat	15	Nat	5	Nat	5
FAC	2Pr	FAC	2P	FAC	2P	FAC	4P	FAC	4Qr	FAC	2Pr	FAC	1Pr	FAC	4Q	FAC	1P
FLC	1P	FLC	1P	FLC	4P	FLC	1P	FAT	QF	FAT	1P	FAT	1P	FAT	1Pr	FAT	1P

League Honours: Isthmian League Division Three 1992-93, Division One 97-98, Premier Division 2002-03.
Conference 2007-08.

County FA Honours: Hampshire Senior Cup 1998-99, 99-2000, 01-02, 02-03, 06-07.

FA Cup (As a non-League side) Third Round Proper - 2006-07. (Football League side) Fourth Round Proper - 2012-13.

FA Trophy Semi-Finals 2003-04, 07-08.

FA Vase Quarter-Finals 1993-94.

Victory: 8-0 v Bishop's Stortford (A) Isthmian Premier 05/09/1998

Defeat: 0-6 v Worthing (A) Isthmian League Cup 02/03/99

Goalscorer: Mark Butler - 155 (1992-98)

Appearances: Jason Chewings - 489 (August 1994 - May 2004)

Additional: Paid an undisclosed record fee to Woking for Marvin Morgan (05/2008)
Received £130,000 from Crewe Alexandra for Joel Grant (11/2008)

Exit from the M3 at junction 4 and take the A331 to Aldershot , after 3 miles take the 4th exit off the A331 and take the Town Centre route to Aldershot.
1.25 miles from the A331 junction the ground will be on your right hand side. Located on the High Street in Aldershot.

BARNET

The Bees

Club Colours Amber and black

Founded 1885

Club Contact Details 020 8381 3800 tellus@thehivelondon.com

The Hive, Camrose Avenue, Edgware, Middlesex, HA8 6AG

2018-19 SEASON
Nat 12
FAC 4Pr
FAT 4P

Record
P 58 W 23 D 16 L 19

Top Goalscorer
Coulthirst (20)

Honours
-

Previous Names: New Barnet 1885-88. Barnet 1888-1902 (folded). Barnet Alston 1904-19.

Previous Leagues: Post 1945 - Athenian 1945-65. Southern 1965-79. Conference 1979-91, 2001-05, 13-15. Football League 1991-2001, 05-13.

Ground Capacity: 6,500 **Seats:** 3,434 **Covered:** 5,176 **Clubhouse:** Yes **Shop:** Yes

Previous Grounds: Underhill 1907-2013

Record Attendance: 11,026 v Wycombe Wanderers FA Amateur Cup 01/01/1953

09-10		10-11		11-12		12-13		13-14		14-15		15-16		16-17		17-18	
FL 2	11	FL 2	22	FL 2	22	FL 2	23	Conf	8	Conf	1	FL 2	15	FL 2	15	FL 2	24
FAC	2Pr	FAC	1Pr	FAC	2P	FAC	1P	FAC	1P	FAC	1P	FAC	2P	FAC	1P	FAC	1P
FLC	1P	FLC	1P	FLC	2P	FLC	1P	FAT	2P	FAT	1Pr	FLC	2P	FLC	1P	FLC	2P

League Honours: Athenian League 1931-32, 32-33, 46-47, 58-59, 63-64, 64-65. Southern League Division One 1965-66, Division One South 1977-78. Football Conference 1990-91, 2004-05, 2014-15.

County FA Honours: Herts Senior Cup 1985-86, 90-91, 91-92, 92-93, 95-96, 2006-07, 10-11.

FA Cup (As a non-League side) 4th Rnd Proper Replay - 2018-19. (FL) 4th Rnd Proper - 2006-07, 07-08.

FA Am Cup Winners 1945-46

FA Trophy Finalists 1971-72

Victory: 7-0 v Blackpool Division 3 11/11/2000

Defeat: 1-9 v Peterborough Division 3 05/09/1998

Goalscorer: Arthur Morris - 403 (1927-36)

Appearances: Les Eason - 648 (1965-74, 77-78)

Leave M1 at junction 4, take the A41 towards Edgware, at the first roundabout turn right on to the A410 towards Stanmore (London Road), pass the Stanmore Tube Station on your left, at the next set of lights, turn left on the A4140 (Marsh Lane into Honeypot Lane) towards Queensbury/Kingsbury after approx 2 miles turn left at the roundabout by the Tesco petrol station in to Taunton Way, then Camrose Avenue, The Hive is on your left hand side.

Nearest Railway Station Canons Park Underground (Jubilee line) is a 5 min walk away.

Bus Route 340, 186 & 79 from Edgware to Canons Park.

BARROW

The Bluebirds

Club Colours Blue & white

Founded 1901

Club Contact Details 01229 666 010 office@barrowafc.com

Furness Building Society Stadium, (Holker Street), Wilkie Road, Barrow-in-Furness LA14 5UW

2018-19 SEASON
Nat 10
FAC 4Q
FAT 1P

Record
P 48 W 17 D 13 L 18

Top Goalscorer
Hindle (12)

Honours
-

Previous Names: None

Previous Leagues: Lancashire Combination 1901-21. Football League 1921-72. Northern Premier 1972-79, 83-84, 86-89, 92-98, 99-04. Conference 1979-83, 84-86, 89-92, 98-99.

Ground Capacity: 5,045 **Seats:** 1,000 **Covered:** 2,200 **Clubhouse:** Yes **Shop:** Yes

Previous Grounds: Strawberry & Little Park, Roose.

Record Attendance: 16,854 v Swansea Town - FA Cup 3rd Round 1954

09-10		10-11		11-12		12-13		13-14		14-15		15-16		16-17		17-18	
Conf	15	Conf	18	Conf	13	Conf	22	Conf N	11	Conf N	1	Nat	11	Nat	7	Nat	20
FAC	3P	FAC	4Q	FAC	1P	FAC	2Pr	FAC	4Qr	FAC	2Q	FAC	4Q	FAC	3P	FAC	4Q
FAT	F	FAT	1P	FAT	2P	FAT	QF	FAT	2P	FAT	3Q	FAT	2P	FAT	QF	FAT	2Pr

League Honours: Northern Premier League 1983-84, 88-89, 97-98. Conference North 2014-15.

County FA Honours: Lancashire Senior Cup 1954-55. Lancashire Challenge Trophy 1980-81.

FA Cup Third Round Proper - 1945-46, 53-54(r), 55-56, 58-59, 63-64, 66-67(r), 67-68, 90-91, 2008-09, 09-10, 16-17

FA Trophy Winners 1989-90, 2009-10

Victory: 12-0 v Cleator - FA Cup 1920

Defeat: 1-10 v Hartlepool United - Football League Division 4 1959

Goalscorer: Colin Cowperthwaite - 282 (December 1977 - December 1992)

Appearances: Colin Cowperthwaite - 704

Additional: Paid £9,000 to Ashton United for Andy Whittaker (07/94)
Received £40,000 from Barnet for Kenny Lowe (01/91)

M6 Junction 36, onto A590 signposted Barrow. Follow A590 all the way to the outskirts of Barrow (approx. 27 miles) entering via Industrial route. In a further 2 miles you pass the Fire Station on the right hand side, take next left into Wilkie Road, the ground is on the right.

Nearest Railway Station Barrow-in-Furness half a mile away.

BOREHAM WOOD

Founded 1948

The Wood **Club Colours** White & black

Club Contact Details 0208 953 5097 matt@borehamwoodfootballclub.co.uk
Meadow Park, Broughinge Road, Boreham Wood WD6 5AL

2018-19 SEASON
Nat 20
FAC 1P
FAT 2P

Record
P 52 W 14 D 18 L 20

Top Goalscorer
Shaibu (13)

Honours
Herts Senior Cup

Previous Names: Boreham Wood Rovers and Royal Retournez amalgamated in 1948 to form today's club

Previous Leagues: Mid Herts 1948-52, Parthenon 1952-57, Spartan 1957-66, Athenian 1966-74, Isthmian 1974-2004, Southern 2004-10

Ground Capacity: 4,502 **Seats:** 1,700 **Covered:** 2,800 **Clubhouse:** Yes **Shop:** Yes
Previous Grounds: Eldon Avenue 1948-63
Record Attendance: 4,030 v Arsenal - Friendly 13/07/2001

09-10	10-11	11-12	12-13	13-14	14-15	15-16	16-17	17-18
Isth P 4	Conf S 14	Conf S 8	Conf S 9	Conf S 13	Conf S 2	Nat 19	Nat 11	Nat 4
FAC 2Q	FAC 4Q	FAC 2Q	FAC 1P	FAC 1Pr	FAC 4Q	FAC 1Pr	FAC 1Pr	FAC 2P
FAT 1P	FAT 1P	FAT 1P	FAT 1Pr	FAT 3Q	FAT 3Q	FAT 1P	FAT QF	FAT 2Pr

League Honours: Athenian League Div. Two 1968-69, Div.One 73-74. Isthmian League Division Two 1976-77, Division One 1994-95, 2000-01, Premier Division Play-off 2009-10. Southern Div. One East 2005-06, Conference South Play-off 2014-15.

County FA Honours: Herts Senior cup 1971-72, 98-99, 2001-02, 07-08, 13-14, 18-19. Herts Charity Cup 1980-81, 83-84, 85-86, 88-89, 89-90. London Challenge Cup 1997-98.

FA Cup Second Round Proper - 1996-97, 97-98, 2017-18.
FA Trophy Semi-Finals - 2005-06
Goalscorer: Mickey Jackson
Appearances: Dave Hatchett - 714
Additional: Received £5,000 from Dagenham & Redbridge for Steve Heffer

From M25 – Exit J23, A1 Southbound to London. Exit slip road to Borehamwood join A5135, straight over two roundabouts, at third 3rd roundabout take 2nd exit into Brook Road, Broughinge Road is first turning on the right, after big car park.
From M1 Southbound – Exit J4 to Edgware onto A41 (Watford by pass), Keep going straight over at the roundabout and two sets of traffic lights until you hit Apex Corner, turn left towards A1, over Stirling Corner, exit slip road into Borehamwood join A5135 at the third roundabout take 2nd exit into Brook Road, Broughinge Road is first turning on the right, after big car park.

Nearest Railway Station Elstree & Boreham Wood.

BROMLEY

Founded 1892

The Ravens or The Lillywhites **Club Colours** White and black

Club Contact Details 020 8460 5291 info@bromleyfc.net
The Stadium, Hayes Lane, Bromley, Kent BR2 9EF

2018-19 SEASON
Nat 11
FAC 1P
FAT 1P

Record
P 49 W 18 D 12 L 19

Top Goalscorer
Hooper (14)

Honours
-

Previous Names: None

Previous Leagues: South London, Southern, London, West Kent, South Surburban, Kent, Spartan 1907-08, Isthmian 1908-11, 52-2007, Athenian 1919-1952

Ground Capacity: 5,000 **Seats:** 1,300 **Covered:** 2,500 **Clubhouse:** Yes **Shop:** Yes
Previous Grounds: White Hart Field. Widmore Road. Plaistow Cricket Ground.
Record Attendance: 10,798 v Nigeria - 1950

09-10	10-11	11-12	12-13	13-14	14-15	15-16	16-17	17-18
Conf S 12	Conf S 11	Conf S 17	Conf S 15	Conf S 3	Conf S 1	Nat 14	Nat 10	Nat 9
FAC 1P	FAC 3Qr	FAC 1P	FAC 1P	FAC 3Q	FAC 1P	FAC 4Q	FAC 4Q	FAC 1P
FAT 3Q	FAT 3Q	FAT 3Q	FAT 3P	FAT 3Q	FAT 2P	FAT 1P	FAT 2P	FAT F

League Honours: Spartan 1907-08. Isthmian League 1908-09, 09-10, 53-54, 60-61. Athenian League 1922-23, 48-49, 50-51. Conference South 2014-15.

County FA Honours: Kent Senior Cup 1949/50, 76-77, 91-92, 96-97, 2005-06, 06-07. Kent Amateur Cup x12. London Senior Cup 1909-10, 45-46, 50-51, 2002-03, 12-13.

FA Cup Second Round Proper 1937-38, 45-46.
FA Trophy Third Round Proper 1999-00, 2012-13.
Victory: 13-1 v Redhill - Athenian League 1945-46
Defeat: 1-11 v Barking - Athenian League 1933-34
Goalscorer: George Brown - 570 (1938-61)
Appearances: George Brown
Additional: Received £50,000 from Millwall for John Goodman

From M25 Motorway: Leaving the M25 at Junction 4, follow the A21 to Bromley and London, for approximately 4 miles and then fork left onto the A232 signposted Croydon/Sutton. At the 2nd set of traffic lights turn right into Baston Road (B265), following it for about 2 miles as it becomes Hayes Street and then Hayes Lane. Bromley FC is on right hand side of road just after a mini roundabout. From the Croydon/Surrey areas use the A232, turn left into Baston Road (B265), following it for about 2 miles as it becomes Hayes Street and then Hayes Lane. From West London use the South Circular Road as far as West Dulwich and then via Crystal Palace, Penge, Beckenham and Bromley South areas. From North and East London use the Blackwall Tunnel and then the A20 road as far as Sidcup. Then use the A232 to Keston Common, turn right into Baston Road (B265), following it for about 2 miles as it becomes Hayes Street and then Hayes Lane.

CHESTERFIELD

Founded 1866

The Spireites **Club Colours** Blue & white

Club Contact Details 01246 269 300 fans@chesterfield-fc.co.uk

The Proact Stadium, 1866 Sheffield Road, Whittington Moor, Chesterfield S41 8NZ

2018-19 SEASON
Nat 14
FAC 2P
FAT 3P

Record
P 53 W 18 D 18 L 17

Top Goalscorer
Denton (14)

Honours
-

Previous Names: Chesterfield Town 1891-1915, Chesterfield Municipal 1915-20.

Previous Leagues: Sheffield & District 1892-96. Midland 1896-99, 1909-15, 19-20. Football League 1899-1909, 1921-2018.

Ground Capacity: 10,000 **Seats:** 10,000 **Covered:** Yes **Clubhouse:** Yes **Shop:** Yes

Previous Grounds: Athletic Ground 1866-72. Saltergate (Recreation Ground) 1872-2010.

Record Attendance: 30,561 (Saltergate) v Tottenham, 12/02/1938. 10,089 (1866 Sheffield Rd) v Rotherham

09-10	10-11	11-12	12-13	13-14	14-15	15-16	16-17	17-18
FL 2 8	FL 2 1	FL 1 22	FL 2 8	FL 2 1	FL 1 6	FL 1 18	FL 1 24	FL 2 23
FAC 1P	FAC 2P	FAC 1P	FAC 2P	FAC 2P	FAC 4P	FAC 2Pr	FAC 2P	FAC 1P
FLC 1P	FLC 1P	FLC 1P	FLC 1P	FLC 1P	FLC 1P	FLC 1P	FLC 1P	FLC 1P

League Honours: Midland 1909-10, 19-20. League Division Three North 1930-31, 35-36, Division Four/League Two 69-70, 84-85, 2010-11, 13-14.

County FA Honours: Derbyshire Senior Cup 1898-99, 1920-21, 21-22, 24-25, 32-33, 36-37, 2017-18.

FA Cup (As a non-League side) Second Round Proper - 2018-19. (Football League side) Semi-Finals 1996-97 (r).

FA Trophy Third Round Proper 2018-19.

Appearances: Mark Allott - 385 (League) 2001-12.

Goalscorer: Jack Lester - 92 (League) 2007-13.

Victory: 8-1 v Barrow 13/11/1926 and v Gateshead 25/04/1931.

From the M1. Leave the motorway at Junction 29 at he roundabout take the second exit A617 its dual carriageway for 7 miles or so. At the end of the A617 get in the right hand lane and at the roundabout take the 4th exit the A61 north dual carriageway. At the next roundabout take the first exit at the Tesco's roundabout. Gordon Lamb garage on the left. Donkey Derby on the right. At the next roundabout take the 3rd exit and drive along the B6057 Sheffield Road. You should be able to see the ground on your left just past Tesco's entrance.

Nearest Railway Station Chesterfield

CHORLEY

Founded 1875

Magpies **Club Colours** Black and white

Club Contact Details 01257 230 007 graham.watkinson@chorleyfc.com

Victory Park Stadium, Duke Street, Chorley, Lancashire PR7 3DU

2018-19 SEASON
Nat N 2
FAC 1Pr
FAT 3Q

Record
P 50 W 27 D 12 L 11

Top Goalscorer
CARVER (15)

Honours
National North Play-off

Previous Names: Founded as a Rugby Union side in 1875 then switched to football in 1883.

Previous Leagues: Lancashire Jr 1889-90. Lancashire All 1890-94. Lancashire 1894-1903. Lancashire Comb 1903-68, 69-70. NPL (FM) 1968-69, 70-72, 82-88, 90-2014. Cheshire Co 1972-82. Conference 1988-90.

Ground Capacity: 3,550 **Seats:** 900 **Covered:** 2,800 **Clubhouse:** Yes **Shop:** Yes

Previous Grounds: Dole Lane 1883-1901, Rangletts Park 1901-05, St George's Park 1905-20.

Record Attendance: 9,679 v Darwen, FA Cup Fourth Qualifying Round, 15/11/1932.

09-10	10-11	11-12	12-13	13-14	14-15	15-16	16-17	17-18
NP1N 16	NP1N 3	NP P 3	NP P 8	NP P 1	Conf N 4	Nat N 8	Nat N 6	Nat N 6
FAC 3Q	FAC P	FAC 1Qr	FAC 2Q	FAC 2Q	FAC 4Qr	FAC 4Qr	FAC 3Q	FAC 1P
FAT 1Q	FAT 3Q	FAT 1Q	FAT 1Q	FAT 3P	FAT 2Pr	FAT 3Qr	FAT 1P	FAT 1P

League Honours: Lancs All. 1892-93. Lancashire 1896-97, 98-99. Lancs Comb. 1919-20, 22-23, 27-28, 28-29, 32-33, 33-34, 39-40, 45-46, 59-60, 60-61, 63-64. Cheshire County 1975-76, 76-77, 81-82. NPL Premier 1987-88, 2013-14.

County FA Honours: Lancashire FA Trophy (Record 18 times) 1893-94, 1908-09, 23-24, 39-40, 45-46, 57-58, 58-59, 60-61, 63-64, 64-65, 75-76, 79-80, 81-82, 82-83, 2011-12, 14-15, 15-16, 17-18.

FA Cup Second Round Proper 1986-87, 90-91.

FA Trophy Semi-finals 1995-96.

Victory: 14-1 v Morecambe, April 1946.

Goalscorer: Peter Watson - 372 (1958-66).

Additional: Received £30,000 from Newcastle United for David Eatock 1996.

M61 (Junc.6) follow A6 to Chorley, going past the Yarrow Bridge Hotel on Bolton Rd. Left at first set of traffic lights into Pilling Lane, first right into Ashley St. Ground 2nd entrance on left. **M6** (Junc.27) follow Chorley, left at lights, A49 continue for 2½ miles, right onto B5251. Drive through Coppull and into Chorley for about 2 miles. Entering Chorley turn right into Duke St. 200yds past Plough Hotel. Right into Ashby St. and first right into Ground.

Nearest Railway Station Chorley - half a mile from the ground.

Bus Route Bus station half a mile from the ground.

DAGENHAM & REDBRIDGE

The Daggers **Club Colours** Red & blue

Founded 1992

Club Contact Details 0208 592 1549 info@daggers.co.uk
Chigwell Construction Stadium, Victoria Road, Dagenham, Essex RM10 7XL

2018-19 SEASON
Nat 18
FAC 4Q
FAT 2P
Record
P 50 W 16 D 12 L 22
Top Goalscorer
Wilkinson (12)
Honours
-

Previous Names: Formed by the merger of Dagenham and Redbridge Forest

Previous Leagues: Football Conference 1992-96, 2000-2007. Isthmian 1996-2000. Football League 2007-16.

Ground Capacity: 6,078 **Seats:** 2,200 **Covered:** Yes **Clubhouse:** Yes **Shop:** Yes
Previous Grounds: None
Record Attendance: 5,949 v Ipswich Town (05/01/2002) FA Cup Third Round Proper

09-10	10-11	11-12	12-13	13-14	14-15	15-16	16-17	17-18
FL 2 7	FL 1 21	FL 2 19	FL 2 22	FL 2 9	FL 2 14	FL 2 23	Nat 4	Nat 11
FAC 1P	FAC 1Pr	FAC 3Pr	FAC 1P	FAC 1P	FAC 1Pr	FAC 3P	FAC 1Pr	FAC 4Qr
FLC 1P	FLC 1P	FLC 1P	FLC 1P	FLC 1P	FLC 1P	FLC 1P	FAT 1P	FAT 1P

League Honours: Isthmian League Premier Division 1999-2000. Football Conference 2006-07.

County FA Honours: Essex Senior Cup 1997-98, 2000-01.

FA Cup Fourth Round Proper 2002-03.
FA Trophy Finalists 1996-97.
Victory: 8-1 v Woking, Football Conference, 19.04.94
Defeat: 0-9 v Hereford United, Football Conference, 27.02.04.
Goalscorer: Danny Shipp - 105
Appearances: Tony Roberts - 507
Additional: Transfer fee received: £470,000 Dwight Gayle to Peterborough United

If you are coming from the **North or West**, follow the M25 Clockwise until junction 27 and take the M11 towards London. Proceed along the M11 and as the road splits at the end of the motorway follow the signs for A406 South & A13. There are speed cameras along this road and the speed limit is 50 mph. After 5 miles, take the slip road on the left signposted A13 Dagenham, Tilbury and Southend. Go under the underpass and over the flyover and with the leisure complex on your left bear left onto the A1306 signposted Dagenham East. At the fifth set of lights with McDonalds in front of you, tern left onto the A1112, Ballards Road. The speed limit is 30mph and there is a speed camera on your left. At the Bull Roundabout bear left and go past Dagenham East Tube Station. Victoria Road is the fifth turning on the left. **South & East Via Dartford Crossing:** Follow signs for A13 to Dagenham/ Central London. Proceed along this road and take the turn off signposted Elm Park & Dagenham East and turn right at the roundabout at the bottom of the slip road. Proceed to the set of lights and turn left onto a dual carriageway. After about half a mile you will see a McDonalds on your right. Get into the right hand filter lane and turn right onto the A1112 Ballards Road, then as above.

Nearest Railway Station Dagenham East Underground (District line), exit left and take fifth turning on the left 400 metres away.
Bus Route The 103 runs from Romford Station and stops outside the ground.

DOVER ATHLETIC

The Whites **Club Colours** White & black

Founded 1983

Club Contact Details 01304 822 373 enquiries@doverathletic.com
Crabble Athletic Ground, Lewisham Road, Dover, Kent CT17 0JB

2018-19 SEASON
Nat 13
FAC 1P
FAT 2P
Record
P 51 W 18 D 13 L 20
Top Goalscorer
Effiong (11)
Honours
-

Previous Names: Dover F.C. until club folded in 1983

Previous Leagues: Southern 1983-93, 2002-04, Conference 1993-2002, Isthmian 2004-2009

Ground Capacity: 6,500 **Seats:** 1,010 **Covered:** 4,900 **Clubhouse:** Yes **Shop:** Yes
Previous Grounds: None
Record Attendance: 4,186 v Oxford United - FA Cup 1st Round Proper November 2002

09-10	10-11	11-12	12-13	13-14	14-15	15-16	16-17	17-18
Conf S 2	Conf S 7	Conf S 7	Conf S 3	Conf S 5	Conf 8	Nat 5	Nat 6	Nat 8
FAC 4Q	FAC 3P	FAC 4Q	FAC 3Qr	FAC 2P	FAC 3P	FAC 1P	FAC 1Pr	FAC 4Qr
FAT 3P	FAT 3Q	FAT 3Q	FAT 3Qr	FAT 3P	FAT QFr	FAT QF	FAT 1Pr	FAT 3P

League Honours: Southern League Southern Division 1987-88, Premier Division 1989-90, 92-93. Isthmian League Division 1 South 2007-08, Premier Division 2008-09. Conference South Play-offs 2013-14.

County FA Honours: Kent Senior Cup 1990-91, 2016-17.

FA Cup Third Round Proper 2010-11, 14-15.
FA Trophy Semi-Finals 1997-98.
Victory: 7-0 v Weymouth - 03/04/1990
Defeat: 1-7 v Poole Town
Goalscorer: Lennie Lee - 160
Appearances: Jason Bartlett - 520+
Additional: Paid £50,000 to Farnborough Town for David Lewworthy August 1993
Received £50,000 from Brentford for Ricky Reina 1997

From outside of Kent, find your way to the M25, then take the M2/A2 (following the signs to Canterbury, then from Canterbury follow signs to Dover) as far as the Whitfield roundabout (there is a McDonald's Drive-Thru on the left). Take the fourth exit at this roundabout, down Whitfield Hill. At the bottom of the hill turn left at the roundabout and follow this road until the first set of traffic lights. At the lights turn right (180 degrees down the hill) and follow the road under the railway bridge, the ground is a little further up the road on the left. There is no parking for supporters within the ground, although parking is available in the rugby ground, which is just inside the main entrance - stewards will direct you. If you have to take the M20/A20 leave the A20 in Folkestone (the exit immediately after the tunnel through the hill) and travel through the Alkham Valley (turn left at the roundabout at the end of the slip-road and then left again, following the signs for Alkham) which will eventually take you near Kearsney train station (turn right into Lower Road just before the railway bridge, before you get to the station).

Nearest Railway Station Main line - Dover Priory 2 miles away. Kearsney Station is a 10-15 minute walk from the ground.

EASTLEIGH

Founded 1946

The Spitfires **Club Colours** Blue

Club Contact Details 02380 613 361 admin@eastleighfc.com

The Silverlake Stadium 'Ten Acres', Stoneham Lane, Eastleigh SO50 9HT

2018-19 SEASON
Nat 7
FAC 4Q
FAT 1P
Record
P 50 W 23 D 9 L 18
Top Goalscorer
McCallum (27)
Honours
-

Previous Names: Swaythling Athletic 1946-59, Swaythling 1973-80

Previous Leagues: Southampton Junior & Senior 1946-59, Hampshire 1950-86, Wessex 1986-2003, Southern 2003-04, Isthmian 2004-05

Ground Capacity: 3,000 **Seats:** 2,700 **Covered:** Yes **Clubhouse:** Yes **Shop:** Yes

Previous Grounds: Southampton Common. Walnut Avenue >1957.

Record Attendance: 5,250 v Bolton Wanderers, FA Cup Third Round 09/01/2016

09-10		10-11		11-12		12-13		13-14		14-15		15-16		16-17		17-18	
Conf S	11	Conf S	8	Conf S	12	Conf S	4	Conf S	1	Conf	4	Nat	7	Nat	15	Nat	14
FAC	1P	FAC	4Q	FAC	3Q	FAC	3Q	FAC	3Q	FAC	2P	FAC	3Pr	FAC	3P	FAC	4Q
FAT	3Q	FAT	3P	FAT	3Q	FAT	3Q	FAT	QF	FAT	1P	FAT	2P	FAT	1P	FAT	1P

League Honours: Southampton Senior (West) 1949-50. Hampshire Division Three 1950-51, 53-54, Division Two 1967-68. Wessex Division One 2002-03. Conference South 2013-14.

County FA Honours: Hampshire Intermediate Cup 1950-51, Senior Cup 2011-12.

FA Cup Third Round Proper 2015-16 (r), 16-17.

FA Trophy Quarter Finals 2013-14.

FA Vase Fourth Round 1982-83, 90-91, 94-95.

Victory: 12-1 v Hythe & Dibden (H) - 11/12/1948

Defeat: 0-11 v Austin Sports (A) - 01.01.1947

Goalscorer: Johnnie Williams - 177

Appearances: Ian Knight - 611

Additional: Paid £10,000 to Newport (I.O.W.) for Colin Matthews

From junction 13 of M3, turn right into Leigh Road, turn right at Holiday Inn, at mini roundabout take second exit, at the next mini roundabout take second exit, then next mini roundabout take first exit. Then take the first turning right (signposted) ground 200 metres on the left.

EBBSFLEET UNITED

Founded 1946

The Fleet **Club Colours** Red & white

Club Contact Details 01474 533 796 info@eufc.co.uk

Stonebridge Road, Northfleet, Kent DA11 9GN

2018-19 SEASON
Nat 8
FAC 1Pr
FAT 1P
Record
P 50 W 19 D 14 L 17
Top Goalscorer
Cheek (16)
Honours
-

Previous Names: Gravesend United and Northfleet United merged in 1946 to form Gravesend and Northfleet > 2007

Previous Leagues: Southern 1946-79, 82-97. Alliance (FM) 1979-82. Isthmian 1997-2002.

Ground Capacity: 4,184 **Seats:** 2,300 **Covered:** 3,000 **Clubhouse:** Yes **Shop:** Yes

Previous Grounds: Gravesend United: Central Avenue

Record Attendance: 12,036 v Sunderland - FA Cup 4th Round 12/02/1963

09-10		10-11		11-12		12-13		13-14		14-15		15-16		16-17		17-18	
Conf	22	Conf S	3	Conf	14	Conf	23	Conf S	4	Conf S	8	Nat S	2	Nat S	2	Nat	6
FAC	4Q	FAC	1Pr	FAC	4Q	FAC	1P	FAC	4Qr	FAC	3Q	FAC	2Qr	FAC	4Q	FAC	1P
FAT	1P	FAT	2P	FAT	3P	FAT	1P	FAT	3P	FAT	QF	FAT	1P	FAT	2P	FAT	2Pr

League Honours: Southern League 1957-58, Division One South 1974-75, Southern Division 1993-94. Isthmian League Premier 2001-02.

County FA Honours: Kent Senior Cup 1948-49, 52-53, 80-81, 99-00, 00-01, 01-02, 07-08, 13-14

FA Cup Fourth Round Proper 1962-63

FA Trophy Winners 2007-08

Victory: 8-1 v Clacton Town - Southern League 1962-63

Defeat: 0-9 v Trowbridge Town - Southern League Premier DIvision 1991-92

Goalscorer: Steve Portway - 152 (1992-94, 97-2001)

Appearances: Ken Burrett - 537

Additional: Paid £8,000 to Wokingham Town for Richard Newbery 1996 and to Tonbridge for Craig Williams 1997
Received £35,000 from West Ham United for Jimmy Bullard 1998

Exit the M25 at Junction 2 and take the A2 signposted Canterbury. Leave the A2 at the Northfleet/Gravesend West junction. At roundabout, follow signs to Ebbsfleet International Station/A226 which will take you on to Thamesway and past Ebbsfleet International. The stadium is at the end of the road.

Nearest Railway Station Northfleet - 300 yards from the ground.
Bus Route 480/490 or FASTRACK 'B' Service

FC HALIFAX TOWN

Founded 1911

The Shaymen **Club Colours** Blue and white trim

Club Contact Details 01422 341 222 tonyallen@fchalifaxtown.com

The Shay Stadium, Shay Syke, Halifax HX1 2YT

2018-19 SEASON
Nat 15
FAC 2P
FAT 2Pr

Record
P 54 W 16 D 23 L 15

Top Goalscorer
Southwell (8)

Honours
-

Previous Names: Halifax Town 1911-2008 then reformed as F.C. Halifax Town

Previous Leagues: Yorkshire Combination 1911-12, Midland 1912-21, Football League (FM Division Three North)1921-93, 98-2002, Conference 1993-98, 2002-08

Ground Capacity: 10,401 **Seats:** 5,830 **Covered:** Yes **Clubhouse:** Yes **Shop:** Yes

Previous Grounds: Sandhall Lane 1911-15, Exley 1919-21.

Record Attendance: 36,885 v Tottenham Hotspur - FA Cup 5th Round 14/02/1953

09-10		10-11		11-12		12-13		13-14		14-15		15-16		16-17		17-18	
NP1N	1	NP P	1	Conf N	3	Conf N	5	Conf	5	Conf	9	Nat	21	Nat N	3	Nat	16
FAC	4Q	FAC	4Q	FAC	1P	FAC	4Qr	FAC	1P	FAC	1P	FAC	1P	FAC	2Pr	FAC	4Q
FAT	3Q	FAT	2Q	FAT	3Qr	FAT	QFr	FAT	1P	FAT	QF	FAT	F	FAT	3Qr	FAT	2P

League Honours: Conference 1997-98. Northern Premier League Division One North 2009-10, Premier Division 2010-11.

County FA Honours: West Riding County Cup 2012-13.

FA Cup Fifth Round Proper 1932-33, 52-53 as Halifax Town. Second Round Proper 2016-17 (r) as FC Halifax Town.

FA Trophy Winners 2015-16

Victory: 12-0 v West Vale Ramblers - FA Cup 1st Qualifying Road 1913-14

Defeat: 0-13 v Stockport County - Division 3 North 1933-34

Goalscorer: Ernie Dixon - 132 (1922-30)

Appearances: John Pickering - 402 (1965-74)

Additional: Recorded a 30 game unbeaten run at The Shay between 18/04/2009 - 20/11/2010 (W 24 D 6 F 79 A 20).
Fee paid - £150,000 for Chris Tate, July 1999. Fee Received - £350,000 for Geoff Horsfield, October 1998.

From the North: Take the A629 to Halifax Town Centre, take the 2nd exit at the roundabout following signs for A629 (Huddersfield), then into Skircoat Road where you will find the ground. General: Take the M62 exiting at junction 24, follow signs for A629 Halifax into Skircoat Road, then onto Shaw hill where you will find the ground.

Nearest Railway Station Halifax - 5-10min walk from the ground.

HARROGATE TOWN

Founded 1914

Town and Sulphurites **Club Colours** Yellow & black

Club Contact Details 01423 210 600 enquiries@harrogatetownafc.com

The CNG Stadium, Wetherby Road, Harrogate HG2 7SA

2018-19 SEASON
Nat 6
FAC 4Qr
FAT 3P

Record
P 52 W 23 D 12 L 17

Top Goalscorer
Muldoon (17)

Honours
-

Previous Names: Harrogate AFC 1914-32. Harrogate Hotspurs 1935-48.

Previous Leagues: West Riding 1919-20, Yorkshire (FM) 20-21, 22-31, 57-82, Midland 21-22, Northern 31-32, Harrogate & Dist. 35-37, 40-46, W.Riding Co.Am. 37-40, W.Yorks. 46-57, NCE (FM) 82-87, NPL (FM) 87-2004

Ground Capacity: 3,800 **Seats:** 500 **Covered:** 1,300 **Clubhouse:** Yes **Shop:** Yes

Previous Grounds: Starbeck Lane 1919-20.

Record Attendance: 4,280 v Railway Athletic - Whitworth Cup Final 1950

09-10		10-11		11-12		12-13		13-14		14-15		15-16		16-17		17-18	
Conf N	21	Conf N	12	Conf N	15	Conf N	6	Conf N	9	Conf N	15	Nat N	4	Nat N	11	Nat N	2
FAC	2Q	FAC	3Q	FAC	2Qr	FAC	2Pr	FAC	2Q	FAC	2Q	FAC	4Q	FAC	4Q	FAC	4Q
FAT	1Pr	FAT	1P	FAT	1P	FAT	1P	FAT	3Qr	FAT	1P	FAT	3Q	FAT	1Pr	FAT	3Pr

League Honours: Yorkshire 1926-27. Northern Premier League Division One 2001-02.

County FA Honours: West Riding Challenge Cup 1924-25, 31-32, 62-63, 72-73, 85-86, 2001-02, 02-03, 07-08.

FA Cup Second Round Proper 2012-13 (r)

FA Trophy Third Round Proper 1999-2000, 18-19 **FA Vase** Fourth Round Proper 1989-90

Victory: 13-0 v Micklefield

Defeat: 1-10 v Methley United - 1956

Goalscorer: Jimmy Hague - 135 (1956-58 and 1961-76)

Appearances: Paul Williamson - 428 (1980-81, 1982-85, and 1986-93)

A61 to Harrogate, turn right on to A658, and at roundabout take A661, proceed through second set of lights (Woodlands pub) ground approx. 500 mtrs on the right. From A1 Wetherby. Leave A1 at Wetherby on to A661 to Harrogate. Stay on this road and when reaching Harrogate at Woodland pub lights, ground 500mtrs on the right.

Nearest Railway Station Harrogate - 25min walk from the ground.
Bus Route 770 / 771 TransDev from Town Centre.

HARTLEPOOL UNITED

Founded 1908

Monkey Hangers **Club Colours** Blue & white

Club Contact Details 01429 272 584 enquiries@hartlepoolunited.co.uk

The Super 6 Stadium (Victoria Park), Clarence Road, Hartlepool TS24 8BZ

2018-19 SEASON
Nat 16
FAC 1Pr
FAT 2P

Record
P 51 W 17 D 15 L 19

Top Goalscorer
Noble (13)

Honours
-

Previous Names: Hartlepools United 1908-68. Hartlepool 1968-77.

Previous Leagues: North Eastern 1908-21. Football League 1921-2017.

Ground Capacity: 7,865 **Seats:** 4,359 **Covered:** Yes **Clubhouse:** Yes **Shop:** Yes

Previous Grounds: None

Record Attendance: 17,264 v Manchester United, FA Cup Third Round Proper, 1957

09-10		10-11		11-12		12-13		13-14		14-15		15-16		16-17		17-18	
FL 1	20	FL 1	16	FL 1	13	FL 1	23	FL 2	19	FL 2	22	FL 2	16	FL 2	23	Nat	15
FAC	1P	FAC	3P	FAC	1P	FAC	1P	FAC	2Pr	FAC	2P	FAC	3P	FAC	2P	FAC	1P
FLC	2P	FLC	2P	FLC	1P	FLC	1P	FLC	1P	FLC	1P	FLC	2P	FLC	1P	FAT	1P

League Honours: None

County FA Honours: None

FA Cup 4th Rd Proper 1954-55(r), 77-78, 88-89(r), 92-93, 2004-05(r), 08-09 as a League club. 1st Rd Proper 2017-18, 18-19(r) as a N-Lge Club.

FA Trophy 2nd Round Proper 2018-19

Goalscorer: Joshie Fletcher - 111

Appearances: Ritchie Humphreys - 543 (Includes a run of 234 consecutive appearances)

Exit the A19 at signpost Hartlepool A689, Motorway A1(M). At r'about turn right (s/p Hartlepool A689) and continue on the A689 for 4.3 miles, through the village of Newton Bewley, to the r'about by the Owton Lodge pub. Go straight on (s/p Town Centre A689) and follow Town Centre signs for 2.8 miles, over two r'abouts. At the traffic lights just past the Blacksmiths Arms on your left, go straight on. At the next traffic lights go straight on again over the bridge into the new marina complex and straight on again at the r'about into Marina Way. This is the area for the Jackson's Wharf parking. To get to the ground itself continue to the next r'about and turn left (s/p The North A179, A1048). Turn left at the lights into Clarence Road to the ground.

Nearest Railway Station Hartlepool is about half a mile away.

MAIDENHEAD UNITED

Founded 1870

Magpies **Club Colours** Black & white

Club Contact Details 01628 636 314 social@maidenheadunitedfc.org

York Road, Maidenhead, Berkshire SL6 1SF

2018-19 SEASON
Nat 19
FAC 1P
FAT 1P

Record
P 49 W 16 D 7 L 26

Top Goalscorer
Clifton (13)

Honours
-

Previous Names: After WWI Maidenhead F.C and Maidenhead Norfolkians merged to form Maidenhead Town >1920.

Previous Leagues: Southern (FM) 1894-1902, 2006-07, West Berkshire 1902-04, Gr. West Suburban 04-22, Spartan 1922-39, Gr. West Comb. 1939-45, Corinthian 45-63, Athenian 63-73, Isthmian 73-2004, Conference 04-09

Ground Capacity: 4,500 **Seats:** 550 **Covered:** 2,000 **Clubhouse:** Yes **Shop:** Yes

Previous Grounds: Kidwells Park (Norfolkians)

Record Attendance: 7,989 v Southall - FA Amateur Cup Quarter final 07/03/1936

09-10		10-11		11-12		12-13		13-14		14-15		15-16		16-17		17-18	
Conf S	16	Conf S	19	Conf S	20	Conf S	19	Conf S	18	Conf S	18	Nat S	7	Nat S	1	Nat	12
FAC	2Q	FAC	4Q	FAC	1Pr	FAC	3Q	FAC	2Q	FAC	3Qr	FAC	1Pr	FAC	2Q	FAC	1P
FAT	2P	FAT	3Q	FAT	1Pr	FAT	1P	FAT	3P	FAT	2Pr	FAT	2P	FAT	3Q	FAT	3Pr

League Honours: West Berkshire 1902-03. Spartan 1926-27, 31-32, 33-34. Corinthian 1957-58, 60-61, 61-62. National South 2016-17.

County FA Honours: Berks & Bucks Senior Cup 1894-95, 95-96, 1911-12, 27-28, 29-30, 30-31, 31-32, 38-39, 45-46, 55-56, 56-57, 60-61, 62-63, 65-66, 69-70, 97-98, 98-99, 2001-02, 02-03, 09-10, 14-15, 16-17. Wycombe Senior Cup 1999

FA Cup As United - First Round Proper 1960-61, 62-63, 63-64, 71-72, 2006-07, 07-08, 11-12 (r), 15-16 (r), 18-19.

FA Trophy Quarter-finals 2003-04 **FA Vase** Second Round Proper 1989-90

Victory: 14-1 v Buckingham Town - FA Amateur Cup 06/09/1952

Defeat: 0-14 v Chesham United (A) - Spartan League 31/03/1923

Goalscorer: George Copas - 270 (1924-35). Most goals in a season: Jack Palethorpe - 65 in 39 apps (1929-30).

Appearances: Bert Randall - 532 (1950-64)

Additional: Received £5,000 from Norwich City for Alan Cordice 1979

The Ground is in the town centre.
200 yards from the station and two minutes walk from the High Street.
Access from M4 Junctions 7 or 8/9.

Nearest Railway Station Maidenhead - 200 yards from the ground.

NOTTS COUNTY

The Magpies **Club Colours** Black & white

Founded 1862

Club Contact Details 0115 952 9000 office@nottscountyfc.co.uk
Meadow Lane Stadium, Meadow Lane, Nottingham NG2 3HJ

2018-19 SEASON
FL 2 23
FAC 1P
FLC 1P

Record
P 52 W 10 D 14 L 28

Top Goalscorer
-

Honours
-

Previous Names: None

Previous Leagues: Football League (FM) 1888-2019

Ground Capacity: 19,841 **Seats:** 19,841 **Covered:** Yes **Clubhouse:** Yes **Shop:** Yes
Previous Grounds: 1862-63 Park Hollow, 63-73 Meadows Cket Gd, 73-77, 94-1910 Trent Bridge, 77-78 Beeston Cket Gd, 80–94 Castle Gd
Record Attendance: 47,310 v York City, FA Cup Six Round, 12/03/1955

09-10		10-11		11-12		12-13		13-14		14-15		15-16		16-17		17-18	
FL 2	1	FL 1	19	FL 1	7	FL 1	12	FL 1	20	FL 1	21	FL 2	7	FL 2	16	FL 2	5
FAC	5P	FAC	4Pr	FAC	4P	FAC	2Pr	FAC	1P	FAC	1Pr	FAC	1P	FAC	2Pr	FAC	4Pr
FLC	1P	FLC	3P	FLC	1P	FLC	1P	FLC	2P	FLC	1P	FLC	2P	FLC	1P	FLC	1P

League Honours: Football League Division Two 1896-97, 1913-14, 22-23, Division Three South 1930-31, 49-50, Division Four 1970-71, Division Three 1997-98, League Two 2009-10.

County FA Honours:

FA Cup Winners 1893-94.

Victory: (League) 11-1 v Newport County, Division Three South, 15/01/1949
Victory: (Cup) 15-0 v Rotherham Town, FA Cup 1st Round Proper, 24/10/1885
Goalscorer: (League) Les Bradd - 125 (1967-78). In a season: Tom Keetley - 39 (1930-31)
Appearances: (League) Albert Iremonger - 564 (1904-26)

Leave the M1 at junction 26 and follow signs for Nottingham via the A610 Nuthall Road until you meet the A6514 at Western Boulevard. Turn right and follow the A6514 ('the Ring Road south'). Carry straight on at the next roundabout ('the Crown Island') and join Middleton Boulevard. Stay on Middleton Boulevard, which becomes Clifton Boulevard after the Queen's Medical Centre. Turn left for Riverside P&R if you are heading for the Embankment, or Riverside Way Park & Ride, and follow signs for Matchday Parking. Continue around the ring road, following the 'Football Traffic' signs until you reach the Gamston roundabout. Take the first exit left onto the A6011 ('Radcliffe Road'). Continue along the A6011 and bear right on to Lady Bay Bridge (do not follow signs for city via Trent Bridge). Leave the M1 at Junction 24 and follow signs to join the A453 towards Nottingham. After passing through Clifton, continue on the A453 following signs for football and cricket traffic. Join the A52 eastbound towards Grantham and carry straight on at the Nottingham Knight Island and the Wheatcroft Island until you reach the Gamston Island. Take the first exit on to the A6011 ('Radcliffe Road'). Continue along the A6011, following the road as it bends to the right and continue over Lady Bay Bridge. Follow local signs for matchday parking.

Nearest Railway Station The ground is 10min walk from Nottingham train station.
Bus Route None directly to the ground only to Nottingham's coach station on Station Street, the ground is a short walk from there.

SOLIHULL MOORS

Moors **Club Colours** Blue with yellow

Founded 2007

Club Contact Details 0121 705 6770 info@solihullmoorsfc.co.uk
The Automated Technology Group Stadium, Damson Park, Damson Parkway, Solihull B91 2PP

2018-19 SEASON
Nat 2
FAC 2Pr
FAT 4P

Record
P 56 W 30 D 13 L 13

Top Goalscorer
Yussuf (21)

Honours
-

Previous Names: Today's club was formed after the amalgamation of Solihull Borough and Moor Green in 2007.

Previous Leagues: None

Ground Capacity: 5,500 **Seats:** 2,131 **Covered:** Yes **Clubhouse:** Yes **Shop:** Yes
Previous Grounds: None
Record Attendance: 3,681 v Leyton Orient, National, 22/04/2019.

09-10		10-11		11-12		12-13		13-14		14-15		15-16		16-17		17-18	
Conf N	17	Conf N	7	Conf N	19	Conf N	9	Conf N	8	Conf N	12	Nat N	1	Nat	16	Nat	18
FAC	3Q	FAC	3Q	FAC	4Q	FAC	3Q	FAC	4Q	FAC	2Q	FAC	3Q	FAC	2P	FAC	1P
FAT	3Q	FAT	3Q	FAT	1P	FAT	2P	FAT	3Q	FAT	1P	FAT	1P	FAT	1P	FAT	2P

League Honours: National North 2015-16.

County FA Honours: Birmingham Senior Cup 2015-16.

FA Cup Second Round Proper 2016-17(r)
FA Trophy Fourth Round Proper 2018-19
Victory: 7-2 v Corby Town, Conference North, 12/02/2011.
Defeat: 0-9 v Tranmere Rovers, National, 08/04/2017.
Appearances: Carl Motteram - 71 (2007-08)

Leave the M42 at Junction 6 and take the A45 towards Birmingham, after approximately 2 miles, at the traffic lights, take the left hand filter lane onto Damson Parkway. Follow the road for approximately 1 mile where the Autotech Stadium is situated on the right hand side, continue over the traffic lights (for the Land Rover factory entrance) to the traffic island and come back on yourself to find the entrance to the Football Club on the left just after the traffic lights. Use B92 9EJ as the postcode for SatNav purposes.

Nearest Railway Station Solihull & Birmingham within 3 miles away.
Bus Route Nos. X12 or 966 from Town Centre.

STOCKPORT COUNTY

County or Hatters **Club Colours** Blue and white

Founded 1883

Club Contact Details 0161 286 8888 mark.lockyear@stockportcounty.com

Edgeley Park, Hardcastle Road, Stockport SK3 9DD

2018-19 SEASON
Nat N 1
FAC 2P
FAT SF

Record
P 55 W 33 D 12 L 10

Top Goalscorer
Warburton (27)

Honours
National North

Previous Names: Heaton Norris Rovers 1883-88, Heaton Norris 1888-90.

Previous Leagues: Lancashire 1863-1900. Football League 1900-2011.

Ground Capacity: 10,800 **Seats:** 10,800 **Covered:** Yes **Clubhouse:** Yes **Shop:** Yes

Previous Grounds: Heaton Norris Recreation Ground & other various locations 1883-89. Green Lane 1889-1902.

Record Attendance: 27,833 v Liverpool, FA Cup 5th Round 11/02/1950. 10,273 (all seated) v Leeds United,

09-10	10-11	11-12	12-13	13-14	14-15	15-16	16-17	17-18
FL 1 24	FL 2 24	Conf 16	Conf 21	Conf N 14	Conf N 11	Nat N 9	Nat N 8	Nat N 5
FAC 2P	FAC 1Pr	FAC 4Q	FAC 1P	FAC 3Q	FAC 4Q	FAC 2Q	FAC 1P	FAC 3Qr
FLC 1P	FLC 1P	FAT 1Pr	FAT 2Pr	FAT 3Qr	FAT 2Pr	FAT 3Q	FAT 2Pr	FAT 4Pr

League Honours: Lancashire 1899-1900. League Division Three North 1921-22, 36-37, Division Four 1966-67. National North 2018-19.

County FA Honours: Manchester S.C. 1897-98,98-99, 1914-15,22-23. Cheshire Medal 1922-23,24-25,28-29,29-30,30-31. Ches' Bowl 1933-34,48-49, 52-53,55-56,56-57,58-59,60-61,62-63. Ches' S.C.1905-06,46-47,48-49,65-66,2015-16. Ches' Prem. Cup 1969-70,70-71, 2010-11.

FA Cup Fifth Round Proper 1934-35, 49-50, 2000-01.

FA Trophy Semi-finals 2018-19.

Victory: 13-0 v Halifax Town, Division Three North 06/01/1934.

Defeat: 0-9 v Everton Reserves, Lancashire League, 09/12/1893.

Goalscorer: (League) Jack Connor - 132, 1951-56.

Appearances: (League) Andy Thorpe - 555, 1978-86, 88-92.

Additional: Paid, £800,000 for Ian Moore from Nottingham Forest, 07/1998.
Received, £1,600,000 for Alun Armstrong from Middlesbrough, 02/1998.

Via M60, exit at Junction 1 ('sign-posted 'Stockport Town Centre and West'). At the r'about turn right and continue through to the second set of lights and turn left (ignoring the sign directing you to Stockport Co.) and follow the road to the left, which is Chestergate. At the lights turn right up King Street, past the fire station on the right to the top of the hill, turn right at the r'about signed Edgeley. Continue down Hardcastle street turning left after the bus stop signed Caroline Street.

Nearest Railway Station Stockport - Approx. half a mile from the ground.

SUTTON UNITED

The U's **Club Colours** Amber & brown

Founded 1898

Club Contact Details 0208 644 4440 info@suttonunited.net

Borough Sports Ground, Gander Green Lane, Sutton, Surrey SM1 2EY

2018-19 SEASON
Nat 9
FAC 1Pr
FAT 2P

Record
P 53 W 19 D 17 L 17

Top Goalscorer
Collins & Eastmond 7

Honours
-

Previous Names: Club formed after the merger of Sutton Guild Rovers and Sutton Association (formerley Sutton St Barnabas FC).

Previous Leagues: Sutton Junior, Southern Suburban, Athenian 1921-63, Isthmian 1963-86, 91-99, 2000-04, 2008-11, Conference 1999-2000, 04-08

Ground Capacity: 5,013 **Seats:** 765 **Covered:** 1,250 **Clubhouse:** Yes **Shop:** Yes

Previous Grounds: Western Road, Manor Lane, London Road, The Find

Record Attendance: 14,000 v Leeds United - FA Cup 4th Round 24/01/1970

09-10	10-11	11-12	12-13	13-14	14-15	15-16	16-17	17-18
Isth P 2	Isth P 1	Conf S 4	Conf S 6	Conf S 2	Conf S 15	Nat S 1	Nat 12	Nat 3
FAC 1P	FAC 1Q	FAC 2P	FAC 2Q	FAC 1P	FAC 3Q	FAC 4Q	FAC 5P	FAC 1P
FAT 1Q	FAT 1Pr	FAT 3Q	FAT 3P	FAT 3Q	FAT 1P	FAT 3Pr	FAT 3Pr	FAT 3P

League Honours: Athenian League 1927-28, 45-46, 57-58. Isthmian League 1966-67, 84-85, 85-86, 98-99, 2010-11. National League South 2015-16.

County FA Honours: London Senior Cup 1957-58, 82-83. Surrey Senior Cup 1945-46, 64-65, 67-68, 69-70, 79-80, 82-83, 83-84, 84-85, 85-86, 86-87, 87-88, 92-93, 94-95, 98-99, 2002-03.

FA Cup Fifth Round Proper 2016-17

FA Trophy Runners-up 1980-81

Victory: 11-1 v Clapton - 1966 and v Leatherhead - 1982-83 both Isthmian League

Defeat: 0-13 v Barking - Athenian League 1925-26

Goalscorer: Paul McKinnon - 279

Appearances: Larry Pritchard - 781 (1965-84)

Additional: Received £100,000 from AFC Bournemouth for Efan Ekoku 1990

Travel along the M25 to junction 8. Then north on the A217 for about 15-20 minutes. Ignoring signs for Sutton itself, stay on the A217 to the traffic lights by the Gander Inn (on the left), turn right into Gander Green Lane. The Borough Sports Ground is about 200 yards up this road on the left hand side, if you reach West Sutton station you have gone too far.

Nearest Railway Station West Sutton a few minutes walk from the ground.
Bus Route 413

TORQUAY UNITED

The Gulls **Club Colours** Yellow

Founded 1899

Club Contact Details 01803 328 666 reception@torquayunited.com
Plainmoor, Torquay, Devon TQ1 3PS

2018-19 SEASON
Nat S 1
FAC 1P
FAT 1P

Record
P 48 W 30 D 8 L 10

Top Goalscorer
Reid (32)

Honours
National South

Previous Names: Torquay United & Ellacombe merged to form Torquay Town 1910, then merged with Babbacombe to form Torquay United in 1921

Previous Leagues: Western 1921-27. Football League 1927-2007, 09-14. Conference 2007-09.

Ground Capacity: 6,500 **Seats:** 2,950 **Covered:** Yes **Clubhouse:** Yes **Shop:** Yes
Previous Grounds: Recreation Ground. Cricketfield Road > 1910.
Record Attendance: 21,908 v Huddersfield Town, FA Cup 4th Rnd, 29/01/1955.

09-10		10-11		11-12		12-13		13-14		14-15		15-16		16-17		17-18	
FL 2	17	FL 2	7	FL 2	5	FL 2	19	FL 2	24	Conf	13	Nat	18	Nat	17	Nat	22
FAC	3P	FAC	4P	FAC	2P	FAC	1P	FAC	1P	FAC	4Q	FAC	4Q	FAC	4Qr	FAC	4Q
FLC	1P	FLC	1P	FLC	1P	FLC	1P	FLC	1P	FAT	SF	FAT	QF	FAT	1P	FAT	1P

League Honours: Torquay & District 1909-09. Plymouth & District 1911-12. Southern Western Section 1926-27. National South 2018-19.

County FA Honours: Devon Senior Cup 1910-11, 21-22. Devon Bowl/Devon St Luke's Bowl 1933-34, 34-35, 36-37,45-46, 47-48, 48-49, 54-55 (shared), 57-58, 60-61, 69-70, 70-71, 71-72, 95-96 (shared), 97-98, 2006-07.

FA Cup Fourth Round Proper 1948-49, 54-55, 70-71, 82-83, 89-90, 2008-09, 10-11.

FA Trophy Finalists 2007-08

Victory: 9-0 v Swindon Town, Division Three South, 08/03/1952
Defeat: 2-10 v Fulham, Division Three South, 07/09/1931
Goalscorer: Sammy Collins - 219 in 379 games (1948-58) Scored 40 during the 1955-56 season.
Appearances: Dennis Lewis - 443 (1947-59)
Additional: Paid £75,000 for Leon Constantine from Peterborough United, December 2004.
Received £650,000 from Crewe for Rodney Jack, July 1998.

BY ROAD FROM THE NORTH/EAST (A30/M5): At the junction of the A30/M5 take A38 signposted Plymouth. After 3 miles take left fork on A380 signposted Torquay. After a further 10 miles at Penn Inn roundabout take 2nd exit to Torquay. At Kerswell Gardens take the A3022 to Torquay. At Lowes Bridge turn left into Hele Rd (B3199) and continue until a double roundabout is reached. Turn left and immediately right into Westhill Road. Take the fifth turning on the right (St Marychurch Rd) then second left into St Paul's Rd. Continue on into St Paul's Crescent and the ground is on the left. Main entrance from Westlands Lane.

Nearest Railway Station Torre, 25 mins away. Main Torquay 2+ miles away.

WOKING

The Cards **Club Colours** Red, white & black

Founded 1889

Club Contact Details 01483 772 470 admin@wokingfc.co.uk
The Laithwaite Community Stadium, Kingfield Road, Woking, Surrey GU22 9AA

2018-19 SEASON
Nat S 2
FAC 3P
FAT 1Pr

Record
P 53 W 30 D 10 L 13

Top Goalscorer
Hyde (15)

Honours
National South Play-off

Previous Names: None

Previous Leagues: West Surrey 1895-1911. Isthmian 1911-92.

Ground Capacity: 6,000 **Seats:** 2,500 **Covered:** 3,900 **Clubhouse:** Yes **Shop:** Yes
Previous Grounds: Wheatsheaf, Ive Lane (pre 1923)
Record Attendance: 6,000 v Swansea City - FA Cup 1978-79 and v Coventry City - FA Cup 1996-97

09-10		10-11		11-12		12-13		13-14		14-15		15-16		16-17		17-18	
Conf S	5	Conf S	5	Conf S	1	Conf	12	Conf	9	Conf	7	Nat	12	Nat	18	Nat	21
FAC	1P	FAC	P	FAC	3Q	FAC	4Q	FAC	4Q	FAC	1P	FAC	4Q	FAC	2P	FAC	2Pr
FAT	2P	FAT	3P	FAT	3Q	FAT	2P	FAT	2P	FAT	3Pr	FAT	QF	FAT	1Pr	FAT	1P

League Honours: West Surrey 1895-96. Isthmian League Division Two South 1986-87, Premier Division 1991-92. Conference South 2011-12.

County FA Honours: Surrey Senior Cup 1912-13, 26-27, 55-56, 56-57, 71-72, 90-91, 93-94, 95-96, 99-00, 03-04, 2011-12, 13-14, 16-17.

FA Cup Fourth Round Proper 1990-91.

FA Am Cup Winners 1957-58.

FA Trophy Winners 1993-94, 94-95, 96-97, Runners-up 2005-06.

Victory: 17-4 v Farnham - 1912-13
Defeat: 0-16 v New Crusaders - 1905-06
Goalscorer: Charlie Mortimore - 331 (1953-65)
Appearances: Brian Finn - 564 (1962-74)
Additional: Paid £60,000 to Crystal Palace for Chris Sharpling
Received £150,000 from Bristol Rovers for Steve Foster

The ground is situated on the A247, opposite the entrance to Woking Park, midway between the town centre and Old Woking. Leave the M25 at either junctions 10 (Wisley) or 11 (Chertsey) and follow the signs towards Woking. When nearing the town centre follow the brown signs showing Heathside car park. The ground is about 15 minutes' walk from the car park. Come out of the car park and follow the signs for Woking FC. Travelling supporters are requested to use Heathside car park as there are no parking areas around the Stadium.

Nearest Railway Station Woking - about 15 mins from the ground.

WREXHAM

Founded 1864

The Robins **Club Colours** Red & white

Club Contact Details 01978 891 864 info@wrexhamfc.tv
Racecourse Ground, Mold road, Wrexham LL11 2AH

2018-19 SEASON
Nat 4
FAC 2Pr
FAT 2P

Record
P 54 W 28 D 11 L 15

Top Goalscorer
Four players (6)

Honours
-

Previous Names: Wrexham Athletic for the 1882-83 season only

Previous Leagues: The Combination 1890-94, 1896-1906, Welsh League 1894-96, Birmingham & District 1906-21, Football League 1921-2008

Ground Capacity: 10,771 **Seats:** 10,771 **Covered:** Yes **Clubhouse:** Yes **Shop:** Yes
Previous Grounds: Rhosddu Recreation Ground during the 1881-82 and 1882-83 seasons.
Record Attendance: 34,445 v Manchester United - FA Cup 4th Round 26/01/57

09-10		10-11		11-12		12-13		13-14		14-15		15-16		16-17		17-18	
Conf	11	Conf	4	Conf	2	Conf	5	Conf	17	Conf	11	Nat	8	Nat	13	Nat	10
FAC	2P	FAC	4Q	FAC	3Pr	FAC	1P	FAC	2P	FAC	3P	FAC	4Q	FAC	4Qr	FAC	4Q
FAT	1Pr	FAT	2P	FAT	1P	FAT	F	FAT	2P	FAT	F	FAT	2P	FAT	1P	FAT	1P

League Honours: Welsh Senior League 1894-95, 95-96. Combination 1900-01, 01-02, 02-03, 04-05. Football League Division Three 1977-78.

County FA Honours: Denbighshire & Flintshire (Soames) Charity Cup 1894-95, 98-99, 1902-03, 04-05, 05-06, 08-09.

FA Cup Quarter-Finals 1973-74, 77-78, 96-97
FA Trophy Winners 2012-13
Victory: 10-1 v Hartlepool United - Division Four 03/03/62
Defeat: 0-9 v v Brentford - Division Three
Goalscorer: Tommy Bamford - 201 (1928-34)
Appearances: Arfon Griffiths - 591 (1959-61 & 62-79)
Additional: Paid £800,000 to Birmingham City for Bryan Hughes March 1997
Received £212,000 from Liverpool for Joey Jones October 1978

From Wrexham by-pass (A483) exit at Mold junction (A451).
Follow signs for Town Centre and football ground is half a mile on the left hand side.

Nearest Railway Station Wrexham General is right next to the ground.

YEOVIL TOWN

Founded 1895

The Glovers **Club Colours** Green & white

Club Contact Details 01935 423 662
Huish Park, Lufton Way, Yeovil BA22 8YF

2018-19 SEASON
FL 2 24
FAC 1P
FLC 1P

Record
P 50 W 10 D 14 L 26

Top Goalscorer
-

Honours
-

Previous Names: Yeovil Casuals 1895-1907. Yeovil Town & Petters United >1946.

Previous Leagues: Somerset Senior. Dorset District. Bristol Charity. Western. Southern 1946-79. Alliance 1979-85. Isthmian 1985-88, 95-97. Conference 1988-95, 97-2002. Football League 2002-19.

Ground Capacity: 9,565 **Seats:** 5,212 **Covered:** Yes **Clubhouse:** Yes **Shop:** Yes
Previous Grounds: Pen Mill Athletic Ground. Huish > 1990.
Record Attendance: 9,527 v Leeds United, League One, 25/04/2008

09-10		10-11		11-12		12-13		13-14		14-15		15-16		16-17		17-18	
FL 1	15	FL 1	14	FL 1	7	FL 1	4	FLCh	24	FL 1	24	FL 2	20	FL 2	20	FL 2	19
FAC	1P	FAC	2P	FAC	2Pr	FAC	4P	FAC	4P	FAC	3P	FAC	3Pr	FAC	1Pr	FAC	4P
FLC	1P	FLC	1P	FLC	1P	FLC	2P	FLC	2P	FLC	1P	FLC	1P	FLC	2P	FLC	1P

League Honours: Somerset Sen 1896-97, 1901-02, 12-13, 20-21. Dorset Dist 08-09. Bristol Charity 21-22. Western 21-22, 24-25, 29-30, 34-35. Sthn Western Div 23-24, 31-32, 34-35, Prem 54-55, 63-64, 70-71. Isth P 87-88, 96-97. Conf 2002-03. FLge2 04-05.

County FA Honours: Somerset Professional/Premier Cup x25 firstly in 1912-13 and most recently in 2004-04.

FA Cup Fifth Round Proper 1948-49
FA Trophy Winners 2001-02
Goalscorer: Johnny Hayward - 548 (1906-28). Most league goals Dave Taylor - 284 (1960-69).
Appearances: Len Harris - 691 (1958-72)

Huish Park is located on the very outskirts of Yeovil and is signposted from the A303. Leave the A303 at the Cartgate roundabout and take the A3088 towards Yeovil. Follow the road for around four miles until you reach a roundabout on the outskirts of Yeovil with the Westlands Airfield directly in front of you. Turn left at this roundabout and then continue straight on, crossing a number of roundabouts. As you pass the entrance to an Asda superstore, take the next left for the ground, which can be seen from the road.

Nearest Railway Station Pen Mill Junction and Yeovil Junction - taxi ride away from the ground.
Bus Route No 68 from the above stations takes you to the town centre where you can get the First traveller No 1 to near the ground

AFC TELFORD UNITED

The Bucks **Club Colours** White and navy

Founded 1892

Club Contact Details 01952 640 064 enquiries@afctu.co.uk

New Bucks Head Stadium, Watling Street, Wellington, Telford TF1 2TU

2018-19 SEASON
Nat N 8
FAC 3Q
FAT SF

Record
P 51 W 23 D 14 L 14

Top Goalscorer
Udoh (26)

Honours
-

Previous Names: Wellington Town 1892-1969. AFC Telford United was formed when Telford United folded in May 2004

Previous Leagues: Shropshire 1892-98. Birmingham & District 1898-1901, 02-06, 08-38, 39-45. The Combination 1901-02. Cheshire County 1938-39, 45-58. Southern 1958-79. Alliance/Conference 1979-2004. Northern Premier 2004-06.

Ground Capacity: 6,380 **Seats:** 2,200 **Covered:** 4,800 **Clubhouse:** Yes **Shop:** Yes

Previous Grounds: None - Renovation of the old Bucks Head started in 2000 and was completed in 2003.

Record Attendance: 5,710 vs Burscough 28/04/2007

09-10		10-11		11-12		12-13		13-14		14-15		15-16		16-17		17-18	
Conf N	11	Conf N	2	Conf	20	Conf	24	Conf N	1	Conf	22	Nat N	18	Nat N	17	Nat N	14
FAC	1P	FAC	3Qr	FAC	1P	FAC	4Qr	FAC	2Q	FAC	2P	FAC	2Q	FAC	2Qr	FAC	1P
FAT	3Qr	FAT	3P	FAT	2P	FAT	2P	FAT	1Pr	FAT	2P	FAT	1P	FAT	1P	FAT	1P

League Honours: Birmingham & District 1920-21, 34-35, 35-36, 39-40. Cheshire County 1945-46, 46-47, 51-52. NPL Div. 1 Play-off 2004-05, Premier Division Play-off 2006-07. Conference North Play-off 2010-11, Champions 13-14.

County FA Honours: Birmingham Senior Cup 1946-47. Walsall Senior Cup 1946-47. Shropshire Senior Cup 2008-09, 13-14, 16-17.

FA Cup Fifth Round Proper 1984-85. As AFC Telford United - Second Round Proper 2014-15.

FA Trophy Winners 1970-71, 82-83. As AFC Telford United - Semi-Finals 2008-09, 18-19.

Victory: 7-0 v Runcorn (A) - Northern Premier League Division One, 17/04/06.

Defeat: 1-6 v Guiseley (A) - Conference North, 01/04/14.

Goalscorer: Andy Brown - 56 (2008-12)

Appearances: Ryan Young - 367 (2007-14)

Additional: Paid £5,000 to Tamworth for Lee Moore 08/12/06
Received £25,000 from Burnley for Duane Courtney 31/08/05

(Sat Nav follow TF1 2NW into Haybridge Road) From M54 Junction 6, A5223 towards Wellington, straight over first roundabout (retail park). Straight over second roundabout (B5067). Left at third roundabout (Furrows garage). Continue over railway bridge and follow road round to the right, then turn left into AFC Telford United Car Park.

Nearest Railway Station Wellington (Shropshire) - 20min walk to ground.

Bus Route 44 - every 10 mins from Town centre.

ALFRETON TOWN

The Reds **Club Colours** All red

Founded 1959

Club Contact Details 01773 830 277 a.raisin@alfretontownfc.com

The Impact Arena, North Street, Alfreton, Derbyshire DE55 7FZ

2018-19 SEASON
Nat N 15
FAC 1P
FAT 3Q

Record
P 48 W 16 D 13 L 19

Top Goalscorer
Styche (11)

Honours
-

Previous Names: Formed when Alfreton Miners Welfare and Alfreton United merged.

Previous Leagues: Central Alliance 1959-61. Midland 1961-82. Northern Counties East 1982-87, 99-02. Northern Premier 1987-99, 02-04.

Ground Capacity: 3,600 **Seats:** 1,500 **Covered:** 2,600 **Clubhouse:** Yes **Shop:** Yes

Previous Grounds: None

Record Attendance: 5,023 v Matlock Town - Central Alliance 1960

09-10		10-11		11-12		12-13		13-14		14-15		15-16		16-17		17-18	
Conf N	3	Conf N	1	Conf	15	Conf	13	Conf	11	Conf	21	Nat N	10	Nat N	18	Nat N	17
FAC	3Qr	FAC	2Qr	FAC	1P	FAC	2P	FAC	1P	FAC	4Qr	FAC	4Q	FAC	1Pr	FAC	3Q
FAT	3Qr	FAT	3Pr	FAT	3P	FAT	1P	FAT	1P	FAT	2P	FAT	3Q	FAT	2P	FAT	3Q

League Honours: Midland 1969-70, 73-74, 76-77. Northern Counties East 1986-87, 2001-02 Northern Premier League Division One 2002-03. Conference North 2010-11

County FA Honours: Derbyshire Senior Cup 1960-61, 69-70, 72-73, 73-74, 81-82, 94-95, 2001-02, 02-03, 15-16, 18-19

FA Cup Second Round Proper 2008-09, 12-13

FA Vase Fifth Round Proper 1999-00

FA Trophy Fourth Round Proper 2002-03 (r), 2004-05

Victory: 15-0 v Loughbrough Midland League 1969-70

Defeat: 1-9 v Solihull - FAT 1997. 0-8 v Bridlington - 1992

Goalscorer: John Harrison - 303

Appearances: John Harrison - 561

Additional: Paid £2,000 to Worksop Town for Mick Goddard
Received £150,000 from Swindon Town for Aden Flint, January 2011

From M1 Junction 28 Take A38 towards Derby for 2 miles.
Then take slip road onto B600 Turn right at Tjunction towards town centre.
At pedestrian crossing turn left into North Street and the ground is 150-yards down on the right hand side.

Nearest Railway Station Alfreton - Approx. 15min walk from the ground

ALTRINCHAM

Founded 1891

The Robins **Club Colours** Red & white stripes

Club Contact Details 0161 928 1045 office@altrinchamfootballclub.co.uk
The J Davidson Stadium, Moss Lane, Altrincham, Cheshire WA15 8AP

2018-19 SEASON
Nat N 5
FAC 4Q
FAT 1P

Record
P 49 W 23 D 13 L 13

Top Goalscorer
Hancock (20)

Honours
-

Previous Names: Rigby Memorial Club 1891-93. Merged with the 'Grapplers' to form Broadheath FC 1893-1903.

Previous Leagues: Manchester (Founder members) 1893-1911. Lancashire Combination 1911-19. Cheshire County (FM) 1919-68. Northern Premier (FM) 1968-79, 97-99, 00-04, 17-18. Alliance/Conference/National (FM) 1979-97, 99-00, 04-17.

Ground Capacity: 6,085 **Seats:** 1,323 **Covered:** Yes **Clubhouse:** Yes **Shop:** Yes
Previous Grounds: Pollitts Field 1903-10.
Record Attendance: 10,275 - Altrincham Boys v Sunderland Boys English Schools Shield 28/02/1925.

09-10	10-11	11-12	12-13	13-14	14-15	15-16	16-17	17-18
Conf 14	Conf 22	Conf N 8	Conf N 4	Conf N 3	Conf 17	Nat 22	Nat N 22	NP P 1
FAC 4Q	FAC 4Q	FAC 2Q	FAC 1Pr	FAC 2Q	FAC 1P	FAC 2P	FAC 1P	FAC 3Q
FAT 2P	FAT 2P	FAT 3Q	FAT 1P	FAT 1P	FAT 3P	FAT 2P	FAT 1Pr	FAT 1Pr

League Honours: Manchester 1904-05, 06-07. Cheshire 1965-66, 66-67. Football Alliance 1979-80, 80-81. Northern Premier League Premier Division 1998-99, 2017-18.

County FA Honours: Cheshire Amateur Cup 1903-04. Cheshire Senior Cup Winners 1904-05, 33-34, 66-67, 81-82, 98-99, 04-05, 08-09.

FA Cup Fourth Round Proper 1985-86
FA Trophy Winners 1977-78, 85-86
Victory: 14-2 v Sale Holmfield, Cheshire Amateur Cup, 05/12/1903
Defeat: 1-13 v Stretford (H) - 04.11.1893
Goalscorer: Jack Swindells - 252 (1965-71)
Appearances: John Davison - 677 (1971-86)
Additional: Transfer fee paid - £15k to Blackpool for Keith Russell. Received - £50k from Leicester for Kevin Ellison

From M6 junction19, turn right towards Altrincham into town centre (approx 15 minutes). Turn down Lloyd Street, past Sainsburys on the right. Tesco Extra on left. Then follow signs for Altrincham F.C.

Nearest Railway Station Altrincham - Approx. 10min walk from the ground
Bus Route Arriva 263 & Stagecoach X41

BLYTH SPARTANS

Founded 1899

Spartans **Club Colours** Green and white

Club Contact Details 01670 352 373 generalmanager@blythspartans.com
Croft Park, Blyth, Northumberland NE24 3JE

2018-19 SEASON
Nat N 6
FAC 4Q
FAT 3P

Record
P 51 W 25 D 11 L 15

Top Goalscorer
Maguire (26)

Honours
-

Previous Names: None

Previous Leagues: Northumberland 1901-07, Northern All. 1907-13, 46-47, North Eastern 1913-39, Northern Com. 1945-46, Midland 1958-60, Northern Counties 1960-62, Northern 1962-94, NPL 1994-2006, 13-17. Conference 2006-13.

Ground Capacity: 4,435 **Seats:** 563 **Covered:** 1,000 **Clubhouse:** Yes **Shop:** Yes
Previous Grounds: None
Record Attendance: 10,186 v Hartlepool United - FA Cup 08/12/1956

09-10	10-11	11-12	12-13	13-14	14-15	15-16	16-17	17-18
Conf N 13	Conf N 9	Conf N 21	NP P 16	NP P 8	NP P 6	NP P 2	NP P 1	Nat N 10
FAC 4Qr	FAC 2Q	FAC 1P	FAC 2Qr	FAC 1Q	FAC 3P	FAC 1Q	FAC 2Q	FAC 2Q
FAT 2P	FAT QF	FAT 3Q	FAT 1Q	FAT 2Q	FAT 2Qr	FAT 3Q	FAT 3Qr	FAT 2P

League Honours: North Eastern 1935-36. Northern 1972-73, 74-75, 75-76, 79-80, 80-81, 81-82, 82-83, 83-84, 86-87, 87-88. Northern Division 1 1994-95. Northern Premier Premier Division 2005-06, 16-17.

County FA Honours: Northumberland Senior Cup 2014-15, 16-17.

FA Cup Fifth Round Proper 1977-78(r).
FA Trophy Quarter-finals 1979-80(r), 82-83(r), 2010-11.
Victory: 18-0 v Gateshead Town - Northern Alliance 28/12/1907
Defeat: 0-10 v Darlington - North Eastern League 12/12/1914
Appearances: Robbie Dale (pictured) became Blyth's record appearance holder during the 2018-19 season.
Additional: Received £30,000 from Hull City for Les Mutrie

From the Tyne Tunnel, take the A19 signposted MORPETH. At second roundabout take the A189 signposted ASHINGTON. From A189 take A1061 signposted BLYTH. At 1st roundabout follow signs A1061 to BLYTH. Go straight across next two roundabouts following TOWN CENTRE/SOUTH BEECH. At next roundabout turn left onto A193 go straight across next roundabout, and at the next turn right into Plessey Rd and the ground is situated on your left. Team coach should the turn left into William St (3rd left) and reverse up Bishopton St to the designated parking spot.

BOSTON UNITED

The Pilgrims **Club Colours** Amber and black

Founded 1933

Club Contact Details 01205 364 406 admin@bufc.co.uk
Jakemans Stadium, York Street, Boston PE21 6JN

2018-19 SEASON
Nat N 11
FAC 2Q
FAT 1P
Record
P 45 W 18 D 7 L 20
Top Goalscorer
Allott (10)
Honours
-

Previous Names: Reformed as Boston United when Boston Town folded in 1933

Previous Leagues: Midland 1933-58, 62-64, Southern 1958-62, 98-2000, United Counties 1965-66, West Midlands 1966-68, NPL 1968-79, 93-98, 2008-10, Alliance/Conference 1979-93, 2000-02, 07-08, Football League 2002-07.

Ground Capacity: 6,778 **Seats:** 5,711 **Covered:** 6,645 **Clubhouse:** Yes **Shop:** Yes
Previous Grounds: None
Record Attendance: 11,000 v Derby County, FA Cup Third Round Proper Replay, 09/01/1974

09-10		10-11		11-12		12-13		13-14		14-15		15-16		16-17		17-18	
NP P	3	Conf N	3	Conf N	11	Conf N	16	Conf N	6	Conf N	3	Nat N	5	Nat N	15	Nat N	9
FAC	2Q	FAC	2Q	FAC	2Qr	FAC	4Q	FAC	3Q	FAC	3Q	FAC	2Q	FAC	3Q	FAC	4Qr
FAT	2Qr	FAT	2P	FAT	2P	FAT	1Pr	FAT	2P	FAT	1Pr	FAT	3Q	FAT	3Q	FAT	3Qr

League Honours: Central Alliance League 1961-62. United Counties League 1965-66. West Midlands League 1966-67, 67-68. Northern Premier League 1972-73, 73-74, 76-77, 77-78. Southern League 1999-2000. Conference 2001-02.

County FA Honours: Lincolnshire Senior Cup 1934-35, 36-37, 37-38, 45-46, 49-50, 54-55, 55-56, 56-57, 59-60, 76-77, 78-79, 85-86, 87-88, 88-89, 05-06. East Anglian Cup 1960-61.

FA Cup Third Round Proper 1971-72, 73-74 (r), 2004-05 (r)
FA Trophy Final 1984-85
Victory: 12-0 v Spilsby Town - Grace Swan Cup 1992-93
Defeat: 2-9 v AFC Fylde - (A) National North, 19/11/2017
Goalscorer: Chris Cook - 181
Appearances: Billy Howells - 500+
Additional: Paid £30,000 to Scarborough for Paul Ellender, 08/2001
Received £50,000 from Bolton Wanderers for David Norris 2000

A1 to A17 Sleaford to Boston-Over Boston Railway Station crossing, bear right at the Eagle Public House-To light over Haven Bridge-straight along John Adams Way(Dual Carriageway) - Turn right at traffic lights into main ridge, then right again into York Street (This is opposite Eagle Fisheries) Ground is signposted after Railway crossing.

Nearest Railway Station Boston - less than 1 mile from the ground

BRACKLEY TOWN

Saints **Club Colours** Red and white

Founded 1890

Club Contact Details 01280 704 077 janenebutters@brackleytownfc.co.uk
St James Park, Churchill Way, Brackley NN13 7EJ

2018-19 SEASON
Nat N 3
FAC 3Q
FAT 4P
Record
p 51 W 27 D 13 L 11
Top Goalscorer
Ndlovu (17)
Honours
-

Previous Names: N/A

Previous Leagues: Oxfordshire Senior. North Bucks & District. Banbury & District. Hellenic 1977-83, 94-97, 99-2004. United Counties 1983-84. Southern 1997-99.

Ground Capacity: 3,500 **Seats:** 600 **Covered:** 1,500 **Clubhouse:** Yes **Shop:** Yes
Previous Grounds: Manor Road 1890-1968. Buckingham Road 1968-74.
Record Attendance: 2,604 v FC Halifax Town, Conference North Play-off final, 12/05/13.

09-10		10-11		11-12		12-13		13-14		14-15		15-16		16-17		17-18	
SthP	5	SthP	9	SthP	1	Conf N	3	Conf N	7	Conf N	18	Nat N	19	Nat N	7	Nat N	3
FAC	2Q	FAC	2Q	FAC	1Q	FAC	3Q	FAC	2P	FAC	3Q	FAC	1Pr	FAC	2P	FAC	4Qr
FAT	2Qr	FAT	3Q	FAT	1P	FAT	1P	FAT	3Qr	FAT	3Q	FAT	3Q	FAT	QF	FAT	F

League Honours: United Counties Division One 1983-84. Hellenic Premier Division 1996-97, 2003-04. Southern Division One Midlands 2006-07, Premier Division 2011-12.

County FA Honours: Northamptonshire Senior Cup 2010-11, 11-12, 14-15.

FA Cup Second Round Proper 2013-14, 16-17.
FA Vase Third Round Proper 1987-88.
FA Trophy Winners 2017-18
Goalscorer: Paul Warrington - 320
Appearances: Terry Muckelberg - 350
Additional: Received £2,000 from Oxford City for Phil Mason 1998

Take A43 from Northampton or Oxford, or A422 from Banbury to large roundabout south of town. Take exit marked Brackley (South) and follow towards the town (Tesco store on left). Pass the Locomotive public house and take first turning right, signposted Football Club, into Churchill Way - road leads into Club car park.

Nearest Railway Station Banbury - Approx. 10 miles from the ground.
Bus Route Stagecoach No. 500 from Banbury.

BRADFORD PARK AVENUE

Avenue **Club Colours** Green and white

Founded 1863

Club Contact Details 01274 674 584 info@bpafc.com

Horsfall Stadium, Cemetery Road, Bradford, West Yorkshire BD6 2NG

2018-19 SEASON
Nat N 7
FAC 3Q
FAT 3Q

Record
P 46 W 19 D 11 L 16

Top Goalscorer
Beesley (21)

Honours
-

Previous Names: Bradford FC. 1863-1907. Reformed as a Sunday club in 1974, then as a Saturday club in 1988.

Previous Leagues: West York. 1895-98. Yorkshire 98-99. Southern 1907-08. Football Lge 08-70. NPL 70-74, 95-04, 05-12. Bradford Am Sun. 74-76. Bradford Sun.All. 76-92. W. Riding Co. Am. 88-89. Cen Mids 89-90. NWC 90-95. Conf 2004-05

Ground Capacity: 3,500 **Seats:** 1,800 **Covered:** 2,000 **Clubhouse:** Yes **Shop:** Yes

Previous Grounds: Park Ave1907-73,87-88, Valley Parade73-74, Bingley Rd, Hope Ave, Ave Rd, Bramley, M'nt Pleasant

Record Attendance: 2,100 v Bristol City - FA Cup 1st Round 2003

09-10		10-11		11-12		12-13		13-14		14-15		15-16		16-17		17-18	
NP P	2	NP P	3	NP P	4	Conf N	7	Conf N	10	Conf N	13	Nat N	14	Nat N	16	Nat N	7
FAC	3Qr	FAC	1Q	FAC	1P	FAC	1P	FAC	4Qr	FAC	2Qr	FAC	3Qr	FAC	2Q	FAC	3Qr
FAT	1Q	FAT	1Q	FAT	1Qr	FAT	3Q	FAT	2P	FAT	1P	FAT	2Pr	FAT	3Q	FAT	3Qr

League Honours: West Yorkshire 1895-96 (Shared). Football League Division Three North 1927-28. North West Counties Div.One 1994-95 Northern Premier Division One 2000-01, Division One North 2007-08.

County FA Honours: West Riding Senior Cup x9. West Riding County Cup 1990-91, 2014-15, 15-16.

FA Cup Quarter-finals 1912-13, 19-20, 45-46.

FA Vase Second Round Proper 1994-95.

FA Trophy Fourth Round Proper 1998-99.

Victory: 11-0 v Derby Dale - FA Cup 1908
Defeat: 0-7 v Barnsley - 1911
Goalscorer: Len Shackleton - 171 (1940-46)
Appearances: Tommy Farr - 542 (1934-50)
Additional: Paid £24,500 to Derby County for Leon Leuty 1950
Received £34,000 from Derby County for Kevin Hector 1966

M62 to junction 26. Join M606 leave at second junction. At the roundabout take 2nd exit (A6036 signposted Halifax) and pass Odsal Stadium on the left hand side. At next roundabout take the 3rd exit (A6036 Halifax, Horsfall Stadium is signposted). After approximately one mile turn left down Cemetery Road immediately before the Kings Head Public House. Ground is 150 yards on the left.

Nearest Railway Station Bradford Foster Square or Bradford Interchange
Bus Route From Interchange - 681 (682 Eve & Sun)

CHESTER

The Blues **Club Colours** Blue & white

Founded 2010

Club Contact Details 01244 371 376 info@chesterfc.com

Swansway Chester Stadium, Bumpers Lane, Chester CH1 4LT

2018-19 SEASON
Nat N 9
FAC 3Q
FAT 3Qr

Record
P 46 W 17 D 15 L 14

Top Goalscorer
DUDLEY (11)

Honours
-

Previous Names: Formed after the demise of Chester City, which itself was formed in 1983 after the original Chester of 1885 folded.

Previous Leagues: Northern Premier League 2010-12.

Ground Capacity: 5,376 **Seats:** 4,170 **Covered:** Yes **Clubhouse:** Yes **Shop:** Yes

Previous Grounds: None

Record Attendance: 5,009 v Northwich Victoria, April 2012

09-10		10-11		11-12		12-13		13-14		14-15		15-16		16-17		17-18	
		NP1N	1	NP P	1	Conf N	1	Conf	21	Conf	12	Nat	17	Nat	19	Nat	23
						FAC	3Qr	FAC	4Q	FAC	2Pr	FAC	4Q	FAC	4Q	FAC	4Q
				FAT	2P	FAT	3Qr	FAT	1P	FAT	1Pr	FAT	3P	FAT	2P	FAT	2P

League Honours: Northern Premier League Division One North 2010-11, Premier Division 2011-12. Conference North 2012-13.

County FA Honours: Cheshire Senior Cup 2012-13.

FA Cup Fourth Qualifying Round 2013-14, 15-16, 16-17, 17-18

FA Trophy Third Round Proper 2015-16

Goalscorer: League - Michael Wilde - 41 (2010-12)
Appearances: League - Craig Mahon - 187 (2013-)

Stay on the M56 until you reach a roundabout at the end of the motorway. Follow the signs to North Wales & Queensferry A5117. After around one and a half miles you will reach a set of traffic lights where you need to bear left on to the A550 (signposted North Wales & Queensferry). Then from the A550, take the A548 towards Chester. Head straight through the first set of traffic lights and after passing a Vauxhall and then a Renault garage on your left, turn right at the next lights into Sovereign Way. Continue to the end of Sovereign Way and then turn right into Bumpers Lane and the entrance to the Club car park is just down on the right.

Nearest Railway Station Chester - 2.5 miles away.
Bus Route No.10A from City Centre Bus Exchange.

CURZON ASHTON

Founded 1963

The Nash **Club Colours** Royal blue and

Club Contact Details 0161 330 6033 rob@curzon-ashton.co.uk

Tameside Stadium, Richmond Street, Ashton-u-Lyme OL7 9HG

2018-19 SEASON
Nat N 18
FAC 3Q
FAT 3Q
Record
P 45 W 14 D 10 L 21
Top Goalscorer
Crankshaw (9)
Honours
-

Previous Names: Club formed when Curzon Road Methodists and Ashton Amateurs merged, and were initially known as Curzon Amateurs.

Previous Leagues: Manchester Amateur. Manchester > 1978. Cheshire (FM of Div.2) 1978-82. North West Counties (FM) 1983-87, 98-2007.Northern Premier (FM) 1987-97, 2007-15. Northern Counties East 1997-98.

Ground Capacity: 4,000 **Seats:** 527 **Covered:** 1,100 **Clubhouse:** Yes **Shop:** Yes
Previous Grounds: National Park 1963-2004. Stalybridge Celtic FC 2004-05.
Record Attendance: 3,210 v FC United of Manchester, North West Counties Challenge Cup Final, 03/05/07.

09-10	10-11	11-12	12-13	13-14	14-15	15-16	16-17	17-18
NP1N 3	NP1N 4	NP1N 2	NP1N 7	NP1N 1	NP P 4	Nat N 11	Nat N 14	Nat N 18
FAC Pr	FAC 1Qr	FAC Pr	FAC 2Q	FAC 3Q	FAC 3Q	FAC 2Q	FAC 1Pr	FAC 2Q
FAT P	FAT 1P	FAT 3Q	FAT 1Q	FAT 1P	FAT 2Q	FAT 2P	FAT 2P	FAT 3Q

League Honours: Manchester Amateur Division One 1963-64, 65-66. Manchester Premier Division 1977-78. Northern Premier Division One North 2013-14, Premier Division Play-off 2014-15.

County FA Honours: Manchester Premier Cup 1981-82, 83-84, 85-86, 87-87, 89-90.

FA Cup Second Round Proper 2008-09. **FA Vase** Semi-finals 1979-80, 2006-07.
FA Trophy Second Round Proper 2015-16.
Victory: 10-1 v Wakefield, 2012-13
Defeat: 0-8 v Bamber Bridge
Goalscorer: Rod Lawton - 376
Appearances: Alan Sykes

M60 (from Stockport) Junction 23 turn left off slip road, then get into the second from left lane to go through the lights onto the A6140 sign-posted Ashton. Keep on the A6140 until you come to a set of traffic lights with a cinema on your right, turn left at these lights, follow road over a bridge then over a mini-roundabout then turn left after the mini-roundabout. Ground is at the bottom.

Nearest Railway Station Ashton-under-Lyne - Approx. one mile from ground.
Bus Route Also 5mins from Ashton West Metrolink.

DARLINGTON 1883

Founded 1883

The Quakers **Club Colours** Black and white

Club Contact Details 01325 363 777 Dave.watson@darlingtonfc.org

Blackwell Meadows, Grange Road, Darlington DL1 5NR

2018-19 SEASON
Nat N 18
FAC 2Q
FAT 3Q
Record
P 44 W 12 D 14 L 18
Top Goalscorer
Nicholson (11)
Honours
-

Previous Names: Darlington FC 1883-2012

Previous Leagues: Northern League 1883-1908, 2012-13, North Eastern 1908-21, Football League 1921-89, 91-2010, Conference 1989-90, 10-12.

Ground Capacity: 3299 **Seats:** 588 **Covered:** Yes **Clubhouse:** Yes **Shop:**
Previous Grounds: Feethams 1883-2003. Darlington Arena 2003-12. Bishop Auckland 2012-16.
Record Attendance: 21,023 v Bolton Wanderers - League Cup 3rd Round 14/11/1960

09-10	10-11	11-12	12-13	13-14	14-15	15-16	16-17	17-18
FL 2 24	Conf 7	Conf 22	NL 1 1	NP1N 2	NP1N 2	NP P 1	Nat N 5	Nat N 12
FAC 1P	FAC 2P	FAC 4Qr			FAC 1Qr	FAC 1Q	FAC 2Q	FAC 2Q
	FAT F	FAT 1P		FAT 1Qr	FAT 2Q	FAT 2Q	FAT 3Qr	FAT 3Q

League Honours: Northern 1895-96, 99-1900, 2012-13. North Eastern 1912-13, 20-21. Football League Division Three North 1924-25, Division Four 1990-91. Conference 1989-90. NPL Division One North Play-off 2014-15, Premier Division 2015-16.

County FA Honours: Durham Challenge Cup 1884-85, 90-91, 92-93, 96-97, 1919-20, 99-2000.

FA Cup Fifth Round Proper 1910-11, 57-58.
FA Trophy Winners 2010-11.
Victory: 13-1 v Scarborough, FA Cup, 24/10/1891
Defeat: 0-10 v Doncaster Rovers - Division 4 25/01/1964
Goalscorer: Alan Walsh - 100, Jerry Best - 80
Appearances: Ron Greener - 490, John Peverell - 465, Brian Henderson - 463
Additional: Paid £95,000 to Motherwell for Nick Cusack January 1992.
Received £400,000 from Dundee United for Jason Devos October 1998

(SOUTH) From A1M exit at junction 57 , A66 (M) take slip road left towards Darlington & Airport. At the roundabout end of motorway, take first exit A66
Follow this to roundabout take 2nd exit A167 Darlington . Blackwell Meadows is on your right after approx. 400 yards.
(NORTH) From A1M junction 59, take the A167 towards the town centre, and when you reach the town centre in 5 miles, take the A167 to Northallerton along Grange Road. The ground is on your left after South Park. There is limited car parking at the ground, it is recommended to use the town centre car parks, a 10 minute walk away.

Nearest Railway Station Darlington - 1.5 miles away

FARSLEY CELTIC

Founded 2010

The Celt Army **Club Colours** Green & white

Club Contact Details 0113 255 7292 office@farsleyceltic.com

The Citadel, Newlands, Pudsey, Leeds, LS28 5BE

2018-19 SEASON
NP P 1
FAC 2Q
FAT 1P

Record
P 42 W 30 D 6 L 6

Top Goalscorer
Spencer (27)

Honours
Northern Premier Premier Division

Previous Names: Farsley AFC 2010-15.

Previous Leagues: Northern Counties East 2010-11. Northern Premier 2011-19.

Ground Capacity: 4,000 **Seats:** 300 **Covered:** 1,500 **Clubhouse:** Yes **Shop:** Yes

Previous Grounds: None

Record Attendance: 11,000 v Tranmere Rovers, FA Cup First Round Proepr, 1974-75 (at Elland Road)

09-10	10-11	11-12	12-13	13-14	14-15	15-16	16-17	17-18
	NCEP 1	NP1N 4	NP1N 14	NP1N 7	NP1N 12	NP1N 9	NP1N 2	NP P 5
			FAC 1Qr	FAC P	FAC 2Q	FAC 1Q	FAC 3Q	FAC 1Q
		FAT 1Qr	FAT Pr	FAT P	FAT 1Q	FAT 1Q	FAT 1P	FAT 1Qr

League Honours: Northern Counties East Premier Division 2010-11. Northern Premier League Premier Division 2018-19.

County FA Honours: West Riding County Cup 2016-17.

FA Cup Third Qualifying Round 2016-17.

FA Trophy First Round Proper 2016-17, 18-19.

Victory: 8-0 v Arnold Town (H) Northern Counties East Premier 2010-11.

Defeat: 5-1 v Tadcaster Albion, President's Cup Final 27/04/11.

Farsley is sandwiched between Leeds and Bradford approximately 1 mile from the junction of the Leeds Outer Ring Road (A6110) and the A647 towards Bradford. At the junction, take the B6157 towards Leeds, passing the police station on the left hand side. At New Street (the junction cornered by Go Outdoors) turn left. Newlands is approximately 300 yards on the right. Throstle Nest is situated at the end of Newlands with parking available outside the ground.

Nearest Railway Station New Pudsey - 1km

Bus Route Town Street - stop 500m away

GATESHEAD

Founded 1930

Tynesiders, The Heed **Club Colours** White & black

Club Contact Details 01914 783 883 info@gateshead-fc.com

The International Stadium, Neilson Road, Gateshead NE10 0EF

2018-19 SEASON
Nat 17
FAC 1P
FAT 1P

Record
P 49 W 20 D 9 L 20

Top Goalscorer
Boden (12)

Honours
-

Previous Names: Gateshead AFC (formerly South Shields)1930-73. Gateshead Town 1973-74. Gateshead Utd (formerly South Shields) 1974-77.

Previous Leagues: Football League 1930-60, NCE 60-62, North Regional 62-68, Northern Prem 68-70, 73-83, 85-86, 87 -90, Wearside 70-71, Midland 71-72, Northern Comb 73-74. Alliance/Conf 1983-85, 86-87, 90-98.

Ground Capacity: 11,795 **Seats:** 11,795 **Covered:** 7,271 **Clubhouse:** Yes **Shop:** Yes

Previous Grounds: Redheugh Park 1930-71

Record Attendance: 11,750 v Newcastle United - Friendly 07/08/95

09-10	10-11	11-12	12-13	13-14	14-15	15-16	16-17	17-18
Conf 20	Conf 15	Conf 8	Conf 17	Conf 3	Conf 10	Nat 9	Nat 8	Nat 17
FAC 1Pr	FAC 1P	FAC 2P	FAC 4Q	FAC 1Pr	FAC 3P	FAC 4Q	FAC 4Qr	FAC 2P
FAT 3Pr	FAT SF	FAT QF	FAT 3P	FAT 2P	FAT 3Pr	FAT QFr	FAT 2P	FAT SF

League Honours: Northern Regional 1963-64. Northern Premier League 1982-83, 85-86.

County FA Honours: Durham Senior Professional Cup 1930-31, 48-49, 501-51, 54-55, 58-59. Durham Challenge Cup 2010-11 (Reserve Team)

FA Cup Quarter Finals 1952-53 as a League club. Third Round Proper 2014-15 as a Non-League Club.

FA Trophy Semi-Finals 2010-11

Victory: 8-0 v Netherfield - Northern Premier League

Defeat: 0-9 v Sutton United - Conference 22/09/90

Goalscorer: Paul Thompson - 130

Appearances: James Curtis - 506 (2003-present)

Additional: Record transfer fee paid; £9,000 - Paul Cavell, Dagenham & Redbridge 1994
Record transfer fee received; £150,000 Lee Novak, Huddersfield Town 2009

Travelling up on the A1, turn off at the junction with the A194 just north of the Washington Services. Follow the A194 until the roundabout junction with the A184, turn left onto this road. The International Stadium is on the right after approximately 3 miles.

Nearest Railway Station Gateshead Stadium Metro stop 5min walk away.

GLOUCESTER CITY

Founded 1883

The Tigers **Club Colours** Red & amber

Club Contact Details 01386 442 303 info@gcafc.co.uk

Evesham United FC, The Spiers & Hartwell Jubilee Stadium, Cheltenham Road WR11 2LZ

2018-19 SEASON
Nat S 17
FAC 4Q
FAT 3Q

Record
P 47 W 15 D 12 L 20

Top Goalscorer
Jackson (9)

Honours
-

Previous Names: Gloucester 1883-86,1889-1901, Gloucester Nomads 1888-89, Gloucester YMCA 1910-25, Gloucester City 1902-10,1925 to date

Previous Leagues: Bristol & District (now Western) 1893-96, Gloucester & Dist. 1897-1907, North Gloucestershire 1907-10, Gloucestershire Northern Senior (FM) 1920-34, Birmingham Comb 1934-39, Southern 1939-2000

Ground Capacity: 3,000 **Seats:** 300 **Covered:** Yes **Clubhouse:** Yes **Shop:** Yes

Previous Grounds: Longlevens 1934-64. Horton Rd 1964-86. Meadow Pk 1986-2007. FGR 07-08. Cirencester T. 08-10. Cheltenham 10-17.

Record Attendance: Longlevens: 10,500 v Tottenham - Friendly 1952. Meadow Park: 4,500 v Dagenham &

09-10		10-11		11-12		12-13		13-14		14-15		15-16		16-17		17-18	
Conf N	18	Conf N	14	Conf N	14	Conf N	11	Conf N	17	Conf N	14	Nat N	15	Nat N	10	Nat S	14
FAC	4Qr	FAC	2Q	FAC	4Qr	FAC	1P	FAC	1P	FAC	4Q	FAC	4Q	FAC	3Qr	FAC	2Q
FAT	3Q	FAT	3P	FAT	3Qr	FAT	3Q	FAT	1P	FAT	3Qr	FAT	3Qr	FAT	3Q	FAT	3Q

League Honours: Gloucester & District Division One 1897-98, 99-1900, 03-04. North Gloucestershire Division One 1907-08, 08-09. Gloucestershire Northern Senior 1933-34. Southern League Midland Division 1988-89, Premier Division Play-off 2008-09.

County FA Honours: Glos Junior Cup 1902-03. Glos Senior Amateur Cup 1931-32. Glos Senior Cup 1937-38, 49-50, 50-51, 52-53, 54-55, 55-56, 57-58, 65-66, 68-69, 70-71, 74-75, 78-79, 79-80, 81-82, 82-83, 83-84, 90-91, 92-93.

FA Cup Second Round Proper 1989-90 (r). **Welsh Cup** Quarter-finals 1958-59 (r).

FA Trophy Semi-finals 1996-97 (r)

Victory: 12-1 v Bristol Saint George, April 1934

Defeat: 0-14 v Brimscombe FC, January 1923

Goalscorer: Jerry Causon - 206 (1930-36)

Appearances: Tom Webb - 675+ (2001 to date)

Additional: Paid £25,000 to Worcester City for Steve Ferguson 1990-91
Received £25,000 from AFC Bournemouth for Ian Hedges 1990

M5 (J10) follow A4019 - Cheltenham, through lights until you reach a r'about, PC World on left, McDonalds on right, turn left. After 500yds you'll come to a double r'about, straight over, keep going for 300yds, turn right into Swindon Lane, go over the level crossing and 2 mini r'abouts until you come to a large r'about, straight over, past Racecourse and turn right into Albert Rd at the end turn left at r'about (Prestbury Rd) 200yds turn into Whaddon Road.

Nearest Railway Station Evesham - 30/40 mins walk from the ground.

GUISELEY

Founded 1909

The Lions **Club Colours** White and navy

Club Contact Details 01943 873 223 (Office) 872 872 (Club) admin@guiseleyafc.co.uk

Nethermoor Park, Otley Road, Guiseley, Leeds LS20 8BT

2018-19 SEASON
Nat N 19
FAC 2P
FAT 3Qr

Record
P 50 W 13 D 19 L 18

Top Goalscorer
Liburd (12)

Honours
-

Previous Names: None

Previous Leagues: Wharfedale, Leeds, West Riding Counties, West Yorkshire, Yorkshire 1968-82, Northern Counties East 1982-91, Northern Premier 1991-2010

Ground Capacity: 4,200 **Seats:** 500 **Covered:** 1,040 **Clubhouse:** Yes **Shop:** Yes

Previous Grounds: None

Record Attendance: 2,486 v Bridlington Town - FA Vase Semi-final 1st Leg 1989-90

09-10		10-11		11-12		12-13		13-14		14-15		15-16		16-17		17-18	
NP P	1	Conf N	5	Conf N	2	Conf N	2	Conf N	5	Conf N	5	Nat	20	Nat	20	Nat	24
FAC	3Qr	FAC	1P	FAC	3Q	FAC	1Pr	FAC	2Q	FAC	4Q	FAC	4Qr	FAC	4Qr	FAC	2P
FAT	3P	FAT	QF	FAT	3P	FAT	2P	FAT	3P	FAT	1P	FAT	3Pr	FAT	2P	FAT	1P

League Honours: Wharfedale 1912-13. Yorkshire Division Two 1975-76. Northern Counties East 1990-91. NPL Division One 1993-94, Premier Division 2009-10. Conference North Play-off 2014-15.

County FA Honours: West Riding County Cup 1978-79, 79-80, 80-81, 93-94, 95-96, 2004-05, 10-11, 11-12.

FA Cup First Round Proper 1991-92, 94-95, 99-00, 02-03, 10-11, 12-13(r) **FA Vase** Winners 1990-91(r), Runners-up 91-92.

FA Trophy Semi-Finals 1993-94.

Misc: Highest points total gained - 93 - NPL 1 (1st) 1993-94 and NPL P (3rd) 1994-95.

From the West M62, M606 then follow signs to A65 through Guiseley to Ground on Right. From South and East M1 and M621 towards Leeds City Centre. Continue on M621 to Junction 2, follow Headingly Stadium signs to A65 towards Ilkley then as above. From North West From Skipton, A65 Ilkley, via Burley By-pass A65 towards Leeds, Ground quarter of a mile on left after Harry Ramsden's roundabout From North/NE A1M, leave at A59, towards Harrogate, then A658 signed Leeds Bradford Airport, at Pool turn right onto A659 Otley, continue towards Bradford/Leeds, to Harry Ramsden roundabout then A65 Leeds ground quarter of a mile on left.

Nearest Railway Station Nethermoor is about 5 min walk away.

Bus Route There are two bus stops directly outside.

HEREFORD

The Bulls **Club Colours** White and black

Founded 2014

Club Contact Details 01432 268 257 info@herefordfc.co.uk
Edgar Street, Hereford HR4 9JU

2018-19 SEASON
Nat N 17
FAC 3Q
FAT 2P

Record
P 48 W 14 D 17 L 17

Top Goalscorer
Owen-Evans (11)

Honours
-

Previous Names: Formed in 2014 after the demise of Hereford United who folded during the 2014-15 season.

Previous Leagues: Midland 2015-16. Southern 2016-18.

Ground Capacity: 8,843 **Seats:** 2,761 **Covered:** 6,082 **Clubhouse:** Yes **Shop:** Yes
Previous Grounds: None
Record Attendance: 4,712 v AFC Telford United, FA Cup 1P, 04/11/2017.

09-10	10-11	11-12	12-13	13-14	14-15	15-16	16-17	17-18
						MidL 1	Sthsw 1	SthP 1
							FAC 3Q	FAC 2P
						FAV F	FAT P	FAT 1P

League Honours: Midland League 2015-16. Southern Division One South & West 2016-17, Premier Division 17-18.

County FA Honours: Herefordshire County Cup 2015-16, 17-18

FA Cup Second Round Proper 2017-18
FA Vase Runners-up 2015-16
FA Trophy Second Round Proper 2018-19

Victory: 8-0 v Heanor Town - Midland League 23/04/16 & v Godalming Town (H), FAC 1Q, 02/09/2017.
Defeat: 4-5 v Coleshill Town - Midland League 2015-16.
Goalscorer: John Mills

Edgar Street is part of the main A49 road running through the centre of Hereford. Coming from the M5, take junction 7 (Worcester South) and follow signs for A4103 Hereford. At Hereford follow the A4103 until it joins the A49. Follow the A49 to the ground on the left, turn left immediately after the ground into Blackfriars Street. Turn left into the Merton Meadow car park. The main Club entrance is ten yards after the turning on the left, the players entrance is midway down the main stand.

Nearest Railway Station Hereford - 0.6km

KETTERING TOWN

The Poppies **Club Colours** Red & black

Founded 1872

Club Contact Details 01536 217 006 info@ketteringtownfc.com
Latimer Park, Burton Latimer, Kettering NN15 5PS

2018-19 SEASON
SthPC 1
FAC 4Q
FAT 2Q

Record
P 42 W 28 D 4 L 10

Top Goalscorer
Hoenes (17)

Honours
Southern League Premier Central

Previous Names: Kettering > 1924

Previous Leagues: Midland 1892-1900, also had a team in United Counties 1896-99, Southern 1900-30, 1950-79, 2001-02, 12-19. Birmingham 1930-50, Alliance/Conference 1979-2001, 02-03, 04-12. Isthmian 2003-04.

Ground Capacity: 2,500 **Seats:** 332 **Covered:** Yes **Clubhouse:** Yes **Shop:**
Previous Grounds: North Park, Green Lane, Rockingham Road > 2011. Nene Park 2011-13.
Record Attendance: 11,536 v Peterborough - FA Cup 1st Round replay 1958-59

09-10	10-11	11-12	12-13	13-14	14-15	15-16	16-17	17-18
Conf 6	Conf 14	Conf 24	SthP 22	SthC 3	SthC 1	SthP 6	SthP 9	SthP 4
FAC 2Pr	FAC 4Q	FAC 1P	FAC 2Q	FAC P	FAC 2Q	FAC 3Qr	FAC 4Q	FAC 4Qr
FAT 1P	FAT 1Pr	FAT 1P	FAT 1Q	FAT 1Q	FAT 1Q	FAT 2Q	FAT 2Q	FAT 1Q

League Honours: Midland 1895-96, 99-1900. United Counties 1904-05, 38-39. Southern 1927-28, 56-57, 72-73, 2001-02, Division One Central 2014-15, Premier Central 2018-19. Conference North 2007-08.

County FA Honours: Northamptionshire Senior Cup 2016-17, 17-18.

FA Cup Fourth Round Proper 1988-89, 2008-09.
FA Trophy Runners-up 1978-79, 1999-2000.

Victory: 16-0 v Higham YMCI - FA Cup 1909
Defeat: 0-13 v Mardy - Southern League Division Two 1911-12
Goalscorer: Roy Clayton - 171 (1972-81)
Appearances: Roger Ashby
Additional: Paid £25,000 to Macclesfield for Carl Alford 1994.
Recieved £150,000 from Newcastle United for Andy Hunt

From Jct 10 of the A14 turn due South at the roundabout onto Kettering Road (signposted Burton Latimer). After 200 yards turn right at the roundabout onto Attendiez Way. Go over the next roundabout and follow the road around Morrison's warehouse. The road becomes Polwell Lane and the entrance to Latimer Park is on the left just after Morrison's warehouse. **If approaching from the South**, take the A6 to its junction with the A14 and follow the directions above or, if travelling up the A509 turn right at the roundabout just after Isham (signposted Burton Latimer) onto Station Road and continue for half a mile past the Weetabix and Alumasc factories before turning left onto Polwell Lane. The entrance to Latimer Park is on the right after 50 yds.

Nearest Railway Station Kettering - 4.1km
Bus Route Station Road - stop 150m away

KIDDERMINSTER HARRIERS

Harriers **Club Colours** Red and white

Founded 1886

Club Contact Details 01562 823 931 info@harriers.co.uk
Aggborough Stadium, Hoo Road, Kidderminster DY10 1NB

2018-19 SEASON
Nat N 10
FAC 3Q
FAT 3Q

Record
P 45 W 18 D 9 L 18

Top Goalscorer
Ironside (19)

Honours
-

Previous Names: Kidderminster Harriers and Football Club 1886-90. Kidderminster FC 1890-1891.

Previous Leagues: B'ham & Dist (FM) 1889-90, 91-1939, 47-48, 60-62. Midland 1890-91. Southern 1939-45, 48-60, 72-83. B'ham Comb 1945-47. West Mids (Reg) 1962-72. Conference 1983-2000. Football Lg 2000-05.

Ground Capacity: 6,444 **Seats:** 3,140 **Covered:** 3,062 **Clubhouse:** Yes **Shop:** Yes
Previous Grounds: Chester Road 1886-87.
Record Attendance: 9,155 v Hereford United, FA Cup First Round Proper, 27/11/48

09-10	10-11	11-12	12-13	13-14	14-15	15-16	16-17	17-18
Conf 13	Conf 6	Conf 6	Conf 2	Conf 7	Conf 16	Nat 23	Nat N 2	Nat N 4
FAC 4Qr	FAC 4Q	FAC 4Qr	FAC 1P	FAC 4P	FAC 4Q	FAC 4Q	FAC 1P	FAC 1P
FAT SF	FAT 1P	FAT 3P	FAT 2P	FAT 1P	FAT 2P	FAT 1P	FAT 3Q	FAT 2Pr

League Honours: Birmingham & District 1937-38. West Midlands (Regional) 1964-65, 68-69, 69-70, 70-71. Conference 1993-94, 1999-2000.

County FA Honours: Worcestershire Senior Cup (27 times) Firstly in 1895-96 and most recently 2016-17. Birmingham Senior Cup (7x) Firstly in 1933-34 and most recently in 1966-67. Staffordshire Senior Cup (4x) Firstly in 1980-81 and most recently in 1984-85.

FA Cup Fifth Round Proper 1993-94
Welsh Cup Finalists 1985-86, 1988-89
FA Trophy Winners 1986-87; Runners-up 1990-91, 94-95, 2006-07

Victory: 25-0 v Hereford (H), Birmingham Senior Cup First Round, 12/10/1889
Defeat: 0-13 v Darwen (A), FA Cup First Round Proper, 24/01/1891
Goalscorer: Peter Wassell - 448 (1963-74)
Appearances: Brendan Wassell - 686 (1962-74)
Additional: Paid £80,000 to Nuneaton Borough for Andy Ducros July 2000
Recieved £380,000 from W.B.A. for Lee Hughes July 1997

From North M5 Junc 3 onto A456 to Kidderminster, From South M5 Junc 6 onto A449 to Kidderminster. Alternatively M40/42 Junc 1 onto A38 to Bromsgrove/A448 to Kidderminster. (All routes follow Brown signs to (SVR) Steam Railway then follow signs to Aggborough). Aggborough is signposted at either end of Hoo Road.

Nearest Railway Station Kidderminster - half a mile from the ground.

KING'S LYNN TOWN

The Linnets **Club Colours** Yellow & blue

Founded 2010

Club Contact Details 01553 760 060 office@kltown.co.uk
The Walks Stadium, Tennyson Road, King's Lynn PE30 5PB

2018-19 SEASON
SthPC 2
FAC 3Q
FAT 1Qr

Record
P 42 W 24 D 12 L 6

Top Goalscorer
Marriott (28)

Honours
Super Play-off

Previous Names: King's Lynn Town formed in 2010 after King's Lynn FC folded.

Previous Leagues: United Counties 2010-12. Northern Premier 2012-15. Southern 2015-19.

Ground Capacity: 8,200 **Seats:** 1,400 **Covered:** 5,000 **Clubhouse:** Yes **Shop:** Yes
Previous Grounds: None
Record Attendance:

09-10	10-11	11-12	12-13	13-14	14-15	15-16	16-17	17-18
	UCL P 2	UCL P 2	NP1S 1	NP P 11	NP P 18	SthP 9	SthP 13	SthP 2
		FAC 4Q	FAC 1Qr	FAC 1Q	FAC 4Q	FAC 3Q	FAC 3Q	FAC 2Q
	FAV SF	FAV 2P	FAT 3P	FAT 1Q	FAT 3Q	FAT 2Q	FAV 1P	FAT 1Q

League Honours: Northern Premier Division One South 2012-13.

County FA Honours: Norfolk Senior Cup 2016-17.

FA Cup Fourth Qualifying Round 2011-12, 14-15.
FA Vase Semi-finals 2010-11.
FA Trophy Third Round Proper 2012-13.

Victory: 7-1 v Gosport Borough (A), Southern Premier, 06/02/2018

At the roundabout, at the junction of A47 and the A17, follow the A47, signposted King's Lynn and Norwich. Travel along the dual carriageway for approx. one and a half miles branching off left, following the signs for Town Centre, onto the Hardwick roundabout. Take the first exit, following the signs for Town Centre, travel through two sets of traffic lights until reaching a further set of traffic lights at the Southgates roundabout. Take the fourth exit onto Vancouver Avenue, and travel for approx. 300 metres, going straight across a mini roundabout, The Walks is a further 200 metres along on the left hand side, with car parking outside the ground. The changing rooms and hospitality suite are located at the rear of the main stand.

Nearest Railway Station King's Lynn - 5min walk away.
Bus Route Serviced by Eastern Counties & Norfolk Green

LEAMINGTON

The Brakes **Club Colours** Gold and black

Founded 1892

Club Contact Details 01926 430 406 info@leamingtonfc.co.uk
Phillips 66 Community Stadium, Harbury Lane, Whitmarsh, Leamington CV33 9QB

2018-19 SEASON
Nat N 13
FAC 2Q
FAT 2P
Record
P 45 W 14 D 15 L 16
Top Goalscorer
Bishop (22)
Honours
Birmingham Senior Cup

Previous Names: Leamington Town 1892-1937, Lockheed Borg & Beck 1944-46 , Lockheed Leamington 1946-73, AP Leamington 1973-88

Previous Leagues: B'ham Comb, B'ham & Dist, West Mids (Reg), Midland Counties, Southern, Midland Combination, Midland Alliance 2005-07. Southern 2007-13, 15-17. Football Conference 2013-15.

Ground Capacity: 2,300 **Seats:** 294 **Covered:** 720 **Clubhouse:** Yes **Shop:** Yes
Previous Grounds: Old Windmill Ground
Record Attendance: 1,380 v Retford United - 17/02/2007

09-10		10-11		11-12		12-13		13-14		14-15		15-16		16-17		17-18	
SthP	10	SthP	5	SthP	7	SthP	1	Conf N	13	Conf N	21	SthP	3	SthP	2	Nat N	19
FAC	1Q	FAC	1Qr	FAC	2Q	FAC	2Q	FAC	2Qr	FAC	3Qr	FAC	1Qr	FAC	1Q	FAC	3Qr
FAT	1Q	FAT	3Q	FAT	1Q	FAT	1Qr	FAT	2P	FAT	3Q	FAT	1Pr	FAT	1Q	FAT	1P

League Honours: Birmingham & Dist 1961-62. West Mids Regional 1962-63. Midland Co 1964-65. Southern League 1982-83, 2012-13, Division One Midlands 2008-09. Midland Comb Div Two 2000-01, Premier Div 2004-05. Midland All 2006-07.

County FA Honours: Birmingham Senior Cup 2016-17, 18-19.

FA Cup First Round Proper 2005-06
FA Vase Quarter-finals 2006-07
FA Trophy Second Round Proper 2013-14, 18-19
Goalscorer: Josh Blake - 187
Appearances: Josh Blake - 406

From West and North – M40 Southbound – Exit J14 and take A452 towards Leamington. Ahead at 1st island. Next island take 2nd exit A452 (Europa Way). Next island take 4th exit (Harbury Lane) signposted Harbury and Bishops Tachbrook. Next island take 3rd exit (Harbury Lane). At traffic lights continue straight ahead Harbury Lane. Ground is 1.5 miles on left.
From South – M40 northbound – Exit J13. Turn right onto A452 towards Leamington. At 1st island take 3rd exit A452 (Europa Way) and follow as above (Europa Way onwards).

Nearest Railway Station Leamington Spa - 3 miles away
Bus Route Nos. 65 & 66

SOUTHPORT

The Sandgrounders **Club Colours** Yellow & black

Founded 1881

Club Contact Details 01704 533 422 secretary@southportfc.net
Merseyrail Community Stadium, Haig Avenue, Southport, Merseyside PR8 6JZ

2018-19 SEASON
Nat N 14
FAC 2Pr
FAT 1P
Record
P 51 W 18 D 16 L 17
Top Goalscorer
CHARLES (16)
Honours
-

Previous Names: Southport Central 1888-1918, Southport Vulcan 1918-21.

Previous Leagues: Preston & District, Lancashire 1889-1903, Lancashire Combination 1903-11, Central 1911-21, Football League 1921-78, Northern Premier 1978-93, 2003-04, Conference 1993-2003.

Ground Capacity: 6,008 **Seats:** 1,660 **Covered:** 2,760 **Clubhouse:** Yes **Shop:** Yes
Previous Grounds: Sussex Road Sports Ground, Scarisbrick New Road 1886-1905, Ash Lane (later named Haig Ave)
Record Attendance: 20,010 v Newcastle United - FA Cup 1932

09-10		10-11		11-12		12-13		13-14		14-15		15-16		16-17		17-18	
Conf N	1	Conf	21	Conf	7	Conf	20	Conf	18	Conf	19	Nat	16	Nat	23	Nat N	15
FAC	1P	FAC	1P	FAC	1P	FAC	4Q	FAC	1P	FAC	3P	FAC	4Q	FAC	1Pr	FAC	2Q
FAT	1Pr	FAT	1Pr	FAT	1P	FAT	QF	FAT	1P	FAT	1Pr	FAT	2P	FAT	2P	FAT	3Qr

League Honours: Football League Division Four 1972-73. Northern Premier League Premier Division 1992-93. Conference North 2004-05, 2009-10.

County FA Honours: Lancs Senior Cup 1904-05. Lancs Junior Cup 1919-20, 92-93, 96-97, 97-98, 2001-01, 05-06, 07-08, 09-10. Liverpool Senior Cup 1930-31, 31-32, 43-44, 62-63, 74-75, 90-91, 92-93, 98-99, 2011-12.

FA Cup Quarter-Finals 1930-31. As a Non-League side - Third Round Proper 1998-99, 2014-15.
FA Trophy Runners-up 1998-98
Victory: 8-1 v Nelson - 01/01/31
Defeat: 0-11 v Oldham Athletic - 26/12/62
Goalscorer: Alan Spence - 98
Appearances: Arthur Peat - 401 (1962-72)
Additional: Paid £20,000 to Macclesfield Town for Martin McDonald

Leave M6 at junction 26. Join M58 to junction 3. Join A570 signposted Southport, follow A570 through Ormskirk Town Centre following signs for Southport. At the big roundabout (McDonalds is on the left) take the fourth exit. Proceed along this road until you reach the 2nd set of pedstrian lights and take the next left into Haig Avenue.

Nearest Railway Station Meols Cop - 1mile away. Southport - 1.5miles away.
Bus Route 44 Arriva from the Southport Station.

SPENNYMOOR TOWN

The Moors **Club Colours** Black and white

Founded 2005

Club Contact Details 01388 827 248

The Brewery Field, Durham Road, Spennymoor DL16 6JN

2018-19 SEASON

Nat N 4

FAC 2Q

FAT 3P

Record

P 50 W 26 D 12 L 12

Top Goalscorer

TAYLOR (32)

Honours

-

Previous Names: Evenwood Town and Spennymoor United merged to form today's club in 2005.

Previous Leagues: Northern League 2005-14. Northern Premier 2014-17.

Ground Capacity: 3,000 **Seats:** 224 **Covered:** 800 **Clubhouse:** Yes **Shop:** Yes

Previous Grounds: None

Record Attendance: 2,670 v Darlington, Northern League 2012-13.

09-10		10-11		11-12		12-13		13-14		14-15		15-16		16-17		17-18	
NL 1	1	NL 1	1	NL 1	1	NL 1	2	NL 1	1	NP1N	5	NP1N	2	NP P	2	Nat N	8
FAC	2Q	FAC	1Q	FAC	3Q	FAC	2Q	FAC	1Q	FAC	4Qr	FAC	2Q	FAC	1P	FAC	2Q
FAV	2Pr	FAV	5P	FAV	3P	FAV	F	FAV	5P	FAT	1P	FAT	3Q	FAT	1Q	FAT	4Pr

League Honours: Northern League Division One 2009-10, 2010-11, 2011-12, 2013-14, Division Two 2006-07.

County FA Honours: Durham Challange Cup 2011-12.

FA Cup First Round Proper 1956-57, 2016-17.

FA Vase Winners 2012-13.

FA Trophy First Round Proper 2014-14.

Victory: 10-0 v Billingham Town (H), Northern League Division One, 18/03/2014

Defeat: 2-8 v Clitheroe (A), FA Cup 2nd Qualifying Round, 29/09/2007

Goalscorer: Gavin Cogdon - 103

Appearances: Lewis Dodds - 227

Additional: Northern League record points tally of 109 during 2012-13.

Leave the A1(M) at junction 59, then at roundabout take the 1st exit onto the A167. At roundabout take the 2nd exit onto the A167 At Rushyford roundabout take the 3rd exit onto the A167. At roundabout take the 3rd exit onto the A167. At Thinford Roundabout take the 1st exit onto the A688. At roundabout take the 1st exit onto the A688. At roundabout take the 3rd exit onto Saint Andrew's Lane. At roundabout take the 1st exit onto Saint Andrew's Lane. At mini roundabout take 2nd exit onto King Street. At mini roundabout take 2nd exit onto King Street/Durham Road. Bear right onto Durham Road. Take 3rd exit on left onto Wood Vue.

YORK CITY

Minstermen **Club Colours** Red and navy blue

Founded 1922

Club Contact Details 01904 624 447 / 559 500 enquiries@yorkcityfootballclub.co.uk

Bootham Crescent, York YO30 7AQ

2018-19 SEASON

Nat N 12

FAC 1P

FAT 1P

Record

P 48 W 20 D 10 L 18

Top Goalscorer

Burrow (19)

Honours

-

Previous Names: None

Previous Leagues: Midland 1922-29. Football League 1929-2004, 2012-16. Conference 2004-12.

Ground Capacity: 8,256 **Seats:** 3,409 **Covered:** Yes **Clubhouse:** Yes **Shop:** Yes

Previous Grounds: Fulfordgate 1922-32. New 8,000 all-seater stadium, at Monks Cross, open during 2019-20 season.

Record Attendance: 28,123 v Huddersfield Town - FA Cup Sixth Round Proper 1938

09-10		10-11		11-12		12-13		13-14		14-15		15-16		16-17		17-18	
Conf	5	Conf	8	Conf	4	FL 2	17	FL 2	7	FL 2	18	FL 2	24	Nat	21	Nat N	11
FAC	3P	FAC	3P	FAC	4Q	FAC	1Pr	FAC	1Pr	FAC	1Pr	FAC	1P	FAC	4Qr	FAC	3Q
FAT	QF	FAT	1P	FAT	F	FLC	1P	FLC	1P	FLC	1P	FLC	2P	FAT	F	FAT	1P

League Honours: Football League Division Four 1983-84, Third Division Play-offs 1992-93. Conference Premier Play-offs 2011-12.

County FA Honours: North Riding Senior Cup 1949-50, 56-57, 69-70, 79-80, 87-88. 88-89, 95-96, 98-99, 99-00, 05-06, 09-10.

FA Cup Semi-Finals 1954-55.

FA Trophy Winners 2011-12, 16-17. Runners-up 08-09.

Victory: 9-1 v Southport - Division Three North 1957

Defeat: 0-12 v Chester City - Division Three North 1936

Goalscorer: Norman Wilkinson - 143 (1954-66)

Appearances: Barry Jackson - 539 (1958-70)

Additional: Paid £140,000 to Burnley for Adrian Randall December 1995
Received £950,000 from Sheffield Wednesday for Richard Cresswell 25/03/1999

From Tadcaster (A64) take left turning onto A1237 (Outer Ringroad) continue for approx 5 miles to A19 and then turn right into York. Continue for just over 1 mile and turn left into Bootham Crescent opposite Grange Hotel.

Nearest Railway Station York - 20 min walk away.

BATH CITY

Founded 1889

The Romans **Club Colours** Black & white

Club Contact Details 01225 423 087 info@bathcityfootballclub.co.uk

Twerton Park, Twerton, Bath, Somerset BA2 1DB

2018-19 SEASON
Nat S 5
FAC 4Q
FAT 1P

Record
P 48 W 23 D 11 L 14

Top Goalscorer
Stearn (14)

Honours
-

Previous Names: Bath AFC 1889-92. Bath Railway FC 1902-05. Bath Amateurs 1913-23 (Reserve side)

Previous Leagues: Western 1908-21. Southern 1921-79, 88-90, 97-2007. Football League Division Two North 1939-45. Alliance/Conference 1979-88, 90-97.

Ground Capacity: 8,880 **Seats:** 1,006 **Covered:** 4,800 **Clubhouse:** Yes **Shop:** Yes

Previous Grounds: The Belvoir Ground 1889-92 & 1902-15. Lambridge Show Ground 1919-32.

Record Attendance: 18,020 v Brighton & Hove Albion - FA Cup 1960

09-10		10-11		11-12		12-13		13-14		14-15		15-16		16-17		17-18	
Conf S	4	Conf	10	Conf	23	Conf S	11	Conf S	7	Conf S	14	Nat S	14	Nat S	9	Nat S	9
FAC	2P	FAC	4Qr	FAC	1Pr	FAC	3Qr	FAC	4Q	FAC	4Q	FAC	3Qr	FAC	4Q	FAC	4Qr
FAT	3Q	FAT	2P	FAT	3P	FAT	1P	FAT	3Q	FAT	SF	FAT	3Q	FAT	1P	FAT	1P

League Honours: Western Division Two 1928-29, Premier 1933-34. Southern Premier Division 1959-60, 77-78, 2006-07.

County FA Honours: Somerset Premier Cup 1929-30, 33-34, 35-36, 51-52, 52-53, 57-58, 59-60, 65-66, 67-68, 69-70, 77-78, 80-81, 81-82, 83-84, 84-85, 85-86, 88-89, 89-90, 93-94, 94-95, 2007-08.

FA Cup Third Round Proper 1963-64 (r), 93-94 (r).

FA Trophy Semi-Finals 2014-15.

Victory: 8-0 v Boston United - 1998-99

Defeat: 0-9 v Yeovil Town - 1946-47

Goalscorer: Paul Randall - 106

Appearances: David Mogg - 530

Additional: Paid £15,000 to Bristol City for Micky Tanner.
Received £80,000 from Southampton for Jason Dodd.

Take Junction 18 off M4. 3rd exit off roundabout and follow A46 (10 miles) to Bath City Centre. Along Pulteney Road then right into Claverton Street and then follow A36 Lower Bristol Road (1.5 miles). Left under Railway bridge (signs Bath City FC) into Twerton High Street and ground is 2nd turning on left.

Nearest Railway Station Bath Spa - 2 miles from ground or Avon Street - 1 mile

Bus Route No.5 - every 12mins from Town Centre.

BILLERICAY TOWN

Founded 1880

Town or Blues **Club Colours** All blue

Club Contact Details 01277 286 474 info@billericaytownfc.co.uk

New Lodge, Blunts Wall Road, Billericay CM12 9SA

2018-19 SEASON
Nat S 8
FAC 1Pr
FAT 1P

Record
P 50 W 23 D 10 L 17

Top Goalscorer
Emmanuel (25)

Honours
-

Previous Names: Billericay FC.

Previous Leagues: Romford & Dist 1890-1914, Mid Essex 1918-47, South Essex Comb 1947-66, Essex Olympian 1966-71, Essex Senior 1971-77, Athenian 1977-79. Isthmian 1979-2012. Conference 2012-13.

Ground Capacity: 3,500 **Seats:** 424 **Covered:** 2,000 **Clubhouse:** Yes **Shop:** Yes

Previous Grounds: None

Record Attendance: 3,841 v West Ham United - Opening of Floodlights 1977

09-10		10-11		11-12		12-13		13-14		14-15		15-16		16-17		17-18	
Isth P	13	Isth P	11	Isth P	1	Conf S	21	Isth P	10	Isth P	8	Isth P	9	Isth P	8	Isth P	1
FAC	2Q	FAC	2Qr	FAC	3Q	FAC	3Qr	FAC	2Q	FAC	3Q	FAC	1Qr	FAC	4Q	FAC	1Pr
FAT	1P	FAT	3Q	FAT	3Q	FAT	1P	FAT	2Qr	FAT	1Q	FAT	1Q	FAT	2Q	FAT	4P

League Honours: Chelmsford & District Division Three 1932-33. Essex Olympian 1969-70, 70-71. Essex Senior 1972-73, 74-75, 75-76. Athenian 1977-78, 78-79. Isthmian Division Two 1979-80, Premier Division 2011-12.

County FA Honours: Essex Senior Cup 1975-76, 2010-11, 17-18. Essex Senior Trophy 1977-78, 79-80, 2017-18.

FA Cup First Round Proper 1997-98, 2004-05, 07-08, 18-19(r). **FA Vase** Winners 1975-76, 76-77, 78-79.

FA Trophy Fifth Round Proper 2000-01.

Victory: 11-0 v Stansted (A) - Essex Senior League 05/05/1976

Defeat: 3-10 v Chelmsford City (A) - Essex Senior Cup 04/01/1993

Goalscorer: Freddie Claydon - 273

Appearances: J Pullen - 418

Additional: Leon Gutzmore scored 51 goals during the 1997-98 season.
Received £22,500+ from West Ham United for Steve Jones November 1992

From the M25 (J29) take the A127 to the Basildon/Billericay (A176) turn-off, (junction after the Old Fortune of War roundabout). Take second exit at roundabout (Billericay is signposted). Then straight over (2nd exit) at the next roundabout. Continue along that road until you enter Billericay. At the first roundabout take the first available exit. At the next r'about (with Billericay School on your left) go straight over (1st exit). At yet another roundabout!, turn left into the one-way system. Keep in the left-hand lane and go straight over roundabout. At first set of lights, turn left. Blunts Wall Road is the second turning on your right.

Nearest Railway Station Billericay - 1.4km

Bus Route London Road - stop 300m away

BRAINTREE TOWN

The Iron **Club Colours** Orange & blue

Founded 1898

Club Contact Details 01376 345 617 braintreeTFC@aol.com
Cressing Road Stadium, off Clockhouse Way, Braintree CM7 3DE

2018-19 SEASON
Nat 23
FAC 4Q
FAT 1P

Record
P 48 W 11 D 8 L 29

Top Goalscorer
Bettamer (6)

Honours
-

Previous Names: Manor Works 1898-1921, Crittall Athletic 1921-68, Braintree and Crittall Athletic 1968-81, Braintree 1981-83.

Previous Leagues: N.Essex 1898-1925, Essex & Suffolk B 1925-29, 55-64, Spartan 28-35, Eastern Co. 35-37, 38-39, 52-55, 70-91, Essex Co. 37-38, London 45-52, Gt London 64-66, Met 66-70, Southern 91-96, Isthmian 96-2006

Ground Capacity: 4,222 **Seats:** 553 **Covered:** 1,288 **Clubhouse:** Yes **Shop:** Yes
Previous Grounds: The Fiar Field 1898-1903, Spalding Meadow 1903-23.
Record Attendance: 4,000 v Tottenham Hotspur - Testimonial May 1952

09-10		10-11		11-12		12-13		13-14		14-15		15-16		16-17		17-18	
Conf S	7	Conf S	1	Conf	12	Conf	9	Conf	6	Conf	14	Nat	3	Nat	22	Nat S	6
FAC	2Qr	FAC	3Q	FAC	4Q	FAC	1P	FAC	1Pr	FAC	1P	FAC	1Pr	FAC	2P	FAC	3Q
FAT	3Q	FAT	1P	FAT	2Pr	FAT	1Pr	FAT	2P	FAT	3Pr	FAT	2P	FAT	3Pr	FAT	1Pr

League Honours: North Essex 1905-06, 10-11, 11-12. Eastern Counties League 1936-37, 83-84, 84-85. Essex & Suffolk Border 1959-60. Isthmian League Premier Division 2005-06. Conference South Champions 2010-11.

County FA Honours: Essex Senior Cup 1995-96. Essex Senior Trophy 1986-87.

FA Cup Second Round Proper 2016-17

FA Trophy Fifth Round Proper 2001-02 (r) **FA Vase** Fifth Round Proper 1984-85 (r)

Victory: 12-0 v Thetford - Eastern Counties League 1935-36
Defeat: 0-14 v Chelmsford City (A) - North Essex League 1923
Goalscorer: Chris Guy - 211 (1963-90). Gary Bennett scored 57 goals during season 1997-98
Appearances: Paul Young - 524 (1966-77)
Additional: Received £10,000 from Brentford for Matt Metcalf and from Colchester United for John Cheesewright

Leave M11 at junction 8A (for Stansted Airport) and follow A120 towards Braintree and Colchester for 17 miles. At Gallows Corner roundabout (with WestDrive Kia on your right) take first exit into Cressing Road. Clockhouse Way and the entrance to the ground are three quarters of a mile on the left and are clearly sign-posted.

Nearest Railway Station Braintree - less than a mile from the ground.

CHELMSFORD CITY

City or Clarets **Club Colours** Claret and white

Founded 1878

Club Contact Details 01245 290 959
Melbourne Community Stadium, Salerno Way, Chelmsford CM1 2EH

2018-19 SEASON
Nat S 4
FAC 2Q
FAT 3Q

Record
P 45 W 21 D 9 L 15

Top Goalscorer
Murphy (24)

Honours
-

Previous Names: Chelmsford FC 1878-1938.

Previous Leagues: North Essex (FM) 1895-1900. South Essex 1900-13. Athenian (FM) 1912-22. Middlesex Co 1922-38. Essex & Suffolk Border 1923-24. London 1924-35. Eastern Co (FM) 1935-38. Southern 1938-2004. Isthmian 2004-08

Ground Capacity: 3,000 **Seats:** 1,300 **Covered:** 1,300 **Clubhouse:** Yes **Shop:** Yes
Previous Grounds: New Writtle Street 1938-97, Maldon Town 1997-98, Billericay Town 1998-2005
Record Attendance: 3,201 v AFC Wimbledon, 15/03/2008.

09-10		10-11		11-12		12-13		13-14		14-15		15-16		16-17		17-18	
Conf S	3	Conf S	4	Conf S	6	Conf S	5	Conf S	17	Conf S	10	Nat S	15	Nat S	4	Nat S	3
FAC	4Q	FAC	2P	FAC	2Pr	FAC	2P	FAC	2Q	FAC	4Qr	FAC	3Q	FAC	2Q	FAC	1P
FAT	3P	FAT	3Q	FAT	1P	FAT	3P	FAT	3Q	FAT	3Q	FAT	1P	FAT	3Pr	FAT	3Qr

League Honours: Middlesex County 1923-24. London League 1930-31. Southern League 1930-40 (joint), 45-46, 67-68, 71-72, Division One South 88-89. Isthmian League Premier Division 2007-08.

County FA Honours: Essex Senior Cup 1892-93, 1901-02, 85-86, 88-89, 92-93, 2002-03, 08-09 16-17. East Anglian Cup 1924-25, 26-27, 28-29. Essex Professional Cup 1957-58, 69-70, 70-71, 73-74, 74-75.

FA Cup Fourth Round Proper 1938-39.

FA Trophy Semi-Finals 1969-70.

Victory: 10-1 v Bashley (H) - Southern League 26/04/2000
Defeat: 1-10 v Barking (A) - FA Trophy 11/11/1978
Goalscorer: Tony Butcher - 286 (1956-71)
Appearances: Tony Butcher - 560 (1956-71)
Additional: Paid £10,000 to Dover Athletic for Tony Rogers, 1992 and to Heybridge Swifts for Kris Lee ,2001
Received £50,000 from Peterborough United for David Morrison, 1994

Leave A12 at J15 and head towards Chelmsford. At the roundabout turn left into Westway. Turn left onto the A1060 signposted Sawbridgeworth. At the second set of traffic lights turn right into Chignal Road. Turn right into Melbourne Avenue. Salerno Way is on your left. At the end of the football pitches and immediately before the block of flats, turn left at the mini roundabout in Salerno Way to enter the Stadium car park.

Nearest Railway Station Chelmsford - take bus or taxi to ground.
Bus Route No. 54 and 56 opposite the train station.

CHIPPENHAM TOWN

Founded 1873

The Bluebirds **Club Colours** All royal blue

Club Contact Details 01249 650 400
Hardenhuish Park, Bristol Road, Chippenham SN14 6LR

2018-19 SEASON
Nat S 13
FAC 4Qr
FAT 3Qr

Record
P 49 W 18 D 10 L 21

Top Goalscorer
Jarvis (19)

Honours
-

Previous Names: None

Previous Leagues: Western 1904-06, 30-65, 73-2001. Wiltshire Senior. Wiltshire Premier. Hellenic 1968-73. Southern 2001-17.

Ground Capacity: 3,000 **Seats:** 300 **Covered:** 1,000 **Clubhouse:** Yes **Shop:** Yes
Previous Grounds: Played at four different locations before moving in to Hardenhuish on 24/09/1919.
Record Attendance: 4,800 v Chippenham United - Western League 1951

09-10		10-11		11-12		12-13		13-14		14-15		15-16		16-17		17-18	
SthP	3	SthP	7	SthP	11	SthP	15	SthP	18	SthP	11	SthP	8	SthP	1	Nat S	1
FAC	4Q	FAC	2Q	FAC	1Q	FAC	4Q	FAC	1Q	FAC	3Q	FAC	4Q	FAC	3Q	FAC	2Q
FAT	2P	FAT	2Qr	FAT	1P	FAT	2Q	FAT	2Q	FAT	2Q	FAT	1Q	FAT	2Q	FAT	3Q

League Honours: Western League 1951-52. Southern League Premier Division 2016-17.

County FA Honours: Wiltshire Senior Cup. Wiltshire Senior Shield x4.

FA Cup First Round Proper 1951-52, 2005-06(r).
FA Vase Runners-up 1999-2000.
FA Trophy Second Round Proper 2002-03, 09-10.

Victory: 9-0 v Dawlish Town (H) - Western League
Defeat: 0-10 v Tiverton Town (A) - Western League
Goalscorer: Dave Ferris
Appearances: Ian Monnery

Exit 17 from M4. Follow A350 towards Chippenham for three miles to first roundabout, take second exit (A350); follow road to third roundabout (junction with A420). Turn left and follow signs to town centre. Ground is 1km on left hand side adjacent to pedestrian controlled traffic lights. Car/Coach park next to traffic lights.

Nearest Railway Station Chippenham - 1km
Bus Route Bus stops within 200m of the ground.

CONCORD RANGERS

Founded 1967

Beach Boys **Club Colours** Yellow and blue

Club Contact Details 01268 515 750 media@concordrangers.co.uk
Aspect Arena, Thames Road, Canvey Island, Essex SS8 0HH

2018-19 SEASON
Nat S 6
FAC 4Q
FAT 3Q

Record
P 46 W 22 D 13 L 11

Top Goalscorer
WALL (22)

Honours
-

Previous Names: None

Previous Leagues: Thundermite Boys League 1967-73. Vange & District 1973-79. Mid-Essex 1979-88. Essex Intermediate 1988-91. Essex Senior 1991-2008. Isthmian 2008-13.

Ground Capacity: 3,250 **Seats:** 375 **Covered:** Yes **Clubhouse:** Yes **Shop:**
Previous Grounds: Waterside 70s-85
Record Attendance: 1,537 v Mansfield Town, FA Cup First Round Replay, 25/11/2014.

09-10		10-11		11-12		12-13		13-14		14-15		15-16		16-17		17-18	
Isth1N	2	Isth P	8	Isth P	14	Isth P	4	Conf S	9	Conf S	7	Nat S	10	Nat S	18	Nat S	17
FAC	2Q	FAC	3Q	FAC	2Qr	FAC	2Qr	FAC	4Q	FAC	1Pr	FAC	2Q	FAC	3Q	FAC	4Qr
FAT	3Q	FAT	1Q	FAT	1Q	FAT	2Q	FAT	1P	FAT	2P	FAT	3Q	FAT	3Q	FAT	3Q

League Honours: Essex Intermediate League Division 2 1990-91. Essex Senior League 1997-98, 2003-04, 07-08.

County FA Honours: Essex Senior Cup 2013-14, 14-15, 15-16.

FA Cup First Round Proper 2014-15
FA Vase Quarter-Finals 2007-08
FA Trophy Second Round Proper 2014-15

Goalscorer: Tony Stokes - 120
Appearances: Steve King - 312 (2013-16)

Take the A13 to Sadlers Farm at Benfleet, follow the road onto Canvey Way signposted Canvey Island (A130) next r'about (Waterside Farm) take 3rd exit onto Canvey Island 1st exit, signposted seafront / Industrial area next r'about 1st exit, next r'about 1st exit. Next landmark is a set of traffic lights (King Canute Pub on the left, carry on through to a mini r/bout passing a school on the right turn right into Thorney Bay Road, Thames Road is the 3rd turning on the right, Concord Rangers is approx 1 mile along Thames Road.

Nearest Railway Station Benfleet - Approx. 3 miles from the ground.
Bus Route First Buses operate a regular service to Thorney Bay Road, 5-10min walk from there

DARTFORD

The Darts — **Club Colours** White and black — **Founded** 1888

Club Contact Details 01322 299 991 info@dartfordfc.com
Princes Park Stadium, Grassbanks, Darenth Road, Dartford DA1 1RT

2018-19 SEASON
Nat S 10
FAC 3Q
FAT 3Qr

Record
P 46 W 19 D 11 L 16

Top Goalscorer
Sherringham (10)

Honours
-

Previous Names: None

Previous Leagues: Kent League (FM) 1894-96, 97-98, 99-1902, 09-14, 21-26, 93-96, Southern (FM) 1896-97, 1926-81, 82-84, 86-92, 96-2006. West Kent 1902-09. Alliance 1981-82, 84-86.

Ground Capacity: 4,097 **Seats:** 642 **Covered:** Yes **Clubhouse:** Yes **Shop:** Yes
Previous Grounds: The Brent/Westgate House, Potters Meadow, Engleys Meadow, Summers Meadow, Watling Street
Record Attendance: 4,097 v Horsham YMCA - Isth Div 1 South 11/11/2006 and v Crystal Palace - Fr 20/07/07

09-10		10-11		11-12		12-13		13-14		14-15		15-16		16-17		17-18	
Isth P	1	Conf S	10	Conf S	2	Conf	8	Conf	22	Conf	23	Nat S	8	Nat S	3	Nat S	2
FAC	3Q	FAC	1Pr	FAC	4Q	FAC	4Qr	FAC	1P	FAC	2P	FAC	2Q	FAC	1P	FAC	1P
FAT	3Q	FAT	3P	FAT	3Pr	FAT	SF	FAT	1Pr	FAT	3Pr	FAT	3Q	FAT	2P	FAT	1Pr

League Honours: Southern League Division 2 1896-97, Eastern Section 1930-31, 31-32, Southern Championship 30-31, 31-32, 73-74, 83-84, Southern Division 1980-81. West Kent 1908-09. Isthmian League Div.1 North 2007-08, Premier Division 2009-10.

County FA Honours: Kent Senior Cup 1930-31, 31-32, 32-33, 34-35, 46-47, 69-70, 72-73, 86-87, 87-88, 2010-11, 15-16. Kent Senior Trophy

FA Cup Third Round Proper 1935-36, 36-37. **FA Vase** First Round Proper 1994-95.
FA Trophy Runners-up 1973-74.
Appearances: Steve Robinson - 692
Additional: Paid £6,000 to Chelmsford City for John Bartley
Received £25,000 from Redbridge Forest for Andy Hessenthaler

From M25 clockwise leave at Junction 1b to r'about controlled by traffic lights. Take third exit onto Princes Road, (A225) then second exit at next roundabout. Continue down hill to traffic lights (ground on your left), turn left into Darenth Road then second turning on your left into Grassbanks leading to car park. From M25 anti-clockwise leave at Junction 2 onto slip road A225 to r'about, then first exit, second exit at next r'about then down hill to traffic lights turn left into Darenth Road, then second turning on your left into Grassbanks.

Nearest Railway Station Dartford - bus ride away from the ground.
Bus Route Fasttrack B towards Bluewater/Dartford.

DORKING WANDERERS

Wanderers — **Club Colours** Red & white stripes — **Founded** 1999

Club Contact Details info@dorkingwanderers.com
Meadowbank Stadium, Mill Lane, Dorking RH4 1DX

2018-19 SEASON
Isth P 1
FAC 3Qr
FAT 1P

Record
P 41 W 29 D 6 L 6

Top Goalscorer
Prior (27)

Honours
Isthmian Premier Division

Previous Names: None

Previous Leagues: Crawley & District 1999-2000. West Sussex 2000-2007. Sussex County 2007-2015.

Ground Capacity: 2,000 **Seats:** 200 **Covered:** Yes **Clubhouse:** Yes **Shop:**
Previous Grounds: Big Field Brockham >2007. West Humble Playing Fields 2007-18.
Record Attendance: N/A

09-10		10-11		11-12		12-13		13-14		14-15		15-16		16-17		17-18	
		SxC3	1	SxC2	3	SxC1	20	SxC1	8	SxC1	2	Isth1S	2	Isth1S	2	Isth P	14
								FAC	Pr	FAC	2Qr	FAC	1Q	FAC	1Q	FAC	3Q
						FAV	2Q	FAV	2Qr	FAV	2Q	FAT	1Qr	FAT	P	FAT	3Q

League Honours: West Sussex Division Four North 2000-01, Division Two North 2003-04, Premier Division 2006-07. Sussex County Division Three 2010-11. Isthmian Premier Division 2018-19.

County FA Honours: None

FA Cup Third Qualifying Round 2018-19(r). **FA Vase** Second Qualifying Round 2012-13, 13-14(r), 14-15.
FA Trophy First Round Proper 2018-19.

From the M25 go off at junction 9, take the A243 exit to A24/Leatherhead/Dorking. At the roundabout, take the 3rd exit onto A243. At the roundabout, take the 2nd exit onto Leatherhead By-Pass Rd/A243. At the roundabout, take the 2nd exit onto Leatherhead By-Pass Rd/A24. At the roundabout, take the 2nd exit and stay on Leatherhead By-Pass Rd/A24. At the roundabout, take the 1st exit onto Dorking Rd/A24. Continue to follow A24. At the roundabout, take the 2nd exit onto London Rd/A24. At the roundabout, take the 4th exit and stay on London Rd/A24.

Nearest Railway Station Dorking West and Dorking Deepdene

DULWICH HAMLET

Founded 1893

Hamlet **Club Colours** Navy and pink

Club Contact Details 020 7274 8707
Champion Hill, Dog Kennell Hill, Edgar Kail Way SE22 8BD

2018-19 SEASON
Nat S 14
FAC 3Q
FAT 1P
Record
P 47 W 15 D 11 L 21
Top Goalscorer
Akinyemi (15)
Honours
-

Previous Names: None

Previous Leagues: Camberwell 1894-97. Southern Suburban 1897-1900, 01-07. Dulwich 1900-01. Spartan 1907-08. Isthmian 1907-2018.

Ground Capacity: 3,000 **Seats:** 500 **Covered:** 1,000 **Clubhouse:** Yes **Shop:** Yes
Previous Grounds: Woodwarde Rd 1893-95,College Farm 95-96,Sunray Ave 1896-02,Freeman's Gd,Champ Hill 02-12, Champ Hill (old grd)12-92. Champion Hill 92-2018. T&M FC 18.
Record Attendance: 3,104 v Bath City, National South, 05/01/2019

09-10	10-11	11-12	12-13	13-14	14-15	15-16	16-17	17-18
Isth1S 12	Isth1S 5	Isth1S 3	Isth1S 1	Isth P 6	Isth P 4	Isth P 5	Isth P 3	Isth P 2
FAC 1Q	FAC Pr	FAC 2Q	FAC 2Q	FAC 3Q	FAC 1Q	FAC 2Q	FAC 2Q	FAC 2Q
FAT P	FAT 2Q	FAT 1Q	FAT P	FAT 3Qr	FAT 2Q	FAT 2P	FAT QFr	FAT 2Q

League Honours: Dulwich 1899-00, 1900-01. Isthmian League Premier Division 1919-20, 25-26, 32-33, 48-49, Division One 1977-78, Division One South 2012-13.

County FA Honours: Surrey Senior Cup x16, firstly in 1904-05 and most recently 74-75. London Senior Cup x5, firstly in 1924-25 and most recently in 2003-04. London Challenge Cup 1998-99.

FA Cup 1RP 1925-26, 26-27, 27-28, 28-29, 29-30, 30-31(r), 32-33, 33-34(r), 34-35, 35-36, 36-37, 37-38, 48-49, 98-99.

FA Trophy Quarter-Finals 1979-80(r), 2016-17(r).

FA Am Cup Winners 1919-20, 31-32, 36-37.

Victory: 13-0 v Walton-on-Thames, Surrey Senior Cup, 1936-37
Defeat: 1-10 v Hendon, Isthmian league, 1963-64
Goalscorer: Edgar Kail - 427 (1919-33)
Appearances: Reg Merritt - 576 (1950-66)
Additional: Received £35,000 from Charlton Athletic for Chris Dickson 2007

Nearest Railway Station East Dulwich 200 yards. Denmark Hill 10 min walk. Herne Hill then bus 37 stops near ground. Mitcham Tram.
Bus Route Buses 40 & 176 from Elephant & Castle, 185 from Victoria.

EASTBOURNE BOROUGH

Founded 1964

Borough **Club Colours** All red

Club Contact Details 01323 766 265 info@ebfc.co.uk
Langney Sports Club, Priory Lane, Eastbourne BN23 7QH

2018-19 SEASON
Nat S 18
FAC 4Q
FAT 1P
Record
P 48 W 13 D 13 L 22
Top Goalscorer
Walker (11)
Honours
-

Previous Names: Langney FC 1964-68. Langney Sports 1968-2001.

Previous Leagues: Eastbourne & Dist 1964-73. Eastbourne & Hastings 1973-83. Sussex County 1983-2000. Southern 2000-2004.

Ground Capacity: 4,151 **Seats:** 542 **Covered:** 2,500 **Clubhouse:** Yes **Shop:** Yes
Previous Grounds: Local Recreation Grounds. Princes Park >1983.
Record Attendance: 3,770 v Oxford United - FA Cup 1st Round 05/11/05

09-10	10-11	11-12	12-13	13-14	14-15	15-16	16-17	17-18
Conf 19	Conf 23	Conf S 18	Conf S 12	Conf S 10	Conf S 11	Nat S 17	Nat S 11	Nat S
FAC 4Qr	FAC 4Q	FAC 4Q	FAC 3Qr	FAC 3Q	FAC 4Qr	FAC 4Q	FAC 1P	FAC 3Q
FAT 2Pr	FAT 3Pr	FAT 3Qr	FAT 3Q	FAT 3Q	FAT 3Q	FAT 2P	FAT 3Qr	FAT 1P

League Honours: Eastbourne & Hastings Premier Division 1981-82. Sussex County League Division Three 1986-87, Division Two 1987-88, Division One 1999-2000, 02-03.

County FA Honours: Sussex Senior Challenge Cup 2001-02, 08-09, 15-16.

FA Cup First Round Proper 2005-06, 07-08, 08-09(r), 16-17.

FA Vase Second Round Proper 1990-91, 91-92, 97-98.

FA Trophy Third Round Proper 2001-02, 02-03, 04-05, 10-11.

Victory: 11-1 v Crowborough, Sussex Senior Cup Quarter-final, 13/01/2009
Defeat: 0-8 v Sheppey United (A) - FA Vase 09/10/93 and v Peachaven & Tels (A) - Sussex Co. Div.1 09/11/93
Goalscorer: Nigel Hole - 146
Appearances: Darren Baker - 952 (1992-2013)
Additional: Paid £1,800 to Yeovil Town for Yemi Odoubade.
Received £25,000 from Oxford United for Yemi Odoubade.

From M25 take M23/A23 eastbound to A27 Polegate by pass pick up and follow signs for crematorium 50yds past crematorium turn right at mini roundabout into Priory Road.
Stadium 100yds on left.

Nearest Railway Station Pevensey & Westham - 15-20 mins walk.
Bus Route The LOOP Bus from the town centre.

HAMPTON & RICHMOND BOROUGH

Founded 1921

HRBFC

Beavers or Borough **Club Colours** Red & blue

Club Contact Details 0208 979 2456 secretary@hamptonfc.net

Beveree Stadium, Beaver Close, Station Road, Hampton TW12 2BX

2018-19 SEASON
Nat S 15
FAC 1P
FAT 3Q

Record
P 47 W 16 D 10 L 21

Top Goalscorer
Dickson (19)

Honours
-

Previous Names: Hampton 1921-99

Previous Leagues: Kingston & District 1921-33. South West Middlesex 1933-59. Surrey Senior 1959-64. Spartan 1964-71. Athenian 1971-73. Isthmian 1973-2007, 12-16. Conference 2007-12.

Ground Capacity: 3,500 **Seats:** 644 **Covered:** 800 **Clubhouse:** Yes **Shop:** Yes

Previous Grounds: Moved to the Beveree Stadium in 1959

Record Attendance: 3,500 v Hayes & Yeading United, Conference South Play-off Final, 2008-09

09-10		10-11		11-12		12-13		13-14		14-15		15-16		16-17		17-18	
Conf S	14	Conf S	18	Conf S	21	Isth P	13	Isth P	12	Isth P	15	Isth P	1	Nat S	7	Nat S	4
FAC	4Q	FAC	3Q	FAC	3Q	FAC	3Q	FAC	4Q	FAC	1Q	FAC	1Q	FAC	3Q	FAC	4Q
FAT	1Pr	FAT	2P	FAT	3P	FAT	1Pr	FAT	3Q	FAT	1Q	FAT	3Q	FAT	3Qr	FAT	1Pr

League Honours: Surrey Senior 1963-64. Spartan 1964-65, 65-66, 66-67, 69-70. Isthmian Premier Division 2006-07, 2015-16.

County FA Honours: Middlesex Charity Cup 1969-70, 95-96, 97-98, 98-99. Middlesex Super Cup 1999-00, 06-07. Middlesex Senior Cup 2005-06, 07-08, 11-12, 13-14, 16-17.

FA Cup First Round Proper 2000-01, 07-08.

FA Trophy Third Round Proper 2011-12.

Victory: 11-1 v Eastbourne United - Isthmian League Division 2 South 1990-91

Defeat: 0-13 v Hounslow Town - Middlesex Senior Cup 1962-63

Goalscorer: Peter Allen - 176 (1964-73)

Appearances: Tim Hollands - 750 (1977-95)

Additional: Paid £3,000 to Chesham United for Matt Flitter June 2000
Received £40,000 from Queens Park Rangers for Leroy Phillips

Exit M25 at Junction 12 (M3 Richmond). Exit M3 at Junction 1 and take 4th exit (Kempton Park, Kingston).
After approximately 2 miles turn left into High Street, Hampton. Immediately turn left on to Station Road.
The entrance to the ground is 200 yards on the right hand side.

Nearest Railway Station Hampton - less than half a mile from the ground.

HAVANT AND WATERLOOVILLE

Founded 1998

HWFC Havant and Waterlooville Football Club

The Hawks **Club Colours** White & sky blue

Club Contact Details 02392 787 822 generalmanager@havantandwaterloovillefc.co.uk

Westleigh Park, Martin Road, West Leigh, Havant PO9 5TH

2018-19 SEASON
Nat 22
FAC 4Q
FAT 1Pr

Record
P 49 W 9 D 14 L 26

Top Goalscorer
Rutherford (16)

Honours
-

Previous Names: Havant Town and Waterlooville merged in 1998

Previous Leagues: Southern 1998-2004. Conference/National 2004-16. Isthmian 2016-17.

Ground Capacity: 5,300 **Seats:** 710 **Covered:** Yes **Clubhouse:** Yes **Shop:** Yes

Previous Grounds: None

Record Attendance: 4,400 v Swansea City - FA Cup 3rd Round 05/01/2008

09-10		10-11		11-12		12-13		13-14		14-15		15-16		16-17		17-18	
Conf S	6	Conf S	9	Conf S	19	Conf S	10	Conf S	6	Conf S	5	Nat S	20	Isth P	1	Nat S	10
FAC	3Q	FAC	1P	FAC	3Q	FAC	2Q	FAC	2Qr	FAC	1P	FAC	4Qr	FAC	3Q	FAC	4Q
FAT	1P	FAT	3Qr	FAT	3Qr	FAT	2P	FAT	SF	FAT	2P	FAT	3P	FAT	3Q	FAT	1P

League Honours: Southern League Southern Division 1998-99. Isthmian League Premier Division 2016-17. National South 2017-18.

County FA Honours: Hampshire Senior Cup 2015-16, 17-18.

FA Cup Fourth Round Proper 2007-08 (Eventually going out to Liverpool at Anfield 5-2)

FA Trophy Semi-finals 2013-14

Victory: 9-0 v Moneyfields - Hampshire Senior Cup 23/10/2001

Defeat: 0-5 v Worcester City - Southern Premier 20/03/2004

Goalscorer: James Taylor - 138

Appearances: James Taylor - 297

Additional: Paid £5,000 to Bashley for John Wilson
Received £15,000 from Peterborough United for Gary McDonald

Ground is a mile and a half from Havant Town Centre. Take A27 to Havant then turn onto B2149 (Petersfield Road).
Turn right at next junction after HERON pub into Bartons Road then take first right into Martin Road.

Nearest Railway Station Havant - within 2 miles of the ground.

HEMEL HEMPSTEAD TOWN

Founded 1885

The Tudors **Club Colours** All red

Club Contact Details 01442 259 777

Vauxhall Road, Adeyfield Road, Hemel Hempstead HP2 4HW

2018-19 SEASON
Nat S 16
FAC 4Qr
FAT 3P

Record
P 51 W 17 D 14 L 20

Top Goalscorer
Parkes (15)

Honours
-

Previous Names: Apsley End 1885-99. Hemel Hempstead 1899-1955, 72-99. Hemel H'stead Town 1955-72. Merged with Hemel H'stead Utd '72.

Previous Leagues: West Herts 1885-99. Herts County 1899-1922. Spartan 1922-52. Delphian 1952-63. Athenian 1963-77. Isthmian 1977-2004. Southern 2004-14.

Ground Capacity: 3,152 **Seats:** 300 **Covered:** 900 **Clubhouse:** Yes **Shop:** Yes

Previous Grounds: Salmon Meadow 1885-1928. Gees Meadow 1928-29. Crabtree Lane (Wood Lane Ground) 1929-72.

Record Attendance: 3,500 v Tooting & Mitcham - Amateur Cup 1962 (Crabtree Lane)

09-10		10-11		11-12		12-13		13-14		14-15		15-16		16-17		17-18	
SthP	20	SthP	15	SthP	19	SthP	4	SthP	1	Conf S	9	Nat S	6	Nat S	12	Nat S	5
FAC	1Qr	FAC	1Q	FAC	2Q	FAC	1Q	FAC	4Qr	FAC	1P	FAC	3Qr	FAC	4Qr	FAC	3Q
FAT	1Q	FAT	1Q	FAT	2Q	FAT	1Qr	FAT	3Q	FAT	3P	FAT	1P	FAT	3Qr	FAT	3Qr

League Honours: West Herts 1894-95, 97-98, 1904-05. Herts County 1899-1900. Spartan Division One 1933-34. Isthmian League Division Three 1997-98, Division Two 1999-2000. Southern Premier Division 2013-14.

County FA Honours: Herts Senior Cup 1905-06, 07-08, 08-09, 25-26, 2012-13, 14-15. Herts Charity Shield 1925-26, 34-35, 51-52,63-64, 76-77, 83-84. Herts Charity Cup 2004-05, 08-09, 09-10.

FA Cup First Round Proper 2014-15

FA Vase Third Round Proper 1999-00, 00-01

FA Trophy Third Round Proper 2018-19

Victory: 13-0 v RAF Uxbridge (A), Spartan Division One, 1933-34. and v Chipperfield Corinthians (H), St Mary's Cup QF, 2014-15.

Defeat: 1-13 v Luton Town, FA Cup First Qualifying Round, 05/10/1901.

Goalscorer: Dai Price

Appearances: John Wallace - 1012

Leave at Junction 8, straight over (2nd exit) first roundabout, straight over (2nd exit) second roundabout at which point you need to get in the right hand lane - take first right across the dual carriageway which leads in to Leverstock Green Road. First left at mini-roundabout in to Vauxhall Road, the entrance to the ground is on the right hand side by an out of place looking roundabout.

Nearest Railway Station Hemel Hempstead - Taxi ride away from the ground

Bus Route 320 from Stop 'A' outside the station

HUNGERFORD TOWN

Founded 1886

The Crusaders **Club Colours** White & black

Club Contact Details 01488 682 939 nmatthews@rhsystems.co.uk

Bulpitt Lane, Hungerford RG17 0AY

2018-19 SEASON
Nat S 19
FAC 3Q
FAT 3Q

Record
P 46 W 11 D 11 L 24

Top Goalscorer
Oris-Dadomo (9)

Honours
-

Previous Names: None

Previous Leagues: Hungerford League. Newbury League (FM) 1909-39. Newbury & District. Swindon & District. Hellenic 1958-78, 2003-09. Isthmian 1978-2003. Southern 2009-16.

Ground Capacity: 2,500 **Seats:** 400 **Covered:** 400 **Clubhouse:** Yes **Shop:** Yes

Previous Grounds: Hungerford Marsh Field.

Record Attendance: 1,684 v Sudbury Town - FA Vase Semi-final 1988-89

09-10		10-11		11-12		12-13		13-14		14-15		15-16		16-17		17-18	
Sthsw	17	Sthsw	7	Sthsw	5	Sthsw	2	SthP	6	SthP	4	SthP	5	Nat S	6	Nat S	19
FAC	2Q	FAC	3Q	FAC	2Qr	FAC	2Qr	FAC	3Q	FAC	1Q	FAC	1Qr	FAC	3Q	FAC	3Qr
FAT	3Q	FAT	1Qr	FAT	P	FAT	P	FAT	3P	FAT	1Qr	FAT	2P	FAT	3Q	FAT	3Q

League Honours: Newbury League 1912-13, 13-14, 19-20, 21-22. Hellenic Division One 1970-71, Premier Division 2008-09.

County FA Honours: Berks & Bucks Senior Cup 1981-82. Basingstoke Senior Cup 2012-13, 14-15.

FA Cup First Round Proper 1979-80.

FA Vase Semi-Finals 1977-78, 79-80, 88-89.

FA Trophy Third Round Proper 2014-15.

Goalscorer: Ian Farr - 268

Appearances: Dean Bailey and Tim North - 400+

Additional: Paid £4,000 to Yeovil Town for Joe Scott. Received £3,800 from Barnstaple Town for Joe Scott. Isthmian representatives in Anglo Italian Cup 1981.

From M4 Junction, take A338 to Hungerford. First Roundabout turn right on to A4, next roundabout first left, 100 yards roundabout 1st left up High Street, go over three roundabouts, at fourth roundabout turn first left signposted 'Football Club'. Take second left into Bulpitt Lane, go over crossroads, ground on left.

Nearest Railway Station Hungerford - Approx. one mile from the ground.

Bus Route Priory Close stop - 120m away

MAIDSTONE UNITED

The Stones

Club Colours Amber & black

Founded 1992

Club Contact Details 01622 753 817 info@maidstoneunited.co.uk

The Gallagher Stadium, James Whatman Way, Maidstone, Kent ME14 1LQ

2018-19 SEASON
Nat 24
FAC 2P
FAT 4Pr

Record
P 56 W 14 D 10 L 32

Top Goalscorer
Turgott (16)

Honours
Kent Senior cup

Previous Names: Maidstone Invicta > 1997

Previous Leagues: Kent County 1993-2001, Kent 2001-06. Isthmian 2006-15.

Ground Capacity: 4,200 **Seats:** 792 **Covered:** 1,850 **Clubhouse:** Yes **Shop:** Yes

Previous Grounds: London Rd 1993-01, Central Pk 01-02 & Bourne Pk 02-09 (S'bourne), 11-12, The Homelands (A'ford) 09-11.

Record Attendance: 3,560 v Oldham Athletic, FA Cup 2nd Round, 1 December 2018

09-10		10-11		11-12		12-13		13-14		14-15		15-16		16-17		17-18	
Isth P	18	Isth P	20	Isth1S	6	Isth1S	2	Isth P	7	Isth P	1	Nat S	3	Nat	14	Nat	19
FAC	3Q	FAC	1Q	FAC	2Q	FAC	3Q	FAC	3Q	FAC	2P	FAC	1P	FAC	1Pr	FAC	2P
FAT	2P	FAT	3Q	FAT	P	FAT	2P	FAT	3Q	FAT	2Q	FAT	1P	FAT	1P	FAT	3Pr

League Honours: Kent County Division Four 1993-94, Div. Two 1994-95, Div. One 1998-99, Premier 2001-02. Kent 2000-02, 05-06. Isthmian Division One South 2006-07, Premier 2014-15. National League South Play-offs 2015-16.

County FA Honours: Kent Junior Cup 1994-95, Weald of Kent Charity Cup 1999-00, 00-01, Kent Senior Trophy 2002-03. Kent Senior Cup 2017-18, 18-19.

FA Cup Second Round Proper 2014-15, 18-19

FA Vase Third Round Proper 2005-06 (r)

FA Trophy Fourth Round Proper 2018-19 (r)

Victory: 12-1 v Aylesford - Kent League 1993-94

Defeat: 2-8 v Scott Sports - 1995-96

Goalscorer: Richard Sinden - 98

Appearances: Tom Mills

Additional: Paid £2,000 for Steve Jones - 2000

M20 (junction 6) and M2 (junction 3).
Follow signs to Maidstone on the A229.
At the White Rabbit roundabout, take the third exit on to James Whatman Way.

Nearest Railway Station Maidstone East & Maidstone Barracks a walk away

Bus Route Nos. 101 or 155 from the Mall Bus Station

OXFORD CITY

The Hoops

Club Colours Blue & white

Founded 1990

Club Contact Details 01865 744 493

Court Place Farm, Marsh Lane, Marston, Oxford OX3 0NQ

2018-19 SEASON
Nat S 12
FAC 1Pr
FAT 2P

Record
P 51 W 22 D 7 L 22

Top Goalscorer
Tshimanga (34)

Honours
-

Previous Names: The original club, founded in 1882, folded in 1988 when they were evicted from their White House ground and did not reform until 1990.

Previous Leagues: South Midlands 1990-93. Isthmian 1993-2004. Southern 2004-05, 06-12. Spartan South Midlands 2005-06.

Ground Capacity: 3,500 **Seats:** 520 **Covered:** 400 **Clubhouse:** Yes **Shop:** Yes

Previous Grounds: Cuttleslowe Park 1990-91, Pressed Steel 1991-93.

Record Attendance: 2,276 v Oxford United, pre-season friendly, 08/07/2017

09-10		10-11		11-12		12-13		13-14		14-15		15-16		16-17		17-18	
SthP	13	SthP	14	SthP	2	Conf N	10	Conf N	20	Conf N	6	Nat S	12	Nat S	14	Nat S	16
FAC	1P	FAC	1Q	FAC	1Pr	FAC	2Q	FAC	4Q	FAC	2Q	FAC	3Q	FAC	2Qr	FAC	2P
FAT	2Q	FAT	1Q	FAT	1Q	FAT	2P	FAT	3Q	FAT	2Pr	FAT	3P	FAT	3Q	FAT	3Q

League Honours: Spartan South Midlands Premier Division 1992-93, 2005-06. Isthmian Division One 1995-96.

County FA Honours: Oxford Senior Cup 1996-97, 98-99, 99-00, 02-03, 17-18.

FA Cup Second Round Proper 2017-18

FA Vase Runners-up 1994-95

FA Trophy Third Round Proper 1999-00, 02-03, 15-16

Follow the A40 to the Headington roundabout going straightover towards Banbury & Northampton A40. Within a mile a flyover is visible as the exit from the Ring Road. Turn left under the flyover and left again toward Marsh Lane. Turn right at the T Junction and the ground is on your left just before the Pedestrian Crossing.

Nearest Railway Station Oxford - three miles from the ground.

Bus Route 14A from the Station to the ground.

SLOUGH TOWN

The Rebels **Club Colours** Yellow & blue

Founded 1890

Club Contact Details 07792 126 124 gensec@sloughtownfc.net
Arbour Park, Stoke Road, Slough SL2 5AY (do not send correspondence to the ground)

2018-19 SEASON
Nat S 11
FAC 2P
FAT 3Q

Record
P 51 W 20 D 16 L 15

Top Goalscorer
Dobson (11)

Honours
Berks & Bucks Senior Cup

Previous Names: Slough FC. Slough United.

Previous Leagues: Southern All 1892-93, Berks & Bucks 1901-05, Gt Western Suburban 09-19, Spartan 20-39, Herts & Middx 40-45, Corinthian 46-63, Athenian 63-73, Isthmian 73-90, 94-95, 98-2007, Conf 90-94, 95-98, Southern 2007-2018.

Ground Capacity: 2,000 **Seats:** 250 **Covered:** Yes **Clubhouse:** Yes **Shop:** Yes
Previous Grounds: Dolphin Stad 1890-1936. Wrexham Park >2003. Stag Meadow W & Eton 03-07. Holloways Park B'field SYCOB 07-16.
Record Attendance: 1,401 v Hayes & Yeading United, Southern Premier, 29/08/2016

09-10		10-11		11-12		12-13		13-14		14-15		15-16		16-17		17-18	
SthM	5	SthC	5	SthC	2	SthC	6	SthC	5	SthP	16	SthP	17	SthP	5	SthP	3
FAC	3Q	FAC	1Q	FAC	3Qr	FAC	1Pr	FAC	Pr	FAC	1Q	FAC	2Q	FAC	3Q	FAC	2P
FAT	2Q	FAT	1Qr	FAT	P	FAT	1Qr	FAT	1Q	FAT	2Qr	FAT	2Q	FAT	3Q	FAT	3Qr

League Honours: Isthmian League 1980-81, 89-90. Athenian League x3.

County FA Honours: Berks & Bucks Senior Cup 1902-03, 19-20, 23-24, 26-27, 35-36, 54-55, 70-71, 71-72, 76-77, 80-81, 2018-19

FA Cup Second Round Proper 1970-71, 79-80, 82-83, 85-86(r), 86-87, 2004-05, 17-18, 18-19.

FA Trophy Semi-finals 1976-77, 97-98 **FA Am Cup** Runners-up 1972-73

Victory: 17-0 v Railway Clearing House - 1921-22
Defeat: 1-11 v Chesham Town - 1909-10
Goalscorer: Ted Norris - 343 in 226 appearances. Scored 84 during the 1925-26 season.
Appearances: Terry Reardon - 475 (1964-81)
Additional: Paid £18,000 to Farnborough Town for Colin Fielder
Received £22,000 from Wycombe Wanderers for Steve Thompson

From the M4: Exit at Junction 5 (signposted Colnbrook/Datchet/Langley) and head west on London Road (A4). Pass the Sainsbury's Superstore on your right hand side and drive straight over the roundabout, continuing on London Road. Pass the Tesco Slough Extra store and then the turning to Slough Rail station on your right and at the next junction, turn right onto Stoke Road (B416). Continue along Stoke Road for 0.7 miles, going straight ahead at the crossroads with Shaggy Calf Lane and Elliman Avenue (following the signpost to Slough Cemetery & Crematorium, Wexham Park Hospital and Stoke Poges). The entrance to Arbour Park is a few hundred yards further on the right hand side.

Nearest Railway Station Slough
Bus Route First Group 1, 13, 12, 14, 353.

ST ALBANS CITY

The Saints **Club Colours** Yellow & blue

Founded 1908

Club Contact Details 01727 848 914
Clarence Park, York Road, St. Albans, Herts AL1 4PL

2018-19 SEASON
Nat S 9
FAC 3Q
FAT 3Qr

Record
P 47 W 19 D 12 L 16

Top Goalscorer
Moyo (15)

Honours
-

Previous Names: None

Previous Leagues: Herts County 1908-10. Spartan 1908-20. Athenian 1920-23. Isthmian 1923-2004. Conference 2004-11. Southern 2011-14.

Ground Capacity: 5,007 **Seats:** 667 **Covered:** 1,900 **Clubhouse:** Yes **Shop:** Yes
Previous Grounds: N/A
Record Attendance: 9,757 v Ferryhill Athletic - FA Amateur Cup 1926

09-10		10-11		11-12		12-13		13-14		14-15		15-16		16-17		17-18	
Conf S	13	Conf S	22	SthP	8	SthP	11	SthP	4	Conf S	13	Nat S	18	Nat S	10	Nat S	8
FAC	2Q	FAC	4Q	FAC	2Qr	FAC	3Q	FAC	1P	FAC	4Q	FAC	1P	FAC	1P	FAC	4Q
FAT	3Q	FAT	1P	FAT	1Q	FAT	1Q	FAT	2P	FAT	3Qr	FAT	3Q	FAT	3Qr	FAT	2Pr

League Honours: Herts County Western Division 1909-09, Western & Championship 09-10. Spartan B Division 1909-10, Spartan 11-12. Athenian League 1920-21, 21-22. Isthmian League 1923-24, 26-27, 27-28, Division One 1985-86.

County FA Honours: London Senior Cup 1970-71.

FA Cup Second Round Proper 1968-69 (r), 80-81 (r), 96-97.

FA Trophy Semi-final 1998-99.

Victory: 14-0 v Aylesbury United (H) - Spartan League 19/10/1912
Defeat: 0-11 v Wimbledon (H) - Isthmian League 1946
Goalscorer: Wilfred Minter - 356 in 362 apps. (Top scorer for 12 consecutive seasons from 1920-32)
Appearances: Phil Wood - 900 (1962-85)
Additional: Wilfred Minter scored seven goals in an 8-7 defeat by Dulwich Hamlet, the highest tally by a player on the losing side of an FAC tie.
Paid £6,000 to Yeovil Town for Paul Turner 1957. Received £92,759 from Southend United for Dean Austin 1990.

M25 (Clockwise) exit at junc. 21A(A405). Follow signs to St. Albans from slip road. At Noke Hotel r'about, bear right on A405 and stay on A405 until London Colney r'about (traffic light controlled). Turn left onto A1081. Follow road for approx 1 mile until mini r'about (Great Northern pub on left). Turn right into Alma Rd. At traffic lights turn right into Victoria St. and continue to junction with Crown pub. Go straight across into Clarence Rd, ground is first on left. M25 (C-clockwise) exit at junc. 22 (A1081). Follow signs to St. Albans. At London Colney r'about exit onto A1081. Then as above.

Nearest Railway Station St. Albans City - 5-10 minute walk from the ground.

TONBRIDGE ANGELS

Angels **Club Colours** Blue and white

Founded 1947

Club Contact Details 01732 352 417 charlie.cole@tonbridgeangels.co.uk

Longmead Stadium, Darenth Avenue, Tonbridge, Kent TN10 3JF

2018-19 SEASON
Isth P 4
FAC 2Q
FAT 2Q

Record
P 39 W 17 D 6 L 16

Top Goalscorer
Turner (16)

Honours
Super Play-off

Previous Names: Tonbridge FC 1947-94.

Previous Leagues: Southern 1948-80, 93-2004, Kent 1989-93, Isthmian 2004-11.

Ground Capacity: 3,000 **Seats:** 760+ **Covered:** 1,500 **Clubhouse:** Yes **Shop:** Yes

Previous Grounds: The Angel 1948-80

Record Attendance: 8,236 v Aldershot - FA Cup 1951 at The Angel.

09-10	10-11	11-12	12-13	13-14	14-15	15-16	16-17	17-18
Isth P 8	Isth P 2	Conf S 9	Conf S 16	Conf S 21	Isth P 20	Isth P 4	Isth P 6	Isth P 11
FAC 3Q	FAC 1Q	FAC 2Q	FAC 2Q	FAC 3Q	FAC 2Q	FAC 2Q	FAC 4Q	FAC 1Q
FAT 3Q	FAT 3Q	FAT 3Qr	FAT 2P	FAT 1Pr	FAT 3Qr	FAT 2Q	FAT 2Qr	FAT 1Qr

League Honours: Kent 1992-93.

County FA Honours: Kent Senior Cup 1964-65, 74-75. Kent Senior Shield 1951-52, 55-56, 57-58, 58-59, 63-64.

FA Cup First Round Proper 1967-68, 72-73.

FA Vase Third Round Proper 1993-94.

FA Trophy Third Round Proper 2004-05(r).

Victory: 11-1 v Worthing - FA Cup 1951

Defeat: 2-11 v Folkstone - Kent Senior Cup 1949

Goalscorer: Jon Main scored 44 goals in one season including seven hat-tricks

Appearances: Mark Giham

From M25. Take A21 turning at Junction 5 to junction with A225/b245 (signposted Hildenborough). After passing Langley Hotel on left thake slightly hidden left turn into Dry Hill Park Road. Left again at mini roundabout into Shipbourne Road (A227) and then left again at next roundabout into Darenth Avenue' Longmead stadium can be found at the bottom of the hill at the far end of the car park.

Nearest Railway Station Tonbridge - 3.1km

Bus Route Heather Walk - stop 250m away

WEALDSTONE

The Stones **Club Colours** Blue & white

Founded 1899

Club Contact Details 07790 038 095

Grosvenor Vale, Ruislip, Middlesex HA4 6JQ

2018-19 SEASON
Nat S 7
FAC 4Q
FAT 1P

Record
P 49 W 22 D 12 L 15

Top Goalscorer
Pratt (12)

Honours
-

Previous Names: None

Previous Leagues: Willesden & District 1899-1906, 08-13, London 1911-22, Middlesex 1913-22, Spartan 1922-28, Athenian 1928-64, Isthmian 1964-71, 95-2006, 2007-14. Southern 1971-79, 81-82, 88-95, Conference 1979-81, 82-88

Ground Capacity: 3,607 **Seats:** 329 **Covered:** 1,166 **Clubhouse:** Yes **Shop:** No

Previous Grounds: Locket Road, Belmont Road, Lower Mead Stadium 1922-91, Watford FC, Yeading FC, Edgware Town, Northwood FC

Record Attendance: 13,504 v Leytonstone - FA Amateur Cup 4th Round replay 05/03/1949 (at Lower Mead)

09-10	10-11	11-12	12-13	13-14	14-15	15-16	16-17	17-18
Isth P 6	Isth P 12	Isth P 4	Isth P 3	Isth P 1	Conf S 12	Nat S 13	Nat S 8	Nat S 11
FAC 1P	FAC 3Qr	FAC 1Q	FAC 2Q	FAC 3Q	FAC 2Qr	FAC 1P	FAC 4Q	FAC 3Q
FAT 3Q	FAT 1Pr	FAT SF	FAT 3Qr	FAT 2Qr	FAT 2P	FAT 1P	FAT 3P	FAT SF

League Honours: Athenian 1951-52. Southern Division One South 1973-74, Southern Division 1981-82. Conference 1984-85. Isthmian Division Three 1996-97, Premier 2013-14.

County FA Honours: Middlesex Junior Cup 1912-13. Senior 1929-30, 37-38, 40-41, 41-42, 42-43, 45-46, 58-59, 62-63, 63-64, 67-68, 84-85. Charity Cup 1929-30, 30-31, 37-38, 38-39, 49-50, 63-64, 68-68, 03-04, 10-11 Prem Cup 2003-04, 07-08, 08-09, 10-11. London Senior 1961-62.

FA Cup Third Round Proper 1977-78.

FA Vase Third Round Proper 1997-98.

FA Trophy Winners 1984-85.

FA Am Cup Winners 1965-66.

Victory: 22-0 v The 12th London Regiment (The Rangers) - FA Amateur Cup 13/10/1923

Defeat: 0-14 v Edgware Town (A) - London Senior Cup 09/12/1944

Goalscorer: George Duck - 251

Appearances: Charlie Townsend - 514

Additional: Became the first club to win the 'Non-League Double' when they won the Conference and FA Trophy in 1984-85. Paid £15,000 to Barnet for David Gipp. Received £70,000 from Leeds United for Jermaine Beckford.

From the M1: Follow Signs for Heathrow Airport on the M25. Come off at Junction 16 onto the A40, come off at The Polish War Memorial junction A4180 sign posted to Ruislip, continue on West End Road, right into Grosvenor Vale after approx 1.5 miles, the ground is at the end of the road.
From the M25: Follow Take Junction 16 Off M25 onto A40. Then come off at The Polish War Memorial junction A4180 sign posted to Ruislip, continue on West End Road, right into Grosvenor Vale after approx 1.5 miles, the ground is at the end of the road.

Nearest Railway Station Ruislip and Ruislip Gardens both walking distance.

Bus Route E7

WELLING UNITED

The Wings **Club Colours** Red & white

Founded 1963

Club Contact Details 0208 301 1196 info@wellingunited.com

Park View Road Ground, Welling, Kent DA16 1SY

2018-19 SEASON
Nat S 3
FAC 4Q
FAT 3Qr

Record
P 49 W 26 D 8 L 15

Top Goalscorer
Kiernan (15)

Honours
-

Previous Names: None

Previous Leagues: Eltham & District Sunday 1963-71, Metropolitan 1971-75, London Spartan 1975-78, Athenian 1978-81, Southern 1981-86, 2000-04, Conference 1986-2000

Ground Capacity: 4,000 **Seats:** 1,070 **Covered:** 1,500 **Clubhouse:** Yes **Shop:** Yes

Previous Grounds: Butterfly Lane, Eltham 1963-77.

Record Attendance: 4,100 v Gillingham - FA Cup First Round Proper, 22nd November 1989

09-10		10-11		11-12		12-13		13-14		14-15		15-16		16-17		17-18	
Conf S	9	Conf S	6	Conf S	3	Conf S	1	Conf	16	Conf	20	Nat	24	Nat S	16	Nat S	10
FAC	3Q	FAC	2Q	FAC	2Q	FAC	4Q	FAC	2P	FAC	4Q	FAC	2P	FAC	4Q	FAC	2Q
FAT	1P	FAT	1Pr	FAT	1P	FAT	3P	FAT	1P	FAT	1Pr	FAT	2P	FAT	3P	FAT	3Q

League Honours: Southern League Premier Division 1985-86. Conference South 2012-13.

County FA Honours: Kent Senior Cup 1985-86, 98-99, 2008-09. London Senior Cup 1989-90. London Challenge Cup 1991-92.

FA Cup Third Round Proper 1988-89. **FA Vase** Third Round Proper 1979-80.

FA Trophy Quarter-finals 1988-89, 2006-07.

Victory: 7-1 v Dorking - 1985-86

Defeat: 0-7 v Welwyn Garden City - 1972-73

Additional: Paid £30,000 to Enfield for Gary Abbott
Received £95,000 from Birmingham City for Steve Finnan 1995

M25 to Dartford then A2 towards London.
Take Bexleyheath/Blackfen/Sidcup,turn off (six miles along A2) then follow A207 signed welling.
Ground is 1 mile From A2 on main road towards Welling High Street.

Nearest Railway Station Welling - 15-20 minute walk from the ground.

Bus Route Numbers 89, 486 and B16.

WEYMOUTH

The Terras **Club Colours** Claret & blue

Founded 1890

Club Contact Details 01305 785 558 info@theterras.co.uk

Bob Lucas Stadium, Radipole Lane, Weymouth DT4 9XJ

2018-19 SEASON
SthPS 1
FAC 1Qr
FAT 2Pr

Record
P 44 W 24 D 13 L 7

Top Goalscorer
Goodship (38)

Honours
Southern Premier South

Previous Names: None

Previous Leagues: Dorset, Western 1907-23, 28-49, Southern 1923-28, 49-79, 89-2005, Alliance/Conference 1979-89, 2005-10.

Ground Capacity: 6,600 **Seats:** 900 **Covered:** Yes **Clubhouse:** Yes **Shop:** Yes

Previous Grounds: Recreation Ground > 1987.

Record Attendance: 4,995 v Manchester United - Ground opening 21/10/97

09-10		10-11		11-12		12-13		13-14		14-15		15-16		16-17		17-18	
Conf S	22	SthP	18	SthP	17	SthP	9	SthP	12	SthP	7	SthP	7	SthP	10	SthP	5
FAC	2Q	FAC	2Q	FAC	3Q	FAC	2Q	FAC	4Q	FAC	4Qr	FAC	1Q	FAC	4Q	FAC	3Q
FAT	1P	FAT	2Q	FAT	2P	FAT	2Q	FAT	2Q	FAT	1Pr	FAT	3Q	FAT	1Pr	FAT	1Q

League Honours: Dorset 1897-98, 1913-14, Division One 1921-22. Western Division One 1922-23, 36-37, 37-38, Division Two 33-34. Southern 1964-65, 65-66, Southern Division 1997-98, Southern Premier South 2018-19. Conference South 2005-06.

County FA Honours: Dorset Senior Cup x12 - Firstly in 1985-86 and most recently in 2016-17.

FA Cup Fourth Round Proper 1961-62.

FA Trophy Quarter-finals 1973-74, 76-77(r).

Goalscorer: W 'Farmer' Haynes - 275

Appearances: Tony Hobsons - 1,076

Additional: Paid £15,000 to Northwich Victoria for Shaun Teale
Received £100,000 from Tottenham Hotspur for Peter Guthrie 1988

Defeat: 0-9 v Rushden & Diamonds, Conference South, 21/02/2009 - this was a game which, due to an administration issue, the club had to field their U18 team.

Approach Weymouth from Dorchester on the A354.
Turn right at first roundabout onto Weymouth Way, continue to the next roundabout then turn right (signposted Football Ground).
At the next roundabout take third exit into the ground.

Nearest Railway Station Weymouth - 2.2km

Bus Route Bus stops outside the ground

ISTHMIAN PREMIER INS: Bowers & Pitsea (P - IsthN), Cheshunt (IsthSC), Cray Wanderers (P - IsthSE), East Thurrock United (R - NatS), Horsham (P - IsthSE).

BISHOP'S STORTFORD

Founded 1874

Nickname: Blues or Bishops **Club Colours:** Blue and white

Club Contact Details 01279 306 456

ProKit Uk Stadium, Woodside Park, Dunmow Road, Bishop's Stortford CM23 5RG

Previous Names: None

Previous Leagues: East Herts 1896-97, 1902-06, 19-21, Stansted & Dist. 1906-19, Herts Co. 1921-25, 26-29, Herts & Essex Border 1925-26, Spartan 1929-51, Delphian (FM) 1951-63, Athenian 1963-71, Isthmian 1971-2004, Conference 2004-17, Southern 2017-18.

09-10		10-11		11-12		12-13		13-14		14-15		15-16		16-17		17-18		18-19	
Conf S	18	Conf S	16	Conf N	10	Conf N	17	Conf S	15	Conf S	16	Nat S	11	Nat S	21	SthP	18	Isth P	7
FAC	2Q	FAC	2Qr	FAC	4Q	FAC	1P	FAC	1P	FAC	2Qr	FAC	2Q	FAC	3Q	FAC	1Q	FAC	1Q
FAT	1P	FAT	3Q	FAT	1P	FAT	1P	FAT	3Q	FAT	1P	FAT	3Q	FAT	3Q	FAT	2Q	FAT	2Q

HONOURS / RECORDS

FA Comps: FA Amateur Cup 1973-74. FA Trophy 1980-81.

League: Stansted & District 1910-11, 12-13, 19-20. Spartan Division Two East 1931-32. Delphian 1954-55. Athenian Division One 1965-66, Premier 69-70. Isthmian Division One 1980-81, 93-94.

County FA: Herts Senior Cup 1932-33, 58-59, 59-60, 63-64, 70-71, 72-73, 73-74, 75-76, 86-87, 2005-06, 09-10, 11-12. London Senior Cup 1973-74.

Victory: 11-0 v Nettleswell & Buntwill - Herts Junior Cup 1911

Defeat: 0-13 v Cheshunt (H) - Herts Senior Cup 1926

Goalscorer: Post 1929 Jimmy Badcock - 123

Appearances: Phil Hopkins - 543

Ground Capacity: 4,000 **Seats:** 525 **Covered:** 700 **Clubhouse:** Yes **Shop:** Yes

Previous Grounds: Silver Leys 1874-97. Hadham Rd 97-1900. Havers Lane 00-03. Laundry Field 03-19. Brazier's Field 1919-97.Shared>99

Record Attendance: 6,000 v Peterborough Utd - FAC 2nd Rnd 1972-73 and v Middlesbrough - FA Cup 3rd Rnd replay 1982-83

DIRECTIONS

Woodside Park is situated 1/4 mile from Junction 8 of M11.
Follow A1250 towards Bishop's Stortford Town Centre, entrance to the ground is signposted through Woodside Park Industrial Estate.

Nearest Railway Station Bishop's Stortford - 20 minute walk from ground.

BOGNOR REGIS TOWN

Founded 1883

Nickname: The Rocks **Club Colours:** White & green

Club Contact Details 01243 822 325

Nyewood Lane, Bognor Regis PO21 2TY

Previous Names: None

Previous Leagues: West Sussex 1896-1926, Brighton & Hove District 1926-27, Sussex County 1927-72, Southern League 1972-81, Isthmian 1982-2004, 2009-17, Conference 2004-09, 17-18.

09-10		10-11		11-12		12-13		13-14		14-15		15-16		16-17		17-18		18-19	
Isth P	22	Isth1S	2	Isth1S	2	Isth P	14	Isth P	3	Isth P	14	Isth P	2	Isth P	2	Nat S	22	Isth P	14
FAC	1Q	FAC	2Q	FAC	3Q	FAC	2Q	FAC	2Qr	FAC	1Qr	FAC	4Q	FAC	2Q	FAC	4Q	FAC	2Qr
FAT	2Q	FAT	3Qr	FAT	P	FAT	3Q	FAT	3Q	FAT	1Qr	FAT	SF	FAT	1Q	FAT	2P	FAT	2Qr

HONOURS / RECORDS

FA Comps: None

League: West Sussex 1920-21, 21-22, 22-23, 23-24, 24-25. Sussex County Division One 1948-49 71-72, Division Two 70-71.

County FA: Sussex Professional Cup 1973-74.
Sussex Senior Cup 1954-55, 55-56, 79-80, 80-81, 81-82, 82083, 83084, 86-87, 2018-19.

Victory: 24-0 v Littlehampton - West Sussex League 1913-14

Defeat: 0-19 v Shoreham - West Sussex League 1906-07

Goalscorer: Kevin Clements - 216 (1978-89). On 16/12/14 Jason Prior scored his 100th goal for the club making it the fastest century of goals.

Appearances: Mick Pullen - 967 (20 seasons)

Ground Capacity: 4,100 **Seats:** 350 **Covered:** 2,600 **Clubhouse:** Yes **Shop:** Yes

Previous Grounds: None

Record Attendance: 3,642 v Swnsea City - FA Cup 1st Round replay 1984

DIRECTIONS

West along sea front from pier past Aldwick shopping centre then turn right into Nyewood Lane.

If walking from Bognor Railway Station - Walk along Linden Road until you reach Parklands Avenue, just after Parklands Avenue is a footpath on your left (opposite Town Cross Avenue) that if followed leads all the way to the entrance of the football club.

Nearest Railway Station Bognor is within walking distance to the ground.

BOWERS & PITSEA

Founded 1946

Nickname: **Club Colours:** Red & white

Club Contact Details 01268 452 068

Len Salmon Stadium, Crown Avenue, Pitsea, Basildon SS13 2BE

Previous Names: Bowers United > 2004.

Previous Leagues: Thurrock & Thameside Combination. Olympian. Essex Senior >2016.

09-10	10-11	11-12	12-13	13-14	14-15	15-16	16-17	17-18	18-19
ESen 17	ESen 14	ESen 15	ESen 19	ESen 14	ESen 2	ESen 1	Isth1N 6	Isth1N 3	IsthN 1
FAC P	FAC P	FAC EP	FAC EP	FAC EP	FAC 1Q	FAC EP	FAC Pr	FAC P	FAC 2Q
FAV 1Q	FAV 2Q	FAV 2Q	FAV 1Q	FAV 1P	FAV 1P	FAV SF	FAT 1Q	FAT 1Qr	FAT EP

HONOURS / RECORDS

FA Comps: None

League: Thurrock & Thameside Combination 1958-59. Essex Senior 1980-81, 98-99, 2015-16. Isthmian North Division 2018-19.

County FA: None

Victory: 14-1 v Stansted, 2006-07

Defeat: 0-8 v Ford United, 1996-97

Goalscorer: David Hope scored 50 during the 1998-99 season.

Ground Capacity: 2,000 **Seats:** 200 **Covered:** 1,000 **Clubhouse:** Yes **Shop:** Yes

Previous Grounds: Pitsea Market. Gun Meadow.

Record Attendance: 1,800 v Billericay Town, FA Vase.

DIRECTIONS

From A13, Take the turn off for Pitsea. At the roundabout take the first exit so that you pass Tesco's on your left. At the next roundabout take the third exit (Ashlyns). Go straight at the next roundabout (approx. 20 metres). Follow the road until the next roundabout and take the second exit and then take the first left into Kenneth Road. Follow the road to the end and turn right and then immediate left into the grounds. Visitors car park is at far end of clubhouse building. Access to clubhouse via pathway between clubhouse and football pitch then side door beside patio area. A130: Take the Canvey Island turn off and follow road to join A13 then follow above. Coming from A127 Take the Wickford turn off and take the third exit at roundabout. Follow road going straight over two roundabouts At third roundabout turn left (Ashlyns) then follow above.

Nearest Railway Station Pitsea - 1.7km

Bus Route Wilsner - stop 200m award

BRIGHTLINGSEA REGENT

Founded 1928

Nickname: The Rs **Club Colours:** Red & black

Club Contact Details 01206 304 119

Tydal Stadium, North Road, Brightlingsea, Essex CO7 0PL

Previous Names: Brightlingsea Athletic & Brightlingsea Town merged to form Brightlingsea United 1928-2005. Merged with Regent Park Rangers.

Previous Leagues: Essex Senior 1972-91. Eastern Counties 1990-02, 2011-14. Essex & Suffolk Border 2002-2011.

09-10	10-11	11-12	12-13	13-14	14-15	15-16	16-17	17-18	18-19
EsSuP 4	EsSuP 1	EC1 5	EC1 3	ECP 2	Isth1N 6	Isth1N 8	Isth1N 1	Isth P 20	Isth P 13
				FAC EPr	FAC 1Q	FAC Pr	FAC 1Q	FAC 1Q	FAC 3Q
		FAV 1Q	FAV 3P	FAV 5P	FAT 1Q	FAT Pr	FAT 2Qr	FAT 1Q	FAT 3Qr

HONOURS / RECORDS

FA Comps: None

League: Essex & Suffolk Border Division One 1946-47, 60-61, Division Two 2005-06, Premier 10-11. Essex Senior 1988-89, 89-90. Isthmian Division One North 2016-17.

County FA: None

Best FA Cup Third Qualifying Round 2018-19.

FA Trophy Third Qualifying Round 2018-19(r).

FA Vase Fifth Round Proper 2013-14.

Ground Capacity: 1,000 **Seats:** Yes **Covered:** Yes **Clubhouse:** Yes **Shop:**

Previous Grounds: Bell Green (Bellfield Close). Recreation Ground (Regent Road) > 1920.

Record Attendance: 1,200 v Colchester United, friendly, 1988.

DIRECTIONS

Take exit 28 off M25, take slip road left for A12 toward Brentwood / Chelmsford / Romford, turn left onto slip road, merge onto A12, take slip road left for A120, take slip road left for A133, at roundabout, take 2nd exit, turn left onto B1029 / Great Bentley Road, turn right onto B1027 / Tenpenny Hill, and then immediately turn left onto B1029 / Brightlingsea Road, turn left to stay on B1029 / Ladysmith Avenue, bear left onto Spring Road, turn left onto North Road.

Nearest Railway Station Alresford - 4.8km

Bus Route Spring Chase - stop 300m away

CARSHALTON ATHLETIC

Founded 1905

Nickname: Robins **Club Colours:** All red

Club Contact Details 020 8642 2551 secretary@carshaltonathletic.co.uk
War Memorial Sports Ground, Colston Avenue, Carshalton SM5 2PN

Previous Names: Mill Lane Mission 1905-07.
Previous Leagues: Croydon & District 1905-10. Southern Suburban 1910-22. Surrey Senior (Founding Members) 1922-23. London 1923-46. Corinthian 1946-56. Athenian 1956-73. Isthmian 1973-2004. Conference 2004-06.

09-10		10-11		11-12		12-13		13-14		14-15		15-16		16-17		17-18		18-19	
Isth P	17	Isth P	13	Isth P	16	Isth P	20	Isth P	23	Isth1S	20	Isth1S	10	Isth1S	6	Isth1S	1	Isth P	2
FAC	1Q	FAC	4Qr	FAC	2Q	FAC	2Q	FAC	1Q	FAC	1Q	FAC	2Q	FAC	1Qr	FAC	2Q	FAC	P
FAT	2Pr	FAT	2Q	FAT	3P	FAT	2Q	FAT	3Q	FAT	P	FAT	P	FAT	Pr	FAT	P	FAT	3Pr

HONOURS / RECORDS
FA Comps: None
League: Corinthian 1952-53, 53-54. Isthmian Division One South 2002-03, 17-18.

County FA: Surrey Intermediate Cup 1921-22, 31-32. Surrey Senior Shield 1975-76. Surrey Senior Cup 1988-89, 89-90, 91-92. London Challenge Cup 1991-92.

Victory: 13-0 v Worthing - Isthmian League Cup 28/01/1991
Defeat: 0-11 v Southall - Athenian League March 1963
Goalscorer: Jimmy Bolton - 242 during seven seasons
Appearances: Jon Warden - 504
Additional: Paid £15,000 to Enfield for Curtis Warmington. Received £30,000 from Crystal Palace for Ian Cox 1994

Ground Capacity: 8,000 **Seats:** 240 **Covered:** 4,500 **Clubhouse:** Yes **Shop:** Yes
Previous Grounds: Various before moving to Colston Avenue during the 1920-21 season.
Record Attendance: 7,800 v Wimbledon - London Senior Cup, Jan 1959.

DIRECTIONS
Turn right out of Carshalton Station exit,
turn right again,
and then left into Colston Avenue.

Nearest Railway Station Carshalton - 0.3km

CHESHUNT

Founded 1946

Nickname: Ambers **Club Colours:** Amber & black

Club Contact Details 01992 625 793 info@cheshuntfc.com
Cheshunt Stadium, Theobalds Lane, Cheshunt, Herts EN8 8RU

Previous Names: None
Previous Leagues: London 1946-51, 55-59, Delphian 1951-55, Aetolian 1959-62, Spartan 1962-64, 88-93, Athenian 1964-77, Isthmian 1977-87, 94-2005, Southern 2006-08

09-10		10-11		11-12		12-13		13-14		14-15		15-16		16-17		17-18		18-19	
Isth1N	15	Isth1N	18	Isth1N	18	Isth1N	11	Isth1N	15	Isth1N	18	Isth1N	6	Isth1N	10	Isth1N	19	IsthSC	3
FAC	P	FAC	1Q	FAC	Pr	FAC	Pr	FAC	P	FAC	P	FAC	P	FAC	1Q	FAC	2Q	FAC	1Qr
FAT	P	FAT	P	FAT	P	FAT	P	FAT	1Q	FAT	P	FAT	2Q	FAT	1Q	FAT	1Q	FAT	EPr

HONOURS / RECORDS
FA Comps: None
League: London Division One 1947-48, 48-49, Premier 49-50, Division One 1948, 49. Spartan 1962-63. Athenian 1967-68, 75-76. Isthmian Division Two 2002-03.
County FA: London Charity Cup 1974. East Anglian Cup 1975. Herts Charity Cup 2006, 2008.

Defeat: 0-10 v Eton Manor - London League 17/04/1956
Goalscorer: Darrell Cox - 152 (1997-2005, 07-08, 2010)
Appearances: John Poole - 526 (1970-76, 79-83)
Additional: Received £10,000 from Peterborough United for Lloyd Opara

Ground Capacity: 3,500 **Seats:** 424 **Covered:** 600 **Clubhouse:** Yes **Shop:** No
Previous Grounds: Gothic Sports Ground 1946-47. College Road 1947-50. Brookfield Lane 1950-52, 53-58.
Record Attendance: 5,000 v Bromley - FA Amateur Cup 2nd Round 28/01/1950

DIRECTIONS
M25, junction 25 take A10 north towards Hertford.
Third exit at roundabout towards Waltham Cross A121.
First exit at roundabout towards Cheshunt B176.
Under railway bridge then left onto Theobalds Lane.
Ground is 800 yard on the right.

Nearest Railway Station Theobalds Grove - 0.6km

CORINTHIAN-CASUALS

Founded 1939

Nickname: Casuals **Club Colours:** Chocolate and pink

Club Contact Details 020 8397 3368 secretary@ccfcltd.co.uk

King George's Field, Queen Mary Close, Hook Rise South, KT6 7NA

Previous Names: Casuals and Corinthians merged in 1939

Previous Leagues: Isthmian 1939-84, Spartan 1984-96, Combined Counties 1996-97

09-10		10-11		11-12		12-13		13-14		14-15		15-16		16-17		17-18		18-19	
Isth1S	13	Isth1S	20	Isth1S	13	Isth1S	14	Isth1S	17	Isth1S	13	Isth1S	6	Isth1S	4	Isth1S	5	Isth P	17
FAC	P	FAC	1Q	FAC	P	FAC	P	FAC	1Q	FAC	P	FAC	P	FAC	1Q	FAC	1Q	FAC	2Qr
FAT	1Q	FAT	P	FAT	P	FAT	P	FAT	P	FAT	Pr	FAT	1P	FAT	1Q	FAT	2Q	FAT	1Q

HONOURS / RECORDS

FA Comps: None

League: London Spartan Senior Division 1985-86.

County FA: Surrey Senior Cup 1953-54, 2010-11.

Goalscorer: Cliff West - 215

Appearances: Simon Shergold - 526

Best FA Cup First Round Proper 1965-66, 83-84.

FA Amateur C Runners-up 1955-56. **FA Trophy:** Second Round Proper 2002-03.

FA Vase First Round Proper 1983-84.

Ground Capacity: 2,000 **Seats:** 161 **Covered:** 700 **Clubhouse:** Yes **Shop:** Yes

Previous Grounds: Kingstonian's Richmond Road 1939-46. Polytechnic Ground in Chiswick 46-50. Oval 50-63. Dulwich Hamlet's Champion Hill 63-68, Tooting & Mitcham United's Sandy Lane 68-83, Molesey's Walton Road 83-84, 86-88. Wimbledon Park Athletics Stadium 84-86.

Record Attendance:

DIRECTIONS

The ground is situated just off the A3 not far from the Tolworth roundabout. If you are travelling from the M25 you can join the A3 at junction 10 towards London. Stay on the A3 until you reach the 50mph speed limit, continue under the Hook roundabout and move into the lefthand lane for ca. 174 yds. Bear LEFT onto Hook Rise North for 0.2 mile (Tolworth Junction). At roundabout, take the FOURTH exit (as if you were going to rejoin the A3 going towards Portsmouth) then almost immediately take slip road on left onto Hook Rise South for 0.5 mile. If you are travelling from London on the A3 take the Tolworth Junction exit. At roundabout, take the SECOND exit (as if you were going to rejoin the A3 going towards Portsmouth) then almost immediately take slip road on left onto Hook Rise South for 0.5 mile. Turn LEFT into Queen Mary Close. Ground and car park under railway bridge on right hand side. Youth Section pitches and changing rooms are in the park on the left.

Nearest Railway Station Tolworth - 0.6km

CRAY WANDERERS

Founded 1860

Nickname: Wanderers or Wands **Club Colours:** Amber & black

Club Contact Details 020 8460 5291

Bromley FC, Hayes Lane, Bromley, Kent BR2 9EF

Previous Names: Cray Old Boys (immediately after WW1); Sidcup & Footscray (start of WW2).

Previous Leagues: Kent 1894-1903, 06-07, 09-14, 34-38, 78-2004; West Kent & Sth Suburban (before WW1); London 20-34, 51-59; Kent Am 38-39, 46-51; South London All 43-46; Aetolian 59-64; Gr London 64-66; Metropolitan 66-71; Met. London 71-15; London Spartan 75-78.

09-10		10-11		11-12		12-13		13-14		14-15		15-16		16-17		17-18		18-19	
Isth P	15	Isth P	9	Isth P	9	Isth P	17	Isth P	24	Isth1N	16	Isth1N	4	Isth1S	11	Isth1S	3	IsthSE	1
FAC	1Q	FAC	2Qr	FAC	3Q	FAC	3Q	FAC	1Q	FAC	1Q	FAC	1Q	FAC	1Q	FAC	P	FAC	1Q
FAT	1Q	FAT	2Q	FAT	1Q	FAT	3Q	FAT	1Q	FAT	3Q	FAT	P	FAT	2Q	FAT	3Q	FAT	P

HONOURS / RECORDS

FA Comps: None

League: Kent 1901-02, 80-81, 2002-03, 03-04. London 1956-57, 57-58. Aetolian 1962-63. Greater London 1965-66. Metropolitan London 1974-75; London Spartan 1976-77, 77-78. Isthmian South East Division 2018-19.

County FA: Kent Amateur Cup 1930-31, 62-63, 63-64, 64-65. Kent Senior Trophy 1992-93, 2003-04.

Victory: 15-0 v Sevenoaks - 1894-95.

Defeat: 2-15 (H) and 0-14 (A) v Callenders Athletic - Kent Amateur League, 1947-48.

Goalscorer: Ken Collishaw 274 (1954-1965)

Appearances: John Dorey - 454 (1961-72).

Additional: Unbeaten for 28 Ryman League games in 2007-2008.

Ground Capacity: 5,000 **Seats:** 1,300 **Covered:** 2,500 **Clubhouse:** Yes **Shop:** Yes

Previous Grounds: Northfield Farm (1950-51), Tothills (aka Fordcroft, 1951-1955), Grassmeade (1955-1973), Oxford Road (1973-1998).

Record Attendance: (Grassmeade) 2,160vLeytonstone,FAAm.R3, 68-69; (Oxford R) 1,523vStamford,FAVQF 79-80; (Hayes L)1,082vAFC Wim, 04-05

DIRECTIONS

From M25: Leaving the motorway at junction 4, follow the A21 to Bromley and London, for approximately 4 miles and then fork left onto the A232 signposted Croydon/Sutton. At the second set of traffic lights, turn right into Baston Road (B265), following it for about two miles as it becomes Hayes Street and then Hayes Lane. Cray Wanderers FC is on the right hand side of the road just after the mini roundabout. There is ample room for coaches to drive down the driveway, turn round and park.

Nearest Railway Station Bromley South - 1km

Bus Route Hayes Road - stop 160m away

EAST THURROCK UNITED

Founded 1969

Nickname: The Rocks **Club Colours:** Amber & black

Club Contact Details 01375 644 166 secretary.eastthurrockunited@gmail.com

Rookery Hill, Corringham, Essex SS17 9LB

Previous Names: Corringham Social > 1969 (Sunday side)

Previous Leagues: South Essex Comb 1969-70. Greater London 1970-72. Metropolitan London 1972-75. London Spartan 1975-79. Essex Senior 1979-92. Isthmian 1992-2004, 05-16. Southern 2004-05. National 16-19.

09-10		10-11		11-12		12-13		13-14		14-15		15-16		16-17		17-18		18-19	
Isth1N	5	Isth1N	1	Isth P	10	Isth P	5	Isth P	20	Isth P	13	Isth P	3	Nat S	13	Nat S	15	Nat S	21
FAC	2Q	FAC	2Qr	FAC	1P	FAC	4Qr	FAC	1Qr	FAC	1P	FAC	3Q	FAC	2Q	FAC	4Qr	FAC	2Q
FAT	P	FAT	P	FAT	2Pr	FAT	2Qr	FAT	1Pr	FAT	3Q	FAT	1P	FAT	2P	FAT	3Pr	FAT	3Q

HONOURS / RECORDS

FA Comps: None

League: Metropolitan London Division Two 1972-73.
Isthmian League Division Three 1999-2000, Division One North 2010-11.

County FA: East Anglian Cup 2002-03.

Victory: 7-0 v Coggeshall (H) - Essex Senior League 1984

Defeat: 0-9 v Eton Manor (A) - Essex Senior League 1982

Goalscorer: Graham Stewart - 102

Appearances: Glen Case - 600+

Additional: £22,000 from Leyton Orient for Greg Berry 1990

Ground Capacity: 3,500 **Seats:** 160 **Covered:** 1,000 **Clubhouse:** Yes **Shop:** Yes

Previous Grounds: Billet, Stanford-le-Hope 1970-73, 74-76, Grays Ath 73-74, TilburyFC 77-82, New Thames Club 82-84.

Record Attendance: 1,661 vs Dulwich Hamlet, Isthmian League Premier Division Play-off final, 2016

DIRECTIONS

From M25 Junction 30. Take A13 towards Southend. Exit A13 at Stanford-le-hope exit (A1014), this is just after the BP garage. Turn right at the roundabout (3rd exit) onto a1014. Straight over first roundabout. Through traffic lights. Ground is 200 yards on your left.

Nearest Railway Station Stanford-le-Hope or Basildon.

Bus Route 100 - Stops 100 metres from the ground.

ENFIELD TOWN

Founded 2001

Nickname: ET's or Towners **Club Colours:** White & blue

Club Contact Details 07787 875 650

Queen Elizabeth Stadium, Donkey Lane, Enfield EN1 3PL

Previous Names: Broke away from Enfield F.C. in 2001

Previous Leagues: Essex Senior 2001-2005. Southern 2005-2006.

09-10		10-11		11-12		12-13		13-14		14-15		15-16		16-17		17-18		18-19	
Isth1N	4	Isth1N	6	Isth1N	2	Isth P	16	Isth P	19	Isth P	7	Isth P	6	Isth P	4	Isth P	17	Isth P	10
FAC	2Q	FAC	3Q	FAC	P	FAC	2Q	FAC	2Qr	FAC	2Qr	FAC	4Q	FAC	1Q	FAC	4Qr	FAC	1Q
FAT	2Q	FAT	2Q	FAT	1Q	FAT	3Q	FAT	2Q	FAT	1Q	FAT	2Q	FAV	2Q	FAT	1Q	FAT	2Q

HONOURS / RECORDS

FA Comps: None

League: Essex Senior 2002-03, 04-05.

County FA: Middlesex Charity Cup 2001-02, 07-08.

Victory: 7-0 v Ilford (A) - 29/04/2003

Goalscorer: Liam Hope - 108 (2009-15)

Appearances: Rudi Hall

Ground Capacity: 2,500 **Seats:** Yes **Covered:** Yes **Clubhouse:** Yes **Shop:** No

Previous Grounds: Brimsdown Rovers FC 2001-2010

Record Attendance: 969 v Tottenham Hotspur, friendly, November 2011.

DIRECTIONS

From the M25: Head towards London on the A10 from junction 25. Turn right into Carterhatch Lane at the Halfway House pub. Donkey Lane is first left after the pub.

From London/North Circular Road: Head north up the A10 and turn left to Carterhatch Lane at the Halfway House pub. Donkey Lane is first left after the pub.

Nearest Railway Station Southbury - 1.2km

FOLKESTONE INVICTA

Founded 1936

Nickname: The Seasiders **Club Colours:** Yellow & black

Club Contact Details 01303 257 461
The Fullicks Stadium, Cheriton Road CT19 5JU

Previous Names: None
Previous Leagues: East Kent Amateur. Kent County Eastern Section. Kent 1990-98, Southern 1998-2004

09-10		10-11		11-12		12-13		13-14		14-15		15-16		16-17		17-18		18-19	
Isth1S	2	Isth P	22	Isth1S	4	Isth1S	5	Isth1S	2	Isth1S	2	Isth1S	1	Isth P	16	Isth P	4	Isth P	6
FAC	1Q	FAC	2Qr	FAC	1Q	FAC	1Q	FAC	2Q	FAC	1Qr	FAC	1Qr	FAC	3Q	FAC	4Q	FAC	1Q
FAT	P	FAT	3Q	FAT	3Q	FAT	Pr	FAT	2Qr	FAT	2Qr	FAT	Pr	FAT	2Q	FAT	1Qr	FAT	3Q

HONOURS / RECORDS
FA Comps: None
League: Kent County Eastern Division One 1969-70, Premier 78-79. Kent Division Two 1991-92.
Isthmian Division One South 2015-16.
County FA: Kent Intermediate Shield 1991-92.

Victory: 13-0 v Faversham Town - Kent League Division One, May 1995.
Defeat: 1-7 v Crockenhill - Kent League Division One, February 1993 & v Welling United, Kent Senior Cup, February 2009.
Goalscorer: James Dryden - 141
Appearances: Michael Everitt - 631

Ground Capacity: 4,000 **Seats:** 900 **Covered:** Yes **Clubhouse:** Yes **Shop:** Yes
Previous Grounds: South Road Hythe > 1991, County League matches on council pitches
Record Attendance: 2,332 v West Ham United, benefit match, 1996-97.

DIRECTIONS
Leave the M20 motorway at junction 13, and head south onto the A20 (Cherry Garden Avenue). At the traffic lights, turn left onto the A2034 (Cheriton Road), pass the Harvey Grammar School and Stripes club - the ground is next left before Morrisons' supermarket; opposite the cemetery. Some car parking is available at Stripes.

Nearest Railway Station Folkestone West - 0.4km

HARINGEY BOROUGH

Founded 1973

Nickname: Borough **Club Colours:** Yellow & blue

Club Contact Details 0208 888 9933
Coles Park, White Hart Lane, Tottenham, London N17 7JP

Previous Names: Edmonton & Haringey 1973-76. Haringey Borough 1976-95. Tufnell Park 1995-96.
Previous Leagues: Athenian 1973-84. Isthmian 1984-89. Spartan South Midlands 1989-2013. Essex Senior 2013-15.

09-10		10-11		11-12		12-13		13-14		14-15		15-16		16-17		17-18		18-19	
SSM P	15	SSM P	8	SSM P	5	SSM P	9	ESen	2	ESen	1	Isth1N	15	Isth1N	5	Isth1N	4	Isth P	3
FAC	EPr	FAC	P	FAC	P	FAC	EP	FAC	2Q	FAC	EP	FAC	1Q	FAC	1Q	FAC	4Q	FAC	4Q
FAV	1Qr	FAV	1P	FAV	3P	FAV	2Q	FAV	3P	FAV	1Pr	FAT	2Qr	FAT	P	FAT	1P	FAT	1Qr

HONOURS / RECORDS
FA Comps: None
League: Essex Senior 2014-15.

County FA: London Senior Cup 1990-91

Best FA Cup First Round Proper 2018-19.
FA Trophy First Round Proper 2017-18.
FA Vase Quarter Finals 1977-78.

Ground Capacity: 2,500 **Seats:** 280 **Covered:** yes **Clubhouse:** Yes **Shop:** No
Previous Grounds: None
Record Attendance: 2,710 v AFC Wimbledon, FA Cup First Round Proper, 09/11/2018.

DIRECTIONS
At junction 25 of the M25 or from the A406 (North Circular Road) turn south onto the A10 (Great Cambridge Road) towards Central London. At the junction of the A10 and White Hart Lane turn right (use slip road at traffic lights) into White Hart Lane and the ground is about 500 yards on the left, some 150 yards after a petrol station. PUBLIC TRANSPORT: Bus W3 from Finsbury Park station to Northumberland Park station via Alexandra Palace station and Wood Green underground station passes ground. In other direction W3 can be boarded at White Hart Lane station).

Nearest Railway Station White Hart Lane - 1.5km. Wood Green (UG) - 1.5km
Bus Route W3 stops outside the ground.

HORNCHURCH

Founded 2005

Nickname: The Urchins **Club Colours:** Red and white

Club Contact Details 01708 220 080

The Stadium, Bridge Avenue, Upminster, Essex RM14 2LX

Previous Names: Formed in 2005 after Hornchurch F.C. folded. AFC Hornchurch 2005-18.

Previous Leagues: Essex Senior 2005-06. Isthmian 2006-12. Conference 2012-13.

09-10		10-11		11-12		12-13		13-14		14-15		15-16		16-17		17-18		18-19	
Isth P	9	Isth P	10	Isth P	2	Conf S	20	Isth P	5	Isth P	23	Isth1N	5	Isth1N	4	Isth1N	1	Isth P	15
FAC	1Q	FAC	2Qr	FAC	1Q	FAC	2Q	FAC	4Q	FAC	1Qr	FAC	4Q	FAC	1Q	FAC	3Q	FAC	3Q
FAT	3Qr	FAT	1P	FAT	2P	FAT	3Q	FAT	1Q	FAT	3Q	FAT	1Q	FAT	P	FAT	Pr	FAT	2Q

HONOURS / RECORDS

FA Comps: None

League: Essex Senior 2005-06. Isthmian League Division One North 2006-07, 17-18.

County FA: Essex Senior Cup 2012-13.

Misc: Won the Essex League with a record 64 points in 2005-06

Ground Capacity: 3,500 **Seats:** 800 **Covered:** 1,400 **Clubhouse:** Yes **Shop:** Yes

Previous Grounds: None

Record Attendance:

DIRECTIONS

Bridge Avenue is off A124 between Hornchurch and Upminster.

Nearest Railway Station Upminster Bridge Underground - 0.4km

HORSHAM

Founded 1881

Nickname: Hornets **Club Colours:** Yellow & green

Club Contact Details 01403 458 854 admin@horshamfc.co.uk

Hop Oast, Worthing Road, Horsham RH13 0AD

Previous Names: None

Previous Leagues: West Sussex Senior, Sussex Co 1926-51, Metropolitan 1951-57, Corinthian 1957-63, Athenian 1963-73, Isthmian 1973-2015. Southern Combination 2015-16,

09-10		10-11		11-12		12-13		13-14		14-15		15-16		16-17		17-18		18-19	
Isth P	11	Isth P	17	Isth P	22	Isth1S	15	Isth1S	16	Isth1S	24	SCom	1	Isth1S	16	Isth1S	15	IsthSE	2
FAC	1Q	FAC	1Q	FAC	2Qr	FAC	2Q	FAC	3Q	FAC	1Q	FAC	Pr	FAC	P	FAC	2Q	FAC	3Qr
FAT	1Qr	FAT	2Q	FAT	1Q	FAT	P	FAT	1Q	FAT	3Q	FAV	1P	FAT	1Q	FAT	P	FAT	3Q

HONOURS / RECORDS

FA Comps: None

League: West Sussex Senior 1899-00, 1900-01, 01-02, 25-26. Sussex County 1931-32, 32-33, 34-35, 36-37, 37-38, 46-47. Metropolitan 1951-52. Athenian Division Two 1969-70, Division One 72-73. Isthmian Division Three 1995-96. Southern Combination 2015-16.

County FA: Sussex Senior Cup 1933-34, 38-39, 49-50, 53-54, 71-72, 73-74, 75-76.

Victory: 16-1 v Southwick - Sussex County League 1945-46

Defeat: 1-11 v Worthing - Sussex Senior Cup 1913-14

Goalscorer: Mick Browning

Appearances: Mark Stepney

Additional: Paid £2,500 to Lewes for Lee Farrell, July 2007. Received £10,000 from Tonbridge Angels for Carl Rook, Dec 2008.

Ground Capacity: **Seats:** Yes **Covered:** Yes **Clubhouse:** Yes **Shop:** Yes

Previous Grounds: Queens Street 1904-2008. Worthing FC 08-09. Horsham YMCA 2009-17. Culver Road (Sussex FA) 2017-19.

Record Attendance: 7,134 v Swindon - FA Cup First Round Proper, November 1966

DIRECTIONS

The Stadium is situated off the A24 and all supporters arriving by car will be directed to the Hop Oast Park & Ride, which is located opposite the access lane to the Stadium. The Post Code is RH13 0AR. It is a five minute walk to the Stadium.

Nearest Railway Station Horsham from which you can catch a bus to the stadium.

Bus Route No.98 from Roffey, Southwater and Horsham Railway and Bus Stations. No.23 can be taken from Crawley & Worthing.

KINGSTONIAN

Founded 1885

Nickname: The K's **Club Colours:** Red and white hoops

Club Contact Details 020 8330 6869 secretary@kingstonian.com

Corinthian-Casuals FC, King George's Field, Queen Mary Close, Hook Rise South, KT6 7NA

Previous Names: Kingston & Suburban YMCA 1885-87, Saxons 1887-90, Kingston Wanderers 1893-1904, Old Kingstonians 1908-19

Previous Leagues: Kingston & District, West Surrey, Southern Suburban, Athenian 1919-29, Isthmian 1929-98, Conference 1998-2001

09-10		10-11		11-12		12-13		13-14		14-15		15-16		16-17		17-18		18-19	
Isth P	5	Isth P	7	Isth P	11	Isth P	11	Isth P	2	Isth P	11	Isth P	7	Isth P	17	Isth P	13	Isth P	18
FAC	2Q	FAC	3Qr	FAC	1Q	FAC	2Q	FAC	1Q	FAC	3Q	FAC	2Q	FAC	1Q	FAC	2Q	FAC	1Q
FAT	3Q	FAT	2Q	FAT	1Q	FAT	1P	FAT	1Q	FAT	1Q	FAT	3Q	FAT	3Q	FAT	3Qr	FAT	1Qr

HONOURS / RECORDS

FA Comps: FA Amateur Cup 1932-33. FA Trophy 1998-99, 99-2000.

League: Athenian League 1923-24, 25-26. Isthmian 1933-34, 36-37, 97-98, Division One South 2008-09.

County FA: Surrey Senior Cup 1910-11, 13-14, 25-26, 30-31, 31-32, 34-35, 38-39, 51-52, 62-63, 63-64, 66-67, 97-98, 2005-06.
London Senior Cup 1962-63, 64-65, 86-87.

Victory: 15-1 v Delft - 1951

Defeat: 0-11 v Ilford - Isthmian League 13/02/1937

Goalscorer: Johnnie Whing - 295 (1948-62)

Appearances: Micky Preston - 555 (1967-85)

Additional: Paid £18,000 to Rushden & Diamonds for David Leworthy 1997 Received £150,000 from West Ham for Gavin Holligan 1999

Ground Capacity: 3,400 **Seats:** 125 **Covered:** Yes **Clubhouse:** Yes **Shop:** Yes

Previous Grounds: Several > 1921, Richmond Road 1921-89. Kingsmeadow 1989-2017. Leatherhead FC 2017-18.

Record Attendance: 8,760 v Dulwich Hamlet at Richmond Road 1933.

DIRECTIONS

M25 junction 9 to Leatherhead.
Follow signs to the Leisure Centre, ground adjacent.

Nearest Railway Station Tolworth - 0.6km

LEATHERHEAD

Founded 1946

Nickname: The Tanners **Club Colours:** Green & white

Club Contact Details 01372 360 151

Fetcham Grove, Guildford Road, Leatherhead, Surrey KT22 9AS

Previous Names: Club was formed when Leatherhead Rose and Leatherhead United merged in 1946.

Previous Leagues: Surrey Senior 1946-50, Metropolitan 1950-51, Delphian 1951-58, Corinthian 1958-63, Athenian 1963-72

09-10		10-11		11-12		12-13		13-14		14-15		15-16		16-17		17-18		18-19	
Isth1S	5	Isth1S	4	Isth P	19	Isth1S	6	Isth1S	3	Isth P	10	Isth P	11	Isth P	13	Isth P	6	Isth P	8
FAC	2Qr	FAC	P	FAC	4Qr	FAC	2Q	FAC	3Q	FAC	1Q	FAC	1Qr	FAC	1Q	FAC	2P	FAC	4Qr
FAT	1Q	FAT	P	FAT	1Q	FAT	3Qr	FAT	2Q	FAT	3Q	FAT	1Q	FAT	1Q	FAT	2Q	FAT	1Q

HONOURS / RECORDS

FA Comps: None

League: Surrey Senior 1946-47, 47-48, 48-49, 49-50. Corinthian 1962-63. Athenian Division One 1963-64.

County FA: Surrey Senior Cup 1968-69. Surrey Senior Shield 1968-69. Surrey Intermediate Cup 1968-69.

Victory: 13-1 v Leyland Motors - Surrey Senior League 1946-47

Defeat: 1-11 v Sutton United

Goalscorer: Steve Lunn scored 46 goals during 1996-97

Appearances: P Caswell - 200

Additional: Paid £1,500 to Croydon for B Salkeld. Received £1,500 from Croydon for B Salkeld.

Ground Capacity: 3,400 **Seats:** 125 **Covered:** Yes **Clubhouse:** Yes **Shop:** Yes

Previous Grounds: None

Record Attendance: 5,500 v Wimbledon - 1976

DIRECTIONS

M25 junction 9 to Leatherhead,
follow signs to Leisure Centre,
ground adjacent.

Nearest Railway Station Leatherhead - half a mile away

LEWES

Founded 1885

Nickname: Rooks **Club Colours:** Red & black

Club Contact Details 01273 470 820

The Dripping Pan, Mountfield Road, Lewes, East Sussex BN7 2XA

Previous Names: None

Previous Leagues: Mid Sussex 1886-1920, Sussex County 1920-65, Athenian 1965-77, Isthmian 1977-2004, Conference 2004-11.

09-10		10-11		11-12		12-13		13-14		14-15		15-16		16-17		17-18		18-19	
Conf S	19	Conf S	21	Isth P	6	Isth P	19	Isth P	16	Isth P	19	Isth P	23	Isth1S	9	Isth1S	2	Isth P	11
FAC	3Q	FAC	4Q	FAC	1Q	FAC	2Q	FAC	3Q	FAC	2Q	FAC	1Q	FAC	1Qr	FAC	1Q	FAC	3Q
FAT	2P	FAT	3Q	FAT	2Q	FAT	2Qr	FAT	1Q	FAT	3Q	FAT	1Qr	FAT	1Q	FAT	3Q	FAT	3Qr

HONOURS / RECORDS

FA Comps: None

League: Mid Sussex 1910-11, 13-14. Sussex County 1964-65. Athenian Division Two 1967-68, Division One 1969-70. Isthmian Division Two 2001-02, Division One South 2003-04. Conference South 2007-08.

County FA: Sussex Senior Cup 1964-65, 70-71, 84-85, 2000-01, 05-06.

Goalscorer: 'Pip' Parris - 350

Appearances: Terry Parris - 662

Additional: Paid £2,000 for Matt Allen
Received £2,500 from Brighton & Hove Albion for Grant Horscroft

Ground Capacity: 3,000 **Seats:** 600 **Covered:** 1,400 **Clubhouse:** Yes **Shop:** Yes

Previous Grounds: Played at Convent Field for two seasons before WWI

Record Attendance: 2,500 v Newhaven - Sussex County League 26/12/1947

DIRECTIONS

After leaving the M23, follow the A23 to Brighton. On the outskirts of Brighton join the A27 eastbound. Stay on the A27 for about 5 miles. At the roundabout take first exit into Lewes. Follow this road until you reach traffic lights outside Lewes Prison. Turn right at the lights and follow the road down the hill until you reach a mini roundabout outside the Swan public house. Turn left at roundabout into Southover High Street and continue over next mini roundabout outside the Kings Head public house. At the next roundabout go straight over into Mountfield Road. The Dripping Pan is on your right.

Nearest Railway Station Lewes - 0.3km

Bus Route Priory School - stop 100m away

MARGATE

Founded 1896

Nickname: The Gate **Club Colours:** Blue & white

Club Contact Details 01843 221 769 secretary@margate-fc.com

Hartsdown Park, Hartsdown Road, Margate, Kent CT9 5QZ

Previous Names: Margate Town 1896-1929. Thanet United 1981-89.

Previous Leagues: Kent 1911-23, 24-28, 29-33, 37-38, 46-59. Southern 1933-37, 59-2001, Conference 2001-05, 15-17. Isthmian 2005-15.

09-10		10-11		11-12		12-13		13-14		14-15		15-16		16-17		17-18		18-19	
Isth P	19	Isth P	16	Isth P	15	Isth P	9	Isth P	11	Isth P	2	Nat S	19	Nat S	22	Isth P	7	Isth P	12
FAC	1Qr	FAC	2Qr	FAC	3Q	FAC	3Q	FAC	2Q	FAC	2Q	FAC	4Q	FAC	4Qr	FAC	4Q	FAC	2Q
FAT	1Q	FAT	2Q	FAT	2Qr	FAT	1Q	FAT	3Q	FAT	1Q	FAT	3Q	FAT	3Qr	FAT	3Q	FAT	1Q

HONOURS / RECORDS

FA Comps: None

League: Kent 1932-33, 37-38, 46-47, 47-48. Southern League Eastern Section & Championship 1935-36, Division One 1962-63, Division One South 1977-78, Premier Division 2000-01.

County FA: Kent Senior Cup 1935-36, 36-37, 73-74, 93-94, 97-98, 2002-03, 03-04, 04-05.

Victory: 12-1 v Deal Cinque Ports, FA Cup 1Q, 1919-20 and v Erith & Belvedere, Kent League, 1927-28.

Defeat: 0-11 v AFC Bournemouth (A), FA Cup, 20/11/1971.

Goalscorer: Martin Buglione - 158

Appearances: Bob Harrop - 564

Additional: Paid £5,000 to Dover Athletic for Steve Cuggy

Ground Capacity: 3,000 **Seats:** 400 **Covered:** 1,750 **Clubhouse:** Yes **Shop:** Yes

Previous Grounds: At least six before moving to Hartsdown in 1929. Shared with Dover Ath. 2002-03 and Ashford Town 04-05.

Record Attendance: 14,169 v Tottenham Hotspur - FA Cup 3rd Round 1973

DIRECTIONS

From M25 continue onto M26 merge onto M20, at junction 7, exit onto Sittingbourne Rd/A249 toward Sheerness/Canterbury/Ramsgate, continue to follow A249, take the ramp onto M2, continue onto A299 (signs for Margate/Ramsgate) keep right at the fork, at the roundabout, take the 2nd exit onto Canterbury Rd (Birchington)/A28 continue to follow A28, turn right onto The Square/A28 continue to follow A28, turn right onto George V Ave/B2052, turn right onto Hartsdown Rd/B2052, ground will be on the left.

Nearest Railway Station Margate - 0.7 miles from the ground.

MERSTHAM

Founded 1892

Nickname: The Moatsiders **Club Colours:** Yellow & black

Club Contact Details 01737 644 046

Moatside Stadium, Weldon Way, Merstham, Surrey RH1 3QB

Previous Names: None

Previous Leagues: Redhill & District. Surrey Intermediate. Surrey Senior 1965-78. London Spartan 1978-84. Combined Counties 1984-2008.

09-10		10-11		11-12		12-13		13-14		14-15		15-16		16-17		17-18		18-19	
Isth1S	16	Isth1S	19	Isth1S	9	Isth1S	12	Isth1S	7	Isth1S	4	Isth P	10	Isth P	20	Isth P	18	Isth P	5
FAC	Pr	FAC	P	FAC	2Q	FAC	P	FAC	2Q	FAC	2Q	FAC	1Q	FAC	1P	FAC	1Q	FAC	1Qr
FAT	2Q	FAT	P	FAT	1Q	FAT	2Q	FAT	Pr	FAT	2Q	FAT	1Qr	FAT	2Q	FAT	1Qr	FAT	2Q

HONOURS / RECORDS

FA Comps: None

League: Redhill & District 1934-35, 35-36, 49-50, 50-51. Surrey Intermediate 1952-53. Surrey Senior 1971-72. Combined Counties Premier Division 2007-08.

County FA: East Surrey Junior Cup 1929-30. Surrey Senior Charity Cup 1976-77. East Surrey Charities Senior Cup 1979-80, 80-81. East Surrey Charity Cup 1998-99, 2004-05, 06-07. Surrey Senior Cup 2007-08, 15-16, 17-18.

Defeat: 1-8 v Aldershot Town, FA First Qualifying Round, 1996-97.

Best FA Cup First Round Proper 2016-17.

FA Trophy Second Qualifying Round 2009-10, 12-13, 16-17, 18-19.

FA Vase Quarter Finals 2007-08.

Ground Capacity: 2,500 **Seats:** 174 **Covered:** 100 **Clubhouse:** Yes **Shop:** No

Previous Grounds: None

Record Attendance: 1,920 v Oxford United, FAC First Round Proper, 05/11/2016

DIRECTIONS

Leave Merstham village (A23) by School Hill, take 5th right (Weldon Way). Clubhouse and car park on the right. Ten minutes walk from Merstham BR.

Nearest Railway Station Merstham - 0.7km

POTTERS BAR TOWN

Founded 1960

Nickname: Grace or Scholars **Club Colours:** Maroon & white

Club Contact Details 01707 654 833

Pakex Stadium, Parkfield, Watkins Rise, Potters Bar EN6 1QB

Previous Names: Mount Grace Old Scholars 1960-84. Mount Grace 1984-91.

Previous Leagues: Barnet & District 1960-65, North London Combination 1965-68, Herts Senior County 1968-91, Spartan South Midlands 1991-2005, Southern 2005-06, 13-17. Isthmian 2006-13.

09-10		10-11		11-12		12-13		13-14		14-15		15-16		16-17		17-18		18-19	
Isth1N	14	Isth1N	13	Isth1N	12	Isth1N	10	SthC	15	SthC	14	SthC	12	SthC	9	Isth1N	2	Isth P	16
FAC	3Q	FAC	P	FAC	P	FAC	1Qr	FAC	P	FAC	P	FAC	2Q	FAC	4Q	FAC	2Qr	FAC	1Q
FAT	Pr	FAT	1Qr	FAT	2Q	FAT	1Q	FAT	1Qr	FAT	Pr	FAT	Pr	FAT	P	FAT	2Qr	FAT	2Q

HONOURS / RECORDS

FA Comps: None

League: North London Combination Premier Division 1967-68. Herst Senior county Premier Division 1990-91. Spartan South Midlands Premier Division 1996-97, 2004-05.

County FA: None

Goalscorer: Micky Gray scored 51 during a single season. Richard Howard has come closest to that record having scored 49 goals during seasons 2004-05 and 2006-07 respectively.

Best FA Cup Fourth Qualifying Round 2006-07, 16-17.

FA Trophy Second Round Qualifying 2011-12, 17-18(r).

FA Vase Sixth Round Proper 1997-98.

Ground Capacity: 2,000 **Seats:** 150 **Covered:** 250 **Clubhouse:** Yes **Shop:** Yes

Previous Grounds: None

Record Attendance: 268 v Wealdstone - FA Cup 1998 (4,000 watched a charity match in 1997)

DIRECTIONS

M25 junction 24 enter Potters Bar along Southgate Road (A111) turn right into High Street at first lights (A1000) then left into The Walk after half a mile. Ground is 200 yards on the right - opposite Potters Bar Cricket Club.

Nearest Railway Station Potters Bar - 0.9km

IsthSE - Cray Wanderers v Whitsatable - Aaron Rhule slides the ball under Whitstable keeper Dan Eason to score for Cray Wanderers.

IsthSE - Phonix Sports v Whitsatable - Whitstables Robert Gillman blocks this effort from Phoenix Sports Alfie Aldridge.

IsthSE - VCD Athletic v Whitstable Town - Ali Fuseini (9) scores against Whitstable. Photos: Alan Coomes.

WINGATE & FINCHLEY

Founded 1991

Nickname: Blues **Club Colours:** Blue

Club Contact Details 0208 446 2217
Maurice Rebak Stadium, Summers Lane, Finchley N12 0PD

Previous Names: Wingate (founded 1946) and Finchley (founded late 1800s) merged in 1991
Previous Leagues: South Midlands 1991-95, Isthmian 1995-2004, Southern 2004-2006

09-10		10-11		11-12		12-13		13-14		14-15		15-16		16-17		17-18		18-19	
Isth1N	3	Isth1N	3	Isth P	13	Isth P	18	Isth P	21	Isth P	12	Isth P	13	Isth P	5	Isth P	9	Isth P	19
FAC	2Qr	FAC	Pr	FAC	1Q	FAC	2Q	FAC	1Qr	FAC	3Q	FAC	3Q	FAC	2Q	FAC	2Qr	FAC	1Q
FAT	Pr	FAT	1Q	FAT	1Q	FAT	2Qr	FAT	2Qr	FAT	1Q	FAT	1Q	FAT	1Pr	FAT	1P	FAT	2P

HONOURS / RECORDS
FA Comps: None
League: None

County FA: London Senior Cup 2010-11.

Victory: 9-1 v Winslow, South Midlands League, 23/11/1991
Defeat: 0-9 v Edgware, Isthmian Division Two, 15/01/2000
Goalscorer: Marc Morris 650 (including with Wingate FC)
Appearances: Marc Morris 720 (including with Wingate FC)

Ground Capacity: 1,500 **Seats:** 500 **Covered:** 500 **Clubhouse:** Yes **Shop:** No
Previous Grounds: None
Record Attendance: 528 v Brentwood Town (Division One North Play-Off) 2010/11

DIRECTIONS
The simplest way to get to The Harry Abrahams Stadium is to get on to the A406 North Circular Road.
If coming from the West (eg via M1), go past Henlys Corner (taking the left fork after the traffic lights) and then drive for about 1 mile. The exit to take is the one immediately after a BP garage. Take the slip road and then turn right at the lights onto the A1000.
If coming from the East (eg via A10, M11) take the A1000 turn off. At the end of the slip road turn left at the lights. Go straight over the next set of lights. Then after 100m pass through another set of lights, then at the next set of lights turn right into Summers Lane.
The Stadium is a few hundred metres down on the right hand side.

Nearest Railway Station New Southgate - 2.3km

WORTHING

Founded 1886

Nickname: Rebels **Club Colours:** All red

Club Contact Details 01903 233 444 secretary@worthingfc.com
Woodside Road, Worthing, West Sussex BN14 7HQ

Previous Names: None
Previous Leagues: West Sussex 1896-1904, 1905-14, 19-20, Brighton Hove & District 1919-20, Sussex County 1920-48, Corinthian 1948-63, Athenian 1963-77

09-10		10-11		11-12		12-13		13-14		14-15		15-16		16-17		17-18		18-19	
Isth1S	3	Isth1S	14	Isth1S	7	Isth1S	10	Isth1S	15	Isth1S	6	Isth1S	3	Isth P	15	Isth P	16	Isth P	9
FAC	2Q	FAC	2Q	FAC	3Q	FAC	1Q	FAC	P	FAC	2Q	FAC	3Q	FAC	3Q	FAC	1Q	FAC	4Q
FAT	Pr	FAT	1Q	FAT	2Q	FAT	P	FAT	P	FAT	2Q	FAT	1Q	FAT	2Pr	FAT	2Q	FAT	3Q

HONOURS / RECORDS
FA Comps: None
League: Sussex League 1920-21, 21-22, 26-27, 28-29, 30-31, 33-34, 38-39, 39-40. Sussex League West 1945-46.
Isthmian League Division Two 1981-82, 92-93, Division One 1982-83.
County FA: Sussex Senior Cup x21.

Victory: 25-0 v Littlehampton (H) - Sussex League 1911-12
Defeat: 0-14 v Southwick (A) - Sussex County League 1946-47
Goalscorer: Mick Edmonds - 276
Appearances: Mark Knee - 414
Additional: Received £7,500 from Woking for Tim Read 1990

Ground Capacity: 3,650 **Seats:** 500 **Covered:** 1,500 **Clubhouse:** Yes **Shop:** No
Previous Grounds: None
Record Attendance: 3,600 v Wimbledon - FA Cup 14/11/1936

DIRECTIONS
A24 or A27 to Grove Lodge roundabout.
A24 (Town Centre exit) and right into South Farm Road.
Over five roundabouts take last on right (Pavilion Road) before level crossing.
Woodside Road on right, ground on left. 1/2 mile from BR.

Nearest Railway Station Worthing - 0.6km

AFC SUDBURY

Founded 1999

Nickname: Yellows or The Suds **Club Colours:** Yellow & blue

Club Contact Details 01787 376 213
Brundon Lane, Sudbury CO10 7HN

Previous Names: Sudbury Town (1874) and Sudbury Wanderers (1958) merged in 1999
Previous Leagues: Eastern Counties 1999-2006, Isthmian 2006-08, Southern 2008-10.

09-10		10-11		11-12		12-13		13-14		14-15		15-16		16-17		17-18		18-19	
SthM	14	Isth1N	7	Isth1N	8	Isth1N	17	Isth1N	10	Isth1N	3	Isth1N	1	Isth P	23	Isth1N	12	IsthN	8
FAC	1Q	FAC	Pr	FAC	3Q	FAC	1Q	FAC	3Q	FAC	1Q	FAC	2Q	FAC	2Q	FAC	3Q	FAC	3Q
FAT	1Qr	FAT	1P	FAT	1Q	FAT	P	FAT	3Qr	FAT	1P	FAT	2Q	FAT	2P	FAT	1Q	FAT	EP

HONOURS / RECORDS
FA Comps: None
League: Eastern Counties League 2000-01, 01-02, 02-03, 03-04, 04-05. Isthmian League Division One North 2015-16.

County FA: Suffolk Premier Cup 2001-02, 02-03, 03-04.

Goalscorer: Gary Bennett - 172
Appearances: Paul Betson - 376
Best FA Cup First Round Proper 2000-01.
FA Trophy First Round Proper 2006-07, 08-09, 10-11, 14-15.

Ground Capacity: 2,500 **Seats:** 200 **Covered:** 1,500 **Clubhouse:** Yes **Shop:** Yes
Previous Grounds: The Priory Stadium
Record Attendance: 1,800

DIRECTIONS
From Braintree: Take A131 through Halstead to Sudbury. On descending hill into Sudbury turn left at first set of traffic lights (Kings Head), and then take the first right into Brundon Lane. The road narrows before reaching ground on the right hand sideFrom Colchester, Bury St Edmunds and Ipswich: Enter Sudbury and follow signs for Halstead/Chelmsford. Go aross the river bridge and go under the old rail bridge, then turn right at the traffic lights (Kings Head) into Bulmer Road and the first right again into Brundon Lane. The road narrows before reaching ground on the right hand side.

Nearest Railway Station Sudbury - 1.5km
Bus Route Bulmer Road - stop 100m away

AVELEY

Founded 1927

Nickname: The Millers **Club Colours:** All blue

Club Contact Details 07946 438 540 craigjohnson.aveleyfc@gmail.com
Parkside, Park Lane, Aveley RM15 4PX

Previous Names: Lodge Meadow 1927-51.
Previous Leagues: Thurrock Combination 1946-49, London 1949-57, Delphian 1957-63, Athenian 1963-73, Isthmian 1973-2004, Southern 2004-06

09-10		10-11		11-12		12-13		13-14		14-15		15-16		16-17		17-18		18-19	
Isth P	3	Isth P	19	Isth P	20	Isth P	5	Isth1N	13	Isth1N	9	Isth1N	12	Isth1N	7	Isth1N	14	IsthN	2
FAC	3Qr	FAC	1Q	FAC	2Q	FAC	2Q	FAC	1Q	FAC	3Q	FAC	3Q	FAC	P	FAC	P	FAC	P
FAT	1Q	FAT	1Q	FAT	1Q	FAT	P	FAT	P	FAT	P	FAT	P	FAT	P	FAT	1Q	FAT	2Q

HONOURS / RECORDS
FA Comps: None
League: London Division One 1950-51, Premier Division 54-55. Athenian 1970-71. Isthmian Division One North 2008-09.

County FA: Essex Thameside Trophy 1979-80, 2004-05, 06-07.

Victory: 11-1 v Histon - 24/08/1963
Defeat: 0-8 v Orient, Essex Thameside Trophy
Goalscorer: Jotty Wilks - 214
Appearances: Ken Riley - 422

Ground Capacity: 3,500 **Seats:** 424 **Covered:** Yes **Clubhouse:** Yes **Shop:** No
Previous Grounds: Lodge Meadow 1927-52. Mill Field 1952-2018.
Record Attendance: 3,741 v Slough Town - FA Amateur Cup 27/02/1971

DIRECTIONS
Clockwise on M25: At junction 30/31, Use the 2nd from the left lane to take the A13 exit to Dagenham/Tilbury/Thurrock (Lakeside). Take Ship Lane to Park Lane in Aveley. At Mar Dyke Interchange, take the 2nd exit. At the roundabout, exit onto Ship Lane. At the roundabout, take the 2nd exit onto High Street. Continue onto Stifford Rd. At the roundabout, take the 1st exit onto Aveley Bypass/B1335. At the roundabout, take the 3rd exit. Merge onto Park Lane. Parkside will be on the right.

Nearest Railway Station Purfleet
Bus Route 372 (Hornchurch to Lakeside) passes the ground.

OUTS: Barking (Tr - IsthSC), Bowers & Pitsea (P - IsthP), Mildenhall Town (R - ECP).

BASILDON UNITED

Founded 1963

Nickname: The Bees **Club Colours:** Yellow & black

Club Contact Details 01268 521 278

Gardiners Close, Basildon SS14 3AW

Previous Names: Armada Sports.

Previous Leagues: Grays & Thurrock. Greater London. Essex Senior. Athenian. Isthmian. Essex Senior >2018.

09-10		10-11		11-12		12-13		13-14		14-15		15-16		16-17		17-18		18-19	
ESen	12	ESen	12	ESen	18	ESen	13	ESen	8	ESen	12	ESen	2	ESen	9	ESen	2	IsthN	17
FAC	P	FAC	EP	FAC	EP	FAC	1Q	FAC	P	FAC	P	FAC	1Q	FAC	P	FAC	P	FAC	1Q
FAV	1P	FAV	2Q	FAV	1P	FAV	1Q	FAV	1Q	FAV	1Q	FAV	3P	FAV	3P	FAV	1P	FAT	P

HONOURS / RECORDS

FA Comps: None

League: Essex Senior 1976-77, 77-78, 78-79, 79-80, 93-94.
Isthmian Division Two 1983-84.

County FA: Essex Senior Trophy 1978-79.

Best FA Cup Third Qualifying Round 1983-84, 98-99.

FA Trophy Second Qualifying Round 1985-86.

FA Vase Quarter Finals 1980-81.

Ground Capacity: 2,000 **Seats:** 400 **Covered:** 1,000 **Clubhouse:** Yes **Shop:** No

Previous Grounds: Gloucester Park Bowl 1963-70.

Record Attendance: 4,000 v West Ham, ground opening 11/08/1970 (4,999 watched a West Ham XI open Gloucester Park Bowl)

DIRECTIONS

Gardiners Close is sandwiched between the Southend Arterial Road (A127) and Cranes Farm Road (A1235).
Take 5 bus from Basildon Town Centre get off at Jolly Friar pub. 400 yard walk.

Nearest Railway Station Basildon (C2C), 2 miles

Bus Route 5 (First), 400 metres from ground

BRENTWOOD TOWN

Founded 1954

Nickname: Blues **Club Colours:** Sky blue & white

Club Contact Details 07768 006 370 info@brentwoodtownfc.co.uk

The Arena, Brentwood Centre, Doddinghurst Road, Brentwood CM15 9NN

Previous Names: Manor Athletic, Brentwood Athletic, Brentwood F.C.

Previous Leagues: Romford & District, South Essex Combination, London & Essex Border, Olympian, Essex Senior

09-10		10-11		11-12		12-13		13-14		14-15		15-16		16-17		17-18		18-19	
Isth1N	12	Isth1N	5	Isth1N	9	Isth1N	9	Isth1N	19	Isth1N	4	Isth P	22	Isth1N	14	Isth1N	21	IsthN	13
FAC	P	FAC	3Qr	FAC	1Qr	FAC	3Q	FAC	1Qr	FAC	2Q	FAC	4Q	FAC	P	FAC	P	FAC	1Q
FAV	1Q	FAV	1Q	FAV	1Q	FAV	3Qr	FAV	P	FAV	1Qr	FAV	2Q	FAV	P	FAT	3Q	FAT	2Qr

HONOURS / RECORDS

FA Comps: None

League: Essex Senior 2000-01, 2006-07.

County FA: None

Best FA Cup Third Round Proper 1969-70.

FA Trophy First Round Proper 1969-70.

FA Vase First Round 2004-05, 06-07.

Ground Capacity: 1,000 **Seats:** 150 **Covered:** 250 **Clubhouse:** Yes **Shop:** No

Previous Grounds: King George's Playing Fields (Hartswood), Larkins Playing Fields 1957-93

Record Attendance: 763 v Cheshunt, Isthmian Division One North, 23/04/2011.

DIRECTIONS

From High Street (Wilson's Corner) turn north into Ongar Road.
Then at third mini roundabout turn right into Doddinghurst Road.

Nearest Railway Station Shenfield - 2.1km

Bus Route Leisure Centre - stop 150m away

BURY TOWN

Founded 1872

Nickname: The Blues **Club Colours:** Blue & white

Club Contact Details 01284 754 721
Ram Meadow, Cotton Lane, Bury St Edmunds IP33 1XP

Previous Names: Bury St Edmunds 1872-1885, 1895-1908. Bury Town 1885-95. Bury United 1908-23.
Previous Leagues: Norfolk & Suffolk Border, Essex & Suffolk Border, Eastern Counties 1935-64, 76-87, 97-2006, Metropolitan 1964-71, Southern 1971-76, 87-97

09-10		10-11		11-12		12-13		13-14		14-15		15-16		16-17		17-18		18-19	
SthC	1	Isth P	3	Isth P	5	Isth P	7	Isth P	15	Isth P	24	Isth1N	13	Isth1N	11	Isth1N	9	IsthN	6
FAC	4Q	FAC	3Qr	FAC	2Q	FAC	4Q	FAC	1Q	FAC	1Q	FAC	2Q	FAC	P	FAC	P	FAC	1Q
FAT	P	FAT	2Q	FAT	3Qr	FAT	1Qr	FAT	1P	FAT	1Q	FAT	1P	FAT	1Q	FAT	2Q	FAT	EP

HONOURS / RECORDS
FA Comps: None
League: Metropolitan 1965-66, 68-69. Eastern Counties1963-64. Southern Division One Central 2009-10

County FA: Suffolk Senior Cup 1936-37, 37-38, 38-39, 44-45, 84-85.
Suffolk Premier Cup x12 - Firstly in 1958-59 and most recently in 2013-14.

Goalscorer: Doug Tooley - 251 in nine seasons
Appearances: Dick Rayner - 610 over 12 seasons
Additional: Paid £1,500 to Chelmsford City for Mel Springett
Received £5,500 from Ipswich Town for Simon Milton

Ground Capacity: 3,500 **Seats:** 300 **Covered:** 1,500 **Clubhouse:** Yes **Shop:** Yes
Previous Grounds: Kings Road 1888-1976. Temporary Ground 1976-77.
Record Attendance: 2,500 v Enfield - FA Cup Fourth Qualifying Round 1986

DIRECTIONS
Follow signs to Town Centre from A14. At second roundabout take first left into Northgate Street then left into Mustow Street at T junction at lights and left again into Cotton Lane. Ground is 350 yards on the right.

Nearest Railway Station Bury St Edmunds - 0.7km

CAMBRIDGE CITY

Founded 1908

Nickname: Lilywhites **Club Colours:** Black and white

Club Contact Details 07720 678 585 info@cambridge-city-fc.com
Histon FC, Bridge Road, Impington, Cambridge CB24 9PH

Previous Names: Cambridge Town 1908-51
Previous Leagues: Bury & District 1908-13, 19-20, Anglian 1908-10, Southern Olympian 1911-14, Southern Amateur 1913-35. Spartan 1935-50. Athenian 1950-58. Southern 1958-2004, 08-19. Conference 2004-08.

09-10		10-11		11-12		12-13		13-14		14-15		15-16		16-17		17-18		18-19	
SthP	6	SthP	4	SthP	5	SthP	8	SthP	3	SthP	13	SthP	18	SthP	21	Sth1E	6	SthC	12
FAC	3Q	FAC	3Q	FAC	1Qr	FAC	1Pr	FAC	2Q	FAC	1Q	FAC	1Q	FAC	2Q	FAC	2Qr	FAC	1Q
FAT	2Q	FAT	3Q	FAT	2Q	FAT	1Q	FAT	2Qr	FAT	1Q	FAT	1Q	FAT	1Q	FAT	1Q	FAT	1Q

HONOURS / RECORDS
FA Comps: None
League: Southern 1962-63, Southern Division 1985-86.

County FA: Suffolk Senior Cup 1909-10. East Anglian x9. Cambridgeshire Professional Cup 2012-13, 14-15, Invitational Cup 2014-15.

Goalscorer: Gary Grogan
Appearances: Mal Keenan
Additional: Paid £8,000 to Rushden & Diamonds for Paul Coe
Received £100,000 from Millwall for Neil Harris 1998

Ground Capacity: 3,250 **Seats:** 450 **Covered:** Yes **Clubhouse:** Yes **Shop:** Yes
Previous Grounds: City Ground.
Record Attendance: 12,058 v Leytonstone - FA Amateur Cup 1st Round 1949-50

DIRECTIONS
From the M11 (Northbound) Junc 14, take the A14 eastbound signed towards Newmarket. Take the first exit off the A14 and at the roundabout, take the first exit onto the B1049. Go straight over the traffic lights, past the Holiday Inn Hotel (on your right) and the entrance to the club is half a mile on your right.

Nearest Railway Station Cambridge - the following buses run every 20 minutes,
Bus Route Citi 8 and Guided Busway routes A, B and C

CANVEY ISLAND

Founded 1926

Nickname: The Gulls **Club Colours:** Yellow & blue

Club Contact Details 01268 682 991

Park Lane, Canvey Island, Essex SS8 7PX

Previous Names: None

Previous Leagues: Southend & District, Thurrock & Thames Combination, Parthenon, Metropolitan, Greater London 1964-71, Essex Senior 1971-95, Isthmian 1995-2004, Conference 2004-06

09-10		10-11		11-12		12-13		13-14		14-15		15-16		16-17		17-18		18-19	
Isth P	16	Isth P	6	Isth P	8	Isth P	8	Isth P	13	Isth P	17	Isth P	14	Isth P	22	Isth1N	6	IsthN	9
FAC	2Q	FAC	3Qr	FAC	2Q	FAC	1Q	FAC	4Q	FAC	4Qr	FAC	1Q	FAC	2Qr	FAC	P	FAC	P
FAT	1Q	FAT	1Q	FAT	3Q	FAT	3Qr	FAT	2Q	FAT	1Qr	FAT	2Q	FAT	1Q	FAT	P	FAT	1Q

HONOURS / RECORDS

FA Comps: FA Trophy 2000-01.

League: Thurrock Combination 1955-56. Greater London Division One 1967-68, 68-69. Essex Senior 1986-87, 92-93. Isthmian Division Two 1995-96, 97-98, Division One 1998-99, Premier Division 2003-04.

County FA: Essex Senior Cup 1998-99, 99-00, 01-02, 11-12.

Goalscorer: Andy Jones

Appearances: Steve Ward

Additional: Paid £5,000 to Northwich Victoria for Chris Duffy
Received £4,500 from Farnborough Town for Brian Horne

Ground Capacity: 4,100 **Seats:** 500 **Covered:** 827 **Clubhouse:** Yes **Shop:** Yes

Previous Grounds: None

Record Attendance: 3,553 v Aldershot Town - Isthmian League 2002-03

DIRECTIONS

A130 from A13 or A127 at Sadlers Farm roundabout.
One mile through Town Centre, first right past old bus garage.

Nearest Railway Station Leigh-on-Sea - 3.2km

Bus Route Transport Museum - stop 100m away

COGGESHALL TOWN

Founded 1878

Nickname: Seed Growers **Club Colours:** Red & black

Club Contact Details 01376 562 843 secretary@coggeshalltownfc.co.uk

West Street, Coggeshall CO6 1NT

Previous Names: None

Previous Leagues: North Essex 1899-1909. Colchester & District/Essex & Suffolk Border 1909-39, 58-72, 90-96, 2000-2016. North Essex. Braintree & Dist. Colchester & E Essex 1950-58. Essex Senior 1972-90. Essex Inter. 1996-98, 99-00. Eastern Co 2016-18.

09-10		10-11		11-12		12-13		13-14		14-15		15-16		16-17		17-18		18-19	
EsSu1	4	EsSu1	5	EsSu1	5	EsSu1	2	EsSuP	7	EsSuP	6	EsSuP	1	EC1	2	ECP	1	IsthN	4
																		FAC	3Q
																FAV	2Q	FAT	EP

HONOURS / RECORDS

FA Comps: None

League: North Essex x4. Essex & Suffolk Border Division II B 1909-10, 10-11, Division One 1962-63, Premier Division 1966-67, 67-68, 69-70, 2015-16. Eastern Counties Premier 2017-18.

County FA: Essex Intermediate Cup 1970-71.

Best FA Cup Third Qualifying Round 2018-19.

FA Trophy Extra Preliminary Round 2018-19.

FA Vase Second Qualifying Round 2017-18.

Ground Capacity: **Seats:** Yes **Covered:** Yes **Clubhouse:** Yes **Shop:**

Previous Grounds: Mynheer Park. Barnard Field 1880-81. Highfields Farm Park 1881-90, 95-1960. Fabians Field 1890-95.

Record Attendance: 1,124 v Tiptree United, Essex & Suffolk Border League, 1967-68.

DIRECTIONS

From the M11 take junction 8, take the A120 exit to Stansted Airport/Colchester/B. Stortford.
At the roundabout, take the 1st exit onto Thremhall Ave/A120.
At Priory Wood Roundabout, take the 3rd exit onto the A120 ramp to Colchester.
Continue onto A120. At the roundabout, take the 2nd exit and stay on A120.
At the roundabout, take the 3rd exit onto Coggeshall Rd/A120. Turn right onto West Street.

Nearest Railway Station Kelvedon - 3.6km

DEREHAM TOWN

Founded 1884

Nickname: Magpies **Club Colours:** Black & white

Club Contact Details 01362 690 460 enquiries@derehamtownfc.co.uk

Aldiss Park, Norwich Road, Dereham, Norfolk NR20 3PX

Previous Names: Dereham and Dereham Hobbies.

Previous Leagues: Norwich District. Dereham & District. Norfolk & Suffolk. Anglian Comb. Eastern Counties > 2013.

09-10		10-11		11-12		12-13		13-14		14-15		15-16		16-17		17-18		18-19	
ECP	10	ECP	2	ECP	10	ECP	1	Isth1N	7	Isth1N	7	Isth1N	9	Isth1N	18	Isth1N	8	IsthN	14
FAC	1Q	FAC	EP	FAC	EP	FAC	3Qr	FAC	1Q	FAC	2Q	FAC	P	FAC	2Q	FAC	2Q	FAC	P
FAV	2P	FAV	1Q	FAV	1P	FAV	2P	FAT	1Q	FAT	2Q	FAT	P	FAT	P	FAT	Pr	FAT	P

HONOURS / RECORDS

FA Comps: None

League: Anglian Combination Division One 1989-90, Premier Division 97-98. Eastern Counties Premier Division 2012-13.

County FA: Norfolk Senior Cup 2005-06, 06-07, 15-16.

Best FA Cup Third Qualifying Round replay 2012-13.

FA Trophy Second Qualifying Round 2014-15.

FA Vase Fifth Round Proper 2008-09.

Ground Capacity: 2,500 **Seats:** 150 **Covered:** 500 **Clubhouse:** Yes **Shop:** Yes

Previous Grounds: Bayfields Meadow. Recreation Ground >1996.

Record Attendance: 3000 v Norwich City, Friendly, 07/2001.

DIRECTIONS

Take the A47 towards Swaffham & Dereham. Do not take first slip road into Dereham. Carry on along the by-pass and take the second slip road, onto the B1110, sign posted B1147 to Bawdeswell, Swanton Morley and the Dereham Windmill. Follow the slip road round and Aldiss Park is 500 yards on your right.

Bus Route Paget Adams Drive - stop 300m away

FELIXSTOWE & WALTON UNITED

Founded 2000

Nickname: Seasiders **Club Colours:** Red & white

Club Contact Details 01394 282 627 secretary@felixstowefootball.co.uk

Dellwood Avenue, Felixstowe IP11 9HT

Previous Names: Felixstowe Port & Town and Walton United merged in July 2000.

Previous Leagues: Eastern Counties 2000-18.

09-10		10-11		11-12		12-13		13-14		14-15		15-16		16-17		17-18		18-19	
ECP	7	ECP	18	ECP	18	ECP	14	ECP	3	ECP	5	ECP	4	ECP	2	ECP	2	IsthN	11
FAC	EP	FAC	2Qr	FAC	P	FAC	Pr	FAC	P	FAC	1Q	FAC	EPr	FAC	3Q	FAC	EP	FAC	P
FAV	1Pr	FAV	1P	FAV	2P	FAV	2Q	FAV	1Q	FAV	1P	FAV	1Q	FAV	2P	FAV	1P	FAT	EP

HONOURS / RECORDS

FA Comps: None

League: None

County FA: None

Best FA Cup Third Qualifying Round 2016-17.

FA Vase Second Round Proper 2011-12, 16-17.

FA Trophy Extra Preliminary Round 2018-19.

Ground Capacity: 2,000 **Seats:** 200 **Covered:** 200 **Clubhouse:** Yes **Shop:** Yes

Previous Grounds: None

Record Attendance: 1,541 v Coggeshall Town, Eastern Counties Premier Division, 01/05/2018

DIRECTIONS

The A12 meets the A14 (Felixstowe to M1/M6 trunk road) at Copdock interchange, just to the South of Ipswich. For Felixstowe take the A14 heading east over the Orwell Bridge. Follow the A14, for approx. 14 miles until you come to a large roundabout with a large water tower on your right, take the 1st exit off the roundabout, which is straight on. Take the first exit at the next roundabout, straight ahead again. At the next roundabout take the fourth exit onto Beatrice Avenue, take the first left into Dellwood Avenue. The ground is 100 yards down on the left behind tall wooden fencing.

Nearest Railway Station Felixstowe - 0.3km

GRAYS ATHLETIC

Founded 1890

Nickname: The Blues **Club Colours:** All royal blue

Club Contact Details 07913 566 706 graysathleticfc@hotmail.co.uk

Aveley FC, Parkside, Park Lane, Aveley RM15 4PX

Previous Names: Grays Juniors 1890.

Previous Leagues: Grays & District. South Essex. Athenian 1912-14, 58-83. London 1914-24, 26-39,.Kent 1924-26. Corinthian 1945-58. Isthmian 1983-2004. Conference 2004-10

09-10		10-11		11-12		12-13		13-14		14-15		15-16		16-17		17-18		18-19	
Conf	23	Isth1N	10	Isth1N	5	Isth1N	1	Isth P	14	Isth P	6	Isth P	15	Isth P	24	Isth1N	16	IsthN	7
FAC	4Q	FAC	2Qr	FAC	1Q	FAC	2Q	FAC	3Q	FAC	3Qr	FAC	4Qr	FAC	1Q	FAC	1Qr	FAC	P
FAT	1P	FAT	3Qr	FAT	2Q	FAT	2Qr	FAT	3Q	FAT	2Q	FAT	3Qr	FAT	1Qr	FAT	1Qr	FAT	P

HONOURS / RECORDS

FA Comps: FA Trophy 2004-05, 05-06.

League: South Essex Division Two B 1908-09. Corinthian 1945-46. London Prmier (Amateur) 1914-15, Premier 1921-22, 26-27, 29-30. Isthmian Division Two South 1984-85, Division One North 2012-13. Conference South 2004-05.

County FA: Essex Senior Cup 1914-15, 20-21, 22-23, 44-45, 56-57, 87-88, 93-94, 94-95. East Anglian Cup 1944-45.

Victory: 12-0 v Tooting & Mitcham United - London League 24/02/1923

Defeat: 0-12 v Enfield (A) - Athenian League 20/04/1963

Goalscorer: Harry Brand - 269 (1944-52)

Appearances: Phil Sammons - 673 (1982-97)

Additional: Paid £12,000 to Welling United for Danny Kedwell. Received £150,000 from Peterborough United for Aaron McLean.

Ground Capacity: 3,500 **Seats:** 424 **Covered:** Yes **Clubhouse:** Yes **Shop:** No

Previous Grounds: Recreation Ground Bridge Road. Rookery Hill (East Thurrock Utd). Rush Green Road. Mill Field (Aveley FC).

Record Attendance: 9,500 v Chelmsford City - FA Cup 4th Qualifying Round 1959

DIRECTIONS

Clockwise on M25: At junction 30/31, Use the 2nd from the left lane to take the A13 exit to Dagenham/Tilbury/Thurrock (Lakeside). Take Ship Lane to Park Lane in Aveley. At Mar Dyke Interchange, take the 2nd exit. At the roundabout, exit onto Ship Lane. At the roundabout, take the 2nd exit onto High Street. Continue onto Stifford Rd. At the roundabout, take the 1st exit onto Aveley Bypass/B1335. At the roundabout, take the 3rd exit. Merge onto Park Lane. Parkside will be on the right.

Nearest Railway Station Purfleet

Bus Route 372 (Hornchurch to Lakeside) passes the ground.

GREAT WAKERING ROVERS

Founded 1919

Nickname: Rovers **Club Colours:** Green & white

Club Contact Details 01702 217 812

Burroughs Park, Little Wakering Hall Lane, Great Wakering SS3 0HH

Previous Names: None

Previous Leagues: Southend & District 1919-81, Southend Alliance 1981-89, Essex Intermediate 1989-92, Essex Senior 1992-99, 2012-14, Isthmian 1999-2004, 14-17, Southern 2004-05.

09-10		10-11		11-12		12-13		13-14		14-15		15-16		16-17		17-18		18-19	
Isth1N	9	Isth1N	15	Isth1N	22	ESen	4	ESen	1	Isth1N	15	Isth1N	18	Isth1N	24	ESen	1	IsthN	15
FAC	Pr	FAC	1Q	FAC	Pr	FAC	P	FAC	P	FAC	P	FAC	P	FAC	P	FAC	EP	FAC	2Q
FAT	P	FAT	1Q	FAT	P	FAV	1P	FAV	3P	FAT	P	FAT	P	FAT	P	FAV	3P	FAT	P

HONOURS / RECORDS

FA Comps: None

League: Essex Intermediate Division Three 1990-91, Division Two 91-92. Essex Senior 1994-95, 2013-14, 17-18.

County FA: None

Victory: 9-0 v Eton Manor - 27/12/1931

Defeat: 1-7 v Bowers United - Essex Senior League 01/04/1998

Appearances: John Heffer - 511

Best FA Cup Second Qualifying Round 1998-99, 2006-07, 18-19.

FA Trophy First Round Proper 2002-03, 04-05. **FA Vase:** Fifth Round 1997-98, 2001-02.

Ground Capacity: 3,000 **Seats:** 250 **Covered:** Yes **Clubhouse:** Yes **Shop:**

Previous Grounds: Great Wakering Rec

Record Attendance: 1,150 v Southend United - Friendly 19/07/2006

DIRECTIONS

A127 towards Southend and follow signs for Shoeburyness for about four miles.
Turn left to Great Wakering on B1017 at Bournes Green.
Go down High Street for half a mile and ground is on the left.

Nearest Railway Station Shoeburyness - 3.2km

Bus Route Barrow Hall Rd (Little Wakering Rd) - 631m

HEYBRIDGE SWIFTS

Founded 1880

Nickname: Swifts **Club Colours:** Black & white

Club Contact Details 01621 852 978 secretaryhsfc@btinternet.com
Scraley Road, Heybridge, Maldon, Essex CM9 8JA

Previous Names: Heybridge FC.
Previous Leagues: Essex & Suffolk Border, North Essex, South Essex, Essex Senior 1971-84

09-10		10-11		11-12		12-13		13-14		14-15		15-16		16-17		17-18		18-19	
Isth1N	6	Isth1N	9	Isth1N	16	Isth1N	6	Isth1N	3	Isth1N	12	Isth1N	20	Isth1N	21	Isth1N	5	IsthN	5
FAC	3Qr	FAC	Pr	FAC	1Q	FAC	2Q	FAC	4Q	FAC	P	FAC	1Q	FAC	1Qr	FAC	1P	FAC	2Q
FAT	P	FAT	Pr	FAT	P	FAT	P	FAT	1Q	FAT	1Q	FAT	2Qr	FAT	1Q	FAT	2P	FAT	EP

HONOURS / RECORDS
FA Comps: None
League: Essex & Suffolk Border Division Two (West) 1920-21, Division One 30-31. Essex Senior 1981-82, 82-83, 83-84. Isthmian Division Two North 1989-90.
County FA: Essex Junior Cup 1931-32. East Anglian Cup 1993-94, 94-95.

Goalscorer: Arthur 'Stumpy' Moss - 193 (1948-60)
Appearances: John Pollard - 543
Additional: Paid £1,000 for Dave Rainford and for Lee Kersey
Received £35,000 from Southend United for Simon Royce

Ground Capacity: 3,000 **Seats:** 550 **Covered:** 1,200 **Clubhouse:** Yes **Shop:** Yes
Previous Grounds: Bentall's Sports Ground 1890-1964. Sadd's Athletic ground share 1964-66.
Record Attendance: 2,477 v Woking - FA Trophy Quarter-finals 1997.

DIRECTIONS
Leave Maldon on the main road to Colchester,
pass through Heybridge then turn right at sign to Tolleshunt Major (Scraley Road).
The ground is on the right.

Bus Route Scylla Close - stop 1km away

HISTON

Founded 1904

Nickname: The Stutes **Club Colours:** Red and black

Club Contact Details 01223 237 373 (Ground)
Bridge Road, Impington, Cambridge CB24 9PH

Previous Names: Histon Institute 1904-51.
Previous Leagues: Cambridgeshire 1904-48. Spartan 1948-60. Delphian 1960-63. Athenian 1963-65. Eastern Counties 1965-2000, 17-19. Southern 2000-05, 14-17. Conference 2005-14.

09-10		10-11		11-12		12-13		13-14		14-15		15-16		16-17		17-18		18-19	
Conf	18	Conf	24	Conf N	16	Conf N	19	Conf N	21	SthP	18	SthP	22	SthC	21	ECP	6	ECP	1
FAC	4Q	FAC	4Q	FAC	2Qr	FAC	3Qr	FAC	3Q	FAC	2Qr	FAC	1Q	FAC	2Q	FAC	EP	FAC	1Qr
FAT	1P	FAT	1P	FAT	3Q	FAT	3Q	FAT	3Q	FAT	2Q	FAT	1Qr	FAT	Pr	FAV	2Q	FAV	2P

HONOURS / RECORDS
FA Comps: None
League: Spartan Division One Eastern 1950-51. Eastern Counties 1999-2000, 18-19. Southern League Premier 2004-05. Conference South 2006-07.
County FA: Cambridgeshire Professional Cup 2012-13, 15-16.

Victory: 11-0 v March Town - Cambridgeshire Invitation Cup 15/02/01
Defeat: 1-8 v Ely City - Eastern Counties Division One 1994
Goalscorer: Neil Kennedy - 292
Appearances: Neil Andrews and Neil Kennedy
Additional: Paid £6,000 to Chelmsford City for Ian Cambridge 2000. Received £30,000 from Man Utd for Guiliano Maiorana.

Ground Capacity: 3,250 **Seats:** 450 **Covered:** 1,800 **Clubhouse:** Yes **Shop:** Yes
Previous Grounds: None
Record Attendance: 6,400 v King's Lynn - FA Cup 1956

DIRECTIONS
From the M11 (Northbound) Junc 14, take the A14 eastbound signed towards Newmarket. Take the first exit off the A14 and at the roundabout, take the first exit onto the B1049. Go straight over the traffic lights, past the Holiday Inn Hotel (on your right) and the entrance to the club is half a mile on your right.

Nearest Railway Station Cambridge - the following buses run every 20 minutes,
Bus Route Citi 8 and Guided Busway routes A, B and C

HULLBRIDGE SPORTS

Founded 1945

Nickname: The Bridge or Sports **Club Colours:** Blue & white

Club Contact Details 01702 230 420
Lower Road, Hullbridge, Hockley Essex SS5 6BJ

Previous Names: None
Previous Leagues: Southend & District. Southend Alliance.

09-10		10-11		11-12		12-13		13-14		14-15		15-16		16-17		17-18		18-19	
ESen	11	ESen	9	ESen	11	ESen	15	ESen	9	ESen	4	ESen	11	ESen	11	ESen	15	ESen	1
FAC	EPr	FAC	EP	FAC	EP	FAC	EP	FAC	P	FAC	EP	FAC	2Q	FAC	P	FAC	Pr	FAC	P
FAV	1Q	FAV	2P	FAV	1P	FAV	1P	FAV	4P	FAV	4P	FAV	4P	FAV	2P	FAV	4P	FAV	2P

HONOURS / RECORDS
FA Comps: None
League: Southend & District Division Two 1951-52, Division Three 1956-57, Division One 1965-66. Essex Senior 2018-19.

County FA: None

Best FA Cup Second Qualifying Round 2015-16.
FA Vase Fourth Round Proper 2014-14, 14-15, 15-16, 17-18.

Ground Capacity: 1,500 **Seats:** 60 **Covered:** 60 **Clubhouse:** Yes **Shop:** No
Previous Grounds: Originally played on land on the junction of Pooles Lane and Long Lane until 1980.
Record Attendance: 800 v Blackburn Rovers, FA Youth Cup 1999-00.

DIRECTIONS
Leave the A127 and head towards Rayleigh on the A129. Turn left at the first mini roundabout and go down Crown Hill towards Rayleigh Station. Go past Rayleigh Station which will be on your left and the road bends round to the left and you will go under the railway bridge. Take the first turning the other side of the railway bridge which will be Down Hall Road. Continue to the end of Down Hall Road and turn left at the end into Hullbridge Rd. Follow Hullbridge Rd until it comes to an end and there will be a sharp right hand bend which goes in to Lower Rd. Continue along Lower Rd, straight over the mini r'about and up the hill. You will see Hilltop Avenue on your left hand side and the turning in to the football ground will be just after this on the right.
Nearest Railway Station Rayleigh, approx. 3 miles
Bus Route 20, bottom of the hill

MALDON & TIPTREE

Founded 1946

Nickname: The Jammers **Club Colours:** Blue & red

Club Contact Details 01621 853 762
Park Drive, Maldon CM9 5JQ

Previous Names: Maldon Town were rebranded in 2010.
Previous Leagues: Chelmsford & Mid-Essex. North Essex. Essex & Suffolk Border. Eastern Counties 1966-72. Essex Senior 1972-2004. Southern 2004-05.

09-10		10-11		11-12		12-13		13-14		14-15		15-16		16-17		17-18		18-19	
Isth1N	17	Isth1N	8	Isth1N	11	Isth1N	2	Isth1N	9	Isth1N	19	Isth1N	7	Isth1N	2	Isth1N	7	IsthN	3
FAC	1Q	FAC	2Q	FAC	3Q	FAC	2Qr	FAC	1Q	FAC	P	FAC	P	FAC	1Q	FAC	1Qr	FAC	P
FAT	P	FAT	P	FAT	3Q	FAT	P	FAT	1Q	FAT	P	FAT	P	FAT	1Q	FAT	2Q	FAT	1Q

HONOURS / RECORDS
FA Comps: None
League: Mid-Essex Premier Division 1949-50, 50-51. Essex & Suffolk Border Premier Division 1965-66. Essex Senior 1984-85.

County FA: Essex Intermediate Cup 1951-52.

Best FA Cup Third Qualifying Round 2000-01, 11-12.
FA Trophy Third Qualifying Round 2011-12.
FA Vase Semi Finals 2002-03.

Ground Capacity: 2,800 **Seats:** 155 **Covered:** 300 **Clubhouse:** Yes **Shop:**
Previous Grounds: Sadd's Ground 1946-47. Promenade 1947-50. Farmbridge Road 1950-1994.
Record Attendance: 1,163 v AFC Sudbury, FA Vase semi-final 2003.

DIRECTIONS
From M25 junction 28 travel north on A12 until A414 to Maldon.
Turn right at Safeways roundabout, then over next two roundabouts.
Ground is on the right.

Bus Route Jersey Road - stop 50m away

ROMFORD

Founded 1876

Nickname: Boro **Club Colours:** Yellow & blue

Club Contact Details 07973 717 074

Brentwood Town FC, The Arena, Brentwood Centre, Doddinghurst Road, Brentwood CM15 9NN

Previous Names: Original club founded in 1876 folded during WW1, Reformed in 1929 folded again in 1978 and reformed in 1992

Previous Leagues: Essex Senior 1992-96, 2002-09. Isthmian 1997-2002.

09-10		10-11		11-12		12-13		13-14		14-15		15-16		16-17		17-18		18-19	
Isth1N	13	Isth1N	12	Isth1N	13	Isth1N	8	Isth1N	11	Isth1N	20	Isth1N	16	Isth1N	16	Isth1N	23	IsthN	19
FAC	1Qr	FAC	2Q	FAC	1Q	FAC	P	FAC	1Q	FAC	2Qr	FAC	Pr	FAC	1Q	FAC	1Q	FAC	1Q
FAT	P	FAT	3Q	FAT	P	FAT	1Q	FAT	P	FAT	Pr	FAT	1Q	FAT	2Q	FAT	P	FAT	EP

HONOURS / RECORDS

FA Comps: None

League: Essex Senior 1995-96, 2008-09. Isthmian Division Two 1996-97.

County FA: East Anglian Cup 1997-98.

Goalscorer: Danny Benstock. Vinny John scored 45 goals during season 1997-98.

Appearances: Paul Clayton - 396 (2006-15)

Victory: 9-0 v Hullbridge Sports, Essex Senior, 21/10/1995.

Misc: Mark Lord became the oldest player to play for the club aged 48yrs 90 days on 03/03/2015.

Ground Capacity: 3,500 **Seats:** 160 **Covered:** 1,000 **Clubhouse:** Yes **Shop:** Yes

Previous Grounds: Hornchurch Stadium 1992-95. Rush Green 1995-96. Sungate 1996-2001. The Mill Field (Aveley FC). Thurrock FC. E.Thurrock

Record Attendance: 820 v Leatherhead - Isthmian Division Two

DIRECTIONS

From High Street (Wilson's Corner) turn north into Ongar Road.
Then at third mini roundabout turn right into Doddinghurst Road.

Nearest Railway Station Shenfield - 2.1km

Bus Route Leisure Centre - stop 150m away

SOHAM TOWN RANGERS

Founded 1947

Nickname: Greens, Town or Rangers **Club Colours:** Green & white stripes

Club Contact Details 01353 720 732

Julius Martin Lane, Soham, Ely, Cambridgeshire CB7 5EQ

Previous Names: Soham Town and Soham Rangers merged in 1947

Previous Leagues: Peterborough & District, Eastern Counties 1963-2008, Southern 2008-11.

09-10		10-11		11-12		12-13		13-14		14-15		15-16		16-17		17-18		18-19	
SthC	11	SthC	17	Isth1N	19	Isth1N	7	Isth1N	8	Isth1N	11	Isth1N	17	Isth1N	19	Isth1N	13	IsthN	16
FAC	Pr	FAC	P	FAC	P	FAC	1Q	FAC	P	FAC	P	FAC	P	FAC	1Qr	FAC	1Qr	FAC	1Q
FAT	1Qr	FAT	1Q	FAT	P	FAT	2Q	FAT	2Q	FAT	P	FAT	P	FAT	1Q	FAT	P	FAT	Pr

HONOURS / RECORDS

FA Comps: None

League: Peterborough & District 1959-60, 61-62. Eastern Counties Premier Division 2007-08.

County FA: Cambridgeshire Challenge Cup 1957-58. Cambridgeshire Invitation Cup 1990-91, 97-98, 98-99, 2005-06.

Best FA Cup Third Qualifying Round 1970-71

FA Trophy Second Qualifying Round 2012-13, 13-14

FA Vase Fifth Round 2004-05

Ground Capacity: 2,000 **Seats:** 250 **Covered:** 1,000 **Clubhouse:** Yes **Shop:** Yes

Previous Grounds: None

Record Attendance: 3,000 v Pegasus - FA Amateur Cup 1963

DIRECTIONS

Take the turning off the A14 for Soham/Ely. Join the A142 following signs for Ely/Soham. On approaching Soham at the Q8 Petrol Station, continue down the Soham by-pass for approx. 1.5 miles. Turn left after the Bypass Motel, continue bearing left across the Common into Bushel Lane, at end of road, turn right into Hall Street. Julius Martin Lane is 2nd left.

Bus Route Julius Martin Lane - stop 200m away

TILBURY

Founded 1895

Nickname: The Dockers **Club Colours:** Black & white

Club Contact Details 01375 843 093

Chadfields, St Chads Road, Tilbury, Essex RM18 8NL

Previous Names: None

Previous Leagues: Grays & District/South Essex, Kent 1927-31, London 1931-39, 46-50, 57-62, South Essex Combination (Wartime), Corinthian 1950-57, Delphian 1962-63, Athenian 1963-73, Isthmian 1973-2004, Essex Senior 2004-05

09-10		10-11		11-12		12-13		13-14		14-15		15-16		16-17		17-18		18-19	
Isth1N	11	Isth1N	19	Isth1N	3	Isth1N	16	Isth1N	16	Isth1N	14	Isth1N	11	Isth1N	12	Isth1N	17	IsthN	10
FAC	P	FAC	1Q	FAC	1Q	FAC	1Q	FAC	2Q	FAC	1Q	FAC	1Q	FAC	1Q	FAC	1Q	FAC	P
FAT	P	FAT	P	FAT	P	FAT	P	FAT	1Q	FAT	Pr	FAT	1P	FAT	Pr	FAT	P	FAT	P

HONOURS / RECORDS

FA Comps: None

League: London 1958-59, 59-60, 60-61, 61-62. Athenian Division One 1968-69. Isthmian Division Two 1975-76.

County FA: Essex Senior Cup x4. East Anglian Cup 2008-09.

Goalscorer: Ross Livermore - 282 in 305 games

Appearances: Nicky Smith - 424 (1975-85)

Additional: Received £2,000 from Grays Athletic for Tony Macklin 1990 and from Dartford for Steve Connor 1985

Best FA Cup Third Round Proper 1977-78 **FA Amateur Cup:** Quarter Finals 1946-47

FA Trophy Third Round Proper 1982-83 **FA Vase:** Fourth Round Proper 1988-89, 99-00

Ground Capacity: 4,000 **Seats:** 350 **Covered:** 1,000 **Clubhouse:** Yes **Shop:**

Previous Grounds: Orient Field 1895-46.

Record Attendance: 5,500 v Gorleston - FA Cup 1949

DIRECTIONS

A13 Southend bound go left at Chadwell St Mary's turning, then right after 400 metres and right again at roundabout (signed Tilbury). Right into St Chads Road after five miles, first right into Chadfields for ground.

Nearest Railway Station Tilbury Town - 1.1km

Bus Route Raphael Avenue - stop 75m away

WITHAM TOWN

Founded 1947

Nickname: Town **Club Colours:** White & blue

Club Contact Details 01376 511 198 withamtownfc@gmail.com

Spa Road, Witham CM8 1UN

Previous Names: Witham Town Football Clubs did exist before both World Wars with both folding due to the conflicts.

Previous Leagues: Mid-Essex 1947-52. South Essex 1952-58. Essex & Suffolk Border 1958-71. Essex Senior 1971-87, 2009-12. Isthmian 1987-2009.

09-10		10-11		11-12		12-13		13-14		14-15		15-16		16-17		17-18		18-19	
ESen	2	ESen	3	ESen	1	Isth1N	4	Isth1N	2	Isth P	22	Isth1N	19	Isth1N	13	Isth1N	11	IsthN	18
FAC	P	FAC	Pr	FAC	P	FAC	1Q	FAC	2Qr	FAC	4Q	FAC	2Q	FAC	2Q	FAC	1Q	FAC	Pr
FAV	1P	FAV	3P	FAV	3P	FAT	P	FAT	1Q	FAT	2Q	FAT	P	FAT	1Q	FAT	1Q	FAT	1Q

HONOURS / RECORDS

FA Comps: None

League: Braintree & District 1920-21, 24-25. Mid-Essex Division Three 1935-36, 47-48, Division Two 48-49. South Essex 1955-56. Essex & Suffolk Border 1964-65, 70-71. Essex Senior 1970-71, 85-86, 2011-12.

County FA: Essex Senior Trophy 1985-86.

Goalscorer: Colin Mitchell.

Appearances: Keith Dent.

Ground Capacity: 2,500 **Seats:** 157 **Covered:** 780 **Clubhouse:** Yes **Shop:** No

Previous Grounds: Crittall Windows works ground 1949-75.

Record Attendance: 800 v Billericay Town, Essex Senior League, May 1976.

DIRECTIONS

From M25: At junction 28, take the A12/A1023 exit to Chelmsford/Romford/Brentwood.
At the roundabout, take the 1st exit onto the A12 ramp to Chelmsford/Harwich/A120.
Merge onto A12. At junction 21, exit onto Hatfield Rd/B1389 toward Witham.
Go through 2 roundabouts. Turn left onto Spinks Lane. Turn right onto Highfields Road.
Turn left ground will be on the right.

Nearest Railway Station Witham - 1.1km

Bus Route Cuppers Close - stop 200m away

ISTHMIAN SOUTH CENTRAL INS: Barking (Tr - IsthN), Chertsey Town (P - CCP), Harlow Town (R - IsthP), Staines Town (R - SthPS).

ASHFORD TOWN (MIDDLESEX)

Founded 1958

Nickname: Ash Trees **Club Colours:** Tangerine, white & black

Club Contact Details 01784 245 908

Robert Parker Stadium, Stanwell, Staines TW19 7BH

Previous Names: Ashford Albion 1958-64.

Previous Leagues: Hounslow & District 1964-68, Surrey Intermediate 1968-82, Surrey Premier 1982-90, Combind Counties 1990-2000, 14-16, Isthmian 20 00-04, 06-10, Southern 2004-06, 10-14, 16-18.

09-10		10-11		11-12		12-13		13-14		14-15		15-16		16-17		17-18		18-19	
Isth P	20	SthC	16	SthC	9	SthC	10	SthC	22	CCP	3	CCP	2	SthC	10	Sth1E	12	IsthSC	11
FAC	3Qr	FAC	1Qr	FAC	P	FAC	2Q	FAC	1Q	FAC	Pr	FAC	1Q	FAC	1Q	FAC	3Q	FAC	P
FAT	1Q	FAT	2P	FAT	2Q	FAT	1Qr	FAT	P	FAV	1P	FAV	1Pr	FAT	1Qr	FAT	2Qr	FAT	1Q

HONOURS / RECORDS

FA Comps: None

League: Surrey Intermediate (Western) Prmeier Division A 1974-75. Surrey Premier 1982-90. Combined Counties 1994-95, 95-96, 96-97, 97-98, 99-00.

County FA: Middlesex Senior Charity Cup 1999-00, 11-12, 16-17. Aldershot Senior Cup 2002-03, 11-12. Middlesex Premier Cup 2006-07. Surrey Senior Cup 2008-09.

Goalscorer: Andy Smith

Appearances: Alan Constable - 650

Additional: Received £10,000 from Wycombe Wanderers for Dannie Bulman 1997

Ground Capacity: 2,550 **Seats:** 250 **Covered:** 250 **Clubhouse:** Yes **Shop:** No

Previous Grounds: Clockhouse Lane Recreation 1958-85.

Record Attendance: 992 v AFC Wimbledon - Isthmian League Premier Division 26/09/2006

DIRECTIONS

M25 junction 13, A30 towards London, third left at footbridge after Ashford Hospital crossroads, ground sign posted after 1/4 mile on the right down Short Lane, two miles from Ashford (BR) and Hatton Cross tube station.

Nearest Railway Station Heathrow Terminal 4 Underground - 1.5km

Bus Route Genesis Close - stop 400m away

BARKING

Founded 1880

Nickname: The Blues **Club Colours:** All blue

Club Contact Details 0203 244 0069 secretary@barking-fc.co.uk

Mayesbrook Park, Lodge Avenue, Dagenham RM8 2JR

Previous Names: Barking Rov. Barking Woodville. Barking Working Lads Institute, Barking Institute. Barking T. Barking & East Ham United.

Previous Leagues: South Essex, London 1896-98, 1909-26. Athenian 1923-52. Isthmian. Southern. Essex Senior >2017.

09-10		10-11		11-12		12-13		13-14		14-15		15-16		16-17		17-18		18-19	
ESen	8	ESen	6	ESen	7	ESen	6	ESen	12	ESen	3	ESen	4	ESen	1	Isth1N	10	IsthN	12
FAC	EP	FAC	P	FAC	EPr	FAC	EPr	FAC	Pr	FAC	EP	FAC	Pr	FAC	Pr	FAC	2Q	FAC	P
FAV	2Qr	FAV	1P	FAV	1P	FAV	1P	FAV	2P	FAV	1Q	FAV	2P	FAV	1P	FAT	1Q	FAT	P

HONOURS / RECORDS

FA Comps: None

League: South Essex Division One 1898-99, 1911-12, Division Two 1900-01. Division Two 1901-02. London Division One A 1909-10, Premier 1920-21. Athenian 1934-35. Isthmian Premier 1978-79. Essex Senior 2016-17.

County FA: Essex Senior Cup 1893-94, 95-96, 1919-20, 45-46, 62-63, 69-70, 89-90. London Senior Cup 1911-12, 20-21, 26-27, 78-79.

Goalscorer: Neville Fox - 242 (1965-73).

Appearances: Bob Makin - 569.

Victory: 14-0 v Sheppey United, Mithras Cup, 02/12/1969

Best FA Cup Second Round Proper replay 1981-82. **FA Amateur Cup:** Finalists 1926-27.

FA Trophy Second Round Proper 1979-80. **FA Vase:** Fifth Round Proper 1996-97.

Ground Capacity: 2,500 **Seats:** 200 **Covered:** 600 **Clubhouse:** Yes **Shop:** Yes

Previous Grounds: Barking Park Recreation Ground. Vicarage Field 1884-1973.

Record Attendance: 1,972 v Aldershot, FA Cup Second Round Proper, 1978.

DIRECTIONS

Take the exit road from the A13 at Becontree Heath onto the A1153 Lodge Avenue turn off. We are approximately one mile down on the left. The 368 bus stops outside or opposite the ground - alternatively, buses 145,364 and number 5 are a short walk from the LIDL supermarket or from the A13 end get the 62 to the bottom of the hill and walk up Lodge Avenue. To reach us by train go to Upney station, turn left and at the bottom of the hill cross the road into the 'The Drive'. Go to the end of The Drive and enter Mayesbrook Park. Go to the left and the ground is about five minutes' walk and past the Sporthouse.

Nearest Railway Station Upney (District Line), 2 miles

Bus Route 368 (50 yards) 5, 145, 364 (400 yards)

OUTS: Cheshunt (P - IsthP), Egham Town (R - CCP), Hayes & Yeading United (P - SthPS), Molesey (R - CCP).

BEDFONT SPORTS

Founded 2000

Nickname: The Eagles **Club Colours:** Red & black

Club Contact Details 0208 831 9067 or 07967 370 109
Bedfont Sports Club, Hatton Road, Bedfont TW14 9QT

Previous Names: Bedfont Sunday became Bedfont Sports in 2002 - Bedfont Eagles (1978) merged with the club shortly afterwards.
Previous Leagues: Hounslow & District 2003-04. Middlesex County 2004-09.

09-10		10-11		11-12		12-13		13-14		14-15		15-16		16-17		17-18		18-19	
CC1	9	CC1	4	CC1	2	CCP	13	CCP	17	CCP	16	CCP	13	CCP	8	CCP	2	IsthSC	12
				FAC	Pr	FAC	EP	FAC	P	FAC	EP	FAC	P	FAC	P	FAC	EP	FAC	P
		FAV	1Q	FAV	1P	FAV	2Q	FAV	2Q	FAV	1P	FAV	1P	FAV	3Pr	FAV	1Q	FAT	P

HONOURS / RECORDS
FA Comps: None
League: Hounslow & District League Division One 2003-04.

County FA: Middlesex County Premier Cup 2009-10.

Best FA Cup Preliminary Round 2011-12(r), 13-14, 15-16, 16-17, 18-19
FA Vase Third Round Proper Replay 2016-17
FA Trophy Preliminary Round 2018-19

Ground Capacity: 3,000 **Seats:** Yes **Covered:** 200 **Clubhouse:** Yes **Shop:**
Previous Grounds: N/A
Record Attendance:

DIRECTIONS
From Junction 13, M25 – Staines.
At Crooked Billet roundabout turn right onto the A30 Signposted C. London, Hounslow.
At Clockhouse Roundabout take the 2nd exit onto the A315 Signposted Bedfont.
Turn left onto Hatton Road.
Arrive on Hatton Road, Bedfont Sports Club.

Nearest Railway Station Hatton Cross or Feltham BR
Bus Route London Transport 203, H25, H26

BRACKNELL TOWN

Founded 1896

Nickname: The Robins **Club Colours:** Red & white

Club Contact Details 01344 412 305
Larges Lane, Bracknell RG12 9AN

Previous Names: Old Bracknell Wanderers 1896-1962.
Previous Leagues: Ascot & District. Reading & District 1949-58. Great Western Comb. 1958-63, Surrey Senior 1963-70, Spartan 1970-75, London Spartan 1975-84, Isthmian 1984-2004, Southern 2004-10, Hellenic 2010-18.

09-10		10-11		11-12		12-13		13-14		14-15		15-16		16-17		17-18		18-19	
Sthsw	22	Hel P	16	Hel P	21	Hel1E	5	Hel P	13	Hel P	9	Hel P	14	Hel P	2	Hel P	2	IsthSC	2
FAC	P	FAC	P	FAC	EP	FAC	1Q	FAC	P	FAC	EP	FAC	1Q	FAC	P	FAC	P		
FAT	1Q	FAV	2P	FAV	2Q	FAV	2Q	FAV	2Q	FAV	2Q	FAV	2Qr	FAV	1P	FAV	QF	FAT	1Qr

HONOURS / RECORDS
FA Comps: None
League: Ascot & District 1911-12, 32-33, Division Two 13-14. Surrey Senior 1969-70.
Spartan Senior Division 1980-81, Premier 1982-83. Isthmian Division Three 1993-94.
County FA: Berks & Bucks Senior Trophy 2016-17

Goalscorer: Justin Day
Goalscorer: James Woodcock
Best FA Cup First Round Proper 2000-01
FA Trophy First Round Proper 2002-03, 03-04, 04-05
FA Vase Quarter Finals 2017-18

Ground Capacity: 2,500 **Seats:** 150 **Covered:** 500 **Clubhouse:** Yes **Shop:** Yes
Previous Grounds: Field next to Downshire Arms. Station Field > 1933
Record Attendance: 2,500 v Newquay - FA Amateur Cup 1971

DIRECTIONS
Leave M4 at J10, take A329M signposted Wokingham & Bracknell. Follow road for 5 miles, over roundabout, pass Southern industrial estate (Waitrose etc.) on right to a 2nd roundabout with traffic lights; take 2nd exit and follow signposts for M3. At next roundabout take 1st exit. At next roundabout take 3rd exit, Church Road dual carriageway. This brings you to another roundabout with Bracknell & Wokingham college on right and Old Manor PH on left, take 5th exit for Ascot - A329. Go down hill on dual carriageway, London Road to next roundabout take 4th exit back up the dual carriageway, London Road, Larges Lane last left turn before reaching roundabout again. Ground 200 yards on right.

Nearest Railway Station Bracknell - 0.5km
Bus Route Larges Bridge Drive stop - 282m away

CHALFONT ST PETER

Founded 1926

Nickname: Saints **Club Colours:** Red & green

Club Contact Details 01753 886 477

Mill Meadow, Gravel Hill, Amersham Road, Chalfont St Peter SL9 9QX

Previous Names: None

Previous Leagues: G W Comb 1948-58. Parthernon 1958-60. London 1960-62. Spartan 1962-75. London Spartan 1975-76. Athenian 1976-84. Isthmian 1984-2006. Spartan South Midlands 2006-11. Southern 2011-19.

09-10		10-11		11-12		12-13		13-14		14-15		15-16		16-17		17-18		18-19	
SSM P	2	SSM P	1	SthC	12	SthC	16	SthC	14	SthC	16	SthC	6	SthC	18	Sth1E	9	IsthSC	14
FAC	P	FAC	P	FAC	1Q	FAC	3Qr	FAC	2Q	FAC	3Q	FAC	P	FAC	1Q	FAC	Pr	FAC	1Qr
FAV	2P	FAV	2Pr	FAT	1Q	FAT	1Q	FAT	Pr	FAT	1Q	FAT	1Q	FAV	2Qr	FAT	1Qr	FAT	P

HONOURS / RECORDS

FA Comps: None

League: Spartan Division Two 1975-76. Isthmian Division Two 1987-88. Spartan South Midlands Premier Division 2010-11.

County FA: Berks & Bucks Intermediate Cup 1952-53, 84-85.

Victory: 10-1 v Kentish Town (away) Spartan League Premier Division 23 Dec 2008

Defeat: 0-13 v Lewes (away) Isthmian Division 3, 7 Nov 2000

Appearances: Colin Davies

Ground Capacity: 4,500 **Seats:** 220 **Covered:** 120 **Clubhouse:** Yes **Shop:** Yes

Previous Grounds: Gold Hill Common 1926-49.

Record Attendance: 2,550 v Watford benefit match 1985

DIRECTIONS

Follow A413 (Amersham Road).
The ground is adjacent to the Chalfont Community Centre off Gravel Hill which is part of the A413.
Players and officials can park inside the ground.
The A413 is the Denham to Aylesbury road.

Nearest Railway Station Gerrards Cross - 2.3km

Bus Route The Waggon & Horses Pub - stop 250m away

CHERTSEY TOWN

Founded 1890

Nickname: Curfews **Club Colours:** Royal blue & white stripes

Club Contact Details 01932 561 774

Alwyns Lane, Chertsey, Surrey KT16 9DW

Previous Names: Chertsey 1890-1950.

Previous Leagues: West Surrey. Surrey Inter 1919-39. Surrey Senior 46-63. Metropolitan 63-66. Greater London 66-67. Spartan 67-75. London Spartan 75-76. Athenian 76-84. Isthmian 84-85, 86-2006. Combined Counties 85-86, 2006-11, 14-19. Southern 2011-14.

09-10		10-11		11-12		12-13		13-14		14-15		15-16		16-17		17-18		18-19	
CCP	2	CCP	2	SthC	17	SthC	20	SthC	21	CCP	20	CCP	18	CCP	19	CCP	15	CCP	1
FAC	P	FAC	2Q	FAC	2Q	FAC	P	FAC	2Q	FAC	EPr	FAC	P	FAC	1Q	FAC	P	FAC	EP
FAV	5Pr	FAV	2P	FAT	3Q	FAT	1Q	FAT	1Q	FAV	1P	FAV	2Q	FAV	1Q	FAV	1Q	FAV	2P

HONOURS / RECORDS

FA Comps: FA Vase 2018-19

League: Surrey Senior 1958-59, 60-61, 61-62. Combined Counties Premier 2018-19

County FA: Surrey Junior Cup 1896-97.

Goalscorer: Alan Brown (54) 1962-63.

FA Cup Third Qualifying Round 1994-95

FA Trophy Third Qualifying Round 2011-12

Ground Capacity: 2,500 **Seats:** 240 **Covered:** 760 **Clubhouse:** Yes **Shop:** Yes

Previous Grounds: Pre 1929 - Willow Walk, Free Prae Road, Staines Lane and Chilsey Green.

Record Attendance: 2150 v Aldershot Town, Isthmian Div.2 04/12/93.

DIRECTIONS

Leave M25 at junction 11, East on St. Peters Way (A317). Left at roundabout in Chertsey Road (A317). Left into Eastworth Road (A317). Straight on into Chilsey Green Road (A320), 3rd exit on roundabout (towards Staines) (A320). 1st right after car showrooms into St. Ann's Road (B375). Right at Coach & Horses in Grove Road (residential). Alwyns Lane is very narrow and not suitable for large motor coaches.

Nearest Railway Station Chertsey

Bus Route Abellio 446, 451, 461, 557

CHIPSTEAD

Founded 1906

Nickname: Chips **Club Colours:** Green, white & black

Club Contact Details 01737 553 250
High Road, Chipstead, Surrey CR5 3SF

Previous Names: None
Previous Leagues: Surrey Intermediate 1962-82, Surrey Premier 1982-86, Combined Counties 1986-2007

09-10		10-11		11-12		12-13		13-14		14-15		15-16		16-17		17-18		18-19	
Isth1S	19	Isth1S	10	Isth1S	12	Isth1S	20	Isth1S	13	Isth1S	15	Isth1S	21	Isth1S	20	Isth1S	20	IsthSC	13
FAC	1Q	FAC	2Qr	FAC	2Q	FAC	1Q	FAC	3Q	FAC	1Qr	FAC	P	FAC	1Q	FAC	2Q	FAC	P
FAT	2Q	FAT	P	FAT	1Q	FAT	P	FAT	P	FAT	P	FAT	1Q	FAT	Pr	FAT	Pr	FAT	2Qr

HONOURS / RECORDS
FA Comps: None
League: Combined Counties Premier 1989-90, 2006-07.

County FA: East Surrey Charity Cup 1960-61.

Goalscorer: Mick Nolan - 124
Best FA Cup Fourth Qualifying Round 2008-09
FA Trophy Second Qualifying Round 2009-10, 18-19(r)
FA Vase Third Round Proper 1997-98, 98-99

Ground Capacity: 2,000 **Seats:** 150 **Covered:** 200 **Clubhouse:** Yes **Shop:** Yes
Previous Grounds: None
Record Attendance: 1,170

DIRECTIONS
From the Brighton Road north bound,
go left into Church Lane and left into Hogcross Lane.
High Road is on the right.

Nearest Railway Station Coulsdon South from where a Taxi can be taken to the ground. Chipstead a dangerous 1.25m walk away
Bus Route 405 to Star Lane, Hooley. Ground is a further 20min walk from there

FC ROMANIA

Founded 2006

Nickname: The Wolves **Club Colours:** Yellow & red

Club Contact Details 01992 625 793
Cheshunt FC, Theobalds Lane, Cheshunt, Herts EN8 8RU

Previous Names: None
Previous Leagues: Sunday London Weekend 2006-07. Essex Business Houses 2007-10. Middlesex County 2010-13. Essex Senior 2013-18.

09-10		10-11		11-12		12-13		13-14		14-15		15-16		16-17		17-18		18-19	
EsxBH2	4	Midx1SE	2	MidxP	2	MidxP	2	ESen	5	ESen	6	ESen	3	ESen	3	ESen	3	IsthSC	16
										FAC	2Q	FAC	EP	FAC	EP	FAC	2Qr	FAC	2Q
						FAV	2Q	FAV	1Q	FAV	2Q	FAV	4P	FAV	3Pr	FAV	2Pr	FAT	P

HONOURS / RECORDS
FA Comps: None
League: None

County FA: None

Best FA Cup Second Qualifying Round 2014-15, 17-18(r), 18-19
FA Vase Fourth Round Proper 2015-16
FA Trophy Preliminary Round 2018-19

Ground Capacity: 3,500 **Seats:** 424 **Covered:** 600 **Clubhouse:** Yes **Shop:**
Previous Grounds: Hackey Marshes 2006-07. Low Hall Rec Walthamstow 2007-10. Leyton Sport Centre 2010-12.
Record Attendance:

DIRECTIONS
Exit the M25 at junction 25 and head north on the A10. At the next roundabout turn right onto the A121, Winston Churchill Way. At next roundabout turn left into the High Street. Pass under the railway bridge and take the next left into Theobalds Lane. The ground is 200 yards down this road on the right hand side. (NOTE: On exit, you can continue down Theobalds Lane and turn left onto the dual carriageway (A10), then straight over the roundabout for the M25)

Nearest Railway Station Theobalds Grove – 5 mins walk

HANWELL TOWN

Founded 1920

Nickname: Magpies **Club Colours:** Black & white

Club Contact Details 020 8998 1701

Preivale Lane, Perivale, Greenford, UB6 8TL

Previous Names: None

Previous Leagues: London 1924-27. Dauntless. Wembley & District. Middlesex County 1970-83. London Spartan/Spartan 1983-97. Spartan South Midlands (FM) 1997-2006, 2007-14. Southern 2006-07, 14-18.

09-10	10-11	11-12	12-13	13-14	14-15	15-16	16-17	17-18	18-19
SSM P 13	SSM P 15	SSM P 21	SSM P 6	SSM P 1	SthC 7	SthC 20	SthC 11	Sth1E 18	IsthSC 8
FAC P	FAC EP	FAC EP	FAC EP	FAC EPr	FAC P	FAC 3Q	FAC 2Qr	FAC 1Q	FAC 3Qr
FAV 2Q	FAV 1Q	FAV 1P	FAV 1Pr	FAV 5P	FAT P	FAT P	FAT 2Q	FAT 1Q	FAT P

HONOURS / RECORDS

FA Comps: None

League: London Spartan Senior Division 1983-84. Spartan South Midlands Premier 2013-14.

County FA: London Senior Cup 1991-92, 92-93.

Goalscorer: Keith Rowlands

Appearances: Phil Player 617 (20 seasons)

Best FA Cup Third Qualifying Round 2015-16, 18-19(r)

FA Trophy Second Qualifying Round 2006-07, 16-17(r)

FA Vase Fifth Round Proper 2013-14

Ground Capacity: 1,250 **Seats:** 175 **Covered:** 600 **Clubhouse:** Yes **Shop:** No

Previous Grounds: Moved to Reynolds Field in 1981.

Record Attendance: 600 v Spurs, floodlight switch on, 1989.

DIRECTIONS

From West - Exit M25 at junction 16 and follow A40(M) towards London. Continue over Greenford Flyover and get into nearside lane, signposted Ealing & Perivale. Exit and turn right across the A40 and the ground is immediatley on the left.
From East - At Hanger Lane Giratory take the A40 exit towards Oxford. The first exit is signposted Perivale/Ealing. Take the slip road and then left at traffic lights . Take the first left again into Perivale Lane.

Nearest Railway Station Perivale Underground - 0.6km

Bus Route Perivale Lane - stop 200m away

HARLOW TOWN

Founded 1879

Nickname: Hawks **Club Colours:** Red & white

Club Contact Details 01279 443 196 harlowtownfc@aol.com

The Harlow Arena, off Elizabeth Way, The Pinnacles, Harlow CM19 5BE

Previous Names: Harlow & Burnt Mill 1898-1902.

Previous Leagues: East Hertfordshire > 1932, Spartan 1932-39, 46-54, London 1954-61, Delphian 1961-63, Athenian 1963-73, Isthmian 1973-92, 93-2004, Inactive 1992-93, Southern 2004-06

09-10	10-11	11-12	12-13	13-14	14-15	15-16	16-17	17-18	18-19
Isth1N 22	Isth1N 4	Isth1N 7	Isth1N 21	Isth1N 4	Isth1N 2	Isth1N 3	Isth P 10	Isth P 21	Isth P 22
FAC Pr	FAC 2Q	FAC P	FAC P	FAC 2Q	FAC 1Qr	FAC 4Q	FAC 2Q	FAC 3Qr	FAC 1Qr
FAT P	FAT 1P	FAT 3Q	FAT Pr	FAT P	FAT 1Q	FAT 2Q	FAT 2P	FAT 3Q	FAT 2Q

HONOURS / RECORDS

FA Comps: None

League: East Herts Division One 1911-12, 22-23, 28-29, 29-30. Athenian Division One 1971-72. Isthmian Division One 1978-79, Division Two North 1988-89.

County FA: Essex Senior cup 1978-79

Victory: 14-0 v Bishop's Stortford - 11/04/1925

Defeat: 0-11 v Ware (A) - Spartan Division 1 East 06/03/1948

Goalscorer: Dick Marshall scored 64 during 1928-29, Alex Read scored 52 during 2013-14.

Appearances: Norman Gladwin - 639 (1951-70)

Ground Capacity: 3,500 **Seats:** 500 **Covered:** 500 **Clubhouse:** Yes **Shop:** Yes

Previous Grounds: Green Man Field 1879-60. Harlow Sportcentre 1960-2006.

Record Attendance: 9,723 v Leicester City - FA Cup 3rd Round replay 08/01/1980

DIRECTIONS

Barrows Farm is situated on the western side of town just off of the Roydon Road (A1169) on the Pinnacles Industrial Estate.
If coming into Harlow from the M11 (North or South) exit at Junction 7 and follow the A414 until the first roundabout where you turn left onto the A1169. Follow the A1169 signed for Roydon until you see the ground ahead of you at the Roydon Road roundabout. Go straight over the roundabout and the entrance to the ground is on the left.
If coming into town from the west on the A414 turn right at the first roundabout (the old ground was straight ahead) signed Roydon A1169. Follow the A1169 for approx 1 mile and the entrance to the ground is on the right.

HERTFORD TOWN

Founded 1901

Nickname: The Blues **Club Colours:** All blue

Club Contact Details 01992 583 716
Hertingfordbury Park, West Street, Hertford SG13 8EZ

Previous Names: Port Vale Rovers 1901.
Previous Leagues: Herts Senior County 1908-20. Middlsex 1920-21. Spartan 1921-59. Delphian 1959-63. Athenian 1963-72. Eastern Counties 1972-73. Spartan South Midlands 1973-2017.

09-10		10-11		11-12		12-13		13-14		14-15		15-16		16-17		17-18		18-19	
SSM P	16	SSM P	9	SSM P	16	SSM P	17	SSM P	16	SSM P	11	SSM P	8	SSM P	2	Isth1N	15	IsthSC	18
FAC	EP	FAC	P	FAC	1Q	FAC	EP	FAC	1Q	FAC	1Q	FAC	EPr	FAC	P	FAC	2Q	FAC	1Q
FAV	2Q	FAV	1P	FAV	1Q	FAV	3P	FAV	1Q	FAV	1P	FAV	3P	FAV	1P	FAT	1Q	FAT	P

HONOURS / RECORDS
FA Comps: None
League: Spartan Division One Eastern Section 1949-50. Delphian 1960-61, 61-62.

County FA: Herts Senior Cup 1966-67. East Anglian Cup 1962-63, 69-70.

Appearances: Robbie Burns
Best FA Cup Fourth Qualifying Round 1973-74
FA Trophy Second Round Proper 1979-80
FA Vase Third Round Proper 1986-87, 2003-04, 12-13, 15-16

Ground Capacity: 6,500 **Seats:** 200 **Covered:** 1,500 **Clubhouse:** Yes **Shop:** Yes
Previous Grounds: Hartham Park 1901-08.
Record Attendance: 5,000 v Kingstonian FA Am Cup 2nd Round 1955-56.

DIRECTIONS
From the A1, follow the A414 from Hatfield to Hertford until you see the Gates Ford Dealership on the right. At the next roundabout take the 4th exit on your left (doubling back) and immediately past the Gates Ford dealership (now on your left), TURN LEFT into West Street, (Hertford Town FC signposted on the railings), continue along West Street until you pass the Scout hut on your right, just as the road begins to bear left there is a sign post bearing a brown tourist football sign, TURN RIGHT down the hill and over the bridge to the ground (situated at the bottom on the right). **From the A10,** from the roundabout at the top of the A10 slip road, continue on the dual carriageway (A414 signposted to Hatfield), over the next roundabout, (Mercedes dealership on your right) continue down the hill and TURN LEFT at the roundabout at the bottom (multi-storey car park on your right). You will pass All Saints Church on your left. Go straight across the next roundabout, and immediately past the Gates Ford dealership, then as above.

Nearest Railway Station Hertford North - 0.8km

MARLOW

Founded 1870

Nickname: The Blues **Club Colours:** All royal blue

Club Contact Details 01628 483 970
Alfred Davies Memorial Ground, Oak tree Road, Marlow SL7 3ED

Previous Names: Great Marlow
Previous Leagues: Reading & District, Spartan 1908-10, 28-65, Gt Western Suburban, Athenian 1965-84, Isthmian 1984-2004. Southern 2004-12, 13-18. Hellenic 2012-13.

09-10		10-11		11-12		12-13		13-14		14-15		15-16		16-17		17-18		18-19	
SthM	15	SthC	11	SthC	22	Hel P	1	SthC	17	SthC	11	Sthsw	13	SthC	4	Sth1E	14	IsthSC	4
FAC	1Q	FAC	P	FAC	1Q	FAC	1Q	FAC	P	FAC	P	FAC	Pr	FAC	Pr	FAC	2Q	FAC	2Q
FAT	2Q	FAT	Pr	FAT	1Qr	FAV	2P	FAT	3Q	FAT	P	FAT	3Q	FAT	1Q	FAT	Pr	FAT	P

HONOURS / RECORDS
FA Comps: None
League: Spartan 1937-38, Division Two West 1929-30. Isthmian Division One 1987-88. Hellenic Premier Division 2012-13.

County FA: Berks & Bucks Senior Cup x11

Goalscorer: Kevin Stone
Appearances: Mick McKeown - 500+
Additional: Paid £5,000 to Sutton United for Richard Evans
Received £8,000 from Slough Town for David Lay

Ground Capacity: 3,000 **Seats:** 250 **Covered:** 600 **Clubhouse:** Yes **Shop:** No
Previous Grounds: Crown ground 1870-1919, Star Meadow 1919-24
Record Attendance: 3,000 v Oxford United - FA Cup 1st Round 1994

DIRECTIONS
From M40 (Junction 4 High Wycombe) or M4 (Junction 8/9 Maidenhead) take A404, leave at the A4155 junction signposted Marlow. Follow A4155 towards Marlow then turn right at Esso service station into Maple Rise.
At crossroads follow straight ahead into Oak Tree Road.
Ground 100 yards on left.

Nearest Railway Station Marlow - 1km
Bus Route Oak Tree Road - stop 100m away

NORTHWOOD

Founded 1926

Nickname: Woods **Club Colours:** All red

Club Contact Details 01923 827 148 enquiries@northwoodfc.com

Northwood Park, Chestnut Avenue, Northwood, Middlesex HA6 1HR

Previous Names: Northwood United 1926-1945.

Previous Leagues: Harrow & Wembley 1932-69, Middlesex 1969-78, Hellenic 1979-84, London Spartan 1984-93, Isthmian 1993-2005, 2007-10, Southern 2005-07, 10-18.

09-10	10-11	11-12	12-13	13-14	14-15	15-16	16-17	17-18	18-19
Isth1N 10	SthC 20	SthC 7	SthC 13	SthC 9	SthC 10	SthC 7	SthC 20	Sth1E 17	IsthSC 10
FAC 1Qr	FAC 1Q	FAC P	FAC 3Q	FAC P	FAC 1Qr	FAC 2Q	FAC P	FAC P	FAC 1Qr
FAT 1Pr	FAT Pr	FAT Pr	FAT P	FAT P	FAT 2Q	FAT 1Q	FAT 1Qr	FAT P	FAT P

HONOURS / RECORDS

FA Comps: None

League: Harrow, Wembley & District Premier 1932-33, 33-34, 34-35, 35-36, 36-37, 47-48, 48-49. Middlesex Premier 1977-78. Hellenic Division One 1978-79. Spartan Premier 1991-92. Isthmian Division One North 2002-03.

County FA: Middlesex Intermediate Cup 1978-79. Middlesex Senior Cup 2006-07, 15-16.

Victory: 15-0 v Dateline (H) - Middlesex Intermediate Cup 1973

Defeat: 0-8 v Bedfont - Middlesex League 1975

Goalscorer: Lawrence Yaku scored 61 goals during season 1999-2000

Appearances: Chris Gell - 493+

Ground Capacity: 3,075 **Seats:** 308 **Covered:** 932 **Clubhouse:** Yes **Shop:** No

Previous Grounds: Northwood Recreation Ground 1926-1928. Northwood Playing Fields 1928-1971.

Record Attendance: 1,642 v Chlesea - Friendly July 1997

DIRECTIONS

M25 Junction 18, take A404 through Rickmansworth to Northwood. After passing under grey railway bridge, take first right into Chestnut Avenue. Ground is in grounds of Northwood Park, entrance is 400 metres on left.
(Ground is 20 minutes from J.18).

Nearest Railway Station Northwood Hills Underground - 0.7km

SOUTH PARK

Founded 1897

Nickname: The Sparks **Club Colours:** All red

Club Contact Details 01737 245 963

King George's Field, Whitehall Lane, South Park RH2 8LG

Previous Names: South Park & Reigate Town 2001-03.

Previous Leagues: Redhill & District. Crawley & District > 2006. Combined Counties 2006-14.

09-10	10-11	11-12	12-13	13-14	14-15	15-16	16-17	17-18	18-19
CC1 6	CC1 3	CCP 8	CCP 4	CCP 1	Isth1S 14	Isth1S 11	Isth1S 8	Isth1S 13	IsthSC 17
	FAC 1Q	FAC P	FAC 4Q	FAC 1Qr	FAC 1Qr	FAC 2Q	FAC 2Q	FAC P	FAC P
FAV 2Qr	FAV 2Q	FAV 4P	FAV 3P	FAV 3P	FAT 1Q	FAT 1Q	FAT 2P	FAT Pr	FAT P

HONOURS / RECORDS

FA Comps: None

League: Combined Counties Premier Division 2013-14.

County FA: Surrey Premier Cup 2010-11.

Best FA Cup Fourth Qualifying Round 2012-13

FA Vase Fourth Round Proper 2011-12

FA Trophy Preliminary Round 2018-19

Ground Capacity: 2,000 **Seats:** 113 **Covered:** Yes **Clubhouse:** Yes **Shop:** Yes

Previous Grounds: Crescent Road. Church Road.

Record Attendance: 643 v Metropolitan Police, 20/10/2012

DIRECTIONS

From junction 8 of the M25, take A217 and follow signs to Gatwick. Follow through the one way system via Reigate town centre and continue on until traffic lights and crossroads by The Angel public house, turn right at these lights, into Prices Lane, and continue on road. After a sharp right bend into Sandcross Lane past Reigate Garden Centre. Take next left after school into Whitehall Lane.

Nearest Railway Station Reigate - 2km

Bus Route Sandcross Lane - stop 200m away

STAINES TOWN

Founded 1892

Nickname: The Swans **Club Colours:** Yellow and blue

Club Contact Details 01784 469 240

Wheatsheaf Park, Wheatsheaf Lane, Staines TW18 2PD

Previous Names: Staines Albany & St Peters Institute merged in 1895. Staines 1905-18, Staines Lagonda 1918-25, Staines Vale (WWII)

Previous Leagues: Great Western Suburban, Hounslow & District 1919-20, Spartan 1924-35, 58-71, Middlesex Senior 1943-52, Parthenon 1952-53, Hellenic 1953-58, Athenian 1971-73, Isthmian 1973-2009, 15-18. Conference 2009-15. Southern 2018-19.

09-10		10-11		11-12		12-13		13-14		14-15		15-16		16-17		17-18		18-19	
Conf S	8	Conf S	15	Conf S	15	Conf S	18	Conf S	8	Conf S	21	Isth P	16	Isth P	12	Isth P	8	SthPS	22
FAC	2Pr	FAC	4Q	FAC	4Q	FAC	2Q	FAC	1P	FAC	3Qr	FAC	1P	FAC	3Q	FAC	1Q	FAC	1Q
FAT	3Q	FAT	3Q	FAT	2P	FAT	3Qr	FAT	1Pr	FAT	3Qr	FAT	1Q	FAT	1Q	FAT	1Q	FAT	1Q

HONOURS / RECORDS

FA Comps: None

League: Spartan League 1959-60. Athenian League Division Two 1971-72, Division One 1974-75, 88-89.

County FA: Middlesex Senior cup 1975-76, 76-77, 77-78, 88-89, 90-91, 94-95, 97-98, 2009-10, 12-13. Barassi Cup 1975-76.

Victory: 14-0 v Croydon (A) - Isthmian Division 1 19/03/1994
Defeat: 1-18 - Wycombe Wanderers (A) - Great Western Suburban League 27/12/1909
Goalscorer: Alan Gregory - 122
Appearances: Dickie Watmore - 840

Ground Capacity: 3,000 **Seats:** 300 **Covered:** 850 **Clubhouse:** Yes **Shop:** Yes
Previous Grounds: Groundshared with Walton & Hersham and Egham Town whilst new Wheatsheaf stadium was built 2001-03.
Record Attendance: 2,860 v Stokcport County, FAC, 2007

DIRECTIONS

Leave M25 at Junction 13. If coming from the North (anticlockwise), bear left onto A30 Staines By-Pass; if coming from the South (clockwise), go round the roundabout and back under M25 to join By-Pass. Follow A30 to Billet Bridge roundabout, which you treat like a roundabout, taking last exit, A308, London Road towards Town Centre. At 3rd traffic lights, under iron bridge, turn left into South Street, passing central bus station, as far as Thames Lodge (formerly Packhorse). Turn left here, into Laleham Road, B376, under rail bridge. After 1km, Wheatsheaf Lane is on the right, by the traffic island. Ground is less than 100 yds on left. Please park on the left.

Nearest Railway Station Staines - 1.3km
Bus Route Penton Hook Road - stop 100m away

TOOTING & MITCHAM UNITED

Founded 1932

Nickname: The Terrors **Club Colours:** Black and white stripes

Club Contact Details 020 8685 6193

Imperial Fields, Bishopsford Road, Morden, Surrey SM4 6BF

Previous Names: Tooting Town (Founded in 1887) and Mitcham Wanderers (1912) merged in 1932 to form Tooting & Mitcham FC.

Previous Leagues: London 1932-37, Athenian 1937-56

09-10		10-11		11-12		12-13		13-14		14-15		15-16		16-17		17-18		18-19	
Isth P	12	Isth P	14	Isth P	21	Isth1S	16	Isth1S	11	Isth1S	11	Isth1S	17	Isth1S	1	Isth P	24	IsthSC	6
FAC	1P	FAC	2Q	FAC	1Q	FAC	1Q	FAC	P	FAC	3Q	FAC	2Q	FAC	P	FAC	2Q	FAC	2Q
FAT	2Q	FAT	1Q	FAT	1Q	FAT	1Q	FAT	P	FAT	P	FAT	1Q	FAT	1Q	FAT	1Q	FAT	EP

HONOURS / RECORDS

FA Comps: None

League: Athenian 1949-50, 54-55. Isthmian 1975-76, 59-60, Division Two 2000-01, Division One South 2016-17.

County FA: London Senior Cup 1942-43, 48-49, 58-59, 59-60, 2006-07, 07-08, 15-16. Surrey Senior cup 1937-38, 43-44, 44-45, 52-53, 59-60, 75-76, 76-77, 77-78, 2007-07. Surrey Senior Shield 1951-52, 60-61, 61-62, 65-66.

Victory: 11-0 v Welton Rovers - FA Amateur Cup 1962-63
Defeat: 1-8 v Kingstonian - Surrey Senior Cup 1966-67
Goalscorer: Alan Ives - 92
Appearances: Danny Godwin - 470
Additional: Paid £9,000 to Enfield for David Flint. Received £10,000 from Luton Town for Herbie Smith.

Ground Capacity: 3,500 **Seats:** 612 **Covered:** 1,200 **Clubhouse:** Yes **Shop:** Yes
Previous Grounds: Sandy Lane, Mitcham
Record Attendance: 17,500 v Queens Park Rangers - FA Cup 2nd Round 1956-57 (At Sandy Lane)

DIRECTIONS

M25 Jct 8, take the A217 northbound, this goes through Tadworth and Cheam. It's dual carriageway most of the way, although long stretches have a 40mph speed limit. This leads to a major roundabout with lights (Rose Hill). Take the third exit (Mitcham A217), this is Bishopsford Road and the ground is a mile further on. Go through two sets of lights, the road dips, and the entrance is on the right opposite a petrol station.
From the South: M25 Jct 7, M23 then A23 northbound. Turn left onto the A237 after passing under a railway bridge at Coulsdon South station. Through Hackbridge and Beddington, then turn left onto the A239. Turn left at lights by Mitcham Cricket Green into the A217, the ground is 800 yards on the left.

Nearest Railway Station Mitcham Tram Stop - 0.5km

UXBRIDGE

Founded 1871

Nickname: The Reds **Club Colours:** Red & white

Club Contact Details 01895 443 557 sec@uxbridgefc.co.uk

Honeycroft, Horton Road, West Drayton, Middlesex UB7 8HX

Previous Names: Uxbridge Town 1923-45

Previous Leagues: Southern 1894-99, Greatt Western Suburban 1906-19, 20-23, Athenian 1919-20, 24-37, 63-82, Spartan 1937-38, London 1938-46, Great Western Comb. 1939-45, Corinthian 1946-63, Athenian 1963-82. Isthmian 1982-2004. Southern 2004-18.

09-10		10-11		11-12		12-13		13-14		14-15		15-16		16-17		17-18		18-19	
Sthsw	15	SthC	13	SthC	4	SthC	11	SthC	10	SthC	12	SthC	15	SthC	17	Sth1E	15	IsthSC	15
FAC	2Q	FAC	P	FAC	P	FAC	1Q	FAC	1Q	FAC	2Q	FAC	3Q	FAC	2Q	FAC	P	FAC	P
FAT	1Qr	FAT	2P	FAT	1P	FAT	2Qr	FAT	P	FAT	2Q	FAT	P	FAT	1Q	FAT	P	FAT	EPr

HONOURS / RECORDS

FA Comps: None

League: Corinthian 1959-60.

County FA: Middlesex Senior Cup 1893-94, 95-96, 1950-51, 2000-01, Charity Cup 1907-08, 12-13, 35-36, 81-82, 2012-13, 13-14.
London Challenge Cup 1993-94, 96-97, 98-99.

Goalscorer: Phil Duff - 153

Appearances: Roger Nicholls - 1,054

Best FA Cup Second Round Proper 1873-74 **FA Amateur Cup:** Finalists 1897-98

FA Trophy Second Round Proper 1998-99, 99-2000, 00-01, 08-09

FA Vase Fourth Round Proper 1983-84

Ground Capacity: 3,770 **Seats:** 339 **Covered:** 760 **Clubhouse:** Yes **Shop:**

Previous Grounds: RAF Stadium 1923-48, Cleveland Road 1948-78

Record Attendance: 1,000 v Arsenal - Opening of the floodlights 1981

DIRECTIONS

M4 to Junction 4 (Heathrow),
take A408 towards Uxbridge for 1 mile,
turn left into Horton Road.
Ground 1/2 mile on right.

Nearest Railway Station West Drayton - 1km

WALTHAM ABBEY

Founded 1944

Nickname: Abbotts **Club Colours:** Green and white hoops

Club Contact Details 01992 711 287

Capershotts, Sewardstone Road, Waltham Abbey, Essex EN9 1NX

Previous Names: Abbey Sports amalgamated with Beechfield Sports in 1974 to form Beechfields. Club then renamed to Waltham Abbey in 1976

Previous Leagues: London Spartan/Spartan. Essex & Herts Border. Essex Senior.

09-10		10-11		11-12		12-13		13-14		14-15		15-16		16-17		17-18		18-19	
Isth1N	21	Isth1N	11	Isth1N	14	Isth1N	12	Isth1N	18	Isth1N	10	Isth1N	21	Isth1N	20	Isth1N	18	IsthSC	9
FAC	1Q	FAC	P	FAC	1Q	FAC	2Q	FAC	1Q	FAC	3Q	FAC	P	FAC	1Q	FAC	P	FAC	P
FAT	1Q	FAT	P	FAT	Pr	FAT	1Q	FAT	1Q	FAT	P	FAT	2Q	FAT	1Q	FAT	1Q	FAT	EP

HONOURS / RECORDS

FA Comps: None

League: London Spartan Division One 1977-78, Senior Division 1978-79.

County FA: London Senior Cup 1998-99. Essex Senior Cup 2004-05.

Best FA Cup Third Qualifying Round 2014-15

FA Trophy First Qualifying Round 2006-07, 09-10, 12-13, 13-14

FA Vase Second Round Proper 1997-98

Ground Capacity: 3,500 **Seats:** 200 **Covered:** 500 **Clubhouse:** Yes **Shop:** No

Previous Grounds: None

Record Attendance:

DIRECTIONS

Exit M25 at junction 26 and take 2nd left at roundabout into Honey Lane (A121).
At the Sewardstone roundabout, take third right into Sewarstone Road which takes you over the M25.
Ground is first right before cemetery.

Nearest Railway Station Waltham Cross - 2km

Bus Route Catersfield - stop 100m away

WARE

Founded 1892

Nickname: Blues **Club Colours:** Blue & white

Club Contact Details 01920 462 064
Wodson Park, Wadesmill Road, Ware, Herts SG12 0UQ

Previous Names: Ware Town.
Previous Leagues: East Herts, North Middlesex 1907-08, Herts County 1908-25, Spartan 1925-55, Delphian 1955-63, Athenian 1963-75, Isthmian 1975-2015. Southern 2015-16.

09-10		10-11		11-12		12-13		13-14		14-15		15-16		16-17		17-18		18-19	
Isth1N	19	Isth1N	14	Isth1N	21	Isth1N	19	Isth1N	21	Isth1N	10	SthC	11	Isth1N	22	Isth1N	20	IsthSC	7
FAC	1Q	FAC	P	FAC	P	FAC	1Q	FAC	P	FAC	P	FAC	P	FAC	P	FAC	2Q	FAC	1Q
FAT	P	FAT	P	FAT	P	FAT	P	FAT	Pr	FAT	1Q	FAT	P	FAT	2Q	FAT	1Q	FAT	P

HONOURS / RECORDS
FA Comps: None
League: East Herts 1897-88, 98-99, 99-1900, 02-03, 03-04, 05-06 (shared), 06-07. Herts County 1908-09, 21-22. Spartan Division Two B 1926-27, Division One 51-52, Premier 52-53. Isthmian Division Two 2005-06.
County FA: Herts Senior Cup 1898-99, 1903-04, 06-07, 21-22, 53-54. Herts Charity Shield 1926-27, 52-53, 56-57, 58-59, 62-63, 85-86. East Anglian Cup 1973-74.

Victory: 10-1 v Wood Green Town
Defeat: 0-11 v Barnet
Goalscorer: George Dearman scored 98 goals during 1926-27
Appearances: Gary Riddle - 654

Ground Capacity: 3,300 **Seats:** 500 **Covered:** 312 **Clubhouse:** Yes **Shop:** Yes
Previous Grounds: Highfields, Canons Park, London Road, Presdales Lower Park 1921-26
Record Attendance: 3,800 v Hendon - FA Amateur Cup, January 1957.

DIRECTIONS
A10 off junction A602 and B1001 turn right at roundabout after 300 yards and follow Ware sign, past Rank factory. Turn left at main road onto A1170 (Wadesmill Road) Stadium is on the right after 3/4 mile.

Nearest Railway Station Ware - 1.9km
Bus Route Wodson Park - stop 100m away

WESTFIELD

Founded 1953

Nickname: The Field **Club Colours:** Amber & black

Club Contact Details 01483 771 106
Woking Park, off Elmbridge Lane, Kingfield, Woking GU22 9BA

Previous Names: None
Previous Leagues: Woking & District. Surrey Intermediate > 1962. Parthenon 1962-63. Surrey Senior 1963-78. Combined Counties (FM) 1978-2018

09-10		10-11		11-12		12-13		13-14		14-15		15-16		16-17		17-18		18-19	
CC1	16	CC1	13	CC1	8	CC1	3	CCP	4	CCP	14	CCP	9	CCP	2	CCP	1	IsthSC	5
FAC	N/A	FAC	N/A	FAC	EP	FAC	EP	FAC	1Qr	FAC	P	FAC	EPr	FAC	EP	FAC	2Q	FAC	P
FAV	1Q	FAV	1Q	FAV	2Q	FAV	1Q	FAV	1P	FAV	2P	FAV	2Q	FAV	2Q	FAV	3P	FAT	Pr

HONOURS / RECORDS
FA Comps: None
League: Surrey Senior League 1972-73, 73-74. Combined Counties Premier 2017-18.

County FA: Surrey County Junior Charity Cup 1954-55

Best FA Cup Second Qualifying Round 2017-18
FA Vase Fourth Round Proper 2000-01
FA Trophy Preliminary Round 2018-19(r)

Ground Capacity: 1000 **Seats:** Yes **Covered:** Yes **Clubhouse:** Yes **Shop:**
Previous Grounds: Moved to Woking Park in 1960
Record Attendance: 325 v Guernsey, Combined Counties Division One, 2011-12

DIRECTIONS
Follow signs to Woking Leisure Centre on the A247.

Nearest Railway Station Woking
Bus Route Arriva 34, 35

ASHFORD UNITED

Founded 1930

Nickname: The Nuts & Bolts **Club Colours:** Green & white

Club Contact Details 01233 611 838 info@ashfordunitedfc.com

The Homelands, Ashford Road TN26 1NJ

Previous Names: Ashford Town 1930-2010.

Previous Leagues: Kent 1930-59. Southern 1959-2004. Isthmian 2004-10. Kent Invicta 2011-2013. Southern Counties East 2013-17.

09-10		10-11		11-12		12-13		13-14		14-15		15-16		16-17		17-18		18-19	
Isth1S	20			K_lv	5	K_lv	3	SCEP	2	SCEP	2	SCEP	3	SCEP	1	Isth1S	21	IsthSE	4
FAC	1Q					FAC	P	FAC	P	FAC	P	FAC	EP	FAC	1Q	FAC	1Q	FAC	P
FAT	1Q			FAV	1Qr	FAV	2Q	FAV	4P	FAV	4P	FAV	QF	FAV	2P	FAT	P	FAT	EPr

HONOURS / RECORDS

FA Comps: None

League: Kent 1948-49. Southern Counties East 2016-17.

County FA: Kent Senior Cup 1958-59, 62-63, 92-93, 95-96. Kent Senior Trophy 2016-17.

Victory: 15-0 v Erith & Belvedere, Kent League, 28/04/1937.

Defeat: 3-14 v Folkestone Reserves, Kent League, 1933-34.

Goalscorer: Dave Arter - 197. Shaun Welford scored 48 goals during the 2016-17 season.
Stuart Zanone scored 7 v Lingfield (A), Southern Counties East, 24/03/2015.

Appearances: Peter McRobert - 765

Ground Capacity: 3,200 **Seats:** 500 **Covered:** Yes **Clubhouse:** Yes **Shop:**

Previous Grounds: Essella Park 1931-1987.

Record Attendance: At Essella Park - 6,525 v Crystal Palace, FAC 1st Rnd, 1959-60. At Homelands - 3,363 v Fulham, FAC 1st , 1994-95.

DIRECTIONS

Take Junction 10 off the M20 following signs for the A2070. Continue along A2070 eventually merging onto A2042. At the roundabout take first exit on to Avenue Jacques Faucheux. At the next roundabout take second exit onto Ashford Road. Ground will be on the right handside.

Nearest Railway Station Ham Street - 4.2km

Bus Route Smithfields Crossroads - stop 600m away

BURGESS HILL TOWN

Founded 1882

Nickname: Hillians **Club Colours:** Green & black

Club Contact Details 01444 871 514

Green Elephant Stadium, Leylands Park, Maple Drive, Burgess Hill, West Sussex RH15 8DL

Previous Names: Burgess Hill 1882-1969.

Previous Leagues: Mid Sussex >1958, Sussex County 1958-2003, Southern 2003-04

09-10		10-11		11-12		12-13		13-14		14-15		15-16		16-17		17-18		18-19	
Isth1S	7	Isth1S	7	Isth1S	20	Isth1S	8	Isth1S	6	Isth1S	1	Isth P	21	Isth P	20	Isth P	23	Isth P	21
FAC	P	FAC	2Q	FAC	P	FAC	P	FAC	2Q	FAC	4Q	FAC	1Q	FAC	4Qr	FAC	4Q	FAC	2Q
FAT	2Q	FAT	1Q	FAT	1Q	FAT	Pr	FAT	Pr	FAT	2P	FAT	1Q	FAT	3Q	FAT	2Q	FAT	1Qr

HONOURS / RECORDS

FA Comps: None

League: Mid-Sussex 1900-01, 03-04, 39-40, 56-57. Sussex County Division Two 1974-75, Division One 75-76, 96-97, 98-99, 2001-02, 02-03. Isthmian Division One South 2014-15.

County FA: Sussex Senior Cup 1883-84, 84-85, 85-86.

Goalscorer: Ashley Carr - 208

Appearances: Paul Williams - 499

Best FA Cup Fourth Qualifying Round 1999-2000, 08-09, 14-15, 16-17(r), 17-18.

FA Trophy Second Round Proper 2003-04, 04-05, 14-15.

FA Vase Quarter Finals 2001-02.

Ground Capacity: 2,500 **Seats:** 408 **Covered:** Yes **Clubhouse:** Yes **Shop:** Yes

Previous Grounds: Moved to Leylands Park in 1969.

Record Attendance: 2,005 v AFC Wimbledon - Isthmian League Division One 2004-05

DIRECTIONS

Turn east from A273 London Road into Leylands Road,
Take 4th left sign posted Leyland Park.
Nearest station is Wivelsfield.

Nearest Railway Station Wivelsfield - 0.4km

OUTS: Cray Wanderers (P - IsthP), Greenwich Borough (R - SCEP), Horsham (P - IsthP), Thamesmead Town (F).

CHICHESTER CITY

Founded 2000

Nickname: Lillywhites **Club Colours:** White & green

Club Contact Details 01243 533 368 secretary@chichestercityfc.co.uk
Oaklands Park, Chichester, W Sussex PO19 6AR

Previous Names: Chichester FC (pre 1948), Chichester City 1948-2000. Merged with Portfield in 2000, Chicester City United 2000-09
Previous Leagues: None

09-10		10-11		11-12		12-13		13-14		14-15		15-16		16-17		17-18		18-19	
SxC1	3	SxC1	14	SxC1	20	SxC1	19	SxC1	11	SxC1	14	SCP	5	SCP	3	SCP	6	SCP	1
FAC	P	FAC	EP	FAC	EPr	FAC	EP	FAC	EP	FAC	EP	FAC	P	FAC	EP	FAC	EP	FAC	EP
FAV	1P	FAV	1P	FAV	2P	FAV	2Q	FAV	1Q	FAV	1Q	FAV	1Q	FAV	4P	FAV	5P	FAV	2P

HONOURS / RECORDS
FA Comps: None
League: Sussex County Division One 2003-04. Southern Combination Premier 2018-19.

County FA: Sussex RUR Cup 2006-07

FA Cup First Qualifying Round 2001-02
FA Vase Fifth Round Proper 2017-18

Ground Capacity: 2,000 **Seats:** none **Covered:** 200 **Clubhouse:** Yes **Shop:** Yes
Previous Grounds: Church Road (Portfield) 2000-08.
Record Attendance:

DIRECTIONS
Half a mile north of the city centre, adjacent to festival theatre.
Turn into Northgate car park and entrance to the ground is next to the Chichester Rackets Club.

Nearest Railway Station Chichester - 1.2km
Bus Route University - stop 182m away

CRAY VALLEY PAPER MILLS

Founded 1919

Nickname: Millers **Club Colours:** Green & black

Club Contact Details 07838 344 451
Badgers Sports Ground, Middle Park Avenue, Eltham SE9 5HT

Previous Names: None
Previous Leagues: Sidcup & Kent 1919. Kent County Amateur >55. South London Alliance 55-91. Spartan 1991-97, Spartan South Midlands 1997-98, London Intermediate 1998-01, Kent County 2001-11.

09-10		10-11		11-12		12-13		13-14		14-15		15-16		16-17		17-18		18-19	
KC P	6	KC P	3	Kent P	11	Kent P	8	SCE	7	SCE	7	SCE	10	SCEP	4	SCEP	6	SCEP	1
								FAC	P	FAC	EP	FAC	P	FAC	P	FAC	1Q	FAC	2Q
						FAV	1Q	FAV	2Pr	FAV	2Q	FAV	1P	FAV	1Q	FAV	1P	FAV	F

HONOURS / RECORDS
FA Comps: None
League: Sidcup & Kent Division Two 1919-20. South Kent County Division Three (Western) 1933-37, Division One West 2002-03, Premier Division 2004-05. London Alliance Premier Division 1980-81. Southern Counties Premier 2018-19.
County FA: Kent Junior Cup 1921-22, 77-78, 80-81. Kent Intermediate Shield 2004-05.
London Intermediate Cup 2002-03, 03-04, 09-10. London Senior Cup 2016-17.

FA Cup Second Qualifying Round 2018-19
FA Vase Runners-up 2018-19

Ground Capacity: 1,000 **Seats:** 100 **Covered:** Yes **Clubhouse:** Yes **Shop:**
Previous Grounds: St Paul's Cray paper mills sports ground 1919-81. Played at many grounds until permanent move to Badgers.
Record Attendance: 663 v Canterbury City, FA Vase semi-final, 17/03/2019

DIRECTIONS
From A20 Kent - Sidcup bypass to 'Big Yellow Storage' roundabout. Take last exit (back on yourself), then 1st left onto Eltham Palace Rd. 1st left onto Middle Park avenue. Badgers Sports will be on your left.
From A2 Kent - To A205 exit, left onto Westhorne Avenue, to 'Yorkshire Grey' McDonalds roundabout. 2nd exit onto Middle Park Avenue. Badgers Sports will be on your right.

Nearest Railway Station Mottingham - 30min walk from ground.
Bus Route 160 stops outside the ground.

EAST GRINSTEAD TOWN

Founded 1890

Nickname: The Wasps **Club Colours:** Amber & black stripes (Blue & yellow)

Club Contact Details 01342 325 885

College Lane, East Court, East Grinstead RH19 3LS

Previous Names: East Grinstead 1890-1997.

Previous Leagues: Mid Sussex, Sussex County, Souhern Amateur 1928-35. Sussex County 1935-2014.

09-10		10-11		11-12		12-13		13-14		14-15		15-16		16-17		17-18		18-19	
SxC1	15	SxC1	7	SxC1	9	SxC1	8	SxC1	2	Isth1S	22	Isth1S	20	Isth1S	18	Isth1S	22	IsthSE	13
FAC	1Q	FAC	1Q					FAC	EP	FAC	Pr	FAC	P	FAC	P	FAC	1Q	FAC	2Q
FAV	1P	FAV	2Q			FAV	1Qr	FAV	2P	FAT	Pr	FAT	1Q	FAT	1Q	FAT	P	FAT	1Q

HONOURS / RECORDS

FA Comps: None

League: Mid-Sussex 1901-02, 36-37. Southern Amateur DivisioN Three 1931-32. Sussex County Division Two 2007-08.

County FA: Sussex RUR Cup 2003-04.

Appearances: Guy Hill

Best FA Cup Second Qualifying Round 1947-48, 50-51, 52-53, 71-72, 2018-19

FA Trophy First Qualifying Round 2015-16, 16-17, 18-19

FA Vase Third Round Proper 1974-75

Ground Capacity: 3,000 **Seats:** Yes **Covered:** Yes **Clubhouse:** Yes **Shop:** No

Previous Grounds: West Ground 1890-1962. King George's Field 1962-67.

Record Attendance: 2,006 v Lancing F A Am Cup, November 1947

DIRECTIONS

A264 Tunbridge Wells road (Moat Road) until mini roundabout at bottom of Blackwell Hollow,
turn immediately right by club sign then 1st left,
ground 200 yards down lane past rifle club on right.

Nearest Railway Station East Grinstead - 1.1km

Bus Route East Court - stop 100m away

FAVERSHAM TOWN

Founded 1884

Nickname: Lillywhites **Club Colours:** White & black

Club Contact Details 01795 591 000

Salters Lane, Faversham Kent ME13 8ND

Previous Names: Faversham Invicta, Faversham Services, Faversham Railway and Faversham Rangers pre War.

Previous Leagues: Kent 1884-1900, 1904-12, 24-34, 37-59, 66-71, 76-2003. Kent County 1934-37. Aetolian 1959-63. Greater London 1964-66. Metropolitan London 1971-73. Athenian 1973-76. Kent County 2005-10.

09-10		10-11		11-12		12-13		13-14		14-15		15-16		16-17		17-18		18-19	
Kent P	1	Isth1S	8	Isth1S	17	Isth1S	3	Isth1S	10	Isth1S	3	Isth1S	5	Isth1S	10	Isth1S	19	IsthSE	17
FAC	1Q	FAC	1Q	FAC	1Q	FAC	1Qr	FAC	2Q	FAC	2Q	FAC	1Qr	FAC	3Qr	FAC	2Q	FAC	1Q
FAV	2P	FAT	1Q	FAT	2Q	FAT	1Q	FAT	P	FAT	1Q	FAT	P	FAT	1Q	FAT	P	FAT	P

HONOURS / RECORDS

FA Comps: None

League: Kent 1969-70, 70-71, 77-78, 89-90, Division Two 1895-96. Kent County 2009-10.

County FA: Kent Amateur Cup 1956-57, 58-59, 71-72, 72-73, 73-74. Kent Senior Trophy 1976-77, 77-78.

Best FA Cup Third Qualifying Round 2016-17

FA Trophy Second Qualifying Round 201-12

FA Vase Third Round Proper 1991-92

Ground Capacity: 2,000 **Seats:** 200 **Covered:** 1,800 **Clubhouse:** Yes **Shop:** No

Previous Grounds: Moved in to Salters Lane in 1948.

Record Attendance:

DIRECTIONS

From the M25 continue onto M26 9.9 miles. Continue onto M20 8.1 miles. Exit onto Slip Road (M20 J7) 0.2 miles. Bear left 0.1 miles. Continue onto Sittingbourne Road A249 0.9 miles. Bear right onto Detling Hill A249 4.6 miles. Bear left 0.1 miles. Continue onto Slip Road (M2 J5) 0.4 miles. Continue onto M2 10.5 miles. Exit onto Slip Road (M2 J6) 0.1 miles. Turn left onto Ashford Road A251 0.5 miles. Turn right onto Canterbury Road A2 0.2 miles. Turn right onto Westwood Place 0.1 miles.

Nearest Railway Station Faversham - 0.6km

GUERNSEY

Founded 2011

Nickname: Green Lions **Club Colours:** Green & white

Club Contact Details 01481 747 279
Footes Lane Stadium, St Peter Port, Guernsey GY1 2UL

Previous Names: None
Previous Leagues: Combined Counties 2011-13.

09-10	10-11	11-12	12-13	13-14	14-15	15-16	16-17	17-18	18-19
		CC1 1	CCP 2	Isth1S 4	Isth1S 10	Isth1S 13	Isth1S 21	Isth1S 18	IsthSE 18
				FAC 2Q	FAC P	FAC Pr	FAC Pr	FAC Pr	FAC Pr
			FAV SF	FAT 1Q	FAT 1Q	FAT P	FAT P	FAT P	

HONOURS / RECORDS
FA Comps: None
League: Combined Counties Division One 2011-12.

County FA: None

Victory: 11-0 v Crawley Down Gatwick, Isthmian Division One South, 01/01/2014
Defeat: 0-8 v Merstham, Isthmian Division One South, 18/11/2014
Goalscorer: Ross Allen - 239 in 226 appearances. (Scored 57 in all competitions during 2011-12)

Ground Capacity: 5,000 **Seats:** 720 **Covered:** Yes **Clubhouse:** Yes **Shop:** No
Previous Grounds: None
Record Attendance: 4,290 v. Spennymoor Town, FA Vase semi-final first leg, 23/03/2013

DIRECTIONS
The ground is located centrally in the island, is easily accessible with parking for several hundred cars in the immediate vicinity and on a regular bus route stopping immediately outside the stadium. It is approximately three miles north easterly from Guernsey Airport and one mile west from St Peter Port, the island's capital.

Bus Route Bus stops outside the ground

HASTINGS UNITED

Founded 1894

Nickname: The U's or The Arrows **Club Colours:** All white

Club Contact Details 01424 444 635
The Pilot Field, Elphinstone Road, Hastings TN34 2AX

Previous Names: Rock-a-Nore 1894-1921. Hastings and St Leonards Amateurs 1921-79. Hastings Town 1979-2002.
Previous Leagues: South Eastern 1904-05, Southern 1905-10, Sussex County 1921-27, 52-85, Southern Amateur 1927-46, Corinthian 1946-48

09-10	10-11	11-12	12-13	13-14	14-15	15-16	16-17	17-18	18-19
Isth P 7	Isth P 18	Isth P 18	Isth P 22	Isth1S 5	Isth1S 19	Isth1S 7	Isth1S 5	Isth1S 9	IsthSE 3
FAC 1Q	FAC 1Q	FAC 1Q	FAC 3P	FAC 1Q	FAC 2Q	FAC 3Q	FAC 3Qr	FAC 1Q	FAC 3Q
FAT 1Q	FAT 1Qr	FAT 1Qr	FAT 1Q	FAT 2Q	FAT P	FAT 2Q	FAT 2Qr	FAT 1Q	FAT P

HONOURS / RECORDS
FA Comps: None
League: Southern Division Two B 1909-10, Southern Division 1991-92, Eastern Division 2001-01.
Sussex County Division Two 1979-80.
County FA: Sussex Senior Cup 1935-36, 37-38, 95-96, 97-98.

Goalscorer: Terry White scored 33 during 1999-2000
Additional: Paid £8,000 to Ashford Town for Nicky Dent
Received £50,000 from Nottingham Forest for Paul Smith

Ground Capacity: 4,050 **Seats:** 800 **Covered:** 1,750 **Clubhouse:** Yes **Shop:** Yes
Previous Grounds: Bulverhythe Recreation > 1976
Record Attendance: 4,888 v Nottingham Forest - Friendly 23/06/1996

DIRECTIONS
From A1 turn left at third roundabout into St Helens Road.
Then left after one mile into St Helens Park Road leading into Downs Road.
Turn left at T-junction at the end of the road. Ground is 200 yards on the right.

Nearest Railway Station Ore - 0.9km. Hastings - 1.9km.

HAYWARDS HEATH TOWN

Founded 1888

Nickname: The Blues **Club Colours:** Blue & white

Club Contact Details 07796 677 661

Hanbury Park Stadium, Haywards Heath RH16 3PT

Previous Names: Haywards Heath Juniors 1888-94. Haywards Heath Excelsior 1894-95. Haywards Heath 1895-1989.

Previous Leagues: Mid-Sussex 1888-1927. Sussex County/Southern Combination 1927-52, 61-2018. Metropolitan 1952-61.

09-10		10-11		11-12		12-13		13-14		14-15		15-16		16-17		17-18		18-19	
SxC3	3	SxC3	8	SxC3	15	SxC3	2	SxC2	5	SxC2	9	SC1	1	SCP	2	SCP	1	IsthSE	5
										FAC	EP			FAC	P	FAC	1Qr	FAC	EP
FAV	1Q			FAV	1Qr			FAV	2Q	FAV	1Q	FAV	2P	FAV	2P	FAV	2P	FAT	P

HONOURS / RECORDS

FA Comps: None

League: Sussex County/Southern Combination 1949-50, 69-70, 2017-18, Eastern Division 45-46/ Division One 2015-16.

County FA: Sussex Senior Cup 1941-42, 57-58. Sussex RUR Cup 1943-44, 66-67, 74-75, 75-76. Sussex Intermediate Cup 2012-13

Best FA Cup Fourth Qualifying Round 1945-46

FA Vase Third Round Proper 1990-91

FA Trophy Preliminary Round 2018-19

Ground Capacity: 2,000 **Seats:** Yes **Covered:** Yes **Clubhouse:** Yes **Shop:**

Previous Grounds:

Record Attendance:

DIRECTIONS

A272 to Haywards Heath Town Centre. At Sussex roundabout, north on B2708 (Hazelgrove Road) take first right into New England Road. Fourth right Allen Road leads to ground.
Allen Road is the only vehicular and pedestrian access to the ground.

Nearest Railway Station Haywards HEath - 1.9km

Bus Route Market Square - stop 84m away

HERNE BAY

Founded 1886

Nickname: The Bay **Club Colours:** Blue & white

Club Contact Details 01227 374 156

Winch's Field, Stanley Gardens, Herne Bay CT6 5SG

Previous Names: None.

Previous Leagues: East Kent. Faversham & Dist. Cantebury & Dist. Kent Am. Aetolian 1959-64. Athenian 1964-74.

09-10		10-11		11-12		12-13		13-14		14-15		15-16		16-17		17-18		18-19	
Kent P	2	Kent P	2	Kent P	1	Isth1S	19	Isth1S	18	Isth1S	9	Isth1S	8	Isth1S	17	Isth1S	12	IsthSE	15
FAC	EP	FAC	EP	FAC	1Q	FAC	P	FAC	Pr	FAC	1Q	FAC	2Qr	FAC	2Qr	FAC	3Q	FAC	1Q
FAV	2P	FAV	4P	FAV	SF	FAT	P	FAT	1Qr	FAT	P	FAT	2Qr	FAT	1Qr	FAT	P	FAT	2Q

HONOURS / RECORDS

FA Comps: None

League: East Kent 1902-03, 03-04, 04-05, 05-06. Athenian Division Two 1970-71. Kent 1991-92, 93-94, 96-97, 97-98, 2011-12, Division Two 1954-55.

County FA: Kent Amateur Cup 1957-58. Kent Senior Trophy 1978-79, 1996-97.

Victory: 19-3 v Hythe Wanderers - Feb 1900.

Defeat: 0-11 v 7th Dragon Guards - Oct 1907.

Misc: Most League Victories in a Season: 34 - 1996-97.

Ground Capacity: 3,000 **Seats:** 200 **Covered:** 1,500 **Clubhouse:** Yes **Shop:** Yes

Previous Grounds: Mitchell's Athletic Ground. Herne Bay Memorial Park.

Record Attendance: 2,303 v Margate, FA Cup 4th Qual. 1970-71.

DIRECTIONS

From M25 exit onto Sittingbourne Rd/A249 toward Sheerness. Continue to follow A249. At the roundabout, take the 1st exit onto the M2 ramp to Canterbury/Dover/Ramsgate. Merge onto M2. Continue onto Thanet Way/A299. Continue to follow A299. Take the A291 exit toward Canterbury/Herne Bay. At the roundabout, take the 2nd exit onto A291. At the roundabout, take the 1st exit onto Canterbury Rd/B2205. Turn left onto Spenser Rd. Take the 1st left onto Stanley Gardens. Take the 1st left to stay on Stanley Gardens.

Nearest Railway Station Herne Bay - 0.8km

HYTHE TOWN

Founded 1910

Nickname: The Cannons **Club Colours:** Red & white

Club Contact Details 01303 264 932 / 238 256

Reachfields Stadium, Fort Road, Hythe CT21 6JS

Previous Names: Hythe Town 1910-1992, Hythe United 1992-2001

Previous Leagues: Kent Amateur League, Kent League, Southern League, Kent County League, Kent League.

09-10	10-11	11-12	12-13	13-14	14-15	15-16	16-17	17-18	18-19
Kent P 3	Kent P 1	Isth1S 8	Isth1S 4	Isth1S 8	Isth1S 16	Isth1S 4	Isth1S 7	Isth1S 7	IsthSE 7
FAC 2Qr	FAC 1P	FAC 2Q	FAC P	FAC P	FAC 2Q	FAC P	FAC 2Q	FAC Pr	FAC 1Q
FAV 1P	FAV 3P	FAT 2Q	FAT 1Qr	FAT 2Qr	FAT 1Q	FAT P	FAT 1P	FAT 1Q	FAT 1Q

HONOURS / RECORDS

FA Comps: None

League: Kent County Eastern Division Two 1936-37, Division One 71-72, Premier Division 73-74, 74-75, 75-76.
Kent League 1988-89, 2010-11.

County FA: Kent Senior Cup 2011-12.
Kent Senior Trophy 1990-91.

Victory: 10-1 v Sporting Bengal, 2008-09

Defeat: 1-10 v Swanley Furness, 1997-98

Goalscorer: Dave Cook - 130

Appearances: John Walker - 354, Jason Brazier - 349, Dave Cook - 346, Lee Winfield - 344

Ground Capacity: 3,000 **Seats:** 350 **Covered:** 2,400 **Clubhouse:** Yes **Shop:** Yes

Previous Grounds: South Road 1910-77.

Record Attendance: 2,147 v Yeading, FA Vase Semi-Final, 1990.

DIRECTIONS

Leave the M20 at junction 11, then at the r'dabout take the 3rd exit onto the B2068, signposted Hastings, Hythe. At the next r'dabout take the 2nd exit onto Ashford Road, A20. Continue onto Ashford Road, A20. Entering Newingreen, at the T-junction turn left onto Hythe Rd, A261, signposted Hythe. Continue down London Rd, A261. Entering Hythe, continue at the traffic lights onto Scanlons Bridge Rd, A2008. Turn right at the next set of lights onto Dymchurch Rd, A259. Either take the 1st left down Fort Rd and turn right at the end of Fort Rd for the car-park, or after a few hundred yards turn left onto the Reachfields estate. Follow the road round and the stadium will be on your right.

Nearest Railway Station Hythe - 0.5km

PHOENIX SPORTS

Founded 1935

Nickname: None **Club Colours:** Green & black

Club Contact Details 07795 182 927

Mayplace Ground, Mayplace Road East, Barnehurst, Kent DA7 6JT

Previous Names: St Johns Welling. Lakeside. Phoenix.

Previous Leagues: Spartan League. Kent County > 2011. Kent Invicta 2011-13.

09-10	10-11	11-12	12-13	13-14	14-15	15-16	16-17	17-18	18-19
KC P 4	KC P 5	K_Iv 2	K_Iv 1	SCE 6	SCE 1	Isth1N 14	Isth1N 8	Isth1N 11	IsthSE 9
					FAC EPr	FAC 2Q	FAC P	FAC 3Q	FAC 1Qr
				FAV 1P	FAV 5P	FAT 1Qr	FAT 2Q	FAT P	FAT Pr

HONOURS / RECORDS

FA Comps: None

League: Kent County Division One West 1999-2000, 2007-08, Division Two West 2004-05. Kent Invicta 2012-13.
Southern Counties East 2014-15.

County FA: London Senior Trophy 2017-18

Best FA Cup Third Qualifying Round 2017-18

FA Trophy Second Qualifying Round 2016-17

FA Vase Fifth Round Proper 2014-15

Ground Capacity: 2,000 **Seats:** 108 **Covered:** Yes **Clubhouse:** Yes **Shop:** No

Previous Grounds: Danson Park >1950.

Record Attendance: Not known

DIRECTIONS

Take A206/Bob Dunn Way towards Erith (Jct 1a off the A282). Continue on the A206 through five roundabouts, at the sixth take the second exit onto A2000/Perry Street. Follow the A2000 for half a mile and turn right onto Mayplace Road. At the next roundabout take the second exit and stay on Mayplace Road East. Ground will be on the left.

Nearest Railway Station Barnehurst - 1.1km

Bus Route Woodside Road - stop 50m away

RAMSGATE

Founded 1945

Nickname: The Rams **Club Colours:** All red

Club Contact Details 01843 591 662

Southwood Stadium, Prices Avenue, Ramsgate, Kent CT11 0AN

Previous Names: Ramsgate Athletic > 1972

Previous Leagues: Kent 1945-59, 1976-2005, Southern 1959-76

09-10		10-11		11-12		12-13		13-14		14-15		15-16		16-17		17-18		18-19	
Isth1S	14	Isth1S	9	Isth1S	10	Isth1S	7	Isth1S	12	Isth1S	21	Isth1S	12	Isth1S	12	Isth1S	16	IsthSE	11
FAC	P	FAC	Pr	FAC	Pr	FAC	P	FAC	P	FAC	1Q	FAC	P	FAC	1Q	FAC	2Q	FAC	3Q
FAT	3Q	FAT	1Qr	FAT	P	FAT	3Q	FAT	3Q	FAT	P	FAT	1Q	FAT	P	FAT	P	FAT	1Q

HONOURS / RECORDS

FA Comps: None

League: Kent Division One 1949-50, 55-56, 56-57, Premier 1998-99, 2004-05. Isthmian Division One 2005-06.

County FA: Kent Senior Shield 1960-61, 67-68, 68-69. Kent Senior Cup 1963-64. Kent Senior Trophy 1987-88, 88-89, 98-99.

Victory: 11-0 & 12-1 v Canterbury City - Kent League 2000-01
Goalscorer: Mick Willimson
Best FA Cup First Round Proper 1955-56, 2005-06
FA Trophy Third Qualifying Round 1969-70, 75-76, 2008-09, 09-10, 12-13, 13-14
FA Vase Quarter Finals 1999-2000

Ground Capacity: 2,500 **Seats:** 400 **Covered:** 600 **Clubhouse:** Yes **Shop:** Yes
Previous Grounds: None
Record Attendance: 5,038 v Margate - 1956-57

DIRECTIONS

Approach Ramsgate via A299 (Canterbury/London) or A256 (Dover/Folkestone) to Lord of Manor roundabout.
Follow the signpost to Ramsgate along Canterbury Road East, counting via 2nd exit of the 1st roundabout.
At the 2nd roundabout, continue towards Ramsgate on London Road (2nd exit).
Take the 3rd turning on the left, into St Mildred's Avenue, then 1st left into Queen Bertha Road.
After the right hand bend, take left into Southwood Road, and 1st left into Prices Ave. The stadium is at the end of Prices Avenue.

Nearest Railway Station Ramsgate - 1km

SEVENOAKS TOWN

Founded 1883

Nickname: Town **Club Colours:** Blue & black

Club Contact Details 07876 444 274 secretary@sevenoakstownfc.co.uk

Greatness Park, Mill Lane, Sevenoaks TN14 5BX

Previous Names: None.

Previous Leagues: Sevenoaks League. Kent Amateur/County. Kent/Southern Counties East >2018.

09-10		10-11		11-12		12-13		13-14		14-15		15-16		16-17		17-18		18-19	
Kent P	6	Kent P	7	Kent P	14	Kent P	17	SCE	16	SCE	8	SCE	5	SCEP	3	SCEP	1	IsthSE	10
FAC	Pr	FAC	EP	FAC	P	FAC	EP	FAC	EP	FAC	EP	FAC	EPr	FAC	2Qr	FAC	1Q	FAC	1Qr
FAV	1Q	FAV	1Q	FAV	2Q	FAV	1P	FAV	1P	FAV	1Q	FAV	2Q	FAV	2Q	FAV	3P	FAT	1Q

HONOURS / RECORDS

FA Comps: None

League: Kent County 1984-85, 95-96, 2002-03. Southern Counties East Premier 2017-18.

County FA:

Best FA Cup Second Qualifying Round 2016-17(r)
FA Vase Third Round Proper 2017-18
FA Trophy First Qualifying Round 2018-19

Ground Capacity: 2,000 **Seats:** 150 **Covered:** 200 **Clubhouse:** Yes **Shop:**
Previous Grounds: None
Record Attendance:

DIRECTIONS

Sevenoaks Town's ground can be accessed from the A25 (Seal Road).

Nearest Railway Station Bat & Ball - 0.4km

SITTINGBOURNE

Founded 1886

Nickname: Brickies **Club Colours:** Red & black

Club Contact Details 01795 410 777
Woodstock Park, Broadoak Road, Sittingbourne ME9 8AG

Previous Names: Sittingbourne United 1881-86
Previous Leagues: Kent 1894-1905, 1909-27, 30-39, 46-59, 68-91, South Eastern 1905-09, Southern 1927-30, 59-67

09-10		10-11		11-12		12-13		13-14		14-15		15-16		16-17		17-18		18-19	
Isth1S	9	Isth1S	11	Isth1S	19	Isth1S	9	Isth1S	14	Isth1S	12	Isth1S	18	Isth1S	15	Isth1S	14	IsthSE	16
FAC	2Q	FAC	P	FAC	1Q	FAC	1Q	FAC	3Q	FAC	P	FAC	2Q	FAC	Pr	FAC	Pr	FAC	1Q
FAT	1Q	FAT	P	FAT	1Q	FAT	1Q	FAT	P	FAT	P	FAT	P	FAT	P	FAT	2Qr	FAT	1Q

HONOURS / RECORDS
FA Comps: None
League: Kent 1902-03, 57-58, 58-59, 75-76, 83-84, 90-91. Southern Southern Division 1992-93, 95-96.

County FA: Kent Senior Cup 1901-02, 28-29, 29-30, 57-58.

Victory: 15-0 v Orpington, Kent League 1922-23)
Defeat: 0-10 v Wimbledon, SL Cup 1965-66)
Additional: Paid £20,000 to Ashford Town for Lee McRobert 1993
Received £210,000 from Millwall for Neil Emblem and Michael Harle 1993

Ground Capacity: 3,000 **Seats:** 300 **Covered:** 600 **Clubhouse:** Yes **Shop:** Yes
Previous Grounds: Sittingbourne Rec. 1881-90, Gore Court 1890-92, The Bull Ground 1892-1990. Central Park 1990-2001
Record Attendance: 5,951 v Tottenham Hotspur - Friendly 26/01/1993

DIRECTIONS
From the M2 exit at Junction 5, take A249 towards Sheerness, leave A249 at 1st junction, raised section to Key Street roundabout, take A2 to Sittingbourne. One way system to town centre, first right into Park Road, Follow signs to Kent Science Park, Park Road becomes Gore Court Road, Gore Court Road becomes Woodstock Road, Woodstock Road becomes Ruins Barn Road.
When houses disappear approximately half a mile, take left as signposted Kent Science Park/Sittingbourne Research Centre into Broadoak Road, down hill passed Research Centre on right, carry on up hill, take left into car park Woodstock Park.

Nearest Railway Station Sittingbourne - 3.1km
Bus Route Kent Science Park - stop 500m away

THREE BRIDGES

Founded 1901

Nickname: Bridges **Club Colours:** Yellow & black

Club Contact Details 01293 442 000
Jubilee Walk, Three Bridges Road, Crawley, RH10 1LQ

Previous Names: Three Bridges Worth 1936-52. Three Bridges United 1953-64.
Previous Leagues: Mid Sussex, E Grinstead, Redhill & Dist 36-52. Sussex County/Southern Combintion >2012, 2017-18. Isthmian 2012-17.

09-10		10-11		11-12		12-13		13-14		14-15		15-16		16-17		17-18		18-19	
SxC1	7	SxC1	5	SxC1	1	Isth1S	21	Isth1S	19	Isth1S	7	Isth1S	14	Isth1S	23	SCP	2	IsthSE	14
FAC	EP	FAC	P	FAC	EP	FAC	P	FAC	1Q	FAC	Pr	FAC	P	FAC	P	FAC	P	FAC	P
FAV	2Q	FAV	3P	FAV	4Pr	FAT	2Q	FAT	2Q	FAT	1Q	FAT	P	FAT	P	FAV	1P	FAT	P

HONOURS / RECORDS
FA Comps: None
League: Sussex County Division One 1953-54, 2011-12.

County FA: Sussex RUR Charity Cup 1982-83, 87-88, 2007-08

Appearances: John Malthouse
Best FA Cup Second Qualifying Round 1982-83, 83-84, 2002-03
FA Vase Fifth Round Proper 1981-82

Ground Capacity: 3,500 **Seats:** 120 **Covered:** 600 **Clubhouse:** Yes **Shop:**
Previous Grounds: None
Record Attendance: 2,000 v Horsham 1948

DIRECTIONS
Leave the M23 at Junction 10 heading towards Crawley on the A2011 (Crawley Avenue). At the roundabout take the first left heading towards Three Bridges Train Station (Hazelwick Avenue). Pass Tesco on your left and head straight over the roundabout (second exit). As you approach the traffic lights remain in the right hand side lane. After turning right in to Haslett Avenue at these lights move immediately in to the right turn lane at the next set of lights. Turn right at these lights in to Three Bridges Road. Follow the road round to the left then turn left after one hundred yards in to Jubilee Walk (directly opposite the Plough Pub). Follow the road to the end and turn right (still Jubilee Walk) and head straight on where Three Bridges Jubilee Field Stadium is at the far end.

Nearest Railway Station: Three Bridges - 0.4km
Bus Route Jubilee Walk - stop 71m away

VCD ATHLETIC

Founded 1916

Nickname: The Vickers **Club Colours:** Green & white

Club Contact Details 01322 524 262 davejoyo@yahoo.co.uk

Oakwood, Old Road, Crayford DA1 4DN

Previous Names: Vickers (Erith). Vickers (Crayford) Now Vickers Crayford Dartford Athletic.
Previous Leagues: Dartford & District. Kent County 1997-2009, 2010-13. Isthmian 2009-10.

09-10		10-11		11-12		12-13		13-14		14-15		15-16		16-17		17-18		18-19	
Isth1N	8	Kent P	3	Kent P	3	Kent P	2	Isth1N	1	Isth P	18	Isth P	24	Isth1N	15	Isth1S	17	IsthSE	6
FAC	1Q	FAC	Pr	FAC	2Qr	FAC	1Q	FAC	P	FAC	2Q	FAC	1Qr	FAC	2Q	FAC	P	FAC	P
FAT	1Q	FAV	2P	FAV	3Pr	FAV	1Pr	FAT	Pr	FAT	1Q	FAT	2Q	FAT	1Q	FAT	P	FAT	1Q

HONOURS / RECORDS
FA Comps: None

League: Kent County 1952-53, 63-64, 96-97. Kent 2008-09. Isthmian Division One North 2013-14.

County FA: Kent Junior Cup 1926-27. Kent Amateur Cup 1961-62, 63-64. Kent Intermediate Cup 1995-96.
Kent Senior Trophy 2005-06, 08-09.

Best FA Cup Second Qualifying Round 2002-03, 08-09, 11-12(r), 14-15, 16-17
FA Trophy Second Qualifying Round 2015-16
FA Vase Fifth Round Proper 2005-06, 06-07

Ground Capacity: 1,180 **Seats:** Yes **Covered:** Yes **Clubhouse:** Yes **Shop:** No
Previous Grounds: Groundshared with Thamesmead (5 seasons), Lordswood (2) and Greenwich Boro' (1) whilst waiting for planning at Oakwood.
Record Attendance: 13,500 Away v Maidstone, 1919.

DIRECTIONS

Follow A2 until you reach the exit for A220/A223 towards Bexleyheath and Crayford. At the roundabout, take the second exit on to Bourne Road/A223. After just over half a mile, turn right onto the A207 London Road. Keep left at the fork, then turn left onto Crayford High Street/A2000. Where the A2000 bends right, go straight on to pick up Old Road, and the ground is on your right.

Nearest Railway Station Crayford - 0.9km

WHITEHAWK

Founded 1945

Nickname: Hawks **Club Colours:** Red and white

Club Contact Details 01273 601 244

East Brighton Park, Wilson Avenue, Brighton BN2 5TS

Previous Names: Whitehawk & Manor Farm Old Boys untill 1960.
Previous Leagues: Brighton & Hove District >1952. Sussex County 1952-2010. Isthmian 2010-13. Conference/National 2013-18.

09-10		10-11		11-12		12-13		13-14		14-15		15-16		16-17		17-18		18-19	
SxC1	1	Isth1S	3	Isth1S	1	Isth P	1	Conf S	19	Conf S	4	Nat S	5	Nat S	17	Nat S	21	Isth P	20
FAC	EP	FAC	3Q	FAC	2Qr	FAC	2Qr	FAC	2Q	FAC	3Qr	FAC	2Pr	FAC	1Pr	FAC	2Q	FAC	3Q
FAV	SF	FAT	1Q	FAT	1Q	FAT	3Q	FAT	2Pr	FAT	3Q	FAT	1P	FAT	2P	FAT	1P	FAT	1Q

HONOURS / RECORDS
FA Comps: None

League: Sussex County League Division One 1961-62, 63-64, 83-84, 2009-10, Division Two 1967-68, 80-81.
Isthmian League Division One South 2011-12, Premier Division 2012-13.
County FA: Sussex Senior Cup 1950-51, 61-62, 2011-12, 14-15. Sussex RUR Charity Cup 1954-55, 58-59, 90-91.

Goalscorer: Billy Ford
Appearances: Ken Powell - 1,103
Victory: 14-0 v Southdown (H), Sussex Junior Cup Second Round, 27/03/1948.
Defeat: 2-13 v St Luke's Terrace Old Boys (A), Brighton & Hove District Division Two, 02/11/1946.
Misc: Scored 127 goals in 32 matches during the 1961-62 season.

Ground Capacity: 3,000 **Seats:** 800 **Covered:** Yes **Clubhouse:** Yes **Shop:** No
Previous Grounds: N/A
Record Attendance: 2,174 v Dagenham & Redbridge, FA Cup Second Round Proper replay, 6th December 2015.

DIRECTIONS

From N (London) on M23/A23 – after passing Brighton boundary sign & twin pillars join A27 (sp Lewes); immediately after passing Sussex University (on L) leave A27 via slip rd at sp B2123, Falmer, Rottingdean; at roundabout at top of slip rd turn R onto B2123 (sp Falmer, Rottingdean); in 2m at traffic lights in Woodingdean turn R by Downs Hotel into Warren Road; in about 1m at traffic lights turn L into Wilson Ave, crossing racecourse; in 1¼m turn L at foot of hill (last turning before traffic lights) into East Brighton Park; follow lane for the ground.

Nearest Railway Station Brighton Central - two & half miles from the ground.
Bus Route B&H Bus No.7 or 27

WHITSTABLE TOWN

Founded 1886

Nickname: Oystermen or Natives **Club Colours:** Red & white

Club Contact Details 01227 266 012

The Belmont Ground, Belmont Road, Belmont, Whitstable CT5 1QP

Previous Names: None

Previous Leagues: East Kent 1897-1909, Kent 1909-59, 67-2007, Aetolian 1959-60, 63-64, Kent Amateur 1960-62, 64-67, South East Anglian 1962-63, Isthmian 2007-16. Southern Counties East 2016-18.

09-10		10-11		11-12		12-13		13-14		14-15		15-16		16-17		17-18		18-19	
Isth1S	18	Isth1S	15	Isth1S	18	Isth1S	17	Isth1S	20	Isth1S	8	Isth1S	23	SCEP	5	SCEP	2	IsthSE	12
FAC	2Q	FAC	2Q	FAC	P	FAC	P	FAC	Pr	FAC	1Q	FAC	1Qr	FAC	Pr	FAC	EP	FAC	1Q
FAT	Pr	FAT	P	FAT	P	FAT	2Q	FAT	2P	FAT	P	FAT	P	FAV	1Qr	FAV	3P	FAT	1Q

HONOURS / RECORDS

FA Comps: None

League: Kent Division Two (Mid Kent) 1927-28, Division Two 33-34, 49-50, Premier Division 2006-07.
Kent Amateur Eastern Division 1960-61

County FA:

Goalscorer: Barry Godfrey

Appearances: Frank Cox - 429 (1950-60)

Best FA Cup Third Qualifying Round 1957-58, 88-89, 89-90

FA Trophy Second Round Proper 2013-14

FA Vase Fifth Round Proper 1996-97

Ground Capacity: 3,000 **Seats:** 500 **Covered:** 1,000 **Clubhouse:** Yes **Shop:** Yes

Previous Grounds: None

Record Attendance: 2,500 v Gravesend & Northfleet - FA Cup 19/10/1987. **Previous Lges:** Greater London 1964-67, Kent 1967

DIRECTIONS

Approach East Kent on the M2 from the London direction towards Margate. Continue to the end of the motorway at Faversham. Proceed onto the A299 Thanet Way. (signposted Margate and Ramsgate). Continue on the A299 for approx 6 miles (passing Seasalter marshes on your left). Take the Whitstable turn off A2990. Continue until you reach the Long Reach roundabout and go straight ahead (second exit). Turn left at the second roundabout (Tesco). Descend Millstrood Hill. After passing the cemetery on your right, turn left into Grimshill Road. The entrance to the Belmont Ground is on the right, 140 yards along Grimshill Road. (SAT NAV - CT5 4LN)

Nearest Railway Station Whitstable 400 yards away

WHYTELEAFE

Founded 1946

Nickname: The Leafe **Club Colours:** White with green

Club Contact Details 0208 660 5491

15 Church Road, Whyteleafe, Surrey CR3 0AR

Previous Names: None

Previous Leagues: Caterham & Ed, Croydon. Thornton Heath & District. Surrey Interm. (East) 1954-58. Surrey Senior 1958-75. Spartan 1975-81. Athenian 1981-84. Isthmian 1984-2012.

09-10		10-11		11-12		12-13		13-14		14-15		15-16		16-17		17-18		18-19	
Isth1S	15	Isth1S	16	Isth1S	21	Kent P	6	SCE	1	Isth1S	5	Isth1S	15	Isth1S	14	Isth1S	8	IsthSE	8
FAC	P	FAC	P	FAC	Pr	FAC	EP	FAC	2Q	FAC	1Q	FAC	Pr	FAC	2Q	FAC	Pr	FAC	1Qr
FAT	2Qr	FAT	Pr	FAT	1Q	FAV	1P	FAV	2P	FAT	2Q	FAT	P	FAT	P	FAT	P	FAT	1Q

HONOURS / RECORDS

FA Comps: None

League: Surrey Senior Premier Division 1968-69. Southern Counties East 2013-14.

County FA: Surrey Senior Cup 1968-69.

Misc: Paid £1,000 to Carshalton Athletic for Gary Bowyer
Received £25,000 for Steve Milton

Best FA Cup First Round Proper 1999-2000

FA Trophy Fourth Round Proper 1998-99

FA Vase FiFth Round Proper 1980-81, 85-86

Ground Capacity: 2,000 **Seats:** 400 **Covered:** 600 **Clubhouse:** Yes **Shop:** Yes

Previous Grounds: None

Record Attendance: 2,210 v Chester City - FA Cup 1999-2000

DIRECTIONS

FROM THE M25 AND THE SOUTH: From Junction 6 of the M26 head north along the A22 (signposted to London, Croydon and Caterham). At Wapses Lodge Roundabout, the Ann Summers building is clearly visible opposite, take the third exit. Take the first left adjacent to Whyteleafe South railway station and cross the level crossing. Fork right after 200 yards into Church Road. The ground is a quarter of a mile down the road on the right. FROM THE NORTH: From Purley Cross (where the A23 crosses the A22), head south signposted to Eastbourne and the M25. Pass 'My Old China' (Chinese restaurant) on your right and continue under a railway bridge. Follow the A22 through Kenley and into Whyteleafe. At the first roundabout (with Whyteleafe Tavern opposite), turn right and cross a level crossing adjacent to Whyteleafe Station. Take first left into Church Road keeping St Luke Church to your right. The ground is a quarter of a mile up the road on the left.

Nearest Railway Station Whyteleafe South - 0.4km

NPL PREMIER INS: Ashton United (R - NatN), Atherton Collieries (P - NPLW), FC United of Manchester (R - NatN), Morpeth Town (P - NPLE), Radcliffe (P - NPLW).

ASHTON UNITED

Founded 1878

Nickname: Robins **Club Colours:** Red and white

Club Contact Details 0161 339 4158
Hurst Cross, Surrey Street, Ashton-u-Lyne OL6 8DY

Previous Names: Hurst 1878-1947
Previous Leagues: Manchester, Lancashire Combination 1912-33, 48-64, 66-68, Midland 1964-66, Cheshire County 1923-48, 68-82, North West Counties 1982-92. NPL 92-2018. National 2018-19.

09-10		10-11		11-12		12-13		13-14		14-15		15-16		16-17		17-18		18-19	
NP P	12	NP P	14	NP P	12	NP P	10	NP P	5	NP P	3	NP P	3	NP P	11	NP P	2	Nat N	20
FAC	2Q	FAC	2Q	FAC	2Q	FAC	2Q	FAC	3Q	FAC	3Q	FAC	3Q	FAC	1Q	FAC	2Q	FAC	4Q
FAT	1Q	FAT	1Qr	FAT	1Q	FAT	1Q	FAT	1Q	FAT	1Q	FAV	1P	FAT	1Q	FAT	2Pr	FAT	3Q

HONOURS / RECORDS
FA Comps: None
League: Manchester League 1911-12. Lancashire Combination 1916-17.
North West Counties Division Two 1987-88, Division One 1991-92.
County FA: Manchester Senior Cup 1894-95, 1913-14, 75-76, 77-78.
Manchester Premier Cup 1979-80, 82-83, 91-92, 2000-01, 01-02, 02-03. Manchester Challenge Shield 1992-93.

Victory: 11-3 v Stalybridge Celtic - Manchester Intermediate Cup 1955
Defeat: 1-11 v Wellington Town - Cheshire League 1946-47
Appearances: Micky Boyle - 462
Additional: Paid £9,000 to Netherfield for Andy Whittaker 1994
Received £15,000 from Rotherham United for Karl Marginson 1993

Ground Capacity: 4,500 **Seats:** 250 **Covered:** 750 **Clubhouse:** Yes **Shop:** Yes
Previous Grounds: Rose HIll 1878-1912
Record Attendance: 11,000 v Halifax Town - FA Cup 1st Round 1952

DIRECTIONS
From the M62 (approx 7.5 miles) Exit at Junction 20, take A627M to Oldham exit (2.5 miles) Take A627 towards Oldham town centre At King Street Roundabout take Park Road Continue straight onto B6194 Abbey Hills Road Follow B6194 onto Lees Road Turn right at the stone cross memorial and 1st right into the ground. From the M60 (approx 2.5 miles); Exit at Junction 23, take A635 for Ashton town centre Follow by-pass to B6194 Mossley Road. At traffic lights turn left into Queens Road Continue onto B6194 Lees Road Turn left at the stone cross memorial and 1st right into the ground.

Nearest Railway Station Ashton-under-Lyne - 1.4km
Bus Route Kings Road - stop 50m away

ATHERTON COLLIERIES

Founded 1916

Nickname: Colls **Club Colours:** Black & white

Club Contact Details 07968 548 056
Alder Street, Atherton, Greater Manchester M46 9EY

Previous Names: None
Previous Leagues: Bolton Combination 1918-21, 52-71. Lancashire Alliance 1921. Manchester 1945-48. West Lancashire 1948-50. Lancashire Combination 1950-52, 71-78. Cheshire Co 1978-82. North West Co 1982-2017.

09-10		10-11		11-12		12-13		13-14		14-15		15-16		16-17		17-18		18-19	
NWC1	6	NWC1	5	NWC1	4	NWC1	4	NWC1	5	NWC1	1	NWCP	3	NWCP	1	NP1N	10	NP1W	1
FAC	P	FAC	Pr	FAC	P	FAC	1Q	FAC	Pr	FAC	Pr	FAC	Pr	FAC	P	FAC	2Q	FAC	1Q
FAV	2Q	FAV	2Q	FAV	2Q	FAV	1Q	FAV	1Q	FAV	2P	FAV	3P	FAV	5P	FAT	2Q	FAT	Pr

HONOURS / RECORDS
FA Comps: None
League: Bolton Combination 1919-20, 36-37, 37-38, 38-39, 40-41, 44-45, 56-57, 58-59, 60-61, 64-65.
North West Counties Division Three 1986-87, Division One 2014-15, Premier 2016-17. NPL Division One West 2018-19.
County FA: Lancashire County FA Shield 1919-20, 22-23, 41-42, 45-46, 56-57, 64-65.

Best FA Cup Third Qualifying Round 1994-95
FA Vase Fifth Round 2016-17
FA Trophy Second Qualifying Round 2017-18

Ground Capacity: 2,500 **Seats:** Yes **Covered:** Yes **Clubhouse:** Yes **Shop:** No
Previous Grounds: None
Record Attendance: 3,300 in the Bolton Combination 1920's.

DIRECTIONS
M61 to junction 5, follow sign for Westhoughton, turn left onto A6, turn right onto A579 (Newbrook Road/Bolton Road) into Atherton. At first set of traffic lights turn left into High Street, then second left into Alder Street to ground.

Nearest Railway Station Atherton - 0.7km
Bus Route High Street - stop 100m away

BAMBER BRIDGE

Founded 1952

Nickname: Brig **Club Colours:** White & black

Club Contact Details 01772 909 690 admin@bamberbridgefc.com

Sir Tom Finney Stadium, Brownedge Road, Bamber Bridge PR5 6UX

Previous Names: None

Previous Leagues: Preston & District 1952-90, North West Counties 1990-93

09-10		10-11		11-12		12-13		13-14		14-15		15-16		16-17		17-18		18-19	
NP1N	14	NP1N	7	NP1N	10	NP1N	9	NP1N	4	NP1N	3	NP1N	12	NP1N	11	NP1N	4	NP P	16
FAC	2Q	FAC	2Qr	FAC	1Q	FAC	2Q	FAC	1Qr	FAC	3Q	FAC	4Q	FAC	P	FAC	1Q	FAC	2Qr
FAT	1Q	FAT	2Q	FAT	1Q	FAT	P	FAT	P	FAT	1Q	FAT	P	FAT	1Q	FAT	1Q	FAT	1Q

HONOURS / RECORDS

FA Comps: None

League: Preston & District Premier Division 1980-81, 85-86, 86-87, 89-90. North West Counties Division Two 1991-92. Northern Premier Premier Division 1995-96.

County FA: Lancashire FA Amateur Shield 1981-82, Trophy 1994-95.

Victory: 8-0 v Curzon Ashton - North West Counties 1994-95

Additional: Paid £10,000 to Horwich RMI for Mark Edwards
Received £15,000 from Wigan Athletic for Tony Black 1995

Ground Capacity: 3,000 **Seats:** 554 **Covered:** 800 **Clubhouse:** Yes **Shop:** Yes

Previous Grounds: King George V, Higher Wallton 1952-86

Record Attendance: 2,300 v Czech Republic - Pre Euro '96 friendly

DIRECTIONS

Junction 29, A6 (Bamber Bridge by-pass)onto London Way. First roundabout take 3rd exit Brownedge Road (East) then take first right. Ground on left at the bottom of the road.

Nearest Railway Station Lostock Hall - 0.9km. Bamber Bridge - 0.9km

Bus Route Irongate - stop 100m away

BASFORD UNITED

Founded 1900

Nickname: Community **Club Colours:** All amber

Club Contact Details 0115 924 4491

Mill Street Playing Field, Greenwich Avenue, off Bagnall Road, Basford, Nottingham NG6 0LD

Previous Names: None

Previous Leagues: Notts Alliance 1905-39, 1946-2004. Notts Amateur League 1939-46. Notts Amateur Alliance 2004-06. Notts Senior 2006-11. Central Midlands 2011-12. East Midlands Counties 2012-13. Northern Counties East 2013-14. Midland League 2014-15.

09-10		10-11		11-12		12-13		13-14		14-15		15-16		16-17		17-18		18-19	
NottS	2	NottS	2	CMSth	1	EMC	1	NCEP	5	MFLP	1	NP1S	4	NP1S	6	NP1S	1	NP P	7
								FAC	1Q	FAC	Pr	FAC	2Q	FAC	P	FAC	3Q	FAC	1Q
						FAV	2P	FAV	2Q	FAV	2Q	FAT	2Q	FAT	P	FAT	1Q	FAT	1P

HONOURS / RECORDS

FA Comps: None

League: Notts Alliance 1905-06, 07-08, 19-20, Division One 1997-98. Central Midlands Southern 2011-12. East Midland Counties 2012-13. Midland Football Premier Division 2014-15. Northern Premier Division One South 2017-18.

County FA: Notts Senior Cup 1946-47, 87-88, 2014-15, 15-16, 17-18, Intermediate Cup 2005-06.

Misc: Former club secretary, Wallace Brownlow, who took up the post when 19 in 1907, remained in the position until his death in 1970 - a world record of 63 years.

Ground Capacity: 2,200 **Seats:** Yes **Covered:** Yes **Clubhouse:** Yes **Shop:**

Previous Grounds: Old Peer Tree Inn, Dolly Tub > 1903, Catchems Corner 1903-30, Vernon Avenue 1930-34, Mill Street 1934-91.

Record Attendance: 3,500 v Grantham United, FACup 1937.

DIRECTIONS

From M1 junction 26 take the A610 to Nottingham for 1.3 miles, turn left at the 2nd roundabout by the Gateway Hotel onto Cinderhill Road. After ¼ mile turn right onto Bagnall Road, take the 4th left onto Greenwich Avenue and the ground is at the end of the road. NB. This is the best route and the route via the A453 should be avoided if possible.

Nearest Railway Station Highbury Vale Tram Stop - 400m

Bus Route Christina Avenue - stop 150m away

BUXTON

Founded 1877

Nickname: The Bucks **Club Colours:** Blue & white

Club Contact Details 01298 23197

The Silverlands, Buxton, Derbyshire SK17 6QH

Previous Names: None

Previous Leagues: Combination 1891-99. Manchester 1899-1932. Cheshire County 1932-40, 46-73. Northern Premier 1973-98, 2006- Northern Counties East 1998-2006.

09-10		10-11		11-12		12-13		13-14		14-15		15-16		16-17		17-18		18-19	
NP P	8	NP P	6	NP P	13	NP P	7	NP P	13	NP P	10	NP P	11	NP P	7	NP P	8	NP P	5
FAC	4Q	FAC	4Q	FAC	2Q	FAC	4Q	FAC	2Q	FAC	3Q	FAC	3Qr	FAC	1Q	FAC	4Q	FAC	2Qr
FAT	2Q	FAT	1Q	FAT	2Q	FAT	1Pr	FAT	2Q	FAT	2Q	FAT	3Q	FAT	2Q	FAT	1Q	FAT	2Qr

HONOURS / RECORDS

FA Comps: None

League: Manchester 1931-32. Cheshire County 1972-73.
Northern Counties East 2005-06. Northern Premier Division One 2006-07.

County FA: Derbyshire Senior Cup 1938-39, 45-46, 56-57, 59-60, 71-72, 80-81, 85-86, 86-87, 2008-09, 11-12.

Goalscorer: Mark Reed - 251 (469 appearances)

Appearances: David Bainbridge - 642

Additional: Paid £5,000 to Hyde United for Gary Walker 1989
Received £16,500 from Rotherham for Ally Pickering 1989

Ground Capacity: 5,200 **Seats:** 490 **Covered:** 2,500 **Clubhouse:** Yes **Shop:** Yes

Previous Grounds: The Park (Cricket Club) 1877-78. Fields at Cote Heath and Green Lane 1878-84.

Record Attendance: 6,000 v Barrow - FA Cup 1st Round 1962-63

DIRECTIONS

FROM MANCHESTER (A6): Drop down hill into Buxton on the A6. Junction with A53 (Buxton) At mini-roundabout turn left (signposted Matlock) A6. At Safeway roundabout take 2nd exit (right) B5059 (not shown) (signposted Poole's Cavern and Country Park)
Turn right onto High Street (London Road Lights) - A515. Turn right on Buxton Market at Joe Royle's shop. Turn left onto Concert Place (signposted for Police Station) then Hardwick Square South. Continue forward onto Silverlands. Ground on right after 400 metres.

Nearest Railway Station Higher Buxton - walking distance from the gorund.

FC UNITED OF MANCHESTER

Founded 2005

Nickname: F.C. **Club Colours:** Red/white/black

Club Contact Details 0161 769 2005 office@fc-utd.co.uk

Broadhurst Park, 310 Lightbowne Road, Moston, Manchester, M40 0FJ

Previous Names: None

Previous Leagues: North West Counties 2005-07. Northern Premier 2007-15. National 2015-19.

09-10		10-11		11-12		12-13		13-14		14-15		15-16		16-17		17-18		18-19	
NP P	13	NP P	4	NP P	6	NP P	3	NP P	2	NP P	1	Nat N	13	Nat N	13	Nat N	16	Nat N	21
FAC	4Q	FAC	2Pr	FAC	2Q	FAC	4Q	FAC	1Q	FAC	2Q	FAC	1P	FAC	3Qr	FAC	4Q	FAC	3Q
FAT	3Q	FAT	3Q	FAT	1P	FAT	2Q	FAT	1Qr	FAT	QF	FAT	3Q	FAT	3Q	FAT	3Q	FAT	3Q

HONOURS / RECORDS

FA Comps: None

League: North West Counties League Division Two 2005-06, Division One 2006-07.
Northern Premier League Division One North Play-off 2007-08, Premier Division 2014-15.

County FA: Manchester Premier Cup 2016-17, 17-18.

Victory: 10-2 v Castleton Gabriels 10/12/2005. 8-0 v Squires Gate 14/10/06, Glossop N.E. 28/10/06 & Nelson 05/09/10

Defeat: 0-5 v Harrogate Town, 20 February 2016

Goalscorer: Rory Patterson - 99 (2005-08). Simon Carden scored 5 goals against Castleton Gabriels 10/12/2005.

Appearances: Jerome Wright - 400

Additional: Longest unbeaten run (League): 22 games 03/12/2006 - 18/08/2007.

Ground Capacity: 4,400 **Seats:** 696 **Covered:** Yes **Clubhouse:** Yes **Shop:** Yes

Previous Grounds: Gigg Lane(Bury FC) 2005-14. Bower Fold (Stalybridge C) Aug-Dec'14. Tameside Stad (Curzon A)

Record Attendance: 6,731 v Brighton & Hove Albion, FA Cup 2nd Round 08/12/2010 (Gigg Lane)

DIRECTIONS

From South leave M60 at J21 turn left and immediately right to Manchester City Centre A663. After 350 yards bear right onto A6104 to Manchester. At Greengate roundabout take first exit onto Lightbowne Road. Ground is half a mile on the left.
From North leave M60 at J20, turn right onto A664 Blackley. After 700 yards turn left at lights onto A6104 Oldham. After 1.5 miles take 4th exit off Greengate roundabout onto Lightbowne Road.

Nearest Railway Station Moston - 11min walk from the ground.

Bus Route Matchday Special and Shuttle Bus

GAINSBOROUGH TRINITY

Founded 1873

Nickname: The Blues **Club Colours:** All blue

Club Contact Details 07500 838 068
The Martin & Co Arena, Gainsborough, Lincolnshire DN21 2QW

Previous Names: Trinity Recreationists
Previous Leagues: Midland (FM) 1889-96, 1912-60, 61-68. Football League 1896-1912. Yorkshire 1960-61.
Northern Premier (FM) 1968-2004.

09-10		10-11		11-12		12-13		13-14		14-15		15-16		16-17		17-18		18-19	
Conf N	14	Conf N	18	Conf N	4	Conf N	8	Conf N	16	Conf N	17	Nat N	18	Nat N	19	Nat N	20	NP P	6
FAC	3Q	FAC	2Q	FAC	4Q	FAC	2Qr	FAC	2Q	FAC	4Q	FAC	1P	FAC	2Q	FAC	1P	FAC	3Q
FAT	2Pr	FAT	3Q	FAT	3Q	FAT	SF	FAT	3Q	FAT	1P	FAT	3Qr	FAT	3Qr	FAT	1P	FAT	1Qr

HONOURS / RECORDS
FA Comps: None
League: Midland 1890-91, 1927-28, 48-49, 66-67.

County FA: Lincolnshire County Senior Cup 1889-90, 92-93, 94-95, 97-98, 1903-04, 04-05, 06-07, 10-11, 46-47, 47-48, 48-49, 50-51, 51-52, 57-58, 58-59, 63-64, 70-71, 2002-03, 15-16, 17-18. Lincolnshire Shield 2007-08.

Victory: 7-0 v Fleetwood Town and v Great Harwood Town
Defeat: 1-7 v Stalybridge Celtic - Northern Premier 2000-01 and v Brentford - FA Cup 03-04.
Additional: Paid £3,000 to Buxton for Stuart Lowe
Received £30,000 from Lincoln City for Tony James

Ground Capacity: 4,340 **Seats:** 504 **Covered:** 2,500 **Clubhouse:** Yes **Shop:** Yes
Previous Grounds: Played at Bowling Green Ground and Sincil Bank when Northolme was being used for cricket.
Record Attendance: 9,760 v Scunthorpe United - Midland League 1948

DIRECTIONS

The Northolme is situated on the A159, Gainsborough to Scunthorpe road, approximately a third of a mile north of the Town Centre. Public Car Park on the right 150 yards before the Ground. Any person parked illegally in the Streets around the Ground will be issued with a ticket from the Police.

Nearest Railway Station Gainsborough Central - less than half a mile away.

GRANTHAM TOWN

Founded 1874

Nickname: Gingerbreads **Club Colours:** Black & white stripes

Club Contact Details 01476 591 818 psnixon@hotmail.com
South Kesteven Sports Stadium, Trent Road, Gratham NG31 7XQ

Previous Names: Grantham FC 1874-1987.
Previous Leagues: Midland Amateur Alliance, Central Alliance 1911-25, 59-61, Midland Counties 1925-59, 61-72,
Southern 1972-79, 85-2006, Northern Premier 1979-85

09-10		10-11		11-12		12-13		13-14		14-15		15-16		16-17		17-18		18-19	
NP1S	11	NP1S	5	NP1S	1	NP P	19	NP P	15	NP P	12	NP P	18	NP P	8	NP P	4	NP P	18
FAC	Pr	FAC	Pr	FAC	3Q	FAC	2Q	FAC	1Qr	FAC	3Q	FAC	1Q	FAC	1Qr	FAC	2Q	FAC	2Qr
FAT	Pr	FAT	P	FAT	1Q	FAT	1Q	FAT	1Qr	FAT	1Q	FAT	1Q	FAT	2Q	FAT	3Q	FAT	1Q

HONOURS / RECORDS
FA Comps: None
League: Midland Amateur 1910-11. Central Alliance 1924-25. Midland 1963-64, 70-71, 71-72.
Southern Division One North 1972-73, 78-79, Midland Division 97-98. Northern Premier Division One South 2011-12.
County FA: Lincolnshire Senior Cup 1884-85, 1971-72, 82-83, County Senior Cup 1936-37, Senior Cup 'A' 1953-54, 60-61, 61-62, County Shield 2003-04, 04-05.

Victory: 13-0 v Rufford Colliery (H) - FA Cup 15/09/1934
Defeat: 0-16 v Notts County Rovers (A) - Midland Amateur Alliance 22/10/1892
Goalscorer: Jack McCartney - 416
Appearances: Chris Gardner - 664
Additional: Received £20,000 from Nottingham Forest for Gary Crosby

Ground Capacity: 7,500 **Seats:** 750 **Covered:** 1,950 **Clubhouse:** Yes **Shop:** Yes
Previous Grounds: London Road >1990-91. Spalding United FC 1990-91.
Record Attendance: 6,578 v Middlesbrough, FA Cup Third Round Proper, 1973-74.

DIRECTIONS

FROM A1 NORTH: Leave A1 At A607 Melton Mowbray exit. Turn left at island on slip road into Swingbridge Lane. At T junction turn left into Trent Road ground is 100yds on right. **FROM A52 NOTTINGHAM:** Pass over A1 and at first island turn right into housing estate & Barrowby Gate. Through housing estate to T junction. Turn right and then immediately left into Trent road ground is 100 yards on the left.
FROM A607 MELTON MOWBRAY: Pass under A1 and take next left A1 South slip road. At island turn right into Swingbridge Road then as for A1 North above. From all directions follow brown signs for Sports Complex, which is immediately behind the stadium.

Nearest Railway Station Grantham - 1.5km
Bus Route Meres Leisure Centre - stop 100m away

HYDE UNITED

Founded 1919

Nickname: The Tigers **Club Colours:** Red & navy

Club Contact Details 0161 367 7273
Ewen Fields, Walker Lane, Hyde SK14 5PL

Previous Names: Hyde United 1919-2010, Hyde F.C. 2010-15.
Previous Leagues: Lancashire & Cheshire 1919-21, Manchester 1921-30, Cheshire County 1930-68, 1970-82, Northern Premier 1968-70, 1983-2004. Football Conference 2004-15.

09-10		10-11		11-12		12-13		13-14		14-15		15-16		16-17		17-18		18-19	
Conf N	15	Conf N	19	Conf N	1	Conf	18	Conf	24	Conf N	22	NP P	22	NP1N	10	NP1N	3	NP P	10
FAC	2Qr	FAC	2Qr	FAC	3Q	FAC	4Qr	FAC	4Q	FAC	2Q	FAC	2Qr	FAC	2Q	FAC	1P	FAC	1Q
FAT	3Qr	FAT	1P	FAT	1P	FAT	1Pr	FAT	1P	FAT	2P	FAT	1Qr	FAT	P	FAT	P	FAT	2Q

HONOURS / RECORDS
FA Comps: None
League: Manchester 1920-21, 21-22, 22-23, 28-29, 29-30. Cheshire 1954-55, 55-56, 81-82.
Northern Premier Division One North 2003-04, Premier Division 2004-05. Conference North 2011-12.
County FA: Cheshire Senior Cup 1945-46, 62-63, 69-70, 80-81, 89-90, 96-97. Manchester Senior Cup 1974-75, Premier Cup 1993-94, 94-95, 95-96, 98-99.

Victory: 13-1 v Eccles United, 1921-22.
Goalscorer: Pete O'Brien - 247. Ernest Gillibrand 86 goals during the 1929-30 season, including 7 against New Mills.
Appearances: Steve Johnson - 623 (1975-1988)
Additional: Paid £8,000 to Mossley for Jim McCluskie 1989
Received £50,000 from Crewe Alexandra for Colin Little 1995

Ground Capacity: 4,250 **Seats:** 530 **Covered:** 4,073 **Clubhouse:** Yes **Shop:** Yes
Previous Grounds: None
Record Attendance: 7,600 v Nelson - FA Cup 1952

DIRECTIONS
M60 (Manchester Orbital Motorway) to Junction 24, take the M67 (towards Sheffield) to junction 3 (Hyde/Dukinfield/Stalybridge). Once on exit slipway, keep to the right-hand lane heading for Hyde town centre. At the traffic lights at end of the slipway turn right, then at the second set of lights turn left (Morrisons on left) onto Mottram Road. Turn right at next lights onto Lumn Road. Left at Give Way sign onto Walker Lane. Ground entrance is on left, just after Hyde Leisure Pool, and is clearly signposted. Please note for Satnav, use SK14 5PL

Nearest Railway Station Newton for Hyde - 0.8km
Bus Route Walker Lane - stop 110m away

LANCASTER CITY

Founded 1911

Nickname: Dolly Blues **Club Colours:** Blue & white

Club Contact Details 01524 382 238 secretary@lancastercityfc.com
Giant Axe, West Road, Lancaster LA1 5PE

Previous Names: Lancaster Town 1911-37
Previous Leagues: Lancashire Combination 1911-70, Northern Premier League 1970-82, 87-2004, North West Counties 1982-87, Conference 2004-07

09-10		10-11		11-12		12-13		13-14		14-15		15-16		16-17		17-18		18-19	
NP1N	2	NP1N	8	NP1N	6	NP1N	13	NP1N	6	NP1N	11	NP1N	6	NP1N	1	NP P	17	NP P	12
FAC	1Q	FAC	P	FAC	3Q	FAC	1Q	FAC	2Qr	FAC	3Q	FAC	2Q	FAC	3Q	FAC	3Q	FAC	1Q
FAT	2Qr	FAT	2Q	FAT	P	FAT	P	FAT	1Q	FAT	Pr	FAT	Pr	FAT	1Q	FAT	1P	FAT	1P

HONOURS / RECORDS
FA Comps: None
League: Northern Premier Division One 1995-96, Division One North 2016-17.
County FA: Lancashire Junior Cup (ATS Challenge Trophy) 1927-28, 28-29, 30-31, 33-34, 51-52, 74-75.

Victory: 17-2 v Appleby, FA Cup, 1915.
Defeat: 0-10 v Matlock Town - Northern Premier League Division 1 1973-74
Goalscorer: David Barnes - 130, 1979-84, 88-91. Jordan Connerton scored 38 during the 2009-10 season.
Appearances: Edgar J Parkinson - 591, 1949-64.
Additional: Paid £6,000 to Droylsden for Jamie Tandy. Received £25,000 from Birmingham City for Chris Ward.

Ground Capacity: 3,500 **Seats:** 513 **Covered:** 900 **Clubhouse:** Yes **Shop:** Yes
Previous Grounds: None
Record Attendance: 7,506 v Carlisle United - FA Cup Fourth Qualifying Round, 17/11/1927

DIRECTIONS
From the South: Exit M6 at Junction 33. At roundabout take the second exit onto the A6, pass through Galgate and then Lancaster University on the right until the next roundabout. Take the second main exit into Lancaster and follow signs for the railway station. At the traffic lights by Waterstones Bookshop turn immediately left. Take the second right onto Station Road and follow downhill on West Road and take the first right into the ground. **From the North:** Exit M6 at Junction 34 and turn left onto the A683. Follow signs for railway station into City around the one way system. Move over to the right hand side lane at the police station and through traffic lights. Manoeuvre into the left-hand lane until traffic lights at Waterstones Bookshop. Follow directions as from the south.

MATLOCK TOWN

Founded 1885

Nickname: The Gladiators **Club Colours:** Blue & white

Club Contact Details 01629 583 866
Causeway Lane, Matlock, Derbyshire DE4 3AR

Previous Names: None
Previous Leagues: Midland Combination 1894-96, Matlock and District, Derbyshire Senior, Central Alliance 1924-25, 47-61, Central Combination 1934-35, Chesterfield & District 1946-47, Midland Counties 1961-69

09-10		10-11		11-12		12-13		13-14		14-15		15-16		16-17		17-18		18-19	
NP P	7	NP P	11	NP P	14	NP P	17	NP P	12	NP P	14	NP P	17	NP P	9	NP P	14	NP P	15
FAC	2Qr	FAC	3Q	FAC	2Q	FAC	1Qr	FAC	2Q	FAC	1Q	FAC	1Qr	FAC	4Q	FAC	2Q	FAC	1Q
FAT	1P	FAT	2Qr	FAT	3Q	FAT	2P	FAT	3Q	FAT	1Q	FAT	1P	FAT	2P	FAT	1Q	FAT	1Q

HONOURS / RECORDS
FA Comps: FA Trophy 1974-75. Anglo Italian Non-League Cup 1979.
League: Central Alliance North Division 1959-60, 60-61. Midland Counties 1961-62, 68-69.

County FA: Derbyshire Senior Cup 1974-75, 76-77, 77-78, 83-84, 84-85, 91-92, 2003-04, 09-10, 14-15, 16-17.

Victory: 10-0 v Lancaster City (A) - 1974
Defeat: 0-8 v Chorley (A) - 1971
Goalscorer: Peter Scott
Appearances: Mick Fenoughty
Additional: Paid £2,000 for Kenny Clark 1996. Received £10,000 from York City for Ian Helliwell.

Ground Capacity: 2,757 **Seats:** 560 **Covered:** 1,200 **Clubhouse:** Yes **Shop:** Yes
Previous Grounds: None
Record Attendance: 5,123 v Burton Albion - FA Trophy Semi-final, 1975

DIRECTIONS
On A615, ground is 500 yards from Town Centre and Matlock BR. Sat Nav users can enter DE4 3AR

Nearest Railway Station Matlock - 0.3km
Bus Route Causeway Lane - stop 100m away

MICKLEOVER SPORTS

Founded 1948

Nickname: Sports **Club Colours:** Red & black

Club Contact Details 01332 512 826
Mickleover Sports Club, Station Road, Mickleover Derby DE3 9FE

Previous Names: Mickleover Old Boys 1948-93
Previous Leagues: Derby & District Senior 1948-93. Central Midlands 1993-99, Northern Counties East 1999-2009

09-10		10-11		11-12		12-13		13-14		14-15		15-16		16-17		17-18		18-19	
NP1S	1	NP P	15	NP P	21	NP1S	21	NP1S	5	NP1S	1	NP P	20	NP P	16	NP P	12	NP P	19
FAC	2Q	FAC	3Q	FAC	2Q	FAC	Pr	FAC	2Qr	FAC	3Q	FAC	1Q	FAC	2Q	FAC	3Q	FAC	3Q
FAT	P	FAT	2Q	FAT	1Q	FAT	P	FAT	2Q	FAT	3Q	FAT	1Q	FAT	3Qr	FAT	1Q	FAT	2Qr

HONOURS / RECORDS
FA Comps: None
League: Central Midlands Supreme Division 1998-99. Northern Counties East Division One 2002-03, Premier Division 2008-09. Northern Premier League Division One South 2009-10, 14-15.
County FA: None

Misc: Won 16 consecutive League matches in 2009-10 - a Northern Premier League record
Best FA Cup Third Qualifying Round 2010-11, 14-15, 17-18, 18-19
FA Trophy Third Qualifying Round 2014-15, 16-17(r)
FA Vase Fourth Round Proper 2000-01

Ground Capacity: 1,500 **Seats:** 280 **Covered:** 500 **Clubhouse:** Yes **Shop:** Yes
Previous Grounds: None
Record Attendance: 1,074 v FC United of Manchester, Northern Premier League Premier Division, 02/10/10.

DIRECTIONS
M1 NORTH - J28. A38 to Derby. At Markeaton Island right A52 Ashbourne, 2nd left Radbourne Lane, 3rd Left Station Road 50 yds.

M1 SOUTH – J25. A52 to Derby. Follow signs for Ashbourne, pick up A52 at Markeaton Island (MacDonalds) then as above.

FROM STOKE A50 – Derby. A516 to A38 then as above.

Nearest Railway Station Peartree - 5.1km
Bus Route Buxton Drive - stop 100m away

MORPETH TOWN

Founded 1909

Nickname: Highwaymen **Club Colours:** Amber & black

Club Contact Details 07882 991 356
Craik Park, Morpeth Common, Morpeth, Northumberland NE61 2YX

Previous Names: None
Previous Leagues: Northern Alliance 1936-1994. Northern League 1994-2018.

09-10		10-11		11-12		12-13		13-14		14-15		15-16		16-17		17-18		18-19	
NL 1	21	NL 2	20	NL 2	4	NL 2	3	NL 2	17	NL 1	8	NL 1	4	NL 1	2	NL 1	2	NP1E	1
FAC	1Q	FAC	EP			FAC	EP	FAC	1Q	FAC	EP	FAC	P	FAC	3Q	FAC	EP	FAC	1Qr
FAV	2P	FAV	2Q	FAV	1Q	FAV	2P	FAV	5P	FAV	2P	FAV	F	FAV	4P	FAV	2P	FAT	P

HONOURS / RECORDS
FA Comps: FA Vase 2015-16.
League: Northern Alliance 1983-84, 93-94. Northern Division Two 1995-96.

County FA: Northumberland Benevolent Bowl 1978-79, 85-86. Northumberland Senior Cup 2006-07.

Best FA Cup Fourth Qualifying Round 1998-99
FA Trophy Preliminary Round 2018-19

Ground Capacity: 1,000 **Seats:** 100 **Covered:** Yes **Clubhouse:** Yes **Shop:**
Previous Grounds: Stobhill Cricket Hill. Storey Park 1954-94.
Record Attendance:

DIRECTIONS
From south. Turn off the A1 onto A197, sign posted Morpeth.
Turn left at sign pointing Belsay (B6524).
Take right turn just before bridge under the A1.
Ground is signposted and up a small track is on the right.

Nearest Railway Station Morpeth - 1.9km
Bus Route Whalton Road - stop 670m away

NANTWICH TOWN

Founded 1884

Nickname: The Dabbers **Club Colours:** All green

Club Contact Details 01270 621 771 secretary@nantwichtownfc.com
Weaver Stadium, Water Lode, Kingsley Fields, Nantwich, CW5 5UP

Previous Names: Nantwich
Previous Leagues: Shropshire & Dist. 1891-92, Combination 1892-94, 1901-10, Cheshire Junior 1894-95, Crewe & Dist. 1895-97, North Staffs & Dist. 1897-1900, Cheshire 1900-01, Manchester 1910-12, 65-68, Lancs. Com. 1912-14, Cheshire Co. 1919-38, 68-82, Crewe & Dist. 1938-39, 47-48, Crewe Am. Comb. 1946-47, Mid-Cheshire 1948-65, North West Co. 1982-2007

09-10		10-11		11-12		12-13		13-14		14-15		15-16		16-17		17-18		18-19	
NP P	10	NP P	17	NP P	10	NP P	14	NP P	19	NP P	15	NP P	8	NP P	5	NP P	15	NP P	4
FAC	1Q	FAC	2Q	FAC	1P	FAC	1Q	FAC	1Q	FAC	1Q	FAC	1Q	FAC	4Q	FAC	1P	FAC	2Qr
FAT	1P	FAT	1P	FAT	1Q	FAT	2Qr	FAT	3Q	FAT	2Q	FAT	SF	FAT	1P	FAT	1Q	FAT	1Q

HONOURS / RECORDS
FA Comps: FA Vase 2005-06.
League: Mid-Cheshire 1963-64. Cheshire County 1980-81.

County FA: Crew Amateur Combination 1946-47. Cheshire Amateur Cup 1895-96, 1963-64.
Cheshire Senior Cup 1932-33, 75-76, 2007-08, 11-12, 17-18.

Victory: 20-0 v Whitchurch Alexandra (home) 1900/01 Cheshire League Division 1, 5 April 1901
Defeat: 2-16 v Stalybridge Celtic (away) 1932/33 Cheshire County League, 22 Oct 1932
Goalscorer: John Scarlett 161 goals (1992/3 to 2005/6).
Bobby Jones scored 60 goals during season 1946-47, Gerry Duffy scored 42 during season 1961-62
Additional: Received £20,000 from Crewe Alexandra for Kelvin Mellor - Feb 2008

Ground Capacity: 3,500 **Seats:** 350 **Covered:** 495 **Clubhouse:** Yes **Shop:** Yes
Previous Grounds: London Road/Jackson Avenue (1884-2007)
Record Attendance: 5,121 v Winsford United - Cheshire Senior Cup 2nd Round 1920-21

DIRECTIONS
M6 Jun 16 A500 towards Nantwich. Over 4 roundabouts onto A51 towards Nantwich Town Centre, through traffic lights and over railway crossing. Over next r/bout then left at next r/bout past Morrisons supermarket on right. Continue over r/bout through traffic lights. Ground on right at next set of traffic lights.
SATNAV Postcode: CW5 5UP

Nearest Railway Station Nantwich - 1.1km
Bus Route Malbank School - stop 150m away

RADCLIFFE

Founded 1949

Nickname: The Boro **Club Colours:** Blue

Club Contact Details 0161 724 8346 secretary@radcliffefc.com
Stainton Park, Pilkington Road, Radcliffe, Lancashire M26 3PE

Previous Names: Radcliffe Borough >2018
Previous Leagues: South East Lancashire, Manchester 1953-63, Lancashire Combination 1963-71, Cheshire County 1971-82, North West Counties 1982-97

09-10		10-11		11-12		12-13		13-14		14-15		15-16		16-17		17-18		18-19	
NP1N	10	NP1N	18	NP1N	15	NP1N	15	NP1N	18	NP1N	19	NP1N	18	NP1N	20	NP1N	20	NP1W	2
FAC	3Q	FAC	1Q	FAC	3Q	FAC	Pr	FAC	1Q	FAC	1Q	FAC	P	FAC	1Q	FAC	1Q	FAC	2Q
FAT	1Qr	FAT	2Qr	FAT	2Qr	FAT	1Q	FAT	1Q	FAT	P	FAT	2Q	FAT	P	FAT	P	FAT	P

HONOURS / RECORDS
FA Comps: None
League: South Lancashire Division Two 1950-51, Division One 51-52, Premier 80-81. North West Counties Division Two 1982-83, Division One 84-85. Northern Premier Division One 1996-97.
County FA: Manchester Premier Cup 2007-08.

Goalscorer: Ian Lunt - 147. Jody Banim scored 46 during a single season.
Appearances: Simon Kelly - 502
Additional: Paid £5,000 to Buxton for Gary Walker 1991
Received £20,000 from Shrewsbury Town for Jody Banim 2003

Ground Capacity: 4,000 **Seats:** 350 **Covered:** 1,000 **Clubhouse:** Yes **Shop:** Yes
Previous Grounds: Ashworth Street. Bright Street > 1970.
Record Attendance: 2,495 v York City - FA Cup 1st Round 2000-01

DIRECTIONS
M62 junction 17 – follow signs for 'Whitefield' and 'Bury'.
Take A665 to Radcliffe via by-pass to Bolton Road. Signposted to turn right into Unsworth Street opposite Turf Hotel.
The Stadium is on the left approximately half a mile turning Colshaw Close East.

Nearest Railway Station Radcliffe - 1.3km
Bus Route Lowe Street - 100m away

SCARBOROUGH ATHLETIC

Founded 2007

Nickname: The Seadogs **Club Colours:** Red & white

Club Contact Details 07538 903 723 club.secretary@scarboroughathletic.com
Scarborough Leisure Village, Ashburn Road YO11 2JW

Previous Names: Formed after Scarborough F.C. folded in 2007.
Previous Leagues: Northern Counties East 2007-13.

09-10		10-11		11-12		12-13		13-14		14-15		15-16		16-17		17-18		18-19	
NCEP	5	NCEP	10	NCEP	3	NCEP	1	NP1S	7	NP1N	6	NP1N	20	NP1N	3	NP1N	2	NP P	8
FAC	EP	FAC	P	FAC	1Q	FAC	EP	FAC	2Q	FAC	2Q	FAC	P	FAC	P	FAC	4Q	FAC	1Qr
FAV	2P	FAV	3P	FAV	1P	FAV	1P	FAT	3Q	FAT	1Q	FAT	P	FAT	P	FAT	P	FAT	1Q

HONOURS / RECORDS
FA Comps: None
League: Northern Counties East Division One 2008-09, Premier 2012-13.

County FA: None

Victory: 13-0 v Brodsworth, Northern Counties East, 2009-10.
Defeat: 0-6 v Thackley 16/04/2013 and AFC Telford United 16/11/2013.
Goalscorer: Ryan Blott - 231, including 42 scored during the 2008-09 season and 5 each against Yorkshire Amateur's (08/11/08) and Armthorpe Welfare (14/04/12).
Appearances: Ryan Blott - 376 (20/10/07 - 29/04/16).

Ground Capacity: 2,000 **Seats:** 250 **Covered:** Yes **Clubhouse:** Yes **Shop:** No
Previous Grounds: Queensgate - Bridlington FC >2017.
Record Attendance: 2,038 v Sheffield United, Opening of the new ground friendly, 15/07/2017.

DIRECTIONS
From the A64 turn right onto Valley Road, at the next roundabout take teh second exit, continue along Valley Road until right turn into Ashburn Road.

Nearest Railway Station Scarborough - 1km

SOUTH SHIELDS

Founded 1974

Nickname: Mariners **Club Colours:** Claret & white

Club Contact Details 0191 454 7800

Mariners Park, Shaftesbury Avenue, Jarrow, Tyne & Wear NE32 3UP

Previous Names: South Shields Mariners.

Previous Leagues: Northern Alliance 1974-76, Wearside 1976-95.

09-10	10-11	11-12	12-13	13-14	14-15	15-16	16-17	17-18	18-19
NL 1 11	NL 1 11	NL 1 13	NL 1 23	NL 2 17	NL 2 15	NL 2 1	NL 1 1	NP1N 1	NP P 2
FAC EP	FAC Pr	FAC Pr	FAC 1Q	FAC Pr			FAC EP	FAC 4Q	FAC 2Q
FAV 1P	FAV 1P	FAV 1P	FAV 1P	FAV 1P	FAV 2Q	FAV 3P	FAV F	FAT 2Q	FAT 3Q

HONOURS / RECORDS

FA Comps: FA Vase 2016-17.

League: Northern Alliance 1975-76. Wearside 1976-77, 92-93, 94-95. Northern Division Two 2015-16, Division One 2016-17.

County FA: Monkwearmouth Charity Cup 1986-87. Durham Senior Challenge Cup 2016-17.

Best FA Cup Fourth Qualifying Round 2017-18

FA Trophy Third Qualifying Round 2018-19

Ground Capacity: 3,500 **Seats:** Yes **Covered:** Yes **Clubhouse:** Yes **Shop:** No

Previous Grounds: Filtrona Park (renamed Mariners Park in 2015) 1992-2013. Eden Lane 2013-15.

Record Attendance: 3,464 v Coleshill Town, FA Vase semi-final, 2016-17.

DIRECTIONS

The ground is within walking distance of Bede Metro Station. Alight at the station and go down the stairs before turning right if you have departed a train heading for South Shields, or turning left if departing a train going towards Newcastle. At the next junction you come to, turn right, and there is then a short walk along Shaftesbury Avenue to reach the ground.

Nearest Railway Station Bede - 0.2km

Bus Route Taunton Avenue - stop 200m away

STAFFORD RANGERS

Founded 1876

Nickname: Rangers **Club Colours:** Black & white

Club Contact Details 01785 602 430 secretary@staffordrangersfc.co.uk

Marston Road, Stafford ST16 3UF

Previous Names: None

Previous Leagues: Shropshire 1891-93, Birmingham 1893-96, N. Staffs. 1896-1900, Cheshire 1900-01, Birmingham Combination 1900-12, 46-52, Cheshire County 1952-69, N.P.L. 1969-79, 83-85, Alliance 1979-83, Conf. 1985-95, 2005-11. Southern >2005.

09-10	10-11	11-12	12-13	13-14	14-15	15-16	16-17	17-18	18-19
Conf N 16	Conf N 20	NP P 16	NP P 15	NP P 22	NP1S 6	NP1S 1	NP P 13	NP P 13	NP P 14
FAC 2Qr	FAC 2Qr	FAC 2Q	FAC 2Q	FAC 2Q	FAC 1Qr	FAC P	FAC 1Q	FAC 4Q	FAC 2Q
FAT 3Q	FAT 3Q	FAT 2Q	FAT 1P	FAT 1Q	FAT 1Q	FAT 1Qr	FAV 3Q	FAT 3Q	FAT 2Q

HONOURS / RECORDS

FA Comps: FA Trophy 1971-72.

League: Birmingham Combination 1912-13. Cheshire County 1968-69. Northern Premier 1971-72, 84-85, Division One South 2015-16. Southern Premeir Division 2002-03. Coference North 2005-06.

County FA: Staffordshire Senior Cup 1954-55, 56-57, 62-63, 71-72, 77-78, 86-87, 91-92, 2002-03, 04-05, 14-15, 17-18.

Victory: 15-0 v Kidsgrove Athletic - Staffordshire Senior Cup 2003

Defeat: 0-12 v Burton Town - Birmingham League 1930

Goalscorer: M. Cullerton - 176. Les Box scored seven against Dudley Town, FA Cup, 06/09/1958.

Appearances: Jim Sargent

Additional: Paid £13,000 to VS rugby for S. Butterworth. Received £100,000 from Crystal Palace for Stan Collymore.

Ground Capacity: 4,000 **Seats:** 530 **Covered:** Yes **Clubhouse:** Yes **Shop:** Yes

Previous Grounds: None

Record Attendance: 8,536 v Rotherham United - FA Cup 3rd Round 1975

DIRECTIONS

M6 Junction 14. Follow signs for Uttoxeter and Stone. Straight over at 1st and 2nd (A34) islands, 3rd right sign posted Common Road and Astonfields Road Ind. Estate. The ground is straight ahead after three quarters of a mile. The route from the Motorway is highlighted by the standard football road signs.
*Sat Nav ST16 3UF

Nearest Railway Station Stafford - 1.8km

Bus Route Co-operative Strret - stop 200m away

STALYBRIDGE CELTIC

Founded 1909

Nickname: Celtic **Club Colours:** Royal blue & white

Club Contact Details 0161 338 2828 secretary@stalybridgeceltic.co.uk
Bower Fold, Mottram Road, Stalybridge, Cheshire SK15 2RT

Previous Names: None
Previous Leagues: Lancs & Cheshire Am. 1909-11. Lancashire Comb 1911-12, Central 1912-14, 15-21, Southern 1914-15, Football Lge 1921-23, Cheshire Co. 1923-82, North West Co. 1982-87, N.P.L. 1987-92, 98-2001, 02-04, Conference 1992-98, 01-02, 04-17.

09-10		10-11		11-12		12-13		13-14		14-15		15-16		16-17		17-18		18-19	
Conf N	9	Conf N	10	Conf N	6	Conf N	13	Conf N	19	Conf N	19	Nat N	12	Nat N	21	NP P	22	NP P	17
FAC	3Qr	FAC	4Q	FAC	2Q	FAC	4Q	FAC	2Q	FAC	2Q	FAC	1P	FAC	3Q	FAC	3Q	FAC	1Q
FAT	2P	FAT	2P	FAT	2P	FAT	3Q	FAT	1P	FAT	3Qr	FAT	3Q	FAT	3Qr	FAT	3Q	FAT	3Q

HONOURS / RECORDS
FA Comps: None
League: Lancashire Combination Division Two 1911-12. Cheshire County 1979-80. North West Counties 1983-84, 86-87.
Northern Premier League Premier Division 1991-92, 2000-01.
County FA: Manchester Senior Cup 1922-23.
Cheshire Senior Cup 1952-53, 2000-01.

Victory: 16-2 v Manchester NE - 01/05/1926 and v Nantwich - 22/10/1932
Defeat: 1-10 v Wellington Town - 09/03/1946
Goalscorer: Harry Dennison - 215. Cecil Smith scored 77 goals during the 1931-32 season
Appearances: Kevan Keelan - 395
Additional: Paid £15,000 to Kettering Town for Ian Arnold 1995. Received £16,000 from Southport for Lee Trundle.

Ground Capacity: 6,500 **Seats:** 1,500 **Covered:** 2,400 **Clubhouse:** Yes **Shop:** Yes
Previous Grounds: None
Record Attendance: 9,753 v West Bromwich Albion - FA Cup replay 1922-23

DIRECTIONS
Via the B6174 (Stalybridge Road). At a mini r'about, turn left (exit 1 of 5) onto Roe Cross Road (A6018). Follow for 1 3/4 miles passing the Roe Cross Inn on the right and through the cutting (the road is now called Mottram Road). When you pass the Dog and Partridge on the right, you will be almost there. Bower Fold is on the left opposite a sharp right turn next to the Hare and Hounds pub. If the car park is full, parking can be found on the streets.

Nearest Railway Station Stalybridge - 1.5 miles from the ground.

WARRINGTON TOWN

Founded 1949

Nickname: The Wire **Club Colours:** Yellow & blue

Club Contact Details 01925 653 044
Cantilever Park, Loushers Lane, Warrington WA4 2RS

Previous Names: Stockton Heath Albion 1949-61
Previous Leagues: Warrington & District 1949-52, Mid Cheshire 1952-78, Cheshire County 1978-82, North West Counties 1982-90 Northern Premier 1990-97

09-10		10-11		11-12		12-13		13-14		14-15		15-16		16-17		17-18		18-19	
NP1N	9	NP1N	9	NP1N	11	NP1N	10	NP1N	3	NP1N	9	NP1N	1	NP P	10	NP P	3	NP P	3
FAC	2Qr	FAC	3Q	FAC	2Q	FAC	2Q	FAC	2Qr	FAC	2P	FAC	P	FAC	1Q	FAC	3Qr	FAC	4Qr
FAT	1Q	FAT	P	FAT	Pr	FAT	P	FAT	P	FAT	P	FAT	3Q	FAT	1Q	FAT	3P	FAT	1Q

HONOURS / RECORDS
FA Comps: None
League: Mid-Cheshire 1960-61. North West Counties 1989-90, Division Two 2000-01.
Northern Premier Division One North 2015-16.
County FA: None

Goalscorer: Steve Hughes - 167
Appearances: Neil Whalley
Additional: Paid £50,000 to Preston North End for Liam Watson Received £60,000 from P.N.E. for Liam Watson
Players to progress - Roger Hunt, Liverpool legend and 1966 World Cup winner.

Ground Capacity: 2,500 **Seats:** 350 **Covered:** 650 **Clubhouse:** Yes **Shop:** Yes
Previous Grounds: Stockton Lane 1949-50, 55-56. London Road 1950-53. Loushers Lane 1953-55.
Record Attendance: 2,600 v Halesowen Town - FA Vase Semi-final 1st leg 1985-86

DIRECTIONS
From M62 Junction 9 Warrington Town Centre: Travel 1 mile south on A49, turn left at traffic lights into Loushers Lane, ground ½ mile on right hand side. From M6 North or South Junction 20: Follow A50 (Warrington signs) for 2 miles, cross Latchford Swingbridge, turn immediate left into Station Road, ground on left.

Nearest Railway Station Warrington Central - 2.3km
Bus Route Fairfield Gardens - stop 200m away

A close call for Maddison (Darlington). Photos: Keith Clayton.

Barrows (Grantham) Abadaki (Witton).

Carberry (Bootle) takes on Guffogg (Ashton).

WHITBY TOWN

Founded 1926

Nickname: Seasiders **Club Colours:** All royal blue

Club Contact Details Office: 01947 604 847
Turnbull Ground, Upgang Lane, Whitby, North Yorks YO21 3HZ

Previous Names: Whitby Whitehall Swifts and Whitby Town merged in 1926 to form Whitby United. Name changed to Whitby Town in 1949.
Previous Leagues: Northern 1926-97

09-10		10-11		11-12		12-13		13-14		14-15		15-16		16-17		17-18		18-19	
NP P	14	NP P	16	NP P	17	NP P	13	NP P	9	NP P	13	NP P	19	NP P	6	NP P	21	NP P	11
FAC	2Q	FAC	1Q	FAC	3Q	FAC	3Q	FAC	1Qr	FAC	1Qr	FAC	1Qr	FAC	2Q	FAC	2Q	FAC	1Q
FAT	2Q	FAT	3Qr	FAT	1Q	FAT	3Q	FAT	1Q	FAT	1Q	FAT	2Q	FAT	2Q	FAT	1Q	FAT	1Q

HONOURS / RECORDS
FA Comps: FA Vase 1996-97.
League: Northern 1992-93, 96-97.
Northern Premier Division One 1997-98.
County FA: North Riding Senior Cup 1964-65, 67-68, 82-83, 89-90, 2004-05, 16-17.

Victory: 11-2 v Cargo Fleet Works - 1950
Defeat: 3-13 v Willington - 24/03/1928
Goalscorer: Paul Pitman - 382
Appearances: Paul Pitman - 468
Additional: Paid £2,500 to Newcastle Blue Star for John Grady 1990. Received £5,000 from Gateshead for Graham Robinson 1997

Ground Capacity: 3,500 **Seats:** 622 **Covered:** 1,372 **Clubhouse:** Yes **Shop:** Yes
Previous Grounds: None
Record Attendance: 4,000 v Scarborough - North Riding Cup 18/04/1965

DIRECTIONS
On entering Whitby from both the A169 and A171 roads, take the first fork and follow signs for the "West Cliff".
Then turn left at the Spa Shop and Garage, along Love Lane to junction of the A174.
Turn right and the ground is 600 yards on the left.

Nearest Railway Station Whitby - 1km
Bus Route Argyle Road - 120m away

WITTON ALBION

Founded 1887

Nickname: The Albion **Club Colours:** Red & white stripes

Club Contact Details 01606 430 08
Wincham Park, Chapel Street, Wincham, CW9 6DA

Previous Names: None
Previous Leagues: Lancashire Combination, Cheshire County > 1979, Northern Premier 1979-91, Conference 1991-94

09-10		10-11		11-12		12-13		13-14		14-15		15-16		16-17		17-18		18-19	
NP1S	7	NP1N	10	NP1N	3	NP P	4	NP P	16	NP P	22	NP1N	11	NP1S	2	NP P	7	NP P	9
FAC	P	FAC	P	FAC	4Q	FAC	2Q	FAC	1Q	FAC	1Q	FAC	2Q	FAC	2Qr	FAC	1Q	FAC	4Q
FAT	3Qr	FAT	3Qr	FAT	3Q	FAT	2Q	FAT	2Q	FAT	2Qr	FAT	1Q	FAT	1Pr	FAT	1Q	FAT	3Q

HONOURS / RECORDS
FA Comps: None
League: Cheshire County 1948-49, 49-50, 53-54. Northern Premier Premier Division 1990-91.

County FA: Cheshire Senior Cup x7.

Victory: 13-0 v Middlewich (H)
Defeat: 0-9 v Macclesfield Town (A) - 18/09/1965
Goalscorer: Frank Fidler - 175 (1947-50)
Appearances: Brian Pritchard - 729
Additional: Paid £12,500 to Hyde United for Jim McCluskie 1991. Received £11,500 from Chester City for Peter Henderson.

Ground Capacity: 4,813 **Seats:** 650 **Covered:** 2,300 **Clubhouse:** Yes **Shop:** Yes
Previous Grounds: Central Ground (1910-1989)
Record Attendance: 3,940 v Kidderminster Harries - FA Trophy Semi-final 13/04/1991

DIRECTIONS
M6 Junction 19: Follow A556 for Northwich for three miles, through two sets of traffic lights. Turn right at the beginning of the dual carriageway onto A559. After ¾ mile turn right at traffic lights by Slow & Easy Public House, still following A559. After a further ¾ mile turn left a Black Greyhound Public House (signposted). Follow the road through the industrial estate for about ½ mile. Turn left immediately after crossing the canal bridge (signposted) **From M56 Junction 10:** Follow the A558 (Northwich Road) towards Northwich for approximately 6 miles. Turn right at the crossroads by the Black Greyhound Public House (signposted). Follow the road through the industrial estate for about ½ mile. Turn left immediately after crossing the canal bridge (signposted).

Nearest Railway Station Northwich - 1.2km

BRIGHOUSE TOWN

Founded 1963

Nickname: Town **Club Colours:** Orange & black

Club Contact Details 07483 119 054
St Giles Road, Hove Edge, Brighouse, HD6 3PL

Previous Names: Blakeborough
Previous Leagues: Huddersfield Works 1963-75. West Riding County Amateur 1975-08.

09-10	10-11	11-12	12-13	13-14	14-15	15-16	16-17	17-18	18-19
NCE1 2	NCEP 16	NCEP 4	NCEP 2	NCEP 1	NP1N 14	NP1N 14	NP1N 9	NP1N 17	NP1E 3
	FAC EP	FAC EP	FAC P	FAC 2Q	FAC 1Q	FAC 1Q	FAC 1Q	FAC P	FAC P
FAV 2Q	FAV 1Pr	FAV 1Q	FAV 4P	FAV 3Pr	FAT P	FAT 1Q	FAT P	FAT P	FAT 1Q

HONOURS / RECORDS
FA Comps: None
League: Hudersfield Works 1966-67, 68-69, 73-74, 74-75. West Riding County Amateur Premier Division 1990-91, 94-95, 95-96, 2000-01, 01-02, Division One 88-89. Northern Counties East Premier 2013-14.
County FA: West Riding county Cup 1991-92.

Best FA Cup Second Qualifying Round 2013-14
FA Trophy First Qualifying Round 2015-16
FA Vase Fourth Round Proper 2012-13

Ground Capacity: 1,000 **Seats:** 100 **Covered:** 200 **Clubhouse:** Yes **Shop:** No
Previous Grounds: Woodhouse Recreation Ground. Green Lane.
Record Attendance: 1,059 v Scarborough Athletic, Northern Counties East Premier Division, 13/04/2013.

DIRECTIONS
Leave M62 at jct 26 go onto A58 Halifax. Carry on to third set of traffic lights at Hipperholme. Turn left at lights onto A644 Brighouse past Brighouse Juniors pitch on right. Take next left in 100 metres then next left into Spout House Lane. Follow road past Old Pond PH road bears right, carry on and as road begins to bear left turn right into lane, gate 20 metres on left into car park.

Nearest Railway Station Brighouse - 2.5km

CITY OF LIVERPOOL

Founded 2015

Nickname: The Purps **Club Colours:** All purple

Club Contact Details 07831 494 885 contact@colfc.co.uk
Vesty Road, off Bridle Road, Bootle, Liverpool L20 1NY

Previous Names: None
Previous Leagues: North West Counties 2016-19.

09-10	10-11	11-12	12-13	13-14	14-15	15-16	16-17	17-18	18-19
							NWC1 4	NWCP 4	NWCP 1
								FAC 1Q	FAC 2Q
								FAV 3P	FAV 1P

HONOURS / RECORDS
FA Comps: None
League: North West Counties Premier 2018-19.

County FA: None

Victory: 10-0 v Stockport Town, North West Counties Division One, 31/12/2016
FA Cup Second Qualifying Round 2018-19
FA Vase Third Round Proper 2017-18

Ground Capacity: 1,750 **Seats:** Yes **Covered:** Yes **Clubhouse:** Yes **Shop:**
Previous Grounds: Sharing with Bootle FC (current agreement ends 2021). Hope to move in to a new 3,000 capacity stadium.
Record Attendance: 1,024 v Nantwich Town, FA Cup First Qualifying Round, 01/09/2017

DIRECTIONS
At Liverpool end of M57and M58 follow signs for Liverpool (A59 (S)), for 1 1/2 miles. At Aintree racecourse on left and Aintree Train Station on right ,turn right at lights into Park Lane. Turn left at second set of lights into Bridle Road. After 200 yards turn left at lights into Vestey Estate , ground 200 yards.

Nearest Railway Station Aintree - 0.5km
Bus Route Arriva 15, 135 & 157

CLITHEROE

Founded 1877

Nickname: The Blues **Club Colours:** All blue

Club Contact Details 01200 423 344 secretary@clitheroefc.co.uk
Shawbridge, off Pendle Road, Clitheroe, Lancashire BB7 1LZ

Previous Names: Clitheroe Central 1877-1903.
Previous Leagues: Blackburn & District, Lancashire Combination 1903-04, 05-10, 25-82, North West Counties 1982-85

09-10		10-11		11-12		12-13		13-14		14-15		15-16		16-17		17-18		18-19	
NP1N	8	NP1N	6	NP1N	19	NP1N	8	NP1N	17	NP1N	13	NP1N	7	NP1N	7	NP1N	12	NP1W	18
FAC	1Q	FAC	P	FAC	2Q	FAC	1Q	FAC	P	FAC	1Q	FAC	1Q	FAC	P	FAC	1Q	FAC	1Q
FAT	2Q	FAT	2Q	FAT	Pr	FAT	Pr	FAT	Pr	FAT	1Q	FAT	P	FAT	P	FAT	1Q	FAT	1Q

HONOURS / RECORDS
FA Comps: None
League: Lancashire Combination Division Two 1959-60, Division One 1979-80.
North West Counties Division Three 1983-84, Division Two 1984-85, Division One 1985-86, 2003-04.
County FA: Lancashire Challenge Trophy 1892-93, 1984-85.

Goalscorer: Don Francis
Appearances: Lindsey Wallace - 670
Additional: Received £45,000 from Crystal Palace for Carlo Nash.

Ground Capacity: 2,000 **Seats:** 250 **Covered:** 1,400 **Clubhouse:** Yes **Shop:** No
Previous Grounds: None
Record Attendance: 2,050 v Mangotsfield - FA Vase Semi-final 1995-96

DIRECTIONS
M6 junction 31, A59 to Clitheroe (17 miles) at 5th roundabout turn left after half a mile at Pendle Road. Ground is one mile behind Bridge Inn on the right.

Nearest Railway Station Clitheroe - 0.6km
Bus Route Hayhurst Street - 50m away

COLNE

Founded 1996

Nickname: The Reds **Club Colours:** Red & white

Club Contact Details 01282 862 545 secretary@colnefootballclub.com
Harrison Drive, Colne, Lancashire BB8 9SL

Previous Names: None
Previous Leagues: North West Counties 1996-2016.

09-10		10-11		11-12		12-13		13-14		14-15		15-16		16-17		17-18		18-19	
NWCP	8	NWCP	5	NWCP	8	NWCP	8	NWCP	9	NWCP	4	NWCP	1	NP1N	5	NP1N	8	NP1W	4
FAC	EP	FAC	P	FAC	EP	FAC	EPr	FAC	EPr	FAC	EP	FAC	1Q	FAC	1Q	FAC	1Q	FAC	2Q
FAV	1P	FAV	1P	FAV	1P	FAV	2Q	FAV	2Q	FAV	1P	FAV	2P	FAT	P	FAT	P	FAT	EP

HONOURS / RECORDS
FA Comps: None
League: North West Counties League Division Two 2003-04, Premier Division 2015-16.

County FA: None

Goalscorer: Geoff Payton
Appearances: Richard Walton

Ground Capacity: 1,800 **Seats:** 160 **Covered:** 1,000 **Clubhouse:** Yes **Shop:** Yes
Previous Grounds: None
Record Attendance: 1,742 v AFC Sudbury F.A. Vase SF 2004. 2,762 (at Accrington Stanley) v FC United, NWC Challenge Cup,

DIRECTIONS
Follow M65 to end of motorway. Turn left and follow signs for Skipton and Keighley, continue to roundabout, take 1st left up Harrison Drive, across small roundabout, follow road to ground.

Nearest Railway Station Colne - 0.6km
Bus Route Tennyson Road - stop 100m away

DROYLSDEN

Founded 1892

Nickname: The Bloods **Club Colours:** All red

Club Contact Details 0161 301 1352
Market Street, Droylsden, M43 7AY

Previous Names: None
Previous Leagues: Manchester, Lancashire Combination 1936-39, 50-68, Cheshire County 1939-50, 68-82, North West Counties 1982-87, Northern Premier 1986-2004

09-10		10-11		11-12		12-13		13-14		14-15		15-16		16-17		17-18		18-19	
Conf N	5	Conf N	8	Conf N	9	Conf N	21	NP P	24	NP1N	10	NP1N	19	NP1N	13	NP1N	13	NP1W	14
FAC	2Q	FAC	2Pr	FAC	4Qr	FAC	2Q	FAC	1Q	FAC	2Q	FAC	3Q	FAC	Pr	FAC	2Q	FAC	Pr
FAT	3Q	FAT	3Pr	FAT	2P	FAT	3Q	FAT	1Q	FAT	P	FAT	P	FAT	Pr	FAT	3Q	FAT	1Qr

HONOURS / RECORDS
FA Comps: None
League: Manchester 1930-31, 32-33. North West Counties Division Two 1986-87. Northern Premier Division One 1998-99. Conference North 2006-07.
County FA: Manchester Junior Cup 1922-23, Manchester Premier Cup x12 - Firstly in 1946-47 and most recently in 2009-10, Manchester Senior Cup 1972-73, 75-76, 78-79.

Victory: 13-2 v Lucas Sports Club
Goalscorer: E. Gillibrand - 275 (1931-35)
Appearances: Paul Phillips - 326
Additional: Received £11,000 from Crewe Alexandra for Tony Naylor 1990
Defeat: 1-13 v Chorley, Northern Prmeier Premier Division, 05/04/2014.

Ground Capacity: 3,000 **Seats:** 500 **Covered:** 2,000 **Clubhouse:** Yes **Shop:** Yes
Previous Grounds: None
Record Attendance: 15,000 v Hyde United, Manchester League, 1921.

DIRECTIONS
From junction 23 M60 follow signs A635 Manchester, then A662 signed Droylsden, at town centre traffic lights turn right into Market Street, through next set of lights and the main entrance to the ground is 75 yards on your left.

Nearest Railway Station Droylsden - 240m away
Bus Route Bus stops outside the ground

DUNSTON UTS

Founded 1975

Nickname: The Fed **Club Colours:** All blue

Club Contact Details 0191 493 2935
UTS Stadium, Wellington Road, Dunston, Gateshead NE11 9JL

Previous Names: Whickham Sports 1975-82. Dunston Mechanics 82-87. Dunston Federation Brewery 87-2007. Dunston Federation 07-09.
Previous Leagues: Newcastle City Amateur. Northern Amateur. Northern Combination 1980-87. Wearside 1987-91. Northern 91-2019.

09-10		10-11		11-12		12-13		13-14		14-15		15-16		16-17		17-18		18-19	
NL 1	4	NL 1	7	NL 1	3	NL 1	5	NL 1	7	NL 1	6	NL 1	11	NL 1	15	NL 1	10	NL 1	1
FAC	EPr	FAC	2Q	FAC	1Q	FAC	1Qr	FAC	P	FAC	2Q	FAC	1Q	FAC	2Q	FAC	P	FAC	4Q
FAV	2P	FAV	QF	FAV	F	FAV	4P	FAV	QF	FAV	5Pr	FAV	5Pr	FAV	3P	FAV	2P	FAV	2P

HONOURS / RECORDS
FA Comps: FA Vase 2011-12.
League: Northern Amateur 1977-78. Northern Combination 1986-87. Wearside 1988-89, 89-90. Northern Division Two 1992-93, Division One 2003-04, 04-05, 18-19.
County FA: None

Goalscorer: Paul King
Appearances: Paul Dixon

Ground Capacity: 2,000 **Seats:** 150 **Covered:** 400 **Clubhouse:** Yes **Shop:** No
Previous Grounds:
Record Attendance: 2,520 v Gateshead, FA Cup Fourth Qualifying Round, 20/10/2018

DIRECTIONS
From south take Dunston/Whickham exit off A1M.
Turn right at top of slip road into Dunston Road and head down the bank.
As the road veers left, the road becomes Wellington Road, and the ground is situated on your left.

Nearest Railway Station Metrocentre - 0.9km. Dunston - 1km.
Bus Route Wellington Road - stop 24m away

KENDAL TOWN

Founded 1919

Nickname: The Mintcakes / The Field **Club Colours:** Black and white stripes

Club Contact Details 01539 738 818
Parkside Road, Kendal, Cumbria LA9 7BL

Previous Names: Netherfield AFC 1919-2000
Previous Leagues: Westmorland, North Lancashire Combination 1945-68, Northern Premier 1968-83, North West Counties 1983-87

09-10		10-11		11-12		12-13		13-14		14-15		15-16		16-17		17-18		18-19	
NP P	5	NP P	8	NP P	11	NP P	21	NP1N	10	NP1N	16	NP1N	15	NP1N	12	NP1N	18	NP1W	19
FAC	4Q	FAC	1Q	FAC	3Q	FAC	3Q	FAC	P	FAC	Pr	FAC	2Q	FAC	P	FAC	1Q	FAC	1Q
FAT	1Q	FAT	3Q	FAT	2Qr	FAT	1Qr	FAT	1Qr	FAT	P	FAT	1Q	FAT	2Q	FAT	1Q	FAT	P

HONOURS / RECORDS
FA Comps: None
League: Lancashire Combination 1948-49, 64-65.

County FA: Westmorlands Senior Cup x12. Lancashire Senior Cup 2002-03.

Victory: 11-0 v Great Harwood - 22/03/1947
Defeat: 0-10 v Stalybridge Celtic - 01/09/1984
Goalscorer: Tom Brownlee
Additional: Received £10,250 from Manchester City for Andy Milner 1995

Ground Capacity: 2,490 **Seats:** 450 **Covered:** 1000 **Clubhouse:** Yes **Shop:** Yes
Previous Grounds: None
Record Attendance: 5,184 v Grimsby Town - FA Cup 1st Round 1955

DIRECTIONS
M6 junction 36, via A590/591/A6 to Kendal (South). At first traffic lights turn right, left at roundabout, right into Parkside Road. Ground on right over brow of hill.

Nearest Railway Station Kendal - 1.3km
Bus Route Castle Circle - stop 200m away

MARINE

Founded 1894

Nickname: Mariners **Club Colours:** Gold & black

Club Contact Details 0151 924 1743
College Road, Crosby, Liverpool L23 3AS

Previous Names: None
Previous Leagues: Liverpool Zingari, Liverpool County Combination, Lancashire Combination 1935-39, 46-69, Cheshire County 1969-79

09-10		10-11		11-12		12-13		13-14		14-15		15-16		16-17		17-18		18-19	
NP P	9	NP P	9	NP P	7	NP P	11	NP P	20	NP P	21	NP P	15	NP P	18	NP P	19	NP P	20
FAC	1Q	FAC	1Qr	FAC	1Q	FAC	4Q	FAC	1Q	FAC	3Q	FAC	3Q	FAC	2Qr	FAC	2Q	FAC	4Q
FAT	1Q	FAT	2Q	FAT	3Q	FAT	1Q	FAT	2Q	FAT	2Q	FAT	3Q	FAT	1P	FAT	2P	FAT	1Q

HONOURS / RECORDS
FA Comps: None
League: I Zingari Division Two 1901-02, Division One 02-03, 03-04, 09-10, 19-20, 20-21, 22-23. Liverpool Combination Division One 1927-28, 30-31, 33-34, 34-35, 43-44. Cheshire County 1973-74, 75-76, 76-77. Northern Premier Premier Division 1993-94, 84-95.
County FA: Lancashire Amateur Cup 1921-22, 25-26, 30-31, Junior Cup /Trophy 78-79, 87-88, 90-91, 99-00. Liverpool Challenge Cup 42-43, 44-45, 71-72, Non-League Cup 1968-69, 75-76, 76-77, Senior Cup 78-79, 84-85, 87-88, 89-90, 93-94, 99-00, 07-08.

Victory: 14-0 v Sandhurst - FA Cup 1st Qualifying Round 01/10/1938
Defeat: 2-11 v Shrewsbury Town - FA Cup 1st Round 1995
Goalscorer: Paul Meachin - 200
Appearances: Peter Smith 952
Additional: Paid £6,000 to Southport for Jon Penman October 1985. Received £20,000 from Crewe for Richard Norris 1996.

Ground Capacity: 3,185 **Seats:** 400 **Covered:** 1,400 **Clubhouse:** Yes **Shop:** Yes
Previous Grounds: Waterloo Park 1894-1903
Record Attendance: 4,000 v Nigeria - Friendly 1949

DIRECTIONS
From the East & South: Leave the M62 at junction 6 and take the M57 to Switch Island at the end. At the end of the M57 take the A5036 (signposted Bootle & Docks). At the roundabout, at the end of the road (by Docks), turn right onto the A565 following signs for 'Crosby' and 'Marine AFC' and follow this road for 1 mile. After passing the Tesco Express on your right, turn left at the traffic lights (by Merchant Taylors' School) into College Road. The ground is half a mile on your left. **From the North:** Leave the M6 at junction 26 and join the M58. Travel along the M58 to Switch Island at the end. Take the A5036 (signposted Bootle & Docks) and follow directions above.

Nearest Railway Station Blunellsands & Crosby - 0.5km
Bus Route Brompton Avenue - stop 175m away

MARSKE UNITED

Founded 1956

Nickname: The Seasiders **Club Colours:** Yellow & navy

Club Contact Details 07803 248 709 admin@marskeunitedfc.com

Mount Pleasant Avenue, Marske by the Sea, Redcar TS11 7BW

Previous Names: None

Previous Leagues: Local leagues 1956-76. Teeside 1976- 85. Wearside 1985-97. Northern League 1997-2018.

09-10		10-11		11-12		12-13		13-14		14-15		15-16		16-17		17-18		18-19	
NL 2	4	NL 2	3	NL 1	18	NL 1	19	NL 1	16	NL 1	1	NL 1	2	NL 1	5	NL 1	1	NP1E	10
FAC	EP	FAC	1Q	FAC	P	FAC	P	FAC	4Q	FAC	1Qr	FAC	Pr	FAC	1Q	FAC	Pr	FAC	P
FAV	5Pr	FAV	2P	FAV	2Q	FAV	1Qr	FAV	1P	FAV	3P	FAV	4P	FAV	2P	FAV	SF	FAT	3Q

HONOURS / RECORDS

FA Comps: None

League: Teesside 1980-81, 84-85. Wearside 1995-96. Northern Division One 2014-15, 17-18.

County FA: None

Defeat: 3-9

Goalscorer: Chris Morgan 169.

Appearances: Mike Kinnair 583.

Victory: 16-0

Ground Capacity: 2,500 **Seats:** Yes **Covered:** Yes **Clubhouse:** Yes **Shop:**

Previous Grounds: None

Record Attendance: 1,359 v Bedlington Terriers FA Vase.

DIRECTIONS

Leave A19 and join Parkway (A174) to Marske until Quarry Lane r'about. Take exit (A1085) into Marske. Take the next right after you pass under a railway, into Meadow Rd. Take the next left into Southfield Rd and the entrance is on your left shortly before a T-junc.

Nearest Railway Station Marske - 0.4km

Bus Route Windy Hill Lane - stop 84m away

MOSSLEY

Founded 1903

Nickname: Lilywhites **Club Colours:** White & black

Club Contact Details 01457 832 369

Seel Park, Market Street, Mossley, Lancashire OL5 0ES

Previous Names: Park Villa 1903-04, Mossley Juniors

Previous Leagues: Ashton, South East Lancashire, Lancashire Combination 1918-19, Cheshire County 1919-72, Northern Premier 1972-95, North West Counties 1995-2004

09-10		10-11		11-12		12-13		13-14		14-15		15-16		16-17		17-18		18-19	
NP1N	7	NP1N	15	NP1N	14	NP1N	5	NP1N	15	NP1N	7	NP1N	13	NP1N	17	NP1N	19	NP1W	8
FAC	P	FAC	4Q	FAC	Pr	FAC	P	FAC	Pr	FAC	Pr	FAC	Pr	FAC	1Q	FAC	1Qr	FAC	2Q
FAT	3Qr	FAT	2Q	FAT	P	FAT	1Qr	FAT	2Q	FAT	1Q	FAT	1Q	FAT	1Q	FAT	1Q	FAT	EP

HONOURS / RECORDS

FA Comps: None

League: Ashton & District 1911-12, 14-15. Northern Premier 1978-79, 79-80, Division One 2005-06.

County FA: Manchester Premier Cup 1937-38, 48-49, 60-61, 66-67, 67-68, 88-89, 90-91, 2011-12, 12-13, 14-15, 15-16. Manchester Challenge Trophy 2011-12.

Victory: 9-0 v Urmston, Manchester Shield, 1947

Defeat: 2-13 v Witton Albion, Cheshire League, 1926

Goalscorer: David Moore - 235 (1974-84). Jackie Roscoe scored 58 during the 1930-31 season.

Appearances: Jimmy O'Connor - 613 (1972-87)

Additional: Paid £2,300 to Altrincham for Phil Wilson. Received £25,000 from Everton for Eamonn O'Keefe.

Ground Capacity: 4,000 **Seats:** 220 **Covered:** 1,500 **Clubhouse:** Yes **Shop:** Yes

Previous Grounds: Moved to Seel Park in 1911.

Record Attendance: 7,000 v Stalybridge Celtic 1950

DIRECTIONS

Exit M60 Junction 23 following A635 Ashton-under-Lyne. Take 3rd exit off roundabout then 3rd exit off next roundabout (Asda) and then 3rd exit off next roundabout signed Mossley A670. At junction turn right on to Mossley Rd through traffic lights. After approx 2.5 miles drop down hill entering Mossley town centre. Passing supermarket on left turn right before next traffic lights. Continue up the hill and left into Market Street. Ground is approx 200 yards on the left.

Nearest Railway Station Mossley - 0.3km

Bus Route Stamford Street - 200m away

OSSETT UNITED

Founded 2018

Nickname: United **Club Colours:** Blue

Club Contact Details 01924 272 960 secretary@ossettunited.com
Ingfield Stadium, Prospect Road, Ossett WF5 9HA

Previous Names: Formed after the merger of Ossett Albion (1944) and Ossett Town (1936).
Previous Leagues: None

09-10	10-11	11-12	12-13	13-14	14-15	15-16	16-17	17-18	18-19
									NP1E 5
									FAC Pr
									FAT 2Q

HONOURS / RECORDS
FA Comps: None
League: None

County FA: West Riding County Cup 2018-19.

Ground Capacity: 1,950 **Seats:** 360 **Covered:** 1,000 **Clubhouse:** Yes **Shop:** Yes
Previous Grounds: None
Record Attendance: 1,118 v AFC Guiseley, West Riding County Cup Final, 9/04/2019

DIRECTIONS
From M1 Junction 40: Take A638 signposted Ossett Town Centre. Take first left off A638 onto Wakefield Road, sixth left turn into Dale Street (B6120) to traffic lights. Turn left at lights. The Ground is in front of you opposite the bus station. The entrance to the Ground is just before the Esso petrol station.

Nearest Railway Station Dewsbury - 3.9km
Bus Route Prospect Road - stop 50m away

PICKERING TOWN

Founded 1888

Nickname: Pikes **Club Colours:** All blue

Club Contact Details 01751 473 317
Recreation Club, off Mill Lane, Malton Road, Pickering YO18 7DB

Previous Names: None
Previous Leagues: Beckett, York & District, Scarborough & District, Yorkshire 1972-82. Northern Counties East 1982-2018.

09-10	10-11	11-12	12-13	13-14	14-15	15-16	16-17	17-18	18-19
NCEP 7	NCEP 7	NCEP 12	NCEP 5	NCEP 7	NCEP 11	NCEP 6	NCEP 2	NCEP 2	NP1E 16
FAC EP	FAC EP	FAC 1Qr	FAC EPr	FAC EP	FAC EP	FAC P	FAC Pr	FAC P	FAC P
FAV 4P	FAV 2P	FAV 2Q	FAV 2P	FAV 2Q	FAV 2Q	FAV 1Q	FAV 2P	FAV 1P	FAT 3Qr

HONOURS / RECORDS
FA Comps: None
League: Scarborough & District Division One 1930-31, 50-51. York Division Two 1953-54, Division One 55-56, 66-67, 69-70. Yorkshire Division Three 1973-74. Northern Counties East Division Two 1987-88.
County FA: North Riding Cup 1990-91. North Riding Senior Cup 2012-13.

Best FA Cup Second Qualifying Round 1999-2000, 01-02, 03-04
FA Vase Quarter Finals 2005-06
FA Trophy Third Qualifying Round 2018-19(r)

Ground Capacity: 2,000 **Seats:** 200 **Covered:** 500 **Clubhouse:** Yes **Shop:** Yes
Previous Grounds: Not known
Record Attendance: 1,412 v Notts County (friendly) in August 1991

DIRECTIONS
A169 from Malton. On entering Pickering, take 1st left past Police Station and BP garage into Mill Lane, ground 200 yds on right.

Nearest Railway Station Pickering - 650m
Bus Route Millfield Close - stop 62m away

PONTEFRACT COLLIERIES

Founded 1958

Nickname: Colls **Club Colours:** All blue

Club Contact Details 01977 600 818
Beechnut Lane, Pontefract, WF8 4QE

Previous Names: None
Previous Leagues: West Yorkshire 1958-79. Yorkshire 1979-82. Northern Counties East 1982-2018.

09-10		10-11		11-12		12-13		13-14		14-15		15-16		16-17		17-18		18-19	
NCE1	5	NCE1	5	NCE1	5	NCE1	5	NCE1	9	NCE1	2	NCEP	20	NCE1	2	NCEP	1	NP1E	2
FAC	EP	FAC	EP	FAC	P	FAC	EPr	FAC	EP	FAC	EP	FAC	P	FAC	1Q	FAC	P	FAC	P
FAV	2Q	FAV	2Q	FAV	1P	FAV	2Q	FAV	2Q	FAV	1Q	FAV	1Q	FAV	1Q	FAV	4P	FAT	P

HONOURS / RECORDS
FA Comps: None
League: Yorkshire Division Three 1981-82.
Northern Counties East Division One North 1983-84, Premier Division 2017-18.
County FA: Castleford & District FA Embleton Cup 1982-83, 86-87, 95-96, 99-2000, 05-06, 06-07, 07-08.

Best FA Cup First Qualifying Round 1995-96, 97-98, 2016-17
FA Vase Second Round Proper 2002-03
FA Trophy Preliminary Round 2018-19

Ground Capacity: 1,200 **Seats:** 300 **Covered:** 400 **Clubhouse:** Yes **Shop:** Yes
Previous Grounds: Not known
Record Attendance: 1,000 v Hull City, floodlight opening 1987.

DIRECTIONS
M62 jct32 (Xscape) towards Pontefract.
Left at lights after roundabout for park entrance and retail park.
Traffic through town should follow racecourse signs through lights to roundabout and back to lights.

Nearest Railway Station pontefract Tanshelf - ¼ mile

PRESCOT CABLES

Founded 1884

Nickname: Tigers **Club Colours:** Amber & black

Club Contact Details 0151 426 0527
Volair Park, Eaton Street, Prescot L34 6ND

Previous Names: Prescot > 1995
Previous Leagues: Liverpool County Combination, Lancashire Combination 1897-98, 1918-20, 27-33, 36-76, Mid Cheshire 1976-78, Cheshire County 1978-82, North West Counties 1982-2003

09-10		10-11		11-12		12-13		13-14		14-15		15-16		16-17		17-18		18-19	
NP1N	15	NP1N	21	NP1N	16	NP1N	17	NP1N	20	NP1N	20	NP1N	16	NP1N	16	NP1N	5	NP1W	7
FAC	P	FAC	1Qr	FAC	P	FAC	1Q	FAC	1Q	FAC	1Q	FAC	P	FAC	P	FAC	Pr	FAC	P
FAT	P	FAT	1Q	FAT	P	FAT	1Q	FAT	P	FAT	1Q	FAT	P	FAT	1Q	FAT	1Qr	FAT	2Q

HONOURS / RECORDS
FA Comps: None
League: Lancashire Combination Division Two 1951-52, Premier 1956-57. Mid-Cheshire 1976-77.
Cheshire County Division Two 1979-80. North West Counties 2002-03.
County FA: Liverpool Challenge Cup 1927-28, 28-29, 29-30, 48-49, 61-62, 77-78. Liverpool Non-League Cup 1952-53, 58-59, 60-61.
Liverpool Senior Cup 2016-17, 17-18.

Victory: 18-3 v Great Harwood - 1954-55
Defeat: 1-12 v Morecambe - 1936-37
Goalscorer: Freddie Crampton
Appearances: Harry Grisedale

Ground Capacity: 3,200 **Seats:** 500 **Covered:** 600 **Clubhouse:** Yes **Shop:** Yes
Previous Grounds: None
Record Attendance: 8,122 v Ashton National - 1932

DIRECTIONS
From North: M6 to Jct 26, onto M58 to Junction 3. Follow A570 to junction with A580 (East Lancs Road). (Approach junction in right hand lane of the two lanes going straight on). Cross A580 and take first road on right (Bleak Hill Road). Follow this road through to Prescot (2 miles). At traffic lights turn right, straight on at large r'about (do not follow route onto Prescot by-pass) and right at next lights. 100 yards turn right at Hope and Anchor pub into Hope Street. Club will be in sight at bottom of road. **From South:** M6 to Junction 21a (M62 Jct 10). Follow M62 towards Liverpool, to junction 7. Follow A57 to Rainhill and Prescot. Through traffic lights at Fusilier pub, 100 yards turn right at Hope and Anchor pub (as above).
From East: Follow M62 as described in 'From South' or A580 East Lancs Road to Junction with A570 (Rainford by-pass), turn left and take first right. Follow route as 'From North'.

RAMSBOTTOM UNITED

Founded 1966

Nickname: The Rams **Club Colours:** Blue & white

Club Contact Details 01706 822 799 secretary@rammyunited.co.uk

The Harry Williams Stadium, Acrebottom (off Bridge Street) BL0 0BS.

Previous Names: None

Previous Leagues: Bury Amateur 1966-69. Bolton Combination 1969-89. Manchester 1989-95. North West Counties 1995-2012.

09-10		10-11		11-12		12-13		13-14		14-15		15-16		16-17		17-18		18-19	
NWCP	4	NWCP	2	NWCP	1	NP1N	6	NP1N	5	NP P	17	NP P	24	NP1N	14	NP1N	14	NP1W	5
FAC	P	FAC	1Q	FAC	1Q	FAC	1Q	FAC	2Q	FAC	1Q	FAC	1Q	FAC	P	FAC	P	FAC	Pr
FAV	1P	FAV	1P	FAV	2P	FAT	2Q	FAT	3Q	FAT	1P	FAT	1Qr	FAT	3Q	FAT	2Q	FAT	3Pr

HONOURS / RECORDS

FA Comps: None

League: Bolton Combination Division One 1972-73, Premier Division 76-77. Manchester Division One 1990-91.
North West Counties Division Two 1996-97, Premier Division 2011-12.

County FA: None

Victory: 9-0 v Stantondale (H), NWCFL Division Two, 9th November 1996.

Defeat: 0-7 v Salford City (A), NWCFL Division One, 16th November 2002.

Goalscorer: Russell Brierley - 176 (1996-2003). Russell Brierley scored 38 during the 1999-2000 season.

Ground Capacity: 2,000 **Seats:** Yes **Covered:** Yes **Clubhouse:** Yes **Shop:** No

Previous Grounds: None

Record Attendance: 2,104 v FC United of Manchester, Northern Premier League Premier Division, 04/04/15.

DIRECTIONS

From South,M66(north) to junction1,take the A56 towards Ramsbottom, after 1 mile turn left at traffic lights down Bury New Road follow the road towards the centre then turn left just before the railway crossing, ground runs parallel with the railway line.

From the North leave the A56 (Edenfield by pass) at the start of the M66, follow the signs for Ramsbottom into the centre turn left down Bridge street then after 100 yards turn immediately right after the railway level crossing ground parallel with railway line.

RUNCORN LINNETS

Founded 2006

Nickname: Linnets **Club Colours:** Yellow & green

Club Contact Details 08454 860 705 secretary@runcornlinnetsfc.co.uk

Millbank Linnets Stadium, Stockham Lane, Murdishaw, Runcorn, Cheshire WA7 6GJ

Previous Names: None

Previous Leagues: North West Counties 2006-18.

09-10		10-11		11-12		12-13		13-14		14-15		15-16		16-17		17-18		18-19	
NWCP	11	NWCP	12	NWCP	5	NWCP	6	NWCP	2	NWCP	2	NWCP	2	NWCP	4	NWCP	1	NP1W	6
FAC	P	FAC	P	FAC	2Q	FAC	EPr	FAC	3Q	FAC	P	FAC	1Q	FAC	EP	FAC	P	FAC	P
FAV	2Q	FAV	1P	FAV	1P	FAV	1P	FAV	1P	FAV	1P	FAV	2P	FAV	1P	FAV	3P	FAT	EP

HONOURS / RECORDS

FA Comps: None

League: North West Counties Premier 2017-18.

County FA: None

Best FA Cup Third Qualifying Round 2013-14

FA Vase Third Round Proper 2008-09, 17-18

FA Trophy Extra Preliminary Round 2018-19

Ground Capacity: 1,600 **Seats:** Yes **Covered:** Yes **Clubhouse:** Yes **Shop:**

Previous Grounds: Not known

Record Attendance: 1,037 v Witton Albion, pre season friendly July 2010

DIRECTIONS

A533 Queensway take ramp to Daresbury Expressway follow A533 to roundabout take 1st exit onto Murdishaw Avenue to ground.

Nearest Railway Station Runcorn East - 1.2km

Bus Route Halton Arms stop - 62m away

TADCASTER ALBION

Founded 1892

Nickname: The Brewers / Taddy **Club Colours:** White & blue

Club Contact Details 01904 606 000
Ings Lane, Tadcaster LS24 9AY

Previous Names: John Smith's FC > 1923.
Previous Leagues: York, Harrogate, Yorkshire 1973-82. Northern Counties East 1982-2016.

09-10		10-11		11-12		12-13		13-14		14-15		15-16		16-17		17-18		18-19	
NCE1	1	NCEP	4	NCEP	8	NCEP	6	NCEP	2	NCEP	3	NCEP	1	NP1N	19	NP1N	7	NP1E	
		FAC	1Qr	FAC	2Q	FAC	3Q	FAC	EPr	FAC	P	FAC	P	FAC	2Q	FAC	P	FAC	1Q
FAV	1P	FAV	4P	FAV	2P	FAV	1Q	FAV	1Q	FAV	QFr	FAV	3P	FAT	P	FAT	P	FAT	Pr

HONOURS / RECORDS
FA Comps: None
League: York Division One 1909-10, 23-24, 32-33, Premier 47-48.
Northern Counties East Division One 2009-10, Premier Division 2015-16.
County FA: None

Victory: 13-0 v Blidworth Welfare, NCEL Division One, 1997-98
Defeat: 10-2 v Thackley, 1984-85

Ground Capacity: 2,000 **Seats:** 159 **Covered:** 259 **Clubhouse:** Yes **Shop:** No
Previous Grounds: None
Record Attendance: 1,307 v Highworth Town, FA Vase, 2014-15.

DIRECTIONS
From A64 follow Tadcaster signs (A659) either from the west or east. From the west, on reaching John Smiths Brewery turn right down Centre Lane or New Street. From the east, go over the river bridge, turn left after pedestrian lights and down New Street.

Nearest Railway Station Ulleskelf - 4.3km
Bus Route John Smith's Brewery - stop 300m away

TRAFFORD

Founded 1990

Nickname: The North **Club Colours:** All white

Club Contact Details 0161 747 1727
Shawe View, Pennybridge Lane, Flixton Urmston M41 5DL

Previous Names: North Trafford 1990-94
Previous Leagues: Mid Cheshire 1990-92, North West Counties 1992-97, 2003-08, Northern Premier 1997-2003

09-10		10-11		11-12		12-13		13-14		14-15		15-16		16-17		17-18		18-19	
NP1N	12	NP1N	14	NP1N	12	NP1N	4	NP P	10	NP P	23	NP1N	8	NP1N	6	NP1N	6	NP1W	9
FAC	Pr	FAC	1Q	FAC	1Q	FAC	3Q	FAC	3Q	FAC	1Q	FAC	P	FAC	2Q	FAC	Pr	FAC	2Q
FAT	P	FAT	P	FAT	P	FAT	2Q	FAT	2Q	FAT	2Q	FAT	P	FAT	2Q	FAT	P	FAT	P

HONOURS / RECORDS
FA Comps: None
League: North West Counties Division One 1996-97, 2007-08.

County FA: Manchester Challenge Trophy 2004-05.

Victory: 10-0 v Haslingden St.Mary's (Lancs Amt Shield 1991)
Goalscorer: Scott Barlow - 100
Appearances: Lee Southwood - 311
Additional: NWC League Record: 18 consecutive league wins in 2007-08
Most Points In One Season: 95 points from 38 games 2007-08

Ground Capacity: 2,500 **Seats:** 292 **Covered:** 740 **Clubhouse:** Yes **Shop:** Yes
Previous Grounds: None
Record Attendance: 803 v Flixton - Northern Premier League Division 1 1997-98. 2,238 (at Altrincham FC) FAC P v FC United

DIRECTIONS
Anti-Clockwise exit at J10 (Trafford Centre) and turn right towards Urmston B5214. Straight across two roundabouts. First lights turn right into Moorside Road, at next roundabout take second exit in to Bowfell Road. At next lights turn sharp left then immediately right in to Pennybridge Lane next to Bird In Hand Pub, parking on left 100 yards. Or Leave M60 at J8, taking A6144 towards Lymm, Partington, Carrington. At second set of traffic lights turn right on B5158 towards Flixton. Remain on B5158 crossing railway bridge at Flixton Station and turn right at next set of traffic lights. Passing Bird in Hand Pub take immediate right in to Pennybridge Lane. Parking on left 100 yards.

Nearest Railway Station Urmston - 0.3km

WIDNES

Founded 2003

Nickname: Vikings **Club Colours:** White & black

Club Contact Details 07917 428 609
Lowerhouse Lane, Widnes, Cheshire WA8 7DZ

Previous Names: Formed as Dragons AFC in 2003. Widnes Dragons > 2012. Widnes Vikings 2012-14.
Previous Leagues: Junior Leagues 2003-12. West Cheshire 2012-13. North West Counties 2013-18.

09-10	10-11	11-12	12-13	13-14	14-15	15-16	16-17	17-18	18-19
			WCh3 4	NWC1 14	NWC1 16	NWC1 13	NWC1 1	NWCP 2	NP1W 12
								FAC EP	FAC EPr
					FAV 2Q		FAV 2Q	FAV 1Q	FAT EP

HONOURS / RECORDS
FA Comps: None
League: North West Counties Division One 2016-17.

County FA: None

Victory: (League) 8-0 v St Helens Town, 08/04/2017
Defeat: (League) 1-10 v Northwich Manchester Villa, 13/12/2014

Ground Capacity: 13,350 **Seats:** Yes **Covered:** Yes **Clubhouse:** Yes **Shop:**
Previous Grounds: The club moved to Halton Stadium in 2012.
Record Attendance: 462 v Charnock Richard, North West Counties Division One, 22/04/2017

DIRECTIONS
From the M62 - Exit at Junction 7, take A568 dual carriageway towards Widnes (Following brown signs to Halton Stadium). Keep right after junction onto Ashley Way (A562). Take 2nd exit off roundabout (McDonald's on the right). Take 2nd exit off mini-roundabout into Lowerhouse Lane. From Runcorn & the South: Cross Widnes/Runcorn Bridge (A533). Follow signs to Widnes (A562). At roundabout take 3rd exit towards Widnes Town Centre. Take first left following brown signs to Halton Stadium (McDonald's on the right). Take 2nd exit off mini-roundabout into Lowerhouse Lane.

Nearest Railway Station Widnes - 1.5km
Bus Route Cricketers Arms stop - 121m away

WORKINGTON

Founded 1921

Nickname: Reds **Club Colours:** Red and white

Club Contact Details 01900 602 871
Borough Park, Workington, Cumbria CA14 2DT

Previous Names: Workington AFC 1921-
Previous Leagues: North Eastern 1921-51, Football League 1951-77, Northern Premier 1977-2005. Conference 2005-14.

09-10	10-11	11-12	12-13	13-14	14-15	15-16	16-17	17-18	18-19
Conf N 4	Conf N 11	Conf N 13	Conf N 14	Conf N 22	NP P 2	NP P 5	NP P 4	NP P 11	NP P 21
FAC 4Q	FAC 4Qr	FAC 2Q	FAC 4Q	FAC 4Q	FAC 2Q	FAC 2Q	FAC 3Qr	FAC 2Q	FAC 3Qr
FAT QF	FAT 3Qr	FAT 3Q	FAT 3Q	FAT 3Q	FAT 3Q	FAT 1Q	FAT 1Q	FAT 3Pr	FAT 1P

HONOURS / RECORDS
FA Comps: None
League: North West Counties 1998-99

County FA: Cumberland County Cup x25 (Most recently 2016-17).

Victory: 17-1 v Cockermouth Crusaders - Cumberland Senior League 19/01/1901
Defeat: 0-9 v Chorley (A) - Northern Premier League 10/11/1987
Goalscorer: Billy Charlton - 193
Appearances: Bobby Brown - 469
Additional: Paid £6,000 to Sunderland for Ken Chisolm 1956. Received £33,000 from Liverpool for Ian McDonald 1974.

Ground Capacity: 3,101 **Seats:** 500 **Covered:** 1,000 **Clubhouse:** Yes **Shop:** Yes
Previous Grounds: Lonsdale Park 1921-37.
Record Attendance: 21,000 v Manchester United - FA Cup 3rd round 04/01/1958

DIRECTIONS
A66 into Workington. At traffic lights at bottom of hill (HSBC opposite), turn left towards town centre. Approach traffic lights in centre lane (Washington Central Hotel on your right) and turn right. Continue on this road, passing over a mini roundabout, a pedestrian crossing and a further set of traffic lights. You will come to the Railway Station (facing you), carry on through the junction and bear right, passing the Derwent Park Stadium (Rugby League/speedway), then left and Borough Park becomes visible ahead of you.

Nearest Railway Station Workington - 0.6km
Bus Route Tesco - stop 100m away

NPL SOUTH EAST INS: Ilkeston Town (P - MFLP), Worksop Town (P - NCEP), Chasetown, Glossop North End, Kidsgrove Athletic, Leek Town, Market Drayton Town & Newcastle Town (Tr - NPLNW). Sutton Coldfield Town (Tr - SthC).

BELPER TOWN

Founded 1883

Nickname: The Nailers **Club Colours:** Yellow & black

Club Contact Details 01773 825 549

Christchurch Meadow, Bridge Street, Belper DE56 1BA

Previous Names: None

Previous Leagues: Derbyshire Senior (Founder members) 1890-1911. Notts & Derbyshire (FM) 1911-12. Central Alliance 1957-61, Midland Counties 1961-82, Northern Counties East 1982-97

09-10		10-11		11-12		12-13		13-14		14-15		15-16		16-17		17-18		18-19	
NP1S	6	NP1S	14	NP1S	6	NP1S	3	NP1S	4	NP P	24	NP1S	13	NP1S	10	NP1S	16	NP1E	9
FAC	Pr	FAC	P	FAC	P	FAC	2Qr	FAC	2Q	FAC	1Qr	FAC	1Q	FAC	2Q	FAC	Pr	FAC	1Q
FAT	Pr	FAT	P	FAT	2Q	FAT	2Q	FAT	1Q	FAT	1Q	FAT	1Qr	FAT	P	FAT	P	FAT	Pr

HONOURS / RECORDS

FA Comps: None

League: Central Alliance 1958-59. Midland Counties 1979-80. Northern Counties East 1984-85.

County FA: Derbyshire Senior Cup 1958-59, 61-62, 63-64, 79-80, 2007-08.

Victory: 15-2 v Nottingham Forest 'A' - 1956

Defeat: 0-12 v Goole Town - 1965

Goalscorer: Mick Lakin - 231

Appearances: Craig Smithurst - 678

Additional: Paid £2,000 to Ilkeston Town for Jamie Eaton 2001. Received £2,000 from Hinckley United for Craig Smith.

Ground Capacity: 2,650 **Seats:** 500 **Covered:** 850 **Clubhouse:** Yes **Shop:** Yes

Previous Grounds: Acorn Ground > 1951

Record Attendance: 3,200 v Ilkeston Town - 1955

DIRECTIONS

From North: Exit M1: Exit junction 28 onto A38 towards Derby. Turn off at A610 (signposted 'Ripley/Nottingham') 4th exit at roundabout towards Ambergate. At junction with A6 (Hurt Arms Hotel) turn left to Belper. Ground on right just past first set of traffic lights. Access to the ground is by the lane next to the church. **From South:** Follow A6 north from Derby towards Matlock. Follow A6 through Belper until junction with A517. Ground on left just before traffic lights at this junction. Access to the ground is by the lane next to the church.

NB. Please do not attempt to bring coaches into the ground – these can be parked outside

Nearest Railway Station Belper - 0.4km

Bus Route The Lion Hotel - stop 200m away

CARLTON TOWN

Founded 1904

Nickname: The Millers **Club Colours:** Yellow & blue

Club Contact Details 01159 403 192

Bill Stokeld Stadium, Stoke Lane, Gedling NG4 2QS

Previous Names: Sneinton FC

Previous Leagues: Notts Alliance, Central Midlands, Northern Counties East

09-10		10-11		11-12		12-13		13-14		14-15		15-16		16-17		17-18		18-19	
NP1S	9	NP1S	8	NP1S	2	NP1S	12	NP1S	10	NP1S	18	NP1S	18	NP1S	19	NP1S	19	NP1E	19
FAC	2Qr	FAC	2Q	FAC	2Q	FAC	3Q	FAC	3Q	FAC	1Q	FAC	P	FAC	P	FAC	P	FAC	P
FAT	2Q	FAT	1Qr	FAT	P	FAT	P	FAT	Pr	FAT	1Qr	FAT	2Q	FAT	1Q	FAT	1Q	FAT	2Q

HONOURS / RECORDS

FA Comps: None

League: Notts Alliance 1905-06, 07-08, 08-09, 09-10, Division Two 1984-85, Division One 1992-93. Central Midlands Supreme Division 2002-03. Northern Counties East Division One 2005-06.

County FA: Notts Senior Cup 2012-13, 16-17.

Best FA Cup Third Qualifying Round 2012-13, 13-14

Amateur Cup Third Round Proper 1910-11, 19-20, 30-31

FA Trophy Second Qualifying Round 2009-10, 15-16

FA Vase Third Round Proper 2005-06

Ground Capacity: 1,500 **Seats:** 164 **Covered:** Yes **Clubhouse:** Yes **Shop:** No

Previous Grounds: Club played at several grounds before moving to Stoke Lane (Bill Stokeld Stadium) in the 1990s.

Record Attendance: 1,000 - Radio Trent Charity Match

DIRECTIONS

From M1 J26 take A610 to Nottingham Ring Road. Follow signs for Mansfield (A60) for approx 4 miles via 2 roundabouts until reaching junction with A60 at Arnold. Take right turn at Vale Hotel on to Thackerays Lane. Proceed to roundabout and take 3rd exit on to Arno Vale Road. Proceed through traffic lights to top of hill and continue straight on at next lights on to Arnold Lane. Continue past golf course, the old Gedling Colliery and church to mini roundabout. Continue straight on to the old junction with A612. (Southwell) must turn right here and at next set of lights turn left and follow the loop road to the next junction. Take left turn on to the new A612 Gedling By Pass and follow to the next set of traffic lights at Severn Trent Works. Turn left on to Stoke Lane. Entrance to Carlton Town is immediate right. **[Ground must be accessed via the new A612 between Netherfield and Burton Joyce. Football club is signposted in both directions on the approach to the ground).** *Sat Nav postcode NG4 2QW

Nearest Railway Station Carlton - 1.1km. Netherfield - 1.5km

Bus Route Stoke Lane - stop 50m away

CHASETOWN

Founded 1954

Nickname: The Scholars **Club Colours:** Royal blue & white

Club Contact Details 01543 682 222
The Scholars, Church Street, Chasetown, Walsall WS7 3QL

Previous Names: Chase Terrace Old Scholars 1954-72
Previous Leagues: Cannock Youth 1954-58, Lichfield & District 1958-61, Staffordshire County 1961-72, West Midlands 1972-94, Midland Alliance 1994-2006, Southern 2006-09

09-10		10-11		11-12		12-13		13-14		14-15		15-16		16-17		17-18		18-19	
NP1S	2	NP P	10	NP P	20	NP1S	5	NP1S	12	NP1S	13	NP1S	7	NP1S	17	NP1S	5	NP1W	13
FAC	Pr	FAC	1Q	FAC	2Q	FAC	2Q	FAC	1Qr	FAC	1Qr	FAC	3Qr	FAC	2Q	FAC	2Q	FAC	1Qr
FAT	1Qr	FAT	QF	FAT	2Q	FAT	2Q	FAT	1Q	FAT	3Q	FAT	Pr	FAT	P	FAT	2Q	FAT	1Q

HONOURS / RECORDS
FA Comps: None
League: West Midlands 1978. Midland Alliance 2004-05.

County FA: Walsall Senior Cup 1990-91, 92-93, 2004-05.

Victory: 14-1 v Hanford - Walsall Senior Cup 1991-92
Defeat: 1-8 v Telford United Reserves - West Midlands League
Goalscorer: Tony Dixon - 197. Mick Ward scored 39 goals during the 1987-88 season, whilst a player by the name of Keith Birch scored 11 in a 21-1 win over Lichfield Laundry.
Misc: Became the first club from the eighth tier of English football to reach the FA Cup Third Round Proper during the 2007-08 season.

Ground Capacity: 2,000 **Seats:** 151 **Covered:** 220 **Clubhouse:** Yes **Shop:** Yes
Previous Grounds: Burntwood Recreation
Record Attendance: 2,420 v Cardiff City - FA Cup 3rd Round January 2008

DIRECTIONS
From the M42 junction10 towards Tamworth or from the M6 Junction 11 or 12 towards Cannock or the A38 southbound from Derby - follow signs for A5 towards Brownhills, At the traffic lights at the Terrace Restaurant turn towards Burntwood onto the A5195. Straight over first island towards Chasetown and Hammerwich, over toll road and at second island turn left into Haney Hay Road which leads into Highfields Road signposted Chasetown, up the hill to mini island, then straight on into Church Street past the church on left and school on right. Ground is on the left at end of road. If using M6 Toll exit at junction T6 Burntwood - turn left out of Toll booths and left at second island and follow over toll road as above.

Nearest Railway Station Hednesford - 6.4km
Bus Route Queen Street - stop 160m away

CLEETHORPES TOWN

Founded 1998

Nickname: The Owls **Club Colours:** Blue & black

Club Contact Details 01472 693 601
The Linden Club, Clee Road, Grimsby DN32 8QL

Previous Names: Lincolnshire Soccer School Lucarlys 1998-2008.
Previous Leagues: Lincolnshire 2003-05, 10-12. Central Midlands 2005-06. Humber Premier 2006-09. Northern Counties East 2012-17.

09-10		10-11		11-12		12-13		13-14		14-15		15-16		16-17		17-18		18-19	
Humb	Exp	Lincs	3	Lincs	1	NCE1	4	NCE1	1	NCEP	4	NCEP	3	NCEP	1	NP1S	10	NP1E	7
										FAC	2Q	FAC	P	FAC	P	FAC	1Q	FAC	3Qr
								FAV	2P	FAV	2P	FAV	5P	FAV	F	FAT	3Q	FAT	1Q

HONOURS / RECORDS
FA Comps: None
League: Lincolnshire 2011-12. Northern Counties East Division One 2013-14, Premier 2016-17.

County FA: Lincolnshire Senior Trophy 2016-17.

Best FA Cup Second Qualifying Round 2014-15
FA Vase Runners-up 2016-17
FA Trophy Third Qualifying Round 2017-18

Ground Capacity: 1,875 **Seats:** 190 **Covered:** Yes **Clubhouse:** Yes **Shop:**
Previous Grounds: None
Record Attendance: 1,154 v Bromsgrove Sporting, FA Vase Semi-Final second leg, 18/03/2017.

DIRECTIONS
Head East along the M180/A180. Exit at the Great Coates Interchange. Travel back over motorway to first roundabout. Take first exit and follow for two miles to Trawl Pub roundabout. Take second exit, follow for two miles to Bradley roundabout. Take second exit on to Bradley Road. The ground is approximately 500 yards on the left.

There is plenty of parking at the ground.

Nearest Railway Station Grimsby - then a 5 min walk to main bus station (see below).
Bus Route From the bus station, take either No.14 or No.13 bus.

FRICKLEY ATHLETIC

Founded 1910

Nickname: The Blues **Club Colours:** All royal blue

Club Contact Details 01977 642 460
Westfield Lane, South Elmsall, Pontefract WF9 2EQ

Previous Names: Frickley Colliery
Previous Leagues: Sheffield, Yorkshire 1922-24, Midland Counties 1924-33, 34-60, 70-76, Cheshire County 1960-70, Northern Premier 1976-80, Conference 1980-87

09-10		10-11		11-12		12-13		13-14		14-15		15-16		16-17		17-18		18-19	
NP P	15	NP P	18	NP P	19	NP P	18	NP P	21	NP P	19	NP P	7	NP P	22	NP1S	3	NP1E	12
FAC	3Qr	FAC	3Qr	FAC	3Q	FAC	3Q	FAC	2Q	FAC	1Q	FAC	2Q	FAC	1Q	FAC	1Q	FAC	2Q
FAT	2Q	FAT	1Q	FAT	1Q	FAT	1Q	FAT	1Q	FAT	1Q	FAT	1Q	FAT	1Q	FAT	1Q	FAT	1Q

HONOURS / RECORDS
FA Comps: None
League: None

County FA: Sheffield & Hallamshire Senior Cup x14 - Firstly in 1927-28 and most recently in 2015-16.

Goalscorer: K Whiteley
Additional: Received £12,500 from Boston United for Paul Shirtliff and from Northampton Town for Russ Wilcox

Ground Capacity: 2,087 **Seats:** 490 **Covered:** 700 **Clubhouse:** Yes **Shop:** Yes
Previous Grounds: None
Record Attendance: 5,800 v Rotherham United - FA Cup 1st Round 1971

DIRECTIONS
From North: Leave A1 to join A639, go over flyover to junction. Turn left and immediately right, signed South Elmsall. Continue to roundabout and take 2nd exit to traffic lights and turn left onto Mill Lane (B6474). Turn right at the T-junction and continue down hill to next T-junction. Turn right and immediately left up Westfield Lane. The ground is signposted to the left after about half a mile.
From South: Exit M18 at J2 onto A1 (North). Leave A1 for A638 towards Wakefield. Continue on A638, going straight on at the first roundabout and turn left at next roundabout to traffic lights. Continue as above from traffic lights.

Nearest Railway Station South Elmsall - 0.7km. Moorthorpe - 0.9km
Bus Route Westfield Lane - stop 100m away

GLOSSOP NORTH END

Founded 1886

Nickname: Peakites / The Hillmen **Club Colours:** All royal blue

Club Contact Details 07740 265 711
Surrey Street, Glossop, Derbys SK13 7AJ

Previous Names: Glossop North End1886-1896 and Glossop FC 1898-1992. Reformed in 1992.
Previous Leagues: North Cheshire 1890-94. Combination 1894-96. Midland 1896-98. The Football League 1898-1918. Lancashire Comb. 1919-20, 57-66. Manchester 1920-57, 66-78. Cheshire County (Founder member) 1978-82. North West Counties (FM)1982-2015.

09-10		10-11		11-12		12-13		13-14		14-15		15-16		16-17		17-18		18-19	
NWCP	7	NWCP	14	NWCP	6	NWCP	13	NWCP	3	NWCP	1	NP1N	4	NP1N	8	NP1N	11	NP1W	17
FAC	1Q	FAC	1Q	FAC	EP	FAC	P	FAC	1Q	FAC	2Q	FAC	1Qr	FAC	Pr	FAC	P	FAC	Pr
FAV	3P	FAV	1P	FAV	3P	FAV	2Qr	FAV	2P	FAV	F	FAT	Pr	FAT	1Q	FAT	3Qr	FAT	EP

HONOURS / RECORDS
FA Comps: None
League: Manchester 1927-28. North West Counties Premier Division 2014-15.

County FA: Manchester FA Premier Cup 1996-97, 97-98. Derbyshire Senior Cup 2000-01.

Best FA Cup First Round Proper 1896-97
FA Trophy Third Qualifying Round 2017-18
FA Vase Finalists 2014-15

Ground Capacity: 2,374 **Seats:** 209 **Covered:** 509 **Clubhouse:** Yes **Shop:** Yes
Previous Grounds: Pyegrove. Silk Street. Water Lane. Cemetery Road. North Road 1890-1955.
Record Attendance: 10,736 v Preston North End F.A. Cup 1913-1914

DIRECTIONS
From M67 follow A57 signposted Glossop/Sheffield. On approaching Town Centre turn left at traffic lights by Tesco Store into Glossop Brook Road, continue up the hill to the ground. For Sat/Nav enter Glossop Brook Road for easiest access to ground.

Nearest Railway Station Glossop - 0.4km
Bus Route St Mary's Road - stop 300m away

ILKESTON TOWN

Founded 2017

Nickname: The Robins **Club Colours:** Red & white

Club Contact Details 07876 492 902
New Manor Ground, Awsworth Road, Ilkeston, Derbyshire DE7 8JF

Previous Names: None
Previous Leagues: Midland 2017-19.

09-10	10-11	11-12	12-13	13-14	14-15	15-16	16-17	17-18	18-19
								MFL1 2	MFLP 1
									FAV 2P

HONOURS / RECORDS
FA Comps: None
League: Midland Premier 2018-19.

County FA: None

Victory: 8-1 v Loughborough University, Midland Premier, 27/04/2019
Defeat: 0-4 v Coventry Sphinx, Midland Premier, 15/12/2018

Ground Capacity: 3,029 **Seats:** 550 **Covered:** 2,000 **Clubhouse:** Yes **Shop:** Yes
Previous Grounds: None.
Record Attendance: Not known

DIRECTIONS
M1 Junction 26, take the A610 signed Ripley, leave at the first exit on to the A6096 signed Awsworth / Ilkeston, at the next island take the A6096 signed Ilkeston, keep on this road for about half a mile, then turn right into Awsworth Road, Signed Cotmanhay (Coaches can get down this road) the ground is about half a mile on the left hand side down this road. Car Parking available at the ground £1 per car.

KIDSGROVE ATHLETIC

Founded 1952

Nickname: The Grove **Club Colours:** All blue

Club Contact Details 01782 782 412
Hollinwood Road, Kidsgrove, Staffs ST7 1DH

Previous Names: None
Previous Leagues: Buslem and Tunstall 1953-63, Staffordshire County 1963-66, Mid Cheshire 1966-90, North West Counties 1990-2002

09-10	10-11	11-12	12-13	13-14	14-15	15-16	16-17	17-18	18-19
NP1S 4	NP1S 7	NP1S 13	NP1S 18	NP1S 21	NP1S 20	NP1S 15	NP1S 12	NP1S 18	NP1W 10
FAC 1Q	FAC 2Q	FAC 4Q	FAC P	FAC 1Q	FAC P	FAC Pr	FAC 2Q	FAC 2Q	FAC 4Q
FAT P	FAT Pr	FAT 1Q	FAT 1Q	FAT 2Q	FAT P	FAT 2Qr	FAT 2Q	FAT 2Q	FAT P

HONOURS / RECORDS
FA Comps: None
League: Staffordshire County Division Two 1963-64, Premier 65-66. Mid-Cheshire 1970-71, 77-78, 86-87, 87-88.
North West Counties Premier Division 1997-98, 2001-02.
County FA: Staffordshire Senior Cup 2003-04, 06-07, 08-09, 10-11, 11-12.

Victory: 23-0 v Cross Heath W.M.C. - Staffordshire Cup 1965
Defeat: 0-15 v Stafford Rangers - Staffordshire Senior Cup 20/11/2001
Goalscorer: Scott Dundas - 53 (1997-98)
Additional: Paid £10,000 to Stevenage Borough for Steve Walters
Received £3,000 for Ryan Baker 2003-04

Ground Capacity: 2,000 **Seats:** 1,000 **Covered:** 800 **Clubhouse:** Yes **Shop:** Yes
Previous Grounds: Vickers and Goodwin 1953-60
Record Attendance: 1,903 v Tiverton Town - FA Vase Semi-final 1998

DIRECTIONS
Leave the M6 at Junction 16, join the A500 towards Stoke-on-Trent. Take the 2nd exit signposted Newcastle & Kidsgrove. Top of the slip road, turn left onto A34 Kidsgrove/Congleton. Straight over at roundabout. At 1st set of traffic lights (by Caudwell Arms pub) turn right onto A34. Continue to next set of lights, turn right into Cedar Avenue. Continue then take 2nd right into Lower Ash Road. Take 3rd left into Hollinwood Road, Ground on left at top.

Nearest Railway Station Kidsgrove - 0.8km
Bus Route Grove Avenue - stop 200m away

LEEK TOWN

Founded 1946

Nickname: The Blues **Club Colours:** All blue

Club Contact Details 01538 399 278
Harrison Park, Macclesfield Road, Leek, Cheshire ST13 8LD

Previous Names: None
Previous Leagues: Staffordshire Co., Manchester 1951-54, 57-73, West Midlands (B'ham) 1954-56,Cheshire Co. 1973-82, North West Counties 1982-87, Northern Premier 1987-94, 95-97, Southern 1994-95, Conference 1997-99

09-10		10-11		11-12		12-13		13-14		14-15		15-16		16-17		17-18		18-19	
NP1S	8	NP1S	16	NP1S	5	NP1S	10	NP1S	3	NP1S	2	NP1S	8	NP1S	9	NP1S	7	NP1W	3
FAC	P	FAC	P	FAC	3Qr	FAC	3Q	FAC	Pr	FAC	4Q	FAC	1Qr	FAC	1Q	FAC	1Q	FAC	2Q
FAT	2Q	FAT	P	FAT	2Qr	FAT	2Qr	FAT	2P	FAT	2Qr	FAT	P	FAT	2Q	FAT	2Q	FAT	1Qr

HONOURS / RECORDS
FA Comps: None
League: Staffordshire County 1949-50, 50-51. Manchester 1951-52, 71-72, 72-73. Cheshire County 1974-75.
Northern Premier Division One 1989-90, Premier Division 1996-97.
County FA: Staffordshire Senior Cup 1995-96.

Goalscorer: Dave Sutton - 144
Appearances: Gary Pearce - 447
Additional: Paid £2,000 to Sutton Town for Simon Snow
Received £30,000 from Barnsley for Tony Bullock

Ground Capacity: 3,600 **Seats:** 650 **Covered:** 3,000 **Clubhouse:** Yes **Shop:** Yes
Previous Grounds: None
Record Attendance: 3,512 v Macclesfield Town - FA Cup 1973-74

DIRECTIONS
From the South: Leave M6 at J15, over roundabout on to the A500, go over the flyover, up the slip road, onto the A50 and follow the signs to Leek. Go straight over the roundabout (Britannia Building on the left) to large set of lights. Go straight across St. Georges Street to top of road to junction, turn left, go down the hill for about a half a mile. The Ground is on the left. **From the North:** Leave M6 at J19. Take Macclesfield signs. Follow into Macclesfield then take A523 Leek/Buxton signs. Follow these to Leek. Ground is situated on the right as you come into Leek. From West Midlands: M6 J15. A500 towards Stoke, over flyover, take A50 past Brittania Stadium. After approx 3 miles join A53 signposted Leek. On entering the town, straight ahead up St Edwards St. (Remainder as above)

LINCOLN UNITED

Founded 1938

Nickname: United **Club Colours:** White & red

Club Contact Details 01522 609 674
Ashby Avenue, Hartsholme, Lincoln LN6 0DY

Previous Names: Lincoln Amateurs > 1954
Previous Leagues: Lincolnshire 1945-46, 60-67, Lincoln 1946-60, Yorkshire 1967-82,
Northern Counties East 1982-86, 92-95, Central Midlands 1982-92

09-10		10-11		11-12		12-13		13-14		14-15		15-16		16-17		17-18		18-19	
NP1S	19	NP1S	12	NP1S	18	NP1S	20	NP1S	17	NP1S	9	NP1S	5	NP1S	8	NP1S	8	NP1E	14
FAC	4Q	FAC	2Q	FAC	P	FAC	P	FAC	P	FAC	1Q	FAC	2Q	FAC	4Q	FAC	1Q	FAC	P
FAT	P	FAT	1Qr	FAT	1Q	FAT	1Q	FAT	P	FAT	P	FAT	2Q	FAT	3Q	FAT	P	FAT	P

HONOURS / RECORDS
FA Comps: None
League: Yorkshire Division Two 1967-68, Division One 70-71, 73-74. Central Midlands Supreme Division 1991-92.
Northern Counties East Division One (South) 82-83, Division Two 1985-86, Division One 92-93, Premier Division 1994-95.
County FA: Lincolnshire Senior Cup 2016-17.

Victory: 12-0 v Pontefract Colliery - 1995
Defeat: 0-7 v Huddersfield Town - FA Cup 1st Round 16/11/1991
Goalscorer: Tony Simmons - 215
Appearances: Steve Carter - 447
Additional: Paid £1,000 to Hucknall Town for Paul Tomlinson Dec 2000. Received £3,000 from Charlton for Dean Dye July 1991.

Ground Capacity: 2,200 **Seats:** 400 **Covered:** 1,084 **Clubhouse:** Yes **Shop:** Yes
Previous Grounds: Skew Bridge 1940s, Co-op Sports Ground > 1960s, Hartsholme Cricket Club > 1982
Record Attendance: 2,000 v Crook Town - FA Amateur Cup 1st Round 1968

DIRECTIONS
Along Lincoln Relief Road (A46) until reaching roundabout with exit for Birchwood. Take this exit which is Skellingthorpe Road for approximately 1 mile, at 30 mph sign turn right into Ashby Avenue. Entrance to ground is 200 yards on right.

Nearest Railway Station Hkeham - 2.1km
Bus Route Eccleshare Court - stop 75m away

LOUGHBOROUGH DYNAMO

Founded 1955

Nickname: The Moes **Club Colours:** Gold & black

Club Contact Details 01509 215 972
Watermead Lane, Loughborough LE11 3TN

Previous Names: None
Previous Leagues: Loughborough Alliance 1957-66, Leicestershire & District 1966-71, East Midlands 1971-72, Central Alliance 1972-89, Leicestershire Senior 1989-2004, Midland Alliance 2004-08

09-10		10-11		11-12		12-13		13-14		14-15		15-16		16-17		17-18		18-19	
NP1S	14	NP1S	17	NP1S	8	NP1S	16	NP1S	14	NP1S	14	NP1S	20	NP1S	20	NP1S	14	NP1E	8
FAC	1Q	FAC	2Q	FAC	2Q	FAC	1Qr	FAC	P	FAC	P	FAC	P	FAC	P	FAC	1Q	FAC	P
FAT	1Q	FAT	P	FAT	P	FAT	P	FAT	P	FAT	2Q	FAT	P	FAT	P	FAT	P	FAT	Pr

HONOURS / RECORDS
FA Comps: None
League: Loughborough Alliance Division Three 1959-60, Division One 64-65. Leicester & District Division One 1969-70. Leicestershire Senior Division One 2001-02, Premier Division 2003-04.
County FA: Leicestershire Charity Cup 1987-88, 2003-04, 11-12, Senior Cup 2002-03, 03-04.

Best FA Cup Second Qualifying Round 2010-11, 11-12
FA Trophy Second Qualifying Round 2014-15
FA Vase Second Round Proper 2004-05

Ground Capacity: 1,500 **Seats:** 75 **Covered:** Yes **Clubhouse:** Yes **Shop:** No
Previous Grounds: None
Record Attendance: Not known

DIRECTIONS
From M1: At Junction 23 turn towards Loughborough (A512). At 1st set of traffic lights turn right on to Snells Nook Lane.. At 1st crossroads ("Priory" pub on left) turn left on to Nanpantan Rd. Turn (1st) right after 0.75 miles on to Watermead Lane. The ground is at the end of the lane. **From Leicester (A6):** Turn left at 3rd roundabout on Epinal Way (Ring Road) on to Forest Road. After 2 miles turn (5th) left on to Watermead Lane. **From Nottingham (A60):** Turn right at 1st set of traffic lights in Loughborough. Go through next 4 sets of traffic lights. Turn left at the first roundabout on to Epinal Way straight on at next roundabout and then take the third exit at following r'about on to Forest Road. After 2 miles turn (5th) left on to Watermead Lane.
Nearest Railway Station Loughborough - 4.6km
Bus Route Nursery School - stop 500m away

MARKET DRAYTON TOWN

Founded 1969

Nickname: None **Club Colours:** All red

Club Contact Details 07453 960 650
Greenfields Sports Ground, Greenfields Lane, Market Drayton TF9 3SL

Previous Names: Little Drayton Rangers > 2003
Previous Leagues: West Midlands (Regional) 1969-2006, Midland Alliance 2006-09

09-10		10-11		11-12		12-13		13-14		14-15		15-16		16-17		17-18		18-19	
NP1S	13	NP1S	18	NP1S	16	NP1S	15	NP1S	19	NP1S	19	NP1S	11	NP1S	14	NP1S	21	NP1W	16
FAC	2Q	FAC	2Q	FAC	P	FAC	1Qr	FAC	P	FAC	1Q	FAC	1Q	FAC	P	FAC	1Q	FAC	Pr
FAT	Pr	FAT	1Qr	FAT	P	FAT	P	FAT	P	FAT	1Qr	FAT	P	FAT	1Q	FAT	P	FAT	EP

HONOURS / RECORDS
FA Comps: None
League: West Midlands (Regional) 2005-06. Midland Alliance 2008-09.

County FA: None

Victory: (League) 9-0 Home vs. Racing Club Warwick 10/03/09
Best FA Cup Second Qualifying Round 2007-08, 10-11
FA Trophy First Qualifying Round 2010-11, 14-15, 15-16
FA Vase Fifth Round Proper 2008-09

Ground Capacity: 1,000 **Seats:** Yes **Covered:** Yes **Clubhouse:** Yes **Shop:** No
Previous Grounds: Not known
Record Attendance: 440 vs. AFC Telford, Friendly 11/07/09. 229 vs. Witton Albion, Unibond South 25/08/09

DIRECTIONS
Take the A41 to Ternhill Island, turn right on A53 for Newcastle-under-Lyne. Straight on at first island (by Muller factory). At next island turn right to town centre (by Gingerbread Inn). Approx 200yds take 2nd right into Greenfields Lane. Ground 150 yards on right, car park opposite.

From Stoke-on-Trent take A53 for Shrewsbury, at Gingerbread Inn turn left for town centre then as above.

Bus Route Cmetery Road Jct - stop 400m away

NEWCASTLE TOWN

Founded 1964

Nickname: The Castle **Club Colours:** Blue & white

Club Contact Details 01782 662 350 secretary@newcastletownfc.co.uk
Buckmaster Avenue, Clayton ST5 3BX

Previous Names: Parkway Hanley, Clayton Park & Parkway Clayton. Merged as NTFC in 1986.
Previous Leagues: Newcatle & District, Staffs Co & Mid Cheshire, North West Counties

09-10		10-11		11-12		12-13		13-14		14-15		15-16		16-17		17-18		18-19	
NWCP	1	NP1S	2	NP1S	15	NP1S	17	NP1S	8	NP1S	3	NP1S	14	NP1S	7	NP1S	20	NP1W	15
FAC	P	FAC	4Q	FAC	1Qr	FAC	P	FAC	1Qr	FAC	Pr	FAC	1Qr	FAC	P	FAC	1Q	FAC	P
FAV	2P	FAT	1Q	FAT	1Qr	FAT	1Q	FAT	P	FAT	1Q	FAT	1Qr	FAT	P	FAT	1Qr	FAT	2Qr

HONOURS / RECORDS

FA Comps: None

League: Mid Cheshire Division Two 1982-83, 90-91, Division One 85-86. North West Counties Premier Division 2009-10.

County FA: Walsall Senior Cup 1993-94, 94-95. Staffordshire Senior Cup 2009-10.

Goalscorer: Andy Bott - 149
Appearances: Dean Gillick - 632

Ground Capacity: 4,000 **Seats:** 300 **Covered:** 1,000 **Clubhouse:** Yes **Shop:** Yes
Previous Grounds: None
Record Attendance: 3,948 v Notts County - FA Cup 1996

DIRECTIONS

FROM M6: Leave the M6 at Junction 15 and immediately turn left up the bank (signposted A519 Newcastle.) Go to the second roundabout and turn right into Stafford Avenue. Take the first left into Tittensor Road (signposted Newcastle Town FC.) Go to the end and the ground is below in the parkway. (Entrance through the gateway signposted Newcastle Town FC.)
FROM A50 DERBY: Follow the A50 to the end and join the A500 (signposted M6 South) just past Stoke City Football Ground. Follow the A500 to the Motorway and at the roundabout turn right up the bank (A519 Newcastle.) Go to the second roundabout and turn right into Stafford Avenue. Take the first left into Tittensor Road (signposted Newcastle Town FC.) Go to the end and the ground is below in the parkway. (Entrance through the gateway signposted Newcastle Town FC.)

SHEFFIELD

Founded 1857

Nickname: The Club **Club Colours:** Red & black

Club Contact Details 0114 362 7016
The Home of Football Stadium, Sheffield Road, Dronfield S18 2GD

Previous Names: None
Previous Leagues: Yorkshire 1949-82

09-10		10-11		11-12		12-13		13-14		14-15		15-16		16-17		17-18		18-19	
NP1S	5	NP1S	11	NP1S	4	NP1S	9	NP1S	16	NP1S	15	NP1S	17	NP1S	15	NP1S	15	NP1E	4
FAC	1Q	FAC	4Qr	FAC	P	FAC	P	FAC	1Q	FAC	2Qr	FAC	Pr	FAC	1Q	FAC	P	FAC	P
FAT	P	FAT	1Qr	FAT	3Q	FAT	P	FAT	3Q	FAT	1Q	FAT	1Q	FAT	P	FAT	P	FAT	EPr

HONOURS / RECORDS

FA Comps: FA Amateur Cup 1902-03.

League: Northern Counties East Division One 1988-89, 90-91.

County FA: Sheffield and Hallamshire Senior Cup 1993-94, 2004-05, 05-06, 07-08, 09-10.

Misc: Oldest Football Club in the World.
Paid £1,000 to Arnold Town for David Wilkins. Received £1,000 from Alfreton for Mick Godber 2002.

Best FA Cup Fourth Round Proper 1877-78, 79-80.
FA Trophy Third Qualifying Round 2007-08, 11-12, 13-14
FA Vase Finalists 1976-77

Ground Capacity: 2,089 **Seats:** 250 **Covered:** 500 **Clubhouse:** Yes **Shop:** Yes
Previous Grounds: Abbeydale Park, Dore 1956-89, Sheffield Amateur Sports Stadium, Hillsborough Park 1989-91, Don Valley Stadium 1991-97
Record Attendance: 2,000 v Barton Rovers - FA Vase Semi-final 1976-77

DIRECTIONS

From the South – M1 to Junc 29, A617 into Chesterfield. At Roundabout follow A61 Sheffield. This is a dual carriageway passing over 2 roundabouts. At the 3rd roundabout take the 3rd exit signposted Dronfield. The Coach and Horses Public House is at the bottom of the hill on the right and the BT Local Business Stadium directly behind it. Entrance to the ground is by turning right at the traffic lights and immediate right into the Club Car Park. **From the East** - M18 to M1 north to Junc 33 (Sheffield). Turn towards Sheffield and take the 3rd exit from dual carriageway signposted' Ring Road / Chesterfield'. Go straight on at traffic island so that you are travelling alongside dual carriageway for a short period. At the junction turn left onto A61 Chesterfield. This is a dual carriageway passing through numerous traffic lights and two traffic islands. Follow Chesterfield sign at all times. After passing Graves Tennis centre on your left, turn left at next traffic island (still signposted Chesterfield). At next traffic island take 2nd exit signposted Dronfield The Coach and Horses Public House is at the bottom of the hill on the right and the BT Local Business Stadium directly behind it. Entrance to the ground is by turning right at the traffic lights and immediate right into the Club Car Park.
Nearest Railway Station Dronfield - 1.1km

SPALDING UNITED

Founded 1921

Nickname: Tulips **Club Colours:** Blue & yellow

Club Contact Details 01778 713 328

Sir Halley Stewart Playing Fields, Winfrey Avenue, Spalding PE11 1DA

Previous Names: None

Previous Leagues: Peterborough, United Counties 1931-55,68-78,86-88,91-99,03-04, 11-14 Eastern Counties 1955-60, Central Alliance 1960-61, Midland Co. 1961-68, Northern Counties East 1982-86, Southern 1988-91, 99-03. NPL 2003-11.

09-10	10-11	11-12	12-13	13-14	14-15	15-16	16-17	17-18	18-19
NP1S 21	NP1S 22	UCL P 13	UCL P 3	UCL P 1	NP1S 7	NP1S 12	NP1S 3	NP1S 13	NP1E 18
FAC P	FAC 1Qr	FAC EP	FAC EP	FAC 2Q	FAC 2Q	FAC 3Qr	FAC 1Q	FAC Pr	FAC 1Q
FAT 1Q	FAT P	FAV 2P	FAV 5P	FAV 3P	FAT 1Qr	FAT P	FAT P	FAT 1Q	FAT P

HONOURS / RECORDS

FA Comps: None

League: Peterborough & District 1930-31. United Counties 1954-55, 75-75, 87-88, 98-99, 2003-04, 13-14. Northern Counties East 1983-84.

County FA: Lincolnshire Senior Cup 1952-53.

Best FA Cup First Round Proper 1957-58, 64-65

FA Trophy Third Round Proper 1999-2000

FA Vase Quarter Finals 1989-90, 96-97

Ground Capacity: 3,500 **Seats:** 1,000 **Covered:** 1,000 **Clubhouse:** Yes **Shop:** Yes

Previous Grounds: Stadium known as the Black Swan Ground before being renamed after Halley Stewart MP in 1954.

Record Attendance: 6,972 v Peterborough - FA Cup 1982

DIRECTIONS

From the North follow the A52 and pick up the A16 south, as you near Spalding follow A16 By-pass past the New Power Station (on right). Carry on the by-pass to Springfields Roundabout, (McDonalds is on the left) turn right. Follow signs to Spalding Town Centre over Fulney Bridge on the Holbeach Road and travel approx ¾ mile from by-pass. Turn right over second bridge forming the roundabout then straight over into West Elloe Avenue. Continue down to traffic lights (Approx 400 yards). Turn left into Pinchbeck Road. After approx 300 yards turn right at the traffic lights. Turn left at the next set of traffic lights into Winfrey Avenue. The Ground is on the left.

Nearest Railway Station Spalding - 0.2km

Bus Route Broad Street - stop 100m away

STAMFORD

Founded 1896

Nickname: The Daniels **Club Colours:** Red with white trim

Club Contact Details 01780 751 471

Borderville Sports Centre, Ryhall Road, Stamford PE9 1US

Previous Names: Stamford Town and Rutland Ironworks amalgamated in 1894 to form Rutland Ironworks > 1896

Previous Leagues: Peterborough, Northants (UCL) 1908-55, Central Alliance 1955-61, Midland counties 1961-72, United Counties 1972-98, Southern 1998-2007

09-10	10-11	11-12	12-13	13-14	14-15	15-16	16-17	17-18	18-19
NP1S 10	NP1S 19	NP1S 7	NP1S 4	NP P 18	NP P 20	NP P 21	NP1S 16	NP1S 6	NP1E 11
FAC P	FAC 2Q	FAC P	FAC 2Q	FAC 4Q	FAC 2Q	FAC 2Q	FAC 1P	FAC P	FAC Pr
FAT P	FAT 1Q	FAT 1Q	FAT 3Q	FAT 1Q	FAT 1Q	FAT 1Q	FAT 1Q	FAT 2Q	FAT 3Qr

HONOURS / RECORDS

FA Comps: FA Vase 1979-80.

League: United Counties 1911-12, 75-76, 77-78, 79-80, 80-81, 81-82, 96-97, 97-98.

County FA: Lincolnshire Senior Cup 2000-01, Senior Shield 2006-07, 08-09, 10-11, 13-14, 14-15.

Victory: 13-0 v Peterborough Reserves - Northants League 1929-30

Defeat: 0-17 v Rothwell - FA Cup 1927-28

Goalscorer: Bert Knighton - 248

Appearances: Dick Kwiatkowski - 462

Ground Capacity: 2,000 **Seats:** 300 **Covered:** 1,250 **Clubhouse:** Yes **Shop:** Yes

Previous Grounds: Hanson's Field 1894-2014.

Record Attendance: 1,573 v Peterborough United, pre-season friendly, 10/07/2019.

DIRECTIONS

From the North using the A1: Leave the A1 at the B1081 exit signposted Stamford. Continue into Great Casterton. Turn left at the crossroads (signposted Ryhall) for about 2.5 miles. At the end of the road turn right and immediately right again. Continue for about 1.5 miles across several mini roundabouts and the stadium is on the right. **From the South using the A1:** Leave A1 at A606 exit signposted Oakham. Turn right over the A1 then left as if going back onto A1 south. Then, before joining the south bound carriageway, take the first right signposted Great Casterton for 0.5 mile. Turn left for one mile into Great Casterton (ignore first turning right for Little Casterton) then turn right at the crossroads (signposted Ryhall) for about 2.5 miles. At the end of the road turn right and immediately right again. Continue for about 1.5 miles across several mini roundabouts and the stadium on the right. **From the West using the A43:** Join A1 north as you approach Stamford. Then follow directions as A1 from the South. **From the East using the A1175:** Go straight over roundabout for Morrisons. At the mini-roundabout, take the 3rd exit and follow road. You will pass Sainsbury's and then Travis Perkins on your right. The stadium is on your left at bottom of dip. Sat Nav PE9 4QN.

Nearest Railway Station Stamford - 2.1km

Bus Route Gush Way - stop 300m away

STOCKSBRIDGE PARK STEELS

Founded 1986

Nickname: Steels **Club Colours:** Yellow & royal blue

Club Contact Details 0114 288 8305 (Match days)
Bracken Moor Lane, Stocksbridge, Sheffield S36 2AN

Previous Names: Stocksbridge Works and Oxley Park merged in 1986
Previous Leagues: Northern Counties East 1986-96

09-10		10-11		11-12		12-13		13-14		14-15		15-16		16-17		17-18		18-19	
NP P	11	NP P	13	NP P	18	NP P	20	NP P	23	NP1S	17	NP1S	6	NP1S	4	NP1S	11	NP1E	13
FAC	2Q	FAC	2Q	FAC	3Q	FAC	1Q	FAC	1Qr	FAC	P	FAC	Pr	FAC	P	FAC	P	FAC	P
FAT	1Q	FAT	3Q	FAT	1Qr	FAT	1P	FAT	1Q	FAT	P	FAT	1P	FAT	1P	FAT	P	FAT	P

HONOURS / RECORDS
FA Comps: None
League: Northern Counties East Division One 1991-92, Premier Division 1993-94.

County FA: Sheffield Senior Cup 1951-52, 92-93, 95-96, 98-99, 2006-07, 08-09.

Victory: 17-1 v Oldham Town - FA Cup 2002-03
Defeat: 0-6 v Shildon
Goalscorer: Trevor Jones - 145
Appearances: Paul Jackson scored 10 v Oldham Town in the 2002-03 FA Cup - a FA Cup record
Received £15,000 from Wolverhampton Wanderers for Lee Mills

Ground Capacity: 3,500 **Seats:** 450 **Covered:** 1,500 **Clubhouse:** Yes **Shop:** Yes
Previous Grounds: Stonemoor 1949-51, 52-53
Record Attendance: 2,050 v Sheffield Wednesday - opening of floodlights October 1991

DIRECTIONS
From the West onto A616. Immediately you reach the Stocksbridge bypass turn Right signed (Stocksbridge West), then continue until you reach the shopping centre approx 1.5 miles. 300 yards past the centre you will see Gordons Autos on your left. Turn right directly opposite signed (Nanny Hill) and continue up the hill for Approx 500 yds, Ground is on the Left. **From M1**- From North Junction 36 on to A61 Sheffield to McDonalds Roundabout. **From South** Junction 35a on to A616 Manchester to McDonalds Roundabout. From McDonalds roundabout on A616 Manchester for approx 6 miles then take Stocksbridge West exit, then continue until you reach the shopping centre approx 1.5 miles. 300yds past the centre you will see Gordons Autos on your Left. Turn right directly opposite signed (Nanny Hill) and continue up the hill for Approx 500yds, ground on Left.

SUTTON COLDFIELD TOWN

Founded 1879

Nickname: Royals **Club Colours:** All blue

Club Contact Details 0121 354 2997 murralln@gmail.com
Central Ground, Coles Lane, Sutton Coldfield B72 1NL

Previous Names: Sutton Coldfield F.C. 1879-1921
Previous Leagues: Central Birmingham, Walsall Senior, Staffordshire County, Birmingham Combination 1950-54, West Midlands (Regional) 1954-65, 79-82, Midlands Combination 1965-79. Northern Premier 2010-18. Southern 2018-19.

09-10		10-11		11-12		12-13		13-14		14-15		15-16		16-17		17-18		18-19	
SthM	6	NP1S	6	NP1S	12	NP1S	6	NP1S	6	NP1S	4	NP P	12	NP P	20	NP P	24	SthC	5
FAC	3Qr	FAC	1Q	FAC	P	FAC	1Q	FAC	2Q	FAC	1Q	FAC	1Q	FAC	2Q	FAC	1Q	FAC	2Qr
FAT	1Qr	FAT	P	FAT	1Q	FAT	P	FAT	P	FAT	P	FAT	1P	FAT	1Q	FAT	1Q	FAT	EP

HONOURS / RECORDS
FA Comps: None
League: West Midlands League 1979-80. Midland Combination x2.
NPL Division One South Play-off 2014-15.
County FA: Birmingham Senior Cup 2010-11.

Goalscorer: Eddie Hewitt - 288
Appearances: Andy Ling - 550
Additional: Paid £1,500 to Gloucester for Lance Morrison, to Burton Albion for Micky Clarke and to Atherstone United for Steve Farmer 1991. Received £25,000 from West Bromwich Albion for Barry Cowdrill 1979

Ground Capacity: 4,500 **Seats:** 200 **Covered:** 500 **Clubhouse:** Yes **Shop:** Yes
Previous Grounds: Meadow Plat 1879-89, Coles Lane 1890-1919
Record Attendance: 2,029 v Doncaster Rovers - FA Cup 1980-81

DIRECTIONS
From M42 Junc 9, take A4097 [Minworth sign]. At island, follow signs to Walmley Village. At traffic lights turn right [B4148]. After shops turn left at traffic lights into Wylde Green Road. Over railway bridge turn right into East View Road, which becomes Coles Lane.

Nearest Railway Station Sutton Coldfield - 1.1km
Bus Route Douglas Road - stop 100m away

WISBECH TOWN

Founded 1920

Nickname: Fenmen **Club Colours:** All red

Club Contact Details 01945 581 511
Fenland Stadium, Lynn Road, Wisbech PE14 7AL

Previous Names: None
Previous Leagues: Peterborough 1920-35. United Counties 1935-50, 2013-18. EC 1950-52, 70-97, 2003-13. Midland 1952-58. Southern 1958-70, 97-2002.

09-10		10-11		11-12		12-13		13-14		14-15		15-16		16-17		17-18		18-19	
ECP	11	ECP	4	ECP	4	ECP	2	UCL P	7	UCL P	3	UCL P	8	UCL P	6	UCL P	2	NP1E	17
FAC	P	FAC	P	FAC	1Q	FAC	1Qr	FAC	EP	FAC	1Q	FAC	P	FAC	P	FAC	1Q	FAC	1Q
FAV	2Q	FAV	2P	FAV	4Pr	FAV	4P	FAV	QF	FAV	3P	FAV	1P	FAV	1Qr	FAV	4P	FAT	1Qr

HONOURS / RECORDS
FA Comps: None
League: United Counties 1946-47, 47-48. Southern Division one 1961-62.
Eastern Counties 1971-72, 76-77, 90-91.
County FA: None

Goalscorer: Bert Titmarsh - 246 (1931-37)
Appearances: Jamie Brighty - 731
Best FA Cup Second Round Proper 1957-58, 97-98
FA Trophy Second Round Proper 1999-2000
FA Vase Semi Finals 1984-85, 85-86

Ground Capacity: **Seats:** 118 **Covered:** Yes **Clubhouse:** Yes **Shop:**
Previous Grounds: Played on several grounds before moving to Fenland Park in 1947, then moving to their new stadium in 2008.
Record Attendance: 8,044 v Peterborough United, Midland League 25/08/1957

DIRECTIONS
From A1 follow signs for Wisbech (A47). At the outskirts of Wisbech, take 2nd exit off roundabout, signposted A47. After 1.5 miles, go straight over at the next roundabout. At next roundabout (another 3.1 miles on, Total Garage on right) take first exit (signposted B198 West Walton/Walsoken). Cross over next roundabout (which is new, so not marked on some maps and sat navs) and follow road for just over a mile. The entrance to the stadium is on the right via the right turn lane.

Bus Route Pumping Station - stop 370m away

WORKSOP TOWN

Founded 1861

Nickname: Tigers **Club Colours:** Amber & black

Club Contact Details 07952 365 224
Babbage Way, Worksop S80 1UJ

Previous Names: None
Previous Leagues: Sheffield Association. Midland 1949-60, 61-68, 69-74, Northern Premier 1968-69, 74-2004, 2007-14, Conf. 2004-07. Northern Counties East 2014-19.

09-10		10-11		11-12		12-13		13-14		14-15		15-16		16-17		17-18		18-19	
NP P	18	NP P	7	NP P	15	NP P	9	NP P	4	NCEP	2	NCEP	4	NCEP	13	NCEP	18	NCEP	1
FAC	1Qr	FAC	1Q	FAC	1Q	FAC	1Q	FAC	3Q	FAC	EP	FAC	EP	FAC	Pr	FAC	EP	FAC	1Q
FAT	1Qr	FAT	1P	FAT	2P	FAT	1P	FAT	1Q	FAV	4P	FAV	2P	FAV	2P	FAV	3P	FAV	2Q

HONOURS / RECORDS
FA Comps: None
League: Sheffield Association 1898-99 (joint), 47-48, 48-49. Midland 1921-22, 65-66, 72-73. Northern Counties east Premier 2018-19.

County FA: Sheffield & Hallamshire Senior Cup 1923-24, 52-53, 54-55, 65-66, 69-70, 72-73, 81-82, 84-85, 94-95, 96-97, 2002-03, 11-12

Victory: 20-0 v Staveley - 01/09/1984
Defeat: 1-11 v Hull City Reserves - 1955-56
Goalscorer: Kenny Clark - 287
Appearances: Kenny Clark - 347
Additional: Paid £5,000 to Grantham Town for Kirk Jackson. Received £47,000 from Sunderland for Jon Kennedy 2000.

Ground Capacity: 2,500 **Seats:** 200 **Covered:** 750 **Clubhouse:** Yes **Shop:** Yes
Previous Grounds: Central Avenue, Sandy Lane, shared with Ilkeston Town (New Manor Ground)
Record Attendance: 8,171 v Chesterfield - FA Cup 1925 (Central Avenue)

DIRECTIONS
From M1 junc 31 take A57 Worksop after 7 miles carry on to by-pass at 3rd roundabout take 1st exit Sandy Lane industrial estate Ground 1ml on left at side of Tyre Centre.
From A1 junc34 take B6045 Blyth, then take A57 Worksop at 1st set of lights go straight on pass the Hospital on the left,next set of lights straight on, at the next set go under the bridge,the next set of lights turn right,100mts up the road 1st right then turn first left into the ground.

Nearest Railway Station Worksop - 0.5km
Bus Route Grafton Street - stop 114m away

AFC RUSHDEN & DIAMONDS

Founded 2011

Nickname: The Diamonds **Club Colours:** White & blue

Club Contact Details 01933 359 206 secretary@afcdiamonds.com

Rushden & Higham United FC, Hayden Road, Rushden NN10 0HX

Previous Names: None

Previous Leagues: United Counties 2012-15. Southern 2015-16. Northern Premier 2016-17.

09-10	10-11	11-12	12-13	13-14	14-15	15-16	16-17	17-18	18-19
			UCL 1 2	UCL P 3	UCL P 1	SthC 5	NP1S 5	Sth1E 2	SthPC 9
				FAC 3Q	FAC 1Q	FAC 4Qr	FAC 3Q	FAC 2Qr	FAC 1Q
			FAV 3P	FAV 4P	FAV 2P	FAT P	FAT 2Q	FAT P	FAT 1Q

HONOURS / RECORDS

FA Comps: None

League: United Counties Premier Division 2014-15.

County FA: Northamptonshire Senior Cup 2015-16.

Victory: 9-0 v Buckingham Town (A) 15/12/12 and v Desborough Town (A) 21/02/15

Goalscorer: Tom Lorraine - 54 in 150 appearances, 2014- present.

Appearances: Brad Harris - 213, 2013 - present

Additional: 28 matches unbeaten, 13/01/2015 - 31/10/2015.

Ground Capacity: 2,654 **Seats:** 100 **Covered:** 250 **Clubhouse:** Yes **Shop:** Yes

Previous Grounds: The Dog & Duck Wellingborough Town FC 2011-17.

Record Attendance: 1,162 v Barwell, 27/10/2015.

DIRECTIONS

Take the A6 Rushden and Higham bypass, and exit at the junction with Newton Road. Follow the road past the cemetery, and take the sharp right hand turn immediately after the Risdene Academy onto Hayden Road. The ground is approximately a quarter of a mile on the left.

Nearest Railway Station Wellingborough and Bedford

Bus Route X46/X47, 49, 50, 26 to Rushden town centre a 10 min walk from the ground

ALVECHURCH

Founded 1929

Nickname: The Church **Club Colours:** Amber & black.

Club Contact Details 0121 445 2929 info@alvechurchfc.club

Lye Meadow, Redditch Road, Alvechurch B48 7RS

Previous Names: Alvechurch FC >1993. Re-formed in 1994 as Alvechurch Villa > 1996.

Previous Leagues: Worcestershire Combination/Midland Combination 1961-73, 94-2003. West Midlands (Reg) 1973-78. Southern 1978-93. Midland Alliance 2003-14. Midland Football League 2014-17. Northern Premier 2017-18.

09-10	10-11	11-12	12-13	13-14	14-15	15-16	16-17	17-18	18-19
MidAl 7	MidAl 20	MidAl 13	MidAl 11	MidAl 13	MFLP 15	MFLP 2	MFLP 1	NP1S 2	SthPC 4
FAC P	FAC EP	FAC 1Q	FAC EPr	FAC EP	FAC EP	FAC P	FAC P	FAC 3Q	FAC 2Q
FAV 2Q	FAV 2Q	FAV 2Q	FAV 2Q	FAV 3P	FAV 1Q	FAV 4P	FAV 2P	FAT 2Q	FAT 1Qr

HONOURS / RECORDS

FA Comps: None

League: Worcestershire Combination Division 1962-63, 64-65, 66-67. Midland Combination Division One 1971-72, Premier 2002-03. West Midlands (Reg) Premier 1973-74, 74-75, 75-76, 76-77. Southern Midland Division 1980-81. Midland Football Premier 2016-17.

County FA: Worcestershire Senior Cup 1972-73, 73-74, 76-77, Senior Urn 2003-04, 04-05, 07-08, 12-13.

Victory: 13-0 v (A) Alcester Town.

Defeat: 0-9 v (H) Coalville Town.

Goalscorer: Graham Allner. Keith Rostill scored 53 goals during the 2002-03 season.

Appearances: Kevin Palmer.

Additional: In 1971, the club played out the longest FA Cup tie in history when it took six games to beat Oxford City in the 4Q Round.

Ground Capacity: 3,000 **Seats:** 100 **Covered:** 300 **Clubhouse:** Yes **Shop:**

Previous Grounds: Played in the local park until moving to Lye Meadow.

Record Attendance: 13,500 v Enfield, FA Amateur Cup Quarter-final, 1964-65.

DIRECTIONS

Exit M42 at junction 2, take the A441 dual carriageway towards Redditch. At the 1st island, take the B4120 to Alvechurch. The ground is approximately 1 mile of the right (car park entrance is before the ground)

Nearest Railway Station Alvechurch - 0.7km

Bus Route Bus stops at the ground.

BANBURY UNITED

Founded 1931

Nickname: Puritans **Club Colours:** Red

Club Contact Details 01295 263 354 bworsley@btinternet.com
Station Approach, Banbury OX16 5AB

Previous Names: Spencer Villa 1931-34. Banbury Spencer. Club reformed in 1965 as Banbury United
Previous Leagues: Banbury Junior 1933-34, Oxon Senior 1934-35, Birmingham Combination 1935-54, West Midlands 1954-66, Southern 1966-90, Hellenic 1991-2000

09-10		10-11		11-12		12-13		13-14		14-15		15-16		16-17		17-18		18-19	
SthP	12	SthP	16	SthP	16	SthP	16	SthP	19	SthP	21	Sthsw	2	SthP	6	SthP	9	SthPC	17
FAC	1Qr	FAC	1Q	FAC	1Q	FAC	1Qr	FAC	1Q	FAC	2Q	FAC	P	FAC	3Q	FAC	3Q	FAC	2Q
FAT	2Qr	FAT	2Q	FAT	3Qr	FAT	1Qr	FAT	1Q	FAT	3Q	FAT	1Qr	FAT	1Q	FAT	2Qr	FAT	2Q

HONOURS / RECORDS
FA Comps: None
League: Oxfordshire Junior Banbury Division 1933-34. Oxfordshire Senior 1934-35. Hellenic Premier 1999-2000.

County FA: Oxford Senior Cup 1978-79, 87-88, 2003-04, 05-06, 06-07, 14-15.

Victory: 12-0 v RNAS Culham - Oxon Senior Cup 1945-46
Defeat: 2-11 v West Bromwich Albion 'A' - Birmingham Combination 1938-39
Goalscorer: Dick Pike and Tony Jacques - 222 (1935-48 and 1965-76 respectively). Jacues also scored 62 in a single season, 1967-68.
Appearances: Jody McKay - 576
Additional: Paid £2,000 to Oxford United for Phil Emsden. Received £20,000 from Derby County for Kevin Wilson 1979.

Ground Capacity: 4,000 **Seats:** 250 **Covered:** 250 **Clubhouse:** Yes **Shop:** Yes
Previous Grounds: Middleton Road 1931-34.
Record Attendance: 7,160 v Oxford City - FA Cup 3rd Qualifying Round 30/10/1948

DIRECTIONS
From M40, Junction 11, head towards Banbury, over first roundabout, left at next roundabout into Concorde Avenue. Straight on at next roundabout, taking left hand lane, and turn left at traffic lights, turn first right into Station Approach. At station forecourt and car park, take narrow single track road on extreme right and follow to Stadium.

Nearest Railway Station Banbury - 0.2km

BARWELL

Founded 1992

Nickname: Canaries **Club Colours:** Green & yellow

Club Contact Details 07961 905 141
Kirkby Road Sports Ground, Kirkby Road, Barwell LE9 8FQ

Previous Names: Barwell Athletic FC and Hinckley FC amalgamated in 1992.
Previous Leagues: Midland Alliance 1992-2010, Northern Premier League 2010-11, 13-18. Southern 2011-13.

09-10		10-11		11-12		12-13		13-14		14-15		15-16		16-17		17-18		18-19	
MidAl	1	NP1S	1	SthP	9	SthP	7	NP P	14	NP P	8	NP P	9	NP P	14	NP P	10	SthPC	16
FAC	EP	FAC	4Q	FAC	2Q	FAC	3Qr	FAC	1Q	FAC	4Q	FAC	1P	FAC	2Q	FAC	3Q	FAC	1Q
FAV	SF	FAT	P	FAT	2Q	FAT	1Q	FAT	1Q	FAT	3Qr	FAT	1Q	FAT	2Q	FAT	2Q	FAT	1P

HONOURS / RECORDS
FA Comps: None
League: Midland Alliance 2009-10.
Northern Premier Division One South 2010-11.
County FA: Leicestershire Challenge Cup 2014-15, 16-17.

Goalscorer: Andy Lucas
Appearances: Adrian Baker

Ground Capacity: 2,500 **Seats:** 256 **Covered:** 750 **Clubhouse:** Yes **Shop:** Yes
Previous Grounds: None
Record Attendance: 1,279 v Whitley Bay, FA Vase Semi-Final 2009-10.

DIRECTIONS
FROM M6 NORTH/M42/A5 NORTH: From M6 North join M42 heading towards Tamworth/Lichfield, leave M42 at Junction 10(Tamworth Services) and turn right onto A5 signposted Nuneaton. Remain on A5 for approx 11 miles, straight on at traffic lights at Longshoot Motel then at next roundabout take first exit signposted A47 Earl Shilton. In about 3 miles at traffic lights go straight on and in 1 mile at roundabout take first exit signposted Barwell. In about 1.5 miles, centre of village, go straight over mini roundabout and then in 20 metres turn right into Kirkby Road. Entrance to complex is 400 metres on right opposite park.
FROM M1 SOUTH: From M1 South Take M69)Signposted Coventry) Take Junction 2 Off M69 (Signposted Hinckley) Follow signs to Hinckley . Go straight on at traffic lights with Holywell Pub on the right. The road bears to the right at next traffic lights turn right signposted Earl Shilton/Leicester. Keep on this road past golf club on right at Hinckley United Ground on left and at large roundabout take second exit signposted Barwell. In about 1.5 miles, centre of village, go straight over mini roundabout and then in 20 metres turn right into Kirkby Road. Entrance to complex is 400 metres on right opposite park.
Nearest Railway Station Hinckley - 7 miles away

BIGGLESWADE TOWN

Founded 1874

Nickname: The Waders **Club Colours:** Green & white

Club Contact Details 01767 318 802 (Matchdays) michaeldraxler@hotmail.com

The Langford Road Stadium, Langford Road, Biggleswade SG18 9JT

Previous Names: Biggleswade FC. Biggleswade & District.

Previous Leagues: Biggleswade & District 1902-20. Bedford & District. Northamptsonshire/United Counties 1920-39 / 1951-55, 1963-80. Spartan 1945-51. Eastern Counties 1955-63. South Midlands/SSM 1980-2009.

09-10		10-11		11-12		12-13		13-14		14-15		15-16		16-17		17-18		18-19	
SthM	12	SthC	4	SthC	8	SthC	4	SthP	9	SthP	19	SthP	14	SthP	7	SthP	16	SthPC	7
FAC	P	FAC	1Q	FAC	2Qr	FAC	1Q	FAC	1P	FAC	3Q	FAC	2Q	FAC	2Q	FAC	3Q	FAC	1Q
FAT	1Q	FAT	1Q	FAT	1Q	FAT	P	FAT	1Q	FAT	2Q	FAT	1Q	FAT	2Qr	FAT	1Q	FAT	2P

HONOURS / RECORDS

FA Comps: None

League: Biggleswade & District 1902-03. Spartan South Midlands Premier Division 2008-09.

County FA: Bedfordshire Senior Cup 1902-03, 07-08, 46-47, 50-51, 61-62, 62-63, 66-67, 73-74.
Bedfordshire Premier Cup 2009. Bedfordshire Senior Challenge Cup 2012-13.

Victory: 12-0 v Newmarket Town (A), Eastern Counties.
Best FA Cup First Round Proper 2013-14
FA Trophy Second Round Proper 2018-19
FA Vase Quarter Finals 2008-09

Ground Capacity: 3,500 **Seats:** 300 **Covered:** 400 **Clubhouse:** Yes **Shop:**
Previous Grounds: Fairfield
Record Attendance: 2,000

DIRECTIONS

From the south – up the A1, past the first roundabout (Homebase) signposted Biggleswade. At next roundabout (Sainsburys) turn right onto A6001. As you approach the Town Centre, go straight over the mini roundabout following signs for Langford (Teal Road). At traffic lights, turn right (still heading towards Langford). Continue along Hitchin Street over two mini roundabouts and as you pass under the A1, the ground entrance is 200 yards on the right. From the north – exit A1 at the Sainsburys roundabout and follow instructions as above.

Nearest Railway Station Biggleswade - 1km

BROMSGROVE SPORTING

Founded 2009

Nickname: The Rouslers **Club Colours:** Red & white

Club Contact Details 01527 876 949 info@bromsgrovesporting.co.uk

The Victoria Ground, Birmingham Road, Bromsgrove, Worcs, B61 0DR

Previous Names: None

Previous Leagues: Midland Combination 2010-14.

09-10		10-11		11-12		12-13		13-14		14-15		15-16		16-17		17-18		18-19	
		MCm2	3	MCm1	3	MCmP	6	MCmP	2	MFL1	2	MFL1	2	MFL1	1	MFLP	1	SthC	2
										FAC	Pr	FAC	P	FAC	P	FAC	P	FAC	P
								FAV	1P	FAV	3P	FAV	1P	FAV	SF	FAV	5P	FAT	EP

HONOURS / RECORDS

FA Comps: None

League: Midland Football League Division One 2016-17, Premier 2017-18.

County FA: Worcestershire Senior Urn 2017-18

Best FA Cup Preliminary Round 2014-15(r), 15-16, 16-17, 17-18, 18-19
FA Vase Semi Final 2016-17
FA Trophy Extra Preliminary Round 2018-19

Ground Capacity: 5,008 **Seats:** Yes **Covered:** Yes **Clubhouse:** Yes **Shop:** Yes
Previous Grounds: None
Record Attendance: 3,349 v Cleethorpes Town, FA Vase Semi Final First Leg, 11/03/2017

DIRECTIONS

From M5 - leave at Junction 4 and follow the signs for the the A38 towards Bromsgrove. Proceed across the M42 junction (you can use this junction if you are heading south for your return journey). After half a mile turn right at the first set of traffic lights onto the Birmingham Road. After three quarters of a mile the ground is on your right.
From M42: Leave at Junction 1 and take second roundabout exit onto A38 towards Bromsgrove. Continue as for M5.

Nearest Railway Station Bromsgrove - 2km
Bus Route All Saints Road stop - 214m away

COALVILLE TOWN

Founded 1926

Nickname: The Ravens **Club Colours:** Black & white

Club Contact Details 07496 792 650 coalvilletownfc@gmail.com

Owen Street Sports Ground, Owen St, Coalville LE67 3DA

Previous Names: Ravenstoke Miners Ath. 1926-58. Ravenstoke FC 1958-95. Coalville 1995-98.

Previous Leagues: Coalville & Dist. Amateur. North Leicester. Leicestershire Senior. Midland Alliance > 2011. Northern Premier 2011-18.

09-10		10-11		11-12		12-13		13-14		14-15		15-16		16-17		17-18		18-19	
MidAl	2	MidAl	1	NP1S	14	NP1S	2	NP1S	2	NP1S	10	NP1S	3	NP P	17	NP P	20	SthPC	6
FAC	P	FAC	2Q	FAC	P	FAC	1Q	FAC	2Q	FAC	2Qr	FAC	2Q	FAC	2Q	FAC	2Q	FAC	3Qr
FAV	3P	FAV	F	FAT	P	FAT	2Q	FAT	1Pr	FAT	P	FAT	1Q	FAT	1Q	FAT	3Q	FAT	1Qr

HONOURS / RECORDS

FA Comps: None

League: Coalville & District Amateur 1952-53. North Leicestershire 1988-89, 89-90. Leicestershire Senior 2001-02, 02-03. Midland Football Alliance 2010-11.

County FA: Leicestershire Senior Cup 1999-00. Leicestershire Challenge Cup 2012-13, 17-18.

Appearances: Nigel Simms.

Additional: 153 goals scored during 2010-11 season.

Ground Capacity: 2,000 **Seats:** 240 **Covered:** 240 **Clubhouse:** Yes **Shop:** Yes

Previous Grounds: None

Record Attendance: 1,500.

DIRECTIONS

From the M42/A42 take the exit signposted Ashby and follow A511 to Coalville and Leicester. After approx. 3 miles and at the first roundabout take the second exit (A511). At the next roundabout take the 3rd exit into Coalville Town Centre. At the traffic lights go straight over to mini-roundabout then straight on for 50 meters before turning right into Owen Street. Ground is at the top of Owen Street on the left.

Nearest Railway Station Loughborough and Leicester

Bus Route Arriva No.137 can be taken to Coalville from both Loughborough and Leicester.

HEDNESFORD TOWN

Founded 1880

Nickname: The Pitmen **Club Colours:** White and black

Club Contact Details 01543 422 870 office@hednesfordtownfc.com

Keys Park, Park Road, Hednesford, Cannock WS12 2DZ

Previous Names: Hednesford 1938-74

Previous Leagues: Walsall & District, Birmingham Comb. 1906-15, 45-53, West Mids 1919-39, 53-72, 74-84, Midland Counties 1972-74, Southern 1984-95, 2001-2005, 2009-11, Conference 1995-2001, 05-06, 13-16. Northern Premier 2006-09, 11-13, 16-19.

09-10		10-11		11-12		12-13		13-14		14-15		15-16		16-17		17-18		18-19	
SthP	4	SthP	2	NP P	5	NP P	2	Conf N	4	Conf N	8	Nat N	21	NP P	15	NP P	16	NP P	13
FAC	1Q	FAC	1Q	FAC	3Q	FAC	3Qr	FAC	1P	FAC	2Q	FAC	3Q	FAC	1Q	FAC	2Q	FAC	3Q
FAT	1Q	FAT	1Q	FAT	2Qr	FAT	1P	FAT	1P	FAT	3Q	FAT	3Q	FAT	2Qr	FAT	2Qr	FAT	1Qr

HONOURS / RECORDS

FA Comps: FA Trophy 2003-04.

League: Birmingham Combination 1909-10, 50-51. West Midlands (Reg) 1940-41, 77-78. Southern League Premier Division 1994-95.

County FA: Staffordshire Senior Cup 1897-98, 1969-70, 73-74, 2012-13. Birmingham Senior Cup 1935-36, 2008-09, 12-13.

Victory: 12-1 v Redditch United - Birmingham Combination 1952-53

Defeat: 0-15 v Burton - Birmingham Combination 1952-53

Goalscorer: Joe O'Connor - 220 in 430 games

Appearances: Kevin Foster - 470

Additional: Paid £12,000 to Macclesfield Town for Steve Burr. Received £40,000 from Blackpool for Kevin Russell.

Ground Capacity: 6,039 **Seats:** 1,011 **Covered:** 5,335 **Clubhouse:** Yes **Shop:** Yes

Previous Grounds: The Tins 1880-1903. The Cross Keys 1903-95.

Record Attendance: 4,412 v FC United of Manchester, Northern Premier League Premier Division play-off final, 11/05/13.

DIRECTIONS

Leave M6 at J11 and follow the signs for Cannock. At the next island take the third exit towards Rugeley (A460). On reaching the A5 at Churchbridge island, rejoin the A460 signposted Rugeley and follow this road over five traffic islands. At the sixth traffic island, by a Texaco petrol station, turn right past a McDonalds restaurant and follow this road to the next island which is 'Cross Keys Island'. Go over this island to the next small island and turn right. Keys Park football ground is on left.

Nearest Railway Station Hednesford - 1.6km

Bus Route Brickworks Road - stop 200m away

HITCHIN TOWN

Founded 1865

Nickname: Canaries **Club Colours:** Yellow & green

Club Contact Details 01462 459 028 (match days only) roy.izzard@outlook.com

Top Field, Fishponds Road, Hitchin SG5 1NU

Previous Names: Hitchin FC 1865-1911. Re-formed in 1928

Previous Leagues: Spartan 1928-39, Herts & Middlesex 1939-45, Athenian 1945-63, Isthmian 1964-2004

09-10		10-11		11-12		12-13		13-14		14-15		15-16		16-17		17-18		18-19	
SthC	2	SthC	2	SthP	14	SthP	13	SthP	13	SthP	9	SthP	3	SthP	4	SthP	11	SthPC	18
FAC	1Qr	FAC	2Qr	FAC	1Q	FAC	3Qr	FAC	1Qr	FAC	2Q	FAC	3Qr	FAC	2Qr	FAC	1Qr	FAC	1P
FAT	3Qr	FAT	P	FAT	2Q	FAT	3Q	FAT	1Qr	FAT	1Qr	FAT	3Q	FAT	1P	FAT	1Q	FAT	1Q

HONOURS / RECORDS

FA Comps: None

League: Spartan 1934-35. Isthmian League Division One 1992-93.

County FA: AFA Senior Cup 1931-32. London Senior Cup 1969-70. East Anglian Cup 1972-73.
Herts Senior Cup x14 Most recently 2016-17.

Victory: 13-0 v Cowley and v RAF Uxbridge - both Spartan League 1929-30

Defeat: 0-10 v Kingstonian (A) and v Slough Town (A) - 1965-66 and 1979-80 respectively

Goalscorer: Paul Giggle - 214 (1968-86)

Appearances: Paul Giggle - 769 (1968-86)

Additional: Paid £2,000 to Potton United for Ray Seeking. Received £30,000 from Cambridge United for Zema Abbey, Jan 2000

Ground Capacity: 5,000 **Seats:** 500 **Covered:** 1,250 **Clubhouse:** Yes **Shop:** Yes

Previous Grounds: None

Record Attendance: 7,878 v Wycombe Wanderers - FA Amateur Cup 3rd Round 08/02/1956

DIRECTIONS

From East A1 to J8 onto A602 to Hitchin.
At Three Moorhens Pub roundabout, take third exit (A600) towards Bedford, over next roundabout and lights, turn right at next roundabout, turnstiles on left, parking 50 yards on.

Nearest Railway Station Hitchin - 1.3km

Bus Route Buss stops outside the ground

KING'S LANGLEY

Founded 1886

Nickname: Kings **Club Colours:** White & black

Club Contact Details 07730 410 330

Gaywood Park, Hempstead Road, Kings Langley Herts WD4 8BS

Previous Names: None

Previous Leagues: West Herts (Founder Member) 1891-1920, 22-34. Southern Olympian 1934-39.
Hertfordshire County 1920-22, 46-52, 55-2001. Parthenon 1952-55. Spartan South Midlands 2001-2015.

09-10		10-11		11-12		12-13		13-14		14-15		15-16		16-17		17-18		18-19	
SSM1	7	SSM1	3	SSM1	4	SSM1	6	SSM1	2	SSM P	1	SthC	1	SthP	20	SthP	21	SthPS	6
				FAC	EP	FAC	EPr	FAC	1Q	FAC	Pr	FAC	P	FAC	2Q	FAC	2Q	FAC	2Qr
		FAV	1Q	FAV	2Q	FAV	1Q	FAV	1Q	FAV	2P	FAT	1Q	FAT	3Q	FAT	1Q	FAT	1Q

HONOURS / RECORDS

FA Comps: None

League: West Herts Div.3 1911-12, Div.2 1919-20, 30-31, 34-35. Southern Olympian Div.1 1936-37. Herts County 1949-50, 51-52, 65-66, 66-67, Div.1 1975-76. Spartan South Midlands Div.2 2007-08, Premier 2014-15. Southern Div.1 Central 2015-16.

County FA: Herts Charity Shield 1966-67. Herts Intermediate Cup 2006-07, 07-08. Herts Senior Centenary Trophy 2011-12.

Misc: 47 consecutive matches unbeaten in all competitions between 15-09-07 and 15-10-08.

Ground Capacity: 1,963 **Seats:** Yes **Covered:** Yes **Clubhouse:** Yes **Shop:**

Previous Grounds: Groomes Meadow. Blackwell Meadow. Kings Langley Common. Home Park 1913-80.
Oxhey, Rolls Royce & Buncefield Lane and Leavesden Hospital Ground between 1980-97.

Record Attendance: Not known

DIRECTIONS

From M25 leave at Junction 20. Take A4251 to Kings Langley. Go over first roundabout and through village, past 'Young Pretender' Pub & restaurant on left. Go past Coniston Road on left and immediately indicate and move into 'turn right lane' in middle of road. Turn RIGHT into Ground. If car park is full, use lay-byes on road outside ground. Total distance from junction 20 :- 1.4 miles approx.
From Hemel Hempstead, take A4251 through Apsley. Continue under railway bridge and ground is approx. a quarter of a mile on LEFT, immediately before lay-bye.

Nearest Railway Station Kings Langley - 1.6km

LEISTON

Founded 1880

Nickname: The Blues **Club Colours:** All blue

Club Contact Details 01728 830 308 info@leistonfc.co.uk

Victory Road, Leiston IP16 4DQ

Previous Names: Leiston Works Athletic 1919-35.

Previous Leagues: North Suffolk. Suffolk & Ipswich. South East Anglian/East Anglian. Essex & Suffolk Border. Norfolk & Suffolk. Ipswich & District 1953-2001. Eastern Counties 2001-2011. Isthmian 2011-18.

09-10		10-11		11-12		12-13		13-14		14-15		15-16		16-17		17-18		18-19	
ECP	3	ECP	1	Isth1N	1	Isth P	12	Isth P	9	Isth P	9	Isth P	8	Isth P	7	Isth P	5	SthPC	19
FAC	EP	FAC	4Qr	FAC	1Q	FAC	2Q	FAC	1Q	FAC	2Q	FAC	3Q	FAC	4Q	FAC	3Q	FAC	2Q
FAV	3P	FAV	QF	FAT	P	FAT	3Qr	FAT	1Q	FAT	1P	FAT	2Q	FAT	1Pr	FAT	2Q	FAT	3Q

HONOURS / RECORDS

FA Comps: None

League: Suffolk & Ipswich/Ipswich & District 1900-01, 01-02, 02-03, Division 2B 1937-38 / Division One 83-84. Eastern Counties Premier Division 2010-11. Isthmian Division One North 2011-12.

County FA: Suffolk Junior Cup 1894-95, 82-83, 83-84, Premier Cup 2017-18. East Anglian Cup 2007-08.

Goalscorer: Lee McGlone - 60 (League).

Appearances: Gareth Heath - 201 (League).

Ground Capacity: 2,250 **Seats:** 250 **Covered:** 500 **Clubhouse:** Yes **Shop:**

Previous Grounds: Leiston Recreation Ground 1880-1921.

Record Attendance: 1,250 v Fleetwood Town, FA Cup First round Proper, 2008-09.

DIRECTIONS

Take junction 28 off the M25, take the A12/A1023 exit to Chelmsford/Romford/Brentwood, keep left at the fork, follow signs for Chelmsford/A12 (E) and merge onto A12, at the roundabout, take the 3rd exit onto the A14 ramp, merge onto A14, at junction 58, exit toward A12, keep left at the fork, follow signs for Lowestoft/Woodbridge/A12 (N) and merge onto A12, go through 7 roundabouts, turn right onto A1094, turn left onto Snape Rd/B1069, continue to follow B1069, turn left onto Victory Rd, ground will be on the left.

Nearest Railway Station Saxmundham - 6 miles

Bus Route Alde Valley Sixth Form - stop 300m away

LOWESTOFT TOWN

Founded 1880

Nickname: The Trawler Boys or Blues **Club Colours:** Blue & white

Club Contact Details 01502 573 818 admin@lowestofttownfc.co.uk

Crown Meadow, Love Road, Lowestoft NR32 2PA

Previous Names: Original club merged with Kirkley in 1887 to form Lowestoft and became Lowestoft Town in 1890

Previous Leagues: North Suffolk 1897-35, Eastern Counties 1935-2009. Isthmian 2009-2014, 16-18. Conference 2014-16.

09-10		10-11		11-12		12-13		13-14		14-15		15-16		16-17		17-18		18-19	
Isth1N	1	Isth P	4	Isth P	3	Isth P	2	Isth P	4	Conf N	16	Nat N	20	Isth P	11	Isth P	22	SthPC	14
FAC	1P	FAC	2Q	FAC	3Q	FAC	4Q	FAC	1Q	FAC	3Q	FAC	2Q	FAC	1Q	FAC	2Q	FAC	2Q
FAT	1Q	FAT	1P	FAT	1P	FAT	1Q	FAT	1Q	FAT	1P	FAT	1P	FAT	1Q	FAT	1Q	FAT	1Q

HONOURS / RECORDS

FA Comps: None

League: Eastern Counties League 1935-36 (shared), 37-38, 62-63, 64-65, 65-66, 66-67, 67-68, 69-70, 70-71, 77-78, 2005-06, 08-09. Isthmian League Division One North 2009-10.

County FA: Suffolk Senior Cup 1902-03, 22-23, 25-26, 31-32, 35-36, 46-47, 47-48, 48-49, 55-56, Premier Cup 1966-67, 71-72, 74-75, 78-79, 79-80, 99-00, 00-01, 04-05, 05-06, 08-09, 11-12, 14-15, 15-16. East Anglian Cup 1929-30, 70-71, 77-78.

Best FA Cup First Round Proper 1926-27, 38-39, 66-67, 67-68, 77-78, 2009-10

FA Trophy Second Round Proper 1971-72

FA Vase Runners-up 2007-08

Ground Capacity: 3,250 **Seats:** 466 **Covered:** 500 **Clubhouse:** Yes **Shop:** Yes

Previous Grounds: Crown Meadow Athletic Ground 1880-1889. North Denes 1889-94.

Record Attendance: 5,000 v Watford - FA Cup 1st Round 1967

DIRECTIONS

Head for Lowestoft town centre. After crossing Bascule Bridge and railway station turn right at traffic lights (sp A12 Yarmouth) into Katwyck Way. After 300 yards take 1st exit at roundabout into Raglan Street. At 'T' junction turn left into Love Road and ground is about 100 yards on right.

Nearest Railway Station Lowestoft - 0.7km

NEEDHAM MARKET

Founded 1919

Nickname: The Marketmen **Club Colours:** All red

Club Contact Details 01449 721 000 m.easlea@sky.com

Bloomfields, Quinton Road, Needham Market IP6 8DA

Previous Names: None

Previous Leagues: Suffolk & Ipswich Senior, Eastern Counties. Isthmian 2010-2018.

09-10		10-11		11-12		12-13		13-14		14-15		15-16		16-17		17-18		18-19	
ECP	1	Isth1N	2	Isth1N	4	Isth1N	16	Isth1N	5	Isth1N	1	Isth P	20	Isth P	9	Isth P	19	SthPC	11
FAC	2Q	FAC	3Q	FAC	2Q	FAC	1Q	FAC	4Q	FAC	3Q	FAC	1Qr	FAC	1Q	FAC	3Q	FAC	2Qr
FAV	QF	FAT	1Qr	FAT	1Q	FAT	P	FAT	P	FAT	P	FAT	1Q	FAT	2Q	FAT	2Q	FAT	1P

HONOURS / RECORDS

FA Comps: None

League: Eastern Counties Premier Division 2009-10. Isthmian Division One North 2014-15.

County FA: Suffolk Senior Cup 1989-90, 2004-05. Suffolk & Ipswich Senior League 1995-96. East Anglian Cup 2006-07. Suffolk Premier Cup 2016-17.

Victory: 10-1 v I[swich Wanderers (A) , FA Cup Preliminary Round, 01/09/2007

Defeat: 2-6 v Lowestoft Town (A), FA Trophy First round Qualifier, 19/10/2010

Goalscorer: Craig Parker - 111 (2007-2011) Most goals in a season - Craig Parker 40 (2011-11).

Appearances: Rhys Barber - 334 (2006-2012)

Additional: Most goals scored in a season - 196 in 70 games (2007-08)

Ground Capacity: 2,250 **Seats:** 250 **Covered:** 250 **Clubhouse:** Yes **Shop:** Yes

Previous Grounds: Young's Meadow 1919. Crowley Park >1996.

Record Attendance: 1,784 v Cambridge United, FAC Fourth Qualifying Round, 26/10/2013.

DIRECTIONS

Enter Needham Market on B1113 and turn right into Barking Road (B1078) from North approach. Then turn right into Chainhouse Road. Continue up to the top of the hill and turn right into Quinton Road. Continue along the road for a few hundred yards and the ground is situated on the left hand side signposted Bloomfields, Needham Market FC. Follow the driveway round to the left to enter the car park.

Nearest Railway Station Needham Market - 0.6km

Bus Route Quinton Road stop - 38m away

NUNEATON BOROUGH

Founded 1889

Nickname: The Boro / The Town **Club Colours:** Blue and white

Club Contact Details 024 7634 9690

Liberty Way, Nuneaton CV11 6RR

Previous Names: Nuneaton St. Nicholas 1889-1894. Nuneaton Town 1894-37. Nuneaton Borough 1937-2008.

Previous Leagues: Local 1894-1906. Birmingham Jr/Comb 06-15, 26-33, 38-52. Birmingham 19-24, 33-37. Central Am. 37-38. Birmingham 52-58. Southern 24-25, 58-79 81-82, 87-99, 2003-04, 08-10. Conference/National 79-81, 82-87, 99-03, 04-08, 10-19.

09-10		10-11		11-12		12-13		13-14		14-15		15-16		16-17		17-18		18-19	
SthP	2	Conf N	6	Conf N	5	Conf	15	Conf	13	Conf	24	Nat N	6	Nat N	12	Nat N	13	Nat N	22
FAC	1P	FAC	1P	FAC	4Q	FAC	1Pr	FAC	4Q	FAC	4Qr	FAC	3Q	FAC	2Q	FAC	3Q	FAC	2Qr
FAT	1P	FAT	3Q	FAT	1P	FAT	1P	FAT	2Pr	FAT	1P	FAT	1P	FAT	3P	FAT	1P	FAT	3Q

HONOURS / RECORDS

FA Comps: None

League: Coventry & Dist. 1902-03. Coventry & North Warwicks' 1904-05. Birmingham Junior 1906-07, Combination 1914-15, 28-29, 30-31. Birmingham League North 1954-55, Div.One 55-56. Southern League Midland Div. 1981-82, 92-93, 95-96, Premier Division 1988-99.

County FA: Birmingham Senior Cup 1930-31, 48-49, 54-55, 59-60, 77-78, 79-80, 92-93, 2001-02, 09-10.

Victory: 11-1 - 1945-46 and 1955-56

Defeat: 1-8 - 1955-56 and 1968-69

Goalscorer: Paul Culpin - 201 (55 during season 1992-93)

Appearances: Alan Jones - 545 (1962-74)

Misc: Paid £35,000 to Forest green Rovers for Marc McGregor 2000

Ground Capacity: 4,614 **Seats:** 514 **Covered:** Yes **Clubhouse:** Yes **Shop:** Yes

Previous Grounds: Higham Lane/Rose Inn/Arbury Rd/Edward St. 1889-1903. Queens Rd 03-08. Newdegate Arms 08-15. Manor Pk 19-07.

Record Attendance: 22,114 v Rotherham Utd, FAC 3P 28/01/1967 (Manor Park). 3,480 v Luton Town, Conf. Prem., 22/02/14

DIRECTIONS

From the South, West and North West, exit the M6 at Junction 3 and follow the A444 into Nuneaton. At the Coton Arches r'about turn right into Avenue Road which is the A4254 signposted for Hinckley. Continue along the A4254 following the road into Garrett Street, then Eastboro Way, then turn left into Townsend Drive. Follow the road round before turning left into Liberty Way for the ground.

Nearest Railway Station Nuneaton - approx. 35min walk from the ground.

PETERBOROUGH SPORTS

Founded 1919

Nickname: The Turbines **Club Colours:** All blue

Club Contact Details 01733 567 835

Lincoln Road, Peterborough PE1 3HA

Previous Names: Brotherhoods Engineering Works 1919-99. Bearings Direct during 1999-2001.

Previous Leagues: Northants League (former UCL) 1919-23. Peterborough & District 1923-2013. United Counties 2013-17. Northern Premier 2017-18.

09-10	10-11	11-12	12-13	13-14	14-15	15-16	16-17	17-18	18-19
		P&D P 3	P&D P 3	UCL 1 16	UCL 1 5	UCL 1 1	UCL P 1	NP1S 12	SthC 1
						FAC 1Qr	FAC 1Q	FAC 1Q	FAC 3Q
					FAV 2P	FAV 1Q	FAV 4P	FAT P	FAT P

HONOURS / RECORDS

FA Comps: None

League: Northants 1919-20, United Counties 1919-20, Division One 2015-16, Premier 2016-17.
Peterborough & Dist Division Three 1925-26, Division Three South 1980-81, Premier 2006-07. Southern Div1 Central 18-19.

County FA: Northants Junior Cup 2006-07, 15-16,

Ground Capacity: 1,500 **Seats:** Yes **Covered:** Yes **Clubhouse:** Yes **Shop:** No

Previous Grounds: None

Record Attendance: Not known

DIRECTIONS

From the North, come in on the A15 Southbound and cross the large A47 roundabout just after Morrisons on your right hand side. Take the left hand slip road and at the traffic lights, affter approximately 400 yards, turn right. At the t-junction after 50 yards, the entrance to the ground is approximately 400 yards on the left hand side, in front of a Church and before the crossing.
From the East, take the turning from the A47 and take City Centre and follow as above.
From the South and West, Take A47 and take exit signposted City Centre. Go straight on at roundabout (back up on the A47). Take the third right at a large roundabout with the A15 and follow instructions above.

Nearest Railway Station Peterborough - 3 miles

REDDITCH UNITED

Founded 1891

Nickname: The Reds **Club Colours:** Red & black

Club Contact Details 01527 67450 info@redditchutdfc.co.uk

Bromsgrove Road, Redditch B97 4RN

Previous Names: Redditch Town

Previous Leagues: Birmingham Combination 1905-21, 29-39, 46-53, West Midlands 1921-29, 53-72, Southern 1972-79, 81-2004, Alliance 1979-80. Conference 2004-11.

09-10	10-11	11-12	12-13	13-14	14-15	15-16	16-17	17-18	18-19
Conf N 19	Conf N 21	SthP 15	SthP 19	SthP 10	SthP 6	SthP 2	SthP 17	SthP 14	SthPC 15
FAC 4Qr	FAC 4Q	FAC 1Q	FAC 1Q	FAC 1Qr	FAC 1Qr	FAC 1Q	FAC 1Q	FAC 2Q	FAC 1Q
FAT 1P	FAT 1P	FAT 1Q	FAT 1Q	FAT 3Q	FAT 3Q	FAT 1Q	FAV 2Q	FAT 1Q	FAT 1Q

HONOURS / RECORDS

FA Comps: None

League: Birmingham Combination 1913-14, 32-33, 52-53. Birmingham & District Southern Division 1954-55.
Southern Division One North 1975-76, Western Division 2003-04.

County FA: Worcestershire Senior Cup 1893-94, 29-30, 74-75, 76-76, 2007-08, 13-14.
Birmingham Senior Cup 1924-25, 31-32, 38-39, 76-77, 2004-05. Staffordshire Senior Cup 1990-91.

Misc: Paid £3,000 to Halesowen Town for Paul Joinson. Received £40,000 from Aston Villa for David Farrell.
Played nine games in nine days at the end of the 1997-98 season.

Victory: 7-1 v Farnborough (H), Southern Premier, 06/01/2018

Ground Capacity: 4,000 **Seats:** 400 **Covered:** 2,000 **Clubhouse:** Yes **Shop:** Yes

Previous Grounds: HDA Sports Ground, Millsborough Road

Record Attendance: 5,500 v Bromsgrove Rovers - Wets Midlands League 1954-55

DIRECTIONS

M42 J2, at island first exit onto the A441 for 2 miles, next island first exit onto Birmingham Road A441 for 1.2 miles then at island third exit onto Middlehouse Lane B4184 for 0.3 miles. At traffic lights (next to the fire station) turn left onto Birmingham Road for 0.2 miles then turn right into Clive Road for 0.3 miles. At island take first exit onto Hewell Road for 0.2 miles then at 'T' junction right onto Windsor Street for 0.1 miles. At traffic lights (next to bus station) continue straight ahead onto Bromsgrove Road for 0.3 miles and at the brow of the hill, turn right into the ground's entrance.

Nearest Railway Station Redditch - 0.4km

Bus Route Bus stops outside the ground

ROYSTON TOWN

Founded 1875

Nickname: The Crows **Club Colours:** White & black

Club Contact Details 01763 241 204 secretary@roystontownfc.co.uk

Garden Walk, Royston, Herts SG8 7HP

Previous Names: None

Previous Leagues: Buntingford & District 1919-29. Cambridgeshire 1929-48. Herts County 1948-60, 63-77. South Midlands 1960-63, 77-84. Isthmian 1984-94. Spartan South Midlands 1994-2012.

09-10		10-11		11-12		12-13		13-14		14-15		15-16		16-17		17-18		18-19	
SSM P	4	SSM P	3	SSM P	1	SthC	7	SthC	7	SthC	2	SthC	2	SthC	1	SthP	7	SthPC	10
FAC	1Q	FAC	EP	FAC	P	FAC	1Qr	FAC	2Q	FAC	P	FAC	Pr	FAC	P	FAC	2Qr	FAC	1Q
FAV	5P	FAV	2Pr	FAV	4P	FAT	1Qr	FAT	P	FAT	1Q	FAT	2Q	FAT	1Pr	FAT	3P	FAT	3Qr

HONOURS / RECORDS

FA Comps: None

League: Cambridgeshire Division Two 1929-30. Herts County Division One 1969-70, 72-73, Premier 1976-77.
South Midlands Division One 1977-78, 2008-09, Premier Division 2011-12. Southern Division One Central 2016-17.

County FA: Herts Charity Shield 1981-82, 96-97. Herts Intermediate Cup 1988-89.

Best FA Cup Third Qualifying Round 1998-99

FA Trophy First Round Proper Reply 2016-17

FA Vase Fifth Round Proper 2009-10

Ground Capacity: 1,900 **Seats:** 300 **Covered:** Yes **Clubhouse:** Yes **Shop:** No

Previous Grounds: Newmarket Road, Baldock Road and Mackerell Hall before acquiring Garden Walk in 1932.

Record Attendance: 876 v Aldershot Town, 1993-94.

DIRECTIONS

From A505 (Town Bypass) take A10 towards town centre (signposted London).
Go straight on at next roundabout.
Garden Walk is on the left after the 3rd set of pedestrian lights (opposite Catholic Church).
Entrance to ground is approx 75 metres on left.

Nearest Railway Station Royston - 0.7km

Bus Route St Mary's School - stop 150m away

RUSHALL OLYMPIC

Founded 1951

Nickname: The Pics **Club Colours:** Gold and black

Club Contact Details 01922 641 021 philfisher.secretary@gmail.com

Dales Lane off Daw End Lane, Rushall, Nr Walsall WS4 1LJ

Previous Names: None

Previous Leagues: Walsall Amateur 1952-55, Staffordshire County (South) 1956-78, West Midlands 1978-94, Midland Alliance 1994-2005, Southern 2005-08. Northern Premier 2008-18.

09-10		10-11		11-12		12-13		13-14		14-15		15-16		16-17		17-18		18-19	
NP1S	12	NP1S	3	NP P	8	NP P	6	NP P	7	NP P	9	NP P	10	NP P	12	NP P	8	SthPC	8
FAC	1Q	FAC	Pr	FAC	4Q	FAC	1Q	FAC	4Q	FAC	2Q	FAC	3Q	FAC	2Q	FAC	3Qr	FAC	1Qr
FAT	1Q	FAT	2Q	FAT	1Q	FAT	1P	FAT	2Q	FAT	3Qr	FAT	2Qr	FAT	1Q	FAT	2Q	FAT	1Q

HONOURS / RECORDS

FA Comps: None

League: West Midlands (Reg) Division One 1979-80. Midland Alliance 2004-05.

County FA: Staffordshire Senior Cup 2015-16. Walsall Senior Cup 2015-16, 17-18.

Goalscorer: Graham Wiggin

Appearances: Alan Dawson - 400+

Ground Capacity: 1,980 **Seats:** 200 **Covered:** 200 **Clubhouse:** Yes **Shop:** Yes

Previous Grounds: Rowley Place 1951-75, Aston University 1976-79

Record Attendance: 2,000 v Leeds United Ex players

DIRECTIONS

M6 J10 follow signs for Walsall stay on this dual carriage way for about four miles until you come to the Walsall Arboretum and turn left following signs for Lichfield A461. Go under the bridge and you will come to McDonald's on your right, turn right into Daw End Lane. Go over the canal bridge and turn right opposite the Royal Oak Public House and the ground is on the right.
Alternative: From the A38 to it's junction with the A5 (Muckley Corner Hotel) take the A461 to Walsall after about five miles you will reach some traffic lights in Rushall by Mcdonald's, turn left into Daw End Lane go over the canal bridge and turn right opposite The Royal Oak Public House the ground is on the right.

Nearest Railway Station Walsall - 3km.

Bus Route Royal Oak - stop 50m away

ST. IVES TOWN

Founded 1887

Nickname: The Ives **Club Colours:** Red & white

Club Contact Details 01480 463 207 sitfcsecretary@aol.com

Westwood Road, St. Ives PE27 6DT

Previous Names: None

Previous Leagues: Cambridgeshire, Central Amateur, Hunts, Peterborough & District. United Counties > 2013.

09-10	10-11	11-12	12-13	13-14	14-15	15-16	16-17	17-18	18-19
UCL P 10	UCL P 11	UCL P 3	UCL P 2	SthC 13	SthC 9	SthC 4	SthP 15	SthP 22	SthPC 13
FAC 1Q	FAC EP	FAC Pr	FAC P	FAC 2Q	FAC Pr	FAC 2Q	FAC 1Q	FAC 2Q	FAC 3Q
FAV 5P	FAV 4P	FAV QF	FAV 2Pr	FAT 2Q	FAT P	FAT 1Q	FAV 3Q	FAT 1Q	FAT 1Q

HONOURS / RECORDS

FA Comps: None

League: Southern Division One Central Play-offs 2015-16.

County FA: Hunts Senior Cup 1900/01, 11-12, 22-23, 25-26, 29-30, 81-82, 86-87, 87-88, 2006-07, 08-09, 11-12, 15-16.
Hunts Premier Cup 2006-07, 08-09.

Victory: 0-6 v Stafford Rangers (A), FAT 1Q, 28/10/2017 & v Dorchester Town (A), Southern Premier, 16/12/2017

Best FA Cup Third Qualifying Round 2018-19

FA Vase Quarter Finals 2011-12

FA Trophy First Qualifying Round 2017-18, 18-19

Ground Capacity: 2,000 **Seats:** Yes **Covered:** Yes **Clubhouse:** Yes **Shop:** No

Previous Grounds: Meadow Lane.

Record Attendance: 1,523 v AFC Rushden & Diamonds, Southern Division One Central Play-off Final, 02/05/2016.

DIRECTIONS

From the A14 (Junction 26) continue along London Road (A1096). On entering the Town of St Ives (avoiding Town Centre), continue over the first roundabout and over the bypass (Harrison Way), continue over the next two roundabouts (still on Harrison Way). Turn left at the next two mini roundabouts onto the A1123 (St Audrey Lane). Turn left at the traffic lights onto Ramsey Road, then turn right into Westwood Road (opposite the Fire Station). Continue to the top where the ground is on the right hand side before the Recreation Centre.

Nearest Railway Station Huntingdon - 6.2 miles

STOURBRIDGE

Founded 1876

Nickname: The Glassboys **Club Colours:** Red and white

Club Contact Details 01384 394 040 clive1974eades@gmail.com

War Memorial Athletic Ground, High Street, Amblecote DY8 4HN

Previous Names: Stourbridge Standard 1876-87

Previous Leagues: West Midlands (Birmingham League) 1892-1939, 54-71, Birmingham Combination 1945-53, Southern 1971-2000. Midland Alliance 2000-06. Southern 2006-14. Northern Premier 2014-18.

09-10	10-11	11-12	12-13	13-14	14-15	15-16	16-17	17-18	18-19
SthP 9	SthP 8	SthP 6	SthP 2	SthP 5	NP P 16	NP P 6	NP P 3	NP P 11	SthPC 3
FAC 1P	FAC 2Q	FAC 2P	FAC 1Qr	FAC 2P	FAC 3Qr	FAC 2P	FAC 3P	FAC 4Q	FAC 4Q
FAT 3Qr	FAT 3Q	FAT 3Q	FAT 1Q	FAT 3Qr	FAT 2Q	FAT 3P	FAT 1Q	FAT 2P	FAT 1Q

HONOURS / RECORDS

FA Comps: None

League: Birmingham 1923-24. Birmingham Combination 1951-52. Southern Division One North 1973-74, Midland Division 1990-91.
Midland Alliance 2001-02, 02-03.

County FA: Worcestershire Junior Cup 1927-28. Hereford Senior Cup 1954-55. Birmingham Senior Cup 1949-50, 58-59, 67-68, 2017-18. Worcestershire Senior Cup x11 - Firstly in 1904-05 and most recently in 2012-13.

Goalscorer: Ron Page - 269

Appearances: Ron Page - 427

Additional: Received £20,000 from Lincoln City for Tony Cunningham 1979

Ground Capacity: 2,626 **Seats:** 250 **Covered:** 750 **Clubhouse:** Yes **Shop:** Yes

Previous Grounds: None

Record Attendance: 5,726 v Cardiff City - Welsh Cup Final 1st Leg 1974

DIRECTIONS

From M6: Leave the M5 Southbound at Junction 3 and take the A456 towards Kidderminster. Upon entering Hagley (following a long downhill approach), take the right hand filter lane at the traffic lights (Signposted A491 Stourbridge). Continue to follow the A491 towards Stourbridge Town Centre and continue to follow the Ring Road (watching the Speed Camera), and take the A491 exit now signposted Wolverhampton. The ground is on the left hand side of the road immediately after the 3rd set of traffic lights (approximately 500 yards) and opposite the Vets for Pets. Please note that Parking is Extremely Limited on the Ground. **From M42:** Leave the M5 Northbound at Junction 4 and follow the A491 towards Stourbridge and in Hagley, take the left hand filter lane to continue on the A491 and proceed as above.

Nearest Railway Station Stourbridge - 1km

Bus Route Bus 246 from Dudley, 256 from Wolverhampton and 257 all pass the War Memorial Athletic Ground.

AFC Rushden & Diamonds v Bedworth United. Photo: Bill Wheatcroft.

Hippolyte-Patrick (Hendon) cuts his way through the Salisbury defence. Photos: Keith Clayton.

Butterworth (Yaxley) tackled by Gaughran (Wisbech).

Arthur (Met Police) Kearney (Harrow Boro).

STRATFORD TOWN

Founded 1941

Nickname: The Town **Club Colours:** All blue

Club Contact Details 01789 269 336 stratfordtownfcsecretary@outlook.

The DCS Stadium, Knights Lane, Tiddington, Stratford Upon Avon CV37 7BZ

Previous Names: Straford Rangers 1941-49. Stratford Town Amateurs 1964-70.

Previous Leagues: Local leagues > 1954. Worcestershire/Midland Combination 1954-57, 70-75, 77-94. Birmingham & District/West Midlands (Reg) 1957-70. Hellenic 1975-77. Midland Alliance (Founder Members) 1994-2013.

09-10		10-11		11-12		12-13		13-14		14-15		15-16		16-17		17-18		18-19	
MidAl	3	MidAl	5	MidAl	8	MidAl	1	Sthsw	10	Sthsw	3	SthP	19	SthP	14	SthP	15	SthPC	5
FAC	2Qr	FAC	P	FAC	3Q	FAC	EP	FAC	P	FAC	P	FAC	1Q	FAC	1Q	FAC	3Qr	FAC	1Q
FAV	2P	FAV	1P	FAV	1P	FAV	2Q	FAT	Pr	FAT	2Q	FAT	2Q	FAT	1Qr	FAT	2Q	FAT	1P

HONOURS / RECORDS

FA Comps: None

League: Worcestershire/Midland Combination 1956-57, 86-87.
Midland Alliance 2012-13.

County FA: Birmingham Senior Cup 1962-63.

Best FA Cup Third Qualifying Round 2004-05, 06-07, 11-12, 17-18(r)

Amateur Cup Third Round 1962-63

FA Trophy First Round Proper 2018-19

FA Vase Fifth Round Proper 2008-09

Ground Capacity: 1,400 **Seats:** Yes **Covered:** Yes **Clubhouse:** Yes **Shop:** Yes

Previous Grounds: A number of pitches before Alcester Road by the late 1940s where they stayed until 2007.

Record Attendance: 1,078 v Aston Villa, Birmingham Senior Cup, Oct. 1996.

DIRECTIONS

From Town Centre follow signs for Banbury (A422) and Oxford (A3400). Cross Clopton Bridge and turn immediately left onto B4086 towards Wellesbourne. After approx 1 mile you enter the village of Tiddington. Turn 1st right into Knights Lane. Ground is approx 800 yards on right (100 yards after school).

Nearest Railway Station Stratford-upon-Avon - 2.8km

Bus Route Alveston Primary School - stop 50m away

TAMWORTH

Founded 1933

Nickname: The Lambs **Club Colours:** All red

Club Contact Details 01827 657 98 clubsec@thelambs.co.uk

The Lamb Ground, Kettlebrook, Tamworth, Staffordshire B77 1AA

Previous Names: None

Previous Leagues: Birmingham Combination 1933-54. West Midlands (originally Birmingham & District League) 1954-72, 84-88. Southern 1972-79, 83-84, 89-2003. Northern Premier 1979-83. Conference/National 2003-18.

09-10		10-11		11-12		12-13		13-14		14-15		15-16		16-17		17-18		18-19	
Conf	16	Conf	19	Conf	18	Conf	19	Conf	23	Conf N	7	Nat N	7	Nat N	9	Nat N	21	SthPC	12
FAC	4Q	FAC	2P	FAC	3P	FAC	4Q	FAC	2P	FAC	4Qr	FAC	2Q	FAC	2Q	FAC	2Q	FAC	1Q
FAT	QF	FAT	1P	FAT	1P	FAT	3P	FAT	QF	FAT	3Q	FAT	1P	FAT	3Qr	FAT	3Pr	FAT	2Q

HONOURS / RECORDS

FA Comps: FA Vase 1988-89.

League: West Midlands League 1963-64, 65-66, 71-72, 87-88.
Southern League Divison One Midland 1996-97, Premier Division 2002-03. Conference North 2008-09.

County FA: Staffordshire Senior Cup 1958-59, 63-64, 65-66, 2001-02.
Birmingham Senior Cup 1960-61, 65-66, 68-69.

Victory: 14-4 v Holbrook Institue (H) - Bass Vase 1934

Defeat: 0-11 v Solihull (A) - Birmingham Combination 1940

Goalscorer: Graham Jessop - 195

Appearances: Dave Seedhouse - 869

Additional: Paid £7,500 to Ilkeston Town for David Hemmings, Dec 2000. Received £12,000 from Kidderminster H for Scott Rickards, 2003

Ground Capacity: 4,565 **Seats:** 518 **Covered:** 1,191 **Clubhouse:** Yes **Shop:** Yes

Previous Grounds: Jolly Sailor Ground 1933-34

Record Attendance: 5,500 v Torquay United - FA Cup 1st Round 15/11/69

DIRECTIONS

Take the A5 towards Tamworth. Follow the A5 bypass into the Town and follow signs towards the Town Centre.

Continue to follow signs towards Snowdome and when you see this on your left hand side you should also see the ground immediately on your right.

Nearest Railway Station Tamworth - within walking distance of the ground.

BEACONSFIELD TOWN

Founded 1994

Nickname: The Rams **Club Colours:** Red

Club Contact Details 01494 676 868 info@beaconsfieldtownfc.co.uk

Holloways Park, Windsor Road, Beaconsfield, Bucks HP9 2SE

Previous Names: Slough YCOB and Beaconsfield United merged in 1994. Beaconsfield SYCOB 1994-2017.
Previous Leagues: Spartan South Midlands 1004-2004, 07-08, Southern 2004-07.

09-10		10-11		11-12		12-13		13-14		14-15		15-16		16-17		17-18		18-19	
SthM	19	SthC	22	SthC	5	SthC	5	SthC	8	SthC	20	SthC	9	SthC	16	Sth1E	1	SthPS	12
FAC	P	FAC	P	FAC	2Qr	FAC	P	FAC	1Q	FAC	2Q	FAC	1Q	FAC	4Q	FAC	1Q	FAC	3Q
FAT	1Q	FAT	1Q	FAT	P	FAT	Pr	FAT	P	FAT	P	FAT	P	FAT	1Q	FAT	2Qr	FAT	1P

HONOURS / RECORDS

FA Comps: None

League: Spartan South Midlands 2000-01, 03-04, 07-08. Southern Division One East 2017-18.

County FA: Berks and Bucks Senior Trophy 2003-04, Senior Cup 2012-13.

Goalscorer: Allan Arthur
Appearances: Allan Arthur
Best FA Cup Fourth Qualifying Round 2016-17
FA Trophy First Round Proper 2018-19
FA Vase Second Round Proper 2003-04

Ground Capacity: 2,900 **Seats:** Yes **Covered:** Yes **Clubhouse:** Yes **Shop:** No
Previous Grounds: None
Record Attendance: Not known

DIRECTIONS

Leave Junction 2 of M40, take A355 towards Slough, 50 yards off roundabout turn left and at next roundabout turn complete right, coming back towards A355 to continue across A355, then turn right and 150 yards on left is sign to club. Go through gate and clubhouse is 200 yards on right.

Nearest Railway Station Beaconsfield - 2.8km

BLACKFIELD & LANGLEY

Founded 1935

Nickname: Watersiders **Club Colours:** Green

Club Contact Details 02380 893 603 d-sangster@sky.com

Gang Warily Rec., Newlands Rd, Southampton SO45 1GA

Previous Names: None
Previous Leagues: Southampton Junior. Southampton Senior. Hampshire 1950-2000. Wessex 2000-18.

09-10		10-11		11-12		12-13		13-14		14-15		15-16		16-17		17-18		18-19	
WexP	8	WexP	14	WexP	16	WexP	1	WexP	6	WexP	5	WexP	3	WexP	4	WexP	1	SthS	1
FAC	EP	FAC	P	FAC	1Q	FAC	4Q	FAC	EP	FAC	2Qr	FAC	3Q	FAC	P	FAC	EPr	FAC	P
FAV	2Q	FAV	1P	FAV	2P	FAV	4P	FAV	4P	FAV	3P	FAV	1P	FAV	3P	FAV	4Pr	FAT	P

HONOURS / RECORDS

FA Comps: None

League: Southampton Junior Division One 1945-46. Southampton West Division 1946-47. Hampshire Division Three West 1951-52, Division Two 1984-85, Premier Division 97-98. Wessex Premier Division 2012-13, 17-18. Southern D1S 2018-19.

County FA: None

Best FA Cup Fourth Qualifying Round 2012-13
FA Vase Fourth Round Proper 2012-13, 13-14
FA Trophy Preliminary Round 2018-19

Ground Capacity: 2,000 **Seats:** 180 **Covered:** Yes **Clubhouse:** Yes **Shop:**
Previous Grounds: Yes
Record Attendance: 240

DIRECTIONS

Leave M27 at Junction 2 signposted A326 to Fawley. Head South along A326 through several roundabouts. Pass the Holbury P/H on your right at roundabout take the right fork signposted Lepe and Fawley.At the 1st set of traffic lights turn left then turn left into the ground, approx 200 yards. There is a sign at the traffic lights indicating Blackfield & Langley FC. Postcode for Satellite Navigation systems SO45 1GA

Nearest Railway Station Beaulieu Road - 7.2 miles
Bus Route Gang Warily Leisure Centre - stop 50m away

OUTS: Basingstoke Town (R - Sth1S), Frome Town (R - Sth1S), Kings Langley (Tr - Sth1C), Staines Town (R - Sth1S), Weymouth (P- NatS).

CHESHAM UNITED

Founded 1917

Nickname: The Generals **Club Colours:** Claret & blue

Club Contact Details 01494 783 964 secretary@cheshamunited.co.uk

The Meadow, Amy Lane, Amersham Road, Chesham HP5 1NE

Previous Names: Chesham Town and Chesham Generals merged in 1917 to form Chesham United.

Previous Leagues: Spartan 1917-47, Corinthian 1947-63, Athenian 1963-73, Isthmian 1973-2004

09-10		10-11		11-12		12-13		13-14		14-15		15-16		16-17		17-18		18-19	
SthM	4	SthP	6	SthP	4	SthP	3	SthP	2	SthP	12	SthP	13	SthP	11	SthP	8	SthPS	10
FAC	3Q	FAC	2Qr	FAC	2Q	FAC	1Q	FAC	1Q	FAC	1Qr	FAC	2P	FAC	1P	FAC	2Q	FAC	2Q
FAT	1Qr	FAT	1Qr	FAT	2Qr	FAT	2P	FAT	1P	FAT	1Q	FAT	1Pr	FAT	2Q	FAT	1P	FAT	2Q

HONOURS / RECORDS

FA Comps: None

League: Spartan 1921-22, 22-23, 24-25, 32-33. Isthmian Division Two North 1986-87, Division One 1986-87, 97-97, Premier Division 1992-93.

County FA: Berks & Bucks Senior Cup x13. Most recently 2017-18

Goalscorer: John Willis

Appearances: Martin Baguley - 600+

Additional: Received £22,000 from Oldham Athletic for Fitz Hall

Victory: 13-1 v Merthyr Town (H), Southern Premier, 18/11/2017

Ground Capacity: 5,000 **Seats:** 284 **Covered:** 2,500 **Clubhouse:** Yes **Shop:** Yes

Previous Grounds: None

Record Attendance: 5,000 v Cambridge United - FA Cup 3rd Round 1979

DIRECTIONS

From M25 Junction 20 take A41 (Aylesbury), leave A41 at turn-off for Chesham (A416), pass through Ashley Green into Chesham. Follow signs to Amersham, still on A416 pass two petrol stations opposite each other and at next roundabout take third exit into ground.

From M1 Junction 8 follow signs for Hemel Hempstead then joining the A41 for Aylesbury, then as above.

Nearest Railway Station Chesham underground - 0.7km

Bus Route The Wild Rover Pub - stop 250m away

DORCHESTER TOWN

Founded 1880

Nickname: The Magpies **Club Colours:** Black & white

Club Contact Details 01305 267 623 office@dorchestertownfc.co.uk

The Avenue Stadium, Weymouth Avenue, Dorchester DT1 2RY

Previous Names: None

Previous Leagues: Dorset, Western 1947-72

09-10		10-11		11-12		12-13		13-14		14-15		15-16		16-17		17-18		18-19	
Conf S	17	Conf S	17	Conf S	11	Conf S	8	Conf S	22	SthP	17	SthP	12	SthP	18	SthP	19	SthPS	15
FAC	3Q	FAC	3Q	FAC	2Q	FAC	2P	FAC	2Q	FAC	4Q	FAC	1Qr	FAC	1Q	FAC	2Q	FAC	2Q
FAT	3Q	FAT	2Pr	FAT	3Q	FAT	1Pr	FAT	3Q	FAT	1Q	FAT	2Qr	FAT	2Q	FAT	2Q	FAT	2P

HONOURS / RECORDS

FA Comps: None

League: Western Division One 1954-55. Southern Southern Division 1979-80, 86-87, Division One East 2002-03.

County FA: Dorset Senior Cup x12 - Firstly in 1950-51 and most recently in 2011-12.

Victory: 7-0 v Canterbury (A) - Southern League Southern Division 1986-87

Defeat: 0-13 v Welton Rovers (A) - Western League 1966

Appearances: Mark Jermyn - 600+ over 14 seasons

Additional: Denis Cheney scored 61 goals in one season. Paid £12,000 to Gloucester City for Chris Townsend 1990. Received £35,000 from Portsmouth for Trevor Sinclair.

Ground Capacity: 4,939 **Seats:** 710 **Covered:** 2,846 **Clubhouse:** Yes **Shop:** Yes

Previous Grounds: Council Recreation Ground, Weymouth Avenue 1908-1929, 1929-90, The Avenue Ground 1929

Record Attendance: 4,159 v Weymouth - Southern Premier 1999

DIRECTIONS

The stadium is located at the junction of A35 Dorchester Bypass and the A354 to Weymouth, adjacent to Tesco. There is a coach bay for the team coach at the front of the stadium. Any supporters coach should park on the railway embankment side of the stadium.

Nearest Railway Station Dorchester South & West - 0.9km

FARNBOROUGH

Founded 1967

Nickname: Boro **Club Colours:** Yellow and blue

Club Contact Details 0844 807 9900 info@farnboroughfc.co.uk

The Rushmoor Stadium, Cherrywood Road, Farnborough, Hants GU14 8DU

Previous Names: Farnborough Town 1967-2007

Previous Leagues: Surrey Senior 1968-72, Spartan 1972-76, Athenian 1976-77, Isthmian 1977-89, 99-2001, 15-16. Alliance/Conference 1989-90, 91-93, 94-99, 2010-15. Southern 1990-91, 93-94, 2007-10.

09-10		10-11		11-12		12-13		13-14		14-15		15-16		16-17		17-18		18-19	
SthP	1	Conf S	2	Conf S	16	Conf S	13	Conf S	16	Conf S	20	Isth P	18	SthC	2	SthP	20	SthPS	9
FAC	4Qr	FAC	4Qr	FAC	2Qr	FAC	2Q	FAC	2Qr	FAC	2Qr	FAC	2Qr	FAC	2Q	FAC	1Q	FAC	1Qr
FAT	1P	FAT	3Q	FAT	1Pr	FAT	1P	FAT	3Qr	FAT	3P	FAT	1Qr	FAT	P	FAT	3Q	FAT	1Q

HONOURS / RECORDS

FA Comps: None

League: Spartan 1972-73, 73-74, 74-75. London Spartan 1975-76. Athenian Division Two 1976-77. Isthmian Division Two 1978-79, Division One 84-85, Premier 2000-01. Southern Premier 1990-91, 93-94, 2009-10, Division One South & West 2007-08.

County FA: Hampshire Senior Cup 1974-75, 81-82, 83-84, 85-86, 90-91, 2003-04, 05-06.

Victory: 7-0 v Newport (I.O.W.) (A) - Southern League Division 1 South & West 01/12/2007

Defeat: 0-4 v Hednesford Town (A) - Southern League Premier Division 04/03/2010

Goalscorer: Dean McDonald - 35 (in 53+3 Appearances 2009-10)

Appearances: Nic Ciardini - 147 (2007-10)

Ground Capacity: 6,500 **Seats:** 627 **Covered:** 1,350 **Clubhouse:** Yes **Shop:** Yes

Previous Grounds: Queens Road Recreation ground.

Record Attendance: 2,230 v Corby Town - Southern Premier 21/03/2009

DIRECTIONS

Leave the M3 at Junction 4 and take the A331 signed to Farnham, after a few hundred yards exit at the second slip road- signed A325 Farnborough, turn right at the roundabout and cross over the dual carriageway and small roundabout, passing the Farnborough Gate shopping centre on your left hand side, at the next roundabout turn left (first exit) onto the A325. Go over a pelican crossing and at the next set of lights take the right filter into Prospect Avenue. At the end of this road turn rightat the roundabout into Cherrywood Road, the ground is half a mile on the right hand side.

Nearest Railway Station Frimley - 0.7km

GOSPORT BOROUGH

Founded 1944

Nickname: The 'Boro' **Club Colours:** Yellow & blue

Club Contact Details 023 9250 1042 enquiries@gosportboroughfc.co.uk

Privett Park, Privett Road, Gosport, Hampshire PO12 3SX

Previous Names: Gosport Borough Athletic

Previous Leagues: Portsmouth & District 1944-45, Hampshire 1945-78. Southern 1978-92, 2007-13. Wessex 1992-2007. Conference 2013-17.

09-10		10-11		11-12		12-13		13-14		14-15		15-16		16-17		17-18		18-19	
Sthsw	8	Sthsw	13	Sthsw	3	SthP	5	Conf S	12	Conf S	6	Nat S	9	Nat S	20	SthP	23	SthPS	19
FAC	P	FAC	Pr	FAC	P	FAC	4Qr	FAC	2Q	FAC	1P	FAC	3Qr	FAC	2Q	FAC	2Q	FAC	2Q
FAT	2Q	FAT	P	FAT	1P	FAT	2Q	FAT	F	FAT	2P	FAT	3Q	FAT	1P	FAT	2Q	FAT	1Q

HONOURS / RECORDS

FA Comps: None

League: Portsmouth & District 1944-45. Hampshire 1945-46, 76-77, 77-78. Wessex 2006-07.

County FA: Hampshire Senior Cup 1987-88, 2014-15.

Victory: 19-1 v Widbrook United, Portsmouth Senior Cup, 2016-17.

Defeat: 0-9 v Gloucester City - Southern Premier Division 1989-90 and v Lymington & N.M. - Wessex Lge 99-2000

Goalscorer: Justin Bennett- 257

Appearances: Tony Mahoney - 765

Ground Capacity: 4,500 **Seats:** 1,000 **Covered:** Yes **Clubhouse:** Yes **Shop:** Yes

Previous Grounds: None

Record Attendance: 4,770 v Pegasus - FA Amateur Cup 1953

DIRECTIONS

Leave the M27 at junction 11 and follow the signs "A32 Gosport". After approximately four miles you will reach two roundabouts in quick succession. Go straight ahead at the first and take the third exit (signposted Alverstoke, Stokes Bay, Privett Park) at the second.
Follow this road (Military Road) until reaching the roundabout at the Cocked Hat pub. Take the first exit into Privett Road. The ground is signposted on the left after 300 yards. SatNav users should use **PO12 3SY** as the postcode for their destination.

Nearest Railway Station Portsmouth Harbour

Bus Route X5 (to Southampton) & 9/9A (to Fareham)

HARROW BOROUGH

Founded 1933

Nickname: Boro **Club Colours:** All red

Club Contact Details 0844 561 1347
Earlsmead Stadium, Carlyon Avenue, South Harrow HA2 8SS

Previous Names: Roxonian 1933-38, Harrow Town 1938-66
Previous Leagues: Harrow & District 1933-34, Spartan 1934-40, 45-58, West Middlesex Combination 1940-41, Middlesex Senior 1941-45, Delphian 1956-63, Athenian 1963-75. Isthmian 1975-2018.

09-10		10-11		11-12		12-13		13-14		14-15		15-16		16-17		17-18		18-19	
Isth P	14	Isth P	5	Isth P	17	Isth P	15	Isth P	18	Isth P	16	Isth P	17	Isth P	21	Isth P	12	SthPS	7
FAC	1Qr	FAC	1P	FAC	2Q	FAC	1Q	FAC	1Qr	FAC	4Qr	FAC	1Qr	FAC	1P	FAC	1Q	FAC	1Q
FAT	2Qr	FAT	1Q	FAT	2Qr	FAT	1Q	FAT	1Q	FAT	1Q	FAT	1Q	FAV	3Q	FAT	1Qr	FAT	1Q

HONOURS / RECORDS
FA Comps: None
League: Isthmian League 1983-84.

County FA: Middlesex Senior Cup 1982-83, 92-93, 2014-15. Middlesex Premier Cup 1981-82.
Middlesex Senior Charity Cup 1979-80, 92-93, 2005-06, 06-07, 14-15.

Victory: 13-0 v Handley Page (A) - 18/10/1941
Defeat: 0-8 on five occasions
Goalscorer: Dave Pearce - 153
Appearances: Les Currell - 582, Colin Payne - 557, Steve Emmanuel - 522

Ground Capacity: 3,068 **Seats:** 350 **Covered:** 1,000 **Clubhouse:** Yes **Shop:** Yes
Previous Grounds: Northcult Road 1933-34.
Record Attendance: 3,000 v Wealdstone - FA Cup 1st Qualifying Road 1946

DIRECTIONS
From the M25 junction 16, take the M40 East towards Uxbridge and London. Continue onto A40, passing Northolt Aerodrome on the left hand side. At the Target Roundabout junction (A312) turn left towards Northolt. Just after passing Northolt Underground Station on the left hand side, turn left at the next set of traffic lights, onto Eastcote Lane, becoming Field End Road.
At next roundabout, turn right onto Eastcote Lane. At a small parade of shops, take the turning on the right into Carlyon Avenue. Earlsmead is the second turning on the right.

Nearest Railway Station Northolt Underground - 1.1km

HARTLEY WINTNEY

Founded 1897

Nickname: The Row **Club Colours:** All orange

Club Contact Details 01252 843 586 (Clubhouse)
Memorial Playing Fields, Green Lane, Hartley Wintney RG27 8DL

Previous Names: None
Previous Leagues: Basingstoke & District. Aldershot & District >1978. Founder members of the Home Counties League (renamed Combined Counties League) 1978- 2017.

09-10		10-11		11-12		12-13		13-14		14-15		15-16		16-17		17-18		18-19	
CC1	5	CC1	7	CC1	3	CCP	19	CCP	7	CCP	9	CCP	1	CCP	1	Sth1E	4	SthPS	8
FAC	EP	FAC	Pr	FAC	3Q	FAC	P	FAC	4Q	FAC	Pr	FAC	3Q	FAC	EP	FAC	2Q	FAC	1Q
FAV	2Q	FAV	1Q	FAV	1P	FAV	1Q	FAV	2P	FAV	2Q	FAV	5P	FAV	2P	FAT	1P	FAT	1Qr

HONOURS / RECORDS
FA Comps: None
League: Combined Counties League 1982-83, 2015-16, 16-17.

County FA: None

Best FA Cup Fourth Qualifying Round 2013-14
FA Vase Fifth Round 2015-16
FA Trophy First Qualifying Round 2018-19(r)

Ground Capacity: 1,500 **Seats:** 113 **Covered:** Yes **Clubhouse:** Yes **Shop:** Yes
Previous Grounds: Causeway Farm 1897-1953.
Record Attendance: 1,392 v AFC Wimbledon , Combined Counties League Premier, 25/01/03.

DIRECTIONS
On entering Hartley Wintney via the A30 take the turn at the mini roundabout signposted A323 Fleet. Take the 1st right turn, Green Lane, which has St John's Church on the corner. Continue down Green Lane for about 800 metres and turn right into car park, which has a shared access with Greenfields School. Turn left at St John's Church if coming down the A323 from Fleet.

Nearest Railway Station Winchfield - 1.9km
Bus Route Green Lane - stop 100m away

HAYES & YEADING UNITED

Founded 2007

Nickname: United **Club Colours:** Red & white

Club Contact Details 0208 573 2075 info@hyufc.com

SKYex Community Stadium, Beaconsfield Road, Hayes UB4 0SL

Previous Names: Hayes - Botwell Mission 1909-29. Hayes and Yeading merged to form today's club in 2007

Previous Leagues: Isthmian. Conference 2007-16. Southern 2016-18.

09-10		10-11		11-12		12-13		13-14		14-15		15-16		16-17		17-18		18-19	
Conf	17	Conf	16	Conf	21	Conf S	17	Conf S	20	Conf S	19	Nat S	21	SthP	23	Sth1E	3	IsthSC	1
FAC	4Q	FAC	1P	FAC	4Q	FAC	4Q	FAC	2Qr	FAC	2Q	FAC	2Q	FAC	2Q	FAC	3Q	FAC	2Q
FAT	1P	FAT	1P	FAT	1P	FAT	1P	FAT	1P	FAT	1P	FAT	3Qr	FAT	1Q	FAT	1Q	FAT	1P

HONOURS / RECORDS

FA Comps: None

League: Isthmian South Central 2018-19.

County FA: None

Victory: 8-2 v Hillingdon Borough (A) - Middlesex Senior Cup 11/11/08

Defeat: 0-8 v Luton Town (A) - Conference Premier 27/03/10

Goalscorer: Josh Scott - 40 (2007-09)

Appearances: James Mulley - 137 (2007-10)

Ground Capacity: 6,000 **Seats:** 2,500 **Covered:** 3,900 **Clubhouse:** Yes **Shop:** Yes

Previous Grounds: Kingfield Stadium (Woking FC) 2012-13.

Record Attendance: 1,881 v Luton Town - Conference Premier 06/03/2010

DIRECTIONS

From the M40/A40(M) Head eastbound towards London, take the Target Roundabout exit signposted Northolt, Harrow & Hayes. At the top of the slip road take the fourth exit (the first after the exit towards London) onto the A312 towards Hayes. The next roundabout (The White Hart) is about is about 1 mile and a half on. Here ignore signs to Yeading (third exit) instead take the second exit towards Hayes & Heathrow to stay on the A312 (Hayes-By - Pass). At the next roundabout again ignore signs to Yeading and carry straight over. Take the next exit signposted Southall and Uxbridge (A4020 Uxbridge Road). At the top of the slip road take the first exit towards Southall and follow the directions below Head eastbound along the (A4020) Uxbridge Road. Head eastbound along the (A4020) Uxbridge Road signposted towards Southall. Get into the far right hand lane as soon as you can and turn right into Springfield Road at the next set of Traffic Lights (There is a petrol station and a retail development with a Wickes on the corner of Springfield Road). Follow the road to the School, the Road bears left into Beaconsfield Road, and about 100 yards on your right is the entrance to the ground.

Nearest Railway Station Hayes & Harlington - 5-10min taxi ride from ground

Bus Route From Uxbridge Underground take bus towards Shep Bush, alight at Springfield Rd

HENDON

Founded 1908

Nickname: Dons or Greens **Club Colours:** Green and white

Club Contact Details 020 8205 1645 Secretaryhendonfc@gmail.com

Silver Jubilee Park, Townsend Lane, Kingsbury, London NW9 7NE

Previous Names: Christ Church Hampstead > 1908, Hampstead Town > 1933, Golders Green > 1946

Previous Leagues: Finchley & District 1908-11, Middlesex 1910-11, London 1911-14, Athenian 1914-63. Isthmian 1963-2018.

09-10		10-11		11-12		12-13		13-14		14-15		15-16		16-17		17-18		18-19	
Isth P	10	Isth P	15	Isth P	7	Isth P	10	Isth P	8	Isth P	2	Isth P	19	Isth P	19	Isth P	3	SthPS	16
FAC	4Q	FAC	1P	FAC	4Q	FAC	1P	FAC	2P	FAC	3Q	FAC	1Q	FAC	4Q	FAC	1Qr	FAC	3Q
FAT	2Q	FAT	2Q	FAT	1Q	FAT	1Q	FAT	1P	FAT	3Q	FAT	1Q	FAT	1Q	FAT	2P	FAT	2Q

HONOURS / RECORDS

FA Comps: FA Amateur Cup 1959-60, 64-65, 71-72. European Amateur Champions 1972-73.

League: Finchley & District Division Three 1908-09, DivisioN Two 09-10, Division One 10-11. Middlesex 1912-13, 13-14. Athenian 1952-53, 55-56, 60-61. Isthmian 1964-65, 72-73.

County FA: London Senior Cup 1963-64, 68-69, 2008-09, 11-12 14-15. Middlesex Senior Cup x16 - Firstly in 1933-34 / Most recently 2017-18. Middlesex Intermediate Cup 1964-65, 66-67, 72-73. London Intermediate Cup 1962-63, 64-65, 72-73, 75-76, 79-80.

Victory: 13-1 v Wingate - Middlesex County Cup 02/02/1957

Defeat: 2-11 v Walthamstowe Avenue, Athenian League 09/11/1935

Goalscorer: Freddie Evans - 176 (1929-35)

Appearances: Bill Fisher - 787 - (1940-64)

Additional: Received £30,000 from Luton Town for Iain Dowie

Ground Capacity: 3,070 **Seats:** 350 **Covered:** 1,000 **Clubhouse:** Yes **Shop:**

Previous Grounds: Claremont Road. Vale Farm (Wembley FC). Earlsmead (Harrow Borough FC).

Record Attendance: 9,000 v Northampton Town - FA Cup 1st Round 1952

DIRECTIONS

From Staples Corner travel north along the A5, towards Edgware, through West Hendon, to the junction with Kingsbury Road (Red Lion public house on corner). Turn into Kingsbury Road and Townsend Lane is the 3rd turning on the left, at the top of the hill. The ground is in the bottom left hand corner of the Silver Jubilee Park.

Nearest Railway Station Hendon - 1.1km

Bus Route Queensbury Road - 700m away

MERTHYR TOWN

Founded 2010

Nickname: Martyrs **Club Colours:** White & black

Club Contact Details 01685 359 921 merthyrsec@gmail.com
Penydarren Park, Park Terrace CF47 8RF

Previous Names: None
Previous Leagues: Western League 2010-12.

09-10	10-11		11-12		12-13		13-14		14-15		15-16		16-17		17-18		18-19	
	West1	1	WestP	1	Sthsw	3	Sthsw	2	Sthsw	1	SthP	10	SthP	3	SthP	17	SthPS	13
	FAC	EP	FAC	1Qr	FAC	3Q	FAC	1Q	FAC	P	FAC	2Q	FAC	3Q	FAC	2Q	FAC	2Q
	FAV	2Q	FAV	2Q	FAT	1P	FAT	3Q	FAT	3Qr	FAT	3Qr	FAT	2Qr	FAT	1Q	FAT	2Q

HONOURS / RECORDS
FA Comps: None
League: Western League Division One 2010-11, Premier Division 2011-12.
Southern Division One South & West 2014-15.
County FA: None

Victory: 9-0 v Bishops Cleeve, Southern Division One South & West, 06/04/2015.
Defeat: 1-13 v Chesham United (A), Southern Premier, 18/11/2017

Ground Capacity: 4,000 **Seats:** Yes **Covered:** Yes **Clubhouse:** Yes **Shop:**
Previous Grounds: Rhiw Dda'r (Taff's Well AFC) 2010-11.
Record Attendance: Not known

DIRECTIONS
Leave the M4 at Junction 32 and join the A470 to Merthyr Tydfil. After approx 22 miles at the fourth roundabout take 3rd exit. At next roundabout go straight on and go straight on through two sets of traffic lights. At third set turn left (ground signposted Merthyr Tydfil FC from here). After 50 yards take first right, then first right just after Catholic Church into Park Terrace. The ground is at the end of the road approx. 200 yards on.

Nearest Railway Station Merthyr Tydfil - 0.6km
Bus Route St Mary's Church - stop 100m away

METROPOLITAN POLICE

Founded 1919

Nickname: The Blues **Club Colours:** All blue

Club Contact Details 020 8398 7358
Imber Court, Ember Lane, East Molesey, Surrey KT8 0BT

Previous Names: None
Previous Leagues: Spartan 1928-60, Metropolitan 1960-71, Southern 1971-78. Isthmian 1978-2018.

09-10		10-11		11-12		12-13		13-14		14-15		15-16		16-17		17-18		18-19	
Isth1S	10	Isth1S	1	Isth P	12	Isth P	6	Isth P	17	Isth P	5	Isth P	12	Isth P	18	Isth P		SthPS	3
FAC	1Q	FAC	4Qr	FAC	1Q	FAC	1P	FAC	1Qr	FAC	2Q	FAC	1Qr	FAC	2Q	FAC	2Q	FAC	1P
FAT	1Q	FAT	Pr	FAT	1Q	FAT	2Qr	FAT	2Q	FAT	3Q	FAT	3Q	FAV	1Q	FAT	3Q	FAT	1Qr

HONOURS / RECORDS
FA Comps: None
League: Spartan League Eastern Division and overall 1928-29, 29-30, 36-37, 38-39, 46-47, 53-54, 54-55, Central Division 45-46.
Isthmian League Division One South 2010-11.
County FA: Middlesex Senior Cup 1927-28, Surrey Senior Cup 1932-33, 2014-15. London Senior Cup 2009-10.

Victory: 10-1 v Tilbury - 1995
Defeat: 1-11 v Wimbledon - 1956
Goalscorer: Mario Russo
Appearances: Pat Robert

Ground Capacity: 3,100 **Seats:** 297 **Covered:** 1,800 **Clubhouse:** Yes **Shop:** No
Previous Grounds: None
Record Attendance: 4,500 v Kingstonian - FA Cup 1934

DIRECTIONS
Take M3 to junction 1, then take A308. At roundabout take the fourth exit onto Staines Road (A308) towards Kingston. After 3.7 miles at roundabout take the second exit onto Hampton Court Way (A309). After 1 mile at roundabout take the third exit onto Ember Court Road, then 300 yards ahead of you is the entrance to the ground.

Nearest Railway Station Thames Ditton - 0.8km

POOLE TOWN

Founded 1890

Nickname: The Dolphins **Club Colours:** Red & white

Club Contact Details 01794 517 991 secretary@pooletownfc.co.uk

Tatnam Ground, Oakdale School, School Lane, Poole BH15 3JR

Previous Names: Poole Rovers and Poole Hornets merged in 1890 to form Poole FC > 1934 (Known as Poole & St. Mary's 1919-20).

Previous Leagues: Dorset 1896-1903, 04-05, 10-11. Hampshire 1903-04, 05-10, 11-23, 34-35, 96-2004. Western 1923-26, 30-34, 35-57. Southern 1926-30, 57-96, 2011-16. Wessex 2004-11. National 2016-18.

09-10	10-11	11-12	12-13	13-14	14-15	15-16	16-17	17-18	18-19
WexP 1	WexP 1	Sthsw 2	Sthsw 1	SthP 7	SthP 2	SthP 1	Nat S 5	Nat S 20	SthPS 5
FAC 1Q	FAC 4Q	FAC 3Q	FAC P	FAC 4Qr	FAC 2Qr	FAC 4Q	FAC 2Q	FAC 3Q	FAC 4Q
FAV 4P	FAV SF	FAT 1Qr	FAT 2Qr	FAT 2Q	FAT 1P	FAT 1Q	FAT 3Qr	FAT 3Q	FAT 3Q

HONOURS / RECORDS

FA Comps: None

League: Western 1956-57. Hampshire Division One 1999-00. Wessex Premier Division 2008-09, 09-10, 10-11. Southern Division One South & West 2012-13, Premier 2015-16.

County FA: Dorset Senior Cup 1894-95, 96-97, 98-99, 1901-02, 03-04, 06-07, 25-26, 26-27, 37-38, 46-47, 74-75, 88-89, 97-98, 2008-09, 12-13, 13-14.

Victory: 12-0 v Welton Rovers (H) Western League 26/04/1939.

Defeat: 1-12 v Boscombe (A) Hampshire League (West) 20/12/1913.

Additional: Transfer fee paid £5,000 for Nicky Dent 1990.
Transfer fee received reported as £180,000 for Charlie Austin from Swindon Town 2009.

Ground Capacity: 3,100 **Seats:** 268 **Covered:** Yes **Clubhouse:** Yes **Shop:** Yes

Previous Grounds: Ye Old Farm Ground. Wimborne Road Rec > 1933. Poole Stadium 1933-94. Hamworthy Utd 1994-96. Holt Utd 1996.

Record Attendance: 6,575 v Watford, FAC 1Pr, 1962-63 (at Poole Stadium). 2,203 v Corby, Southern Prem, 2014-15 (at Tatnam).

DIRECTIONS

Follow the A35 into Poole and at the roundabout by the fire station take the second exit into Holes Bay Road (A350). At next roundabout take 1st exit onto Broadstone Way (A349) and turn right at Wessex Gate East traffic lights into Willis Way. Turn right into Fleets Way and continue until you see Poole Motor Cycles. Turn left into Palmer Road opposite Poole Motor Cycles and take first right into School Lane which will take you into the Club/School car park. The ground is on the right hand side.

Nearest Railway Station Poole - 3/4 mile from the ground.

SALISBURY

Founded 2015

Nickname: The Whites **Club Colours:** White and black

Club Contact Details 01722 776 655 info@salisburyfc.co.uk

Raymond McEnhill Stadium, Partridge Way, Old Sarum SP4 6PU

Previous Names: None

Previous Leagues: Wessex 2015-16.

09-10	10-11	11-12	12-13	13-14	14-15	15-16	16-17	17-18	18-19
						WexP 1	Sthsw 2	Sth1W 2	SthPS 4
							FAC 2Q	FAC 2Q	FAC 2Qr
						FAV SF	FAT 1Q	FAT P	FAT 2P

HONOURS / RECORDS

FA Comps: None

League: Wessex Premier Division 2015-16.

County FA: None

Victory: 9-1 v Bournemouth - Wessex Premier 25/08/15.

Defeat: 4-1 v AFC Porchester - Wessex Premier 30/04/16.

Goalscorer: Sam Wilson - 40 - 2015-16.

Appearances: Thomas Whelan - 54 - 2015-16.

Ground Capacity: 4,000 **Seats:** 500 **Covered:** 2,247 **Clubhouse:** Yes **Shop:**

Previous Grounds: None

Record Attendance: 3,450 v Hereford FC, FA Vase Semi-final 2nd leg, 2015-16.

DIRECTIONS

From North/East/West: Leave A303 at Countess roundabout at Amesbury and take A345 towards Salisbury until Park and Ride roundabout from where the ground is signposted. From South: Proceed to A345 and then follow directions to Amesbury until Park and Ride roundabout from where the ground is signposted.

Nearest Railway Station Salisbury - 4km

Bus Route Bus stops outside the ground

SWINDON SUPERMARINE

Founded 1992

Nickname: Marine **Club Colours:** All blue

Club Contact Details 01793 828 778 supermarinefc@aol.com

The Webbswood Stadium, South Marston, Swindon SN3 4BZ

Previous Names: Club formed after the amalgamation of Swindon Athletic and Supermarine

Previous Leagues: Wiltshire, Hellenic1992-2001.

09-10		10-11		11-12		12-13		13-14		14-15		15-16		16-17		17-18		18-19	
SthP	14	SthP	10	SthP	21	Sthsw	4	Sthsw	5	Sthsw	14	Sthsw	4	Sthsw	7	Sth1W	5	SthPS	11
FAC	1Q	FAC	2P	FAC	2Q	FAC	1Q	FAC	P	FAC	2Q	FAC	1Q	FAC	3Q	FAC	3Q	FAC	2Qr
FAT	1Q	FAT	3Q	FAT	1P	FAT	1Q	FAT	1Q	FAT	P	FAT	2Q	FAT	1Q	FAT	1Q	FAT	1Qr

HONOURS / RECORDS

FA Comps: None

League: Hellenic League Premier Division 1997-98, 2000-01.

County FA: Wiltshire Premier Shield 1996-97, 2006-07. Senior Cup 2016-17.

Goalscorer: Damon York - 136 (1990-98)

Appearances: Damon York - 314 (1990-98)

Additional: Paid £1,000 to Hungerford Town for Lee Hartson

Ground Capacity: 2,000 **Seats:** 325 **Covered:** Yes **Clubhouse:** Yes **Shop:** Yes

Previous Grounds: Supermarine: Vickers Airfield > Mid 1960s

Record Attendance: 1,550 v Aston Villa

DIRECTIONS

From M5 Junction 11a, take the A417 to Cirencester, then A419 Swindon. At the A361 junction by Honda Factory take road to Highworth. After one mile Club is on 4th roundabout.
From M4 Junction 15, take A419 towards Swindon Cirencester, take A361, then as above .
From A420 Swindon take A419 to Cirencester, near Honda factory take A361, then as above.

Nearest Railway Station Swindon - 5.8km

Bus Route Stanton Fitzwarren Turn - stop 300m away

TAUNTON TOWN

Founded 1947

Nickname: The Peacocks **Club Colours:** Claret and sky blue

Club Contact Details 01823 254 909 admin@tauntontown.com

Wordsworth Drive, Taunton, Somerset TA1 2HG

Previous Names: Taunton > 1968

Previous Leagues: Western 1954-77, 83-2002, Southern 1977-83

09-10		10-11		11-12		12-13		13-14		14-15		15-16		16-17		17-18		18-19	
Sthsw	19	Sthsw	9	Sthsw	17	Sthsw	18	Sthsw	8	Sthsw	4	Sthsw	3	Sthsw	4	Sth1W	1	SthP	2
FAC	1Q	FAC	1Q	FAC	1Qr	FAC	1Qr	FAC	Pr	FAC	1Q	FAC	2Qr	FAC	1Pr	FAC	1Qr	FAC	4Qr
FAT	1Q	FAT	Pr	FAT	1Q	FAT	2Q	FAT	P	FAT	Pr	FAT	2Q	FAT	3Q	FAT	1P	FAT	1Q

HONOURS / RECORDS

FA Comps: FA Vase 2000-01.

League: Western League 1968-69, 89-90, 95-96, 98-99, 99-2000, 2000-01.
Southern Division One 2017-18.

County FA: Somerset Senior Cup 1969-70, Premier Cup 2002-03, 05-06, 13-14, 14-15, 16-17.

Victory: 12-0 v Dawlish Town (A) - FA Cup Preliminary Round 28/08/1993

Defeat: 0-8 v Cheltenham Town (A) - FA Cup 2nd Qualifying Round 28/09/1991

Goalscorer: Tony Payne. Reg Oram scored 67 in one season

Appearances: Tony Payne

Ground Capacity: 2,500 **Seats:** 300 **Covered:** 1,000 **Clubhouse:** Yes **Shop:** Yes

Previous Grounds: Mountfields. French Weir. Victoria Park. Huish Old Boys. Denman's Park > 1953.

Record Attendance: 3,284 v Tiverton Town - FA Vase Semi-final 1999

DIRECTIONS

From M5 Junction 25 follow signs to Town Centre.
Proceed along Toneway then bear left at roundabout into Chritchard Way.
At traffic lights proceed into Wordsworth Drive and the ground is on the left.

Nearest Railway Station Taunton - 1.4km

Bus Route Milford Road - stop 20m away

TIVERTON TOWN

Founded 1913

Nickname: Tivvy **Club Colours:** All yellow

Club Contact Details 01884 252 397 jayrichdevon24@googlemail.com

Ladysmead, Bolham Road, Tiverton, Devon EX16 6SG

Previous Names: Tiverton Athletic.

Previous Leagues: East Devon 1913-28. North Devon 1928-32. Exeter & District 1932-73. Western 1973-99.

09-10		10-11		11-12		12-13		13-14		14-15		15-16		16-17		17-18		18-19	
SthP	19	SthP	20	Sthsw	9	Sthsw	16	Sthsw	3	Sthsw	16	Sthsw	8	Sthsw	3	SthP	6	SthPS	18
FAC	1Q	FAC	1Qr	FAC	P	FAC	P	FAC	P	FAC	1Qr	FAC	P	FAC	Pr	FAC	1Q	FAC	3Qr
FAT	1Q	FAT	1Q	FAT	3Q	FAT	1Q	FAT	3Qr	FAT	1Q	FAT	2Q	FAT	1Q	FAT	2Qr	FAT	2Q

HONOURS / RECORDS

FA Comps: FA Vase 1997-98, 98-99.

League: East Devon Senior Division 1924-25, 25-26, 26-27, 27-28. North Devon 1931-32.
Exeter & District 1933-34, 64-65, 65-66. Western 1993-94, 94-95, 96-97, 97-98.

County FA: Devon Senior Cup 1955-56, 65-66.
Devon St Luke's Cup 1990-91, 91-92, 92-93, 93-94, 94-95, 96-97, 1999-2000, 02-03, 05-06, 16-17.

Victory: 14-1 v University College SW, 11/02/1933.

Defeat: 0-10 v Dawlish Town, 27/12/1969.

Goalscorer: Phil Everett - 378.

Appearances: Tom Gardner - 510.

Ground Capacity: 2,983 **Seats:** 520 **Covered:** 2,300 **Clubhouse:** Yes **Shop:** Yes

Previous Grounds: Athletic Ground (Amory Park) 1913-21. Elm Field (The Elms) 1921-46.

Record Attendance: 3,000 v Leyton Orient - FA Cup 1st Round Proper 12/11/1994.

DIRECTIONS

M5 Junction 27, follow A361 to Tiverton's second exit at roundabout, turning left.
Continue for about 400 yards, crossing roundabout until reaching mini-roundabout.
Carry on straight across. Ground is 200 yards on right.

Nearest Railway Station Tiverton Parkway - 2km

Bus Route Park Road - stop 300m away

TRURO CITY

Founded 1889

Nickname: City, White Tigers, The Tinmen **Club Colours:** All white

Club Contact Details 01872 225 400 info@trurocityfc.net

Treyew Road, Truro TR1 2TH

Previous Names: None

Previous Leagues: Cornwall County. Plymouth & District >1951. South Western (FM) 1951-2006. Western 2006-08. Southern 2008-11, 13-15. Conference 2011-13.

09-10		10-11		11-12		12-13		13-14		14-15		15-16		16-17		17-18		18-19	
SthP	11	SthP	1	Conf S	14	Conf S	22	SthP	17	SthP	3	Nat S	4	Nat S	19	Nat S	7	Nat S	20
FAC	3Qr	FAC	2Q	FAC	3Q	FAC	2Q	FAC	2Q	FAC	1Q	FAC	3Q	FAC	2Q	FAC	1P	FAC	2Qr
FAT	1Pr	FAT	3Q	FAT	1P	FAT	3Q	FAT	1Q	FAT	3Q	FAT	2Pr	FAT	1Pr	FAT	3Q	FAT	2P

HONOURS / RECORDS

FA Comps: FA Vase 2006-07.

League: Plymouth & District 1936-37. South Western League 1960-61, 69-70, 92-93, 95-96, 97-98. Western Div. One 2006-07,
Premier Division 07-08. Southern Division One South & West 2008-09, Premier Division 2010-11.

County FA: Cornwall Senior Cup 1894-95, 1901-02, 02-03, 10-11, 23-24, 26-27, 27-28, 37-38, 58-59, 66-67, 69-70, 94-95, 97-98, 2005-06, 06-07, 07-08.

Misc: 115 points & 185 goals, Western League Division One (42 games) 2006-07.
Became first British club to achieve five promotions in six seasons.

Ground Capacity: 3,200 **Seats:** 1,675 **Covered:** Yes **Clubhouse:** Yes **Shop:** Yes

Previous Grounds: Truro School. Tolgarrick > mid-1900s Treyew Road Mid 1900s-2018. Plainmoor (Torquay) 18.

Record Attendance:

DIRECTIONS

On arriving at Exeter, leave the M5 at junction 31 and join the A30. Travel via Okehampton, Launceston, and Bodmin.. At the end of the dual carriageway (windmills on right hand side) take left hand turning signposted Truro. After approximately 7 miles turn right at traffic lights, travel downhill crossing over three roundabouts, following signs for Redruth. Approximately 500 metres after third roundabout signed 'Arch Hill', ground is situated on left hand side.

Nearest Railway Station Truro - 10min walk from the ground.

WALTON CASUALS

Founded 1948

Nickname: The Stags **Club Colours:** Orange and black

Club Contact Details 01932 260 300 info@waltoncasuals.com

Elmbridge Sports Hub, Waterside Drive, Walton-on-Thames, Surrey KT12 2JP

Previous Names: None

Previous Leagues: Surrey Intermediate 1948-69. Surrey Senior 1969-71. Suburban 1971-92. Surrey County 1992-95. Combined Counties 1995-2005.

09-10		10-11		11-12		12-13		13-14		14-15		15-16		16-17		17-18		18-19	
Isth1S	21	Isth1S	12	Isth1S	15	Isth1S	22	Isth1S	9	Isth1S	18	Isth1S	16	Isth1S	13	Isth1S	6	SthPS	17
FAC	3Q	FAC	1Q	FAC	P	FAC	P	FAC	P	FAC	Pr	FAC	P	FAC	3Q	FAC	1Q	FAC	2Q
FAT	Pr	FAT	1Q	FAT	Pr	FAT	P	FAT	Pr	FAT	1Q	FAT	1Qr	FAT	1P	FAT	1Q	FAT	3Q

HONOURS / RECORDS

FA Comps: None

League: Surban Southern Section 1982-83, Premier B 2012-13. Combined Counties Premier Division 2004-05.

County FA: None

Goalscorer: Paul Mills - 111 in 123 appearances (1993-99).

Appearances: Lawrence Ennis - 288

Victory: 10-0 v Chessington United, Combined Counties Premier, 28/12/2004.

Defeat: 0-7 v Redhill, Surrey Senior Cup 1st Rnd, 08/12/98. v Chipstead, Combined Counties Premier, 09/11/2002. v Faversham Town, Isthmian Division One, 08/12/2012. v Faversham Town, Isthmian Division One, 09/04/2016.

Ground Capacity: 2,217 **Seats:** 153 **Covered:** 403 **Clubhouse:** Yes **Shop:** Yes

Previous Grounds: Elm Grove Rec. 1948-69. Franklyn Road 69-71. Stompond Lane 71-72. Liberty Lane 72-80. Waterside Stadium 80-2015. Moatside 2015-16. Church Road 2016-17.

Record Attendance: 1,748 v AFC Wimbledon - Combined Counties League 12/04/2004

DIRECTIONS

Follow A308 towards Staines/Kingston/Sunbury, continue until roundabout with second exit taking you onto Hampton Court Way/A309. Continue onto A3050, follow the A3050 via Bridge Road and Riverbank. After travelling along the latter for just over 3 miles take the second exit off the roundabout onto Waterside Drive. Follow until Sports Hub appears on the right.

Nearest Railway Station Both Walton and Hersham stations about 43min walk.

Bus Route Nos. 461 & 459 stop nearest the hub.

WESTON-SUPER-MARE

Founded 1887

Nickname: Seagulls **Club Colours:** White & black

Club Contact Details 01934 621 618 enquiries@wsmafc.co.uk

Winterstoke Road, Weston-super-Mare BS24 9AA

Previous Names: Borough or Weston-super-Mare

Previous Leagues: Western League 1900-02, 10-18, 48-92. Bristol & District and Somerset County 1921-45. Southern 1992-04.

09-10		10-11		11-12		12-13		13-14		14-15		15-16		16-17		17-18		18-19	
Conf S	21	Conf S	12	Conf S	13	Conf S	7	Conf S	11	Conf S	17	Nat S	16	Nat S	15	Nat S	12	Nat S	22
FAC	2Q	FAC	3Q	FAC	4Q	FAC	3Qr	FAC	3Q	FAC	1P	FAC	4Q	FAC	2Q	FAC	2Q	FAC	1P
FAT	3Qr	FAT	3Q	FAT	3Q	FAT	3Q	FAT	1Pr	FAT	1P	FAT	2P	FAT	3Q	FAT	2Pr	FAT	1P

HONOURS / RECORDS

FA Comps: None

League: Western League 1991-92.

County FA: Somerset Senior Cup 1926-67.
Somerset Premier Cup 2010-11, 11-12, 17-18.

Victory: 11-0 v Paulton Rovers

Defeat: 1-12 v Yeovil Town Reserves

Goalscorer: Matt Lazenby - 180

Appearances: Harry Thomas - 740

Additional: Received £20,000 from Sheffield Wednesday for Stuart Jones

Ground Capacity: 3,500 **Seats:** 350 **Covered:** 2,000 **Clubhouse:** Yes **Shop:** Yes

Previous Grounds: 'Great Ground' Locking Road >1955. Langford Road 1955-83. Woodspring Park 1983-2004.

Record Attendance: 2,949 v Doncaster Rovers, FA Cup First Round Proper, 18th November 2014.

DIRECTIONS

Leave the M5 at Junction 21, take the dual carriageway A370 and continue straight until the 4th roundabout with ASDA on the right. Turn left into Winterstoke Road, bypassing a mini roundabout and continue for 1/2 mile. Woodspring Stadium is on the right.

Nearest Railway Station Weston-Super-Mare - 25-30 minute walk away.

Herbert (Salisbury) clears the danger from Hippolyer-Patrick (Hendon). Photo: Keith Clayton.

Moss (Harrow Boro) gets in his shot with McLaughlin (Met Police) watching on. Photo: Keith Clayton.

WIMBORNE TOWN

Founded 1878

Nickname: Magpies **Club Colours:** Black and white

Club Contact Details 01202 884 821 info@wimbornetownfc.co.uk
The Cuthbury, Cowgrove Road, Wimborne, Dorset BH21 4EL

Previous Names: None
Previous Leagues: Dorset, Dorset Combination, Western 1981-86, Wessex 1986-2010

09-10		10-11		11-12		12-13		13-14		14-15		15-16		16-17		17-18		18-19	
WexP	2	Sthsw	19	Sthsw	19	Sthsw	12	Sthsw	13	Sthsw	13	Sthsw	17	Sthsw	11	Sth1W	3	SthPS	14
FAC	1Q	FAC	1Q	FAC	P	FAC	P	FAC	P	FAC	1Q	FAC	2Q	FAC	Pr	FAC	Pr	FAC	1Qr
FAV	2P	FAT	1Qr	FAT	P	FAT	2Q	FAT	P	FAT	1P	FAT	P	FAT	2Q	FAT	1Q	FAT	1Q

HONOURS / RECORDS
FA Comps: FA Vase 1991-92.
League: Dorset Division One 1980-81. Wessex 1991-92, 93-94, 99-2000.

County FA: Dorset Minor Cup 1912-13, Senior Amateur Cup 1936-37, 63-64, Senior Cup 91-92, 96-97.

Goalscorer: Jason Lovell
Appearances: James Sturgess

Ground Capacity: 1,716 **Seats:** 275 **Covered:** 425 **Clubhouse:** Yes **Shop:** Yes
Previous Grounds: None
Record Attendance: 3,250 v Bamber Bridge

DIRECTIONS
On the Wimborne To Blandford Road (B3082), turn left into Cowgrove Road just past Victoria Hospital.

Nearest Railway Station Poole - 8 miles
Bus Route First School - stop 400m away

YATE TOWN

Founded 1906

Nickname: The Bluebells **Club Colours:** White & navy blue

Club Contact Details 01454 228 103 yatetownfootballclub@outlook.com
Lodge Road, Yate, Bristol BS37 7LE

Previous Names: Yate Rovers 1906-1930s. Yate YMCA 1933-58.
Previous Leagues: Bristol Premier Combination > 1968, Gloucestershire County 1968-83, Hellenic 1983-89, 2000-03, Southern 1989-2000

09-10		10-11		11-12		12-13		13-14		14-15		15-16		16-17		17-18		18-19	
Sthsw	13	Sthsw	14	Sthsw	13	Sthsw	6	Sthsw	9	Sthsw	6	Sthsw	16	Sthsw	18	Sth1W	14	SthS	3
FAC	1Qr	FAC	P	FAC	2Qr	FAC	1P	FAC	3Qr	FAC	1Q	FAC	P	FAC	P	FAC	P	FAC	1Qr
FAT	2Qr	FAT	P	FAT	2Q	FAT	Pr	FAT	Pr	FAT	P	FAT	P	FAT	1Q	FAT	1Q	FAT	1Qr

HONOURS / RECORDS
FA Comps: None
League: Hellenic 1987-88, 88-89.

County FA: Gloucestershire Senior Cup 2004-05, 05-06.

Victory: 13-3 v Clevedon - Bristol Premier Combination 1967-68
Goalscorer: Kevin Thaws
Appearances: Gary Hewlett
Additional: Paid £2,000 to Chippenham Town for Matt Rawlings 2003
Received £15,000 from Bristol Rovers for Mike Davis

Ground Capacity: 2,300 **Seats:** 236 **Covered:** 400 **Clubhouse:** Yes **Shop:** Yes
Previous Grounds: Yate Aerodrome 1954-60. Sunnyside Lane 1960-84.
Record Attendance: 2,000 v Bristol Rovers v Bristol Rovers Past XI - Vaughan Jones testimonial 1990

DIRECTIONS
From East: leave M4 J18, enter Yate on A432 via Chipping Sodbury bypass. Turn right at first small roundabout (Link Road), straight over next roundabout into Goose Green Way, over more roundabouts and 2 major sets of traffic lights. Turn right at third set of lights (by The Fox), then immediately left into Lodge Road. Ground 200m on right. From North: M5 (South) exit J14, B4509/B4060 into Chipping Sodbury. Turn right into Chipping Sodbury High Street, down Bowling Hill and right at first roundabout into Goose Green Way – then as above. From South: Leave M5 at J15, then join M5. Leave M4 at J19, take second exit onto M32. Leave M32 at J1, at roundabout take first exit onto A4174. Continue on A4174 over traffic lights, then at roundabout take first exit onto A432. Enter Yate on A432, at traffic lights turn left into Stover Road (B4059), then at roundabout take second exit – still on B4059. Left at traffic lights (Fox PH) and immediately left into Lodge Road.

Nearest Railway Station Yate - 1km
Bus Route North Road - stop 100m away

AFC DUNSTABLE

Founded 1981

Nickname: Od's **Club Colours:** All royal blue

Club Contact Details 01582 891 433 afcdunstable2016@gmail.com

Creasey Park, Creasey Park Drive, Brewers Hill Road LU6 1BB

Previous Names: Old Dunstablians 1981- 2004.

Previous Leagues: Dunstable Alliance 1981-83. Luton District & South Bedfordshire 1983-95. South Midlands/Spartan South Midlands 1995-2016.

09-10		10-11		11-12		12-13		13-14		14-15		15-16		16-17		17-18		18-19	
SSM1	5	SSM1	2	SSM P	3	SSM P	8	SSM P	9	SSM P	3	SSM P	1	SthC	7	Sth1E	5	SthC	10
				FAC	P	FAC	2Qr	FAC	EP	FAC	P	FAC	1Q	FAC	2Q	FAC	P	FAC	Pr
		FAV	2P	FAV	2Q	FAV	1P	FAV	1Qr	FAV	3P	FAV	4P	FAT	P	FAT	P	FAT	P

HONOURS / RECORDS

FA Comps: None

League: Spartan South Midlands Division Two 2003-04, 06-07, Premier Division 2015-16.

County FA: Bedfordshire Junior Cup 1989-90. Bedfordshire Senior Trophy 2006-07, 07-08. Bedfordshire Senior Cup 2016-17.

Best FA Cup Second Qualifying Round 2012-13(r), 16-17

FA Trophy Preliminary Round 2016-17, 17-18, 18-19

FA Vase Fourth Round Proper 2015-16

Ground Capacity: 3,200 **Seats:** 350 **Covered:** 1,000 **Clubhouse:** Yes **Shop:** Yes

Previous Grounds: Manshead School 1981-94. Dunstable Cricket Club (Totternhoe) 1994-2009.

Record Attendance: Not known.

DIRECTIONS

From the South: When travelling north on the A5, go straight across the lights in the centre of Dunstable. Turn left at the next main set of lights into Brewers Hill Road. You will immediately pass the Fire Station on your left. Carry on until you hit the first roundabout. Go over the roundabout and take the immediate right into Creasey Park Drive. From North: When travelling south on the A5, go through the chalk cutting and over the first set of traffic lights. At the next set of lights turn right into Brewers Hill Road. Go over the roundabout and take the immediate right into Creasey Park Drive. Public Transport: Creasey Park is well served by buses. Arriva and Centrebus services from Luton, Houghton Regis Leighton Buzzard and Aylesbury all stop at the bottom of Brewers Hill Road. Some 24 services stop directly opposite Creasey Park Drive in Weatherby.

Nearest Railway Station Luton Leagrave - 4 miles

AYLESBURY UNITED

Founded 1897

Nickname: The Ducks **Club Colours:** Green & white

Club Contact Details 01296 487 367 (Office) info@aylesburyunitedfc.co.uk

Chesham United FC, The Meadow, Amy Lane, Chesham HP5 1NE

Previous Names: None

Previous Leagues: Post War: Spartan1908-51, Delphian 51-63, Athenian 63-76, Southern 76-88, 2004-10, Conf. 88-89, Isthmian 89-2004. Spartan South Midlands 2010-13.

09-10		10-11		11-12		12-13		13-14		14-15		15-16		16-17		17-18		18-19	
SthM	22	SSM P	6	SSM P	4	SSM P	2	SthC	12	SthC	13	SthC	19	SthC	13	Sth1E	13	SthC	15
FAC	1Qr	FAC	1Q	FAC	Pr	FAC	P	FAC	2Q	FAC	P	FAC	P	FAC	P	FAC	3Q	FAC	1Qr
FAT	P	FAV	2P	FAV	2Q	FAV	1P	FAT	1Q	FAV	P	FAT	P	FAT	1Q	FAT	Pr	FAT	P

HONOURS / RECORDS

FA Comps: None

League: Spartan 1908-09, Western Division 28-29. Delphian 1953-54. Southern 1987-88.

County FA: Berks & Bucks Senior Cup 1913-14, 85-86, 96-97, 99-00. Berks & Bucks Senior Shield 2012-13.

Victory: 10-0 v Hornchurch & Upminster (H), Delphain League 17/04/1954

Defeat: 0-9 v Bishop's Stortford (A), Delphain League 08/10/1955

Goalscorer: Cliff Hercules - 301 (1984-2002)

Appearances: Cliff Hercules - 651+18 (1984-2002)

Ground Capacity: 5,000 **Seats:** 284 **Covered:** Yes **Clubhouse:** Yes **Shop:** No

Previous Grounds: Turnfurlong Lane. Buckingham Road >2006. Meadow View Park (Thame Utd) 2006-17.

Record Attendance: Turnfurlong Lane - 7,440 v Watford FAC 1st Rnd 1951-52. Buckingham Road - 6,031 v England 04/06/1988.

DIRECTIONS

From M25 Junction 20 take A41 (Aylesbury), leave A41 at turn-off for Chesham (A416), pass through Ashley Green into Chesham. Follow signs to Amersham, still on A416 pass two petrol stations opposite each other and at next roundabout take third exit into ground.
From M1 Junction 8 follow signs for Hemel Hempstead then joining the A41 for Aylesbury, then as above.

Nearest Railway Station Chesham underground - 0.7km

Bus Route The Wild Rover Pub - stop 250m away

OUTS: Aylesbury (R - SSMP), Bromsgrove Sporting (P - SthPC), Cambridge City (Tr - IsthN), Dunstable Town (R - SSMP), Peterborough Sports (P _ SthPC), Sutton Coldfield Town (Tr - NPLSE).

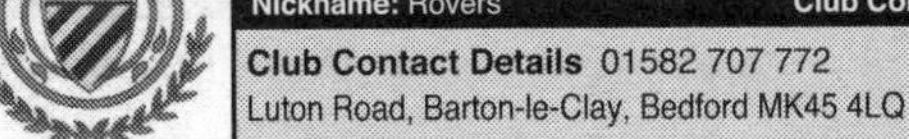

BARTON ROVERS

Founded 1898

Nickname: Rovers **Club Colours:** All royal blue

Club Contact Details 01582 707 772 bartonrovers@talktalk.net

Luton Road, Barton-le-Clay, Bedford MK45 4LQ

Previous Names: None

Previous Leagues: Local village football leagues >1939. Luton & District 1947-54, South Midlands 1954-79, Isthmian 1979-2004

09-10		10-11		11-12		12-13		13-14		14-15		15-16		16-17		17-18		18-19	
SthM	21	SthC	12	SthC	11	SthC	14	SthC	6	SthC	5	SthC	18	SthC	3	Sth1E	20	SthC	16
FAC	P	FAC	P	FAC	1Qr	FAC	1Q	FAC	2Qr	FAC	3Q	FAC	1Q	FAC	2Q	FAC	P	FAC	1Q
FAT	2Qr	FAT	1Q	FAT	1Q	FAT	1Q	FAT	P	FAT	P	FAT	Pr	FAT	P	FAT	P	FAT	EP

HONOURS / RECORDS

FA Comps: None

League: South Midlands Division Two 1954-55, Division One 64-65, Premier 70-71, 71-72, 72-73, 74-75, 75-76, 76-77, 77-78, 78-79.

County FA: Bedfordshire Senior Cup 1971-72, 72-73, 80-81, 81-82, 89-90, 97-98, 98-99, 2014-15, Premier Cup 1995-96, Senior Challenge Cup 2015-16.

Goalscorer: Richard Camp - 152 (1989-98)

Appearances: Tony McNally - 598 (1988-2005)

Additional: Paid £1,000 to Hitchin Town for Bill Baldry 1980
Received £2,000 from AFC Wimbledon for Paul Barnes

Ground Capacity: 2,000 **Seats:** 160 **Covered:** 1,120 **Clubhouse:** Yes **Shop:** Yes

Previous Grounds: None

Record Attendance: 1,900 v Nuneaton Borough - FA Cup 4th Qualifying Round 1976

DIRECTIONS

Leave M1 at J12 head towards Harlington.
Follow signs through Sharpenhoe Village to Barton.
At T-junction in village turn right, continue 500 yards and turn right into ground on concrete roadway adjacent to playing fields.

Nearest Railway Station Harlington - 4.6km

Bus Route The Memorial - stop 200m away

Bedford Town F.C.

BEDFORD TOWN

Founded 1989

Nickname: The Eagles **Club Colours:** All blue

Club Contact Details 01234 831 558

The Eyrie, Meadow Lane, Cardington, Bedford MK44 3LW

Previous Names: Original Bedford Town founded in 1908 folded in 1982

Previous Leagues: South Midlands 1989-94, Isthmian 1994-2004, Southern 2004-06, Conference 2006-07

09-10		10-11		11-12		12-13		13-14		14-15		15-16		16-17		17-18		18-19	
SthP	18	SthP	17	SthP	10	SthP	10	SthP	22	SthC	17	SthC	14	SthC	8	Sth1E	8	SthC	4
FAC	3Qr	FAC	2Q	FAC	1Q	FAC	1Q	FAC	2Q	FAC	Pr	FAC	1Q	FAC	P	FAC	1Q	FAC	2Q
FAT	1Q	FAT	1Q	FAT	1Q	FAT	2Q	FAT	1Qr	FAT	3Qr	FAT	2Q	FAT	P	FAT	1Qr	FAT	2P

HONOURS / RECORDS

FA Comps: None

League: South Midlands Division One 1992-93, Premier Division 93-94. Isthmian Division Two 1998-99.

County FA: Bedfordshire Senior Cup 1994-95.

Defeat: 0-10 v Merthyr Tydfil, 1950-51, v Yeovil Town 1960-61

Goalscorer: Jason Reed. Joe Chamberlain scored 9 v Rushden Fosse, December 1911

Appearances: David Skinn

Victory: 9-0 v Weymouth, Southern League, 1954-55, v Poole 1958-59, v Ickleford, v Cardington

Ground Capacity: 3,000 **Seats:** 300 **Covered:** 1,000 **Clubhouse:** Yes **Shop:** Yes

Previous Grounds: Allen Park, Queens Park, Bedford Park Pitch 1991-93

Record Attendance: 3,000 v Peterborough United - Ground opening 06/08/1993. At Queens Park - 18,407 v Everton, FAC, 1965-66

DIRECTIONS

From A1: Take A603 from Sandy to Bedford, go through Willington and ground is a mile and a half on right, signposted Meadow Lane. From M1: Off at Junction 13, take A421, carry on A421 onto Bedford Bypass and take A603 Sandy turn off. Ground is on left.

Nearest Railway Station Bedford St Johns - 3.8km

Bus Route Meadow Lane - stop 150m away

BEDWORTH UNITED

Founded 1895

Nickname: Greenbacks **Club Colours:** All green

Club Contact Details 02476 314 752 secretary@bedworthunitedfc.co.uk

The Oval, Coventry Road, Bedworth CV12 8NN

Previous Names: Bedworth Town 1947-68

Previous Leagues: Birmingham Combination 1947-54, Birmingham/West Midlands 1954-72. Southern 1972-2013, 14-16. Northern Premier 2013-14, 16-18.

09-10		10-11		11-12		12-13		13-14		14-15		15-16		16-17		17-18		18-19	
SthM	16	SthC	15	SthC	3	SthP	21	NP1S	20	SthC	4	SthP	21	NP1S	11	NP1S	4	SthPC	22
FAC	4Q	FAC	2Q	FAC	1Q	FAC	2Q	FAC	P	FAC	2Qr	FAC	2Q	FAC	3Q	FAC	P	FAC	P
FAT	P	FAT	1Q	FAT	1Q	FAT	1Q	FAT	P	FAT	P	FAT	1Q	FAT	1Q	FAT	1Q	FAT	1Q

HONOURS / RECORDS

FA Comps: None

League: Birmingham Combination 1948-49, 49-50.

County FA: Birmingham Senior Cup 1978-79, 80-81, 81-82.

Goalscorer: Peter Spacey - 1949-69

Appearances: Peter Spacey - 1949-69

Additional: Paid £1,750 to Hinckley Town for Colin Taylor 1991-92
Received £30,000 from Plymouth Argyle for Richard Landon

Ground Capacity: 2,900 **Seats:** 300 **Covered:** 300 **Clubhouse:** Yes **Shop:** Yes

Previous Grounds: British Queen Ground 1911-39

Record Attendance: 5,172 v Nuneaton Borough - Southern League Midland Division 23/02/1982

DIRECTIONS

1.5 miles from M6 J3, take B4113 Coventry–Bedworth Road and after third set of traffic lights (Bedworth Leisure Centre).
Ground 200 yards on right opposite cemetery.
Coaches to park in Leisure Centre.

Nearest Railway Station Bedworth - 0.5km

Bus Route Bus stops at the Leisure Centre

BERKHAMSTED

Founded 2009

Nickname: Comrades **Club Colours:** Yellow and blue

Club Contact Details 07525 872 914

Broadwater, Lower Kings Road, Berkhamsted HP4 2AL

Previous Names: None

Previous Leagues: Spartan South Midlands 2009-18.

09-10		10-11		11-12		12-13		13-14		14-15		15-16		16-17		17-18		18-19	
SSM2	1	SSM1	1	SSM P	7	SSM P	11	SSM P	5	SSM P	6	SSM P	5	SSM P	8	SSM P	2	SthC	6
				FAC	1Qr	FAC	2Q	FAC	1Q	FAC	EP	FAC	P	FAC	EP	FAC	1Q	FAC	1Qr
		FAV	2Q	FAV	2Q	FAV	2P	FAV	2P	FAV	1P	FAV	5P	FAV	4P	FAV	3P	FAT	1Q

HONOURS / RECORDS

FA Comps: None

League: Spartan South Midlands Division Two 2009-10, Division One 10-11.

County FA: Hertfordshire Charity Shield 2016-17

Victory: 12-1 v Stotfold, FA Cup Extra Preliminary Round, 05/08/2017

Defeat: 1-7 v Hanwell Town, Spartan South Midlands Premier Division, 2011-12

Ground Capacity: 1,500 **Seats:** 170 **Covered:** 350 **Clubhouse:** Yes **Shop:** Yes

Previous Grounds: None

Record Attendance: 366 v Slough Town, FA Cup First Qualifying Round, 02/09/2017

DIRECTIONS

Exit A41 onto A416. Go straight over the town centre traffic lights into Lower Kings Road. Go over the canal bridge and take first left into Broadwater. Follow the road to the left, going parallel to the canal. The ground is on the right hand side, sandwiched between the canal and the railway.

Nearest Railway Station Berkhamsted - 0.3km

Bus Route Castel Hill Avenue - stop 190m away

BIGGLESWADE FC

Founded 2016

Nickname: FC **Club Colours:** Green & white

Club Contact Details
Biggleswade Town FC, Langford Road, Biggleswade SG18 9JT

Previous Names: Based on Biggleswade Town's U18 side.
Previous Leagues: Spartan South Midlands 2016-19.

09-10	10-11	11-12	12-13	13-14	14-15	15-16	16-17	17-18	18-19
							SSM1 1	SSM P 5	SSM P 1
								FAC EP	FAC P
							FAV 2P	FAV 4P	FAV 2P

HONOURS / RECORDS
FA Comps: None
League: Spartan South Midlands Division One 2016-17, Premier Division 2018-19.

County FA: None

FA Cup Preliminary Round 2018-19
FA Vase Fourth Round Proper 2017-18

Ground Capacity: 3,000 **Seats:** 300 **Covered:** Yes **Clubhouse:** Yes **Shop:**
Previous Grounds: None
Record Attendance: Not known

DIRECTIONS
From the south – up the A1, past the first roundabout (Homebase) signposted Biggleswade. At next roundabout (Sainsburys) turn right onto A6001. As you approach the Town Centre, go straight over the mini roundabout following signs for Langford (Teal Road). At traffic lights, turn right (still heading towards Langford). Continue along Hitchin Street over two mini roundabouts and as you pass under the A1, the ground entrance is 200 yards on the right. From the north – exit A1 at the Sainsburys roundabout and follow instructions as above.

Nearest Railway Station Biggleswade - 1km
Bus Route Eldon Way - stop 260m away

COLESHILL TOWN

Founded 1894

Nickname: The Coleman **Club Colours:** White & blue

Club Contact Details 01675 464 905 paul@unique-brass-finishes.co.uk
Pack Meadow, Packington Lane, Coleshill B46 3JJ

Previous Names: Coleshill & District. Coleshill FC. Coleshill United 1919.
Previous Leagues: Birmingham Youth & Old Boys 1906-07, 56-67. Sutton & Erdington 1907-08. Trent Valley 1912. Sutton & District 1919-56. Worcestershire Combination/Midland Combination 1967-2008. Midland Alliance 2008-2014.

09-10	10-11	11-12	12-13	13-14	14-15	15-16	16-17	17-18	18-19
MidAl 8	MidAl 12	MidAl 16	MidAl 15	MidAl 4	MFLP 2	MFLP 5	MFLP 2	MFLP 2	SthC 9
FAC P	FAC 3Q	FAC Pr	FAC EPr	FAC EP	FAC 1Q	FAC 3Q	FAC 1Q	FAC 1Q	FAC EP
FAV 1P	FAV 1Q	FAV 1Q	FAV 1Q	FAV 4P	FAV 2P	FAV 4P	FAV SF	FAV 5P	FAT EP

HONOURS / RECORDS
FA Comps: None
League: Sutton & District Division One 1952-53, 54-5. Birmingham Youth & Old Boys Suburban Division 1958-59. Midland Combination Division Two 1969-70, Premier 07-08.
County FA: Walsall Senior Cup 1982-83

Best FA Cup Third Qualifying Round 2015-16
FA Vase Semi Finals 2016-17
FA Trophy Extra Preliminary Round 2018-19

Ground Capacity: 2,000 **Seats:** 570 **Covered:** **Clubhouse:** Yes **Shop:**
Previous Grounds: Memorial Ground >1974
Record Attendance:

DIRECTIONS
From M6 Junction 4 take A446 signposted Lichfield. Straight over 1st roundabout then immediately turn right across dual carriageway onto B4117 signposted Coleshill. After school on right, turn right into Packington Lane. Ground is ½ mile on left.

Nearest Railway Station Coleshill Parkway - 3.6km
Bus Route St Edmunds Primary School - 258m away

CORBY TOWN

Founded 1948

Nickname: The Steelmen **Club Colours:** Black and white

Club Contact Details 01536 406 640 media@corbytownfc.co.uk

Steel Park, Jimmy Kane Way, Rockingham Road, Corby NN17 2FB

Previous Names: Stewart & Lloyds (Corby) > 1947

Previous Leagues: United Counties 1935-52. Midland 1952-58. Southern 1958-2009, 13-15. Football Conference 2009-13, 15-16. Northern Premier 2016-18.

09-10	10-11	11-12	12-13	13-14	14-15	15-16	16-17	17-18	18-19
Conf N 6	Conf N 13	Conf N 17	Conf N 20	SthP 11	SthP 1	Nat N 22	NP P 21	NP1S 9	SthC 3
FAC 2Q	FAC 1Pr	FAC 1P	FAC 4Q	FAC 1P	FAC 1Qr	FAC 2Qr	FAC 1Q	FAC P	FAC 3Q
FAT 3P	FAT 3Q	FAT 3Qr	FAT 2Pr	FAT 1Q	FAT 1Q	FAT 3Q	FAT 1Q	FAT 1Q	FAT P

HONOURS / RECORDS

FA Comps: None

League: United Counties League 1950-51, 51-52. Southern League Premier Division 2008-09, 2014-15.

County FA: Northants Senior Cup 1950-51, 62-63, 75-76, 82-83, 2009-10, 12-13.

Goalscorer: David Holbauer - 159 (1984-95)

Appearances: Derek Walker - 601

Additional: Paid £2,700 to Barnet for Elwun Edwards 1981
Received £20,000 from Oxford United for Matt Murphy 1993

Ground Capacity: 3,893 **Seats:** 577 **Covered:** 1,575 **Clubhouse:** Yes **Shop:** Yes

Previous Grounds: Occupation Road 1948-85.

Record Attendance: 2,240 v Watford - Friendly 1986-87

DIRECTIONS

From A14, Exit at Jnc 7, Keep left, at first roundabout take A6003 Oakham/Uppingham stay on this road for approx. 7 miles (ignore signs for Corby to your right en route) straight over two roundabouts at second B.P. petrol station on right. At next roundabout approx 1 mile ahead turn right onto A6116 for 300 yards entrance to Ground between Rugby Club and Rockingham Forest Hotel (Great Western).

Nearest Railway Station Corby - 2.2km

Bus Route Dalton Road - stop 500m away

DAVENTRY TOWN

Founded 1886

Nickname: Purple Army **Club Colours:** Purple

Club Contact Details 01327 311 239 club.secretary@dtfc.co.uk

Browns Road, Daventry, Northants NN11 4NS

Previous Names: None

Previous Leagues: Northampton Town (pre-1987), Northants Comb 1987-89, United Counties 1989-2010, 16-19. Southern 2010-15. Northern Premier 2015-16.

09-10	10-11	11-12	12-13	13-14	14-15	15-16	16-17	17-18	18-19
UCL P 1	SthC 2	SthC 16	SthC 8	SthC 4	SthC 19	NP1S 21	UCL 1 1	UCL P 10	UCL P 1
FAC 1Q	FAC P	FAC 3Q	FAC 2Q	FAC 1P	FAC 1Q	FAC P	FAC EP	FAC EP	FAC 1Q
FAV 5P	FAT 2Q	FAT 2Q	FAT P	FAT 1P	FAT P	FAT P	FAV 1P	FAV 2Q	FAT P

HONOURS / RECORDS

FA Comps: None

League: Northants Combination Division One 1987-88, Premier 88-89.
United Counties Division One 1989-90, 90-91, 2000-01, 2007-08, 16-17, Premier Division 2009-10, 18-19.

County FA: Northants Junior Cup 1930-31, 60-61.

FA Cup First Round Proper 2013-14

FA Trophy First Round Proper 2013-14

FA Vase Fifth Round 2009-10

Ground Capacity: 3,000 **Seats:** 250 **Covered:** 250 **Clubhouse:** Yes **Shop:**

Previous Grounds: Hollow Ground.

Record Attendance: 850 v Utrecht (Holland) - 1989

DIRECTIONS

From Northampton or J.16 of the M1, follow A45 westbound into Daventry, crossing the A5 on the way.
At first roundabout bear left along A45 Daventry Bypass.
At next roundabout go straight over onto Browns Road.
The Club is at the top of this road on the left.

Bus Route The Cherwell - stop 330m away

DIDCOT TOWN

Founded 1907

Nickname: Railwaymen **Club Colours:** Red & white

Club Contact Details 01235 813 138 info@didcottownfc.co.uk

Loop Meadow Stadium, Bowmont Water, Didcot OX11 7GA

Previous Names: Didcot Village and Northbourne Wanderers amalgamated to form Didcot Town in 1907.

Previous Leagues: Metropolitan 1957-63, Hellenic 1963-2006

09-10		10-11		11-12		12-13		13-14		14-15		15-16		16-17		17-18		18-19	
SthP	15	SthP	19	Sthsw	16	Sthsw	17	Sthsw	12	Sthsw	7	Sthsw	10	Sthsw	12	Sth1W	6	SthC	7
FAC	2Q	FAC	3Q	FAC	1Qr	FAC	4Q	FAC	3Q	FAC	P	FAC	1P	FAC	P	FAC	1Q	FAC	2Qr
FAT	1Q	FAT	1Q	FAT	1P	FAT	3Q	FAT	Pr	FAT	1Pr	FAT	1Q	FAT	P	FAT	P	FAT	2Q

HONOURS / RECORDS

FA Comps: FA Vase 2004-05.

League: Hellenic Premier Division 1953-54, 2005-06, Division One 1976-77, 87-88.

County FA: Berks & Bucks Senior Trophy 2001-02, 02-03, 05-06.

Goalscorer: Ian Concanon

Best FA Cup First Round Proper 2015-16

FA Trophy First Round Proper 2011-12, 14-15(r)

Ground Capacity: 2,800 **Seats:** 350 **Covered:** 200 **Clubhouse:** Yes **Shop:** Yes

Previous Grounds: Fleet Meadow. Edmonds Park. Cow Lane. Haydon Road. Station Road 1923-99.

Record Attendance: 2,707 - v Exeter City, FA Cup 1st Round, 08/11/2015

DIRECTIONS

From A34 take A4130 towards Didcot.
At first roundabout take first exit, at next roundabout take third exit, then straight across next two roundabouts.
At fifth roundabout turn right into Avon Way.
Follow Avon Way for 1/2 mile till you get to a mini roundabout.
Straight across it, ground is on the left after 100 yards, in Bowmont Water.

Nearest Railway Station Didcot Parkway - 0.4km

HALESOWEN TOWN

Founded 1873

Nickname: Yeltz **Club Colours:** All blue

Club Contact Details 0121 629 0727 info@ht-fc.com

The Grove, Old Hawne Lane, Halesowen B63 3TB

Previous Names: None

Previous Leagues: Birmingham & District/West Midlands 1892-1905, 06-11, 46-86, Birmingham Combination 1911-39. Southern 1986-12. Northern Premier 2012-18.

09-10		10-11		11-12		12-13		13-14		14-15		15-16		16-17		17-18		18-19	
SthP	8	SthP	21	Sthsw	12	NP1S	7	NP1S	1	NP P	11	NP P	13	NP P	19	NP P	23	SthPC	21
				FAC	P	FAC	P	FAC	3Q	FAC	3Q	FAC	2Q	FAC	3Qr	FAC	2Q	FAC	2Q
		FAT	1Q	FAT	P	FAT	2Q	FAT	1Q	FAT	1P	FAT	1Q	FAT	2Q	FAT	1Q	FAT	3Q

HONOURS / RECORDS

FA Comps: FA Vase 1984-85, 85-86

League: West Midlands (Reg) 1946-47, 82-83, 83-84, 84-85, 85-86. Southern League Midland Division 1989-90, Western Division 2001-02. Northern Premier Division One South 2013-14.

County FA: Worcestershire Senior Cup 1951-52, 61-62, 2002-03, 04-05. Birmingham Senior Cup 1983-84, 97-98. Staffordshire Senior Cup 1988-89.

Victory: 13-1 v Coventry Amateurs - Birmingham Senior cup 1956

Defeat: 0-8 v Bilston - West Midlands League 07/04/1962

Goalscorer: Paul Joinson - 369

Appearances: Paul Joinson - 608

Additional: Paid £7,250 to Gresley Rovers for Stuart Evans. Received £40,000 from Rushden & Diamonds for Jim Rodwell.

Ground Capacity: 3,150 **Seats:** 525 **Covered:** 930 **Clubhouse:** Yes **Shop:** Yes

Previous Grounds: None

Record Attendance: 5,000 v Hendon - FA Cup 1st Round Proper 1954

DIRECTIONS

Get to Junction 3 of the M5. Head towards Kidderminster on the A458 for a mile or so to the first traffic island at the bottom of the hill. Turn right on to the A459 towards Dudley (the cricket ground should now be on your left) and continue past where the road splits to the next island. Turn left here on to the A456 towards Stourbridge until you get to the next island. Take the 3rd exit (Old Hawne Lane) and the ground is about 400 yards away, at the top of the hill on the left.

Nearest Railway Station Old Hill - 1.8km

Bus Route Cranmoor Crescent - stop 50m away

KEMPSTON ROVERS

Founded 1884

Nickname: Walnut Boys **Club Colours:** Red, white & black

Club Contact Details 01234 852 346 afckempston@yahoo.co.uk

Hillgrounds Leisure, Hillgrounds Road, Kempston, Bedford MK42 8SZ

Previous Names: Kempston Rovers 1884-2004. AFC Kempston Rovers 2004-16.

Previous Leagues: Bedford & District. Biggleswade & District. Bedfordshire & District County/South Midlands 1927-53. United Counties 1957-2016.

09-10	10-11	11-12	12-13	13-14	14-15	15-16	16-17	17-18	18-19
UCL 1 5	UCL 1 1	UCL P 10	UCL P 17	UCL P 12	UCL P 8	UCL P 1	SthC 6	Sth1E 7	SthC 13
	FAC 1Q	FAC EP	FAC 1Q	FAC EP	FAC P	FAC P	FAC 2Qr	FAC 2Q	FAC 3Q
FAV 2Q	FAV 1Q	FAV 2Q	FAV 2Q	FAV 1Q	FAV 2P	FAV 2P	FAT 1Q	FAT P	FAT 1Qr

HONOURS / RECORDS

FA Comps: None

League: Bedford & District Division One 1907-08, 08-09, Division Two South 22-23, 33-34. Biggleswade & District 1910-11. United Counties Premier Division 1957-58, 73-74, 2015-16, Division One 85-86, 2010-11, Division Two 1955-56,

County FA: Bedfordshire Senior Cup 1908-09, 37-38, 76-77, 91-92. Huntingdonshire Premier Cup 1999-2000, 00-01.

Best FA Cup Fourth Qualifying Round 1978-79

FA Trophy First Qualifying Round 2016-17, 18-19(r)

FA Vase Fifth Round Proper 1974-75, 80-81

Ground Capacity: 2,000 **Seats:** 100 **Covered:** 250 **Clubhouse:** Yes **Shop:** Yes

Previous Grounds: None

Record Attendance: Not known

DIRECTIONS

Take A421 Bedford by pass turning as indicated to Kempston onto A5140 Woburn Road. At roundabout turn left into St John's Street then right into Bedford Road. After the shops and park on the left turn immediately left into Hillgrounds Road. Ground is past the swimming pool on right hand side.

Nearest Railway Station Bedford - 1.3km

Bus Route Prentice Gardens - stop 100m away

KIDLINGTON

Founded 1909

Nickname: Greens **Club Colours:** Green

Club Contact Details 01865 849 777

Yarnton Road, Kidlington, Oxford OX5 1AT

Previous Names: None.

Previous Leagues: Villages Leagues > 1945. Oxford City Junior 1945-51. Oxfordshire Senior 1951-54. Hellenic 1954-2016.

09-10	10-11	11-12	12-13	13-14	14-15	15-16	16-17	17-18	18-19
Hel P 11	Hel P 7	Hel P 18	Hel P 13	Hel P 6	Hel P 4	Hel P 1	SthC 12	Sth1W 12	SthC 18
FAC 1Q	FAC EP	FAC P	FAC EPr	FAC EPr	FAC P	FAC 2Q	FAC P	FAC 2Q	FAC P
FAV 1P	FAV 1P	FAV 2Q	FAV 3P	FAV 3P	FAV 1Q	FAV QFr	FAT P	FAT 1Q	FAT P

HONOURS / RECORDS

FA Comps: None

League: Oxfordshire Senior 1952-53. Hellenic Premier Division 2015-16.

County FA: Oxfordshire Intermediate Cup 1952-53, 69-70, 84-85.

Best FA Cup Second Qualifying Round 2015-16, 17-18

FA Trophy First Qualifying Round 2017-18

FA Vase Fifth Round 1976-77

Ground Capacity: 2,086 **Seats:** Yes **Covered:** Yes **Clubhouse:** Yes **Shop:** No

Previous Grounds: None

Record Attendance: 2,000 v Showbiz XI, 1973.

DIRECTIONS

From Kidlington Roundabout take A4260 into Kidlington. After 3rd set of traffic lights take 2nd left into Yarnton Road. Ground 300 yards on left, just past Morton Avenue.

Nearest Railway Station Oxford Parkway - 1.9km

Bus Route Treeground Place - stop 100m away

NORTH LEIGH

Founded 1908

Nickname: The Millers **Club Colours:** Yellow and black

Club Contact Details 01993 880 157 commercial@northleighfc.co.uk

Eynsham Hall Park, North Leigh, Witney, Oxon OX29 6SL

Previous Names: None

Previous Leagues: Witney & District, Hellenic 1990-2008

09-10		10-11		11-12		12-13		13-14		14-15		15-16		16-17		17-18		18-19	
Sthsw	10	Sthsw	6	Sthsw	6	Sthsw	9	Sthsw	7	Sthsw	8	Sthsw	9	Sthsw	6	Sth1W	18	SthC	17
FAC	1Q	FAC	P	FAC	1Q	FAC	3Q	FAC	1Q	FAC	P	FAC	3Q	FAC	4Q	FAC	1Qr	FAC	P
FAT	P	FAT	1Qr	FAT	P	FAT	1Qr	FAT	1Q	FAT	1Q	FAT	1Q	FAT	1Pr	FAT	P	FAT	Pr

HONOURS / RECORDS

FA Comps: None

League: Witney & District Premier 1985-86, 86-87, 87-88, 88-89, 89-90. Hellenic Premier Division 2002-03, 07-08.

County FA: Oxfordshire Senior Cup 2011-12, 16-17.

Goalscorer: P Coles

Appearances: P King

Best FA Cup Fourth Qualifying Round 2016-17

FA Trophy First Round Proper 2016-17

FA Vase Fourth Round Proper 2003-04

Ground Capacity: 1,500 **Seats:** 175 **Covered:** 200 **Clubhouse:** Yes **Shop:** No

Previous Grounds: None

Record Attendance: 426 v Newport County - FA Cup 3rd Qualifying Round 16/10/2004

DIRECTIONS

Ground is situated off A4095 Witney to Woodstock road, three miles east of Witney.
Entrance 300 yards east of main park entrance.

Nearest Railway Station Combe - 3.3km

ST. NEOTS TOWN

Founded 1879

Nickname: Saints **Club Colours:** Dark blue & light blue

Club Contact Details 01480 470 012 enquiries@stneotstownfc.co.uk

Rowley Park, Kester Way, Cambridge Road, St Neots, PE19 6SN

Previous Names: St Neots 1879-1924. St. Neots & District 1924-1957.

Previous Leagues: Biggleswade & Dist. Bedfordshire & Dist/South Midlands 1927-36, 46-49. United Co. 1936-39, 51-56, 66-69, 73-88, 94-2011. Metropolitan (Founder Members) 1949-51, 60-66. Central Alliance 1956-60. Eastern Co. 1969-73. Hunts Junior 1990-94.

09-10		10-11		11-12		12-13		13-14		14-15		15-16		16-17		17-18		18-19	
UCL P	2	UCL P	1	SthC	1	SthP	12	SthP	16	SthP	5	SthP	20	SthP	19	SthP	12	SthPC	20
FAC	P	FAC	1Q	FAC	P	FAC	2Q	FAC	2Qr	FAC	1Qr	FAC	2Qr	FAC	1Qr	FAC	1Q	FAC	4Q
FAV	2Q	FAV	5P	FAT	2Q	FAT	1Q	FAT	2Q	FAT	3Qr	FAT	2Q	FAT	2Qr	FAT	2Q	FAT	2Q

HONOURS / RECORDS

FA Comps: None

League: South Midlands 1932-33. Metropolitan 1949-50. United Counties 1967-68, 2010-11, Division One 1994-95.
Huntingdonshire 1990-91, 91-92, 92-93, 93-94. Southern Division One Central 2011-12.

County FA: Huntingdonshire Senior Cup x38 - Firstly in 1888-89 and most recently in 2017-18.
Huntingdonshire Premier Cup 2001-02.

Misc: 105 points obtained in the 2010-11 season - a United Counties record.

In 1968-69 the club won the Huntingdonshire Senior Cup for the 12th consecutive time - an English record for Senior cups.

Ground Capacity: 3,500 **Seats:** 250 **Covered:** 850 **Clubhouse:** Yes **Shop:** No

Previous Grounds: Town Common 1879-1899. Shortsands 1899-1988. Priory Park 1990-93. Old Rowley Park 1993-2008.

Record Attendance: 2,000 v Wisbech 1966

DIRECTIONS

From St Neots town centre, take the B1428 Cambridge Road, after going under the railway bridge, turn left at the first roundabout into Dramsell Rise. Follow the road up the hill to Kester Way and the ground. If approaching from Cambridge on the A428, turn right at the first roundabout as you approach St Neots onto the Cambridge Road. At the second roundabout, turn right into Dramsell Rise and follow as above. If travelling via the A1, follow signs for the A428 Cambridge. Go straight over roundabout with Tescos on left hand side, then turn left at next roundabout. Follow final instructions above as if approaching from Cambridge.

Nearest Railway Station St Neots - 06.km

THAME UNITED

Founded 1883

Nickname: Red Kites **Club Colours:** Red & black

Club Contact Details 01844 214 401 jake@jcpc.org.uk

Meadow View Park, Tythrop Way, Thame, Oxon OX9 3RN

Previous Names: Thame F.C.

Previous Leagues: Oxon Senior. Hellenic 1959-88, 2006-17. South Midlands 1988-91. Isthmian 1991-2004. Southern 2004-06.

09-10		10-11		11-12		12-13		13-14		14-15		15-16		16-17		17-18		18-19	
Hel1E	1	Hel P	10	Hel P	9	Hel P	9	Hel P	10	Hel P	5	Hel P	6	Hel P	1	Sth1E	11	SthC	8
FAC	1Q	FAC	2Qr	FAC	2Q	FAC	P	FAC	EP	FAC	1Q	FAC	EPr	FAC	P	FAC	1Q	FAC	P
FAV	2Qr	FAV	2Q	FAV	2Q	FAV	2P	FAV	2Q	FAV	2P	FAV	3P	FAV	1P	FAT	3Q	FAT	2Q

HONOURS / RECORDS

FA Comps: None

League: Hellenic 1961-62, 69-70, 2016-17, Division One East 2009-10. South Midlands League 1990-91. Isthmian Division Two 1994-95.

County FA: None

Appearances: Steve Mayhew

Best FA Cup Fourth Qualifying Round 2003-04, 04-05

FA Trophy Third Round Proper 2002-03

FA Vase Semi Finals 1998-99

Ground Capacity: 3,000 **Seats:** Yes **Covered:** Yes **Clubhouse:** Yes **Shop:**

Previous Grounds: Windmill Road 1883-2005. Aylesbury United FC 2005-06. AFC Wallingford 2006-11.

Record Attendance: 1,382 v Oxford United Jan 2011.

DIRECTIONS

From the west: At the Oxford Road roundabout on the edge of Thame take the first left (sign posted Aylesbury) and follow the by-pass. At the next roundabout take the third exit on to Tythrop Way. The ground is 200 yards on the left.
From the east: Leave the M40 at Junction 6 and follow the signposts to Thame. On arriving in Thame, take the first right on to Wenman Road (B4012). Stay on the B4012 as it by-passes Thame, going straight over two roundabouts. The ground is on the right, directly off the by-pass, approximately half a mile after you pass Chinnor Rugby Club.

Nearest Railway Station Haddenham & Thame Parkway - 2.9km

Bus Route Queens Close - stop 350m away

WANTAGE TOWN

Founded 1892

Nickname: Alfredians **Club Colours:** Green & white

Club Contact Details 01235 764 781 (Ground) wantagetownfc-secretary@outlook.com

Alfredian Park, Manor Road, Wantage OX12 8DW

Previous Names: None.

Previous Leagues: Swindon & District. North Berkshire. Reading & District. Hellenic > 2014, 17-19. Southern 2014-17.

09-10		10-11		11-12		12-13		13-14		14-15		15-16		16-17		17-18		18-19	
Hel P	5	Hel P	1	Hel P	12	Hel P	2	Hel P	1	Sthsw	20	Sthsw	20	Sthsw	21	Hel P	4	Hel P	1
FAC	1Q	FAC	EP	FAC	P	FAC	1Q	FAC	P	FAC	1Qr	FAC	P	FAC	1Qr	FAC	P	FAC	2Qr
FAV	1P	FAV	3P	FAV	3P	FAV	2P	FAV	2P	FAT	P	FAT	P	FAT	1Qr	FAV	2P	FAT	1Q

HONOURS / RECORDS

FA Comps: None

League: Swindon & District 1907-08, 33-34, 52-53, 55-56. North Berks Division One 1919-20, 21-22. Hellenic Division 1 East 1980-81, 03-04, Premier Division 2010-11, 13-14, 18-19.

County FA: Berks & Bucks Intermediate Cup 1954-55. Reading Senior Cup 1982-83.

FA Cup Second Qualifying Round 2018-19

FA Trophy First Qualifying Round 2016-17

FA Vase Third Round Proper 1974-75, 83-84, 86-87, 2010-11, 11-12

Ground Capacity: 1,500 **Seats:** 50 **Covered:** 300 **Clubhouse:** Yes **Shop:**

Previous Grounds: Not known

Record Attendance: 550 v Oxford United, July 2003.

DIRECTIONS

Proceed to Market Square. Take road at southeast corner (Newbury Street signposted to Hungerford). Continue for approximately a quarter of a mile take right turning into the ground. Clearly marked 'Wantage Town FC'.

Bus Route King Alfreds School stop - 423m away

WELWYN GARDEN CITY

Founded 1921

Nickname: Citizens **Club Colours:** Claret & sky blue

Club Contact Details 01707 329 358 welwyngardencityfc@gmail.com

Herns Lane, Welwyn Garden City, Herts AL7 1TA

Previous Names: Original club folded in 1935 and was reformed in 1937.

Previous Leagues: Mid-Herts 1922-26, 44-45. Beds & Dist 26-27. Spartan 27-35, 37-39, 45-51, 55-59. East, North & Mid-Herts Comb. 1939. Beds & Herts Comb 1940. London 51-55. Herts Senior Co 59-70. Greater London 70-71. Met London (FM) 71-73.

09-10		10-11		11-12		12-13		13-14		14-15		15-16		16-17		17-18		18-19	
SSM P	22	SSM1	17	SSM1	17	SSM1	13	SSM1	4	SSM1	1	SSM P	4	SSM P	6	SSM P	1	SthC	14
FAC	EP	FAC	EP							FAC	1Q	FAC	1Q	FAC	P	FAC	EP	FAC	P
FAV	1Q	FAV	2Q	FAV	1Q	FAV	1Q	FAV	3P	FAV	1P	FAV	1P	FAV	3P	FAV	3P	FAT	P

HONOURS / RECORDS

FA Comps: None

League: South Midlands 1973-74, Division One 1981-82. Spartan South Midlands Division One 2014-15, Premier 17-18.

County FA: Hertfordshire FA Charity Shield 1927-28, 86-87, 87-88. Herts FA Senior Centenary Trophy 1984-85.

Best FA Cup Third Qualifying Round 1998-99(r), 2005-06
FA Vase Fourth Round Proper Replay 2005-06
Goalscorer: Jason Caswell scored 51 goals during the 2014-15 season
FA Trophy Preliminary Round 2018-19

Ground Capacity: 2,500 **Seats:** Yes **Covered:** Yes **Clubhouse:** Yes **Shop:**
Previous Grounds: Several before moving to Herns Lane in 1968
Record Attendance: Unknown

DIRECTIONS

Best Route to the Ground: From A1 (M) follow Welwyn Garden City signpost A1000.
Take second exit off one-way system, sign-posted Panshanger. Ground is 400 yards on left.

Nearest Railway Station Welwyn Garden City - 1.9km
Bus Route Hernes Way - stop 160m away

YAXLEY

Founded 1962

Nickname: The Cuckoos **Club Colours:** Navy and orange

Club Contact Details 01733 244 928 info@yaxleyfc.com

Leading Drove, Holme Road, Yaxley, Peterborough PE7 3NA

Previous Names: Yaxley British Legion 1963-86. Coalite Yaxley 1986-90. Clarksteel Yaxley 1990.

Previous Leagues: Peterborough & District 1962-88. Eastern Counties (Founder Member) 1988-92. Huntingdonshire 1992-94. West Anglia 1994-95. United Counties 1995-2018.

09-10		10-11		11-12		12-13		13-14		14-15		15-16		16-17		17-18		18-19	
UCL P	19	UCL P	16	UCL P	18	UCL P	12	UCL P	6	UCL P	4	UCL P	12	UCL P	3	UCL P	1	SthC	11
FAC	EP	FAC	EP	FAC	EP	FAC	P	FAC	EP	FAC	EP	FAC	1Q	FAC	Pr	FAC	1Q	FAC	P
FAV	2Q	FAV	1Q	FAV	1P	FAV	1P	FAV	1Q	FAV	4P	FAV	3P	FAV	1P	FAV	3P	FAT	2Qr

HONOURS / RECORDS

FA Comps: None

League: Peterborough & District Division Three South 1968-69, Division Two 70-71, Premier 76-77, 83-84.
West Anglia 1994-95. United Counties Division One 1996-97, Premier 2017-18.

County FA: Hunts Senior Cup 1974-75, 75-76, 82-83, 83-84, 98-99, 2003-04, 04-05, 07-08. Hunts Premier Cup 2004-05

Best FA Cup Second Qualifying Round 2002-03, 06-07
FA Vase Fourth Round Proper 2014-15
FA Trophy Second Qualifying Round 2018-19(r)

Ground Capacity: 1,500 **Seats:** 150 **Covered:** yes **Clubhouse:** Yes **Shop:** Yes
Previous Grounds: Middleton Road 1962-94
Record Attendance: 300v Wisbech Town, FA Vase Preliminary Round 1982-83

DIRECTIONS

Leave A1 at Norman Cross and travel towards Peterborough. Turn off A15 at traffic lights. Bear immediately right and go past cemetery. At bottom of hill turn right into Main Street then left into Holme Road. After short distance go over small bridge and turn left between a bungalow and house into Leading Drove. Ground on left hand side.

Nearest Railway Station Peterborough - 8 miles
Bus Route Churhc Street stop 300m away

STH D1 SOUTH INS: Basingstoke Town (R - SthPS), Frome Town (R - SthPS), Sholing (P - WsexP), Willand Rovers (P WestP).

AFC TOTTON

Founded 1886

Nickname: Stags **Club Colours:** Blue and white

Club Contact Details 02380 868 981 enquiries@afctotton.com

Testwood Stadium, Salisbury Road, Calmore, Totton SO40 2RW

Previous Names: Totton FC until merger with Totton Athletic in 1975

Previous Leagues: New Forest (Founder Members) 1904. Southampton Senior. Hampshire 1920-86, Wessex 1986-2008.

09-10		10-11		11-12		12-13		13-14		14-15		15-16		16-17		17-18		18-19	
Sthsw	2	Sthsw	1	SthP	3	SthP	14	SthP	21	Sthsw	15	Sthsw	15	Sthsw	19	Sth1W	10	SthS	10
FAC	4Q	FAC	P	FAC	2P	FAC	4Q	FAC	1Q	FAC	1Q	FAC	P	FAC	P	FAC	1Q	FAC	P
FAT	2Q	FAT	2Q	FAT	1Q	FAT	1P	FAT	1Q	FAT	1Q	FAT	P	FAT	Pr	FAT	Pr	FAT	2Q

HONOURS / RECORDS

FA Comps: None

League: New Forest 1905-06, 10-11, 13-14, 19-20, 25-26, 26-27, 47-48, 60-61, 61-62. Hampshire West 1924-25. Hampshire Division Two 1930-31, 66-67, Division One 81-82, 84-85. Wessex Premier Division 2007-08. Southern Division South & West 2010-11.

County FA: Hampshire Junior Cup 1913-14, Intermediate Cup 1946-47, 66-67, 81-82, 82-83, Senior Cup 2009-10, 10-11.

Appearances: Michael Gosney - 427

Best FA Cup Second Round Proper 2011-12

FA Trophy Third Qualifying Round 2006-07, 08-09(r)

FA Vase Runners-up 2008-09

Ground Capacity: 2,375 **Seats:** 500 **Covered:** 500 **Clubhouse:** Yes **Shop:** Yes

Previous Grounds: South Testwood Park 1886-1933.

Record Attendance: 2,315 v Bradford Park Avenue, 12/11/2011.

DIRECTIONS

From the M27 Junction 2. From the east take the first exit at the roundabout or from the west take the third exit at the roundabout. Take the first left within 100 yards, signposted Totton Central.

At the T junction turn left and you will find the entrance to the ground approximately 1 mile on the left hand side, just before the Calmore Roundabout.

Nearest Railway Station Totton - 2.9km

Bus Route Cooks Lane - stop 300m away

BARNSTAPLE TOWN

Founded 1904

Nickname: Barum **Club Colours:** Red

Club Contact Details 01271 343 469

Mill Road, Barnstaple, North Devon EX31 1JQ

Previous Names: Pilton Yeo Vale

Previous Leagues: North Devon, Devon & Exeter, South Western. Western >2016.

09-10		10-11		11-12		12-13		13-14		14-15		15-16		16-17		17-18		18-19	
WestP	15	WestP	11	WestP	15	WestP	20	West1	3	West1	1	WestP	2	Sthsw	17	Sth1W	21	SthS	19
FAC	P	FAC	EP	FAC	P	FAC	EP	FAC	EP	FAC	EP	FAC	1Q	FAC	1Q	FAC	1Q	FAC	P
FAV	1P	FAV	2Q	FAV	3P	FAV	1P	FAV	2P	FAV	2Q	FAV	2P	FAT	1Q	FAT	P	FAT	P

HONOURS / RECORDS

FA Comps: None

League: North Devon 1904-05, 08-09. Exeter & District 1946-47. Western 1952-53, 79-80, Division One 1993-94, 2014-15.

County FA: Devon Pro Cup 1952-53, 62-63, 64-65, 67-68, 69-70, 71-72, 72-73, 74-75, 76-77, 77-78, 78-79, 79-80. 80-81. Devon St Lukes Cup 1987-88. Devon Senior Cup 1992-93.

Victory: 12-1 v Tavistock, F.A. Cup 3rd Qualifying Round 1954.

Defeat: 0-11 v Odd Down, Western, 25/04/2013.

Appearances: Ian Pope

Additional: Paid £4,000 to Hungerford Town for Joe Scott.
Received £6,000 from Bristol City for Ian Doyle.

Ground Capacity: 2,000 **Seats:** 250 **Covered:** 1,000 **Clubhouse:** Yes **Shop:** Yes

Previous Grounds: None

Record Attendance: 6,200 v Bournemouth & Boscombe Athletic, FA Cup 1st Round, 1951-52.

DIRECTIONS

Exit M5 at junction 27 and take the A361 to Barnstaple. As you approach the Town, turn left at the first roundabout and follow signs to Ilfracombe (A361). Turn right at the second roundabout, straight over ⊠Stones⊠ roundabout and over the bridge. Stay in the right-hand lane and turn right at the second set of lights, towards the Town Centre. After 600 yards turn right at the lights into Pottington Road. The ground is located 200 yards on the right.

Nearest Railway Station Barnstaple - 1km

BASINGSTOKE TOWN

Founded 1896

Nickname: Dragons **Club Colours:** All blue

Club Contact Details 01256 327 575 admin@basingstoketown.net

The Ark Cancer Charity Stadium, Western Way, Basingstoke RG22 6EZ

Previous Names: The club was formed by the merger of Aldworth United and Basingstoke Albion in 1896.

Previous Leagues: Hampshire 1900-40, 45-71, Southern 1971-87, Isthmian 1987-2004. Conference 2004-16.

09-10		10-11		11-12		12-13		13-14		14-15		15-16		16-17		17-18		18-19	
Conf S	15	Conf S	13	Conf S	5	Conf S	14	Conf S	14	Conf S	3	Nat S	22	SthP	12	SthP	10	SthPS	20
FAC	3Q	FAC	4Q	FAC	1P	FAC	3Q	FAC	2Q	FAC	1Pr	FAC	1P	FAC	2Q	FAC	1Qr	FAC	2Q
FAT	3Q	FAT	1P	FAT	2P	FAT	3Q	FAT	1Pr	FAT	1Pr	FAT	3Q	FAT	3Q	FAT	1Q	FAT	3Q

HONOURS / RECORDS

FA Comps: None

League: Hampshire North Division 1911-12, 19-20, Division One 1967-68, 69-70, 70-71.
Southern Southern Division 1984-85.

County FA: Hampshire Senior Cup 1970-71, 89-90, 95-96, 96-97, 2007-08, 13-14, 16-17.

Victory: 10-1 v Chichester City (H) - FA Cup 1st Qualifying Round 1976

Defeat: 0-8 v Aylesbury United - Southern League April 1979

Goalscorer: Paul Coombs - 159 (1991-99)

Appearances: Billy Coomb

Additional: Paid £4,750 to Gosport Borough for Steve Ingham

Ground Capacity: 2,402 **Seats:** 651 **Covered:** 2,000 **Clubhouse:** Yes **Shop:** Yes

Previous Grounds: Castle Field 1896-1947

Record Attendance: 5,085 v Wycombe Wanderers - FA Cup 1st Round replay 1997-98

DIRECTIONS

Leave M3 at junction 6 and turn left onto South Ringway which is the A30.
Straight over first roundabout. At second roundabout turn left into Winchester Road.
Proceed past ground on right to roundabout.
Take fifth exit into Western Way. Ground on right.

Nearest Railway Station Basingstoke - 2.6km

Bus Route Mansfield Road - 50m away

BIDEFORD

Founded 1947

Nickname: The Robins **Club Colours:** All red

Club Contact Details 01237 474 974 enquiries@bidefordafc.com

The Sports Ground, Kingsley Road, Bideford EX39 2NG

Previous Names: Bideford Town

Previous Leagues: Devon & Exeter 1947-49, Western 1949-72, 75-2010, Southern 1972-75

09-10		10-11		11-12		12-13		13-14		14-15		15-16		16-17		17-18		18-19	
WestP	1	Sthsw	10	Sthsw	1	SthP	20	SthP	8	SthP	15	SthP	23	Sthsw	10	Sth1W	8	SthS	9
FAC	P	FAC	P	FAC	2Q	FAC	2Q	FAC	2Q	FAC	2Q	FAC	2Q	FAC	1Q	FAC	3Q	FAC	Pr
FAV	2P	FAT	3Q	FAT	1Q	FAT	1Q	FAT	2Q	FAT	1Qr	FAT	3Q	FAT	P	FAT	P	FAT	P

HONOURS / RECORDS

FA Comps: None

League: Western 1963-64, 70-71, 71-72, 81-82, 82-83, 2001-02, 03-04, 04-05, 05-06, 09-10, Division Two 1951-52, Division Three 1949-50. Southern Division One South & West 2011-12.

County FA: Devon Pro Cup 1960-61, 61-62, 63-64, 65-66, 66-67, 68-69, 70-71. Devon Senior Cup 1979-80.
Devon St Lukes Bowl 1981-82, 83-84, 85-86, 95-96, 2009-10.

Victory: 16-1 v Soundwell, 1950-51

Defeat: 1-10 v Taunton Town, 1998-99

Goalscorer: Tommy Robinson - 259

Appearances: Derek May - 647

Ground Capacity: 4,000 **Seats:** 375 **Covered:** 1,000 **Clubhouse:** Yes **Shop:**

Previous Grounds: None

Record Attendance: 5,975 v Gloucester City - FA Cup 4th Qualifying Round 1949

DIRECTIONS

Exit M5 at junction 27 and follow A361 to Barnstaple. At Barnstaple turn left onto A39 to Bideford. After 9 miles and crossing bridge over river, turn left at roundabout into Bideford. The Ground is on the right hand side as you enter the Town centre.

Nearest Railway Station Barnstaple - 9 miles

Bus Route The Dairy - stop 100m away

BRISTOL MANOR FARM

Founded 1960

Nickname: The Farm **Club Colours:** Red & black

Club Contact Details 0117 968 3571
The Creek, Portway, Sea Mills, Bristol BS9 2HS

Previous Names: None
Previous Leagues: Bristol Suburban 1964-69. Somerset Senior 1969-77. Western 1977-2017.

09-10		10-11		11-12		12-13		13-14		14-15		15-16		16-17		17-18		18-19	
WestP	7	WestP	7	WestP	8	WestP	18	WestP	2	WestP	4	WestP	3	WestP	1	Sth1W	9	SthS	15
FAC	1Q	FAC	2Qr	FAC	EPr	FAC	EP	FAC	2Qr	FAC	P	FAC	1Q	FAC	EPr	FAC	P	FAC	3Qr
FAV	4P	FAV	2P	FAV	2Q	FAV	2Q	FAV	1P	FAV	2P	FAV	QF	FAV	5P	FAT	1Q	FAT	1Q

HONOURS / RECORDS
FA Comps: None
League: Western Division One 1982-83, Premier 2016-17.

County FA: Gloucestershire Challenge Trophy 1987-88, 2015-16. Gloucestershire Amateur Cup 1989-90.

Appearances: M. Baird
Victory: 10-0 v Devizes Town, Les Phillips Cup, 19/11/2016.
Defeat: 0-11 v Bristol City, Community Match, 09/07/2017

Ground Capacity: 1,700 **Seats:** 200 **Covered:** 350 **Clubhouse:** Yes **Shop:** No
Previous Grounds: None
Record Attendance: 1,417 v Bristol City, pre-season friendly, 09/07/2017.

DIRECTIONS
Leaving M5 at Junction 18, take A4 marked Bristol. U-turn on dual carriageway by Bristol and West Sports Ground and then ground is half-mile on left hand side.

Nearest Railway Station Sea Mills - 0.3km
Bus Route Riverleaze - stop 50m away

CINDERFORD TOWN

Founded 1922

Nickname: The Foresters **Club Colours:** Black and white

Club Contact Details 01594 824 080
The Causeway, Edge Hills Road, Cinderford, Gloucestershire GL14 2QH

Previous Names: None
Previous Leagues: Gloucestershire Northern Senior 1922-39, 60-62, Western 1946-59, Warwickshire Combination 1963-64, West Midlands 1965-69, Gloucestershire Co. 1970-73, 85-89, Midland Comb. 1974-84, Hellenic 1990-95

09-10		10-11		11-12		12-13		13-14		14-15		15-16		16-17		17-18		18-19	
Sthsw	16	Sthsw	12	Sthsw	10	Sthsw	10	Sthsw	15	Sthsw	9	Sthsw	1	SthP	24	Sth1W	13	SthS	5
FAC	P	FAC	3Q	FAC	2Q	FAC	1Qr	FAC	P	FAC	P	FAC	1Q	FAC	1Q	FAC	3Q	FAC	2Q
FAT	1Q	FAT	2Q	FAT	P	FAT	1Q	FAT	P	FAT	Pr	FAT	P	FAT	1Q	FAT	P	FAT	1Qr

HONOURS / RECORDS
FA Comps: None
League: Western Division Two 1956-57. Warwickshire Combination Western Division 1964-65. Hellenic Premier Division 1994-95. Southern Division One South & West 2015-16.
County FA: Gloucestershire Senior Amateur Cup North x6. Gloucestershire Junior Cup North 1980-81. Gloucestershire Senior Cup 2000-01.

Victory: 13-0 v Cam Mills - 1938-39
Defeat: 0-10 v Sutton Coldfield - 1978-79
Appearances: Russel Bowles - 528

Ground Capacity: 2,200 **Seats:** 250 **Covered:** 1,000 **Clubhouse:** Yes **Shop:** Yes
Previous Grounds: Mousel Lane, Royal Oak
Record Attendance: 4,850 v Minehead - Western League 1955-56

DIRECTIONS
Take A40 west out of Gloucester, then A48 for 8 miles. Turn right at Elton Garage onto A4151 (Forest of Dean). Continue through Littledean, climb steep hill, turn right at crossroads (football ground), then second left into Latimer Road. Or if coming from Severn Bridge take A48 Chepstow through Lydney, Newnham then left at Elton Garage – then as above.

Nearest Railway Station Gloucester - 15 miles
Bus Route Forest High School - stop 200m away

CIRENCESTER TOWN

Founded 1889

Nickname: Centurions **Club Colours:** Red & black

Club Contact Details 01285 654 543 enquiries@cirentownfc.com

The Corinium Stadium, Kingshill Lane, Cirencester GL7 1HS

Previous Names: None

Previous Leagues: Cheltenham 1889-1935. Gloucestershire Northern Senior 1935-68. Gloucestershire County (Founder Members) 1968-69. Hellenic 1969-96.

09-10		10-11		11-12		12-13		13-14		14-15		15-16		16-17		17-18		18-19	
Sthsw	5	SthP	13	SthP	22	Sthsw	11	Sthsw	1	SthP	8	SthP	15	SthP	22	Sth1W	7	SthS	2
FAC	3Q	FAC	1Qr	FAC	1Q	FAC	P	FAC	3Q	FAC	1Qr	FAC	2Q	FAC	2Q	FAC	P	FAC	3Q
FAT	1Q	FAT	1Pr	FAT	2Q	FAT	P	FAT	1Q	FAT	1Q	FAT	1Pr	FAT	1Q	FAT	1Qr	FAT	P

HONOURS / RECORDS

FA Comps: None

League: Cheltenham Division One 1927-28, 29-30, 48-49, 54-55, 55-56. Gloucestershire Northern Senior 1966-67, 67-68. Hellenic Division One 1973-74, Premier Division 95-96. Southern Division One South & West 2013-14.

County FA: Gloucestershire Senior Amateur Cup 1989-90. Gloucestershire Senior Challenge Cup 1995-96, 2015-16.

Misc: Paid £4,000 to Gloucester City for Lee Smith

Best FA Cup Fourth Qualifying Round 2001-02, 03-04

FA Trophy Third Round Proper 2002-03

FA Vase Third Round Proper 1975-76, 76-77

Ground Capacity: 2,564 **Seats:** 550 **Covered:** 1,250 **Clubhouse:** Yes **Shop:** Yes

Previous Grounds: Smithfield Stadium >2002.

Record Attendance: 2,600 v Fareham Town - 1969

DIRECTIONS

Go along the dual carriageway, the Cirencester North-South outer bypass which links the M4 at Junction 15, Swindon, with the M5 at Junction 11a, Gloucester. That road is identified on the road signs and road maps as A419(T) from Swindon or A417(T) from the M5. It is about 20 or so minutes road time from both the M4 and the M5 junctions, traffic permitting. Come off the bypass at the Burford Road Junction (named on the road signs). There is a big services located there - fuel, food and a Travelodge. At that junction, go up the slip road to a roundabout. At the roundabout, turn away from Cirencester Town Centre, (If you are coming from the south, go over the bypass and straight over another roundabout) and up to the traffic lights. Turn right at the traffic lights and follow the road to a T-junction. Turn right, the road takes you back over the bypass, and then turn first left into Kingshill Lane. The Ground is half a mile on the right, past Kingshill School and the Council Playing Fields.

Nearest Railway Station Kemble - 6 miles

Bus Route Kingshill School - stop 150m away

EVESHAM UNITED

Founded 1945

Nickname: The Robins **Club Colours:** Red and white

Club Contact Details 01386 442 303 eveshamunitedsecretary@hotmail.com

Jubilee Stadium, Cheltenham Road, Evesham WR11 2LZ

Previous Names: None

Previous Leagues: Worcester, Birmingham Combination, Midland Combination 1951-55, 65-92, West Midlands (Regional) 1955-62

09-10		10-11		11-12		12-13		13-14		14-15		15-16		16-17		17-18		18-19	
SthP	16	SthP	12	SthP	20	Sthsw	14	Sthsw	16	Sthsw	2	Sthsw	6	Sthsw	5	Sth1W	4	SthS	7
FAC	2Q	FAC	1Q	FAC	3Q	FAC	P	FAC	1Q	FAC	4Q	FAC	P	FAC	1Qr	FAC	Pr	FAC	P
FAT	2Qr	FAT	2Q	FAT	1Qr	FAT	P	FAT	1Q	FAT	1Qr	FAT	2Q	FAT	1Qr	FAT	P	FAT	EP

HONOURS / RECORDS

FA Comps: None

League: Midland Combination Premier Division 1991-92, Division One 1965-66, 67-68, 68-69. Southern Division One Midlands 2007-08.

County FA: Worcestershire Senior Urn 1976-77, 77-78, Senior Cup 2008-09, 17-18.

Victory: 11-3 v West Heath United

Defeat: 1-8 v Ilkeston Town

Goalscorer: Sid Brain

Appearances: Rob Candy

Additional: Paid £1,500 to Hayes for Colin Day 1992. Received £5,000 from Cheltenham Town for Simon Brain.

Ground Capacity: 3,000 **Seats:** Yes **Covered:** Yes **Clubhouse:** Yes **Shop:** Yes

Previous Grounds: The Crown Meadow > 1968, Common Reed 1968-2006. Ground shared with Worcester City 2006-12.

Record Attendance: 2,338 v West Bromwich Albion - Friendly 18/07/1992

DIRECTIONS

FROM M5 NORTH: Leave M5 motorway at Junction 7 and follow B4084 through Pershore onto Evesham. At traffic lights in Evesham with River Avon and Bridge on left, take right hand lane and turn right into Cheltenham Road signposted A46, M5 Southbound, Oxford and Cheltenham. Continue through two sets of traffic lights passing Tesco Garage and Ambulance Station on left before reaching roundabout. Ground situated on right at roundabout. **FROM M5 SOUTH:** Leave M5 motorway at Junction 9 signposted Tewkesbury and Evesham. Take 3rd exit signposted Ashchurch and Evesham. Follow A46 (Evesham) through Beckford before reaching roundabout on outskirts of Evesham. Ground situated on left at roundabout. **FROM M42:** Leave M42 motorway at Junction 3 (A435) signposted Redditch and Evesham. Continue on A435 (Evesham) through Studley then A46 until reaching roundabout on outskirts of Evesham. Take left hand exit onto Evesham by-pass (A46), signposted M5 South, Cheltenham and Oxford. Proceed on by-pass going over three r'abouts before reaching ground, which is situated on 4th r'about at end of by-pass.

Nearest Railway Station Evesham - 2.9km

Bus Route Lavender Walk - stop 400m away

FROME TOWN

Founded 1904

Nickname: The Robins **Club Colours:** Red

Club Contact Details 01373 464 087 gary@frometownfc.co.uk

Badgers Hill, Berkley Road, Frome BA11 2EH

Previous Names: None

Previous Leagues: Wiltshire Premier 1904, Somerset Senior 1906-19, Western 1919, 63-2009

09-10		10-11		11-12		12-13		13-14		14-15		15-16		16-17		17-18		18-19	
Sthsw	6	Sthsw	4	SthP	12	SthP	18	SthP	14	SthP	20	SthP	16	SthP	8	SthP	13	SthPS	21
FAC	P	FAC	2Q	FAC	2Qr	FAC	2Q	FAC	1Qr	FAC	3Qr	FAC	1Qr	FAC	1Q	FAC	2Q	FAC	1Qr
FAT	1Q	FAT	1Q	FAT	1Q	FAT	1Q	FAT	1Qr	FAT	1Q	FAT	3Qr	FAT	3Q	FAT	1Q	FAT	1Q

HONOURS / RECORDS

FA Comps: None

League: Somerset County 1906-07, 08-09, 10-11.
Western Division Two 1919-20, Division One 2001-02, Premier Division 1978-79.

County FA: Somerset Senior Cup 1932-33, 33-34, 50-51 Somerset Premier Cup 1966-67, 68-69 (shared), 82-83, 2008-09.

Victory: 7-2 v kings Langley (A), Southern Premier, 09/12/2017

Defeat: 0-7 v Gosport Borough (A), Southern Premier, 21/04/2018

Ground Capacity: 2,331 **Seats:** 250 **Covered:** Yes **Clubhouse:** Yes **Shop:** Yes

Previous Grounds: None

Record Attendance: 8,000 v Leyton Orient - FA Cup 1st Round 1958

DIRECTIONS

From Bath, take A36 and then A361. At third roundabout, follow A361 and at fourth roundabout take A3098. Take first right and ground is one mile on left hand side. From south follow A36 (Warminster) and take A3098 to Frome. At T Junction turn right and take second exit at roundabout. Ground is first right and follow road for one mile on left hand side.

Nearest Railway Station Frome - 0.9km

Bus Route Bus stops outside the ground

HIGHWORTH TOWN

Founded 1893

Nickname: Worthians **Club Colours:** Red and black

Club Contact Details 01793 766 263

Elms Recreation Ground, Highworth SN6 7DD

Previous Names: None.

Previous Leagues: Cirencester & District. Swindon & District. Wiltshire Combination. Hellenic >2018.

09-10		10-11		11-12		12-13		13-14		14-15		15-16		16-17		17-18		18-19	
Hel P	9	Hel P	4	Hel P	6	Hel P	16	Hel P	11	Hel P	7	Hel P	7	Hel P	6	Hel P	3	SthS	14
FAC	1Q	FAC	1Qr	FAC	EP	FAC	1Q	FAC	EP	FAC	P	FAC	P	FAC	2Q	FAC	P	FAC	EPr
FAV	2Q	FAV	1Q	FAV	2Pr	FAV	1Qr	FAV	1Q	FAV	SF	FAV	3P	FAV	2P	FAV	1P	FAT	EP

HONOURS / RECORDS

FA Comps: None

League: Cirencester & District Division Two 1931-32. Swindon & District Division Three 1933-34, 54-55, Two 1955-56, One 1956-57, Premier 57-58, 58-59, 60-61, 61-62, 62-63, 63-64, 65-66, 66-67, 67-68. Hellenic Premier 2004-05.

County FA: Wiltshire Senior Cup 1963-64, 72-73, 95-96, 97-98.

Goalscorer: Kevin Higgs

Appearances: Rod Haines

Ground Capacity: 1,500 **Seats:** 150 **Covered:** 250 **Clubhouse:** Yes **Shop:** No

Previous Grounds: Unknown

Record Attendance: 2,000 v QPR, opening of floodlights.

DIRECTIONS

From the A419 (Honda) roundabout travel in a North Easterly direction for 3.5 miles towards Highworth along the A361. Upon reaching Highworth, take the first exit at the Fox roundabout and immediately left into The Elms. After 100 yards, turn left into the Rec car park and the club is at the opposite end.

Nearest Railway Station Swindon - 7 miles

Bus Route Swindon Street stop - 90m away

LARKHALL ATHLETIC

Founded 1914

Nickname: Larks **Club Colours:** All royal blue

Club Contact Details 01225 334 952
Plain Ham, Charlcombe Lane, Larkhall, Bath BA1 8DJ

Previous Names: None
Previous Leagues: Somerset Senior. Western 1976-2014.

09-10		10-11		11-12		12-13		13-14		14-15		15-16		16-17		17-18		18-19	
WestP	14	WestP	1	WestP	3	WestP	5	WestP	1	Sthsw	5	Sthsw	11	Sthsw	13	Sth1W	15	SthS	13
FAC	P	FAC	P	FAC	1Q	FAC	1Qr	FAC	1Q	FAC	2Qr	FAC	2Qr	FAC	P	FAC	P	FAC	P
FAV	3P	FAV	1Q	FAV	5P	FAV	5P	FAV	5P	FAT	P	FAT	1Q	FAT	P	FAT	1Q	FAT	Pr

HONOURS / RECORDS
FA Comps: None
League: Western Division One 1988-89, 08-09, Premier Division 2010-11, 13-14.

County FA: Somerset Junior Cup 1962-63, Senior Cup 1975-76, 2003-04.

Victory: 8-0 v Oldland Abbotonians, 2007
Defeat: 1-6 v Exmouth Town, 2001
Goalscorer: Ben Highmore scored 52 goals during the 2008-09 season.
Appearances: Luke Scott - 600+ (as at July 2014)

Ground Capacity: 1,429 **Seats:** Yes **Covered:** 50 **Clubhouse:** Yes **Shop:** No
Previous Grounds: None
Record Attendance: 280 v Tunbridge Wells, FA Vase, Feb 2013

DIRECTIONS
Take the A4 east from Bath City Centre towards Chippenham/M4. After approximately 1 mile after Cleveland Bridge junction (keep straight ahead) fork left into St Saviours Road (turning is signposted 'Larkhall Local Shops'). In Larkhall Square take first left exit (Salisbury Road) and turn right at t-junction. Follow the road round to the left and up the hill. You are now on Charlcombe Lane. The ground is on the right, on a parallel lane, as Charlcombe Lane narrows. Continue for approximately 100 yards, turn around in Woolley Lane on the right and go back down the hill, this time keeping to the top lane on the left hand side. Plain Ham is on the left just past the junction with Charlcombe Lane.

Nearest Railway Station Bath Spa - 2.8km
Bus Route Charlcombe Lane - stop 200m away

MANGOTSFIELD UNITED

Founded 1950

Nickname: The Field **Club Colours:** Claret and sky blue

Club Contact Details 0117 956 0119 davidj693@hotmail.co.uk
Cossham Street, Mangotsfield, Bristol BS16 9EN

Previous Names: None
Previous Leagues: Bristol & District 1950-67. Avon Premier Combination 1967-72. Western 1972-2000.

09-10		10-11		11-12		12-13		13-14		14-15		15-16		16-17		17-18		18-19	
Sthsw	9	Sthsw	3	Sthsw	14	Sthsw	13	Sthsw	11	Sthsw	10	Sthsw	14	Sthsw	8	Sth1W	16	SthS	16
FAC	4Q	FAC	2Q	FAC	P	FAC	1Q	FAC	2Q	FAC	1Q	FAC	1Q	FAC	P	FAC	P	FAC	P
FAT	Pr	FAT	Pr	FAT	2Qr	FAT	Pr	FAT	2Q	FAT	2Q	FAT	2Q	FAT	P	FAT	P	FAT	1Qr

HONOURS / RECORDS
FA Comps: None
League: Bristol & District Div.7 1951-52, Div.6 52-53, Div.4 53-54, Div.3 54-55, Div.2 55-56, Premier Comb Div.1 68-69. Somerset Senior Div.3 74-75, Div.2 75-76, 97-98, Prem 2004-05. Western 1990-91. Southern Division One West 2004-05.
County FA: Gloucestershire Senior Cup 1968-69, 75-76, 2002-03, 12-13. Gloucestershire F.A. Trophy x6. Somerset Premier Cup 1987-88.

Victory: 17-0 v Hanham Sports (H) - 1953 Bristol & District League
Defeat: 3-13 v Bristol City United - Bristol & District League Division One
Goalscorer: John Hill. **Appearances:** John Hill - 600+
Misc: In the last 10 matches of the 2003/04 season, the club went 738 minutes (just over 8 games) without scoring and then finished the campaign with 13 goals in the last two, which included a 9-0 away win.

Ground Capacity: 3,038 **Seats:** 300 **Covered:** 800 **Clubhouse:** Yes **Shop:** Yes
Previous Grounds: None
Record Attendance: 1,253 v Bath City - F.A. Cup 1974

DIRECTIONS
Exit M4 at junction 19 and join the M32 to Bristol. Exit M32 at junction 1 and take first exit for A4174. At traffic lights continue forward and at next lights bear right to join a roundabout. Take first exit at the roundabout, through lights and continue until next lights. Turn left and go up Cleeve Hill. At traffic lights go straight ahead and over double mini roundabout. Continue forward for 1 mile until the next Pedestrian traffic lights, then turn left into Cossham Street. The ground is 500 yards on the right hand side.

Nearest Railway Station Bristol Parkway - 5 miles. Temple Meads - 7 miles.
Bus Route Cossham Street - stop 50m away

MELKSHAM TOWN

Founded 1876

Nickname: Town **Club Colours:** Yellow and black

Club Contact Details 01225 302 977
Oakfield Stadium, Eastern Way, Melksham SN12 7GU

Previous Names: Melksham FC 1876-1951.
Previous Leagues: Wiltshire (Founder Members) 1894-1974. Western 1974-2018.

09-10		10-11		11-12		12-13		13-14		14-15		15-16		16-17		17-18		18-19	
WestP	19	WestP	8	West1	2	WestP	13	WestP	7	WestP	1	WestP	5	WestP	3	WestP	2	SthS	12
FAC	EP	FAC	EP	FAC	P	FAC	1Q	FAC	EPr	FAC	EPr	FAC	EPr	FAC	EP	FAC	EP	FAC	1Q
FAV	1P	FAV	2P	FAV	2P	FAV	2Q	FAV	2Q	FAV	4P	FAV	2P	FAV	4Pr	FAV	QF	FAT	2Q

HONOURS / RECORDS
FA Comps: None
League: Wiltshire 1903-04, Premier 1993-94.
Western Division One 1979-80, 96-97, Premier Division 2014-15.
County FA: Wiltshire Senior Cup 1904-05, 69-70, 77-78, 2002-03, 07-08, 12-13, 13-14, 15-16.

Best FA Cup Third Qualifying Round 1954-55, 57-58
FA Trophy Second Qualifying Round 1982-83, 84085, 85-86, 87-87, 87-88, 2018-19
FA Vase Quarter Finals 2017-18
Goalscorer: Gareth Lewis scored 72 goals during the 1968-69 season

Ground Capacity: 3,000 **Seats:** Yes **Covered:** Yes **Clubhouse:** Yes **Shop:**
Previous Grounds: Challymead Common 1876-83. Old Bear Field 1883-1920. Conigre 1920-2017.
Record Attendance: 2,821 v Trowbridge Town, FA Cup 1957-58.

DIRECTIONS
If you are travelling on the A3102 take the first exit at the roundabout situated after new road turning on your right. Continue on this road, going across the next 2 roundabouts, the Stadium and complex will be on your left, there is a Drive way up to the ground opposite the Right hand turning for Hawthorn Road. If you are travelling on the on the A365 take the 3rd exit at the Bowerhill roundabout, which will take you towards the town centre. At the first roundabout you come to take the 3rd exit onto snowberry lane. Follow this road to the next round about and take the 3rd Exit onto Eastern Way. After about 300 yards there is right hand turning into the new complex after you pass Hawthorn Road turning.

Nearest Railway Station Melksham - 2.7km
Bus Route New Road - stop 300m away

MONEYFIELDS

Founded 1987

Nickname: Moneys **Club Colours:** Yellow and navy

Club Contact Details 02392 665 260 kat.close@ntlworld.com
Moneyfields Sports Ground, Moneyfield Ave, Copnor, Portsmouth PO3 6LA

Previous Names: Portsmouth Civil Service 1987-94.
Previous Leagues: Portsmouth 1987-91. Hampshire 1991-98. Wessex 1998-2017.

09-10		10-11		11-12		12-13		13-14		14-15		15-16		16-17		17-18		18-19	
WexP	12	WexP	7	WexP	4	WexP	4	WexP	9	WexP	4	WexP	8	WexP	2	Sth1E	10	SthS	4
FAC	P	FAC	P	FAC	1Qr	FAC	P	FAC	1Q	FAC	EP	FAC	P	FAC	1Q	FAC	1Q	FAC	3Q
FAV	2P	FAV	3P	FAV	2Q	FAV	2P	FAV	3P	FAV	2Q	FAV	4P	FAV	2P	FAT	2Qr	FAT	P

HONOURS / RECORDS
FA Comps: None
League: Portsmouth Premier 1990-91.
Hampshire Division Three 1991-92, Division Two 1992-93, Division One 1996-97.
County FA: Hampshire Intermediate 1991-92, 92-93.

Victory: 9-0v Blackfield & Langley 01-02.
Goalscorer: Lee Mould - 86
Appearances: Matt Lafferty - 229

Ground Capacity: 1,500 **Seats:** 150 **Covered:** 150 **Clubhouse:** Yes **Shop:** Yes
Previous Grounds: Copnor Road 1987-94.
Record Attendance: 250 v Fareham, Wessex Division One 2005-06

DIRECTIONS
Leave the A27 from both West and East at the Southsea turn off (A2030) Head down the Eastern Road and turn right into Tangiers Road at the fourth set of traffic lights. Continue along this road until you pass the school and shops on your left and take the next right into Folkestone Road. This becomes Martins Road and the ground is directly in front of you at the end of the road.

Nearest Railway Station Hilsea - 1.6km
Bus Route Chichester Road - stop 400m away

PAULTON ROVERS

Founded 1881

Nickname: The Robins or Rovers **Club Colours:** Claret and white

Club Contact Details 01761 412 907

Athletic Ground, Winterfield Road, Paulton, Bristol BS39 7RF

Previous Names: None

Previous Leagues: Wiltshire Premier, Somserset Senior, Western

09-10		10-11		11-12		12-13		13-14		14-15		15-16		16-17		17-18		18-19	
Sthsw	7	Sthsw	11	Sthsw	7	Sthsw	5	Sthsw	4	SthP	10	SthP	24	Sthsw	15	Sth1W	19	SthS	17
FAC	1P	FAC	2Q	FAC	P	FAC	Pr	FAC	P	FAC	2Qr	FAC	2Q	FAC	1Q	FAC	4Q	FAC	1Qr
FAT	P	FAT	2Q	FAT	2Q	FAT	Pr	FAT	1Q	FAT	2Q	FAT	1Q	FAT	P	FAT	2Q	FAT	P

HONOURS / RECORDS

FA Comps: None

League: None

County FA: Somerset Junior Cup 1898-99, Senior Cup x12 - Firstly in 1900-01 and most recently in 1974-75, Premier Cup 2012-13.

Goalscorer: Graham Colbourne

Appearances: Steve Tovey

Best FA Cup First Round Proper 2009-10

FA Trophy First Round Proper 2004-05

FA Vase Fifth Round Proper 1989-90

Ground Capacity: 2,500 **Seats:** 253 **Covered:** 2,500 **Clubhouse:** Yes **Shop:** Yes

Previous Grounds: Chapel Field, Cricket Ground, Recreation Ground

Record Attendance: 2,000 v Crewe Alexandra - FA Cup 1906-07

DIRECTIONS

From the A39 at Farrington Gurney follow the A362 (signposted Radstock) for 2 miles. Continue straight over the first roundabout (by Tesco) and at the second roundabout turn left onto the B3355 (signposted Paulton). The ground is on the right hand side just past the La Campagna (Italian Restaurant).

Nearest Railway Station Bath Spa - 13 miles

Bus Route Alexandra Park - stop 150m away

SHOLING

Founded 1884

Nickname: The Boatmen **Club Colours:** Red & white stripes

Club Contact Details 07496 804 555 secretary@sholingfc.com

Portsmouth Road, Sholing, SO19 9PW

Previous Names: Woolston Works, Thornycrofts (Woolston) 1918-52, Vospers 1960-2003, Vosper Thorneycroft FC/VTFC 2003-10

Previous Leagues: Hampshire 1991-2004, Wessex 2004-09, 2013-14, 15-19. Southern 2009-13, 2014-15.

09-10		10-11		11-12		12-13		13-14		14-15		15-16		16-17		17-18		18-19	
Sthsw	4	Sthsw	2	Sthsw	4	Sthsw	7	WexP	1	Sthsw	17	WexP	2	WexP	3	WexP	3	WexP	1
FAC	2Q	FAC	2Qr	FAC	2Q	FAC	3Q	FAC	2Q	FAC	1Q	FAC	P	FAC	1Q	FAC	EP	FAC	2Qr
FAV	P	FAT	P	FAT	1Q	FAT	3Q	FAV	F	FAT	3Q	FAV	2P	FAV	1P	FAV	3P	FAT	3Q

HONOURS / RECORDS

FA Comps: FA Vase 2013-14.

League: Hampshire Premier Division 2000-01, 03-04.
Wessex Premier 2013-14, 18-19.

County FA: Southampton Senior Cup 2001-02, 03-04, 05-06, 06-07, 07-08, 09-10, 13-14, 16-17

Goalscorer: George Diaper - 100+

FA Cup Third Qualifying Round 2012-13

FA Trophy Third Qualifying Round 2012-13, 14-15

Ground Capacity: 1,400 **Seats:** 150 **Covered:** 250 **Clubhouse:** Yes **Shop:**

Previous Grounds: Not known

Record Attendance: 150

DIRECTIONS

Using the Motorway coming from the West, leave the M27 at Junction 8 (marked Soton East, Hamble A3024). Get in right hand land and turn right at the roundabout (left hand lane & turn left if coming from the East) Get into the left hand lane for the B3397 to Hamble. At the roundabout, take the 2nd exit towards Hamble, go past Tescos (get in right hand land, left hand lane is to Tesco's only). Go straight across roundabout and then straight across the following one. Then turn right at the sign marked for Woolston A3025. This takes you onto Portsmouth Road, go past the Plough Pub on your left and after quarter of a mile, turn right into Sholing FC (opposite layby).

Nearest Railway Station Netley - 1.9km

Bus Route Bus stop outside the ground.

SLIMBRIDGE

Founded 1899

Nickname: The Swans **Club Colours:** All blue

Club Contact Details 01453 899 982 info@slimbridgeafc.co.uk

Thornhill Park, Cambridge, Glos GL2 7AF

Previous Names: None

Previous Leagues: Stroud & District. Gloucester Northern. Gloucestershire County >2009. Hellenic 2009-2013. Western 2013-15.

09-10		10-11		11-12		12-13		13-14		14-15		15-16		16-17		17-18		18-19	
Hel1W	1	Hel P	5	Hel P	5	Hel P	6	WestP	16	WestP	3	Sthsw	18	Sthsw	20	Sth1W	20	SthS	18
				FAC	P	FAC	EP	FAC	EPr	FAC	P	FAC	2Q	FAC	2Q	FAC	P	FAC	Pr
		FAV	1Q	FAV	1P	FAV	1Q	FAV	2Q	FAV	2Pr	FAT	P	FAT	P	FAT	P	FAT	P

HONOURS / RECORDS

FA Comps: None

League: Stroud & District Division Three 1951-52, Division Two 1952-53, Division one 1953-54, 98-99, Division Four 1989-90. Hellenic Division 1 West 2003-04, 09-10, Premier 06-07. Gloucester Northern 2007-08. Gloucestershire County 2008-09.

County FA: Gloucester Challenge Trophy 2003-04, 05-06, 06-07. Gloucester Northern Senior Cup 2000-01.

Victory: 12-1 v Cheltenham Civil Service, Reg Davis Cup, 18/08/2007

Defeat: 0-9 v Cinderford Town (A), 19/04/2018 and v Taunton Town (A), 24/04/2018

Goalscorer: Marvyn Roberts - 104 (in 221 appearances)

Appearances: Fred Ward - 505

Ground Capacity: 1,500 **Seats:** Yes **Covered:** Yes **Clubhouse:** Yes **Shop:** Yes

Previous Grounds: Various venues around Slimbridge before moving to Wisloe Road (now Thornhill Park) in 1951.

Record Attendance: 525 v Shortwood United, Hellenic Premier, 24/08/2003.

DIRECTIONS

From North - Exit M5 at junction 13 turning right onto the A419. At roundabout turn left onto A38 towards Bristol/Dursely. Continue on the A38 through Cambridge and at next roundabout turn left and Wisloe Road is the first turning on the left hand side.

From South - Exit M5 at juntion 14 turning left and then turn right at the traffic lights onto the A38 towards Gloucester. Pass therough the villages of Stone, Woodford and Newport, then at the next roundabout turn right for Cam/Dursley. Wisloe Road is the first turning on the left hand side.

Nearest Railway Station Cam & Dursley - 1 mile

Bus Route Wisloe Road - stop 300m away

THATCHAM TOWN

Founded 1895

Nickname: Kingfishers **Club Colours:** Blue and white

Club Contact Details 01635 862 016

Waterside Park, Crookham Hill, Thatcham, Berks RG19 4PA

Previous Names: Thatcham 1895-1974.

Previous Leagues: Reading Temperance 1896-1953. Hellenic (founder member) 1953-82, Athenian 1982-84, London Spartan 1984-86, Wessex 1986-2006. Southern 2006-14.

09-10		10-11		11-12		12-13		13-14		14-15		15-16		16-17		17-18		18-19	
Sthsw	12	Sthsw	5	Sthsw	8	SthC	17	Sthsw	19	Hel P	12	Hel P	2	Hel P	4	Hel P	1	SthS	11
FAC	P	FAC	1Q	FAC	P	FAC	2Q	FAC	P	FAC	EPr	FAC	1Q	FAC	EP	FAC	2Q	FAC	Pr
FAT	2Q	FAT	P	FAT	2Qr	FAT	P	FAT	P	FAV	1P	FAV	2Q	FAV	3P	FAV	F	FAT	1Q

HONOURS / RECORDS

FA Comps: FA Vase 2017-18.

League: Reading Temperance Division Two 1905-06. Hellenic Division One 1958-59, 64-65, 72-73, Premier 1974-75, 2017-18. Wessex 1995-96.

County FA: Berks & Bucks Junior Cup 1935-36, Senior Cup 74-75, Senior Trophy 2004-05. Basingstoke Senior Cup 2008-09, 10-11, 11-12.

Best FA Cup Fourth Qualifying Round 1996-97

FA Trophy Second Qualifying Round 2008-09, 09-10, 11-12(r)

Ground Capacity: 2,500 **Seats:** 300 **Covered:** 300 **Clubhouse:** Yes **Shop:** Yes

Previous Grounds: Station Road 1946-52, Lancaster Close 1952-92

Record Attendance: 1,400 v Aldershot - FA Vase

DIRECTIONS

From North, follow A34/A339 towards Newbury. Then follow A4 signposted Thatcham, continue on A4 through Thatcham until you come to a roundabout with a signpost to the Railway Station off to the right (Pipers Way). Continue to the station and go over the level crossing, ground is approximately 250m on left.
From West leave the M4 at junction 13 then follow the directions above. From the East, leave the M4 at junction 12 and follow A4 towards Newbury/Thatcham then follow directions above to the Railway station.

Nearest Railway Station Thatcham - 1.6km

Bus Route Vincent Road stop - 287m away

WILLAND ROVERS

Founded 1946

Nickname: Rovers **Club Colours:** White and blue

Club Contact Details 01884 33885
Silver Street, Willand, Collumpton, Devon EX15 2RG

Previous Names: None.
Previous Leagues: Devon & Exeter >1992. Devon County (Founder Members) 1992-2001. Western 2001-19.

09-10		10-11		11-12		12-13		13-14		14-15		15-16		16-17		17-18		18-19	
WestP	2	WestP	4	WestP	5	WestP	11	WestP	8	WestP	6	WestP	6	WestP	6	WestP	3	WestP	1
FAC	2Q	FAC	1Q	FAC	EP	FAC	EP	FAC	EP	FAC	4Q	FAC	EP	FAC	EPr	FAC	1Q	FAC	P
FAV	5Pr	FAV	4P	FAV	4P	FAV	2P	FAV	1P	FAV	1Q	FAV	2Q	FAV	1P	FAV	2P	FAV	QF

HONOURS / RECORDS
FA Comps: None
League: Devon County 1998-99, 2000-01, Western Division One 2004-05, Premier 18-19.

County FA: None

Goalscorer: Paul Foreman
FA Cup Fourth Qualifying Round 2014-15
FA Vase Quarter finals 2018-19

Ground Capacity: 1,000 **Seats:** 75 **Covered:** 150 **Clubhouse:** Yes **Shop:**
Previous Grounds: Not known
Record Attendance: 650 v Newton Abbot 1992-3

DIRECTIONS
Leave M5 Junction 27 and take first left at roundabout. Follow signs to Willand. After passing Halfway House pub on right, go straight over mini-roundabout (signposted to Cullompton) ground is 400 metres on left hand side.

Nearest Railway Station Tiverton Parkway - 3.2km
Bus Route Garage (Silver St) - stop 50m away

WINCHESTER CITY

Founded 1884

Nickname: The Capitals **Club Colours:** Red & black

Club Contact Details 07768 828 918 secretary.wcfc@outlook.com
Hillier Way, Winchester SO23 7SR

Previous Names: None
Previous Leagues: Hampshire 1898-71, 73-03. Southern 1971-73, 2006-09, 2012-13. Wessex 2003-06. 2009-12, 13-15.

09-10		10-11		11-12		12-13		13-14		14-15		15-16		16-17		17-18		18-19	
WexP	11	WexP	3	WexP	1	SthC	22	WexP	5	WexP	2	Sthsw	5	Sthsw	14	Sth1W	11	SthS	6
FAC	EP	FAC	EP	FAC	P	FAC	1Q	FAC	1Q	FAC	3Q	FAC	2Qr	FAC	3Q	FAC	1Q	FAC	4Q
FAV	1P	FAV	2Q	FAV	2P	FAT	P	FAV	1P	FAV	1P	FAT	1Q	FAT	3Q	FAT	P	FAT	EPr

HONOURS / RECORDS
FA Comps: FA Vase 2004.
League: Hampshire Division Two 1973-74, 91-92, Division One 2000-01, Premier Division 2002-03.
Wessex Division One 2003-04, 05-06, Premier Division 2011-12.
County FA: Hants Senior Cup 1930-31, 2004-05.

Goalscorer: Andy Forbes.
Appearances: Ian Mancey.

Ground Capacity: 3,000 **Seats:** 180 **Covered:** 275 **Clubhouse:** Yes **Shop:** Yes
Previous Grounds: None
Record Attendance: 1,818 v Bideford, FA Vase Semi-final.

DIRECTIONS
From Junction 9 on the M3 take the A33/A34 for one mile then follow A33 for a further mile.
Take the first left into Kings Worthy and follow the road for about three miles.
When you enter the 30mph zone take the second left, first right, then left into Hillier Way, Ground is on the right.

Nearest Railway Station Winchester - 0.9km
Bus Route Simonds Court - stop 250m away

PREMIER DIVISION INS: Ascot United (Tr - HelP), Egham Town (R - IsthSC), Frimley Green (P - CC1), Molesey (R - IsthSC), Sheerwater (P - CC1).

ABBEY RANGERS

Nickname: **Club Colours:** Black & white

Founded 1976

Club Contact Details 01932 422 962 graham.keable@ntlworld.com

Ground: Addlestone Moor, Addlestone, KT15 2QH

Capacity: **Seats:** Yes **Covered:** Yes

Previous Names: None

Previous Leagues: Surrey Elite 2011-2015

HONOURS: FA Comps: None

League: Surrey & Hants Border League 2004-05.
Surrey Intermediate League (Western) Division One 2008-09.

10 YEAR RECORD

09-10	10-11	11-12	12-13	13-14	14-15	15-16	16-17	17-18	18-19
SuIP	SuIP	SuEl 10	SuEl 7	SuEl 3	SuEl 4	CC1 3	CCP 10	CCP 17	CCP 3
							FAC EP	FAC EP	FAC EP
						FAV 2P	FAV 3P	FAV 2Q	FAV 2P

From Junction 11 M25.
Exit A317 St. Peter's Way towards Chertsey, Addlestone and Weybridge.
At roundabout take 2nd exit towards Addlestonemoor.

Nearest Railway Station Addlestone
Bus Route No.461

ASCOT UNITED

Nickname: Yellaman **Club Colours:** Yellow and blue

Founded 1965

Club Contact Details 01344 291 107 (Ground)

Ground: Ascot Racecourse, Car Park 10, Winkfield Rd, Ascot SL5 7RA

Capacity: 1,150 **Seats:** **Covered:** **Shop:** Yes

Previous Names: None.

Previous Leagues: Reading Senior. Hellenic >2019.

HONOURS: FA Comps: None

League: Reading Senior Division 2006-07.

10 YEAR RECORD

09-10	10-11	11-12	12-13	13-14	14-15	15-16	16-17	17-18	18-19
Hel P 15	Hel P 12	Hel P 14	Hel P 7	Hel P 3	Hel P 3	Hel P 4	Hel P 15	Hel P 14	Hel P 7
		FAC EP	FAC P	FAC EP	FAC P	FAC EP	FAC 1Qr	FAC P	FAC P
	FAV 2Q	FAV 2Q	FAV QFr	FAV 2P	FAV QF	FAV 3Pr	FAV 2P	FAV 1Q	FAV 1Q

Directions to Racecourse – New postcode SL5 7LJ (If your sat nav does not have this postcode try SL5 7LN for A330 Winkfield Road) From Bracknell take A329 to Ascot. From Heatherwood Hospital roundabout take Ascot High Street. At first mini-roundabout go straight. At mini roundabout at end of High Street turn left along A330 Winkfield Road. Go under bridge and take first right signposted Car Park 7&8. Continue forwards past golf club, through gates and follow track to the end. Please arrive from Ascot High Street as some sat navs will direct you by a back road which ends in a locked gate and you will have to retrace your route.

Nearest Railway Station Ascot - 1.3km
Bus Route Hilltop Close (Cheapside Rd) stop - 934m

BADSHOT LEA

Nickname: Baggies **Club Colours:** Claret & sky blue

Founded 1907

Club Contact Details

Ground: Westfield Lane, Wrecclesham, Farnham, Surrey GU10 4PF

Capacity: 1,200 **Seats:** Yes **Covered:** Yes

Previous Names: None

Previous Leagues: Surrey Intermediate. Hellenic > 2008.

HONOURS: FA Comps: None

League: Surrey Intermediate Division One 1936-37, 37-38, 85-86, Division Two 92-93

10 YEAR RECORD

09-10	10-11	11-12	12-13	13-14	14-15	15-16	16-17	17-18	18-19
CCP 10	CCP 6	CCP 17	CCP 7	CCP 15	CCP 8	CCP 17	CCP 21	CC1 3	CCP 9
FAC 2Q	FAC EP	FAC P	FAC 3Q	FAC P	FAC P	FAC P	FAC P	FAC P	FAC EP
FAV 3P	FAV 1Q	FAV 2Q	FAV 1Q	FAV 1Q	FAV 1Q	FAV 2Q	FAV 2Q	FAV 2Q	FAV 2P

FROM M3: Exit via junction 5, follow signs for the A287 (4th exit off the roundabout). Take 2nd exit at the next roundabout and then the 2nd exit again onto Farnham Road/A287. After almost 4.5 miles right onto Dora's Green Lane. After just over 1.5 miles take left onto Crondall Lane, then right on to Dippenhall Road after 300yards or so. Then take the next left onto Clarks Hill, followed by the next left onto Runwick Lane. At next major junction turn left onto Alton Road/A31. At the next roundabout take the 3rd exit onto Wrecclesham Road/A325. At the next roundabout again take the 3rd exit continuing on the A325. Turn right onto Riverdale followed by the next left towards Westfield Lane. At the juntio turn right onto Westfield Lane.

Nearest Railway Station Aldershot
Bus Route Stagecoach 18 from Aldershot bus station - about 28min journey via 31 stops to Westfield Lane.

BALHAM

Founded 2011

Nickname:

Club Colours: Red and white

Club Contact Details 020 8942 8062

Ground: Colliers Wood Utd, Wibbandune Stadium, Lincoln Green, Wimbledon SW20 0AA

Capacity: 2000 **Seats:** 120 **Covered:** 420

Previous Names: None

Previous Leagues: Surrey South Eastern Combination 2011-15. Surrey Elite Intermediate 2015-2016

HONOURS: FA Comps: None

League: Surrey South Eastern Combination Intermediate Division One 2013-14.

10 YEAR RECORD

09-10	10-11	11-12	12-13	13-14	14-15	15-16	16-17	17-18	18-19
		SSECJ1 4	SSECI2 3	SSECI1 1	SuEI 3	SuEI 2	CC1 3	CCP 5	CCP 18
									FAC P
								FAV 1P	FAV 1Q

On A3 Southbound 1 mile from Robin Hood Gate.

Nearest Railway Station Raynes Park

Bus Route London Transport 265

BANSTEAD ATHLETIC

Founded 1944

Nickname: The A's

Club Colours: Amber & black

Club Contact Details 01737 350 982 terrymolloy@leyfield.eclipse.co.uk

Ground: Merland Rise, Tadworth, Surrey KT20 5JG

Capacity: 4000 **Seats:** 250 **Covered:** 800 **Shop:** Yes

Previous Names: Banstead Juniors 1944-46.

Previous Leagues: Surrey Senior 1949-65. Spartan 1965-75. London Spartan 1975-79. Athenian 1979-85. Isthmian 1985-2006.

HONOURS: FA Comps: None

League: Surrey Senior League 1950-51, 51-52, 52-53, 53-54, 56-57, 64-65.
Combined Counties League Division One 2016-17.

10 YEAR RECORD

09-10	10-11	11-12	12-13	13-14	14-15	15-16	16-17	17-18	18-19
CCP 20	CCP 17	CCP 22	CC1 17	CC1 12	CC1 6	CC1 6	CC1 1	CCP 19	CCP 8
FAC EPr	FAC P	FAC 1Q	FAC EP			FAC EPr	FAC Pr	FAC 1Q	FAC EP
FAV 2Q	FAV 2Q	FAV 2Q	FAV 2Q	FAV 2Q	FAV 1P	FAV 2Q	FAV 1P	FAV 1Q	FAV 2P

From M25 Junction 8 Follow Signs To Banstead Sports Centre.

Nearest Railway Station Tattenham Corner

Bus Route Metro 420 & 460

CAMBERLEY TOWN

Founded 1895

Nickname: The Krooners

Club Colours: Red and white stripes

Club Contact Details 01276 65 392

Ground: Krooner Park, Wilton Road, Camberley, Surrey GU15 2QW

Capacity: 1,976 **Seats:** 196 **Covered:** 300 **Shop:** Yes

Previous Names: St Michael's FC (St Michael's Camberley) 1895-1901. Camberley & Yorktown 1901-46. Camberley 1946-67.

Previous Leagues: East & West Surrey (West Surrey) 1898-99, 1910-22. Aldershot Comb 1902-03. Ascot & Dist 1903-10. Surrey Senior 1922-73. Spartan 1973-75. Athenian 1975-77, 82-84. Isthmian 1977-82, 84-2006.

HONOURS: FA Comps: None

League: Ascot & Dist. 1904-05, 07-08, 08-09, 09-10. Aldershot Sen. Civilian 1912-13. West Surrey 1913-14. Surrey Senior 1930-31, 31-32, 32-33.

10 YEAR RECORD

09-10	10-11	11-12	12-13	13-14	14-15	15-16	16-17	17-18	18-19
CCP 3	CCP 4	CCP 6	CCP 16	CCP 2	CCP 2	CCP 3	CCP 6	CCP 7	CCP 16
FAC EP	FAC P	FAC P	FAC P	FAC 1Qr	FAC EP	FAC EP	FAC 1Q	FAC P	FAC EP
FAV 1P	FAV 2P	FAV 1P	FAV 2Q	FAV 2Q	FAV 1P	FAT QF	FAV 2P	FAV 1P	FAV 2Q

Exit M3 Motorway at Junction 4. At the end of the slip road take the right hand land signposted A331, immediately take the left hand lane signposted Frimley and Hospital (Red H Symbol) and this will lead you up onto the A325. Continue to the roundabout and turn left onto the B3411 (Frimley Road) Continue past Focus DIY store on Left and stay on B3411 for approx 1.5 miles. At the next Mini roundabout turn left into Wilton Road, proceed through industrial estate (past the Peugeot garage) and the entrance to the ground is right at the end.

Nearest Railway Station Camberley

Bus Route Stagecoach 1

CB HOUNSLOW UNITED

Nickname: None **Club Colours:** Green and black

Founded 1989

Club Contact Details

Ground: Green Lane, Hounslow TW4 6DH

Capacity: 1200 **Seats:** 100 **Covered:** Yes

Previous Names: CB United 1989-94. (Named after Cater Bank, a company owned by the father of the club chairman.)

Previous Leagues: Hounslow & District 1989-94. Middlesex County 1994-2006.

HONOURS: FA Comps: None

League: Combined Counties League Division One 2015-16.

10 YEAR RECORD

09-10		10-11		11-12		12-13		13-14		14-15		15-16		16-17		17-18		18-19	
CC1	15	CC1	14	CC1	15	CC1	8	CC1	14	CC1	7	CC1	1	CCP	20	CCP	9	CCP	17
														FAC	1Q	FAC	P	FAC	P
										FAV	1Q	FAV	2Q	FAV	2Q	FAV	2Q	FAV	1P

Hatton Road runs alongside the A30 at Heathrow.
Ground is opposite the Duke of Wellington Public House.

Nearest Railway Station Hatton Cross (Underground) Piccadilly Line

Bus Route London Transport 203, H25, H26

COBHAM

Nickname: Hammers **Club Colours:** Red & black

Founded 1892

Club Contact Details 07813 643 336

Ground: Leg O'Mutton Field, Anvil Lane, Cobham KT11 1AA

Capacity: 2000 **Seats:** 112 **Covered:** 200

Previous Names: None

Previous Leagues: Surrey Senior 1937-78.

HONOURS: FA Comps: None

League: Kingston & District Division One 1928-29, 29-30.

10 YEAR RECORD

09-10		10-11		11-12		12-13		13-14		14-15		15-16		16-17		17-18		18-19	
CC1	7	CC1	8	CC1	11	CC1	11	CC1	16	CC1	11	CC1	7	CC1	11	CC1	2	CCP	14
FAC	P	FAC	1Q	FAC	EPr	FAC	EPr											FAC	P
FAV	1Q	FAV	1Q	FAV	1Q	FAV	2Q	FAV	2Q	FAV	2Q	FAV	2Q	FAV	2Q	FAV	1P	FAV	1P

From Cobham High Street, turn right into Downside Bridge Road and turn right into Leg of Mutton Field.

Nearest Railway Station Cobham

Bus Route Green Line 715

COLLIERS WOOD UNITED

Nickname: The Wood **Club Colours:** Royal blue & black

Founded 1874

Club Contact Details 0208 942 8062 collierswoodunited@yahoo.co.uk

Ground: Wibbandune Sports Ground, Lincoln Green, Wimbledon SW20 0AA

Capacity: 2000 **Seats:** 102 **Covered:** 100 **Shop:** Yes

Previous Names: Vandyke 1874-1997. Vandyke Colliers United 1997-99.

Previous Leagues: Wimbledon & Sutton. Surrey Intermediate. Surrey County Senior

HONOURS: FA Comps: None

League: Surrey County Premier League 1997-98.

10 YEAR RECORD

09-10		10-11		11-12		12-13		13-14		14-15		15-16		16-17		17-18		18-19	
CCP	19	CCP	11	CCP	19	CCP	18	CCP	16	CCP	11	CCP	8	CCP	15	CCP	16	CCP	13
FAC	P	FAC	EP	FAC	EPr	FAC	P	FAC	P	FAC	EP	FAC	EP	FAC	2Qr	FAC	Pr	FAC	EPr
FAV	1Q	FAV	3P	FAV	1P	FAV	3P	FAV	1Q	FAV	4P	FAV	3P	FAV	1Q	FAV	1Q	FAV	2Q

On A3 Southbound 1 mile from Robin Hood Gate.

Nearest Railway Station Raynes Park

Bus Route London Transport 265

EGHAM TOWN

Nickname: Sarnies **Club Colours:** Red & white

Founded 1877

Club Contact Details 01784 437 055

Ground: Runnymead Stadium, Tempest Road, Egham TW20 8XD

Capacity: 5500 **Seats:** 262 **Covered:** 3300

Previous Names: Runnymead Rovers 1877-1905. Egham F.C. 05-63.

Previous Leagues: West Surrey. Surrey Senior 1922-28, 33-39, 65-67. Spartan 1928-33, 67-74. Athenian 1964-77. Isthmian 1977-2004, 05-06, 18-19. Southern 2004-05, 13-18. Combined Counties 2006-13.

HONOURS: FA Comps: None

League: West Surrey 1921-22. Surrey Senior 1922-23. Spartan 1971-72. Athenian Division Two 1974-75. Combined Counties 2012-13.

10 YEAR RECORD

09-10	10-11	11-12	12-13	13-14	14-15	15-16	16-17	17-18	18-19
CCP 4	CCP 13	CCP 4	CCP 1	SthC 11	SthC 15	SthC 3	SthC 5	Sth1E 16	IsthSC 20
FAC EPr	FAC EP	FAC Pr	FAC P	FAC P	FAC P	FAC Pr	FAC 4Q	FAC 1Qr	FAC 2Qr
FAV 2Q	FAV 2P	FAV 2P	FAV 1P	FAT 2Q	FAT 1Q	FAT 1Q	FAT P	FAT 2Q	FAT P

From M25 - J13 - Take the A30, heading south. The road runs parallel with the M25 briefly, and sweeps round a sharp left hand bend, under the M25. Stay right, down to the r'about in front of you just the other side of the M25. Go round the r'about and back under the M25.This road is called The Causeway. Carry on down this road, over the small r'about at Sainsbury's and at the bigger r'about turn right (signposted B3376 - Thorpe, Chertsey, Woking). Proceed down Thorpe Rd, over a level crossing, to a mini r'about, go over, and on the left, after the green turn into Pond Road. Left into Wards Place then first right and you will see the entrance to the football ground.

Nearest Railway Station Egham - 1km

Bus Route Charta Road - stop 200m away

FRIMLEY GREEN

Nickname: The Green **Club Colours:** All blue

Founded 1919

Club Contact Details 01252 835 089

Ground: Frimley Green Rec. Ground, Frimley Green, Camberley GU16 6JY

Capacity: 2000 **Seats:** No **Covered:** Yes

Previous Names: None

Previous Leagues: Surrey Senior 1960-74. London Spartan 1974-75. London Spartan 1975-81. Combined Counties 1981-94. Surrey County Premier 1999-2002.

HONOURS: FA Comps: None

League: Combined Counties Division One 2012-13.

10 YEAR RECORD

09-10	10-11	11-12	12-13	13-14	14-15	15-16	16-17	17-18	18-19
CC1 13	CC1 15	CC1 10	CC1 1	CCP 12	CCP 21	CC1 12	CC1 13	CC1 7	CC1 2
FAC EP	FAC EP			FAC P	FAC EP	FAC EP			FAC P
FAV 2Q	FAV 2Q	FAV 1Q	FAV 2P	FAV 1Q	FAV 2Q	FAV 2Q	FAV 2Q	FAV 1P	FAV 1Q

Exit M3 at junction 4 and follow the signs to Frimley High Street. At the mini roundabout in front of the White Hart public house turn into Church Road. At the top of the hill by the Church the road bends right and becomes Frimley Green Road. Follow the road for approx of a mile, go over the mini roundabout which is the entrance to Johnson's Wax factory, and the Recreation Ground is the second turning on the left, just past Henley Drive, which is on your right.

Nearest Railway Station Frimley

Bus Route Stagecoach 3, Arriva 49

GUILDFORD CITY

Nickname: The Sweeney **Club Colours:** Red & white stripes

Founded 1996

Club Contact Details 01483 443 322

Ground: Spectrum Leisure Centre, Parkway, Guildford GU1 1UP

Capacity: 1,320 **Seats:** 255 **Covered:** Yes **Shop:** Yes

Previous Names: AFC Guildford 1996-2005. Guildford United 2005-06.

Previous Leagues: Surrey Senior. Combined Counties > 2012. Southern 2012-14.

HONOURS: FA Comps: None

League: Southern League 1937-38, 55-56, League cup 1962-63, 66-67. Combined Counties Division One 2003-04, Premier Division 2010-11, 11-12

10 YEAR RECORD

09-10	10-11	11-12	12-13	13-14	14-15	15-16	16-17	17-18	18-19
CCP 7	CCP 1	CCP 1	SthC 9	Sthsw 22	CCP 17	CCP 14	CCP 16	CCP 12	CCP 7
FAC 1Qr	FAC 2Q	FAC EP	FAC 1Q	FAC P	FAC EP	FAC P	FAC 1Q	FAC 1Q	FAC EP
FAV 2Q	FAV 4P	FAV 2P	FAT 1Q	FAT P	FAV 1P	FAV 1Q	FAV 1Q	FAV 1Q	FAV 2Q

From A3, exit at Guildford – follow signs to leisure centre.
From Guildford main line station, take no.100 shuttle bus to Spectrum.
From London Road Station walk via Stoke Park.

Nearest Railway Station Guildford Main Line (2 miles) & Guildford (London Rd) (1 mile)

Bus Route Arriva 100

HANWORTH VILLA

Nickname: The Vilans **Club Colours:** Red & white

Founded 1976

Club Contact Details 0208 831 9391 db1959@btinternet.com
Ground: Rectory Meadows, Park Road, Hanworth TW13 6PN
Capacity: 600 **Seats:** 100 **Covered:** Yes

Previous Names: None
Previous Leagues: Hounslow & District Lge. West Middlesex Lge. Middlesex County League.

HONOURS: FA Comps: None
League: Hounslow & District Div.1 & Prem. West Middlesex Division One & Division Two.
Middlesex County 2002-03, 04-05.

10 YEAR RECORD

09-10	10-11	11-12	12-13	13-14	14-15	15-16	16-17	17-18	18-19
CCP 17	CCP 5	CCP 3	CCP 9	CCP 8	CCP 19	CCP 7	CCP 3	CCP 11	CCP 15
		FAC 4Q	FAC P	FAC P	FAC Pr	FAC EP	FAC P	FAC P	FAC Pr
	FAV 2Q	FAV 3Pr	FAV 4P	FAV 4P	FAV 3P	FAV 1P	FAV 1Q	FAV 2P	FAV 1P

From M25 and M3 once on the M3 towards London. This becomes the A316, take the A314 (Hounslow Rd) exit signposted Feltham & Hounslow. Turn left onto Hounslow Rd, at the second mini round about (Esso garage on the corner) turn left into Park Rd. Continue down Park Road past the Hanworth Naval Club on the right and Procter's Builders Merchants on the left. Follow the road around the 90 degree bend and continue to the end of the road past the Hanworth Village Hall. Once past the two houses next to the village hall turn left into Rectory Meadows.

Nearest Railway Station Feltham or Hampton
Bus Route London United 111 or H25

KNAPHILL

Nickname: The Knappers **Club Colours:** Red and black

Founded 1924

Club Contact Details 01483 475 150
Ground: Brookwood Country Park, Redding Way, Knaphill GU21 2AY
Capacity: 1,000 **Seats:** 100 **Covered:** Yes

Previous Names: None
Previous Leagues: Woking & District. Surrey Intermediate (Western) > 2007

HONOURS: FA Comps: None
League: Woking & District League 1978-79.
Surrey Intermediate League Division Three 1980-81, Division One 2005-06, Premier 06-07.

10 YEAR RECORD

09-10	10-11	11-12	12-13	13-14	14-15	15-16	16-17	17-18	18-19
CC1 3	CC1 9	CC1 12	CC1 12	CC1 3	CCP 13	CCP 5	CCP 14	CCP 8	CCP 11
					FAC 1Q	FAC EP	FAC EPr	FAC 2Q	FAC EP
		FAV 1Q	FAV 1Q	FAV 2P	FAV 2P	FAV 4P	FAV 3P	FAV 2Q	FAV 1Q

From A3: A322 from Guildford through towards Worplesdon. At Fox Corner rounabaout, take 2bd exit onto Bagshot Road, A322 signposted Bagshot. Pat West Hill Golf Club, at traffice lights turn right onto Brookwood Lye Road, A324 signposted Woking. Turn left into Hermitage Road on A324, up to roundabout, take 1st exit onto Redding Way, then 1st left entering driveway towards car park and ground.

Nearest Railway Station Brookwood or Woking
Bus Route Arriva 34, 35

MOLESEY

Nickname: The Moles **Club Colours:** White & black

Founded 1946

Club Contact Details 020 8979 4823
Ground: 412 Walton Road, West Molesey KT8 2JG
Capacity: 4,000 **Seats:** 160 **Covered:** Yes **Shop:** Yes

Previous Names: None.
Previous Leagues: Surrey Intermediate 1946-53. Surrey Senior 1953-59. Spartan 1959-73. Athenian 1973-77. Isthmian 1977-2008, 15-19. Combined Counties 2008-15.
HONOURS: FA Comps: None
League: Surrey Intermediate 1946-47. Surrey Senior 1957-58. Combined Counties Premier Division 2014-15.

10 YEAR RECORD

09-10	10-11	11-12	12-13	13-14	14-15	15-16	16-17	17-18	18-19
CCP 8	CCP 3	CCP 5	CCP 10	CCP 11	CCP 1	Isth1S 9	Isth1S 19	Isth1S 23	IsthSC 19
FAC 1Q	FAC EP	FAC EP	FAC EP	FAC Pr	FAC P	FAC 1Q	FAC P	FAC P	FAC Pr
FAV 1P	FAV 1P	FAV 1P	FAV 1Q	FAV 1Q	FAV 2Q	FAT 3Q	FAT P	FAT P	FAT 1Q

Take A3 towards Cobham/London & exit at Esher-Sandown turn. 1st exit at roundabout to A244 through Esher to Marquis of Granby Pub. 1st exit A309 at next roundabout. 1st exit at end of road turn right, follow until mini roundabout left into Walton Road after 1 mile ground on left.

Nearest Railway Station Hampton - 1.5km
Bus Route Grange Road - stop 150m away

RAYNES PARK VALE

Nickname: The Vale **Club Colours:** Blue and yellow

Founded 1995

Club Contact Details 0208 540 8843

Ground: Prince George's Playing Field, Raynes Park SW20 9NB

Capacity: 1500 **Seats:** 120 **Covered:** 100

Previous Names: Malden Vale and Raynes Park merged in 1995

Previous Leagues: None

HONOURS: FA Comps: None

League: Combined Counties Division One 2002-03.

10 YEAR RECORD

09-10	10-11	11-12	12-13	13-14	14-15	15-16	16-17	17-18	18-19
CCP 18	CCP 15	CCP 9	CCP 11	CCP 10	CCP 15	CCP 15	CCP 23	CC1 5	CCP 5
FAC P	FAC P	FAC P	FAC Pr	FAC Pr	FAC Pr	FAC EP	FAC EP	FAC EP	FAC Pr
FAV 1Q	FAV 1P	FAV 1P	FAV 2Q	FAV 1Q	FAV 1P	FAV 1Q	FAV 1Q	FAV 1Q	FAV 1Q

Exit Raynes Park station into Grand Drive cross Bushey Road at the traffic lights continue up Grand Drive for 400 yards entrance on the left follow drive to clubhouse. From the A3. Onto Bushey Road towards South Wimbledon. Grand Drive on the right, ground in Grand Drive on the left hand side.

Nearest Railway Station Raynes Park

Bus Route London Buses 152 & 163

REDHILL

Nickname: Reds/Lobsters **Club Colours:** Red & white

Founded 1894

Club Contact Details 01737 762 129

Ground: Kiln Brow, Three Arch Road, Redhill, Surrey RH1 5AE

Capacity: 2,000 **Seats:** 150 **Covered:** 150 **Shop:** Yes

Previous Names: None

Previous Leagues: E & W Surrey. Spartan 1909-10. Southern Sub. London 1921-23. Athenian 1923-84. Sussex County 1984-2013. Isthmian 2013-15.

HONOURS: FA Comps: None

League: London League 1922-23. Athenian League 1924-25, 83-84.

10 YEAR RECORD

09-10	10-11	11-12	12-13	13-14	14-15	15-16	16-17	17-18	18-19
SxC1 5	SxC1 8	SxC1 10	SxC1 2	Isth1S 22	Isth1S 23	CCP 20	CC1 2	CCP 6	CCP 12
FAC EP	FAC EP	FAC 1Q	FAC 1Q	FAC 1Q	FAC 3Q	FAC EP	FAC P	FAC P	FAC EP
FAV 2P	FAV 2Q	FAV 2Q	FAV 1Q	FAT P	FAT Pr	FAV 2Q	FAV 1Q	FAV 1Q	FAV 1P

On left hand side of A23 two and a half miles south of Redhill.

Nearest Railway Station Redhill (mainline) Earlswood

Bus Route 100, 400, 420, 430, 435, 460

SHEERWATER

Nickname: Sheers **Club Colours:** All royal blue

Founded 1958

Club Contact Details 07791 612 008

Ground: Sheerwater Recreation Ground, Blackmore Crescent, Woking GU21 5NS

Capacity: 1,000 **Seats:** 67 **Covered:** 25

Previous Names: None

Previous Leagues: Woking & District 1958-67. Surrey County Intermediate 1967-78. Surrey Senior 1972-78. Combined Counties 1978-82. Surrey Premier (FM) 1982-93, 94-2000. Surrey County Senior 2000-03.

HONOURS: FA Comps: None

League: Combined Counties Division One 2018-19

10 YEAR RECORD

09-10	10-11	11-12	12-13	13-14	14-15	15-16	16-17	17-18	18-19
CC1 17	CC1 17	CC1 18	CC1 15	CC1 11	CC1 14	CC1 13	CC1 9	CC1 4	CC1 1
									FAV 1P

From M25(J11) take the A320 towards Woking, At Six Cross roundabout take the exit to Monument Road.
At the lights turn left into Eve Road for Sheerwater Estate.
First left is Blackmore Crescent, Entrance is Quarter of a mile on left.

Nearest Railway Station Woking or West Byfleet

Bus Route Arriva 436 and Abellio 446

SOUTHALL

Founded 1871

Nickname: None **Club Colours:** Red and white

Club Contact Details enquiries@southallfc.com
Ground: Robert Parker Stadium, Short Lane, Stanwell TW19 7BH
Capacity: 3,000 **Seats:** **Covered:**

Previous Names: Southall 1871-1975. Southall & Ealing Borough 1975-80.
Previous Leagues: West London (FM) 1892-93. Southern 1896-1905. Great Western Suburban 1907-14. Athenian 1919-73. Isthmian 1973-75, 80--2000. Combined Counties 2000-06. Middlesex County 2006-12. Spartan South Midlands 2012-18.
HONOURS: FA Comps: None
League: Great Western Suburban 1912-13. Athenian 1926-27.
Spartan South Midlands Division One 2017-18.

10 YEAR RECORD

09-10	10-11	11-12	12-13	13-14	14-15	15-16	16-17	17-18	18-19
MidxP 10	MidxP 8	MidxP 3	SSM1 9	SSM1 11	SSM1 12	SSM1 12	SSM1 5	SSM1 1	CCP 4
								FAC P	FAC EP
				FAV 1Q	FAV 2Q	FAV 1P	FAV QF	FAV 2P	FAV 2P

SPELTHORNE SPORTS

Founded 1922

Nickname: Spelly **Club Colours:** Navy & sky blue

Club Contact Details 01932 961 055
Ground: Spelthorne Sports Club, 296 Staines Rd West, Ashford Common, TW15 1RY
Capacity: 1,500 **Seats:** 50 **Covered:** Yes

Previous Names: None
Previous Leagues: Surrey Intermediate (West) > 2009. Surrey Elite Intermediate 2009-11.

HONOURS: FA Comps: None
League: Surrey Elite Intermediate League 2010-11. Combined Counties Division One 2013-14.

10 YEAR RECORD

09-10	10-11	11-12	12-13	13-14	14-15	15-16	16-17	17-18	18-19
SuEl 5	SuEl 1	CC1 7	CC1 6	CCP 1	CCP 6	CCP 11	CCP 9	CCP 10	CCP 6
						FAC P	FAC P	FAC EP	FAC 1Q
					FAV 1P	FAV 1Q	FAV 1Qr	FAV 1P	FAV 2P

From M25 (J13) take the A30 exit to London (W)/Hounslow/Staines. At the roundabout, take the 1st exit onto Staines Bypass/A30 heading to London(W)/Hounslow/Staines/Kingston/A308. Turn left onto Staines Bypass/A308. Continue to follow A308. Go through one roundabout. Make a U-turn at Chertsey Rd. Ground will be on the left.

Nearest Railway Station Sunbury
Bus Route 290 to outside the club.

SUTTON COMMON ROVERS

Founded 1978

Nickname: Commoners **Club Colours:** All yellow

Club Contact Details 020 8644 4440
Ground: Sutton United FC, Gander Green Lane, Sutton. Surrey SM1 2EY
Capacity: 5,013 **Seats:** 765 **Covered:** 1,250 **Shop:** Yes

Previous Names: Inrad FC. Centre 21 FC . SCR Plough, SCR Grapes, SRC Litten Tree, SCR Kingfisher, Mole Valley SCR >2015.
Previous Leagues: South Eastern Combination.

HONOURS: FA Comps: None
League: Combined Counties League Division One 2009-10.

10 YEAR RECORD

09-10	10-11	11-12	12-13	13-14	14-15	15-16	16-17	17-18	18-19
CC1 1	CCP 8	CCP 21	CC1 2	CCP 18	CCP 18	CCP 19	CCP 12	CCP 3	CCP 2
	FAC EP	FAC EP	FAC EPr	FAC EP	FAC P	FAC EP	FAC EPr	FAC P	FAC EP
FAV 1P	FAV 1Q	FAV 2Q	FAV 2Q	FAV 2Q	FAV 1Q	FAV 4P	FAV 3P	FAV 1Q	FAV 2P

Travel along the M25 to junction 8. Then north on the A217 for about 15-20 minutes. Ignoring signs for Sutton itself, stay on the A217 to the traffic lights by the Gander Inn (on the left), turn right into Gander Green Lane. The Borough Sports Ground is about 200 yards up this road on the left hand side, if you reach West Sutton station you have gone too far.

Nearest Railway Station West Sutton a few minutes walk from the ground.
Bus Route 413

CC DIVISION ONE INS: AFC Hayes (R - CCP), Jersey Bulls (N), Walton & Hersham (R - CCP), Westside (P - SEI), Kensington & Ealing Borough (NC from Kensington Borough). **OUTS:** AC London (Expelled), Frimley Green (P - CCP), Sheerwater (P -CCP).

AFC HAYES

Founded: 1976 Nickname: The Brooks

Club Contact Details 020 8845 0110

Ground: Farm Park, Kingshill Avenue, Hayes UB4 8DD **Club Colours:** Blue and white stripes

HONOURS **League:** Spartan South Midlands Premier South 1997-98.

FA Comps: None

10 YEAR RECORD

09-10		10-11		11-12		12-13		13-14		14-15		15-16		16-17		17-18		18-19	
Sthsw	21	SthC	19	SthC	10	SthC	15	SthC	18	SthC	22	CCP	16	CCP	17	CCP	18	CCP	19
FAC	P	FAC	P	FAC	1Q	FAC	P	FAC	P	FAC	1Q	FAC	Pr	FAC	P	FAC	EP	FAC	EP
FAT	P	FAT	1Q	FAT	1Q	FAT	P	FAT	1Q	FAT	Pr	FAV	2Q	FAV	1Q	FAV	2Q	FAV	1Q

From the A40 McDonalds Target roundabout take A312 south towards Hayes.
At White Hart roundabout take third exit into Yeading Lane.
Turn right at first traffic lights into Kingshill Avenue.
Ground approx one miles on the right-hand side.

Nearest Railway Station Northholt or Haye & Harlington

Bus Route No.90

ASH UNITED

Founded: 1911 Nickname: Green Army

Club Contact Details 01252 320 385 / 345 757

Ground: Shawfield Stadium, Youngs Drive off Shawfield Road, Ash, GU12 6RE. **Club Colours:** Green & red.

HONOURS **League:** Combined Counties 1981-82, 86-87, 98-99.

FA Comps: None

10 YEAR RECORD

09-10		10-11		11-12		12-13		13-14		14-15		15-16		16-17		17-18		18-19	
CCP	11	CCP	18	CCP	13	CCP	20	CCP	1	CC1	10	CC1	10	CC1	12	CC1	10	CC1	7
FAC	1Q	FAC	EP	FAC	EP	FAC	EP	FAC	EP	FAC	EP								
FAV	1P	FAV	2Q	FAV	1Q	FAV	2P	FAV	1Q	FAV	1Q	FAV	1Q	FAV	1P	FAV	1Q	FAV	1Q

FROM M3: Get off the M3 at J4, onto the A331: Take 3rd Exit off to Woking. Up to the roundabout turn left into Shawfields Road, follow road for about 500 yards, Football Ground is on the left, take next turning on your left into Youngs Drive where club is 50yards on.
FROM M25: Get onto the A3 heading to Guildford/Portsmouth. Keep on this until you reach the A31(Hog's Back). Then go onto the A31 until you reach the exit for the A331 to Aldershot. Follow the signs for Aldershot, which will be the 1st exit off the A331.When you reach the r'about take the exit for Woking, which will be the 3rd exit off. Up to the r'about turn left into Shawfields Road, then as above.

Nearest Railway Station Ash or Ash Vale

Bus Route Stagecoach 20A, 550

BAGSHOT

Founded: 1906 Nickname:

Club Contact Details

Ground: Camberley Town FC, Krooner Park, Wilton Rd, Camberley GU15 2QW **Club Colours:** Yellow & blue

HONOURS **League:** Aldershot & District Division Two 2005-06, Division One 2008-09, Senior Division 2011-12, 12-13, 13-14, 15-16.

FA Comps: None

10 YEAR RECORD

09-10		10-11		11-12		12-13		13-14		14-15		15-16		16-17		17-18		18-19	
A&DS	2	A&DS	3	A&DS	1	A&DS	1	A&DS	1	A&DS	1	A&DS	1	CC1	8	CC1	19	CC1	13
																FAV	1Q	FAV	1Q

Exit M3 Motorway at Junction 4. At the end of the slip road take the right hand land signposted A331, immediately take the left hand lane signposted Frimley and Hospital (Red H Symbol) and this will lead you up onto the A325. Continue to the roundabout and turn left onto the B3411 (Frimley Road) Continue past Focus DIY store on Left and stay on B3411 for approx 1.5 miles. At the next Mini roundabout turn left into Wilton Road, proceed through industrial estate (past the Peugeot garage) and the entrance to the ground is right at the end.

Nearest Railway Station Camberley

Bus Route Stagecoach 1

BEDFONT & FELTHAM

Founded: 2012 Nickname: The Yellows

Club Contact Details 020 8890 7264

Ground: The Orchard, Hatton Road, Bedfont TW14 9QT **Club Colours:** Yellow & blue

HONOURS **League:** None

FA Comps: None

10 YEAR RECORD

09-10		10-11		11-12		12-13		13-14		14-15		15-16		16-17		17-18		18-19	
						CC1	13	CC1	5	CC1	5	CC1	2	CCP	22	CC1	17	CC1	5
										FAC	1Q	FAC	1Q	FAC	EP	FAC	EP	FAC	EP
						FAV	2Q	FAV	1P	FAV	1Q	FAV	1Q	FAV	2Q	FAV	1Q	FAV	1P

Hatton Road runs alongside the A30 at Heathrow.
Ground is opposite the Duke of Wellington Public House.

Nearest Railway Station Hatton Cross (Piccadilly Line)

Bus Route London Transport 203, H25, H26

BRITISH AIRWAYS

Founded: 1947 Nickname:

Club Contact Details

Ground: Bedfont & Feltham FC, The Orchard, Hatton Road, Bedfont TW14 9QT **Club Colours:** Blue and white

HONOURS **League:** Middlesex County Premier Division 2012-13, 17-18.

FA Comps: None

10 YEAR RECORD

09-10	10-11	11-12	12-13	13-14	14-15	15-16	16-17	17-18	18-19
LonCom 2	LonCom 2	LonCom 1	MidxP 1	MidxP 7	MidxP 11	MidxP 6	MidxP 2	MidxP 1	CC1 10
									FAV 1Q

Hatton Road runs alongside the A30 at Heathrow.
Ground is opposite the Duke of Wellington Public House.

Nearest Railway Station Hatton Cross (Piccadilly Line)

Bus Route London Transport 203, H25, H26

CHESSINGTON & HOOK UNITED

Founded: 1921 Nickname: Chessey

Club Contact Details

Ground: Chalky Lane, Chessington, Surrey KT9 2NF **Club Colours:** Blue and white

HONOURS **League:** Kingston & District Division Four 1922-23, Division Two 1955-56, Division One 1957-58.

FA Comps: None

10 YEAR RECORD

09-10	10-11	11-12	12-13	13-14	14-15	15-16	16-17	17-18	18-19
CCP 6	CCP 12	CCP 20	CCP 17	CCP 22	CC1 3	CCP 21	CC1 5	CC1 13	CC1 9
FAC EP	FAC EP	FAC P	FAC P	FAC P	FAC 1Q	FAC 1Q	FAC Pr	FAC P	
FAV 1Q	FAV 1Q	FAV 1Q	FAV 2Q	FAV 2P	FAV 2P	FAV 1Q	FAV 1Qr	FAV 2Q	FAV 2Q

Chalky Lane is off A243 (Opposite Chessington World of Adventures) which leads to Junction 9 on M25 or Hook Junction on the A3.

Nearest Railway Station Chessington South

Bus Route London United 71, 465

COVE

Founded: 1897 Nickname: None

Club Contact Details

Ground: Oak Farm Fields, 7 Squirrels Lane, Farnborough GU14 8PF **Club Colours:** Yellow and black

HONOURS **League:** Combined Counties League 2000-01.

FA Comps: None

10 YEAR RECORD

09-10	10-11	11-12	12-13	13-14	14-15	15-16	16-17	17-18	18-19
CCP 12	CCP 9	CCP 11	CCP 3	CCP 5	CCP 4	CCP 22	CC1 17	CC1 18	CC1 18
FAC P	FAC EPr	FAC EP	FAC P	FAC 1Q	FAC EP	FAC P	FAC EP		
FAV 2Q	FAV 1P	FAV 2Q	FAV 2Q	FAV 2P	FAV 1Q	FAV 1P	FAV 1Q	FAV 1Q	FAV 1Q

From M3 junction 4, follow signs for A325, then follow signs for Cove FC.

Nearest Railway Station Farnborough Main

DORKING WANDERERS RES.

Founded: 1999 Nickname: Wanderers

Club Contact Details info@dorkingwanderers.com

Ground: Meadowbank Stadium, Mill Lane, Dorking RH4 1DX **Club Colours:** Red & white

HONOURS **League:** None

FA Comps: None

10 YEAR RECORD

09-10	10-11	11-12	12-13	13-14	14-15	15-16	16-17	17-18	18-19
						CC1 15			CC1 11

From the M25 go off at junction 9, take the A243 exit to A24/Leatherhead/Dorking. At the roundabout, take the 3rd exit onto A243. At the roundabout, take the 2nd exit onto Leatherhead By-Pass Rd/A243. At the roundabout, take the 2nd exit onto Leatherhead By-Pass Rd/A24. At the roundabout, take the 2nd exit and stay on Leatherhead By-Pass Rd/A24. At the roundabout, take the 1st exit onto Dorking Rd/A24. Continue to follow A24. At the roundabout, take the 2nd exit onto London Rd/A24. At the roundabout, take the 4th exit and stay on London Rd/A24.

Nearest Railway Station Dorking West and Dorking Deepdene

EPSOM & EWELL

Founded: 1960 Nickname: E's or Salts

Club Contact Details 01737 553 250

Ground: Chipstead FC, High Road, Chipstead, Surrey CR5 3SF **Club Colours:** Royal blue & white

HONOURS **League:** Surrey Senior 1974-75. Isthmian Division Two 1977-78.

FA Comps: None

10 YEAR RECORD

09-10		10-11		11-12		12-13		13-14		14-15		15-16		16-17		17-18		18-19	
CCP	5	CCP	10	CCP	14	CCP	5	CCP	3	CCP	7	CCP	4	CCP	4	CCP	21	CC1	8
FAC	P	FAC	1Q	FAC	P	FAC	1Q	FAC	EPr	FAC	Pr	FAC	EP	FAC	P	FAC	EP	FAC	Pr
FAT	3P	FAV	2Q	FAV	2Q	FAV	1Q	FAV	2Q	FAV	1P	FAV	1Q	FAV	2P	FAV	2P	FAV	1Q

From M25 Junction 8. Take the A217.
At 1st Roundabout take the 2nd Exit.
At the end of the Road Turn Left.
Ground is 2 Miles on the Right.

Nearest Railway Station Kingswood

EVERSLEY & CALIFORNIA

Founded: 1910 Nickname: The Boars

Club Contact Details

Ground: ESA Sports Complex, Fox Lane, Eversley RG27 0NS **Club Colours:** Yellow and blue

HONOURS **League:** Surrey Elite Intermediate 2008-09.

FA Comps: None

10 YEAR RECORD

09-10		10-11		11-12		12-13		13-14		14-15		15-16		16-17		17-18		18-19	
CC1	8	CC1	11	CC1	5	CC1	4	CC1	2	CC1	9	CC1	5	CC1	6	CC1	9	CC1	16
																FAC	EP		
										FAV	2Q			FAV	2Q	FAV	1Q	FAV	1P

Leave the M3 at junction 4a signposted Fleet/Farnborough. At the roundabout take the 2nd exit towards Yateley.
At the roundabout take the 2nd exit towards Yateley. At the roundabout take the 2nd exit towards Yateley.
At the roundabout take the 1st exit and proceed through Yateley on the Reading Road. At the roundabout take the 2nd exit and follow the road for about 1 mile. Turn right down the first turning for Fox Lane and then follow the road round to the right where the ground will be signposted.

Nearest Railway Station Fleet, Sandhurst

FARNHAM TOWN

Founded: 1906 Nickname: The Town

Club Contact Details 01252 715 305

Ground: Memorial Ground, West Street, Farnham GU9 7DY **Club Colours:** Claret & sky blue

HONOURS **League:** Surrey Intermediate 1929-30, 30-31. Surrey Senior 1965-66, 66-67, 67-68.
Combined Counties 1990-91, 91-92, Division One 2006-07.

FA Comps: None

10 YEAR RECORD

09-10		10-11		11-12		12-13		13-14		14-15		15-16		16-17		17-18		18-19	
CC1	11	CC1	2	CCP	12	CCP	8	CCP	15	CCP	10	CCP	10	CCP	18	CCP	22	CC1	4
FAC	EPr	FAC	P	FAC	P	FAC	EP	FAC	P	FAC	EP	FAC	1Q	FAC	P	FAC	P	FAC	EP
FAV	2Q	FAV	2Q	FAV	1P	FAV	2Q	FAV	1P	FAV	1Pr	FAV	1P	FAV	1Q	FAV	2P	FAV	2Q

Follow A31 to Coxbridge roundabout (passing traffic lights at Hickleys corner.
Farnham station to left.) At next roundabout take 3rd exit to Farnham town centre.
At the mini roundabout take 2nd exit.
The ground is to the left.

Nearest Railway Station Farnham
Bus Route Stagecoach 5, 14, 18, 19, 46, 64, 71, 536

FC DEPORTIVO GALICIA

Founded: 1968 Nickname: Depor

Club Contact Details

Ground: Hatten Road, Feltham, Middlesex TW14 9JR **Club Colours:** Blue and white

HONOURS **League:** Middlesex County Premier Division 2016-17.

FA Comps: None

10 YEAR RECORD

09-10		10-11		11-12		12-13		13-14		14-15		15-16		16-17		17-18		18-19	
MidxP	14	MidxP	7	MidxP	12	MidxP	13	MidxP	6	MidxP	12	MidxP	13	MidxP	1	CC1	12	CC1	14
														FAV	1Q	FAV	2Q	FAV	1P

From Junction 13, M25 – Staines. At Crooked Billet roundabout turn right onto the A30 Signposted C. London, Hounslow.
At Clockhouse Roundabout take the 2nd exit onto the A315 Signposted Bedfont.
Turn left onto Hatton Road. Arrive on Hatton Road, Bedfont Sports Club.

Nearest Railway Station Hatton Cross or Feltham BR
Bus Route London Transport 203, H25, H26

FLEET SPURS

Founded: 1948 Nickname: Spurs

Club Contact Details

Ground: Kennels Lane, Farnborough Hampshire, GU14 0ST **Club Colours:** Red and blue

HONOURS **League:** Surrey Premier A Division 1968-69. Aldershot Senior 1990-91. Hampshire Division Two 1997-98.

FA Comps: None

10 YEAR RECORD

09-10	10-11	11-12	12-13	13-14	14-15	15-16	16-17	17-18	18-19
Wex1 3	Wex1 10	Wex1 7	Wex1 10	Wex1 12	Wex1 9	Wex1 12	Wex1 16	CC1 16	CC1 17
		FAC EP	FAC EP						
	FAV 2Q	FAV 1Q	FAV 2Q	FAV 1Q	FAV 1Qr	FAV 1Q	FAV 2Q	FAV 1Q	FAV 2Q

From exit 4a on the M3, take the A327 towards Farnborough/Cove.Continuing on the A327 Filter Left at Traffic Lights - follow A327Take 1st exit at next roundabout into Summit Ave - A327Make a U turn around the next rounaboutKennels Lane is the first left. The grounds entrance is 250 yards on the left.

GODALMING TOWN

Founded: 1950 Nickname: The G's

Club Contact Details 01483 417 520 godalmingtownfootballclub@gmail.com

Ground: The Bill Kyte Stadium, Wey Court, Meadrow, Guildford, Surrey GU7 3JF **Club Colours:** Yellow & green

HONOURS **League:** Combined Counties Premier Division 1983-84, 2005-06.

FA Comps: None

10 YEAR RECORD

09-10	10-11	11-12	12-13	13-14	14-15	15-16	16-17	17-18	18-19
Isth1S 4	Isth1S 17	Isth1S 5	SthC 3	Sthsw 18	SthC 8	SthC 10	Isth1S 24	CCP 20	CC1 12
FAC P	FAC 1Q	FAC 4Q	FAC 1Qr	FAC P	FAC 1Qr	FAC 1Q	FAC 1Q	FAC 1Q	FAC EP
FAT 3Q	FAT 2Qr	FAT 2Q	FAT P	FAT P	FAT P	FAT P	FAT P	FAV 2Q	FAV 1Q

A3100 from Guildford, pass the Manor Inn on the left and then the petrol station on the right. Wey Court is 50 yards further along the road on the right hand side.
A3100 from Godalming, pass the Three Lions pub on the left and then turn left into Wey Court immediately after the Leathern Bottle pub. Parking: Please note that the club car park is for players and officials only. Spectators are asked to use the public car park next door to the ground.

Nearest Railway Station Farncombe - 1/2 a mile from the ground.

JERSEY BULLS

Founded: 2018 Nickname: Bulls

Club Contact Details info@bulls.je

Ground: Springfield Stadium, Saint Helier, Jersey JE2 4LF **Club Colours:** Red & white

HONOURS **League:** None

FA Comps: None

10 YEAR RECORD

09-10	10-11	11-12	12-13	13-14	14-15	15-16	16-17	17-18	18-19

KENSINGTON & EALING BOROUGH

Founded: 2012 Nickname:

Club Contact Details

Ground: Leatherhead FC, Fetcham Grove, Guildford Road, Leatherhead, Surrey **Club Colours:** Green and white

HONOURS **League:** None

FA Comps: None

10 YEAR RECORD

09-10	10-11	11-12	12-13	13-14	14-15	15-16	16-17	17-18	18-19
				Midx2 3	Midx1SE 6	SSM2 5	SSM1 12	CC1 15	CC1 15
								FAV 1P	FAV 2P

From Beaconsfield and High Wycombe follow the signposts to Amersham Old Town. Turn left at the bottom of the hill (Tesco roundabout). Go straight on through the next roundabout. From London at the first roundabout take the second exit signposted Amersham Old Town. Go straight on through the second, third (Tesco) and fourth roundabout. At the roundabout in front of the old Market Hall turn right into Church Street. Go past the Church on your right and take the first left into School Lane. Go past the recreation ground on your left and the road on your left (Mill Lane). The ground is one hundred yards on your left past Mill Lane.

Nearest Railway Station Leatherhead half a mile away

SANDHURST TOWN

Founded: 1910 Nickname: Fizzers

Club Contact Details info@sandhursttownfc.org

Ground: Bottom Meadow, Memorial Ground, Yorktown Rd, GU47 9BJ **Club Colours:** Red and black

HONOURS **League:** Reading & Disttrict Division One 1932-33, Premier 33-34. Aldershot & District Division One 1980-81.

FA Comps: None

10 YEAR RECORD

09-10	10-11	11-12	12-13	13-14	14-15	15-16	16-17	17-18	18-19
CCP 9	CCP 7	CCP 15	CCP 21	CC1 13	CC1 16	CC1 11	Hel1E 8	Hel1E 4	CC1 6
FAC EPr	FAC EP	FAC EP	FAC EP	FAC EPr					FAC EPr
FAV 1Q	FAV 2Q	FAV 1Q	FAV 1P	FAV 1Q			FAV 1Q	FAV 1P	FAV 1Q

Coming from Camberley: Once on the A321 (Yorktown Road), drive past the pitches and memorial park on your left, continue past the large car parks. Turn left in to a small car park opposite Park Road. There is a café (Pistachios in the Park), some skateboard ramps and a large barrier/gate. Drive through the gate and park on the grass area on the right-hand side. The Stadium itself is about 50 yards further down the track (it is visible in the corner). **Coming from Sandhurst Village:** Once on the A321 (Yorktown Road), driving away from the village shops, continue until you see a petrol station on your right. Continue for a further 50 yards where you need to turn right in to a small car park opposite Park Road. There is a café (Pistachios in the Park), some skateboard ramps and a large barrier/gate. Drive through the gate and park on the grass area on the right-hand side. The Stadium itself is about 50 yards further down the track (it is visible in the corner).

Nearest Railway Station Sandhurst - 0.9km

Bus Route Wellington Arms stop - 194m away

TOOTING BEC

Founded: 2004 Nickname:

Club Contact Details

Ground: Imperial Fields, Bishopsford Road, Morden SM4 6BF **Club Colours:** Black & white

HONOURS **League:** Surrey Elite Intermediate Division One 2009-10, Premier 2017-18.

FA Comps: None

10 YEAR RECORD

09-10	10-11	11-12	12-13	13-14	14-15	15-16	16-17	17-18	18-19
SuI1 1	SuEI 15	SuEI 13	SuEI 9	SuEI 7	SuEI 10	SuEI 7	SuEI 2	SuEI 1	CC1 3
								FAV 2Q	FAV 1Q

Nearest Railway Station Mitcham Junction - then take the tram to Mitcham Tram stop, ground an 8min walk from there.

WALTON & HERSHAM

Founded: 1945 Nickname: Swans

Club Contact Details waltonhersham2019@gmail.com

Ground: Waterside Drive, Walton-on-Thames, Surrey KT12 2JP **Club Colours:** Red and white

HONOURS **League:** Corinthian 1946-47, 47-48, 48-49. Athenian League 1968-69.

FA Comps: Amateur Cup 1972-73

10 YEAR RECORD

09-10	10-11	11-12	12-13	13-14	14-15	15-16	16-17	17-18	18-19
Isth1S 8	Isth1S 6	Isth1S 11	Isth1S 18	Isth1S 21	Isth1S 17	Isth1S 22	CCP 5	CCP 4	CCP 20
FAC 3Q	FAC 1Q	FAC 1Q	FAC 1Qr	FAC P	FAC P	FAC P	FAC Pr	FAC Pr	FAC EP
FAT 1Q	FAT P	FAT P	FAT 1Q	FAT P	FAT 1Q	FAT P	FAV 2P	FAV 3P	FAV 1P

On leaving bridge, follow sign to Hampton Court (A3050), keeping in left lane at traffic lights. Bear right and go through traffic lights in town centre, keeping in left lane. Go through pedestrian lights, straight over mini-roundabout and through another set of pedestrian lights by shopping parade. Turn left at next roundabout (school on right). Turn right just before leisure centre. Car park and ground is at end of road.

Nearest Railway Station Walton-on-Thames less a mile from the ground.

WESTSIDE

Founded: 1996 Nickname:

Club Contact Details

Ground: Mayfield Stadium, off Mayfield Road, Thornton Heath CR7 6DN **Club Colours:**

HONOURS **League:** Surrey South Eastern Combination Division Two 2014-15, Division One 2015-16.

FA Comps: None

10 YEAR RECORD

09-10	10-11	11-12	12-13	13-14	14-15	15-16	16-17	17-18	18-19
	SSECI2 10	SSECI2 5	SSECI2 6	SSECI2 3	SSECI2 1	SSECI1 1	SuEI 6	SuEI 12	SuEI 4
								FAV 1Q	FAV 1Q

From M25: Exit at either Junction 6 and then take the A22 to Purley Cross and then join the A23 London Road and then directions below from Purley, or exit at Junction 7 and take the A23 London Road all the way. **From Streatham and Norbury:** Take the A23 London Road to the roundabout at Thornton Heath, continue down the A23 Thornton Road. Then take the 1st on the Right past the No Entry road (Fairlands Avenue), Silverleigh Road, 50 yards, at the fork, keep left (signposted Croydon Athletic FC) into Trafford Road, then Mayfield Road (which is a continuation of Trafford Road) Go to the end of Mayfield Road, then left at the last house. Follow the lane, passed allotments, past an open car park space and continue along the lane to our club car park.

INS: Dunkirk (R - MidP), Hucknall Town (P - CMidS), Shirebrook Town (Tr - NCE1), FC Bolsover (Tr - NCE1)

BARROW TOWN

Founded: Late 1800s Nickname: The Riversiders

Club Contact Details 07904 289 690 newton-chris@sky.com

Ground: Riverside Park, Bridge Street, Quorn, Leicestershire LE12 8EN **Club Colours:** Red & black

HONOURS
FA Comps: None
League: Leicester Senior Division One 1992-93.

10 YEAR RECORD

09-10		10-11		11-12		12-13		13-14		14-15		15-16		16-17		17-18		18-19	
EMC	12	EMC	5	EMC	5	EMC	2	EMC	19	EMC	9	EMC	13	EMC	14	EMC	11	EMC	8
FAC	EP	FAC	P	FAC	3Q	FAC	EP	FAC	EP	FAC	EP	FAC	EP						
FAV	1Q	FAV	1Q	FAV	2Q	FAV	1Q	FAV	2Q	FAV	2Q	FAV	2Q	FAV	1Q	FAV	1Q	FAV	1P

Leave A6 south of Loughborough near Quorn. From A6 take Barrow/Quorn exit and follow signs to Barrow. Ground 400 metres on right.

From Nottingham: Take A60 and as you exit Hoton village follow signs for Prestwold and Barrow. On reaching Barrow go through village to roundabout at end of main street, turn right down hill and over river. Ground on left.

Nearest Railway Station Barrow upon Soar - 1.7km

BELPER UNITED

Founded: 1920 Nickname:

Club Contact Details

Ground: Christchurch Meadow, Bridge Street, Belper DE56 1BA **Club Colours:** Green and black

HONOURS
FA Comps: None
League: Midlands Regional Alliance Premier Division 1985-86, 94-95, Division One 2004-05.

10 YEAR RECORD

09-10		10-11		11-12		12-13		13-14		14-15		15-16		16-17		17-18		18-19	
MidRAP	13	MidRAP	10	CMSth	9	CMSth	3	CMSth	10	CMSth	5	CMSth	2	EMC	13	EMC	5	EMC	10
																FAC	P	FAC	EP
								FAV	1Q	FAV	1P	FAV	1Q	FAV	1Q	FAV	2Q	FAV	1P

M1 to junction 25 then A52 towards Derby. After 7 miles at roundabout take 2nd exit onto Eastgate/The Underpass. Continue onto A601 St. Alkmunds Way and after 0.2 miles merge onto A6 going through one roundabout. After 2 miles take 3rd exit at roundabout onto Duffield Road A6. Continue going through 1 roundabout for 6 miles then after shops turn left into concealed entrance onto Bridge Street or continue on for 100 yards into next concealed entrance and park inside ground.

Nearest Railway Station Belper

BORROWASH VICTORIA

Founded: 1911 Nickname: The Vics

Club Contact Details 07540 938 780

Ground: Borrowash Road, Spondon, Derby DE21 7PH **Club Colours:** Red & white stripes

HONOURS
FA Comps: None
League: Derby & District 1952-53. East Midlands regional Premier 1977-78. Midland Division One 1980-81. Northern Counties East Div.1 South 1983-84.

10 YEAR RECORD

09-10		10-11		11-12		12-13		13-14		14-15		15-16		16-17		17-18		18-19	
EMC	11	EMC	2	EMC	2	EMC	4	EMC	5	EMC	16	EMC	9	EMC	12	EMC	19	EMC	19
FAC	Pr	FAC	P	FAC	P	FAC	P	FAC	P	FAC	EP								
FAV	1P	FAV	2Q	FAV	2Q	FAV	4P	FAV	2P	FAV	2P	FAV	1P	FAV	1Q			FAV	1Q

From M1 Junction 25 travel towards Derby on A52. Take third turning left (directly under pedestrian footbridge) onto Borrowash Road. Past golf driving range on left and in approximately 400 metres turn left into the Asterdale Sports Centre.

Nearest Railway Station Spondon - 1.2km

CLIFTON ALL WHITES

Founded: 1963 Nickname: All Whites

Club Contact Details 07775 615 237

Ground: Green Lane, Clifton, Nottingham NG11 9AZ **Club Colours:** All white

HONOURS
FA Comps: None
League: Notts Alliance Division One 1998-99. Central Midlands 2013-14. Notts Senior Premier Division 2016-17.

10 YEAR RECORD

09-10		10-11		11-12		12-13		13-14		14-15		15-16		16-17		17-18		18-19	
				NottS1	2	CMSth	4	CMSth	1	CMSth	8	NottSP	6	NottSP	1	EMC	12	EMC	12
												FAV	2Q	FAV	2Q	FAV	1Qr	FAV	1Qr

At junction 24 of the M1, take the A453 exit to Nottingham (S). Take Remembrance Way/A453 to Farnborough Rd in Clifton. Merge onto Kegworth Interchange. Turn right to stay on Kegworth Interchange. Continue straight onto Remembrance Way/A453. At Mill Hill Roundabout, take the 2nd exit onto Barton Ln/Remembrance Way/A453. At the roundabout, take the 2nd exit onto Clifton Ln/Remembrance Way/A453. At the roundabout, take the 2nd exit onto Green Lane.

Nearest Railway Station Beeston - 3.2km
Bus Route Clifton Centre Tram Stop 426m from ground.

OUTS: Arnold Town (R - CMidS), Ashby Ivanoe (Tr - Mid1), FC Bolsver (resigned), Newark Flowserve (P - MidP), Selston (P - MidP).

CLIPSTONE

Founded: 1928 Nickname: The Cobras

Club Contact Details 07792 113 376 enquiries@clipstonefc.co.uk

Ground: The Lido Ground, Clipstone Road East, Clipstone Village NG21 9AB **Club Colours:** Black & white

HONOURS **League:** Central Midlands 1993-94, 96-97. Northern Counties East Division One 2014-15.

FA Comps: None

10 YEAR RECORD

09-10	10-11	11-12	12-13	13-14	14-15	15-16	16-17	17-18	18-19
CM Su 10	CM Su 9	CMN 4	NCE1 11	NCE1 7	NCE1 1	NCEP 13	NCEP 16	NCEP 22	EMC 18
					FAC 1Q	FAC 1Q	FAC EP	FAC P	FAC P
				FAV 2Q	FAV 2Q	FAV 1P	FAV 2Q	FAV 1P	FAV 1Q

From M1 J29, take exit signposted A617 Mansfield. At next roundabout, take third exit continuing on the A617. Keep going straight on until you get to the Mansfield ring road with Riley's snooker hall on your right and a miner's statue on your left. Follow the road round underneath a pedestrian bridge and take the next left onto the A6191 (Ratcliffe Gate). After around half a mile, turn left onto the B6030 (Carter Lane). Follow the B6030 for about 3 miles, go straight on at a roundabout and the ground will be on your left.

Nearest Railway Station Mansfield Woodhouse - 4.9km

Bus Route Station Road - stop 27m away

DUNKIRK

Founded: 1946 Nickname: The Boatmen

Club Contact Details 0115 985 0803

Ground: Ron Steel Spts Ground, Lenton Lane, Clifton Bridge, Nottingham NG7 **Club Colours:** Red and black

HONOURS **League:** Notts Alliance Division Two 1981-82, Division One 1984-85.
Central Midlands Supreme Division 2004-05. East Midlands 2009-10, 17-18.

FA Comps: None

10 YEAR RECORD

09-10	10-11	11-12	12-13	13-14	14-15	15-16	16-17	17-18	18-19
EMC 1	MidAl 8	MidAl 18	MidAl 10	MidAl 19	MFLP 19	MFLP 20	EMC 5	EMC 1	MFLP 19
FAC EP	FAC 1Q	FAC EP	FAC P	FAC 1Q	FAC EP	FAC 3Q	FAC 1Q	FAC 1Q	FAC EP
FAV 3P	FAV 3P	FAV 2Q	FAV 1P	FAV 2Q	FAV 2Q	FAV 2P	FAV 2Q	FAV 1P	FAV 2Q

From M1 Junction 24 take A453 towards Nottingham, through Clifton and join A52 onto Clifton Bridge. Get in middle lane down the slip road onto the island under the flyover signposted Industrial Estate. Take immediate 1st left and 1st left again onto Lenton Lane. Follow the road past Greenwood Meadows and the ground is 200 yards on the right.

Nearest Railway Station Beeston - 2.3km

EASTWOOD COMMUNITY

Founded: 2014 Nickname: Red Badgers

Club Contact Details 01773 432 414 / 07713 478 246

Ground: Chewton Street, Eastwood, Notts NG16 3HB **Club Colours:** Red and black

HONOURS **League:** Central Midlands South 2017-18.

FA Comps: None

10 YEAR RECORD

09-10	10-11	11-12	12-13	13-14	14-15	15-16	16-17	17-18	18-19
					CMSth 13	CMSth 10	CMSth 2	CMSth 1	EMC 6
						FAV 1Q	FAV 2Q	FAV 2Q	FAV 2P

From J26 M1 Take A610 towards Matlock / Ilkeston then take first exit towards Matlock/ Ilkeston, take the B610 – Nottingham Road for about 1 mile then turn left into Chewton Street, where entrance to club will be on the right hand side.

Nearest Railway Station Langley Mill via Chesterfield station. Walk to Acorn Centre to catch bus.

Bus Route Rainbow one bus from Acorn Centre. 11min journey via seven stops to Edward Road, ground 1min walk from there.

GEDLING MINERS WELFARE

Founded: 1919 Nickname: Miners

Club Contact Details 0115 926 6300

Ground: Plains Social Club, Plains Road, Mapperley, Nottingham NG3 5RH **Club Colours:** Yellow and royal blue

HONOURS **League:** Notts Alliance 1945-46, 49-50, 50-51, 51–52, 53-54, 55-56, 57-58, 58-59,
59-60, 60-61, Division Two 2000-01.

FA Comps: None

10 YEAR RECORD

09-10	10-11	11-12	12-13	13-14	14-15	15-16	16-17	17-18	18-19
EMC 8	EMC 4	EMC 13	EMC 13	EMC 12	EMC 12	EMC 14	EMC 20	EMC 10	EMC 16
FAC EPr	FAC P	FAC EPr							
FAV 1Q	FAV 2Q	FAV 1Q	FAV 2Q	FAV 1Q	FAV 1P	FAV 1Q	FAV 1Q	FAV 1Q	FAV 1Q

Situated on B684 in Mapperley.
From Nottingham the ground is approached via Woodborough Road.
From the north via A614 by Lime Lane Junction to Plains Road.

Nearest Railway Station Carlton - 3.5km

GRAHAM STREET PRIMS

Founded: 1904 Nickname: Prims

Club Contact Details 07902 403 074

Ground: The Gred Harding Ground, Borrowash Road, Spondon DE21 7PH **Club Colours:** Red & white

HONOURS **League:** Central Alliance Premier Division 1970-71.
East Midlands Regional 1978-79.

FA Comps: None

10 YEAR RECORD

09-10	10-11	11-12	12-13	13-14	14-15	15-16	16-17	17-18	18-19
EMC 18	EMC 14	EMC 14	EMC 8	EMC 10	EMC 18	EMC 11	EMC 19	EMC 16	EMC 7
				FAC EP	FAC EP				
FAV 2Q	FAV 2Q	FAV 1Q	FAV 1P	FAV 3P	FAV 1P	FAV 2Q	FAV 1Q	FAV 1Q	FAV 2Q

From M1 Junction 25 travel towards Derby on A52. Take third turning left (directly under pedestrian footbridge) onto Borrowash Road. Past golf driving range on left and in approximately 400 metres turn left into the Asterdale Sports Centre.

Nearest Railway Station Spondon - 1.2km

HEANOR TOWN

Founded: 1883 Nickname: The Lions

Club Contact Details 07581 015 868

Ground: The Town Ground, Mayfield Avenue, Heanor DE75 7EN **Club Colours:** White & black

HONOURS **League:** Central Midlands Supreme Division 1994-95, 96-97.
East Midlands Counties 2011-12.

FA Comps: None

10 YEAR RECORD

09-10	10-11	11-12	12-13	13-14	14-15	15-16	16-17	17-18	18-19
EMC 7	EMC 3	EMC 1	NCEP 11	NCEP 8	NCEP 6	MFLP 6	MFLP 6	MFLP 13	EMC 4
FAC EP	FAC EPr	FAC 1Q	FAC P	FAC EP	FAC P	FAC EP	FAC 1Q	FAC EP	FAC EP
FAV 2Qr	FAV 2P	FAV 1Q	FAT 1Pr	FAV 1P	FAV 4P	FAV 2P	FAV 1P	FAV 1Q	FAV 1P

From M1: J26, take A610 Ripley Road to end of dual carriageway then take A608 to Heanor via Langley Mill. At traffic lights at top of long hill take left lane signed Ilkeston. First right into Mundy Street, second left onto Godfrey Street. Ground on left where road forks. From A608 Derby: Enter town and see Tesco on left. Turn right at roundabout to the Market Place. Turn right at end of square and at crossroads right again onto Mundy Street. Then left into Godfrey Street and ground on left where road forks.

Nearest Railway Station Langley Mill - 2km

Bus Route Sports Ground stop - 132m away

HUCKNALL TOWN

Founded: 1987 Nickname: The Town

Club Contact Details 07572 473 037

Ground: Watnall Road, Hucknall, Notts NG15 6EY **Club Colours:** Yellow and black

HONOURS **League:** Central Midlands South Division 2018-19.

FA Comps: None

10 YEAR RECORD

09-10	10-11	11-12	12-13	13-14	14-15	15-16	16-17	17-18	18-19
NP P 17	NP P 20	NP1S 11	NP1S 22	CMSth 13	CMSth 4	CMSth 3	CMSth 4	CMSth 3	CMSth 1
FAC 3Qr	FAC 1Q	FAC 1Q	FAC P	FAC EP					
FAT 1Qr	FAT 1Q	FAT 1Q	FAT 2Q	FAV 1P		FAV 1P	FAV 3P	FAV 2Q	FAV 2P

Exit the M1 at Junction 27 and take the A608 towards Hucknall. Turn right onto the A611 to Hucknall then take the Hucknall bypass. At the second roundabout join Watnall Road (B6009) and the ground is 100 yards on the right.

INGLES

Founded: 1972 Nickname:

Club Contact Details 07703 730 872

Ground: The Dovecote, Little Haw Lane, Shepshed, Leicestershire. LE12 9BN **Club Colours:** Red and white

HONOURS **League:** North Leicestershire Division Three 1973-74, Division Two 74-75, Premier 92-93, 95-96, 2013-14.
Leicestershire Senior Premier Division 2017-18.

FA Comps: None

10 YEAR RECORD

09-10	10-11	11-12	12-13	13-14	14-15	15-16	16-17	17-18	18-19
				NLeiP 1	LeicSP 3	LeicSP 5	LeicSP 7	LeicSP 1	EMC 11
									FAV 2Q

Turn right off Ashby Road to Charnwood Road then take the second left down Anson Road.
Then take the fifth right to Chatsworth Close, this will bring you on to Little Haw Lane.

KIMBERLEY MINERS WELFARE

Founded: 1926 Nickname: Miners

Club Contact Details 07803 267 825

Ground: Kimberley MWFC, The Stag Ground, Kimberley, Nottingham NG16 2NB **Club Colours:** Red & black

HONOURS **League:** Spartan League 1947-48, 64-65, 65-66. Notts Amateur League 1985-86. Notts Alliance Division Two 1994-95, Division One 95-96.

FA Comps: None

10 YEAR RECORD

09-10	10-11	11-12	12-13	13-14	14-15	15-16	16-17	17-18	18-19
		NottSP 13	NottSP 5	NottSP 2	EMC 13	EMC 15	EMC 8	EMC 6	EMC 9
								FAC P	FAC P
						FAV 1Q	FAV 2Qr	FAV 2P	FAV 2Q

Leave the M1 at Junction 26. Take A610 to Nottingham before you reach Nuthall Island.
As Island take first exit signposted B600 Kimberley.
Follow road for around 2 miles before you see Stag PH on the right hand side.
Continue down road for a further 200 yards, entrance to ground between HAMA Medical Centre and Roots Emporium.

Nearest Railway Station Ilkeston - 3.4km and Bulwell - 3.8km.

RADFORD

Founded: 1964 Nickname: The Pheasants

Club Contact Details 0115 942 3250

Ground: Selhurst Street, Off Radford Road, Nottingham NG7 5EH **Club Colours:** Claret and sky blue

HONOURS **League:** East Midlands Regional League 1982-83.

FA Comps: None

10 YEAR RECORD

09-10	10-11	11-12	12-13	13-14	14-15	15-16	16-17	17-18	18-19
EMC 19	EMC 19	EMC 17	EMC 19	EMC 15	EMC 3	EMC 2	EMC 7	EMC 7	EMC 5
FAC EP						FAC P	FAC EP	FAC EPr	FAC EP
FAV 2Q	FAV 1Q	FAV 2Q	FAV 2Q	FAV 1Q	FAV 1Q	FAV 1P	FAV 2P	FAV 2Q	FAV 1Q

Leave the M1 at junction 26 (signposted Nottingham, Ilkeston), at roundabout take the 1st exit onto the A610 (signposted Nottingham) At r'about take the 3rd exit onto the A610 (signposted Nottingham) Entering Nottingham. At next r'about take the 2nd exit onto Nuthall Road - A610 (signposted Nottingham, Arnold), at traffic signals continue forward onto Nuthall Rd - A610 (signposted City Centre) At traffic signals turn left onto Western Boulevard - A6514 (signposted Ring Road, Mansfield) Turn immediately right onto Wilkinson St; go to top of street, past Tram Depot, follow tram line towards Nottingham At top of hill, (traffic lights turn right onto Radford Road – 4th turning on the right onto Selhurst St - Ground immediately on right.

Nearest Railway Station Nottingham - 2.8km

RAINWORTH M.W.

Founded: 1922 Nickname: The Wrens

Club Contact Details 01623 792 495

Ground: Welfare Ground, Kirklington Road, Rainworth, Mansfield NG21 0JY **Club Colours:** All white

HONOURS **League:** Notts Alliance 1971-72, 77-78, 78-79, 79-80, 80-81, 81-82, 82-83, 90-91, 95-96, 96-97.

FA Comps: None

10 YEAR RECORD

09-10	10-11	11-12	12-13	13-14	14-15	15-16	16-17	17-18	18-19
NCEP 2	NP1S 20	NP1S 19	NP1N 14	NP1S 15	NP1S 21	NCEP 9	NCEP 18	NCEP 10	EMC 17
FAC 2Q	FAC P	FAC P	FAC 1Qr	FAC Pr	FAC P	FAC EPr	FAC EP	FAC EP	FAC P
FAV 3P	FAT Pr	FAT P	FAT 1Q	FAT P	FAT Pr	FAV 1Q	FAV 1Q	FAV 1Q	FAV 1Q

From M1 (Junction 29) – take A617. At Pleasley turn right onto the new Mansfield Bypass road which is still the A617 and follow to Rainworth. At roundabout with B6020 Rainworth is off to the right, but it is better to go straight over onto the new Rainworth Bypass and then right at the next roundabout (the ground can be seen on the way along the Bypass) At mini roundabout, turn right onto Kirklington Road and go down the hill for ¼ mile – ground and car park on the right Alternatively you can reach the new A617 Bypass from the A38 via Junction 28 on the M1. From A614 at roundabout, take the A617 to Rainworth for 1 mile. Left at 1st r'about into village. At mini r'about right into Kirklington road - ¼ mile down hill as above.

Nearest Railway Station Mansfield - 4¼ miles

Bus Route Garden Avenue - stop 24m away

SHERWOOD COLLIERY

Founded: 2008 Nickname: The Wood

Club Contact Details 07813 718 302

Ground: Debdale Lane, Mansfield Woodhouse, Mansfield NG19 7NS **Club Colours:** Black and blue

HONOURS **League:** None

FA Comps: None

10 YEAR RECORD

09-10	10-11	11-12	12-13	13-14	14-15	15-16	16-17	17-18	18-19
			CMN 15	CMN 11	CMN 17	CMN 5	CMN 3	CMN 2	EMC 3
							FAV 2P	FAV 2Q	FAV 2Q

Take junction 28 off the M1 to Mansfield/Matlock. At Pinxton Interchange take 4th exit onto Alfreton Road/A38. After 2 miles take left onto Alfreton Road/B6023. After just over a mile (having gone over a roundabout) turn right onto B6023. Continue on B6023 until left onto Dalestorth Street. Continue along Dalestorth Street until it's end and turn left onto Beck Lane. Continue straight for 0.6 miles and onto Abbott Road/A6075. After two miles turn left onto Mallard Court. Ground on your left.

Nearest Railway Station Mansfield Woodhouse - 6min walk from the ground.

SHIREBROOK TOWN

Founded: 1985 Nickname: None

Club Contact Details

Ground: Langwith Road, Shirebrook, Mansfield, NG20 8TF **Club Colours:** Red and black

HONOURS

FA Comps: None

League: Central Midlands League Supreme Division 2000-01, 01-02.
Northern Counties East Division One 2003-04.

10 YEAR RECORD

09-10	10-11	11-12	12-13	13-14	14-15	15-16	16-17	17-18	18-19
NCEP 19	NCE1 13	NCE1 13	NCE1 6	NCE1 5	NCE1 4	NCE1 7	NCE1 18	NCE1 5	NCE1 18
FAC P	FAC 1Q	FAC Pr	FAC EP	FAC Pr	FAC EPr	FAC EP	FAC EPr		FAC EP
FAV 2Q	FAV 1Q	FAV 2Q	FAV 2Pr	FAV 2Q	FAV 1Q	FAV 2P	FAV 2Q	FAV 1P	FAV 2Q

Depart M1 at Junction 29, at roundabout take A617 towards Mansfield (for 3.5 miles), at next roundabout take 2nd Exit B6407 Common Lane towards Shirebrook (or 1.8 miles), go straight on at next roundabout (for 300 yards), at staggered crossroads turn right onto Main Street (for 1.1 miles), at T Junction turn right (for 100 yards), take the first road on your left (Langwith Road). The ground is 400 yards on the right.

Nearest Railway Station Shirebrook - 0.2km

Bus Route Langwith Road End - stop 36m away

TEVERSAL

Founded: 1918 Nickname: Tevie Boys

Club Contact Details 01623 554 924

Ground: Teversal Grange Sports and Social Centre, Carnarvon Street, Teversal, **Club Colours:** Black and red

HONOURS

FA Comps: None

League: Central Midlands Division Two 1987-88.

10 YEAR RECORD

09-10	10-11	11-12	12-13	13-14	14-15	15-16	16-17	17-18	18-19
NCE1 11	NCE1 18	NCE1 15	NCE1 10	NCE1 15	NCE1 20	NCE1 14	NCE1 16	EMC 3	EMC 15
FAC EPr	FAC EPr		FAC EP	FAC EP					FAC EP
FAV 1Q	FAV 1Q	FAV 2Q	FAV 2Q	FAV 2Q	FAV 1Q	FAV 2Q	FAV 1Q	FAV 2Q	FAV 2Q

From North: Travel South on the M1 to junc 29 take the A6175 to Heath and Holmewood. Travel through Holmewood, and at the r'dabout take the B6039 to Hardstaff and Tibshelf. At the T-junction in Tibshelf (pub on your left) turn left onto B6014 travelling over the motorway into Teversal. Follow the road round passing the Carnarvon Arms pub and under a bridge, take 2nd left onto Coppywood Close, travel to the top and following the road round with the ground at the top. **From South:** From the M1 junc 28, take the A38 to Mansfield. Travel through a number of sets of traffic lights and after passing the Kings Mill Reservoir you will come to a major junction (King & Miller Pub and McDonalds on your left). Travel straight on taking the A6075 towards Mansfield Woodhouse, at the next set of lights turn left onto the B6014 to Stanton Hill. You will come to a r'dabout with a Co-op on your left, continue on the B6014 towards Tibshelf. Take the second right onto Coppywood Close, then as above.

Nearest Railway Station Sutton Parkway - 4.5 miles

Bus Route Trent Barton No.241 from Mansfield bus station to Teversal (Carnarvon Street) - 1/4 mile walk to ground from there.

WEST BRIDGFORD

Founded: 1990 (Colts) Nickname:

Club Contact Details

Ground: Regatta Way, Gamston, West Bridgford, Nottingham NG2 5AT **Club Colours:** Black & red

HONOURS

FA Comps: None

League: East Midlands Counties 2016-17.

10 YEAR RECORD

09-10	10-11	11-12	12-13	13-14	14-15	15-16	16-17	17-18	18-19
		NottS2 2	NottS1 5	NottS1 2	NottSP 2	NottSP 3	EMC 1	EMC 15	EMC 13
								FAC EP	
							FAV 2Q	FAV 1Q	FAV 1Q

Follow M5 and M42 to A42 in Leicestershire. Continue on A42 to your destination in Nottinghamshire. Continue onto A42 after 13.7miles Keep left at the fork, follow signs for A453/A6/Nott'm(S)/Derby/East Midlands Airport. At Finger Farm Roundabout, take the 3rd exit onto Ashby Rd/A453. Ashby Rd/A453 turns slightly left and becomes Kegworth Interchange. Turn right to stay on Kegworth Interchange. Continue straight onto Remembrance Way/A453. At Mill Hill Roundabout, take the 2nd exit onto Barton Ln/Remembrance Way/A453. At the roundabout, take the 2nd exit onto Clifton Ln/Remembrance Way/A453. At the roundabout, take the 1st exit and stay on Clifton Ln/Remembrance Way/A453. At The Farnborough Rd Roundabout, take the 2nd exit onto Clifton Ln/A453. Take the Newark (A46) exit toward Melton (A606)/Grantham (A52). At the roundabout, take the 1st exit onto Clifton Ln/B679. At the roundabout, take the 2nd exit onto the A52 ramp to A606/A46/Grantham/Melton/Newark/Tollerton. Merge onto Clifton Blvd/A52. At the roundabout, take the 2nd exit onto A52. At Wheatcroft Island, take the 2nd exit onto Gamston Lings Bar Rd/A52. Continue to follow A52. At Gamston Roundabout, take the 1st exit onto Radcliffe Rd/A6011. Turn right onto Regatta Way. **Nearest Railway Station:** Nottingham - 2.7km.

PREMIER DIVISION INS: Mildenhall Town (R - IsthN). Stanway Rovers (Tr - ExS), Swaffham Town (P - ECo1N).
OUTS: Framlington Town (R - ECo1N), Great Yarmouth Town (R - ECo1N), Histon (P - IsthN).

BRANTHAM ATHLETIC

Nickname: Blue Imps **Club Colours:** All blue

Founded 1887

Club Contact Details 01206 392 506 (ground) secretary@branthamathletic.com
Ground: Brantham Leisure Centre, New Village, Brantham CO11 1RZ
Capacity: 1,200 **Seats:** 200 **Covered:** 200

Previous Names: Brantham & Stutton United 1996-98.
Previous Leagues: Eastern Counties. Suffolk & Ipswich.

HONOURS: FA Comps: None
League: Essex & Suffolk Border 1972-73, 73-74, 75-76, 76-77. Suffolk & Ipswich Senior League 2007-08.

10 YEAR RECORD

09-10		10-11		11-12		12-13		13-14		14-15		15-16		16-17		17-18		18-19	
EC1	3	ECP	13	ECP	3	ECP	4	ECP	11	ECP	8	ECP	11	ECP	8	ECP	5	ECP	8
		FAC	P	FAC	P	FAC	P	FAC	1Q	FAC	EPr	FAC	1Q	FAC	EP	FAC	P	FAC	2Q
FAV	2Q	FAV	1Q	FAV	1P	FAV	5P	FAV	4P	FAV	3P	FAV	1P	FAV	2Q	FAV	1Q	FAV	2Q

Turn off the A12 heading towards East Bergholt, stay on the B1070 through East Bergholt and go straight across the roundabout with the A137. Turn left immediately at the T-junction and follow this road around the sharp curve to the right and turn right immediately before the Village Hall. Follow this road around the sharp left hand turn and the Social Club and the car park are on the right.

Nearest Railway Station Manningtree - 1.5km
Bus Route Temple Pattle (Brooklands Close) - 120m

ELY CITY

Nickname: Robins **Club Colours:** Red

Founded 1885

Club Contact Details 01353 662 035 (ground) derek.oakey11@gmail.com
Ground: The Ellgia Stadium, Downham Road, Ely CB6 2SH
Capacity: 1,500 **Seats:** 200 **Covered:** 350 **Shop:** Yes

Previous Names: None.
Previous Leagues: Cambridgeshire 1901-02, 03-51. Peterborough & District 1951-58. Central Alliance 1958-60.

HONOURS: FA Comps: None
League: Peterborough & District 1955-56.
Eastern Counties Division One 1996-97.

10 YEAR RECORD

09-10		10-11		11-12		12-13		13-14		14-15		15-16		16-17		17-18		18-19	
ECP	9	ECP	15	ECP	2	ECP	11	ECP	17	ECP	20	EC1	2	ECP	13	ECP	14	ECP	18
FAC	EP	FAC	1Q	FAC	1Qr	FAC	Pr	FAC	EP	FAC	EP	FAC	EPr	FAC	EP	FAC	EP	FAC	EP
FAV	3P	FAV	1Qr	FAV	1Q	FAV	4P	FAV	2Pr	FAV	1Q	FAV	2Q	FAV	5P	FAV	2P	FAV	2Q

Follow signs for Kings Lynn/Downham Market as you approach Ely. Don't go into the city centre. After the Little Chef roundabout (junction of A10/A142) continue for approx half a mile until the next roundabout. Turn left for Little Downham (the B1411). There is also a sign for a Golf Course. The Golf Course is part of a Sports Complex which includes the football club. After turning left at the roundabout take another left after only about 50 metres into the Sports Complex entrance. The football club is at the end of the drive past the rugby club and tennis courts.

Nearest Railway Station Ely - 2.5km

FC CLACTON

Nickname: The Seasiders **Club Colours:** White & royal blue

Founded 1892

Club Contact Details 07527 222 088 (ground) secretaryfcclacton@gmail.com
Ground: Rush Green Bowl, Rush Green Rd, Clacton-on-Sea CO16 7BQ
Capacity: 3,000 **Seats:** 200 **Covered:** Yes **Shop:** Yes

Previous Names: Clacton Town > 2007
Previous Leagues: Eastern Counties 1935-37, 38-58. Essex County 1937-38. Southern League 1958-64.

HONOURS: FA Comps: None
League: North Essex D2 1898-99, 99-1900. Clacton & District 1905-06. South East Anglian D2 1907-08. Colchester & District D2 1909-10. East Anglian 1910-11. Southern D1 1959-60. Eastern Counties D1 1994-95, 98-99.

10 YEAR RECORD

09-10		10-11		11-12		12-13		13-14		14-15		15-16		16-17		17-18		18-19	
EC1	2	ECP	16	ECP	15	ECP	20	ECP	15	ECP	16	ECP	10	ECP	20	ECP	18	ECP	6
FAC	P	FAC	Pr	FAC	P	FAC	EP	FAC	2Qr	FAC	P	FAC	P	FAC	EP	FAC	EP	FAC	P
FAV	2P	FAV	1P	FAV	1P	FAV	2Q	FAV	1Q	FAV	2Q	FAV	1P	FAV	1Q	FAV	1Q	FAV	3P

Leave the A12 at junction 29, then at roundabout take the 1st exit, then merge onto the A120 (sign posted Clacton, Harwich). Branch left, then merge onto the A133 (sign posted Clacton). Continue along the A133 following signs to Clacton until St Johns Roundabout (tiled Welcome to Clacton sign) take the 4th exit onto St Johns Rd - B1027 (sign posted St Osyth) Entering Clacton On Sea B1027 (fire station on left). B1027 At second mini-roundabout turn left onto Cloes Lane (Budgens on right). Continue down Cloes Lane for about 1/2 mile, passing St.Clares School on your right, at traffic lights, turn right onto Rush Green Rd. Rush Green Bowl will then appear on the right after 1/4 mile.

Nearest Railway Station Clacton-on-Sea - 1.8km

GODMANCHESTER ROVERS

Nickname: Goody/Rovers **Club Colours:** Royal blue

Founded 1911

Club Contact Details 07734 136 419 (Ground) secretary@godmanchesterroversfc.co.uk

Ground: The David Wilson Homes Ground, Godmanchester, Huntingdon PE29 2LQ

Capacity: **Seats:** Yes **Covered:** Yes

Previous Names: None

Previous Leagues: Huntingdonshire County. Cambridgeshire >2002.

HONOURS: FA Comps: None

League: Eastern Counties League Division One 2011-12.

10 YEAR RECORD

09-10	10-11	11-12	12-13	13-14	14-15	15-16	16-17	17-18	18-19
EC1 12	EC1 9	EC1 1	ECP 5	ECP 5	ECP 2	ECP 2	ECP 12	ECP 4	ECP 3
FAC 1Q	FAC EPr	FAC P	FAC P	FAC P	FAC P	FAC P	FAC Pr	FAC EP	FAC 1Q
FAV 1Qr	FAV 2P	FAV 3P	FAV 1P	FAV 1P	FAV 1Pr	FAV 1Pr	FAV 1P	FAV 2Q	FAV 4P

From Junction 24 of the A14, take exit A1198 signposted Godmanchester, Wood Green Animal Shelter, Papworth, Royston. After approx 3/4 mile turn left into Bearscroft Lane where the ground is on the right hand side.

Nearest Railway Station Huntingdon - 3.1km

GORLESTON

Nickname: The Greens **Club Colours:** Green

Founded 1887

Club Contact Details 01493 602 802 (Ground) colin-bray@sky.com

Ground: Emerald Park, Woodfarm Lane, Gorleston, Norfolk NR31 9AQ

Capacity: **Seats:** Yes **Covered:** Yes

Previous Names: None

Previous Leagues: Aldred/Yamouth & District 1900-08. Norfolk & Suffolk/Anglian Combination 1908-35, 60-69. Eastern Counties 1935-60.

HONOURS: FA Comps: None

League: Yamouth & District 1905-06, 07-08. Norfolk & Suffolk/Anglian Comb. 1920-21, 25-26, 29-30, 31-32, 32-33, 33-34, 34-35, 68-69. Eastern Counties 1952-53, 72-73, 79-80, 80-81, Division One 1995-96, 2010-11.

10 YEAR RECORD

09-10	10-11	11-12	12-13	13-14	14-15	15-16	16-17	17-18	18-19
EC1 4	EC1 1	ECP 12	ECP 3	ECP 4	ECP 12	ECP 16	ECP 4	ECP 7	ECP 15
FAC Pr	FAC EP	FAC 1Q	FAC P	FAC 1Q	FAC EP	FAC EP	FAC EP	FAC 1Q	FAC EP
FAV 2Qr	FAV 2P	FAV 2Q	FAV 1P	FAV 1P	FAV 1P	FAV 2P	FAV 4P	FAV 3P	FAV 2Q

On Magdalen Estate follow signs to Crematorium, turn left and follow road to ground.

HADLEIGH UNITED

Nickname: Brettsiders **Club Colours:** Navy blue

Founded 1892

Club Contact Details 01473 822 165 (Ground) waffhenderson@aol.com

Ground: The Millfield, Tinkers Lane, Duke St, Hadleigh IP7 5NF

Capacity: 3,000 **Seats:** 250 **Covered:** 500

Previous Names: None

Previous Leagues: Ipswich & District/Suffolk & Ipswich 1929-91.

HONOURS: FA Comps: None

League: Suffolk & Ipswich 1953-54, 56-57, 73-74, 76-77, 78-79, Division Two 1958-59. Eastern Counties 1993-94, 2013-14.

10 YEAR RECORD

09-10	10-11	11-12	12-13	13-14	14-15	15-16	16-17	17-18	18-19
ECP 18	ECP 9	ECP 11	ECP 8	ECP 1	ECP 7	ECP 7	ECP 18	ECP 21	ECP 16
FAC EP	FAC EP	FAC P	FAC 1Q	FAC P	FAC 1Q	FAC EP	FAC EP	FAC P	FAC P
FAV 2Q	FAV 1P	FAV 1Q	FAV QF	FAV 5P	FAV 2P	FAV 2Q	FAV 2Q	FAV 2Q	FAV 2Q

On reaching Hadleigh High Street turn into Duke Street (right next to Library), continue on for approximately 150 metres and take left turn into narrow lane immediately after going over small bridge, continue to end of the lane where you will find the entrance to club car park.

HAVERHILL ROVERS

Founded 1886

Nickname: Rovers **Club Colours:** Red

Club Contact Details 01440 702 137 (ground) barbarajoneshrfc@outlook.com

Ground: The New Croft, Chalkstone Way, Haverhill, Suffolk CB9 0BW

Capacity: 3,000 **Seats:** 200 **Covered:** 200

Previous Names: None.

Previous Leagues: East Anglian. Essex & Suffolk Border.

HONOURS: FA Comps: None

League: Essex & Suffolk Border 1947-48, 62-63, 63-64.
Eastern Counties 1978-79.

10 YEAR RECORD

09-10		10-11		11-12		12-13		13-14		14-15		15-16		16-17		17-18		18-19	
ECP	12	ECP	8	ECP	14	ECP	10	ECP	7	ECP	17	ECP	12	ECP	16	ECP	19	ECP	12
FAC	EPr	FAC	Pr	FAC	1Q	FAC	P	FAC	P	FAC	EPr	FAC	EP	FAC	EP	FAC	Pr	FAC	2Q
FAV	1P	FAV	1P	FAV	1P	FAV	1P	FAV	1Q	FAV	2Q	FAV	1Q	FAV	2Q	FAV	1Q	FAV	2Q

Take the A143 in to Haverhill and, at the roundabout by Tesco, turn left and then right in the one in front of the store. Carry on over the next roundabout past Aldi on the left and past the Sports Centre, Cricket Club and garage on the left. Just after the Workspace Office Solutions building take a right towards the town centre (towards Parking (South). The drive way into Hamlet Croft is a small turning on the left just after Croft Lane (look for the sign for Tudor Close).

KIRKLEY & PAKEFIELD

Founded 1886

Nickname: The Kirks **Club Colours:** Royal blue

Club Contact Details 01502 513 549 (ground) secretarykpfc@outlook.com

Ground: The Bungalow, Walmer Road, Lowestoft NR33 7LE

Capacity: 2,000 **Seats:** 150 **Covered:** 150 **Shop:** Yes

Previous Names: Kirkley. Kirkley & Waveney 1929-33. Merged with Pakefield in 2007.

Previous Leagues: North Suffolk. Norfolk & Suffolk. Anglian Combination.

HONOURS: FA Comps: None

League: North Suffolk 1894-95, 96-97, 1901-02, 05-06, 07-08, 08-09.
Anglian Combination Premier Division 2001-02, 02-03.

10 YEAR RECORD

09-10		10-11		11-12		12-13		13-14		14-15		15-16		16-17		17-18		18-19	
ECP	4	ECP	12	ECP	13	ECP	12	ECP	12	ECP	4	ECP	5	ECP	11	ECP	10	ECP	5
FAC	2Q	FAC	EP	FAC	EP	FAC	P	FAC	P	FAC	P	FAC	2Q	FAC	P	FAC	EP	FAC	EPr
FAV	4P	FAV	2P	FAV	1Q	FAV	1Q	FAV	2Q	FAV	2P	FAV	2P	FAV	1Q	FAV	2Q	FAV	2P

From A12 to Lowestoft town centre and go over roundabout at Teamways Garage and past Teamways Pub.
Take next left into Walmer Road.

Nearest Railway Station Oulton Broad South - 1.8km

LONG MELFORD

Founded 1868

Nickname: The Villagers **Club Colours:** Black & white

Club Contact Details 01787 312 187 (Ground) richardjpowell@outlook.com

Ground: Stoneylands Stadium, New Road, Long Melford, Suffolk CO10 9JY

Capacity: **Seats:** Yes **Covered:** Yes

Previous Names: N/A

Previous Leagues: Essex & Suffolk Border > 2003

HONOURS: FA Comps: None

League: Essex & Suffolk Border Champions x5.
Eastern Counties Division One 2014-15.

10 YEAR RECORD

09-10		10-11		11-12		12-13		13-14		14-15		15-16		16-17		17-18		18-19	
EC1	16	EC1	12	EC1	9	EC1	13	EC1	11	EC1	1	ECP	9	ECP	17	ECP	16	ECP	17
				FAC	P	FAC	EP					FAC	P	FAC	P	FAC	P	FAC	1Qr
FAV	2Qr	FAV	2Q	FAV	1Q	FAV	1P	FAV	2Q	FAV	2Q	FAV	2Q	FAV	2Q	FAV	1Q	FAV	1Q

Turn down St Catherine Road off Hall St (Bury-Sudbury road) and then turn left into New Road.

Nearest Railway Station Sudbury - 4.6km

MILDENHALL TOWN

Nickname: The Hall **Club Colours:** Amber & black

Founded 1898

Club Contact Details 01638 713 449 (ground) bhensby@talktalk.net

Ground: Recreation Way, Mildenhall, Suffolk IP28 7HG

Capacity: 2,000 **Seats:** 100 **Covered:** 200 **Shop:** Yes

Previous Names: None

Previous Leagues: Bury & District. Cambridgeshire. Cambridgeshire Premier. Eastern Counties > 2017. Isthmian 2017-19.

HONOURS: FA Comps: None

League: Eastern Counties Premier Division 2016-17.

10 YEAR RECORD

09-10		10-11		11-12		12-13		13-14		14-15		15-16		16-17		17-18		18-19	
ECP	6	ECP	5	ECP	7	ECP	7	ECP	10	ECP	10	ECP	6	ECP	1	Isth1N	22	IsthN	20
FAC	2Q	FAC	EP	FAC	EP	FAC	EP	FAC	1Qr	FAC	1Q	FAC	2Q	FAC	EP	FAC	1Qr	FAC	P
FAV	1Q	FAV	1Q	FAV	2Q	FAV	1Q	FAT	1Pr	FAT	2Q	FAT	2P	FAT	2Q	FAT	3Q	FAT	1Q

Next to swimming pool and car park a quarter of a mile from town centre.

Bus Route Maids Head - stop 250m away

NEWMARKET TOWN

Nickname: The Jockeys **Club Colours:** Yellow & royal blue

Founded 1877

Club Contact Details 01638 663 637 (ground) domszary123@hotmail.com

Ground: The Bloorie Stadium, Cricket Field Road, Off Cheveley Rd, Newmarket CB8 8BT

Capacity: 2,750 **Seats:** 144 **Covered:** 250 **Shop:** Yes

Previous Names: None

Previous Leagues: Cambridgeshire Senior. Bury & District. Suffolk & Ipswich >1937. Eastern Counties 1937-52. Peterborough & District 1952-59.

HONOURS: FA Comps: None

League: Cambridgeshire Senior 1919-20. Bury & District 1926-27. Suffolk & Ipswich 1931-32, 32-33, 33-34. Peterborough & District 1957-58. Eastern Counties Division One 2008-09.

10 YEAR RECORD

09-10		10-11		11-12		12-13		13-14		14-15		15-16		16-17		17-18		18-19	
ECP	16	ECP	19	ECP	20	EC1	2	ECP	9	ECP	6	ECP	13	ECP	3	ECP	9	ECP	10
FAC	EP	FAC	P	FAC	EP	FAC	EP	FAC	Pr	FAC	1Q	FAC	P	FAC	EP	FAC	P	FAC	1Q
FAV	1P	FAV	2Q	FAV	2Q	FAV	2Q	FAV	2P	FAV	2Q	FAV	1P	FAV	2Q	FAV	1P	FAV	1P

Four hundred yards from Newmarket BR.Turn right into Green Road and right at cross roads into new Cheveley Road.
Ground is at top on left.

Nearest Railway Station Newmarket - 0.4km

NORWICH UNITED

Nickname: Planters **Club Colours:** Yellow & blue

Founded 1903

Club Contact Details 01603 716 963 (ground) norwich.utd.fc@gmail.com

Ground: Plantation Park, Blofield, Norwich NR13 4PL

Capacity: 3,000 **Seats:** 100 **Covered:** 1,000 **Shop:** Yes

Previous Names: Poringland & District > 1987

Previous Leagues: Norwich & District. Anglian Combination. Eastern Counties >2016. Isthmian 2016-18.

HONOURS: FA Comps: None

League: Anglian Combination Premier Division 1988-99. Eastern Counties Division One 1990-91, 01-02, Premier Division 2014-15, 15-16.

10 YEAR RECORD

09-10		10-11		11-12		12-13		13-14		14-15		15-16		16-17		17-18		18-19	
ECP	15	ECP	6	ECP	9	ECP	13	ECP	6	ECP	1	ECP	1	Isth1N	9	Isth1N	24	ECP	11
FAC	P	FAC	Pr	FAC	EP	FAC	1Q	FAC	EP	FAC	2Qr	FAC	Pr	FAC	P	FAC	P	FAC	EP
FAV	2Q	FAV	1P	FAV	2Q	FAV	2Q	FAV	4P	FAV	5P	FAV	2P	FAT	P	FAT	P	FAV	1Q

Follow A11 towards Norwich until A47 roundabout - take the 5th exit onto the A47 ramp to Gt Yarmouth/Ipswich/Lowestoft/A4146/A140.
Continue on the A47 for just over ten miles until exit toward Blofield/Heath, take this exit.
Then turn right onto Shack Lane. Turn right onto Woodbastwick Road.
Turn left onto Plantation Road.

Nearest Railway Station Brundall - 2.1km

Bus Route Surgery (Plantation Rd) stop - 48m away.

STANWAY ROVERS

Founded 1956

Nickname: Rovers **Club Colours:** Yellow

Club Contact Details 01206 578 187 (ground) ivan_senter@tiscali.co.uk

Ground: Hawthorns, New Farm Road, Stanway, Colchester CO3 0PG

Capacity: 1,500 **Seats:** 100 **Covered:** 250 **Shop:** Yes

Previous Names: None.

Previous Leagues: Colchester & East Essex. Essex & Suffolk Border. Eastern Counties >2018. Essex Senior 2018-19.

HONOURS: FA Comps: None

League: Colchester & East Essex Premier Division 1973-74. Essex & Suffolk Border Division Two 1981-82, 85-86. Eastern Counties Division One 2005-06.

10 YEAR RECORD

09-10		10-11		11-12		12-13		13-14		14-15		15-16		16-17		17-18		18-19	
ECP	5	ECP	7	ECP	5	ECP	9	ECP	13	ECP	3	ECP	3	ECP	6	ECP	8	ESen	15
FAC	1Qr	FAC	1Qr	FAC	EP	FAC	EP	FAC	EPr	FAC	EP	FAC	2Q	FAC	1Q	FAC	EP	FAC	P
FAV	3P	FAV	3P	FAV	2Q	FAV	2Q	FAV	2Q	FAV	5P	FAV	3P	FAV	2P	FAV	2Q	FAV	2Q

Leave A12 at Jct 26 to A1124. Turn right(from London)or left from Ipswich onto Essex Yeomanry Way.
A1124 towards Colchester 1st right into Villa Road, then left into Chaple Road, and left into New Farm Road.
Ground 400 yds on left.

Nearest Railway Station Colchester - 3.7km

STOWMARKET TOWN

Founded 1883

Nickname: Gold and Blacks **Club Colours:** Old Gold & black

Club Contact Details 01449 612 533 (ground) davidwalker545@gmail.com

Ground: Stowmarket Community Sports & Social Club, Greens Meadow, Bury Road, Stowmarket, Suffolk IP14 1JQ

Capacity: **Seats:** Yes **Covered:** Yes

Previous Names: Stowuplands Corinthians. Stowmarket Corinthians. Stowmarket FC

Previous Leagues: Ipswich & District 1896-1925. Essex & Suffolk Border 1925-52.

HONOURS: FA Comps: None

League: Ipswich & District/Suffolk & Ipwich 1896-97, 97-98, 99-1900, 21-22. Essex & Suffolk Border 1950-51. Eastern Counties Division One 2016-17.

10 YEAR RECORD

09-10		10-11		11-12		12-13		13-14		14-15		15-16		16-17		17-18		18-19	
EC1	15	EC1	7	EC1	15	EC1	17	EC1	14	EC1	11	EC1	14	EC1	1	ECP	3	ECP	4
FAC	EP			FAC	EP											FAC	Pr	FAC	EP
FAV	2Q	FAV	2Q	FAV	2Q	FAV	1Q	FAV	2Q	FAV	2Q	FAV	2Q	FAV	1Q	FAV	2Q	FAV	4P

Exit the A14 at junction 49 signposted Haughley/Stowmarket.
Take the 2nd exit towards Stowmarket. Follow the road all the way until you go under the A14 and reach another roundabout.
At this roundabout take the 1st exit and you will see the club to your immediate left.

Nearest Railway Station Stowmarket - 1km

SWAFFHAM TOWN

Founded 1892

Nickname: Pedlars **Club Colours:** Black & white

Club Contact Details 01760 722 700 (ground) rayewart@aol.com

Ground: The Pavillion, Shoemakers Lane, Swaffham, Norfolk PE37 7NT

Capacity: **Seats:** Yes **Covered:** Yes

Previous Names: None

Previous Leagues: Anglian Combination

HONOURS: FA Comps: None

League: Anglian Combination Division Two 1973-74. Eastern Counties Division One 2000-01, Division One North 18-19.

10 YEAR RECORD

09-10		10-11		11-12		12-13		13-14		14-15		15-16		16-17		17-18		18-19	
EC1	14	EC1	15	EC1	13	EC1	9	EC1	7	EC1	2	ECP	18	ECP	21	EC1	4	EC1N	1
								FAC	P	FAC	EP	FAC	EP	FAC	EP	FAC	P	FAC	EP
FAV	1Q	FAV	2Q	FAV	1Q	FAV	1P	FAV	1Pr	FAV	1Q	FAV	1P	FAV	1P	FAV	2Q	FAV	3Pr

Follow A11 until roundabout signposted A134, take first exit.
At the next roundabout, take the 3rd exit onto Swaffham Road/A1065.
Continue to follow A1065. At the next roundabout, take the 1st exit onto Brandon Road/A1065.
Continue to follow A1065. Turn left onto Haspalls Road.
Turn right onto Cley Road. Turn left onto Shoemakers Lane.

Bus Route Greenhoe Place (Haspalls Rd) stop - 212m away

WOODBRIDGE TOWN

Founded 1885

Nickname: The Woodpeckers **Club Colours:** Black & white

Club Contact Details 01394 385 308 (ground) richardnscott@btinternet.com

Ground: Notcutts Park, Fynn Road, Woodbridge IP12 4LS

Capacity: 3,000 **Seats:** 50 **Covered:** 200 **Shop:** No

Previous Names: None.

Previous Leagues: Ipswich & District. Suffolk & Ipswich.

HONOURS: FA Comps: None

League: Ipswich & District/Suffolk & Ipswich Senior 1912-13, 88-89, Division One 1986-87, 70-71.
Eastern Counties Division One 2017-18.

10 YEAR RECORD

09-10		10-11		11-12		12-13		13-14		14-15		15-16		16-17		17-18		18-19	
ECP	19	ECP	10	ECP	6	ECP	15	ECP	20	EC1	17	EC1	9	EC1	4	EC1	1	ECP	2
FAC	EP	FAC	EP	FAC	EPr	FAC	EP	FAC	EP	FAC	EP					FAC	EP	FAC	1Q
FAV	2P	FAV	2Q	FAV	1Pr	FAV	2Q	FAV	2Q	FAV	1P	FAV	2Q	FAV	2Q	FAV	2Q	FAV	2P

Get on A14 from A137.
Follow A14 and A12 to Ipswich Road/B1438.
Continue on Ipswich Road/B1438.
Drive to Fynn Road in Woodbridge.

Nearest Railway Station Woodbridge - 1.7km

Bus Route Ashton House (California) - 201m away

WROXHAM

Founded 1892

Nickname: Yachtsmen **Club Colours:** Royal blue

Club Contact Details 01603 783 538 (ground) ray.bayles@ntlworld.com

Ground: Trafford Park, Skinners Lane, Wroxham NR12 8SJ

Capacity: 2,500 **Seats:** 50 **Covered:** 250

Previous Names: None

Previous Leagues: East Norfolk. Norwich City. East Anglian. Norwich & Dist. Anglian Comb.

HONOURS: FA Comps: None

League: Anglian County League 1981-82, 82-83, 83-84, 84-85, 86-87.
Eastern Counties Division One 1988-89, Prem 91-92, 92-93, 93-94, 96-97, 97-98, 98-99, 2006-07, 11-12.

10 YEAR RECORD

09-10		10-11		11-12		12-13		13-14		14-15		15-16		16-17		17-18		18-19	
ECP	8	ECP	3	ECP	1	Isth1N	14	Isth1N	22	Isth1N	8	Isth1N	22	Isth1N	23	ECP	13	ECP	7
FAC	P	FAC	Pr	FAC	3Q	FAC	1Q	FAC	1Q	FAC	2Q	FAC	1Q	FAC	P	FAC	EP	FAC	EPr
FAV	F	FAV	3P	FAV	1P	FAT	1Qr	FAT	1Q	FAT	P	FAT	P	FAT	1Q	FAV	2Q	FAV	1P

Head North East from Norwich on the A1151 (Wroxham Road).
Over the railway bridge and straight over the mini roundabout.
Take the next left after the petrol station into Castle Street.
Over another railway bridge and turn left into Skinners Lane.
The entrance to the football ground is at the end on the left hand side.

Nearest Railway Station Hoveton & Wroxham - 1.6km

Bus Route 722, 724 and 717.

ECo DIVISION ONE NORTH INS: Framlington Town (R - ECoP), Great Yarmouth Town (R - ECoP), Sheringham (P - AngCom).
OUTS: Harleston Town (Demoted - AngCom), Swaffham Town (P - ECoP).

AFC SUDBURY RESERVES

Founded: 1999 Nickname: AFC

Club Contact Details 01787 376 213 dave-afc@supanet.com

Ground: Kings Marsh Stadium, Brundon Lane, Sudbury CO10 7HN **Club Colours:** Yellow & blue

HONOURS **League:** None

FA Comps: None

10 YEAR RECORD

09-10	10-11	11-12	12-13	13-14	14-15	15-16	16-17	17-18	18-19
				EC1 16	EC1 14	EC1 10	EC1 18	EC1 11	EC1N 13

From Colchester, Bury St Edmunds and Ipswich: Enter Sudbury and follow signs for Halstead/Chelmsford. Go aross the river bridge and go under the old rail bridge, then turn right at the traffic lights (Kings Head) into Bulmer Road and the first right again into Brundon Lane. The road narrows before reaching ground on the right hand side.

Nearest Railway Station Sudbury - 1.5km

CORNARD UNITED

Founded: 1964 Nickname: Ards

Club Contact Details 07834 773 416 paulw_66@outlook.com

Ground: Backhouse Lane, Great Cornard, Sudbury, Suffolk CO10 0NL **Club Colours:** All blue

HONOURS **League:** Colchester & East Essex Div.6 1971-72, Div.5 72-73, Div.4 73-74, Div.3 74-75
Essex & Suffolk Border 1988-89. Eastern Counties Division One 1989-90.

FA Comps: None

10 YEAR RECORD

09-10	10-11	11-12	12-13	13-14	14-15	15-16	16-17	17-18	18-19
EC1 13	EC1 17	EC1 16	EC1 18	EC1 18	EC1 18	EC1 15	EC1 15	EC1 15	EC1N 12
FAC EP									
FAV 1Q	FAV 1Q	FAV 2Q	FAV 1Q	FAV 2Q	FAV 1Q	FAV 1Q	FAV 1Q	FAV 1Q	FAV 1Q

Left off roundabout on A134 coming from Ipswich/Colchester into Sudbury, follow signs for Country Park - ground is immediately opposite along Blackhouse Lane.

Nearest Railway Station Sudbury - 2.2km

DEBENHAM LC

Founded: 1991 Nickname: The Hornets

Club Contact Details 01728 861 101 (ground)

Ground: Debenham Leisure Centre, Gracechurch Street, Debenham IP14 6BL **Club Colours:** Yellow & black

HONOURS **League:** Suffolk & Ipswich Division Seven 1991-92, Four 96-97, Three 99-2000,
One 03-04.

FA Comps: None

10 YEAR RECORD

09-10	10-11	11-12	12-13	13-14	14-15	15-16	16-17	17-18	18-19
ECP 14	ECP 22	EC1 7	EC1 15	EC1 12	EC1 7	EC1 13	EC1 12	EC1 7	EC1N 11
		FAC EP	FAC EP			FAC EP			
	FAV 2Q	FAV 2Q	FAV 1Qr	FAV 1P	FAV 2Q	FAV 2Q	FAV 1Q	FAV 1Pr	FAV 1Pr

Approach Ipswich along the A14. Turn left at junction 51 onto the A140 signposted towards Norwich.
After approx 4 miles turn right towards Mickfield and follow the road into Debenham turning left into Gracechurch Street.
Debenham Leisure Centre is approx 1 mile on the right hand side.

DISS TOWN

Founded: 1888 Nickname: Tangerines

Club Contact Details 01379 651 223 (ground) pamdisstownfc@gmail.com

Ground: Brewers Green Lane, Diss, Norfolk IP22 4QP **Club Colours:** Tangerine & navy

HONOURS **League:** Anglian Combination Division One 1967-68, 73-74, Premier 76-77, 78-79.
Eastern Counties Division One 1991-92.

FA Comps: FA Vase 1993-94.

10 YEAR RECORD

09-10	10-11	11-12	12-13	13-14	14-15	15-16	16-17	17-18	18-19
EC1 5	EC1 3	ECP 16	ECP 17	ECP 18	ECP 19	EC1 7	EC1 6	EC1 12	EC1N 15
FAC EP	FAC EP	FAC EP	FAC EP	FAC EP	FAC EP	FAC EP		FAC EP	
FAV 2Qr	FAV 1Q	FAV 3P	FAV 2P	FAV 1P	FAV 1Q	FAV 1P	FAV 2Q	FAV 2Q	FAV 1Q

Off B1066 Diss -Thetford road near Roydon school.

Nearest Railway Station Diss - 0.5 miles

DOWNHAM TOWN

Founded: 1881 Nickname: Town

Club Contact Details george.dickson@me.com

Ground: Memorial Field, Lynn Road, Downham Market PE38 9AU **Club Colours:** Red

HONOURS **League:** Peterborough & District 1962-63, 73-74, 78-79, 86-87, 87-88.

FA Comps: None

10 YEAR RECORD

09-10	10-11	11-12	12-13	13-14	14-15	15-16	16-17	17-18	18-19
EC1 18	EC1 16	EC1 14	EC1 16	EC1 17	EC1 9	EC1 16	EC1 14	EC1 9	EC1N 8
		FAV 2Q	FAV 2Q	FAV 1Q		FAV 2Q	FAV 2Q	FAV 1Q	FAV 1Q

One and a quarter miles from Downham Market (BR) - continue to town clock, turn left and ground is three quarters of a mile down Lynn Road.

Nearest Railway Station Downham Market - 1.25 miles

FAKENHAM TOWN

Founded: 1884 Nickname: Ghosts

Club Contact Details 01328 851 735 (ground) chilvers.paul@yahoo.com

Ground: Clipbush Park, Clipbush Lane, Fakenham, Norfolk NR21 8SW **Club Colours:** Amber & black

HONOURS **League:** Anglian Combination Division One 1971-72.

FA Comps: None

10 YEAR RECORD

09-10	10-11	11-12	12-13	13-14	14-15	15-16	16-17	17-18	18-19
EC1 19	EC1 14	EC1 11	EC1 5	EC1 2	ECP 13	ECP 17	ECP 15	ECP 22	EC1N 6
			FAC EP	FAC EP	FAC EPr	FAC P	FAC EP	FAC EP	FAC EP
FAV 2Q	FAV 1Qr	FAV 1Q	FAV 2Q	FAV 2Q	FAV 2P	FAV 2Q	FAV 2Q	FAV 1Q	FAV 1Q

From Kings Lynn: Follow A148 from Kings Lynn towards Cromer. On approaching Fakenham, you will come to a roundabout, where the A148 and the A1065 join. Take the first exit, continuing on the A148, towards Cromer. continue to the next roundabout, and take the third exit into Clipbush Lane. Continue to the next roundabout, and the entrance to the ground is the first exit, and is well signposted.
From Norwich: Those travelling from Norwich, will be approaching on the A1067, which will take you directly into Fakenham. At the first roundabout, turn right into Clipbush lane. Continue to the next r'about, and the entrance to the ground is the third exit from the roundabout, and is well signposted.

Bus Route Sanders Coaches No.9

FELIXSTOWE & WALTON UNITED RES

Founded: 2000 Nickname: Seasiders

Club Contact Details 01394 282 627 (ground) secretary@felixstowefootball.co.uk

Ground: Goldstar Ground, Dellwood Avenue, Felixstowe IP11 9HT **Club Colours:** Red & white

HONOURS **League:** None

FA Comps: None

10 YEAR RECORD

09-10	10-11	11-12	12-13	13-14	14-15	15-16	16-17	17-18	18-19
									EC1N 19

FRAMLINGHAM TOWN

Founded: 1887 Nickname: The Castlemen

Club Contact Details fionawhatling@tiscali.co.uk

Ground: Framingham Sports Club, Badingham Road, Framlingham IP13 9HS **Club Colours:** Green & white

HONOURS **League:** Suffolk & Ipswich Division Two 1980-81, Senior Division 91-92.

FA Comps: None

10 YEAR RECORD

09-10	10-11	11-12	12-13	13-14	14-15	15-16	16-17	17-18	18-19
S&I S 11	S&I S 10	S&I S 16	S&I 1 10	S&I 1 5	S&I 1 2	S&I S 5	EC1 7	EC1 2	ECP 20
								FAC P	FAC EPr
	FAV 1P	FAV 2Q					FAV 1Q	FAV 2P	FAV 2Qr

Via the A14, take the A140 ramp to Diss/Norwich/B1078. At the roundabout, take the 1st exit onto A140, Follow A1120 and B1119 to your destination in Framlingham. Turn right onto Stowmarket Rd/A1120, Continue to follow A1120. Turn right onto B1119. Turn right onto College Rd/B1116. At the roundabout, take the 2nd exit onto Well Cl Square/B1116, Continue to follow B1116. Turn left onto Fore St/B1119, Continue to follow B1119. Slight left onto Badingham Rd/B1120

GREAT YARMOUTH TOWN

Founded: 1897 Nickname: The Bloaters

Club Contact Details 07776 147 508 (Secretary) jglewsley@btinternet.com

Ground: The Wellesley, Sandown Road, Great Yarmouth NR30 1EY **Club Colours:** Yellow & black

HONOURS **League:** Norfolk & Suffolk 1913-14, 26-27, 27-28. Eastern Counties 1968-69, Division One 2009-10.

FA Comps: None

10 YEAR RECORD

09-10	10-11	11-12	12-13	13-14	14-15	15-16	16-17	17-18	18-19
EC1 1	ECP 14	ECP 21	EC1 10	EC1 8	EC1 4	EC1 3	ECP 5	ECP 15	ECP 19
FAC P	FAC EP	FAC EP	FAC P	FAC EP	FAC P	FAC EP	FAC EP	FAC 1Q	FAC EP
FAV 1Q	FAV 2Q	FAV 2Q	FAV 2Q	FAV 2P	FAV 3P	FAV 1P	FAV 1P	FAV 2Q	FAV 2P

Approaching Great Yarmouth on the A47 at the end of the single carriageway you will come to a roundabout where the A12 and A47 meet. Take the second exit onto the A149 towards the town centre. Continue to the next roundabout (Fuller's Hill roundabout) and take the second exit. Keep in the left hand lane and at the traffic lights turn left onto Northgate Street. Follow this road to the roundabout and take the second exit onto Kitchener Road. At the crossroads go straight ahead onto Sandown Road and you will see the Wellesley on the right.

Nearest Railway Station Great Yarmouth - 1/2 mile away.

HAVERHILL BOROUGH

Founded: 2011 Nickname: Borough

Club Contact Details 01440 702 137 (Ground)

Ground: The New Croft, Chalkestone Way, Haverhill, Suffolk CB9 0BW **Club Colours:** Blue

HONOURS **League:** Essex & Suffolk Border Division One 2011-12.

FA Comps: None

10 YEAR RECORD

09-10	10-11	11-12	12-13	13-14	14-15	15-16	16-17	17-18	18-19
		EsSu1 1	EsSuP 2	EC1 4	EC1 6	EC1 8	EC1 3	ECP 20	EC1N 16
	-				FAC 1Q	FAC EP		FAC 1Q	FAC EP
				FAV 1Q	FAV 1P	FAV 1Q	FAV 1P	FAV 1Q	FAV 1P

Take the A143 in to Haverhill and, at the roundabout by Tesco, turn left and then right in the one in front of the store. Carry on over the next roundabout past Aldi on the left and past the Sports Centre, Cricket Club and garage on the left. Just after the Workspace Office Solutions building take a right towards the town centre (towards Parking (South). The drive way into Hamlet Croft is a small turning on the left just after Croft Lane (look for the sign for Tudor Close).

IPSWICH WANDERERS

Founded: 1980 Nickname: Wanderers

Club Contact Details 01473 720 691 (Ground)

Ground: SEH Sports Centre, Humber Doucy Lane, Ipswich IP4 3NR **Club Colours:** All blue

HONOURS **League:** Eastern Counties Division One 1997-98, 04-05.

FA Comps: None

10 YEAR RECORD

09-10	10-11	11-12	12-13	13-14	14-15	15-16	16-17	17-18	18-19
EC1 17	EC1 10	EC1 12	EC1 4	EC1 3	ECP 9	ECP 15	ECP 10	ECP 23	EC1N 10
		FAC Pr	FAC EP	FAC P	FAC 1Qr	FAC 2Q	FAC EPr	FAC EP	FAC EP
FAV 2Q	FAV 1P	FAV 2Q	FAV 1P	FAV 1P	FAV 2P	FAV 5Pr	FAV 2P	FAV 1Q	FAV 1Q

Exit the M25 At junction 28, exit toward A12/Chelmsford E/A1023/Brentwood/London/Romford. Keep left at the fork, follow signs for C'ford/A12 and merge onto A12. Continue on A12. Drive to Humber Doucy Ln in Suffolk. Merge onto A12. At the r'about, take the 3rd exit onto the A14 (E) ramp to A12 (N)/Felixstowe/Lowestoft. Merge onto A14. At junction 57, exit onto Nacton Rd/A1189 toward Ipswich. At the r'about, take the 3rd exit onto Ransomes Way/A1189. At the r'about, take the 2nd exit and stay on Ransomes Way/A1189. At the r'about, take the 1st exit onto Felixstowe Rd/A1156. At the r'about, continue straight onto Bixley Rd/A1189. Continue to follow A1189. At the r'about, take the 2nd exit onto Woodbridge Rd E/A1214. Slight left toward Playford Rd. Continue onto Playford Rd. Turn left onto Humber Doucy Lane.

Nearest Railway Station Derby Road (Ipswich) 2.1km.

KING'S LYNN TOWN RESERVES

Founded: 1879 Nickname: The Linnets

Club Contact Details 01553 760 060 (Ground) ncesar1947@yahoo.co.uk

Ground: The Walks Stadium, Tennyson Road, King's Lynn PE30 5PB. **Club Colours:** Blue

HONOURS **League:** None

FA Comps: None

10 YEAR RECORD

09-10	10-11	11-12	12-13	13-14	14-15	15-16	16-17	17-18	18-19
ECP Exp					EC1 5	EC1 5	EC1 10	EC1 6	EC1N 14

At the roundabout, at the junction of A47 and the A17, follow the A47, signposted King's Lynn and Norwich. Travel along the dual carriageway for approx. one and a half miles branching off left, following the signs for Town Centre, onto the Hardwick roundabout. Take the first exit, following the signs for Town Centre, travel through two sets of traffic lights until reaching a further set of traffic lights at the Southgates roundabout. Take the fourth exit onto Vancouver Avenue, and travel for approx. 300 metres, going straight across a mini roundabout, The Walks is a further 200 metres along on the left hand side, with car parking outside the ground. The changing rooms and hospitality suite are located at the rear of the main stand.

Nearest Railway Station King's Lynn - 5min walk away.

Bus Route Serviced by Eastern Counties & Norfolk Green

LAKENHEATH

Founded: Nickname:

Club Contact Details lakenheathfc.secretary@gmail.com

Ground: The Nest, Wings Road, Lakenheath IP27 9HN **Club Colours:** Green & white

HONOURS **League:** Cambridgeshire County Senior Division A 2007-08, Premier 10-11.

FA Comps: None

10 YEAR RECORD

09-10	10-11	11-12	12-13	13-14	14-15	15-16	16-17	17-18	18-19
CamP 3	CamP 1	CamP 2	CamP 9	CamP 5	CamP 2	CamP 6	CamP 3	CamP 8	EC1N 5

Take the A14, followed by the A1101 and then finally the B1112 which will bring you in to the village of Lakenheath.

Nearest Railway Station Lakenheath 4.5km walk

Bus Route 201 from Mildenhall, 200 from Thetford

LEISTON RESERVES

Founded: 1880 Nickname: Blues

Club Contact Details 01728 830 308 (ground)

Ground: The LTAA, Victory Road, Leiston, Suffolk IP16 4DQ **Club Colours:** All blue

HONOURS **League:** None

FA Comps: None

10 YEAR RECORD

09-10	10-11	11-12	12-13	13-14	14-15	15-16	16-17	17-18	18-19
					EC1 19	EC1 6	EC1 21	EC1 13	EC1N 9

Take junction 28 off the M25, take the A12/A1023 exit to Chelmsford/Romford/Brentwood, keep left at the fork, follow signs for Chelmsford/A12 (E) and merge onto A12, at the roundabout, take the 3rd exit onto the A14 ramp, merge onto A14, at junction 58, exit toward A12, keep left at the fork, follow signs for Lowestoft/Woodbridge/A12 (N) and merge onto A12, go through 7 roundabouts, turn right onto A1094, turn left onto Snape Rd/B1069, continue to follow B1069, turn left onto Victory Rd, ground will be on the left.

MARCH TOWN UNITED

Founded: 1885 Nickname: Hares

Club Contact Details 01354 653 073 (ground) chris@gbshealthandsafety.co.uk

Ground: GER Sports Ground, Robin Goodfellow Lane, March, Cambs PE15 8HS **Club Colours:** Amber & black

HONOURS **League:** United Counties Division One 1953-54. Eastern Counties 1987-88.

FA Comps: None

10 YEAR RECORD

09-10	10-11	11-12	12-13	13-14	14-15	15-16	16-17	17-18	18-19
EC1 7	EC1 8	EC1 4	EC1 14	EC1 19	EC1 8	EC1 11	EC1 16	EC1 17	EC1N 4
FAC EP	FAC P	FAC Pr	FAC EP						
FAV 1P	FAV 1Q	FAV 1Q	FAV 1Q	FAV 2Q			FAV 2Q	FAV 1Q	FAV 2Q

Follow signs for A14 E. Continue onto A14. At the roundabout, take the 2nd exit onto Thrapston Rd/A14. Continue to follow A14. At the next roundabout, take the 2nd exit onto A141. Continue on the A141 until roundabout signposted B1099, take the 4th exit onto Wisbech Rd/B1099. At the next roundabout, take the 1st exit onto Norwood Road. Turn right onto Maple Grove. Turn right onto Robingoodfellow's Lane.

Nearest Railway Station March - 0.7km

Bus Route Darthill Road stop - 290m away

MULBARTON WANDERERS

Founded: 2002 Nickname: Wanderers

Club Contact Details 07545 470 130 j.nurse21@btinternet.com

Ground: Mulberry Park, Mulbarton Common, Norfolk NR14 8AE **Club Colours:** Blue & black

HONOURS **League:** Anglian Combination Division Five 2010-11, Division Four 11-12, Division One 14-15.

FA Comps: None

10 YEAR RECORD

09-10	10-11	11-12	12-13	13-14	14-15	15-16	16-17	17-18	18-19
AnC6 2	AnC5 1	AnC4 1	AnC3 2	AnC3 2	AnC1 1	AnCP 8	AnCP 3	AnCP 2	EC1N 3
									FAV 2Q

Nearest Railway Station Norwich (6.5 miles away)

Bus Route Regular services from Norwich City centre to the village of Mulbarton.

NEEDHAM MARKET RESERVES

Founded: 1919 Nickname: The Marketmen

Club Contact Details 01449 721 000 (ground) m.easlea@sky.com

Ground: Bloomfields, Quinton Road, Needham Market IP6 8DA. **Club Colours:** Red

HONOURS **League:** None

FA Comps: None

10 YEAR RECORD

09-10	10-11	11-12	12-13	13-14	14-15	15-16	16-17	17-18	18-19
				EC1 15	EC1 16	EC1 19	EC1 19	EC1 20	EC1N 17

Quinton Road is off Barretts Lane which in turn is off Needham Market High Street.

Nearest Railway Station Needham Market - 0.6km

Bus Route Quinton Road stop - 38m away

NORWICH CBS

Founded: 1888 Nickname:

Club Contact Details 01603 748 944 (ground) norwichcbsfc@outlook.com

Ground: The FDC, Bowthorpe Park, Clover Hill Road, Norwich NR5 9ED **Club Colours:** Sky blue

HONOURS **League:** Anglian Combination Premier Division 2016-17.

FA Comps: None

10 YEAR RECORD

09-10	10-11	11-12	12-13	13-14	14-15	15-16	16-17	17-18	18-19
AnCP 12	AnCP 11	AnCP 4	AnCP 2	AnCP 2	AnCP 5	AnCP 2	AnCP 1	EC1 8	EC1N 7
								FAV 4P	FAV 2P

Follow A11 towards Norwich until roundabout with 2nd exit signposted A47 (Swaffham). Merge onto Norwich Southern Bypass/A47. Take the A1074 exit toward Norwich. At the next roundabout, take the 4th exit. At the next roundabout, take the 2nd exit onto Dereham Road/A1074. At the next roundabout, take the 3rd exit onto Wendene. Turn left onto Clover Hill Road.

Bus Route Breckland Road stop - 176m away

SHERINGHAM

Founded: 1897 Nickname: The Shannocks

Club Contact Details 07961 435261 (Secretary) info@sheringhamfc.co.uk

Ground: Sheringham Recreation, Weybourne Road, Sheringham NR26 8WD **Club Colours:** Red

HONOURS **League:** Norfolk & Suffolk 1957-58. Anglian Combination Premier 1969-70, 2008-09, 18-19, Division Three 02-03, Division Two 03-04, Division One 04-05.

FA Comps: None

10 YEAR RECORD

09-10	10-11	11-12	12-13	13-14	14-15	15-16	16-17	17-18	18-19
AnCP 13	AnCP 10	AnCP 11	AnCP 14	AnCP 13	AnCP 16	AnC1 6	AnC1 11	AnC1 2	AnCP 1

WISBECH ST MARY

Founded: 1993 Nickname: The Saints

Club Contact Details 01945 410 243 (ground) martin@jsholmes.com

Ground: ABC Meats Stadium, Beechings Close, Wisbech St Mary PE13 4SS **Club Colours:** Purple

HONOURS **League:** Cambridgeshire County Division 1B 2008-09, Senior B 10-11,

FA Comps: None

10 YEAR RECORD

09-10	10-11	11-12	12-13	13-14	14-15	15-16	16-17	17-18	18-19
CamSB 3	CamSB 1	CamSA 3	CamP 7	CamP 8	CamP 15	CamP 5	EC1 13	EC1 18	EC1N 18
						FAV 2Q	FAV 1Q	FAV 2P	FAV 1Q

Follow A47 towards Wisbech. Just before Ring's End turn left onto Gull Road/B1187.
Then turn right onto Gull Road.
Gull Road turns slightly left and becomes High Road, follow for just over 4 miles and then turn left onto Station Road.
Then turn left onto Beechings Close less than half a mile later.

Bus Route St Mary's Close (High Rd) stop - 362m away

BARKINGSIDE

Founded: 1898 Nickname: The Side / Sky Blues

Club Contact Details 020 8552 3995 confclothing@aol.com

Ground: Cricketfield Stadium, 3 Cricklefield Place, Ilford IG1 1FY **Club Colours:** Sky blue

HONOURS **League:** Spartan Premier Division 1996-97. Spartan South Midlands 1998-99.

FA Comps: None

10 YEAR RECORD

09-10	10-11	11-12	12-13	13-14	14-15	15-16	16-17	17-18	18-19
ESen 9	ESen 15	ESen 8	ESen 2	Isth1N 20	Isth1N 22	Isth1N 23	ESen 10	ESen 16	ESen 19
FAC EP	FAC EP	FAC EP	FAC EPr	FAC P	FAC 1Q	FAC P	FAC P	FAC EP	FAC EPr
FAV 2Q	FAV 2Q	FAV 2Qr	FAV 1Q	FAT P	FAT 2Q	FAT P	FAV 2Q	FAV 2Q	FAV 2Q

Taking the A127, from the east travel towards London before coming to the traffic light controlled junction at Barley Lane, Goodmayes (B177) . Turn Left by taking the slip road and follow Barley Lane to its junction with the traffic light controlled High Road, Goodmayes (A118) (it is the first set of traffic control lights for traffic rather than pedestrians on that road). Turn Right and follow the road past Seven Kings station (which should be on your right) and on towards Ilford. The entrance to the ground is some 400 yards past the station with the Ilford Swimming Baths on the left being the point at which both coaches and those in cars or on foot should turn left into the car parks.

Nearest Railway Station Ilford (underground) / Seven Kings (BR) ½ mile

Bus Route 86 outside ground

BENFLEET

Founded: 1922 Nickname:

Club Contact Details 01268 682 991 (Canvey Island FC)

Ground: Canvey Island FC, Frost Financial Stadium, 1 Park Lane, Canvey Island **Club Colours:** Sky and navy blue

HONOURS **League:** Essex Olympian Division One 1988-89, Division Two 2006-07, Division Three 15-16.

FA Comps: None

10 YEAR RECORD

09-10	10-11	11-12	12-13	13-14	14-15	15-16	16-17	17-18	18-19
EsxOP 13	EsxO1 5	EsxO1 11	EsxO1 9	EsxO1 11	EsxO2 Exp	EsxO3 1	EsxO2 3	EsxO2 4	EC1S 12

BRIGHTLINGSEA REGENT RES

Founded: 1928 Nickname: The Rs

Club Contact Details 01206 304 199 (ground)

Ground: Taydal Stadium, North Road, Brightlingsea, Essex CO7 0PL **Club Colours:** Red & black

HONOURS **League:** None

FA Comps: None

10 YEAR RECORD

09-10	10-11	11-12	12-13	13-14	14-15	15-16	16-17	17-18	18-19
									EC1S 18

Take exit 28 off M25, take slip road left for A12 toward Brentwood / Chelmsford / Romford, turn left onto slip road, merge onto A12, take slip road left for A120, take slip road left for A133, at roundabout, take 2nd exit, turn left onto B1029 / Great Bentley Road, turn right onto B1027 / Tenpenny Hill, and then immediately turn left onto B1029 / Brightlingsea Road, turn left to stay on B1029 / Ladysmith Avenue, bear left onto Spring Road, turn left onto North Road.

Nearest Railway Station Alresford - 4.8km

Bus Route Spring Chase - stop 300m away

BURNHAM RAMBLERS

Founded: 1900 Nickname: Ramblers

Club Contact Details 01621 784 383 (Ground) martin.leno@btopenworld.com

Ground: Leslie Fields Stadium, Springfield Road CM0 8TE **Club Colours:** Blue & black

HONOURS **League:** Mid-Essex 1927-28, 54-55, 62-63. Essex Olympian 1966-67. Essex Senior League 2012-13.

FA Comps: None

10 YEAR RECORD

09-10	10-11	11-12	12-13	13-14	14-15	15-16	16-17	17-18	18-19
ESen 3	ESen 7	ESen 4	ESen 1	Isth1N 17	Isth1N 24	ESen 14	ESen 21	ESen 20	EC1S 13
FAC EP	FAC 1Q	FAC Pr	FAC P	FAC 1Q	FAC P	FAC EP	FAC EP	FAC EP	FAC EP
FAV 1P	FAV 2P	FAV 1P	FAV 2P	FAT 1Q	FAT P	FAV 1Qr	FAV 2Q	FAV 1P	FAV 1Q

A12 Proceed along the A12 until you reach the turn off for Maldon. Carry on through Danbury and then follow the signs for Burnham on Crouch (B1010). *Just before you get to Burnham on Crouch there is a garage on the left-hand side. Springfield Road is about quarter of a mile past the garage on the right. Turn right into Springfield Road, then take the second turning on the right and then first right and drive through the gates of the ground. **A127** Proceed along the A127, and take the A130 turn off sign-posted to Chelmsford. At Rettendon Turnpike (a large roundabout), take the A132 to South Woodham Ferrers. Burnham on Crouch is sign-posted from there (B1012 and then B1010). Continue from * above. **A13** Proceed along A13 and take the A130 turn off sign-posted to Chelmsford. At Rettendon Turnpike (a large roundabout) take the A132 to South Woodham Ferrers. Burnham on Crouch is sign-posted from there (B1012 and then B1010). Continue from * above.

Nearest Railway Station Burnham on Crouch (Greater Anglia).

Bus Route 31X (Eastern National)

COGGESHALL UNITED

Founded: 2017 Nickname: Weavers

Club Contact Details 01376 562 962 (Ground) secretary@coggeshallunitedfc.co.uk

Ground: West Street, Coggeshall, Essex CO6 1NT **Club Colours:** Blue

HONOURS **League:** None

FA Comps: None

10 YEAR RECORD

09-10	10-11	11-12	12-13	13-14	14-15	15-16	16-17	17-18	18-19
								EsSuP 2	EC1S 2
									FAV 2Q

FIRE UNITED

Founded: 2012 Nickname:

Club Contact Details 02075 114 477 & 077446 952 176 (ground) fire_united_secretary@hotmail.com

Ground: Terence MacMillan Stadium, Plaistow E13 8SD **Club Colours:** Gold & blue

HONOURS **League:** None

FA Comps: None

10 YEAR RECORD

09-10	10-11	11-12	12-13	13-14	14-15	15-16	16-17	17-18	18-19
			Midx1SE 9	Midx1SE 7	Midx1SE 12		Midx1SE 9	Midx1SE 4	EC1S 19
									FAV 1Q

FRENFORD

Founded: 1945 Nickname:

Club Contact Details 020 8518 0992 (ground)

Ground: Jack Carter Centre, The Drive, Ilford, Essex, IG1 3PS **Club Colours:** Red & white

HONOURS **League:** Ilford & District Premier 1975-76. Essex Olympian Division Two 1995-96, Premier 2011-12, 12-13.

FA Comps: None

10 YEAR RECORD

09-10	10-11	11-12	12-13	13-14	14-15	15-16	16-17	17-18	18-19
EsxOP 4	EsxOP 3	EsxOP 1	EsxOP 1	EsxOP 3	EsxOP 7	EsxOP 7	EsxOP 5	EsxOP 2	EC1S 9

HACKNEY WICK

Founded: 1995 Nickname: The Wickers

Club Contact Details 07388 372 989 (Secretary)

Ground: The Old Spotted Dog, Upton Lane, Forest Gate E7 9NP **Club Colours:** Yellow & black

HONOURS **League:** Essex Sunday Corinthian 2011-12.

FA Comps: None

10 YEAR RECORD

09-10	10-11	11-12	12-13	13-14	14-15	15-16	16-17	17-18	18-19
		EsxSC 1	ESen 10	ESen 20	ESen 15	ESen 8	ESen 17	ESen 21	EC1S 6
						FAC EP	FAC EP	FAC EP	FAC P
					FAV 2Q	FAV 1Q	FAV 1P	FAV 1Q	FAV 2Q

Five minute walk along Upton Lane from Romford Road.

Nearest Railway Station Wanstead Park, 10 min walk or Stratford, 25 min walk

Bus Route 25, 6 min walk from Woodgrange Park bus stop

HALSTEAD TOWN

Founded: 1879 Nickname: Humbugs

Club Contact Details 01787 472 082 (ground) halsteadtownfc@aol.com

Ground: Rosemary Lane, Broton Industrial Estate, Halstead, Essex CO9 1HR **Club Colours:** Black & white

HONOURS
FA Comps: None

League: Essex & Suffolk Border Premier Division 1957-58, 68-69, 77-78.
Eastern Counties 1994-95, 95-96, Division One 2002-03.

10 YEAR RECORD

09-10	10-11	11-12	12-13	13-14	14-15	15-16	16-17	17-18	18-19
EC1 6	EC1 11	EC1 6	EC1 11	EC1 6	EC1 10	EC1 4	EC1 9	EC1 10	EC1S 3
FAC 1Qr	FAC P	FAC EP	FAC P	FAC EP	FAC EPr		FAC 1Q		
FAV 2Pr	FAV 2Q	FAV 1P	FAV 2Q	FAV 2Q	FAV 1Q	FAV 2Q	FAV 2Q	FAV 2Q	FAV 1Q

From A1311 Chelmsford to Braintree road follow signs to Halstead.

HARWICH & PARKESTON

Founded: 1875 Nickname: Shrimpers

Club Contact Details 01255 503 643

Ground: Royal Oak, Main Road, Dovercourt, Harwich CO12 4AA **Club Colours:** Black & white stripes

HONOURS
FA Comps: None

League: Essex & Suffolk Border Senior Division 1908-09, 13-14, 20-21, 21-22, 22-23, 28-29, 31-32, 32-33, 33-34. Eastern Counties 1935-36 (joint). Essex County 1937-38. Athenian Division Two 1964-65

10 YEAR RECORD

09-10	10-11	11-12	12-13	13-14	14-15	15-16	16-17	17-18	18-19
ECP Exp	EsSuP	EsSuP 2	EsSuP 5	EsSuP 3	EsSu1 5	EsSuP 9	EsSuP 6	EsSuP 10	EC1S 5

HOLLAND

Founded: 2006 Nickname:

Club Contact Details 07778 142 118 (ground) mark.sorrell@btinternet.com

Ground: Eastcliff Sports Ground, Dulwich Road, Holland-on-Sea CO15 5HP **Club Colours:** Orange

HONOURS
FA Comps: None

League: Essex & Suffolk Border Division One 2008-09.

10 YEAR RECORD

09-10	10-11	11-12	12-13	13-14	14-15	15-16	16-17	17-18	18-19
EsSuP 7	EsSuP 5	EsSuP 12	EsSuP 4	EsSuP 10	EsSuP 4	EsSuP 4	EC1 5	EC1 16	EC1S 11
								FAV 1P	FAV 2Q

From Colchester, Get on A12 in Mile End from A134 and Via Urbis Romanae, Head south on Rotary Way. At the roundabout, take the 2nd exit and stay on Rotary Way. Turn left onto Westway/A134. At the roundabout, take the 5th exit and stay on Westway/A134. At the roundabout, take the 2nd exit and stay on Westway/A134. At Essex Hall Roundabout, take the 2nd exit onto A134. Turn left onto Turner Rd/A134. Continue to follow A134. Continue straight onto Via Urbis Romanae. At the roundabout, take the 2nd exit. At the roundabout, take the 3rd exit. At the roundabout, take the 2nd exit onto the A12 ramp to Ipswich/Felixstowe/A14/Harwich/A120. Take A120 and A133 to St John's Rd/B1027 in Clacton-on-Sea. Merge onto A12. Take the A120 ramp to Calchester North/A1232/Clacton Harwich. Keep right to continue on A120. At the roundabout, take the 1st exit onto Colchester Rd/A133. At the roundabout, take the 3rd exit onto A133. At the roundabout, take the 2nd exit and stay on A133. Go through 1 r'dabout. Continue on B1027. Drive to Dulwich Rd in Holland-on-Sea.

Nearest Railway Station Clacton-on-Sea - 1.7km

LEYTON ATHLETIC

Founded: 2008 Nickname: Wad Army

Club Contact Details 07903 061 692 wadamlodge.fc@hotmail.com

Ground: Wadham Lodge Sports Ground, Kitchener Road, Walthamstow E17 4JP **Club Colours:** All white

HONOURS
FA Comps: None

League: Essex Olympian Division Three 2009-10, Division Two 2010-11.

10 YEAR RECORD

09-10	10-11	11-12	12-13	13-14	14-15	15-16	16-17	17-18	18-19
EsxO3 1	EsxO2 1	EsxO1 4	EsxO1 2	EsxOP 9	EsxOP 4	ESen 6	ESen 15	ESen 19	ESen 20
								FAC EPr	FAC P
							FAV 2P	FAV 1Q	FAV 1Q

From North and West London - Use the M25 or any other means to get onto the North Circular Road (A406). Leave A406 at Crooked Billet roundabout slip road. At roundabout take the 4th turn off signposted Leyton/Walthamstow. After 300 yards you will see a church on your left. Turn left here into Brookscroft Road. Follow the road until you are forced to turn left. Turn left into Kitchener Road and you will see the gates to the ground and car park on your right. **From East London** - From the M11/A406 junction, follow road flow onto the Southend Road. Exit when you see sign for the A112. This takes you to the Crooked Billet Roundabout. Take the first exit to Walthamstow, then turn left into Brookscroft Road and follow directions above. **From South London** - The easiestway is through Blackwell Tunnel then follow signs for Stansted Airport until you get onto the M11 link road. You'll come through to Leytonstone and to the Redbridge roundabout. Keep left until you flow onto the North Circular Road (A406). Take the A406, then follow the instructions for East London.B

Nearest Railway Station Walthamstow Central - Victoria Line/London Overground, 1.4 miles

Bus Route 34,97, 215, 357, approx. ¼ mile

LITTLE OAKLEY

Founded: 1947 Nickname: The Acorns

Club Contact Details 01255 880 370 (ground)

Ground: Memorial Ground, Harwich Road, Little Oakley, Harwich CO12 5ED **Club Colours:** Blue & black

HONOURS
League: Essex & Suffolk Border Division One 1985-86,
Premier Division 1986-87, 87-88, 92-93, 2003-04, 15-16, 16-17.
FA Comps: None

10 YEAR RECORD

09-10	10-11	11-12	12-13	13-14	14-15	15-16	16-17	17-18	18-19
EsSuP 6	EsSuP 13	EsSuP 6	EsSuP 7	EsSuP 6	EsSuP 2	EsSuP 4	EsSuP 1	EC1 14	EC1S 7
								FAV 2Q	FAV 1Pr

Follow M5, M4 and M25 to Brentwood. Take exit 28 from M25 toward A12/Chelmsford E/A1023/Brentwood/London/Romford. Keep left at the fork, follow signs for C'ford/A12 and merge onto A12. Take the A120 ramp to Calchester North/A1232/Clacton Harwich. Keep right to continue on A120. At the roundabout, take the 2nd exit and stay on A120. Turn right at Main Rd/B1352. Slight left onto Church Hill/B1352. Turn right onto Mayes Lane. At the roundabout, take the 1st exit and stay on Mayes Lane. Turn right onto Harwich Rd/B1414

Nearest Railway Station Harwich International - 3.3km

Bus Route Mayes Lane stop - 173m away

LOPES TAVARES

Founded: 2015 Nickname:

Club Contact Details 0300 124 0123/07756 417255 secretary.ltlondonfc@gmail.com

Ground: 281 Prince Regent Lane, London E13 8SD **Club Colours:** Red

HONOURS
League: None
FA Comps: None

10 YEAR RECORD

09-10	10-11	11-12	12-13	13-14	14-15	15-16	16-17	17-18	18-19
							EsxAIP 8	EsxAIP 5	EC1S 16

MAY & BAKER E.C.

Founded: Nickname: Bakers

Club Contact Details 0208 919 2156 / 3156 mwright@cvc.com

Ground: Parkside, Park Lane, Aveley RM15 4PX **Club Colours:** Red & black

HONOURS
League: Essex Olympian Division One 2009/10.
FA Comps: None

10 YEAR RECORD

09-10	10-11	11-12	12-13	13-14	14-15	15-16	16-17	17-18	18-19
EsxO1 1	EsxOP 6	EsxOP 11	EsxOP 8	EsxOP 10	EsxOP 9	EsxOP 11	EsxOP 3	EsxOP 7	EC1S 8
									FAV 2P

Nearest Railway Station Purfleet

NEWBURY FOREST

Founded: 2003 Nickname:

Club Contact Details 0208 550 3611 ron.dangerfield@newburyforestfc.co.uk

Ground: Redbridge FC, Oakside Stadium, Station Road, Barkingside, IG6 1NB **Club Colours:** Navy blue

HONOURS
League: Romford & District Senior 2009-10.
FA Comps: None

10 YEAR RECORD

09-10	10-11	11-12	12-13	13-14	14-15	15-16	16-17	17-18	18-19
RomS 1			EsxO1 3	EsxOP 7	EsxOP 10	EsxOP 14	EsxO1 6	EsxO1 8	EC1S 17
						FAV 2Q	FAV 1Q		FAV 1P

Take junction 26 off the M25, exit toward A121/Loughton/Waltham Abbey. Take A121, A1168, A113 and A123 to Station Road in Ilford.
Having turned off onto the A123 take the 2nd exit off the next roundabout onto Craven Gardens.
Then turn left onto Carlton Drive, turn left to stay on Carlton Drive.
Slight right onto Station Road.

Nearest Railway Station Barkingside Underground - 186m

Bus Route Barkingside - 395m away

WHITE ENSIGN

Founded: 1951 Nickname:

Club Contact Details 01702 217 812 (ground)

Ground: Burroughs Park, Little Wakering Hall Lane, Great Wakering SS3 0HH **Club Colours:** Red

HONOURS **League:** Essex Intermediate/Olympian Division Two 2002-03, Division One 03-04, 04-05, 06-07, 07-08.

FA Comps: None

10 YEAR RECORD

09-10	10-11	11-12	12-13	13-14	14-15	15-16	16-17	17-18	18-19
EsxOP 10	EsxOP 12	EsxOP 8	EsxOP 7	EsxOP 13	EsxO1 2	EsxOP 5	EsxOP 12	EsxOP 4	EC1S 4
									FAV 1Q

A127 towards Southend and follow signs for Shoeburyness for about four miles.
Turn left to Great Wakering on B1017 at Bournes Green.
Go down High Street for half a mile and Great Wakering Rovers FC's ground is on the left.

Nearest Railway Station Shoeburyness - 3.2km

Bus Route Barrow Hall Rd (Little Wakering Rd) - 631m

WIVENHOE TOWN

Founded: 1925 Nickname: The Dragons

Club Contact Details lorraineosman1969@yahoo.com

Ground: Broad Lane Ground, Elmstead Road, Wivenhoe CO7 7HA **Club Colours:** Blue & white

HONOURS **League:** Brightlingsea & Dist 1932-33, 36-37, 47-48. Colchester & East Essex Prem 1952-53, 55-56, D1 59-60, 69-70. Essex & Suffolk D2 1971-72, D1 72-73, Prem 78-79. Isth D2N 1987-88, D1 1989-90. Eastern C. D1 2015-16.

FA Comps: None

10 YEAR RECORD

09-10	10-11	11-12	12-13	13-14	14-15	15-16	16-17	17-18	18-19
ECP 20	ECP 20	ECP 19	ECP 18	ECP 19	ECP 18	EC1 1	ECP 19	ECP 24	EC1S 14
FAC EPr			FAC EPr	FAC EPr	FAC P	FAC EP	FAC EP	FAC EP	FAC EP
FAV 1P		FAV 1Q	FAV 2Qr	FAV 1Q	FAV 1P	FAV 2Q	FAV 1Q	FAV 1Q	FAV 1Q

The ground is situated off the B1027 on the junction of Elmstead Road and Brightlingsea Road to the north of Wivenhoe.

Nearest Railway Station Wivenhoe - 2.4km.

Bus Route No.62.

WORMLEY ROVERS

Founded: 1921 Nickname:

Club Contact Details 01992 460 650 (ground)

Ground: Wormley Sports Club, Church Lane, Wormley EN10 6LB **Club Colours:** Red & black

HONOURS **League:** Herts Senior County Division Three 1976-77, Division One 86-87.

FA Comps: None

10 YEAR RECORD

09-10	10-11	11-12	12-13	13-14	14-15	15-16	16-17	17-18	18-19
HertP 2	HertP 7	HertP 8	HertP 7	HertP 8	HertP 5	HertP 15	HertP 8	HertP 5	EC1S 10
									FAV 1Q

Off the A10

INS: Cockfosters (Tr - SSMP), Hadley (Tr - SSMP), Hashtag United (P - ECo1S).
OUTS: Barkingside (R - EC1S), Hullbridge Sports (P - IsthN), Leyton Athletic (R - ECo1S), Stanway Rovers (Tr - ECoP).

CLAPTON

Nickname: Tons **Club Colours:** Red & white Founded 1878

Club Contact Details 0203 652 2951 (ground) secretary@claptonfc.com
Ground: The Old Spotted Dog, Upton Lane, Forest Gate E7 9NP
Capacity: 2,000 **Seats:** 100 **Covered:** 180 **Shop:** No

Previous Names: None
Previous Leagues: Southern (FM). London. Isthmian (FM) 1905-2006.

HONOURS: FA Comps: FA Amateur Cup 1906-07, 08-09, 14-15, 23-24, 24-25.
League: Isthmian 1910-11, 22-23, Division Two 1982-83.

10 YEAR RECORD

09-10	10-11	11-12	12-13	13-14	14-15	15-16	16-17	17-18	18-19
ESen 16	ESen 17	ESen 17	ESen 18	ESen 10	ESen 8	ESen 7	ESen 2	ESen 6	ESen 11
FAC EP	FAC EP	FAC EP	FAC EP	FAC P	FAC EPr	FAC EP	FAC P	FAC 1Q	FAC EPr
FAV 1Q	FAV 2Q	FAV 2Q	FAV 1P	FAV 1P	FAV 2Q	FAV 2Q	FAV 1Q	FAV 1P	FAV 2Q

A13 to Plaistow junction (A112) follow A112 along Prince Regent's Lane straight across two sets of lights.
At 3rd set of lights, turn right onto Clegg St. Go straight across the next set of lights onto Upton Lane, (A114).
The Ground is approximately half a mile down on the left hand side.

Nearest Railway Station Forest Gate, 8-10 min walk or Plaistow (District Line), 5-7 min
Bus Route 325, stops outside ground

COCKFOSTERS

Nickname: Fosters **Club Colours:** All red Founded 1921

Club Contact Details 0208 449 5833 graham.bint@btinternet.com
Ground: Cockfosters Sports Ground, Chalk Lane, Cockfosters, Herts EN4 9JG
Capacity: **Seats:** Yes **Covered:** Yes

Previous Names: Cockfosters Athletic 1921-68.
Previous Leagues: Barnet 1921-30s. Wood Green 1930s-46. Northern Suburban Int. 1946-66. Hertfordshire County 1966-1991. Spartan 1991-97. Spartan South Midlands 1997-2019.
HONOURS: FA Comps: None
League: Wood green Division Two 1931-32, Division One 33-34, Premier 38-39. Northern Suburban Inter. Division One 1949-50, 60-61, Premier 61-62. Hertfordshire Senior County Division One 1966-67, Premier 78-79, 80-81, 83-84

10 YEAR RECORD

09-10	10-11	11-12	12-13	13-14	14-15	15-16	16-17	17-18	18-19
SSM1 11	SSM1 15	SSM1 9	SSM1 2	SSM P 8	SSM P 18	SSM P 9	SSM P 3	SSM P 20	SSM P 18
FAC Pr	FAC Pr	FAC P	FAC P	FAC 1Qr	FAC P	FAC 1Q	FAC EP	FAC 1Q	FAC EP
FAV 1P	FAV 1P	FAV 1Q	FAV 2P	FAV 2P	FAV 1P	FAV 1Qr	FAV 2P	FAV 1P	FAV 1Q

Leaving the M25 motorway at junction 24 (Potters Bar), take the A111 signposted to Cockfosters. The ground is situated approximately 2 miles from the motorway on the right immediately before Cockfosters Underground Station. VEHICLE DRIVERS PLEASE BE AWARE THAT THE YELLOW LINES & PARKING RESTRICTIONS IN CHALK LANE ARE STRICTLY ENFORCED UP TO 6.30PM INCLUDING SATURDAYS.

Nearest Railway Station New Barnet - 1.5km
Bus Route Cockfosters - stop 200m away

ENFIELD 1893 FC

Nickname: The E's **Club Colours:** White & royal blue Founded 1893

Club Contact Details 07957 647 820 enfieldfc@sky.com
Ground: The Harlow Arena, Elizabeth Way, Harlow, Essex CM19 5BE
Capacity: 3,500 **Seats:** 500 **Covered:** Yes

Previous Names: Enfield Spartans > 1900. Enfield > 2007.
Previous Leagues: Tottenham & District. North Middlesex. London 1903-12, 20-21. Athenian 1912-14, 21-63. Isthmian 1963-81, 90-2005, 06-07. Conference 1981-90. Southern 2005-06.
HONOURS: FA Comps: FA Amateur Cup 1966-67, 69-70. FA Trophy 1981-82, 87-88.
League: Alliance 1982-83, 85-86. Essex Senior 2010-11.

10 YEAR RECORD

09-10	10-11	11-12	12-13	13-14	14-15	15-16	16-17	17-18	18-19
ESen 4	ESen 1	ESen 7	ESen 9	ESen 3	ESen 16	ESen 20	ESen 18	ESen 9	ESen 14
FAC 2Q	FAC EP	FAC Pr	FAC EP	FAC EPr	FAC EP	FAC EP	FAC EP	FAC EP	FAC EP
FAV 2P	FAV 1P	FAV 4P	FAV 4P	FAV 4P	FAV 1P	FAV 1Q	FAV 2Q	FAV 3P	FAV 2P

Exit M11 at Junction 7. Follow the A414 towards Harlow until the first set of traffic lights where you filter off to the left onto the A1169. Follow the A1169, signed for Roydon, over several mini roundabouts until you get to a large grassed roundabout where you turn right (2nd exit). Continue straight down the road until you meet another roundabout where you turn left (2nd exit). Keep going until you reach the GSK roundabout where you turn right, then keep going straight until you see the ground ahead of you at the Roydon Road roundabout. Go straight over the roundabout and the entrance to the ground is on the left. If coming into town from the west on the A414 turn right at the first roundabout (the old ground was straight ahead) signed Roydon A1169. Follow the A1169 for approx 1 mile and the entrance to the ground is on the right.

Nearest Railway Station Harlow Town, 1.2 miles
Bus Route No direct bus to the ground

HADLEY

Nickname: Bricks **Club Colours:** Red and black

Founded 1882

Club Contact Details info@hadleyfc.co.uk

Ground: Hadley Sports Ground, Brickfield Lane, Arkley, Barnet EN5 3LD

Capacity: 2,000 **Seats:** 150 **Covered:** 250 **Shop:** Yes

Previous Names: None

Previous Leagues: Barnet & Dist. 1922-57, North Suburban 1957-70, Mid-Herts 1970-77, Herts Senior County 1977-85, 99-2007, Southern Olymian 1985-99, West Herts 2007-08. Spartan South Mildlands 08-19.

HONOURS: FA Comps: None

League: Mid-Herts Premier 1975-76, 76-77. Hertfordshire Senior County Division Three 1977-78, Division One 2001-02, Premier 2003-04, 04-05. West Hertfordshire 2007-08.

10 YEAR RECORD

09-10	10-11	11-12	12-13	13-14	14-15	15-16	16-17	17-18	18-19
SSM1 2	SSM P 14	SSM P 15	SSM P 12	SSM P 13	SSM P 9	SSM P 6	SSM P 19	SSM P 6	SSM P 3
	FAC EPr	FAC EPr	FAC P	FAC P	FAC EPr	FAC EP	FAC 3Qr	FAC 1Q	FAC 1Qr
FAV 2P	FAV 2Q	FAV 1P	FAV 1Pr	FAV 2P	FAV 2Qr	FAV 1P	FAV 1Q	FAV 2Qr	FAV 2Q

From M25, exit junction 23 (South Mimms) go south on the A1 to Stirling Corner roundabout. Take the left exit onto Barnet Road and continue until the first set of traffic lights. Go straight over and then take the immediate first left opposite the Gate Oublic House into Brickfield Lane. The ground is approximately 75 yards on the left.

Nearest Railway Station Elstree & Borehamwood - 2.8km

Bus Route Brickfield Lane - stop 70m away

HASHTAG UNITED

Nickname: **Club Colours:** Blue & yellow

Founded 2016

Club Contact Details 0208 889 1415 (Matchday) jay@hashtagunited.co.uk

Ground: Chadfields, St Chads Road, Tilbury, Essex RM18 8NL

Capacity: 4,000 **Seats:** 350 **Covered:** 1,000

Previous Names: Spencer FC.

Previous Leagues: Eastern Counties 2018-19

HONOURS: FA Comps: None

League: Eastern Counties Division One South 2018-19

10 YEAR RECORD

09-10	10-11	11-12	12-13	13-14	14-15	15-16	16-17	17-18	18-19
									EC1S 1

A13 Southend bound go left at Chadwell St Mary's turning, then right after 400 metres and right again at roundabout (signed Tilbury). Right into St Chads Road after five miles, first right into Chadfields for ground.

Nearest Railway Station Tilbury Town - 1.1km

Bus Route Raphael Avenue - stop 75m away

HODDESDON TOWN

Nickname: Lilywhites **Club Colours:** White & black

Founded 1879

Club Contact Details 07860 423 977 jdsinden1@gmail.com

Ground: The Stewart Edwards Stadium, Lowfield, Park View, Hoddesdon, Herts. EN11 8PX

Capacity: 3,000 **Seats:** 150 **Covered:** Yes

Previous Names: None

Previous Leagues: Hertfordshire County 1920-25. Spartan 1925-75. London Spartan 1975-77. Athenian 1977-84. Spartan SM 1984-2018.

HONOURS: FA Comps: FA Vase 1974-75 (1st Winners).

League: Spartan 1970-71, Division One 1935-36, Division Two 'B' 1927-28.

10 YEAR RECORD

09-10	10-11	11-12	12-13	13-14	14-15	15-16	16-17	17-18	18-19
SSM1 4	SSM1 9	SSM1 3	SSM1 3	SSM P 6	SSM P 19	SSM P 3	SSM P 7	SSM P 12	ESen 9
FAC P	FAC EP	FAC EP	FAC EPr	FAC EPr	FAC P	FAC 3Qr	FAC P	FAC EP	FAC P
FAV 3P	FAV 1Q	FAV 1P	FAV 1P	FAV 2Q	FAV 2Q	FAV 1P	FAV 3P	FAV 1Q	FAV 2Q

From A10 take the Hoddesdon turn off, A1170. Follow slip road to roundabout at bottom of the hill and turn right into Amwell Street (morrisons will be on your left). Take the first right, at church, into Pauls Lane. Follow road round to the left, which becomes Taverners Way, and at mini roundabout at end (opposite Iceland store) turn right into Brocket Road. At T-junction turn left into Park View and ground is approximately 200 yards on right. Please note that there are strict parking restrictions on Saturday in Park View.
For Sat-Nav use the postcode EN11 8PU which will take you to Park Road, directly opposite the ground.

Nearest Railway Station Broxbourne

Bus Route 310 - Hoddesdon High Street

ILFORD

Founded 1987

Nickname: The Foxes **Club Colours:** Blue and white hoops

Club Contact Details 020 8514 8352

Ground: Cricklefield Stadium, 486 High Road, Ilford, Essex IG1 1FY

Capacity: 3,500 **Seats:** 216 **Covered:** Yes **Shop:** No

Previous Names: Reformed as Ilford in 1987 after the original club merged with Leytonstone in 1980.

Previous Leagues: Spartan 1987-94, Essex Senior 1996-2004, Isthmian 2004-05, 2006-13, Southern 2005-06.

HONOURS: FA Comps: FA Amateur Cup 1928-29, 29-30.

League: Isthmian 1906-07, 20-21, 21-22, Division Two 2004-05.

10 YEAR RECORD

09-10		10-11		11-12		12-13		13-14		14-15		15-16		16-17		17-18		18-19	
Isth1N	20	Isth1N	20	Isth1N	20	Isth1N	22	ESen	16	ESen	10	ESen	5	ESen	6	ESen	13	ESen	10
FAC	P	FAC	1Q	FAC	Pr	FAC	P	FAC	EP	FAC	EP	FAC	P	FAC	P	FAC	P	FAC	EP
FAT	Pr	FAT	1Q	FAT	P	FAT	1Q	FAV	1P	FAV	2Q	FAV	1P	FAV	1P	FAV	2Q	FAV	1Q

Taking the A127, from the east travel towards London before coming to the traffic light controlled junction at Barley Lane, Goodmayes (B177) . Turn Left by taking the slip road and follow Barley Lane to its junction with the traffic light controlled High Road, Goodmayes (A118) (it is the first set of traffic control lights for traffic rather than pedestrians on that road). Turn Right and follow the road past Seven Kings station (which should be on your right) and on towards Ilford. The entrance to the ground is some 400 yards past the station with the Ilford Swimming Baths on the left being the point at which both coaches and those in cars or on foot should turn left into the car parks.

Nearest Railway Station Seven Kings (BR), approx. ½ mile

Bus Route 86, outside ground

REDBRIDGE

Founded 1958

Nickname: Motormen **Club Colours:** Royal blue

Club Contact Details r.holloway338@btinternet.com

Ground: Oakside Stadium, Station Road, Barkingside, Essex IG6 1NB

Capacity: 3,000 **Seats:** **Covered:**

Previous Names: Ford United 1958-2004

Previous Leagues: Aetolian 1959-64, Greater London 1964-71, Metropolitan London 1971-74, Essex Senior 1974-97, Isthmian 1997-2004, 05-16. Conference 2004-05.

HONOURS: FA Comps: None

League: Aetolian 1959-60, 61-62. Greater London 1970-71. Essex Senior 1991-92, 96-97. Isthmian Division Three 1998-99, Division One 2001-02.

10 YEAR RECORD

09-10		10-11		11-12		12-13		13-14		14-15		15-16		16-17		17-18		18-19	
Isth1N	18	Isth1N	16	Isth1N	6	Isth1N	20	Isth1N	14	Isth1N	23	Isth1N	24	ESen	14	ESen	4	ESen	12
FAC	P	FAC	2Q	FAC	2P	FAC	P	FAC	P	FAC	Pr	FAC	P	FAC	EP	FAC	P	FAC	EP
FAT	P	FAT	1Q	FAT	3Q	FAT	1Q	FAT	P	FAT	P	FAT	1Q	FAV	2Q	FAV	2Qr	FAV	3P

Take junction 26 off the M25, exit toward A121/Loughton/Waltham Abbey. Take A121, A1168, A113 and A123 to Station Road in Ilford.
Having turned off onto the A123 take the 2nd exit off the next roundabout onto Craven Gardens.
Then turn left onto Carlton Drive, turn left to stay on Carlton Drive.
Slight right onto Station Road.

Nearest Railway Station Barkingside Underground - 186m

Bus Route Barkingside - 395m away

SAFFRON WALDEN TOWN

Founded 1872

Nickname: The Bloods **Club Colours:** Red & black

Club Contact Details 01799 520 980

Ground: Catons Lane Stadium, Saffron Walden, Essex CB10 2DU

Capacity: **Seats:** Yes **Covered:** Yes

Previous Names: Saffron Walden > 1967. Resigned from ECo in August 2011 rejoining for 2012-13 season.

Previous Leagues: Herts County 1955-71. Essex Senior 1971-74, 96-2003. Eastern Counties 1974-84 2004-11, 12-18. Isthmian 1984-96.

HONOURS: FA Comps: None

League: Essex Senior 1973-74, 99-00. Eastern Counties 1982-83.

10 YEAR RECORD

09-10		10-11		11-12		12-13		13-14		14-15		15-16		16-17		17-18		18-19	
EC1	14	EC1	6			EC1	6	ECP	5	EC1	3	ECP	8	ECP	9	ECP	11	ESen	4
FAC	EP	FAC	Pr					FAC	EP	FAC	Pr	FAC	1Q	FAC	1Q	FAC	Pr	FAC	1Qr
FAV	1Q	FAV	2Q			FAV	2Q	FAV	2Q	FAT	4P	FAV	3P	FAV	1P	FAV	1Q	FAV	2Q

Into Castle Street off Saffron-Walden High Street.
Then left at T-junction and first left by Victory Pub.

Nearest Railway Station Audley End - 3.5km

Bus Route Saffron Walden High Street

SAWBRIDGEWORTH TOWN

Founded 1897

Nickname: Robins **Club Colours:** Red & black

Club Contact Details 01279 722 039

Ground: Crofters End, West Road, Sawbridgeworth CM21 0DE

Capacity: 2,500 **Seats:** 175 **Covered:** 300

Previous Names: Sawbridgeworth > 1976.

Previous Leagues: Stortford. Spartan 1936-39, 46-53. Herts County. Essex Olympian.

HONOURS: FA Comps: None
League: Essex Olympian 1971-72.

10 YEAR RECORD

09-10		10-11		11-12		12-13		13-14		14-15		15-16		16-17		17-18		18-19	
ESen	10	ESen	16	ESen	6	ESen	14	ESen	6	ESen	5	ESen	10	ESen	5	ESen	8	ESen	18
				FAC	EP	FAC	EP	FAC	EP	FAC	EP	FAC	EP	FAC	1Q	FAC	EP	FAC	EP
		FAV	2Q	FAV	2Q	FAV	2Q	FAV	2Q	FAV	1Q	FAV	1Q	FAV	2Q	FAV	1P	FAV	1P

From junction 7 of M11 take the A414 towards Harlow and go through three roundabouts. At the 4th roundabout take the 3rd exit onto Cambridge Rd (A1184). Continue on A1184 and at the roundabout take the 1st exit onto West Road. Turn right onto Crofters and ground will be facing.

Nearest Railway Station Sawbridgeworth, approx. ½ mile

Bus Route 510 & 511, approx. ½ mile

SOUTHEND MANOR

Founded 1955

Nickname: The Manor **Club Colours:** Yellow & black

Club Contact Details 07788 580 360 southendmanor@btinternet.com

Ground: The Arena, Southchurch Park, Northumberland Crescent, Southend SS1 2XB

Capacity: 2,000 **Seats:** 500 **Covered:** 700 **Shop:** No

Previous Names: None

Previous Leagues: Southend Borough Combination. Southend & District Alliance.

HONOURS: FA Comps: None
League: Southend Borough Combination 1971-72, 73-74, 78-79, 79-80, 80-81, 81-82.
Southend & District Alliance 1983-84, 84-85. Essex Senior 1990-91.

10 YEAR RECORD

09-10		10-11		11-12		12-13		13-14		14-15		15-16		16-17		17-18		18-19	
ESen	7	ESen	5	ESen	2	ESen	7	ESen	19	ESen	18	ESen	16	ESen	7	ESen	14	ESen	17
FAC	EPr	FAC	P	FAC	4Q	FAC	1Q	FAC	EPr	FAC	EP	FAC	P	FAC	EPr	FAC	P	FAC	EP
FAV	1P	FAV	2Q	FAV	3Pr	FAV	3P	FAV	2Q	FAV	2Q	FAV	2Qr	FAV	2Q	FAV	1Q	FAV	1P

Take junction 29 off the M25, merge onto Southend Arterial Road/A127. At the rnext oundabout, take the 3rd exit onto Prince Ave/A127. At the next roundabout, take the 2nd exit onto Priory Cres/A1159. Continue to follow A1159. Go through 1 roundabout then at the next roundabout, take the 2nd exit onto Eastern Ave/A1159. At the next roundabout, take the 3rd exit onto Hamstel Road. Go through 1 roundabout then continue onto Lifstan Way, in less than half a mile turn right onto Woodgrange Drive. Then turn third left at the 3rd cross street onto Marlborough Road, Northumberland Crescent will be at the end of this road.

Nearest Railway Station Southend East (C2C), ½ mile to ground

Bus Route 7 & 8 (Arriva) to Woodgrange Drive, ¼ mile

SPORTING BENGAL UNITED

Founded 1996

Nickname: Bengal Tigers **Club Colours:** All royal blue

Club Contact Details 020 8980 1885

Ground: Mile End Stadium, Rhodeswell Rd, Off Burdett Rd E14 7TW

Capacity: 2,000 **Seats:** Yes **Covered:** Yes

Previous Names: None.

Previous Leagues: Asian League. London Intermediate, Kent 2003-11.

HONOURS: FA Comps: None
League: None

10 YEAR RECORD

09-10		10-11		11-12		12-13		13-14		14-15		15-16		16-17		17-18		18-19	
Kent P	15	Kent P	15	ESen	10	ESen	11	ESen	13	ESen	20	ESen	12	ESen	19	ESen	10	ESen	8
FAC	EP					FAC	EPr	FAC	EPr	FAC	EP	FAC	EP	FAC	1Q	FAC	EP	FAC	Pr
FAV	1Q			FAV	3P	FAV	1P	FAV	1P	FAV	1Q	FAV	2P	FAV	1P	FAV	1Q	FAV	2Q

Come off the Great West Road/A4 onto Earls Court Road/A3220. Continue straight to stay on Earls Ct Rd/A3220. Turn left onto Cremorne Rd/A3220. Continue onto Cheyne Walk/A3212. Turn right onto Peckham - Camberwell - Vauxhall - Westminster Hwy/A202. Continue straight onto Kennington Ln/Peckham - Camberwell - Vauxhall - Westminster Hwy/A202/A3204. Turn left onto Kennington Ln/A3. A3 turns slightly right and becomes Elephant and Castle. Continue onto New Kent Rd/A201. Keep left to continue on New Kent Rd. At the r'about, take the 2nd exit onto Tower Bridge Rd/A100. Turn right onto Abbey St/B202. Turn right onto Jamaica Rd/A200. At the r'about, take the 2nd exit onto Rotherhithe Tunnel/A101. Continue to follow A101. Slight left onto Yorkshire Rd. Turn right onto Salmon Ln. Continue onto Rhodeswell Rd. Keep right to continue on Turners Rd. Turn right onto St Paul's Way/B140. Turn left onto Burdett Rd/A1205. Turn left and then left again.

Nearest Railway Station Mile End – approx. 5 mins walk

Bus Route 277, 309, D6, D7 – outside ground

ST MARGARETSBURY

Founded 1894

Nickname: The Bury **Club Colours:** Red & black

Club Contact Details 01920 870 473

Ground: Recreation Ground, Station Road, St Margarets SG12 8EH

Capacity: 1,000 **Seats:** 60 **Covered:** 60

Previous Names: Stanstead Abbots > 1962

Previous Leagues: East Herts, Hertford & District, Waltham & District 1947-48, Herts Senior County 1948-92. Spartan SM 1992-2018.

HONOURS: FA Comps: None

League: Spartan 1995-96.

10 YEAR RECORD

09-10		10-11		11-12		12-13		13-14		14-15		15-16		16-17		17-18		18-19	
SSM P	14	SSM P	18	SSM P	12	SSM P	4	SSM P	4	SSM P	8	SSM P	19	SSM P	20	SSM P	16	ESen	7
FAC	P	FAC	P	FAC	EP	FAC	1Q	FAC	1Q	FAC	P	FAC	P	FAC	EP	FAC	1Q	FAC	P
FAV	2Q	FAV	1Q	FAV	2Q	FAV	2Q	FAV	1P	FAV	3P	FAV	1Q	FAV	3P	FAV	1Qr	FAV	1Q

A10 heading north from M25 for 7.3 miles, or A10 heading south turn off at next junction after Hertford. Turn off at A414 Harlow & Chelmsford/A1170 Ware. Proceed on A414 feeder road for 400yards to Amwell roundabout and take the 3rd exit, B181 to Stanstead Abbotts. The ground is a ¼ mile on right.

Nearest Railway Station St Margarets - 5mins from the ground

STANSTED

Founded 1892

Nickname: Blues **Club Colours:** Royal blue

Club Contact Details 07921 403 842

Ground: Hargrave Park, Cambridge Road, Stansted CM24 8BX

Capacity: 2,000 **Seats:** 200 **Covered:** 400 **Shop:** No

Previous Names: None.

Previous Leagues: Spartan 1946-53. London 1953-56. Herts Premier 1956-71.

HONOURS: FA Comps: FA Vase 1983-84.

League: East Herts 1934-35. Essex Senior 2009-10.

10 YEAR RECORD

09-10		10-11		11-12		12-13		13-14		14-15		15-16		16-17		17-18		18-19	
ESen	1	ESen	2	ESen	16	ESen	17	ESen	17	ESen	7	ESen	9	ESen	8	ESen	18	ESen	2
FAC	EP	FAC	EP	FAC	1Q	FAC	EP	FAC	EPr	FAC	EP	FAC	Pr	FAC	EP	FAC	EP	FAC	P
FAV	2P	FAV	5P	FAV	2P	FAV	2Q	FAV	2Q	FAV	2Q	FAV	1Q	FAV	1Q	FAV	1Q	FAV	1Q

Exit M11 at junction 8, take A120 west and cross first roundabout. At next roundabout take right exit, follow road into Stansted Mountfitchet. Once in Stansted Mountfitchet look for Esso Petrol Station on your left. Drive past and ground entrance is approx. 200 yards on the left.

Nearest Railway Station Stansted Mountfitchet - ¼ mile

Bus Route 301 100 yards from ground

TAKELEY

Founded 1904

Nickname: **Club Colours:** Royal blue

Club Contact Details 01279 870 404 Takeleyfc@mail.com

Ground: Station Road, Takeley, Bishop's Stortford CM22 6SQ

Capacity: 2,000 **Seats:** Yes **Covered:** Yes

Previous Names: None.

Previous Leagues: Essex Intermediate/Olympian.

HONOURS: FA Comps: None

League: Essex Olympian/Intermediate 1987-88, 2001-02, Division Two 1993-94.

10 YEAR RECORD

09-10		10-11		11-12		12-13		13-14		14-15		15-16		16-17		17-18		18-19	
ESen	6	ESen	13	ESen	3	ESen	3	ESen	7	ESen	11	ESen	18	ESen	4	ESen	5	ESen	5
		FAC	EP	FAC	EPr	FAC	P	FAC	EP	FAC	EPr	FAC	EP	FAC	EP	FAC	1Q	FAC	1Q
FAV	2Q	FAV	1P	FAV	2Q	FAV	2P	FAV	2P	FAV	1Q	FAV	2Qr	FAV	2Q	FAV	1P	FAV	1P

Take the A120 (W) exit from the M11.
Follow Dunmow Road/B1256 after 3 miles turn right into Station Road/B183.
Ground will be on your left.

Nearest Railway Station Stansted Airport (overground) Epping (underground)

Bus Route from Stansted Airport to Four Ashes Pub.

TOWER HAMLETS

Founded 2000

Nickname: Green Army **Club Colours:** Orange & black

Club Contact Details 020 8980 1885

Ground: Mile End Stadium, Rhodeswell Rd, Poplar E14 7TW

Capacity: 2,000 **Seats:** Yes **Covered:** Yes

Previous Names: Bethnal Green United 2000-2013.

Previous Leagues: Canery Wharf Summer League. Inner London. London Intermediate. Middlesex County >2009.

HONOURS: FA Comps: None

League: Middlesex County Premier Division 2008-09.

10 YEAR RECORD

09-10	10-11	11-12	12-13	13-14	14-15	15-16	16-17	17-18	18-19
ESen 5	ESen 4	ESen 9	ESen 12	ESen 4	ESen 17	ESen 17	ESen 20	ESen 11	ESen 16
				FAC P	FAC EP	FAC Pr	FAC P	FAC P	FAC EP
				FAV 1P	FAV 1P	FAV 1Q	FAV 1Q	FAV 2P	FAV 1Q

From A12(A406/M11), leave A12 at junction with A11/A118 and turn right onto A11 (signposted Central London, Bow, Mile End). Keep driving along Bow Road until you come to Mile End Station. At this junction, turn left onto A1205 Burdett Road (signposted Rotherhithe Tunnel, Poplar). Keep going down this road until you come to a railway bridge, go under that and at the next junction do a right onto St Pauls Way. Go through the lights and bear right onto Rhodeswell Road, the ground/car park are on the right.
From A13, pass through Poplar along the East India Dock Road. At big junction turn right onto A1205 Burdett Road (signposted Mile End). Continue up this road up until you arrive at a junction and turn left onto St Pauls Way. Go through the lights and bear right onto Rhodeswell Road, the ground/car park are on the right.

Nearest Railway Station Mile End (Central, Dist, Hammersmith & City Lines), 5mins walk.

Bus Route 309, D6, D7, 277

WALTHAMSTOW

Founded 1964

Nickname: The Stags **Club Colours:** Royal blue

Club Contact Details 07748 983 792

Ground: Wadham Lodge, Kitchener Road, Walthamstow E17 4JP

Capacity: 3,500 **Seats:** 216 **Covered:** Yes

Previous Names: Pennant 1964-88. Walthamstow Pennant 88-95. Merged with Leyton to form Leyton Pennant 95-2003. Waltham Forest 03-18.

Previous Leagues: Isthmian 2003-04, 06-14. Southern 2004-06.

HONOURS: FA Comps: None

League: None

10 YEAR RECORD

09-10	10-11	11-12	12-13	13-14	14-15	15-16	16-17	17-18	18-19
Isth1N 16	Isth1N 21	Isth1N 17	Isth1N 18	Isth1N 23	ESen 9	ESen 19	ESen 12	ESen 17	ESen 3
FAC 1Q	FAC P	FAC 2Q	FAC 2Q	FAC P	FAC EP	FAC EP	FAC 2Q	FAC EPr	FAC 1Q
FAT 1Qr	FAT 1Q	FAT 1Q	FAT 1Q	FAT P	FAV 1P	FAV 2Q	FAV 1P	FAV 1Q	FAV 1Q

From the Crooked Billet roundabout (A406 North Circular Road) head south onto the A112 (Chingford Road) towards Walthamstow.
Take the 1st left into Brookscroft Road (St John's Church on the corner).
Follow this road to the end where it turns left into Kitchener Road and the ground is on the right.
Using postcode E17 4LJ should direct you correctly.

Nearest Railway Station Walthamstow Central - Victoria Line/London Overground.

Bus Route 158

WEST ESSEX

Founded 1989

Nickname: **Club Colours:** Red & black

Club Contact Details 07956 557 438

Ground: Barking FC, Mayesbrook Park, Lodge Avenue, Dagenham RM8 2JR

Capacity: 2,500 **Seats:** 200 **Covered:** 600

Previous Names: None

Previous Leagues: Ilford & District 1989-94. Essex Business Houses 1994-2010. Middlesex County 2010-2016.

HONOURS: FA Comps: None

League: Essex Business Houses Division One 2008-09.
Middlesex County Division One (Central & East) 2010-11, Premier Division 2015-16.

10 YEAR RECORD

09-10	10-11	11-12	12-13	13-14	14-15	15-16	16-17	17-18	18-19
EsxBHP 8	Midx1SE 1	MidxP 11	MidxP 10	MidxP 9	MidxP 7	MidxP 1	ESen 13	ESen 7	ESen 13
								FAC P	FAC P
							FAV 1Q	FAV 2Q	FAV 1P

Take the exit road from the A13 at Becontree Heath onto the A1153 Lodge Avenue turn off. The ground is approximately one mile down on the left. The 368 bus stops outside or opposite the ground - alternatively, buses 145, 364 and number 5 are a short walk from the LIDL supermarket or from the A13 end get the 62 to the bottom of the hill and walk up Lodge Avenue. To reach us by train go to Upney station, turn left and at the bottom of the hill cross the road into the 'The Drive'. Go to the end of The Drive and enter Mayesbrook Park. Go to the left and the ground is about five minutes' walk and past the Sporthouse.

Nearest Railway Station Barking. Upney (District Line) 2 miles

Bus Route 5, 62, 145, 364, 368

WOODFORD TOWN

Founded 2007

Nickname: The Woods **Club Colours:** Blue

Club Contact Details

Ground: The Harlow Arena, Elizabeth Way, Harlow Essex CM19 5BE

Capacity: 3,500 **Seats:** Yes **Covered:** Yes

Previous Names: Mauritius Sports merged with Walthamstow Ave & Pennant 2007. Mauritius Sports Ass. 09-11. Haringey & Waltham Dev. 11-13. Grhouse London 13-15

Previous Names Cont: Greenhouse Sports 15-16. Haringey & Waltham 16-17.

Previous Leagues: London Intermediate 2001-03. Middlesex County 2003-2007.

HONOURS: FA Comps: None

League: None

10 YEAR RECORD

09-10	10-11	11-12	12-13	13-14	14-15	15-16	16-17	17-18	18-19
ESen 18	ESen 11	ESen 12	ESen 8	ESen 18	ESen 19	ESen 15	ESen 22	ESen 12	ESen 6
	FAC EP	FAC Pr	FAC P	FAC 1Q					
FAV 1Q	FAV 1Q	FAV 2P	FAV 1Qr	FAV 2Q		FAV 2P			

Leave M25 at Junction 25. Take A10 northbound. Turn first exit at roundabout. Straight over the next roundabout then 3rd exit at the next roundabout after that. Ground entrance is 50 yards on the right.

Nearest Railway Station Harlow Town, 1 mile

ARDLEY UNITED

Nickname: None **Club Colours:** All sky blue

Founded 1945

Club Contact Details 07711 009 198 sharon.smith23@talk21.com
Ground: The Playing Fields, Fritwell Road, Ardley OX27 7PA
Capacity: 1,000 **Seats:** 100 **Covered:** 200 **Shop:** No

Previous Names: None
Previous Leagues: Oxford Senior. Volunteered for relegation after 2016-17 season.

HONOURS: FA Comps: None
League: Banbury District & Lord Jersey FA Divion One 1984-85. Oxfordshire Senior Division One 1988-89, Premier 1990-91. Hellenic Division One 1996-97, 97-98, Division One West 2017-18.

10 YEAR RECORD

09-10	10-11	11-12	12-13	13-14	14-15	15-16	16-17	17-18	18-19
Hel P 7	Hel P 3	Hel P 3	Hel P 5	Hel P 2	Hel P 8	Hel P 13	Hel P 5	Hel1W 1	Hel P 17
FAC EPr	FAC EP	FAC Pr	FAC P	FAC 1Qr	FAC 2Q	FAC EP	FAC P	FAC EP	FAC P
FAV 1P	FAV 2Q	FAV 1P	FAV 3P	FAV 1Q	FAV 1P	FAV 1Q	FAV 2Q	FAV 1Q	FAV 1Q

From M40 travelling North. At the end of the slip road at junction 10 turn left onto B430. Take the first right and the ground is 10 yards on your right. **From M40 travelling South** at the end of the slip road at junction 10 turn right, cross the motorway keeping in the right hand lane follow signs for B430. Take the first right and the ground is 10 yards on the right. **From the A34.** Leave the A34 after the BP garage signed Middleton Stoney / Weston on the Green. Stay on this road some 10 miles to Ardley. After entering the village take the first left after passing the Fox and Hounds public house, and the ground is 10 yards on your right.

Nearest Railway Station Bicester North - 6.3km
Bus Route Water Lane stop - 121m away

BINFIELD

Nickname: Moles **Club Colours:** All red

Founded 1892

Club Contact Details 07515 336 989 robchallis@binfieldfc.com
Ground: Stubbs Lane off Hill Farm Lane, Binfield RG42 5NR
Capacity: 1,500 **Seats:** yes **Covered:** yes

Previous Names: None.
Previous Leagues: Ascot & District. Great Western Combination. Reading & Dist. Chiltonian.

HONOURS: FA Comps: None
League: Great Western Combination 1946-47. Reading & District Division One 1975-76, 87-88, Division Two 86-87. Hellenic Division One East 2008-09.

10 YEAR RECORD

09-10	10-11	11-12	12-13	13-14	14-15	15-16	16-17	17-18	18-19
Hel P 8	Hel P 2	Hel P 8	Hel P 3	Hel P 5	Hel P 6	Hel P 8	Hel P 8	Hel P 7	Hel P 9
FAC EP	FAC 1Q	FAC P	FAC EP	FAC 2Q	FAC EP	FAC P	FAC EP	FAC P	FAC 2Q
FAV 1Q	FAV 2P	FAV 4P	FAV 3P	FAV 3P	FAV 2Q	FAV 1Qr	FAV 2Q	FAV 2Q	FAV 2Q

From M4 Junction 10 take A329 signposted Wokingham & Binfield, at roundabout take 1st exit. Go through 1st set of traffic lights, turn left at 2nd set opposite Travel Lodge. Follow road through village over two mini-roundabouts, at 'T' junction with church in front of you turn right. Take left filter road after 150 yards into Stubbs Lane. Ground is on left at end of short lane.

Nearest Railway Station Bracknell - 3.9km
Bus Route Church Lane North stop - 628m

BISHOP'S CLEEVE

Nickname: The Mitres **Club Colours:** All Green

Founded 1905

Club Contact Details 01242 676 166 (Ground) themitres@outlook.com
Ground: Kayte Lane, Bishop's Cleeve, Cheltenham GL52 3PD
Capacity: 1,500 **Seats:** 50 **Covered:** 50 Yes

Previous Names: None
Previous Leagues: Cheltenham. North Gloucestershire. Hellenic 1983-2006. Southern 2006-18.

HONOURS: FA Comps: None
League: Cheltenham Division Two 1924-25, 30-31, 58-59, Division One 31-32, 34-35, 61-62, 63-64, 65-66, 66-67. Gloucestershire Northern Senior Division Two 1967-68, Division One 68-69, 69-70, 72-73. Hellenic Division One

10 YEAR RECORD

09-10	10-11	11-12	12-13	13-14	14-15	15-16	16-17	17-18	18-19
Sthsw 11	Sthsw 15	Sthsw 11	Sthsw 21	Sthsw 20	Sthsw 21	Sthsw 12	Sthsw 16	Sth1W 22	Hel P 4
FAC 3Q	FAC 2Q	FAC P	FAC 2Q	FAC Pr	FAC 1Q	FAC P	FAC Pr	FAC 1Q	FAC 1Q
FAT P	FAT 1Q	FAT P	FAT 1Q	FAT P	FAT 1Q	FAT P	FAT 2Q	FAT P	FAV 2Q

From Cheltenham take A435 towards Evesham.
Pass racecourse, take right at traffic lights then first left into Kayte Lane.
Ground 1/2 mile on left.

Nearest Railway Station Cheltenham Spa - 4.9km
Bus Route Bus stops outside the ground

BRACKLEY TOWN SAINTS

Nickname: The Saints **Club Colours:** Red and white

Founded 1890

Club Contact Details 01280 704 077 (Ground) pat.ashby55@btinternet.com

Ground: St James Park, Churchill Way, Brackley, Northamptonshire, NN13 7EF

Capacity: 3,500 **Seats:** 300 **Covered:** 1,500

Previous Names: Brackley Town Development > 2015

Previous Leagues: None

HONOURS: FA Comps: None

League: None

10 YEAR RECORD

09-10		10-11		11-12		12-13		13-14		14-15		15-16		16-17		17-18		18-19	
										Hel1E	2	Hel P	16	Hel P	13	Hel P	12	Hel P	3
																FAC	EP	FAC	Pr
														FAV	1Qr	FAV	1Q	FAV	2Q

Take A43 from Northampton or Oxford, or A422 from Banbury to large roundabout south of town. Take exit marked Brackley (South) and follow towards the town (Tesco store on left). Pass the Locomotive public house and take first turning right, signposted Football Club, into Churchill Way - road leads into Club car park.

Bus Route Tesco (Oxford Rd) stop - 38m away

BRIMSCOMBE & THRUPP

Nickname: Lilywhites **Club Colours:** White and blue

Founded 1886

Club Contact Details 07833 231 464 allanboulton370@btinternet.com

Ground: 'The Meadow', London Road, Brimscombe Stroud, Gloucestershire GL5 2SH

Capacity: 1,500 **Seats:** Yes **Covered:** Yes

Previous Names: Brimscombe AFC 1886- late 1970s. Brimscombe and Thrupp merged.

Previous Leagues: Stroud & District. Gloucestershire Northern Senior. Gloucestershire County

HONOURS: FA Comps: None

League: Stroud & Dist. 1902-03, 06-07, 07-08, 12-13. Gloucestershire Northern Senior 1922-23, 30-31, 47-48, Division Two 2004-05. Gloucestershire County 2010-11. Hellenic Division One West 2012-13.

10 YEAR RECORD

09-10		10-11		11-12		12-13		13-14		14-15		15-16		16-17		17-18		18-19	
GlCo	5	GlCo	1	Hel1W	4	Hel1W	1	Hel P	12	Hel P	10	Hel P	5	Hel P	7	Hel P	6	Hel P	2
										FAC	EP	FAC	Pr	FAC	3Q	FAC	P	FAC	P
								FAV	2P	FAV	1P	FAV	3Pr	FAV	2Pr	FAV	1Q	FAV	1P

9 miles north of Cirencester on A419. 2 miles south of Stroud on A419

Nearest Railway Station Stroud - 2.9km

Bus Route Brewery Lane stop - 261m away

BURNHAM

Nickname: The Blues **Club Colours:** Blue & white

Founded 1878

Club Contact Details 01628 668 654 (Ground) burnhamfcsec@aol.com

Ground: The Gore, Wymers Wood Road, Burnham, Slough SL1 8JG

Capacity: 2,500 **Seats:** Yes **Covered:** Yes **Shop:** Yes

Previous Names: Burnham & Hillingdon 1985-87

Previous Leagues: Hellenic 1971-77, 95-99, Athenian 1977-84, London Spartan 1984-85, Southern 1985-95, 99-16.

HONOURS: FA Comps: None

League: Hellenic 1975-76, 98-99, Division One East 2018-19. London Spartan 1984-85. Southern Division One Central 2012-13.

10 YEAR RECORD

09-10		10-11		11-12		12-13		13-14		14-15		15-16		16-17		17-18		18-19	
SthM	3	SthC	14	SthC	15	SthC	1	SthP	20	SthP	23	Sthsw	21	Hel P	17	Hel P	20	Hel1E	1
FAC	2Qr	FAC	2Q	FAC	3Q	FAC	P	FAC	2Q	FAC	2Q	FAC	Pr	FAC	EP	FAC	EP	FAC	2Q
FAT	3Q	FAT	1Qr	FAT	Pr	FAT	2Q	FAT	2Q	FAT	2Qr	FAT	P	FAV	2Q	FAV	2Q	FAV	2Q

Approx. 2 miles from M4 junction 7 and 5 miles from M40 junction 2. From M40 take A355 to A4 signposted Maidenhead. From M4 take A4 towards Maidenhead until you reach roundabout with Sainsbury Superstore on left. Turn right into Lent Rise Road and travel approx 11/2 miles over 2 double roundabouts. 100 yards after second double roundabout fork right into Wymers Wood Road. Ground entrance on right.

Nearest Railway Station Taplow - 1.9km

Bus Route Pink Lane stop - 239m away

EASINGTON SPORTS

Founded 1946

Nickname: The Clan **Club Colours:** Red & white

Club Contact Details 07791 681 204 jamiehunter@hotmail.co.uk

Ground: Addison Road, Banbury OX16 9DH

Capacity: 1,500 **Seats:** 50 **Covered:** Yes

Previous Names:

Previous Leagues: Warwick Combination.

HONOURS: FA Comps: None

League: Oxfordshire Senior Premier Division 1957-58, 58-59, Division One 1965-66.
Hellenic Division One West 2018-19.

10 YEAR RECORD

09-10	10-11	11-12	12-13	13-14	14-15	15-16	16-17	17-18	18-19
Hel1W 6	Hel1W 11	Hel1W 6	Hel1W 8	Hel1W 9	Hel1W 4	Hel1W 5	Hel1W 4	Hel1W 3	Hel1W 1
									FAC P
								FAV 1Q	FAV 2Q

From North/South M40 - Leave M40 at J11, follow A422 to Banbury, 2nd roundabout take A4260 to Adderbury. Go through three sets of traffic lights, at top of hill at T-junction turn left. Take 3rd right into Addison Road.
From South West A361 – Entering Banbury take 1st right turning into Springfield Ave after 'The Easington' PH.
Follow road and take T-junction right into Grange Road, 1st right into Addison Road. Ground on left at end of road.

Nearest Railway Station Banbury - 1.6km
Bus Route Springfield Avenu stop - 117m away

FAIRFORD TOWN

Founded 1891

Nickname: The Reds **Club Colours:** All red.

Club Contact Details 01285 712 071 (Ground) clake@fairfordtownfc.co.uk

Ground: Cinder Lane, London Road, Fairford GL7 4AX

Capacity: 2,000 **Seats:** 100 **Covered:** 250 **Shop:** Yes

Previous Names: None.

Previous Leagues: Cirencester & District. Swindon & District.

HONOURS: FA Comps: None

League: Swindon & District Prmeier Division 1964-65, 68-69.
Hellenic Division One A 1971-72, Division One West 2016-17.

10 YEAR RECORD

09-10	10-11	11-12	12-13	13-14	14-15	15-16	16-17	17-18	18-19
Hel P 20	Hel P 21	Hel P 20	Hel1W 4	Hel1W 4	Hel1W 14	Hel1W 4	Hel1W 1	Hel P 18	Hel P 13
FAC EP	FAC EPr	FAC P	FAC EP	FAC EP	FAC EP		FAC EP	FAC EPr	FAC EP
FAV 2Q	FAV 1P	FAV 1P	FAV 1P	FAV 2Q	FAV 1Q	FAV 1P	FAV 1P	FAV 1Q	FAV 1Q

Take A417 from Lechlade, turn left down Cinder Lane 150 yards after 40 mph sign. From Cirencester take Lechlade Road, turn right down Cinder Lane 400 yards after passing the Railway Inn.

Bus Route Hatherop Lane stop - 124m

FLACKWELL HEATH

Founded 1907

Nickname: Heathens **Club Colours:** All red.

Club Contact Details 07932 952 538 joparsons19@sky.com

Ground: Wilks Park, Magpie Lane, Heath End Rd, Flackwell Hth HP10 9EA

Capacity: 2,000 **Seats:** 150 **Covered:** Yes

Previous Names: None.

Previous Leagues: High Wycombe & District 1907-50. Great Western Combination 1950-76. Hellenic 1976-82. Athenian 1982-84. Isthmian 1984-2007.

HONOURS: FA Comps: None

League: Great Western Combination Division Two 1950-51, Premier 1957-58, 62-63.
Hellenic Premier Division 2014-15.

10 YEAR RECORD

09-10	10-11	11-12	12-13	13-14	14-15	15-16	16-17	17-18	18-19
Hel P 4	Hel P 8	Hel P 4	Hel P 10	Hel P 8	Hel P 1	Hel P 3	Hel P 3	Hel P 5	Hel P 8
FAC 2Q	FAC P	FAC EP	FAC EP	FAC EPr	FAC 3Q	FAC EP	FAC 1Q	FAC P	FAC EP
FAV 3P	FAV 2P	FAV 3P	FAV 1P	FAV 1Q	FAV 5P	FAV 2P	FAV 1P	FAV 1P	FAV 1P

Junction 4 of M40 Follow signs A404 (High Wycombe) Turn right at traffic lights halfway down Marlow Hill, signposted Flackwell Heath. Ground three (3) miles on left.

Nearest Railway Station Bourne End - 3km
Bus Route Fernlea Close stop - 106m

HOLMER GREEN

Nickname: The Greens **Club Colours:** All Green

Founded 1908

Club Contact Details 01494 711 485 (Ground) j.ostinelli@sky.com
Ground: Airedale Park, Watchet Lane, Holmer Green, Bucks HP15 6UF
Capacity: 1,000 **Seats:** 25 **Covered:** yes

Previous Names: None
Previous Leagues: Chesham & District 1908-38, Wycombe Combination 1984-95, Chiltonian 1995-98. Spartan South Midlands 1998-2018.

HONOURS: FA Comps: None
League: Wycombe Combination 1971-72, 73-74, 76-77, 80-81. Chiltonian Prmeier 1984-85, 85-86, 93-94.
South Midlands Senior 1995-96. Spartan South Midlands 1998-99, Division One 2009-10.

10 YEAR RECORD

09-10	10-11	11-12	12-13	13-14	14-15	15-16	16-17	17-18	18-19
SSM1 1	SSM P 17	SSM P 20	SSM P 22	SSM P 12	SSM P 20	SSM P 7	SSM P 14	SSM P 14	Hel P 12
		FAC EP	FAC EP	FAC EP	FAC Pr	FAC EP	FAC EP	FAC P	FAC EP
	FAV 1Q	FAV 1Q	FAV 2Q	FAV 2Q	FAV 1Pr	FAV 1Q	FAV 2P	FAV 1Q	FAV 1Q

From Amersham on A404 High Wycombe Road. After approx 2 miles turn right into Sheepcote Dell Road. Continue until end of road at Bat & Ball pub. Turn right, then immediately left. Continue approx 1/2 mile until double mini-roundabouts. Turn left in front of the Mandarin Duck restaurant into Airedale Park 150 yards on the right

Nearest Railway Station Great Missenden - 4.3km
Bus Route Copners Drive - stop 350m away

LONGLEVENS AFC

Nickname: Levens **Club Colours:** Red & black

Founded 1954

Club Contact Details 01452 530 388 (Clubho) 07526 958 972 bill1853@outlook.com
Ground: Saw Mills End, Corinium Avenue, Gloucester GL4 3DG
Capacity: 500 **Seats:** Yes **Covered:** Yes

Previous Names: None
Previous Leagues: Gloucestershire Northern Senior > 2011. Gloucestershire County 2011-14.

HONOURS: FA Comps: None
League: Gloucestershire Northern Division One 2008-09. Gloucestershire County 2012-13, 13-14.
Hellenic Division One West 2014-15.

10 YEAR RECORD

09-10	10-11	11-12	12-13	13-14	14-15	15-16	16-17	17-18	18-19
GlN1 5	GlN1 4	GlCo 9	GlCo 1	GlCo 1	Hel1W 1	Hel P 10	Hel P 12	Hel P 9	Hel P 16
							FAC P	FAC P	FAC P
						FAV 1Q	FAV 2Q	FAV 1P	FAV 1P

From South: From M5 Gloucester exit junction 11a, and bear left onto A417. At roundabout take 2nd exit continue on A417 for ½ mile. At next roundabout take 2nd exit (look for coroners court sign) for ½ mile then turn left on Sawmills End (Ibis Hotel). Ground is on the left just past hotel. **From North:** From M5 Gloucester exit junction 11, at roundabout take third exit onto A40 for approx 2 miles. At roundabout take 2nd exit (A417) for 1 mile. At roundabout take 3rd exit (look for coroners court sign) for ½ mile then turn left on Sawmills End (Ibis Hotel). Ground is on the left just past hotel.

Nearest Railway Station Gloucester - 1.9km
Bus Route Budgen's Garage stop - 146m away

LYDNEY TOWN

Nickname: The Town **Club Colours:** Black & white

Founded 1911

Club Contact Details 01594 844 523 (Ground) rogersansom@outlook.com
Ground: Lydney Recreation Ground, Swan Road, Lydney GL15 5RU
Capacity: 1,000 **Seats:** Yes **Covered:** Yes

Previous Names: None
Previous Leagues: Local leagues 1911-52. Gloucestershire Northern Senior 1952-80, 84-. Hellenic 1980-84. Gloucestershire County 2005-06.

HONOURS: FA Comps: None
League: Gloucesteeshire Northern Senior 1979-80. Gloucestershire County 2005-06. Hellenic League Division One West 2006-07.

10 YEAR RECORD

09-10	10-11	11-12	12-13	13-14	14-15	15-16	16-17	17-18	18-19
Hel1W 8	Hel1W 5	Hel1W 13	Hel1W 10	Hel1W 2	Hel1W 3	Hel P 12	Hel P 9	Hel P 16	Hel P 11
FAC EP	FAC P	FAC EP					FAC EP	FAC EP	FAC 1Qr
FAV 1Q	FAV 1P	FAV 1P	FAV 2Q	FAV 2Q		FAV 2Q	FAV 1P	FAV 2Q	FAV 1Q

From Gloucester – take Lydney road off A48 down Highfield Hill and into the town centre. Take 1st left into Swan Road after 2nd set of pelican lights.

From Chepstow – at by-pass roundabout take Lydney road. Go over railway crossing then take 2nd right into Swan Road.

Nearest Railway Station Lydney Town - 144m
Bus Route Forest Parade - 156m away

READING CITY

Nickname: Mighty Moor **Club Colours:** Blue

Founded 2001

Club Contact Details 07918 880 777 media@readingcity.co.uk

Ground: The Rivermoor, Scours Lane, Tilehurst, Reading RG30 6AY

Capacity: **Seats:** Yes **Covered:** Yes

Previous Names: Highmoor and Ibis merged to form today's club in 2001. Highmoor Ibis 2001-18.

Previous Leagues: Reading 2001-2011.

HONOURS: FA Comps: None

League: Reading Senior Division 2003-04, 10-11.

10 YEAR RECORD

09-10	10-11	11-12	12-13	13-14	14-15	15-16	16-17	17-18	18-19
ReadS 4	ReadS 1	Hel1E 2	Hel P 12	Hel P 4	Hel P 2	Hel P 11	Hel P 14	Hel P 17	Hel P 18
				FAC 1Q	FAC P	FAC EP	FAC P	FAC P	FAC EPr
			FAV 2Q	FAV 1P	FAV 1P	FAV 1P	FAV 1P	FAV 1Q	FAV 1Q

Come off J12 of the M4 head along the A4 towards Reading, take a left onto Langley Hill and follow it all the way up onto Park Lane, continue onto School Road past the Tilehurst shops and then down onto Kentwood Hill. At the bottom of the hill take a right onto the Oxford Road towards Reading and just past the Waitrose Shop you need to take a left into an industrial estate and under the railway bridge and the ground will be in front of you to your right.

Nearest Railway Station Tilehurst - 1.2km

Bus Route Cold Store stop - 277m away

ROYAL WOOTTON BASSETT

Nickname: Bassett **Club Colours:** All blue

Founded 1882

Club Contact Details 01793 853 880 (Ground) ian.thomas@wbtfc.co.uk

Ground: Gerrard Buxton Sports Ground Malmesbury Rd Royal Wootton Bassett SN4 8DS

Capacity: 4,500 **Seats:** 550 **Covered:** 1,250 **Shop:** No

Previous Names: Wootton Bassett Town > 2015.

Previous Leagues: Vale of White 1898-99. Swindon & District 1899-1903. Wiltshire County 1903-08, 35-69, 76-88. Calne & District 1930. Wiltshire Combination 1969-76.

HONOURS: FA Comps: None

League: Calne & District 1931-32, 34-35, 35-36.
Wiltshire Division One 1958-59, Division Two 1984-85, Division One 1987-88.

10 YEAR RECORD

09-10	10-11	11-12	12-13	13-14	14-15	15-16	16-17	17-18	18-19
Hel1W 2	Hel P 15	Hel1W 5	Hel1W 2	Hel P 14	Hel P 11	Hel P 15	Hel P 11	Hel P 15	Hel P 10
FAC P	FAC 1Qr	FAC EP	FAC 2Q	FAC EP	FAC P	FAC EP	FAC EP	FAC EP	FAC Pr
FAV 1Q	FAV 1P	FAV 1Q	FAV 1Q	FAV 2Q	FAV 2Q	FAV 2Q	FAV 2Q	FAV 2P	FAV 2Q

Exit A417 AT Burford Road Junction and follow signs for Cirencester Town FC.

Bus Route The Farm stop - 69m

SHRIVENHAM

Nickname: Shrivvy **Club Colours:** Blue & white

Founded 1900

Club Contact Details 07711 263 113 c.rawle@shrivenhamfc.co.uk

Ground: The Recreation Ground, Barrington Park, Shrivenham SN6 8BJ

Capacity: 1,500 **Seats:** Yes **Covered:** Yes

Previous Names: None.

Previous Leagues: North Berkshire.

HONOURS: FA Comps: None

League: North Berks Division Two 1994-95, Division One 1997-98, 2000-01.
Hellenic Division One West 2004-05.

10 YEAR RECORD

09-10	10-11	11-12	12-13	13-14	14-15	15-16	16-17	17-18	18-19
Hel P 16	Hel P 20	Hel P 16	Hel P 19	Hel P 15	Hel P 19	Hel1W 8	Hel1W 7	Hel1W 2	Hel P 5
FAC 1Q	FAC EP	FAC EP	FAC P	FAC EP	FAC P	FAC EP			
FAT 1P	FAT 1P	FAV 2Q	FAV 2Q	FAV 2Q	FAV 1Q	FAV 2Q	FAV 1Q		FAV 2Q

Shrivenham village is signposted off A420 Oxford to Swindon road, six miles east of Swindon, four miles west of Faringdon. Drive through village turn into Highworth Road, ground is on right, parking is before the ground on the left Martens Rd, No parking allowed by the ground.

Bus Route Green (Townsend Rd) stop - 268m away

TUFFLEY ROVERS

Nickname: Rovers **Club Colours:** Claret & blue

Founded 1929

Club Contact Details 07545 492 261 admin@tuffleyroversfc.co.uk

Ground: Glevum Park, Lower Tuffley Lane, Tuffley, Gloucester GL2 5DT

Capacity: 1,000 **Seats:** 100 **Covered:** yes

Previous Names: None

Previous Leagues: Gloucestershire County 1988-91, 2007-13. Hellenic 1991-06. Gloucestershire Northern 2006-07.

HONOURS: FA Comps: None

League: Gloucester County 1990-91. Gloucestershire Northern Division One 2006-07.

10 YEAR RECORD

09-10	10-11	11-12	12-13	13-14	14-15	15-16	16-17	17-18	18-19
GlCo 3	GlCo 6	GlCo 3	GlCo 2	Hel1W 6	Hel1W 2	Hel P 17	Hel P 10	Hel P 10	Hel P 15
						FAC 1Q	FAC EP	FAC 1Q	FAC EP
					FAV 1P	FAV 1Q	FAV 2P	FAV 1Q	FAV 2Qr

From the motorway junction 12 of the M5 motorway head towards Gloucester for a short distance on the B4008 down to a roundabout. At this roundabout take the second exit A38 towards Gloucester. After 1/2 mile you will reach another roundabout with a Holiday Inn on your right. Take the first exit continuing along the A38 on towards Gloucester until you reach a large traffic light junction at the end of the dual carriageway (approx 1.5 miles). At these lights continue straight over ignoring sign for Tuffley to the right. Once through this first set of lights keep to the right and keep in the right filter lane to the next lights. Turn right here and head towards City Centre and Historic Docks along the Old Bristol Road. Just after the newly shaped road straightens along the old road take the turning right in to Lower Tuffley Lane. Continue almost to the end and the entrance to the ground is on the left through a gateway directly after the commercial premises of Marshall Langston and opposite a large transport depot.

Nearest Railway Station Gloucester - 3.5km

Bus Route Pearce Way stop - 197m away

VIRGINIA WATER

Nickname: The Waters **Club Colours:** Maroon

Founded 1920

Club Contact Details 01753 860 656 (Ground) gp738@hotmail.com

Ground: Windsor FC, Stag Meadow, St Leonards Road Windsor SL4 3DR

Capacity: 4,500 **Seats:** 450 **Covered:** 650

Previous Names:

Previous Leagues: Surrey Senior 1968-75. London Spartan 1975-79. Combined Counties 1979-87, 93-94. Surrey County Premier 1992-93, 94-2002. Surrey Intermediate (West) 2002-10. Surrey Elite Intermediate 2010-17.

HONOURS: FA Comps: None

League: Surrey County Premier Division 1992-93, 96-97. Surrey Elite Intermediate 2016-17. Hellenic Division One East 2017-18.

10 YEAR RECORD

09-10	10-11	11-12	12-13	13-14	14-15	15-16	16-17	17-18	18-19
	SuEI 6	SuEI 14	SuEI 11	SuEI 8	SuEI 7	SuEI 5	SuEI 1	Hel1E 1	Hel P 14
									FAV 2Q

Exit M4 at Junction 6 – follow signs for Windsor – now on Royal Windsor Way relief road (A355/A322) – continue down this road over the River Thames and the flyover – until reaching a very large roundabout – take the 3rd exit into Imperial Road (signposted M3, Ascot and Legoland) until reaching T Junction with traffic lights – turn left at lights into St Leonards Road - after approx. a quarter of a mile take a right where the PREMIER (bright YELLOW signage) shop is. Ground entrance/car park is 200 metres.

Nearest Railway Station Windsor & Eton Central - 1.5km

Bus Route Stag Meadow stop - 131m away

WESTFIELDS

Nickname: The Fields **Club Colours:** All Maroon & sky blue

Founded 1966

Club Contact Details 07860 410 548 andrewmorris@westfieldsfc.com

Ground: Allpay Park, Widemarsh Common, Hereford HR4 9NA

Capacity: 2,250 **Seats:** 220 **Covered:** 400 **Shop:** Yes

Previous Names: None.

Previous Leagues: Herefordshire Sunday 1966-73. Worcester & Dist. 1973-78. West Midlands (Regional) 1978-04. Midland Alliance 2004-14. Midland 2014-19.

HONOURS: FA Comps: None

League: West Midlands (Regional) Division One 1986-87, Premier 2002-03.

10 YEAR RECORD

09-10	10-11	11-12	12-13	13-14	14-15	15-16	16-17	17-18	18-19
MidAl 5	MidAl 6	MidAl 2	MidAl 2	MidAl 12	WMP 8	MFLP 16	MFLP 5	MFLP 12	MFLP 4
FAC 1Q	FAC P	FAC EP	FAC 2Qr	FAC EP	FAC P	FAC 1Q	FAC 1P	FAC 2Q	FAC EP
FAV 2P	FAV 3P	FAV 1P	FAV 1P	FAV 4P	FAV 3P	FAV 1P	FAV 3P	FAV 4P	FAV 3P

On reaching the outskirts of Hereford from Worcester, continue along A4103, over roundabout signposted Holmer and Leisure Centre. Proceed for 1 mile to large roundabout by the "Starting Gate Inn" and turn left towards Hereford. Proceed for ½ mile, past Hereford Leisure Centre and at mini roundabout, turn right. Proceed 150 yards and bear left around the Common, in front of Cricket Pavilion and immediately turn right into the driveway for Allpay Park.

Nearest Railway Station Hereford - 1km

Bus Route Priory Place stop - 165m away

WINDSOR

Nickname: The Royals | **Club Colours:** Red, white & green | Founded 1892

Club Contact Details 01753 860 656 (Ground) secretary@windsorfc.net

Ground: Stag Meadow, St Leonards Road, Windsor, Berks SL4 3DR

Capacity: 4,500 **Seats:** 450 **Covered:** 650 **Shop:** Yes

Previous Names: Formed when Windsor Phoenix and Windsor St. Albans merged in 1892. Windsor & Eton 1892-2011.

Previous Leagues: W.Berks, Gt Western, Suburban, Athenian 22-29,63-81, Spartan 29-39, Gt W.Comb. Corinthian 45-50, Met 50-60, Delphian 60-63, Isthmian 1963-2006, Stouthern 2006-11. Combined Counties 2011-17.

HONOURS: FA Comps: None

League: Athenian League 1979-80, 80-81. Isthmian League Division 1 1983-84. Southern League Division 1 South & West 2009-10.

10 YEAR RECORD

09-10		10-11		11-12		12-13		13-14		14-15		15-16		16-17		17-18		18-19	
Sthsw	1	SthP	Exp	CCP	2	CCP	6	CCP	6	CCP	5	CCP	12	CCP	11	Hel P	8	Hel P	6
FAC	2Q	FAC	1Q			FAC	1Q	FAC	P	FAC	P	FAC	EP	FAC	EP	FAC	EP	FAC	P
FAT	1Qr	FAT	2Q	FAV	2Q	FAV	1P	FAV	1P	FAV	1P	FAV	1P	FAV	1Q	FAV	QF	FAV	5P

Exit M4 at Junction 6 – follow signs for Windsor – now on Royal Windsor Way relief road (A355/A322) – continue down this road over the River Thames and the flyover – until reaching a very large roundabout – take the 3rd exit into Imperial Road (signposted M3, Ascot and Legoland) until reaching T Junction with traffic lights – turn left at lights into St Leonards Road - after approx. a quarter of a mile take a right where the PREMIER (bright YELLOW signage) shop is. Ground entrance/car park is 200 metres.

Nearest Railway Station Windsor & Eton - 1.5km

Bus Route Stag Meadow stop - 131m away

Hellenic League Division Two North

ADDERBURY PARK	Luck Plackett Playing Fields, Round Close Road, Abberbury OX17 3EE
BANBURY UNITED DEV	Station Approach, Banbury OX16 5AB
BUCKINGHAM ATHLETIC DEV	Stratford Fields, Stratford Road, Buckingham MK18 1NY
CHINNOR RESERVES	Chinnor Community Sports Ground, Station Road, Chinnor OX39 4PX
EASINGTON SPORTS DEV	Addison Road, Banbury OX16 9DH
HEADINGTON AMATEURS	Horspath Sports Ground, Oxford Rd, Horspath, Oxford OX4 2RR
HEYFORD ATHLETIC	King George Playing Field, Mill Lane, Lower Heyford OX25 5PG
LONG CRENDON DEV	Oxford City FC, Court Place farm, Marsh Lane, Marston Oxford OX3 0NQ
MILTON UNITED DEV	The Heights, Potash Lane, Milton, Abingdon OX13 6AG
MORETON RANGERS DEV	London Road, Moreton-in-Marsh, Glos Gl56 0HN
OLD BRADWELL UNITED	Abbey Road, Bradwell, Milton Keynes MK13 9AR
RISBOROUGH RANGERS DEV	Windsors, Horsenden Lane, Horseden, Prince Risborough HP27 9NE
SOUTHAM UNITED	Bobby Hancocks Park, Saints Drive, Southam CV47 2UZ
WOODSTOCK TOWN	New Road, Woodstock OX20 1PD

Hellenic League Division Two South

ABINGDON UNITED DEV	Northcourt Road, Abingdon OX14 1PL
AFC ALDERMASTON RESERVES	Aldermaston Recreational Society, AWE, Aldermaston, Reading RG7 4PR
ASTON CLINTON SPORTS	Aston Clinton Park, London Road, Aston Clinton HP22 5HL
CHALFONT WASPS	Crossleys, Bowstridge Lane Chalfont, St Giles HP8 4QN
CHALVEY SPORTS RESERVES	Chalvey Recreation Ground, High Street, Chalvey, Slough SL1 2SS
HAZLEMERE SPORTS	
LANGLEY DEV	Summerleaze Road, Maidenhead SL6 8SP
PEN & TYLERS GREEN DEV	French School Meadows, Elm Road, Penn HP10 8LF
STOKENCHURCH	Longburrow, Park Lane, Stokenchurch HP14 3TQ
TAPLOW UNITED	Stanley Jones Field, Berry Hill, Taplow SL6 0DA
VIRGINIA WATER DEV	The Timbers, Crown Road, Viginia Water GU25 4HS
WALLINGFORD TOWN RES	Wallingford Sports Ground, Hithercroft Road
WOKINGHAM & EMMBROOK RES	Emmbrook Sports & Social Club, Forest Road, Wokingham RG41 1JB
YATELEY UNITED	Cody Sports Club, The Fairway, Farnborough GU14 0LP

ABINGDON TOWN

Founded: 1870 Nickname: The Abbots

Club Contact Details 07585 443 656 sec@abingdontownfc.com

Ground: Culham Road, Abingdon OX14 3HP **Club Colours:** Yellow and green

HONOURS
FA Comps: None
League: Oxford & District 1899-00, 1900-01. North Berks 1919-20, 22-23. Reading & District 1947-48. Spartan Premier 1988-89. Hellenic Premier 1956-57, 58-59, 59-60, 86-87, Division One 75-76.

10 YEAR RECORD

09-10	10-11	11-12	12-13	13-14	14-15	15-16	16-17	17-18	18-19
Hel P 12	Hel P 14	Hel P 11	Hel P 18	Hel P 20	NBk 1 3	NBk 1 5		Hel2E 7	Hel1E 12
FAC EP	FAC EP	FAC Pr	FAC P	FAC EP					
FAV 2Q	FAV 2Q	FAV 1P	FAV 1Q	FAV 1P					

Abingdon can be reached in a number of different ways, depending exactly where you are coming from. Generally if coming directly from the North or South it is probably easier to take the A34 from either the M40 (North), or M4 (South). Exit the A34 at Abingdon South (A415) and head into Abingdon centre. From the centre take the A415 out of town (signposted Dorchester). As you come over the bridge crossing the river, the ground is approximately 300 yards on the right. If coming from the Reading direction you can travel via Henley and then take the A415 from Dorchester into Abingdon and the ground will be on your left.

ABINGDON UNITED

Founded: 1946 Nickname: The Yellows

Club Contact Details 01235 203 203 secretaryaufc@virginmedia.com

Ground: The Northcourt, Northcourt Road, Abingdon OX14 1PL **Club Colours:** Yellow and blue

HONOURS
FA Comps: None
League: North Berks 1952-53.

10 YEAR RECORD

09-10	10-11	11-12	12-13	13-14	14-15	15-16	16-17	17-18	18-19
Sthsw 14	Sthsw 16	Sthsw 18	Sthsw 20	Hel P 17	Hel P 15	Hel P 19	Hel1W 2	Hel P 13	Hel P 19
FAC 2Qr	FAC P	FAC 1Q	FAC P	FAC EPr	FAC 2Q	FAC EP	FAC EPr		FAC EPr
FAT 1Q	FAT 1Q	FAT P	FAT P	FAV 1P	FAV 2Pr	FAV 1Q	FAV 1P	FAV 2Q	FAV 1P

From the north – Leave A34 at Abingdon north turning. Ground on right at first set of traffic lights.
From the south – Enter Town Centre, leave north on A4183 (Oxford Road).
Ground on left after one mile.

Nearest Railway Station Radley - 2.5km
Bus Route Boundary House (Oxford Rd) stop - 215m

AFC ALDERMASTON

Founded: 1952 Nickname: The Atomics

Club Contact Details 01189 824 454 (Ground) martin.desay@gmail.com

Ground: AWE, Aldermaston, Reading RG7 4PR **Club Colours:** Red & black

HONOURS
FA Comps: None
League: None

10 YEAR RECORD

09-10	10-11	11-12	12-13	13-14	14-15	15-16	16-17	17-18	18-19
Wex1 21	HantP 15	HantP 9	HantP 8	HantP 10	ReadP 5	ReadP 7	Hel1E 7	Hel1E 11	Hel1E 3
								FAV 1Q	

From A4 at Padworth, take A340 (Aldermaston/Tadley) to Calleva Park Roundabout. Take first left on A340, and then take next left at mini roundabout into AWE West Gate. Follow signs for Aldermaston Recreational Society. Car Park directly ahead. Enter ground through gate at end of car park. Ground is on right hand side.

Nearest Railway Station Midgham - 4km
Bus Route Calleva Park stop - 48m away

CHALVEY SPORTS

Founded: 1885 Nickname: The Stab Monks

Club Contact Details 07768 010 760 chalveysportsfc@gmail.com

Ground: Arbour Park, Stoke Road, Slough SL2 5AY **Club Colours:** All royal blue

HONOURS
FA Comps:
League: Great Western Combination 1954-55. East Berkshire Division One 1992-93, Premier 96-97. Hellenic Division Two East 2016-17, 17-18.

10 YEAR RECORD

09-10	10-11	11-12	12-13	13-14	14-15	15-16	16-17	17-18	18-19
EBkP 8	EBkP 10	EBkP 8	EBkP 7	EBkP 2	EBkP 2	EBkP 2	Hel2E 1	Hel2E 1	Hel1E 8

CHINNOR

Founded: 1971 Nickname: The Chalkmen

Club Contact Details 01844 350 049 daryl.ridgley@btopenworld.com

Ground: Station Road, Chinnor, Oxon OX39 4PX **Club Colours:** Yellow and black

HONOURS **League:** None

FA Comps: None

10 YEAR RECORD

09-10	10-11	11-12	12-13	13-14	14-15	15-16	16-17	17-18	18-19
Hel1E 10	Hel1E 13	Hel1E 10	Hel1E 6	Hel1E 8	Hel1E 5	Hel1E 6	Hel1E 10	Hel1E 12	Hel1E 13
				FAC EP		FAC EP			
			FAV 2Q	FAV 2Q	FAV 1P	FAV 1Q			

Leave the M40 at Junction 6 & follow the B4009 sign posted Princes Risborough. After 3 miles you will enter Chinnor. Turn left at The Crown P/H roundabout & the ground is 400 yards on the right opposite the Black Boy P/H.

Nearest Railway Station Princes Risborough - 4.9km

Bus Route Duck Square stop - 56m away

DIDCOT TOWN DEVELOPMENT

Founded: 1907 Nickname: Railwaymen

Club Contact Details 01235 813 138

Ground: Loop Meadow Stadium, Bowmont Water, Didcot OX11 7GA **Club Colours:** Red and white

HONOURS **League:** None

FA Comps: None

10 YEAR RECORD

09-10	10-11	11-12	12-13	13-14	14-15	15-16	16-17	17-18	18-19
Hel1E 15	Hel1E 14	Hel1E 16	Hel1E 3	Hel1E 12	Hel1E 12	Hel1E 11	Hel1E 9	Hel1E 10	Hel1E 5

From A34 take A4130 towards Didcot, at first roundabout take first exit, at next roundabout take third exit, then straight across next two roundabouts, at 5th roundabout turn right into Avon Way, ground is on the left. Also footpath direct from Didcot Railway Station.

Nearest Railway Station Didcot Parkway - 0.4km

Bus Route Ladygrove Park Primary School stop - 171m

HOLYPORT

Founded: 1934 Nickname: The Villagers

Club Contact Details 07515 789 415 richardtyrell@googlemail.com

Ground: Summerleaze Village, 7 Summerleaze Road SL6 8SP **Club Colours:** Claret & green

HONOURS **League:** Hayes & Giles Premier Division 1998-99, 99-2000, 01-02.
Hellenic Division One East 2010-11.

FA Comps: None

10 YEAR RECORD

09-10	10-11	11-12	12-13	13-14	14-15	15-16	16-17	17-18	18-19
Hel1E 3	Hel1E 1	Hel P 13	Hel P 14	Hel P 18	Hel P 16	Hel1E 7	Hel1E 13	Hel1E 5	Hel1E 4
	FAC EP	FAC EP	FAC EP	FAC EP	FAC EPr	FAC EP			FAC EP
FAV 2Q	FAV 2P	FAV 1Q	FAV 1P	FAV 2Q	FAV 1Q	FAV 1Qr	FAV 1Q	FAV 2Q	FAV 1Pr

From the A4 Maidenhead take the B4447 towards Cookham after ¼ mile turn right into Ray Mill Road West, at the T-junction turn left into Blackamoor Lane. As road bends sharply you will see the entrance to the ground on left, signposted Holyport FC. Please observe speed limit down track to the ground. Please note a new electric gate has been installed at the entrance to Summerleaze, it will automatically open upon approach on match days.

Nearest Railway Station Furze Platt - 1km

Bus Route Veterinary Hospital stop - 133m away

KIDLINGTON DEVELOPMENT

Founded: 1909 Nickname: Greens

Club Contact Details 01865 849 777 (Ground) barry.hiles@btinternet.com

Ground: Yarnton Road, Kidlington, Oxford OX5 1AT **Club Colours:** All green

HONOURS **League:** None

FA Comps: None

10 YEAR RECORD

09-10	10-11	11-12	12-13	13-14	14-15	15-16	16-17	17-18	18-19
								Hel1W 11	Hel1W 6

From Kidlington roundabout (Sainsburys) take the A4260 into Kidlington, at the fifth set of lights turn left into Yarnton Road, ground is approx 300 metres on left, just past left turn to Morton Ave.

Nearest Railway Station Oxford Parkway - 1.9km

Bus Route Treeground Place stop - 63m away

LANGLEY

Founded: Nickname: The Villagers

Club Contact Details 07935 046 504 langleyfc2016@gmail.com

Ground: Summerleaze Park, Maidenhead, Berkshire SL6 8SP **Club Colours:** Red and white

HONOURS **League:** East Berkshire Division One 2013-14, Premier Division 2016-17.

FA Comps: None

10 YEAR RECORD

09-10	10-11	11-12	12-13	13-14	14-15	15-16	16-17	17-18	18-19
				EBk1 1	EBkP 5	EBkP 4	EBkP 1	EBkP 2	Hel2E 2

From the A4 Maidenhead take the B4447 towards Cookham after ¼ mile turn right into Ray Mill Road West, at the T-junction turn left into Blackamoor Lane. As road bends sharply you will see the entrance to the ground on left, signposted Holyport FC. Please observe speed limit down track to the ground. Please note a new electric gate has been installed at the entrance to Summerleaze, it will automatically open upon approach on match days.

Nearest Railway Station Furze Platt - 1km
Bus Route Veterinary Hospital stop - 133m away

LONG CRENDON

Founded: 1886 Nickname: The Robins

Club Contact Details 07937 423 781 admin@longcrendonfc.co.uk

Ground: Court Place Farm, Marsh Lane, Marston, Oxford OX3 0NQ **Club Colours:** Red and white

HONOURS **League:** Aylesbury & District Division Two 2014-15, Hellenic Division Two East 2018-19

FA Comps: None

10 YEAR RECORD

09-10	10-11	11-12	12-13	13-14	14-15	15-16	16-17	17-18	18-19
				AyD2 9	AyD2 1	AyD1 2	AyDP 2	Hel2E 3	Hel2E 1

Follow the A40 to the Headington roundabout going straightover towards Banbury & Northampton A40. Within a mile a flyover is visible as the exit from the Ring Road. Turn left under the flyover and left again toward Marsh Lane. Turn right at the T Junction and the ground is on your left just before the Pedestrian Crossing.

Nearest Railway Station Oxford - three miles from the ground.
Bus Route 14A from the Station to the ground.

MARLOW UNITED

Founded: 1977 Nickname: The Flying Blues

Club Contact Details 01628 436 166

Ground: Alfred Davies Memorial Ground, Oak tree Road, Marlow SL7 3ED **Club Colours:** Blue and white

HONOURS **League:** East Berks 1979-80. Wycombe & District Division One 83-84, Premier 84-85.
Reading Premier 99-00, Senior 04-05. Thames Valley Premier 2014-15, 18-19

FA Comps: None

10 YEAR RECORD

09-10	10-11	11-12	12-13	13-14	14-15	15-16	16-17	17-18	18-19
Hel P 18	ReadP 4	ReadS 4	ReadS 3	ReadS 3	THVaP 1	THVaP 2	THVaP 2	THVaP 6	THVaP 1
FAC EP									
FAV 1Q									

From M40 (Junction 4 High Wycombe) or M4 (Junction 8/9 Maidenhead) take A404, leave at the A4155 junction signposted Marlow.
Follow A4155 towards Marlow then turn right at Esso service station into Maple Rise.
At crossroads follow straight ahead into Oak Tree Road.
Ground 100 yards on left.

Nearest Railway Station Marlow - 1km
Bus Route Oak Tree Road - stop 100m away

MILTON UNITED

Founded: 1909 Nickname: Miltonians

Club Contact Details 01235 832 999 milton.united.fc@hotmail.co.uk

Ground: The Heights, Potash Lane, Milton Heights, OX13 6AG **Club Colours:** Claret & sky blue

HONOURS **League:** Hellenic 1990-91, Division One East 2013-14.

FA Comps: None

10 YEAR RECORD

09-10	10-11	11-12	12-13	13-14	14-15	15-16	16-17	17-18	18-19
Hel1E 7	Hel1E 4	Hel1E 14	Hel1E 14	Hel1E 1	Hel P 14	Hel P 18	Hel1W 12	Hel1E 13	Hel1E 10
FAC P	FAC EP	FAC EP			FAC 1Q	FAC P	FAC EP		
FAV 2Q	FAV 1Q	FAV 2Q	FAV 2Q	FAV 1P	FAV 2Q	FAV 2Q	FAV 2Q	FAV 1Q	FAV 1Q

Exit A34 at Milton, 10 miles south of Oxford & 12 miles north of junction 13 of M4. Take A4130 towards Wantage approximately 200 metres turn 1st left then right into Milton Hill. Ground 400 metres on the left.

Nearest Railway Station Didcot Parkway - 4.7km. Appleford - 5.9km
Bus Route The Pack Horse stop - 69m away

PENN & TYLERS GREEN

Founded: 1905 Nickname: Penn

Club Contact Details 01494 676 868 hsvlatta1955@yahoo.co.uk

Ground: Beaconsfield Town FC, Holloways Park, Windsor Road HP9 2SE **Club Colours:** Blue & white

HONOURS **League:** Wycombe Comb. Div.A 1911-12, Div.2 35-36, 56,57, 60-61, North 39-40, Div.1 46-47, Div.3 55-56, Prem 62-63. Wycombe & Dist Sen 83-84. Hellenic D1E 2015-16, 16-17

FA Comps: None

10 YEAR RECORD

09-10	10-11	11-12	12-13	13-14	14-15	15-16	16-17	17-18	18-19
Hel1E 17	Hel1E 10	Hel1E 12	Hel1E 4	Hel1E 5	Hel1E 9	Hel1E 1	Hel1E 1	Hel1E 3	Hel1E 9
									FAV 1Q

Leave Junction 2 of M40, take A355 towards Slough, 50 yards off roundabout turn left and at next roundabout turn complete right, coming back towards A355 to continue across A355, then turn right and 150 yards on left is sign to club. Go through gate and clubhouse is 200 yards on right.

Nearest Railway Station Beaconsfield - 2.8km

RISBOROUGH RANGERS

Founded: 1971 Nickname: Rangers or Boro

Club Contact Details 07855 958 236 nick@lloydlatchford.co.uk

Ground: " Windsors" Horsenden Lane, Princes Risborough. Bucks HP27 9NE **Club Colours:** All red

HONOURS **League:** None

FA Comps: None

10 YEAR RECORD

09-10	10-11	11-12	12-13	13-14	14-15	15-16	16-17	17-18	18-19
SSM2 10	SSM2 5	SSM2 2	SSM2 4	SSM1 14	SSM1 5	SSM1 7	SSM1 6	SSM1 8	SSM1 7
						FAC P	FAC EP	FAC EPr	
					FAV 2Q	FAV 2Q	FAV 1Q	FAV 1Q	FAV 1Q

On entering Prices Risborough from Aylesbury, turn left at first roundabout.
At the second roundabout turn right. Go pass Esso petrol station on left hand side.
After approximately 400 yards take the right fork. Take second turn on left (Picts Lane).
At junction turn right over the railway bridge and then immediately right again.
Ground is approximately 200 yards on the right hand side.

Nearest Railway Station Princes Rosborough - 0.2km
Bus Route Railway Station - stop 0.2km away

THAME RANGERS

Founded: Nickname: None

Club Contact Details 01844 214 401 rjcarr5@btinternet.com

Ground: Meadow View Park, Tythrop Way, Thame OX9 3RN **Club Colours:** Red & black

HONOURS **League:** Wycombe & District Senior Division 2015-16.
Spartan South Midlands Division Two 2016-17.

FA Comps: None

10 YEAR RECORD

09-10	10-11	11-12	12-13	13-14	14-15	15-16	16-17	17-18	18-19
						WyDS 1	SSM2 1	Hel1E 8	Hel1E 2
									FAV 2P

From the west: At the Oxford Road roundabout on the edge of Thame take the first left (sign posted Aylesbury) and follow the by-pass. At the next roundabout take the third exit on to Tythrop Way. The ground is 200 yards on the left.
From the east: Leave the M40 at Junction 6 and follow the signposts to Thame. On arriving in Thame, take the first right on to Wenman Road (B4012). Stay on the B4012 as it by-passes Thame, going straight over two roundabouts. The ground is on the right, directly off the by-pass, approximately half a mile after you pass Chinnor Rugby Club.

Nearest Railway Station Haddenham & Thame Parkway - 2.9km
Bus Route Queens Close stop - 309m away

WALLINGFORD TOWN

Founded: 1995 Nickname: Wally

Club Contact Details 01491 835 044

Ground: Wallingford Sports Park, Hithercroft Road, Wallingford OX10 9RB **Club Colours:** Red & white

HONOURS **League:** None

FA Comps: None

10 YEAR RECORD

09-10	10-11	11-12	12-13	13-14	14-15	15-16	16-17	17-18	18-19
NBk 1 5	NBk 1 4	NBk 1 11	NBk 1 9	NBk 1 9	NBk 1 4	NBk 1 6	NBk 1 3	Hel1E 7	Hel1E 7
FAV 1Q	FAV 1P	FAV 1Q						FAV 2Q	FAV 1Q

N, S & E A4130 Wallingford Ring Road, signposted Didcot. Right at Hithercroft Road roundabout (signposted Hithercroft Industrial Estate). Ground 200 yds on left. West A4130 signs for Reading taking Ring Road (right first roundabout) along Calvin Thomas Way. Left 2nd roundabout Hithercroft Road. Ground on left. Wallingford centre East along High Street past Waitrose car park. Left 1st mini roundabout to Croft Road. Next mini roundabout right into Hithercroft Road. Ground is 0.5 miles on the right.

Nearest Railway Station Wallingford - 366m
Bus Route Moses Winter Way stop - 58m away

WOKINGHAM & EMMBROOK

Founded: 2004 Nickname: Satsumas

Club Contact Details 07525 736 797 senior@wefc.club

Ground: Lowther Road Wokingham RG41 1JB **Club Colours:** Orange and black

HONOURS **League:** Hellenic Division One East 2014-15.

FA Comps: None

10 YEAR RECORD

09-10	10-11	11-12	12-13	13-14	14-15	15-16	16-17	17-18	18-19
Hel1E 2	Hel P 11	Hel P 10	Hel P 8	Hel1E 2	Hel1E 1	Hel P 20	Hel1E 12	Hel1E 6	Hel1E 6
		FAC 1Q	FAC EP						
	FAV 2Q	FAV 2Q	FAV 1P			FAV 1P			

From M4 – exit J10 – take left slip road signposted Reading . After 100 yds exit to Winnersh Triangle /Earley . As you approach traffic lights go through both sets bearing right towards Earley/Winnersh /Wokingham . Continue to next set of traffic lights and keep left bearing left under Railway Bridge . Keep left and bear left at next set of traffic lights to Winnersh/Wokingham on A329 –Reading Road . Continue straight ahead to traffic lights – go straight ahead continuing on A329 –Reading Road passing Sainsbury's on your right . Continue through next lights, under bridge and past BP garage on the left . Once past the garage take next left into Old Forest Road . Go over the bridge to next turn on the right hand side into Lowther Road and immediately right into the Emmbrook Sports and Social Club.

Nearest Railway Station Winnersh - 1.6km

Bus Route Toutley Close stop - 154m away

WOODLEY UNITED

Founded: 1904 Nickname: Woods or United

Club Contact Details 0118 9453 555 info@woodleyunitedfc.co.uk

Ground: Rivermoor Stadium, Scours Lane, Reading, Berkshire, RG30 6AY **Club Colours:** Sky blue

HONOURS **League:** Wargrave & District 1909-10, 26-27. Reading & District Division Three 28-29, Division One 32-33, Division Two 50-51, Premier 57-58, 58-59, 85-86. Reading Division Four Kennet 91-92, Division Three Kennet 92-93,

FA Comps: None

10 YEAR RECORD

09-10	10-11	11-12	12-13	13-14	14-15	15-16	16-17	17-18	18-19
Hel1E 4	Hel1E 5	Hel1E 5	Hel1E 3	Hel1E 14	Hel1E 8	Hel1E 13	Hel1E 2	Hel P 19	Hel1E 11
								FAC EP	FAC EP
					FAV 2Q	FAV 1Q	FAV 1Q	FAV 1Q	FAV 1Q

Come off J12 of the M4 head along the A4 towards Reading, take a left onto Langley Hill and follow it all the way up onto Park Lane, continue onto School Road past the Tilehurst shops and then down onto Kentwood Hill. At the bottom of the hill take a right onto the Oxford Road towards Reading and just past the Waitrose Shop you need to take a left into an industrial estate and under the railway bridge and the ground will be in front of you to your right.

Nearest Railway Station Tilehurst - 1.2km

Bus Route Cold Store stop - 277m away

BOURTON ROVERS

Founded: 1894 Nickname: Rovers

Club Contact Details 01451 821 977

Ground: Rissington Road, Bourton-on-the-Water, Cheltenham GL54 2EB **Club Colours:** All blue

HONOURS **League:** Hellenic Division Two West 2016-17

FA Comps: None

10 YEAR RECORD

09-10	10-11	11-12	12-13	13-14	14-15	15-16	16-17	17-18	18-19
							Hel2W 1	Hel2W 2	Hel2W 5

CHELTENHAM SARACENS

Founded: 1964 Nickname: The Sarries

Club Contact Details 07468 515 471 saracenschairman@outlook.com

Ground: Petersfield Park, Tewkesbury Road GL51 9DY **Club Colours:** All blue

HONOURS **League:** Hellenic Division One 1999-2000.

FA Comps: None

10 YEAR RECORD

09-10	10-11	11-12	12-13	13-14	14-15	15-16	16-17	17-18	18-19
Hel1W 4	Hel1W 3	Hel P 15	Hel P 11	Hel P 16	Hel P 20	Hel1W 2	Hel1W 14	Hel1W 10	Hel1W 2
				FAC Pr	FAC P	FAC 1Q			
FAV 2Q	FAV 1Q	FAV 1Q	FAV 1P	FAV 1Q	FAV 1Q	FAV 1Q			FAV 2Q

Follow directions into Cheltenham following signs for railway station. At Station roundabout take Gloucester Road, in a Northerly direction for approx 2 miles. Turn left at lights past Tesco entrance onto Tewkesbury Road, follow road past 'The Range' store over railway bridge. Take 1st left and then 1st left again, then left into service road into car park.

Nearest Railway Station Cheltenham Spa - 1.4km

Bus Route Moors Avenue stop - 171m away

CIRENCESTER TOWN DEV.

Founded: 2011 Nickname: Centurions

Club Contact Details 01285 654 543 scott.griffin@cirentownfc.com

Ground: Corinium Stadium, Kingshill Lane, Cirencester Glos GL7 1HS **Club Colours:** Red & black

HONOURS **League:** None

FA Comps: None

10 YEAR RECORD

09-10	10-11	11-12	12-13	13-14	14-15	15-16	16-17	17-18	18-19
			Hel2W 3	Hel2W 3	Hel1W 4	Hel1W 11	Hel1W 5	Hel1W 5	Hel1W 8

Leave bypass at Burford Road roundabout.
Aim for Stow, turn right at traffic lights, then right again at next junction, first left into Kingshill Lane.
Ground 500 yards on right.

Bus Route Kingshill School Grounds stop - 55m away

CLANFIELD 85

Founded: 1890 Nickname: Robins

Club Contact Details 01367 810 770 peter.osborne1@virgin.net

Ground: Radcot Road, Clanfield OX18 2ST **Club Colours:** All red

HONOURS **League:** North Berks Division Two 1924-25.
Hellenic Division One 1969-70.

FA Comps: None

10 YEAR RECORD

09-10	10-11	11-12	12-13	13-14	14-15	15-16	16-17	17-18	18-19
Hel1W 10	Hel1W 4	Hel1W 8	Hel1W 11	Hel1W 5	Hel1W 9	Hel1W 12	Hel1W 10	Hel1W 8	Hel1W 5
	FAC EP	FAC EP							
FAV 1Qr	FAV 2P	FAT 1P	FAV 1Q					FAV 2Q	FAV 2Q

Situated on A4095 at southern end of village, 8 miles west of Witney and 4 miles east of Faringdon.

Bus Route Carter Institute stop - 399m away

HEREFORD LADS CLUB

Founded: 1925 Nickname: Lads Club

Club Contact Details 07557 128 790

Ground: Widemarsh Common, Hereford HR4 9NA **Club Colours:** Blue

HONOURS **League:** Herefordshire Division One 2002-03.
West Midlands Division One 2016-17.

FA Comps: None

10 YEAR RECORD

09-10	10-11	11-12	12-13	13-14	14-15	15-16	16-17	17-18	18-19
		WM2 2	WM2 3	WM1 10	WM1 5	WM1 2	WM1 1	WMP 12	WMP 7
								FAV 1Q	FAV 2P

Driving north through Hereford on the A49/Edgar Street, continue on A49 until road merges onto Newtown Road (first exit off roundabout). In less than half a mile turn left for the ground.
Driving South into Hereford on the A49/Holmer Road, continue on A49 until road merges onto Newtown Road. In less than half a mile turn right for the ground.

Nearest Railway Station Hereford - 1km
Bus Route Priory Place - stop 150m away

HEREFORD PEGASUS

Founded: 1955 Nickname: The Redmen or Peggy

Club Contact Details 07931 971 765 nikmarsh1982@gmail.com

Ground: Old School Lane, Hereford HR1 1EX **Club Colours:** Red and white

HONOURS **League:** Hellenic Division One 1984-85, 98-99.

FA Comps: None

10 YEAR RECORD

09-10	10-11	11-12	12-13	13-14	14-15	15-16	16-17	17-18	18-19
Hel P 14	Hel P 22	WMP 17	WMP 7	WMP 2	WMP 9	WMP 9	WMP 9	WMP 19	WMP 20
FAC 2Q	FAC EPr	FAC EPr	FAC P	FAC EP	FAC EPr	FAC EP			
FAV 2Q	FAV 2Q	FAV 1Q	FAV 1P	FAV 1Q	FAV 2P	FAV 1Q	FAV 2Q	FAV 1Q	FAV 1Q

pegasus juniors - Old School Lane hr1 1ex - 07980 456 995
Approach City on A4103 (from Worcester) at roundabout on outskirts take 2nd exit (A4103) over railway bridge, traffic light controlled.
Take 2nd turning on left into Old School Lane, ground entrance 150 metre's on left.

Nearest Railway Station Hereford - 1.3km
Bus Route Bus stops outside the ground

MALMESBURY VICTORIA

Founded: 1896 Nickname: The Vics

Club Contact Details 01666 822 141 brendon@innov.co.uk

Ground: Flying Monk Ground, Gloucester Road, SN16 9JS **Club Colours:** Black & white

HONOURS **League:** Wiltshire Premier 1999-00, 2014-15.

FA Comps: None

10 YEAR RECORD

09-10	10-11	11-12	12-13	13-14	14-15	15-16	16-17	17-18	18-19
Hel P 19	Hel1W 13	Hel1W 16	Hel1W 15	Hel1W 12	Wilt 1	Wilt 3	West1 9	West1 15	Hel1W 4
FAV 2Q	FAV 1Q			FAV 1Q	FAV 1P	FAV 2Q	FAV 1Q	FAV 2Q	FAV 2P

At M4 Junction 14, take A429 to Cirencester, at priory roundabout take Second exit. At Wychurch roundabout take second exit, after 500 yards at roundabout take first exit B4014, after ½ mile at roundabout take first exit towards town centre. At bottom of hill club is behind the Supermarket. Entrance is via lane opposite the bus stop. Enter with caution as the lane is narrow and used by the general public.

Bus Route Bus stops outside the Supermarket

MALVERN TOWN

Founded: 1947 Nickname: The Hillsiders

Club Contact Details 01684 564 746 marg@malverntown.co.uk

Ground: Langlands Avenue, Malvern WR14 2EQ **Club Colours:** Sky blue and claret

HONOURS **League:** Midland Combination Division One 1955-56.

FA Comps: None

10 YEAR RECORD

09-10	10-11	11-12	12-13	13-14	14-15	15-16	16-17	17-18	18-19
MidAl 19	MidAl 23	WMP 13	WMP 13	WMP 14	WMP 5	WMP 3	WMP 4	WMP 3	WMP 4
FAC Pr	FAC P	FAC EPr				FAC EP	FAC EP	FAC P	FAC P
FAV 1P	FAV 1P	FAV 1Q	FAV 1Q	FAV 1Q	FAV 1Q	FAV 2Q	FAV 1P	FAV 1Q	FAV 1Q

Leave M5 at Junction 7 and turn towards Worcester. Turn left at next roundabout onto A4440 towards Malvern. Straight over next two roundabouts and take left slip road onto A449 at next roundabout. When approaching Malvern, turn left onto B4208 signposted Welland. Straight over three roundabouts and then take the third left into Orford Way. Take the third left into Langland Avenue. Ground is 300 yards on left.

Nearest Railway Station Great Malvern - 1.2km. Malvern Link - 1.5km

Bus Route Bus stops outside the ground

MORETON RANGERS

Founded: 1997 Nickname: The Townsmen

Club Contact Details 07568 469 120

Ground: London Road, Moreton-in-Marsh, Glos GL56 0HN **Club Colours:** Claret and blue

HONOURS **League:** Cheltenham Division One 2009-10. Hellenic Division Two West 2018-19

FA Comps: None

10 YEAR RECORD

09-10	10-11	11-12	12-13	13-14	14-15	15-16	16-17	17-18	18-19
Chelt1 1						Hel2W 3	Hel2W 5	Hel2W 3	Hel2W 1

Nearest Railway Station Moreton-in-Marsh - 1min walk away

NEW COLLEGE SWINDON

Founded: 1984 Nickname: Blue College

Club Contact Details 01793 824 828 (Ground) newcollegeswinfcsec@yahoo.co.uk

Ground: Supermarine S&S Club, Supermarine Drive, Swindon SN3 4SY **Club Colours:** Blue

HONOURS **League:** Wiltshire Premier Division 2008-09, 09-10.

FA Comps: None

10 YEAR RECORD

09-10	10-11	11-12	12-13	13-14	14-15	15-16	16-17	17-18	18-19
Wilt 1	Wilt 3	Hel1W 11	Hel1W 14	Hel1W 11	Hel1W 12	Hel1W 13	Hel1W 13	Hel1W 13	Hel1W 3
				FAV 2Q	FAV 2Q	FAV 1Q	FAV 2Q	FAV 1Q	FAV 2Q

Off main A361 Swindon – Highworth Road. 2 miles north East of Swindon leave a 419 at the a 361 junction and head to Highworth. Ground is on left after roundabout exit.

Nearest Railway Station Swindon - 5.8km

Bus Route Stanton Fitzwarren Turn stop - 284m away

NEWENT TOWN AFC

Founded: Nickname: The Daff's

Club Contact Details 01531 821 509 (Ground) phil@calendarlady.co.uk

Ground: Wildsmith Meadow, Malswick, Newent GL18 1HE **Club Colours:** Yellow & blue

HONOURS **League:** North Gloucestershire Premier 2012-13. Hellenic Division Two West 2017-18

FA Comps: None

10 YEAR RECORD

09-10		10-11		11-12		12-13		13-14		14-15		15-16		16-17		17-18		18-19	
NGIP	3	NGIP	6	NGIP	3	NGIP	1	GIN2	3	GIN1	14	GIN1	3	GIN1	7	Hel2W	1	Hel1W	9

SHORTWOOD UNITED

Founded: 1900 Nickname: The Wood

Club Contact Details 07931 971 765 jimcunneen1951@gmail.com

Ground: Meadowbank, Shortwood, Nailsworth GL6 0SJ **Club Colours:** Red and white

HONOURS **League:** Gloucestershire 1981-82. Hellenic 1984-85, 91-92.

FA Comps: None

10 YEAR RECORD

09-10		10-11		11-12		12-13		13-14		14-15		15-16		16-17		17-18		18-19	
Hel P	2	Hel P	6	Hel P	2	Sthsw	8	Sthsw	6	Sthsw	11	Sthsw	7	Sthsw	9	Sthsw	17	WestP	20
FAC	1Qr	FAC	Pr	FAC	Pr	FAC	P	FAC	1P	FAC	3Qr	FAC	2Q	FAC	P	FAC	P	FAC	EP
FAV	4P	FAV	2P	FAV	QF	FAT	3Qr	FAT	1Q	FAT	1Q	FAT	P	FAT	P	FAT	3Q	FAV	2Q

When entering Nailsworth from Stroud turn right at mini roundabout, when coming from Cirencester go straight over roundabout, and when from Bath turn left at mini roundabout.
Proceed up Spring Hill 30 yards turn left at Raffles Wine Warehouse, straight through town turn left at Brittannia Pub carry on for 1 mile until you come to Shortwood village you will see sign post on fork in the road keep to the left follow on for quarter of a mile ground opposite church.

Bus Route Homefield Turn - stop 250m away

STONEHOUSE TOWN

Founded: 1898 Nickname: The Magpies

Club Contact Details 07849 551 656

Ground: Oldends Lane, Stonehouse, Glos GL10 2DG **Club Colours:** Black and white

HONOURS **League:** Dursley & Dist 1900-01. Stroud & Dist 1908-09, 20-12, 27-28. North Glos 1919-20. Glos Nth Senior 1934-35, 35-36, 36-37, Div.2 2008-09, Wiltshire 1967-68. Glos Co 1968-69. Western Div.2 1950-51.

FA Comps: None

10 YEAR RECORD

09-10		10-11		11-12		12-13		13-14		14-15		15-16		16-17		17-18		18-19	
														GlCo	3	GlCo	4	GlCo	3

Nearest Railway Station Stonehouse - 3min walk to Wycliffe College bus stop.
Bus Route No.61 (Woodmancote) from Wycliffe College 5min journey to Oldends Lane.

THORNBURY TOWN

Founded: 1898 Nickname: Thorns

Club Contact Details 01454 413 645 (Ground) pengelly.mike@gmail.com

Ground: Mundy Playing Fields, Kington Lane, Thornbury BS35 1NA **Club Colours:** Red & black

HONOURS **League:** Bristol Premier Combination x2. Gloucestershire County 2009-10, 17-18.

FA Comps: None

10 YEAR RECORD

09-10		10-11		11-12		12-13		13-14		14-15		15-16		16-17		17-18		18-19	
GlCo	1	GlCo	13	GlCo	16	GlCo	14	GlCo	6	GlCo	4	GlCo	4	GlCo	4	GlCo	1	Hel1W	3

Nearest Railway Station Bristol Parkway - 40min bus journey from the ground.
Bus Route No.77 (Thornbury) to Rock Street - 14min walk to ground from there.

TYTHERINGTON ROCKS

Founded: 1896 Nickname: The Rocks

Club Contact Details 07837 555 776 (Ground) tramar1618@btinternet.com

Ground: Hardwicke Playing Field, Woodlands Rd, Tytherington Glos GL12 8UQ **Club Colours:** Amber & black

HONOURS

FA Comps: None

League: Iron Acton & District 1944-45. Bristol & Suburban Div.3 1949-50, Prem Div.2 93-94, Prem Div.1 96-97, Prem Div.1 97-98. Hellenic Div.1W 2011-12, 13-14.

10 YEAR RECORD

09-10	10-11	11-12	12-13	13-14	14-15	15-16	16-17	17-18	18-19
Hel1W 11	Hel1W 8	Hel1W 1	Hel1W 3	Hel1W 1	Hel1W 15	Hel1W 14	Hel1W 15	Hel1W 14	Hel1W 11
						FAV 2Qr	FAV 1Q	FAV 2Q	FAV 1Q

From M5 Junction 14 take A38 for Bristol. Tytherington turn-off is approx three (3) miles. Enter village, ground is signposted.

Bus Route Stowell Hill Road stop - 102m away

WELLINGTON

Founded: 1968 Nickname: The Wellies

Club Contact Details 07842 186 643 (MD) wellingtonherefordfc@gmail.com

Ground: Wellington Playing Field, Wellington, Hereford HR4 8AZ **Club Colours:** Orange

HONOURS

FA Comps: None

League: West Midlands (Reg) Division One South 1998-99.

10 YEAR RECORD

09-10	10-11	11-12	12-13	13-14	14-15	15-16	16-17	17-18	18-19
WMP 6	WMP 10	WMP 11	WMP 15	WMP 8	WMP 11	WMP 11	WMP 5	WMP 10	WMP 9
FAC EP	FAC EPr	FAC EP	FAC P		FAC P			FAC EP	
FAV 3P	FAV 1Q	FAV 2Q	FAV 1Q	FAV 1Q	FAV 1P	FAV 2Q	FAV 2Q	FAV 1P	FAV 1Pr

The Ground is situated in Wellington, behind School and opposite the Church. Wellington is 8 miles South of Leominster or 6 miles North of Hereford on the A49. At the Hereford end of the dual carriageway take the turn for Wellington.

Bus Route Wellington Village - stop 270m away

Hellenic League Division Two West

BRIMSCOMBE & THRUP DEV	The Meadow, London Road, Brimscombe, Stroud GL5 2SH
CHIPPENHAM TOWN DEV	Stanley Park Sports Ground, Stanley Lane, Chippenham SN15 3XB
CLANFIELD 85 DEV	Radcot Road, Main Street, Clanfield OX18 2ST
FAIRFORD TOWN RESERVES	Cinder Lane, Fairford GL7 4AX
FARINGDON TOWN	Tucker Park, Park Road, Faringdon SN7 7DP
HIGHWORTH TOWN RESERVES	The Elms Recreation Ground, Highworth SN6 7DD
KINTBURY RANGERS DEV	The Recreation Ground, Kintbury
LETCOMBE	Bassett Road, Letcombe Regis OX12 9LJ
NEWENT TOWN DEV	Wildsmith Meadow, Malswick, Newent GL18 1HE
SHORTWOOD UNITED DEV	Meadowbank Stadium, Shortwood GL6 0SJ
SHRIVENHAM DEV	Shrivenham Recreation Ground, Highworth Road, Shrivenham SN6 8BL
SWINDON ROBINS	Beversbrook Sports Facility, Beversbrook Road, Calne SN11 9FL
WANTAGE TOWN DEV	Alfredian Park, Manor Road, Wantage OX12 8DW

PREMIER DIVISION INS: Gresley (R - NPLE), Haughmond (P - WMidP), Heather St John's (P - MFL1), Newark Flowserve (P - EMC), Racing Club Warwick (P - MFL1), Selston (P - EMC), Tividale (P - WMidP).

AFC WULFRUNIANS

Nickname: The Wulfs **Club Colours:** Red and black

Founded 2005

Club Contact Details 07765 141 410 birchkeith@yahoo.co.uk

Ground: Castlecroft Stadium, Castlecroft Road, Wolverhampton WV3 8NA

Capacity: 2,000 **Seats:** Yes **Covered:** Yes

Previous Names: None

Previous Leagues: West Midlands (Regional). Midland Alliance 2013-14.

HONOURS: FA Comps: None

League: West Midlands (Regional) League Division Two 2005-06, Premier Division 2008-09, 12-13.

10 YEAR RECORD

09-10	10-11	11-12	12-13	13-14	14-15	15-16	16-17	17-18	18-19
WMP 3	WMP 3	WMP 5	WMP 1	MidAl 8	MFLP 7	MFLP 13	MFLP 17	MFLP 17	MFLP 12
FAC 2Q	FAC EP	FAC 1Q	FAC 1Q	FAC 2Q	FAC P	FAC 1Q	FAC EP	FAC Pr	FAC EP
FAV 1P	FAV 2Q	FAV 2Q	FAV 3P	FAV 2P	FAV 1Pr	FAV 4P	FAV 2P	FAV 1Pr	FAV 2Q

Follow A454 (signposted Bridgnorth) and turn left at Mermaid Pub onto Windmill Lane. Turn right onto Castlecroft Avenue. Ground is straight across past Wightwick Cricket Ground.

Nearest Railway Station Wolverhampton - 5km

Bus Route Castlecroft Hotel stop - 218m away

BOLDMERE ST. MICHAELS

Nickname: The Mikes **Club Colours:** White & black

Founded 1883

Club Contact Details 07866 122 254 clivefaulkner457@gmail.com

Ground: Trevor Brown Memorial Ground, Church Road, Boldmere B73 5RY

Capacity: 2,500 **Seats:** 230 **Covered:** 400

Previous Names: None.

Previous Leagues: West Midlands (Regional) 1949-63. Midland Combination. Midland Alliance > 2014.

HONOURS: FA Comps: None

League: Midland Combination Premier 1985-86, 88-89, 89-90.

10 YEAR RECORD

09-10	10-11	11-12	12-13	13-14	14-15	15-16	16-17	17-18	18-19
MidAl 6	MidAl 3	MidAl 12	MidAl 9	MidAl 2	MFLP 9	MFLP 11	MFLP 12	MFLP 14	MFLP 5
FAC EP	FAC EP	FAC 1Q	FAC EP	FAC EP	FAC 1Q	FAC EPr	FAC P	FAC 1Q	FAC EPr
FAV 3P	FAV 2P	FAV 2P	FAV 2Q	FAV 2Q	FAV 1P	FAV 1P	FAV 2Q	FAV 2Q	FAV 2P

A38(M) from M6 junction 6 and A5127 from Birmingham to Yenton Traffic Lights.
Left on A452 Chester Road, then 6th.right into Church Road.
From M6 junction 5 A452 Brownhills to Yenton Traffic Lights. Straight on then 6th right into Church Road.

Nearest Railway Station Chester Road - 0.9km

Bus Route Church Road stop - 106m away

COVENTRY SPHINX

Nickname: Sphinx **Club Colours:** Sky blue & white

Founded 1946

Club Contact Details 07979 233 845 sharon@coventrysphinx.co.uk

Ground: Sphinx Sports & Social Club, Sphinx Drive, Coventry CV3 1WA

Capacity: 1,000 **Seats:** Yes **Covered:** Yes

Previous Names: Armstrong Siddeley Motors. Sphinx > 1995.

Previous Leagues: Midland Combination. Midland Alliance 2007-14.

HONOURS: FA Comps: None

League: Midland Combination Premier 2006-07.

10 YEAR RECORD

09-10	10-11	11-12	12-13	13-14	14-15	15-16	16-17	17-18	18-19
MidAl 9	MidAl 16	MidAl 3	MidAl 14	MidAl 7	MFLP 18	MFLP 19	MFLP 10	MFLP 10	MFLP 9
FAC 3Q	FAC 2Q	FAC P	FAC P	FAC 2Q	FAC Pr	FAC P	FAC EP	FAC EP	FAC EP
FAV 2Q	FAV 2P	FAV 2Q	FAV 2P	FAV 2P	FAV 2Q	FAV 2P	FAV 2Q	FAV 1Q	FAV 1Qr

From M6. Leave M6 at Junction 3 and take A444 towards Coventry. Continue to Binley Road (6 roundabouts) and turn left on A428 Binley Road towards Binley. Pass a row of shops on left and Bulls Head public house on right. After the Bulls Head, turn 1st right into Biggin Hall Crescent. Then take the 5th left turn into Siddeley Avenue. Take 1st left into Sphinx Drive and the ground is at the end.
From M42 & A45. Follow A45 towards Coventry and take A4114 Coventry at Coventry Hill Hotel. At roundabout take 2nd exit to next roundabout and take 3rd exit onto Holyhead Road. After approx 2.5 miles you will come to Coventry Ring Road where you turn left and then get over to your right onto the ring road. Continue on Ring Road and leave at Junction 3 signposted M69 and Football Stadium. Follow signs for A428 Binley until you see Bulls Head public house on your right. Then follow the above instructions.

Nearest Railway Station Coventry - 2.6km

Bus Route Bulls Head Lane stop - 363m away

COVENTRY UNITED

Founded 2013

Nickname: Cov United **Club Colours:** Red and green

Club Contact Details 07863 563 943 graham.wood@coventryunited.co.uk

Ground: Coventry RFC, Butts Park Arena, The Butts, Coventry CV1 3GE

Capacity: 3,000 **Seats:** Yes **Covered:** Yes

Previous Names: None

Previous Leagues: Midland Combination 2013-14.

HONOURS: FA Comps: None

League: Midland Football League Division Two 2014-15, Division One 2015-16.

10 YEAR RECORD

09-10	10-11	11-12	12-13	13-14	14-15	15-16	16-17	17-18	18-19
				MCm2 2	MFL2 1	MFL1 1	MFLP 8	MFLP 8	MFLP 8
							FAC 1Q	FAC EP	FAC EP
						FAV 2P	FAV 1P	FAV 3Pr	FAV 4P

Head for Coventry Ring Road, once on the Ring Road come off at junction 7 (B4101/Earlsdon/Tile Hill).
At the next roundabout take the first exit onto Butts Road/B4101.

Nearest Railway Station Coventry - 1km

Bus Route Albany Road stop - 156m away

GRESLEY

Founded 2009

Nickname: The Moatmen **Club Colours:** Red & white

Club Contact Details 07733 055 212 ian.collins@gresleyfc.com

Ground: The Moat Ground, Moat Street, Church Gresley, Derbyshire DE11 9RE

Capacity: 2,400 **Seats:** Yes **Covered:** Yes Yes

Previous Names: Gresley Rovers

Previous Leagues: East Midlands 2009-11. Midland Football Alliance 2011-12. Northern Premier 2012-19.

HONOURS: FA Comps: None

League: East Midlands Counties 2010-11. Midland Alliance 2011-12.

10 YEAR RECORD

09-10	10-11	11-12	12-13	13-14	14-15	15-16	16-17	17-18	18-19
EMC 2	EMC 1	MidAl 1	NP1S 11	NP1S 9	NP1S 5	NP1S 16	NP1S 18	NP1S 17	NP1E 20
FAC EPr	FAC 1Qr	FAC 1Q	FAC 3Q	FAC 2Qr	FAC Pr	FAC Pr	FAC 2Qr	FAC P	FAC P
FAV QF	FAV 4P	FAV 5P	FAT 1Q	FAT 1P	FAT 3Q	FAT 1Q	FAT 1Q	FAT P	FAT P

From the South: Follow the M42 northbound to Junction 11, turn off onto the A444 toward Burton Upon Trent. Turn right onto the A514 (Castle Road) toward Gresley and follow the road up the hill to the traffic island at the top. Continue on the A514 over the island and take the second road on the left (School Street), the next left into Moat Street where the Moat Ground is located. **From the North-East:** Follow the M1 south to junction 23a, turn off on to the A42 southbound. Continue on the A42 to Ashby-de-la-Zouch then turn off onto the A511 toward Swadlincote. At Woodville turn off the A511 onto the A514 toward Church Gresley, follow the road signs to Gresley, the School Street turn off is second on the right after the Gresley island. Take the first turn on the left in School Street to take you to the ground. **From the North-West:** From Stoke-on-Trent follow the A50 toward Burton-Upon-Trent, turn on to the A511 and continue through Burton. Turn off the A511 onto the A444 toward Nuneaton. Follow the A444 until you reach the turn off for the A514. Turn left onto the A514 (Castle Road) toward Gresley and follow the road up the hill to the traffic island at the top. Continue on the A514 over the island and take the second road on the left (School Street), the next left into Moat Street where the Moat Ground is located.

Bus Route Church Street - stop 200m away

HAUGHMOND

Founded 1980

Nickname: Academicals **Club Colours:** White and black

Club Contact Details 07785 531 754 stuartlwilliams@btinternet.com

Ground: Sundorne Sports Village, Sundorne Road, Shrewsbury. SY1 4RQ

Capacity: **Seats:** Yes **Covered:** Yes

Previous Names: None

Previous Leagues: West Midlands >2017. Midland Football 2017-18. West Midlands 2018-19.

HONOURS: FA Comps: None

League: Shropshire County Premier Division 2010-11. West Midlands Division Two 2011-12, Premier Division 2016-17.

10 YEAR RECORD

09-10	10-11	11-12	12-13	13-14	14-15	15-16	16-17	17-18	18-19
ShCP 2	ShCP 1	WM2 1	WM1 4	WM1 2	WMP 8	WMP 5	WMP 1	MFLP 20	WMP 2
							FAC EP	FAC 2Qr	FAC 1Q
						FAV 2P	FAV 1P	FAV 1P	FAV 1Q

Head in to Shrewsbury on the A5, at the Preston Island, take the 1st exit onto the A49.
At the next roundabout take the 1st exit onto Sundorne Road/B5062.
At the next roundabout take the 1st exit for the ground.

Nearest Railway Station Shrewsbury - 2.6km

Bus Route Ta Centre stop - 109m away

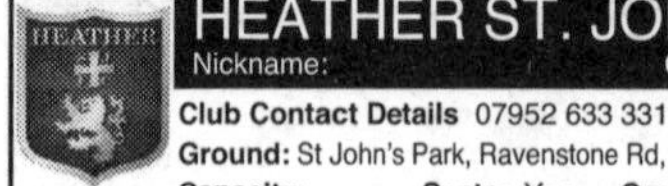

HEATHER ST. JOHN'S

Founded 1949

Nickname: **Club Colours:** All royal blue

Club Contact Details 07952 633 331 adrianrock@hotmail.co.uk

Ground: St John's Park, Ravenstone Rd, Heather LE67 2QJ

Capacity: **Seats:** Yes **Covered:** Yes

Previous Names: Heather Athletic 1949-2007.

Previous Leagues: Midland Combination > 2011. Midland Alliance 2011-14.

HONOURS: FA Comps: None

League: Leicester & District Division One 1965-66., 69-70, 71-72.
Midland Combination Division One 2006-07, Premier 10-11. Midland Division One 2018-19.

10 YEAR RECORD

09-10		10-11		11-12		12-13		13-14		14-15		15-16		16-17		17-18		18-19	
MCmP	2	MCmP	1	MidAl	19	MidAl	20	MidAl	22	MFL1	16	MFL1	16	MFL1	8	MFL1	7	MFL1	1
FAC	P	FAC	P					FAC	EP	FAC	EP							FAC	EP
FAV	2Q	FAV	3P			FAV	1P	FAV	2Q	FAV	2Q	FAV	1Q	FAV	1Q	FAV	1P	FAV	2P

Exit M42 at Junction 11. Take the road towards Measham, pass the Car Auctions and go over the traffic lights. At 2nd mini island take 2nd exit onto Leicester Road. After approximately 3 miles you will enter Heather. At T junction turn left. At mini island take 2nd exit onto Ravenstone Road and go up the hill. Ground is 200 metres on the left.

Bus Route Holyoake Drive stop - 160m away

HIGHGATE UNITED

Founded 1948

Nickname: Red or Gate **Club Colours:** All red

Club Contact Details 07527 941 993 jimmymerry777@gmail.com

Ground: The Coppice, Tythe Barn Lane, Shirley Solihull B90 1PH

Capacity: 2,000 **Seats:** **Covered:**

Previous Names: None.

Previous Leagues: Worcestershire/Midland Combination. Midland Alliance 2008-14.

HONOURS: FA Comps: None

League: Midland Combination Premier 1972-73, 73-74, 74-75.

10 YEAR RECORD

09-10		10-11		11-12		12-13		13-14		14-15		15-16		16-17		17-18		18-19	
MidAl	18	MidAl	18	MidAl	20	MidAl	19	MidAl	3	MFL1	1	MFLP	9	MFLP	7	MFLP	3	MFLP	14
FAC	EPr	FAC	EP	FAC	P	FAC	EPr							FAC	2Q	FAC	EPr	FAC	1Q
FAV	2Qr	FAV	2Q	FAV	1P	FAV	2Q					FAV	2P	FAV	2Q	FAV	3P	FAV	1P

Take junction 3 off the M42 (A435/Birmingham (S)/Redditch/Evesham) take first exit off the roundabout.
Continue on the A435 until the next roundabout, take the 4th exiti onto Station Road. Continue onto Norton Lane.
Take next left onto Lowbrook Lane and after just under half a mile turn left into Tilehouse Lane.
Just under a mile later turn right onto Tythe Barn Lane and the ground will be on the right.

Nearest Railway Station Whitlocks End - 0.4km

Bus Route Whitlocks End stop - 302m away

LONG EATON UNITED

Founded 1956

Nickname: Blues **Club Colours:** Blue and black

Club Contact Details 07971 416 444 secretary@longeatonutd.co.uk

Ground: Grange Park, Station Road, Long Eaton, Derbys NG10 2EF

Capacity: 1,500 **Seats:** 450 **Covered:** 500 **Shop:** No

Previous Names: None

Previous Leagues: Central Alliance 1956-61, Mid Co Football Lge 1961-82, NCE 1982-89, 2002-14. Central Midlands 1989-2002

HONOURS: FA Comps: None

League: Northern Counties East Division One South 1984-85.

10 YEAR RECORD

09-10		10-11		11-12		12-13		13-14		14-15		15-16		16-17		17-18		18-19	
NCEP	10	NCEP	12	NCEP	15	NCEP	12	NCEP	11	MFLP	3	MFLP	18	MFLP	14	MFLP	9	MFLP	15
FAC	P	FAC	EPr	FAC	EP			FAC	1Q	FAC	EP	FAC	1Q	FAC	P	FAC	EP	FAC	P
FAV	2P	FAV	1Q	FAV	2P	FAV	3P	FAV	2P	FAV	1P	FAV	2P	FAV	3P	FAV	2Q	FAV	1P

M1 Junc 25, take A52 towards Nottingham, to island by Bardills Garden Centre, right onto B6003. Approx 2 miles to end of road to T-junction. At traffic lights, turn right A453 and take 2nd left into Station Road. Entrance on left down un-named road opposite disused car park next to Grange School.

Nearest Railway Station Attenborough - 1.9km

Bus Route School stop - 158m away

LYE TOWN

Nickname: The Flyers **Club Colours:** Blue & white

Founded 1930

Club Contact Details 07429 887 570 dprobbo@gmail.com

Ground: Sports Ground, Stourbridge Road, Lye, Stourbridge, West Mids DY9 7DH

Capacity: 1,000 **Seats:** **Covered:**

Previous Names: Lye & Wollescote 1930-31.

Previous Leagues: Worcestershire Combination 1931-39. Birmingham & Dist/West Midlands (Regional) 1947-62/1962-2014.

HONOURS: FA Comps: None

League: West Midlands (Regional) 2013-14.

10 YEAR RECORD

09-10	10-11	11-12	12-13	13-14	14-15	15-16	16-17	17-18	18-19
WMP 19	WMP 11	WMP 15	WMP 2	WMP 1	MFLP 6	MFLP 8	MFLP 4	MFLP 16	MFLP 10
FAC EP		FAC EP	FAC P	FAC P	FAC EP	FAC EPr	FAC P		
FAV 1Q	FAV 2Q	FAV 1Q	FAV 1P	FAV 1Q	FAV 2Q	FAV 2Q	FAV 1Q		FAV 4P

Situated on A458 Birmingham to Stourbridge RoadFrom M5 Junction 3, take road marked Kidderminster, as far as lights at the bottom of Hagley Hill. Turn right, then take the third turning off the first island. Carry straight on at the next island. Turn left at Lights/Crossroads, onto the A458. Ground approximately 400 yards on the left hand side.

Nearest Railway Station Lye - 0.5km

Bus Route Cemetery Road stop - 93m away

NEWARK FLOWSERVE

Nickname: Simmos **Club Colours:** Orange

Founded 1901

Club Contact Details 07760 334 155 kmpnewark@aol.com

Ground: Lowfields, Hawton Lane, Newark, Nottinghamshire NG24 3BU

Capacity: **Seats:** Yes **Covered:** Yes

Previous Names: Worthington Simpsons >1998, IDP Newark 1998-2001.

Previous Leagues: Nottingham Alliance. Nottinghamshire Senior >2004, 2009-18. Central Midlands 2004-09. East Midlands Counties 2018-19.

HONOURS: FA Comps: None

League: Notts Alliance 1952-53, 65-66. Nottinghamshire Senior Premier Division 2017-18.

10 YEAR RECORD

09-10	10-11	11-12	12-13	13-14	14-15	15-16	16-17	17-18	18-19
				NottS2 3	NottS1 2	NottSP	NottSP	NottSP 1	EMC 2
									FAV 1Q

Enter Newark on the B6166, bear right onto Boundary Road towards Newark Hospital. Take 2nd exit at the next roundabout to continue on Boundary Road. At the next junction turn right onto Bowbridge Road. Continue along Bowridge Road for almost a mile then turn left onto Hawton Lane.

Nearest Railway Station Nottingham - walk to Eugene Gardens (Stop ME03).

Bus Route From Eugene Gardens take 90 Fosseway Flyer getting off at Princes Street in Newark - the ground is 1.5 miles.

RACING CLUB WARWICK

Nickname: Racers **Club Colours:** Gold and black

Founded 1919

Club Contact Details 07926 188 553 pja.murphy@hotmail.co.uk

Ground: Townsend Meadow, Hampton Road, Warwick, Warwickshire CV34 6JP

Capacity: 1,300 **Seats:** **Covered:**

Previous Names: Warwick Saltisford Rovers > 1970.

Previous Leagues: Warwick. Leamington & District. West Midlands (regional) 1967-72. Midland Combination 1972-89, 2009-14. Southern 1989-2003. Midland Alliance 2003-09.

HONOURS: FA Comps: None

League: Warwick 1933-34, 34-35, 35-36. Leamington & District 37-38, 45-46, 46-47, 47-48. Midland Combination Premier Division 1987-88.

10 YEAR RECORD

09-10	10-11	11-12	12-13	13-14	14-15	15-16	16-17	17-18	18-19
MCmP 22	MCmP 19	MCmP 13	MCmP 17	MCmP 12	MFL1 18	MFL1 10	MFL1 6	MFL1 5	MFL1 2
									FAC 1Q
	FAV 1Q	FAV 2P	FAV 2Q	FAV 1P	FAV 1Q	FAV 2P	FAV 1Q	FAV 3P	FAV 2Q

M40 Junction 15, signposted Warwick. At roundabout with traffic lights take A429 to Warwick. Follow this road for ½ mile and you will come to houses on your left. Take the 2nd turn on the left into Shakespeare Avenue. Follow to T-junction. Turn right into Hampton Road. Entrance to ground is 50 yards on left.

Nearest Railway Station Warwick Parkway - 1.4km

Bus Route Shakespeare Avenue stop - 131m away

ROMULUS

Nickname: The Roms **Club Colours:** Red and white stripes/red/red

Founded 1979

Club Contact Details 07515 991 621 sarah.romulusfc@virginmedia.com

Ground: Vale Stadium, Farnborough Road, Castle Vale, Birmingham B35 7LQ

Capacity: **Seats:** **Covered:**

Previous Names: None

Previous Leagues: Midland Combination 1999-2004, Midland Alliance 2004-07, Southern 2007-2010. Northern Premier 2010-18.

HONOURS: FA Comps: None

League: Midland Combination Division One 1999-00, Premier Division 2003-04.

10 YEAR RECORD

09-10		10-11		11-12		12-13		13-14		14-15		15-16		16-17		17-18		18-19	
SthM	8	NP1S	10	NP1S	20	NP1S	19	NP1S	11	NP1S	12	NP1S	10	NP1S	13	NP1S	22	MFLP	17
FAC	2Q	FAC	1Q	FAC	1Q	FAC	P	FAC	P	FAC	1Q	FAC	P	FAC	1Qr	FAC	1Q	FAC	2Q
FAT	1Q	FAT	2Q	FAT	2Q	FAT	3Q	FAT	Pr	FAT	1Q	FAT	Pr	FAT	Pr	FAT	P	FAV	2P

From M42 Junc 9, take A4097 (Minworth sign). At island, follow signs to Walmley Village. At traffic lights turn right (B4148). After shops turn left at traffic lights into Wylde Green Road. Over railway bridge turn right into East View Road, which becomes Coles Lane.

SELSTON

Nickname: The Parishioners **Club Colours:** Blue & black

Founded 1968

Club Contact Details 07973 364 188 clanclif@hotmail.co.uk

Ground: Parish Hall, Mansfield Road, Selston, Nottinghamshire NG16 6EE

Capacity: **Seats:** Yes **Covered:** Yes

Previous Names: None

Previous Leagues: Midland Regional Alliance >2011. Notts Senior 2011-15. Central Midlands 2015-17. East Midlands Counties 2017-19.

HONOURS: FA Comps: None

League: Midland Regional Alliance Division Two 2007-08. Notts Senior 2013-14.
Central Midlands South Division 2015-16, 16-17. East Midlands Counties 2018-19.

10 YEAR RECORD

09-10		10-11		11-12		12-13		13-14		14-15		15-16		16-17		17-18		18-19	
MidRA1	3	MidRA1	5	NottSP	11	NottSP	11	NottSP	1	NottSP	4	CMSth	1	CMSth	1	EMC	4	EMC	1
																		FAV	1P

Follow M1 to Nottinghamshire. Take exit 27 from M1. Continue on Mansfield Rd/A608.
Take B600 to Mansfield Rd/B6018 in Selston
At the roundabout, take the 1st exit onto Mansfield Rd/A608. Turn right onto Sandhill Road.
Turn right onto Alfreton Rd/B600. Continue to follow B600.
Turn right onto Mansfield Rd/B6018. Ground will be on the left.

Nearest Railway Station Kirkby in Ashfield - 4.5km

SOUTH NORMANTON ATHLETIC

Nickname: The Shiners **Club Colours:** Blue & white

Founded 1926

Club Contact Details 07961 186 320 richardstrzyzewski@hotmail.co.uk

Ground: M J Robinson Structures Arena, Lees Lane South Normanton, Derby DE55 2AD

Capacity: **Seats:** 150 **Covered:** 300

Previous Names: South Normanton Miners Welfare 1926-90. Folded in 2008, reformed in 2009.

Previous Leagues: Alfreton &District Sunday Lge 1980-87, Mansfield Sunday Lge 1987-90, Central Midlands League 1990-2003, East Midlands Counties 2002-17.

HONOURS: FA Comps: None

League: None

10 YEAR RECORD

09-10		10-11		11-12		12-13		13-14		14-15		15-16		16-17		17-18		18-19	
CM P	11	CM P	3	CMSth	3	CMSth	9	CMSth	2	EMC	7	EMC	4	EMC	2	MFLP	19	MFLP	16
												FAC	Pr	FAC	P	FAC	EP	FAC	P
				FAV	1Q	FAV	2Q			FAV	2Q	FAV	2Q	FAV	1Q	FAV	1Q	FAV	2Q

M1 Junction 28 take B6019 to Alfreton, turn right onto Market Street at the Shell petrol station, then take the 5th turning on the left onto Lees Lane opposite Ladbrooks. The ground is at the end of the lane.

Nearest Railway Station Alfreton - 1.8km
Bus Route Market Street stop - 105m away

SPORTING KHALSA

Founded 1991

Nickname: Sporting **Club Colours:** Yellow & blue

Club Contact Details 07976 220 444 manjit.gill@globeproperty.co.uk

Ground: Aspray Arena, Noose Lane, Willenhall WV13 3BB

Capacity: 5,000 **Seats:** Yes **Covered:** Yes

Previous Names: None

Previous Leagues: Walsall & District Sunday 1991-96. West Midlands (Regional) 1996-97, 2005-15.

HONOURS: FA Comps: None

League: West Midlands (Regional) Premier Division 2014-15.

10 YEAR RECORD

09-10	10-11	11-12	12-13	13-14	14-15	15-16	16-17	17-18	18-19
WM1 17	WM1 3	WMP 14	WMP 11	WMP 6	WMP 1	MFLP 3	MFLP 3	MFLP 5	MFLP 3
			FAC Pr		FAC P	FAC 4Q	FAC P	FAC Pr	FAC P
FAV 1Q	FAV 1Q	FAV 1Q	FAV 1Q	FAV 2Q	FAV 2Qr	FAV 1P	FAV QF	FAV 2P	FAV 5P

From M6 junction 10, take 2nd exit onto A454 to Wolverhampton/Dudley A463. Take the A454 exit towards Wolverhampton. At Keyway junction take 2nd exit onto the Keyway A454 and continue on A454 going through one roundabout. At next traffic lights make a u turn at Nechells Lane. Turn left into Noose Lane and over roundabout. Ground is located on your left.

Nearest Railway Station Wolverhampton - 3.9km

Bus Route Fibbersley Bridge stop - 125m away

STOURPORT SWIFTS

Founded 1882

Nickname: Swifts **Club Colours:** Gold & black

Club Contact Details 07780 997 758 ghaighway@hotmail.co.uk

Ground: Walshes Meadow, Harold Davis Drive, Stourport on Severn DY13 0AA

Capacity: 2,000 **Seats:** 250 **Covered:** 150 **Shop:** Yes

Previous Names: None

Previous Leagues: Kidderminster/Worcestershire/West Midlands (Regional) > 1998, Midland Alliance 1998-2001, 12-14, Southern 2001-12.

HONOURS: FA Comps: None

League: Midland Alliance 2000-01.

10 YEAR RECORD

09-10	10-11	11-12	12-13	13-14	14-15	15-16	16-17	17-18	18-19
SthM 17	Sthsw 17	Sthsw 21	MidAl 5	MidAl 10	MFLP 10	MFLP 10	MFLP 13	MFLP 15	MFLP 13
								FAC EPr	FAC 1Q
								FAV 5P	FAV 2P

Follow the one way system through Stourport Town Centre signposted 'Sports Centre'.
Go over river bridge and turn left into Harold Davies Drive.
Ground is at rear of Sports Centre.

Nearest Railway Station Hartlebury - 4.2km

Bus Route Swimming Pool stop - 104m away

TIVIDALE

Founded 1953

Nickname: The Dale **Club Colours:** Yellow and blue

Club Contact Details 07939 234 813 leon@tividalefc.com

Ground: The Beeches, Packwood Road, Tividale, West Mids B69 1UL

Capacity: 3,000 **Seats:** 200 **Covered:** Yes

Previous Names: Tividale Hall Youth Club 1953-56

Previous Leagues: Warwickshire & West Midlands Alliance 1956-66. West Midlands (Regional) 1966- 2011. Midland Alliance 2011-14.

HONOURS: FA Comps: None

League: Warwickshire & West Midlands Alliance Premier 1964-65. West Midlands (Reg) Division One 1972-73, Premier Division 2010-11, 18-19. Midland Alliance 2013-14.

10 YEAR RECORD

09-10	10-11	11-12	12-13	13-14	14-15	15-16	16-17	17-18	18-19
WMP 7	WMP 1	MidAl 4	MidAl 8	MidAl 1	NP1S 8	NP1S 22	MFLP 22	WMP 2	WMP 1
FAC 1Qr	FAC EP	FAC EP	FAC 2Q	FAC 1Q	FAC 2Qr	FAC 1Q	FAC P	FAC 1Q	FAC EP
FAV 2P	FAV 1P	FAV 5P	FAV 2Q	FAV 2Q	FAT P	FAT P	FAV 1Q	FAV 1Q	FAV 2Q

M5 Junction 2. Take A4123 towards Dudley. After approx 1.5 miles and after footbridge, take left up Trafalgar Road. Take 2nd right into Elm Terrace and then 1st left into Birch Crescent. Take 1st right into Packwood Road and ground is at end of road.

Nearest Railway Station Dudley Port - 1.6km

Bus Route Regent Road - stop 100m away

WALSALL WOOD

Nickname: Wood or Prims **Club Colours:** All Red

Founded 1915

Club Contact Details 07775 512 373 gevangelou67@gmail.com

Ground: Oak Park, Lichfield Road, Walsall Wood, Walsall WS9 9NP

Capacity: 1,000 **Seats:** Yes **Covered:** Yes

Previous Names: Walsall Borough (formed when Walsall Wood & Walsall Sportsco merged) 1982-96.

Previous Leagues: Midland Combinataion 1986-92, 2006-13. Staffordshire Senior 1992-93. West Midlands 1993-2006. Mid Alliance 2013-14.

HONOURS: FA Comps: None

League: Worcestershire/Midland Combination 1951-52, 2012-13. Midland Football Division One 2017-18.

10 YEAR RECORD

09-10		10-11		11-12		12-13		13-14		14-15		15-16		16-17		17-18		18-19	
MidCo	6	MidCo	9	MidCo	14	MidCo	1	MidAl	6	WMP	4	MFLP	7	MFLP	20	MFL1	1	MFLP	2
FAC	EP	FAC	EP	FAC	EP			FAC	1Qr	FAC	P	FAC	EPr	FAC	EP	FAC	P	FAC	1Q
FAV	1P	FAV	2Q	FAV	2Q	FAV	QFr	FAV	2P	FAV	4Pr	FAV	3P	FAV	1P	FAV	3P	FAV	3P

From North- Leave M6 at Junction 12 and take A5 until big island just outside Brownhills (next island after 'The Turn' pub on left). Take A452 Chester Road North through Brownhills High Street to traffic lights at Shire Oak (Pub at junction on right hand side). Turn right onto A461 towards Walsall, go to next set of traffic lights, cross over and turn right immediately onto Oak Park Leisure Centre Car park (rear of Kentucky Fried Chicken). Proceed diagonally over car park and follow road round to ground entrance.

From South using M5/M6 motorways- M5 North past Junction 1 onto M6 North. Leave at Junction 9 (Wednesbury turn off) and take A4148 to Walsall. Proceed for about 2 miles over several islands until going down a hill alongside the Arboretum. At big island at bottom, turn right onto A461 for Lichfield. Take A461 for about 4 miles and go through Walsall Wood village (after Barons Court Hotel on right) up the hill after village, Oak Park is on the left opposite Fitness First. Turn left and go diagonally across Oak Park Leisure Centre car park. Follow road round to ground entrance.

WORCESTER CITY

Nickname: City **Club Colours:** Blue & white

Founded 1902

Club Contact Details 07811 076 933 kevinpreece1987@gmail.com

Ground: The Victoria Ground, Birmingham Road, Bromsgrove B61 0DR

Capacity: 3,500 **Seats:** 400 **Covered:** Yes **Shop:** Yes

Previous Names: Formed when Berwick Rangers and Worcester Rovers amalgamated

Previous Leagues: Birmingham & District 1902-38. Southern 1938-79, 85-2004. Alliance 1979-85. Conference 2004-17.

HONOURS: FA Comps: None

League: Birmingham League 1913-14, 24-25, 28-29, 29-30.
Southern League Division One North 1967-68, 76-77, Premier 1978-79.

10 YEAR RECORD

09-10		10-11		11-12		12-13		13-14		14-15		15-16		16-17		17-18		18-19	
Conf S	20	Conf N	16	Conf N	7	Conf N	15	Conf N	15	Conf N	9	Nat N	17	Nat N	20	MFLP	4	MFLP	11
FAC	3Qr	FAC	3Q	FAC	2Q	FAC	4Q	FAC	4Qr	FAC	2Pr	FAC	1P	FAC	3Q	FAC	Pr	FAC	EPr
FAT	3P	FAT	2Pr	FAT	3Q	FAT	3Q	FAT	2P	FAT	1P	FAT	1Pr	FAT	1P	FAV	2P	FAV	2P

From M5 J4 take A38 to Bromsgrove, after island at M42 J1, take 1st right at Traffic Lights (signposted Bromsgrove North).
Ground is 1000 metres on right (opposite Tesco Garage).
From M42 J1, follow above directions from islands.

Nearest Railway Station Bromsgrove - two miles from the ground.

Bus Route 144/144a from Crowngate Bus Station

Midland Football League Division Two

ALCESTER TOWN	Old Stratford Road, Oversley Green, Alcester, B49 6LN
BARNT GREEN SPARTEK	The Pavilions, Malthouse Lane, Earlswood, Solihull, B94 5DX
BOLDMERE S & S	Boldmere Sports & Social Club, 323 Boldmere Road, Boldmere, B73 5HQ
BOLEHILL SWIFTS	Rene Road, Bolehall, Tamworth, Staffordshire B77 3NN
COTON GREEN	New Mill Lane, Fazeley, Tamworth, B78 3RX
COVENTRY ALVIS	Alvis Sports & Social Club, Green Lane, Coventry, CV3 6EH
EARLSWOOD TOWN	The Pavilions, Malthouse Lane, Earlswood, Solihull, B94 5DX
FAIRFIELD VILLA	Recreation Ground, Stourbridge Road, Fairfield, Bromsgrove, Worcs, B61 9LZ
FC STRATFORD	Stratford Town FC, Knights Lane, Tiddington, Stratford Upon Avon, CV37 7BZ
FECKENHAM	Studley Sports & Social Club, Eldorado Close, Studley, Warwickshire, B80 7HP
HAMPTON	Hampton Sports Club, Field Lane, Solihull, B91 2RT
KNOWLE	The Robins Nest, Hampton Road, Knowle, Solihull, B93 0NX
LANE HEAD	Red Lion ground, Somerfield Road, Walsall WS3 2EH
MOORS GREEN ACADEMY	The Trevor Brown Memorial Grd, Church Road, Boldmere, Sutton Coldfield, B73 5RY
NORTHFELD TOWN	Shenley Lane Com. Assoc., 472 Shenley Lane, Selly Oak, Birmingham B29 4HZ
REDDITCH BOROUGH	The Meitis & SS Club, Cherry Tree Walk, Batchley, Redditch B97 6PB

ASHBY IVANHOE

Founded: 1948 Nickname: The Knights

Club Contact Details 07966 293 355 ctissington1962@btinternet.com
Ground: Lower Packington Road, Ashby de la Zouch LE65 1TS **Club Colours:** Blue and red

HONOURS
FA Comps: None
League: North Leicestershire 1994-95, 96-97, 98-99, 2002-03.
Leicestershire Senior Premier Division 2010-11.

10 YEAR RECORD

09-10	10-11	11-12	12-13	13-14	14-15	15-16	16-17	17-18	18-19
LeicSP 5	LeicSP 1	LeicSP 8	LeicSP 4	LeicSP 3	EMC 6	EMC 3	EMC 10	EMC 17	EMC 14
							FAC 1Q		
FAV 1Q	FAV 2Q	FAV 2Q				FAV 1Q	FAV 1P	FAV 2Q	FAV 2Q

From A42 junction 12, follow signs for Ashby, pass golf club on the left, then pass car wash garage on right and take the second right onto Avenue Road.
Turn right at the end of the road onto Lower Packington Road, follow road around bends and the ground is on the right.

ATHERSTONE TOWN

Founded: 2004 Nickname: The Adders

Club Contact Details 07980 037 883 trn700@aol.com
Ground: Sheepy Road, Atherstone, Warwickshire CV9 3AD **Club Colours:** Red & white

HONOURS
FA Comps: None
League: Midland Combination Division 1 2004-05, Premier Division 2005-06. Midland Alliance 2007-08.

10 YEAR RECORD

09-10	10-11	11-12	12-13	13-14	14-15	15-16	16-17	17-18	18-19
SthM 13	SthC 21	MidAl 21	MCmP 9	MCmP 9	MFL1 13	MFL1 13	MFL1 4	MFL1 3	MFL1 3
FAC P	FAC Pr	FAC P	FAC EP	FAC 3Q	FAC EPr			FAC EP	FAC 2Q
FAT 1Q	FAT P	FAV 1P	FAV 1Q	FAV 1P	FAV 2Q	FAV 1Q	FAV 2Q	FAV 1P	FAV 2Q

Take M42 towards Atherstone. Exit at Junction 10. Travel southbound on A5 towards Nuneaton for approximately 4 miles. At third roundabout take first exit to Holly Lane Industrial Estate. Over railway bridge (Aldi HQ on left). At the next roundabout turn right onto Rowlands Way. Ground is 300 yards on the right. Car park and street parking in Rowlands Way.

Nearest Railway Station Atherstone - 0.6km
Bus Route Lister Road stop - 118m away

BROCTON

Founded: 1937 Nickname: The Badgers

Club Contact Details 07791 841 774 terryhomer@yahoo.co.uk
Ground: Silkmore Lane Sports Grd, Silkmore Lane, Stafford, Staffordshire ST17 **Club Colours:** Green and white

HONOURS
FA Comps: None
League: Midland Combination Premier 2013-14.

10 YEAR RECORD

09-10	10-11	11-12	12-13	13-14	14-15	15-16	16-17	17-18	18-19
MCmP 7	MCmP 8	MCmP 6	MCmP 5	MCmP 1	MFLP 13	MFLP 15	MFLP 21	MFL1 17	MFL1 11
FAC P	FAC EPr	FAC EP	FAC EPr	FAC 1Q	FAC Pr	FAC EP	FAC P	FAC 1Q	
FAV 2Q	FAV 2Q	FAV 3Pr	FAV 1Q	FAV 4P	FAV 4P	FAV 3P	FAV 2Q	FAV 2P	FAV 2P

From M6 J13 take A449 towards Stafford for 1.5 miles until reaching traffic lights by Esso petrol station. Turn right at lights into Rickescote Road, follow road round over railway bridge to mini island, at island bear left into Silkmore Lane. At next mini island take 4th exit for entrance to ground. **From Lichfield/Rugeley**. After passing Staffs Police HQ at Baswick go downhill past BMW garage and pub to large island, take 1st exit into Silkmore Lane, at next mini island take 2nd exit into ground entrance. Do not turn into Lancaster Road or Silkmore Crescent as directed by Sat Navs **Hospitality:** Spittle Brook, Queensville Bridge. At end of driveway go over Splitter Island and turn right at mini island, at next island take 2nd exit (Stafford Town Centre). Go over Railway Bridge, at bottom of bridge turn immediately right, travelling back on yourself. Spittle Brook is 100 yds on left.

Nearest Railway Station Stafford - 2km
Bus Route Silkmore Crescent stop - 30m away

CADBURY ATHLETIC

Founded: 1994 Nickname:

Club Contact Details 07827 963 212 cafc.sec@gmail.com
Ground: Eckersall Road, Kings Norton, Birmingham, B38 8SR **Club Colours:** Purple & white

HONOURS
FA Comps: None
League: Midland Combination Division One 2013-14.

10 YEAR RECORD

09-10	10-11	11-12	12-13	13-14	14-15	15-16	16-17	17-18	18-19
MCmP 19	MCmP 6	MCmP 12	MCm1 3	MCm1 1	MFL1 6	MFL1 15	MFL1 5	MFL1 15	MFL1 8
FAC EP		FAC EP				FAC P		FAC EP	
FAV 1Q	FAV 1Q	FAV 1Q	FAV 1Q	FAV 1Q	FAV 1Q	FAV 1Q	FAV 1P	FAV 1Q	FAV 4P

Exit M42 at junction 2, take the A441 dual carriageway towards Redditch. At the 1st island, take the B4120 to Alvechurch. The ground is approximately 1 mile of the right (car park entrance is before the ground).

Nearest Railway Station Kings Norton - 0.5km
Bus Route Meadow Hill Road stop - 266m away

CHELMSLEY TOWN

Founded: 1927 Nickname:

Club Contact Details 07837 509 752 louisehelenhughes@gmail.com

Ground: Coleshill FC Pack Meadow, Packington Lane, Coleshill, B46 3JQ **Club Colours:** Sky blue, white & black

HONOURS
FA Comps: None **League:** Midland Combination Division One 1987-88.

10 YEAR RECORD

09-10	10-11	11-12	12-13	13-14	14-15	15-16	16-17	17-18	18-19
MCm2 13	MCm2 11	MCm2 3	MCm1 13	MCm1 6	MCm2 6	MCm2 2	MCm1 17	MFL1 16	MFL1 12
								FAV 2Q	FAV 1P

From M6 Junction 4 take A446 signposted Lichfield. Straight over 1st roundabout then immediately turn right across dual carriageway onto B4117 signposted Coleshill. After school on right, turn right into Packington Lane. Ground is ½ mile on left.

Nearest Railway Station Coleshill Parkway - 3.6km
Bus Route St Edwards Primary School stop - 258m away

COVENTRY COPSEWOOD

Founded: 1923 Nickname: The G's

Club Contact Details 07884 585 440 davide.wilson@hotmail.co.uk

Ground: Copsewood Sports & Social Club, Allard Way, Coventry CV3 1JP **Club Colours:** All blue

HONOURS
FA Comps: None **League:** Midland Combination Division One 1996-97.

10 YEAR RECORD

09-10	10-11	11-12	12-13	13-14	14-15	15-16	16-17	17-18	18-19
MCmP 5	MCmP 4	MCmP 3	MCmP 12	MCmP 16	MFL1 8	MFL1 11	MFL1 12	MFL1 13	MFL1 15
FAV 2Qr	FAV 2P	FAV 1P	FAV 1Q	FAV 1Q	FAV 1Q	FAV 1Q	FAV 1P	FAV 2Q	FAV 2Q

M6 South: Leave at junction 2 and follow A4600 signs for City Centre. Go over 3 roundabouts and past 1 set of traffic lights, on reaching the 2nd set of traffic lights with Coventry Oak pub on left, turn left down Hipswell Highway. Follow road for 1 mile and reach another set of lights (Fire Station is on left and Mill Pool pub is on right). Go over lights and the ground is 300 yards on the left. **From M40:** Follow A46 signs to Coventry and Leicester, stay on this road until very end, you then reach a roundabout with a flyover, go round the roundabout following M69 signs. This road takes you past Asda and you reach a set of traffic lights with a roundabout. Take 2nd left turn off the roundabout, again following M69 signs, This is Allard Way and takes you past Matalan on left, Go under railway bridge and ground is 400 yards on the right. A45 from Birmingham Direction: Follow A45 until reaching a slip road signposted A46, this slip road has the Festival Pub on left side of it. It is after a roundabout with big Peugeot car showroom on left. Go down slip road and take 2nd exit. , this is another slip road leading to A46, signposted B4114 Coventry. Follow road until reaching roundabout with a flyover, and then follow as M40 directions above.

GNP SPORTS

Founded: 1983 Nickname:

Club Contact Details 07875 690 471 jasingh84@hotmail.com

Ground: Sphinx Drive, off Siddeley Drive, Coventry, CV3 1WA **Club Colours:** Red and black

HONOURS
FA Comps: None **League:** Midland Division Three 2017-18

10 YEAR RECORD

09-10	10-11	11-12	12-13	13-14	14-15	15-16	16-17	17-18	18-19
								MFL3 1	MFL2 2

From M6. Leave M6 at Junction 3 and take A444 towards Coventry. Continue to Binley Road (6 roundabouts) and turn left on A428 Binley Road towards Binley. Pass a row of shops on left and Bulls Head public house on right. After the Bulls Head, turn 1st right into Biggin Hall Crescent. Then take the 5th left turn into Siddeley Avenue. Take 1st left into Sphinx Drive and the ground is at the end.
From M42 & A45. Follow A45 towards Coventry and take A4114 Coventry at Coventry Hill Hotel. At roundabout take 2nd exit to next roundabout and take 3rd exit onto Holyhead Road. After approx 2.5 miles you will come to Coventry Ring Road where you turn left and then get over to your right onto the ring road. Continue on Ring Road and leave at Junction 3 signposted M69 and Football Stadium. Follow signs for A428 Binley until you see Bulls Head public house on your right. Then follow the above instructions.

Nearest Railway Station Coventry - 2.6km
Bus Route Bulls Head Lane stop - 363m away

HEATH HAYES

Founded: 1965 Nickname: The Hayes

Club Contact Details 07974 851 604 tony.hhfc@gmail.com

Ground: Coppice Colliery Grd, Newlands Lane, Heath Hayes, Cannock, WS12 **Club Colours:** Blue

HONOURS
FA Comps: None **League:** Staffordshire County Division One 1977-78. West Midlands (Regional) Division One North 1998-99. Midland Combination Premier Division 2009-10.

10 YEAR RECORD

09-10	10-11	11-12	12-13	13-14	14-15	15-16	16-17	17-18	18-19
MCmP 1	MidAl 11	MidAl 14	MidAl 18	MidAl 8	MFLP 22	MFL1 8	MFL1 14	MFL1 14	MFL1 18
FAC P	FAC P	FAC EP	FAC P	FAC EP	FAC EP	FAC EP	FAC EP		
FAV 1Q	FAV 3P	FAV 1P	FAV 1Q	FAV 1Q	FAV 1Q	FAV 1Q	FAV 1Q	FAV 2Q	FAV 2Q

From M6 Junction 11 take the A4601 towards Cannock and at the 1st island turn right onto the A460 signposted Rugeley/Cannock Business Parks. At the double island (A5) go straight on still on A460 and over two islands. At the 3rd island, turn right onto A5190 signposted Lichfield. Pass Texaco garage on the right and take the next right turn into Newlands Lane. Entrance to the ground is 50 yards down the lane on the left under the barrier.

Nearest Railway Station Cannock - 2.7km
Bus Route Five Ways Inn stop - 253m away

HINCKLEY AFC

Founded: 2014 Nickname:

Club Contact Details 07954 996 796 jackson.dh18@gmail.com

Ground: Ibstock Miner's Welfare Stadium, Leicester Road, Ibstock, LE67 6HN **Club Colours:** Red & blue

HONOURS **League:** None

FA Comps: None

10 YEAR RECORD

09-10	10-11	11-12	12-13	13-14	14-15	15-16	16-17	17-18	18-19
					MFL1 3	MFL1 5	MFL1 2	MFL1 6	MFL1 16
						FAC 2Q	FAC EPr	FAC 1Q	FAC EPr
					FAV 1Q	FAV 1P	FAV 5P	FAV 4P	FAV 3P

Exit M42 at Junction 11. Take the road towards Measham, pass the Car Auctions and go over the traffic lights. At 2nd mini island take 2nd exit onto Leicester Road. After approximately 3 miles you will enter Heather. At the T-junction turn left. At mini island take 2nd exit onto Ravenstone Road and go up the hill. Ground is 200 metres on the left.

KIRBY MUXLOE

Founded: 1910 Nickname:

Club Contact Details 07715 403 409 kirbymuxloefc@outlook.com

Ground: Kirby Muxloe Sports Club, Ratby Lane LE9 2AQ **Club Colours:** Blue

HONOURS **League:** Leicestershire Senior Premier Division 2007-08.
East Midlands Counties 2008-09.

FA Comps: None

10 YEAR RECORD

09-10	10-11	11-12	12-13	13-14	14-15	15-16	16-17	17-18	18-19
MidAl 10	MidAl 9	MidAl 11	MidAl 12	MidAl 14	MFLP 5	UCL P 9	UCL P 18	UCL P 12	UCL P 19
FAC P	FAC P	FAC EP	FAC P	FAC P	FAC P	FAC Pr	FAC 2Q	FAC P	FAC EP
FAV 1P	FAV 1Q	FAV 2Q	FAV 1P	FAV 1P	FAV 2Q	FAV 2Q	FAV 1P	FAV 2Q	FAV 1Q

From M1 leave at JCTT 21A and follow the signposts for Kirby Muxloe. As you enter the village, at the roundabout take 2nd exit onto Ratby Lane. At mini Roundabout take 2nd exit and the ground is 200 yards on the right hand side. From A47 at Traffic lights turn right onto Colchester Road A563 Continue on A563 for approximately 6 miles turning onto A5630 Anstey Lane. After approximately 2 miles turn left on A46 towards M1 just before next left and then follow directions to Kirby Muxtoe, as you enter the village, at the roundabout take 2nd exit onto Ratby Lane. At mini roundabout take 2nd exit and the ground is 200 yards on the right hand side.

Bus Route Kirby Corner - stop 55m away

LEICESTER ROAD

Founded: 2013 Nickname: The Knitters

Club Contact Details 07814 414 726 stuart.millidge43@hotmail.com

Ground: Leicester Road Stadium, Leicester Road, Hinckley, LE10 3DR **Club Colours:** Blue & red

HONOURS **League:** None

FA Comps: None

10 YEAR RECORD

09-10	10-11	11-12	12-13	13-14	14-15	15-16	16-17	17-18	18-19
					MFL2 2	MFL1 4	MFL1 3	MFL1 4	MFL1 5
							FAC 1Qr	FAC P	FAC P
						FAV 2Q	FAV 1P	FAV 1Q	FAV 1Qr

From North West: A5 Southbound at Dodwells roundabout (A5/A47) take 1st exit (Earl Shilton, A47 and Industrial Estates), straight over 3 roundabouts, straight over traffic lights, at next roundabout take the 3rd exit (B4668) towards Hinckley, the entrance is 200 yards on the right.
From M69, Junction 1: take A5 north (Tamworth/Nuneaton) then as above.

Nearest Railway Station Hinckley - 2.7km

Bus Route Leicester Road stop - 262m away

LICHFIELD CITY

Founded: 1970 Nickname:

Club Contact Details 07779 295 033 darrenleaver@outlook.com

Ground: Brownsfield Road, Lichfield, Staffs, WS13 6AY **Club Colours:** All royal blue

HONOURS **League:** None

FA Comps: None

10 YEAR RECORD

09-10	10-11	11-12	12-13	13-14	14-15	15-16	16-17	17-18	18-19
MCm2 3	MCm2 4	MCm1 4	MCmP 10	MCmP 7	MFL1 12	MFL1 7	MFL1 7	MFL1 10	MFL1 4
					FAC P		FAC P		
				FAV 1Q	FAV 2Q	FAV 1Q	FAV 2P	FAV 1Q	FAV 1Q

From M42 J10, follow A5 towards Brownhills, or J9 and follow A446 to Lichfield, then follow signs for A38 Lichfield/Derby. From Swinfen Roundabout take 3rd exit for A38 north and then take next off A38 onto A5192 (Cappers Lane). Follow A5192 through 2 islands onto Eastern Avenue. The Ground is on the right at the top of the hill next to Norgreen factory.
From M6 J12, follow A5 towards Lichfield then A38 to Lichfield Derby, then follow instructions as above. (Sat Nav: WS13 6RZ)

Nearest Railway Station Lichfield Trent Valley High Level/Lichfield Trent Valley - 1.4km

Bus Route Netherstowe Lane stop - 78m away

NKF BURBAGE

Founded: 2009 | Nickname: Panthers

Club Contact Details 07471 933 001 | andy.crossland@sky.com

Ground: Kirkby Road Sports Ground, Kirkby Road, Barwell LE9 8FQ | **Club Colours:** Orange and black

HONOURS
FA Comps: None
League: Midland Football League Division Two 2016-17, 17-18.

10 YEAR RECORD

09-10	10-11	11-12	12-13	13-14	14-15	15-16	16-17	17-18	18-19
						LeicS1 2	MFL2 1	MFL2 1	MFL1 6
									FAV 3P

FROM M6 NORTH/M42/A5 NORTH: From M6 North join M42 heading towards Tamworth/Lichfield, leave M42 at Junction 10(Tamworth Services) and turn right onto A5 signposted Nuneaton. Remain on A5 for approx 11 miles, straight on at traffic lights at Longshoot Motel then at next roundabout take first exit signposted A47 Earl Shilton. In about 3 miles at traffic lights go straight on and in 1 mile at roundabout take first exit signposted Barwell. In about 1.5 miles, centre of village, go straight over mini roundabout and then in 20 metres turn right into Kirkby Road. Entrance to complex is 400 metres on right opposite park. **FROM M1 SOUTH:** From M1 South Take M69)Signposted Coventry) Take Junction 2 Off M69 (Signposted Hinckley) Follow signs to Hinckley . Go straight on at traffic lights with Holywell Pub on the right. The road bears to the right at next traffic lights turn right signposted Earl Shilton/Leicester. Keep on this road past golf club on right at Hinckley United Ground on left and at large roundabout take second exit signposted Barwell. In about 1.5 miles, centre of village, go straight over mini roundabout and then in 20 metres turn right into Kirkby Road. Entrance to complex is 400 metres on right opposite park.

Nearest Railway Station Hinckley - 7 miles away

NUNEATON GRIFF

Founded: 1972 | Nickname: The Heartlanders

Club Contact Details 07944 457 250 | nuneatongriff@sky.com

Ground: The Pingles Stadium, Avenue Road, Nuneaton, Warwickshire CV11 4LX | **Club Colours:** Blue & white

HONOURS
FA Comps: None
League: Coventry Alliance Premier 1996-97, 97-98.
Midland Combination Premier Division 1999-2000, 00-01.

10 YEAR RECORD

09-10	10-11	11-12	12-13	13-14	14-15	15-16	16-17	17-18	18-19
MCmP 12	MCmP 2	MCmP 11	MCmP 4	MCmP 3	MFL1 17	MFL1 3	MFL1 10	MFL1 19	MFL1 19
FAC P	FAC P	FAC EP	FAC 2Q	FAC EP	FAC EP		FAC EPr		
FAV 1Q	FAV 1Q	FAV 1Q	FAV 2Q	FAV 2Q	FAV 1P	FAV 5P	FAV 3P	FAV 1Q	FAV 2Q

From M5, M42 & M6: Take M6 south to junction 3 and leave by turning left onto A444 (Nuneaton). Stay on A444 through Bermuda Park, McDonalds and George Eliot Hospital roundabouts until reaching large roundabout with footbridge over road. Carry straight on (2nd exit) and downhill, taking right hand lane. At bottom of hill you reach Coton Arches Island, take 2nd exit (A4252 Avenue Road) and travel ½ mile to Cedar Tree Pub traffic lights, turn left into Stadium car park service road. It is unsuitable for coaches to turn around in. **From A5:** Travel south following signs for Nuneaton. After passing through Atherstone travel for 2½ miles until junction with A444. At this junction (Royal Red Gate Pub) turn right at staggered junction and continue on A444 through Caldecote and Weddington into Nuneaton. Join one-way system at Graziers Arms by turning left and immediately take right hand lane for 300 yards and follow A444 for Coventry. At Third Island turn left on to dual carriageway (Coton Road) for ½ mile and turn left at Coton Arches island on to A4252 (Avenue Road) then as above. **Hospitality:** Attleborough Liberal Club, Bull Street, Nuneaton. Leave ground, turn left at Cedar Pub traffic lights, take 3rd turn on right, club car park is 2nd on the riaht.

PAGET RANGERS

Founded: 2011 | Nickname: Bears or The Wee Gers

Club Contact Details 07528 177 046 | paterson_r3@sky.com

Ground: Central Ground, Coles Lane, Sutton Coldfield, B72 1NL | **Club Colours:** Gold and black

HONOURS
FA Comps: None
League: None

10 YEAR RECORD

09-10	10-11	11-12	12-13	13-14	14-15	15-16	16-17	17-18	18-19
				MCm2 3	MFL2 11	MFL2 4	MFL2 2	MFL1 12	MFL1 10
						FAV 1Q	FAV 2P	FAV 2Q	FAV 1P

A38(M) from M6 junction 6 and A5127 from Birmingham to Yenton Traffic Lights.
Left on A452 Chester Road, then 6th.right into Church Road.
From M6 junction 5 A452 Brownhills to Yenton Traffic Lights. Straight on then 6th right into Church Road.

ROCESTER

Founded: 1876 | Nickname: Romans

Club Contact Details 07885 836 094 | sam.goldsworthy@rocesterfc.net

Ground: Hillsfield, Mill Street, Rocester, Uttoxeter ST14 5JX | **Club Colours:** Amber & black

HONOURS
FA Comps: None
League: Staffordshire Senior 1985-86, 86-87. West Mids (Regional) Division One 1987-88.
Midland Alliance 1998-99, 2003-04.

10 YEAR RECORD

09-10	10-11	11-12	12-13	13-14	14-15	15-16	16-17	17-18	18-19
MidAl 16	MidAl 14	MidAl 6	MidAl 13	MidAl 20	MFLP 12	MFLP 12	MFLP 16	MFLP 22	MFL1 14
FAC P	FAC EP	FAC 1Q	FAC P	FAC EPr	FAC EPr	FAC Pr	FAC P	FAC EPr	FAC EP
FAV 1Q	FAV 1Q	FAV 1Q	FAV 4P	FAV 2P	FAV 1P	FAV 1P	FAV 2P	FAV 2Q	FAV 1Q

From Uttoxeter take the B5030, signposted Ashbourne/Alton Towers After 3 miles turn right opposite the JCB factory over humpback bridge into Rocester village. Turn right at mini island into Mill Street, ground is 500 yards on the left immediately past the JCB Academy.

Bus Route Ashbourne Road Garage stop - 152m away

STAFFORD TOWN

Founded: 1976 Nickname: Reds or Town

Club Contact Details 07789 110 923 staffordtown@hotmail.co.uk

Ground: Evans Park, Riverway, Stafford ST16 3TL **Club Colours:** All red

HONOURS **League:** Midland Combination Division Two 1978-79.

FA Comps: None West Midlands (Regional) Division One 1993-94, Premier 1999-2000.

10 YEAR RECORD

09-10	10-11	11-12	12-13	13-14	14-15	15-16	16-17	17-18	18-19
WM1 2	WMP 15	WMP 18	MCmP 11	MCmP 8	MFL1 14	MFL1 18	MFL1 16	MFL1 20	StfSP 5
				FAC EP	FAC P				
	FAV 1Q	FAV 2P	FAV 2Q	FAV 2Q	FAV 1Q	FAV 2Q	FAV 1Q	FAV 1P	FAV 1Q

From M6 junction 13, take A449 towards Stafford for 1½ miles until reaching traffic lights by an Esso petrol station. Turn right at the lights into Rickerscote Road, follow the road round over railway bridge to a mini island. At the island bear left into Silkmore Lane, after approximately 600 yards take the 2nd exit at the mini island and carry on until a large island, take the 2nd exit towards Stafford town centre (A34 Lichfield Road). Go over the railway bridge with Alstrom factory on the left hand side. Straight on at 1st set of traffic lights, then bear left at next set of lights (A518 Uttoxeter) and follow road round with B&Q and Argos on your left hand side. At the roundabout (with KFC and Pizza Hut in front of you) take the 2nd exit (A518 Uttoxeter) and follow to traffic lights. Go straight over lights into Riverway, the ground entrance is approximately 80 yards on the right hand side. Follow the driveway behind the cricket pavilion to the stadium entrance.

Nearest Railway Station Stafford - 1.1km

Bus Route Hatherton Street stop - 99m away

STAPENHILL

Founded: 1947 Nickname: The Swans

Club Contact Details 07411 832 333 stapenhillsecretary@yahoo.com

Ground: Edge Hill, Maple Grove, Stapenhill DE15 9NN. **Club Colours:** All red

HONOURS **League:** Leicestershire Senior 1958-59, 59-60, 86-87, 88-89, 2006-07.

FA Comps: None

10 YEAR RECORD

09-10	10-11	11-12	12-13	13-14	14-15	15-16	16-17	17-18	18-19
LeicSP 12	LeicSP 4	LeicSP 5	LeicS1 5	EMC 2	EMC 15	EMC 12	EMC 11	EMC 13	MFL1 13
					FAC EPr				
			FAV 1Q	FAV 1Q	FAV 1Q	FAV 1Q	FAV 2Q	FAV 1Q	FAV 1Q

From North: Exit A38 at Clay Mills and follow A5018 towards Burton. Follow A444 (Nuneaton). At Swan junction traffic lights turn right onto Stapenhill Road. At roundabout go straight over – 6th left onto Sycamore Road. Ground 500 yards on Maple Grove

From South: Follow A511 to Burton on Trent, at Swan junction traffic lights turn left onto Stapenhill Road. At roundabout go straight over – 6th left onto Sycamore Road. Ground 500 yards on Maple Grove

Nearest Railway Station Burton-on-Trent - 3km

STUDLEY

Founded: 1971 Nickname: Bees

Club Contact Details 07745 310 077 bobtheat@hotmail.co.uk

Ground: The Beehive, Abbeyfields Drive, Studley B80 7BF **Club Colours:** Sky blue and navy

HONOURS **League:** Midland Combination Division One 1991-92.

FA Comps: None

10 YEAR RECORD

09-10	10-11	11-12	12-13	13-14	14-15	15-16	16-17	17-18	18-19
MidAl 11	MidAl 7	MidAl 17	MidAl 21	MCmP 6	MFL1 10	MFLP 12	MFLP 15	MFL1 9	MFL1 9
FAC P	FAC EP	FAC P	FAC P	FAC P	FAC EP				
FAV 1P	FAV 1P	FAV 2Q	FAV 1Q	FAV 2Q	FAV 1P	FAV 2Q	FAV 1Q	FAV 2Q	FAV 2Q

From M42 Junction 3, take exit towards Redditch (A435).
Head South for 5 miles, Abbeyfield Drive is on the left hand side ½ mile past "The Boot" Public House, adjacent to a sharp left hand bend.

Nearest Railway Station Redditch - 4.6km

Bus Route Red Hill Close stop - 49m away

UTTOXETER TOWN

Founded: 1983 Nickname: Town

Club Contact Details 07970 383 822 uttoxetertfc@gmail.com

Ground: Oldfields Sports Ground, Springfield Road, Uttoxeter, ST14 7JX **Club Colours:** Yellow & blue

HONOURS **League:** None

FA Comps: None

10 YEAR RECORD

09-10	10-11	11-12	12-13	13-14	14-15	15-16	16-17	17-18	18-19
				StfSP 2	MFL1 5	StfSP 6	MFL1 11	MFL1 11	MFL1 7
						FAV 3P	FAV 2P	FAV 2Q	FAV 2Qr

Exit M6 at junction 15 onto A500, head for Uttoxeter, then turn onto A50 following signs for Uttoxeter
Turn right at B5030 onto Ashbourne Road then continue onto Cheadle Road.
At Smithfield Hotel mini roundabout turn right onto Smithfield Road., then turn right onto Springfield Road.
The ground is on the left with parking in front.

Nearest Railway Station Uttoxeter - 1.1km

Bus Route Smithfield Road stop - 178m away

PREMIER DIVISION INS: Avro (P - NWC1N), Longridge Town (P - NWC1N), Rylands (P - NWC1S), Skelmersdale United (R - NPLW).

1874 NORTHWICH

Founded 2012

Nickname: **Club Colours:** Green and black

Club Contact Details 07975 679 624

Ground: Townfield, Tonwfield Lane, Barnton Northwich, Cheshire CW8 4LH

Capacity: 6,000 **Seats:** Seats **Covered:** Yes

Previous Names: None

Previous Leagues: None

HONOURS: FA Comps: None

League: None

10 YEAR RECORD

09-10	10-11	11-12	12-13	13-14	14-15	15-16	16-17	17-18	18-19
				NWC1 3	NWCP 3	NWCP 4	NWCP 5	NWCP 7	NWCP 10
					FAC Pr	FAC P	FAC Pr	FAC 3Qr	FAC EPr
				FAV 1Q	FAV 3P	FAV 2P	FAV 2P	FAV SF	FAV 2P

Turn off the A533 (Northwich to Runcorn) onto Beech Lane, Barnton. Turn right at the 'T' junction with Townfield Lane - the ground is 200 yards on the left signed Memorial Hall. Note parking restrictions well signed.

Nearest Railway Station Greenbank

Bus Route No.4 from Northwich interchange. Embark at Beech Road which is a short walk from the ground.

ASHTON ATHLETIC

Founded 1968

Nickname: Yellows **Club Colours:** Yellow and blue

Club Contact Details 01942 716 360

Ground: Brocstedes Park, Downall Green, Ashton in Makerfield WN4 0NR

Capacity: 600 **Seats:** 100 **Covered:** 300

Previous Names: None.

Previous Leagues: Lancashire Combination 1978-82. Manchester Amateur League

HONOURS: FA Comps: None

League: None

10 YEAR RECORD

09-10	10-11	11-12	12-13	13-14	14-15	15-16	16-17	17-18	18-19
NWCP 21	NWCP 22	NWCP 14	NWCP 20	NWCP 6	NWCP 5	NWCP 7	NWCP 9	NWCP 12	NWCP 5
FAC EP	FAC EP	FAC Pr	FAC Pr	FAC P	FAC EP	FAC EPr	FAC 2Q	FAC 3Q	FAC 2Q
FAV 1Q	FAV 2Q	FAV 2Q	FAV 1Q	FAV 2Q	FAV 2Q	FAV 1Qr	FAV 2Q	FAV 3P	FAV 1Q

From South: M6 to junction 25, turn right onto A49, after 1/2 mile turn right into Soughers Lane, at T junction turn right into Downall Green Road, pass over M6 and turn 2nd right into Boothbrow Road, turn 2nd right in Brocstedes Road. From North: M6 to junction 24, rejoin north bound M6 to junction 25, directions as above.

Nearest Railway Station Bryn - 1.6km.

Bus Route 156/157 St Helens/Bryn route

AVRO

Founded 1936

Nickname: **Club Colours:** Blue, black and white

Club Contact Details 07920 779 382

Ground: Vestacare Stadium, White Bank Road, Oldham OL8 3JH

Capacity: **Seats:** **Covered:**

Previous Names:

Previous Leagues: Manchester.

HONOURS: FA Comps: None

League: Manchester Division One 1988-89, 2003-04, Premier 09-10, 10-11, 17-18.

10 YEAR RECORD

09-10	10-11	11-12	12-13	13-14	14-15	15-16	16-17	17-18	18-19
MancP 1	MancP 1	MancP 6	MancP 5	MancP 9	MancP 3	MancP 9	MancP 11	MancP 1	NWC1N 2
									FAV 3P

M60 J22 then A62 towards Manchester/Failsworth. First left onto Hollins Rd – signposted Oldham South and Hollinwood. Follow Hollins Rd to junction with Oak Rd – just before petrol station – then Oak Rd to Whitebank Rd. Stadium is directly in front of you.

Nearest Railway Station Manchester Victoria or Moston (mainline). Hollinwood (metrolink) 20 mins walk or 180 bus.

Bus Route No.180 from Oldham Street (Manchester City centre) to Hollins Road/Oak Road, then 5 mins down Oak Road to ground.

OUTS: Abbey Hey (R - NWC1S), City of Liverpool (P - NPLNW), Silsden (Tr - NCEP), West Didsbury & Chorlton (R - NWC1S).

BARNOLDSWICK TOWN

Nickname: Town or Barlick **Club Colours:** All blue

Founded 1972

Club Contact Details 07528 410 204
Ground: Silentnight Stadium, West Close Road, Barnoldswick, Colne, BB18 5LJ
Capacity: **Seats:** Yes **Covered:** Yes

Previous Names: Today's club formed after the merger of Barnoldswick United and Barnoldswick Park Rovers in 2003
Previous Leagues: Craven, East Lancashire, West Lancashire.

HONOURS: FA Comps: None
League: West Lancashire Division One 1998-99.

10 YEAR RECORD

09-10	10-11	11-12	12-13	13-14	14-15	15-16	16-17	17-18	18-19
NWC1 2	NWCP 7	NWCP 4	NWCP 9	NWCP 16	NWCP 19	NWCP 9	NWCP 11	NWCP 9	NWCP 11
		FAC EP	FAC EP	FAC EPr	FAC EP	FAC EP	FAC EPr	FAC 1Q	FAC P
	FAV 2Q	FAV 2P	FAV 3P	FAV 2Q	FAV 2Q	FAV 2Q	FAV 1P	FAV 1Q	FAV 2Q

M65 to end (Colne), straight on at round-a-bout, through two sets of traffic lights to round-a-bout. Turn left to Barnoldswick. On entering Barnoldswick through traffic lights straight on at mini round-a-bout, through built up area. On leaving built up area turn right into Green Berfield Lane (Club signposted). Bear right on track to rear of ground and car park. From A56 Gisburn turn right signposted Barnoldswick. On entering built up area turn left onto Green Berfield lane, (Club signposted). Bear on track to rear of ground and car park.

Nearest Railway Station Colne or Skipton
Bus Route Greenberfield Road stop - 97m away

BOOTLE

Nickname: Bucks **Club Colours:** All blue

Founded 1953

Club Contact Details 0151 525 4796
Ground: Vestey Road, Off Bridle Road, Bootle L30 1NY
Capacity: 1,750 **Seats:** **Covered:** Yes

Previous Names: Langton Dock 1953 - 1973.
Previous Leagues: Liverpool Shipping. Lancashire Combination 1974-78. Cheshire County 1978-82. Liverpool County Combination 1982-2006.

HONOURS: FA Comps: None
League: Liverpool County Combination 1964-65, 65-66, 67-68, 68-69, 69-70, 70-71, 71-72, 72-73, 73-74. Lancashire Comb. 1975-76, 76-77. Cheshire County Div.2 1978-79. North West Counties Div.1 2008-09.

10 YEAR RECORD

09-10	10-11	11-12	12-13	13-14	14-15	15-16	16-17	17-18	18-19
NWCP 3	NWCP 6	NWCP 3	NWCP 3	NWCP 8	NWCP 7	NWCP 8	NWCP 2	NWCP 5	NWCP 2
FAC P	FAC P	FAC P	FAC 1Q	FAC 1Qr	FAC EP	FAC EP	FAC P	FAC EP	FAC EP
FAV 4P	FAV 2P	FAV 2Q	FAV 2P	FAV 1P	FAV 1P	FAV 2Q	FAV 3P	FAV 2P	FAV 2Q

At Liverpool end of M57 and M58 follow signs for Liverpool (A59 (S)), for 1 1/2 miles. At Aintree racecourse on left and Aintree Train Station on right ,turn right at lights into Park Lane. Turn left at second set of lights into Bridle Road. After 200 yards turn left at lights into Vestey Estate , ground 200 yards.

Nearest Railway Station Aintree - 0.5km
Bus Route Hereford Drive stop - 251m away

BURSCOUGH

Nickname: Linnets **Club Colours:** All green

Founded 1946

Club Contact Details 01704 896 776
Ground: Victoria Park, Bobby Langton Way, Mart Lane, Burscough L40 0SD
Capacity: 2,500 **Seats:** 270 **Covered:** 1,000 **Shop:** Yes

Previous Names: None
Previous Leagues: Liverpool County Combination 1946-53, Lancashire Combination 1953-70, Cheshire County 1970-82, North West Counties 1982-98, Northern Premier League 1998-2007, 09-17, Conference 2007-09.

HONOURS: FA Comps: FA Trophy 2002-03.
League: Lancashire Combination Division Two 1953-54. North West Counties Division One 1982-83. Northern Premier Premier Division 2006-07.

10 YEAR RECORD

09-10	10-11	11-12	12-13	13-14	14-15	15-16	16-17	17-18	18-19
NP P 16	NP P 19	NP P 22	NP1N 11	NP1N 14	NP1N 15	NP1N 5	NP1N 22	NWCP 18	NWCP 12
FAC 3Q	FAC 1Q	FAC 1Qr	FAC 1Q	FAC 2Q	FAC 1Q	FAC 3Q	FAC 2Q	FAC Pr	FAC 1Q
FAT 1Q	FAT 1Q	FAT 1Q	FAT 2Q	FAT 1Qr	FAT P	FAT 1Pr	FAT P	FAV 1P	FAV 2Q

M6 to J27. Follow signs for 'Parbold' (A5209), carry on through Newburgh into Burscough passing Briars Hall Hotel on left. Turn right at second mini-roundabout into Junction Lane (signposted 'Burscough & Martin Mere') into village, over canal. Take second left into Mart Lane to ground at end.

Nearest Railway Station Burscough Bridge - 0.2km
Bus Route Tesco stop - 105m away

CHARNOCK RICHARD

Founded 1933

Nickname: **Club Colours:** Green & white

Club Contact Details 01257 792 558

Ground: Mossie Park, Charter Lane, Charnock Richard, Chorley PR7 5LZ

Capacity: **Seats:** Yes **Covered:** Yes

Previous Names: None

Previous Leagues: Chorley Alliance (Sunday). Preston & District. West Lancashire >2016

HONOURS: FA Comps: None

League: Chorley Alliance 1947-48, 56-57. Preston & District 1960-61, 66-67, 67-68, 68-69, 89-90.
West Lancashire Division One 1997-98, Premier 2002-03, 08-09, 11-12, 12-13, 13-14, 14-15.

10 YEAR RECORD

09-10	10-11	11-12	12-13	13-14	14-15	15-16	16-17	17-18	18-19
WLaP 4	WLaP 2	WLaP 1	WLaP 1	WLaP 1	WLaP 1	WLaP 2	NWC1 2	NWCP 6	NWCP 6
								FAC EP	FAC Pr
							FAV 2P	FAV 1P	FAV 1P

M6 to junction 28 (Leyland) at end of slip road turn right. Travel to the traffic lights and turn right onto the A49 towards Wigan, through Euxton and into Charnock Richard. Pass the Bowling Green Pub on the right, continue for ¾ mile and turn left into Church Lane. Turn first right into Charter lane, ground 500 yards on the right. M61 to junction 8 (Chorley) follow the signs for Southport on reaching the A49 follow signs for Wigan, through Charnock Richard directions then as above. PLEASE USE THE CLUB PARK. Do not park on the road.

Nearest Railway Station Euxton Balshaw Lane - 3km

Bus Route Leeson Avenue stop - 299m away

CONGLETON TOWN

Founded 1901

Nickname: Bears **Club Colours:** Black & white

Club Contact Details 01260 274 460

Ground: Ivy Gardens, Booth Street, Crescent Road, Congleton, Cheshire CW12 4GA

Capacity: 1,450 **Seats:** 250 **Covered:** 1,200 **Shop:** Yes

Previous Names: Congleton Hornets

Previous Leagues: Crewe & District, North Staffs, Macclesfield, Cheshire County 1920-39, 46-65, 78-82. Mid Cheshire, NW Co, NPL

HONOURS: FA Comps: None

League: Crewe & District 1901-02, 02-03, 03-04. North Staffs & District 1919-20. Macclesfield & District 1939-40.
Mid Cheshire 1973-74, 75-76, 77-78.

10 YEAR RECORD

09-10	10-11	11-12	12-13	13-14	14-15	15-16	16-17	17-18	18-19
NWCP 5	NWCP 8	NWCP 11	NWCP 7	NWCP 10	NWCP 8	NWCP 6	NWCP 16	NWCP 15	NWCP 3
FAC 2Q	FAC Pr	FAC P	FAC P	FAC Pr	FAC Pr	FAC 2Q	FAC P	FAC P	FAC 1Q
FAV 2P	FAV 1Q	FAV 1Q	FAV 1P	FAV 4P	FAV 2P	FAV 1P	FAV 1P	FAV 2Qr	FAV 1Q

On approach to Congleton from M6, past Waggon & Horses Pub, at 1st roundabout 2nd exit, past fire station, 2nd right into Booth Street. Ground at top of road.

Nearest Railway Station Congleton - 1.9km

Bus Route Booth Street stop - 75m away

HANLEY TOWN

Founded 1966

Nickname: **Club Colours:** All royal blue

Club Contact Details 07977 519 498

Ground: Potteries Park, Abbey Lane, Bucknall, Stoke-on-Trent, Staffordshire ST2 8AJ

Capacity: **Seats:** Yes **Covered:** Yes

Previous Names: None

Previous Leagues: London 1966-67. Staffordshire County Senior 1967-76. Mid-Cheshire 1976-88, 96-98.
Midland/Staffordshire County 1998-2013.

HONOURS: FA Comps: None

League: London 1966-67. Staffordshire County Div.2 67-68, Div.1 68-69, Premier 72-73, 75-76. Mid-Cheshire Div.1 81-82.
Midland/Staffordshire County Senior 2004-05, 2006-07, 11-12, 12-13. North West Counties Div.1 2015-16.

10 YEAR RECORD

09-10	10-11	11-12	12-13	13-14	14-15	15-16	16-17	17-18	18-19
	StfSP 2	StfSP 1	StfSP 1	NWC1 4	NWC1 4	NWC1 1	NWCP 10	NWCP 8	NWCP 17
						FAC P	FAC EPr	FAC P	FAC EPr
					FAV 1P	FAV 1Q	FAV 1P	FAV 1P	FAV 1P

From Stoke-on-Trent take the A52/Leek Road.
After almost 2 miles turn right onto Bucknall Road/A52, continue for just over half a mile and turn left onto Fellbrook Lane.
Continue onto Abbey Lane.

Nearest Railway Station Stoke-on-Trent - 3.2km

Bus Route Abbey Lane stop - 229m away

IRLAM

Nickname: Mitchells/Shack **Club Colours:** All blue

Founded 1969

Club Contact Details 07969 946 277
Ground: Silver Street, Irlam, Manchester M44 6JJ
Capacity: **Seats:** 150 **Covered:** Yes

Previous Names: Mitchell Shackleton.
Previous Leagues: Manchester Amateur. Manchester.

HONOURS: FA Comps: None
League: Manchester Amateur Division Three 1973-74, Division Two 74-75. Manchester Premier Division 2002-03.

10 YEAR RECORD

09-10		10-11		11-12		12-13		13-14		14-15		15-16		16-17		17-18		18-19	
NWC1	10	NWC1	9	NWC1	10	NWC1	14	NWC1	10	NWC1	14	NWC1	2	NWCP	8	NWCP	13	NWCP	13
		FAC	EP	FAC	EP	FAC	P							FAC	EP	FAC	EP	FAC	2Q
FAV	2Q	FAV	2P	FAV	1Q	FAV	1Q	FAV	1Q	FAV	1Q	FAV	1Qr	FAV	1P	FAV	1P	FAV	5P

M60 to junction 10, take A57 to Irlam, then B5320 into Lower Irlam.
Turn right into Silver Street, Ground approx 300 yards on the right.

Nearest Railway Station Flixton - 2.3km
Bus Route Silver Street stop - 23m away

LITHERLAND REMYCA

Nickname: The REMY **Club Colours:** Red and black

Founded 1959

Club Contact Details 0151 288 6288
Ground: Litherland Sports Park, Boundary Road, Litherland, Liverpool L21 7LA
Capacity: **Seats:** 100 **Covered:** Yes

Previous Names:
Previous Leagues: Liverpool County >2015.

HONOURS: FA Comps: None
League: Zingari Premier Division 1987-88, 93-94, 94-95, 95-96, Division Two 2005-06. Liverpool County Division Two 2006-07.

10 YEAR RECORD

09-10		10-11		11-12		12-13		13-14		14-15		15-16		16-17		17-18		18-19	
LivCP	3	LivCP	13	LivCP	15	LivCP	9	LivCP	5	NWC1	9	NWC1	9	NWC1	3	NWC1	2	NWCP	15
																FAC	P	FAC	EP
												FAV	1Q	FAV	1P	FAV	1P	FAV	1P

End of M57/M58 Along Dunningsbridge Road towards Docks, turn right at Junction of Bootle Golf Course on the right hand side into Boundary Road, 2nd turning on the left into sports park.

Nearest Railway Station Aintree - 1.7km
Bus Route Moss Lane stop - 98m away

LONGRIDGE TOWN

Nickname: **Club Colours:** All red

Founded 1996

Club Contact Details 01772 786365 / 07710 514767
Ground: The Mike Riding Ground, Inglewhite Road, Longridge, Preston PR3 2NA
Capacity: **Seats:** Yes **Covered:** Yes

Previous Names:
Previous Leagues: Preston & District 1996-2009.

HONOURS: FA Comps: None
League: Preston & District Division Three 2003-04. West Lancashire Division One 2011-12, Premier 16-17. North West Counties Division One North 2018-19.

10 YEAR RECORD

09-10		10-11		11-12		12-13		13-14		14-15		15-16		16-17		17-18		18-19	
WLa2	2	WLa1	4	WLa1	1	WLaP	3	WLaP	12	WLaP	6	WLaP	4	WLaP	1	WLaP	3	NWC1N	1
																		FAV	1Q

From M6 South,exit at J31a and follow signs to Longridge. On entering Longridge take left fork at Old Oak pub. Continue to ground on Inglewhite Road.

From M6 North, exit at J32. Take A6 to Broughton,Turn Right onto B5269. Follow signs to Longridge. On Entering Longridge take left onto Halfpenny Lane. Ground is at end of the road.

Nearest Railway Station Preston (7.7 miles)
Bus Route No.1 bus Preston to Berry Lane Longridge

NORTHWICH VICTORIA

Founded 1874

Nickname: Vics, Greens or Trickies **Club Colours:** Green and white

Club Contact Details 01606 43008

Ground: Wincham Park, Chapel Street, Northwich CW9 6DA

Capacity: **Seats:** Yes **Covered:** Yes

Previous Names: None

Previous Leagues: The Combination 1890-92, 1894-98, Football League 1892-94, Cheshire 1898-1900, Manchester 1900-12 Lancashire 1912-19, Cheshire County 1919-68, Northern Premier 1968-79, Conference 1979-2010

HONOURS: FA Comps: FA Trophy 1983-84.

League: Manchester 1902-03. Cheshire County 1956-57. Conference North 2005-06.

10 YEAR RECORD

09-10	10-11	11-12	12-13	13-14	14-15	15-16	16-17	17-18	18-19
Conf N 12	NP P 12	NP P 2	NP1S 8	NP1N 9	NP1N 4	NP1N 3	NP1S 22	NWCP 16	NWCP 4
FAC 2P	FAC 2Qr	FAC 2Q	FAC Pr	FAC 1Q	FAC 1Qr	FAC 2P	FAC P	FAC EPr	FAC P
FAT 3P	FAT 1P	FAT 3P	FAT 1Q	FAT 1Pr	FAT 1Qr	FAT 1Q	FAT Pr	FAV 1Q	FAV SF

Turn off the A533 (Northwich to Runcorn) at the Beech Tree Inn (Barnton Village) into Beech Lane. Turn right at the 'T' junction with Townfield Lane - the ground is 200 yards on the left signed Memorial Hall. Note parking restrictions well signed.

Nearest Railway Station Northwich (1.3 miles)

PADIHAM

Founded 1878

Nickname: Caldersiders **Club Colours:** All blue.

Club Contact Details 01282 773 742

Ground: Arbories Memorial Sports Ground, Well Street, Padiham BB12 8LE

Capacity: 1,688 **Seats:** 159 **Covered:** Yes

Previous Names: None

Previous Leagues: Lancashire Combination 1894-98, 1900-06, 10-16, 49-68, 77-82. East Lancs Am. North East Lancs. West Lancs. North West Counties > 2013. NPL 2013-15.

HONOURS: FA Comps: None

League: West Lancashire Division Two 1971-72, 76-77, Division One 1999-00. North West Counties 2012-13.

10 YEAR RECORD

09-10	10-11	11-12	12-13	13-14	14-15	15-16	16-17	17-18	18-19
NWCP 10	NWCP 4	NWCP 15	NWCP 1	NP1N 19	NP1N 22	NWCP 11	NWCP 7	NWCP 17	NWCP 18
FAC P	FAC EP	FAC EP	FAC P	FAC 1Q	FAC P	FAC 1Q	FAC P	FAC EP	FAC EP
FAV 2P	FAV 2Qr	FAV 2P	FAV 1Q	FAT P	FAT 1Q	FAV 1Q	FAV 2P	FAV 1Q	FAV 2Qr

M65 to Junction 8, then follow A6068 signposted Clitheroe and Padiham. At traffic lights at bottom of hill turn right into Dean Range/Blackburn Road towards Padiham. At next junction turn into Holland Street opposite church, then into Well St at the side of Hare & Hounds Pub to ground.

Nearest Railway Station Hapton - 2.2km

Bus Route Memorial Park stop - 110m away

RUNCORN TOWN

Founded 1967

Nickname: Town **Club Colours:** Sky and navy blue

Club Contact Details 07808 737 773

Ground: Sandy Lane, Weston Point, Runcorn WA7 4ET

Capacity: 1,530 **Seats:** Yes **Covered:** Yes

Previous Names: Mond Rangers 1967-2005 (Amalgamated with ICI Weston 1974-75).

Previous Leagues: Runcorn Sunday 1967-73, Warrington & District 1973-84, West Cheshire 1984-10.

HONOURS: FA Comps: None

League: West Cheshire League Division Two 2006-07.

10 YEAR RECORD

09-10	10-11	11-12	12-13	13-14	14-15	15-16	16-17	17-18	18-19
WCh1 3	NWC1 2	NWCP 2	NWCP 4	NWCP 5	NWCP 13	NWCP 13	NWCP 3	NWCP 3	NWCP 7
		FAC 1Q	FAC 1Q	FAC P	FAC 3Q	FAC P	FAC EP	FAC P	FAC 1Q
	FAV 4P	FAV 4Pr	FAV 5P	FAV 2P	FAV 2P	FAV 3Pr	FAV 1P	FAV 1P	FAV 3P

M56 J12. Head towards Liverpool. Come off at fourth exit (Runcorn Docks), turn left at the top of slip road, left at T-Junction, then left into Pavilions. ;M62 J7. Head towards Runcorn. When crossing Runcorn Bridge, stay in the right hand lane. Follow road around and come off at second exit (Runcorn Docks). Turn right at the top of slip road, left at T-Junction, then left into Pavilions.

Nearest Railway Station Runcorn - 1.6km

Bus Route South Parade stop - 69m away

RYLANDS

Founded 1911

Nickname: **Club Colours:** All blue

Club Contact Details 01925 635 880

Ground: Rylands Recreation Club, Gorsey Lane, Warrington WA2 7RZ

Capacity: 1345 **Seats:** Yes **Covered:** Yes

Previous Names: Merged with Crosfields and became Crosfields/Rylands between 2008-10

Previous Leagues: Mid-Cheshire 1968-2007. Cheshire 2008-18.

HONOURS: FA Comps: None

League: Mid-Cheshire 1980-81, 83-84. North West Counties Division One South 2018-19.

10 YEAR RECORD

09-10		10-11		11-12		12-13		13-14		14-15		15-16		16-17		17-18		18-19	
Ches1	10	Ches1	7	Ches1	12	Ches1	6	Ches1	8	ChesP	9	ChesP	14	ChesP	10	ChesP	11	NWC1S	1
																		FAV	2Q

Nearest Railway Station Warrington Central (1.4 miles)

Bus Route No.3 from Warrington to Beresford Street

SKELMERSDALE UNITED

Founded 1882

Nickname: Skem / Blueboys **Club Colours:** All blue

Club Contact Details

Ground: Prescot Cables FC, Volair Park, Eaton Street, Prescot L34 6HD

Capacity: 3,200 **Seats:** 500 **Covered:** 600 Yes

Previous Names: Skelmsdale Young Rovers. Skelmersdale Wesleyans.

Previous Leagues: Liverpool County Combination, Lancashire Combination 1891-93, 1903-07, 21-24, 55-56, 76-78, Cheshire County 1968-71, 78-82, Northern Premier 1971-76, 06-19. North West Counties 1983-2006.

HONOURS: FA Comps: FA Amateur Cup 1970-71. Barassi Anglo-Italian Cup 1970-71.

League: Northern Premier Division One North 2013-14.

10 YEAR RECORD

09-10		10-11		11-12		12-13		13-14		14-15		15-16		16-17		17-18		18-19	
NP1N	5	NP1N	2	NP1N	7	NP1N	1	NP P	6	NP P	7	NP P	16	NP P	24	NP1N	21	NP1W	20
FAC	P	FAC	2Q	FAC	P	FAC	2Q	FAC	2Q	FAC	2Q	FAC	2Q	FAC	1Qr	FAC	1Q	FAC	P
FAT	2Q	FAT	1Q	FAT	P	FAT	3P	FAT	1Q	FAT	1Q	FAT	1Pr	FAT	1Q	FAT	P	FAT	P

From North: M6 to Jct 26, onto M58 to Jct 3. Follow A570 to junction with A580 (East Lancs Road). (Approach junction in right hand lane of the two lanes going straight on). Cross A580 and take first road on right (Bleak Hill Road). Follow this road through to Prescot (2 miles). At traffic lights turn right, straight on at large r'about (do not follow route onto Prescot by-pass) and right at next lights. 100 yards turn right at Hope and Anchor pub into Hope Street. Club will be in sight at bottom of road. **From South:** M6 to Jct 21a (M62 junction 10). Follow M62 towards Liverpool, to junction 7. Follow A57 to Rainhill and Prescot. Through traffic lights at Fusilier pub, 100 yards turn right at Hope and Anchor pub (as above).
From East: Follow M62 as described in 'From South' or A580 East Lancs Road to Junction with A570 (Rainford by-pass), turn left and take first right. Follow route as 'From North'.

SQUIRES GATE

Founded 1948

Nickname: Gate **Club Colours:** All blue.

Club Contact Details 01253 348 512

Ground: Brian Addison Stadium, School Road, Marton, Blackpool, Lancs FY4 5DS

Capacity: 1,000 **Seats:** 100 **Covered:** Yes

Previous Names: Squires Gate British Legion FC >1953.

Previous Leagues: Blackpool & District Amateur 1958-61. West Lancashire 1961-91.

HONOURS: FA Comps: None

League: Blackpool & District Amateur League Division One 1955-56, 56-57. West Lancashire League Division Two 1980-81.

10 YEAR RECORD

09-10		10-11		11-12		12-13		13-14		14-15		15-16		16-17		17-18		18-19	
NWCP	13	NWCP	9	NWCP	16	NWCP	21	NWCP	19	NWCP	6	NWCP	19	NWCP	19	NWCP	11	NWCP	8
FAC	EPr	FAC	EP	FAC	1Qr	FAC	EP	FAC	EP	FAC	1Qr	FAC	EPr	FAC	1Q	FAC	EP	FAC	1Q
FAV	2Q	FAV	2Q	FAV	3P	FAV	2Q	FAV	2Q	FAV	1Q	FAV	2Q	FAV	1Q	FAV	1Q	FAV	2P

M55 to junction 4, turn left onto the A583, at first set of traffic lights turn right (Whitehill Road) follow sign for airport, at round-a-bout thake Lytham St Annes exit.
Ground approx. 11/2 on right.

Nearest Railway Station Squires Gate - 2.4km

Bus Route St Nicholas School stop - 75m away

WHITCHURCH ALPORT

Nickname: **Club Colours:** Red and white

Founded 1946

Club Contact Details

Ground: Yockings Park, Black Park Road, Whitchurch SY13 1PG

Capacity: **Seats:** Yes **Covered:** Yes

Previous Names: None

Previous Leagues: Cheshire. Mercian Regional League.

HONOURS: FA Comps: WFA Am Cup 1973-74

League: Shrewsbury & District 1947-48. Mid Cheshire 1969-70.

10 YEAR RECORD

09-10	10-11	11-12	12-13	13-14	14-15	15-16	16-17	17-18	18-19
Ches2 9	Ches2 3	Ches2 7	MerRP 11	MerRP 5	MerRP 4	NWC1 18	NWC1 5	NWC1 4	NWCP 14
								FAC EP	FAC P
							FAV 1Q	FAV 1Q	FAV 2Q

From the North either A41 or A49 into town. At main set of traffic lights turn first left (sign posted Whitchurch Alport FC) into Talbot Street, follow a long to Black Park Road, ground on the left. From the East A525 into Whitchurch, under the railway bridge and turn right into Queens Road, first left into Sainsbury Road then first right into Talbot Street than as above.

Nearest Railway Station Whitchurch - 0.4km

Bus Route Railway Station stop - 501m away

WINSFORD UNITED

Nickname: Blues **Club Colours:** Navy blue

Founded 1883

Club Contact Details 01606 558 447

Ground: The Barton Stadium, Kingsway, Winsford, Cheshire CW7 3AE

Capacity: 3,000 **Seats:** 200 **Covered:** 5,000 **Shop:** Yes

Previous Names: Over Wanderers 1883-1887

Previous Leagues: The Combination 1902-04. Cheshire County 1919-40, 47-82. Northern Premier League 1987-2001.

HONOURS: FA Comps: None

League: Cheshire County 1920-21, 76-77.
North West Counties League Division Two 2006-07.

10 YEAR RECORD

09-10	10-11	11-12	12-13	13-14	14-15	15-16	16-17	17-18	18-19
NWCP 19	NWCP 3	NWCP 7	NWCP 5	NWCP 14	NWCP 12	NWCP 14	NWCP 13	NWCP 14	NWCP 16
FAC EPr	FAC EP	FAC EPr	FAC P	FAC P	FAC EP	FAC EPr	FAC 1Qr	FAC EP	FAC EP
FAV 2P	FAV 2Q	FAV 2P	FAV 3P	FAV 2Pr	FAV 1P	FAV 1P	FAV 1Q	FAV 2Q	FAV 1P

M6 to junction 18, follow A54 through Middlewich for approx. 3 miles, bear right at round-a-bout at Winsford Railway Station, follow road for approx. 1 mile, turn right into Kingsway, ground is on the right.

Nearest Railway Station Winsford - 1.2km

Bus Route Wesley Court stop - 34m away

AFC BLACKPOOL

Founded: 1947 Nickname: Mechanics

Club Contact Details 01253 761 721
Ground: Jepson Way, Common Edge Road, Blackpool FY4 5DY **Club Colours:** Tangerine

HONOURS
FA Comps: None
League: West Lancashire League 1960-61, 61-62.
North West Counties League Division Three 1985/86, Division One 2010-11.

10 YEAR RECORD

09-10	10-11	11-12	12-13	13-14	14-15	15-16	16-17	17-18	18-19
NWC1 15	NWC1 1	NWCP 9	NWCP 10	NWCP 13	NWCP 18	NWCP 22	NWC1 19	NWC1 7	NWC1N 13
		FAC Pr	FAC EP	FAC EP	FAC EP	FAC 1Q	FAC EP		
FAV 2Q	FAV 2P	FAV 1Q	FAV 2Q	FAV 1P	FAV 1Q	FAV 1Q	FAV 2Q	FAV 1Q	FAV 2Q

M6 to M55, exit at junction 4.
At roundabout turn left along A583 to traffic lights, turn right into Whitehill Road, to traffic lights (2 miles).
Go straight across the main road into Jepson Way, ground at top.

Nearest Railway Station Squires Gate - 2.2km
Bus Route Borough Boundary stop - 109m away

AFC DARWEN

Founded: 2009 (reformed) Nickname: Salmoners

Club Contact Details 01254 776 193
Ground: WEC Group Anchor Ground, Anchor Road, Darwen, Lancs BB3 0BB **Club Colours:** All red

HONOURS
FA Comps: None
League: None

10 YEAR RECORD

09-10	10-11	11-12	12-13	13-14	14-15	15-16	16-17	17-18	18-19
WLaP 8	NWC1 13	NWC1 13	NWC1 5	NWC1 9	NWC1 3	NWCP 18	NWCP 18	NWCP 23	NWC1N 10
						FAC EP	FAC EPr	FAC EP	FAC P
		FAV 1P		FAV 2Q	FAV 2P	FAV 2Q	FAV 1Q	FAV 1P	FAV 2Q

M65 to junction 4. At traffic lights turn left onto A666 (signposted Darwen). After approx 1/2 mile turn left between Anchor Car sales and the Anchor Pub. Bear right and ground is on the left.

Nearest Railway Station Darwen - 1.7km
Bus Route Birch Hall Avenue stop - 256m away

AFC LIVERPOOL

Founded: 2008 Nickname: Little Reds

Club Contact Details 0151 924 1743 or 0151 286 9101
Ground: Marine FC, College Road, Crosby, Liverpool L23 3AS **Club Colours:** All red

HONOURS
FA Comps: None
League: None

10 YEAR RECORD

09-10	10-11	11-12	12-13	13-14	14-15	15-16	16-17	17-18	18-19
NWC1 5	NWC1 4	NWCP 19	NWCP 11	NWCP 7	NWCP 9	NWCP 17	NWCP 12	NWCP 20	NWC1N 3
	FAC EP	FAC EPr	FAC P	FAC P	FAC EP	FAC 1Q	FAC EPr	FAC EP	FAC EPr
FAV 2Q	FAV 3P	FAV 2Qr	FAV 1P	FAV 1Q	FAV 2Q	FAV 1Q	FAV 1P	FAV 2Q	FAV 1Q

M57/M58 take the A5036 signposted Bootle & Docks, at the roundabout under the flyover turn right onto the A565 following signs for Crosby and Marine AFC. After passing Tesco Express on the right, turn left at the traffic lights (by Merchants Taylors School) into College Road, ground is approx ½ mile on the left.

Nearest Railway Station Blundellsands & Crosby - 0.5km
Bus Route Brompton Avenue stop - 175m away

ASHTON TOWN

Founded: 1953 Nickname: The Town

Club Contact Details 01942 724 448
Ground: Edge Green Street, Ashton-in-Makerfield, Wigan, WN4 8SL **Club Colours:** All red

HONOURS
FA Comps: None
League: St Helens Combination Division Two 1957-58.
Warrington & District League Division One 1959-60, 60-61, 62-63, 63-64, 64-65, 69-70.

10 YEAR RECORD

09-10	10-11	11-12	12-13	13-14	14-15	15-16	16-17	17-18	18-19
NWC1 13	NWC1 16	NWC1 18	NWC1 6	NWC1 12	NWC1 17	NWC1 11	NWC1 22	ChesP 6	NWC1N 9
	FAC EP			FAC EP					
FAV 2Q	FAV 2Q	FAV 1Q	FAV 2Q	FAV 1Q	FAV 1P	FAV 2Q	FAV 1P	FAV 1Q	FAV 2Q

M6 to Junction 23, A49 to Ashton-in-Makerfield. Turn right at the traffic lights onto the A58 towards Bolton. After approx. three quarters of a mile, turn right into Golbourne Road. After 200 yards turn right into Edge Green Street. Ground at bottom of street.

Nearest Railway Station Bryn
Bus Route 600 or 601

ATHERTON L.R.

Founded: 1956 Nickname: The Panthers

Club Contact Details 01942 575 173

Ground: Crilly Park, Spa Road, Atherton, Manchester M46 9XG **Club Colours:** Yellow and royal blue

HONOURS
FA Comps: None
League: Bolton Combination Division Two A 1965-66.
North West Counties 1992-93, 93-94.

10 YEAR RECORD

09-10	10-11	11-12	12-13	13-14	14-15	15-16	16-17	17-18	18-19
NWCP 20	NWCP 10	NWCP 22	NWC1 13	NWC1 3	NWC1 12	NWC1 17	NWC1 20	NWC1 18	NWC1N 20
FAC 1Qr	FAC Pr	FAC P	FAC P						
FAV 1Q	FAV 1P	FAV 1P	FAV 1Q	FAV 1P		FAV 2Q	FAV 1P	FAV 1Q	FAV 2Q

M61 to Junction 5, follow signs for Westhoughton, turn left onto A6, turn right at first lights into Newbrook Road, then turn right into Upton Road, passing Atherton Central Station. Turn left into Spa Road.

Nearest Railway Station Atherton - 0.3km
Bus Route Devonshire Rad stop - 97m away

BACUP BOROUGH

Founded: 1875 Nickname: The Boro

Club Contact Details 01706 878 655

Ground: Brian Boys Stadium, Cowtoot Lane, Blackthorn, Bacup OL13 8EE **Club Colours:** White and black

HONOURS
FA Comps: None
League: Lancashire Combination 1946-47.
North West Counties Division Two 2002-03

10 YEAR RECORD

09-10	10-11	11-12	12-13	13-14	14-15	15-16	16-17	17-18	18-19
NWCP 12	NWCP 11	NWCP 17	NWCP 17	NWCP 21	NWCP 21	NWC1 5	NWC1 18	NWC1 17	NWC1N 8
FAC EPr	FAC 1Q	FAC EP	FAC P			FAC EP	FAC EP		
FAV 2P	FAV 2P	FAV 2P	FAV 1Qr			FAV 2Q	FAV 2Q	FAV 2Q	FAV 2Q

From M62/M60: Follow onto M66, follow to end signed Rawtenstall. Continue for approx 4 miles to Bacup, turn left into Burnley Road, turn right before the Irwell Inn into Cooper Street. At top of hill turn right and second left into Cowtoot Lane. From M6/M65: To junction 9 (Halifax/ Burnley West) then take A679 and follow to Irwell Inn, turn left directions as above.

Bus Route Thorn Cp School stop - 119m away

CHADDERTON

Founded: 1946 Nickname: Chaddy

Club Contact Details 07506 104 005 (MD)

Ground: Andrew Street, Chadderton, Oldham, Greater Manchester OL9 0JT **Club Colours:** All red

HONOURS
FA Comps: None
League: Manchester Amateur League 1955-56, Division One 1962-63.
Manchester League Division Two 1964-65, Division One 1966-67.

10 YEAR RECORD

09-10	10-11	11-12	12-13	13-14	14-15	15-16	16-17	17-18	18-19
NWC1 4	NWC1 6	NWC1 6	NWC1 12	NWC1 13	NWC1 6	NWC1 14	NWC1 9	NWC1 16	NWC1N 16
FAC EPr	FAC P	FAC EP	FAC P			FAC EP			
FAV 2Qr	FAV 1Q	FAV 2Q	FAV 2Q	FAV 1P	FAV 4P	FAV 2P	FAV 1P	FAV 2Q	FAV 1Q

M62 to junction 20, follow A627(M) towards Manchester. Motorway becomes a dual carriageway, turn left at first major traffic lights (A699) Middleton Road, then second left into Burnley Street, towards Asda Chadderton then second left past Chadderton Sports Centre into Andrew Street Chadderton FC ground on right at the end of Andrew St. Directions from M60 Junction 21 A663 towards Chadderton/Oldham Thru lights at Gorse St Thru lights at Whitegate Lane (McDonalds on left) Thru lights at Foxdenton Lane (garage on left & pub on right Pass new School on left Thru lights at Hunt Lane Right next lights A669 Middleton Road 2nd Left into Burnley St (towards Asda) 2nd left into Andrew St - ground entrance is 2nd on right.

Nearest Railway Station Freehold (Manc. Metrolink) - 1.1km
Bus Route Middleton Road stop - 133m away

CLEATOR MOOR CELTIC

Founded: 1909 Nickname:

Club Contact Details 07710 251 421

Ground: McGrath Park, Birks Road, Cleator Moor, Cumbria CA25 5HP **Club Colours:** Green and white

HONOURS
FA Comps: None
League: None

10 YEAR RECORD

09-10	10-11	11-12	12-13	13-14	14-15	15-16	16-17	17-18	18-19
Wear 5	Wear 15	Wear 7	Wear 4	Wear 4	Wear 3	Wear 4	Wear 3	Wear 2	NWC1N 11
		FAV 1Q							

Travel on the M6 to junction 40, Penrith, Keswick and Workington. Take the first exit on the roundabout onto the A66, travel 26 miles to the third roundabout and take first exit onto the A5086. Travel 11 miles, and at the mini roundabout take the second exit staying on Frizington Road A5086. In 0.1 mile, turn right on to Church Street B5294. In 0.8 miles turn left onto Church Street B5294, and in 0.8 miles turn left on to Birks Road. Travel 0.7 miles over the bridge towards Main Street, school and Health Centre. Turn right at the Health Centre and follow the road round to JBV Park.

Nearest Railway Station Whitehaven
Bus Route Buses run on a regular basis from Whitehaven to Cleator Moor.

DAISY HILL

Founded: 1894 Nickname: The Daisies

Club Contact Details 01942 818 544

Ground: New Sirs, St James Street, Westhoughton, Bolton BL5 2EB **Club Colours:** All royal blue and white

HONOURS
FA Comps: None

League: Wigan & District 1896-97.
Bolton Combination Premier Division 1962-63, 72-73, 75-76, 77-78.

10 YEAR RECORD

09-10	10-11	11-12	12-13	13-14	14-15	15-16	16-17	17-18	18-19
NWC1 11	NWC1 14	NWC1 12	NWC1 16	NWC1 18	NWC1 8	NWC1 12	NWC1 16	NWC1 21	NWC1N 19
	FAC EP		FAC EP						
FAV 2P	FAV 1Q	FAV 1Q	FAV 2Q	FAV 1Q	FAV 1P	FAV 2P	FAV 2Q	FAV 1Q	FAV 2Q

M61 to junction 5, A58 (Snydale Way/Park Road) for one and a half mile, left into Leigh Road (B5235) for 1 mile to Daisy Hill. Turn right into village 200 yards after mini roundabout, then left between church and school into St James Street. Ground 250 yards on left.

Nearest Railway Station Daisy Hill - 0.7km
Bus Route Hindley Road stop - 173m away

EMLEY AFC

Founded: 2005 Nickname: Pewits

Club Contact Details 01924 849 392

Ground: The Welfare Ground, Off Upper Lane, Emley, nr Huddersfield HD8 9RE **Club Colours:** Maroon and sky blue

HONOURS
FA Comps: None

League: None

10 YEAR RECORD

09-10	10-11	11-12	12-13	13-14	14-15	15-16	16-17	17-18	18-19
NCE1 8	NCE1 8	NCE1 10	NCE1 7	NCE1 8	NCE1 5	NCE1 4	NCE1 3	NCE1 12	NCE1 12
FAC EP	FAC P	FAC EP	FAC EP	FAC P	FAC P	FAC P	FAC P	FAC EP	
FAV 2Q	FAV 2P	FAV 1P	FAV 4P	FAV 1P	FAV 1P	FAV 2Q	FAV 2P	FAV 1P	FAV 1Q

From M1 J38: Travel on road signposted to Huddersfield through the village of Bretton to the first roundabout. Take first exit off this roundabout signposted Denby Dale. After approximately one mile turn right at road signposted Emley. After 2 miles enter the village of Emley. Entrance to ground is opposite a white bollard in centre of road. (Narrow entrance).
From M1 J39: Travel on road signposted toward Denby Dale. Travel for approximately 3 miles up hill to first roundabout. Take 2nd exit and follow directions as above.

Nearest Railway Station Denby Dale - 5km
Bus Route Upper Lane Church Street - stop 61m away

GARSTANG

Founded: 1895 Nickname:

Club Contact Details 07501 119 458

Ground: The Riverside, Lancaster Road, Garstang PR3 1EB **Club Colours:** Red and black

HONOURS
FA Comps: None

League: West Lancashire Premier 2007-08, 17-18.

10 YEAR RECORD

09-10	10-11	11-12	12-13	13-14	14-15	15-16	16-17	17-18	18-19
WLaP 6	WLaP 13	WLaP 16	WLa1 2	WLaP 10	WLaP 5	WLaP 9	WLaP 4	WLaP 1	NWC1N 7
									FAV 2P

Turn off A6 onto B6430.
The Riverside ground is 100 yards north of LBT Motors in Garstang Town Centre.

Nearest Railway Station Lancaster (12 miles) or Preston (14.5)
Bus Route From Preston/Lancaster/Blackpool stop High St.

GOLCAR UNITED

Founded: 1904 Nickname:

Club Contact Details 07825 744 829

Ground: Longfield Avenue, Golcar, Huddersfield HD7 4AZ **Club Colours:** green and black

HONOURS
FA Comps: None

League: West Riding County Amateur Premier Division 2004-05, 17-18, 18-19

10 YEAR RECORD

09-10	10-11	11-12	12-13	13-14	14-15	15-16	16-17	17-18	18-19
WRCP 11	WRCP 12	WRCP 7	WRCP 6	WRCP 6	WRCP 2	WRCP 7	WRCP 5	WRCP 1	WRCP 1

A62 Manchester Road to Milnsbridge.
Left up Scar Lane, right on Sycamore Avenue, left into Longfield Avenue.

Nearest Railway Station Huddersfield - 2.9 miles or Slaithwaite - 3.7 miles.
Bus Route 301/302 Golcar Circular.

HOLKER OLD BOYS

Founded: 1936 Nickname: Cobs

Club Contact Details 01229 828 176

Ground: Rakesmoor, Rakesmoor Lane, Hawcoat, Barrow-in-Furness LA14 4QB **Club Colours:** Green and white

HONOURS **League:** West Lancashire 1986-87.

FA Comps: None

10 YEAR RECORD

09-10	10-11	11-12	12-13	13-14	14-15	15-16	16-17	17-18	18-19
NWC1 7	NWC1 3	NWC1 9	NWC1 7	NWC1 6	NWC1 5	NWC1 8	NWC1 17	NWC1 9	NWC1N 18
FAC EP	FAC P	FAC P	FAC 1Q		FAC EPr	FAC P			
FAV 2Q	FAV 2Q	FAV 2Q	FAV 1Q	FAV 1P	FAV 1P	FAV 2Q	FAV 1P	FAV 1Q	FAV 1Q

M6 to junction 36, A590 to Barrow until you reach Kimberley-Clark Paper Mill. Turn 1st left into Bank Lane, signposted Hawcoat & and Barrow Golf Club, At the T junction turn left into Rakesmoor Lane. Ground 200 yards on the right.

Nearest Railway Station Barrow-in-Furness - 2.6km

Bus Route Dunmail Raise stop - 151m away

LOWER BRECK

Founded: 2010 Nickname:

Club Contact Details 0151 263 6186

Ground: Anfield Sports & Community Centre, Lower Breck Rd, Liverpool L6 0AG **Club Colours:** Red and white

HONOURS **League:** Liverpool County Division Two 2012-13, Premier 17-18.

FA Comps: None

10 YEAR RECORD

09-10	10-11	11-12	12-13	13-14	14-15	15-16	16-17	17-18	18-19
			LivC2 1	LivC1 4	LivCP 11	LivCP 3	LivCP 2	LivCP 1	NWC1N 4
									FAV 1P

From the North, join the M62 to the end at then turn right onto Queens Drive. After 1.5 miles turn left onto Mill Bank, then after 0.5 miles turn right onto Lower Breck Road. The ground is on your right.

From the North, join the A580 East Lancs Road. 2.5 miles after you pass the M57, bear left onto Townsend Road then after 1.3 miles turn left onto Lower Breck Road. The ground is on your left.

Nearest Railway Station Liverpool Lime Street

Bus Route Arriva Bus 68 stops at the ground

NELSON

Founded: 1883 Nickname: Admirals

Club Contact Details 01772 794 103

Ground: Little Wembley, Lomeshaye Way, Nelson, Lancs BB9 7BN. **Club Colours:** All blue

HONOURS **League:** Lancashire 1895-96. Lancashire Combination 1949-50, 51-52. Football League Division Three North 1922-23. North West Counties Division One 2013-14.

FA Comps: None

10 YEAR RECORD

09-10	10-11	11-12	12-13	13-14	14-15	15-16	16-17	17-18	18-19
NWCP 17		NWC1 15	NWC1 10	NWC1 1	NWCP 11	NWCP 16	NWCP 21	NWC1 22	NWC1N 14
					FAC EP	FAC EP	FAC P	FAC EP	
FAV 3P			FAV 2Q	FAV 1P	FAV 2Qr	FAV 2Q	FAV 1Q	FAV 2Q	FAV 1P

M65 to junction 13, take first exit towards Fence A6068, take second left towards nelson B6249, after ½ mile turn right (signposted Lomeshaye Village), ground 200 yards on the right.

Nearest Railway Station Nelson - 1km

Bus Route Business Village stop - 83m away

PILKINGTON

Founded: 1938 Nickname:

Club Contact Details

Ground: Ruskin Drive, Dentons Green, St Helens WA10 6RP **Club Colours:** Green

HONOURS **League:** Cheshire Premier Division 2018-19.

FA Comps: None

10 YEAR RECORD

09-10	10-11	11-12	12-13	13-14	14-15	15-16	16-17	17-18	18-19
ChesP 12	ChesP 2	ChesP 9	ChesP 13	ChesP 15	ChesP 16	Ches1 6	Ches1 3	Ches1 2	ChesP 1

From the North: Leave the M6 at Junction 26 (M58) and leave at junction 3 (A570) for St. Helens. Continue on A570 until you reach the junction with the A580 (Starbucks and petrol station on the opposite).
From Manchester or the South: Leave the M6 at junction 23 (A580) and proceed 5 miles to junction with A570 (Starbucks and petrol station on the right). All traffic should then follow signs for St. Helens, passing into one-way system, keep to the right hand lane entering Dentons Green Lane and make a U-turn where the road opens out by the bus shelter, take the left lane and Ruskin Drive is second on the left after Rivington Road and the pedestrian crossing.

Nearest Railway Station St Helens Central

Bus Route The 37, 38 and 38A go past the end of Ruskin Drive.

PRESTWICH HEYS

Founded: 1938 Nickname: The Heys

Club Contact Details 0161 7773 8888 (MD)

Ground: Adie Moran Park, Sandgate Road, Whitefield M45 6WG **Club Colours:** Red and white

HONOURS **League:** Lancashire Combination 1970-71. Manchester Division One 1996-97, Premier Division 2004-05, 04-05, 05-06, 06-07, 15-16.

FA Comps: None

10 YEAR RECORD

09-10	10-11	11-12	12-13	13-14	14-15	15-16	16-17	17-18	18-19
MancP 11	MancP 12	MancP 13	MancP 8	MancP 4	MancP 6	MancP 1	NWC1 8	NWC1 3	NWC1N 5
									FAC P
								FAV 1Q	FAV 2Pr

M60 to junction 17 towards Whitefield, turn right into Clyde Avenue continue over traffic lights onto Thatch Leach Lane, turn right at the Frigate Public House, over motorway bridge, ground on the left.

Nearest Railway Station Clifton - 3.5km
Bus Route Sandgate Road stop - 73m away

SHELLEY

Founded: 1903 Nickname:

Club Contact Details 07931 853 881

Ground: Storthes Hall, Huddersfield HD8 0WA **Club Colours:** Red and black

HONOURS **League:** Huddersfield & District Division Two A 1904-05, Division Two 28-29, 2000-01, Division Three 60-61, 86-87, 2010-11, Division Four 2009-10. West Yorkshire Division Two 2011-12.

FA Comps: None

10 YEAR RECORD

09-10	10-11	11-12	12-13	13-14	14-15	15-16	16-17	17-18	18-19
	HudD3 3	WYk2 1	WYk1 2	WYkP 12	WYkP 10	WYkP 11	WYkP 8	WYkP 10	NWC1N 12
									FAV 2Q

M62 to Huddersfield then A629 towards Sheffield out of Huddersfield. Right turn signposted University Student Village onto Storthes Hall Lane. Turn left into student village complex and follow road over a series of speed bumps until turning left at sign for The Stafflex Arena.

Nearest Railway Station Brockholes (2.5 miles), Stockmoor (2.3) Huddersfield (5.2)
Bus Route 398 Huddersfield Uni to Storthes Hall Park

ST HELENS TOWN

Founded: 1946 Nickname: Town or Saints

Club Contact Details

Ground: Ruskin Drive, Dentons Green, St Helens WA10 6RP **Club Colours:** All blue

HONOURS **League:** Lancashire Combination Division Two 1950-51, Premier 1971-72 .

FA Comps: FA Vase 1986-87.

10 YEAR RECORD

09-10	10-11	11-12	12-13	13-14	14-15	15-16	16-17	17-18	18-19
NWCP 9	NWCP 17	NWCP 21	NWCP 19	NWCP 17	NWCP 20	NWC1 7	NWC1 13	NWC1 20	NWC1N 17
FAC 1Q	FAC Pr	FAC EP	FAC EP	FAC EPr	FAC EP	FAC EP			
FAV 1Q	FAV 3P	FAV 2Q	FAV 1P	FAV 1Q	FAV 3P	FAV 2Q	FAV 1Q	FAV 1Q	FAV 1Q

From South: M6 to junction 25, turn right onto A49, after 1/2 mile turn right into Soughers Lane, at T junction turn right into Downall Green Road, pass over M6 and turn 2nd right into Boothbrow Road, turn 2nd right in Brocstedes Road. (Ashton Athletic FC)

Nearest Railway Station St Helens Central - 1.9km
Bus Route Ruskin Drive stop - 153m away

STEETON

Founded: 1905 Nickname:

Club Contact Details 01535 606 044

Ground: Cougar Park, Royd Ings Avenue, Keighley BD21 3RF **Club Colours:** All green

HONOURS **League:** Keighley & District 1937-38, 38-39, 54-55. Craven & District 1959-60. West Riding County Amateur Division Two 1988-89, 2000-01, Division One 2009-10.

FA Comps: None

10 YEAR RECORD

09-10	10-11	11-12	12-13	13-14	14-15	15-16	16-17	17-18	18-19
WRC1 1	WRCP 8	WRCP 6	WRCP 2	WRCP 5	WRCP 7	WRCP 10	WRCP 3	WRCP 3	NWC1N 15
									FAV 1P

From the South: Follow SatNav for BD21-3RF, the gound is on your right hand side behind a petrol station, opposite McDonald's. Go past the ground and double back on yourself at the roundabout, turn left down Royd Way, then right at the bottom onto Royd Ings Avenue. Entrance is to your right. **From the North:** The gound is behind a petrol station, opposite McDonald's. Follow SatNav for BD21-3RF, at the end of the A629 take the first turn off the roundabout, and quick left down Royd Way, then right at the bottom onto Royd Ings Avenue. Entrance is to your right.
If on foot there is a second entrance to the ground on Hard Ings Road opposite the petrol station.

Nearest Railway Station Keighly (0.8 miles)
Bus Route 662 (Bradford) & 760 (Leeds)

ABBEY HEY

Founded: 1902 Nickname: Red Rebels

Club Contact Details 0161 231 7147

Ground: The Abbey Stadium, Goredale Avenue, Gorton, Manchester M18 7HD **Club Colours:** Red and black

HONOURS
FA Comps: None
League: Manchester Amateur League 1964-65. South East Lancashire 1966-67, 68-69. Manchester League Division One 1970-71, Premier 1981-82, 88-89, 88-89, 91-92, 93-94, 94-95.

10 YEAR RECORD

09-10	10-11	11-12	12-13	13-14	14-15	15-16	16-17	17-18	18-19
NWCP 22	NWC1 15	NWC1 3	NWC1 2	NWCP 20	NWCP 14	NWCP 10	NWCP 14	NWCP 19	NWCP 20
FAC EP	FAC EPr		FAC 2Q	FAC EP	FAC EP	FAC 2Q	FAC EP	FAC 1Qr	FAC EP
FAV 2Q	FAV 2Qr	FAV 2Q	FAV 1Q	FAV 1Q	FAV 2Q	FAV 1P	FAV 2Q	FAV 1Q	FAV 1Q

M60 to junction 24, take A57 to Manchester City Centre for approx 1 mile, at first set of major traffic lights (MacDonalds on right) pass through for approx 300yards, turn left immediatley before overhead railway bridge (A.H.F.C. sign) into Woodland Avenue. Take first right, pass under railway bridge, turn first left into Goredale Avenue.

Nearest Railway Station Ryder Brow - 0.5km
Bus Route Ryder Brow Road stop - 124m away

ABBEY HULTON UNITED

Founded: 1947 Nickname:

Club Contact Details 01782 570 302

Ground: Birches Head Road, Abbey Hulton, Stoke-on-Trent ST2 8DD **Club Colours:** Orange and black

HONOURS
FA Comps: None
League: Staffordshire County Senior Premier Division 2016-17.

10 YEAR RECORD

09-10	10-11	11-12	12-13	13-14	14-15	15-16	16-17	17-18	18-19
		StfSP 5	StfSP 4	StfSP 7	StfSP 3	StfSP 8	StfSP 1	NWC1 13	NWC1S 8
									FAV 1Q

From the A500, take Leed Road A5009 towards Leek,
Turn left onto Birches Head Road.
Go over the narrow bridge, and continue past the junction with Redhills Road, then turn right into the ground. (if you go over the canal bridge you have gone too far)
For satnavs, use post code ST2 8DD for Trent Squash Club, which is next door to the football club.

Nearest Railway Station Stoke-on-Trent - 4.2km
Bus Route Woodhead Road stop - 262m away

ALSAGER TOWN

Founded: 1968 Nickname: The Bullets

Club Contact Details 07888 750 532

Ground: Woodpark Stadium, Woodland Court, Alsager ST7 2DP **Club Colours:** White & black

HONOURS
FA Comps: None
League: None

10 YEAR RECORD

09-10	10-11	11-12	12-13	13-14	14-15	15-16	16-17	17-18	18-19
NWCP 18	NWCP 20	NWCP 13	NWCP 15	NWCP 18	NWCP 17	NWCP 20	NWC1 7	NWC1 8	NWC1S 17
FAC EP	FAC EP	FAC EP	FAC EP	FAC EP	FAC EP	FAC 1Q	FAC P	FAC EP	
FAV 2P	FAV 2Q	FAV 1Q	FAV 2Q	FAV 2Q	FAV 1Q	FAV 3P	FAV 2Q	FAV 2P	FAV 1Q

M6 to Junction 16, A500 towards Stoke, leave A500 at 2nd exit (A34 to Congleton) at 2nd set of traffic lights on A34 turn left for Alsager (B5077). After 500 yards (opposite Caradon/Twyfords Factory) turn right into Moorhouse Avenue. Ground is off West Grove 1/4 mile on right. Entrance to ground is down drive on the bottom right hand corner, between the houses.

Nearest Railway Station Alsager - 0.9km
Bus Route Curzon Avenue stop - 374m away

BARNTON

Founded: 1946 Nickname: Villagers

Club Contact Details 07484 793 822

Ground: Townfield, Townfield Lane, Barnton, Cheshire CW8 4LH **Club Colours:** Black and white

HONOURS
FA Comps: None
League: Mid-Cheshire/Cheshire 1979-80, 82-83, 88-89, 96-97, 97-98, 98-99, 99-2000, 2000-01, 01-02, 02-03, 04-05, Division Two 2012-13.

10 YEAR RECORD

09-10	10-11	11-12	12-13	13-14	14-15	15-16	16-17	17-18	18-19
Ches2 10	Ches2 13	Ches2 13	Ches2 1	Ches1 5	NWC1 7	NWC1 3	NWCP 17	NWCP 22	NWC1S 12
							FAC EP	FAC EP	FAC EP
						FAV 2Q	FAV 2Q	FAV 2Q	FAV 2Q

Turn off the A533 (Northwich to Runcorn) at the Beech Tree Inn (Barnton Village) into Beech Lane. Turn right at the 'T' junction with Townfield Lane - the ground is 200 yards on the left signed Memorial Hall. Note parking restrictions well signed.

Nearest Railway Station Greenbank - 2.6km
Bus Route Crocus Street stop - 128m away

OUTS: Rylands (P - NWCP), Stone Dominoes (R - StaffsCS).

CAMMELL LAIRD 1907

Founded: 1907 Nickname: Lairds

Club Contact Details 0151 645 3121

Ground: Kirklands, St Peter's Road, Rock Ferry, Birkenhead CH42 1PY **Club Colours:** All royal blue

HONOURS **League:** West Cheshire x19 (Firstly in 1954-55 and most recently 2000-01).

FA Comps: None North West Counties Division Two 2004-05, Division One 2005-06.

10 YEAR RECORD

09-10		10-11		11-12		12-13		13-14		14-15		15-16		16-17		17-18		18-19	
NP1S	16	NP1N	19	NP1N	22	NP1N	2	NP1N	11	NWC1	2	NWCP	15	NWCP	22	NWC1	6	NWC1S	15
FAC	2Q	FAC	P	FAC	1Q	FAC	1Q	FAC	2Q	FAC	EP					FAC	P		
FAT	1Q	FAT	1Q	FAT	P	FAT	3Q	FAT	1Q	FAV	1Q					FAV	1Q	FAV	1P

From Chester: M563/A41 towards Birkenhead, at New ferry signpost take the B5136 towards New ferry, approx 1 mile, turn right at traffic island into Proctor Road, ground at the bottom of Proctor Road. From Liverpool: Take the Birkenhead Tunnel, A41 for approx 1 mile, take the B5136 signposted New Ferry / Rock Ferry at big round-a-bout. Follow until the 2nd set of traffic lights, turn left, then first right into St Peters Road, ground at the bottom of the road on the left.

Nearest Railway Station Rock Ferry - 0.7km

Bus Route St Peters Road stop - 58m away

CHEADLE HEATH NOMADS

Founded: 2004 Nickname:

Club Contact Details

Ground: The Heath, Norbreck Avenue, Cheadle, Stockport SK8 2ET **Club Colours:** Maroon and blue

HONOURS **League:** Cheshire Premier 2014-15.

FA Comps: None

10 YEAR RECORD

09-10		10-11		11-12		12-13		13-14		14-15		15-16		16-17		17-18		18-19	
Ches1	7	Ches1	16	Ches1	6	Ches1	12	Ches1	10	ChesP	1	ChesP	2	ChesP	5	ChesP	4	NWC1S	9

If travelling AntiClockwise on the M60, come off at Junction 1, take the inside lane slip road taking the first turning off the roundabout. Take the filter lane right lane to Cheadle (note both lanes filter right) and at the second set of lights turn right onto the A560 Brinksway.Follow the A560 for approx 1.5 miles passing Morrisons on the left and Aldi on the right. Take left lane at the next lights and turn left onto Edgeley Road. Follow for 500 yards and turn left at the mini roundabout onto Birdhall Lane. Take second right onto Cheltenham Road and second left onto Normanton Avenue which leads to Norbreck Avenue. Note this is a single lane under the railway arch and the ground is immediately on the right under the arch. If travelling Clockwise on the M60, come off at Junction 2 and take the second exit towards Stockport (A560). You will come to a set of lights, fork right onto Edgeley Road.

Nearest Railway Station Stockport

Bus Route 11, 11a and 309

CHEADLE TOWN

Founded: 1961 Nickname:

Club Contact Details 0161 428 2510

Ground: Park Road Stadium, Cheadle, Cheshire SK8 2AN **Club Colours:** Red and white

HONOURS **League:** Manchester Division One 1979-80.

FA Comps: None

10 YEAR RECORD

09-10		10-11		11-12		12-13		13-14		14-15		15-16		16-17		17-18		18-19	
NWC1	14	NWC1	10	NWC1	8	NWC1	7	NWC1	11	NWC1	10	NWC1	6	NWC1	12	NWC1	12	NWC1S	
FAC	EP	FAC	P	FAC	P	FAC	EPr	FAC	EP					FAC	1Q				
FAV	1Pr	FAV	1Q	FAV	1P	FAV	1P	FAV	2P	FAV	1Q	FAV	2Q	FAV	1Q	FAV	1Q	FAV	2Qr

M60 to junction 2 (formerly M63 junction 11), follow A560 to Cheadle. Go through first main set of traffic lights and then first left after shops into Park Road. Ground at end of road.

Nearest Railway Station Gatley - 1.8km

Bus Route Stockport Road stop - 161m away

ECCLESHALL

Founded: 1971 Nickname: The Eagles

Club Contact Details 01785 851 351 (MD)

Ground: Pershall Park, Chester Road, Eccleshall ST21 6NE **Club Colours:** All royal blue

HONOURS **League:** Staffordshire County Premier 1982-83. Staffordshire Senior 1989-90.

FA Comps: None Midland 2001-02, 02-03.

10 YEAR RECORD

09-10		10-11		11-12		12-13		13-14		14-15		15-16		16-17		17-18		18-19	
NWC1	9	NWC1	11	NWC1	7	NWC1	15	NWC1	17	NWC1	15	NWC1	16	NWC1	21	NWC1	15	NWC1S	13
FAC	EP	FAC	1Q	FAC	Pr	FAC	EP												
FAV	1Qr	FAV	1P	FAV	1Q	FAV	1P	FAV	2Q	FAV	1P	FAV	2Q	FAV	1Q	FAV	1Q	FAV	1Q

M6 to junction 15, follow signs for Eccleshall A519 (approx. 10 miles). Turn right towards Loggerheads B5026, continue passed church, cricket and tennis clubs until signpost for Pershall. Ground 100 yards on the right.

Nearest Railway Station Stafford - 8.5 miles

Bus Route Pershall Farm stop - 228m away

ELLESMERE RANGERS

Founded: 1969 Nickname: The Rangers

Club Contact Details 07947 864 357 john.edge2@homecall.co.uk

Ground: Beech Grove, Ellesmere, Shropshire SY12 0BZ **Club Colours:** Sky blue & navy blue

HONOURS **League:** West Midlands (Reg) Division One 2005-06, Premier 2009-10.

FA Comps: None

10 YEAR RECORD

09-10		10-11		11-12		12-13		13-14		14-15		15-16		16-17		17-18		18-19	
WMP	1	MidAl	13	MidAl	15	MidAl	22	WMP	11	WMP	4	WMP	10	WMP	7	WMP	6	NWC1S	19
FAC	EP	FAC	EP	FAC	EP	FAC	EP	FAC	P	FAC	EP	FAC	EP					FAC	EP
FAV	1Q	FAV	2Q	FAV	2P	FAV	1Qr	FAV	2Q	FAV	EP	FAV	1P	FAV	1Q	FAV	1Q	FAV	1Q

Follow A5 Wellington and take A495 to Ellesmere. On Approaching Ellesmere, straight over at roundabout, then turn left into housing estate opposite Lakelands School. At crossroads, turn left and the 1st right down the lane to Beech Grove Playing Fields.

Nearest Railway Station Gobowen (7 miles)

Bus Route Lakelands School - stop 50m away

FC OSWESTRY TOWN

Founded: 2013 Nickname: Town

Club Contact Details

Ground: The Venue, Burma Road, Oswestry, Shropshire SY11 4AS **Club Colours:** All blue

HONOURS **League:** Mercain Regional Premier Division 2015-16.

FA Comps: None

10 YEAR RECORD

09-10		10-11		11-12		12-13		13-14		14-15		15-16		16-17		17-18		18-19	
						MerR1	7	MerR1	3	MerRP	5	MerRP	1	NWC1	15	NWC1	19	NWC1S	6
														FAV	1Q	FAV	1Q		

From Chester take the A483 towards Wrexham / Oswestry.
Once entering Oswestry at the 2nd round-a-bout turn left and left again to ground.

Nearest Railway Station Gobowen - 2.1km

Bus Route Park Crescent Jct stop - 325m away

MAINE ROAD

Founded: 1955 Nickname: Blues

Club Contact Details 0161 861 0344

Ground: Brantingham Road, Chorlton-cum-Hardy M21 0TT **Club Colours:** All sky blue.

HONOURS **League:** Manchester Amateur Sunday 1971-72. Manchester Premier 1982-83, 83-84, 84-85, 85-86.
North West Counties Division Two 1989-90.

FA Comps: None

10 YEAR RECORD

09-10		10-11		11-12		12-13		13-14		14-15		15-16		16-17		17-18		18-19	
NWCP	6	NWCP	13	NWCP	18	NWCP	2	NWCP	4	NWCP	15	NWCP	12	NWCP	15	NWCP	21	NWC1S	14
FAC	1Q	FAC	EPr	FAC	1Q	FAC	1Q	FAC	EP	FAC	EP	FAC	P	FAC	1Q	FAC	Pr	FAC	EP
FAV	1Q	FAV	1Pr	FAV	2Q	FAV	1P	FAV	2P	FAV	1P	FAV	2Q	FAV	1Q	FAV	1Q	FAV	2Q

M60 junction 7, A56 towards Manchester, A5145 (Stockport), A6010 Wilbraham Road to Chorlton. Left at traffic lights into Withington Road, first left into Brantingham Road. Ground on left.

Nearest Railway Station Chorlton (Manc. Metrolink) - 768m

Bus Route Manley Road stop - 170m away

NEW MILLS

Founded: pre1890 Nickname: The Millers

Club Contact Details 01663 747 435

Ground: Church Lane, New Mills SK22 4NP **Club Colours:** Amber & black

HONOURS **League:** Manchester Premier Division 1924, 26, 56, 63, 65, 66, 67, 68, 70, 71.
North West Counties Division Two 2007-08, Premier Division 2010-11.

FA Comps: None

10 YEAR RECORD

09-10		10-11		11-12		12-13		13-14		14-15		15-16		16-17		17-18		18-19	
NWCP	2	NWCP	1	NP1S	9	NP1N	3	NP1N	16	NP1N	21	NP1N	22	NWCP	20	NWC1	14	NWC1S	18
FAC	P	FAC	2Q	FAC	1Q	FAC	2Q	FAC	1Qr	FAC	P	FAC	P	FAC	EP	FAC	EP		
FAV	5P	FAV	2P	FAT	P	FAT	3Q	FAT	P	FAT	2Q	FAT	P	FAV	2Q	FAV	1Q	FAV	1Q

Via Buxton: Follow the A6 By-Pass, go straight through the roundabout, under railway bridge and about 1 mile further on turn right onto Marsh Lane (Past Furness Vale primary school), this road takes you straight to the ground. Coach drivers should proceed on the A6 a couple of miles turning right opposite the Swan.
From Chesterfield, take the A619 then the A623 and after the hair pin bend at Sparrow pit, proceed down the A623 turning right onto the A6 By-Pass, Follow directions as above.

Nearest Railway Station New Mills Central - 0.7km

Bus Route School (Bus Park) stop - 72m away

SANDBACH UNITED

Founded: 2004 Nickname:

Club Contact Details 07974 710 924

Ground: Hind Heath Road, Sandbach CW11 3LZ **Club Colours:** Blue and white

HONOURS **League:** None

FA Comps: None

10 YEAR RECORD

09-10	10-11	11-12	12-13	13-14	14-15	15-16	16-17	17-18	18-19
	StfSP	Ches2 5	Ches2 6	Ches2 2	ChesP 11	ChesP 4	NWC1 6	NWC1 5	NWC1S 7
									FAC EP
								FAV 2Q	FAV 1P

M6 to junction 17, take the A534 towards Sandbach, travel to traffic lights and go straight across, travel to round-a-bout, take the 2nd exit, travel to nest round-a-bout and take the 1st exit onto Crewe Road. Dtay on this roard for 1 mile and turn right at the traffic lights into Hind Heath Road ground approx ¾ mile on the right.

Nearest Railway Station Sandbach - 1.4km
Bus Route Salt Line Way stop - 260m away

ST MARTINS

Founded: 1897 Nickname: Saints

Club Contact Details 01691 684 840

Ground: The Venue, Burma Road, Parkhall, Oswestry, Shrops. SY11 4AS **Club Colours:** Yellow and black

HONOURS **League:** Oswestry & District 1919-20, 52-53, 54-55. West Shropshire Alliance Division Three 1973-74, Premier 89-90, 2000-01. Shropshire County Division One 1997-98, 2007-08, Premier 2009-10.

FA Comps: None

10 YEAR RECORD

09-10	10-11	11-12	12-13	13-14	14-15	15-16	16-17	17-18	18-19
ShrCP 1	WM2 2	WM2 5	WM1 16	WM1 14	WM1 3	WM1 6	WM1 8	WM1 4	NWC1S 11
								FAV 1Q	FAV 1Q

From Chester take the A483 towards Wrexham / Oswestry.
Once entering Oswestry at the 2nd roundabout turn left onto A495 and left again to the ground.

Nearest Railway Station Gobowen - 1.9 miles
Bus Route No.53, Oswestry/Gobowen/Ellesmere, bus stop is 500 yards from the ground.

STOCKPORT TOWN

Founded: 2014 Nickname: The Lions

Club Contact Details 0161 494 3140

Ground: Lambeth Grove, Woodley, Stockport SK6 1QX **Club Colours:** Red & white stripes

HONOURS **League:** None

FA Comps: None

10 YEAR RECORD

09-10	10-11	11-12	12-13	13-14	14-15	15-16	16-17	17-18	18-19
						NWC1 4	NWC1 10	NWC1 10	NWC1S 10
							FAV 1P	FAV 2Q	FAV 2Q

Stockport Town Football Club is located at Stockport Sports Village, Lambeth Grove Woodley, SK6 1QX. The ground lies a short distance from the M60. To reach us from the motorway, you should leave at Junction 25, which is signposted for Bredbury. Follow signs from here for the A560 towards Bredbury and Sheffield. Just after passing the McDonalds Drive-Thru, take a left at the traffic lights and proceed down Stockport Road towards Woodley, passing both Morrisons and Homebase on your left before passing under the railway bridge at Bredbury Railway Station.

Nearest Railway Station Woodley - 0.7km. Bredbury - 0.8km
Bus Route Hyde Road stop - 414m away

STONE OLD ALLEYNIANS

Founded: 1962 Nickname:

Club Contact Details 01785 761 891

Ground: Wellbeing Park, Yarnfield Lane, Yarnfield ST15 0NF **Club Colours:** White & black

HONOURS **League:** Mid Staffordshire Division Two 1965-66, 80-81, Division One 71-72, 74-75, 78-79.

FA Comps: None

10 YEAR RECORD

09-10	10-11	11-12	12-13	13-14	14-15	15-16	16-17	17-18	18-19
WM2 4	WM1 6	WM1 5	WM1 10	WM1 8	WM1 2	WMP 14	WMP 12	WMP 13	NWC1S 3
					FAV 2Q	FAV 2Q	FAV 2Qr	FAV 2Q	FAV 2Q

From the South Junction 14 (M6), take A34 towards Stone. Carry on A34 until you see Wayfarer Public House on left. Immediately after Pub, turn left towards Yarnfield. Follow road and once over the motorway bridge, continue for ½ mile. Ground is on left.

Nearest Railway Station Norton Bridge - 2.8km
Bus Route Labour-in-Vain Pub - stop 650m away

VAUXHALL MOTORS

Founded: 1963 Nickname: The Motormen

Club Contact Details 0151 327 2294

Ground: Rivacre Road, Ellesmere Port, South Wirrall CH66 1NJ **Club Colours:** White and navy

HONOURS
FA Comps: None
League: North West Counties Division Two 1988-89, 95-96, Division One 99-2000.

10 YEAR RECORD

09-10	10-11	11-12	12-13	13-14	14-15	15-16	16-17	17-18	18-19
Conf N 20	Conf N 17	Conf N 18	Conf N 12	Conf N 18	WCh1 4	WCh1 4	WCh1 8	WCh1 2	NWC1S 2
FAC 3Q	FAC 1Pr	FAC 2Qr	FAC 2Q	FAC 4Q					
FAT 2P	FAT 3Q	FAT 1Pr	FAT 3Q	FAT 3Q	FAV 1Q	FAV 2Q	FAV 2Q	FAV 1Q	FAV 2P

Leave M53 at junction 5 and take A41 towards North Wales. At first set of traffic lights (Hooton Crossroads) turn left into Hooton Green. At 'T' junction turn left into Hooton Lane. At next 'T' junction turn right into Rivacre Road. Ground is 200 yards on right.

Nearest Railway Station Overpool (1.4 miles) or Hooton (1.7)
Bus Route None near the ground

WEST DIDSBURY & CHORLTON

Founded: 1908 Nickname: West

Club Contact Details

Ground: End of Brookburn Road, Chorlton, Manchester M21 8FE **Club Colours:** White and black

HONOURS
FA Comps: None
League: Lancashire & Cheshire Amateur Division Two 1987-88, Division One 88-89
Manchester League Division One 2010-11.

10 YEAR RECORD

09-10	10-11	11-12	12-13	13-14	14-15	15-16	16-17	17-18	18-19
Manc1 2	Manc1 1	MancP 7	NCE1 3	NWCP 12	NWCP 16	NWCP 5	NWCP 6	NWCP 10	NWCP 19
				FAC Pr	FAC P	FAC EP	FAC P	FAC Pr	FAC EP
		FAV 2Q	FAV 1Q	FAV 1P	FAV 1P	FAV 1P	FAV 2Q	FAV 1P	FAV 1Q

From the M60 take junction 5 onto Princess Road towards city centre. Turn left at Christie Fields offices/Premier Inn onto Barlow Moor Road and continue past Chorlton Park to Chorlton bus station. Turn left into Beech Road, then 2nd left into Reynard Road and continue past the Chorltonville sign passing over 5 speed ramps as far as Brookburn Primary School. Turn left into Brookburn Road and continue to the end of the cul de sac, through the gateway and down the tarmac access which leads into the ground. From Stretford follow Edge Lane and turn right into St Clements Road at church. Continue through Chorlton Green and pass graveyard on left and then Bowling Green PH. Go past school and turn immediately right and continue to end of Brookburn Road as above. There is car parking within the grounds of the club, but restricted access for coaches.

Nearest Railway Station Chorlton Metrolink - 0.9 miles
Bus Route No.86 - Manchester Piccadilly Gardens to Barlow Moor road Bus Station.

WYTHENSHAWE AMATEURS

Founded: 1946 Nickname: The Ammies

Club Contact Details 0161 428 0517

Ground: Hollyhedge Park, Altrincham Road, Wythenshawe M22 4US **Club Colours:** Blue & white

HONOURS
FA Comps: None
League: Lancashire & Cheshire Division Two 1954-55, Division One 56-57, Premier 61-62.
Manchester Division One 1972-73, Premier 89-90, 92-93, 2002-03.

10 YEAR RECORD

09-10	10-11	11-12	12-13	13-14	14-15	15-16	16-17	17-18	18-19
MancP 2	MancP 8	MancP 9	MancP 13	MancP 8	MancP 7	MancP 10	MancP 2	MancP 2	NWC1S 4

From Manchester: Travel south towards the airport along Princess Road/Parkway (A5103), exit at Junction for Sharston, left at the 1st roundabout onto Altrincham Road (A560), straight ahead at 2nd roundabout, right at 3rd roundabout, through first lights then immediate leftat second lights, still on Altrincham Road, Ground is approx. ½ mile on the right.
From the South: The M56 to Junction 3A for Wythenshawe, right at the roundabout for Sharston onto Altrincham Road (A5600) then as above

Nearest Railway Station Benchill Metrolink
Bus Route 102, 103 to Altrincham Road from Mancheter City Centre

WYTHENSHAWE TOWN

Founded: 1946 Nickname:

Club Contact Details

Ground: Ericstan Park, Timpson Road, Wythenshawe M23 9LL **Club Colours:** Royal Blue

HONOURS
FA Comps: None
League: Sth Manc & Wythen Div.2 1949-50. Lancs & Ches Div.C 1958-59, Div.3 59-60, Div.2 64-65, Div.1 66-67, 68-69, 69-70, 70-71. Manc Div.2 73-74, Div.1 2011-12. Cheshire Div.2 2014-15, Div.1 15-16.

10 YEAR RECORD

09-10	10-11	11-12	12-13	13-14	14-15	15-16	16-17	17-18	18-19
Manc1 6	Manc1 4	Manc1 1	MancP 10	MancP 15	Ches2 1	Ches1 1	ChesP 7	ChesP 8	NWC1S 5
									FAV 1Q

From the M56 Junction 3, follow the sign for Wythenshawe Hospital. After 1 mile, after passing the Shell garage, turn left at the traffic lights then right at the next set of traffic lights. The ground is at the end of this road.
From the M60 (CounterClockwise), come off at Junction 5 and join the M56. Come off at the first exit which is Junction 3 and follow signs as above.
From the M60 (Clockwise), head towards the M56 at Junction 4 and come off at the first exit, Junction 2 towards Wythenshawe. At the roundabout go straight ahead towards Altrincham, and at the second roundabout take the second exit, again towards Altrincham. This will bring you to M56 Junction 3, go straight ahead at the roundabout and follow the directions above.
Nearest Railway Station Baguley tram stop is only a 5-10 minute walk from Ericstan Park.
Bus Route 11 / 11a / 109

PREMIER DIVISION INS: Grimsby Borough (P - NCE1), AFC Mansfield (Demotion - NPLE), Silsden (Tr - NWC1N),
OUTS: Hall Road Rangers (R - NCE1), Harrogate Railway Athletic (R - NCE1), Worksop Town (P - NPLSE).

AFC MANSFIELD

Nickname: The Bulls **Club Colours:** All red

Founded 2012

Club Contact Details 07973 491 739

Ground: Forest Town Stadium, Clipstone Road West, Forest Town, Mansfield NG19 0EE

Capacity: **Seats:** Yes **Covered:** Yes

Previous Names: None

Previous Leagues: Central Midlands North 2012-14. Northern Counties East 2014-18. Northern Premier 2018-19 (demoted due to ground grading).

HONOURS: FA Comps: None

League: Central Midlands North 2013-14.

10 YEAR RECORD

09-10	10-11	11-12	12-13	13-14	14-15	15-16	16-17	17-18	18-19
			CMN 2	CMN 1	NCE1 7	NCE1 2	NCEP 7	NCEP 3	NP1E 15
						FAC EP	FAC 3Q	FAC 3Q	FAC 2Q
				FAV 2Pr	FAV 5P	FAV 2Pr	FAV 4P	FAV 2P	FAT 2Qr

The ground is situated approximately 3 miles to the north east of Mansfield town centre and sits on the B6030 Clipstone Road West. Pedestrian access can be gained via gates on Clipstone Road West with vehicle access via Main Avenue and then the 2nd right, turning into Second Avenue.

Nearest Railway Station Mansfield - 2.7km

Bus Route School - stop 64m away

ALBION SPORTS

Nickname: Lions **Club Colours:** Yellow and royal blue

Founded 1974

Club Contact Details 0113 255 7292 contact@albionsports.co.uk

Ground: Throstle Nest, Newlands, Farsley, Leeds, LS28 5BE.

Capacity: 3,500 **Seats:** 1,750 **Covered:** 1,750

Previous Names: None

Previous Leagues: Bradford Amateur Sunday 1974-2007. West Riding County Amateur 2007-11.

HONOURS: FA Comps: None

League: Bradford Amateur Sunday Premier Division 1995-96, 99-2000, 00-01, 02-03, 04-05, 05-06. Northern Counties East Division One 2012-13.

10 YEAR RECORD

09-10	10-11	11-12	12-13	13-14	14-15	15-16	16-17	17-18	18-19
	WRCP 2	NCE1 4	NCE1 1	NCEP 6	NCEP 10	NCEP 11	NCEP 8	NCEP 14	NCEP 16
				FAC 1Q	FAC P	FAC EPr	FAC EPr	FAC 2Q	FAC Pr
			FAV 2Q	FAV 2Q	FAV 2Q	FAV 1Q	FAV 1Q	FAV 1Q	FAV 2Q

Come off the M606 at the roundabout. Take fourth exit onto Rooley Lane which is the A6177, continue to follow A6177 through two roundabouts then turn right onto Leeds Road A647. Continue to follow A647, go through roundabout. At next roundabout, take second exit onto Bradford Road B6157. Follow for ½ mile before turning left onto New Street then turn right onto Newlands. Ground on left.

Nearest Railway Station New Pudsey - 1km

Bus Route Town St Slaters Rd - stop 340m away

ATHERSLEY RECREATION

Nickname: Penguins **Club Colours:** Black and white

Founded 1979

Club Contact Details 07910 121 070 petegoodlad@yahoo.co.uk

Ground: Sheerien Park, Ollerton Road, Athersley North, Barnsley, S71 3DP

Capacity: 2,000 **Seats:** 150 **Covered:** 420 **Shop:** Yes

Previous Names: Athersley North Juniors 1979-86.

Previous Leagues: Barnsley Junior. Barnsley Association. Sheffield & Hallamshire County Senior 1997-2012.

HONOURS: FA Comps: None

League: Barnsley Junior 1986-87. Barnsley Association 91-92, 92-93, 94-95, 95-96, 96-97. Sheffield & Hallamshire County Senior Division Two 1997-98, Premier Division 1999-2000, 03-04, 04-05, 06-07, 08-09, 11-12

10 YEAR RECORD

09-10	10-11	11-12	12-13	13-14	14-15	15-16	16-17	17-18	18-19
SHSP 2	SHSP 2	SHSP 1	NCE1 2	NCEP 10	NCEP 13	NCEP 18	NCEP 10	NCEP 17	NCEP 17
					FAC P	FAC EP	FAC EP	FAC EP	FAC EP
				FAV 2P	FAV 2Q	FAV 1P	FAV 1Q	FAV 1Q	FAV 1Q

From North: M1 J38. Go down slip road, round roundabout and back under motorway. Take first left onto Haigh Lane, go to top of the hill and, at T-junction, turn right. At next T-junction, turn left onto Shaw Lane and go to bottom of hill. At T-junction of A61, turn right to Barnsley, go through first set of traffic lights and take first left onto Newstead Road. Follow to second roundabout and turn right onto Ollerton Road. Follow to second turn on left - do not take it but go past and entrance is between houses 123-125 Ollerton Road. Follow drive into ground.

Nearest Railway Station Barnsley - 3.4km

Bus Route Trowell Way - stop 80m away

BARTON TOWN

Nickname: Swans **Club Colours:** Sky blue & navy blue Founded 1995

Club Contact Details 01652 636 964 bartontown@gmail.com

Ground: Marsh Lane, Barton-on-Humber DN18 5JD

Capacity: 3,000 **Seats:** 240 **Covered:** 540 **Shop:** No

Previous Names: Barton Town Old Boys >2017.

Previous Leagues: Lincolnshire 1995-2000, Humber (Founder member) 2000-01, Central Midlands 2001-07.

HONOURS: FA Comps: None

League: Lincolnshire 1996-97. Central Midlands Supreme Division 2005-06.

10 YEAR RECORD

09-10		10-11		11-12		12-13		13-14		14-15		15-16		16-17		17-18		18-19	
NCE1	6	NCE1	2	NCEP	11	NCEP	8	NCEP	3	NCEP	5	NCEP	10	NCEP	20	NCEP	12	NCEP	11
FAC	1Q	FAC	P	FAC	Pr	FAC	P	FAC	P	FAC	P	FAC	P	FAC	EP	FAC	EP	FAC	EPr
FAV	1Q	FAV	2P	FAV	2P	FAV	1Q	FAV	2Q	FAV	2P	FAV	1Q	FAV	1Q	FAV	2Q	FAV	2P

Approaching from the South on A15, Barton is the last exit before the Humber Bridge. Follow the A1077 into the town. Turn right at the mini roundabout at the bottom of the hill into Holydyke. Take second left onto George Street and then into King Street. Marsh Lane is opposite the junction of King Street and High Street. The ground is at the end of Marsh Lane, on the right, immediately after the cricket ground.

Nearest Railway Station Barton-on-Humber - 0.5km

Bus Route Butts Road - stop 133m away

BOTTESFORD TOWN

Nickname: The Poachers **Club Colours:** Blue & yellow Founded 1974

Club Contact Details 01724 871 883 andrew.susworth@googlemail.com

Ground: Birkdale Park, Ontario Road, Bottesford, Scunthorpe DN17 2TQ

Capacity: 1,000 **Seats:** 90 **Covered:** 300

Previous Names: None

Previous Leagues: Lincolnshire 1974-2000. Central Midlands 2000-07.

HONOURS: FA Comps: None

League: Lincolnshire 1989-90, 90-91, 91-92. Central Midlands Supreme Division 2006-07.

10 YEAR RECORD

09-10		10-11		11-12		12-13		13-14		14-15		15-16		16-17		17-18		18-19	
NCE1	9	NCE1	17	NCE1	16	NCE1	15	NCE1	3	NCE1	8	NCE1	3	NCEP	12	NCEP	8	NCEP	12
FAC	EP	FAC	1Q							FAC	EP	FAC	P	FAC	P	FAC	1Q	FAC	1Q
FAV	1P	FAV	1Q	FAV	2Q	FAV	2P	FAV	1Q	FAV	1Pr	FAV	2Q	FAV	3P	FAV	2Q	FAV	1Pr

Exit M180 via M181-Scunthorpe. At circle (Berkeley Hotel), turn right into Scotter Road. At circle (Asda) straight ahead, 2nd left into South Park road then on to Sunningdale Road, turn right into Goodwood Road, Birch Park at end (right turn). Please note that Goodwood Road is not suitable for large vehicles. Instead, take 2nd right off Sunningdale Road which is Quebec Road, then 2nd right which is Ontario Road down to the bottom and ground is on the left.

Nearest Railway Station Scunthorpe - 3.6km

Bus Route Maple Leaf - stop 149m away

BRIDLINGTON TOWN

Nickname: Seasiders **Club Colours:** All red Founded 1918

Club Contact Details 01262 606 879 dom@bridtownafc.com

Ground: Neil Hudgell Law Stadium, Queensgate, Bridlington YO16 7LN

Capacity: 3,000 **Seats:** 500 **Covered:** 500 **Shop:** Yes

Previous Names: Original Bridlington Town folded in 1994. Greyhound FC changed to Bridlington Town.

Previous Leagues: Yorkshire 1924-39, 59-82, NCEL 1982-90, 99-2003, Northern Premier 1990-94, 2003-08

HONOURS: FA Comps: FA Vase 1992-93

League: Yorkshire League 1974-75. Northern Counties East 1989-90, 2001-02, 09-10, NPL Division One 1992-93.

10 YEAR RECORD

09-10		10-11		11-12		12-13		13-14		14-15		15-16		16-17		17-18		18-19	
NCEP	1	NCEP	3	NCEP	2	NCEP	3	NCEP	12	NCEP	8	NCEP	5	NCEP	3	NCEP	9	NCEP	3
FAC	1Q	FAC	P	FAC	P	FAC	EP	FAC	Pr	FAC	1Q	FAC	EP	FAC	2Qr	FAC	P	FAC	P
FAV	3P	FAV	1Pr	FAV	3P	FAV	1P	FAV	3P	FAV	1Q	FAV	2Q	FAV	1P	FAV	1P	FAV	1P

From South (Hull, Beeford, Barmston): Approach Bridlington on the A165, passing golf course on right and Broadacres Pub, Kingsmead Estate on left. Straight through traffic lights to roundabout by B&Q. Turn right. At traffic lights turn left and over the railway bridge. At roundabout bear left and carry on heading north up Quay Road. After traffic lights turn right into Queensgate. Ground is 800 yards up the road on the right.
From South and West (Driffield, Hull, York): Approach Bridlington on A614. (This was formally the A166). Straight on at traffic lights (Hospital on right) and follow the road round the bend. At roundabout straight across to mini roundabout and bear right (second exit). Follow road around to right and to traffic lights. Straight on. At next traffic lights (just after Kwikfit) turn left into Queensgate. Ground is 800 yards up the road on the right.
From North (Scarborough): Approach Bridlington (Esso garage on right) at roundabout turn left then at mini roundabout second exit. Follow road around to right and to traffic lights. Straight on. At next traffic lights (just after Kwikfit) turn left into Queensgate. Ground is 800 yards up the road on the right.

ECCLESHILL UNITED

Nickname: The Eagles **Club Colours:** Blue & white

Founded 1948

Club Contact Details 01274 615 739

Ground: Kingsway, Wrose, Bradford BD2 1PN

Capacity: 2,225 **Seats:** 225 **Covered:** 415

Previous Names: -

Previous Leagues: Bradford Amateur. West Riding County Amateur >1985

HONOURS: FA Comps: None

League: West Riding County Amateur 1976-77.
Northern Counties East Division One 1996-97.

10 YEAR RECORD

09-10	10-11	11-12	12-13	13-14	14-15	15-16	16-17	17-18	18-19
NCE1 16	NCE1 10	NCE1 6	NCE1 14	NCE1 4	NCE1 13	NCE1 13	NCE1 9	NCE1 4	NCEP 10
FAC EP		FAC 1Q	FAC 1Q		FAC EP				FAC EP
FAV 1Q	FAV 2P	FAV 2P	FAV 1Q	FAV 1P	FAV 1Q	FAV EP	FAV 1Q	FAV 1Q	FAV 1Q

M62 J26 onto M606, right onto Bradford Ring Road A6177, left on to A650 for Bradford at 2nd roundabout. A650 Bradford Inner Ring Road onto Canal Rd, branch right at Staples (Dixons Car showrooms on right), fork left after 30mph sign to junction with Wrose Road, across junction - continuation of Kings Rd, first left onto Kingsway. Ground is 200 yards on right.

Nearest Railway Station Frizinghall - 1.7km

Bus Route Kingsway Plumpton Drive - stop 97m away

GARFORTH TOWN

Nickname: The Miners **Club Colours:** Blue

Founded 1964

Club Contact Details secretary@garforthtown.net

Ground: Community Stadium, Cedar Ridge, Garforth, Leeds LS25 2PF

Capacity: 3,000 **Seats:** 278 **Covered:** 200

Previous Names: Garforth Miners 1964-85

Previous Leagues: Leeds Sunday Comb. 1972-76, West Yorkshire 1976-78, Yorkshire 1978-82, NCE 1982-2007. Northern Premier 2007-13.

HONOURS: FA Comps: None

League: Northern Counties East Division 1 1997-98

10 YEAR RECORD

09-10	10-11	11-12	12-13	13-14	14-15	15-16	16-17	17-18	18-19
NP1N 20	NP1N 13	NP1N 5	NP1N 22	NCEP 14	NCEP 14	NCEP 16	NCEP 15	NCEP 13	NCEP 14
FAC 1Q	FAC P	FAC 1Q	FAC 1Q	FAC EP	FAC P	FAC EP	FAC EP	FAC EP	FAC 1Q
FAT 1Q	FAT 1Qr	FAT 1Q	FAT P	FAV 1P	FAV 2Q	FAV 2P	FAV 1Q	FAV 1P	FAV 1P

From North: travel south on A1 and join M1. Turn off at 1st junc (47). From South: M1 to junc 47. From Leeds area: join M1 at junc 44 or 46 and turn off at junc 47. From West: M62 to junc 29, join M1 and off at junc 47. From junc 47: take turning signe 'Garforth' (A642). Approx. 200 yds turn left into housing estate opposite White House. (Cedar Ridge). Stadium at end of lane. From the South (alternative): A1, turn off on to A63 signposted 'Leeds' immediately after 'Boot & Shoe' Public House. At 1st roundabout turn right on to A656 and follow to next roundabout. Take 1st left on to A642 (Garforth) and follow from M1 junc 47.

Nearest Railway Station East Garforth - 1km. Garforth - 1.2km.

Bus Route Aberford Road - stop 128m away

GOOLE AFC

Nickname: The Vikings **Club Colours:** Red

Founded 1997

Club Contact Details 01405 762 794 (Match days) jumbosmith96@icloud.com

Ground: Victoria Pleasure Gardens, Marcus Road, Goole DN14 6SL

Capacity: 3,000 **Seats:** 300 **Covered:** 800 Yes

Previous Names: Replacement for Goole Town which folded at the end of the 1995-96 season.

Previous Leagues: Central Midlands 1997-98. Northern Counties East 2000-04. Northern Premier 2004-18.

HONOURS: FA Comps: None

League: Central Midlands 1997-98.
Northern Counties East Division One 1999-2000, Premier Division 2003-04.

10 YEAR RECORD

09-10	10-11	11-12	12-13	13-14	14-15	15-16	16-17	17-18	18-19
NP1S 18	NP1S 13	NP1S 10	NP1N 21	NP1S 13	NP1S 16	NP1S 19	NP1N 21	NP1N 22	NCEP 18
FAC P	FAC P	FAC Pr	FAC P	FAC P	FAC Pr	FAC 1Qr	FAC P	FAC P	FAC EP
FAT 1Q	FAT Pr	FAT 1Q	FAT Pr	FAT P	FAT 2Q	FAT 1Q	FAT 1Qr	FAT P	FAV 1Q

Leave the M62 at Junction 36 and follow signs to Goole Town Centre.
Turn right at the 2nd set of traffic lights into Boothferry Road. Turn right again after 300 yards into Carter Street.
The Victoria Pleasure Grounds is at the end of the road. 366 Metres from Goole Railway Station.

Nearest Railway Station Goole - 0.5km

Bus Route Goole Newport Street - stop 200m away

GRIMSBY BOROUGH

Nickname: The Wilderness Boys **Club Colours:** All red

Founded 2003

Club Contact Details 07890 318 054 nigelfanthorpe@hotmail.co.uk

Ground: The Bradley Football Development Centre, Bradley Road, Grimsby, DN37 0AG

Capacity: 1,000 **Seats:** 180 **Covered:** 200 **Shop:** Yes

Previous Names: None

Previous Leagues: Lincolnshire 2003-04. Central Midlands 2004-08.

HONOURS: FA Comps: None

League: None

10 YEAR RECORD

09-10		10-11		11-12		12-13		13-14		14-15		15-16		16-17		17-18		18-19	
NCE1	17	NCE1	15	NCE1	18	NCE1	17	NCE1	16	NCE1	22	NCE1	19	NCE1	4	NCE1	3	NCE1	1
				FAC	EP											FAC	1Q	FAC	1Q
FAV	1P	FAV	2Q	FAV	2Q	FAV	1Q	FAV	2Q	FAV	1Q			FAV	2Q	FAV	1Q	FAV	1Q

Head East along the M180/A180. Exit at the Great Coates Interchange. Travel back over motorway to first Roundabout. Take first exit and follow for two miles to Trawl Pub Roundabout. Take second exit, follow for two miles to Bradley Roundabout. Take second exit on to Bradley Road. The ground is approximately 500 yards on the left.

Nearest Railway Station Grimsby Town - 3km

Bus Route Crowland Avenue - stop 463m away

HANDSWORTH PARRAMORE

Nickname: Amber Parras **Club Colours:** Amber & black

Founded 1986

Club Contact Details 01909 479 955 johnbrunsmeer@hotmail.co.uk

Ground: The Windsor Foodservice Stadium, Sandy Land, Worksop S80 1UJ

Capacity: 2,500 **Seats:** 200 **Covered:** 750

Previous Names: Parramore Sports > 2010. Sheffield Parramore 2010-2011. Worksop Parramore 2011-14.

Previous Leagues: Sheffield & Hallam County Senior 1986-2008. Central Midlands 2008-11

HONOURS: FA Comps: None

League: Central Midland Supreme Division 2010-11.

10 YEAR RECORD

09-10		10-11		11-12		12-13		13-14		14-15		15-16		16-17		17-18		18-19	
CM Su	8	CM Su	1	NCE1	3	NCEP	7	NCEP	4	NCEP	7	NCEP	2	NCEP	4	NCEP	4	NCEP	8
										FAC	P	FAC	P	FAC	3Q	FAC	2Qr	FAC	P
										FAV	1P	FAV	3P	FAV	1P	FAV	1P	FAV	1P

From either the A1 or M1 J31, take the A57 towards Worksop. After approximately 7 miles, look out for the A60/Sandy Lane turnoff at the roundabout. Continue over two mini-roundabouts for ¾mile then turn left into the retail park and left again into the stadium car park.

Nearest Railway Station Worksop - 0.5km

Bus Route Grafton Street - stop 114m away

HEMSWORTH M.W.

Nickname: Wells **Club Colours:** Dark blue

Founded 1981

Club Contact Details 01977 614 997

Ground: Wakefield Road, Fitzwilliam, Pontefract WF9 5AJ

Capacity: 2,000 **Seats:** 100 **Covered:** 100 **Shop:** Yes

Previous Names: None

Previous Leagues: Doncaster Senior. West Riding County Amateur 1995-2008.

HONOURS: FA Comps: None

League: West Riding County Amateur Division One 1996-97.
Northern Counties East Division One 2015-16.

10 YEAR RECORD

09-10		10-11		11-12		12-13		13-14		14-15		15-16		16-17		17-18		18-19	
NCE1	7	NCE1	16	NCE1	8	NCE1	13	NCE1	17	NCE1	3	NCE1	1	NCEP	9	NCEP	6	NCEP	4
		FAC	Pr	FAC	EP	FAC	P					FAC	EP	FAC	P	FAC	EP	FAC	EPr
FAV	1P	FAV	1Q	FAV	2Q	FAV	1Q	FAV	2Q	FAV	2Q	FAV	2P	FAV	2P	FAV	2Q	FAV	2P

From East/West: M62 to J32 towards Pontefract then follow A628 towards Hemsworth. At Ackworth roundabout (Stoneacre Suzuki Garage), take a right on to the A638 Wakefield Road. Travel half a mile to next roundabout then take first exit. Travel one mile to crossroads and turn left into Fitzwilliam. Pass a row of shops on your right and turn left after the bus shelter before an iron bridge. To ground.
From North: A1 South to M62 then follow above directions.
From South: A1(M) North to A638 Wakefield Road. Travel to Ackworth Roundabout (Stoneacre Suzuki Garage) and go straight across and follow the A638 to the next roundabout. Take first exit then to crossroads. Turn left into Fitzwilliam and pass row of shops on your right. Turn left after bus shelter before iron bridge and carry on to the ground.

Nearest Railway Station Fitzwilliam - 0.4km

Bus Route Wakefield Road - stop 22m away

KNARESBOROUGH TOWN

Founded 1902

Nickname: The Boro **Club Colours:** Red and black

Club Contact Details 01423 548 896 knaresboroughtownafc@gmail.com

Ground: Manse Lane, Knaresborough, HG5 8LF

Capacity: 1,000 **Seats:** 73 **Covered:** 173

Previous Names: -

Previous Leagues: York. Harrogate & District. West Yorkshire.

HONOURS: FA Comps: None

League: York 1902-03, 03-04, 04-05, 08-09, 24-25, 25-26, 28-29, 33-34, 34-35, Div.2 51-52, Div.1 52-53. Harrogate & District 64-65, 65-66, 66-67. West Yorkshire Prem 2008-09. Northern Counties East Division One 2017-18.

10 YEAR RECORD

09-10	10-11	11-12	12-13	13-14	14-15	15-16	16-17	17-18	18-19
WYkP 4	WYkP 2	WYkP 3	NCE1 8	NCE1 6	NCE1 12	NCE1 8	NCE1 7	NCE1 1	NCEP 9
					FAC P				FAC 2Q
				FAV 2Q	FAV 1Q	FAV 1Q	FAV 1Q	FAV 2P	FAV 1Q

From West/South Leeds Area: A658 or A61 towards Harrogate. Join A658 southern bypass towards York. At roundabout with B6164, turn left to Knaresborough. Turn left at second roundabout and travel over river bridge. Manse Lane is first on right alongside garage; From East Leeds Area: A58 or A1 to Wetherby. Join B6164 to Knaresborough then as above. From East on A59 from A1: Turn right at first roundabout. Manse Lane is first turn left after speed restriction sign.

Nearest Railway Station Knaresborough - 1.5km

Bus Route Aspin Park School - stop 168 away

LIVERSEDGE

Founded 1910

Nickname: Sedge **Club Colours:** Sky blue

Club Contact Details 01274 862 108 simonturfrey@aol.com

Ground: Clayborn Ground, Quaker Lane, Hightown Road, Cleckheaton WF15 8DF

Capacity: 2,000 **Seats:** 250 **Covered:** 750 **Shop:** Yes

Previous Names: None

Previous Leagues: Bradford 1919-22. West Riding Co. Amateur 1922-27, 49-72. Spen Valley 1947-49. Yorkshire 1972-82.

HONOURS: FA Comps: None

League: West Riding County Amateur 1923-24, 25-26, 26-27, 64-65, 65-66, 68-69. Spen Valley 1948-49.

10 YEAR RECORD

09-10	10-11	11-12	12-13	13-14	14-15	15-16	16-17	17-18	18-19
NCEP 9	NCEP 17	NCEP 14	NCEP 15	NCEP 20	NCEP 18	NCEP 14	NCEP 11	NCEP 11	NCEP 13
FAC EP	FAC EP	FAC Pr	FAC EP	FAC EP	FAC EP	FAC EP	FAC EP	FAC 1Qr	FAC P
FAV 1P	FAV 2Qr	FAV 2Q	FAV 2Q	FAV 1P	FAV 2Q	FAV 1Q	FAV 2Q	FAV 1P	FAV 1Q

M62 J26, A638 into Cleckheaton, right at lights on corner of Memorial Park, through next lights and under railway bridge, first left (Hightown Rd) and Quaker Lane is approx ¼mile on left and leads to ground. From M1 J40, A638 thru Dewsbury and Heckmondwike to Cleckheaton, left at Memorial Park lights then as above. Buses 218 & 220 (Leeds - Huddersfield) pass top of Quaker Lane.

Nearest Railway Station Low Moor - 4.5km

Bus Route Hightown Road - stop 142m away

MALTBY MAIN

Founded 1916

Nickname: Miners **Club Colours:** Red and black

Club Contact Details 07795 693 683 john_mills_@hotmail.co.uk

Ground: Muglet Lane, Maltby, Rotherham S66 7JQ

Capacity: 2,000 **Seats:** 150 **Covered:** 300 **Shop:** No

Previous Names: Maltby Miners Welfare 1970-96

Previous Leagues: Sheffield Association 1919-29, 39-41, 45-49, 65-70, 72-73. Rotherham Minor 1929-36. Sheffield Amateur 1936-39. Rotherham Association 1942-45, 55-58. Yorkshire League 1949-55, 73-82. Doncaster & District 1958-65.

HONOURS: FA Comps: None

League: Sheffield Association 1925-26, 26-27.

10 YEAR RECORD

09-10	10-11	11-12	12-13	13-14	14-15	15-16	16-17	17-18	18-19
NCEP 16	NCEP 11	NCEP 18	NCEP 14	NCEP 15	NCEP 19	NCEP 7	NCEP 14	NCEP 5	NCEP 6
FAC EP	FAC P	FAC EP	FAC 1Q	FAC EP	FAC P	FAC 1Q	FAC EP	FAC EP	FAC 1Q
FAV 2Q	FAV 1Qr	FAV 1Q	FAV 2Q	FAV 1Q	FAV 2Qr	FAV 2P	FAV 1Q	FAV 2Q	FAV 2Q

Exit M18 at Junc 1 with A631.
Two miles into Maltby, right at traffic lights at Queens Hotel corner on to B6427 Muglet Lane.
Ground ¾mile on left.

Nearest Railway Station Rotherham Central - 8 miles

Bus Route Duke Avenue - stop 78m away

PENISTONE CHURCH

Nickname: None **Club Colours:** Black & white

Founded 1906

Club Contact Details penistonechurchfc@gmail.com

Ground: Church View Road, Penistone, Sheffield S36 6AT

Capacity: 1,000 **Seats:** 100 **Covered:** 150 **Shop:** Yes

Previous Names: Formed after the merger of Penistone Choirboys and Penistone Juniors.

Previous Leagues: Sheffield Junior 1906-07. Sheffield Amateur 1907-48. Hatchard League/Sheffield Association 1948-83. Sheffield & Hallamshire County Senior (Founder Members) 1983-14.

HONOURS: FA Comps: None

League: Sheffield & Hallamshire County Senior Division One 1993-94, 2000-01.

10 YEAR RECORD

09-10	10-11	11-12	12-13	13-14	14-15	15-16	16-17	17-18	18-19
Sh&HP 7	Sh&HP 3	Sh&HP 4	Sh&HP 3	Sh&HP 4	NCE1 9	NCE1 5	NCE1 6	NCEP 7	NCEP 2
						FAC EP	FAC EP	FAC 2Q	FAC P
				FAV 1Q	FAV 1Q	FAV 2Q	FAV 1P	FAV 1Q	FAV 1Q

From North: Leave M1 at J37, take 3rd exit A628 Manchester. After ½ mile take 2nd exit A628 Manchester. After approx 4 mile take 2nd exit A628 Manchester then at traffic lights turn left to Penistone Town Centre. On entering town centre after pelican crossing take 1st left Victoria Street then 2nd left. Ground is on your right. From South: Leave M1 at J35A at roundabout take 2nd exit A616 Manchester. At next roundabout take 2nd exit A616 Manchester then take 1st exit signed Penistone, Huddersfield A629. Follow this road through Wortley, Thurgoland and then take B6462 then travel under 3 railway bridges. Turn sharp left after 3rd bridge and follow road to the right onto Church View Road. Ground is approx 600 yards on left.

Nearest Railway Station Penistone - 0.2km

Bus Route Church View Road - stop 149m away

SILSDEN

Nickname: The Cobbydalers **Club Colours:** Red and black

Founded 1904

Club Contact Details 01535 958 850 john.silsdenfc@hotmail.co.uk

Ground: Keighley Road, Keighley Road, Silsden BD20 0EH

Capacity: **Seats:** Yes **Covered:** Yes

Previous Names: Reformed in 1980.

Previous Leagues: Craven & District. West Riding County Amateur. North West Counties >2019.

HONOURS: FA Comps: None

League: Craven Premier Division 1998-99. West Riding County Am. Division Two 99-2000, Division One 2000-01, Premier Division 2002-03. North West Counties Division One 2017-18.

10 YEAR RECORD

09-10	10-11	11-12	12-13	13-14	14-15	15-16	16-17	17-18	18-19
NWCP 14	NWCP 16	NWCP 12	NWCP 18	NWCP 15	NWCP 10	NWCP 21	NWC1 11	NWC1 1	NWCP 9
FAC P	FAC EPr	FAC Pr	FAC EP	FAC EP	FAC EP	FAC P	FAC EPr		FAC EP
FAV 2Q	FAV 1Q	FAV 1Q		FAV 2Q	FAV 1P	FAV 1P	FAV 2Q	FAV 2Q	FAV 3P

A629 Skipton to Keighley road, take A6034, ground in on the left after the golf driving range.

Nearest Railway Station Steeton & Silsden - 1.1km

Bus Route Keighley Road stop - 55m away

STAVELEY MINERS WELFARE

Nickname: The Welfare **Club Colours:** Blue & white

Founded 1989

Club Contact Details 01246 471 441 staveleyed@hotmail.co.uk

Ground: Inkersall Road, Staveley, Chesterfield, S43 3JL

Capacity: 5,000 **Seats:** 220 **Covered:** 400 **Shop:** Yes

Previous Names: None

Previous Leagues: Chesterfield & District Amateur 1989-91. Sheffield & Hallamshire County Senior 1991-93.

HONOURS: FA Comps: None

League: Sheffield & Hallamshire County Senior Division Three 1991-92, Division Two 1992-93. Northern Counties East Division One 2010-11.

10 YEAR RECORD

09-10	10-11	11-12	12-13	13-14	14-15	15-16	16-17	17-18	18-19
NCE1 4	NCE1 1	NCEP 5	NCEP 13	NCEP 17	NCEP 9	NCEP 8	NCEP 6	NCEP 16	NCEP 7
FAC Pr	FAC P	FAC 2Q	FAC Pr	FAC P	FAC 1Q	FAC EP	FAC EP	FAC P	FAC 2Q
FAV 1Q	FAV 4P	FAV SF	FAV 2P	FAV 3P	FAV 1Q	FAV 1Q	FAV 3P	FAV 1P	FAV 1Pr

From M1 J29A, follow the signs to Staveley.
Go past Poolsbrook Country Park and turn left onto Cemetery Road then right onto Inkersall Road.
The ground is on the left on the brow of a hill.

Nearest Railway Station Chesterfield - 5,4km

Bus Route Market Street - stop 156m away

THACKLEY

Founded 1930

Nickname: Dennyboys **Club Colours:** Red and white

Club Contact Details 01274 615 571 mick.lodge@btinternet.com

Ground: Dennyfield, Ainsbury Avenue, Thackley, Bradford BD10 0TL

Capacity: 3000 **Seats:** 300 **Covered:** 600

Previous Names: Thackley Wesleyians 1930-39

Previous Leagues: Bradford Amateur, West Riding County Amateur, West Yorkshire, Yorkshire 1967-82

HONOURS: FA Comps: None

League: West Riding County Amateur x5. West Yorkshire 1965-66, 66-67. Yorkshire Division Two 1973-74.

10 YEAR RECORD

09-10	10-11	11-12	12-13	13-14	14-15	15-16	16-17	17-18	18-19
NCEP 4	NCEP 8	NCEP 10	NCEP 10	NCEP 13	NCEP 12	NCEP 12	NCEP 5	NCEP 15	NCEP 15
FAC EP	FAC 2Q	FAC P	FAC EP	FAC EP	FAC EP	FAC 1Qr	FAC EP	FAC EP	FAC EP
FAV 1Q	FAV 2P	FAV 1P	FAV 3P	FAV 3P	FAV 1Q	FAV 1Qr	FAV 1Q	FAV 2Q	FAV 2P

Via M606 (or M62 Junction 27 and A650) – A6177 (Bradford Ring Road eastbound) and A658 (Harrogate Road) to Greengates traffic lights by (Roebuck Inn). Take 657 towards Shipley and at Thackley corner (beyond "S" bend) turn right into Thackley Road. At crossroads beyond Methodist Church , veer into Ainsbury Avenue and Dennyfield is 200 yards ahead. Alternatively via M621 (Junction 1). A6110 (Leeds Ring Road westbound), A647 to New Pudsey Station – then A6120 to Rodleyand via A657 as above.

Nearest Railway Station Baildon - 1.4km

Bus Route Thackley Road - stop 200m away

YORKSHIRE AMATEUR

Founded 1918

Nickname: Ammers **Club Colours:** White and red

Club Contact Details 0113 289 2886

Ground: Bracken Edge, Roxholme Road, Leeds, LS8 4DZ (Sat. Nav. LS7 4JG)

Capacity: 1,550 **Seats:** 200 **Covered:** 160 **Shop:** Yes

Previous Names: None

Previous Leagues: Yorkshire 1920-24, 30-82.

HONOURS: FA Comps: None

League: Yorkshire 1931-32, Division Two 1958-59, Division Three 1977-78.

10 YEAR RECORD

09-10	10-11	11-12	12-13	13-14	14-15	15-16	16-17	17-18	18-19
NCE1 14	NCE1 3	NCE1 19	NCE1 21	NCE1 19	NCE1 10	NCE1 11	NCE1 13	NCE1 2	NCEP 5
		FAC EP				FAC EP			
FAV 1Q	FAV 2Q	FAV 1P	FAV 2Q	FAV 1Q	FAV 1P	FAV 2Q	FAV 1Q		FAV 1Q

M621 J2: A58 (Wetherby), up Roundhay Road to Fforde Green Hotel. Keep to right hand lane, through lights, double back at next set of lights. When back at first set of lights, right into Harehills Lane. Go uphill to 6th right turn (Sycamore Ave). Left at top. Entrance on right; A1 Nth: Exit at Wetherby junction. A58 towards Leeds. At outer Ring Road, cross roundabout, road becomes dual carriageway (Easterly Road). Cross roundabout. Take right lane until 2nd lights then right into Harehills Lane and as above; A1 Sth: Exit on A64. At Ring Road roundabout, right and at next roundabout left into Wetherby Road and Easterly Road, then as above.

Nearest Railway Station Leeds - 3.5km

Bus Route Harehills Ln Roxholme Ave - stop 168m away

NCE DIVISION ONE INS: Brigg Town (P - LincP), Hall Road Rangers (R - NCEP), Harrogate Railway Athletic (R - NECP), North Ferriby (New), Retford (P - CMN), East Hull (NC from East Yorkshire Carnegie)

ARMTHORPE WELFARE

Founded: 1926 Nickname: Wellie

Club Contact Details armthorpe.welfare@hotmail.co.uk

Ground: Welfare Ground, Church Street, Armthorpe, Doncaster DN3 3AG **Club Colours:** All blue

HONOURS **League:** Doncaster & District Senior 1952-53, 53-54, 54-55, 56-57, 57-58, 60-61, 61-62, 64-65, 82-83, Div.3 77-78, Div.2 78-79, Div.1 81-82. NCE Div.1 Central 1984-85.

FA Comps: None

10 YEAR RECORD

09-10		10-11		11-12		12-13		13-14		14-15		15-16		16-17		17-18		18-19	
NCEP	3	NCEP	13	NCEP	13	NCEP	20	NCEP	18	NCEP	17	NCEP	19	NCEP	21	NCE1	16	NCE1	17
FAC	EP	FAC	P	FAC	1Qr	FAC	EP	FAC	EP	FAC	P	FAC	2Q	FAC	EP	FAC	EPr		
FAV	4Pr	FAV	2Pr	FAV	3P	FAV	2P	FAV	2P	FAV	2Q	FAV	1P	FAV	1Q	FAV	2Q	FAV	1Q

From the north, turn left at main roundabout in the centre of Doncaster and straight across at next roundabout on to Wheatley Hall Road. Turn right on to Wentworth Road, go to top of hill towards the Hospital on to Armthorpe Road. From the south, take the M18 to J4 on to the A630. At 2nd roundabout, turn left and proceed to next roundabout, then turn right. Ground 400 yards on left behind Netto.

Nearest Railway Station Kirk Sandall - 3.4km
Bus Route Beech Road - stop 13m away

BRIGG TOWN

Founded: 1864 Nickname: Zebras

Club Contact Details gavinduncanbriggtownfc@gmail.com

Ground: The Hawthorns, Hawthorn Avenue, Brigg DN20 8PG **Club Colours:** Black and white

HONOURS **League:** Midland Counties 1977-78. Northern Counties East Premier 2000-01. Lincolnshire League x8,

FA Comps: FAV 1995-96, 2002-03

10 YEAR RECORD

09-10		10-11		11-12		12-13		13-14		14-15		15-16		16-17		17-18		18-19	
NP1S	15	NP1S	4	NP1S	17	NP1S	13	NP1S	18	NP1S	22	NCEP	21	NCE1	14	NCE1	21	Lincs	2
FAC	1Q	FAC	2Qr	FAC	P	FAC	P	FAC	1Qr	FAC	P	FAC	EP	FAC	1Q				
FAT	2Q	FAT	P	FAT	1Q	FAT	P	FAT	2Q	FAT	Pr	FAV	1Q	FAV	1Q				

From M180 (Exit 4 - Scunthorpe East) A18 to Brigg. Leave Town via Wrawby Road, following signs for Airport and Grimsby. 100 metres after Sir John Nelthorpe Lower School, and immediately after bus stop/shelter, turn left into Recreation ground (signposted "Football Ground") and follow road into club car park.

*SAT NAV postcode DN20 8DT

Nearest Railway Station Brigg - 0.9km
Bus Route Vale of Ancholme School - stop 189m away

CAMPION

Founded: 1963 Nickname:

Club Contact Details 01274 491 919 campionsecretary@gmail.com

Ground: Scotchman Road, Bradford BD9 5AT. **Club Colours:** Red & black

HONOURS **League:** West Riding Amateur Division Two 1989-90, Division One 92-93.

FA Comps: None

10 YEAR RECORD

09-10		10-11		11-12		12-13		13-14		14-15		15-16		16-17		17-18		18-19	
		WRCP	3	WRCP	9	WRCP	12	WRCP	3	WRCP	3	WRCP	3	NCE1	8	NCE1	9	NCE1	2
																FAV	1Q	FAV	1Q

Leave M62 at J26 to join M606. Stay until end and join A6177 Ring Road (East). Go past Asda supermarket and at first roundabout take first exit and join A650. Go past Leisure Exchange. Road becomes A6037. After approx ¾m turn left into Station Road. At junction, turn left and join A6177. At second set of lights, turn right into Manningham Lane, then turn left into Oak Lane at next lights. At second set of lights, turn right into Heaton Road. Take second left into Scotchman Road. Ground is approx 500m on right.

Nearest Railway Station Frizinghall - 1.9km
Bus Route Toller Lane Masham Place - 109m away

DRONFIELD TOWN

Founded: 1998 Nickname: None

Club Contact Details secretary@dronfieldtownfc.com

Ground: Stonelow Playing Fields, Stonelow Road, Dronfield, S18 2EU **Club Colours:** Red & black

HONOURS **League:** Hope Valley B Div 2001-02, A Div 2002-03, Prem 2003-04. Midland Regional Alliance Division One 2005-06, Premier 2007-08. Central Midlands North 2012-13.

FA Comps: None

10 YEAR RECORD

09-10		10-11		11-12		12-13		13-14		14-15		15-16		16-17		17-18		18-19	
CM P	2	CM Su	7	CMN	3	CMN	1	NCE1	14	NCE1	19	NCE1	15	NCE1	19	NCE1	14	NCE1	6
										FAV	1P	FAV	1P	FAV	1Q	FAV	1P	FAV	2P

From South: At M1 J29, 2nd exit A617 Chesterfield. At roundabout, take 4th exit (A61 Sheffield), then 2nd and 3rd exits at next roundabouts to stay on A61. Leave at first slip road signed Sheepbridge/Unstone. Right towards Unstone/Dronfield. Go across 1st mini roundabout, then right and immediate left at next mini roundabout onto Green Lane. Up hill, 2nd right onto Stonelow Road and 1st right onto Shireoaks. From North: At M1 J30, 3rd exit towards Renishaw. Through Renishaw and Eckington then right for Coal Aston. Left at first mini roundabout, keep on Green Lane, down steep hill and left onto Stonelow Road then take 1st right onto Shireoaks.

Nearest Railway Station Dronfield - 0.9km
Bus Route Oakhill Road Bottom - stop 270m away

OUTS: Grimsby Borough (P - NECP), FC Bolsover (Tr - EMC), Emley (Tr - NWC1N), Harworth Colliery (R - CMN), Shirebrook Town (Tr - EMC)

EAST HULL

Founded: Nickname: Carnegie, EYC

Club Contact Details

Ground: Dunswell Park, Dunswell HU6 0AA **Club Colours:** Black & white

HONOURS

FA Comps: None

League: East Riding County Division One 2009-10, Premier Division 2013-14. Humber Premier Division One 2014-15

10 YEAR RECORD

09-10	10-11	11-12	12-13	13-14	14-15	15-16	16-17	17-18	18-19
ERC1 1	ERCP 7	ERCP 5	ERCP 4	ERCP 1	Humb1 1	HumbP 14	HumbP 5	NCE1 18	NCE1 13

Head North along the A1079 Beverley Road, Hull towards Dunswell. Dunswell Park can be found on the immediate right after exiting the large roundabout on Beverley Road as soon as you enter Dunswell and is prior to the petrol station.

Nearest Railway Station Hull (4 miles)

GLASSHOUGHTON WELFARE

Founded: 1964 Nickname: Welfare or Blues

Club Contact Details 01977 511 234 frankmaclachlan499@gmail.com

Ground: Glasshoughton Centre, Leeds Road, Glasshoughton, Castleford WF10 **Club Colours:** Royal blue & white

HONOURS

FA Comps: None

League: None

10 YEAR RECORD

09-10	10-11	11-12	12-13	13-14	14-15	15-16	16-17	17-18	18-19
NCE1 13	NCE1 7	NCE1 2	NCEP 16	NCEP 16	NCEP 21	NCE1 16	NCE1 11	NCE1 6	NCE1 11
		FAC Pr	FAC EP	FAC EP	FAC EP	FAC EPr			FAC EP
FAV 1Q	FAV 1Q	FAV 2P	FAV 2Q	FAV 2Q	FAV 1Q	FAV 1Q	FAV 2Qr	FAV 2Q	FAV 1P

Leave the M62 J32, signposted Castleford/Pontefract (A639). At the bottom of the slip road take the A656, taking carer to pick up the middle lane for Castleford. After approx. ¼ mile, bear left at the first roundabout and, after a further ¼ mile, left at the next roundabout on to Leeds Road. Ground is then 200 yards on the right.

Nearest Railway Station Glasshoughton - 0.8km

Bus Route Leeds Road Carr Lane - stop 83m away

HALL ROAD RANGERS

Founded: 1959 Nickname: Rangers

Club Contact Details hallroadrangers@live.co.uk

Ground: Hawroth Park, Dawson Drive, Hull HU6 7DY **Club Colours:** Blue & white

HONOURS

FA Comps: None

League: Yorkshire Division Three 1972-73, 79-80. Northern Counties East Division One 2016-17.

10 YEAR RECORD

09-10	10-11	11-12	12-13	13-14	14-15	15-16	16-17	17-18	18-19
NCEP 11	NCEP 14	NCEP 16	NCEP 22	NCE1 11	NCE1 17	NCE1 17	NCE1 1	NCEP 19	NCEP 20
FAC EP	FAC EPr	FAC Pr	FAC EP	FAC EP				FAC EP	
FAV 1P	FAV 1Q	FAV 2Q	FAV 1P	FAV 1Q	FAV 2Q	FAV 2Q	FAV 2P	FAV 2P	

M62 to A63, turn left before Humber Bridge onto A164 to Beverley, after approx. 5 miles turn right onto A1079. In 2 miles, turn left at large roundabout to ground 20 yards on right signed 'Dene Park Sports & Social Club'.

Nearest Railway Station Cottingham - 3.5km

Bus Route Larard Avenue - stop 158m away

HALLAM

Founded: 1860 Nickname: Countrymen

Club Contact Details 0114 230 9484 theclub@hallamfc.co.uk

Ground: Sandygate Road, Crosspool, Sheffield S10 5SE **Club Colours:** Blue and white

HONOURS

FA Comps: None

League: Hatchard 1902-03, 48-49. Sheffield Amateur 1922-23, 26-27. Sheffield Association 1949-50. Yorkshire Division Two 1960-61.

10 YEAR RECORD

09-10	10-11	11-12	12-13	13-14	14-15	15-16	16-17	17-18	18-19
NCEP 15	NCEP 19	NCE1 14	NCE1 12	NCE1 20	NCE1 14	NCE1 6	NCE1 5	NCE1 8	NCE1 3
FAC 1Q	FAC EP	FAC EP	FAC EP				FAC EP	FAC P	FAC EP
FAV 2P	FAV 1P	FAV 1Q	FAV 1Q	FAV 1Q	FAV 2Q	FAV 2P	FAV 2P	FAV 2Q	FAV 2P

A57 Sheffield to Glossop Rd, left at Crosspool shopping area signed Lodge Moor on to Sandygate Rd. Ground half mile on left opposite Plough Inn. 51 bus from Crucible Theatre.

Nearest Railway Station Sheffield - 4.5km

Bus Route Ringstead Crescent - stop 19m away

HARROGATE RAILWAY ATH.

Founded: 1935 **Nickname:** The Rail

Club Contact Details 01423 883 104 shep@therailfc.com

Ground: Station View, Starbeck, Harrogate, North Yorkshire HG2 7JA **Club Colours:** Red and green

HONOURS **League:** West Yorkshire 1953-54.
FA Comps: None Northern Counties East Division Two North 1983-84, Division one 1989-99.

10 YEAR RECORD

09-10	10-11	11-12	12-13	13-14	14-15	15-16	16-17	17-18	18-19
NP1N 17	NP1N 20	NP1N 21	NP1N 18	NP1N 13	NP1N 8	NP1N 21	NCEP 19	NCEP 20	NCEP 19
FAC 1Q	FAC P	FAC 1Q	FAC Pr	FAC Pr	FAC 2Q	FAC Pr	FAC 1Q	FAC Pr	FAC EP
FAT 1Q	FAT 3Q	FAT 1Q	FAT 1Q	FAT P	FAT P	FAT P	FAV 2Q	FAV 1P	FAV 1Q

From All Areas I would suggest using the M1 A1 Link Road heading North. Once on the A1 North stay on it until Junction 47. Exit at Junction 47 and take the 1st Exit at the Roundabout A59 heading towards Knaresborough and Harrogate. At the next Roundabout take the 3rd exit A59 Knaresborough. Stay on the A59 through Knaresborough and on towards Harrogate, after approx 1 mile from Knaresborough you will enter Starbeck. Proceed through Starbeck over the Railway Crossing. Station View is the 1st Right after the Railway Crossing. The Ground is at the far end of Station View. If you are coming from Harrogate towards Knaresborough on the A59 turn left immediately prior to pelican crossing just before the Railway Crossing.

Nearest Railway Station Starbeck - 0.1km
Bus Route Henry Peacock - stop 134m away

NORTH FERRIBY

Founded: 2019 **Nickname:** The Villagers

Club Contact Details 01482 634 601 info@northferriby.co.uk

Ground: The Dransfield Stadium, Grange Lane, Church Road, North Ferriby **Club Colours:** Green and white

HONOURS **League:** None
FA Comps: None

10 YEAR RECORD

09-10	10-11	11-12	12-13	13-14	14-15	15-16	16-17	17-18	18-19

From the West from Leeds toward Hull along M62 – A63 North Ferriby is approximately eight miles west of Hull. Leave A63 signposted North Ferriby via slip road. At roundabout, turn right (crossing over A63), turn left at next roundabout, pass through the traffic lights into North Ferriby. After the Duke of Cumberland public house, turn right at the crossroads onto Church Road, continue down past the church and Grange Lane is on the left. The ground is before the railway bridge.

Nearest Railway Station Ferriby - 5 min walk from the ground.

NOSTELL MINERS WELFARE

Founded: 1928 **Nickname:** The Welfare

Club Contact Details 01924 866 010 nostwellmwfc@hotmail.com

Ground: The Welfare Ground, Crofton Co. Centre, Middle Lane, New Crofton **Club Colours:** Yellow and black

HONOURS **League:** West Yorkshire Premier Division 2004-05
FA Comps: None

10 YEAR RECORD

09-10	10-11	11-12	12-13	13-14	14-15	15-16	16-17	17-18	18-19
NCEP 18	NCEP 9	NCEP 17	NCEP 18	NCEP 21	NCEP 15	NCEP 22	NCE1 22	NCE1 17	NCE1 5
FAC P	FAC EPr	FAC EP	FAC EP	FAC EP	FAC EP	FAC EPr	FAC EPr		
FAV 2Q	FAV 1Q	FAV 2Qr	FAV 1P	FAV 1Q	FAV 2Q	FAV 1Q	FAV 2Q	FAV 2Q	FAV 1Q

From M1 J39/M62 J31: Go towards Wakefield, take A638 Doncaster Road. After 2m, pass transport café/petrol station on right, go under bridge, turn right into Lodge Lane opposite Indian Restaurant. Go through Crofton Village, turn left at 'Slipper' PH, right on to Middle Lane, signposted 'Crofton Community Centre' about 400m; From A1: Take A638 towards Wakefield, turn left in Lodge Lane opposite Indian Restaurant, then as above.

Nearest Railway Station Streethouse - 2.9km
Bus Route The Slipper Pub - stop 372m away

OLLERTON TOWN

Founded: 1988 **Nickname:** The Town

Club Contact Details craigemb99@gmail.com

Ground: The Lane, Walesby Lane, New Ollerton, Newark NG22 9UT **Club Colours:** Red and black

HONOURS **League:** Notts Alliance Division Two 1992-93, Division One 95-96.
FA Comps: None Central Midlands Premier Division 2007-08.

10 YEAR RECORD

09-10	10-11	11-12	12-13	13-14	14-15	15-16	16-17	17-18	18-19
CM Su 3	CM Su 13	CMN 7	CMN 6	CMN 8	CMN 10	CMN 2	NCE1 17	NCE1 15	NCE1 16
FAV 2P	FAV 1Q	FAV 2Q	FAV 1Q	FAV 2Q		FAV 1Q	FAV 1Q	FAV 2Q	FAV 2Q

From north and south on the A614, take the A6075 from the Ollerton roundabout towards Ollerton Village. At the next roundabout, leave at the first exit and immediately take a left (30m from roundabout) onto Walesby Lane. After approx 600m, just after the school, the ground is on the left.

Nearest Railway Station Worksop
Bus Route Rosewood Centre - stop 214m away

PARKGATE

Founded: 1969 Nickname: The Steelmen

Club Contact Details 01709 826 600 brucebickerdike@hotmail.co.uk

Ground: Roundwood Sports Complex, Green Lane, Rawmarsh S62 6LA **Club Colours:** Red & black

HONOURS **League:** Northern Counties East Division One 2006-07.

FA Comps: None

10 YEAR RECORD

09-10		10-11		11-12		12-13		13-14		14-15		15-16		16-17		17-18		18-19	
NCEP	14	NCEP	2	NCEP	7	NCEP	9	NCEP	19	NCEP	16	NCEP	17	NCEP	17	NCEP	21	NCE1	8
FAC	EP	FAC	1Q	FAC	1Q	FAC	EP	FAC	EP	FAC	EP	FAC	EP	FAC	P	FAC	P	FAC	1Qr
FAV	2Q	FAV	2Q	FAV	3P	FAV	3P	FAV	2P	FAV	1Q	FAV	1Q	FAV	1Q	FAV	2Q	FAV	2Q

From Rotherham A633 to Rawmarsh. From Doncaster A630 to Conisbrough, then A6023 through Swinton to Rawmarsh.
Ground at Green Lane - right from Rotherham, left from Conisbrough at the Crown Inn.
Ground 800yds on right.

Nearest Railway Station Swinton - 3.4km
Bus Route Roundwood Grove - stop 57m away

RETFORD

Founded: 2015 Nickname: The Choughs

Club Contact Details 07766 700 536 kevswarfc@gmail.com

Ground: Babworth Road, Retford DN22 6NJ **Club Colours:** All blue

HONOURS **League:** Central Midlands North Division 2018-19

FA Comps: None

10 YEAR RECORD

09-10		10-11		11-12		12-13		13-14		14-15		15-16		16-17		17-18		18-19	
												CMN	7	CMN	6	CMN	5	CMN	1
														FAV	2Q				

From A1 North: Exit at Ranby Head towards Retford. 1st exit at 1st mini roundabout, 3rd exit at next roundabout on to West Carr Road. Ground entrance 100 yards on left under bridge on corner.
From A1 South: Exit at Babworth toward Retford. Turn right at junction onto Babworth Road. 1st exit at 1st mini roundabout, 3rd exit at next roundabout on to West Carr Road. Ground entrance 100 yards on left under bridge on corner.

ROSSINGTON MAIN

Founded: 1919 Nickname: The Colliery

Club Contact Details 01302 864 870 (MD) g-parsons2@sky.com

Ground: Welfare Ground, Oxford Street, Rossington, Doncaster DN11 0TE **Club Colours:** All blue

HONOURS **League:** Doncaster & District Senior 1944-45.
Central Midlands Premier Division 1984-85.

FA Comps: None

10 YEAR RECORD

09-10		10-11		11-12		12-13		13-14		14-15		15-16		16-17		17-18		18-19	
NCE1	10	NCE1	14	NCE1	7	NCE1	18	NCE1	13	NCE1	15	NCE1	20	NCE1	15	NCE1	13	NCE1	14
FAC	P	FAC	EP	FAC	EPr	FAC	EP												
FAV	1P	FAV	1Q	FAV	2Q	FAV	1Q	FAV	2Q	FAV	2Q	FAV	2Q	FAV	2Q	FAV	1P	FAV	2Q

Enter Rossington and go over the railway crossings.
Passing the Welfare Club, Oxford Street is the next road on the right.
The ground is at the bottom of Oxford Street.

Nearest Railway Station Doncaster - 6.4km
Bus Route Grantham Street - stop 149m away

SELBY TOWN

Founded: 1919 Nickname: The Robins

Club Contact Details 01757 210 900 toonarkley@yahoo.co.uk

Ground: Richard Street, Scott Road, Selby YO8 4BN **Club Colours:** All red

HONOURS **League:** Yorkshire 1932-33, 34-35, 35-36, 52-53, 53-54.
Northern Counties East Division One 1995-96.

FA Comps: None

10 YEAR RECORD

09-10		10-11		11-12		12-13		13-14		14-15		15-16		16-17		17-18		18-19	
NCEP	13	NCEP	15	NCEP	20	NCE1	16	NCE1	12	NCE1	11	NCE1	10	NCE1	10	NCE1	7	NCE1	9
FAC	P	FAC	P	FAC	EP	FAC	EP											FAC	Pr
FAV	1P	FAV	2Qr	FAV	1P	FAV	2Q	FAV	1Q	FAV	1P	FAV	1P	FAV	1Q	FAV	1Q	FAV	1Q

From Leeds, left at main traffic lights in Selby down Scott Rd, then 1st left into Richard St. From Doncaster, go straight across main traffic lights into Scott Rd then 1st left. From York, right at main traffic lights into Scott Rd and 1st left. NB: From Feb 14th, roadworks on the A19 mean there are different directions from York - on the A19 travel to the Greencore roundabout and take the first exit onto the Selby bypass. Travel over the new swing bridge and, at the first roundabout, take the third exit and continue to the traffic lights at Selby Abbey. Turn left and travel through town turning right at the end of town into Scott Road. Then, take first left.

Nearest Railway Station Selby - 0.8km
Bus Route Leisure Centre - stop 73m away

SKEGNESS TOWN

Founded: 1947 Nickname: Lilywhites

Club Contact Details 07960 756 351 thegrays23@hotmail.com

Ground: Wainfleet Road, Skegness, Lincolnshire PE25 2EL **Club Colours:** White & red

HONOURS **League:** Lincolnshire 1951-52, 55-56, 2006-07, 07-08, 13-14, 15-16, 16-17.

FA Comps: None

10 YEAR RECORD

09-10	10-11	11-12	12-13	13-14	14-15	15-16	16-17	17-18	18-19
Lincs 5	Lincs 5	Lincs 12	Lincs 8	Lincs 1	Lincs 2	Lincs 1	Lincs 1	Lincs 2	NCE1 15
								FAV 2Q	FAV 2Q

From A52: The ground is located on right hand side next to Pizza Hut.
From A158: Turn right at first set of traffic lights onto Lincoln Road. Go along road for around 700 yards then turn right onto Queens Road (Highwayman Pub on corner). Carry straight on up to junction of A52 (600 yards). Ground is in front of you to the right.

Nearest Railway Station Skegness ½ mile

SWALLOWNEST

Founded: 2006 Nickname: None

Club Contact Details 0114 287 2510 kent97@btinternet.com

Ground: Rotherham Road, Sheffield S26 4UR. **Club Colours:** All royal blue

HONOURS **League:** South Yorkshire Amateur Premier Division 2007-08.
Sheffield & Hallamshire County Senior Div.2 2008-09, Prem 10-11, 16-17.

FA Comps: None

10 YEAR RECORD

09-10	10-11	11-12	12-13	13-14	14-15	15-16	16-17	17-18	18-19
Sh&H1 2	Sh&HP 1	Sh&HP 3	Sh&HP 6	Sh&HP 5	Sh&HP 3	Sh&HP 7	Sh&HP 1	NCE1 11	NCE1 10
									FAV 1P

From M1 J31: Take 3rd exit from north or 1st exit from south. Go a mile on dual carriageway to a second roundabout. Take 3rd exit, Chesterfield Road. Go through traffic lights and Swallownest Miners Welfare is 50 metres on your left.

Nearest Railway Station Woodhouse - 2.2km
Bus Route Park Street - stop 61m away

WINTERTON RANGERS

Founded: 1930 Nickname: Rangers

Club Contact Details 01724 732 628 wintertonrangers2018@mail.com

Ground: West Street, Winterton, Scunthorpe DN15 9QF. **Club Colours:** All blue

HONOURS **League:** Yprkshire Division One 1971-72, 76-77, 78-79.
Northern Counties East Division Two 1989-90, Premier 2007-08.

FA Comps: None

10 YEAR RECORD

09-10	10-11	11-12	12-13	13-14	14-15	15-16	16-17	17-18	18-19
NCEP 6	NCEP 5	NCEP 6	NCEP 19	NCEP 22	NCE1 18	NCE1 8	NCE1 12	NCE1 10	NCE1 4
FAC 1Q	FAC 1Qr	FAC EP	FAC EP	FAC EP	FAC P				
FAV 1P	FAV 2P	FAV 2Q	FAV 2Q	FAV 2Q	FAV 1P	FAV 1Q	FAV 1Q	FAV 1Q	FAV 3P

From Scunthorpe - Take A1077 Barton-on-Humber for 5 miles.
On entering Winterton take 3rd right (Eastgate), 3rd left (Northlands Rd) and 1st Right (West St).
Ground 200 yards on left.

Nearest Railway Station Scunthorpe - 6¼ miles
Bus Route Post Office - stop 150m away

WORSBROUGH BRIDGE ATHLETIC

Founded: 1923 Nickname: The Briggers

Club Contact Details 01226 284 452 mrsmooth705@gmail.com

Ground: Park Road, Worsbrough Bridge, Barnsley S70 5LJ **Club Colours:** All red

HONOURS **League:** Barnsley Division One 1952-53, 58-59, 59-60.
Sheffield Association Division One 1965-66, 69-70.

FA Comps: None

10 YEAR RECORD

09-10	10-11	11-12	12-13	13-14	14-15	15-16	16-17	17-18	18-19
NCE1 18	NCE1 12	NCE1 11	NCE1 9	NCE1 10	NCE1 16	NCE1 21	NCE1 20	NCE1 19	NCE1 7
FAV 1P	FAV 2Q	FAV 2Q	FAV 1Q	FAV 2Q	FAV 2Q	FAV 1Q		FAV 1Q	FAV 2Q

From M1 J36: Travel on the A61 towards Barnsley. The ground is approx. 2 miles from the junc. next to Worsbrough Mill Museum Car Park; From Doncaster: Travel on the A635 to Stairfoot roundabout, then take 2nd exit (B6100) signposted 'Worsbrough' The ground is 2 miles from the roundabout as you reach the A61.

Nearest Railway Station Barnsley - 3.1km
Bus Route West Street - stop 29m away

DIVISION ONE INS: Billingham Town (P - NL2), Nothallerton Town (P - NL2), Thornaby (P - NL2).
OUTS: Dunston UTS - P - NPLNW)

ASHINGTON

Nickname: The Colliers **Club Colours:** Black & White

Founded 1883

Club Contact Details 01670 811 991 exec@ashingtonafc.com
Ground: Woodhorn Lane, Ashington NE63 9FW
Capacity: 2,000 **Seats:** 400 **Covered:** 900 **Shop:** Yes

Previous Names: None
Previous Leagues: East Northumberland. Northern Alliance 1892-93, 1902-14, 69-70. North Eastern 1914-21, 29-58, 62-64. Football League 1921-29. Midland 1958-60. Northern Counties 1960-62. Wearside 1964-65. North Regional 1965-68. N.P.L. 1968-69.

HONOURS: FA Comps: None
League: East Northumberland 1897-98. Northern Alliance 1913-14.
Northern Division Two 2000-01, 03-04.

10 YEAR RECORD

09-10		10-11		11-12		12-13		13-14		14-15		15-16		16-17		17-18		18-19	
NL 1	6	NL 1	8	NL 1	5	NL 1	7	NL 1	6	NL 1	13	NL 1	12	NL 1	16	NL 1	12	NL 1	16
FAC	EP	FAC	3Q	FAC	4Q	FAC	1Q	FAC	P	FAC	1Qr	FAC	P	FAC	EP	FAC	P	FAC	EP
FAV	2Q	FAV	4P	FAV	5P	FAV	4P	FAV	4P	FAV	2P	FAV	2P	FAV	2Q	FAV	1P	FAV	2P

Leave the A1 at the junction with the A19 north of Newcastle. Go along the A19 eastwards untio the next roundabout . Here take the second left (A189) signposted to Bedlington and Ashington.
Continue along A189 until reach Woodhorn roundabout, turn left onto A197. Turn left at first roundabout.
Just before the hospital car park entrance, turn right. Ground is on left.

Bus Route Wansbeck Hospital - stop 71m away

BILLINGHAM TOWN

Nickname: Billy Town **Club Colours:** All blue & white

Founded 1967

Club Contact Details
Ground: Bedford Terrace, Billingham, Cleveland TS23 4AE
Capacity: 3,000 **Seats:** 176 **Covered:** 600 **Shop:** No

Previous Names: Billingham Social Club
Previous Leagues: Stockton & District 1968-74 Teesside 1974-82

HONOURS: FA Comps: None
League: Stockton & District Division Two 1968-69. Teesside 1978-79, 81-82.
Northern Division Two 2018-19.

10 YEAR RECORD

09-10		10-11		11-12		12-13		13-14		14-15		15-16		16-17		17-18		18-19	
NL 1	19	NL 1	15	NL 1	17	NL 1	20	NL 1	23	NL 2	18	NL 2	11	NL 2	5	NL 2	9	NL 2	1
FAC	EP	FAC	EP	FAC	P	FAC	P	FAC	EP	FAC	EP					FAC	EP		
FAV	1Q	FAV	1P	FAV	2P	FAV	1Q	FAV	2Qr	FAV	2Q	FAV	1Q	FAV	4P	FAV	2P	FAV	1P

Leave A19 on A1027 signed Billingham.
Turn left at third roundabout, into Cowpen Lane.
Go over a railway bridge, then first left into Warwick Crescent, then first left again into Bedford Terrace (follow one-way signs) to the ground.

Nearest Railway Station Billingham - 0.4km
Bus Route Warwick Crescent - stop 136m away

BISHOP AUCKLAND

Nickname: Two Blues **Club Colours:** Light & dark blue/blue/blue

Founded 1886

Club Contact Details 01388 604 605
Ground: Heritage Park, Bishop Auckland, Co. Durham DL14 9AE
Capacity: 2,004 **Seats:** 250 **Covered:** 722

Previous Names: Auckland Town 1889-1893
Previous Leagues: Northern Alliance 1890-91, Northern League 1893-1988, Northern Premier 1988-2006

HONOURS: FA Comps: FA Amateur Cup 1895-96, 1899-1900, 1913-14, 20-21, 21-22, 34-35, 38-39, 54-55, 55-56, 56-57.
League: Northern League 1898-99, 1900-01, 01-02, 08-09, 09-10, 11-12, 20-21, 30-31, 38-39, 46-47, 49-50, 50-51, 51-52, 53-54, 54-55, 55-56, 66-67, 84-85, 85-86.

10 YEAR RECORD

09-10		10-11		11-12		12-13		13-14		14-15		15-16		16-17		17-18		18-19	
NL 1	13	NL 1	14	NL 1	8	NL 1	6	NL 1	8	NL 1	11	NL 1	8	NL 1	8	NL 1	19	NL 1	3
FAC	1Q	FAC	Pr	FAC	EP	FAC	2Q	FAC	1Qr	FAC	1Q	FAC	P	FAC	4Q	FAC	EPr	FAC	EP
FAV	2Q	FAV	1P	FAV	2Q	FAV	1P	FAV	2Q	FAV	2P	FAV	1P	FAV	2Q	FAV	2Q	FAV	1P

North: From junction 60 of the A1 follow the A689 to Bishop Auckland. Go straight across the next 2 roundabouts. At the 3rd roundabout turn left onto the A688 and straight across the next 2 roundabouts. At the following roundabout turn left at Aldi and then go straight across at the next roundabout. The stadium is 200 yards on your right. **South:** From junction 58 from the A1, take the A68 towards Bishop Auckland. At the West Auckland by-pass, turn right at the roundabout. Go straight across at the next roundabout and the stadium is located 500 yards on your left.

Nearest Railway Station Bishop Auckland - 2.2km
Bus Route Bus stops right outside the ground.

CONSETT

Nickname: Steelman **Club Colours:** All Red

Founded 1899

Club Contact Details 01207 588 886

Ground: Belle View Stadium, Ashdale Road, Consett DH8 7JP

Capacity: 4,000 **Seats:** 400 **Covered:** 1000 **Shop:** No

Previous Names: Consett Celtic 1899-1922.

Previous Leagues: Northern Alliance 1919-26, 35-37, North Eastern 1926-35, 37-58, 62-64, Midland 1958-60, Northern Counties 1960-62, Wearside 1964-70.

HONOURS: FA Comps: None

League: North Eastern 1939-40, Division Two 26-27. Northern Counties 1961-62. Northern Division Two 1988-89, 05-06.

10 YEAR RECORD

09-10	10-11	11-12	12-13	13-14	14-15	15-16	16-17	17-18	18-19
NL 1 10	NL 1 2	NL 1 15	NL 1 9	NL 1 11	NL 1 9	NL 1 7	NL 1 7	NL 1 9	NL 1 4
FAC Pr	FAC EPr	FAC EP	FAC EPr	FAC EP	FAC 1Q	FAC 2Q	FAC 2Qr	FAC 1Q	FAC 2Qr
FAV 1P	FAV 2Q	FAV 3P	FAV 2P	FAV 2Q	FAV 4P	FAV 2P	FAV 2Q	FAV 2Q	FAV 2Q

Take the A692 from the east into Consett. On the edge of the town, the A692 takes a left at a roundabout. Continue along the A692 for approx 100 yards, before turning right into Leadgate Road. Go along here for approx .25 mile, and turn right into Ashdale Road. There is a road sign for the Leisure Centre pointing into Ashdale Road. The ground is approx 200 yards along Ashdale Road on your right.

Bus Route Mortons Garage - stop 174m away

GUISBOROUGH TOWN

Nickname: Priorymen **Club Colours:** Red & white

Founded 1973

Club Contact Details 01287 636 925

Ground: King George V Ground, Howlbeck Road, Guisborough TS14 6LE

Capacity: **Seats:** Yes **Covered:** Yes

Previous Names: None

Previous Leagues: Middlesbrough & District 1973-77. Northern Alliance 1977-80. Midland 1980-82. Northern Counties East 1982-85.

HONOURS: FA Comps: None

League: Northern Alliance 1979-80.

10 YEAR RECORD

09-10	10-11	11-12	12-13	13-14	14-15	15-16	16-17	17-18	18-19
NL 2 5	NL 2 2	NL 1 16	NL 1 11	NL 1 4	NL 1 3	NL 1 3	NL 1 20	NL 1 15	NL 1 15
FAC 1Q	FAC EP	FAC P	FAC Pr	FAC 3Q	FAC EPr	FAC 1Qr	FAC P	FAC P	FAC 1Q
FAV 1P	FAV 2Q	FAV 1Pr	FAV 1P	FAV 1P	FAV 2P	FAV 2P	FAV 1P	FAV 1Q	FAV 1Pr

Turn off the A19 into the A174, then come off at the second junction, turning right onto the A172. Follow this round until roundabout with A1043, take left exit to join the A1043. Take right at next roundabout to join the A171. At second roundabout turn right into Middlesbrough Road (will be signposted towards Guisborough) then take left turning at traffic lights into Park Lane. Take first left into Howlbeck Road, and the ground is at the end of the road.

Bus Route Howlbeck Road - stop 49m away

HEBBURN TOWN

Nickname: Hornets **Club Colours:** Yellow & black

Founded 1912

Club Contact Details 0191 483 5101

Ground: Hebburn Sports & Social, Victoria Rd West, Hebburn, Tyne & Wear NE31 1UN

Capacity: **Seats:** Yes **Covered:** Yes

Previous Names: Reyrolles, Hebburn Reyrolles > 1988, Hebburn 1988-2000.

Previous Leagues: Tyneside. Northern Combination. Wearside 1960-89.

HONOURS: FA Comps: None

League: Tyneside1938-39. Northern Combination 1943-44. Wearside 1966-67.

10 YEAR RECORD

09-10	10-11	11-12	12-13	13-14	14-15	15-16	16-17	17-18	18-19
NL 2 16	NL 2 10	NL 2 3	NL 1 18	NL 1 22	NL 2 5	NL 2 10	NL 2 11	NL 2 2	NL 1 2
FAC P	FAC EPr	FAC 4Q	FAC P	FAC P	FAC EPr	FAC EP			FAC EP
FAV 2Q	FAV 2P	FAV 1P	FAV 2Q	FAV 1Q	FAV 1Q	FAV 1P	FAV 1Q	FAV 2Q	FAV 5P

Leave A1M on A194(M) (junction 65) and follow signs for Tyne Tunnel. Continue until fourth roundabout and turn left on to B1306 (Hebburn, Mill Lane). Right at traffic lights into Victoria Road. Ground 200 yards long this road on the left.

Nearest Railway Station Hebburn - 1km

Bus Route Victoria Road West - stop 74m away

NEWCASTLE BENFIELD

Nickname: The Lions **Club Colours:** Blue & white hoops/blue/blue

Founded 1988

Club Contact Details 07525 275 641
Ground: Sam Smiths Park, Benfield Road, Walkergate NE6 4NU
Capacity: 2,000 **Seats:** 150 **Covered:** 250

Previous Names: Heaton Corner House. Newcastle Benfield Saints.
Previous Leagues: Northern Alliance 1988-2003

HONOURS: FA Comps: None
League: Northern Alliance Division Two 1989-90, Division One 1994-95, 2002-03.
Northern Division One 2008-09.

10 YEAR RECORD

09-10	10-11	11-12	12-13	13-14	14-15	15-16	16-17	17-18	18-19
NL 1 5	NL 1 4	NL 1 12	NL 1 21	NL 1 14	NL 1 10	NL 1 18	NL 1 10	NL 1 7	NL 1 10
FAC P	FAC 2Q	FAC 1Q	FAC EP	FAC EP	FAC 2Q	FAC P	FAC 1Q	FAC 3Q	FAC 1Qr
FAV 2P	FAV 2Q	FAV 4P	FAV 2P	FAV QF	FAV 3P	FAV 1P	FAV 2P	FAV 4P	FAV 4P

Take the A1058 from either the Tyne Tunnel or central Newcastle. Turn off this road at the junction with Benfield Road. Turn south at this junction, and the Crosslings building will be on your left. Ground is around 400 metres on left, by taking the first turning after passing railway bridge. The ground is 100 yards along this road.

Nearest Railway Station Walkergate - 492m
Bus Route Benfield Comprehensive School - 96m away

NEWTON AYCLIFFE

Nickname: Aycliffe **Club Colours:** Blue & black

Founded 1965

Club Contact Details 01325 312 768
Ground: Moore Lane Park, Moore Lane, Newton Aycliffe, Co. Durham DL5 5AG
Capacity: **Seats:** Yes **Covered:** Yes

Previous Names: None
Previous Leagues: Wearside 1984-94, 2008-09. Darlington & District. Durham Alliance > 2008.

HONOURS: FA Comps: None
League: Darlington & District Division 'A' 2004-05. Durham Alliance 2007-08. Wearside 2008-09.
Northern Division Two 2010-11.

10 YEAR RECORD

09-10	10-11	11-12	12-13	13-14	14-15	15-16	16-17	17-18	18-19
NL 2 9	NL 2 1	NL 1 9	NL 1 17	NL 1 18	NL 1 18	NL 1 6	NL 1 9	NL 1 14	NL 1 12
		FAC EP	FAC EPr	FAC Pr	FAC EP	FAC 2Qr	FAC EPr	FAC P	FAC EPr
	FAV 1Q	FAV 1Qr	FAV 1P	FAV 1Q	FAV 1Q	FAT 5P	FAV 3P	FAV 1Q	FAV 1Qr

From North, leave the A1at junction 60, and travel west along the A689 towards Bishop Auckland. At the roundabout, turn left to join A167. Travel along here for a couple of miles, and at first traffic lights and turn right onto B6443 (Central Avenue). At first roundabout (Tesco's) turn left into Shafto Way then 3rd left into Gunn Way then right into Moore Lane.

Nearest Railway Station Newton Aycliffe - 2km
Bus Route Shafto Way - stop 271m away

NORTH SHIELDS

Nickname: Robins **Club Colours:** All red

Founded 1896

Club Contact Details
Ground: Daren Persson Staduim, West Percy Road, Chirton, North Shields NE29 6UA
Capacity: 1,500 **Seats:** Yes **Covered:** Yes

Previous Names: North Shields Athletic 1896-15, Preston Colliery 1919-1928, North Shields FC 1928-92. North Shields Athletic 1995-99.
Previous Leagues: Northern Combination. Northern Alliance. North Eastern. Midland. Northern Counties/North Eastern 1960-64. Northern 1964-89. Northern Counties East 1989-92. Wearside 1992-2004.

HONOURS: FA Comps: FA Amateur Cup 1968-69. FA Vase 2014-15.
League: Northern Alliance 1906-07, 07-08. North Eastern Div.2 28-29, Div.1 49-50. Northern Counties 60-61.
Northern Div.1 68-69, Div.2 2013-14. Northern Counties East Prem 91-92. Wearside 98-99, 01-02, 03-04.

10 YEAR RECORD

09-10	10-11	11-12	12-13	13-14	14-15	15-16	16-17	17-18	18-19
NL 2 6	NL 2 4	NL 2 8	NL 2 8	NL 2 1	NL 1 4	NL 1 5	NL 1 3	NL 1 8	NL 1 9
	FAC Pr	FAC EPr	FAC EPr	FAC EP	FAC Pr	FAC Pr	FAC P	FAC EPr	FAC EP
FAV 1P	FAV 1Q	FAV 1Q	FAV 1Q	FAV 1Pr	FAV F	FAV 4P	FAV 3P	FAV 3P	FAV 1Q

Continue north on the A19 after Tyne Tunnel. Take right exit at roundabout onto the A1058.
At next roundabout take third exit at Billy Mill, signed to North Shields.
At roundabout with A193, turn right, then take second left into Silkey's Lane.
Ground is 100 yards on left.

Nearest Railway Station Meadow Well - 392m
Bus Route Waterville Road - stop 29m away

NORTHALLERTON TOWN

Nickname: Town **Club Colours:** Black & white

Founded 1994

Club Contact Details 01609 778 337

Ground: The Calvert Stadium, Ainderby Road, Northallerton DL7 8HA

Capacity: **Seats:** **Covered:**

Previous Names: Northallerton FC 1994.

Previous Leagues: Harrogate & District.

HONOURS: FA Comps: None

League: Northern Division Two 1996-97.

10 YEAR RECORD

09-10	10-11	11-12	12-13	13-14	14-15	15-16	16-17	17-18	18-19
NL 2 8	NL 2 9	NL 2 9	NL 2 6	NL 2 7	NL 2 10	NL 2 8	NL 2 9	NL 2 4	NL 2 3
FAC EPr	FAC 1Q	FAC P	FAC EP	FAC EP	FAC P		FAC P		FAC EP
FAV 1P	FAV 1P	FAV 2Q	FAV 1Pr	FAV 1Q	FAV 1Q	FAV 1Q	FAV 2Q	FAV 2Q	FAV 2Q

Leave A1 at Leeming Bar (A684) and follow signs to Northallerton.
Approaching the town take the left turn B1333, signed Romanby.
Ground is on left after 50 yards in Romanby.

Nearest Railway Station Northallerton - 0.3km

Bus Route Chantry Road - stop 81m away

PENRITH

Nickname: Blues **Club Colours:** White and blue

Founded 1894

Club Contact Details 01768 865 990 ianwhite77@hotmail.com

Ground: The Stadium, Frenchfield Park, Frenchfield, Penrith CA11 8UA

Capacity: 1,500 **Seats:** 200 **Covered:** 1,000 **Shop:** No

Previous Names: Penrith 1894-2007. Penrith Town 2007-08. Back to Penrith after a merger with Penrith United.

Previous Leagues: North Eastern. Northern 1947-82. North West Counties 1982-87, 90-97. Northern Premier League 1987-90.

HONOURS: FA Comps: None

League: Northern Division Two 2002-03, 07-08.

10 YEAR RECORD

09-10	10-11	11-12	12-13	13-14	14-15	15-16	16-17	17-18	18-19
NL 1 14	NL 1 17	NL 1 19	NL 1 13	NL 1 13	NL 1 14	NL 1 14	NL 1 12	NL 1 17	NL 1 18
FAC P	FAC EP	FAC 1Q	FAC EP	FAC 3Q	FAC EP	FAC EP	FAC Pr	FAC Pr	FAC EP
FAV 3P	FAV 2Q	FAV 2Q	FAV 1P	FAV 1P	FAV 1Q	FAV 1Q	FAV 3P	FAV 2Q	FAV 2Q

Turn off M6 at junction 40 then onto dual carriageway to Appleby and Scotch Corner. Take the A686 (signposted Alston), for approximately half a mile. Then take a right turn (opposite Carleton Road), and follow the track running parallel with the A66. Turn left into the sports complex and follow the road to the far end.

Nearest Railway Station Penrith North Lakes - 2.3km

Bus Route Oak Road - stop 727m away

RYHOPE COLLIERY WELFARE

Nickname: Colliery Welfare **Club Colours:** Red & white

Founded 1892

Club Contact Details 07901 545 760

Ground: Ryhope Recreation Park, Ryhope Street, Ryhope, Sunderland SR2 0AB

Capacity: **Seats:** Yes **Covered:** Yes

Previous Names: None

Previous Leagues: Wearside >2012, 2013-14.

HONOURS: FA Comps: None

League: Wearside 1927-28, 61-62, 62-63, 63-64, 65-66, 2010-11, 11-12.

10 YEAR RECORD

09-10	10-11	11-12	12-13	13-14	14-15	15-16	16-17	17-18	18-19
Wear 2	Wear 1	Wear 1	NL 2 2	Wear 2	NL 2 6	NL 2 2	NL 1 17	NL 1 11	NL 1 11
						FAC EPr	FAC EPr	FAC EP	FAC EP
					FAV 2P	FAV 1Q	FAV 2P	FAV 2P	FAV 2Q

From the A1 exit onto A168 toward A19/Thirsk/Teesside. Continue onto A19. Take the A1018 ramp to Sunderland. At the roundabout, take the 2nd exit onto Stockton Rd/A1018. Continue to follow Stockton Road. Go through 2 roundabouts. Slight left onto Ryhope Street S/B1286. Ground will be on the left.

Nearest Railway Station Sunderland - 3.8km

Bus Route Ryhope Street-post office - stop 79m away

SEAHAM RED STAR

Founded 1973

Nickname: The Star **Club Colours:** Red & white

Club Contact Details
Ground: Seaham Town Park, Stockton Road, Seaham. Co.Durham SR7 0HP
Capacity: 500 **Seats:** Yes **Covered:** Yes

Previous Names: Seaham Colliery Welfare Red Star 1978-87.
Previous Leagues: Houghton & District 1973-74. Northern Alliance 1974-79. Wearside 1979-83.

HONOURS: FA Comps: None
League: Wearside 1981-82.
Northern League Division Two 2014-15.

10 YEAR RECORD

09-10	10-11	11-12	12-13	13-14	14-15	15-16	16-17	17-18	18-19
NL 2 12	NL 2 17	NL 2 20	NL 2 10	NL 2 4	NL 2 1	NL 1 9	NL 1 14	NL 1 18	NL 1 14
FAC EP	FAC EP			FAC EP	FAC P	FAC EPr	FAC EP	FAC EP	FAC P
FAV 2Q	FAV 1Q	FAV 1Q	FAV 1Q	FAV 1Q	FAV 3P	FAV 3P	FAV 1Q	FAV 2Q	FAV 1P

Leave A19 on B1404 slip road. Follow signs to Seaham/Ryhope. Turn right at traffic lights on to the B1285. Then left at Red Star social club approximately 200 yards after the traffic lights. There is a car park at the next roundabout behid their social club The ground is a short walk at the top of the park.

Nearest Railway Station Seaham - 1.5km
Bus Route Mill Inn (Stockton Rd) - stop 201m away

SHILDON

Founded 1890

Nickname: Railwaymen **Club Colours:** Red and black

Club Contact Details 01388 773 877
Ground: Dean Street, Shildon, Co. Durham DL4 1HA
Capacity: 4,000 **Seats:** 480 **Covered:** 1000

Previous Names: Shildon Athletic > 1923.
Previous Leagues: Auckland & Dist 1892-86, Wear Valley 1896-97, Northern 1903-07, North Eastern 1907-32

HONOURS: FA Comps: None
League: Northern 1933-34, 34-35, 35-36,36-37, 39-40, 2015-16, Division Two 2001-02.

10 YEAR RECORD

09-10	10-11	11-12	12-13	13-14	14-15	15-16	16-17	17-18	18-19
NL 1 2	NL 1 5	NL 1 10	NL 1 8	NL 1 3	NL 1 2	NL 1 1	NL 1 4	NL 1 3	NL 1 6
FAC P	FAC 3Q	FAC 1Qr	FAC 2Q	FAC P	FAC 4Qr	FAC EPr	FAC 2Q	FAC 4Q	FAC P
FAV QF	FAV 3P	FAV 1P	FAV SF	FAV 2P	FAV 3P	FAV 1P	FAV 4P	FAV 2P	FAV 3P

Leave A1M at junction 58. Follow A68 signed Bishop Auckland, turn right at roundabout onto A6072. At Shildon turn right at second roundabout (onto B6282) , then left into Byerley Rd (still the B6282). Right at Timothy Hackworth pub into Main St., then at the top of the bank, left into Dean Street.

Nearest Railway Station Shildon - 1.2km
Bus Route St. Johns Church - stop 149m away

STOCKTON TOWN

Founded 1979

Nickname: **Club Colours:** Yellow and blue

Club Contact Details 01642 604 915
Ground: Bishopton Road West, Stockton-on-Tees TS19 0QD
Capacity: **Seats:** Yes **Covered:** Yes

Previous Names: Hartburn Juniors 1979-2003.
Previous Leagues: Teeside 2009-10. Wearside 2010-2016.

HONOURS: FA Comps: None
League: Wearside 2012-13, 13-14, 14-15,15-16. Northern Division Two 2016-17.

10 YEAR RECORD

09-10	10-11	11-12	12-13	13-14	14-15	15-16	16-17	17-18	18-19
Tee1 4	Wear 10	Wear 3	Wear 1	Wear 1	Wear 1	Wear 1	NL 2 1	NL 1 6	NL 1 7
								FAC EP	FAC EPr
							FAV 2P	FAV F	FAV 3P

From A19: Take the A1027 (towards Stockton/Norton). Take 2nd Exit at first roundabout and 2nd Exit at the second roundabout. At lights (near Sainsburys) turn right onto Bishopton Road West.
From A66: Take the A135 (Yarm Rd) towards Stockton, at 2nd set of lights turn left onto A1027 (Hartburn Lane). Travel along past Park (on right) and as road bears left, get into filter to turn right to follow A1027. At roundabout take 2nd exit, at 2nd set of lights (near Sainsburys) turn left onto Bishopton Road West.

Nearest Railway Station Stockton - 1.4km
Bus Route Whitehouse Drive - stop 101m away

SUNDERLAND RYHOPE C.A.

Nickname: The CA **Club Colours:** Red & white

Founded 1961

Club Contact Details

Ground: Meadow Park, Beachbrooke, Stockton Rd, Ryhope, Sunderland SR2 0NZ

Capacity: 1,500 **Seats:** 150 **Covered:** 200

Previous Names: Ryhope Youth Club 1961-71. Ryhope Community Association 1971-99. Kennek Ryhope CA 1999-2007.

Previous Leagues: Seham & District. Houghton & District. Northern Alliance 1978-82.

HONOURS: FA Comps: None

League: None

10 YEAR RECORD

09-10		10-11		11-12		12-13		13-14		14-15		15-16		16-17		17-18		18-19	
NL 2	2	NL 1	13	NL 1	4	NL 1	22	NL 1	19	NL 1	16	NL 1	13	NL 1	11	NL 1	4	NL 1	5
FAC	EP	FAC	EP	FAC	P	FAC	EPr	FAC	EP	FAC	EPr	FAC	EPr	FAC	EP	FAC	2Q	FAC	Pr
FAV	1Q	FAV	1Q	FAV	1P	FAV	2P	FAV	1P	FAV	2P	FAV	5P	FAV	5P	FAV	2Pr	FAV	4P

From the A19, leave at the junction with the A690, but on that roundabout take the B1286 through Doxford Park. Continue along this road for some time (there are number of roundabouts), but there are signposts to Ryhope along this road. You will eventually come to a T-junction at the end of the B1286, and turn right onto the A1018. After 200 yards you will come to another roundabout, here take a right turn. Then take the next right into a new housing estate. There is a board at the entrance pointing you to Meadow Park, the home of R.C.A. The ground is at the far end of the estate.

Nearest Railway Station Seaham - 3.3km

Bus Route Ryhope Hospital - 94m away

THORNABY

Nickname: The Blues **Club Colours:** All blue

Founded 1980

Club Contact Details 01642 672 896

Ground: Teesdale Park, Acklam Road, Thornaby, Stockton on Tees TS17 7JU

Capacity: **Seats:** **Covered:**

Previous Names: Stockton Cricket Club 1965-1980, Stockton 1980-99 and Thornaby-on-Tees 1999-2000

Previous Leagues: Wearside 1980-85.

HONOURS: FA Comps: None

League: Northern Division Two 1987-88, 91-92.

10 YEAR RECORD

09-10		10-11		11-12		12-13		13-14		14-15		15-16		16-17		17-18		18-19	
NL 2	17	NL 2	14	NL 2	19	NL 2	19	NL 2	14	NL 2	7	NL 2	7	NL 2	16	NL 2	6	NL 2	2
												FAC	EP	FAC	EP				
FAV	2Q	FAV	1Q	FAV	1Q	FAV	1Q	FAV	1Q	FAV	1Q	FAV	1Q	FAV	1Q	FAV	2P	FAV	1Q

Turn off A19 onto A1130 and head towards Thornaby.
Continue along Acklam Road for about half a mile.
Ground is signposted from the main road- on the right up a track between houses after half a mile.

Nearest Railway Station Thornaby - 1.2km

Bus Route Millfield Close - stop 143m away

WEST AUCKLAND TOWN

Nickname: West **Club Colours:** Yellow and black

Founded 1893

Club Contact Details

Ground: Darlington Road, West Auckland, Co. Durham DL14 9AQ

Capacity: 2,000 **Seats:** 250 **Covered:** 250

Previous Names: West Auckland 1893-1914.

Previous Leagues: Wear Valley 1896-1900. South Durham Alliance 1900-05. Mid Durham 1905-08.

HONOURS: FA Comps: None

League: Northern 1959-60, 60-61, Division Two 1990-91.

10 YEAR RECORD

09-10		10-11		11-12		12-13		13-14		14-15		15-16		16-17		17-18		18-19	
NL 1	16	NL 1	6	NL 1	2	NL 1	4	NL 1	5	NL 1	5	NL 1	17	NL 1	18	NL 1	5	NL 1	8
FAC	EPr	FAC	2Q	FAC	EPr	FAC	2Qr	FAC	3Qr	FAC	Pr	FAC	P	FAC	P	FAC	EP	FAC	P
FAV	3P	FAV	2P	FAV	F	FAV	2P	FAV	F	FAV	2P	FAV	1P	FAV	2Q	FAV	4P	FAV	QF

Leave A1 at junction 58 on to the A68. Follow signs to W. Auckland/Corbridge.
On entering village, ground is behind factory on left side.
Ground is up a track on the left side of road next to Oakley Grange Farm.

Nearest Railway Station Bishop Auckland - 4.1km

Bus Route Oakley Grange Farm - stop 128m away

WHICKHAM

Founded 1944

Nickname: The Home Guard **Club Colours:** Black & white

Club Contact Details 0191 420 0186

Ground: Glebe Sports Club, Rectory Lane, Whickham NE16 4PF

Capacity: **Seats:** **Covered:**

Previous Names:

Previous Leagues: Northern Combination 1973-74. Wearside 1974-88.

HONOURS: FA Comps: FA Vase 1980-81.

League: Wearside 1977-78, 87-88. Northern Combination 1969-70, 72-73, 73-74. Northern Division Two 1994-95.

10 YEAR RECORD

09-10	10-11	11-12	12-13	13-14	14-15	15-16	16-17	17-18	18-19
NL 2 10	NL 2 6	NL 2 15	NL 2 16	NL 2 8	NL 2 8	NL 2 12	NL 2 6	NL 2 3	NL 1 17
FAC EP	FAC EP	FAC EP			FAC P	FAC EP			FAC EP
FAV 2P	FAV 1Q	FAV 1Q		FAV 4P	FAV 2P	FAV 2Q	FAV 1Q	FAV 1P	FAV 1P

From A1M take the A692 junction, and travel in the direction signed to Consett. At top of the back the road forks left towards Consett, but you should take the right fork along the B6317 to Whickham. Follow this road for 1.5 miles, left turn into Rectory Lane (B6316). Take first right into Holme Avenue, and then first left. The ground is at top of lane. More car parking can be found further along Rectory Lane, take the next right. Walk past the cricket pitch to access the football club.

Nearest Railway Station Metrocentre - 2.1km

Bus Route Whaggs Lane-south - stop 105m away

WHITLEY BAY

Founded 1897

Nickname: The Seahorses **Club Colours:** Royal blue & white

Club Contact Details 0191 291 3637

Ground: Hillheads Park, Rink Way, Whitley Bay NE25 8HR

Capacity: 4,500 **Seats:** 450 **Covered:** 650 **Shop:** Yes

Previous Names: Whitley Bay Athletic 1950-58

Previous Leagues: Tyneside 1909-10, Northern Alliance 1950-55, North Eastern 1955-58, Northern 1958-88. Northern Premier League 1988-00.

HONOURS: FA Comps: FA Vase 2001-02, 08-09, 09-10, 10-11.

League: Northern Alliance 1952-53, 53-54. Northern 1964-65, 65-66, 06-07. Northern Premier League Division One 1990-91.

10 YEAR RECORD

09-10	10-11	11-12	12-13	13-14	14-15	15-16	16-17	17-18	18-19
NL 1 3	NL 1 3	NL 1 6	NL 1 3	NL 1 10	NL 1 15	NL 1 16	NL 1 6	NL 1 16	NL 1 13
FAC 1Q	FAC 3Q	FAC 1Q	FAC P	FAC EP	FAC EPr	FAC 3Q	FAC EPr	FAC 1Q	FAC 2Q
FAV F	FAV F	FAV 5P	FAV 4P	FAV 3P	FAV 3P	FAV 2P	FAV 2Q	FAV 3P	FAV 2Q

Leave the A19 on the A191, and turn eastwards towards Whitely Bay. Continue along New York Road (A191) which then becomes Rake Lane (A191). Pass hospital on right & then into Shields Rd. and Hillheads Rd (both A191). Ground is to the right, floodlights can be seen from miles away! It is next to an ice rink.

Nearest Railway Station Monkseaton - 768m

Bus Route Whitley Bay Ice Rink - stop 149m away

NL DIVISION TWO INS: Carlisle City (Tr - NWC1N), Newcastle University (P - NAll), Sunderland West End (P - Wear).

BEDLINGTON TERRIERS

Founded: 1949 Nickname: Terriers

Club Contact Details 07935 840 277

Ground: Doctor Pitt Welfare Park, Park Road, Bedlington NE22 5DP **Club Colours:** All red.

HONOURS **League:** Northern Combination 1954-55. Northern Alliance 1966-67.
FA Comps: None Northern DivisioN Two 1993-94, Division One 97-98, 98-99, 99-00, 2000-01, 01-02.

10 YEAR RECORD

09-10	10-11	11-12	12-13	13-14	14-15	15-16	16-17	17-18	18-19
NL 1 7	NL 1 9	NL 1 7	NL 1 15	NL 1 20	NL 1 17	NL 1 22	NL 2 12	NL 2 16	NL 2 14
FAC P	FAC EP	FAC 2Q	FAC 1Q			FAC EPr	FAC EP		
FAV 2P	FAV 1P	FAV 2P	FAV 2P			FAV 2Q	FAV 1Q	FAV 2P	FAV 2P

From the A1:- Take the Seaton Burn turn off and at the roundabout take the second turn off (A1088). At the next roundabout, take the first turnoff to pass Aesica on the left. Straight over at the next roundabout. You will go down a dip, over a bridge and back up the other side, do not turn off, continue on the same road until you come into Bedlington. At the top of the bank there is a roundabout outside the Red Lion pub, go straight over. Down the hill there is another roundabout at the Netto shop, take the second turnoff (turning right). Follow the road past the Police station and Law courts and the road bends sharply to the left. Continue around the corner, take the second right. The ground is at the top of the street.

Nearest Railway Station Cramlington - 5km
Bus Route Allgood Terrace - stop 216m away

BILLINGHAM SYNTHONIA

Founded: 1923 Nickname: Synners

Club Contact Details 01642 530 203

Ground: Norton (Teesside) Sports Complex, Station Road, Norton TS20 1PE **Club Colours:** Green & white

HONOURS **League:** Teeside 1936-37.
FA Comps: None Northern 1956-57, 88-89, 89-90, 95-96. Division Two 86-87.

10 YEAR RECORD

09-10	10-11	11-12	12-13	13-14	14-15	15-16	16-17	17-18	18-19
NL 1 12	NL 1 12	NL 1 11	NL 1 12	NL 1 20	NL 1 20	NL 2 5	NL 2 3	NL 1 22	NL 2 10
FAC P	FAC P	FAC P	FAC EP	FAC Pr	FAC EP	FAC EPr	FAC 1Qr	FAC EP	FAC EPr
FAV 2Qr	FAV 5P	FAV 5Pr	FAV 3P	FAV 3P	FAV 1P	FAV 2Q	FAV 1P	FAV 2Qr	FAV 2Q

Norton Sports Complex is on Station Road, conveniently located just off the A19.
Travelling from the A19, take the A1027 signposted Norton. At the first roundabout take the 3rd exit onto Junction Road. At the first turning on the right take Station Road. The sports complex is on the left, just before the railway crossing.

Nearest Railway Station Billingham - 2.7km
Bus Route Jameson Road - stop 400m away

BIRTLEY TOWN

Founded: 1993 Nickname: The Hoops

Club Contact Details

Ground: Birtley Sports Complex, Durham Road, Birtley DH3 2TB **Club Colours:** Green & white

HONOURS **League:** Wearside Division Two 1994-95, Division One 2002-03, 06-07.
FA Comps: None

10 YEAR RECORD

09-10	10-11	11-12	12-13	13-14	14-15	15-16	16-17	17-18	18-19
NL 2 20	NL 2 13	NL 2 6	NL 2 17	NL 2 13	NL 2 17	NL 2 21	NAl P 8	NAl P 2	NL 2 13
FAC EPr		FAC EP	FAC P						
FAV 2Q	FAV 1P	FAV 2Q	FAV 1Q	FAV 2Q	FAV 2Q	FAV 1Q	FAV 2Q		FAV 2Q

BRANDON UNITED

Founded: 1968 Nickname: United

Club Contact Details 07555 586 305

Ground: Welfare Park, Rear Commercial Street, Brandon DH7 8PL **Club Colours:** All red

HONOURS **League:** Durham & District Sunday Div.2 1969-70, Div.1 73-74, 74-75, 75-76, 76-77.
FA Comps: None Northern Alliance Div.2 77-78, 78-79. Northern 2002-03, Div.2 84-85, 99-2000.

10 YEAR RECORD

09-10	10-11	11-12	12-13	13-14	14-15	15-16	16-17	17-18	18-19
NL 2 15	NL 2 19	NL 2 17	NL 2 18	NL 2 19	NL 2 22	NL 2 15	NL 2 14	NL 2 19	NL 2 19
FAC P	FAC EP								
FAV 1Q	FAV 2Q	FAV 2Q	FAV 1Q		FAV 1Q	FAV 1Q	FAV 1Q	FAV 1Q	FAV 1P

Leave A1 on A690, go through Durham and continue on A690. Once at 'Langley Moor' (you go under a railway bridge), turn right at the "Lord Boyne" pub.
After 100 yards take the next left.
Go up the road for approx half a mile, and turn right at the newsagents.
Take the next left, and Brandon's ground is up a small track.

Nearest Railway Station Durham - 4.4km
Bus Route S Lukes Church - stop 52m away

CARLISLE CITY

Founded: 1975 Nickname: Sky Blues

Club Contact Details 01228 523 777

Ground: Petteril Bank Road, Carlisle CA1 3AF **Club Colours:** All sky blue

HONOURS **League:** Northern Alliance Division One 1991-92.

FA Comps: None

10 YEAR RECORD

09-10	10-11	11-12	12-13	13-14	14-15	15-16	16-17	17-18	18-19
NAI P 10	NAI P 6	NAI P 5	NAI P 3	NAI P 2	NAI P 2	NAI P 3	NWC1 14	NWC1 11	NWC1N 6
							FAV 1Q	FAV 2Q	FAV 2Q

M6 to junction 42, follow the A6 towards Carlisle for approx 2 miles, turn left into Petteril Bank Road, by the Aldi Store. Follow this road for about 1 mile and turn right into the ground. Access road just before the railway bridge.

Nearest Railway Station Carlisle - 1.9km
Bus Route Ridgemount Road stop - 321m away

CHESTER-LE-STREET TOWN

Founded: 1972 Nickname: Cestrians

Club Contact Details 0191 388 7283

Ground: Moor Park, Chester Moor, Chester-le-Street, Co.Durham DH2 3RW **Club Colours:** Blue & white

HONOURS **League:** Washington 1975-76. Wearside 1980-81.
Northern Division Two 1983-84, 97-98.

FA Comps: None

10 YEAR RECORD

09-10	10-11	11-12	12-13	13-14	14-15	15-16	16-17	17-18	18-19
NL 1 20	NL 2 8	NL 2 12	NL 2 13	NL 2 11	NL 2 13	NL 2 3	NL 1 21	NL 2 14	NL 2 5
FAC P	FAC 1Q	FAC EPr	FAC EPr				FAC P	FAC EP	
FAV 2Q	FAV 2Q	FAV 1Q	FAV 2Q	FAV 1Q	FAV 2Q	FAV 1P	FAV 2P	FAV 1Q	FAV 1Q

Leave A1M at junction 63 and take the A167 towards Chester Le Street and Durtham. Keep going along this road for a couple of miles. You will go under a railway bridge, and as the road begins to climb, you will see the Chester Moor pub on your left. Turn into the pub and the ground is accessed along a track at the rear of the pub car park.

Nearest Railway Station Chester-le-Street - 2.2km
Bus Route Inn (A167) - stop 69m away

CROOK TOWN

Founded: 1889 Nickname: Black & Ambers

Club Contact Details 01388 762 959

Ground: The Sir Tom Cowie Millfield, West Road, Crook, Co.Durham DL15 9PW **Club Colours:** Amber and black

HONOURS **League:** Northern 1914-15, 26-27, 52-53, 58-59, 62-63, Division Two 2012-13.

FA Comps: FA Am C 00-01,53-54,

10 YEAR RECORD

09-10	10-11	11-12	12-13	13-14	14-15	15-16	16-17	17-18	18-19
NL 2 13	NL 2 12	NL 2 10	NL 2 1	NL 1 15	NL 1 22	NL 2 18	NL 2 17	NL 2 18	NL 2 9
FAC EP	FAC P	FAC EP	FAC Pr	FAC 1Q	FAC EP	FAC EP			
FAV 3P	FAV 2Q	FAV 2P	FAV 1Q	FAV 2P	FAV 2Q	FAV 1Q	FAV 1Q	FAV 2Q	FAV 2Q

Leave the A1 at Junction 62, and take the A690 towards Durham. Keep on this road through Durham, Meadowfield, Willington and Helmington Row. When you arrive in Crook town centre keep going straight ahead, as the A690 becomes the A689. The ground is situated on this road on your right, approximately 300 yards from the town centre.

Bus Route Bus stops right outside the ground

DURHAM CITY

Founded: 1949 Nickname: City

Club Contact Details 01388 745 912

Ground: Hall Lane, Willington, County Durham DL15 0QG **Club Colours:** Yellow/blue/yellow

HONOURS **League:** Northern 1994-95, 2007-08, Division Two 98-99.
Northern Premier Division One North 2008-09.

FA Comps: None

10 YEAR RECORD

09-10	10-11	11-12	12-13	13-14	14-15	15-16	16-17	17-18	18-19
NP P 20	NP1N 17	NP1N 9	NL 1 14	NL 1 9	NL 1 12	NL 1 20	NL 2 10	NL 2 11	NL 2 20
FAC 1Qr	FAC 1Q	FAC P	FAC 1Q	FAC Pr	FAC P	FAC EP	FAC EP		
FAT 1Q	FAT 1Q	FAT 2Qr	FAV 1P	FAV 2Q	FAV 2Q	FAV 1P	FAV 1Q	FAV 2Q	FAV 1Q

Bus Route Mortons Garage - stop 174m away

EASINGTON COLLIERY

Founded: 1913 Nickname: The Colliery

Club Contact Details

Ground: Memorial Avenue, Seaside Lane, Easington Colliery SR8 3PL **Club Colours:** All green

HONOURS **League:** Wearside 1929-30, 31-32, 32-33, 47-48, 48-49.

FA Comps: None

10 YEAR RECORD

09-10	10-11	11-12	12-13	13-14	14-15	15-16	16-17	17-18	18-19
Wear 7	Wear 2	NL 2 22	Wear 21	Wear 6	Wear 2	NL 2 6	NL 2 7	NL 2 10	NL 2 16
							FAC EP		
FAV 2Q	FAV 1P	FAV 2Q				FAV 2Q	FAV 1P	FAV 1Q	

Travelling on the A1 (M) take the A168 exit toward A19/Thirsk/Teeside. Continue onto A19 and after approximately 41 miles take the A182/B1283 exit toward Houghton-le-Sprng/Easington.
At the next roundabout take the first exit onto Hall Walks/B1283. Continue for just under 2 miles and then turn right onto Memorial Avenue.

Bus Route Black Diamond - stop 43m away

ESH WINNING

Founded: 1885 Nickname: Stags

Club Contact Details 07432 648 072

Ground: West Terrace, Waterhouse, Durham DH7 9BQ **Club Colours:** Yellow and green

HONOURS **League:** Northern 1912-13.
Durham & District Sunday 1978-79, 79-80, Division Two 72-73.

FA Comps: None

10 YEAR RECORD

09-10	10-11	11-12	12-13	13-14	14-15	15-16	16-17	17-18	18-19
NL 1 18	NL 1 21	NL 2 11	NL 2 20	NL 2 22	NL 2 20	NL 2 20	NL 2 21	NL 2 13	NL 2 17
FAC EPr	FAC EP	FAC EP	FAC P						
FAV 1Q	FAV 2Qr	FAV 2Q	FAV 2P	FAV 1Q	FAV 2Q	FAV 1Q	FAV 2Q	FAV 1Q	FAV 1Q

Leave the A1 at Junction 62, and take the A690 towards Durham. Keep on this road through Durham. Once you start to head down a bank on the A690, you will come to a roundabout. Take the right turn onto the B6302, which will be signposted towards Ushaw Moor. Keep on this road though Ushaw Moor (there is a staggered crossroads to negotiate), and carry on the B6302 into Esh Winning. Keep on going as the ground is not in Esh Winning, but the next village along, Waterhouses. When the road takes a sharp left you will see a track continuing straight ahead. The ground is along this track.

Bus Route Church (Russell St) - stop 158m away

HEATON STANNINGTON

Founded: 1910 Nickname: The Stan

Club Contact Details 0191 281 9230

Ground: Grounsell Park, Newton Road, Newcastle upon Tyne NE7 7HP **Club Colours:** Black & white stripes

HONOURS **League:** Northern Amateur 1936-37, 85-86. Tyneside Amateur 1983-84.
Northern Alliance Premier Division 2011-12, 12-13.

FA Comps: None

10 YEAR RECORD

09-10	10-11	11-12	12-13	13-14	14-15	15-16	16-17	17-18	18-19
NAl P 7	NAl P 5	NAl P 1	NAl P 1	NL 2 5	NL 2 9	NL 2 9	NL 2 4	NL 2 5	NL 2 4
						FAC P	FAC EP	FAC P	FAC EPr
					FAV 2Q	FAV 2Q	FAV 2Q	FAV 1Q	FAV 1Q

The ground is a short distance from the Freeman Hospital.
Take the coast road A1058 left for Newcastle, and eventually turn right at traffic lights onto Newton Road.
For satnavers postcode NE7 7HP.

Nearest Railway Station Longbenton - 1.2km
Bus Route No.38 stops at the ground

JARROW

Founded: 1894 Nickname:

Club Contact Details 0191 489 3743

Ground: Perth Green Community Assoc., Inverness Road, Jarrow NE32 4AQ **Club Colours:** Royal blue & white

HONOURS **League:** Northern Alliance 1898-99. Wearside 2016-17.

FA Comps: None

10 YEAR RECORD

09-10	10-11	11-12	12-13	13-14	14-15	15-16	16-17	17-18	18-19
Wear 10	Wear 5	Wear 6	Wear 9	Wear 10	Wear 12	Wear 8	Wear 1	NL 2 12	NL 2 11
									FAV 1Q

Take teh A168 exit off the A1 (M). Continue onto A19. After about 55 miles at the roundabout, take the 2nd exit and stay on A19. After 1.5 miles take the A194 slip road to South Shields. At the next roundabout, take the 4th exit onto Leam Lane/A194, then at the next roundabout, take the 4th exit and stay on Leam Lane/A194, then turn left onto Edinburgh Road and then at the roundabout, take the 2nd exit onto Perth Avenue. Turn left onto Inverness Road.

Nearest Railway Station Brockley Whins - 530m
Bus Route Imverness Road-youth club - stop 75m away

NEWCASTLE UNIVERSITY

Founded: Nickname:

Club Contact Details 07971 852 468

Ground: Prudhoe Town FC, Kimberley Park, Broomhouse Road NE42 5EH **Club Colours:** Blue

HONOURS **League:** Northern Alliance Premier Division 2017-18.

FA Comps: None

10 YEAR RECORD

09-10	10-11	11-12	12-13	13-14	14-15	15-16	16-17	17-18	18-19
NAI P 17	NAI 1 4	NAI 1 8	NAI 1 13	NAI 1 7	NAI 1 8	NAI 1 2	NAI P 2	NAI P 1	NAI P 2

Nearest Railway Station Newcastle

Bus Route No.686 stops 50 metres to the East on Broomhouse Road.

REDCAR ATHLETIC

Founded: 1993 Nickname:

Club Contact Details 01642 470 963

Ground: Green Lane, Redcar TS10 3RW **Club Colours:** Red and navy

HONOURS **League:** Wearside 2017-18.

FA Comps: None

10 YEAR RECORD

09-10	10-11	11-12	12-13	13-14	14-15	15-16	16-17	17-18	18-19
Wear 3	Wear 4	Wear 2	Wear 5	Wear 3	Wear 4	Wear 2	Wear 2	Wear 1	NL 2 7
									FAV 2Q

RYTON & CRAWCROOK ALBION

Founded: 1970 Nickname: The Albion

Club Contact Details 0191 413 4448

Ground: Kingsley Park, Stannerford Road, Crawcrook NE40 3SN **Club Colours:** Black & royal blue

HONOURS **League:** Northern Alliance Division One 1996-97.

FA Comps: None

10 YEAR RECORD

09-10	10-11	11-12	12-13	13-14	14-15	15-16	16-17	17-18	18-19
NL 1 17	NL 1 22	NL 2 18	NL 2 14	NL 2 21	NL 2 12	NL 2 16	NL 2 20	NL 2 17	NL 2 12
FAC 1Q	FAC EP	FAC EP							
FAV 2Q	FAV 2Q	FAV 2Q	FAV 2Q	FAV 2Q	FAV 1Qr	FAV 1Q	FAV 2Q	FAV 1Q	FAV 2Q

Leave the A1 at the south side of the River Tyne (A694). At the roundabout take the A695 (sign posted Blaydon). At Blaydon take the B6317 through Ryton to reach Crawcrook. Turn right at the traffic lights (sign posted Ryton/Clara Vale). Kingsley Park is situated approximately 500 meters on the right.

Nearest Railway Station Wylam - 1.5km

Bus Route Stannerford Road - stop 121m away

SUNDERLAND WEST END

Founded: Nickname:

Club Contact Details

Ground: Washington Road, Sunderland, Tyne & Wear SR5 3NS **Club Colours:** Red & white

HONOURS **League:** None

FA Comps: None

10 YEAR RECORD

09-10	10-11	11-12	12-13	13-14	14-15	15-16	16-17	17-18	18-19
Wear 14	Wear 19	Wear 4	Wear 8	Wear 9	Wear 8	Wear 3	Wear 10	Wear 3	Wear 2

TOW LAW TOWN

Founded: 1890 Nickname: Lawyers

Club Contact Details 01388 731 443

Ground: Ironworks Ground, Tow Law, Bishop Auckland DL13 4EQ **Club Colours:** Black & white

HONOURS
FA Comps: None
League: Northern 1923-24, 24-25, 94-95.

10 YEAR RECORD

09-10	10-11	11-12	12-13	13-14	14-15	15-16	16-17	17-18	18-19
NL 1 9	NL 1 18	NL 1 21	NL 2 11	NL 2 10	NL 2 21	NL 2 14	NL 2 13	NL 2 8	NL 2 15
FAC EPr	FAC EP	FAC EP	FAC EP	FAC EP					
FAV 1P	FAV 1P	FAV 2Q	FAV 1Q	FAV 1Q	FAV 1Q	FAV 2Q	FAV 1Q	FAV 2P	FAV 2Q

Leave the A1 at junction 58 and turn on to A68. Follow signs for Tow Law/Corbridge.
Ground is at far end of Tow Law on the left side.
The ground is situated on Ironworks Road, which is the first left after a sharp left hand bend on the A68 in Tow Law.

Nearest Railway Station Wolsingham - 4.8km
Bus Route Mart (Castle Bank) - stop 241m away

WASHINGTON

Founded: 1947 Nickname: Mechanics

Club Contact Details

Ground: New Ferens Park, Belmont, Durham DH1 1GG **Club Colours:** All red

HONOURS
FA Comps: None
League: North Eastern Division Two 1927-28. Washington Amateur 1955-56, 56-57,57-58, 58-59, 59-60, 61-62,62-63.

10 YEAR RECORD

09-10	10-11	11-12	12-13	13-14	14-15	15-16	16-17	17-18	18-19
NL 2 18	NL 2 16	NL 2 14	NL 2 12	NL 2 9	NL 2 2	NL 1 10	NL 1 19	NL 1 21	NL 2 18
			FAC EP		FAC P	FAC 2Qr	FAC 1Q	FAC EP	FAC EP
FAV 1Q	FAV 1P	FAV 1Q	FAV 2Q	FAV 2Q	FAV 2Q	FAV 2Q	FAV 1Q	FAV 2Q	FAV 2Q

WEST ALLOTMENT CELTIC

Founded: 1928 Nickname: Celtic

Club Contact Details 0191 250 7008

Ground: Druid Park, Callerton Lane, Woolsington NE13 8DF **Club Colours:** Green & white

HONOURS
FA Comps: None
League: Northern Am. 1956-57, 57-58, 58-59, 59-60, 81-82, 82-83, Div 2: 38-39.
Northern All. 1986-87, 90-91, 91-92, 97-98, 98-99, 99-2000, 01-02, 03-04. Northern Div 2 2004-05

10 YEAR RECORD

09-10	10-11	11-12	12-13	13-14	14-15	15-16	16-17	17-18	18-19
NL 1 15	NL 1 20	NL 2 7	NL 2 7	NL 2 2	NL 1 19	NL 1 19	NL 1 22	NL 2 15	NL 2 6
FAC Pr	FAC EP	FAC EPr	FAC P	FAC EP	FAC 1Q	FAC EP	FAC EP	FAC EP	
FAV 2Q	FAV 2Q	FAV 1Q	FAV 1Q	FAV 2Q	FAV 1P	FAV 2Q	FAV 1Q	FAV 1Q	FAV 2Q

2 minutes drive from the A1 and only 200yds from Callerton Parkway Metro.
There is free parking on site for circa 100 cars with extra parking at Callerton Park Metro

Nearest Railway Station Callerton Parkway - 116m
Bus Route Bus stops 70m from the ground.

WILLINGTON

Founded: 1906 Nickname: The Blue & Whites

Club Contact Details 01388 745 912

Ground: Hall Lane, Willington, Co. Durham DL15 0QG **Club Colours:** Blue & white

HONOURS
FA Comps: FA Amateur Cup
League: Northern 1913-14, 25-26, 29-30.

10 YEAR RECORD

09-10	10-11	11-12	12-13	13-14	14-15	15-16	16-17	17-18	18-19
Wear 19	Wear 14	Wear 5	Wear 2	NL 2 15	NL 2 11	NL 2 19	NL 2 18	NL 2 7	NL 2 8
FAV 2Q	FAV 1Q	FAV 2Q	FAV 2Q	FAV 2Q	FAV 1Q	FAV 1Q	FAV 1Q	FAV 2Q	FAV 1Qr

The ground is situated off the A690 in Willington.

Bus Route Police House - stop 129m away

PREMIER EAST INS: Axminster Town, Bovey Tracey, Brixham, Crediton United, Elmore, Honiton Town, Ilfracombe Town, Newton Abbot Spurs, Sidmouth Town, Stoke Gabriel and Torridgeside (all P - SWPD1E) Holsworthy and Plymouth Marjon (P - SWPD1W)), Dartmouth (P - SDLP), Torrington (P - NDevP).

AXMINSTER TOWN

Founded: 1903 Nickname: The Tigers

Club Contact Details martinkeightly@gmail.com

Ground: Tiger Way EX13 5HN **Club Colours:** Amber and black

HONOURS **League:**

FA Comps: None

10 YEAR RECORD

09-10	10-11	11-12	12-13	13-14	14-15	15-16	16-17	17-18	18-19
SW1E 15	SW1E 16	SW1E 16	SW1E 11	SW1E 12	SW1E 18	SW1E 8	SW1E 6	SW1E 10	SW1E 6
								FAV 1Q	FAV 2Q

From B3261 into Axminster, at roundabout proceed onto A358 going through town centre and takings signs for Chard. Continue past Cloakham lawns Sports Centre then take the next left.

BOVEY TRACEY

Founded: 1950 Nickname: Moorlanders

Club Contact Details boveytraceyafc@aol.com

Ground: Mill Marsh Park, Ashburton Rd, Bovey TQ13 9FF **Club Colours:** Red and black

HONOURS **League:**

FA Comps: None

10 YEAR RECORD

09-10	10-11	11-12	12-13	13-14	14-15	15-16	16-17	17-18	18-19
SWPP 17	SWPP 17	SWPP 16	SWPP 15	SWPP 15	SWPP 19	SW1E 16	SW1E 13	SW1E 3	SW1E 2

Western Counties Roofing (Mill Marsh Park), Ashburton Road, Bovey Tracey TQ13 9FF. Tel: 01626 832 780.
Coming off the A38 East or Westbound at Drumbridges take the Bovey Tracey turn-off, straight through the lights at Heathfield. Next roundabout take 2nd exit, next roundabout take 3rd exit, then left, 35 yards, follow road to bottom of drive then enter through gate.

BRIXHAM AFC

Founded: 2012 Nickname: The Blues

Club Contact Details jwharris@talktalk.net

Ground: Wall Park Road TQ5 9UE **Club Colours:** All blue

HONOURS **League:** None

FA Comps: None

10 YEAR RECORD

09-10	10-11	11-12	12-13	13-14	14-15	15-16	16-17	17-18	18-19
			SDevP 4	SDevP 2	SW1E 9	SW1E 9	SW1E 5	SW1E 13	SW1E 3

When entering town take Right fork into Monksbridge Road. At roundabout take first left into Greenover Road and follow to lights at bottom of hill. Go straight ahead and up Rea Barn Hill past rugby club and turn right onto Wall Park Road, ground half a mile on Right.

CREDITON UNITED

Founded: 1910 Nickname: The Kirton

Club Contact Details 01363 774 671

Ground: Lords Meadow, Commercial Road, Crediton EX17 1ER **Club Colours:** All yellow

HONOURS **League:** None

FA Comps: None

10 YEAR RECORD

09-10	10-11	11-12	12-13	13-14	14-15	15-16	16-17	17-18	18-19
SW1E 14	SW1E 15	SW1E 4	SW1E 16	SW1E 6	SW1E 11	SW1E 14	SW1E 8	SW1E 6	SW1E 10
	FAV 1Qr	FAV 2Q	FAV 1Q		FAV 1P	FAV 2Q	FAV 1Q	FAV 1P	FAV 1Q

A377 from Exeter, turn right at the new roundabout at Tesco, taking the sign for Lords Meadow Industrial Estate, when you reach the Sports centre turn right and use the car park on the left.

CULLOMPTON RANGERS

Founded: 1945 Nickname: The Cully

Club Contact Details 01884 33090 alanslark1@gmail.com

Ground: Speeds Meadow, Cullompton EX15 1DW **Club Colours:** Red & black

HONOURS **League:** East Devon Senior Division One 1950-51, 78-79. Devon & Exeter Premier Division 1961-62, 63-64.

FA Comps: None

10 YEAR RECORD

09-10		10-11		11-12		12-13		13-14		14-15		15-16		16-17		17-18		18-19	
SWPP	18	SWPP	16	SWPP	15	SWPP	17	SWPP	18	SWPP	12	SWPP	13	SWPP	9	SWPP	13	SWPP	8
FAC	EP																		
FAV	2Q	FAV	2Q	FAV	2P	FAV	2Q	FAV	2Q	FAV	1Q	FAV	1Q	FAV	2Pr	FAV	2P	FAV	2Q

Leave M5 at junction 28, left at Town Centre, at Meadow Lane turn left past Sports Centre, at end of road turn right, then in 100 yards turn left into ground at end of lane.

DARTMOUTH AFC

Founded: 1999 Nickname: The Darts

Club Contact Details 01803 832 902

Ground: Longcross, Dartmouth TQ5 9LW **Club Colours:** Red & white

HONOURS **League:** Devon 2001-02, 02-03, 06-07. South Devon Division One 2013-14.

FA Comps: None

10 YEAR RECORD

09-10		10-11		11-12		12-13		13-14		14-15		15-16		16-17		17-18		18-19	
SWPP	15	SWPP	18	SWPP	14	SDev1	4	SDev1	1	SDevP	3	SDevP	2	SDevP	5	SDevP	6	SDevP	3

From Townstal Road, on entering the town go past Lidl on your right and the ground is the next right.

ELBURTON VILLA

Founded: 1982 Nickname: The Villa

Club Contact Details 01752 480 025 pope.n@sky.com

Ground: Haye Road, Elburton, Plymouth PL9 8HS **Club Colours:** Red & white stripes

HONOURS **League:** Plymouth & District Division One 1990-91.

FA Comps: None

10 YEAR RECORD

09-10		10-11		11-12		12-13		13-14		14-15		15-16		16-17		17-18		18-19	
SWPP	13	SWPP	19	SWPP	11	SWPP	3	SWPP	12	SWPP	18	SWPP	20	SW1W	2	SW1W	3	SWPP	15
										FAV	1Q	FAV	1Q	FAV	1Q	FAV	1Q	FAV	1P

From Plymouth take the A379 Kingsbridge Road, at 3rd roundabout turn left into Haye Road, (signed Saltram House) and ground is 50 yards on the left.

ELMORE

Founded: 1947 Nickname: Eagles

Club Contact Details 01884 252 341

Ground: Horsdon Park, Heathcoat Way, Tiverton, Devon EX16 6DB **Club Colours:** All green

HONOURS **League:** Devon & Exeter Premier Division 2017-18.

FA Comps: None

10 YEAR RECORD

09-10		10-11		11-12		12-13		13-14		14-15		15-16		16-17		17-18		18-19	
West1	14	West1	19	West1	14	West1	12	SWPP	17	SWPP	Exp	D&EP	5	D&EP	3	D&EP	1	SW1E	5
FAC	EP	FAC	EP			FAC	EP												
FAV	2Q	FAV	1Q	FAV	2Q	FAV	1Q	FAV	1Qr	FAV	1Q								

From Junction 27 of the M5 take the North Devon Link Road. Leave at the first exit (Gornhay Cross) Left at the top of the slip road, then straight over roundabout by Mcdonald's and then ground is on your Right.

HOLSWORTHY AFC

Founded: 1891 Nickname: The Magpies

Club Contact Details 01409 254 295

Ground: Upcott Field, North Road, Holsworthy EX22 6HF **Club Colours:** Black & white

HONOURS **League:** None

FA Comps: None

10 YEAR RECORD

09-10	10-11	11-12	12-13	13-14	14-15	15-16	16-17	17-18	18-19
SWPP 19	SW1W 10	SW1W 15	SW1W 13	SW1W 15	SW1W 13	SW1W 11	SW1W 15	SW1W 11	SW1E 8

Leaving Holsworthy on A388 towards Bideford, ground is on left 100 meters after first roundabout.

HONITON TOWN

Founded: Nickname: The Hippos

Club Contact Details 01404 42379 alanmackay2009@hotmail.com

Ground: Moutbatten Park, Ottery Moor Lane, Honiton EX14 1AW **Club Colours:** Red & black

HONOURS **League:** Devon & Exeter Division One 2014-15, Premier Division 16-17.

FA Comps: None

10 YEAR RECORD

09-10	10-11	11-12	12-13	13-14	14-15	15-16	16-17	17-18	18-19
	D&E1 13	D&E2 8	D&E2 5	D&E1 2	D&E1 1	D&EP 3	D&EP 1	SW1E 14	SW1E 14

From the Exeter direction on the A30, take the Honiton junction, at the roundabout turn Left onto Exeter Road, continue over next Roundabout onto High Street and then take 1st Left into Otter Moor Lane and Mountbatten Park is then before the next bend.

ILFRACOMBE TOWN

Founded: 1902 Nickname: Bluebirds

Club Contact Details 01271 865 939 afalcock@aol.com

Ground: Marlborough Park, Ilfracombe, Devon EX34 8PD **Club Colours:** All blue

HONOURS **League:** North Devon Premier Division 2016-17.

FA Comps:

10 YEAR RECORD

09-10	10-11	11-12	12-13	13-14	14-15	15-16	16-17	17-18	18-19
WestP 3	WestP 3	WestP 11	WestP 16	WestP 18	NDevP 6	NDevP 6	NDevP 1	SW1E 7	SW1E 8
FAC EP	FAC P	FAC EP	FAC EP	FAC P					
FAV 1Q	FAV 1P	FAV 3Pr	FAV 1Q	FAV 1Q	FAV 2Q				FAV 1Q

Take the A361 for Ilfracombe and on entering town take 1st right after the traffic lights, follow Marlborough Road to the top and ground is on your left.

IVYBRIDGE TOWN

Founded: 1925 Nickname: The Ivys

Club Contact Details 01752 896 686 secretary@ivybridgefc.com

Ground: Erme Valley, Ermington Road, Ivybridge PL21 9ES **Club Colours:** Green & black

HONOURS **League:** Devon County 2005-06.

FA Comps: None

10 YEAR RECORD

09-10	10-11	11-12	12-13	13-14	14-15	15-16	16-17	17-18	18-19
SWPP 12	SWPP 7	SWPP 19	SWPP 13	SWPP 4	SWPP 4	SWPP 9	SWPP 17	SWPP 18	SWPP 12
						FAV 2Q	FAV 1Q	FAV 1P	FAV 2P

From Plymouth-leave A38 at Ivybridge and follow signs towards Ermington.
Ground is immediately next to South Devon Tennis Centre.
From Exeter-leave A38 at Ivybridge. Ground is in front of you at the end of the slip road.

Nearest Railway Station Ivybridge - 1.8km
Bus Route Community Centre - stop 251m away

MILLBROOK AFC

Founded: 1888 Nickname: Magpies / Brook

Club Contact Details 01752 822 113

Ground: Jenkins Park PL10 1EN **Club Colours:** Black & white

HONOURS **League:** South West Peninsula Division One West 2017-18.

FA Comps: None

10 YEAR RECORD

09-10	10-11	11-12	12-13	13-14	14-15	15-16	16-17	17-18	18-19
SW1W 15	EC1 5	EC1 2	ECP 6	ECP 3	SW1W 15	SW1W 13	SW1W 4	SW1W 1	SWPP 10

Taking the B3247 into the village, at the Duke of Cornwall bare Right into King Street, after the garage take the left onto the Parade, at mini roundabout take right on to Southdown Road, next Right onto Mill Road where ground is visible.

NEWTON ABBOT SPURS

Founded: 1938 Nickname: The Spurs

Club Contact Details 01626 365 343

Ground: Recreation Ground, Marsh Road, Newton Abbot TQ12 2AR **Club Colours:**

HONOURS **League:** None

FA Comps: None

10 YEAR RECORD

09-10	10-11	11-12	12-13	13-14	14-15	15-16	16-17	17-18	18-19
SW1E 13	SW1E 14	SW1E 9	SW1E 4	SW1E 11	SW1E 17	SW1E 7	SW1E 4	SW1E 2	SW1E 12
									FAV 2Q

At Fire station roundabout or from Railway Station direction enter The Avenue. at bend in that road turn where signposted Recreation Trust, ground shared with South Devon Cricket Club.

PLYMOUTH MAJON

Founded: Nickname: The Johnies

Club Contact Details

Ground: University of Mark & St Johns, Derriford Road PL6 8BH **Club Colours:** Blue and black

HONOURS **League:** Plymouth & West Devon Premier Division 2015-16.

FA Comps: None

10 YEAR RECORD

09-10	10-11	11-12	12-13	13-14	14-15	15-16	16-17	17-18	18-19
		PWDevP 6	PWDevP 4	PWDevP 8	PWDevP	PWDevP 1	SW1W 10	SW1W 12	SW1W 9

Exit the A38 at Manadon (signposted City Centre, Tavistock A386), Keep in left hand lane and at the roundabout take the 2nd exit (signposted Tavistock A386, Hospital, A & E, Airport), Continue at the Derriford roundabout 3rd right following the signs to Uni College/hospital, take left into Derriford Road. Then take the 2nd right.

SIDMOUTH TOWN

Founded: 1895 Nickname: The Vikings

Club Contact Details 01395 577 087

Ground: Manstone Recreation Ground, Manstone Lane, Sidmouth EX10 9TF **Club Colours:** Green and black

HONOURS **League:** Devon & Exeter Premier Division 2010-11

FA Comps: None

10 YEAR RECORD

09-10	10-11	11-12	12-13	13-14	14-15	15-16	16-17	17-18	18-19
	D&EP 1	SW1E 14	SW1E 15	SW1E 13	SW1E 10	SW1E 12	SW1E 11	SW1E 11	SW1E 9
									FAV 1P

Approach Sidmouth on the A3052, turn Right into Woolbrook Road, in half a mile, just past the Lidl Store & Harvest Service station is a mini roundabout, turn left into Manstone Lane, ground 200 meters on right.

STOKE GABRIEL

Founded: 1905 Nickname: The Railwaymen

Club Contact Details 01803 782 913

Ground: G J Churchward Memorial TQ9 6RR **Club Colours:** Maroon & blue

HONOURS **League:** Devon County 1994-95, 96-97.
South West Peninsula Division One East 2013-14, 16-17, 18-19.

FA Comps: None

10 YEAR RECORD

09-10	10-11	11-12	12-13	13-14	14-15	15-16	16-17	17-18	18-19
SW1E 2	SW1E 3	SW1E 2	SW1E 2	SW1E 1	SWPP 14	SWPP 19	SW1E 1	SWPP 12	SW1E 1

At Tweenaway Cross turn Right, after quarter of a mile turn Left at the Parkers Arms Inn.
After approx 1 mile ground entrance is signposted on your right, before the village itself.

Nearest Railway Station Paignton - 4.3km
Bus Route Ramslade Touring Park - stop 344m away

TORPOINT ATHLETIC

Founded: 1887 Nickname: The Point

Club Contact Details 01752 812 889 robbietafc81@live.co.uk

Ground: The Mill, Mill Lane, Carbeile Road, Torpoint PL11 2RE **Club Colours:** Yellow & black

HONOURS **League:** South Western 1964-65, 66-67.

FA Comps: None

10 YEAR RECORD

09-10	10-11	11-12	12-13	13-14	14-15	15-16	16-17	17-18	18-19
SWPP 8	SWPP 4	SWPP 12	SWPP 14	SWPP 10	SWPP 13	SWPP 8	SWPP 12	SWPP 11	SWPP 7
	FAC 1Q	FAC P	FAC EP		FAC EP				
FAV 2Q	FAV QF	FAV 2P		FAV 1Q	FAV 2Q	FAV 2P	FAV 3P	FAV 1Q	FAV 1P

Take turning at Carbeile Inn onto Carbeille Road and first turning on the right into Mill Lane.

Nearest Railway Station Dockyard (plymouth) - 2.5km
Bus Route Carbeile Inn - stop 338m away

TORRIDGESIDE

Founded: 1989 Nickname: T-Side

Club Contact Details andreasussex@btinternet.com

Ground: Donnacroft, Torrington EX38 7HT **Club Colours:** Claret and blue

HONOURS **League:** North Devon Premier Division 2012-13.

FA Comps: None

10 YEAR RECORD

09-10	10-11	11-12	12-13	13-14	14-15	15-16	16-17	17-18	18-19
NDevP 13	NDevP 6	NDevP 5	NDevP 1	NDevP 8	NDevP 3	NDevP 2	SW1E 7	SW1E 8	SW1E 4

Ground is located in Torrington and is adjacent to and uses the same driveway as Torrington Rugby Club.

TORRINGTON

Founded: 1908 Nickname: The Super Greens

Club Contact Details cm@torringtonafc.co.uk

Ground: Vicarage Field, Torrington EX38 7AJ **Club Colours:** All green

HONOURS **League:** Western Division One 2002-03. North Devon Senior Division 2008-09.

FA Comps: None

10 YEAR RECORD

09-10	10-11	11-12	12-13	13-14	14-15	15-16	16-17	17-18	18-19
NDevP 9	NDevP 8	NDevP 15	NDevP 2	NDevP 3	NDevP 10	NDevP 4	NDevP 7	NDevP 7	NDevP 5

From A386 turn left at roundabout onto Calf Street. At the Church turn Right into School Lane then Right at the Swimming Pool.

PREMIER WEST INS: Dobwalls, Liskeard Athletic, Mousehole, Penzance, Porthleven, St Blazey, St Dennis, Wadebridge Town and Wendron United (all P - SWPD1W), Godolphin Atlentic (Newquay) (NC from Godolphin Atlantic).

BODMIN TOWN

Founded: 1889 Nickname: Black & Ambers

Club Contact Details 01208 78165 nickgiles@live.co.uk

Ground: Priory Park, Bodmin, Cornwall PL31 2AE **Club Colours:** Yellow & black

HONOURS **League:** Bodmin & District 1922-23, 26-27. South Western 1990-91, 93-94, 2005-06.
South West Peninsula Premier Division 2007-08, 08-09, 11-12, 12-13, 15-16.

FA Comps: None

10 YEAR RECORD

09-10	10-11	11-12	12-13	13-14	14-15	15-16	16-17	17-18	18-19
SWPP 2	SWPP 2	SWPP 1	SWPP 1	SWPP 7	SWPP 2	SWPP 1	SWPP 3	SWPP 5	SWPP 9
FAC P	FAC 1Q	FAC 3Qr	FAC 1Qr	FAC P	FAC 1Qr	FAC 2Q	FAC Pr	FAC 2Qr	FAC Pr
FAV 1P	FAV 4P	FAV 2Pr	FAV 5P	FAV 4P	FAV 4P	FAV 4P	FAV 3P	FAV 2P	FAV 3P

Situated in Priory Park through main car park. Use football car park on Saturdays.

Nearest Railway Station Bodmin General - 587m

CALLINGTON TOWN

Founded: 1989 Nickname: The Pasty Men

Club Contact Details 01579 382 647

Ground: Ginsters Marshfield Parc PL17 7BT **Club Colours:** Red & black

HONOURS **League:** East Cornwall Combination 1997-98, 98-99.
South West Peninsula Division One West 2013-14.

FA Comps: None

10 YEAR RECORD

09-10	10-11	11-12	12-13	13-14	14-15	15-16	16-17	17-18	18-19
SW1W 10	SW1W 3	SW1W 6	SW1W 5	SW1W 1	SWPP 11	SWPP 16	SWPP 15	SWPP 19	SWPP 17
									FAV 1Q

Ground is in the grounds of Callington Community College which is a quarter of a mile from the town centre.

CAMELFORD

Founded: 1893 Nickname: Camels

Club Contact Details hilarykent35@gmail.com

Ground: Trefew Park, PL32 9TS **Club Colours:** Blue and white

HONOURS **League:** South West Peninsula Division One West 2010-11.

FA Comps: None

10 YEAR RECORD

09-10	10-11	11-12	12-13	13-14	14-15	15-16	16-17	17-18	18-19
SW1W 8	SW1W 1	SWPP 9	SWPP 9	SWPP 14	SWPP 17	SWPP 15	SWPP 14	SWPP 10	SWPP 18
				FAV 2Q	FAV 1Qr	FAV 1P	FAV 1Q	FAV 2Q	FAV 2Qr

From the South drive into Camelford up Victoria Road for 300 yards, turn left into Oakwood Rise.
Follow road around for approximately 300 yards. Entrance is on the right up the lane.
From the North as you enter Camelford turn right into Oakwood Rise then as above.

DOBWALLS

Founded: 1922 Nickname: The Reds

Club Contact Details dodwallsfootball@gmail.com

Ground: Lantoom Park, Duloe Road, Dobwalls PL14 4LR **Club Colours:** Red and black

HONOURS **League:** None

FA Comps: None

10 YEAR RECORD

09-10	10-11	11-12	12-13	13-14	14-15	15-16	16-17	17-18	18-19
SW1W 9	SW1W 11	SW1W 10	SW1W 8	SW1W 8	SW1W 12	SW1W 15	SW1W 11	SW1W 14	SW1W 10

From Dobwalls village take sign for Duloe.
Ground is in half a mile, after the school and on the left before the railway bridge.

FALMOUTH TOWN

Founded: 1949 Nickname: The Ambers

Club Contact Details 01326 375 156 pascoerichard@hotmail.com

Ground: Bickland Park, Bickland Water Road, Falmouth TR11 4PB **Club Colours:** Amber & black

HONOURS **League:** South Western 1961-62, 65-66, 67-68, 70-71, 71-72, 72-73, 73-74, 85-86, 86-87, 88-89, 89-90, 91-92, 96-97, 99-2000. Western 74-75, 75-76, 76-77, 77-78. Cornwall Comb 83-84.

FA Comps: None

10 YEAR RECORD

09-10	10-11	11-12	12-13	13-14	14-15	15-16	16-17	17-18	18-19
SWPP 3	SWPP 5	SWPP 3	SWPP 16	SWPP 16	SWPP 16	SWPP 11	SWPP 10	SWPP 3	SWPP 6
FAC Pr	FAC EPr	FAC EP							
FAV 2Q	FAV 1Qr	FAV 3P			FAV 1P	FAV 1Q			FAV 2P

Take Penryn by-pass from Asda roundabout. Leave by-pass at Hillhead roundabout, take first right and follow industrial estate signs. Ground 1/2 mile on the left.

Nearest Railway Station Penmere - 1.3km
Bus Route Conway Road - stop 54m away

GODOLPHIN ATLANTIC (NEWQUAY)

Founded: 1980 Nickname: G Army

Club Contact Details godolphin.arms@btconnect.com

Ground: Godolphin Way, Newquay TR7 3BU **Club Colours:** Sky blue & white

HONOURS **League:** South West Peninsula Division One West 2012-13.

FA Comps: None

10 YEAR RECORD

09-10	10-11	11-12	12-13	13-14	14-15	15-16	16-17	17-18	18-19
SW1W 6	SW1W 2	SW1W 4	SW1W 1	SWPP 5	SWPP 7	SWPP 5	SWPP 13	SWPP 17	SWPP 14
								FAV 1Q	FAV 2Q

Off Henver Road turn into Godolphin Way and ground is then first entrance on the left.

Nearest Railway Station Newquay - 1.2km
Bus Route Brook House Inn - stop 136m away

HELSTON ATHLETIC

Founded: 1896 Nickname: The Blues

Club Contact Details 01326 573742 (Clubhouse) paul.m.hendy@btinternet.com

Ground: Kellaway Park, Helston TR13 8PJ **Club Colours:** All blue & white

HONOURS **League:** Cornwall Senior 1936-37, 37-38, 39-40. Cornwall Comb. 87-88, 2000-01, 10-11. South West Peninsula Division One West 2014-15.

FA Comps: None

10 YEAR RECORD

09-10	10-11	11-12	12-13	13-14	14-15	15-16	16-17	17-18	18-19
CornC 5	CornC 1	SW1W 2	SW1W 2	SW1W 3	SW1W 1	SWPP 10	SWPP 16	SWPP 9	SWPP 11
							FAV 1P	FAV 1Q	FAV 1Q

From Redruth, go across 5 roundabouts, final one by Tesco, then turn first left.

Bus Route Tesco - stop 101m away

LAUNCESTON

Founded: 1891 Nickname: The Clarets

Club Contact Details 01566 773 279 launcestonfc@aol.com

Ground: Pennygillam Ind. Est., Launceston PL15 7ED **Club Colours:** All claret

HONOURS **League:** South Western 1994-95.

FA Comps: None

10 YEAR RECORD

09-10	10-11	11-12	12-13	13-14	14-15	15-16	16-17	17-18	18-19
SWPP 11	SWPP 11	SWPP 5	SWPP 5	SWPP 8	SWPP 10	SWPP 14	SWPP 11	SWPP 7	SWPP 16
FAC P	FAC EP								
FAV 2Q	FAV 2Q								FAV 2Q

Leave A30 onto Pennygillam roundabout, turn into Pennygillam Industrial Estate.
Ground is 400 yards on the left.

LISKEARD ATHLETIC

Founded: 1946 Nickname: The Blues

Club Contact Details 01579 342 665

Ground: Lux Park PL14 3HZ **Club Colours:** All blue

HONOURS **League:** South Western 1976-77, 78-79. Western Premier Division 1987-88. South West Peninsula Division One West 2018-19.

FA Comps: None

10 YEAR RECORD

09-10	10-11	11-12	12-13	13-14	14-15	15-16	16-17	17-18	18-19
SWPP 16	SWPP 12	SWPP 7	SWPP 18	SWPP 20	SW1W 6	SW1W 7	SW1W 8	SW1W 5	SW1W 1
FAV 1P	FAV 2Q	FAV 1P					FAV 1Q		FAV 1Q

From the parade in the Town Centre, turn left at the Monument, then 1st right and follow signs to Lux Park Leisure Centre, ground adjacent.

MOUSEHOLE

Founded: 1923 Nickname: The Seagulls

Club Contact Details 01736 731 518

Ground: Trungle Parc, Paul, Penzance TR19 6UG **Club Colours:** White and green

HONOURS **League:** South West Peninsula League Division One West 2015-16.

FA Comps: None

10 YEAR RECORD

09-10	10-11	11-12	12-13	13-14	14-15	15-16	16-17	17-18	18-19
SW1W 16	SW1W 14	SW1W 17	SW1W 15	SW1W 2	SW1W 7	SW1W 1	SW1W 6	SW1W 4	SW1W 2

From Penzance head towards Newlyn, at crossroads go straight across and up the hill.
Continue until reaching a T Junction (signposted Mousehole and Paul) Turn left and in half mile before Paul church turn right, at end of road is ground entrance, adjacent to Paul Cricket Club.

NEWQUAY

Founded: 1890 Nickname: The Peppermints

Club Contact Details 01637 872 935

Ground: Mount Wise TR7 2BU **Club Colours:** Red & white

HONOURS **League:** South Western 1958-59, 59-60, 77-78, 79-80, 81-82, 83-84, 87-88. South West Peninsula Division One West 2011-12.

FA Comps: None

10 YEAR RECORD

09-10	10-11	11-12	12-13	13-14	14-15	15-16	16-17	17-18	18-19
SW1W 5	SW1W 9	SW1W 1	SWPP 12	SWPP 11	SWPP 15	SWPP 18	SWPP 19	SWPP 14	SWPP 13
FAV 1P	FAV 1P			FAV EP	FAV 1P	FAV 2Q			FAV 1P

From link road turn right onto Mount Wise, just past traffic lights turn Right into Clevedon Road.

Nearest Railway Station Newquay - 0.8km
Bus Route Windsor Court - stop 117m away

PENZANCE

Founded: 1888 Nickname: The Magpies

Club Contact Details 01736 361 964

Ground: Penlee Park, Alexandra Place, Penzance TR18 4NE **Club Colours:** White and black

HONOURS **League:** South Western 1955-56, 56-57, 74-75. South West Peninsula League Division One West 2008-09.

FA Comps: None

10 YEAR RECORD

09-10	10-11	11-12	12-13	13-14	14-15	15-16	16-17	17-18	18-19
SWPP 7	SWPP 9	SWPP 17	SWPP 19	SW1W 14	SW1W 14	SW1W 10	SW1W 17	SW1W 10	SW1W 12
FAV 2Q	FAV 2Q	FAV 2Q							

Go along Promenade and at the end turn right at mini-roundabout into Alexandra Road.
Take either 1st or 2nd right turnings (Mennaye Rd or Alexander Place).
Ground at end of both Roads.

PORTHLEVEN

Founded: 1898 Nickname: The Fisher Men

Club Contact Details 01326 569 655

Ground: Gala Parc, Mill Lane, Porthleven TR13 9LQ **Club Colours:** Yellow and black

HONOURS **League:** None

FA Comps: None

10 YEAR RECORD

09-10	10-11	11-12	12-13	13-14	14-15	15-16	16-17	17-18	18-19
SW1W 11	SW1W 6	SW1W 12	SW1W 11	SW1W 11	SW1W 11	SW1W 16	SW1W 12	SW1W 6	SW1W 3
FAV 1P	FAV 2Q	FAV 1Q	FAV 2Q		FAV 1Q	FAV 1Q			FAV 2Q

A394 Helston to Penzance Road, turn left at Porthleven.
Ground on your left as you approach the village.

SALTASH UNITED

Founded: 1945 Nickname: The Ashes

Club Contact Details 01752 845 746

Ground: Kimberley Stadium, Callington Road, Saltash PL12 6DX **Club Colours:** Red & white

HONOURS **League:** South Western 1953-54, 75-76. Western Division One 1976-77, Premier 1984-85, 86-87, 88-89.

FA Comps: None

10 YEAR RECORD

09-10	10-11	11-12	12-13	13-14	14-15	15-16	16-17	17-18	18-19
SWPP 9	SWPP 6	SWPP 4	SWPP 6	SWPP 3	SWPP 3	SWPP 6	SWPP 2	SWPP 4	SWPP 4
FAC 1Qr	FAC EPr	FAC EP	FAC EP	FAC EP	FAC 1Q	FAC EP			FAC P
FAV 2P	FAV 2P	FAV 2P	FAV 1P	FAV 3P	FAV 1P	FAV 1Q		FAV 2Q	FAV 3P

At the top of Town Centre fork right at mini-roundabout.
Ground is situated 400m ahead on the left-hand side next to Leisure Centre and Police Station.

Nearest Railway Station Saltash - 0.9km
Bus Route Callington Road St Annes - stop 40m away

ST. AUSTELL

Founded: 1890 Nickname: The Lillywhites

Club Contact Details 01726 66099 hotspurs403@gmail.com

Ground: Poltair Park, Trevarthian Road, St Austell PL25 4LR **Club Colours:** White and black

HONOURS **League:** South Western 1968-69. South West Peninsula Premier 2014-15.

FA Comps: None

10 YEAR RECORD

09-10	10-11	11-12	12-13	13-14	14-15	15-16	16-17	17-18	18-19
SW1W 2	SWPP 10	SWPP 8	SWPP 4	SWPP 9	SWPP 1	SWPP 2	SWPP 4	SWPP 6	SWPP 5
				FAC EP	FAC P	FAC P	FAC EPr	FAC EPr	
			FAV 2P	FAV 1Q	FAV SF	FAV 2P	FAV 2Q	FAV 2Q	FAV 4P

Near Poltair School and St Austell Brewery (5 minutes from St Austell Rail Station).

Nearest Railway Station St Austell - 0.3km
Bus Route Poltair Road - stop 33m away

ST. BLAZEY

Founded: 1896 Nickname: The Green & Blacks

Club Contact Details 01725 814 110 geoallen.spurs1@btinternet.com

Ground: Blaise Park, Station Road, St Blazey PL24 2ND **Club Colours:** Green & black

HONOURS **League:** South Western 1954-55, 57-58, 62-63, 63-64, 80-81, 82-83, 98-99, 2000-01, 01-02, 02-03, 03-04, 04-05, 06-07.

FA Comps: None

10 YEAR RECORD

09-10	10-11	11-12	12-13	13-14	14-15	15-16	16-17	17-18	18-19
SWPP 4	SWPP 8	SWPP 18	SWPP 8	SWPP 13	SWPP 9	SWPP 17	SWPP 20	SW1W 7	SW1W 11
FAC EP	FAC EPr	FAC P		FAC P					
FAV 1P	FAV 3P	FAV 2Q	FAV 3P	FAV 2Q	FAV 2P	FAV 2Q		FAV 1Q	

A390, Lostwithiel to St Austell road, at St Blazey turn left at traffic lights by the church and into Station Road, ground is then 200 yards on your left.

ST. DENNIS

Founded: 1902 Nickname: The Saints

Club Contact Details 01726 822 635

Ground: Boscawen Park, St Dennis PL26 8DW **Club Colours:** Light blue

HONOURS **League:** Cornwall Combination 1975-76. East Cornwall Premier 1991-92, 99-00, 10-11, Division One 09-10.

FA Comps: None

10 YEAR RECORD

09-10	10-11	11-12	12-13	13-14	14-15	15-16	16-17	17-18	18-19
ECor1 1	ECorP 1	SW1W 9	SW1W 6	SW1W 9	SW1W 4	SW1W 6	SW1W 7	SW1W 8	SW1W 5

B3279 into Village, take the first Right and at bottom of hill at T junction turn left and ground entrance is next Right.

STICKER

Founded: 1911 Nickname: The Sticky

Club Contact Details 01726 71003 chrisjohnosborne@aol.com

Ground: Burngullow Park PL26 7EN **Club Colours:** Yellow and blue

HONOURS **League:** South West Peninsula Division One West 2016-17.

FA Comps: None

10 YEAR RECORD

09-10	10-11	11-12	12-13	13-14	14-15	15-16	16-17	17-18	18-19
ECP 8	ECP 3	ECP 2	SW1W 4	SW1W 4	SW1W 5	SW1W 3	SW1W 1	SWPP 15	SWPP 19

From A390 follow signs to Sticker, in the centre of the Village take St Stephen Road (between pub & post office).
After 0.75 miles at cross roads turn Right and ground entrance on your right in 200 meters.

Nearest Railway Station St Austell - 4.4km
Bus Route Hewas Inn (Fore St) - stop 1.1km away

WADEBRIDGE TOWN

Founded: 1894 Nickname: The Bridgers

Club Contact Details 01208 812 537

Ground: Bodieve Park, Bodieve Road, Wadebridge PL27 6EA **Club Colours:** All red

HONOURS **League:** South West Peninsula League Division One West 2007-08.

FA Comps: None

10 YEAR RECORD

09-10	10-11	11-12	12-13	13-14	14-15	15-16	16-17	17-18	18-19
SWPP 14	SWPP 20	SW1W 11	SW1W 3	SW1W 7	SW1W 10	SW1W 14	SW1W 14	SW1W 9	SW1W 4
FAV 1Q	FAV 2Q	FAV 2Q	FAV 1Q	FAV 2Q	FAV 2Q	FAV 2Q			

At the Island Junction off the A39 turn to go into Wadebridge.
200 yards down hill turn Right and the first Right into ground.

WENDRON UNITED

Founded: 1986 Nickname: The Dron

Club Contact Details 01209 860 946

Ground: Underlane TR13 0EH **Club Colours:** Maroon and blue

HONOURS **League:** None

FA Comps: None

10 YEAR RECORD

09-10	10-11	11-12	12-13	13-14	14-15	15-16	16-17	17-18	18-19
SW1W Exp	CornC 10	CornC 11	CornC 12	CornC 2	CornC 2	SW1W 9	SW1W 13	SW1W 13	SW1W 6

A39 to Penryn Campus then A394 towards Helston.
At Rame Cross Post Office turn Right, next junction take the Left fork towards Carnkie then in quarter of a mile turn left into Underlane, ground another quarter of a mile on the Right.

PREMIER DIVISION INS: Alfold (P - SC1), Horley Town (Tr - CCP), Steyning Town (P - SC1).
OUTS: Arundel (R - SC1), Chichester City (P - Isth1S), Shoreham (R - SC1).

AFC UCKFIELD TOWN

Founded 1988

Nickname: The Oakmen **Club Colours:** Red & black

Club Contact Details 01825 890 905 grahamsullivan27@gmail.com
Ground: The Oaks, Old Eastbourne Road, Uckfield TN22 5QL
Capacity: **Seats:** Yes **Covered:** Yes

Previous Names: Wealden 1988-2010. AFC Uckfield & Uckfield Town merged in 2014.
Previous Leagues: None

HONOURS: FA Comps: None
League: Sussex County Division Two 2010-11.

10 YEAR RECORD

09-10	10-11	11-12	12-13	13-14	14-15	15-16	16-17	17-18	18-19
SxC2 8	SxC2 1	SxC1 8	SxC1 21	SxC1 10	SxC2 2	SCP 15	SCP 18	SCP 14	SCP 7
							FAC EP	FAC EPr	FAC 2Q
						FAV 1Q	FAV 2Q	FAV 2Q	FAV 4P

Next to Radutt Restaurant on Old Eastbourne Road, south of Uckfield Town Centre

Nearest Railway Station Uckfield - 2.1km

ALFOLD

Founded 1928

Nickname: Fold **Club Colours:** Maroon

Club Contact Details wayne.mouring@btopenworld.com
Ground: Recreation Ground, Dunsfold Road, Alfold, Surrey GU6 8JB
Capacity: **Seats:** 50 **Covered:** Yes

Previous Names: Formed after the split of Loxwood and Alfold FC (Established 1920) in 1928.
Previous Leagues: Cranleigh & District. Horsham & District. West Sussex > 2016.

HONOURS: FA Comps: None
League: Horsham & District 1953-54. West Sussex Division Two North 1980-81, 93-94, Premier 2002-03. Southern Combination Division One 2018-19.

10 YEAR RECORD

09-10	10-11	11-12	12-13	13-14	14-15	15-16	16-17	17-18	18-19
			WSux2 2	WSux1 9	WSux1 6	SC2 13	SC2 14	SC2 4	SC1 1

A281 Horsham to Alford.
Alford crossways to Dunsfold Road.

BROADBRIDGE HEATH

Founded 1919

Nickname: The Bears **Club Colours:** All royal blue

Club Contact Details 01403 211 311 crispandy@hotmail.com
Ground: Wickhurst Lane Broadbridge Heath Horsham RH12 3YS
Capacity: **Seats:** **Covered:**

Previous Names: None
Previous Leagues: Horsham & District >1971. West Sussex 1971-79. Southern Counties Combination 1979-83.

HONOURS: FA Comps: None
League: West Sussex Division One 1975-76.

10 YEAR RECORD

09-10	10-11	11-12	12-13	13-14	14-15	15-16	16-17	17-18	18-19
SxC2 14	SxC2 6	SxC2 5	SxC2 6	SxC2 2	SxC1 9	SCP 9	SCP 8	SCP 15	SCP 6
								FAC EP	FAC EP
					FAV 2Q	FAV 2Q	FAV 1Q	FAV 2P	FAV 2Q

Alongside A24, Horsham north/south bypass.
From the A24 Horsham Bypass, at the large roundabout/underpass take the Broadbridge Heath Bypass towards Guildford and then at the first roundabout turn left into Wickhurst Lane.

Nearest Railway Station Christs Hospital - 1.5km
Bus Route Tesco - stop 213m away

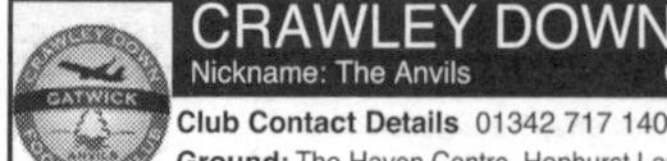

CRAWLEY DOWN GATWICK

Nickname: The Anvils **Club Colours:** All Red

Founded 1993

Club Contact Details 01342 717 140 martinmd@btinternet.com

Ground: The Haven Centre, Hophurst Lane, Crawley Down RH10 4LJ

Capacity: 1,000 **Seats:** Yes **Covered:** 50

Previous Names: Crawley Down United > 1993. Crawley Down Village > 1999. Crawley Down > 2012.

Previous Leagues: Mid Sussex, Sussex County > 2011. Isthmian 2011-14.

HONOURS: FA Comps: None

League: Mid-Sussex Premier Division 1994-95. Sussex County Division One 2010-11.

10 YEAR RECORD

09-10	10-11	11-12	12-13	13-14	14-15	15-16	16-17	17-18	18-19
SxC1 8	SxC1 1	Isth1S 16	Isth1S 13	Isth1S 23	SxC1 19	SC1 2	SCP 11	SCP 12	SCP 9
FAC 1Q	FAC EP	FAC 1Q	FAC P	FAC P	FAC EPr	FAC EP	FAC P	FAC EP	FAC EP
FAV 2Q	FAV 1P	FAT P	FAT 1Q	FAT 1Q	FAV 2P	FAV 1Q	FAV 1Q	FAV 2Q	FAV 1Q

From the North: Turn off the M23 at Junction 10 signposted East Grinstead At the roundabout at the Copthorne Hotel, take the 2nd exit, signed A264 East Grinstead. At the next roundabout (Duke's Head) take the 3rd exit, B2028 south, toward Turners Hill After approx. 1 mile turn left into Sandy Lane. (just after entering the 30mph zone and a telephone box in the layby on the right). At the end of Sandy Lane (war memorial on the right), turn left signed Felbridge. After a couple of bends the Haven Centre is on your left. **From the East:** Travel through East Grinstead on the A22 until the Junction with the A264 at the Felbridge Traffic lights. Turn left (Sign posted Crawley) and after 100 Meters take the Left Fork towards Crawley Down. Approx 1.5 Miles Haven Centre on Right. **From the South:** Travel North through Turners Hill on the B2028 after approx 2 Miles take the 2nd turning on your right (Vicarage Road). This is a Right fork and is sited just after passing over a small bridge. Follow Vicarage Road for approx 1/2 Mile past Junction with Sandy Lane and The Haven Centre is 200 Meters on your left.

EAST PRESTON

Nickname: EP **Club Colours:** Black and white

Founded 1966

Club Contact Details 01903 776 026 keweia@btinternet.com

Ground: Roundstone Recreation Ground, Lashmar Road, East Preston BN16 1ES

Capacity: **Seats:** Yes **Covered:** Yes

Previous Names: None

Previous Leagues: Worthing & District 1966-68. West Sussex 1968-83.

HONOURS: FA Comps: None

League: West Sussex Premier Division 1977-78, 80-81, 81-82, 82-83.
Sussex County Division Three 1983-84, Division Two 1997-98, 2011-12, Division One 2013-14.

10 YEAR RECORD

09-10	10-11	11-12	12-13	13-14	14-15	15-16	16-17	17-18	18-19
SxC2 14	SxC2 14	SxC2 1	SxC1 3	SxC1 1	SxC1 11	SCP 19	SC1 3	SCP 13	SCP 14
FAC 2Q	FAC EP		FAC P	FAC 1Q	FAC 2Q	FAC EP	FAC 1Q	FAC P	FAC EP
FAV 1Q	FAV 2Q	FAV 1P	FAV 2Q	FAV 5P	FAV 2P	FAV 1Q	FAV 2Q	FAV 1Qr	FAV 1P

From Worthing proceed west for six miles on A259 to The Roundstone PH.
From the roundabout, take the first exit, signposted East Preston.
Turn left over the railway crossing. Turn left soon afterwards, and then first right into Roundstone Drive.
Turn left into Lashmar Road and the approach road to the ground is on the right.

Nearest Railway Station Angmering - 0.8km

Bus Route Windlesham Gardens - stop 209m away

EASTBOURNE TOWN

Nickname: Town **Club Colours:** Yellow and blue

Founded 1881

Club Contact Details 01323 724 328 rb.marsh@talk21.com

Ground: The Saffrons, Compton Place Road, Eastbourne BN21 1EA

Capacity: 3,000 **Seats:** 200 **Covered:** Yes

Previous Names: Devonshire Park 1881-89

Previous Leagues: Southern Amateur 1907-46, Corinthian 1960-63, Athenian 1963-76, Sussex County 1976-2007. Isthmian 2007-14.

HONOURS: FA Comps: None

League: Sussex County 1976-77, 2006-07.

10 YEAR RECORD

09-10	10-11	11-12	12-13	13-14	14-15	15-16	16-17	17-18	18-19
Isth1S 22	Isth1S 18	Isth1S 14	Isth1S 11	Isth1S 24	SxC1 4	SCP 2	SCP 5	SCP 5	SCP 3
FAC P	FAC 1Q	FAC P	FAC 2Q	FAC 2Q	FAC P	FAC 3Q	FAC 1Q	FAC 1Q	FAC EP
FAT P	FAT P	FAT 1Q	FAT 1Q	FAT 1Qr	FAV 1P	FAV 3P	FAV 4P	FAV 4P	FAV 3P

Come into Eastbourne following the signs for Eastbourne Railway Station. When arriving at the railway station mini-roundabout turn right into Grove Road, (opposite from the station) and carry on past the Police Station and Town Hall (the large clock building.) Go straight over at the junction past the Caffyns car showroom (you can see the ground on your right), then take the first right turn into Compton Place Road and the entrance to The Saffrons car park is 100 yards on the right.

Nearest Railway Station Eastbourne - 0.4km

Bus Route Saffrons Road Cricket Club - stop 100m away

EASTBOURNE UNITED

Nickname: The U's **Club Colours:** Red and blue

Founded 1894

Club Contact Details 01323 726 989 secretary@eastbourneunitedafc.com

Ground: The Oval, Channel View Road, Eastbourne, BN22 7LN

Capacity: 3,000 **Seats:** 160 **Covered:** 160 **Shop:** Yes

Previous Names: 1st Sussex Royal Engineers. Eastbourne Old Comrades 1922. Eastbourne United (merged with Shinewater Assoc in 2000)

Previous Leagues: Sussex County 1921-28, 32-56. Spartan 1928-32. Metropolitan 1956-64. Athenian 1964-77. Isthmian 1977-92.

HONOURS: FA Comps: None

League: Athenian Division Two 1966-67, Division One 68-69. Sussex County Division One 1954-55, 55-56, 2008-09, Division Two 2013-14.

10 YEAR RECORD

09-10		10-11		11-12		12-13		13-14		14-15		15-16		16-17		17-18		18-19	
SxC1	6	SxC1	20	SxC2	6	SxC2	4	SxC2	1	SxC1	12	SCP	10	SCP	7	SCP	16	SCP	18
FAC	Pr	FAC	EP					FAC	1Q	FAC	P	FAC	1Q	FAC	1Q	FAC	P	FAC	EP
FAV	3P	FAV	2Q			FAV	1Q	FAV	SF	FAV	2P	FAV	2Q	FAV	2P	FAV	1Q	FAV	1Q

From A27 Polegate bypass follow new A22 (Golden Jubilee Way) and cross roundabout into Highfield Link.
At next roundabout take slip road left into Lottbridge Drive.
At second roundabout take third exit into Seaside. 4
00 yards turn left opposite 'Co-op' into Channel View Road.
Oval is second turning left.

Nearest Railway Station Eastbourne - 2km

Bus Route Desmond Road - stop 240m away

HASSOCKS

Nickname: The Robins **Club Colours:** Red and black

Founded 1902

Club Contact Details 01273 846 040 sarahajohn@btinternet.com

Ground: The Beacon, Brighton Road, Hassocks BN6 9LU

Capacity: 1,800 **Seats:** 270 **Covered:** 100

Previous Names: None

Previous Leagues: Mid Sussex, Brighton & Hove & District >1981.

HONOURS: FA Comps: None

League: Brighton, Hove & District Division Two 1965-66, Division One 71-72. Sussex County Division Three 1991-92.

10 YEAR RECORD

09-10		10-11		11-12		12-13		13-14		14-15		15-16		16-17		17-18		18-19	
SxC1	14	SxC1	6	SxC1	4	SxC1	7	SxC1	6	SxC1	15	SCP	13	SCP	13	SCP	18	SCP	12
FAC	EP	FAC	1Q	FAC	EP	FAC	EP	FAC	1Q	FAC	EP					FAC	EP	FAC	EP
FAV	2Q	FAV	1Q	FAV	2Qr	FAV	1P	FAV	1P	FAV	2P			FAV	1Q	FAV	2Q	FAV	1Q

Off A273 Pyecombe Road to Burgess Hill.
Ground is 300 yards south of Stonepound crossroads (B2116) to Hurstpeirpoint or Hassocks.

Nearest Railway Station Hassocks - 1.2km

Bus Route Friars Oak Cottages - stop 211m away

HORLEY TOWN

Nickname: The Clarets **Club Colours:** Claret & blue

Founded 1896

Club Contact Details 01293 822 000 mark@avocettm.co.uk

Ground: The New Defence, Court Lodge Road, Horley RH6 8SP

Capacity: 1800 **Seats:** 150 **Covered:** 100 **Shop:** Yes

Previous Names: Horley >1975

Previous Leagues: Surrey Intermediate 1925-51, 55- Surrey Senior 1951-55, 71-78, London Spartan 1978-81, Athenian 1981-84, Combined Counties 1984-96, 03-19. Surrey County Senior 2002-03.

HONOURS: FA Comps: None

League: Surrey Intermediate 1926-27, Eastern Section 1950-51. Surrey Senior 1976-77.

10 YEAR RECORD

09-10		10-11		11-12		12-13		13-14		14-15		15-16		16-17		17-18		18-19	
CCP	14	CCP	16	CCP	7	CCP	12	CCP	19	CCP	12	CCP	6	CCP	7	CCP	14	CCP	10
FAC	Pr	FAC	P	FAC	1Q	FAC	Pr	FAC	1Q	FAC	EP	FAC	Pr	FAC	EP	FAC	P	FAC	P
FAV	2Q	FAV	1P	FAV	2Q	FAV	1P	FAV	1Q	FAV	3P	FAV	1Q	FAV	1P	FAV	4P	FAV	2P

From centre of town go North up Victoria where it meets the A23, straight across to Vicarage Lane, 2nd left into Court Lodge Road follow it through estate and we are behind adult education centre.

Nearest Railway Station Horley

Bus Route Metrobus 100, 526

HORSHAM YMCA

Nickname: YM's **Club Colours:** White and black

Founded 1898

Club Contact Details 01403 252 689 alan.maguire@hotmail.co.uk

Ground: Gorings Mead, Horsham, West Sussex RH13 5BP

Capacity: 1,575 **Seats:** 150 **Covered:** 200

Previous Names: None

Previous Leagues: Horsham & District, Brighton & Hove, Mid Sussex, Sussex County 1959-2006, 08-09. Isthmian 2006-08, 09-11.

HONOURS: FA Comps: None

League: Sussex County 2004-05, 05-06.

10 YEAR RECORD

09-10	10-11	11-12	12-13	13-14	14-15	15-16	16-17	17-18	18-19
Isth1S 11	Isth1S 22	SxC1 16	SxC1 10	SxC1 4	SxC1 5	SCP 7	SCP 10	SCP 4	SCP 2
FAC 2Q	FAC P	FAC EPr	FAC EP	FAC EP	FAC Pr	FAC 2Qr	FAC EP	FAC EP	FAC 1Q
FAT P	FAT P	FAV 1P	FAV 2P	FAV 1Q	FAV 2P	FAV 2Q	FAV 3P	FAV 1P	FAV 1P

Travel north on the A23, turning off onto the A272 at Bolney.
Continue on the A272 to Cowfold then follow the A281 to Horsham.
On entering the outskirts of the town, follow the A281 (Brighton Road) a short distance and Gorings Mead is a turning on the left.
The entrance to the ground is at the bottom of Gorings Mead.

Nearest Railway Station Horsham - 0.9km

Bus Route Brighton Road - stop 205m away

LANCING

Nickname: The Lancers **Club Colours:** Yellow and blue

Founded 1941

Club Contact Details 01903 767 285 daniel@fuller-smith.co.uk

Ground: Culver Road, Lancing, West Sussex BN15 9AX

Capacity: 2,000 **Seats:** **Covered:**

Previous Names: Lancing Athletic 1941-57

Previous Leagues: Brighton & Hove & District 1946-48.

HONOURS: FA Comps: None

League: Brighton 1946-47, 47-48. Sussex County Division Two 1957-58, 69-70.

10 YEAR RECORD

09-10	10-11	11-12	12-13	13-14	14-15	15-16	16-17	17-18	18-19
SxC2 11	SxC2 2	SxC1 2	SxC1 13	SxC1 18	SxC1 8	SCP 4	SCP 12	SCP 10	SCP 13
FAC EP	FAC P	FAC P	FAC P	FAC EPr	FAC EP	FAC EP	FAC EPr	FAC EPr	FAC 2Q
FAV 2Q	FAV 4P	FAV 3P	FAV 1P	FAV 2Q	FAV 2Q	FAV 1P	FAV 2P	FAV 2Q	FAV 1Q

A27 to Manor Roundabout, south down Grinstead Lane, second right.
Left at mini-roundabout, next turning right Culver Road.
From railway 3rd turning on left (heading north) past Merry Monk public house.

Nearest Railway Station Lancing - 0.2km

Bus Route North Road Post Office - stop 123m away

LANGNEY WANDERERS

Nickname: **Club Colours:** White and red

Founded 2010

Club Contact Details 01323 766 265 saunderstracey@sky.com

Ground: Langney Sports Club, Priory Lane, Eastbourne BN23 7QH

Capacity: 4,151 **Seats:** 542 **Covered:** 2,500 Yes

Previous Names: None

Previous Leagues: East Sussex.

HONOURS: FA Comps: None

League: East Sussex Premier 2012-13. Sussex County Division Three 2013-14.

10 YEAR RECORD

09-10	10-11	11-12	12-13	13-14	14-15	15-16	16-17	17-18	18-19
			EsSuP 1	SxC3 1	SxC3 3	SC1 9	SC1 8	SC1 2	SCP 15
									FAC EP
							FAV 1Qr	FAV 2Q	FAV 1Q

From M25 take M23/A23 eastbound to A27 Polegate by pass pick up and follow signs for crematorium 50yds past crematorium turn right at mini roundabout into Priory Road.
Stadium 100yds on left.

Nearest Railway Station Pevensey & Westham - 15-20 mins walk.

Bus Route The LOOP Bus from the town centre.

LINGFIELD

Founded 1893

Nickname: The Lingers **Club Colours:** Red & Yellow

Club Contact Details 01342 834 269 toveyj@yahoo.co.uk

Ground: Sports Pavillion, Godstone Road, Lingfield, Surrey RH7 6BT

Capacity: 2,000 **Seats:** Yes **Covered:** Yes **Shop:** No

Previous Names: None.

Previous Leagues: Redhill. Surrey Intermediate. Combined Counties. Mid Sussex. Sussex County > 2014. Southern Counties East 2014-15.

HONOURS: FA Comps: None

League: POST WAR: Edenbridge & Caterham 1952-53. Surrey Intermediate Prem B 76-77. Prem A 77-78, 78-79. Mid Sussex Prem 92-93. Sussex County Division Three 97-98.

10 YEAR RECORD

09-10	10-11	11-12	12-13	13-14	14-15	15-16	16-17	17-18	18-19
SxC1 10	SxC1 11	SxC1 7	SxC1 6	SxC1 15	SCE 17	SC1 8	SC1 5	SC1 3	SCP 8
FAC 1Qr	FAC P	FAC 1Qr	FAC 1Q	FAC EP	FAC EP	FAC EP		FAC EP	FAC EP
FAV 2Q	FAV 1Q	FAV 1Q	FAV 1P	FAV 1P	FAV 3P	FAV 2Q	FAV 1P	FAV 1Q	FAV 2Q

A22 (London to Eastbourne Road) 4 miles north of East Grinstead, to Mormon Temple roundabout, take exit Lingfield (B2028) Newchapel Road for 1½ miles. Turn left at mini-roundabout. Ground ½ mile on left.

Nearest Railway Station Lingfield - 1.2km

Bus Route Godstone Road - stop 391m away

LITTLE COMMON

Founded 1966

Nickname: The Green Lane Boys **Club Colours:** Claret & blue

Club Contact Details 01424 845 861 danieleldridge11@btinternet.com

Ground: The Oval, Channel View Road, Eastbourne BN22 7LN

Capacity: 3,000 **Seats:** 160 **Covered:** 160

Previous Names: Albion United 1966-86

Previous Leagues: East Sussex. Sussex County

HONOURS: FA Comps: None

League: East Sussex 1975-76, 76-77, 2004-05. Southern Combination Division One 2017-18.

10 YEAR RECORD

09-10	10-11	11-12	12-13	13-14	14-15	15-16	16-17	17-18	18-19
SxC2 4	SxC2 13	SxC2 16	SxC2 3	SxC2 4	SxC2 7	SC1 7	SC1 2	SC1 1	SCP 16
								FAC EP	FAC EPr
						FAV 1Q	FAV 2Q	FAV 1Q	FAV 2Q

From A27 Polegate bypass follow new A22 (Golden Jubilee Way) and cross roundabout into Highfield Link.
At next roundabout take slip road left into Lottbridge Drive.
At second roundabout take third exit into Seaside. 4
00 yards turn left opposite 'Co-op' into Channel View Road.
Oval is second turning left.

Nearest Railway Station Eastbourne - 25min walk

Bus Route Desmond Road - stop 240m away

LOXWOOD

Founded 1920

Nickname: Magpies **Club Colours:** White and black

Club Contact Details 07791 766 857 secretary@loxwoodfc.co.uk

Ground: Loxwood Sports Ass., Plaistow Road, Loxwood RH14 0SX

Capacity: **Seats:** 100 **Covered:** Yes

Previous Names: None

Previous Leagues: West Sussex 1995-2006.

HONOURS: FA Comps: None

League: West Sussex Division Two North 1998-99, 2001-02. Sussex County Division Three 2007-08.

10 YEAR RECORD

09-10	10-11	11-12	12-13	13-14	14-15	15-16	16-17	17-18	18-19
SxC2 5	SxC2 6	SxC2 5	SxC2 9	SxC2 3	SxC1 6	SCP 8	SCP 6	SCP 11	SCP 17
						FAC EP	FAC P	FAC P	FAC Pr
					FAV 2P	FAV 2P	FAV 1Q	FAV 1Q	FAV 1Q

Leave A272 between Billinghurst and Wisborough Green and join the B2133 for 3.4 miles.
On entering Loxwood Village take 1st left into Plaistow Road, ground situated 100 yards on the left.

Bus Route Plaistow Road - stop 28m away

NEWHAVEN

Nickname: The Dockers **Club Colours:** Red & yellow

Founded 1887

Club Contact Details 01273 513 940 martin.garry@premierfoods.co.uk

Ground: The Trafalgar Ground, Fort Road Newhaven East Sussex BN9 9DA

Capacity: **Seats:** Yes **Covered:** Yes

Previous Names: None

Previous Leagues: Brighton, Hove & District 1887-1920.

HONOURS: FA Comps: None

League: Sussex County Division One 1953-54, 73-74, Division Two 1971-72, 90-91, Division Three 2011-12.

10 YEAR RECORD

09-10	10-11	11-12	12-13	13-14	14-15	15-16	16-17	17-18	18-19
SxC3 9	SxC3 7	SxC3 1	SxC2 2	SxC1 13	SxC1 7	SCP 3	SCP 9	SCP 9	SCP 4
							FAC EPr	FAC Pr	FAC P
FAV 1Q	FAV 1Q	FAV 2Q	FAV 1Q	FAV 1Pr	FAV 1Q	FAV 2P	FAV 3P	FAV 2Q	FAV 2P

From A259, follow the one way system around the town of Newhaven.
Turn left into South Road (pass the Police Station) which becomes Fort Road.
The ground is visible on the right just past a small parade of shops and before the approach road to Newhaven Fort.
Postcode for Sat-nav users: BN9 9DA

Nearest Railway Station Newhaven Harbour - 0.4km

Bus Route Court Farm Road - stop 20m away

PAGHAM

Nickname: The Lions **Club Colours:** White and black

Founded 1903

Club Contact Details 01243 266 112 paghamfootballclub@outlook.com

Ground: Nyetimber Lane, Pagham, West Sussex PO21 3JY

Capacity: 1,500 **Seats:** 200 **Covered:** 200

Previous Names: None

Previous Leagues: Bognor & Chichester 1903-50, West Sussex 50-69

HONOURS: FA Comps: None

League: West Sussex Division One South 1962-63, Prmeier 65-66, 68-69, 69-70.
Sussex County Division Two 1978-79, 86-87, 2006-07, Division One 80-81, 87-88, 88-89.

10 YEAR RECORD

09-10	10-11	11-12	12-13	13-14	14-15	15-16	16-17	17-18	18-19
SxC1 17	SxC1 4	SxC1 6	SxC1 5	SxC1 7	SxC1 3	SCP 6	SCP 4	SCP 3	SCP 11
FAC P	FAC P	FAC EP	FAC 1Qr	FAC EP	FAC 1Q	FAC 1Q	FAC 1Q	FAC 1Q	FAC 1Q
FAV 1P	FAV 2Q	FAV 2P	FAV 1Pr	FAV 2Q	FAV 2P	FAV 2P	FAV 2Q	FAV 1P	FAV 3P

A27 to junction of A259 on the Chichester Bypass.
Exit to Pagham (Vinnetrow Road).
At the Bear Inn (right hand side) turn left into Nyetimber Lane. The ground is 200 metres on right.

Nearest Railway Station Bognor Regis - 4.3km

Bus Route The Bear Inn - stop 119m away

PEACEHAVEN & TELSCOMBE

Nickname: The Tye **Club Colours:** Black and white

Founded 1923

Club Contact Details 01273 582 471 peacehavenfc@hotmail.com

Ground: The Sports Park, Piddinghoe Ave, Peacehaven, BN10 8RJ

Capacity: 3,000 **Seats:** 350 **Covered:** Yes

Previous Names: Formed when Peacehaven Rangers and Telscombe Tye merged.

Previous Leagues: Sussex County 1969-2013. Isthmian 2013-16.

HONOURS: FA Comps: None

League: Brighton, H&D Junior 1951-52, Intermediate 63-64, Senior 68-69. Sussex County Division One 1978-79, 81-82, 82-83, 91-92, 92-93, 94-95, 95-96, 2012-13, Division Three 2005-06, Division Two 2008-09. Isthmian Division One South 2013-14.

10 YEAR RECORD

09-10	10-11	11-12	12-13	13-14	14-15	15-16	16-17	17-18	18-19
SxC1 2	SxC1 3	SxC1 5	SxC1 1	Isth1S 1	Isth P 21	Isth1S 24	SCP 14	SCP 7	SCP 10
FAC EP	FAC P	FAC P	FAC P	FAC 1Q	FAC 1Qr	FAC P	FAC 1Q	FAC EPr	FAC EP
FAV 3P	FAV 2P	FAV 3P	FAV 4P	FAT 1Q	FAT 3Q	FAT 1Q	FAV 2Q	FAV 1Q	FAV 2P

From Brighton on A259, over roundabout & Piddinghoe Ave. is next left after 2nd set of lights-ground at end. From Newhaven, Piddinghoe Ave. is 1st right after 1st set of lights. 3 miles from Newhaven(BR). Peacehaven is served by Brighton to Newhaven & Eastbourne buses.

Nearest Railway Station Newhaven - 3.2km

Bus Route Slindon Avenue - stop 140m away

SALTDEAN UNITED

Founded 1966

Nickname: The Tigers **Club Colours:** Red & black

Club Contact Details 01273 309 898 secretary@saltdeanunitedfc.co.uk

Ground: Hill Park, Coombe Vale Saltdean Brighton East Sussex BN2 8HJ

Capacity: **Seats:** Yes **Covered:** Yes

Previous Names: None

Previous Leagues: None

HONOURS: FA Comps: None

League: Sussex County/Southern Combination Division Three 1988-89, Division Two 95-96 / Division One 2016-17.

10 YEAR RECORD

09-10		10-11		11-12		12-13		13-14		14-15		15-16		16-17		17-18		18-19	
SxC3	8	SxC3	5	SxC3	2	SxC2	18	SxC2	13	SxC2	13	SC1	17	SC1	1	SCP	8	SCP	5
																FAC	EP	FAC	Pr
FAV	2Q	FAV	2Q	FAV	1Q	FAV	1Q	FAV	1Q	FAV	1Q			FAV	1Q	FAV	1P	FAV	1P

From Brighton Pier proceed east along coast road to Rottingdean.
Straight through Rottingdean lights then after ¼ mile turn left at Saltdean Lido.
Proceed inland for approx. ½ mile then bear left down bridleway to Clubhouse.

Nearest Railway Station Southease - 5km

Bus Route Saltdean Vale Shops - stop 175m away

STEYNING TOWN

Founded 1892

Nickname: The Barrowmen **Club Colours:** Red & white

Club Contact Details 01903 814 601 secretary.sfcfc@gmail.com

Ground: The Shooting Field, Steyning, West Sussex BN44 3RQ

Capacity: **Seats:** Yes **Covered:** Yes

Previous Names: Steyning FC 1892-1979.

Previous Leagues: West Sussex (FM) 1896-1919. Brighton, Hove & District 1919-64. Sussex County 1964-86. Wessex (FM) 1986-88. Combined Counties 1988-93.

HONOURS: FA Comps: None

League: Brighton, H&D Division Two 1933-34, 38-39.
Sussex County Division Two 1977-78, Division One 1984-85, 85-86.

10 YEAR RECORD

09-10		10-11		11-12		12-13		13-14		14-15		15-16		16-17		17-18		18-19	
SxC2	17	SxC2	16	SxC2	13	SxC2	10	SxC2	11	SxC2	10	SC1	10	SC1	6	SC1	11	SC1	2
																FAC	P		
				FAV	1Q	FAV	1Q	FAV	1Q	FAV	2Q	FAV	2P	FAV	1Q	FAV	2Q	FAV	3P

Entering Steyning from the west. Take 1st left in the High St (Tanyard Lane) Follow into Shooting Field estate, ground is 4th turn on the left. Entering Steyning from the east. From the High St., turn right into Church St..
Turn left by Church into Shooting Field estate.
NB Coaches MUST park in Church Street Car Park.

Bus Route Middle Mead - stop 52m away

DIVISION ONE INS: Arundel (R - SCP), Roffey (P - SC2), Shoreham (R - SCP).

AFC VARNDEANIANS

Founded: 1929 Nickname:

Club Contact Details stevematthews@utilitymatters.com

Ground: Withdean Stadium, Tongdean Lane, Brighton BN1 5JD **Club Colours:** Red & black

HONOURS
FA Comps: None

League: Brighton & HD Division One 1973-74, 99-2000, 00-01, 02-03.
Mid Sussex Premier 03-04, 06-07, 08-09. Southern Combination Division Two 15-16.

10 YEAR RECORD

09-10	10-11	11-12	12-13	13-14	14-15	15-16	16-17	17-18	18-19
MSuxP 7	MSuxP 9	MSuxP 5	MSuxP 7	MSuxP 2	MSuxP 7	SC2 1	SC1 18	SC1 14	SC1 3
									FAV 2Q

Heading south on the A23, turn right opposite Withdean Park into Togdean Lane, and go under railway bridge.

Nearest Railway Station Preston Park - 0.9km
Bus Route Bottom of Valley Drive - stop 91m away

ARUNDEL

Founded: 1889 Nickname: Mulletts

Club Contact Details 01903 882 548 mullets@btinternet.com

Ground: Mill Road, Arundel, W. Sussex BN18 9PA **Club Colours:** Red and white

HONOURS
FA Comps: None

League: Sussex County Division One 1957-58, 58-59, 86-87.

10 YEAR RECORD

09-10	10-11	11-12	12-13	13-14	14-15	15-16	16-17	17-18	18-19
SxC1 12	SxC1 9	SxC1 17	SxC1 14	SxC1 12	SxC1 10	SCP 12	SCP 15	SCP 17	SCP 19
FAC EP	FAC P	FAC P	FAC EP	FAC EPr	FAC EP	FAC Pr	FAC 1Q	FAC EP	FAC P
FAV 3P	FAV 2Q	FAV 2Q	FAV 2Q	FAV 2Q	FAV 1P	FAV 2Q	FAV 1Q	FAV 1Q	FAV 1Q

On A27 from Worthing over railway bridge to roundabout.
Second exit into Queen St to Town Centre. Cross Bridge over river, and turn right at miniroundabout.
Enter pay and display car par on right. Ground entrance is located at the far left hand corner of the car park.

Nearest Railway Station Arundel - 1.6km

BEXHILL UNITED

Founded: 2002 Nickname: The Pirates

Club Contact Details 07791 368 049 simon_dunne@hotmail.co.uk

Ground: The Polegrove, Brockley Road, Bexhill on Sea TN39 3EX **Club Colours:** White and black

HONOURS
FA Comps: None

League: Sussex County 1956-57, 65-66, 66-67.

10 YEAR RECORD

09-10	10-11	11-12	12-13	13-14	14-15	15-16	16-17	17-18	18-19
SxC3 2	SxC2 4	SxC2 7	SxC2 11	SxC2 8	SxC2 6	SC1 14	SC1 10	SC1 7	SC1 4
						FAC P			
					FAV 2Q	FAV 1Q	FAV 1Q	FAV 2Q	FAV 1Q

From west take A259, at Little Common roundabout take fourth exit into Cooden Sea Road, Turn Left at Cooden Beech Hotel into Cooden Drive. About 1½ miles further, turn right for Brockley Road. Ground at bottom on the right hand side

Nearest Railway Station Collington - 0.3km
Bus Route Polegrove - stop 91m away

BILLINGSHURST

Founded: 1891 Nickname: Hurst

Club Contact Details 01403 786 445 kevtilley@btinternet.com

Ground: Jubilee Fields, Newbridge Road, Billingshurst, West Sussex RH14 9HZ **Club Colours:** Red & black

HONOURS
FA Comps: None

League: West Sussex Premier Division 2011-12.

10 YEAR RECORD

09-10	10-11	11-12	12-13	13-14	14-15	15-16	16-17	17-18	18-19
		WSuxP 1	SxC3 4	SxC3 11	SxC3 6	SC2 5	SC1 15	SC1 16	SC1 12
								FAV 2Q	FAV 1Q

Follow A272 towards Petworth/Midhurst. When leaving the by-pass roundabout appr 50yds further on turn right to Jubilee Fields. (entrance to recycling tip) Follow Road Round.

Nearest Railway Station Billinghurst - 1.7km
Bus Route Hole Farm - stop 126m away

OUTS: Alfold (P - SCP), Steyning Town (SCP).

HAILSHAM TOWN

Founded: 1885 Nickname: The Stringers

Club Contact Details 01323 840 446 robvsquires@yahoo.co.uk

Ground: The Beaconfield, Western Road, Hailsham BN27 3DN **Club Colours:** Yellow & green

HONOURS **League:** Southern Counties Combination 1975-76.

FA Comps: None

10 YEAR RECORD

09-10	10-11	11-12	12-13	13-14	14-15	15-16	16-17	17-18	18-19
SxC1 19	SxC1 16	SxC2 2	SxC1 12	SxC1 16	SxC1 17	SCP 18	SCP 20	SC1 8	SC1 8
FAC EP	FAC EP	FAC EP	FAC EP	FAC EP	FAC EP	FAC EP	FAC EP	FAC EP	
FAV 1Q	FAV 1Q	FAV 1Q	FAV 1Q	FAV 1Q	FAV 1P	FAV 2P	FAV 1Q	FAV 1Q	FAV 2Q

Turn off A22 at Diplocks Way roundabout.
Ground on left (alleyway signposted opposite SETYRES WEALDEN) just before end of Diplocks Way.

Nearest Railway Station Polegate - 4.4km
Bus Route Bramble Drive - stop 190m away

LITTLEHAMPTON TOWN

Founded: 1896 Nickname: Marigolds

Club Contact Details 01903 716 390 paulcox280458@yahoo.co.uk

Ground: St Flora Sportsfield, St Flora's Road, Littlehampton BN17 6BD **Club Colours:** Gold and black

HONOURS **League:** Sussex County Division Two 1996-97, 2003-04, 12-13, Division One 1990-91, 2014-15.

FA Comps: None

10 YEAR RECORD

09-10	10-11	11-12	12-13	13-14	14-15	15-16	16-17	17-18	18-19
SxC2 12	SxC2 11	SxC2 4	SxC2 1	SxC1 3	SxC1 1	SCP 11	SCP 16	SCP 20	SC1 6
FAC EPr	FAC EPr	FAC EP	FAC 1Q	FAC 1Q	FAC 1Q	FAC P	FAC EP	FAC 1Qr	FAC EPr
FAV 1Q	FAV 1Q	FAV 2P	FAV 2Pr	FAV 2P	FAV 3Pr	FAV 1P	FAV 2Qr	FAV 1Q	FAV 2Q

Leave A259 at Waterford Business Park and turn into Horsham Road.
After Shell Garage turn left into St. Floras Road.
Ground is at the end of road on the left.

Nearest Railway Station Littlehampton - 1km
Bus Route Parkside Avenue - stop 79m away

MIDHURST & EASEBOURNE

Founded: 1946 Nickname: The Stags

Club Contact Details 01730 816 557 midhurstfc@gmail.com

Ground: Rotherfield, Dodsley Lane, Easebourne, Midhurst GU29 9BE **Club Colours:** All blue

HONOURS **League:** West Sussex 1955-56, 62-63, 64-65, Premier 67-68.
Sussex County Division Three 94-95, 2002-03.

FA Comps: None

10 YEAR RECORD

09-10	10-11	11-12	12-13	13-14	14-15	15-16	16-17	17-18	18-19
SxC2 18	SxC2 15	SxC2 15	SxC2 8	SxC2 14	SxC2 8	SC1 15	SC1 9	SC1 13	SC1 16
								FAV 2Q	FAV 1Q

Ground one mile out of Midhurst on London Road (A286) opposite Texaco Garage. Ample car parking.

Bus Route Dodsley Grove - Stop 125m away

MILE OAK

Founded: 1960 Nickname: The Oak

Club Contact Details 01273 423 854 tewey62@virginmedia.com

Ground: Mile Oak Recreation Ground, Chalky Road, Portslade BN41 2WF **Club Colours:** Tangerine and black

HONOURS **League:** Brighton & Hove District Div.8 1960-61, Div.4 65-66, Div.2 72-73,
Div.1 73-74, Prem 1980-81. Sussex County Division Two 94-95.

FA Comps: None

10 YEAR RECORD

09-10	10-11	11-12	12-13	13-14	14-15	15-16	16-17	17-18	18-19
SxC1 20	SxC2 7	SxC2 10	SxC2 7	SxC2 7	SxC2 5	SC1 6	SC1 4	SC1 6	SC1 7
FAC P	FAC EP	FAC EPr				FAC EP	FAC EP	FAC EP	
FAV 1Q	FAV 2Q	FAV 2Q		FAV 1Qr	FAV 2Q	FAV 2Q	FAV 2Q	FAV 2Q	FAV 1Qr

From A27 (Brighton Bypass) leave at A293 exit. Right at first roundabout. Ground 1 mile on right.
Parking in the Sports Centre opposite the ground (park) entrance.

Nearest Railway Station Fishersgate - 2.1km
Bus Route New England Rise - stop 11m away

OAKWOOD

Founded: 1962 Nickname: The Oaks

Club Contact Details 01293 515 742 sarah.daly13@hotmail.co.uk

Ground: Tinsley Lane, Three Bridges, Crawley RH10 8AT **Club Colours:** Red & black

HONOURS **League:** Crawley Division One 1973-74. Sussex County Division Three 1984-85, Division Two 2005-06.

FA Comps: None

10 YEAR RECORD

09-10		10-11		11-12		12-13		13-14		14-15		15-16		16-17		17-18		18-19	
SxC2	9	SxC2	17	SxC2	18	SxC2	15	SxC2	12	SxC2	4	SC1	3	SC1	14	SC1	17	SC1	15
FAC	EP	FAC	EP											FAC	EP				
FAV	1Q	FAV	1Q	FAV	1Q	FAV	1Q	FAV	1Q	FAV	1Q	FAV	2Q	FAV	2Q	FAV	1Q	FAV	1Q

From the South on M23, take junction 10 exit left onto A2011, next roundabout take fourth exit right, next roundabout second exit, take first right into Tinsley Lane. Ground entrance 100 metres on left.

Nearest Railway Station Three Bridges - 1.3km

Bus Route Maxwell Way - Stop 98m away

ROFFEY

Founded: 1901 Nickname:

Club Contact Details afchantrill@gmail.com

Ground: Chennells, Bartholomew Way, Horsham RH12 5JL **Club Colours:** Blue and white

HONOURS **League:** Mid Sussex Division One 2009-10.

FA Comps: None

10 YEAR RECORD

09-10		10-11		11-12		12-13		13-14		14-15		15-16		16-17		17-18		18-19	
MSux1	1	MSuxP	2	SxC3	16	SxC3	8	SxC3	3	SxC3	8	SC2	2	SC2	7	SC2	6	SC2	3

SEAFORD TOWN

Founded: 1888 Nickname: The Badgers

Club Contact Details 01323 892 221 secretary@seafordtownfc.com

Ground: The Crouch, Bramber Road, Seaford BN25 1AF **Club Colours:** All red

HONOURS **League:** Lewes 1907-08.
Sussex County Division Three 1985-86, Division Two 1988-89, 2005-06.

FA Comps: None

10 YEAR RECORD

09-10		10-11		11-12		12-13		13-14		14-15		15-16		16-17		17-18		18-19	
SxC2	10	SxC2	5	SxC2	17	SxC2	12	SxC2	17	SxC2	15	SC1	16	SC1	13	SC1	12	SC1	11
				FAV	1P	FAV	2Q	FAV	1Q	FAV	2Q	FAV	1Q	FAV	2Q	FAV	1Q	FAV	2Q

A259 to Seaford. At mini roundabout by station, turn left (coming from Newhaven) or RIGHT (from Eastbourne).
At end of Church Street, across junction, then left at end. After 500m turn left up Ashurst Road Bramber Road is at the top.

Nearest Railway Station Seaford - 0.6km

Bus Route Seaford Head Lower School - stop 168m away

SELSEY

Founded: 1903 Nickname: Blues

Club Contact Details 01243 603 420 selseyfootballclub@yahoo.com

Ground: The Bunn Leisure Stadium, High Street, Selsey, Chichester, PO20 0QG **Club Colours:** All blue

HONOURS **League:** West Sussex Division One 1938-39, 54-55, 56-57, 57-58, 58-59, 60-61.
Sussex County Division Two 1963-64, 75-76.

FA Comps: None

10 YEAR RECORD

09-10		10-11		11-12		12-13		13-14		14-15		15-16		16-17		17-18		18-19	
SxC1	11	SxC1	17	SxC1	12	SxC1	18	SxC1	17	SxC1	20	SC1	13	SC1	7	SC1	9	SC1	5
FAC	2Q	FAC	EP	FAC	P	FAC	EP	FAC	EP	FAC	EP	FAC	EP						
FAV	2Q	FAV	1Q	FAV	1Q	FAV	1Q	FAV	1Q	FAV	1Q	FAV	2Q	FAV	2Q	FAV	2Q	FAV	2Q

Entering Selsey go straight over roundabout and straight over to mini-roundabout to traffic lights.
Turn sharp right at lights, through supermarket car park to ground.

Bus Route Medical Centre - stop 92m away

SHOREHAM

Founded: 1892 Nickname: Musselmen

Club Contact Details 01273 454 261 stuart.slaney@gmail.com

Ground: Middle Road, Shoreham-by-Sea, West Sussex, BN43 6GA **Club Colours:** All blue

HONOURS **League:** West Sussex Junior Division 1897-98, Senior Division 1902-03, 04-05, 05-06. Sussex County Division One 1951-52, 52-53, 77-78, Division Two 1961-62, 76-77, 84-85, 93-94. Southern

FA Comps: None

10 YEAR RECORD

09-10		10-11		11-12		12-13		13-14		14-15		15-16		16-17		17-18		18-19	
SxC1	9	SxC1	18	SxC1	18	SxC1	17	SxC1	14	SxC1	16	SCP	17	SCP	1	Isth1S	24	SCP	20
FAC	P	FAC	EP	FAC	1Q	FAC	EPr	FAC	1Q	FAC	P	FAC	1Q	FAC	P	FAC	1Q	FAC	P
FAV	3P	FAV	1P	FAV	2Q	FAV	1Q	FAV	2Q	FAV	2Q	FAV	1Q	FAV	1P	FAT	P	FAV	2Q

Take the A27 to Shoreham. At the Holmbush Roundabout take the exit towards Southlands Hospital. Immediately before the hospital, turn left down Hammy Lane, then right at the mini roundabout into Middle Road. The entrance to the ground is at the far end of the recreation ground immediately on the right.

Nearest Railway Station Shoreham-by-Sea - 1.1km
Bus Route Hammy Lane - stop 150m away

SIDLESHAM

Founded: 1921 Nickname: The Sids

Club Contact Details 07887 981 267 michael.maiden@aol.com

Ground: Recreation Ground, Selsey Road Sidlesham Nr Chichester PO20 7RD **Club Colours:** Yellow and green

HONOURS **League:** West Sussex Division One 1963-64, Premier 2011-12. Sussex County Division Three 1996-97, 2012-13, Division Two 99-2000

FA Comps: None

10 YEAR RECORD

09-10		10-11		11-12		12-13		13-14		14-15		15-16		16-17		17-18		18-19	
SxC2	11	SxC2	16	WSuxP	1	SxC3	1	SxC3	5	SxC3	2	SC1	11	SC2	3	SC2	2	SC1	10
																FAV	1Q	FAV	1P

sidlesham - Recreation Ground, Selsey Road Sidlesham Nr Chichester PO20 7RD - 01243 641538
From Chichester bypass, take the B2145 (Hunston/Selsey) and head towards Selsey. On entering Sidlesham, pass garage - the ground is on the right between houses.

SOUTHWICK

Founded: 1882 Nickname: The Wickers

Club Contact Details 01273 701 010 clive.harman1966@btinternet.com

Ground: Old Barn Way, Southwick BN42 4NT **Club Colours:** Red & black

HONOURS **League:** West Sussex Senior 1896-97, 97-98. Sussex County Div.1 25-26, 27-28, 29-30, 47-48, 68-69, 74-75, Div.2 2000-01, Div.3 14-15. Isthmian D2S 1985-86.

FA Comps: None

10 YEAR RECORD

09-10		10-11		11-12		12-13		13-14		14-15		15-16		16-17		17-18		18-19	
SxC2	16	SxC2	12	SxC2	8	SxC2	14	SxC3	9	SxC3	1	SC1	5	SC1	11	SC1	18	SC1	13
FAC	Pr	FAC	EP																
FAV	1Q	FAV	2Q			FAV	1Q	FAV	2Q	FAV	2Q	FAV	1Q	FAV	1Q	FAV	1Q	FAV	2Q

A27 from Brighton take first left after Southwick sign to Leisure Centre. Ground adjacent.
Five minutes walk from Fishergate or Southwick stations.

Nearest Railway Station Fishersgate - 0.4km
Bus Route Old Barn Way - stop 151m away

STORRINGTON

Founded: 1920 Nickname: The Swans

Club Contact Details 01903 745 860 keithdalmon@btinternet.com

Ground: Recreation Ground, Pulborough Road, Storrington RH20 4HJ **Club Colours:** All blue

HONOURS **League:** Sussex County Division Three 2004-05.

FA Comps: None

10 YEAR RECORD

09-10		10-11		11-12		12-13		13-14		14-15		15-16		16-17		17-18		18-19	
SxC2	7	SxC2	8	SxC2	9	SxC2	10	SxC2	15	SxC2	14	SC1	4	SC1	12	SC1	15	SC1	14

Turn west on A283 (off A24).
Ground opposite pond to west of village centre.

Nearest Railway Station Pulborough - 5.6km
Bus Route Brow Close - stop 238m away

WICK

Founded: 1892 Nickname: The Wickers

Club Contact Details 01903 713 535 wickfootballclub@outlook.com

Ground: Crabtree Park, Coomes Way, Wick, Littlehampton, W Sussex BN17 7LS **Club Colours:** Red & black

HONOURS **League:** Sussex County Division Two 1981-82, 85-86, 89-90, 93-94.

FA Comps: None

10 YEAR RECORD

09-10		10-11		11-12		12-13		13-14		14-15		15-16		16-17		17-18		18-19	
SxC1	4	SxC1	15	SxC1	14	SxC1	16	SxC2	6	SxC2	3	SCP	16	SCP	19	SC1	5	SC1	9
FAC	P	FAC	EP	FAC	EP									FAC	EP	FAC	EP	FAC	EP
FAV	1P	FAV	1P	FAV	1Q	FAV	2Q							FAV	1P	FAV	1Q	FAV	1P

A27 to Crossbush. A284 towards Littlehampton.
After one mile over level crossing left into Coomes Way next to Locomotive pub. Ground at end.

Nearest Railway Station Littlehampton - 1.7km
Bus Route Seaton Road - stop 250 m away

WORTHING UNITED

Founded: 1952 Nickname: Mavericks

Club Contact Details 01903 234 466 secretary@worthingunitedfc.co.uk

Ground: The Robert Albon Memorial Ground, Lyons Way BN14 9JF **Club Colours:** Sky blue & white

HONOURS **League:** Sussex County Division Two 1973-74, 2014-15, Division Three 1989-90.

FA Comps: None

10 YEAR RECORD

09-10		10-11		11-12		12-13		13-14		14-15		15-16		16-17		17-18		18-19	
SxC2	2	SxC2	3	SxC1	14	SxC1	22	SxC1	20	SxC2	1	SCP	14	SCP	17	SCP	19	SC1	17
FAC	EP	FAC	P					FAC	EPr	FAC	EP	FAC	EPr	FAC	EP	FAC	EP	FAC	P
FAV	2Q	FAV	2Q			FAV	1Qr	FAV	2Q	FAV	2Q	FAV	1P	FAV	1Q	FAV	1Q	FAV	1Q

From the West past Hill Barn roundabout to second set of traffic lights, turn left into Lyons Way.
From East first set of traffic lights at end of Sompting bypass, turn right into Lyons Way.

Nearest Railway Station East Worthing - 1.9km
Bus Route Lyons Farm Sainsbury's - stop 203m away

DIVISION TWO INS: St Francis Rangers (Withdrew from SC1 during 2018-19), TD Shipley (P - WSusxP).
OUTS: ROFFEY (P - SC1)

Southern Combination Division Two	
ANGMERING VILLAGE	Decoy Drive, Angmering BN16 4DN
BOSHAM	Recreation Ground, Walton Lane, Bosham, West Sussex PO10 8QF
BRIGHTON ELECTRICITY	Withdean Stadium, Tongdean Lane, Brighton BN1 5JD
COPTHORNE	King Georges Field, Copthorne Bank, Copthorne RH10 3JQ
COWFOLD	The Sports Ground, Bolney Road, Cowfold, West Sussex RH13 8BL
FERRING	The Glebelands, Ferring, West Sussex BN12 5JL
JARVIS BROOK	Limekiln Playing Fields, Palesgate Lane, Crowborough TN6 3HF
LITTLEHAMPTON UNITED	The Sportsfield, St Flora's Road, Littlehampton BN17 6BD
MONTPELIER VILLA	Falmer Sports Complex, University of Sussex, Pavillion Rd, Brighton BN1 9PJ
ROTTINGDEAN VILLAGE	Rottingdean Sports Centre, Falmer Road, Rottingdean BN2 7DA
RUSTINGTON	Recreation Ground, Jubilee Avenue, Rustington BN16 3NB
ST. FRANCIS RANGERS	Colwell Ground, Princess Royal Hospital, Lewes Rd, Haywards Hth RH16 4SP
TD SHIPLEY	Dragons Lane, Horsham RH13 8GD
UPPER BEEDING	Memorial Playing Fields, High Street, Upper Beeding BN44 3WN
WORTHING TOWN	Palatine Park, Palatine Road, Worthing, Sussex BN12 6JN

PREMIER DIVISION INS: Greenwich Borough (R - IsthSE), Erith & Belvedere (P - SCE1), Welling Town (P - SEC1).
OUTS: Cray Valley PM (P - IsthSE), Croydon (R - SCE1), Rusthall (R - SCE1).

AFC CROYDON ATHLETIC

Nickname: The Rams **Club Colours:** All maroon

Founded 2012

Club Contact Details 020 8689 5322 secretary@afccroydonathletic.co.uk
Ground: Mayfield Stadium, off Mayfield Road, Thornton Heath CR7 6DN
Capacity: 3,000 **Seats:** 301 **Covered:** 660 **Shop:** Yes

Previous Names: None
Previous Leagues: Combined Counties 2012-15.

HONOURS: FA Comps: None
League: None

10 YEAR RECORD

09-10	10-11	11-12	12-13	13-14	14-15	15-16	16-17	17-18	18-19
			CC1 8	CC1 7	CC1 2	SCE 11	SCEP 7	SCEP 13	SCEP 15
				FAC EP	FAC EP	FAC EP	FAC EP	FAC P	FAC 1Q
			FAV 1P	FAV 1P	FAV 2Q	FAV 1Pr	FAV 2Q	FAV 2Q	FAV 2P

From M25: Exit at either Junction 6 and then take the A22 to Purley Cross and then join the A23 London Road and then directions below from Purley, or exit at Junction 7 and take the A23 London Road all the way.
From Streatham and Norbury: Take the A23 London Road to the roundabout at Thornton Heath, continue down the A23 Thornton Road. Then take the 1st on the Right past the No Entry road (Fairlands Avenue), Silverleigh Road, 50 yards, at the fork, keep left (signposted Croydon Athletic FC) into Trafford Road, then Mayfield Road (which is a continuation of Trafford Road) Go to the end of Mayfield Road, then left at the last house. Follow the lane, passed allotments, past an open car park space and continue along the lane to our club car park.

BEARSTED

Nickname: The Bears **Club Colours:** White and blue

Founded 1895

Club Contact Details 07849 089 875 benton951@aol.com
Ground: Otham Sports Ground, White Horse Lane, Otham ME15 8RG
Capacity: **Seats:** Yes **Covered:** Yes

Previous Names: None
Previous Leagues: Maidstone & District. Kent County 1982-2011. Kent Invicta (Founder Member) 2011-16.

HONOURS: FA Comps: None
League: Maidstone & District Div.6 1961-62, Div.3 73-74, Div.2 74-75, Div.1 77-78, Premier 79-80, 80-81, 81-82.
Kent County WD2 82-83, WD1 83-84, WPrem 87-87, WSen 87-88, D1W 96-97, Prem 2000-01, 01-02. Kent Invicta 2015-16.

10 YEAR RECORD

09-10	10-11	11-12	12-13	13-14	14-15	15-16	16-17	17-18	18-19
KC P 8	KC P 8	K_lv 7	K_lv 4	K_lv 6	K_lv 2	K_lv 1	SCEP 12	SCEP 14	SCEP 14
								FAC EP	FAC P
							FAV 1Q	FAV 1Q	FAV 4P

Nearest Railway Station Bearsted - 3.2km
Bus Route Arriva No.13

BECKENHAM TOWN

Nickname: Reds **Club Colours:** All red

Founded 1887

Club Contact Details 07774 728 758 peterpalmer3@sky.com
Ground: Eden Park Avenue, Beckenham Kent BR3 3JL
Capacity: 4,000 **Seats:** 120 **Covered:** 120 **Shop:** Yes

Previous Names: Original club folded in 1969 and reformed based on the Stanhope Rovers Junior team in 1971.
Previous Leagues: London 1923-35, 51-61. Kent County Amateur 1935-51. Aetolian 1961-64. Greater London 1964-69. South East London Amateur 1971-75. London Spartan 1975-82.

HONOURS: FA Comps: None
League: London Division One 1927-28.

10 YEAR RECORD

09-10	10-11	11-12	12-13	13-14	14-15	15-16	16-17	17-18	18-19
Kent P 4	Kent P 10	Kent P 6	Kent P 11	SCE 8	SCE 9	SCE 12	SCEP 18	SCEP 4	SCEP 5
	FAC 2Q	FAC 2Qr	FAC 1Q	FAC EP	FAC EP	FAC P	FAC P	FAC EP	FAC 1Qr
FAV 3P	FAV 3P	FAV 1P	FAV 1P	FAV 3P	FAV 2Q	FAV 2P	FAV 1P	FAV 3P	FAV 1P

374 Eden Park Avenue, Beckenham, Kent BR3 3JL

Nearest Railway Station Eden Park - 0.3km

CANTERBURY CITY

Founded 1904

Nickname: **Club Colours:** Burgundy and white

Club Contact Details 01795 591 900 secretary@cantcityfc.net

Ground: Shepherd Neame Stadium, Salters Lane, Faversham ME13 8ND

Capacity: 2,500 **Seats:** 180 **Covered:** 180 **Shop:** Yes

Previous Names: None

Previous Leagues: Kent 1947-59, 94-01, Metropolitan 1959-60, Southern 1960-94, Kent County 2007-11.

HONOURS: FA Comps: None

League: Kent County Division Two East 2007-08, One East 08-09.

10 YEAR RECORD

09-10	10-11	11-12	12-13	13-14	14-15	15-16	16-17	17-18	18-19
KC P 5	KC P 2	Kent P 9	Kent P 9	SCE 12	SCE 12	SCE 8	SCEP 9	SCEP 10	SCEP 9
				FAC EP	FAC P	FAC P	FAC Pr	FAC EP	FAC EP
			FAV 1P	FAV 1Q	FAV 1Q	FAV 3P	FAV 2P	FAV 2P	FAV SF

From M2, follow into Faversham, turn right onto A2, and next right into Salters Lane. Ground and car park on the left.

CHATHAM TOWN

Founded 1882

Nickname: Chats **Club Colours:** All red & black

Club Contact Details 01634 401 130 secretary@chathamtownfc.com

Ground: Maidstone Road, Chatham ME4 6LR

Capacity: 2,000 **Seats:** 600 **Covered:** 600 **Shop:** Yes

Previous Names: Chatham FC 1882-1974, Medway FC 1974-79

Previous Leagues: Southern 1894-1900, 1920-21, 27-29, 83-88, 2001-06, Kent 1894-96, 1901-1905, 29-59, 68-83, 88-2001, Aetolian 1959-64, Metropolitan 1964-68, Isthmian 2006-17.

HONOURS: FA Comps: None

League: Kent 1894-95, 1903-04, 04-05, 71-72, 73-74, 75-76, 76-77, 79-80, 2000-01. Aetolian 1963-64.

10 YEAR RECORD

09-10	10-11	11-12	12-13	13-14	14-15	15-16	16-17	17-18	18-19
Isth1S 17	Isth1S 21	Isth1N 15	Isth1N 13	Isth1N 12	Isth1N 21	Isth1S 19	Isth1S 22	SCEP 16	SCEP 4
FAC 1Qr	FAC P	FAC 1Q	FAC 1Q	FAC 4Q	FAC P	FAC 2Q	FAC Pr	FAC EPr	FAC P
FAT P	FAT P	FAT P	FAT 1Q	FAT 2Q	FAT 1Qr	FAT 1Q	FAT P	FAV 2Q	FAV 2P

Exit the M2 at junction 3, and follow directions for Chatham & Town Centre. You will then pass a Homebase & Toys 'R' Us on the left hand side. Continue straight over the roundabout and then there is a split in the road, where you bear right for chatham this is Maidstone Road. Follow this, continuing straight over the cross roads and you will see a petrol station on the left. Bournville Road is opposite the petrol station on the left. Ground entrance is first left.

Nearest Railway Station Chatham - 1.4km

Bus Route Bus stops outside the ground.

CORINTHIAN

Founded 1972

Nickname: The Hoops **Club Colours:** Green & white hoops

Club Contact Details 01474 573 116 corinthians@billingsgroup.com

Ground: Gay Dawn Farm, Valley Road, Longfield DA3 8LY

Capacity: **Seats:** Yes **Covered:** Yes

Previous Names: Welling United Reserves > 2009.

Previous Leagues: Southern 1985-91.

HONOURS: FA Comps: None

League: Southern Counties East 2003-04.

10 YEAR RECORD

09-10	10-11	11-12	12-13	13-14	14-15	15-16	16-17	17-18	18-19
Kent P 14	Kent P 12	Kent P 7	Kent P 4	SCE 5	SCE 6	SCE 6	SCEP 10	SCEP 9	SCEP 2
		FAC P	FAC P	FAC P	FAC EP	FAC P	FAC EP	FAC EPr	FAC 1Qr
	FAV 1P	FAV 2Q	FAV 1Q	FAV 1P	FAV 1P	FAV 1P	FAV 4P	FAV 2P	FAV 2P

From the station turn right and at once bear right into footpath alongside railway, and at end right into Ash Road, then up hill, right into Castle Hill, left into Valley Road, out of town and then left into Pennis Lane and ground is on left.

Nearest Railway Station Longfield - 1.5 miles away

CROWBOROUGH ATHLETIC

Nickname: The Crows **Club Colours:** Navy blue and sky blue

Founded 1894

Club Contact Details 07557 107 445 cafcsec@outlook.com

Ground: Crowborough Co. Stadium, Alderbrook Rec, Fermor Road, TN6 3AN

Capacity: 2,000 **Seats:** 150 **Covered:** 150

Previous Names: -

Previous Leagues: Sussex County 1974-2008. Isthmian 2008-09. Sussex County 2009-14.

HONOURS: FA Comps: None

League: Sussex County Division Two 1992-93, 2004-05, Division Three 2003-04, Division One 2007-08.

10 YEAR RECORD

09-10	10-11	11-12	12-13	13-14	14-15	15-16	16-17	17-18	18-19
SxC1 18	SxC1 12	SxC1 13	SxC1 15	SxC1 5	SCE 10	SCE 7	SCEP 2	SCEP 3	SCEP 13
FAC EPr	FAC EP	FAC EP	FAC P	FAC EPr	FAC EPr	FAC EPr	FAC EP	FAC 2Q	FAC EPr
FAV 2P	FAV 1Q	FAV 1Q	FAV 1Q	FAV 2P	FAV 1Q	FAV 1Q	FAV 5P	FAV 4P	FAV 2P

Walking or driving from the Town Centre to the football club - If you use the A26 you'll either turn left or right to get in to the High Street, at the traffic lights, depending if you've come from the Tunbridge Wells or Uckfield direction. Head down the High Street from the lights until you cross the zebra crossing after about 100 yards. Then you'll need to bear right and turn in to Croft Road, you'll go over another zebra crossing, carry straight on past the front of Waitrose and then you'll come to a mini roundabout which you go straight over. After 50 yards there's another mini roundabout, go straight over and follow the road round the 's' bend, an M&S Petrol Station will be on your right, and then head towards the next junction. At the junction of Myrtle Road on your left and Southview Road on your right, Croft Road changes in to Whitehill Road without you ever realising it so carry straight on. Go down the hill and there will be a public house on your right hand side called The Bricklayers, carry on past the pub and then you'll come to another mini roundabout, take the first exit left, this is the start of Fermor Road and take the second right, this is Aldervale Cottages and turn immediately right again into The Crowborough Community Ground, known locally as Alderbrook Rec Ground.

DEAL TOWN

Nickname: The Hoops **Club Colours:** Black & white

Founded 1908

Club Contact Details 01304 375 623 secretary@dealtownfc.co.uk

Ground: Charles Sports Ground, St Leonards Road, Deal CT14 9AU

Capacity: 2,500 **Seats:** 180 **Covered:** 180 **Shop:** Yes

Previous Names: Deal Cinque Ports FC > 1920

Previous Leagues: Thanet. East Kent. Kent 1894-96, 1900-27, 32-39, 45-59, 72-84, Southern 1894-1901 & 84-90, Aetolian 1959-64, Greater London 1964-65, Metropolitan 1965-71, Metropolitan London 1971-72

HONOURS: FA Comps: FA Vase 1999-2000

League: Kent 1953-54. Southern Counties East 1999-2000.

10 YEAR RECORD

09-10	10-11	11-12	12-13	13-14	14-15	15-16	16-17	17-18	18-19
Kent P 9	Kent P 11	Kent P 15	Kent P 12	SCE 13	SCE 13	SCE 9	SCEP 13	SCEP 7	SCEP 11
FAC 1Qr	FAC P	FAC P	FAC EP	FAC P	FAC Pr	FAC 2Q	FAC EP	FAC P	FAC EPr
FAV 1Q	FAV 1Q	FAV 2P	FAV 2P	FAV 1Q	FAV 1Q	FAV 2P	FAV 2Qr	FAV 2P	FAV 1P

Come in on Queen Street, then right into London Road and over bridge, straight on into St Leonard's Road where London Road bears right, and entrance to ground is on left.

Nearest Railway Station Deal - 3/4 mile away

ERITH & BELVEDERE

Nickname: Deres **Club Colours:** Blue & white

Founded 1922

Club Contact Details 07729 358 033 deres.secretary@hotmail.com

Ground: Park View Road, Welling DA16 1SY

Capacity: 4,000 **Seats:** 1,070 **Covered:** 1,000 **Shop:** Yes

Previous Names: Belvedere & District FC (Formed 1918 restructured 1922)

Previous Leagues: Kent 1922-29, 31-39, 78-82. London. Corinthian 1945-63. Athenian 1963-78. Southern. Kent League 2005-13. Isthmian 2013-14.

HONOURS: FA Comps: None

League: Kent Division One / Premier 1981-82 / 2012-13.

10 YEAR RECORD

09-10	10-11	11-12	12-13	13-14	14-15	15-16	16-17	17-18	18-19
Kent P 12	Kent P 5	Kent P 2	Kent P 1	Isth1N 24	SCEP 3	SCEP 16	SCEP 20	SCE1 4	SCE1 2
FAC P	FAC 2Q	FAC 1Q	FAC EP	FAC P	FAC Pr	FAC P	FAC EP	FAC P	FAC EPr
FAV 2P	FAV 2P	FAV 1Q	FAV 3P	FAT P	FAV QF	FAV 2P	FAV 1Q	FAV 1Pr	FAV 1Q

Take the M25 to Junction 2. At the roundabout, take the A2 towards Central London. Leave the A2 at the third exit (Danson Interchange, signposted A221 to Bexleyheath and Sidcup). Turn right (second exit) at the roundabout at the end of the slip road, and then turn right (third exit) at the next roundabout. Go under the A2 Bridge and up the slope to another roundabout. Take the second exit and follow the road (Danson Road) to the traffic lights at the end. Turn left at the lights onto Park View Road. The ground is on the left. There is no car park, but plenty of street parking is available.

Nearest Railway Station Welling - 1.1km

ERITH TOWN

Nickname: The Dockers **Club Colours:** Red & black stripes

Founded 1956

Club Contact Details 07877 766 794 secretary@erithtown.co.uk

Ground: Erith Stadium, Avenue Road, Erith DA8 3AT

Capacity: **Seats:** Yes **Covered:** Yes

Previous Names: Woolwich Town 1959-89 and 1990-97.

Previous Leagues: London Metropolitan Sunday. London Spartan.

HONOURS: FA Comps: None

League: London Metropolitan Sunday Senior Section 1965-66, 70-71, 74-75.

10 YEAR RECORD

09-10	10-11	11-12	12-13	13-14	14-15	15-16	16-17	17-18	18-19
Kent P 12	Kent P 8	Kent P 4	Kent P 3	SCE 3	SCE 19	SCE 13	SCEP 17	SCEP 17	SCEP 6
FAC 1Qr	FAC 2Q	FAC 2Q	FAC EP	FAC P	FAC EP	FAC P	FAC P	FAC 1Q	FAC 2Q
FAV 1P	FAV 2Q	FAV 2P	FAV 2P	FAV 3P	FAV 2P	FAV 2Q	FAV 1Q	FAV 2P	FAV 3P

The stadium is located on the right hand side towards the end of Avenue Road.

Nearest Railway Station Erith

FISHER

Nickname: The Fish **Club Colours:** Black & white stripes

Founded 1908

Club Contact Details 07854 172 490 secretary.fisherfc@yahoo.com

Ground: St Pauls Sports Ground, Salter Road, Rotherhithe, London SE16 5EF

Capacity: **Seats:** Yes **Covered:** Yes

Previous Names: Fisher Athletic. Reformed as Fisher F.C. in 2009.

Previous Leagues: Parthenon, Kent Amateur, London Spartan, Southern, Isthmian, Conference.

HONOURS: FA Comps: None

League: Southern Southern Division 1982-83, Premier 86-87, Eastern 2004-05.

10 YEAR RECORD

09-10	10-11	11-12	12-13	13-14	14-15	15-16	16-17	17-18	18-19
Kent P 13	Kent P 16	Kent P 10	Kent P 14	SCEP 14	SCEP 16	SCEP 17	SCEP 19	SCE1 3	SCEP 3
		FAC P	FAC EPr	FAC EP	FAC P	FAC EP			FAC EP
	FAV 1P	FAV 2Q	FAV 2Q	FAV 2Q	FAV 1Pr	FAV 2P		FAV 1P	FAV 1Qr

The new stadium can be found around 100 yards from the old Surrey Docks Stadium on Salter Road.

The stadium is roughly 10 minutes walk from Rotherhithe Station on the London Overground, and 15 minutes walk from Canada Water Station for the Jubilee Line. The 381 and C10 buses both stop adjacent to the stadium. Nelson Dock Pier is 15 minutes walk away, served by River Bus 4 from Canary Wharf.

Nearest Railway Station Rotherhithe, on the London Overground (1 km)

GLEBE

Nickname: **Club Colours:** Red & black

Founded 2013

Club Contact Details 07432 291 838 lukejefferies@virginmedia.com

Ground: Foxbury Avenue, Chislehurst, Bromley BR7 6SD

Capacity: 1,200 **Seats:** Yes **Covered:** Yes

Previous Names: Glebe Wickham Youth Team founded in 1995 with an adult side formed in 2013.

Previous Leagues: Kent Invicta 2013-16.

HONOURS: FA Comps: None

League: Southern Counties east Division One 2016-17.

10 YEAR RECORD

09-10	10-11	11-12	12-13	13-14	14-15	15-16	16-17	17-18	18-19
				K_Iv 10	K_Iv 7	K_Iv 3	SCE1 1	SCEP 12	SCEP 8
						FAC EP	FAC EP	FAC 2Qr	FAC EP
				FAV 2Q	FAV 1Q	FAV 1Q	FAV 3P	FAV 1Qr	FAV 2Q

The club is located just off the A222 close to the Vauxhall Garage and a stone's throw away from the Sidcup bypass.

Nearest Railway Station Sidcup - 1.9km

Bus Route Nos. 269 & 260.

GREENWICH BOROUGH

Founded 1928

Nickname: Boro **Club Colours:** Red & white

Club Contact Details 0208 850 5220 clubsecretary@greenwichbfc.co.uk

Ground: Phoenix Sports Club, Mayplace Road East, Bexleyheath DA7 6JT

Capacity: 1,000 **Seats:** 100 **Covered:** Yes **Shop:**

Previous Names: Woolwich Borough Council Athletic 1928-65. London Borough of Greenwich 1965-84.

Previous Leagues: Woolwich & District 1928-29. Kent Amateur 1929-39, 46-48. South London Alliance 1948-76. London Spartan 1976-84. Kent/Southern Counties East 1984-2016. Isthmian 2016-19.

HONOURS: FA Comps:

League: Woolwich & District 1928-29. South London Alliance Division Two 1954-55, Division One 1955-56, Premier Division 1960-61, 61-62, 62-63, 63-64, 64-65, 65-66, 73-74. London Spartan 1979-80. Kent 1986-87, 87-88.

10 YEAR RECORD

09-10	10-11	11-12	12-13	13-14	14-15	15-16	16-17	17-18	18-19
Kent P 5	Kent P 4	Kent P 16	Kent P 15	SCE 9	SCE 4	SCE 1	Isth1S 3	Isth1S 4	IsthSE 19
	FAC EP	FAC EP	FAC 1Q	FAC P	FAC 4Q	FAC 1Q	FAC 1Q	FAC 1Q	FAC P
FAV 1P	FAV 1P	FAV 1P	FAV 1Q	FAV 1P	FAV 4P	FAV 2P	FAT Pr	FAT P	FAT 3Q

Take A206/Bob Dunn Way towards Erith (Jct 1a off the A282). Continue on the A206 through five roundabouts, at the sixth take the second exit onto A2000/Perry Street. Follow the A2000 for half a mile and turn right onto Mayplace Road. At the next roundabout take the second exit and stay on Mayplace Road East. Ground will be on the left.

Nearest Railway Station Barnehurst - 1.1km

Bus Route 492 stops at the ground

HOLLANDS & BLAIR

Founded 1967

Nickname: Blair **Club Colours:** All red

Club Contact Details 01634 573 839 laurence.plummer@btinternet.com

Ground: Star Meadow Sports Club, Darland Avenue, Gillingham, Kent ME7 3AN

Capacity: **Seats:** Yes **Covered:** Yes

Previous Names: Hollands & Blair United 1970-74

Previous Leagues: Rochester & District 1970-2004. Kent County 2004-11

HONOURS: FA Comps: None

League: Rochester & District Premier 1989-90, 93-94, 2002-03, 03-04. Kent County Division Two Easy 2004-05, Division One East 05-06, Premier 08-9, 10-11. Kent Invicta 2013-14, 14-15.

10 YEAR RECORD

09-10	10-11	11-12	12-13	13-14	14-15	15-16	16-17	17-18	18-19
KC P 2	KC P 1	K_Iv 3	K_Iv 2	K_Iv 1	K_Iv 1	SCE 2	SCEP 8	SCEP 18	SCEP 18
							FAC Pr	FAC P	FAC EP
						FAV 2Q	FAV 1P	FAV 1P	FAV 1Q

Hollands & Blair FC's home ground can be found on Darland Avenue, Gillingham. The car park entrance is just after The Star Public House car park. The post code for Sat Nav is ME7 3AP.

K SPORTS

Founded 1919

Nickname: The Paperboys **Club Colours:** Black & white

Club Contact Details 07725 941 711 tonyhighsted@yahoo.co.uk

Ground: Cobdown Sports & Social Club, Station Road, Ditton, Aylesford, Kent ME20 6AU

Capacity: **Seats:** **Covered:**

Previous Names: Reeds International. APM. APM Contrast.

Previous Leagues: Kent County >2015.

HONOURS: FA Comps: None

League: Kent Division Two 1929-30, 30-31, 31-32, 46-47. Kent County Senior Division West 1959-60, 63-64, Premier West 1990-91.

10 YEAR RECORD

09-10	10-11	11-12	12-13	13-14	14-15	15-16	16-17	17-18	18-19
KC1E 5	KC1E 2	KC P 6	KC P 6	KC P 3	KC P 4	K_Iv 6	SCE1 5	SCE1 2	SCEP 12
									FAC EPr
								FAV 1P	FAV 2Q

Station Road is off London Road / A20 close to the M20.

Nearest Railway Station Aylesford

LORDSWOOD

Nickname: Lords **Club Colours:** Orange

Founded 1968

Club Contact Details 01634 669 138 slew1953@hotmail.co.uk

Ground: Martyn Grove, Northdane Way, Walderslade, ME5 8YE

Capacity: 600 **Seats:** 123 **Covered:** 123

Previous Names: None.

Previous Leagues: Rochester & Dist. Kent County.

HONOURS: FA Comps: None

League: None

10 YEAR RECORD

09-10	10-11	11-12	12-13	13-14	14-15	15-16	16-17	17-18	18-19
Kent P 16	Kent P 13	Kent P 12	Kent P 5	SCE 11	SCE 15	SCE 4	SCEP 16	SCEP 8	SCEP 10
FAC Pr	FAC EP	FAC P	FAC Pr	FAC EP	FAC Pr	FAC EP	FAC EPr	FAC EP	FAC EP
FAV 1Q	FAV 1P	FAV 1P	FAV 4P	FAV 3P	FAV 1P	FAV 3P	FAV 1P	FAV 3P	FAV 2P

Take Junction 3 of the M2 (signposted Chatham). At the roundabout take the first exit, then turn right onto Walderslade Woods. At the next roundabout take the 2nd exit and follow the road. At the next roundabout take the 2nd exit onto Lordswood Lane, follow the road, and at the next roundabout take the 3rd exit onto Albemarle road. Follow the road all the way to the bottom and then turn left onto North Dane Way. Martin Grove is situated within the grounds of Lordswood Sports and Social Club and Lordswood Leisure Centre - the entrance is approx 400 yards on your right.

Nearest Railway Station Chatham - 4.8km

Bus Route Lords Wood Leisure Centre - stop 30m away

PUNJAB UNITED

Nickname: **Club Colours:** All red with white trim

Founded 2003

Club Contact Details 01474 323 817 jindi_banwait@hotmail.com

Ground: Elite Venue, Hawkins Avenue, Dunkirk Close, Gravesend, Kent DA12 5ND

Capacity: **Seats:** **Covered:**

Previous Names: None

Previous Leagues: Kent County 2016-17.

HONOURS: FA Comps: None

League: Kent County Premier 2016-17. Southern Counties East Division One 2017-18.

10 YEAR RECORD

09-10	10-11	11-12	12-13	13-14	14-15	15-16	16-17	17-18	18-19
							KC P 1	SCE1 1	SCEP 17
									FAV 2Q

Go onto Valley Drive off the A2. Turn left onto Scott Road. Continue on Scott Road T-juction, turn left and then first right until T-juction, turn right ontol Wilberforce Way. Follow Wilberforce Way until Palmer Avenue, take left onto Hawkins Avenue, then first left onto Christian Fields Avenue and then left onto Dunkirk Close at the T-junction.

Nearest Railway Station Gravesend - 2.7km

SHEPPEY UNITED

Nickname: **Club Colours:** Red & white stripes

Founded 1890

Club Contact Details 01795 669 547 jon.longhurst@bond-group.co.uk

Ground: Havill Stadium, Holm Park, Queenborough Road ME12 3DB

Capacity: 1,450 **Seats:** 170 **Covered:** 470

Previous Names: AFC Sheppy 2007-2010. Sheppey & Sheerness United after merger 2013-14.

Previous Leagues: Kent County > 2014.

HONOURS: FA Comps: None

League: Kent 1905-06, 06-07, 72-73, 74-75, 78-79, 94-95. Greater London Section B 1964-65.

10 YEAR RECORD

09-10	10-11	11-12	12-13	13-14	14-15	15-16	16-17	17-18	18-19
KC1E 11	KC1E 11	KC1E 4	KC P Exp	KC P 2	K_lv 5	K_lv 2	SCEP 6	SCEP 11	SCEP 7
							FAC EP	FAC P	FAC EP
						FAV 2Q	FAV 2Q	FAV 2P	FAV 3P

Exit the M2 at Junction 5 (Sheerness, Maidstone) and at the roundabout take the first exit onto the A249 Northbound. Stay on the A249 over the Sheppey Crossing until you reach a roundabout. Take the first left at the roundabout. At the next roundabout take the 2nd exit until you come to a set of traffic lights. At the traffic lights turn right. At the next traffic lights keep straight on. This is the Queenborough Road. Follow the Queenborough Road until you see a church on the right (this is St Peter's Church). Turn left onto St Peter's Close and the ground is a short distance down the road to the left (the ground is signposted as "Sheppey United FC" on the Queenborough Road). The club have a car park at the ground and use of an overflow car park opposite the ground (Holm Sports Football Ground).

TUNBRIDGE WELLS

Founded 1886

Nickname: The Wells **Club Colours:** All red

Club Contact Details 07912 060 857 secretary@twfcexec.com

Ground: Culverden Stadium, Culverden Down, Tunbridge Wells TN4 9SG

Capacity: 3,750 **Seats:** 250 **Covered:** 1,000

Previous Names: None.

Previous Leagues: South Eastern. Southern Amateur 1908-11. Isthminan 1911-13. Spartan 1913-14. Kent.

HONOURS: FA Comps: None

League: Southern Amateur Section B 1909-10. Kent Division One 1984-85.

10 YEAR RECORD

09-10	10-11	11-12	12-13	13-14	14-15	15-16	16-17	17-18	18-19
Kent P 7	Kent P 6	Kent P 5	Kent P 7	SCE 4	SCE 5	SCE 14	SCEP 15	SCEP 15	SCEP 16
FAC EPr	FAC 1Q	FAC P	FAC EP	FAC 1Q	FAC EP	FAC Pr	FAC EPr	FAC 2Q	FAC EPr
FAV 2Q	FAV 3P	FAV 4P	FAV F	FAV 3P	FAV 4Pr	FAV 2P	FAV 1P	FAV 2Qr	FAV 1P

You can access Culverden Down via the A26 / St John's Road.

Nearest Railway Station Tunbridge Wells 1.5km. High Brooms - 1.8km

WELLING TOWN

Founded 2014

Nickname: The Boots **Club Colours:** Green and black

Club Contact Details 07891 431 735 info@wellingtontown.co.uk

Ground: Bayliss Avenue, Thamesmead, London SE28 8NJ

Capacity: **Seats:** **Covered:**

Previous Names: None

Previous Leagues: Kent County 2016-18.

HONOURS: FA Comps: None

League: Kent County Division Two West 2017-18. Southern Counties East Division One 2018-19.

10 YEAR RECORD

09-10	10-11	11-12	12-13	13-14	14-15	15-16	16-17	17-18	18-19
							KC3W 2	KC2W 1	SCE1 1

Nearest Railway Station Abbey Wood - 2 miles

Bus Route 177, 229 401, 472

DIVISION ONE INS: Croydon (R - SCEP), Rusthall (R - SCEP).

BRIDON ROPES

Founded: 1935 — Nickname: The Ropes

Club Contact Details 0208 856 1923 — cburtonsmith@gmail.com

Ground: Charlton Park Lane, Charlton, London SE7 8QS — **Club Colours:** Blue and red

HONOURS
League: Spartan Division Two 1991-92. Kent County Division One West 2009-10.
FA Comps: None

10 YEAR RECORD

09-10	10-11	11-12	12-13	13-14	14-15	15-16	16-17	17-18	18-19
KC1W 1	KC P 4	K_lv 4	K_lv 7	K_lv 8	K_lv 10	K_lv 5	SCE1 7	SCE1 5	SCE1 4
							FAC EP		
						FAV 1P	FAV 1P	FAV 2Q	FAV 2Qr

Exit the M2/A2 (Coming from Kent) at the Sun in the Sands interchange, take third exit along Shooters Hill Road.
Take fifth left turn into Charlton Park Lane and follow road until a mini roundabout.
Take second exit and Meridian is situated on your right.

Nearest Railway Station Charlton - 1.3km

CROYDON

Founded: 1953 — Nickname: The Trams

Club Contact Details 02086 545524 (CH-0208 6548555) — judy@kinetic-foundation.org.uk

Ground: Croydon Sports Arena, Albert Road, South Norwood SE25 4QL — **Club Colours:** Sky & navy blue

HONOURS
League: Spartan 1963-64. Athenian Division Two 1965-66. Isthmian Division One 1999-00.
FA Comps: None

10 YEAR RECORD

09-10	10-11	11-12	12-13	13-14	14-15	15-16	16-17	17-18	18-19
CCP 16	CCP 20	CCP 16	CCP 14	CCP 13	SCE 18	SCE 18	SCEP 11	SCEP 5	SCEP 20
FAC EP	FAC P	FAC EP	FAC EP	FAC P	FAC 1Q	FAC 2Q	FAC Pr	FAC Pr	FAC P
FAV 2P	FAV 1P	FAV 1Q	FAV 3P	FAV 2Q	FAV 1Qr	FAV 1P	FAV 4P	FAV 2P	FAV 1Q

From East Croydon head east on Addiscombe Road towards Addiscombe Grove. Follow Cherry Orchard Rd and B243 to Grasmere Rd in South Norwood. At the end of Grasmere Road, turn left into Albert Road and turn right into the entrance to Croydon FC Sports Arena which is about 100 yards on the right hand side. Drive up to the clubhouse which overlooks the Arena.

Nearest Railway Station Croydon Tramlink - 1/4 mile
Bus Route No.312

FC ELMSTEAD

Founded: 1958 — Nickname: The Cocks

Club Contact Details 07711 287295 — stewartmurphy1001@gmail.com

Ground: Sutton Athletic FC, Lower Road, Hextable, Kent BR8 7RZ — **Club Colours:** Sky blue & red

HONOURS
League: None
FA Comps: None

10 YEAR RECORD

09-10	10-11	11-12	12-13	13-14	14-15	15-16	16-17	17-18	18-19
				KC3W 2	KC2W 2	K_lv 11	SCE1 11	SCE1 8	SCE1 13
						FAV 1Q	FAV 1P	FAV 1Q	FAV 1Q

London Road can be accessed via the B258.

Nearest Railway Station Swanley - 2.4km

FOREST HILL PARK

Founded: 1992 — Nickname:

Club Contact Details 07774 294 236 — info@fhpfc.co.uk

Ground: Ladywell Arena, Silvermere Road, Catford, London SE6 4QX — **Club Colours:** All blue

HONOURS
League: South London Alliance Division One 2005-06. Kent County Division Two West 2009-10.
FA Comps: None

10 YEAR RECORD

09-10	10-11	11-12	12-13	13-14	14-15	15-16	16-17	17-18	18-19
KC2W 1	KC1W 9	KC P 6	KC P 7	KC1W 10	KC1W 5	K_lv 13	SCE1 12	SCE1 16	SCE1 7
								FAV 2Q	FAV 2Q

Either before or after Catford Railway Station (depending on which way you come in) turn in to Doggett Road off the South Circular.
Continue along Doggett Road until arriving at Silvermead Road.

Nearest Railway Station Ladywell and Catford Bridge.
Bus Route 47, 54, 75, 136, 181, 185, 199, 208

GREENWAYS

Founded: 1965 Nickname:

Club Contact Details 07889 313 935 greenwaysfc@hotmail.com

Ground: K Sports, Cobdown, Station Road, Ditton, Aylesford, Kent ME20 6AU **Club Colours:** Green and black

HONOURS **League:** Gravesend Premier x7. Kent County Premier 1988-89.

FA Comps: None

10 YEAR RECORD

09-10	10-11	11-12	12-13	13-14	14-15	15-16	16-17	17-18	18-19
KC1W 8	KC1W 5	KC P 8	KC P 7	KC P 5	KC P 7	KC P 8	KC P 2	KC P 2	SCE1 10

Leave M20 at junction 5. At roundabout turn right onto A20.
Upon entering Ditton turn right into Station Road. Ground is on the left

HOLMESDALE

Founded: 1956 Nickname: The Dalers

Club Contact Details 07875 730 862 mitchell1982@sky.com

Ground: Holmesdale Sp.& Soc.Club, 68 Oakley Rd, Bromley BR2 8HG **Club Colours:** Green & yellow

HONOURS **League:** Thorton Heath & District Division Six 1956-57, Two 61-62, One 71-72, Premier 86-87. Surrey South Eastern Comb. Prem 92-93. Kent County Div.1W 2005-06, Prem 06-07.

FA Comps: None

10 YEAR RECORD

09-10	10-11	11-12	12-13	13-14	14-15	15-16	16-17	17-18	18-19
Kent P 10	Kent P 14	Kent P 13	Kent P 16	SCE 10	SCE 14	SCE 19	SCE1 6	SCE1 7	SCE1 6
FAC P	FAC EP	FAC EP	FAC EP	FAC P	FAC P	FAC P	FAC EP	FAC EP	
FAV 2Q	FAV 1Q	FAV 1Q	FAV 2Q	FAV 2Q	FAV 1Q	FAV 1Qr	FAV 2Q	FAV 1Q	FAV 1Q

Off the A232 on the A233.

Nearest Railway Station Hayes - 2.1km

KENNINGTON

Founded: 1888 Nickname:

Club Contact Details 01233 611 838 kevin@lab-services.co.uk

Ground: Homelands Stadium, Ashford Road, Kingsnorth, Ashford TN26 1NJ **Club Colours:** Amber & black

HONOURS **League:** Kent County Premier 2017-18.

FA Comps: None

10 YEAR RECORD

09-10	10-11	11-12	12-13	13-14	14-15	15-16	16-17	17-18	18-19
KC1E 12	KC1E 10	KC1E 11	KC1E 4	KC1E 4	KC1E 2	KC P 2	KC P 4	KC P 1	SCE1 3

From j10 take 4th exit and follow A2070 past 1 roundabout and turn left at second to A2042 follow road to Ground on left after 1.5 miles

KENT FOOTBALL UNITED

Founded: 2010 Nickname:

Club Contact Details 07875 488 856 m.bolton.kfu@gmail.com

Ground: Glentworth Club, Lowfield Street, Dartford DA1 1JB **Club Colours:** All blue

HONOURS **League:** None

FA Comps: None

10 YEAR RECORD

09-10	10-11	11-12	12-13	13-14	14-15	15-16	16-17	17-18	18-19
		K_lv 13	K_lv 11	K_lv 11	K_lv 15	K_lv 17	SCE1 4	SCE1 9	SCE1 14
		FAV 2Q	FAV 1Q	FAV 1Q					FAV 1Q

Turn off A2 at Black Prince interchange, follow Princes Road to the bottom, turn right at the lights and 2nd right into the ground.

Nearest Railway Station Dartford - 0.8 km

LEWISHAM BOROUGH

Founded: 2003 Nickname: The Boro

Club Contact Details 07712 149980 eno.mwamba@lbcfc.co.uk

Ground: Ladywell Arena, Silvermere Road, Catford, London SE6 4QX **Club Colours:** Blue

HONOURS **League:** Kent County Division One West 2003-04, Premier 2005-06.

FA Comps: None

10 YEAR RECORD

09-10	10-11	11-12	12-13	13-14	14-15	15-16	16-17	17-18	18-19
KC P 10	KC P 6	K_lv 8	K_lv 16	K_lv 13	K_lv 16	K_lv 20	SCE1 19	SCE1 18	SCE1 11
								FAV 1Q	FAV 1Q

Either before or after Catford Railway Station (depending on which way you come in) turn in to Doggett Road off the South Circular. Continue along Doggett Road until arriving at Silvermead Road.

Nearest Railway Station Ladywell and Catford Bridge.

Bus Route 47, 54, 75, 136, 181, 185, 199, 208

LYDD TOWN

Founded: 1885 Nickname: The Lydders

Club Contact Details 01797 321 904 brucemarchant@hotmail.com

Ground: The Lindsey Field, Dengemarsh Road, Lydd, Kent TN29 9JH **Club Colours:** Red and green

HONOURS **League:** Kent County Premier East 1969-70, 70-71, Senior East 1989-90, 90-91, 91-92, Division One East 92-93, 93-94.

FA Comps: None

10 YEAR RECORD

09-10	10-11	11-12	12-13	13-14	14-15	15-16	16-17	17-18	18-19
KC2E 11	KC2E 20	K_lv 12	K_lv 6	K_lv 2	K_lv 3	K_lv 8	SCE1 9	SCE1 10	SCE1 12
								FAV 1Q	FAV 1Q

Travelling along the B2075 into Lydd fork left onto Harden Road before entering the Lydd. Continue along Harden Road across rounadabout onto Robin Hood Lane and eventually onto Dengemarsh Road.

MERIDIAN VP

Founded: 1995 Nickname:

Club Contact Details 07977 274 179 dtamna@globalnet.co.uk

Ground: Meridian Sports & Social Club, Charlton Park Lane, London SE7 8QS **Club Colours:** All sky blue

HONOURS **League:** None

FA Comps: None

10 YEAR RECORD

09-10	10-11	11-12	12-13	13-14	14-15	15-16	16-17	17-18	18-19
KC2W 11	KC2W 12	K_lv 15	K_lv 15	K_lv 14	K_lv 12	K_lv 12	SCE1 17	SCE1 15	SCE1 18
						FAV 1P	FAV 1Q	FAV 2P	FAV 1Q

Charlton Park Lane can be found off the South Circular.

Nearest Railway Station Charlton - 1.3km

ROCHESTER UNITED

Founded: 1982 Nickname:

Club Contact Details 07775 735 543 toniwalker709@gmail.com

Ground: Rochester United Sports Ground, Rede Court Road, Strood ME2 3TU **Club Colours:** Red and black

HONOURS **League:** Rochester & District Division One 1997-98. Kent County Division One West 2007-08. Kent Invicta 2011-12.

FA Comps: None

10 YEAR RECORD

09-10	10-11	11-12	12-13	13-14	14-15	15-16	16-17	17-18	18-19
KC P 12	KC P 15	K_lv 1	Kent P 13	SCE 15	SCE 20	SCE 15	SCEP 14	SCEP 20	SCE1 17
						FAC 1Q	FAC Pr	FAC EPr	FAC EP
					FAV 1P	FAV 2Q	FAV 2Q	FAV 1Q	FAV 1Q

Rochester's ground can be accessed via the A2 in Strood.

Nearest Railway Station Strood - 2.1km

RUSTHALL

Founded: 1899 | Nickname: The Rustics

Club Contact Details 07976 386 527 deanjacquin@icloud.com

Ground: Jockey Farm, Nellington Road, Rusthall, Tunbridge Wells TN4 8SH **Club Colours:** Green & white stripes

HONOURS **League:** Tunbridge Wells 1904-05, 22-23, 23-24, 24-25, 25-26, 29-30, 30-31, 34-35, 37-38, 38-39, 51-52. Kent county Division Two West 1983-84, Division One West 1984-85, 2004-05.

FA Comps: None

10 YEAR RECORD

09-10	10-11	11-12	12-13	13-14	14-15	15-16	16-17	17-18	18-19
KC P 7	KC P 14	K_lv 11	K_lv 12	K_lv 7	K_lv 13	K_lv 19	SCE1 2	SCEP 19	SCEP 19
								FAC EPr	FAC Pr
							FAV 2Q	FAV 1P	FAV 1P

Follow Rusthall High Street through Rusthall and eventually you'll drive onto Nellington Road.

Nearest Railway Station High Rocks - 1.5km

SNODLAND TOWN

Founded: 2012 | Nickname:

Club Contact Details 07799 457 864 terry.reeves55@virginmedia.com

Ground: Potyns Field, Paddlesworth Road, Snodland ME6 5DP **Club Colours:** Royal blue & yellow

HONOURS **League:** None

FA Comps: None

10 YEAR RECORD

09-10	10-11	11-12	12-13	13-14	14-15	15-16	16-17	17-18	18-19
			KC P 11	KC P 4	KC P 9	KC1E 3	SCE1 8	SCE1 6	SCE1 15
								FAV 1Q	FAV 1Q

Coming South on the A228 towards Snodland turn right onto Holborough Road. Follow until a right turn onto Birling Road, take second right onto Constitution Hill. Follow until Paddlesworth Road.
Coming North on the A228 towards Snodland turn left onto Malling Road, take first left onto Hollow Lane. Turn left at the T-junction onto Snodland Road then first right onto St Benedict Road. Continue on this road until T-juction, turn left onto Constitution Hill/Paddlesworth Road.

Nearest Railway Station Snodland - 1.3km

SPORTING CLUB THAMESMEAD

Founded: 1900 | Nickname: The Acre

Club Contact Details 0208 320 4488 montyleach@hotmail.co.uk

Ground: Sporting Club Thamesmead, Bayliss Avenue, Thamesmead SE28 8NJ **Club Colours:** Red & black

HONOURS **League:** South London Alliance Division One 2008-09.

FA Comps: None

10 YEAR RECORD

09-10	10-11	11-12	12-13	13-14	14-15	15-16	16-17	17-18	18-19
KC2W 3	KC2W 4	K_lv 10	K_lv 5	K_lv 9	K_lv 6	K_lv 9	SCE1 10	SCE1 12	SCE1 9
						FAC P	FAC EP		
					FAV 1Q	FAV 1Qr	FAV 2P	FAV 2Q	FAV 2Q

Sporting Club Thamesmead can be accessed via Eastern Way.

Nearest Railway Station Abbey Wood - 1.8km

STANSFELD

Founded: 1961 | Nickname: Palace

Club Contact Details 07861 885 590 stansfeldfc@hotmail.com

Ground: Glebe FC, Foxbury Avenue, Chislehurst, Bromley BR7 6HA **Club Colours:** Yellow & blue stripes

HONOURS **League:** Kent County Division Two (Western) 1958-59, Premier (Western) 62-63, 63-64, 77-78, Senior (Western) 84-85, 86-87, 88-89, 89-90, Premier 94-95, 2009-10.

FA Comps: None

10 YEAR RECORD

09-10	10-11	11-12	12-13	13-14	14-15	15-16	16-17	17-18	18-19
KC P 1	KC P 13	KC P 2	KC P 9	KC P 6	KC P 2	KC P 4	KC P 9	SCE1 13	SCE1 8
								FAV 2Q	FAV 1Q

The club is located just off the A222 close to the Vauxhall Garage and a stone's throw away from the Sidcup bypass.

Nearest Railway Station Sidcup - 1.9km

SUTTON ATHLETIC

Founded: 1898 Nickname:

Club Contact Details 07778 053 433 guy.eldridge@btconnect.com

Ground: London Hire Stadium, Lower Road, Hextable, Kent BR8 7RZ **Club Colours:** Green & white

HONOURS

FA Comps: None

League: Dartford 1952-53, 53-54, 54-55, 56-57, 58-59, 59-60, 60-61, 61-62, 62-63, 63-64, 64-65.
Kent County D2W 68-69, D1W 69-70, PremW 70-71, SeniorW 76-77.

10 YEAR RECORD

09-10		10-11		11-12		12-13		13-14		14-15		15-16		16-17		17-18		18-19	
KC P	3	KC P	11	K_Iv	6	K_Iv	8	K_Iv	3	K_Iv	4	K_Iv	4	SCE1	3	SCE1	11	SCE1	5
																		FAV	1Q

From junction 3 on M25 follow signs to Swanley, then Hextable, turn into Home Hill, then Lower Road.
Ground half a mile away on the left.

Nearest Railway Station Swanley - 2.4km

PREMIER DIVISION INS: Aylesbury Vale Dynamoes (formerly Aylesbury) (R - Sth1C), Broadfields United (P - SSM1), Dunstable Town (R - Sth1C), Eynesbury Rovers (Tr - UCLP), Harefield United (P - SSM1), Newport Pagnell Town (P - UCLP). **OUTS:** Biggleswade (P - Sth1C), Cockfosters (Tr - ESen), Hadley (Tr - ESen), London Tigers (R - SSM1), Stotfold (R - SSM1).

ARLESEY TOWN

Founded 1891

Nickname: The Blues **Club Colours:** Light & dark blue

Club Contact Details 01462 734 504

Ground: New Lamb Meadow, Hitchin Road, Arlesey SG15 6RS

Capacity: 2,920 **Seats:** 150 **Covered:** 600 Yes

Previous Names: None

Previous Leagues: Biggleswade & Dist., Bedfordshire Co. (South Midlands) 1922-26, 27-28, Parthenon, London 1958-60, United Co. 1933-36, 82-92, Spartan South Mid. 1992-2000, Isthmian 2000-04, 06-08, Southern 2004-07, 08-18.

HONOURS: FA Comps: FA Vase 1994-95.

League: South Midlands Premier 1951-52, 52-53, 94-95, 95-96. Spartan South Midlands Premier 1999-2000. United Counties Premier Division 1984-85. Isthmian Division Three 2000-01. Southern Division One Central 2010-11.

10 YEAR RECORD

09-10	10-11	11-12	12-13	13-14	14-15	15-16	16-17	17-18	18-19
SthC 9	SthC 1	SthP 18	SthP 6	SthP 15	SthP 22	SthC 16	SthC 15	SthC 22	SSM P 8
FAC 1Q	FAC 1Q	FAC 1P	FAC 1P	FAC 3Q	FAC 1Q	FAC 1Q	FAC Pr	FAC 1Q	FAC EP
FAT 1Pr	FAT 2Qr	FAT 2Q	FAT 2Qr	FAT 1P	FAT 2Qr	FAT Pr	FAT Pr	FAT 1Q	FAV 2Q

From the A1 exit at Baldock(J10) and follow the signs for Stotfold then Arlesey. You will enter Arlesey from the area known as Church End, this is the opposite end of Arlesey, but as there is only one main street just follow keep driving until you pass the Biggs Wall building and the ground is on your left.
Coming of the M1 at Luton and follow the signs for Hitchin, pass Hitchin Town FC on the Shefford Road and turn right into Turnpike Lane, this is Ickleford. Follow the road out of Ickleford and bear left away from the Letchworth turning, the ground is a little further on, on the right.

Nearest Railway Station Arlesey - 2.6km

Bus Route Prince of Wales - stop 100m away

AYLESBURY VALE DYNAMOES

Founded 1930

Nickname: The Moles **Club Colours:** Red & black

Club Contact Details 01296 431 655

Ground: SRD Stadium, Haywood Way, Aylesbury, Bucks. HP19 9WZ

Capacity: **Seats:** Yes **Covered:** Yes No

Previous Names: Negretti & Zambra FC 1930-54, Stocklake 1954-2000, Haywood United 00, Haywood FC 00-06, Aylesbury Vale 06-09, Aylesbury 09-19

Previous Leagues: Aylesbury District. Wycombe & District. Chiltern, Spartan South Midlands >2010. Southern 2010-19.

HONOURS: FA Comps: None

League: Spartan South Midlands Division One 2003-04, Premier Division 2009-10.

10 YEAR RECORD

09-10	10-11	11-12	12-13	13-14	14-15	15-16	16-17	17-18	18-19
SSM P 1	SthC 8	SthC 20	SthC 12	SthC 16	SthC 3	SthC 8	SthC 19	Sth1E 21	SthC 19
FAC 4Q	FAC Pr	FAC P	FAC P	FAC 1Q	FAC 1Q	FAC 1Qr	FAC P	FAC 1Q	FAC Pr
FAV 1Q	FAT 1Qr	FAT 1Qr	FAT P	FAT 1Q	FAT 1Q	FAT 1Qr	FAT P	FAT 1Qr	FAT P

When entering Aylesbury from all major routes, join the ring road and follow signposts for A41 Bicester and Waddesdon. leave the ring road at the roundabout by the Texaco Garage and Perry dealership. From the Texaco Garage cross straight over four roundabouts. At the fifth roundabout with the Cotton Wheel Pub on the right hand side, turn right into Jackson Road. Take the second left into Haywood Way, club is at the bottom of the road. If entering Aylesbury from Bicester (A41), turn left into Jackson Road by the Cotton Wheel Pub, and then second left into Haywood Way.

Nearest Railway Station Aylesbury Vale Parkway - 1.2km

Bus Route O'grady Way - stop 200m away

BALDOCK TOWN

Founded 1905

Nickname: The Reds **Club Colours:** All red

Club Contact Details 07968 215 395

Ground: Arlesey Town FC, Armadillo Stadium, Hitchin Road, Arlesey SG15 6RS

Capacity: 2,920 **Seats:** 150 **Covered:** 600

Previous Names: Baldock 1905-21. Folded in 2001 reformed as Baldock 2003-06. Baldock Town 2006-08. Baldock Town Letchworth 2008-11.

Previous Leagues: Herts County 1905-25, 46-47, 2007-13. Beds & Dist/South Midlands 1925-39, 47-54, 64-83. Parthenon 1954-59. London 1959-64. United Counties 1983-87. Southern 1987-2001. North Herts 2003-06. North & Mid Herts (FM) 2006-07.

HONOURS: FA Comps: None

League: Herts Senior County Northern Div. 1920-21, Div.1 2007-08, Premier 11-12. South Midlands Div.2 47-38, Div.1 49-50, Premier 27-28, 65-66, 67-68, 69-70.

10 YEAR RECORD

09-10	10-11	11-12	12-13	13-14	14-15	15-16	16-17	17-18	18-19
HertP 3	HertP 4	HertP 1	HertP 2	SSM1 7	SSM1 10	SSM1 3	SSM1 3	SSM1 2	SSM P 5
					FAC P	FAC EP	FAC EP	FAC 2Q	FAC P
FAV 1Q	FAV 1P			FAV 1P	FAV 1P	FAV 2Q	FAV 1P	FAV 1P	FAV 2P

From the A1 exit at Baldock(J10) and follow the signs for Stotfold then Arlesey. You will enter Arlesey from the area known as Church End, this is the opposite end of Arlesey, but as there is only one main street just follow keep driving until you pass the Biggs Wall building and the ground is on your left.
Coming of the M1 at Luton and follow the signs for Hitchin, pass Hitchin Town FC on the Shefford Road and turn right into Turnpike Lane, this is Ickleford. Follow the road out of Ickleford and bear left away from the Letchworth turning, the ground is a little further on, on the right.

Nearest Railway Station Arlesey - 2.6km

Bus Route Prince of Wales - stop 100m away

BIGGLESWADE UNITED

Nickname: United **Club Colours:** Red and navy

Founded 1959

Club Contact Details 07714 661 827 info@biggleswadeunited.com

Ground: Second Meadow, Fairfield Rd, Biggleswade, Beds SG18 0BS

Capacity: 2,000 **Seats:** 260 **Covered:** 130

Previous Names: None

Previous Leagues: North Hertfordshire 1959-69. Midlands 1969-84. Hertfordshire Senior County 1984-86. Bedford & District 1986-96. South Midlands 1996-97.

HONOURS: FA Comps: None

League: Bedford & District Division Two 1990-91, Division One 91-92, Premier 94-95, 95-96. South Midlands Division One 1996-97.

10 YEAR RECORD

09-10	10-11	11-12	12-13	13-14	14-15	15-16	16-17	17-18	18-19
SSM P 20	SSM P 20	SSM P 19	SSM P 18	SSM P 17	SSM P 13	SSM P 10	SSM P 9	SSM P 8	SSM P 4
FAC P	FAC EP	FAC P	FAC P	FAC 1Q	FAC 1Q	FAC 1Q	FAC 1Q	FAC EPr	FAC EPr
FAV 2P	FAV 2Q	FAV 1P	FAV 2Q	FAV 1Q	FAV 2Q	FAV 2P	FAV 2Pr	FAV 1P	FAV 1P

From A1 south take second roundabout (Sainsbury's NOT Homebase). Cross the river bridge and then take second left into Sun Street then take first left into Fairfield Road and travel to the very end and into lane. From A1 north, take first roundabout (Sainsbury's) and follow previous instructions.

Nearest Railway Station Biggleswade - 0.9km

Bus Route Fairfield Road - stop 85m away

BROADFIELDS UNITED

Nickname: The Fighting Cocks **Club Colours:** Blue and white

Founded 1993

Club Contact Details 01895 823 474 websterlocke@aol.com

Ground: Harefield United FC, Breakspear Road North, Harefield, Middlesex UB9 6PE

Capacity: 1,200 **Seats:** 150 **Covered:** Yes

Previous Names: None

Previous Leagues: Middlesex >2015

HONOURS: FA Comps: None

League: Southern Olympian Division Four 1994-95. Middlesex County Senior Division 1996-97.

10 YEAR RECORD

09-10	10-11	11-12	12-13	13-14	14-15	15-16	16-17	17-18	18-19
MidxP Exp	MidxP 5	MidxP 8	MidxP 5	MidxP 15	MidxP 4	SSM1 11	SSM1 11	SSM1 4	SSM1 2
									FAC P
				FAV 2Q	FAV 1Q	FAV 1Q	FAV 2P	FAV 1P	FAV 1P

From the M25 at Junction 16 turn left. At the roundabout turn right towards Denham and at the next roundabout turn left then right at the end of the road. Turn left by the Pub and follow the road over the canal and into the village. Go straight across the roundabout into Breakspear Road and the ground is approximately 800 metres on the right.

Nearest Railway Station Denham - 3km

Bus Route Wickham Close - stop 150m away

COLNEY HEATH

Nickname: Magpies **Club Colours:** Black & white stripes

Founded 1907

Club Contact Details 01727 824 325

Ground: The Recreation Ground, High St, Colney Heath, St Albans AL4 0NP

Capacity: **Seats:** Yes **Covered:** Yes

Previous Names: None

Previous Leagues: Herts Senior County League 1953-2000

HONOURS: FA Comps: None

League: Herts County Division Two 1953-54 Division One A 55-56, Prem 58-99, 99-00, Division One 88-89, Spartan South Midlands Division One 2005-06.

10 YEAR RECORD

09-10	10-11	11-12	12-13	13-14	14-15	15-16	16-17	17-18	18-19
SSM P 5	SSM P 5	SSM P 8	SSM P 13	SSM P 3	SSM P 14	SSM P 20	SSM P 18	SSM P 11	SSM P 6
FAC EP	FAC 1Q	FAC P	FAC 1Q	FAC EP	FAC P			FAC 2Qr	FAC P
FAV 2Q	FAV 1P	FAV 1Q	FAV 2P	FAV 3Pr	FAV 1P		FAV 1P	FAV 1P	FAV 1Pr

From the A1, leave at junction 3 and follow A414 St. Albans. At long roundabout take the left into the village and ground is just past the school on left after 400 yards. **From the M25,** leave at junction 22 and follow B556 Colney Heath. On entering the village turn left at Queens Head PH (roundabout) and follow High Street for ½ mile. The ground is on the right just before the school.

From M1 going south; leave at junction 7. At Park Street roundabout follow A414 Hatfield. Continue on A414 past London Colney. Enter Colney Heath coming round the long roundabout and into village. The ground is past the school on the left after 400 yards.

Nearest Railway Station Welham Green - 3.6km

Bus Route Crooked Billet Ph - stop 50m away

CRAWLEY GREEN

Founded 1992

Nickname: **Club Colours:** All maroon

Club Contact Details
Ground: The Stadium at The Brache, Park Street, Luton LU1 3HH
Capacity: 4,000 **Seats:** 160 **Covered:** Yes

Previous Names: None
Previous Leagues: None

HONOURS: FA Comps: None
League: Spartan South Midlands Division Two 2004-05.

10 YEAR RECORD

09-10		10-11		11-12		12-13		13-14		14-15		15-16		16-17		17-18		18-19	
SSM1	8	SSM1	4	SSM1	6	SSM1	4	SSM1	5	SSM1	7	SSM1	2	SSM P	11	SSM P	18	SSM P	10
FAC	P	FAC	1Qr	FAC	EP	FAC	EP	FAC	P	FAC	EP	FAC	EP	FAC	P	FAC	P	FAC	P
FAV	1Q	FAV	1Q	FAV	2Q	FAV	2Qr	FAV	1Q	FAV	2Q	FAV	2Q	FAV	1P	FAV	2P	FAV	1P

From M1 Junction 10 turn right from south turn left from the North onto the A1081. Keep left at the first slip road marked Harpenden, St Albans and Local Traffic. Follow Local Traffic and take the second exit at the roundabout onto London Road sign posted Local Traffic & Stockwood Park. Proceed approximately ½ mile to the traffic lights and turn right into Cutenhoe Road. At the end of Cutenhoe Road proceed with caution straight over Park Street into the ground.

DUNSTABLE TOWN

Founded 1883

Nickname: The Duns / The Blues **Club Colours:** Blue & white

Club Contact Details 01582 891 433
Ground: Creasey Park Stadium, Brewers Hill Rd, Dunstable LU6 1BB
Capacity: 3,500 **Seats:** 350 **Covered:** 1000 **Shop:** Yes

Previous Names: Dunstable Town 1883-1976. Dunstable FC 1976-98.
Previous Leagues: Metropolitan & District 1950-61, 64-65. United Counties 1961-63. Southern 1965-76, 2004-09, 13-19. Spartan South Midlands 1998-2003, 09-13. Isthmian 2003-04.

HONOURS: FA Comps: None
League: Spartan South Midlands Division One 1999-00, Premier 2002-03, 12-13. Southern Division One Central 2013-14.

10 YEAR RECORD

09-10		10-11		11-12		12-13		13-14		14-15		15-16		16-17		17-18		18-19	
SSM P	7	SSM P	7	SSM P	2	SSM P	1	SthC	1	SthP	14	SthP	11	SthP	16	SthP	24	SthC	20
FAC	P	FAC	EP	FAC	3Q	FAC	1Qr	FAC	2Q	FAC	2Q	FAC	3Q	FAC	1Q	FAC	1Q	FAC	Pr
FAV	1P	FAV	5P	FAV	2P	FAV	3P	FAT	2Q	FAT	1Q	FAT	1Q	FAT	2Q	FAT	1Q	FAT	1Q

From the south: When travelling on the A5, go straight across the lights in the centre of Dunstable. Turn left at the next main set of lights into Brewers Hill Road. You will immediately pass the Fire Station on your left. Carry on until you hit the first r'about, Go over the r'about and take the immediate right into Creasey Park Drive. From the north: When travelling south on the A5, go through the chalk cutting and over the first set of traffic lights. At the next set of lights, turn right into Brewers Hill Road. Then proceed as above. From the East: Turn right at the traffic lights in the centre of Dunstable. Turn left at the next main set of traffic lights into Brewers Hill Road. Then proceed as above. From the east: When coming into Dunstable, go straight across the first r'about you come to. Then turn left at the double mini-r'about into Drovers Way. Follow this road for about 1/2 mile as it bears to the right and becomes Brewers Hill Road. Go over two mini-r'abouts and just before you hit the larger r'about, turn left into Creasey Park Drive.

Bus Route Langridge Court - stop 100m away

EDGWARE TOWN

Founded 1939

Nickname: The Wares **Club Colours:** Green and white

Club Contact Details 0208 205 1645
Ground: Silver Jubilee Park, Townsend Lane, London NW9 7NE
Capacity: 1,990 **Seats:** 298 **Covered:**

Previous Names: Edgware 1972-87. Original Edgware Town folded in 2008 and re-formed in 2014.
Previous Leagues: Corinthian 1946-63. Athenian 1963-84. Spartan 1984-90, 2006-07. Isthmian 1990-2006, 2007-08.

HONOURS: FA Comps: None
League: Middlesex Senior 1939-40, 43-44, 44-45 (shared). London Western Section 1945-46. London Spartan Premier 1987-88, 89-90. Isthmian Division Three 1991-92. Spartan South Midlands Premier 2006-07, Division One 2015-16.

10 YEAR RECORD

09-10		10-11		11-12		12-13		13-14		14-15		15-16		16-17		17-18		18-19	
										SSM1	9	SSM1	1	SSM P	17	SSM P	10	SSM P	13
														FAC	P	FAC	EPr	FAC	EP
												FAV	3P	FAV	2Q	FAV	1P	FAV	2Q

From Edgware tube station, turn left onto Station Road and then left onto Edgware Road. Go South for about two miles on Edgware Road, turn right onto Kingsbury Road. Turn first left onto Townsend Lane down to the bottom of the hill and then turn left into the park through the park barriers..

Nearest Railway Station Hendon - 1.1km
Bus Route Queensbury Road - stop 660m away

EYNESBURY ROVERS

Founded 1897

Nickname: Rovers **Club Colours:** Royal blue & white

Club Contact Details

Ground: Alfred Hall Memorial Ground, Hall Road, Eynesbury, St Neots PE19 2SF

Capacity: **Seats:** Yes **Covered:** Yes

Previous Names: None

Previous Leagues: Biggleswade & District. St Neots Junior. Bed & District. South Midlands 1934-39. United Counties 1946-52, 63-2019. Eastern Counties 1952-63.

HONOURS: FA Comps: None

League: St Neots Junior 1910-11. Bedford & District Division Two 1926-27, 30-31, 31-32. United Counties Division 1 1976-77.

10 YEAR RECORD

09-10	10-11	11-12	12-13	13-14	14-15	15-16	16-17	17-18	18-19
UCL 1 3	UCL 1 6	UCL 1 6	UCL 1 3	UCL 1 2	UCL P 11	UCL P 6	UCL P 5	UCL P 7	UCL P 6
				FAC EP		FAC EP	FAC 1Q	FAC P	FAC Pr
FAV 1P	FAV 2Q	FAV 1Q	FAV 1P	FAV 2P	FAV 1Qr	FAV 1P	FAV 1Q	FAV 1P	FAV 1Q

From the A1 take the A428 towards Cambridge. Turn left at the Tesco roundabout and continue on Barford Road for half a mile going straight on at 4 roundabouts. Turn left into Hardwick Road and left into Hall Road. Ground at end of road.

Nearest Railway Station St Neots - 2.1km

Bus Route Ernulf Academy Forecourt - stop 150m away

HAREFIELD UNITED

Founded 1868

Nickname: Hares **Club Colours:** Red & black

Club Contact Details 01895 823 474

Ground: Preston Park, Breakespeare Road North, Harefield, UB9 6NE

Capacity: 1,200 **Seats:** 150 **Covered:** Yes **Shop:** No

Previous Names: None

Previous Leagues: Uxbridge & District, Great Western Comb, Panthernon, Middlesex, Athenian & Isthmian.

HONOURS: FA Comps: None

League: Great Western Comb. Division Two 1947-48, Division One 50-51. Parthenon 1964-65. Spartan South Midlands Division One 2018-19.

10 YEAR RECORD

09-10	10-11	11-12	12-13	13-14	14-15	15-16	16-17	17-18	18-19
SSM P 6	SSM P 21	SSM P 18	SSM P 10	SSM P 14	SSM P 4	SSM P 21	SSM1 8	SSM1 9	SSM1 1
FAC 2Q	FAC P	FAC Pr	FAC 2Qr	FAC P	FAC P	FAC EPr	FAC 1Q		
FAV 1P	FAV 2Q	FAV 1Q	FAV 1Q	FAV 1Q	FAV 1P	FAV 1P	FAV 2Q	FAV 1Q	FAV 1P

From the M25 at Junction 16 turn left. At the roundabout turn right towards Denham and at the next roundabout turn left then right at the end of the road. Turn left by the Pub and follow the road over the canal and into the village. Go straight across the roundabout into Breakspear Road and the ground is approximately 800 metres on the right.

Nearest Railway Station Denham - 3km

Bus Route Wickham Close - stop 150m away

HARPENDEN TOWN

Founded 1891

Nickname: The Harps **Club Colours:** Yellow & blue

Club Contact Details

Ground: Rothamstead Park, Amenbury Lane, Harpenden AL5 2EF

Capacity: **Seats:** Yes **Covered:** Yes

Previous Names: Harpenden FC 1891-1908.

Previous Leagues: Herts Senior County (founder member) 1898-1900, 1908-22, 48-57. Mid-Herts 1900-08. South Midlands 1957-97.

HONOURS: FA Comps: None

League: Herts Senior County Western Division 1910-11, 11-12, 20-21, Premier 50-51, 52-53, 54-55. South Midlands Division One 1989-90, Premier 61-62, 64-65.

10 YEAR RECORD

09-10	10-11	11-12	12-13	13-14	14-15	15-16	16-17	17-18	18-19
SSM1 12	SSM1 7	SSM1 5	SSM1 7	SSM1 8	SSM1 6	SSM1 4	SSM1 2	SSM P 3	SSM P 14
							FAC P	FAC EP	FAC P
FAV 2Q						FAV 2Q	FAV 1Q	FAV 1P	FAV 1P

Approaching Harpenden from St. Albans, turn left into Leyton Road at mini-roundabout by the Silver Cup and Fire Station. Coming from Luton, go through the town and as you leave (just past The George) turn right into Leyton Road. Turn left in Amenbury Lane and then left into car park after 300 yards. Entrance to the Club is up the pathway, diagonally across the car park in the far corner from the entrance. This is a pay-and-display car park up to 6.30pm.

Nearest Railway Station Harpenden - 0.6km

Bus Route Amenbury Lane - stop 250m away

LEIGHTON TOWN

Nickname: Reds **Club Colours:** Red & white

Founded 1885

Club Contact Details 01525 373 311
Ground: Lake Street, Leighton Buzzard, Beds LU7 1RX
Capacity: 2,800 **Seats:** 400 **Covered:** 300

Previous Names: Leighton United 1922-63
Previous Leagues: Leighton & District. South Midlands 1922-24, 26-29, 46-54, 55-56, 76-92. Spartan 1922-53, 67-74. Isthmian 1992-2004. Southern 2004-16.
HONOURS: FA Comps: None
League: South Midlands 1966-67, 91-92. Isthmian Division Two 2003-04.

10 YEAR RECORD

09-10		10-11		11-12		12-13		13-14		14-15		15-16		16-17		17-18		18-19	
SthM	10	SthC	7	SthC	13	SthC	21	SthC	19	SthC	18	SthC	21	SSM P	16	SSM P	4	SSM P	11
FAC	Pr	FAC	1Q	FAC	3Q	FAC	Pr	FAC	P	FAC	P	FAC	1Q	FAC	EP	FAC	P	FAC	EP
FAT	1Q	FAT	P	FAT	1Q	FAT	P	FAT	P	FAT	1Qr	FAT	1Q	FAV	2Q	FAV	QF	FAV	3P

Ground is situated just south of Town Centre on the A4146 Leighton Buzzard to Hemel Hemstead Road.
Entrance to car park and ground is opposite Morrisons Supermarket Petrol Station.
1/2 mile south of town centre.

Nearest Railway Station Leighton Buzzard - 1.3km
Bus Route Morrisons (Lake St) - stop 60m away

LEVERSTOCK GREEN

Nickname: The Green / The Trees **Club Colours:** White and green

Founded 1895

Club Contact Details 01442 246 280
Ground: Pancake Lane, Leverstock Green, Hemel Hempstead, Herts HP2 4NQ
Capacity: 1,500 **Seats:** 50 **Covered:** 100

Previous Names: None
Previous Leagues: West Herts (pre 1954) & Herts Senior County 1954-91. South Midlands 1991-97.
HONOURS: FA Comps: None
League: Herts Senior County Division One 1978-79.
South Midlands Senior Division 1996-97.

10 YEAR RECORD

09-10		10-11		11-12		12-13		13-14		14-15		15-16		16-17		17-18		18-19	
SSM P	10	SSM P	4	SSM P	11	SSM P	15	SSM P	20	SSM P	15	SSM P	18	SSM P	12	SSM P	7	SSM P	17
FAC	P	FAC	EP	FAC	EP	FAC	EP	FAC	EP	FAC	2Q	FAC	EP	FAC	EP	FAC	Pr	FAC	2Q
FAV	1P	FAV	5P	FAV	2Pr	FAV	1Q	FAV	1Q	FAV	2Q	FAV	2Q	FAV	2P	FAV	2Q	FAV	3P

From M1 at Junction 8, Follow A414 to second roundabout turn left along Leverstock Green Way. Pancake Lane is on the left 300 yards past the Leather Bottle Public House. Ground is 300 yards on left. All visitors are requested to park inside the ground.

Nearest Railway Station Apsley - 3.2km
Bus Route Pancake Lane - stop 300m away

LONDON COLNEY

Nickname: Blueboys **Club Colours:** Royal blue and white

Founded 1907

Club Contact Details 01727 822 132
Ground: Cotlandswick Playing Fields, London Colney, Herts AL2 1DW
Capacity: 1,000 **Seats:** Yes **Covered:** Yes

Previous Names: None
Previous Leagues: Herts Senior 1955-93.
HONOURS: FA Comps: None
League: Herts Senior County 1956-57, 59-60, 86-87, 88-89. 89-90. South Midlands Senior Division 1994-95. Spartan South Midlands Premier Division 2001-02, 16-17, Division One 2011-12.

10 YEAR RECORD

09-10		10-11		11-12		12-13		13-14		14-15		15-16		16-17		17-18		18-19	
SSM1	3	SSM1	5	SSM1	1	SSM P	7	SSM P	7	SSM P	2	SSM P	2	SSM P	1	SSM P	13	SSM P	15
FAC	1Qr	FAC	1Q	FAC	EP	FAC	P	FAC	EPr	FAC	1Q	FAC	P	FAC	1Q	FAC	EPr	FAC	EP
FAV	2P	FAV	1Q	FAV	1Q	FAV	2Q	FAV	1Q	FAV	3P	FAV	2P	FAV	3P	FAV	1Pr	FAV	1P

From M25 J22, follow the A1081 signposted to St Albans. At London Colney roundabout take A414, signposted Hemel Hempstead/Watford. There is a hidden turn into the ground after approximately 500 metres (just after lay-by) signposted Sports Ground and London Colney FC. Follow the ground around between the Rugby and Irish clubs to ground entrance.

Nearest Railway Station Park Street - 2.3km
Bus Route Leisure Centre - stop 430m away

NEWPORT PAGNELL TOWN

Founded 1963

Nickname: Swans **Club Colours:** White & green

Club Contact Details 01908 611 993

Ground: Willen Road, Newport Pagnell MK16 0DF

Capacity: 2,000 **Seats:** 100 **Covered:** 100

Previous Names: Newport Pagnell Wanderers > 1972.

Previous Leagues: North Bucks 1963-71. South Midlands 1971-73. United Counties 1973-2019.

HONOURS: FA Comps: None

League: United Counties Division One 1981-82, 2001-02.

10 YEAR RECORD

09-10		10-11		11-12		12-13		13-14		14-15		15-16		16-17		17-18		18-19	
UCL P	6	UCL P	3	UCL P	5	UCL P	6	UCL P	16	UCL P	10	UCL P	3	UCL P	10	UCL P	3	UCL P	8
FAC	P	FAC	1Q	FAC	Pr	FAC	1Q	FAC	P	FAC	EP	FAC	Pr	FAC	EP	FAC	Pr	FAC	EP
FAV	3P	FAV	1P	FAV	4P	FAV	2P	FAV	2Q	FAV	2Q	FAV	1Q	FAV	QF	FAV	2P	FAV	4P

From the A422 Newport Pagnell by pass turn into Marsh End Road, then first right into Willen Road.

Bus Route Green Park Drive - stop 160m away

NORTH GREENFORD UNITED

Founded 1944

Nickname: Blues **Club Colours:** Royal blue & white

Club Contact Details 0208 422 8923

Ground: Berkeley Fields, Berkley Avenue, Greenford UB6 0NX

Capacity: 2,000 **Seats:** 150 **Covered:** 100

Previous Names: None

Previous Leagues: London Spartan, Combined Counties 2002-10, 16-18. Southern 2010-16.

HONOURS: FA Comps: None

League: Combined Counties League Premier Division 2009-10

10 YEAR RECORD

09-10		10-11		11-12		12-13		13-14		14-15		15-16		16-17		17-18		18-19	
CCP	1	SthC	20	SthC	18	SthC	19	SthC	20	SthC	21	SthC	22	CCP	13	CCP	13	SSM P	16
FAC	EP	FAC	3Q	FAC	3Qr	FAC	P	FAC	3Q	FAC	2Q	FAC	1Qr	FAC	1Q	FAC	P	FAC	P
FAV	2P	FAT	1Q	FAT	P	FAT	P	FAT	2Q	FAT	P	FAT	P	FAV	2Q	FAV	1Q	FAV	1P

A40 going towards London. At the Greenford Flyover come down the slip road, keep in the left hand lane, turn left onto the Greenford Road (A4127). At the third set of traffic lights, turn right into Berkeley Av. Go to the bottom of the road. There is a large car park. We are on the right hand side.

Nearest Railway Station Greenford or Sudbury Hill (Piccadilly Line).

Bus Route No.92

OXHEY JETS

Founded 1972

Nickname: Jets **Club Colours:** Blue and white

Club Contact Details 020 8421 6277

Ground: Boundary Stadium, Altham Way, South Oxhey, Watford WD19 6FW

Capacity: 2,000 **Seats:** 150 **Covered:** 100 **Shop:** No

Previous Names: None

Previous Leagues: Youth Leagues > 1981. Herts Senior County 1981-2004.

HONOURS: FA Comps: None

League: Herts Senior County Premier 2000-01, 01-02, 02-03. Spartan South Midladns Division One 2004-2005.

10 YEAR RECORD

09-10		10-11		11-12		12-13		13-14		14-15		15-16		16-17		17-18		18-19	
SSM P	11	SSM P	19	SSM P	17	SSM P	3	SSM P	18	SSM P	12	SSM P	17	SSM P	15	SSM P	19	SSM P	9
FAC	EP	FAC	1Q	FAC	2Q	FAC	P	FAC	EPr	FAC	EP	FAC	EPr	FAC	P	FAC	EP	FAC	EP
FAV	2Q	FAV	2Q	FAV	1P	FAV	3P	FAV	2P	FAV	2P	FAV	2Q	FAV	1P	FAV	1P	FAV	2Q

From Bushey + Oxhey Station, take Pinner Road (A4008) and continue along Oxhey Lane towards Harrow. At the traffic lights turn right into Little Oxhey Lane. Altham Way is on left just after crossing a narrow railway bridge. Please park in the large swimming pool car park marked "Jets overflow parking" to avoid either blocking in cars, or being blocked in.

Nearest Railway Station Carpenders Park - 1km

Bus Route Lytham Avenue - stop 75m away

POTTON UNITED

Nickname: Royals **Club Colours:** All blue

Founded 1943

Club Contact Details 01767 261 100

Ground: The Hutchinson Hollow, Biggleswade Road, Potton, Beds SG19 2LX

Capacity: 2,000 **Seats:** **Covered:**

Previous Names: None

Previous Leagues: South Midlands 1946-55. United Counties 1961-2018.

HONOURS: FA Comps: None

League: United Counties 1986-87, 88-89, Division One 2003-04.

10 YEAR RECORD

09-10		10-11		11-12		12-13		13-14		14-15		15-16		16-17		17-18		18-19	
UCL 1	11	UCL 1	15	UCL 1	15	UCL 1	16	UCL 1	10	UCL 1	3	UCL 1	7	UCL 1	6	UCL 1	2	SSM P	7
FAC	EPr	FAC	EP									FAC	EP			FAC	1Q	FAC	EP
FAV	2Q	FAV	1Q	FAV	2Q	FAV	2Q	FAV	1Q	FAV	2Q	FAV	2Q	FAV	1Q	FAV	2Q	FAV	2Q

From Sandy, take B1042 into Potton.
Head towards Potton Town Centre and take right turn towards Biggleswade (B1040).
The ground is on left hand side at foot of hill

Nearest Railway Station Sandy - 4.4km

Bus Route The Ridgewy - stop 11m away

TRING ATHLETIC

Nickname: Athletic **Club Colours:** Red and black

Founded 1958

Club Contact Details 01442 891 144 (MD)

Ground: Grass Roots Stadium, Pendley Sports Centre, Cow Lane, Tring HP23 5NS

Capacity: 2,000 **Seats:** 125 **Covered:** 100+ **Shop:** Yes

Previous Names: Tring Athletic Youth 1958-71.

Previous Leagues: West Herts 1958-88.

HONOURS: FA Comps: None

League: West Herts Division One 1961-62, 64-65, 65-66.
Spartan South Midlands Senior Division 1999-2000.

10 YEAR RECORD

09-10		10-11		11-12		12-13		13-14		14-15		15-16		16-17		17-18		18-19	
SSM P	3	SSM P	2	SSM P	6	SSM P	22	SSM P	10	SSM P	10	SSM P	12	SSM P	5	SSM P	17	SSM P	2
FAC	P	FAC	1Q	FAC	P	FAC	Pr	FAC	P	FAC	EP	FAC	P	FAC	EP	FAC	EP	FAC	EP
FAV	2Q	FAV	3P	FAV	2P	FAV	1Q	FAV	3P	FAV	3P	FAV	1P	FAV	4P	FAV	5P	FAV	3Pr

From M25 take A41 to Aylesbury. At roundabout at junction take last exit sign-posted Berkhamsted.
Turn next left into Cow Lane. Stadium is on the right at end of Cow Lane.

Nearest Railway Station Tring - 1.5km

Bus Route Bus stops at the ground.

WEMBLEY

Nickname: The Lions **Club Colours:** Red

Founded 1946

Club Contact Details 0208 904 8169

Ground: Vale Farm, Watford Road, Sudbury, Wembley HA0 3HG.

Capacity: 2450 **Seats:** 350 **Covered:** 950 **Shop:** No

Previous Names: None

Previous Leagues: Middlesex Senior. Spartan 1949-51. Delphian 1951-56. Corinthian 1956-63. Athenian 1963-75. Isthmian 1975-2006. Combined Counties 2006-14.

HONOURS: FA Comps: None

League: Middlesex Senior 1947-48. Spartan Division One Western 1950-51.

10 YEAR RECORD

09-10		10-11		11-12		12-13		13-14		14-15		15-16		16-17		17-18		18-19	
CCP	15	CCP	14	CCP	10	CCP	15	CCP	9	SSM P	7	SSM P	11	SSM P	4	SSM P	9	SSM P	12
FAC	EP	FAC	EP	FAC	1Q	FAC	Pr	FAC	1Q	FAC	EPr	FAC	Pr	FAC	Pr	FAC	P	FAC	EP
FAV	2P	FAV	2Q	FAV	2Qr	FAV	1P	FAV	1P	FAV	2P	FAV	1Q	FAV	3P	FAV	2P	FAV	2Q

Wembley FC is relatively close to both the A440 and the M1.
From Sudbury Town Station 1km along Watford Road.

Nearest Railway Station Sudbury Town Underground - 1km Sudbury & Harrow Road

Bus Route Butlers Green - stop 150m away

DIVISION ONE INS: London Tigers (R - SSMP), New Salamis (P - HertsS), Shefford Town & Campton (P - BedsC), St Panteleimon (MiddxC), Stotfold (R - SSMP).

AMERSHAM TOWN

Founded: 1890 Nickname: The Magpies

Club Contact Details

Ground: Spratleys Meadow, School Lane, Amersham, Bucks HP7 0EL **Club Colours:** Black & white stripes

HONOURS **League:** Wycombe & District Combination 1902-03, 19-20, 20.21.
Hellenic Division One 1962-63, Premier 63-64.

FA Comps: None

10 YEAR RECORD

09-10	10-11	11-12	12-13	13-14	14-15	15-16	16-17	17-18	18-19
SSM1 17	SSM1 20	SSM1 20	SSM1 20	SSM1 16	SSM1 21	SSM2 12	SSM2 16	SSM2 6	SSM1 17
		FAV 2Q	FAV 2P				FAV 1Q	FAV 1Q	FAV 2Q

From Beaconsfield and High Wycombe follow the signposts to Amersham Old Town. Turn left at the bottom of the hill (Tesco roundabout). Go straight on through the next roundabout. From London at the first roundabout take the second exit signposted Amersham Old Town. Go straight on through the second, third (Tesco) and fourth roundabout. At the roundabout in front of the old Market Hall turn right into Church Street. Go past the Church on your right and take the first left into School Lane. Go past the recreation ground on your left and the road on your left (Mill Lane). The ground is one hundred yards on your left past Mill Lane.

AMPTHILL TOWN

Founded: 1881 Nickname: The Amps

Club Contact Details 01525 404 440

Ground: Ampthill Park, Woburn Street, Ampthill MK45 2HX **Club Colours:** Amber and black

HONOURS **League:** South Midlands Premier Division 1959-60.

FA Comps: None

10 YEAR RECORD

09-10	10-11	11-12	12-13	13-14	14-15	15-16	16-17	17-18	18-19
SSM1 13	SSM1 16	SSM1 2	SSM P 5	SSM P 2	SSM P 21	SSM1 14	SSM1 14	SSM1 14	SSM1 10
FAC EP	FAC EP		FAC EP	FAC P	FAC EP	FAC EP			
FAV 1Q	FAV 2Q	FAV 4P	FAV 5P	FAV QF	FAV 2P	FAV 1Q	FAV 1Q	FAV 1P	FAV 1Q

From the South, leave M1 at junction 12 Toddington. Turn right as signposted until you meet the junction with the Ampthill bypass. Go straight across until you meet a mini-roundabout at the town centre. Turn left into Woburn Street. The ground is about half a mile on the right, just past a lay-by. From the North, leave the M1 at J13 and turn left. At first set of traffic lights, turn right onto A507 Ridgmont bypass. Continue until you see the right-hand turning signposted for Ampthill. Ground is about a mile on the left, opposite the rugby ground.

Nearest Railway Station Flitwick - 3.1km. Millbrook - 3.4km
Bus Route Alameda Road - stop 117m away

BEDFORD

Founded: 1957 Nickname: The B's

Club Contact Details

Ground: McMullen Park, Meadow Lane, Cardington, Bedford, MK44 3SB **Club Colours:** Black & white

HONOURS **League:** None

FA Comps: None

10 YEAR RECORD

09-10	10-11	11-12	12-13	13-14	14-15	15-16	16-17	17-18	18-19
SSM1 9	SSM1 13	SSM1 12	SSM1 5	SSM1 3	SSM1 3	SSM P 22	SSM1 19	SSM1 12	SSM1 5
FAC EP	FAC EP	FAC EP			FAC EP	FAC EP	FAC EP		
FAV 2P	FAV 2Q	FAV 2Q		FAV 1Q	FAV 2Q	FAV 1Q	FAV 1Q	FAV 1Qr	FAV 1Q

From the M1 Junction 13: take the A421 on to the Bedford Bypass, take the third exit onto the A603, the ground is 250 yards on the left. From the A1 at Sandy: take A603 to Bedford. The ground is on the right just before you reach the Bedford Bypass.

Nearest Railway Station Bedford St Johns - 3.8km
Bus Route Meadow Lane - stop 141m away

BRIMSDOWN

Founded: 2013 Nickname: The Limers

Club Contact Details gulayermiya1996@googlemail.com

Ground: Ware FC, Wodson Park, Wadesmill Road, Ware SG12 0UQ **Club Colours:** Black and white

HONOURS **League:** None

FA Comps: None

10 YEAR RECORD

09-10	10-11	11-12	12-13	13-14	14-15	15-16	16-17	17-18	18-19
				SSM2 13	SSM2 4	SSM1 15	SSM1 17	SSM1 11	SSM1 18
						FAV 2Q		FAV 1Q	FAV 1P

Nearest Railway Station Ware - 1.9km
Bus Route Wodson Park - stop 100m away

OUTS: Broadfields United (P - SSMP), Codicote (R - SSM2), Harefield United (P - SSMP), Hatfield Town (R - HertsS), Risborough Rangers (Tr - Hell1E)

BUCKINGHAM ATHELTIC

Founded: 1933 Nickname: The Ath

Club Contact Details 01280 816 945 (MD)

Ground: Stratford Fields, Stratford Road, Buckingham MK18 1NY **Club Colours:** Sky blue & navy blue

HONOURS
FA Comps: None
League: North Bucks Premier Division 1984-85. South Midlands Division One 1985-86, 90-91, Spartan South Midlands Division Two 2002-03.

10 YEAR RECORD

09-10	10-11	11-12	12-13	13-14	14-15	15-16	16-17	17-18	18-19
SSM1 16	SSM1 18	SSM1 18	SSM1 11	SSM1 13	SSM1 15	SSM1 8	SSM1 10	SSM1 7	SSM1 4
FAV 1Q	FAV 1Qr	FAV 1Q	FAV 2Q	FAV 2Q	FAV 1Qr	FAV 2Q	FAV 1Q	FAV 1P	FAV 1Pr

From Oxford, Aylesbury or Bletchley: take the Buckingham ring road to the roundabout where the A422 from Stony Stratford/Deanshanger meet-turn left, towards town centre. The ground is situated on the left behind fir trees at the bottom of the hill where 30mph begins (opposite a recently-built block of luxury apartments). From Milton Keynes: Up A5 then (A422) to Buckingham-straight across roundabout towards the town centre-ground location as above. From M1: come off at junction 13 and follow A421 straight through, turning right where it meets the Buckingham ring road – then follow as above, turning left at the next-but-one roundabout.

Bus Route High Street - stop 206m away

ENFIELD BOROUGH

Founded: 2016 Nickname: Panthers

Club Contact Details 07493 377 484

Ground: Wingate & Finchley FC, Maurice Rebak Stadium, Summers Lane, N12 **Club Colours:** Red & black

HONOURS
FA Comps: None
League: None

10 YEAR RECORD

09-10	10-11	11-12	12-13	13-14	14-15	15-16	16-17	17-18	18-19
							SSM2 3	SSM1 10	SSM1 9
								FAV 2P	FAV 1P

Nearest Railway Station New Southgate - 2.3km

FC BROXBOURNE BOROUGH

Founded: 1959 Nickname: Boro

Club Contact Details

Ground: Broxbourne Borough V & E Club, Goffs Lane, Cheshunt, Herts EN7 **Club Colours:** Blue and white

HONOURS
FA Comps: None
League: Herts Senior County Division One 1993-94.

10 YEAR RECORD

09-10	10-11	11-12	12-13	13-14	14-15	15-16	16-17	17-18	18-19
SSM P 9	SSM P 10	SSM P 13	SSM2 3	SSM1 6	SSM1 2	SSM P 16	SSM P 22	SSM1 19	SSM1 8
FAC EP	FAC EP	FAC 1Q				FAC EP	FAC EP	FAC EPr	
FAV 1P	FAV 1Q	FAV 1Q		FAV 1Q	FAV 2Q	FAV 3P	FAV 2Q	FAV 1Q	FAV 2Q

Leave M25 at Junction 25. Take A10 northbound. Turn first exit at roundabout. Straight over the next roundabout then 3rd exit at the next roundabout after that. Ground entrance is 50 yards on the right.

Nearest Railway Station Theobalds Grove - 2.3km
Bus Route Goffs School - stop 37m away

HILLINGDON BOROUGH

Founded: 1990 Nickname: The Hillmen, Boro

Club Contact Details 01895 639 544 accounts@middlesexstadium.com

Ground: Middlesex Stadium, Breakspear Rd, Ruislip HA4 7SB **Club Colours:** White & royal blue

HONOURS
FA Comps: None
League: None

10 YEAR RECORD

09-10	10-11	11-12	12-13	13-14	14-15	15-16	16-17	17-18	18-19
SSM P 18	SSM P 16	SSM P 10	SSM P 19	SSM P 11	SSM P 22	SSM1 16	SSM1 9	SSM1 16	SSM1 16
FAC EP	FAC EP	FAC EP	FAC EP	FAC P	FAC EP	FAC EPr			
FAV 1P	FAV 1P	FAV 1P	FAV 2Q	FAV 1P	FAV 2Q	FAV 1Q	FAV 2Q	FAV 2Q	

From M40/A40 eastbound, leave the A40 at the Swakeleys roundabout, exit is sign-posted Ickenham & Ruislip and take the B467.
At the second mini-roundabout turn left into Breakspear Road South.
After approx 1 mile, turn right into Breakspear Road by the Breakspear Arms PH.
The ground is a further 1/2 mile on the left-hand side.

Nearest Railway Station Willow Lawn - 737m
Bus Route Howletts Lane - stop 98m away

LANGFORD

Founded: 1908 Nickname: Reds

Club Contact Details 01462 816 106

Ground: Forde Park, Langford Road, Henlow, Beds SG16 6AF **Club Colours:** Red & white

HONOURS **League:** Bedford & District 1931-32, 49-50. South Midlands Premier Division 1988-89.

FA Comps: None

10 YEAR RECORD

09-10	10-11	11-12	12-13	13-14	14-15	15-16	16-17	17-18	18-19
SSM P 19	SSM P 23	SSM1 10	SSM1 16	SSM1 19	SSM1 13	SSM1 18	SSM1 4	SSM1 17	SSM1 11
FAC EP	FAC EP	FAC EP						FAC EP	
FAV 1P	FAV 1P	FAV 1Q	FAV 2Q	FAV 1Q	FAV 1Qr	FAV 1Q	FAV 1Q	FAV 2Q	FAV 2Q

From West along A57 to Henlow then north on A6001. Ground at north end of Henlow.
From North and East, leave A1 at Langford water tower then into Langford.
Turn left at Boot Restaurant. Follow A6001 round to the left. Club is 1/2 mile away.

Nearest Railway Station Arlesey - 1.9km
Bus Route Newtown (Langford Rd) - stop 24m away

LONDON LIONS

Founded: 1995 Nickname: Lions

Club Contact Details 0208 441 6051

Ground: Rowley Lane Sports Ground, Rowley Lane, Barnet EN5 3HW **Club Colours:** All blue

HONOURS **League:** Hertfordshire Senior County Division One 1999-2000, Premier 09-10, 16-17. Spartan South Midlands Division One 2012-13.

FA Comps: None

10 YEAR RECORD

09-10	10-11	11-12	12-13	13-14	14-15	15-16	16-17	17-18	18-19
HertP 1	SSM1 8	SSM1 7	SSM1 1	SSM P 22	SSM1 17	HertP 5	HertP 1	SSM1 6	SSM1 6
			FAC 1Q	FAC EPr					FAC P
		FAV 1Q	FAV 2P	FAV 2Q			FAV 1Q	FAV 2P	FAV 2Q

Exit the M25 at junction 23, take the A1(M)/A1081/A1 exit to Hatfield/Barnet/London. At the roundabout, take the 5th exit onto the A1 slip road to London (N&C)/Brent Cross. Continue on A1. Drive to Paddock Lane in Barnet, continue onto A1. In just under 2 miles take the A5135 exit towards Borehamwood/Barnet/Arkley/A411, then turn left onto Rowley Lane, sports ground will be on your right.

Nearest Railway Station Elstree & Borehamwood - 2.4km
Bus Route Buses stop on Rowley Lane.

LONDON TIGERS

Founded: 1986 Nickname: Tigers

Club Contact Details 020 7289 3395 (10am-6pm) info@londontigers.org

Ground: Northwood Park, Cheshunt Avenue, Northwood HA6 1HR **Club Colours:** Amber and black

HONOURS **League:** None

FA Comps: None

10 YEAR RECORD

09-10	10-11	11-12	12-13	13-14	14-15	15-16	16-17	17-18	18-19
SSM P 8	SSM P 12	SSM P 14	SSM P 20	SSM P 15	SSM P 17	SSM P 13	SSM P 21	SSM P 15	SSM P 20
FAC 1Q	FAC EP			FAC P	FAC 2Q	FAC EPr	FAC EPr		
FAV 1P	FAV 1Q		FAV 2Q	FAV 1Q	FAV 1Q	FAV 1P	FAV 2Q		FAV 1Q

MILTON KEYNES ROBINS

Founded: 1883 Nickname: Robins

Club Contact Details 01908 375 978

Ground: Irish Centre, Manor Fields, Bletchley, Milton Keynes MK2 2HX **Club Colours:** All red

HONOURS **League:** Aylesbury & Dist. 1902-03, 67-68. North Bucks 24-25, 28-29, 33-34, 35-36, 36-37, 38-39, 48-49, 49-50. Southern Southern Division 90-91. United Counties 83-84, 85-86.

FA Comps: None

10 YEAR RECORD

09-10	10-11	11-12	12-13	13-14	14-15	15-16	16-17	17-18	18-19
UCL 1 13	UCL 1 16	UCL 1 11	UCL 1 15	UCL 1 11	UCL 1 16	UCL 1 17	UCL 1 5	UCL 1 7	SSM1 14
FAC EP								FAC EP	
FAV 1Q	FAV 1Q	FAV 2P		FAV 2Q		FAV 1Q	FAV 1P	FAV 1Q	

Take A413 out of Buckingham and continue on that road until entering Winslow. As you enter Winslow there is a garage on the right hand side. Take the 1st turn right past the garage (Avenue Road) and then the 1st turn right again into Park Road. Entrance at end of road through the blue gates. Bear left into the car park.

Nearest Railway Station Fenny Stratford - 0.6km
Bus Route Wharfside - stop 300m away

NEW SALAMIS

Founded: 1971 Nickname:

Club Contact Details

Ground: Enfield Town FC, Queen Elizabeth II Stadium,

Club Colours: Red & white

HONOURS

League: KOPA 1984-85, 93-94, 99-00, 00-01, 08-09, 10-11, 11-12, 12-13, 14-15, 15-16, 16-17, 17-18

FA Comps: Sunday Cup 2015

10 YEAR RECORD

09-10	10-11	11-12	12-13	13-14	14-15	15-16	16-17	17-18	18-19
	KOPA 1	KOPA 1	KOPA 1		KOPA 1	KOPA 1	KOPA 1	KOPA 1	HertP 2

From the M25: Head towards London on the A10 from junction 25. Turn right into Carterhatch Lane at the Halfway House pub. Donkey Lane is first left after the pub.

From London/North Circular Road: Head north up the A10 and turn left to Carterhatch Lane at the Halfway House pub. Donkey Lane is first left after the pub.

Nearest Railway Station Southbury - 1.2km

PARK VIEW

Founded: Nickname:

Club Contact Details

Ground: New River Stadium, White Hart Lane, Wood Green N22 5QW

Club Colours: White

HONOURS

League: Middlesex County Division One C&E 2007-08. Amateur Combination Intermediate Division One North 2014-15, Senior Division Two North 15-15, Senior Division One 16-17.

FA Comps:

10 YEAR RECORD

09-10	10-11	11-12	12-13	13-14	14-15	15-16	16-17	17-18	18-19
			LonCom	LonCom 2	AMCI1N 1	AmC2N 1	AmC1 1	SSM2 1	SSM1 13

The Skolars Stadium is located approximately 1 mile from Wood Green Underground Station, which is on the Piccadilly Line, and only 15 minutes from Kings Cross Station.

The W3 bus from Wood Green Station drops very close to the Stadium and, on Friday Night Lights, Skolars run a courtesy bus service to and from the station (check for details). This service is is run by Arriva, one of Skolars long standing sponsors.

RAYNERS LANE

Founded: 1933 Nickname: The Lane

Club Contact Details 0208 868 8724

Ground: Tithe Farm Social Club, Rayners Lane, South Harrow HA2 0XH

Club Colours: Yellow and green

HONOURS

League: Hellenic Division One 1982-83, Division One East 2012-13.

FA Comps: None

10 YEAR RECORD

09-10	10-11	11-12	12-13	13-14	14-15	15-16	16-17	17-18	18-19
Hel1E 12	Hel1E 7	Hel1E 3	Hel1E 1	Hel1E 9	Hel1E 7	Hel1E 5	Hel1E 11	SSM1 13	SSM1 12
						FAV 2Q	FAV 2Q	FAV 2Q	FAV 1P

From A40 Polish War Memorial turn left into A4180 (West End Road), approximately 500 metres turn right into Station Approach, at traffic lights turn right into Victoria Road. At next roundabout continue straight on to traffic lights at junction with Alexandra Avenue (Matrix Bar &taurant on left). Continue straight on over traffic lights and take second turning on left into Rayners Lane. Ground is approximately half a mile on the left.

Nearest Railway Station Rayners Lane underground - 680m
Bus Route Clitheroe Avenue - stop 64m away

SHEFFORD TOWN & CAMPTON

Founded: 2010 Nickname:

Club Contact Details

Ground: Shefford Sports Club, Hitchin Road, Shefford SG17 5JD

Club Colours: Red & white

HONOURS

League: Bedfordshire County Premier Division 2011-12, 17-18, 18-19.

FA Comps: None

10 YEAR RECORD

09-10	10-11	11-12	12-13	13-14	14-15	15-16	16-17	17-18	18-19
	BedCP 2	BedCP 1	BedCP 7	BedCP 11	BedCP 5	BedCP 9	BedCP 7	BedCP 1	BedCP 1

ST PANTELEIMON

Founded: 2015 Nickname: The Saints

Club Contact Details

Ground: North Greenford United, Berkeley Fields **Club Colours:** Yellow & blue

HONOURS **League:** Middlesex County Division One (Central & East) 2018-19.

FA Comps: None

10 YEAR RECORD

09-10	10-11	11-12	12-13	13-14	14-15	15-16	16-17	17-18	18-19
						KOPA	KOPA	KOPA	Midx1SE 1
									FAV 1P

A40 going towards London. At the Greenford Flyover come down the slip road, keep in the left hand lane, turn left onto the Greenford Road (A4127). At the third set of traffic lights, turn right into Berkeley Av. Go to the bottom of the road. There is a large car park. We are on the right hand side.

Nearest Railway Station Greenford or Sudbury Hill (Piccadilly Line).

Bus Route No.92

STOTFOLD

Founded: 1904 Nickname: The Eagles

Club Contact Details 01462 730 765

Ground: Roker Park, The Green, Stotfold, Hitchin, Herts SG5 4AN **Club Colours:** Amber and black

HONOURS **League:** South Midlands 1980-81. United Counties Premier 2007-08.

FA Comps: None

10 YEAR RECORD

09-10	10-11	11-12	12-13	13-14	14-15	15-16	16-17	17-18	18-19
UCL P 7	SSM P 13	SSM P 9	SSM P 14	SSM P 19	SSM P 16	SSM P 15	SSM P 13	SSM P 21	SSM P 19
FAC EP	FAC EP	FAC 1Q	FAC Pr	FAC P	FAC EP	FAC EP	FAC 1Q	FAC EP	FAC EP
FAV 4P	FAV 3P	FAV 1Q	FAV 1Q	FAV 1P	FAV 2Q	FAV 2P	FAV 1Qr	FAV 1Q	FAV 2Q

At A1 junction 10, take the A507 to Stotfold and right into town. Proceed along High Street and at traffic lights turn right (from Hitchin – straight over traffic lights) towards Astwick Turn right at the Crown pub into The Green.
The ground is set back from The Green on the left.

Nearest Railway Station Arlesey - 2.9km

Bus Route The Green - stop 80m away

WINSLOW UNITED

Founded: 1891 Nickname: The Ploughmen

Club Contact Details 01296 713 057

Ground: The Recreation Ground, Elmfields Gate, Winslow, Bucks MK18 3JG **Club Colours:** Yellow and blue

HONOURS **League:** South Midlands Division One 1974-75.

FA Comps: None

10 YEAR RECORD

09-10	10-11	11-12	12-13	13-14	14-15	15-16	16-17	17-18	18-19
	SSM2 4	SSM2 7	SSM1 14	SSM1 9	SSM1 14	SSM1 19	SSM1 16	SSM1 3	SSM1 3
									FAC EP
FAV 1Q		FAV 1P	FAV 2Q	FAV 2Q	FAV 1Qr	FAV 2Q	FAV 2Q	FAV 1Q	FAV 2Q

Best Route to the Ground: A413 from Aylesbury to Winslow, turn right from High Street into Elmfields Gate. Ground is100 yards on left. A421 Milton Keynes to Buckingham, turn left through Great Horwood to Winslow. Turn left from High Street into Elmfields Gate.
PLEASE PARK IN PUBLIC CAR PARK OPPOSITE GROUND IF POSSIBLE.

Bus Route Elmside - stop 210m away

WODSON PARK

Founded: 1997 Nickname:

Club Contact Details 07717 458 446

Ground: Wodson Park Sports Centre, Wadesmill Road, Herts SG12 0UQ **Club Colours:** Sky & navy blue

HONOURS **League:** Hertford & District Division Three 1997-98.

FA Comps: None

10 YEAR RECORD

09-10	10-11	11-12	12-13	13-14	14-15	15-16	16-17	17-18	18-19
SSM2 4	SSM2 14	SSM1 16	SSM1 18	SSM1 17	SSM1 16	SSM1 6	SSM1 7	SSM1 5	SSM1 15
		FAC EP	FAC EP						FAC EP
	FAV 1P	FAV 1Q	FAV 1Q					FAV 2Qr	FAV 2P

From the South: leave the M25 at junction 25 and take the A10 north past Cheshunt and Hoddesdon. After crossing the Lea Valley with Ware below and to your right, leave the A10 at the junction for the A1170 (signposted for Wadesmill and Thundridge). The slip road comes off the A10 onto a roundabout. Turn left (first exit) onto Wadesmill Road (A1170) and come back over the A10 to a second roundabout. Go straight over and take the first turn on the left into Wodson Park Sports Centre. The football ground is on the far left of the car park. From the North: Leave the A10 at the Ware North turn off (A1170). The slip road takes you to a r'about. Turn right (3rd exit) into Wadesmill Road and take the first left into Wodson Park Sports Centre.

Nearest Railway Station Ware - 2.1km

Bus Route Wodspn Park - stop 557m away

Spartan South Midlands Division Two	
ASTON CLINTON	Aston Clinton Park, London Road, Aston Clinton HP22 5HL
BERKHAMSTED RAIDERS	Ashlyns School, Chesham Road, Berkhamsted HP4 3AH
BOVINGDON	Green Lane, Bovingdon, Hemel Hempstead HP3 0LE
BUCKINGHAM UNITED	Lace Hill Sports & Community Centre, Buckingham MK18 7RR
CODICOTE	John Clements Memorial Ground, Bury Lane, Codicote SG4 8XY
GRENDON RANGERS	The Village Hall, Main Street, Grendon Underwood, Aylesbury, Bucks. HP18 0SP
MK GALACTICOS	North Furzton Sports Ground, Lynmouth Crescent, Milton Keynes MK4 1HD
MURSLEY UNITED	The Playing Field, Station Road, Mursley MK17 0SA
NEW BRADWELL ST. PETER	New Bradwell Recreation Ground, Esther Close, Bradville, Milton Keynes MK13 7GA
OLD BRADWELL UNITED	Bradwell Sports & Social Club, Abbey Road, Bradwell, Milton Keynes MK13 9AR
PITSTONE AND IVINGHOE	Pitstone Pavilion & Sports Hall, Marsworth Road, Pitstone LU7 9AP
SARRATT	King George V Playing Fields, George V Way, Sarratt WD3 6AU
THE 61 FC (LUTON)	Kingsway Ground, Beverley Road, Luton LU4 8EU
TOTTERNHOE	Totternhoe Recreation Ground, Dunstable Road, Totternhoe, Beds LU6 1QP
TRING CORINTHIANS	Icknield Way, Tring, Herts HP23 5HJ
UNITE MK	MK Irish Club, Manor Fields, Watling Street, Bletchley, Milton Keynes MK2 2HX

PREMIER DIVISION INS: Anstey Nomads (P - UCL1), Loughborough University (Tr - Mid), Lutterworth Town (P - UCL1), Quorn (Tr - Mid), Shepshed Dynamo (Tr - Mid).

ANSTEY NOMADS

Founded 1947

Nickname: Nomads **Club Colours:** Red & white

Club Contact Details 07946 856 430

Ground: Davidson Homes Park, Cropston Road, Anstey, Leicester LE7 7BP

Capacity: 1000 **Seats:** 100 **Covered:** Yes

Previous Names: -

Previous Leagues: Leicestershire Senior. East Midlands Counties 2009-18.

HONOURS: FA Comps: None

League: Leicestershire Senior 1951-52, 53-54, 81-82, 82-83, 2008-09, Division Two 1973-74.

10 YEAR RECORD

09-10	10-11	11-12	12-13	13-14	14-15	15-16	16-17	17-18	18-19
EMC 20	EMC 12	EMC 9	EMC 14	EMC 17	EMC 14	EMC 4	EMC 17	EMC 2	UCL 1 2
		FAC EP	FAC EP				FAC EP		FAC 2Q
FAV 1Q	FAV 1P	FAV 2Q	FAV 2Q	FAV 1Q	FAV 1Q	FAV 1P	FAV 2Q	FAV 1Q	FAV 1Q

From A46 follow signs to Anstey and enter village by Leicester Road.
Proceed to roundabout in centre of village and take 3rd exit.
Pass Co-op store and car showroom and ground 100 metres on right.

Nearest Railway Station Leicester - 6.2km

BOSTON TOWN

Founded 1964

Nickname: Poachers **Club Colours:** All blue

Club Contact Details 01205 365 470 btfcsec@hotmail.co.uk

Ground: DWB Stadium, Tattershall Road, Boston, Lincs PE21 9LR

Capacity: 6,000 **Seats:** 450 **Covered:** 950

Previous Names: Boston 1964-1994

Previous Leagues: Lincolnshire. Central Alliance 1965-66. Eastern Counties 1966-68. Midland 1968-82. Northern Counties East 1982-87. Central Midlands 1987-91.

HONOURS: FA Comps: None

League: Lincolnshire 1964-65. Central Alliance 1965-65. Midland 1974-75, 78-79, 80-81. Central Midlands Supreme 1988-89. United Counties League 1994-95, 2000-01.

10 YEAR RECORD

09-10	10-11	11-12	12-13	13-14	14-15	15-16	16-17	17-18	18-19
UCL P 5	UCL P 7	UCL P 14	UCL P 10	UCL P 14	UCL P 12	UCL P 16	UCL P 20	UCL P 13	UCL P 17
FAC 1Q	FAC Pr	FAC P	FAC EP	FAC P	FAC 1Q	FAC EP	FAC EP	FAC 3Q	FAC EP
FAV 2Q	FAV 2Q	FAV 2P	FAV 3P	FAV 1P	FAV 2Q	FAV 1Q	FAV 2Q	FAV 2Q	FAV 1Q

Go into town on A16 from Spalding. Turn left at roundabout into Liquor Pond Street becoming Queen Street over railway crossing along Sleaford Road. Turn right into Carlton Road then right at crossroads into Fydell Street. Over railway crossing and river take 2nd left (sharp turn) into Tattershall Road. Continue over railway crossing, ground on left.

Nearest Railway Station Boston - 1.6km

Bus Route Bus stops outside the ground

COGENHOE UNITED

Founded 1967

Nickname: Cooks **Club Colours:** All blue

Club Contact Details 01604 890 521 cogenhoeunited@outlook.com

Ground: Compton Park, Brafield Road, Cogenhoe NN7 1ND

Capacity: 5,000 **Seats:** 100 **Covered:** 200

Previous Names: None

Previous Leagues: Central Northants Combination 1967-85.

HONOURS: FA Comps: None

League: Central Northants Combination Division Two 1951-52, Premier 80-81, 82-83, 83-84. United Counties 2004-05.

10 YEAR RECORD

09-10	10-11	11-12	12-13	13-14	14-15	15-16	16-17	17-18	18-19
UCL P 8	UCL P 15	UCL P 12	UCL P 8	UCL P 5	UCL P 5	UCL P 5	UCL P 13	UCL P 8	UCL P 7
FAC P	FAC P	FAC P	FAC EP	FAC EPr	FAC P	FAC 2Q	FAC P	FAC P	FAC EP
FAV 2P	FAV 1P	FAV 2P	FAV 2Q	FAV 1Q	FAV 1Q	FAV 1P	FAV 1Q	FAV 4P	FAV 2P

From A45 Northampton Ring Road turn as indicated to Billing/Cogenhoe.
Go over River Nene and up hill ignoring first turning on left to Cogenhoe.
Take next left and ground is on right hand side.

Bus Route Orchard Way - stop 190m away

OUTS: Daventry Town (P -Sth1C), Eynesbury Rovers (Tr - SSMP), Kirby Muxloe (R - Mid1), Newport Pagnell Town (Tr - SSMP), Wellingborough Whitworth (R - UCL1).

DEEPING RANGERS

Founded 1964

Nickname: Rangers **Club Colours:** Claret and blue

Club Contact Details 01778 344 701 secretary@deepingrangersfc.co.uk

Ground: The Haydon Whitham Stadium, Outgang Road, Market Deeping PE6 8LQ

Capacity: 2,000 **Seats:** 164 **Covered:** 250

Previous Names: None

Previous Leagues: Peterborough & District 1966 - 1999.

HONOURS: FA Comps: None

League: United Counties Premier Division 2006-07.

10 YEAR RECORD

09-10	10-11	11-12	12-13	13-14	14-15	15-16	16-17	17-18	18-19
UCL P 4	UCL P 14	UCL P 4	UCL P 5	UCL P 4	UCL P 9	UCL P 10	UCL P 2	UCL P 5	UCL P 2
FAC EPr	FAC EP	FAC 2Q	FAC EP	FAC EP	FAC EP	FAC 2Q	FAC 1Q	FAC 2Q	FAC Pr
FAV 1P	FAV 1P	FAV 3P	FAV 2P	FAV 2Q	FAV 3P	FAV 2Q	FAV 1Qr	FAV 3P	FAV 5P

From Town Centre head north on B1524 towards Bourne. Turn right onto Towngate East at Towngate Tavern Pub. Go straight over mini roundabout onto Outgang Road. Ground 1/4 mile on left. From A16 by pass at roundabout with the A15 Bourne Road turn towards Deeping then left into Northfields Road, then left into Towngate/Outgang Road. Ground 1/4 mile on left.

Bus Route Buttercup Court - stop 720m away

DESBOROUGH TOWN

Founded 1896

Nickname: Ar Tam **Club Colours:** All royal blue

Club Contact Details 01536 761 350

Ground: Waterworks Field, Braybrooke Road, Desborough NN14 2LJ

Capacity: 8,000 **Seats:** 250 **Covered:** 500

Previous Names: None

Previous Leagues: Northamptonshire change name to United Counties in 1934.

HONOURS: FA Comps: None

League: Northamptonshire/United Counties 1900-01, 01-02, 06-07, 20-21, 23-24, 24-25, 27-28 / 48-49, 66-67.

10 YEAR RECORD

09-10	10-11	11-12	12-13	13-14	14-15	15-16	16-17	17-18	18-19
UCL P 18	UCL P 19	UCL P 16	UCL P 11	UCL P 4	UCL P 14	UCL P 15	UCL P 4	UCL P 9	UCL P 9
FAC Pr	FAC 1Q	FAC EPr	FAC EPr	FAC P	FAC EP	FAC EP	FAC P	FAC P	FAC P
FAV 2Q	FAV 2Q	FAV 1P	FAV 2P	FAV 2P	FAV 2Q	FAV 1Q	FAV 1P	FAV 4P	FAV 3P

Take exit 3 marked Desborough off the A14 and follow bypass for 2 miles.
At roundabout turn right and ground is 200 yards on the left hand side.

Bus Route Bus stops outside the ground.

HARBOROUGH TOWN

Founded 1976

Nickname: The Bees **Club Colours:** Yellow and black

Club Contact Details 01858 467 339

Ground: Bowden's Park, Northampton Road, Market Harborough, Leics. LE16 9HF

Capacity: **Seats:** Yes **Covered:** Yes

Previous Names: Harborough Town Juniors 1976-2008. Juniors merged with adult team Spencer United to form today's club.

Previous Leagues: Northants Combination.

HONOURS: FA Comps: None

League: Northants Combination Premier Division 2009-10.

10 YEAR RECORD

09-10	10-11	11-12	12-13	13-14	14-15	15-16	16-17	17-18	18-19
NhCo 1	UCL 1 17	UCL 1 2	UCL P 19	UCL P 17	UCL P 20	UCL P 11	UCL P 11	UCL P 11	UCL P 11
				FAC P	FAC EPr	FAC P	FAC P	FAC P	FAC P
		FAV 1Pr	FAV 2Q	FAV 1P	FAV 1Q	FAV 1Q	FAV 1P	FAV 1Q	FAV 2Q

Half a mile south of Market Harborough on the A508. 4 miles north of the A14 junction 2 towards Market Harborough turn left towards Leisure Centre, but keep left passed inflatable dome on the right, then through large car park, club house straight in front, with parking area.

Nearest Railway Station Market Harborough - 1.5km

Bus Route Leisure Centre - stop 200m away

HOLBEACH UNITED

Nickname: Tigers **Club Colours:** Gold & black

Founded 1929

Club Contact Details 01406 424 761

Ground: Carters Park, Park Road, Holbeach, Lincs PE12 7EE

Capacity: 4,000 **Seats:** 200 **Covered:** 450 **Shop:** No

Previous Names: None

Previous Leagues: King's Lynn. Peterborough & District 1936-46. United Counties 1946-55, Eastern 1955-62, Midland Counties 1962-63.

HONOURS: FA Comps: None

League: United Counties 1989-90, 02-03, 12-13.

10 YEAR RECORD

09-10		10-11		11-12		12-13		13-14		14-15		15-16		16-17		17-18		18-19	
UCL P	16	UCL P	17	UCL P	6	UCL P	1	UCL P	11	UCL P	6	UCL P	4	UCL P	7	UCL P	4	UCL P	5
FAC	EPr	FAC	EP	FAC	Pr	FAC	1Q	FAC	P	FAC	P	FAC	2Qr	FAC	1Q	FAC	1Q	FAC	EP
FAV	2Q	FAV	2Q	FAV	1P	FAV	2Q	FAV	1P	FAV	5P	FAV	2P	FAV	2P	FAV	2P	FAV	3P

Approaching Town Centre traffic lights from Spalding Direction take Second Left, or from Kings Lynn direction take sharp right, into Park Road. Ground is 300 yards on the left.

Bus Route Carter's Park - stop 70m away

LEICESTER NIRVANA

Nickname: **Club Colours:** Red and black

Founded 2008

Club Contact Details 01162 660 009 nirvanafc@hotmail.co.uk

Ground: Hamilton Park, Sandhills Avenue, Leicester LE5 1LU

Capacity: **Seats:** Yes **Covered:** Yes

Previous Names: Thurnby Rangers and Leicester Nirvana merged to form today's club in 2008. Thurnby Nirvana 2008-15.

Previous Leagues: Leicestershire Senior >2010 East Midland Counties 2010-14

HONOURS: FA Comps: None

League: Leicestershire Senior Division One 1997-98, 2000-01, Premier Division 04-05. East Midland Counties 2013-14.

10 YEAR RECORD

09-10		10-11		11-12		12-13		13-14		14-15		15-16		16-17		17-18		18-19	
LeicSP	3	EMC	9	EMC	7	EMC	3	EMC	1	UCL P	2	UCL P	2	UCL P	17	UCL P	6	UCL P	12
				FAC	1Qr	FAC	1Qr	FAC	EPr	FAC	P	FAC	P	FAC	EP	FAC	EP	FAC	EP
		FAV	1P	FAV	1Q	FAV	1Q	FAV	2Q	FAV	4P	FAV	4P	FAV	2Q	FAV	2P	FAV	5P

From M1—Exit at Jct 22 (A50/A511 to Leicester/Coalville.
Follow A50 to Leicester, until you reach signs for A563 (Glenfirth Way).
After Sainsbury's, turn right then immediately left in to Gleneagles Avenue. Entrance is at the bottom of the cul de sac.

Nearest Railway Station Syston - 3.9km

Bus Route Lakeview Chase - stop 70m away

LOUGHBOROUGH UNIVERSITY

Nickname: The Scholars **Club Colours:** Purple

Founded 1920

Club Contact Details 07561 468 745 footballsecretary@lboro.ac.uk

Ground: Loughborough Uni Stadium, Holywell Sports Complex, Holywell Park LE11 3QF

Capacity: 3,300 **Seats:** Yes **Covered:** Yes

Previous Names: Loughborough College

Previous Leagues: Leicestershire Senior. Midland Combination. Midland Alliance 2009-14. Midland 2014-19.

HONOURS: FA Comps: None

League: Midland Combination 2008-09.

10 YEAR RECORD

09-10		10-11		11-12		12-13		13-14		14-15		15-16		16-17		17-18		18-19	
MidAl	13	MidAl	4	MidAl	5	MidAl	4	MidAl	14	MFLP	20	MFLP	14	MFLP	18	MFLP	18	MFLP	18
FAC	EP	FAC	EP	FAC	1Q	FAC	P	FAC	1Q	FAC	P	FAC	P	FAC	P	FAC	1Q	FAC	Pr
FAV	1Pr	FAV	2Q	FAV	1P	FAV	1Q	FAV	2P	FAV	1Q	FAV	1Pr	FAV	2Q	FAV	2Q	FAV	1P

From M42/A42 exit at Junction 13 take the A512 towards Loughborough. After crossing Junction 23 of the M1 travel approx 3/4 mile to first traffic island. Turn right into University, following the signs for Holywell park & Holywell Sports Complex (Loughborough University Stadium). After entering the University through the Security barrier, keep straight on at both small islands. Bear left on entry to the large General Spectator Car park. Access to the ground which is on the left hand side of Car Park 'W' (available for spectator parking). Parking at the Stadium is limited to Officials/Team Coach as only a small number of cars can be accommodated. (Sat Nav users use LE11 3QF)

Nearest Railway Station Loughborough - 4km

Bus Route Wheatsheaf stop - 172m away

LUTTERWORTH TOWN

Founded 1955

Nickname: The Swifts **Club Colours:** Orange and black

Club Contact Details 07927 744 247 lutterworthtownfc@hotmail.com

Ground: Dunley Way, Lutterworth, Leicestershire, LE17 4NP

Capacity: **Seats:** Yes **Covered:** Yes

Previous Names: -

Previous Leagues: Leicestershrie Senior >2017

HONOURS: FA Comps: None

League: Leicestershire Senior Division Two 1980-81, Premier 90-91, 2016-17. United Counties Division One 2018-19.

10 YEAR RECORD

09-10	10-11	11-12	12-13	13-14	14-15	15-16	16-17	17-18	18-19
LeicS1 8	LeicS1 15	LeicS1 14	LeicS1 6	LeicS1 6	LeicS1 7	LeicS1 3	LeicSP 1	UCL 1 3	UCL 1 1
									FAC EP
								FAV 1P	FAV 1Q

Travelling North on the A426 turn left into Crescent Road. Follow this road until it merges into Dunley Way. Just before the bend where Dunley Way merges into Sherrier Way take the left. The ground is down the end of this road.
Travelling South on the A426 turn right into Central Avenue. At the T-juction turn right into Dunley Way. Just before the bend where Dunley Way merges into Sherrier Way take the left. The ground is down the end of this road.

Bus Route Elizabethan Way - stop 300m away

NORTHAMPTON O.N.C.

Founded 1946

Nickname: The Chens **Club Colours:** White and navy

Club Contact Details 01604 634 045

Ground: Old Northamptonians Sports Ground, Billing Road NN1 5RT

Capacity: 1,000 **Seats:** Yes **Covered:** Yes

Previous Names: Chenecks FC 1946-60. ON (Old Northamptonians) Chenecks 1960-

Previous Leagues: Northampton Minor 1946-50. Northampton Town 1950-69.

HONOURS: FA Comps: None

League: United Counties Division One 1977-78, 79-80.

10 YEAR RECORD

09-10	10-11	11-12	12-13	13-14	14-15	15-16	16-17	17-18	18-19
UCL 1 4	UCL 1 14	UCL 1 12	UCL 1 11	UCL 1 6	UCL 1 6	UCL 1 2	UCL P 12	UCL P 17	UCL P 15
							FAC EPr	FAC P	FAC EP
						FAV 2Q	FAV 1P	FAV 1P	FAV 1Q

Leave A45 at exit marked Bedford A428 and Town Centre.
Take exit into Rushmere Road marked Abington, Kingsthorpe and County Cricket.
At first set of lights turn left into Billing Road, sports ground 250 yards on the right.

Nearest Railway Station Northampton - 2.7km

Bus Route School for Boys - stop 80m away

OADBY TOWN

Founded 1937

Nickname: The Poachers **Club Colours:** All red

Club Contact Details 01162 715 728

Ground: Freeway Park, Wigston Road, Oadby LE2 5QG

Capacity: 5,000 **Seats:** 224 **Covered:** 224 **Shop:** Yes

Previous Names: Oadby Imperial > 1951.

Previous Leagues: Leicestershire Senior. Midland Alliance > 2011. East Midlands Counties 2011-12.

HONOURS: FA Comps: None

League: Leicestershire Senior Division Two 1951-52, Premier 63-64, 67-68, 68-69, 72-73, 94-95, 96-97, 97-98, 98-99. Midland Alliance 99-00. United Counties Division One 2013-14.

10 YEAR RECORD

09-10	10-11	11-12	12-13	13-14	14-15	15-16	16-17	17-18	18-19
MidAl 14	MidAl 22	EMC 3	UCL 1 4	UCL 1 1	UCL P 13	UCL P 21	UCL P 19	UCL P 19	UCL P 10
FAC EP	FAC 2Q	FAC Pr	FAC P	FAC EP	FAC EP	FAC 2Q	FAC EP	FAC P	FAC EP
FAV 2P	FAV 1Q	FAV 5P	FAV 2P	FAV 2P	FAV 1P	FAV 2Q	FAV 1Q	FAV 1Q	FAV 1Q

A14 Desborough, A6 towards Market Harborough. Follow A6 towards Leicester. Enter Oadby, go past Sainsbury's (traffic lights), next set of lights turn left. Signpost Oadby Town Centre, follow road over mini roundabout (St Peters Church in foreground) bear left towards Wigston. Follow road over roundabout, through the next lights, ground on the left.

Nearest Railway Station South Wigston - 3.6km

Bus Route Brabazon Road - stop 35m away

PETERBOROUGH NORTHERN STAR

Nickname: Star **Club Colours:** Black & white

Founded 1900

Club Contact Details 01733 552 416 clubsecretary@pnsfc.co.uk

Ground: Chestnut Avenue, Peterborough, Cambs PE1 4PE

Capacity: 1,500 **Seats:** Yes **Covered:** yes

Previous Names: Eye United 1900-31. Northam Star SC 1931-51. Eye United 1951-2005.

Previous Leagues: Peterborough Lge >2003

HONOURS: FA Comps: None

League: Peterborough 2002-03. United Counties League Division One 2008-09.

10 YEAR RECORD

09-10	10-11	11-12	12-13	13-14	14-15	15-16	16-17	17-18	18-19
UCL 1 2	UCL P 6	UCL P 7	UCL P 13	UCL P 9	UCL P 7	UCL P 17	UCL P 15	UCL P 16	UCL P 16
			FAC 1Q	FAC P	FAC P	FAC EP	FAC EP	FAC EP	FAC EP
		FAV QF	FAV 2P	FAV 2Q	FAV 3P	FAV 2Q	FAV 1P	FAV 2P	FAV 2P

From A1 turn on to A1139 Fletton Parkway. Follow signs for A47 Wisbech. Exit at Junction 7 (near Perkins Engines Site). At top of slip road turn left into Eastfield Road. At Traffic lights turn right into Newark Avenue and then first right in to Eastern Avenue. Take 2nd left in to Chestnut Avenue and the club is on the right behind steel Palisade Fencing.

Nearest Railway Station Peterborough - 2.6km

Bus Route Hawthorn Road - stop 35m away

PINCHBECK UNITED

Nickname: **Club Colours:** Red and black

Founded 1935

Club Contact Details 07786 984 987

Ground: Sir Harley Stewart Field, Winfrey Avenue, Spalding PE11 1DA

Capacity: **Seats:** Yes **Covered:** Yes

Previous Names: -

Previous Leagues: Peterborough & Distroct >2017

HONOURS: FA Comps: None

League: Peterborough & District Premier Division 1989-90, 90-91, 2011-12.
United Counties Division One 2017-18.

10 YEAR RECORD

09-10	10-11	11-12	12-13	13-14	14-15	15-16	16-17	17-18	18-19
		P&D P 1	P&D P 15	P&D P 15	P&D P 7	P&D P 3	P&D P 2	UCL 1 1	UCL P 4
									FAC EP
								FAV 1Q	FAV 2Q

Follow signs to Spalding Town Centre. From the north drive south down Pinchbeck Road towards Spalding. At traffic lights turn right into Kings Road. At the next set of lights turn left into Winfrey Avenue. The Ground is on the left. From the south follow signs to The Railway station and Bus Stations. The Ground is opposite the Bus Station on Winfrey Avenue. There is parking outside the ground in a pay and display car park.

Nearest Railway Station Spalding - 0.2km

Bus Route Broad Street - stop 100m away

QUORN

Nickname: Reds **Club Colours:** All red

Founded 1924

Club Contact Details 07891 512 346

Ground: Farley Way Stadium, Farley Way, Quorn, Leicestershire LE12 8RB

Capacity: 1,550 **Seats:** 350 **Covered:** 250

Previous Names: Quorn Methodists >1952

Previous Leagues: Leicestershire Senior, Midland Alliance > 2007. NPL 2007-2012. United Counties 2012-13. Midland Alliance 2013-14. Midland 2014-19.

HONOURS: FA Comps: None

League: Leicestershire Senior 2000-01

10 YEAR RECORD

09-10	10-11	11-12	12-13	13-14	14-15	15-16	16-17	17-18	18-19
NP1S 20	NP1S 15	NP1S 21	UCL P 7	MidAl 5	MFLP 11	MFLP 17	MFLP 11	MFLP 11	MFLP 6
FAC 1Q	FAC P	FAC 2Q	FAC 1Q	FAC Pr	FAC P	FAC EP	FAC EP	FAC P	FAC 1Q
FAT 3Q	FAT 1Q	FAT P	FAV 1P	FAV 1Q	FAV 2Q	FAV 2P	FAV 3P	FAV 2P	FAV 2P

Exit Junction 24 M1 Southbound on A6 through Kegworth, continue on A6 signposted Leicester/Loughborough bypass. Through Loughborough and at first roundabout take 2nd exit signposted Quorn. Turn left at traffic lights 200 yards from island and the ground is situated just inside on the left.

Nearest Railway Station Quorn & Woodhouse - 1.5km

Bus Route Alexander Road stop - 189m away

ROTHWELL CORINTHIANS

Founded 1934

Nickname: Corinthians **Club Colours:** Red and white

Club Contact Details 01536 711 706

Ground: Sergeants Lawn, Desborough Road, Rothwell NN14 6JQ

Capacity: **Seats:** 50 **Covered:** 200

Previous Names: None

Previous Leagues: Kettering & District Amateur/East Midlands Alliance 1934-95.

HONOURS: FA Comps: None

League: None

10 YEAR RECORD

09-10		10-11		11-12		12-13		13-14		14-15		15-16		16-17		17-18		18-19	
UCL P	21	UCL P	21	UCL 1	8	UCL 1	17	UCL 1	15	UCL 1	2	UCL P	14	UCL P	16	UCL P	15	UCL P	18
FAC	Pr	FAC	EP	FAC	P	FAC	EP					FAC	EP	FAC	EP	FAC	EP	FAC	P
FAV	1P	FAV	1Qr	FAV	1Q	FAV	1Q	FAV	1Q	FAV	2Q	FAV	2Qr	FAV	2P	FAV	1Qr	FAV	1Q

A14 to Rothwell. Take B669 towards Desborough. Ground on right at rear of cricket field opposite last houses on the left. arking on verge or in adjacent field if gate open. Access to ground via footpath.

Nearest Railway Station Kettering - 5.6km

RUGBY TOWN

Founded 1956

Nickname: The Valley **Club Colours:** Sky blue

Club Contact Details 01788 844 806

Ground: Butlin Road, Rugby, Warwicks CV21 3SD

Capacity: 6,000 **Seats:** 750 **Covered:** 1,000 **Shop:** Yes

Previous Names: Valley Sports 1956-71, Valley Sport Rugby 1971-73, VS Rugby 1973-2000, Rugby United 2000-05

Previous Leagues: Rugby & District 1956-62, Coventry & Partnership, North Warwickshire 1963-69, United Counties 1969-75 West Midlands 1975-83. Southern 1983-2015. Northern Premier 2015-17. Midland Football 2017-18.

HONOURS: FA Comps: FA Vase 1982-83.

League: Southern Midland Division 1986-87. Midland Combination Division 1 2001-02.

10 YEAR RECORD

09-10		10-11		11-12		12-13		13-14		14-15		15-16		16-17		17-18		18-19	
SthP	22	SthC	6	SthC	6	SthC	2	SthC	2	SthC	6	NP1S	9	NP1S	21	MFLP	6	UCL P	3
FAC	2Q	FAC	1Q	FAC	Pr	FAC	1Qr	FAC	3Qr	FAC	2Q	FAC	3Qr	FAC	2Q	FAC	P	FAC	EP
FAT	1Q	FAT	2Q	FAT	Pr	FAT	1Qr	FAT	P	FAT	P	FAT	P	FAT	Pr	FAV	2Pr	FAV	1P

From M6 J.1 North and South, take A426 signed Rugby at third island turn left into Boughton Road.
Continue along Boughton Road after passing under viaduct turn right at traffic lights, B5414 up the hill take second left at mini island into Butlin Road.

Nearest Railway Station Rugby - 1km

Bus Route Jolly Brewers stop - 127m away

SHEPSHED DYNAMO

Founded 1994

Nickname: Dynamo **Club Colours:** Black & white

Club Contact Details 07866 500 187 dannypole@aol.com

Ground: The Dovecote, Butt Hole Lane, Shepshed, Leicestershire LE12 9BN

Capacity: 2,050 **Seats:** 570 **Covered:** 400 **Shop:** Yes

Previous Names: Shepshed Albion/Charterhouse > 1994

Previous Leagues: Leics Sen 1907-16,19-27, 46-50, 51-81, Mid Co 81-82,N.C.E. 82-83, Sth 83-88, 96-04, N.P.L.88-93, 04-12, Mid Com 93-94, Mid All 94-95,13-14. UCL 12-13. Midland 2014-19.

HONOURS: FA Comps: Leicestershire Senior Cup x7

League: Midland Counties 1981-82. Northern Counties East 1982-83. Midland Alliance 1995-96.

10 YEAR RECORD

09-10		10-11		11-12		12-13		13-14		14-15		15-16		16-17		17-18		18-19	
NP1S	17	NP1S	21	NP1S	22	UCL P	9	MidAl	16	MFLP	16	MFLP	4	MFLP	15	MFLP	7	MFLP	7
FAC	P	FAC	Pr	FAC	Pr	FAC	EP	FAC	P	FAC	1Q	FAC	1Qr	FAC	EP	FAC	2Q	FAC	EPr
FAT	2Q	FAT	1Q	FAT	P	FAV	2P	FAV	2Q	FAV	2P	FAV	1Q	FAV	4P	FAV	3P	FAV	4P

From M1: Leave at Junction 23 and take A512 (Ashby). At first traffic lights turn right into Leicester Road and continue to garage on right. Turn right at mini roundabout into Forest Street and continue to Black Swan pub on left. Turn right into Butt Hole Lane, ground 100 yards. **From M6:** Leave at Junction 15 (Stoke-on-Trent) and take A50 to join M1 at Junction 24 South. At Junction 23 leave M1 and continue as above.

Bus Route Market Place stop - 229m away

SLEAFORD TOWN

Nickname: Town **Club Colours:** Green and black

Founded 1968

Club Contact Details 01529 415 951

Ground: Eslaforde Park, Boston Road, Sleaford, Lincs NG34 9GH

Capacity: 1,000 **Seats:** 88 **Covered:** 88

Previous Names: None

Previous Leagues: Lincolnshire 1968-2003.

HONOURS: FA Comps: None

League: United Counties Division One 2005-06.

10 YEAR RECORD

09-10		10-11		11-12		12-13		13-14		14-15		15-16		16-17		17-18		18-19	
UCL P	9	UCL P	18	UCL P	19	UCL P	18	UCL P	13	UCL P	19	UCL P	7	UCL P	14	UCL P	18	UCL P	13
FAC	1Qr	FAC	EP	FAC	EP	FAC	P	FAC	1Q	FAC	EP	FAC	EP	FAC	P	FAC	EP	FAC	EP
FAV	3P	FAV	1Q	FAV	2Q	FAV	1P	FAV	2Q	FAV	2Q	FAV	4P	FAV	3Pr	FAV	1Q	FAV	1Pr

15 Sleaford By-pass, roundabout to A17 Holdingham Roundabout third exit towards Boston on A17.
Take second exit of A17 towards Sleaford ground is 1 mile on right hand side before you enter Sleaford.

Nearest Railway Station Sleaford - 1.4km

Bus Route Eslaforde Park - stop 90m away

WELLINGBOROUGH TOWN

Nickname: Doughboys **Club Colours:** Yellow & blue

Founded 1867

Club Contact Details 01933 441 388

Ground: Dog and Duck, London Road, Wellingborough NN8 2DP

Capacity: 2,500 **Seats:** Yes **Covered:** Yes

Previous Names: Original team (Formed 1867) folded in 2002 reforming in 2004

Previous Leagues: Metropolitan. Southern.

HONOURS: FA Comps: None

League: United Counties 1964-65.

10 YEAR RECORD

09-10		10-11		11-12		12-13		13-14		14-15		15-16		16-17		17-18		18-19	
UCL P	11	UCL P	5	UCL P	8	UCL P	15	UCL P	8	UCL P	15	UCL P	20	UCL P	9	UCL P	14	UCL P	14
FAC	EP	FAC	1Q	FAC	EP	FAC	P	FAC	EPr	FAC	EP	FAC	EP	FAC	EP	FAC	P	FAC	P
FAV	2P	FAV	1P	FAV	1Q	FAV	1Q	FAV	2Q	FAV	2Q	FAV	2Q	FAV	2Q	FAV	1Q	FAV	2P

Leave A.45 at Wellingborough turn-off, pass Tesco's Store on left-hand side, up to roundabout. Take first exit to town centre. Ground is 300 yards on right-hand side. Entry just past the Dog & Duck public house adjacent to entry to Whitworths ground.

Nearest Railway Station Wellingborough - 1.2km

Bus Route The Dog & Duck Pub - stop 50m away

AYLESTONE PARK

Founded: 1967 Nickname:

Club Contact Details 0116 278 5485
Ground: Mary Linwood Recreation Ground, Saffron Lane, Leicester LE2 6TG **Club Colours:** Red
HONOURS **League:** None
FA Comps: None

10 YEAR RECORD

09-10	10-11	11-12	12-13	13-14	14-15	15-16	16-17	17-18	18-19
LeicSP 14	LeicSP 8	LeicSP 3	EMC 7	EMC 18	EMC 19	EMC 5	EMC 4	EMC 9	UCL 1 8
							FAC EP	FAC P	
		FAV 2Q		FAV 2Q	FAV 1Q	FAV 2Q	FAV 1Q	FAV 1Q	FAV 1P

Leave the M1 at Junction 21.
Take Soar Valley Way (A563), over first set of traffic lights and turn right onto Saffron Lane at Southfields roundabout (B5366). Ground 400 metres on left.
From Leicester City Centre, take Saffron Lane to Southfield Roundabout and ground 400 metres on left.

Nearest Railway Station South Wigston - 1.1km

BIRSTALL UNITED

Founded: 1961 Nickname:

Club Contact Details 0116 267 1230
Ground: Meadow Lane, Birstall LE4 4FN **Club Colours:** White and navy
HONOURS **League:** Leicester Mutual Division One 1972-73, 73-74, 75-76.
Leicestershire Senior Division Two 1976-77, Premier 2015-16.
FA Comps: None

10 YEAR RECORD

09-10	10-11	11-12	12-13	13-14	14-15	15-16	16-17	17-18	18-19
LeicSP 9	LeicSP 9	LeicSP 6	LeicSP 11	LeicSP 4	LeicSP 4	LeicSP 1	EMC 3	EMC 8	UCL 1 17
								FAC P	
FAV 1Q		FAV 2Q	FAV 1Q				FAV 2Qr	FAV 1Q	FAV 2Q

At junction 3, exit onto M1 toward Nottingham. At junction 21a, take the A46 exit to Braunstone Frith/Kirby Muxloe/B5380. Keep right at the fork, follow signs for A46/Leicester North/Newark. Continue onto Leicester Western Bypass/A46. Take the A6/Wanlip ramp to Leicester/Loughboro. At the roundabout, take the 2nd exit onto Wanlip. Turn right onto Fillingate. At the roundabout, take the 1st exit and stay on Fillingate. Fillingate turns slightly right and becomes Rectory Rd. Rectory Rd turns slightly left and becomes Wanlip Lane. Turn left onto Lambourne Road. Turn left onto Blenheim Road. Turn right onto Meadow Lane.

Nearest Railway Station Syston

BLACKSTONES

Founded: 1920 Nickname: Stones

Club Contact Details 01780 757 835 imacgilli@outlook.com
Ground: Lincoln Road, Stamford, Lincs PE9 1SH **Club Colours:** Green and white
HONOURS **League:** Peterborough & District 1918-19, Division Two 1961-62, Division One 75-76.
FA Comps: None

10 YEAR RECORD

09-10	10-11	11-12	12-13	13-14	14-15	15-16	16-17	17-18	18-19
UCL P 13	UCL P 9	UCL P 11	UCL P 20	UCL 1 20	UCL 1 17	UCL 1 10	UCL 1 14	UCL 1 8	UCL 1 5
FAC 1Q	FAC EPr	FAC EP	FAC P	FAC EP					
FAV 1P	FAV 2Qr	FAV 1Q	FAV 2Q	FAV 2Q	FAV 2Q	FAV 1P	FAV 2Q	FAV 1Q	FAV 1Q

From Stamford Centre take A6121 towards Bourne. Turn left into Lincoln Road. Ground on the right hand side.
Go into town on A16 from Spalding. Turn left at roundabout into Liquor Pond Street becoming Queen Street over railway crossing along Sleaford Road. Turn right into Carlton Road then right at crossroads into Fydell Street. Over railway crossing and river take 2nd left (sharp turn) into Tattershall Road. Continue over railway crossing, ground on left.

Nearest Railway Station Stamford - 1.5km
Bus Route Junction with Kesteven Rd - stop 75m away

BOURNE TOWN

Founded: 1883 Nickname: Wakes

Club Contact Details 07709 785 273
Ground: Abbey Lawn, Abbey Road, Bourne, Lincs PE10 9EN **Club Colours:** Claret & sky blue
HONOURS **League:** Peterborough & District 1933-34, 39-40, 45-46, 46-47. Central Alliance Division One South 59-60. United Counties Premier 65-66, 68-69, 69-70, 71-72, 90-91.
FA Comps: None

10 YEAR RECORD

09-10	10-11	11-12	12-13	13-14	14-15	15-16	16-17	17-18	18-19
UCL P 17	UCL 1 12	UCL 1 14	UCL 1 10	UCL 1 21	UCL 1 10	UCL 1 5	UCL 1 15	UCL 1 10	UCL 1 13
FAC 2Q									
FAV 1P						FAV 2Q	FAV 1Q	FAV 2Q	FAV 1Q

From Town Centre turn east on A151 towards Spalding into Abbey Road. Ground approximately half a mile on right.

Bus Route Nowells Lane - stop 105m away

BUGBROOKE ST MICHAELS

Founded: 1929 Nickname: Badgers

Club Contact Details 01604 830 707 graybags05@btinternet.com

Ground: Birds Close, Gayton Road, Bugbrooke NN7 3PH **Club Colours:** White and black

HONOURS **League:** Central Northants Combination 1968-69, 69-70, 71-72, 76-77, 85-86.
United Counties Division One 1998-99.

FA Comps: None

10 YEAR RECORD

09-10	10-11	11-12	12-13	13-14	14-15	15-16	16-17	17-18	18-19
UCL 1 7	UCL 1 3	UCL 1 3	UCL 1 7	UCL 1 18	UCL 1 11	UCL 1 18	UCL 1 3	UCL 1 18	UCL 1 4
		FAC P	FAC 1Q	FAC EP					
FAV 2P	FAV 2Q	FAV 1P	FAV 2Q	FAV 2Q	FAV 1Q	FAV 1Q			FAV 2Qr

At M1 Junction 16 take A45 to Northampton.
At first roundabout follow signs to Bugbrooke.
Go straight through village, ground entrance immediately past last house on the left.

Bus Route Bakers Arms Pub - stop 500m away

BURTON PARK WANDERERS

Founded: 1961 Nickname: The Wanderers

Club Contact Details 07794 959 915

Ground: Latimer Park, Polwell Lane, Burton Latimer, Northants NN15 5PS **Club Colours:** Blue & black

HONOURS **League:** None

FA Comps: None

10 YEAR RECORD

09-10	10-11	11-12	12-13	13-14	14-15	15-16	16-17	17-18	18-19
UCL 1 15	UCL 1 8	UCL 1 9	UCL 1 19	UCL 1 8	UCL 1 18	UCL 1 19	UCL 1 19	UCL 1	UCL 1 12
					FAV 2Q	FAV 1Qr	FAV 1Q	FAV 2Q	FAV 2Q

From A14 take J10 towards Burton Latimer, at Alpro roundabout turn right, then straight over roundabout next to Versalift then right at Morrisions. Follow the round around the top of Morrisions continue until you are past the small Alumasc building on the left. Entrance to ground is next left.

Nearest Railway Station Kettering - 4.1km
Bus Route Station Road - stop 120m away

HARROWBY UNITED

Founded: 1949 Nickname: The Arrows

Club Contact Details 01476 401 201

Ground: Harrowby Stadium, Dickens Road, Grantham NG31 9QY **Club Colours:** Blue

HONOURS **League:** Midlands Regional Alliance Premier Division 1989-90.
United Counties Division One 1991-92.

FA Comps: None

10 YEAR RECORD

09-10	10-11	11-12	12-13	13-14	14-15	15-16	16-17	17-18	18-19
CM Su 18			UCL 1 6	UCL 1 3	UCL P 17	UCL P 18	UCL P 21	UCL 1 5	UCL 1 7
					FAC EP	FAC EP	FAC P	FAC EP	
				FAV 1P	FAV 2Q	FAV 1P	FAV 1Q	FAV 1P	FAV 2Q

From A1 take B6403, go past roundabout, to Ancaster and take road for Harrowby.
Follow the road into Grantham, ground on right opposite Cherry Tree public house.

Nearest Railway Station Grantham - 2.6km
Bus Route St Wulframs School - stop 100m away

HOLWELL SPORTS

Founded: 1902 Nickname:

Club Contact Details 01664 812 080

Ground: Welby Road, Asfordby Hill, Melton Mowbray, Leicestershire LE14 3RD **Club Colours:** Yellow and green

HONOURS **League:** Leic Senior Premier 1911-12, 87-88, 91-92, 92-93, Division One 1984-85.
Leicester & District 1907-08, 08-09. Melton Mowbray & Dist Am 1933-34.

FA Comps: None

10 YEAR RECORD

09-10	10-11	11-12	12-13	13-14	14-15	15-16	16-17	17-18	18-19
EMC 13	EMC 13	EMC 11	EMC 5	EMC 9	EMC 8	EMC 16	EMC 16	EMC 18	UCL 1 14
FAC EPr	FAC EPr		FAC EP	FAC EP	FAC 1Q	FAC 1Qr			
FAV 2Q	FAV 2P	FAV 1P	FAV 1Q	FAV 3P	FAV 2Q	FAV 2Q	FAV 1P	FAV 2Q	FAV 1Q

From Derby. Take A52 to M1 J24 then A6 to Loughborough. At Zouch take left on A6006 to Asfordby And Asfordby Hill. At island take left turn and ground 300 metres on left.
From Nottingham A52 to A6006, onto A46. Left onto A6006 and then as above.
From Leicester – turn off A46 at Six Hills Hotel, left at t-junction, right at cross roads and then as above.

Nearest Railway Station Melton Mowbray - 2.8km

HUNTINGDON TOWN

Founded: 1995 Nickname: The Hunters

Club Contact Details 07974 664 818

Ground: Jubilee Park, Kings Ripton Road,, Huntingdon, Cambridgeshire PE28 **Club Colours:** Red & black

HONOURS **League:** Cambridgeshire Division 1B 1999-2000.
United Counties Division One 2011-12.

FA Comps: None

10 YEAR RECORD

09-10	10-11	11-12	12-13	13-14	14-15	15-16	16-17	17-18	18-19
UCL 1 8	UCL 1 5	UCL 1 1	UCL P 4	UCL P 2	UCL P 16	UCL P 22	UCL P 22	UCL 1 12	UCL 1 18
		FAC 1Q	FAC 1Q	FAC 1Q	FAC EP	FAC EPr	FAC EP	FAC EP	
FAV 1Q	FAV 2Q	FAV 2Q	FAV 1Q	FAV 3P	FAV 2P	FAV 1Q	FAV 2Q	FAV 2Q	FAV 1Q

At the A1 Brampton Hut roundabout, follow signs for A14 East until reaching the Spittals Interchange roundabout.
Follow the A141 towards St Ives/March and go over 3 roundabouts.
Take next left turn at traffic lights towards Kings Ripton and the ground is on the left.

Nearest Railway Station Huntingdon - 3.4km
Bus Route Newnham Close - stop 1km away

IRCHESTER UNITED

Founded: 1885 Nickname: The Romans

Club Contact Details 01933 312 877

Ground: Alfred Street, Irchester NN29 7DR **Club Colours:** Red and black

HONOURS **League:** Rushden & District 1928-29, 29-30, 36-37. Northants / United Counties Division Two 1930-31, 31-32 / United Counties Division One 2009-10.

FA Comps: None

10 YEAR RECORD

09-10	10-11	11-12	12-13	13-14	14-15	15-16	16-17	17-18	18-19
UCL 1 1	UCL P 10	UCL P 20	UCL P 21	UCL 1 19	UCL 1 15	UCL 1 16	UCL 1 8	UCL 1 13	UCL 1 10
		FAC EP	FAC EP	FAC EP					
	FAV 1Q	FAV 2Q	FAV 2Q	FAV 2Q	FAV 1P	FAV 1Q	FAV 2Q	FAV 2Q	FAV 2P

From A509 Wellingborough/Newport Pagnell Road turn into Gidsy Lane to Irchester.
Turn left into Wollaston Road B659. Alfred Street is on left hand side with the ground at the end.

Nearest Railway Station Wellingborough - 3.1km
Bus Route Alfred Street - stop 100m away

LONG BUCKBY AFC

Founded: 1937 Nickname: Bucks

Club Contact Details 07749 393 045 lbafc.dja@gmail.com

Ground: Station Road, Long Buckby NN6 7PL **Club Colours:** All claret

HONOURS **League:** United Counties Division Three 1969-70, Division Two 70-71, 71-72, Premier Division 2011-12.

FA Comps: None

10 YEAR RECORD

09-10	10-11	11-12	12-13	13-14	14-15	15-16	16-17	17-18	18-19
UCL P 3	UCL P 4	UCL P 1	UCL P 16	UCL P 18	UCL P 21	UCL 1 6	UCL 1 13	UCL 1 17	UCL 1 15
FAC 1Qr	FAC EP	FAC 3Q	FAC EP	FAC EP	FAC EPr	FAC 1Q			
FAV 5P	FAV 5P	FAV 3P	FAV 1Pr	FAV 1Q	FAV 2Q	FAV 2Q	FAV 1Q	FAV 1Q	FAV 2Q

From the Village Centre turn into Station Road. Ground on left hand side.
Parking is available in South Close adjacent to the Rugby Club.
(do NOT park "half on half off" the pavement outside the ground).

Nearest Railway Station Long Buckby - 0.3km
Bus Route Watson Road - stop 70m away

LUTTERWORTH ATHLETIC

Founded: 1983 Nickname: The Athletic

Club Contact Details 01455 554 046 djones20335783@aol.com

Ground: Weston Arena, Hall Park, Hall Lane, Bitteswell, Lutterworth LE17 4LN **Club Colours:** Green & white

HONOURS **League:** Leicester & District Division Two 1994-95, Premier 2004-05.

FA Comps: None

10 YEAR RECORD

09-10	10-11	11-12	12-13	13-14	14-15	15-16	16-17	17-18	18-19
LeicSP 6	LeicSP 6	LeicSP 2	EMC 13	UCL 1 5	UCL 1 4	UCL 1 11	UCL 1 12	UCL 1 11	UCL 1 6
	FAV 1Q	FAV 1P	FAV 2Q	FAV 1Q		FAV 1Q	FAV 1Q	FAV 1Q	FAV 1Q

Exit the M1 at junction 20 and take the first exit at the roundabout. Then take the third exit at the next roundabout and head into Lutterworth. Continue on through Lutterworth, and when you have left the town continue for half a mile before taking the first left. The ground is immediately on your left.

Bus Route Manor Farm - stop 1.5km away

MELTON TOWN

Founded: 2004 Nickname:

Club Contact Details 01664 480 576 secretarymeltonmowbrayfc@hotmail.com

Ground: Melton Sports Village, Burton Road, Melton Mowbray LE13 1DR **Club Colours:** Red

HONOURS **League:** None

FA Comps: None

10 YEAR RECORD

09-10	10-11	11-12	12-13	13-14	14-15	15-16	16-17	17-18	18-19
LeicS1 9	LeicS1 12	LeicS1 6	LeicS1 2	LeicSP 2	LeicSP 2	LeicSP 3	UCL 1 9	UCL 1 16	UCL 1 3
								FAV 2Q	FAV 1Qr

From Town centre follow signs for A1/Oakham. 1/2 mile up Burton Road ground is on the left.

NORTHAMPTON SILEBY RANGERS

Founded: 1968 Nickname: Rangers

Club Contact Details 01604 670 366

Ground: Fernie Fields Sports Ground, Moulton, Northampton NN3 6BD **Club Colours:** Red and black

HONOURS **League:** Northampton Town 1988-89 89-90. United Counties Division One 1993-94, 2002-03, 04-05, 12-13.

FA Comps: None

10 YEAR RECORD

09-10	10-11	11-12	12-13	13-14	14-15	15-16	16-17	17-18	18-19
UCL 1 9	UCL 1 9	UCL 1 16	UCL 1 1	UCL P 15	UCL P 18	UCL P 19	UCL P 8	UCL P 22	UCL 1 9
					FAC 1Q	FAC P	FAC P	FAC EP	FAC Pr
FAV 1Q				FAV 1P	FAV 1Q	FAV 2P	FAV 2P	FAV 2Q	FAV 2Q

Approach from A43 (Kettering): From large roundabout with traffic lights, take the A5076 Talavera Way exit, signpostedto Market Harborough, Moulton Park and Kingsthorpe. The entrance to the ground is about a quarter of a mile on the left. Approach from A45: Take exit to A43 Ring Road / Kettering / Corby. Go straight over 1 roundabout to large roundabout with traffic lights. Then follow directions above.

Nearest Railway Station Northampton - 5.5km

Bus Route Booth Rise - stop 205m away

RAUNDS TOWN

Founded: 1946 Nickname: Shopmates

Club Contact Details 01933 623 351

Ground: Kiln Park, London Road, Raunds, Northants NN9 6EQ **Club Colours:** Red & black

HONOURS **League:** United Counties Division One 1982-83.

FA Comps: None

10 YEAR RECORD

09-10	10-11	11-12	12-13	13-14	14-15	15-16	16-17	17-18	18-19
UCL P 20	UCL P 20	UCL 1 13	UCL 1 14	UCL 1 12	UCL 1 9	UCL 1 8	UCL 1 7	UCL 1 4	UCL 1 19
FAC EPr	FAC EP	FAC EP				FAC P	FAC EP	FAC EPr	FAC EP
FAV 1Q	FAV 2Q	FAV 2Q	FAV 2Q		FAV 1Q	FAV 1P	FAV 1Q	FAV 2Q	FAV 2Q

From North, East or West, take A14 J13 and follow A45 signs to Raunds.
Turn left at roundabout by BP garage.
From South follow A45 towards Thrapston.
Turn right at roundabout by BP garage. Ground on left.

Bus Route Bus stops outside the ground.

RUSHDEN & HIGHAM UNITED

Founded: Formed: 2007 Nickname: The Lankies

Club Contact Details 01933 410 036 rhufcsec@yahoo.co.uk

Ground: Hayden Road, Rushden, Northants NN10 9LA **Club Colours:** Red and black

HONOURS **League:** None

FA Comps: None

10 YEAR RECORD

09-10	10-11	11-12	12-13	13-14	14-15	15-16	16-17	17-18	18-19
UCL 1 16	UCL 1 10	UCL 1 5	UCL 1 8	UCL 1 14	UCL 1 13	UCL 1 13	UCL 1 16	UCL 1 9	UCL 1 11
		FAC EP	FAC EP	FAC EP					
FAV 2Q	FAV 1Q	FAV 2Q	FAV 2Q	FAV 1Q		FAV 1Q	FAV 1Q	FAV 1P	FAV 1Q

From A6/A45 (Chowns Mill Roundabout) take Higham / Rushden bypass at 3rd roundabout, take the 3rd exit onto Newton Road, then immediately right after Newton Road School into Cromwell road this then leads into Hayden Road. Ground is approx. 100 yards on left hand side. From Bedford (A6) take Rushden / Higham Bypass and at the 1st roundabout take the 1st exit onto Newton Road, then turn immediately right after Newton Road School into Cromwell road this the leads into Hayden Road. Ground is approx. 100 yards on the left hand side.

Bus Route Ashwell Road - stop 60m away

SAFFRON DYNAMO

Founded: 1963 Nickname:

Club Contact Details 07957 151 630

Ground: King's Park, Cambridge Road, Whetstone LE9 1SJ **Club Colours:** Red and black

HONOURS **League:** None

FA Comps: None

10 YEAR RECORD

09-10	10-11	11-12	12-13	13-14	14-15	15-16	16-17	17-18	18-19
LeicSP 7	LeicSP 11	LeicSP 13	LeicSP 13	LeicSP 13	LeicSP 3	LeicSP 7	LeicSP 2	LeicSP 5	LeicSP 2
		FAV 1Q							FAV 2P

ST. ANDREWS

Founded: 1973 Nickname: The Saints

Club Contact Details 0116 283 9298

Ground: Canal Street, Aylestone, Leicester LE2 8DR **Club Colours:** Black & white

HONOURS **League:** Leicestershire City Premier x4. Leicestershire Senior 1989-90, 93-94, 95-96. East Midlands Counties 2015-16.

FA Comps: None

10 YEAR RECORD

09-10	10-11	11-12	12-13	13-14	14-15	15-16	16-17	17-18	18-19
EMC 15	EMC 17	EMC 4	EMC 16	EMC 7	EMC 2	EMC 1	MFLP 9	UCL P 21	UCL 1 16
FAC P	FAC EP		FAC EP		FAC EPr	FAC EP	FAC EP	FAC EPr	FAC EP
FAV 2Q	FAV 2Q	FAV 2P	FAV EP	FAV SF	FAV 2P	FAV 3P	FAV 1P	FAV 2Q	FAV 1Q

From the north to J21 of the M1. 1st left at roundabout and on to next roundabout. 2nd exit and follow A5460 towards Leicester. At 1st set of traffic lights turn right onto Braunstone Lane East. After approximately 1 mile turn left at T-junction and follow Aylestone Road towards Leicester. Take 3rd road on the left. Turn right at T-Junction and turn left at No Entry Signs over the canal bridge and left into ground.

Nearest Railway Station South Wigston - 3km

WELLINGBOROUGH WHITWORTH

Founded: 1973 Nickname: Flourmen

Club Contact Details 07776 160 169

Ground: Victoria Mill Ground, London Road, Wellingborough NN8 2DP **Club Colours:** Red & black

HONOURS **League:** Rushden & District 1975-76, 76-77. United Counties Division One 2006-07.

FA Comps: None

10 YEAR RECORD

09-10	10-11	11-12	12-13	13-14	14-15	15-16	16-17	17-18	18-19
UCL 1 12	UCL 1 13	UCL 1 4	UCL 1 13	UCL 1 17	UCL 1 7	UCL 1 15	UCL 1 2	UCL P 20	UCL P 20
			FAC EP			FAC EP	FAC EP	FAC EP	FAC EP
		FAV 1Q	FAV 2Q	FAV 2Q	FAV 1Q	FAV 1Q	FAV 2Q	FAV 2Q	FAV 1Q

Leave A.45 at Wellingborough turn-off, pass Tesco's Store on left-hand side, up to roundabout. Take first exit to town centre. Ground is 300 yards on right-hand side. Entry just past the Dog & Duck public house adjacent to entry to Whitworths ground.

Nearest Railway Station Wellingborough - 1.2km

Bus Route The Dog & Duck Pub - stop 50m away

WHITTLESEY ATHLETIC

Founded: 2014 Nickname:

Club Contact Details 07941 631 681

Ground: Feldale Field, Drybread Road, Whittlesey, PE7 1YP **Club Colours:** Navy and white

HONOURS **League:** None

FA Comps: None

10 YEAR RECORD

09-10	10-11	11-12	12-13	13-14	14-15	15-16	16-17	17-18	18-19
						P&D P 2	UCL 1 Exp	P&D P 3	P&D P 5

PREMIER DIVISION INS: AFC Stoneham (P - Wex1), Amesbury Town (P - Wex1), Fleet Town (R - Sth1S), Solent University (NC from Team Solent).

AFC PORTCHESTER

Nickname: Portchy/Royals **Club Colours:** Tangerine and black

Founded 1971

Club Contact Details 01329 233 833 (Clubhouse) secretary@afcportchester.co.uk

Ground: The Crest Finance Stadium, Cranleigh Road, Portchester, Hampshire PO16 9DP

Capacity: **Seats:** Yes **Covered:** Yes

Previous Names: Loyds Sports 1971-73. Colourvison Rangers 1973-76. Wilcor Mill 1976-2003.

Previous Leagues: City of Portsmouth Sunday. Portsmouth & District >1998. Hampshire 1998-2004.

HONOURS: FA Comps: None

League: Portsmouth & Football 1997-98. Hampshire Division One 2001-02.

10 YEAR RECORD

09-10	10-11	11-12	12-13	13-14	14-15	15-16	16-17	17-18	18-19
Wex1 6	Wex1 3	Wex1 2	WexP 15	WexP 8	WexP 3	WexP 6	WexP 8	WexP 6	WexP 13
		FAC Pr	FAC EP	FAC 2Q	FAC P	FAC 2Q	FAC 2Q	FAC 2Q	FAC EPr
	FAV 2Q	FAV 2Q	FAV 2Q	FAV 3P	FAV 3P	FAV 1P	FAV 2Q	FAV 1P	FAV 1Q

Leave the M27 at Junction 11 and follow the signs to Portchester into Portchester Road. Carry on for approx 1 mile at the large roundabout, take the 3rd exit into Cornaway Lane and at the 'T' junction turn right in Cranleigh Road and follow the road to the end. Postcode for Satellite Navigation systems PO16 9DP

Nearest Railway Station Porchester - 15.km

Bus Route Sandport Grove stop

AFC STONEHAM

Nickname: The Purples **Club Colours:** All purple

Founded 1919

Club Contact Details 07933 111 381 secretary@afcstoneham.co.uk

Ground: The HP Arena, Jubilee Park, Chestnut Avenue, Eastleigh SO50 9PF

Capacity: **Seats:** Yes **Covered:** Yes

Previous Names: Ordnance Survey > 2006. Stoneham 2006-07.

Previous Leagues: Hampshire Premier League >2015

HONOURS: FA Comps: None

League: Southampton Senior 1982-83, 92-93, 96-97. Hampshire Premier 2007-08. Wessex Division One 2018-19.

10 YEAR RECORD

09-10	10-11	11-12	12-13	13-14	14-15	15-16	16-17	17-18	18-19
HantP 6	HantP 8	HantP 4	HantP 2	HantP 12	HantP 4	Wex1 8	Wex1 8	Wex1 5	Wex1 1
									FAC 1Q
							FAV 1P	FAV 1Q	FAV 1P

Leave M27 at Junction 5. Turn into Stoneham Lane & pass the rear of Eastleigh Football Club. At end of Stoneham Lane (mini roundabout), turn left into Chestnut Avenue. Entrance to ground is on the left and shared with Chandlers Ford Golf Academy.

Nearest Railway Station Southampton Airport Parkway - 1.6km

Bus Route Golf Driving Range stop

ALRESFORD TOWN

Nickname: The Magpies **Club Colours:** White and black

Founded 1898

Club Contact Details 07703 346 672 secretary.alresfordtownfc@gmail.com

Ground: Arlebury Park, The Avenue, Alresford, Hants SO24 9EP

Capacity: **Seats:** Yes **Covered:** Yes

Previous Names: None

Previous Leagues: Winchester League, North Hants league, Hampshire League

HONOURS: FA Comps: None

League: North Hampshire 1999-2000.

10 YEAR RECORD

09-10	10-11	11-12	12-13	13-14	14-15	15-16	16-17	17-18	18-19
WexP 17	WexP 15	WexP 15	WexP 2	WexP 2	WexP 16	WexP 20	WexP 5	WexP 7	WexP 12
FAC P	FAC Pr	FAC P	FAC P	FAC EP	FAC Pr	FAC EP	FAC 2Q	FAC P	FAC EPr
FAV 1Pr	FAV 1Q	FAV 1P	FAV 2Q	FAV 4P	FAV 3P	FAV 1Q	FAV 2P	FAV 2Q	FAV 2P

Alresford is situated on the A31 between Winchester and Alton.
Arlebury Park is on the main avenue into Alresford opposite Perins School.

Nearest Railway Station Alresford - 620m

Bus Route Bridge Road stop

OUTS: Andover New Street (R - Wex1), Bemerton Heath Harlequins (R - Wex1), Sholing (P - Sth1S).

AMESBURY TOWN

Founded 1904

Nickname: Blues **Club Colours:** Royal blue & white

Club Contact Details 01980 623 489 amesburytownfc@gmail.com

Ground: Bonnymead Park Recreation Road Amesbury SP4 7BB

Capacity: **Seats:** Yes **Covered:** Yes

Previous Names: Amesbury FC 1904-1984.

Previous Leagues: Salisbury & District Junior 1904-06. Salisbury & District 1906-56, 97-98. Wiltshire 1956-71. Wiltshire Combination/County 71-. Western 1994-97. Hampshire 1998-2004.

HONOURS: FA Comps: None

League: Salisbury & District Division Two 1954-55, Division One 55-56. Wiltshire Division One 1959-60. Wiltshire Combination/County 1974-75, 79-80 / Division One 90-91, 91-92. Hampshire Premier 1999-2000.

10 YEAR RECORD

09-10	10-11	11-12	12-13	13-14	14-15	15-16	16-17	17-18	18-19
Wex1 11	Wex1 13	Wex1 14	Wex1 14	Wex1 10	Wex1 4	Wex1 2	WexP 19	WexP 20	Wex1 2
FAC EP	FAC EP					FAC EP	FAC P	FAC P	FAC EP
FAV 1Q	FAV 1Q	FAV 1Q	FAV 1Q	FAV 1Q	FAV 2Q	FAV 1Q	FAV 1P	FAV 2Q	FAV 1Q

From Salisbury take A345 to Amesbury, turn left just past the bus station and proceed through the one way system, when road splits with Friar Tuck Café and Lloyds Bank on left turn left and follow road over the river bridge and when road bears sharp right turn left into Recreation Road.
From A303 at Countess Roundabout go into Amesbury, straight over traffic lights, at mini-roundabout turn right into one way system and follow directions as above. Postcode for Satellite Navigation systems SP4 7BB

Bus Route Mandalay Guest House - stop 600m away

BAFFINS MILTON ROVERS

Founded 2011

Nickname: None **Club Colours:** All royal blue

Club Contact Details 07980 403 336

Ground: Kendall Wharf, Eastern Road, Portsmouth PO3 5LY

Capacity: **Seats:** 120 **Covered:** Yes

Previous Names: Formed when Sunday league teams Baffins Milton and Milton Rovers merged.

Previous Leagues: Hampshire Premier >2016

HONOURS: FA Comps: None

League: Portsmouth Saturday Premier Division 2011-12. Hampshire Premier Senior Division , 2013-14, 15-16.

10 YEAR RECORD

09-10	10-11	11-12	12-13	13-14	14-15	15-16	16-17	17-18	18-19
		PorS P 1	PorS P 2	HantP 1	HantP 2	HantP 1	Wex1 2	WexP 9	WexP 5
									FAC P
								FAV 3P	FAV 4P

Travelling towards Portsmouth on the M27 continue onto A27. Take the A2030 (s) exit toward Portsmouth(E)/Southsea. At the roundabout, take the 4th exit onto Eastern Road/A2030. Turn left at Anchorage Road. Destination will be on the left.
Travelling towards Portsmouth on the A3(M) merge onto A27. Take the A2030 exit toward Portsmouth(E)/Central Southsea. At the roundabout, take the 2nd exit onto Eastern Road/A2030. Turn left at Anchorage Road. Destination will be on the left.

Nearest Railway Station Hilsea - 1.3km
Bus Route Robinson Way - stop 420m away

BASHLEY

Founded 1947

Nickname: The Bash **Club Colours:** Gold and black

Club Contact Details 01425 620 280 footballsecretary@bashleyfc.org.uk

Ground: Bashley Road Ground, Bashley Road, New Milton, Hampshire BH25 5RY

Capacity: 4,250 **Seats:** 250 **Covered:** 1,200 **Shop:** Yes

Previous Names: None

Previous Leagues: Bournemouth 1953-83, Hampshire 1983-86, Wessex 1986-89, Southern 1989-2004, 06-16. Isthmian 2004-06

HONOURS: FA Comps: None

League: Hampshire Division Three 1984-85. Wessex 1986-87, 87-88, 88-89. Southern Southern Division 1989-90, Division One South & West 2006-07.

10 YEAR RECORD

09-10	10-11	11-12	12-13	13-14	14-15	15-16	16-17	17-18	18-19
SthP 7	SthP 11	SthP 13	SthP 17	SthP 23	Sthsw 22	Sthsw 22	WexP 14	WexP 14	WexP 9
FAC 2Q	FAC 3Q	FAC 1Q	FAC 1Qr	FAC 2Q	FAC P	FAC P	FAC EP	FAC EP	FAC EP
FAT 1P	FAT 1Q	FAT 1Qr	FAT 1Qr	FAT 1Q	FAT P	FAT 1Q	FAV 2Q	FAV 1P	FAV 1P

Take the A35 from Lyndhurst towards Christchurch, turn left onto B3058 towards New Milton.
The ground is on the left hand side in Bashley village.

Nearest Railway Station New Milton - 1.9km
Bus Route Village Store & PO - stop 230m away

BOURNEMOUTH

Nickname: Poppies **Club Colours:** Red and white

Founded 1875

Club Contact Details 01202 515 123 bournemouthwessex@gmail.com

Ground: Victoria Park, Namu Road, Winton, Bournemouth BH9 2RA

Capacity: 3,000 **Seats:** 205 **Covered:** 205 **Shop:** Yes

Previous Names: Bournemouth Rovers, Bournemouth Wanderers, Bournemouth Dean Park.

Previous Leagues: Hampshire 1896-98, 1903-39 & 46-86.

HONOURS: FA Comps: None

League: None

10 YEAR RECORD

09-10	10-11	11-12	12-13	13-14	14-15	15-16	16-17	17-18	18-19
WexP 4	WexP 5	WexP 9	WexP 13	WexP 15	WexP 18	WexP 18	WexP 17	WexP 18	WexP 3
FAC EP	FAC P	FAC 2Qr	FAC EP	FAC P	FAC Pr	FAC EP	FAC EP	FAC EP	FAC P
FAV 2Q	FAV 3P	FAV QF	FAV 2P	FAV 1Q	FAV 2Q	FAV 2Q	FAV 1P	FAV 2Q	FAV 2P

From the North and East – A338 from Ringwood. Take the 3rd exit signed A3060 Wimborne, going under the road you've just left. Stay on this road passing Castlepoint Shopping Centre (on your right), then the Broadway Hotel on your right, keep straight ahead passing the Horse & Jockey on your left, keep to the nearside lane. At roundabout take the 1st exit marked A347, pass Redhill Common on your right and the fire station on your left: continue on the A347 turning left at the filter with the pub – The Ensbury Park Hotel – immediately in front of you. 1st left into Victoria Avenue, and then third right into Namu Road, turning right at the end into the lane for the ground entrance. **From the West** – A35 from Poole. Take the A3049 Dorset Way passing Tower Park (which is hidden from view) on your right, at the next roundabout take the second exit, and then the first exit at the next roundabout, taking up a position in the outside lane. At the next roundabout (with a pub called the Miller and Carter Steakhouse on your right) take the third exit, Wallisdown Road A3049. Go through the shopping area of Wallisdown across two roundabouts and at the third one take the first exit, you will see the ground on your right as you approach the pelican crossing. Turn right into Victoria Avenue, then third right into Namu Road, turning right at the end into the lane for the ground entrance. Postcode for Satellite Navigation systems BH9 2RA

BROCKENHURST

Nickname: The Badgers **Club Colours:** Blue and white

Founded 1898

Club Contact Details 01590 623 544 brockenhurstfcsec@gmail.com

Ground: Grigg Lane, Brockenhurst, Hants SO42 7RE

Capacity: 2,000 **Seats:** 200 **Covered:** 300

Previous Names: None

Previous Leagues: Hampshire 1924-26, 35-37, 47-86.

HONOURS: FA Comps: None

League: Hampshire Division Three 1959-60, Division Two 70-71, Division One 75-76. Wessex Division One 2012-13.

10 YEAR RECORD

09-10	10-11	11-12	12-13	13-14	14-15	15-16	16-17	17-18	18-19
WexP 13	WexP 22	Wex1 5	Wex1 1	WexP 11	WexP 14	WexP 14	WexP 10	WexP 13	WexP 15
FAC 1Q	FAC EP	FAC 1Q	FAC EP	FAC 1Q	FAC EP	FAC 3Q	FAC P	FAC P	FAC P
FAV 3P	FAV 2Q	FAV 1P	FAV 1Q	FAV 2Q	FAV 1Q	FAV 1Q	FAV 2Q	FAV 2P	FAV 2P

Leave the M27 at Junction 1 and take the A337 to Lyndhurst. From Lyndhurst take the A337 signposted Brockenhurst, turn right at Careys Manor Hotel into Grigg Lane. Ground situated 200 yards on the right. Postcode for Satellite Navigation systems SO42 7RE

Nearest Railway Station Brockenhurst - 0.5km

Bus Route Brockenhurst College - stop 260m away

CHRISTCHURCH

Nickname: The Church **Club Colours:** All Blue

Founded 1885

Club Contact Details 01202 473 792 secretary@christchurchfc.co.uk

Ground: Hurn Bridge Sports Ground, Avon Causeway, Christchurch BH23 6DY

Capacity: 1,200 **Seats:** 215 **Covered:** 265

Previous Names: None

Previous Leagues: Hampshire

HONOURS: FA Comps: None

League: Hampshire Division Two 1937-38, 47-48, 85-86, Division Three 52-53.
Wessex Division One 2017-18.

10 YEAR RECORD

09-10	10-11	11-12	12-13	13-14	14-15	15-16	16-17	17-18	18-19
WexP 5	WexP 6	WexP 3	WexP 3	WexP 16	WexP 21	Wex1 6	Wex1 4	Wex1 1	WexP 16
FAC EP	FAC EP	FAC EP	FAC 1Q	FAC EP	FAC EPr	FAC P	FAC EP	FAC EP	FAC EPr
FAV 2P	FAV 1Pr	FAV 3P	FAV 1P	FAV 1Pr	FAV 2Q	FAV 1Q	FAV 2Q	FAV 3P	FAV 2Q

A338 from Ringwood turn off at sign for Bournemouth International Airport (Hurn) on left. At T junction turn right, continue through traffic lights, at the small roundabout in Hurn turn right away from the Airport, exit signed Sopley and 100 yards on the right is Hurn Bridge Sports Ground. Postcode for Sat. Nav. systems BH23 6DY

Nearest Railway Station Christchurch - 4.6km

Bus Route Post Office - stop 100m away

COWES SPORTS

Nickname: Yachtsmen **Club Colours:** Blue & White

Founded 1881

Club Contact Details 01983 718 277 secretary.cowessportsfc@outlook.com

Ground: Westwood Park Reynolds Close off Park Rd Cowes Isle of Wight PO31 7NT

Capacity: **Seats:** Yes **Covered:** Yes

Previous Names: Cowes

Previous Leagues: Hampshire (FM) 1896-98, 1903-94. Southern 1898-99.

HONOURS: FA Comps: None

League: Hampshire Division One 1896-97, 1908-09 (jt), 26-27, 27-28, 30-31, 36-37, 55-56, 93-94, Division Two 1974-75. Southern Division Two South West 1898-99.

10 YEAR RECORD

09-10		10-11		11-12		12-13		13-14		14-15		15-16		16-17		17-18		18-19	
WexP	22	Wex1	8	Wex1	6	Wex1	4	Wex1	3	Wex1	2	WexP	11	WexP	18	WexP	19	WexP	18
FAC	EP	FAC	EP	FAC	EP	FAC	EP	FAC	P	FAC	P	FAC	P	FAC	EP	FAC	EP	FAC	EP
FAV	2Q	FAV	2Q	FAV	3P	FAV	2Q	FAV	2Q	FAV	1P	FAV	2Q	FAV	2Q	FAV	1Q	FAV	1Q

Turn left out of the Cowes pontoon, 1st right up Park Road approx 1/2 mile take the 4th right into Reynolds Close. Postcode for Sat. Nav. systems PO31 7NT

Bus Route Parklands Avenue - stop 100m away

FAREHAM TOWN

Nickname: Creeksiders **Club Colours:** Red & black stripes

Founded 1947

Club Contact Details 07889 491 903 farehamtnfc@gmail.com

Ground: Cams Alders, Palmerston Drive, Fareham, Hants PO14 1BJ

Capacity: 2,000 **Seats:** 450 **Covered:** 500 **Shop:** Yes

Previous Names: Formed when Fareham FC, Fareham Brotherhood and Fareham Youth Centre merged.

Previous Leagues: Portsmouth 1946-49. Hampshire 1949-79. Southern 1979-98.

HONOURS: FA Comps: None

League: Hampshire League Division 3 East 1949-50, Premier 1959-60, 62-63, 63-64, 64-65, 65-66, 66-67, 72-73, 74-75.

10 YEAR RECORD

09-10		10-11		11-12		12-13		13-14		14-15		15-16		16-17		17-18		18-19	
WexP	6	WexP	8	WexP	12	WexP	9	WexP	10	WexP	19	WexP	12	WexP	12	WexP	16	WexP	17
FAC	EP	FAC	P	FAC	EP	FAC	2Q	FAC	1Q	FAC	P	FAC	EP	FAC	1Qr	FAC	P	FAC	EP
FAV	2P	FAV	2Q	FAV	1P	FAV	2Q	FAV	2P	FAV	1P	FAV	1Q	FAV	2Q	FAV	2P	FAV	1P

Leave the M27 at Junction 11. Follow signs A32 Fareham – Gosport. Pass under the viaduct with Fareham Creek on your left, straight over at the roundabout then fork right – B3385 sign posted Lee-on-Solent. Over the railway bridge, Newgate Lane and turn immediately first right into Palmerston Business Park, follow the road to the ground. Postcode for Satellite Navigation systems PO14 1BJ

Nearest Railway Station Fareham - 0.9km

Bus Route Fairfield Avenue - stop 250m away

FLEET TOWN

Nickname: The Blues **Club Colours:** Blue & white

Founded 1890

Club Contact Details 01252 623 804 Match day only secretary@fleettownfc.co.uk

Ground: Calthorpe Park, Crookham Road, Fleet, Hants GU51 5FA

Capacity: 2,000 **Seats:** 250 **Covered:** 250 **Shop:** Yes

Previous Names: Fleet FC 1890-1963

Previous Leagues: Hampshire 1961-77, Athenian, Combined Counties, Chiltonian, Wessex 1989-95, 2000-02, Southern 1995-2000, 02-04, 07-08, 11-19. Isthmian 2004-07, 2008-11.

HONOURS: FA Comps: None

League: Wessex 1994-95.

10 YEAR RECORD

09-10		10-11		11-12		12-13		13-14		14-15		15-16		16-17		17-18		18-19	
Isth1S	6	Isth1S	13	SthC	21	SthC	18	Sthsw	21	Sthsw	19	SthC	17	SthC	14	Sth1E	19	SthS	20
FAC	Pr	FAC	2Qr	FAC	1Q	FAC	P	FAC	P	FAC	2Q	FAC	1Qr	FAC	1Qr	FAC	Pr	FAC	1Q
FAT	2Q	FAT	1Q	FAT	1Q	FAT	Pr	FAT	P	FAT	1Q	FAT	P	FAT	1Q	FAT	Pr	FAT	1Q

Leave the M3 at Junction 4a, and follow the signs for Fleet. Head along the A3013, Fleet Road. Carry on along the street passing the main shopping street, through several pedestrian crossings for about 1 mile. When you get to the Oatsheaf Pub crossroads head straight across. Ground is 300yds down the hill on the right.

Nearest Railway Station Fllet - 2.1km

Bus Route Leawood Road - stop 150m away

HAMBLE CLUB

Founded 1969

Nickname: The Monks **Club Colours:** All yellow

Club Contact Details 07977 324 923 secretary.hambleclubfc@gmail.com

Ground: Hamble Community Facility, Hamble Lane SO31 4JW

Capacity: **Seats:** Yes **Covered:** Yes

Previous Names: None

Previous Leagues: Hampshire Premier 1993-2016.

HONOURS: FA Comps: None

League: Hampshire Premier 2014-15. Wessex Division One 2016-17.

10 YEAR RECORD

09-10	10-11	11-12	12-13	13-14	14-15	15-16	16-17	17-18	18-19
HantP 12	HantP 16	HantP 15	HantP Exp	Hant1 2	HantP 1	HantP 3	Wex1 1	WexP 10	WexP 7
									FAC P
								FAV 5P	FAV 3Pr

Travelling on the M27 leave at junction 8, take the A3024 exit to Southampton (E)/Hamble. At the roundabout, take the 3rd exit onto A3024. At the roundabout, take the 2nd exit onto Hamble Lane/A3025. At the roundabout, take the 2nd exit and stay on Hamble Lane/A3025. At the roundabout, take the 2nd exit and stay on Hamble Lane/A3025. Continue straight onto Hamble Lane/B3397. At the roundabout, take the 1st exit and stay on Hamble Lane/B3397. Turn right for Hamble Club.

Nearest Railway Station Hamble - 0.4km

Bus Route Hamble Lane School - stop 500m away

HAMWORTHY UNITED

Founded 1926

Nickname: The Hammers **Club Colours:** Maroon & sky blue

Club Contact Details 01202 674 974 hamworthyutdsecretary@gmail.com

Ground: The County Ground, Blandford Close, Hamworthy, Poole BH15 4BF

Capacity: 2,000 **Seats:** **Covered:** Yes **Shop:** No

Previous Names: Hamworthy St. Michael merged with Trinidad Old Boys 1926

Previous Leagues: Dorset Combination (Founder Member) / Dorset Premier 1957-2004.

HONOURS: FA Comps: None

League: Dorset Premier 2002-03, 03-04.

10 YEAR RECORD

09-10	10-11	11-12	12-13	13-14	14-15	15-16	16-17	17-18	18-19
WexP 16	WexP 9	WexP 7	WexP 10	WexP 12	WexP 10	WexP 16	WexP 16	WexP 5	WexP 6
FAC 1Q	FAC Pr	FAC EP	FAC P	FAC 2Q	FAC EP	FAC 1Q	FAC 1Q	FAC 1Q	FAC 1Qr
FAV 1Q	FAV 2Q	FAV 1Q	FAV 2Q	FAV 1P	FAV 2Q	FAV 1Q	FAV 1Q	FAV 2Q	FAV 4P

From M27 to Cadnam – follow A31 to Ringwood – A347/A348 Ferndown - Bearcross – follow on this road until you pass the Mountbatten Arms on your left – turn right at next roundabout onto the A3049 and follow the signs to Dorchester and Poole. Continue on this dual carriageway over the flyover to the next roundabout – straight across and take the 2nd exit left off the dual carriageway to Upton / Hamworthy – go straight across 2 mini roundabouts and continue to Hamworthy passing the Co-op store on your left – then turn left at the 2nd set of traffic lights into Blandford Close. Postcode for Satellite Navigation systems BH15 4BF

Nearest Railway Station Poole - 1.4km

Bus Route Carter School - stop 100m away

HORNDEAN

Founded 1887

Nickname: Deans **Club Colours:** All red (All yellow)

Club Contact Details 02392 591 363 horndeanfc1887@gmail.com

Ground: Five Heads Park Five Heads Road Horndean Hampshire PO8 9NZ

Capacity: **Seats:** Yes **Covered:** Yes

Previous Names: None

Previous Leagues: Waterlooville & District. Portsmouth. Hampshire 1972-86, 1995-2004. Wessex 1986-95

HONOURS: FA Comps: None

League: Waterlooville & District 1926-27, 29-30, 30-31, 31-32. Portsmouth Division Two 1953-54, Premier 68-69, 69-70, 70-71. Hampshire Division Four 1974-75, Division Three 75-76, Division Two 79-80.

10 YEAR RECORD

09-10	10-11	11-12	12-13	13-14	14-15	15-16	16-17	17-18	18-19
Wex1 12	Wex1 2	WexP 17	WexP 11	WexP 17	WexP 11	WexP 5	WexP 6	WexP 4	WexP 2
		FAC 1Q	FAC 1Q	FAC 1Q	FAC 1Q	FAC EP	FAC EP	FAC 1Q	FAC 1Q
	FAV 1Q	FAV 2Q	FAV 3P	FAV 2Q	FAV 2P	FAV 1P	FAV 1P	FAV 3P	FAV 2P

Leave A3(M) at Junction 2 and follow signs to Cowplain. Take the slip road passing Morrisons store on the right crossing over the mini roundabout then continue to the set of traffic lights ensuring you are in the right hand lane signed Horndean. Turn right at these traffic lights and continue on for approximately 400 yards until you reach the Colonial Bar on your left, next junction on your left after the Colonial Bar is Five Heads Road, turn left into Five Heads Road and the ground is approx 1/4 mile along this road. Postcode for Satellite Navigation systems PO8 9NZ

Nearest Railway Station Rowlands Castle - 4.5km

Bus Route Horndean Com. School - stop 560m away

LYMINGTON TOWN

Nickname: Town **Club Colours:** Red and white

Founded 1998

Club Contact Details 01590 671 305 secretary.lymingtontownfc@yahoo.com

Ground: The Sports Ground, Southampton Road, Lymington SO41 9ZG

Capacity: 3,000 **Seats:** 200 **Covered:** 300

Previous Names: None

Previous Leagues: Hampshire 1998-2004.

HONOURS: FA Comps: None

League: Wessex Division Two 2004-05.

10 YEAR RECORD

09-10		10-11		11-12		12-13		13-14		14-15		15-16		16-17		17-18		18-19	
WexP	20	WexP	11	WexP	14	WexP	19	WexP	14	WexP	9	WexP	13	WexP	9	WexP	8	WexP	10
FAC	Pr	FAC	EP	FAC	Pr	FAC	EP	FAC	P	FAC	EP	FAC	EP	FAC	EPr	FAC	EP	FAC	2Q
FAV	2Q	FAV	1P	FAV	1Q	FAV	2Q	FAV	1P	FAV	2Qr	FAV	2P	FAV	1Q	FAV	1P	FAV	2Q

From the North & East – Leave the M27 at Junction 1 (Cadnam/New Forest) and proceed via Lyndhurst then Brockenhurst on the A337. On the outskirts of Lymington proceed through main set of traffic lights with Royal Quarter Housing Development and the Police Station on your right hand side. Continue for just another 250 metres and turn left immediately into St Thomas's Park with he ground in front of you.
Alternatively, turn left at the traffic lights into Avenue Road then first right, Oberland Court, with the Lymington Bowling Club facing you.
If travelling from the direction of Christchurch & New Milton using the A337 pass the White Hart P/H on the outskirts of Pennington and proceed down and up Stanford Hill. Passing the Waitrose Supermarket on your left hand side, the ground is situated immediately on your right hand side sign posted St Thomas Park.

Nearest Railway Station Lymington Town - 0.6km

Bus Route Town Hall - Stop 110m away

PORTLAND UNITED

Nickname: Blues **Club Colours:** All royal blue

Founded 1921

Club Contact Details 01305 861 489 secretary.portlandutdfc@aol.com

Ground: New Grove Corner, Grove Road, Portland DT5 1DP

Capacity: 2,000 **Seats:** Yes **Covered:** Yes

Previous Names: None

Previous Leagues: Western 1925-70. Dorset Combination 1970-76, 77-2001, Dorset Premier 2006-07. Wessex 2001-02.

HONOURS: FA Comps: None

League: Western Division Two 1930-31, 31-32. Dorset Combination 1998-99, 99-2000, Dorset Premier 2007-08, 08-09, 12-13, 13-14. Wessex Division One 2015-16, Premier 2016-17.

10 YEAR RECORD

09-10		10-11		11-12		12-13		13-14		14-15		15-16		16-17		17-18		18-19	
Dor P	8	Dor P	4	Dor P	3	Dor P	1	Dor P	1	Dor P	2	Wex1	1	WexP	1	WexP	15	WexP	4
																FAC	P	FAC	P
														FAV	2P	FAV	2Q	FAV	1Q

On entering the Island of Portland, stay on the main road (signposted for Easton) to the top of the Island (unmistakable - sharp steep hairpin bend with the Portland Heights Hotel in front of you). Continue towards Easton into Yeats Road and Easton Lane. 100 yards after passing the Drill Hall (Castle like building) turn left into Grove Road. New Grove Corner is 200-300 yards on the left.

Bus Route Clifton Hotel - stop 280m away

SHAFTESBURY

Nickname: The Rockies **Club Colours:** Red & white

Founded 1888

Club Contact Details 07769 114 362

Ground: Cockrams, Coppice Street, Shaftesbury SP7 8PD

Capacity: **Seats:** Yes **Covered:** Yes

Previous Names: Shaftesbury Town.

Previous Leagues: Dorset Junior. Dorset Senior 1931-57. Dorset Combination 1957-62, 76-2004. Wessex 2004-11. Dorset Premier 2011-16.

HONOURS: FA Comps: None

League: Dorset Junior 1905-06, 62-63. Dorset Senior 1932-33. Dorset Combination 1988-89, 96-97. Dorset Premier 2015-16. Wessex Division One 2016-17.

10 YEAR RECORD

09-10		10-11		11-12		12-13		13-14		14-15		15-16		16-17		17-18		18-19	
Wex1	20	Wex1	19	Dor P	18	Dor P	11	Dor P	14	Dor P	4	Dor P	1	Wex1	3	WexP	12	WexP	14
FAC	EP															FAC	P	FAC	1Q
FAV	2Q	FAV	2Q									FAV	2Q	FAV	2P	FAV	1Q	FAV	1P

Travelling South on the A350 into Shaftesbury, at the roundabout, take the 2nd exit onto Little Content Lane/A30/A350. Continue to follow A30/A350. Go through one roundabout. Turn right onto Coppice Street. Destination will be on the right. Travelling North on the A350 into Shaftesbury, at the roundabout, take the 2nd exit onto Christy's Lane/A30/A350. Turn left onto Coppice Street. Destination will be on the right.

Bus Route Linden Park - stop 100m away

SOLENT UNIVERSITY

Nickname: The Sparks **Club Colours:** All red

Founded 2007

Club Contact Details 07801 227 232 secretary.teamsolent@solent.ac.uk

Ground: Test Park, Lower Broomhill Road, Southampton SO16 9QZ

Capacity: **Seats:** Yes **Covered:** Yes

Previous Names: None

Previous Leagues: Hampshire Premier 2007-11.

HONOURS: FA Comps: None

League: Wessex Division One 2014-15.

10 YEAR RECORD

09-10	10-11	11-12	12-13	13-14	14-15	15-16	16-17	17-18	18-19
HantP 2	HantP 2	Wex1 3	Wex1 3	Wex1 6	Wex1 1	WexP 7	WexP 7	WexP 17	WexP 11
				FAC EP	FAC EP	FAC EP	FAC P	FAC EP	FAC EP
			FAV 1Q	FAV 1Q	FAV 1Qr	FAV 1P	FAV 5P	FAV 3P	FAV 1Q

Leave the M27 at junction 3 for M271. Take the first slip road off the M271 and then first exit off the roundabout on to Lower Broomhill Road. Carry on to the next roundabout and take the last exit, (coming back on yourself) into Redbridge lane and the entrance to Test Park is approx. 500m on right.
From City centre take the Millbrook road to the M271, first slip road off on to roundabout, 3rd exit on to Lower Broomhill Way and then as above. Postcode for Satellite Navigation systems SO16 9QZ

Nearest Railway Station Redbridge - 1.2km

Bus Route The Saints - stop 450m away

TADLEY CALLEVA

Nickname: The Tadders **Club Colours:** All yellow

Founded 1989

Club Contact Details 07926 830 806 secretarytcfc@gmail.com

Ground: Barlows Park Silchester Road Tadley Hampshire RG26 3PX

Capacity: 1,000 **Seats:** **Covered:**

Previous Names: Tadley FC 1989-99. Tadley Town 1999-2004.

Previous Leagues: Hampshire 1994-2004

HONOURS: FA Comps: None

League: Wessex Division One 2007-08.

10 YEAR RECORD

09-10	10-11	11-12	12-13	13-14	14-15	15-16	16-17	17-18	18-19
Wex1 15	Wex1 16	Wex1 17	Wex1 7	Wex1 5	Wex1 3	Wex1 3	Wex1 7	Wex1 3	WexP 8
				FAC P	FAC EPr	FAC EP	FAC EP		FAC EP
			FAV 1Q	FAV 2Q	FAV 2Q	FAV 3Pr	FAV 1Q	FAV 2Q	FAV 2Q

From M3 Basingstoke Junction 6 take the A340 to Tadley, travel through Tadley and at the main traffic lights turn right into Silchester Road, proceed for 0.5 mile then turn left into the car park. Postcode for Satellite Navigation systems RG26 3PX

Nearest Railway Station Midgham - 5.1km

Bus Route Tadley Common Road - stop 60m away

DIVISION ONE INS: Andover New Street 9R - WexP), Bemerton Heath Harlequins (R - WexP), Pewsey Vale (Tr - Hel1W).
OUTS: AFC Stoneham (P - WexP), Amesbury Town (P - WexP).

ALTON

Founded: 1990 Nickname: The Brewers

Club Contact Details 07709 715 322 secretary@altonfc

Ground: Anstey Park Enclosure, Anstey Road, Alton, Hants GU34 2NB **Club Colours:** White and black

HONOURS **League:** Hampshire Division One 1998-99, Premier 2001-02.

FA Comps: None

10 YEAR RECORD

09-10		10-11		11-12		12-13		13-14		14-15		15-16		16-17		17-18		18-19	
WexP	18	WexP	13	WexP	10	WexP	18	CCP	21	CC1	13	Wex1	7	Wex1	12	Wex1	8	Wex1	13
FAC	P	FAC	2Qr	FAC	P	FAC	P	FAC	P	FAC	1Q	FAC	EP						
FAV	2Q	FAV	2Q	FAV	2Pr	FAV	1P	FAV	1Q	FAV	1Q	FAV	1P	FAV	1P	FAV	1P	FAV	2Q

Leave the A31 at the B3004 signposted to Alton. Follow the road round to the left passing Anstey Park on the right, the ground is then immediately on the left – opposite the turning into Anstey Lane. Postcode for Satellite Navigation systems GU34 2RL

Nearest Railway Station Alton - 0.6km
Bus Route Anstey Lane - stop 32m away

ANDOVER NEW STREET

Founded: 1895 Nickname: The Street

Club Contact Details 01264 358 358 (Wkends from 12) andovernewstreetfc@hotmail.co.uk

Ground: Foxcotte Park Charlton Andover Hampshire SP11 0TA **Club Colours:** Green & black

HONOURS **League:** None

FA Comps: None

10 YEAR RECORD

09-10		10-11		11-12		12-13		13-14		14-15		15-16		16-17		17-18		18-19	
Wex1	19	Wex1	17	Wex1	10	Wex1	15	Wex1	15	Wex1	13	Wex1	16	Wex1	19	Wex1	2	WexP	20
																		FAC	P
		FAV	1P	FAV	2Q	FAV	1Q					FAV	1Q	FAV	1Q	FAV	1Q	FAV	2Q

From Basingstoke follow the A303 to Weyhill roundabout. At roundabout turn right and 2nd roundabout turn left on to A342. Approx 1/2 mile turn right into Short Lane, continue into Harroway Lane to the 'T' junction at the top. Turn right into Foxcotte Lane and continue for about 3/4 mile then turn left, this still Foxcotte Lane, to the top some 3/4 mile to the roundabout straight across into Foxcotte Park. Postcode for Satellite Navigation systems SP11 0TA.

Nearest Railway Station Andover - 2.4km
Bus Route Charlton Cemetery - stop 120m away

ANDOVER TOWN

Founded: 2013 Nickname:

Club Contact Details 07730 590 183

Ground: Portway Stadium, West Portway Industrial Estate, Andover SP10 3LF **Club Colours:** All blue

HONOURS **League:** None

FA Comps: None

10 YEAR RECORD

09-10		10-11		11-12		12-13		13-14		14-15		15-16		16-17		17-18		18-19	
										WexP	12	WexP	4	WexP	13	WexP	2	Wex1	18
												FAC	Pr	FAC	1Q	FAC	1Q	FAC	EP
										FAV	2Q	FAV	1P	FAV	2P	FAV	1Q	FAV	1P

Leave A303 at Junction for A342 . If from the East cross back over A303. At large roundabout take A342 across the face of the Premier Hotel. First right into the Portway Industrial Estate then follow the one way system and after the road swings right at the bottom of the hill the ground is on the left.

Nearest Railway Station Andover - 1.8km
Bus Route Arkwright Gate - stop 130m away

BEMERTON HEATH HARLEQUINS

Founded: 1989 Nickname: Quins

Club Contact Details 01722 331 925 bhhfc@gmail.co.uk

Ground: Moon Park, Western Way, Bemerton Heath Salisbury SP2 9DR **Club Colours:** Black & white

HONOURS **League:** None

FA Comps: None

10 YEAR RECORD

09-10		10-11		11-12		12-13		13-14		14-15		15-16		16-17		17-18		18-19	
WexP	3	WexP	2	WexP	2	WexP	5	WexP	7	WexP	13	WexP	9	WexP	11	WexP	11	WexP	19
FAC	P	FAC	EP	FAC	EP	FAC	EP	FAC	EP	FAC	1Q	FAC	P	FAC	1Q	FAC	EP	FAC	1Q
FAV	2P	FAV	4P	FAV	3P	FAV	5P	FAV	2P	FAV	2P	FAV	2Q	FAV	3P	FAV	1Q	FAV	2Q

Turn off the A36 Salisbury to Bristol road at Skew Bridge (right turn if coming out of Salisbury), 1st left into Pembroke Road for 1/2 mile, 2nd left along Western Way – Ground is 1/4 mile at the end of the road. 40 minutes walk fro Salisbury railway station. Bus service 51 or 52 from the city centre.
Postcode for Satellite Navigation systems SP2 9DP

Nearest Railway Station Salisbury - 2.1km
Bus Route Winding Way - stop 75m away

DOWNTON

Founded: 1905 Nickname: The Robins

Club Contact Details 01725 512 162 secretary@downtonfc.com

Ground: Brian Whitehead Sports Ground Wick Lane Downton Wiltshire SP5 3NF **Club Colours:** Red

HONOURS
FA Comps: None
League: Bournemouth League Division One x5, Senior Division One x7. Wessex League Division One 2010-11.

10 YEAR RECORD

09-10		10-11		11-12		12-13		13-14		14-15		15-16		16-17		17-18		18-19	
Wex1	4	Wex1	1	WexP	6	WexP	8	WexP	21	Wex1	12	Wex1	10	Wex1	11	Wex1	12	Wex1	7
FAC	EPr	FAC	EP	FAC	EPr	FAC	EP	FAC	EP	FAC	EP								
FAV	1P	FAV	2P	FAV	2P	FAV	3P	FAV	2Q			FAV	1Q	FAV	1Q	FAV	1P	FAV	1Q

The ground is situated 6 miles south of Salisbury on the A338 to Bournemouth. In the village – sign to the Leisure Centre (to west) – this is Wick Lane – football pitch and Club approx 1/4 mile on the left. Postcode for Satellite Navigation systems SP5 3NF

Bus Route The Bull - stop 180m away

EAST COWES VICTORIA ATHLETIC

Founded: 1885 Nickname: The Vics

Club Contact Details 01983 297 165 ecvics@gmail.com

Ground: Beatrice Avenue, East Cowes, Isle of Wight PO32 6PA **Club Colours:** Red & white

HONOURS
FA Comps: None
League: Hampshire Division Two 1947-48, 63-64, 71-72, Division One 85-86, 86-87.

10 YEAR RECORD

09-10		10-11		11-12		12-13		13-14		14-15		15-16		16-17		17-18		18-19	
Wex1	17	Wex1	15	Wex1	4	Wex1	8	Wex1	16	Wex1	15	Wex1	18	Wex1	20	Wex1	16	Wex1	10
						FAC	P	FAC	EP										
		FAV	2Q	FAV	1Q	FAV	1Q	FAV	2Q	FAV	2Q	FAV	1Q	FAV	2Q	FAV	1Q	FAV	2Q

From East Cowes ferry terminal follow Well Road into York Avenue until reaching Prince of Wells PH, turn at the next right into Crossways Road then turn left into Beatrice Avenue.
From Fishbourne follow signs to East Cowes and Whippingham Church, ground is 200 yards from the church on Beatrice Avenue.

Bus Route Osborne House - stop 400m away

FAWLEY

Founded: 1923 Nickname: Oilers

Club Contact Details 02380 893 750 (Club) fmahawleyafc@aol.com

Ground: Waterside Spts & Soc. club, 179 Long Lane, Holbury, Soto, SO45 2PA **Club Colours:** Sky and navy blue

HONOURS
FA Comps: None
League: Hampshire Division Three 1994-95.

10 YEAR RECORD

09-10		10-11		11-12		12-13		13-14		14-15		15-16		16-17		17-18		18-19	
Wex1	2	WexP	20	WexP	19	WexP	17	WexP	20	WexP	17	WexP	19	WexP	20	Wex1	9	Wex1	11
						FAC	EP	FAC	EP	FAC	EP	FAC	EP	FAC	EP	FAC	EP		
				FAV	2P	FAV	1P	FAV	2Q	FAV	1Q	FAV	1Q	FAV	1Q	FAV	2Q	FAV	2Q

Leave the M27 at Junction 2 and follow the A326 to Fawley/Beaulieu. Head south for approx 7 miles. The Club is situated on the right hand side 2/3 mile after crossing the Hardley roundabout. The Club is positioned directly behind the service road on the right hand side. Postcode for Satellite Navigation systems SO45 2PA

Nearest Railway Station Netley - 5.3km
Bus Route New Forest Academy - stop 100m away

FOLLAND SPORTS

Founded: 1938 Nickname: Planemakers

Club Contact Details 02380 452 173 follandsportsfc@hotmail.co.uk

Ground: Folland Park, Kings Ave, Hamble, Southampton SO31 4NF **Club Colours:** All red

HONOURS
FA Comps: None
League: Hampshire 1941-42, Division Four 79-80, Division Three 80-81. Southampton Senior 1961-62, 67-68. Wessex Division One 2009-10.

10 YEAR RECORD

09-10		10-11		11-12		12-13		13-14		14-15		15-16		16-17		17-18		18-19	
Wex1	1	WexP	12	WexP	5	WexP	7	WexP	3	WexP	8	WexP	21	Wex1	17	Wex1	18	Wex1	16
FAC	EPr	FAC	3Q	FAC	EP	FAC	P	FAC	P	FAC	2Qr	FAC	EP	FAC	EP				
FAV	2P	FAV	1P	FAV	2Q	FAV	3P	FAV	2P	FAV	2P	FAV	2Q	FAV	1Q	FAV	1Q	FAV	1Q

Leave the M27 at Junction 8 and take the turning for Southampton East At the Windhover roundabout take the exit for Hamble (B3397) Hamble Lane, proceed for 3 miles. Upon entering Hamble the ground is on the right via Kings Avenue, opposite the Harrier P/H. Postcode for Satellite Navigation systems SO31 4NF

Nearest Railway Station Hamble - 1km
Bus Route Verdon Avenue - stop 300m away

HYTHE & DIBDEN

Founded: 1902 Nickname: The Boatmen

Club Contact Details -7789 266 473 hythedibdenfc@aol.com

Ground: Clayfields, Claypit Lane, Dibden SO45 5TN **Club Colours:** Green and white

HONOURS
FA Comps: None
League: Hampshire Division Three West 1949-50. Southampton Division Two 1970-71, 75-76.

10 YEAR RECORD

09-10	10-11	11-12	12-13	13-14	14-15	15-16	16-17	17-18	18-19
Wex1 16	Wex1 14	Wex1 18	Wex1 16	Wex1 4	Wex1 7	Wex1 11	Wex1 18	Wex1 15	Wex1 3
					FAC EP	FAC EP			
	FAV 2Q		FAV 1Q	FAV 1P	FAV 1Q	FAV 2Q	FAV 1Q	FAV 2Q	FAV 1Q

Travel along A326 and at the Dibden Roundabout take the first exit left into Southampton Road. Continue for approximately 1/2 mile and turn right into Claypits Lane just before the Shell Filling Station. The ground is 100 yards on the left and there is car parking in the ground.
Postcode for Satellite Navigation systems SO45 5TN

Nearest Railway Station Southampton Town Quay - 3.5km
Bus Route Drapers Copse - stop 200m away

LAVERSTOCK & FORD

Founded: 1956 Nickname: The Stock

Club Contact Details 01722 327 401 sec.laverstockandfordfc@gmail.com

Ground: The Dell, Church Road, Laverstock, Salisbury, Wilts SP1 1QX **Club Colours:** Green & white hoops

HONOURS
FA Comps: None
League: Hampshire Division Two 2002-03.

10 YEAR RECORD

09-10	10-11	11-12	12-13	13-14	14-15	15-16	16-17	17-18	18-19
WexP 21	WexP 17	WexP 22	Wex1 13	Wex1 9	Wex1 8	Wex1 5	Wex1 6	Wex1 7	Wex1 9
FAC EP	FAC P						FAC EP	FAC P	
FAV 1P	FAV 1P		FAV 1Q	FAV 1P	FAV 2Q	FAV 1P	FAV 1Q	FAV 1Q	FAV 1Q

From Southampton – At the end of the carriageway from Southampton (A36) turn right at traffic lights for the Park & Ride by the Tesco store. Turn left at the traffic lights over the narrow bridge then take the next turning into Manor Farm Road. Take the next turning right into Laverstock Road, (do not turn left under the railway bridge). Keep left into Laverstock village, past the Church and the Club is situated on the left hand side directly opposite the Chinese takeaway and shop. From Bournemouth – Follow the A36 to Southampton past Salisbury College and straight across the Tesco roundabout take left at traffic lights into the Park & Ride (take the corner slowly, the road goes back on itself) then follow directions as above.

Nearest Railway Station Salisbury - 2.5km
Bus Route St Andrews School - stop 40m away

NEW MILTON TOWN

Founded: 1998 Nickname: The Linnets

Club Contact Details 01425 628 191 secretry@newmiltontownfc.co.uk

Ground: Fawcetts Fields, Christchurch Road, New Milton BH25 6QF **Club Colours:** Navy and red

HONOURS
FA Comps: None
League: Wessex 1998-99, 2004-05.

10 YEAR RECORD

09-10	10-11	11-12	12-13	13-14	14-15	15-16	16-17	17-18	18-19
WexP 19	WexP 19	WexP 20	WexP 21	Wex1 11	Wex1 6	Wex1 14	Wex1 14	Wex1 10	Wex1 17
FAC P	FAC EPr	FAC EPr	FAC EP			FAC EP			
FAV 2Q	FAV 1Q	FAV 2Q	FAV 2P		FAV 2Q	FAV 1P	FAV 1Q	FAV 1Q	FAV 2Q

Leave the M27 at Junction 2 and follow the signs to Lyndhurst. Carry on this road over four roundabouts and take the next slip road.At the traffic lights turn right to Lyndhurst. Go around the one way system and follow the signs to Christchurch (A35). After 10 miles at the Cat and Fiddle Public House turn left and continue towards the Chewton Glen Hotel. First exit at roundabout A337 to New Milton. The ground is one mile on the left. Postcode for Sat. Nav. systems BH25 6QB

Nearest Railway Station New Milton - 1.1km
Bus Route Old Milton Green - stop 150m away

NEWPORT (I.O.W.)

Founded: 1888 Nickname: The Port

Club Contact Details 01983 525 027 secretary@niowfc.com

Ground: East Cowes Vics FC, Beatrice Avenue, Isle of Wight PO32 6PA **Club Colours:** Yellow and blue

HONOURS
FA Comps: None
League: Isle of Wight 1907-08, 08-09, 09-10, 23-24. Hampshire 1929-30, 32-33, 38-39, 47-48, 49-50, 52-53, 53-54, 56-57, 79-79, 79-80, 80-81. Southern Eastern Division 2000-01.

10 YEAR RECORD

09-10	10-11	11-12	12-13	13-14	14-15	15-16	16-17	17-18	18-19
WexP 9	WexP 10	WexP 13	WexP 6	WexP 4	WexP 7	WexP 10	WexP 15	WexP 21	Wex1 6
FAC P	FAC 1Q	FAC 1Q	FAC 2Q	FAC P	FAC 2Qr	FAC EP	FAC EP	FAC EP	FAC P
FAV 2Q	FAV 3P	FAV 1Q	FAV 5Pr	FAV 2P	FAV 3P	FAV 4P	FAV 2P	FAV 4P	FAV 2P

From East Cowes ferry terminal follow Wells Road into York Avenue until reaching the Prince of Wales Pubic House. Turn at the next right in to Crossways Road then left into Beatrice Avenue.
From Fishbourne follow signs to East Cowes and Whippingham Church, ground is 200 yards from the church on Beatrice Avenue.

Bus Route Osborne House - stop 400m away

PETERSFIELD TOWN

Founded: 1993 Nickname: Rams

Club Contact Details 01730 233 416 secretary.petersfieldtownfc@outlook.com

Ground: Love Lane, Petersfield, Hampshire GU31 4BW **Club Colours:** Red & black

HONOURS
FA Comps: None
League: Wessex Division One 2013-14, Premier Division 2014-15.

10 YEAR RECORD

09-10		10-11		11-12		12-13		13-14		14-15		15-16		16-17		17-18		18-19	
Wex1	8	Wex1	11	Wex1	12	Wex1	6	Wex1	1	WexP	1	SthC	13	SthC	22	WexP	22	Wex1	15
FAC	EP	FAC	EP	FAC	EP	FAC	EPr	FAC	P	FAC	EP	FAC	3Q	FAC	P	FAC	EP	FAC	P
FAV	1Q	FAV	1Q	FAV	2Q	FAV	1P	FAV	1P	FAV	2Q	FAT	P	FAT	Pr	FAV	2Q	FAV	2Q

Off circulatory one-way system in the town centre. Approx 10 minutes walk from Petersfield train station. Postcode for Satellite Navigation systems GU31 4BW

Nearest Railway Station Petersfield - 0.8km
Bus Route Madeline Road - stop 140m away

PEWSEY VALE

Founded: 1948 Nickname: Vale

Club Contact Details 01672 562 990 (Ground) pewseyvalefc@hotmail.co.uk

Ground: Recreation Ground, Kings Corner Ball Road, Pewsey SN9 5BS **Club Colours:** White and navy

HONOURS
FA Comps: None
League: Wiltshire Division One 1989-90, 92-93.

10 YEAR RECORD

09-10		10-11		11-12		12-13		13-14		14-15		15-16		16-17		17-18		18-19	
Wilt	3	Wex1	4	Wex1	11	Wex1	5	Wex1	8	Wex1	10	Wex1	17	Wex1	21	Hel1W	4	Hel1W	10
				FAC	EP	FAC	P	FAC	EP	FAC	EP							FAC	EP
FAV	2Q	FAV	1Q	FAV	2Qr	FAV	1Q	FAV	1Q	FAV	1Q	FAV	1Q			FAV	1Q	FAV	1Q

From Pewsey High Street/B3087 turn right into Ball Road, keep right to continue on Easterton Lane, turn right to stay on Easterton Lane, turn left and the ground will be on the left.
Park at the top end of the co-operative car park and walk along the path to the pitch.

Nearest Railway Station Pewsey - 0.9km
Bus Route Co-op stop - 316m away

RINGWOOD TOWN

Founded: 1879 Nickname: The Peckers

Club Contact Details 01425 473 448 ringwoodtownfc@live.co.uk

Ground: Long Lane, Ringwood, Hampshire BH24 3BX **Club Colours:** Red and white

HONOURS
FA Comps: None
League: Hampshire Division three 1995-96.

10 YEAR RECORD

09-10		10-11		11-12		12-13		13-14		14-15		15-16		16-17		17-18		18-19	
Wex1	5	Wex1	6	Wex1	9	Wex1	9	Wex1	13	Wex1	11	Wex1	13	Wex1	5	Wex1	11	Wex1	12
FAC	P	FAC	1Q	FAC	EP	FAC	EP									FAC	EP		
FAV	2Q	FAV	1Q	FAV	2Q	FAV	1Q	FAV	1Q	FAV	1P	FAV	2Q	FAV	1Q	FAV	2Q	FAV	1Q

Travel to Ringwood via the A31 (M27). From Ringwood town centre travel 1 mile on the B3347 towards Christchurch. At the Texaco petrol station turn into Moortown Lane and after 200 yards turn right into Long Lane. The ground is situated 250 yards on your left.
Postcode for Satellite Navigation systems BH24 3BX

Bus Route Crow Crossroads - stop 100m away

ROMSEY TOWN

Founded: 1886 Nickname: Town

Club Contact Details 01794 516 691 romseytownfc@gmail.com

Ground: The By-Pass Ground, South Front, Romsey SO51 8GJ **Club Colours:** Red & black

HONOURS
FA Comps: None
League: Post War: Southampton West 1951-52, Senior Div.2 72-73, Senior Div.1 73-74, 76-77, Prem 80-81, 83-84.
Hampshire Div.4 75-76, Div.2 78-79. Wessex 89-90.

10 YEAR RECORD

09-10		10-11		11-12		12-13		13-14		14-15		15-16		16-17		17-18		18-19	
WexP	10	WexP	16	WexP	8	WexP	20	WexP	22	Wex1	14	Wex1	9	Wex1	13	Wex1	6	Wex1	4
FAC	P	FAC	EPr	FAC	EP	FAC	P	FAC	EP	FAC	EP							FAC	EP
FAV	1Q	FAV	2Q	FAV	2Q	FAV	2Q	FAV	2Q	FAV	1Q	FAV	2Q	FAV	1P	FAV	1P	FAV	1Qr

The ground is situated on the south of the town on the A27/A3090 roundabout (Romsey by pass), adjacent to the Romsey Rapids and Broadlands Estate.
Postcode for Satellite Navigation systems SO51 8GJ

Nearest Railway Station Romsey - 0.5km
Bus Route Linden Road - stop 100m away

TOTTON & ELING

Founded: 1925 | Nickname: The Millers

Club Contact Details 07876 776 985 | tefcsecretary@gmail.com

Ground: Millers Park, Salisbury Road, Totton SO40 2RW | **Club Colours:** Red & black

HONOURS
FA Comps: None
League: Hampshire Division three 1974-75, Division One 1987-88, 88-89.
Wessex Division One 2008-09.

10 YEAR RECORD

09-10	10-11	11-12	12-13	13-14	14-15	15-16	16-17	17-18	18-19
WexP 7	WexP 18	WexP 11	WexP 12	WexP 8	WexP 20	Wex1 15	Wex1 15	Wex1 14	Wex1 19
FAC P	FAC 1Q	FAC P	FAC 1Qr	FAC Pr	FAC EP				
FAV 2Q	FAV 1Q	FAV 1Q	FAV 1Q	FAV 1Q	FAV 1Q				FAV 1P

Leave M27 at Junction.2 and take A326 exit signposted Totton/Fawley. Almost immediately leave A326 onto slip road signposted Totton Town Centre which will meet the A36 (Salisbury Road). Turn left on to A36 and proceed for approx. three quarters of a mile and the ground entrance is on the left just before the Calmore Roundabout.

Nearest Railway Station Totton - 2.9km
Bus Route Cooks Lane - stop 280m away

UNITED SERVICES PORTSMOUTH

Founded: 1962 | Nickname: The Navy

Club Contact Details 07887 541 782 | usportsmouthfc@hotmail.co.uk

Ground: Victory Stadium, HMS Temeraire, Burnaby Road, Portsmouth PO1 2HB | **Club Colours:** Royal blue & red

HONOURS
FA Comps: None
League: Hampshire Division Two 1967-68, 77-78, 80-81.

10 YEAR RECORD

09-10	10-11	11-12	12-13	13-14	14-15	15-16	16-17	17-18	18-19
Wex1 9	Wex1 5	Wex1 13	Wex1 12	Wex1 7	Wex1 5	Wex1 4	Wex1 9	Wex1 4	Wex1 5
						FAC EP	FAC P		FAC P
FAV 1P	FAV 1Q	FAV 2Q	FAV 2Q	FAV 2Q	FAV 2P	FAV 2Qr	FAV 1Q	FAV 1P	FAV 2Q

Leave the M27 at Junction 12 and join the M275 to Portsmouth. Follow the signs to Gunwharf, turn right at the traffic lights into Park Road, then at the next set of lights turn left into Burnaby Road and the ground entrance is at the end of the road on your right. Entrance is via HMS Temeraire.

Nearest Railway Station Portsmouth Harbour - 0.7km
Bus Route University - stop 120m away

VERWOOD TOWN

Founded: 1920 | Nickname: The Potters

Club Contact Details 01202 814 007 | secretary@vtfc.co.uk

Ground: Potterne Park Potterne Way Verwood Dorset BH21 6RS | **Club Colours:** Red & black

HONOURS
FA Comps: None
League: Wessex Division One 2011-12.

10 YEAR RECORD

09-10	10-11	11-12	12-13	13-14	14-15	15-16	16-17	17-18	18-19
Wex1 7	Wex1 9	Wex1 1	WexP 14	WexP 19	WexP 15	WexP 17	WexP 22	Wex1 17	Wex1 8
	FAC EPr	FAC EP	FAC EP	FAC EP	FAC EP	FAC P	FAC Pr	FAC EPr	
FAV 1P	FAV 3P	FAV 1Q	FAV 1Qr	FAV 2P	FAV 3P	FAV 2Q	FAV 1Q	FAV 1Q	FAV 2Qr

Turn off the A31 at Verwood/Matchams junctions just West of Ringwood Town centre exit (immediately after garage if coming from the East) to join the B3081. Follow the B3081 through the forest for approximately 4 miles coming into Verwood itself. At the second set of traffic lights turn left into Black Hill. At the roundabout take the 1st exit left into Newtown Road. At the end of Newtown Road turn left and then 1st left into Potterne Way. Note: Along Black Hill on the left you will pass Bradfords Building Merchants and the entrance to the Verwood Sports & Social Club where post match refreshments are made available.

Bus Route Potterne Bridge - stop 280m away

WHITCHURCH UNITED

Founded: 1903 | Nickname: Jam Boys

Club Contact Details 01256 892 493 | secretary.wufc@gmail.com

Ground: Longmeadow, Winchester Road, Whitchurch, Hampshire RG28 7RB | **Club Colours:** Red & white stripes

HONOURS
FA Comps: None
League: Hampshire Division Two 1989-90.

10 YEAR RECORD

09-10	10-11	11-12	12-13	13-14	14-15	15-16	16-17	17-18	18-19
Wex1 10	Wex1 7	Wex1 8	Wex1 2	WexP 13	WexP 6	WexP 15	WexP 21	Wex1 13	Wex1 14
		FAC 2Q	FAC EP	FAC EPr	FAC EPr	FAC EPr	FAC P	FAC EP	
	FAV 1Q	FAV 2Q	FAV 2Q	FAV 1Q	FAV 2Q	FAV 1Pr	FAV 2Q	FAV 2Q	FAV 1Q

From the South – take the A34 (North), 2 miles north of Bullington Cross take the Whitchurch exit. Head for Whitchurch Town Centre. The ground is 500 yards on your right. Postcode for Satellite Navigation systems RG28 7RB

Nearest Railway Station Whitchurch - 1.7km
Bus Route Charcot Close - stop 100m away

PREMIER DIVISION INS: Darlaston Town (1874) (P - WMid1), Littleton (Tr - Mid1), Wolverhampton Sporting Club (R - MidP), Worcester Raiders (P - WMid1).

AFC BRIDGNORTH

Founded: 2013 Nickname: Meadow Men

Club Contact Details

Ground: Crown Meadow, Innage Lane, Bridgnorth WV16 4HS **Club Colours:** Blue & white

HONOURS

FA Comps: None

League: West Midlands (Reg) Division One 2013-14.

10 YEAR RECORD

09-10	10-11	11-12	12-13	13-14	14-15	15-16	16-17	17-18	18-19
				WM1 1	WMP 2	WMP 2	WMP 8	WMP 18	WMP 12
						FAC P	FAC EP		
					FAV 1P	FAV 2P	FAV 1Q	FAV 1Q	FAV 1Q

Follow signs for Shrewsbury A458 over River Bridge on bypass. At next island turn right (Town Centre). At T Junction turn right, first left into Victoria Road. Turn right at crossroads by Woodberry Down. Follow road round to right. Club is on the right 300 yards from crossroads.

Bus Route Bus stops outside the ground.

BEWDLEY TOWN

Founded: 1978 Nickname: None

Club Contact Details 07739 626 169

Ground: Ribbesford Meadows, Ribbesford, Bewdley, Worcs DY12 2TJ **Club Colours:** Royal blue & yellow

HONOURS

FA Comps: None

League: West Midlands (Reg) Division One South 2002-03, Division One 2004-05.

10 YEAR RECORD

09-10	10-11	11-12	12-13	13-14	14-15	15-16	16-17	17-18	18-19
WMP 12	WMP 6	WMP 4	WMP 8	WMP 7	WMP 17	WMP 16	WMP 6	WMP 7	WMP 6
FAC EP	FAC P	FAC 1Q	FAC 1Q	FAC EP	FAC EP			FAC EP	
FAV 2P	FAV 2Q	FAV 1Q	FAV 1P	FAV 1Q	FAV 1Q	FAV 1Q	FAV 2Q	FAV 1Q	FAV 1P

From Kidderminster follow signs to Bewdley on A456 past West Midlands Safari Park and follow signs to Town Centre at next Island. Go over River Bridge into Town and turn left at side of Church (High Street). Stay on this road for 1 ½ miles. Entrance to ground is on left.

Bus Route Burlish Farm - stop 1km away

BILSTON TOWN

Founded: 1894 Nickname: The Steelmen

Club Contact Details

Ground: Queen Street Stadium, Queen Street, Bilston WV14 7EX **Club Colours:** Orange & black

HONOURS

FA Comps: None

League: Walsall & District 1895-96, 1900-01, 01-02, 32-33, 35-36, 47-48. Birmingham & District/West Mids (Reg) Division One 1956-57, Premier 60-61, 72-73.

10 YEAR RECORD

09-10	10-11	11-12	12-13	13-14	14-15	15-16	16-17	17-18	18-19
WM1 12	WM1 9	WM1 9	WM1 2	WMP 16	WMP 13	WMP 20	WMP 15	WMP 11	WMP 13
			FAV 1P	FAV 2Q	FAV 1Q	FAV 2Q	FAV 2Q	FAV 2Q	

From M6 Junction 10 take A454 to Wolverhampton then pick up A563 to Bilston. Turn left at 2nd roundabout and left at mini roundabout by the ambulance station. under the by-pass bridge and first left into Queens Street. Ground is 500 yards on left

Nearest Railway Station Bilston Central - 550m

Bus Route Bus stops outside the ground

BLACK COUNTRY RANGERS

Founded: 1996 Nickname:

Club Contact Details 0121 559 5564

Ground: York Road Stadium, York Road, Oldbury B65 0RR **Club Colours:** Red

HONOURS

FA Comps: None

League: West Midlands (Reg) Division Two 2009-10, Division One 10-11.

10 YEAR RECORD

09-10	10-11	11-12	12-13	13-14	14-15	15-16	16-17	17-18	18-19
WM2 1	WM1 1	WMP 2	WMP 5	WMP 5	WMP 10	WMP 15	WMP 13	WMP 4	WMP 8
				FAC P	FAC EP				
			FAV 2P	FAV 1Q	FAV 1Q	FAV 1Pr	FAV 2Q		FAV 1P

Get to Junction 3 of the M5. Head towards Kidderminster on the A458 for a mile or so to the first traffic island at the bottom of the hill. Turn right on to the A459 towards Dudley (the cricket ground should now be on your left) and continue past where the road splits to the next island. Turn left here on to the A456 towards Stourbridge until you get to the next island. Take the 3rd exit (Old Hawne Lane) and the ground is about 400 yards away, at the top of the hill on the left.

Nearest Railway Station Old Hill - 1.8km

Bus Route Cranmoor Crescent - stop 50m away

OUTS: Haughmond (P - MidP), Hereford Lads Club (Tr - Hel1W), Malvern Town (Tr - Hel1W), Pegasus Juniors (Tr - Hel1W), Tividale (P - MidP), Wellington (Tr - Hel1W).

CRADLEY TOWN

Founded: 1948 Nickname: The Lukes or Hammers

Club Contact Details

Ground: The Beeches, Beeches View Avenue, Cradley, Halesowen B63 2HB **Club Colours:** Red and black

HONOURS **League:** West Midlands (Reg) Division One 1990-91.

FA Comps: None

10 YEAR RECORD

09-10	10-11	11-12	12-13	13-14	14-15	15-16	16-17	17-18	18-19
MidAl 22	WMP 8	WMP 8	WMP 9	WMP 10	WMP 15	WMP 8	WMP 10	WMP 8	WMP 11
FAC 1Q	FAC EP	FAC EPr	FAC Pr	FAC EP			FAC EPr		
FAV 2Q	FAV 1Q	FAV 1Q	FAV 2Q	FAV 1P	FAV 2Q	FAV 1P	FAV 1Q	FAV 2Q	FAV 2Q

A456 Manor Way (SP Kidderminster). Straight on at first island, turn right (second exit) at second island into Hagley Road (B4183). Pass Foxhunt Inn on left and turn third (careful some might say second!!) left into Rosemary Road. Straight on into Lansdowne Road/Dunstall Road and turn left at T-junction into Huntingtree Road/Lutley Mill Road. Left again at next T-junction into Stourbridge Road (A458) and immediately left again into Beecher Road East. First left into Abbey Road and after 250 yards swing right up along Meres Road. Take first left into Hedgefield Grove go straight to the end where the ground entrance is almost opposite in Beeches View Avenue between house numbers 48 and 50.

Nearest Railway Station Cradley Heath - 2km

Bus Route Hedgefield Grove - stop 200m away

DARLASTON TOWN (1874)

Founded: 1874 Nickname:

Club Contact Details 01922 616 165

Ground: Bentley Leisure Pavilion, Bentley Road North, Bentley WS2 0EA **Club Colours:** Blue and white

HONOURS **League:** West Midlands (Regional) Division One 2006-07.

FA Comps: None

10 YEAR RECORD

09-10	10-11	11-12	12-13	13-14	14-15	15-16	16-17	17-18	18-19
WMP 13	WMP 16	WMP 22	WMP 21		WM2 3	WM1 5	WM1 7	WM1 6	WM1 2
	FAV 2Q								

From Junction 10 M6, take (from South 1st exit, from North 3rd exit) onto
Black Country Route. After Approx 400 metres, take 2nd exit off Black Country Route.
At top of slip road take 1st exit and after approx 50 metres turn left and ground is approx 75 metres on your right, past the Premier Inn.

DUDLEY SPORTS

Founded: 1925 Nickname: The Piemen

Club Contact Details 01384 826 420

Ground: Hillcrest Avenue, Brierley Hill, West Mids DY5 3QH **Club Colours:** Green & white

HONOURS **League:** None

FA Comps: None

10 YEAR RECORD

09-10	10-11	11-12	12-13	13-14	14-15	15-16	16-17	17-18	18-19
WMP 15	WMP 14	WMP 12	WMP 17	WMP 17	WMP 12	WMP 6	WMP 17	WMP 16	WMP 15
FAC 1Q			FAC EPr				FAC P		
FAV 1Q	FAV 1Q	FAV 2Q	FAV 1Q	FAV 2Q	FAV 1Q	FAV 2Q	FAV 2Q	FAV 2Q	FAV 2Q

The Ground is situated in Brierley Hill, just off A461. It can be approached from Stourbridge off the Ring Road to Amblecote, turning right at third set of traffic lights or from Dudley passing through Brierley Hill Town centre.

Nearest Railway Station Lye - 2.1km Stourbridge - 2.5km Cradley Heath - 2.8km

Bus Route Lancaster Road - stop 60m away

DUDLEY TOWN

Founded: 1888 Nickname: The Duds or Robins

Club Contact Details

Ground: Sporting Khalsa FC, Asprey Arena, Noose Lane, Willenhall WV13 3BB **Club Colours:** Red & black

HONOURS **League:** Birmingham Combination 1933-34. Southern Midland Division 1984-85.

FA Comps: None

10 YEAR RECORD

09-10	10-11	11-12	12-13	13-14	14-15	15-16	16-17	17-18	18-19
WMP 5	WMP 13	WMP 7	WMP 6	WMP 9	WMP 14	WMP 13	WMP 18	WMP 17	WMP 10
FAC Pr	FAC P		FAC 1Q	FAC EPr	FAC P				
FAV 2Qr	FAV 2Qr	FAV 2Q	FAV 1Q	FAV 2P	FAV 2Q	FAV 1Q	FAV 1Q	FAV 2Q	FAV 2Q

From M6 junction 10 take A454 towards Wolverhampton, after 1 ½ miles branch left, then at Keyway Island take the 2nd exit onto A454.
Go through 1 roundabout and then at traffic lights make a U turn at Neachells Road. Turn left into Noose Lane

LITTLETON

Founded: 1890 Nickname: The Ton

Club Contact Details 01905 909 125

Ground: 5 Acres, Pebworth Road, North Littleton, Evesham, Worcs, WR11 8QL **Club Colours:** Red/red/white

HONOURS **League:** Midland Combination Division Three 2001-02.

FA Comps: None

10 YEAR RECORD

09-10		10-11		11-12		12-13		13-14		14-15		15-16		16-17		17-18		18-19	
MCm1	8	MCm1	5	MCm1	2	MCmP	2	MCmP	11	MFL1	9	MFL1	9	MFL1	9	MFL1	8	MFL1	17
												FAV	2Q	FAV	2Q	FAV	2Q	FAV	2Q

Get on A46 and aim for Bidford-on-Avon, leave A46 at Bidford roundabout and follow signs for B439 (Bidford ½ mile). Come to roundabout in Bidford and take exit B4085 (Cleeve Prior), over a very narrow bridge controlled by traffic lights, straight over crossroads following sign to Honeybourne Broadway. Straight on for approximately 3 miles signpost right turn for the Littletons at crossroads, the ground is 1¼ miles on the right.

Nearest Railway Station Honeybourne - 3.1km
Bus Route The Ivy Inn stop - 1.2km away

PERSHORE TOWN

Founded: 1988 Nickname: Town

Club Contact Details

Ground: King George V Playing Field, King George's Way, Pershore WR10 1QU **Club Colours:** Blue & white

HONOURS **League:** Midland Combination Division Two 1989-90, Premier 1993-94.

FA Comps: None

10 YEAR RECORD

09-10		10-11		11-12		12-13		13-14		14-15		15-16		16-17		17-18		18-19	
MCmP	20	MCmP	13	MCmP	16	MCmP	13	MCmP	15	MFL1	11	MFL1	14	MFL1	18	MFL1	18	WMP	14
FAC	EP																		
FAV	2Q	FAV	2Q	FAV	2Q	FAV	2Q	FAV	2Q	FAV	2Q	FAV	1Q	FAV	1Q	FAV	2Q	FAV	1Q

M5 Junction 7, take B4080 (formerly A44) to Pershore.
On entering the town turn left at 2nd set of traffic lights (signposted Leisure Centre).
The ground is 300 yards on the left hand side.

Nearest Railway Station Pershore - 2.1km
Bus Route Abbey Tea Rooms stop - 167m away

SHAWBURY UNITED

Founded: 1992 Nickname:

Club Contact Details 01939 233 287 daibando161274@aol.com

Ground: Ludlow FC, Bromfield Road, Ludlow SY8 2BN **Club Colours:** Black & white

HONOURS **League:** West Midlands (Regional) Premier Division 2015-16.

FA Comps: None

10 YEAR RECORD

09-10		10-11		11-12		12-13		13-14		14-15		15-16		16-17		17-18		18-19	
WMP	21	WMP	17	WMP	10	WMP	4	WMP	4	WMP	7	WMP	1	MFLP	19	MFLP	21	WMP	6
														FAC	EPr	FAC	EP	FAC	EP
FAV	2Q	FAV	1Q	FAV	2Q	FAV	2P	FAV	1P	FAV	2Q	FAV	1Q	FAV	1P	FAV	1Q	FAV	1Q

Leave A49 and travel under bridge.
Club signposted on right hand side
Ground is approximately 200 yards from Bridge

SHIFNAL TOWN

Founded: 1964 Nickname: The Town or Reds

Club Contact Details 07986 563 156

Ground: Coppice Green Lane, Shifnal, Shrops TF11 8PD **Club Colours:** Red & white

HONOURS **League:** West Midlands (Regional) Division One 1978-79, 2015-16, Premier Division 2006-07.

FA Comps: None

10 YEAR RECORD

09-10		10-11		11-12		12-13		13-14		14-15		15-16		16-17		17-18		18-19	
MidAl	21	WMP	9	WMP	16	WMP	19	WMP	19	WMP	21	WM1	1	WMP	11	WMP	15	WMP	19
FAC	EP	FAC	EPr	FAC	EPr	FAC	EP												
FAV	1Q	FAV	2Pr	FAV	1Q	FAV	1P	FAV	1Q	FAV	2Q	FAV	1Q	FAV	1P	FAV	1P	FAV	1Q

Via the M6 get on to the M54 and follow signs for Wales/Telford/Wolverhampton/Shrewsbury/A5. At junction 3, take the A41 exit to Whitchurch/Weston.
Continue on Newport Road/A41. Turn left and continue onto Stanton Road. Turn right onto Curriers Lane. Turn right onto High Street/B4379. Continue to follow B4379. Turn right onto Drayton Road. Turn right onto Cornwallis Drive.

Nearest Railway Station Shifnal - 0.8km
Bus Route Green (Barn Rd) - stop 100m away

SMETHWICK RANGERS

Founded: 1977 Nickname:

Club Contact Details 01384 826 420

Ground: The Beeches, Packwood Road, Tividale B69 1UL **Club Colours:** Blue & yellow

HONOURS **League:** Midland Combination Division Three 2007-08.
West Midlands Division One 2012-13.

FA Comps: None

10 YEAR RECORD

09-10	10-11	11-12	12-13	13-14	14-15	15-16	16-17	17-18	18-19
MCm2 10	WM2 4	WM1 4	WM1 1	WMP 12	WMP 19	WMP 12	WMP 16	WMP 14	WMP 14
							FAV 1Q	FAV 2Q	FAV 1P

Leave M5 at Junction 2. Follow signs to Dudley A4123. Approximately 1 mile past school and playing fields on right, go under Pedestrian walkway to traffic lights. Turn left into Regent Road. Turn left into Elm Terrace. First left into Birch Crescent. Second left into Packwood Road. Ground is at the end of the Cul-de-sac.

WEDNESFIELD

Founded: 1961 Nickname: The Cottagers

Club Contact Details

Ground: Cottage Ground, Amos Lane, Wednesfield WV11 1ND **Club Colours:** Red & white

HONOURS **League:** West Midlands Division One A 1976-77, Division One 77-78, Premier 95-96, 96-97.

FA Comps: None

10 YEAR RECORD

09-10	10-11	11-12	12-13	13-14	14-15	15-16	16-17	17-18	18-19
WMP 11	WMP 4	WMP 6	WMP 18	WMP 15	WMP 22	WM1 4	WM1 2	WMP 5	WMP 5
FAC EP	FAC 2Q								FAC Pr
FAV 1P	FAV 2P		FAV 1Q	FAV 1Q	FAV 1Q	FAV 1Q	FAV 1Q	FAV 1P	FAV 1P

Going south, leave M6 at Junction 11 onto A460 towards Wolverhampton. After approx. 3 miles turn left at the Millhouse Public House into Pear Tree Lane. Continue on across mini-island into Knowle Lane. At Red Lion Public House continue across mini-island into Long Knowle Lane. Continue across mini-island into Amos Lane. Ground is about ½ mile along on left hand side.
Going north, leave M6 at Junction 10A onto M54. Leave M54 at Junction 1 onto A460 towards Wolverhampton. Turn left at Millhouse Public House and continue as above.

Nearest Railway Station Wolverhampton - 3km
Bus Route Cottages Homes - stop 20m away

WEM TOWN

Founded: 1883 Nickname: Town

Club Contact Details

Ground: Butler Sports Centre, Bowens Field, Wem SY4 5AP **Club Colours:** Red

HONOURS **League:** Shropshire County 2008-09. West Midlands (Reg) Division One 2017-18.

FA Comps: None

10 YEAR RECORD

09-10	10-11	11-12	12-13	13-14	14-15	15-16	16-17	17-18	18-19
WM2 22	WM1 4	WM1 12	WM1 3	WM1 4	WM1 7	WM1 9	WM1 9	WM1 1	WMP 18
									FAV 2Q

From the A5 Shrewsbury bypass take the A49 heading towards Whitchurch. go through the villages of Hadnall & Preston Brockhurst and then take a left turn at the Crossroads onto the B5063 sign posted Wem.
At next junction turn right under railway bridge onto the B5476 into Mill Street.
Enter Wem Town Centre and at the Church turn right into High Street. Take the 1st left after the pedestrian corssing into New Street and then the next left after the Hawkestone Arms public House into Pyms Road. Take the 2nd left turning into Bowens field Ground and car park.

WOLVERHAMPTON CASUALS

Founded: 1899 Nickname: The Cassies

Club Contact Details 01902 783 214

Ground: Brinsford Stadium, Brinsford Lane, Wolverhampton WV10 7PR **Club Colours:** Green

HONOURS **League:** West Midlands (Reg) Division One 1994-95.

FA Comps: None

10 YEAR RECORD

09-10	10-11	11-12	12-13	13-14	14-15	15-16	16-17	17-18	18-19
WMP 16	WMP 12	WMP 3	WMP 3	WMP 3	WMP 6	WMP 7	WMP 2	WMP 9	WMP 3
		FAC EP	FAC 1Qr	FAC P	FAC EP	FAC EP	FAC EPr	FAC P	
FAV 1P	FAV 1P	FAV 1Q	FAV 1Q	FAV 2Q	FAV 1Q	FAV 2Q	FAV 2P	FAV 1Q	FAV 2Q

Turn onto M54 off M6 Northbound. Take Junction 2 and turn right onto A449 to Stafford. Go to next island and come back on yourself towards M54. Brinsford Lane is approximately ½ mile from island on left. Ground is 200 yards on left in Brinsford Lane.

Nearest Railway Station Billbrook - 4.8km
Bus Route Old Heath House - stop 350m away

WOLVERHAMPTON SPORTING CFC

Founded: 2001 Nickname: Wolves Sporting

Club Contact Details

Ground: Pride Park, Hazel Lane, Great Wyrley, Staffs WS6 6AA **Club Colours:** Black & orange

HONOURS **League:** West Midlands (Reg) Division Two 2006-07, Premier 2017-18.

FA Comps: None

10 YEAR RECORD

09-10		10-11		11-12		12-13		13-14		14-15		15-16		16-17		17-18		18-19	
WMP	20	WMP	18	WMP	19	WMP	10	WMP	18	WMP	16	WMP	4	WMP	3	WMP	1	MFLP	20
														FAC	EP	FAC	EP	FAC	EP
		FAV	1P	FAV	2Q	FAV	2Q	FAV	1Q	FAV	1Q	FAV	1Q	FAV	1P	FAV	5P	FAV	2P

Going south, leave M6 at Junction 11 onto A460 towards Wolverhampton. After approx. 3 miles turn left at the Millhouse Public House into Pear Tree Lane. Continue on across mini-island into Knowle Lane. At Red Lion Public House continue across mini-island into Long Knowle Lane. Continue across mini-island into Amos Lane. Ground is about ½ mile along on left hand side.
Going north, leave M6 at Junction 10A onto M54. Leave M54 at Junction 1 onto A460 towards Wolverhampton. Turn left at Millhouse Public House and continue as above.

Nearest Railway Station Ladywood - 1km
Bus Route Hazel Lane - stop 270m away

WORCESTER RAIDERS

Founded: 2001 Nickname: Raiders

Club Contact Details 07532 266 897

Ground: Claines Lane, Worcester, Worcestershire WR3 7SS **Club Colours:** Red and black

HONOURS **League:** West Midlands (Regional) Division One 2018-19.

FA Comps: None

10 YEAR RECORD

09-10		10-11		11-12		12-13		13-14		14-15		15-16		16-17		17-18		18-19	
								WM2	3	WM1	14	WM1	12	WM1	3	WM1	7	WM1	1

Nearest Railway Station Worcester Foregate Street
Bus Route 303 from Foregate Street Station to Bevere Lane (10min journey), ground 14min walk from there.

West Midlands (Regional) Division One

ALLSCOTT	Allscott S&S Club, Shawbirch Road, Allscott, Shropshire TF6 5EQ
BROMYARD TOWN	Delahay Meadow, Stourport Road, Bromyard HR7 4NT
BUSTLEHOLME	York Road Stadium, York Road, Oldbury B65 0RR
DROITWICH SPA	Stourport Swifts FC, Walshes Meadow, Harold Davies Drive, Stourport on Severn DY13 0AA
FC DARLASTON	Queens Street Stadium, Queens Street, Bilston WV14 7EX
GORNAL ATHLETIC	Garden Walk Stadium, Garden Walk, Lower Gornal, Dudley DY3 2NR
GORNAL COLTS	Dell Stadium, Bryce Road, Brierley Hill DY5 4NE
OLD WULFRUNIANS	Brinsford Stadium, Brinsford Lane, Coven Heath, Wolverhampton WV10 7PR
SIKH HUNTERS	Long Lane Park, Long Lane, Essington Wolverhampton WV11 2AA
TEAM DUDLEY	Priory Road - 3G Complex, Priory Road, Dudley, West Midlands DY1 4AD
TIPTON TOWN	Tipton Sports Academy, Wednesbury Oak Road, Tipton DY4 0BS
WELLINGTON AMATEURS	School Grove, Oakengates, Telford, Shrops TF2 6BQ
WILLENHALL TOWN	Cottage Ground, Amos Lane, Wednesfield WV11 1ND
WRENS NEST	The Beeches, Packwood Road, Tividale B69 1UL
WYRLEY	Long Lane, Essington, Wolverhampton. WS6 6AT

PREMIER DIVISION INS: Exmouth Town (P - SWPP), Keynsham Town (West1), Street (Sth1S), Tavistock (P - SWPP).
OUTS: Hengrove Athletic (R - West1), Shortwood United (R - Hel1W), Willand Rovers (P - Sth1S).

BITTON

Nickname: The Ton **Club Colours:** Red & white

Founded 1892

Club Contact Details 01179 323 222 jaynelangdon@btconnect.com
Ground: Bath Road, Bitton, Bristol BS30 6HX
Capacity: 1,000 **Seats:** 48 **Covered:** 200

Previous Names: None
Previous Leagues: Avon Premier Combination, Gloucestershire County 1995-97.

HONOURS: FA Comps: None
League: Western League Premier Division 2008-09.

10 YEAR RECORD

09-10		10-11		11-12		12-13		13-14		14-15		15-16		16-17		17-18		18-19	
WestP	8	WestP	2	WestP	2	WestP	7	WestP	6	WestP	7	WestP	14	WestP	19	WestP	10	WestP	3
FAC	EPr	FAC	1Q	FAC	EPr	FAC	P	FAC	P	FAC	EP	FAC	P	FAC	P	FAC	EPr	FAC	2Q
FAV	2P	FAV	4P	FAV	4P	FAV	4P	FAV	3P	FAV	1Q	FAV	2Q	FAV	2Q	FAV	1Q	FAV	1P

From M4 leave at Junction 18. Take A46 towards Bath, at first roundabout take A420 for Wick / Bridgeyate. On approach to Bridgeyate turn left at mini-roundabout onto A4175 and follow for 2.2 miles, then turn left for Bath on A431. The ground is 100 yards on the right. From Bath take A431, go through Kelston and Bitton village. Ground is on the left. From Chippenham take A420 to Bristol and turn left at mini-roundabout onto A4175 and follow as above.

Nearest Railway Station Bitton - 500m
Bus Route Cherry Garden Road - stop 50m away

BRADFORD TOWN

Nickname: Bobcats **Club Colours:** All royal blue

Founded 1992

Club Contact Details 07912 184 104 secretary@bradfordtownfc.com
Ground: Bradford Sports & Social Club, Trowbridge Rd, Bradford on Avon BA15 1EE
Capacity: **Seats:** Yes **Covered:** Yes

Previous Names: None
Previous Leagues: Wiltshire County 1992-2005.

HONOURS: FA Comps: None
League: Western Division One 2013-14.

10 YEAR RECORD

09-10		10-11		11-12		12-13		13-14		14-15		15-16		16-17		17-18		18-19	
West1	4	West1	6	West1	5	West1	3	West1	1	WestP	8	WestP	8	WestP	5	WestP	4	WestP	7
		FAC	EPr	FAC	EP	FAC	EP	FAC	EP	FAC	1Q	FAC	2Q	FAC	EP	FAC	EP	FAC	P
FAV	2P	FAV	2Q	FAV	1P	FAV	2Q	FAV	1P	FAV	5P	FAV	4P	FAV	4P	FAV	5P	FAV	3P

From Bath or Melksham on entering Bradford on Avon follow the signs for A363 to Trowbridge. The ground is after a mini roundabout and behind a stone wall on the right hand side. From Trowbridge, follow A363 to Bradford-on-Avon. The ground is just past shop on right, behind stone wall on left.

Nearest Railway Station Bradford-upon-Avon - 0.3km
Bus Route Junction Road _ stop 30m away

BRIDGWATER TOWN

Nickname: The Robins **Club Colours:** Red & white

Founded 1984

Club Contact Details 01278 446 899 ianbarber4@gmail.com
Ground: Fairfax Park, College Way, Bath Road, Bridgwater, Somerset TA6 4TZ
Capacity: 2,500 **Seats:** 128 **Covered:** 500 **Shop:** Yes

Previous Names: Bridgwater Town
Previous Leagues: Somerset Senior 1984-94. Western 1994-2007. Southern 2007-2017.

HONOURS: FA Comps: None
League: Somerset Senior Division One 1986-87, Premier 89-90, 90-91, 91-92. Western Division One 1995-96.

10 YEAR RECORD

09-10		10-11		11-12		12-13		13-14		14-15		15-16		16-17		17-18		18-19	
Sthsw	3	Sthsw	18	Sthsw	15	Sthsw	19	Sthsw	14	Sthsw	12	Sthsw	19	Sthsw	22	WestP	8	WestP	4
FAC	3Q	FAC	1Q	FAC	1Q	FAC	P	FAC	3Q	FAC	2Q	FAC	P	FAC	P	FAC	1Q	FAC	EP
FAT	1Qr	FAT	1Q	FAT	P	FAT	2Q	FAT	1Q	FAT	P	FAT	Pr	FAT	Pr	FAV	3Pr	FAV	2Q

Southbound from Bristol M5 J.23- enter town on A39 from Glastonbury. Ground is between Bridgwater College and Rugby Ground by railway bridge.
Northbound from Taunton – M5 J.24- enter town on A38, follow signs for Glastonbury (A39). Ground is between Bridgwater College and Rugby Ground as you pass over railway bridge.

Nearest Railway Station Bridgwater - 0.7km

BRIDPORT

Nickname: Bees **Club Colours:** Red and black

Founded 1885

Club Contact Details 01308 423 834 sevie@tiscali.co.uk
Ground: St Mary's Field, Bridport, Dorset DT6 5LN
Capacity: 2,000 **Seats:** 150 **Covered:** Yes

Previous Names: None
Previous Leagues: Dorset. South Dorset. West Dorset. Perry Street. Dorset Combination (Founding Memeber) 1957-61, 84-88. Western 1961-84.

HONOURS: FA Comps: None
League: Dorset Combination 1985-86, 86-87, 87-88.

10 YEAR RECORD

09-10		10-11		11-12		12-13		13-14		14-15		15-16		16-17		17-18		18-19	
West1	10	West1	3	WestP	14	WestP	14	WestP	12	WestP	14	WestP	16	WestP	16	WestP	7	WestP	13
FAC	1Qr	FAC	P	FAC	P	FAC	EP	FAC	P	FAC	EP	FAC	1Q	FAC	EP	FAC	3Q	FAC	1Q
FAV	2Q	FAV	1P	FAV	1P	FAV	2Q	FAV	1Q	FAV	2P	FAV	1P	FAV	1Q	FAV	1Q	FAV	1P

Follow Bridport by-pass in any direction to the Crown Inn roundabout. Take exit to town centre, at first set of traffic lights (Morrisons) turn left. Ground is 200 yards on the right.

Bus Route Leisure Centre - stop 20m away

BRISLINGTON

Nickname: Bris **Club Colours:** Red & black

Founded 1956

Club Contact Details 01179 774 030 kevinhazell@me.com
Ground: Ironmould Lane, Brislington, Bristol BS4 4TZ
Capacity: 2,000 **Seats:** 144 **Covered:** 1,500

Previous Names: Formed as an U16 team.
Previous Leagues: Bristol Church of England. Bristol & Suburban. Somerset Senior until 1991.

HONOURS: FA Comps: None
League: Somerset Senior 1988-89. Western Division One 1994-95.

10 YEAR RECORD

09-10		10-11		11-12		12-13		13-14		14-15		15-16		16-17		17-18		18-19	
WestP	9	WestP	15	WestP	7	WestP	2	WestP	10	WestP	10	WestP	11	WestP	10	WestP	16	WestP	18
FAC	EPr	FAC	EP	FAC	1Q	FAC	EP	FAC	4Q	FAC	P	FAC	EP	FAC	2Q	FAC	P	FAC	EP
FAV	2P	FAV	1P	FAV	1Q	FAV	1P	FAV	2P	FAV	1P	FAV	1Q	FAV	2Q	FAV	2Q	FAV	1Q

On A4 Bristol to Bath road, about 500 yards on Bath side of Park & Ride. Opposite the Wyevale Garden Centre.

Nearest Railway Station Keynsham - 3km
Bus Route Ironmould Lane - stop 100m away

BUCKLAND ATHLETIC

Nickname: The Bucks **Club Colours:** Yellow with black trim

Founded 1977

Club Contact Details 01626 361 020 phardingham@virginmedia.com
Ground: Homers Heath, South Quarry, Kingskerswell Road, Newton Abbot TQ12 5JU
Capacity: 1,000 **Seats:** Yes **Covered:** Yes

Previous Names: None
Previous Leagues: Torbay Pioneer 1977-87. Devon & Exeter 1987-2000. Devon County 2000-07. South West Peninsula 2007-12.

HONOURS: FA Comps: None
League: Devon & Exeter Senior Third Division 1987-88, Premier 94-95, 99-00.
South West Peninsula Premier 2009-10, 10-11.

10 YEAR RECORD

09-10		10-11		11-12		12-13		13-14		14-15		15-16		16-17		17-18		18-19	
SWPP	1	SWPP	1	SWPP	2	WestP	10	WestP	11	WestP	2	WestP	4	WestP	4	WestP	5	WestP	9
FAC	EPr	FAC	EPr	FAC	Pr	FAC	2Q	FAC	EP	FAC	EP	FAC	P	FAC	EP	FAC	EP	FAC	1Q
FAV	2Q	FAV	2Q	FAV	1P	FAV	2P	FAV	2P	FAV	3P	FAV	3P	FAV	QF	FAV	2P	FAV	2Q

From Exeter: Take the A380 signposted Torquay and travel along this road until you reach Penn Inn roundabout. Take the right hand lane and follow the road around which takes you into the left lane and towards the town centre. Filter left at first set of traffic lights and go passed Sainsbury's, and you are now on the main road towards Decoy. Go under the railway bridge and follow this road to the next mini roundabout. Go straight across, passing the Keyberry Hotel on the left. Go up the hill and down the other side. The ground is situated on the right hand side, opposite Combined linen services. PLEASE NOTE Coaches will not be able to go under the railway bridge at Decoy. Please phone for these directions for alternative route.

Nearest Railway Station Newton Abbot approx 2 miles from the ground.

CADBURY HEATH

Founded 1894

Nickname: The Heathens **Club Colours:** Red & white

Club Contact Details 07971 399 268 martinbristol1955@hotmail.com

Ground: Springfield, Cadbury Heath Road, Bristol BS30 8BX

Capacity: 2,000 **Seats:** Yes **Covered:** Yes

Previous Names: None

Previous Leagues: Bristol & District. Bristol Premier Combination. Gloucestershire County 1968-75, 80-2000. Midland Combination 1975-77.

HONOURS: FA Comps: None

League: Gloucestershire County 1970-71, 71-72, 72-73, 73-74, 93-94, 97-98, 98-99.
Western League Division One 2011-12.

10 YEAR RECORD

09-10	10-11	11-12	12-13	13-14	14-15	15-16	16-17	17-18	18-19
West1 11	West1 4	West1 1	WestP 4	WestP 13	WestP 11	WestP 12	WestP 11	WestP 18	WestP 14
		FAC 2Q	FAC P	FAC EP	FAC EP	FAC EP	FAC 3Q	FAC 2Qr	FAC 1Q
	FAV 4P	FAV 2P	FAV 2P	FAV 1P	FAV 2Q	FAV 2P	FAV 2Q	FAV 1P	FAV 3P

M5-M4-M32 Exit 1 follow signs for ring road, exit roundabout for Cadbury Heath left, 100m mini roundabout straight across, 400m mini roundabout turn right into Tower Road North, 150m turn right into Cadbury Heath Road, ground 50m on right via Cadbury Heath Social Club car park.

Nearest Railway Station Oldland - 1.2km

Bus Route The King William IV - stop 100m away

CHIPPING SODBURY TOWN

Founded 1885

Nickname: The Sods **Club Colours:** Black & white

Club Contact Details 07778 678 823 g.endicott@btopenworld.com

Ground: The Ridings, Wickwar Road, Chipping Sodbury, Bristol BS37 6GA

Capacity: **Seats:** Yes **Covered:** Yes

Previous Names: None

Previous Leagues: Gloucester County 2008-2015.

HONOURS: FA Comps: None

League: Western Division One 2015-16.

10 YEAR RECORD

09-10	10-11	11-12	12-13	13-14	14-15	15-16	16-17	17-18	18-19
GlCo 8	GlCo 3	GlCo 18	GlCo 15	GlCo 11	GlCo 3	West1 1	WestP 13	WestP 13	WestP 10
								FAC P	FAC 1Q
							FAV 1Q	FAV 1Q	FAV 2Q

Travelling north and south M5 – Exit at junction 14, B4509 follow signs to WickWar, at roundabout take third exit onto B4058, turn left onto B4509, at "T" junction turn right onto Wickwar High Street B4060. At mini roundabout continue forward onto Sodbury Road. Road merges into the Wickwar Road, continue on this road for two miles. Ground is on the left hand side. Travelling east and west M4 – Exit at junction 18, A46 Bath Road, follow signs to Yate. At traffic lights bear left onto A432 Badminton Road, stay on this road for three miles. At roundabout take third exit Wickwar Road. Ground is on the right hand side.

Nearest Railway Station Yate - 2.7km

Bus Route Wickwar Road - stop 50m away

CLEVEDON TOWN

Founded 1880

Nickname: Seasiders **Club Colours:** Blue with white

Club Contact Details 01275 871 600 erichowe@hotmail.co.uk

Ground: Everyone Active Stadium, Davis Lane, Clevedon BS21 6TG

Capacity: 3,500 **Seats:** 300 **Covered:** 1,600 **Shop:** Yes

Previous Names: Clevedon FC and Ashtonians merged in 1974

Previous Leagues: Western (Founder Members 1892), 1945-58, 73-93. Bristol & District. Bristol Suburban. Somerset Senior. Southern 1993-2015.

HONOURS: FA Comps: None

League: Bristol & Suburban 1925-26, 27-28, 28-29. Somerset Senior 36-37. Bristol Charity 37-38, 40-41. Western 92-93.
Southern Midland Division 98-99, Divions 1W 2005-06.

10 YEAR RECORD

09-10	10-11	11-12	12-13	13-14	14-15	15-16	16-17	17-18	18-19
SthP 21	Sthsw 20	Sthsw 20	Sthsw 15	Sthsw 17	Sthsw 18	WestP 19	WestP 14	WestP 12	WestP 6
FAC 2Q	FAC 3Q	FAC 2Q	FAC 2Q	FAC 3Qr	FAC P	FAC 3Q	FAC P	FAC P	FAC EP
FAT 1Q	FAT P	FAT P	FAT Pr	FAT 2Q	FAT P	FAV 1Q	FAV 2P	FAV 2Q	FAV 2Q

Exit J20 from M5, at bottom of slip road, turn left at roundabout into Central Way.
At next roundabout turn left to Kenn Road.
Stay on Kenn Road out of town, cross river, take 1st left into Davis Lane, over motorway.
Ground 200m on right.

Nearest Railway Station Yatton - 4km

Bus Route Sercombe Park - stop 400m away

CRIBBS

Nickname: Cribbs **Club Colours:** Blue

Founded 1976

Club Contact Details 0117 950 2303 welshwizard1973@aol.com

Ground: The Lawns, Station Road, Henbury, Bristol BS10 7TB

Capacity: 1,000 **Seats:** 100 **Covered:** Yes

Previous Names: Sun Life Assurance 1976. AXA>2011. Cribbs Friends Life 2011-13

Previous Leagues: Bristol & Avon. Avon Premier Combination. Gloucestershire County > 2012.

HONOURS: FA Comps: None

League: Gloucester County 2011-12.

10 YEAR RECORD

09-10	10-11	11-12	12-13	13-14	14-15	15-16	16-17	17-18	18-19
GlCo 11	GlCo 2	GlCo 1	West1 8	West1 5	West1 3	WestP 5	WestP 8	WestP 11	WestP 8
					FAC P	FAC EP	FAC EPr	FAC EP	FAC EP
				FAV 2Q	FAV 1Q	FAV 1Q	FAV 1Q	FAV 2Q	FAV 4P

From M5 J17 follow signs to Bristol West & Clifton on the A4018 dual carriageway cross two roundabouts, at 3rd roundabout take fourth exit and follow signs to M5, take 1st turning left after car dealers, ground straight ahead.

Nearest Railway Station Pilning - 4.3km. Sea MIlls - 4.5km. Patchway - 4.5km

Bus Route Rugby Club - stop 400m away

EXMOUTH TOWN

Nickname: The Town **Club Colours:** All royal blue

Founded 1933

Club Contact Details 01395 263 348 chardtapp1@hotmail.co.uk

Ground: King George V, Exmouth EX8 3EE

Capacity: **Seats:** 50 **Covered:** Yes

Previous Names: None

Previous Leagues: Western 1973-2006. South West Peninsula (FM) 2007-19.

HONOURS: FA Comps: None

League: Western 1983-84, 85-86.

South West Peninsula Division One East 2012-13.

10 YEAR RECORD

09-10	10-11	11-12	12-13	13-14	14-15	15-16	16-17	17-18	18-19
SW1E 8	SW1E 11	SW1E 5	SW1E 1	SWPP 2	SWPP 8	SWPP 12	SWPP 5	SWPP 16	SWPP 2
								FAC EP	
			FAV 1P	FAV 2Q		FAV 2Q	FAV 5P	FAV 2P	FAV 2P

From Junction 30 of M5 take te A376 to Exmouth, on entering the town the ground is on your right, before the railway station.

Nearest Railway Station Exmouth - 0.6km

Bus Route Exeter Road - stop 143m away

HALLEN

Nickname: The Armadillos **Club Colours:** Blue

Founded 1949

Club Contact Details 01179 505 559 sinbad88@hotmail.co.uk

Ground: Hallen Centre, Moorhouse Lane, Hallen Bristol BS10 7RU

Capacity: 2,000 **Seats:** 200 **Covered:** 200

Previous Names: Lawrence Weston Athletic, Lawrence Weston Hallen

Previous Leagues: Bristol & District. Bristol Premier. Gloucestershire County 1987-92. Hellenic 1992-2000.

HONOURS: FA Comps: None

League: Gloucestershire County 1988-89, 92-93. Hellenic Division One 1996-97. Western Division One 2003-04.

10 YEAR RECORD

09-10	10-11	11-12	12-13	13-14	14-15	15-16	16-17	17-18	18-19
WestP 12	WestP 16	WestP 4	WestP 9	WestP 15	WestP 17	WestP 17	WestP 18	WestP 17	WestP 12
FAC 2Q	FAC P	FAC 1Qr	FAC P	FAC 1Q	FAC P	FAC EPr	FAC EP	FAC EPr	FAC P
FAV 2Q	FAV 2Qr	FAV 2Q	FAV 1P	FAV 5P	FAV 2P	FAV 2P	FAV 2Q	FAV 1Q	FAV 1Q

From Junction 17 M5 follow A4018 towards Bristol. At third roundabout turn right into Crow Lane. Proceed to T junction - turn right and right again at mini roundabout by Henbury Lodge Hotel. At next mini roundabout turn left into Avonmouth Way. Continue for 1.5 miles into Hallen village. At crossroads turn left into Moorhouse Lane

Nearest Railway Station St Andrews Road - 2.7km

Bus Route Moorhouse Park - stop 250m away

KEYNSHAM TOWN

Nickname: K's **Club Colours:** Amber and black

Founded 1895

Club Contact Details jules1233@live.com

Ground: AJN Stadium, Bristol Road, Keynsham BS31 2BE

Capacity: 3,000 **Seats:** **Covered:**

Previous Names: None

Previous Leagues: East Bristol & District >late 1950s. Bristol Premier Combination >1967. Somerset County 1967-73.

HONOURS: FA Comps: None

League: Bristol & District Division Three 1898-99, Division Two 1948-49. Western Division One 1977-78, 2018-19.

10 YEAR RECORD

09-10	10-11	11-12	12-13	13-14	14-15	15-16	16-17	17-18	18-19
West1 8	West1 16	West1 13	West1 13	West1 19	West1 17	West1 9	West1 4	West1 3	West1 1
FAC EP	FAC EP						FAC EP	FAC EP	FAC EPr
FAV 1P	FAV 2P	FAV 2Q	FAV 1Q	FAV 2Q	FAV 2Q	FAV 2Qr	FAV 2Q	FAV 1Q	FAV 1Q

On A4175 off the Bristol to Bath A4. On left immediately after 30mph sign.

Nearest Railway Station Keynsham - 0.7km

Bus Route Rugby Club - stop 50m away

ODD DOWN

Nickname: The Down **Club Colours:** All blue

Founded 1901

Club Contact Details 01225 832 491 lorainebrown@btinternet.com

Ground: Lew Hill Memorial Ground, Combe Hay Lane, Odd Down BA2 8PA

Capacity: 1,000 **Seats:** 160 **Covered:** 250

Previous Names: None

Previous Leagues: Bath & District. Wiltshire. Somerset Senior. Mid-Somerset.

HONOURS: FA Comps: None

League: Western Division One 1992-93, Premier Division 2015-16.

10 YEAR RECORD

09-10	10-11	11-12	12-13	13-14	14-15	15-16	16-17	17-18	18-19
West1 2	WestP 8	WestP 9	WestP 8	WestP 4	WestP 5	WestP 1	WestP 7	WestP 14	WestP 15
FAC Pr	FAC Pr	FAC P	FAC P	FAC EPr	FAC P	FAC P	FAC P	FAC 1Q	FAC EP
FAV 2Q	FAV 2P	FAV 2Q	FAV 2P	FAV 2P	FAV 3P	FAV 2P	FAV 2P	FAV 1P	FAV 1P

Situated behind Odd Down Park & Ride on main A367 Bath to Exeter road.

Nearest Railway Station Oldfield Park - 2.9km

Bus Route St Gregory's School - stop 50m away

PLYMOUTH PARKWAY AFC

Nickname: The Parkway **Club Colours:** All Yellow

Founded 1988

Club Contact Details 07786 571 308 gennyt@sky.com

Ground: Bolitho Park, St Peters Road, Manadon, Plymouth PL5 3JG

Capacity: **Seats:** Yes **Covered:** Yes

Previous Names: None

Previous Leagues: Plymouth & District. South West Peninsula 2007-18.

HONOURS: FA Comps: None

League: Plymouth & District Division Two 1990-91.
South West Peninsula Premier Division 2013-14, 17-18.

10 YEAR RECORD

09-10	10-11	11-12	12-13	13-14	14-15	15-16	16-17	17-18	18-19
SWPP 6	SWPP 3	SWPP 6	SWPP 2	SWPP 1	SWPP 5	SWPP 4	SWPP 7	SWPP 1	WestP 2
			FAC 1Qr	FAC 1Q	FAC P	FAC 1Q	FAC 1Q	FAC EP	FAC 2Q
FAV 4P	FAV 3P	FAV 1P	FAV 1Q	FAV 3P	FAV 2P	FAV 2P	FAV 1Pr	FAV 3P	FAV 1P

From Cornwall/Exeter exit at the Manadon/Tavistock junction off the Plymouth Parkway (A38), off roundabout into St Peters Road. Entrance is one mile on the right.

Nearest Railway Station St Budeaux Road - 2.8km

Bus Route St Peters Road - stop 10m away

ROMAN GLASS ST GEORGE

Nickname: The Glass **Club Colours:** White and black

Founded 1872

Club Contact Details 07770 331 491 adamwolves2@hotmail.com

Ground: Oaklands Park, Gloucester Road, Almondsbury BS32 4AG

Capacity: 2,000 **Seats:** **Covered:**

Previous Names: St George. Bristol St George. Merged with Roman Glass in 1995 to form today's club.

Previous Leagues: Bristol & District/Western (Founder Members) 1892-1903, 1928-35. Bristol & District 1935-57. Bristol Premier Combination (FM) 1957-68. Gloucestershire County (FM) 1968-87, 99-2007. County of Avon Premier Comb 1987-95.

HONOURS: FA Comps: None

League: Bristol & District Div.1 1949-50. Bristol Premier Com. Div.1 1963-64, 64-65, 65-66, 66-67, 67-68, 88-89, Prem 92-93. . Gloucestershire County 1969-70, 2001-02, 06-07.

10 YEAR RECORD

09-10		10-11		11-12		12-13		13-14		14-15		15-16		16-17		17-18		18-19	
West1	18	West1	15	West1	8	West1	17	West1	12	West1	20	West1	18	West1	15	West1	2	WestP	17
																		FAC	EP
						FAV	2Q	FAV	2Q	FAV	2Q	FAV	1Qr	FAV	2Q	FAV	2Q	FAV	1P

Exit M5 at Junction 16. Arriving from the south take the left exit lane.
Turn left at lights and ground is 100m on left hand side.
Arriving from east take right hand lane on slip road. Take 3rd exit nd ground is 100m on left hand side.

Nearest Railway Station Patchway - 2.6km

Bus Route Alondsbury Depot - stop 100m away

SHEPTON MALLET

Nickname: The Mallet **Club Colours:** Black & white

Founded 1986

Club Contact Details 01749 344 609 gkrkb@tiscali.co.uk

Ground: Playing Fields, Old Wells Road, West Shepton, Shepton Mallet BA4 5XN

Capacity: 2,500 **Seats:** 120 **Covered:** Yes

Previous Names: None

Previous Leagues: Somerset Senior.

HONOURS: FA Comps: None

League: Somerset Senior League 2000-01.

10 YEAR RECORD

09-10		10-11		11-12		12-13		13-14		14-15		15-16		16-17		17-18		18-19	
West1	17	West1	14	West1	16	West1	7	West1	2	WestP	9	WestP	10	WestP	12	WestP	6	WestP	11
FAC	EP							FAC	EPr	FAC	Pr	FAC	EP	FAC	P	FAC	EP	FAC	EPr
FAV	2Q	FAV	2Q	FAV	1Q	FAV	1Q	FAV	2P	FAV	3P	FAV	2Q	FAV	1Q	FAV	2Q	FAV	1Q

From the town take B3136 (Glastonbury Road) for approximately 1/2 mile. Turn right at junction of Old Wells Road near King William Public House. Approximately 300 yards up the Old Wells Road turn left into the playing fields.

Bus Route West Lodge - stop 180m away

STREET

Nickname: The Cobblers **Club Colours:** All green

Founded 1880

Club Contact Details 01458 445 987 streetfootballclub@outlook.com

Ground: The Tannery Ground, Middlebrooks, Street BA16 0TA

Capacity: 1,000 **Seats:** 150 **Covered:** 25

Previous Names: None

Previous Leagues: Somerset Senior 1880-1911, 22-30, 60-98. Western 1911-22, 30-39, 46-60, 98-2018. Southern 2018-19.

HONOURS: FA Comps: None

League: Somerset Senior 1892-93, 95-96, 97-98, 98-99, 1909-10, 63-64, 65-66, 1996-97, Division Three 93-94. Western Premier 2017-18.

10 YEAR RECORD

09-10		10-11		11-12		12-13		13-14		14-15		15-16		16-17		17-18		18-19	
WestP	6	WestP	13	WestP	10	WestP	6	WestP	5	WestP	13	WestP	7	WestP	2	WestP	1	SthS	8
FAC	EPr	FAC	P	FAC	EP	FAC	EP	FAC	1Q	FAC	EPr	FAC	P	FAC	1Q	FAC	P	FAC	1Qr
FAV	2Q	FAV	2Q	FAV	1Q	FAV	1P	FAV	2Q	FAV	2Q	FAV	1Q	FAV	1P	FAV	1P	FAT	2Qr

Ground is signposted from both ends of A39 and B3151.

Bus Route Green Lane Ave - stop 220m away

TAVISTOCK

Founded 1888

Nickname: The Lambs **Club Colours:** Red & black

Club Contact Details 01822 614 447 secretary@tavistockfc.com

Ground: Langsford Park, Red & Black Club, Crowndale Road, Tavistock PL19 8JR

Capacity: **Seats:** Yes **Covered:** Yes

Previous Names:

Previous Leagues: South Western 1952-61, 68-2007. South West Peninsula 2007-19.

HONOURS: FA Comps: None

League: Devon 1900-01. Plymouth Combination Division One 1950-51.
South West Peninsula League Division One East 2014-15, Premier 16-17, 18-19.

10 YEAR RECORD

09-10		10-11		11-12		12-13		13-14		14-15		15-16		16-17		17-18		18-19	
SWPP	5	SWPP	13	SWPP	10	SWPP	10	SWPP	19	SW1E	1	SWPP	3	SWPP	1	SWPP	2	SWPP	1
FAC	EP	FAC	P	FAC	1Q	FAC	EP	FAC	EP							FAC	2Q	FAC	EP
FAV	2P	FAV	1P	FAV	1P	FAV	1Q	FAV	2P	FAV	1Q			FAV	1P	FAV	2P	FAV	2P

Take signs for Tavistock College and Sports Centre, go past the College and the ground entrance is a further 100 meters on your left hand side.

Nearest Railway Station Gunnislake - 4.9km

Bus Route Canons Way - stop 694m away

WELLINGTON

Founded 1892

Nickname: Wellie **Club Colours:** Orange and black

Club Contact Details 01823 664 810 jeffandjane@talktalk.net

Ground: Wellington Playing Field, North Street, Wellington TA21 8NE

Capacity: 1,500 **Seats:** 200 **Covered:** 200

Previous Names: None

Previous Leagues: Taunton Saturday, Somerset Senior.

HONOURS: FA Comps: None

League: Western Division One 2007-08, 16-17.

10 YEAR RECORD

09-10		10-11		11-12		12-13		13-14		14-15		15-16		16-17		17-18		18-19	
WestP	13	WestP	18	West1	18	West1	18	West1	8	West1	6	West1	12	West1	1	WestP	15	WestP	16
FAC	EP	FAC	P	FAC	EP											FAC	EP	FAC	EPr
FAV	3P	FAV	2P	FAV	2Q	FAT	2Q			FAV	2Q			FAV	1Q	FAV	2P	FAV	1Q

Leave the M5 motorway at Junction 26 and follow directions to Wellington. At town centre traffic lights take turning into North Street. Take the next left adjacent to the Fire Station and signposted 'Car Park'. The ground is in the corner of the car park.

Bus Route Nth St Police Station - stop 150m away

WESTBURY UNITED

Founded 1920

Nickname: White Horse Men **Club Colours:** Green and black

Club Contact Details 01373 764 197 secretary@westburyunited.co.uk

Ground: Meadow Lane, Westbury, Wiltshire BA13 3AF

Capacity: **Seats:** Yes **Covered:** Yes

Previous Names: Formed after the merger of Westbury Old Comrades FC and Westbury Great Western Railway XI

Previous Leagues: Wiltshire County 1920-1984.

HONOURS: FA Comps: None

League: Wiltshire 1934-35, 37-38, 38-39, 49-50, 50-51, 55-56.
Western Division One 1991-92, 2017-18.

10 YEAR RECORD

09-10		10-11		11-12		12-13		13-14		14-15		15-16		16-17		17-18		18-19	
West1	5	West1	17	West1	17	West1	19	West1	20	West1	22	West1	22	West1	12	West1	1	WestP	5
FAC	EPr	FAC	P															FAC	1Q
FAV	1P	FAV	1Q	FAV	1Q	FAV	1P	FAV	1Q	FAV	1Q	FAV	1Q	FAV	2Q	FAV	2Q	FAV	1P

From town centre proceed along Station Road towards rail station.
At double mini roundabout turn right. Ground is 300 metres on left hand side opposite Fire Station.

Nearest Railway Station Westbury - 1.1km

Bus Route Springfield Road - stop 200m away

ALMONDSBURY

Founded: 1969 Nickname: The Almonds

Club Contact Details 01454 612 240 doug2004.coles@blueyonder.co.uk
Ground: The Field, Gloucester Road, Almondsbury, Bristol BS32 4AA **Club Colours:** Green & white
HONOURS **League:** Bristol Suburban Premier Division 1990-91. Gloucestershire County 2003-04.
FA Comps: None

10 YEAR RECORD

09-10	10-11	11-12	12-13	13-14	14-15	15-16	16-17	17-18	18-19
West1 13	West1 12	West1 9	West1 10	West1 9	West1 5	West1 11	West1 22	West1 13	Hel1W 7
	FAC P	FAC EP	FAC 1Q		FAC EP	FAC 1Q			
FAV 1Q	FAV 2Q	FAV 1Q	FAV 1Q	FAV 1P	FAV 1Q	FAV 2Q	FAV 2Q	FAV 1Q	FAV 2P

Exit M5 at Junction 16. Arriving from the south take the left exit lane. Turn left at lights and ground is 150m on right hand side. Arriving from east take right hand lane on slip road. Take 3rd exit and ground is 150m on right hand side.

Nearest Railway Station Patchway - 2.9km
Bus Route Over Lane - stop 70m away

ASHTON & BACKWELL UNITED

Founded: 2010 Nickname: The Stags

Club Contact Details ashtonbackwellsecretary@gmail.com
Ground: The Lancer Scott Stadium, West Town Road, Backwell. BS48 3HQ **Club Colours:** Maroon & blue
HONOURS **League:** None
FA Comps: None

10 YEAR RECORD

09-10	10-11	11-12	12-13	13-14	14-15	15-16	16-17	17-18	18-19
	SomP 7	SomP 3	SomP 3	West1 14	West1 8	West1 8	West1 7	West1 18	West1 4
						FAC EP	FAC EP		
		FAV 2Q	FAV 2Q	FAV 1P	FAV 2Q	FAV 2Q	FAV 2Q	FAV 2Q	FAV 2Q

Off the main A370 in Backwell, travelling from Bristol the entrance is on the right, apprximately 500 metres after the crossroads. Travelling from Weston Super Mare the entrance to the ground is on the left approximately 500 metrs past the New Inn Pub and Restaurant.

Nearest Railway Station Nailsea & Backwell - 0.9km
Bus Route Spar (Rodney Rd) - stop 150m away

BISHOP SUTTON

Founded: 1977 Nickname: Bishops

Club Contact Details 01275 332 855 bishopsuttonafcsecretary@hotmail.co.uk
Ground: Lakeview, Wick Road, Bishops Sutton, Bristol BS39 5XN. **Club Colours:** All blue
HONOURS **League:** Western Division One 1997-98, Premier Division 2012-13.
FA Comps: None

10 YEAR RECORD

09-10	10-11	11-12	12-13	13-14	14-15	15-16	16-17	17-18	18-19
WestP 4	WestP 5	WestP 6	WestP 1	WestP 9	WestP 19	West1 21	West1 16	West1 12	West1 17
FAC EP	FAC P	FAC 1Q	FAC Pr	FAC P	FAC EP	FAC EP			
FAV 1P	FAV 1Pr	FAV 2P	FAV 2Q	FAV 1P	FAV 1Q	FAV 1P	FAV 2Q	FAV 2Q	FAV 1Q

On main A368 Bath to Weston-Super-Mare road at rear of Butchers Arms Public House.

Bus Route Butchers Arms Pub - stop 50m away

BISHOPS LYDEARD

Founded: 1912 Nickname:

Club Contact Details itspeebee@gmail.com
Ground: Cottlestone Road, Bishops Lydeard, Taunton, TA4 3BA **Club Colours:** Red & black stripes/
HONOURS **League:** Somerset County Division One 2004-05, Premier Division 15-16.
FA Comps: None

10 YEAR RECORD

09-10	10-11	11-12	12-13	13-14	14-15	15-16	16-17	17-18	18-19
SomP 2	SomP 12	SomP 11	SomP 13	SomP 10	SthP 6	SomP 1	West1 6	West1 14	West1 12
									FAV 2Q

Exit M5 at Junction 25, take A358 towards Minehead. Once past Marine Camp
Go straight over roundabout and take first right turn into Bishops Lydeard. At T Junction turn right and
Head through village past the Co-Op. Continue for 1.5 Miles and club is on right hand side.

Nearest Railway Station Bishops Lydeard - 1.5km
Bus Route Darby Way - 80m away

BRISTOL TELEPHONES

Founded: 1948 Nickname: The Phones

Club Contact Details 01275 891 776 steve.watkins56@talktalk.net

Ground: BTRA Sports Ground, Stockwood Lane, Stockwood, Bristol BS14 8SJ **Club Colours:** All pale blue

HONOURS **League:** Bristol & Suburban Premier Division 2010-11, 12-13. Gloucestershire County 2016-17.

FA Comps: None

10 YEAR RECORD

09-10	10-11	11-12	12-13	13-14	14-15	15-16	16-17	17-18	18-19
Br&SuP2 3	Br&SuP1 1	Br&SuP1 3	Br&SuP1 1	GlCo 3	GlCo 8	GlCo 10	GlCo 1	West1 16	West1 20
									FAV 1Q

From Bristol: Leave Bristol via A37 Wells Road. At Whitchurch, turn left at traffic lights at Toby Carvery. Continue on this road, crossing two mini roundabouts, after the second the ground can be found on the right by BS14 Club. From Keynsham: Leave Keynsham towards Bristol. At 'Rest a While' cafe bear left to Stockwood Hill. Continue on past Stockwood Vale GC and across two mini roundabouts. The ground can be found on the left just past the entrance to BS14 Club.

Nearest Railway Station Keynsham - 3.6km
Bus Route Battson Road - stop 50m away

CALNE TOWN

Founded: 1886 Nickname: Lilywhites

Club Contact Details 07795 833 702 wmm498@msn.com

Ground: Bremhill View, Calne, Wiltshire SN11 9EE **Club Colours:** White and black

HONOURS **League:** None

FA Comps: None

10 YEAR RECORD

09-10	10-11	11-12	12-13	13-14	14-15	15-16	16-17	17-18	18-19
WestP 20	West1 11	West1 4	West1 9	West1 13	West1 15	West1 15	West1 21	West1 17	West1 8
FAC P	FAC EP	FAC EP	FAC EP	FAC EP					
FAV 1Q	FAV 1P	FAV 2Q	FAV 1P	FAV 1Q	FAV 2Q	FAV 1P	FAV 1P	FAV 2Q	FAV 1Q

Take A4 to Calne from Chippenham, on approaching Calne turn left at the first roundabout on to A3102 Calne bypass. At the next roundabout turn right, next left and then right and right again.

Bus Route Northend - stop 80m away

CHEDDAR

Founded: 1892 Nickname: The Cheesemen

Club Contact Details 01934 707 271 secretarycheddarfc@gmail.com

Ground: Bowdens Park, Draycott Road, Cheddar BS27 3RL **Club Colours:** Yellow and black

HONOURS **League:** Cheddar Valley 1910-11. Somerset Senior Division One 2003-04.

FA Comps: None

10 YEAR RECORD

09-10	10-11	11-12	12-13	13-14	14-15	15-16	16-17	17-18	18-19
SomP 7	SomP 4	SomP 2	West1 11	West1 17	West1 10	WestP 5	West1 3	West1 4	West1 2
							FAC EPr	FAC EP	FAC P
				FAV 1Q	FAV 1Q	FAV 1Q	FAV 2Q	FAV 1Q	FAV 2P

FROM WELLS: Take the A371 (Weston Super Mare) through Draycott and Bowdens Park is on your left about half a mile past Cheddar Garden Centre (if you get to the church you've gone too far). FROM WESTON: Head towards Wells on the A371 and go through the village of Cheddar. The church is on your right as you come out of the village and Bowdens Park is 200 yards past the church on your right hand side.

Bus Route Church Street - stop 400m away

CORSHAM TOWN

Founded: 1883 Nickname: The Peacocks

Club Contact Details les.bateman63@btinternet.com

Ground: Southbank Ground, Lacock Road, Corsham SN13 9HS **Club Colours:** Red & white

HONOURS **League:** Wiltshire Division Two 1960-61, Division One 97-98. Western Premier Division 2006-07.

FA Comps: None

10 YEAR RECORD

09-10	10-11	11-12	12-13	13-14	14-15	15-16	16-17	17-18	18-19
WestP 17	WestP 10	WestP 18	West1 4	West1 7	West1 9	West1 10	West1 19	West1 20	West1 3
FAC EP	FAC P	FAC EP	FAC EP	FAC 1Qr	FAC EP				
FAV 1P	FAV 2Q	FAV 1Qr	FAV 1Q	FAV 2Q	FAV 2Q	FAV 1P	FAV 2Q	FAV 1Q	FAV 2Q

A4 into Corsham, at Hare and Hounds Roundabout take the Melksham Road B3353 until the War Memorial, then Lacock Road. Ground a half a mile on the right side.

Nearest Railway Station Chippenham - 5.8km
Bus Route St Patrick's School - stop 50m away

DEVIZES TOWN

Founded: 1885 Nickname: The Town

Club Contact Details 01380 722 817 neil@hallmarkflooringltd.co.uk

Ground: Nursteed Road, Devizes, Wiltshire SN10 3DX **Club Colours:** Red & white stripes

HONOURS
FA Comps: None
League: Wiltshire Senior 1895-96, 89-99, 35-36, 48-49, 51-52, 53-54, Premier 61-62, 63-64. Western Premier Division 1972-73, Division One 99-2000.

10 YEAR RECORD

09-10		10-11		11-12		12-13		13-14		14-15		15-16		16-17		17-18		18-19	
West1	19	West1	5	West1	19	West1	21	West1	11	West1	18	West1	19	West1	11	West1	5	West1	11
FAC	EPr			FAC	EP														
FAV	2Q	FAV	2Q	FAV	1P	FAV	1Q	FAV	1Q	FAV	1Q	FAV	1Q	FAV	1P	FAV	1Q	FAV	1Q

Leave Devizes on A342 for Andover. Ground is on the right hand side opposite Eastleigh Road.

Bus Route Eastleigh Road - stop 80m away

HENGROVE ATHLETIC

Founded: 1948 Nickname: The Grove

Club Contact Details 07884 492 217 secretary@hengroveathletic.com

Ground: Norton Lane, Whitchurch, Bristol BS14 0BT **Club Colours:** Green & white

HONOURS
FA Comps: None
League: Somerset County Premier Division 2005-06.

10 YEAR RECORD

09-10		10-11		11-12		12-13		13-14		14-15		15-16		16-17		17-18		18-19	
West1	7	West1	10	West1	10	West1	2	WestP	21	West1	12	West1	7	West1	2	WestP	9	WestP	19
				FAC	EP	FAC	P	FAC	EP	FAC	EP			FAC	EPr	FAC	P	FAC	EP
		FAV	2Pr	FAV	2Q	FAV	2Q	FAV	2Q	FAV	2Q	FAV	3P	FAV	1P	FAV	2P	FAV	1Q

Take A37 from Bristol through Whitchurch village past Maes Knoll pub, over hump bridge taking next turning on right, which is Norton Lane. Ground is immediately after Garden Centre.

Nearest Railway Station Bedminster - 2.5km
Bus Route Wooton Park - stop 100m away

LEBEQ UNITED

Founded: 2008 Nickname:

Club Contact Details Lebequnited@hotmail.com

Ground: Oaklands Park, Almondsbury, Bristol BS32 4AG **Club Colours:** Red

HONOURS
FA Comps: None
League: Bristol & Suburban Division Three 2009-10, Division Two 11-12, Premier Division One 15-16. Gloucestershire County 2018-19.

10 YEAR RECORD

09-10		10-11		11-12		12-13		13-14		14-15		15-16		16-17		17-18		18-19	
Br&Su3	1	Br&Su2	7	Br&Su2	1	Br&Su1	4	Br&SuP2	3	Br&SuP1	8	Br&SuP1	1	GlCo	10	GlCo	2	GlCo	1

Exit M5 at Junction 16. Arriving from the south take the left exit lane.
Turn left at lights and ground is 150m on right hand side.
Arriving from east take right hand lane on slip road.
Take 3rd exit nd ground is 150m on right hand side.

LONGWELL GREEN SPORTS

Founded: 1966 Nickname: The Green

Club Contact Details dainceyt@blueyonder.co.uk

Ground: Longwell Green Com. Centre, Shellards Road BS30 9DU **Club Colours:** Blue & white

HONOURS
FA Comps: None
League: Bristol & District Division Four 1982-83.

10 YEAR RECORD

09-10		10-11		11-12		12-13		13-14		14-15		15-16		16-17		17-18		18-19	
WestP	11	WestP	17	WestP	13	WestP	15	WestP	14	WestP	16	WestP	18	WestP	17	WestP	19	West1	5
FAC	EP	FAC	P	FAC	P	FAC	EPr	FAC	Pr	FAC	1Q	FAC	P	FAC	EP	FAC	EP	FAC	EPr
FAV	2P	FAV	2Q	FAV	1Qr	FAV	2Pr	FAV	1P	FAV	1P	FAV	2Qr	FAV	2Q	FAV	2Q	FAV	1P

Leave Junction 1 M32 follow signs for Ring Road (A4174). At Kingsfield roundabout turn into Marsham Way. At first set of traffic lights turn left into Woodward Drive. Continue to min roundabout and turn right into Parkway Road and continue to Shellards Road. Ground is situated to the rear of the Community Centre.

Nearest Railway Station Bitton - 1.4km
Bus Route Sally Barn Close - stop 500m away

OLDLAND ABBOTONIANS

Founded: 1910 Nickname: The O's

Club Contact Details 01179 328 263 secretary@oldlandfootball.com

Ground: Aitchison Playing Field, Castle Road, Oldland Common, Bristol BS30 **Club Colours:** Blue & white

HONOURS **League:** Somerset County Division One 2004-05.

FA Comps: None

10 YEAR RECORD

09-10	10-11	11-12	12-13	13-14	14-15	15-16	16-17	17-18	18-19
West1 6	West1 2	West1 11	West1 5	West1 21	West1 14	West1 4	West1 17	West1 7	West1 18
				FAC EP			FAC P		
			FAV 1Q	FAV 1Q	FAV 1Q	FAV 2Q	FAV 2Q	FAV 2Q	FAV 1Q

Exit M4 at Jct19 to M32. Exit M32 at Jct 1after 400 yds and take 1st exit from roundabout for A4174. Straight over traffic lights to next roundabout continuing on A4174. Go over five roundabouts for approximately 4.8 miles. At next roundabout take 1st exit to Deanery Road (A420) and continue for 0.9 miles to Griffin Public house and turn right into Bath Road (A4175). Continue for 1.3 miles to Oldland Common High Street and look for Dolphin Public House. Turning for Castle Street is next left between Chinese Chip Shop and Post Office. Ground is at the end of Castle Road.

Nearest Railway Station Oldland - 400m
Bus Route The Clamp - stop 130m away

PORTISHEAD TOWN

Founded: 1912 Nickname: Posset

Club Contact Details 01275 817 600 andy.carling@yahoo.co.uk

Ground: Bristol Road, Portishead, Bristol BS20 6QG **Club Colours:** White and black

HONOURS **League:** Somerset County 1993-94, 94-95, 95-96, 97-98.

FA Comps: None

10 YEAR RECORD

09-10	10-11	11-12	12-13	13-14	14-15	15-16	16-17	17-18	18-19
West1 12	West1 18	West1 12	West1 14	West1 22	West1 21	West1 6	West1 14	West1 21	West1 16
FAC P	FAC EP						FAC 1Q		
FAV 1Q	FAV 2Q	FAV 1Q	FAV 1Q	FAV 1Q	FAV 2Q	FAV 1P	FAV 2Q	FAV 2Q	FAV 1Q

Leave M5 at Junction 19 and take road to Portishead. At outskirts of town take 1st exit from small roundabout signposted Clevedon and Police H.Q. Ground is 150 yds along road on left by bus stop.

Nearest Railway Station Avonmouth - 5.1km
Bus Route Glebe Road - stop 50m away

RADSTOCK TOWN

Founded: 1895 Nickname: The Miners

Club Contact Details 01761 435 004 ianlanning9@gmail.com

Ground: Southfields Recreation Ground, Southfields, Radstock BA3 3NZ **Club Colours:** Red and black

HONOURS **League:** Somerset Senior Division One 1996-97.

FA Comps: None

10 YEAR RECORD

09-10	10-11	11-12	12-13	13-14	14-15	15-16	16-17	17-18	18-19
WestP 16	WestP 12	WestP 16	WestP 17	WestP 1	West1 13	West1 13	West1 5	West1 6	West1 15
FAC EP	FAC P	FAC P	FAC EP	FAC EP	FAC EP				
FAV 1Q	FAV 1P	FAV 1Q	FAV 2Q	FAV 2Q	FAV 1P	FAV 2Q	FAV 1Q	FAV 1P	FAV 2Q

The town of Radstock is situated 15 miles south east of Bristol and 8 miles southwest of Bath on the A367. At the double roundabout in Radstock town centre take the A362 towards Frome. The ground is on the right hand bend, third turning. Turn right into Southfield, ground is 200 yards ahead.

Bus Route Withies Park - stop 80m away

SHERBORNE TOWN

Founded: 1894 Nickname:

Club Contact Details 01935 816 110 michelliethurgood@sky.com

Ground: Raleigh Grove, Terrace Playing Field, Sherborne DT9 5NS **Club Colours:** Black & white

HONOURS **League:** Dorset Premier 1981-82. Western Division One 2012-13.

FA Comps: None

10 YEAR RECORD

09-10	10-11	11-12	12-13	13-14	14-15	15-16	16-17	17-18	18-19
WestP 18	WestP 14	WestP 17	West1 1	WestP 9	WestP 12	WestP 13	WestP 20	WestP 19	West1 13
FAC P	FAC 2Q	FAC EP	FAC 1Q	FAC P	FAC 1Q	FAC Pr	FAC EP	FAC EP	
FAV 2Q	FAV 1Pr	FAV 2Q	FAV 2P	FAV 2Q	FAV 1P	FAV 1Q	FAV 1P	FAV 1Q	FAV 2Q

From Yeovil take A30 - marked Sherborne. On entering town turn right at traffic lights, over next traffic lights and at the next junction turn right. Go over bridge, take second left marked 'Terrace Pling Fields'. Turn into car park, football club car park is situated in the far right-hand corner.

Nearest Railway Station Sherborne - 0.5km
Bus Route Sherborne Station - stop 0.5km away

WARMINSTER TOWN

Founded: 1878 Nickname: The Red & Blacks

Club Contact Details 01985 217 828 chrisjrobbins58@gmail.com

Ground: Weymouth Street, Warminster BA12 9NS **Club Colours:** Red & black stripes

HONOURS **League:** None

FA Comps: None

10 YEAR RECORD

09-10	10-11	11-12	12-13	13-14	14-15	15-16	16-17	17-18	18-19
Wex1 14	Wex1 12	Wex1 16	West1 15	West1 18	West1 16	West1 17	West1 18	West1 22	West1 6
FAC Pr	FAC EP								
FAV 1Q	FAV 2Q		FAV 2Q	FAV 1P	FAV 1Q	FAV 2Q	FAV 1Q	FAV 2Q	FAV 2Q

A36 from Salisbury, head for town centre, turn left at traffic lights in the town centre signposted A350 Shaftesbury. Club is situated approx. 400 yards on left hand side at top of Weymouth Street.

Nearest Railway Station Warminster - 0.9km

Bus Route Glebe Field - stop 80m away

WELLS CITY

Founded: 1890 Nickname:

Club Contact Details 01749 679 971 daveg55@hotmail.co.uk

Ground: Athletic Ground, Rowdens Road, Wells, Somerset BA5 1TU **Club Colours:** All blue

HONOURS **League:** Western Division One 1949-50, 2009-10.

FA Comps: None

10 YEAR RECORD

09-10	10-11	11-12	12-13	13-14	14-15	15-16	16-17	17-18	18-19
West1 1	WestP 9	WestP 12	WestP 19	West1 6	West1 19	West1 2	WestP 15	WestP 20	West1 10
		FAC 2Q	FAC P	FAC 1Q			FAC EPr	FAC P	FAC EP
FAV 2P	FAV 1Q	FAV 1P	FAV 2Q	FAV 1Q	FAV 1Q	FAV 1P	FAV 2Q	FAV 1Q	FAV 2Q

From North & Southwest - Follow A39 to Strawberry Way to roundabout, follow A371 East Somerset Way and take right turn into Rowdens Road. Ground is on left. From East - Follow A371 from Shepton Mallet. After approximately 5 miles on East Somerset Way take left turn into Rowdens Road. Ground is on left.

Bus Route The Police Station - stop 20m away

WELTON ROVERS

Founded: 1887 Nickname: Rovers

Club Contact Details 07970 791 644 garethpaisey@outlook.com

Ground: West Clewes, North Road, Midsomer Norton, Bath BA3 2QD **Club Colours:** Green & white

HONOURS **League:** Western 1911-12, 64-65, 65-66, 66-67, 73-74, Division One 59-60, 87-88.

FA Comps: None

10 YEAR RECORD

09-10	10-11	11-12	12-13	13-14	14-15	15-16	16-17	17-18	18-19
WestP 5	WestP 19	West1 7	West1 16	West1 6	West1 2	WestP 20	West1 20	West1 8	West1 9
FAC EP	FAC EP	FAC EP	FAC EP		FAC EP	FAC EP	FAC EP		
FAV 3P	FAV 1Q	FAV 1Q	FAV 2Q	FAV 1Q	FAV 2P	FAV 3P	FAV 1Q	FAV 1Q	FAV 2Q

The ground is on the main A362 in Midsomer Norton.

Bus Route Elm View - 50m away

WINCANTON TOWN

Founded: 1890 Nickname: Winky

Club Contact Details 01963 31815 cmartin10101981@gmail.com

Ground: Wincanton Sports Ground, Moor Lane, Wincanton. BA9 9EJ **Club Colours:** Yellow & black

HONOURS **League:** Yeovil & District Division Two 1988-89, Division One 89-90, Premier 90-91. Dorset Senior Division 2006-07.

FA Comps: None

10 YEAR RECORD

09-10	10-11	11-12	12-13	13-14	14-15	15-16	16-17	17-18	18-19
Dor P 9	Dor P 7	Dor P 4	Dor P 2	West1 4	West1 4	West1 16	West1 13	West1 10	West1 14
						FAC P			
					FAV 1Q	FAV EP	FAV 1Q	FAV 2Q	FAV 1Q

Travelling to Wincanton on the A357 via Sturminster Newton turn right at the roundabout after passing under the A303 into Laurence Hill and follow the road across three further roundabouts into Southgate Road. Traffic from the A303 will also enter Southgate Road when following the signs to the town. At the junction turn right in the direction of Buckhorn Weston going under the A303 again before entering Moor Lane. Wincanton Sports Centre is on the left.

Nearest Railway Station Templecombe - 4.9km

Bus Route Balsam Lane - stop 1.2km away

Anglian Combination Premier Division

ACLE UNITED	Bridewell Lane, Acle, Norwich NR13 3RA
BECCLES TOWN	College Meadow, Ken Markland Way, Common Lane, Beccles NR34 9BU
BLOFIELD UNITED	Old Yarmouth Road, Blofield, Norwich NR13 4LE
BRADENHAM WANDERERS	Hale Road, Bradenham IP25 7RA
CAISTER	Bowthorpe Park, Clover Hill Road, Norwich NR5 9ED
HARLESTON TOWN	Harleston Recreation Ground, Wilderness Lane, Harleston IP20 9DD
HELLESDON	Hellesdon Community Centre, Woodview Road, Hellesdon, Norwich NR6 5QB
LONG STRATTON	Long Stratton Playing Field, Long Stratton, Manor Road NR15 2XR
MATTISHALL	Mattishall Playing Fields, South Green, Mattishall, Norwich NR20 3JY
MUNDFORD	The Glebe #1, St Leonards St,, Mundford, Norfolk IP26 5DW
NORWICH CEYMS	Hilltops Sports Centre, Main Road, Swardeston, Norwich NR14 8DU
SCOLE UNITED	Scole Playing Field #1, Ransome Avenue, Scole, Norfolk IP21 4EA
ST ANDREWS	Thorpe Recreation Ground, Laundry Lane, Thorpe St Andrew, Norwich NR7 0XQ
UEA	UEA #1, Colney Lane, Norwich, Norfolk NR4 7UE
WAVENEY	Saturn Close Sports Ground, Station Road, Lowestoft NR32 4TD
WROXHAM RESERVES	Trafford Park, Skinners Lane, Wroxham NR12 8SJ

Bedfordshire County Premier Division

AFC KEMPSTON & BEDFORD COL.	Renhold Playing Field, Renhold MK41 0LR
AFC OAKLEY SPORTS M&DH	Oakley Sport & Social Club, Oakley, Bedford MK43 7RP
BEDFORD ALBION	Bedford Borough Council, Woodlands, Ashmead Road, Bedford
BIGGLESWADE RESERVES	Langford Road SG18 9JT
BIGGLESWADE UNITED U23	Second Meadow, Fairfield Road, Biggleswade SG18 0AA
CALDECOTE	The Playing Fields, Harvey Close, Upper Caldecote SG18 9BQ
CRANFIELD UNITED	Crawley Road, Cranfield, Bedfordshire MK43 0AA
CRAWLEY GREEN RESERVES	Crawley Green Recreation Ground, Crawley Green Road, Luton LU2 9AG
FLITWICK TOWN	Flitwick Community Football Centre, Ampthill Road, Flitwick MK45 1BA
MARSTON SHELTON ROVERS	Wotton FC, Weston Park, Bedford Road, Wootton MK43 9JT
QUEENS PARK CRESCENTS	Bedford Borough Council, Allen Park
RISELEY SPORTS	The Playing Field, Gold Street, Riseley MK44 1EG
SHEFFORD TOWN & CAMP RES	Shefford Sports Club, Hitchin Road, Shefford SG17 5JD
STEVINGTON	Pavenham Playing Field, Pavenham, Bedfordshire MK43 7PE
WILSTEAD	Jubilee Playing Fields, Bedford Road, Wilstead MK45 3HN
WOOTTON BLUE CROSS	Weston Park, Bedford Road., Wootton MK43 9JT

Cambridgeshire County Premier Division

BAR HILL	Bar Hill Village Green, The Spinney, Bar Hill, Cambridge CB23 8ST
BRAMPTON	Thrapston Road Playing Fields, Brampton, Huntingdon PE28 4TB
CAMBRIDGE UNIVERSITY PRESS	CUP Sports Ground, Shaftesbury Road, Cambridge CB2 2BS
CHATTERIS TOWN	West Street, Chatteris, Cambridgeshire PE16 6HW
CHERRY HINTON	Recreation Ground, High Street, Cherry Hinton Cambridge CB1 9HZ
COMBERTON UNITED	Comberton Recreation Ground, Hines Lane, Comberton CB23 7BZ
EATON SOCON	River Road, Eaton Ford, St Neots PE19 7AU
ELY CITY RESERVES	The Unwin Ground, Downham Road, Ely CB6 1AQ
EYNESBURY UNITED	Hall Road, Eynesbury PE19 2SF
FOXTON	Hardman Road, off High Street, Foxton CB22 6RN
FULBOURN INSTITUTE	Fulbourn Recreation, Home End, Fulbourn CB21 5HS
GREAT SHELFORD	Recreation Ground, Woollards Lane, Great Shelford CB2 5LZ
HEMINGFORDS UNITED	Peace Memorial Playing Field #1, Manor Road, Hemingford Grey PE28 9BX
LINTON GRANTA	Recreation Ground, Meadow Lane, Linton, Cambridge CB21 6HX
OVER SPORTS	Over Recreation Ground, The Dole, Over, Cambridge CB4 5NW
WEST WRATTING	Recreation Ground, Bull Lane, West Wratting CB21 5NP

Central Midlands Division North

AFC BENTLEY	Bentley MW, 105 The Avenue, Bentley, Doncaster, Sth Yorks DN5 0PN
APPLEBY FRODINGHAM	Brumby Hall Sports Ground, Ashby Road, Scunthorpe, DN16 1AA
ASKERN	Welfare Sports Ground, Manor Way, Doncaster Road, Askern, DN6 0AJ
COLLINGHAM	Station Road, Collingham, Newark, Notts NG23 7RA
CROWLE TOWN COLTS	Windsor Park, Godnow Road, Crowle DN17 4EE
DINNINGTON TOWN	Phoenix Park, 131 Laughton Road, Dinnington, Nr Sheffield S25 2PP
DRONFIELD TOWN RESERVES	The H E Barnes Stadium, Stonelow Road, Dronfield S18 2EU
HARWORTH COLLIERY	Recreation Ground, Scrooby Road, Bircotes, Doncaster DN11 8JT
NEWARK TOWN	YMCA Sports Village, Lord Hawke Way, Newark NG24 4FH
PHOENIX	Phoenix Sports Complex, Bawtry Road, Brinsworth, Rotherham S60 5PA
RENISHAW RANGERS	Stone Close, Kiveton Park S26 6SQ
RETFORD UNITED	Cannon Park, Leverton Road, Retford, Notts DN22 6QF
STAVELEY M.W. RES	Inkersall Road, Staveley, Chesterfield, S43 3JL
SUTTON ROVERS	Askern FC, Manor Way, Askern DN6 0AJ
THORNE COLLIERY	Moorends Welfare, Grange Road, Moorends, Thorne, Doncaster DN8 4NH

Central Midlands Division South

ARNOLD TOWN	Eagle Valley, Oxton Road, Arnold, Nottingham NG5 8PS
ASHLAND ROVERS	Kingsway Park, Hodgkinson Road, Kirkby in Ashfield NG17 7DJ
BLIDWORTH WELFARE	Blidworth Welfare Miners SC, Mansfield Road, Blidworth, Mansfield NG21 0LR
CLAY CROSS TOWN	Coupe Lane, Holmgate, Clay Cross, Chesterfield, Derbyshire S45 9QF
HILTON HARRIERS	The Mease, Hilton, Derbyshire, DE65 5LS
HOLBROOK SPORTS	APC Sealants Ground, Shaw Lane, Holbrook, Derbyshire DE56 0TG
HOLBROOK ST MICHAELS	Holbrook Park, Mackney Road, Holbrook, Belper, Derbyshire DE56 0UH
LINBY COLLIERY WELFARE	Linby Colliery Welfare Ground, Church Lane, Linby, Nottinghamshire NG15 8AB
MANSFIELD HOSIERY MILLS	The Fieldings, Sutton-in-Ashfield NG17 2TF
MICKLEOVER RBL	Mickleover RBL, Poppyfields Drive, Mickleover, Derby DE3 9GQ
PINXTON	Van Elle Welfare Arena, Wharf Road, Pinxton NG16 6LG
ROWSLEY 86	Rowsley Recreation Ground, Peaktor Lane, Rowlsey DE4 2EE
SHERWOOD COLLIERY RES	Debdale Park, Debdale Lane, Mansfield Woodhouse NG19 7NS
SWANWICK PENTRICH ROAD	Highfield Road, Swanwick, Alfreton, Derbyshire DE55 1BW
TEVERSAL RESERVES	Teversal Grange Sports and Social Centre, Carnarvon Street, Teversal, NG17 3HJ
UNDERWOOD VILLA	Bracken Park, Felly Mill Lane, North, Off Mansfield Road, Underwood NG16 5FG

Cheshire League Premier Division

ALTRINCHAM RESERVES	Egerton Youth Club FC, Egerton Youth Club, Mereheath Lane, Knutsford WA16 6SL
BILLINGE	Barrows Farm, Carrmill Road, Billinge WN5 7TX
BLACON YOUTH CLUB	Cairns Crescent Playing Fields, Blacon, Chester CH1 5JG
BROADHEATH CENTRAL	Flixton FC, Valley Road, Urmston , Manchester M41 8RQ
CONGLETON VALE ROVERS	Congleton Town FC, Booth Street, Congleton, Cheshire CW12 4GA
CREWE	Cumberland Arena, Thomas Street, Crewe CW1 2BD
DATEN	Culceth Sports Club, Charnock Road, Culceth WA3 5SH
EAGLE SPORTS	Eagle Sports Club, Thornton Road, Great Sankey, Warrington WA5 2SZ
EGERTON	Egerton Youth Club, Mereheath Lane, Knutsford WA16 6SL
FC ST HELENS	Windleshaw Road, Denton's Green, Saint Helens WA10 6TD
GREENALLS PADGATE ST OS'WLD	Carlsberg Tetley Social Club, Long Lane, Warrington WA2 8PU
KNUTSFORD	Manchester Road, Knutsford WA16 0NX
LOSTOCK GRALAM	Park Stadium, Manchester Road, Lostock Gralam CW9 7PJ
MIDDLEWICH TOWN	Finney's Lane, Middlewich CW10 9DR
POYNTON	Poynton Sports Club, London Road North, Poynton, Cheshire SK12 1AG
WHALEY BRIDGE ATHLETIC	Horwich Park, Park Road, Whaley Bridge, High Peak SK23 7DJ

Devon County League North & East

ALPHINGTON	The Chronicles, Church Road, Alphington, Exeter EX2 8SW
BOVEY TRACEY RESERVES	Recreation Ground, Brimley, Bovery Tracey TQ13 9BY
BRAUNTON	Braunton EX33 1LE
BUDLEIGH SALTERTON	Greenway Lane, Budleigh Salterton EX9 6SG
CHUDLEIGH ATHLETIC	Chudleigh Sports Centre, Kate Brook, Chudleigh TQ13 0QN
CLYST VALLEY	Winslade Park, Exmouth Road, Clyst St Mary, Exeter EX5 1DA
EXMOUTH TOWN RESERVES	Southern Road, Exmouth EX8 3EE
EXWICK VILLA	College Sports Hub, Exwick, Exeter EX4 2BQ
HEAVITREE UNITED	Wingfield Park, Exeter EX1 3BS
LIVERTON UNITED	Halford, Liverton TQ12 6JF
NEWTOWN	RecreatioN Ground, Newton St Cyres
ST. MARTINS AFC	Minster Park, Exminster EX6 8AT
TEIGNMOUTH	Coombe Valley, Coombe Lane, Teignmouth TQ14 9EX
TOPSHAM TOWN	Topsham, Exeter Road
UNIVERSITY OF EXETER	University Sports Ground, Topsham Road, Topsham EX3 0LY
WITHERIDGE	Edge Down Park, Fore Street, Witheridge EX16 8AH

Devon County League South & West

BERE ALSTON UNITED	The Down, Down Road, Bere Alston PL20 7HQ
BUCKLAND ATHLETIC RES	Denbury Playing Fields, Denbury
KINGSTEIGNTON ATHLETIC	Broadpark, Broadway Road, Kingsteignton TQ12 3EH
LAKESIDE ATHLETIC	Parkway Sports Club PL5 2EY
NEWTON ABBOT SPURS RES	Marsh Road, Newton Abbot TQ12 2NR
OTTERY ST MARY	Washbrook Meadows, Butts Road, Ottery St Mary EX11 1EL
PAIGNTON SAINTS	Paignton Community College 3G, Waterleat Road, Paignton TQ3 3WA
PAIGNTON VILLA	Paignton Community College 3G, Waterleat Road, Paignton TQ3 3WA
PLYMOUTH ARGYLE DEV	Manadon Sports Hub PL5 3JG
PLYMPTON ATHLETIC	Lee Moor Recreation Ground, Plymouth PL7 5JH
PLYMSTOCK UNITED	Dean's Cross, Plymstock PL9 7AZ
ROSELANDS	War Memorial Playing Field, Greenway Road, Galmpton, Brixham TQ5 0LN
TAVISTOCK RESERVES	Langsford Park, Crowndale Road, Tavistock PL19 8JR
TOTNES & DARTINGTON	Foxhole Sports Ground, Dartington TQ9 6EB
WALDON ATHLETIC	Windmill Hill, Higher Audley Avenue, Torquay TQ2 7PF
WATCOMBE WANDERERS	Long Lane Playing Field, Long Lane, Newton Abbot TQ12 4SF

Dorset Premier League

BALTI SPORTS	Weymouth Collage, Cranford Avenue, Weymouth, Dorset DT4 7LA
BLANDFORD UNITED	Blandford Recreation Ground, Park Road, Blandford Forum DT11 7BX
BOURNEMOUTH SPORTS	Chapel Gate
BRIDPORT RESERVES	St Marys Field, Skilling Hill Road, Bridport DT6 5LA
CORFE CASTLE	Corfe Castle Sports Field, Hollands Close, Corfe Castle, Dorset BH20 5HB
DORCHESTER SPORTS	The Avenue Stadium, Weymouth Avenue, Dorchester, Dorset DT1 2RY
GILLINGHAM TOWN	Woodwater Lane, Gillingham, Dorset SP8 4HX
HAMWORTHY RECREATION	Hamworthy Rec. Club, Magna Road, Canford Magna, Wimborne BH21 3AE
HOLT UNITED	Petersham Lane, Gaunts Common, Holt, Wimborne BH21 4JR
MERLEY COBHAM SPORTS	Cobham Sports & Social Club, Merley House Lane, Wimborne BH21 3AA
PORTLAND UNITED RES	Weyline Stadium, Grove Road, Portland DT5 1DP
SHAFTESBURY TOWN RES	Cockrams, Coppice Street, Shaftesbury SP7 8PF
SHERBORNE TOWN RESERVES	Raleigh Grove, The Terrace Playing Fields, Sherborne DT9 5NS
STURMINSTER NEWTON UTD	Barnetts Field, Honeymead Lane, Sturminster Newton, Dorset DT10 1EW
SWANAGE TOWN & HERSTON	Day's Park, off De Moulham Road, Swanage BH19 2JW
WAREHAM RANGERS	Purbeck Sports Centre, Worgret Road, Wareham, Dorset BH20 4PH
WESTLAND SPORTS	Alvington Development Centre, Alvington Lane, Yeovil, BA22 8UX

Essex & Suffolk Border League Premier Division

ALRESFORD COLNE RANGERS	Ford Lane, Alresford, Colchester CO7 8AU
BARNSTON	High Easter Road, Barnston, Dunmow CM6 1LZ
BRANTHAM ATHLETIC RES.	Brantham Leisure Centre, New Village, Brantham CO11 1RZ
DEDHAM OLD BOYS	The Duchy Barn Southfields, Dedham, Colchester CO7 6AH
EARLS COLNE	Green Farm Meadow, Halstead Road, Earls Colne, Colchester CO6 2NG
FLITCH UNITED	Alcott Playing Field, Collops Villas, Stebbing, Dunmow CM6 3SY
GAS RECREATION	Gasrec Playing Field, Salary Close, Colchester CO4 3HL
GREAT BENTLEY	The Green, Heckfords Road, Great Bentley, Colchester CO7 8LY
HATFIELD PEVEREL	The Keith Bigden Memorial Ground, Wickham Bishops Rd, Hatfield Peverel CM3 2JL
LAWFORD LADS	School Lane, Lawford, Manningtree CO11 2JA
LITTLE OAKLEY RESERVES	War Memorial Club Ground, Harwich Road, Little Oakley, Harwich CO12 5ED
STANWAY PEGASUS	Stanway School, Winstree Road, Stanway, Colchester CO3 0QA
TIPTREE ENGAINE	Burches Meadow, Pebmarsh Road, Colne Engaine CO6 2HD
TIPTREE HEATH	Tolleshunt Knights Village Hall & Playing Field, Top Road, Tolleshunt Knights, Maldon CM9 8EU
WEST BERGHOLT	Lorkin Daniel Field, Lexden Road, West Bergholt, Colchester CO6 3BW
WHITE NOTLEY	Oak Farm, Faulkbourne, Witham CM8 1SF

Essex Olympian League Premier Division

BASILDON TOWN	Basildon Leisure Club, Gardiners Lane South, Gardiners Way, Basildon, SS14 3AP
BISHOP'S STORTFORD SWIFTS	Silver Leys, Hadham Road (A1250), Bishop's Stortford CM23 2QE
BUCKHURST HILL	Roding Lane, Buckhurst Hill IG9 6BJ
CANNING TOWN	West Ham Community Ground (3G), Albastross Close London E6 5NX
CATHOLIC UNITED	Bowers & Pitsea FC, Len Salmon Stadium, Crown Avenue, Pitsea, Basildon SS13 2BE
HAROLD WOOD ATHLETIC	Harold Wood Recreation Park, Harold View, Harold Wood RM3 0LX
HUTTON	Polo Fields, Hall Green Lane, Hutton, Brentwood CM13 2QT
KELVEDON HATCH	New Hall, School Road, Kelvedon Hatch, Brentwood CM15 0DH
LEIGH RAMBLERS	Belfairs Park, Eastwood Road North, Leigh on Sea, Essex SS9 4LR
OLD SOUTHENDIAN	Garon Park, Main Pitch, Eastern Avenue, Southend-on-Sea SS2 4FA
RAYLEIGH TOWN	Rayleigh Town Sports/Soc. Club, London Road, Rayleigh SS6 9DT
SHENFIELD	St Martins School (3G), Hanging Hill Lane, Hutton CM13 2HG
SPRINGFIELD	Springfield Hall Park, Arun Close, Springfield CM1 7QE
SUNGATE	Ilford Wanderers Rugby Club, Forest Road, Hainault IG6 3HJ

Gloucestershire County League

AEK BOCO	True Clarity Pavilion, Greenbank Road, Hanham, Bristol BS15 3RZ
BROADWELL AMATEURS	The Hawthorns, Broadwell, Gloucestershire GL16 7BE
BROMLEY HEATH UNITED	Pomphrey Hill Pavilion, Pomphrey Hill, Mangotsfield , Bristol BS16 9NF
FRAMPTON UNITED	The Bell Field, Bridge Road, Frampton on Severn, Gloucestershire GL2 7HA
GALA WILTON	The Gala Club, Fairmile Gardens, Tewkesbury Road, Longford, Glou GL2 9EB
HANHAM ATHLETIC	The Playing Fields Pavilion, 16 Vicarage Road, Hanham, Bristol BS15 3AH
HARDWICKE AFC	Hardwicke Playing Field, Green Lane, GL2 4QA
HENBURY	Arnell Drive Playing Field, Lorain Walk, Henbury, Bristol BS10 7AS
LITTLE STOKE	Little Stoke Playing Fields, Little Stoke Lane, Bristol BS34 6HR
PATCHWAY TOWN	Scott Park, Coniston Road, Patchway, Bristol BS34 5JR
QUEDGELEY WANDERERS	Waterwells Sports Centre, Stephenson's Drive, Quedgeley, Gloucester GL2 2AG
ROCKLEAZE RANGERS	Pen Park Sports Pavillion, Jarratts Road, Bristol BS10 6WF
RUARDEAN HILL RANGERS	The Recreation Ground, Ruardean HIll, GL17 9AR
SHARPNESS	Hamfields Leisure Centre, Hamfields Lane, Berkeley, Gloucestershire GL13 9TN
WICK	Wick Sports Ground, Oldbury Lane,, Wick, Bristol BS30 5RJ

Hampshire Premier League

BUSH HILL	Mansel Park, Evenlode Road, Millbrook, Southampton SO16 9LT
CHAMBERLAYNE ATHLETIC	Station Road Recreation Ground, Station Road, Netley Abbey, Southampton SO31 5AE
CLANFIELD	East Moon Recreation Ground, Workhouse Lane, East Meon GU32 1PD
COLDEN COMMON	Oakwood Park, Oakwood Avenue, Otterbourne SO21 2ED
FLEETLANDS	DARA Fleetlands, Lederle Lane, Gosport PO13 0AA
HAYLING UNITED	Park Community School, Middle Park Way, Leigh Park, Havant PO9 4BU
INFINITY	Knowle Village Community Hall, Knowle Avenue, Knowle, Fareham PO17 5LG
LIPHOOK UNITED	Recreation Ground, London Road, Liphook GU30 7AN
LISS ATHLETIC	Newman Collard Playing Fields Liss GU33 7LH
LOCKS HEATH	Locksheath Rec, 419 Warsash Rd, Titchfield Common, Fareham PO14 4JX
LYNDHURST	Wellands Road, Lyndhurst SO43 7AB
OVERTON UNITED	Overton Recreation Centre, Bridge Street, Overton RG25 3HD
PAULSGROVE	Paulsgrove Social Club, Marsden Road, Paulsgrove, Portsmouth PO6 4JB
STOCKBRIDGE	Stockbridge Recreation Ground, High Street, Stockbridge SO20 6EU
SWAY	Jubilee Field, Station Road, Sway Hampshire SO41 6BE
WINCHESTER CASTLE	Hants Co. Council Spts Grd, Petersfield Rd (A31),Chilcombe, Winchester SO23 8ZB

Herts Senior County League Premier Division

BELSTONE	The Medburn Ground, Watling Street, Radlett WD6 3AB
BERKHAMSTED U25	Broadwater, Lower Kings Road, Berkhamsted HP4 2AL
BUSH HILL RANGERS	Enfield Playing Fields, Donkey Lane, Enfield EN1 3PL
CHIPPERFIELD CORINTHIANS	Queens Street, Chipperfield, Kings Langley WD4 9BT
COCKFOSTERS RESERVES	Chalk Lane, Cockfosters EN4 9HZ
COLNEY HEATH DEV	The Recreation Ground, High Street, Colney Heath AL4 0NP
CUFFLEY	King George's Playing Fields, Northaw Road East, Cuffley EN6 4LU
HATFIELD TOWN	Cotlandswick Playing Fields, North Orbital Road, London Colney AL2 1DW
HODDESDON TOWN RES	Lowfield, Park View, Hoddesdon EN11 8PU
KNEBWORTH	Knebworth Recreation Ground, Watton Road, Knebworth, Hertfordshire SG3 6AH
LETCHWORTH GC	Pixmore Playing Fields, Ledgers Lane, Baldock Road, Letchworth SG6 2EN
OXHEY JETS RESERVES	Boundary Stadium, Little Oxhey Lane, Oxhey W19 6FW
ROYSTON DEVELOPMENT	Garden Walk, Royston SG8 7HP
SANDRIDGE ROVERS	Spencer Recreation Ground, Sandridge, St Albans AL4 9DD
WARE SPORTS	Wodson Park Sports Centre, Wadesmill Road, WARE, Hertfordshire SG12 0RB
WESTON	North Herts Arena SG7 5AU

Humber Premier League Premier Division

AFC WALKINGTON	Broadgates Playing Field, Broadgate, Beverley HU17 8RJ
BARTON TOWN RES	Easy Buy Stadium, Marsh Lane, Barton upon Humber DN18 5JD
BEVERLEY TOWN	Norwood Recreation Ground, Norwood, beverley HU17 9HW
CHALK LANE	Hull University (3G), Inglemire Lane, Hull HU6 7TS
DRIFFIELD JUNIORS	Allotment Lane, Driffield YO25 6UH
HEDON RANGERS	Holderness Academy (3G), Station Road, Preston HU12 8UZ
HESSLE RANGERS	Wolfreton School (3G), Well Lane, Willerby HU10 6ER
HORNSEA TOWN	Hollis Recreation Ground, Atwick Road, Hornsea HU18 1EE
HULL UNITED	Steve Prescott Centre (3G), Hull HU5 1HZ
LIV SUPPLIES	Dene Park Sports Club, Dunswell HU6 0AA
NORTH FERRIBY RES	Grange Lane, North Ferriby HU14 3AB
POCKLINGTON TOWN	The Balk, Pocklington YO42 2NZ
RECKITTS AFC	Hull University, Inglemire Lane HUll HU6 7TS
SCULCOATES AMATEURS	St Mary's College, Cranbrook Avenue, Hull HU6 7TN
SOUTH CAVE UNITED	South Cave Sporting Club, Church Street, South Cave HU15 2EP
WESTELLA & WILLERBY	Hill Top Club, Beverley Road, Willerby HU10 6EF

Kent County League Premier Division

BORDEN VILLAGE	Borden Playstool, Wises Lane, Borden, Sittingbourne Kent ME9 8LP
BROMLEIANS	John Cooper Ground, Scrubs Farm, Lower Gravel, Road, Bromley, Kent BR2 8LL
CROCKENHILL	Wested Meadow Ground, Eynesford Road, Crockenhill, Kent BR8 8EJ
FARNBOROUGH OBG	Farnborough Sports Club, Farrow Field, Off High Street, Farnborough, Kent BR6 7BA
FAVERSHAM STRIKE FORCE	Sittingbourne Community College, (3G Pitch), Swanstree Avenue, Kent ME10 4NL
FLEETDOWN UNITED	Heath Lane Open Space, Heath Lane (Lower), Dartford DA1 2QE
HAWKINGE TOWN	Hawkinge Trust Ground, Pavilion Road, Hawkinge, Kent CT18 7UA
IDE HILL	Wrotham School, Borough Green Road, Borough Green, Kent TN15 7RD
K SPORTS RESERVES	K Sports Cobdown, Station Road, Ditton, Aylesford, Kent ME20 6AU
KINGS HILL	Kings Hill Sports Park, 200 Beacon Avenue, Kings Hill, West Malling, Kent ME19 4QP
NEW ROMNEY	The Maude Pavilion, Station Road, New Romney, Kent TN28 8LQ
OTFORD UNITED	Otford Recreation Ground, Off Otford High Street, Otford, Kent TN14 5PG
PECKHAM TOWN	Menace Arena, 37 Dulwich Common, Dulwich, London SE21 7EU
STANSFELD O & B CLUB	Marathon Playing Fields, Forty Foot Way, Avery Hill Road, New Eltham SE9 2EX
STAPLEHURST & MONARCHS UTD	Jubilee Sports Ground, Headcorn Road, Staplehurst TN12 0DS
TUDOR SPORTS	Conservative Club, Oxford Road, Sidcup, Kent DA14 6LW

Leicestershire Senior League Premier Division

ALLEXTON & NEW PARKS	New College, Glenfield Road, Leicester LE3 6DN
ASFORDBY	Asfordby Acres, The Old Quarry, Hoby Road LE14 3TL
ASHBY IVANHOE KNIGHTS	NFU Sports Ground, Greenfield Lower Packington Road, Ashby-de-la-Zouch LE65 1TS
BARLESTONE ST GILES	Barton Road, Barlestone, Nuneaton CV13 0EP
BLABY & WHETSTONE	Warwick Road, Whetstome, Leicester LE8 6LW
COTTESMORE AMATEURS	Westray Park, Main Street, Cottesmore, Oakham LE15 7DH
COUNTY HALL	Linwood Playing Field, Saffron Lane, Leicester LE2 6TG
DESFORD	Sport in Desford, Peckleton Lane, Desford, Leicester LE9 9JU
ELLISTOWN	Terrace Road, Ellistown, Leicestershire LE67 1GD
FC GNG	Riverside Football Ground, Braunstone Lane East, Leicester LE3 2FW
FC KHALSA GAD	TBC
FRIAR LANE & EPWORTH	Knighton Lane East, Leicester. LE2 6FT
HATHERN	Pasture Lane, Hathern, Leicestershire LE12 5LJ
RUGBY BOROUGH	Kilsby Lane, Rugby CV21 4PN
SILEBY TOWN	Sileby Sports Club, 3 Southfield Avenue, Sileby, Leicestershire LE12 7WL
THURNBY RANGERS	Thurnby Rangers Sports Ground, Dakyn Road, Leicester LE5 2ED

Lincolnshire League

BRIGG TOWN RESERVES	The Hawthorns, Wrawby Road, Brigg DN20 8DT
CLEETHORPES TOWN RES	Linden Club, Clee Road, Grimsby DN32 8QL
GAINSBOROUGH TRINITY RES	The Northolme, Northolme, Gainsborough DN21 2QW
GRIMSBY BOROUGH RES	Lucarlys, Wilton Road Ind Estate, Humberston DN36 4AW
HORNCASTLE TOWN	The Wong, Boston Road, Horncastle LN9 6EB
HYKEHAM TOWN	The Priory City of Lincoln Academy, Skellingthorpe Road, Lincoln LN6 0EP
IMMINGHAM TOWN	Blossom Way Sports Ground, Immingham DN40 1PH
LINCOLN MOORLANDS R'WAY	Moorlands Sports & Social Club, Newark Road, Lincoln LN6 8RT
LINCOLN UNITED DEV	Ashby Avenue, Lincoln LN6 0DY
LOUTH TOWN	Main Road, Saltfleetby, Louth LN11 7SS
NETTLEHAM	Mulsanne Park, The Pavilion Field Close, Nettleham LN2 2RX
RUSTON SPORTS	Ruston Sport & Social Club, Newark Road, Lincoln LN6 8RN
SLEAFORD TOWN RANGERS	Eslaforde Park, Boston Road, Sleaford NG34 7ER
WYBERTON	Wyberton Playing Fields, Wyberton, Boston PE21 7BS

Liverpool County Premier League Premier Division

AFC LIVERPOOL RESERVES	Simpson Ground (3G), Hillfoot Road, Liverpool L25 7UJ
ALDER	Liverpool County FA (3G), Wallton Hall Avenue, Liverpool L4 9XP
ALUMNI	Jericho Lane (3G), Otterspool, Liverpool L17 5AR
BANKFIELD OLD BOYS	Simpson Ground (3G), Hillfoot Road, Liverpool L25 7UJ
BRNESC	Long Lane, Liverpool L9 6AG
EAST VILLA	Long Lane, Liverpool L9 6AG
FC PILCHY	Long Lane, Liverpool L9 6AG
LIVER ACADEMY	Liverpool County FA (3G), Wallton Hall Avenue, Liverpool L4 9XP
LIVERPOOL NALGO	Alder Sports Club, Alder Road, Liverpool L12 2BA
LOWER BRECK RESERVES	Anfield Sports & Community Centre (3G), Breckside Park, Lower Breck Road, Liverpool L6 0AG
MSB WOOLTON	Simpson Ground (3G), Hillfoot Road, Liverpool L25 7UJ
OLD XAVERIANS	St Francis Xaviers College, Beconsfield Road, Liverpool L25 6EG
PAGE CELTIC	Liverpool County FA (3G), Wallton Hall Avenue, Liverpool L4 9XP
SEFTON ATHLETIC	Long Lane, Liverpool L9 6AG
WATERLOO DOCK	Anfield Sports & Community Centre (3G), Breckside Park, Lower Breck Road, Liverpool L6 0AG
WATERLOO GSOB	Long Lane, Liverpool L9 6AG

Manchester League Premier Division

BEACHFIELD UNITED	Salford Sports Village (3G), Littleton Road, Salford M7 3NQ
BOLTON COUNTY	Radcliffe Road, Darcy Lever, Bolton, Lancashire BL3 1AN
CHADDERTON RESERVES	Broadway, Andrew Street, Chadderton OL9 0JT
DUKINFIELD TOWN	Woodhams Park, Birch Lane, Dukinfield SK16 5AP
HEYSIDE	Rochdale Road, Shaw, OLDHAM, Lancashire OL2 7HS
HEYWOOD ST JAMES	Phoenix Ground, Shepherd Street, Heywood OL10 1JW
HINDSFORD	Squires Lane, Tyldesley M29 8JF
MANCHESTER GREGORIANS	Belle Vue Sports Village (3G), Kirksmanhulme Lane, Manchester M12 4TF
OLD ALTRINCHAMIANS	Crossford Bridge Sports Ground, Danefield Road, Sale M33 7WR
PENNINGTON	Jubilee Park, Leigh Road, Atherton M46 0SL
ROCHDALE SACRED HEART	Fox Park, Belfield Mill Lane, Rochdale OL16 2UB
ROYTON TOWN	Oldham Academy North (3G), Broadway OL2 5BF
SPRINGHEAD	St John Street, Lees, Oldham OL4 3LN
STOCKPORT GEORGIANS	Cromley Road, Woodsmoor, Stockport SK2 7DT
WALSHAW SPORTS CLUB	Walshaw Sports Club, Sycamore Road, Tottington, Bury BL8 3EG

Mid Sussex League Premier Division

AFC RINGMER	Caburn Ground, Anchor Field, Ringmer BN8 5QN
AFC UCKFIELD TOWN RES	Victoria Pleasure Ground, New Town, Uckfield TN22 5DJ
BALCOMBE	Oakwood Park, Tinsley Lane, Crawley RH10 8AT
BURGESS HILL ALBION	Janes Lane Recreation Ground, Janes Lane, Burgess Hill RH15 0QJ
CHARLWOOD	Hanbury Stadium, Allen Road, Haywards Heath RH16 3PX
CUCKFIELD RANGERS	Whitemans Green, Cuckfield RH17 5HX
EASTBOURNE RANGERS	Eastbourne Sports Park (3G), Cross Levels Way BN21 2UF
FOREST ROW	Oakwood Park, Tinsley Lane, Crawley RH10 8AT
HOLLINGTON UNITED	Gibbons Memorial Field, Wishing Tree Road, St Leonards on Sea TN8 8DJ
LINDFIELD	Whitemans Green, Cuckfield RH17 5HX
ROTHERFIELD	Rotherfield Recreation Ground, North Street, Rotherfield TN6 3LX
SPORTING LINDFIELD	Whitemans Green, Cuckfield RH17 5HX
WILLINGDON ATHLETIC	Huggetts Lane Recreation, Hugget's Lane, Willingdon BN22 0QP

Middlesex County League Premier Division

BRENTHAM	Meadvale Road, Ealing, London W5 1NP
C.B. HOUNSLOW UNITED RES.	Hounslow Sports Club, Green Lane, Hounslow TW4 6DH
CLAPTON COMMUNITY	Wadham Lodge, Kitchener Road, Walthamstow, London E17 4JP
CRICKLEWOOD WANDERERS	Wembley FC, Vale Farm Sports Centre, Watford Road, North Wembley, London HA0 3HE
HILLINGDON	Brunel Uni. Sports Complex, Kingston Park, Kingston Lane, Hillingdon UB8 3PW
HILLTOP	Middlesex Stadium, Breakspear Road, Ruislip HA4 7SB
INDIAN GYMKHANA	Indian Gymkhana Club, Thornbury Avenue, Osterley TW7 4NQ
KENSINGTON DRAGONS	Linford Christie Stadium, Artillery Lane, off Du Cane Road W12 0DF
LAMPTON PARK	Middlesex FA, Rectory Park Facility, Northolt, Middlesex UB5 6ED
LARKSPUR ROVERS	Lord Halsbury Playing Fields, Priors Farm Lane, Off Eastcote Lane, Northolt UB5 5DY
LONDON SAMURAI	Northwood FC, The Acretweed Stadium, Off Chestnut Avenue, Northwood HA6 1HR
NW LONDON	Hadley FC, Brickfield Lane, Arkley, Barnet EN5 3LD
PFC VICTORIA	Hanworth Villa FC, Rectory Meadows, Park Road, off Hounslow Road, Hanworth TW13 6PN
PITSHANGER DYNAMO	Hanwell Town FC, Perivale Lane, Perivale, Greenford Middlesex UB6 8TL
SPORTING HACKNEY	Hackney Marshes, Homerton Road, Hackney, London E9 5PF
STONEWALL	Barn Elms Playing Fields, Queen Elizabeth Walk, Barnes SW13 0DG
YEADING TOWN	Brunel Uni. Sports Complex, Kingston Park, Kingston Lane, Hillingdon UB8 3PW

North Riding League Premier Division

BEADS FC	Beechwood & Easterside Social Club, Marton Road, Middlesbrough TS4 3PP
BEDALE	Heck Food Stadium, Leyburn Road, Bedale DL8 1HA
BORO RANGERS	MFC Foundation, Normanby Road, Eston, Middlesbrough TS6 9AE
FISHBURN PARK	Eskdale School, Broomfield Park, Whitby, N Yorkshire YO22 4EB
GRANGETOWN BOYS CLUB	Grangetown Youth & C. Centre 1,Trunk Road, Grangetown, Middlesbrough TS6 7UP
GUISBOROUGH TOWN RES	Laurence Jackson School, Guisborough, TS14 6RD
KADER	Outwood Academy, Hall Drive, Acklam, TS5 7JY
REDCAR NEWMARKET	Rye Hill School, Redcar Lane, Redcar TS10 2HN
REDCAR TOWN	Mo Mowlam Park #2, Trunk Road, Redcar TS10 5BW
ST MARY'S 1947	Trinity Catholic College, Saltersgill Avenue, Middlesbrough, TS4 3JW
STAITHES ATHLETIC	Staithes Athletic Social Club, Seaton Crescent, Staithes, Saltburn TS13 5AY
STOCKTON WEST END	North Shore Health Academy, Talbot Street, Stockton TS20 2AY
STOKESLEY SPORTS CLUB	Stokesley Sports Club, Broughton Road, Stokesley, TS9 5NY
THIRSK FALCONS	Newsham Road, Thirsk, North Yorkshire, YO7 1QP
THORNABY DUBLINERS	Harold Wilson Sports Complex, Bader Avenue, Thornaby TS17 8PH
YARM & EAGLESCLIFFE	Conyers School, Green Lane, Yarm, TS15 9ET

Northamptonshire Combination Premier Division

CORBY PEGASUS	West Glebe South Pavilion (3), Cottingham Road, Corby, Northants. NN17 1SZ
CORBY S & L KINGSWOOD	Occupation Road, Corby, Northants. NN17 1EH
DESBOROUGH & ROTHWELL U	Montsaye Academy Sports Centre, Rothwell, Northants. NN14 6BB
EARLS BARTON UNITED	Pioneer Sports Ground, Grendon Road, Earls Barton, Northants. NN6 0RB
HARPOLE	Playing Field, Larkhall Lane, Harpole NN7 4DP
HEYFORD ATHLETIC	Playing Field, Middle Street, Nether Heyford PF NN7 3LL
JAMES KING BLISWORTH	Blisworth Playing Field, Courteenhall Road, Blisworth NN7 3DD
KETTERING NOMADS	Isham Cricket Club, Orlingbury Road, Isham NN14 1HY
MOULTON	Brunting Road, Moulton, Northampton NN3 7QF
ROADE	Connolly Way, Hyde Road, Roade NN7 2LU
SPRATTON	Spratton Recreation Ground, Smith Street, Spratton NN6 8HW
THRAPSTON TOWN	Chancery Lane, Thrapston, Northants NN14 4JN
WELDON UNITED	Rockingham Triangle, Jimmy Kane Way, Corby, Northants NN17 2FB
WOLLASTON VICTORIA	Wollaston Playing Field, London Road, Wollaston, Northants NN29 7QP
WOODFORD UNITED	Byfield Road, Woodford Halse, Daventry, Northants NN11 3QS
WOOTTON ST GEORGE	Curtlee Hill, Wootton, Northampton NN4 6ED

Northern Alliance Premier Division

AFC KILLINGWORTH	Blue Flames Sporting Club, Whitley Park, Whitley Road, Newcastle upon Tyne NE12 6SF
AFC NEW FORDLEY	Annitsford Welfare, Barrass Gardens, New Fordley, Cramlington NE23 7RB
ALNWICK TOWN	St. James's Park, Weavers Way, Alnwick, Northumberland NE66 1BG
BLYTH TOWN	South Newsham Pavillion, Blyth NE24 3PW
CULLERCOATS	Links Avenue, Cullercoats, NE30 3TD
GATESHEAD RUTHERFORD	Farnacres, Beggarswood Park, Coach Road, Lobley Hill, Gateshead NE16 1OH
NEWCASTLE BLUE STAR	Scotswood Sports Centre, Denton Road, Scostwood, Newcastle upon Tyne NE15 7HB
NEWCASTLE CHEMFICA	Longbenton Sports Ground, Newcastle University, Coach Lane, Newcastle upon Tyne NE7 7XA
NORTH SHIELDS ATHLETIC	John Spence Community High School, Preston Road, North Shields NE29 9PU
PERCY MAIN AMATEURS	Purvis Park, St Johns Green, Percy Main, North Shields NE29 6HS
PONTELAND UNITED	Ponteland High School, Callerton Lane, Ponteland NE20 9EY
SEATON DELAVAL AMATEURS	Wheatridge Park, Seaton Delaval, Whitley Bay NE25 0QH
SHANKHOUSE	Action Park, Dudley NE23 7HY
WALLINGTON	Oakford Park, Scots Gap, Morpeth NE61 4EJ
WHITLEY BAY RESERVES	Hillheads Park, Rink Way, Whitley Bay NE25 8HP
WINLATON VULCANS	Shibdon Park, Blaydon on Tyne NE21 5LU

Nottinghamshire Senior Premier Division

AFC DUNKIRK	Ron Steel Sports Ground, Lenton Lane, Nottingham NG7 2SA
ASLOCKTON & ORSTON	Orston Recreation Ground, Spa Lane, Orston NG13 9PL
ATTENBOROUGH	Village Green, The Strand, Attenborough, Nottingham NG9 6AU
AWSWORTH VILLA	The Shilo, Attewell Road, Awsworth, Nottingham NG16 2SY
BILBOROUGH TOWN	Harvey Hadden, Wigman Road, Bilborough NG8 4PB
BINGHAM TOWN	Butt Field, Bingham, Nottingham NG13 8GG
BURTON JOYCE	The Poplars, Station Road, Burton Joyce NG14 5AN
CALVERTON MINERS WELFARE	Calverton Miners Welfare, Hollinwood Lane, Calverton NG14 6NR
COTGRAVE	Woodview, Cotgrave Welfare, Woodview, Cotgrave, Nottingham NG12
EASTWOOD COMMUNITY DEV	Play Soccer USA (3G) Arena, Chewton Street, Eastwood NG16 3HB
FC CAVALIERS	The Forest. #1, Gregory Boulevard, Nottingham NG7 2SA
KEYWORTH UNITED	Platt Lane Sports Complex, Platt Lane, Keyworth NG12
MAGDALA AMATEURS	Roko, Wilford Lane, West Bridgford, Nottingham NG2 7RN
SANDIACRE TOWN	St Giles Park, Stanton Road, Sandiacre, Nottingham. NG10 5DE
SOUTHWELL CITY	War Memorial Recreation Ground, Bishop's Drive, Southwell NG25 0JP
STAPLEFORD TOWN	Greenwich Avenue, Basford, Nottingham NG6 0LD
WOLLATON	Wollaton Sports Association, 753 Wollaton Road, Wollaton, NG8 2AN
WOODTHORPE PARK RANGERS	Greenwich Avenue. Basford. Nottingham. NG6 0LD

Oxfordshire Senior League Premier Division

BICESTER TOWN COLTS	Oxford Road, Bicester OX26 6WB
CHARLTON UNITED	Charlton High Street, Charlton-on-Otmoor OX5 2UQ
CHESTERTON	Chesterton Playing Fields, Chesterton OX26 1XD
CROPREDY	Cropredy Sports & Social Club, Williamscott Road, Cropredy OX17 1PG
FREELAND	Wroslyn Road, Freeland OX29 8AQ
GARSINGTON	Denton Lane, Garsington OX44 9EL
HORSPATH	Horspath Athletic Track, Horspath Road, Oxford OX4 2RL
KENNINGTON	Playfield Road, Kennington, Oxford OX1 5RS
LAUNTON	Bicester Road, Launton OX26 5DP
MANSFIELD ROAD	University Club, Mansfield Road, Oxford OX1 3PS
MARSTON SAINTS	Boults Lane, Old Marston, Oxford OX3 0PW
MIDDLETON CHEENEY	Astrop Road, Middleton Cheney OX17 2PQ
SUMMERTOWN	Cuttesslowe Park, Lower Pitch, Oxford OX2 8ES
YARNTON	Littlemarsh Playing Fields, Green Lane, Yarnton Ox5 1QE

Peterborough & District League Premier Division

FC PARSON DROVE	Main Road, Parson Drove, Wisbech PE13 4LA
HOLBEACH UNITED RESERVES	Carters Park, Park Road, Holbeach Spalding PE12 7EE
ICA SPORTS	RSouth Bretton Playing Field, ingwood, South Bretton PE3 9SH
KETTON	Ketton Sports and Community Centre, Pit Lane, Ketton, Stamford, PE9 3SZ
LEVERINGTON SPORTS	Leverington Sports & Social Club, Church Road, Leverington, Wisbech PE13 5DE
LONG SUTTON ATHLETIC	London Road Playing Field, London Road, Long Sutton, Spalding PE12 9EA
MOULTON HARROX	Broad Lane, Moulton, Spalding PE12 6PN
NETHERTON UNITED	The Grange (3G), Charlotte Way, Peterborough PE3 9TT
OAKHAM UNITED	Main Road, Barleythorpe, Oakham, Rutland, LE15 7EE
PETERBOROUGH N E SPORTS	PSL Parkway Club, Lincoln Road, Peterborough PE1 3HA
PETERBOROUGH POLONIA	Nene Valley Community Centre, Candy Street, Peterborough PE2 9RE
STAMFORD LIONS	Blackstone Sports & Social Club, Lincoln Road, Stamford PE9 1UU
SUTTON BRIDGE UNITED	Memorial Park, Bridge Road, Sutton Bridge PE12 9SA
THORNEY	Campbell Drive, Peterborough PE4 7ZL
TYDD	Fenland Stadium, Lynn Road, Wisbech PE14 7AL
UPPINGHAM TOWN	Tods Piece, Wilkes Gardens, Uppingham, Oakham LE15 9QJ

Sheffield & Hallamshire Senior League Premier Division

BURNGREAVE	Firvale Academy, Owler Lane, Sheffield S4 8GB
DODWORTH MW	off High Street, Dodworth, Barnsley S75 3RF
ECCLESFIELD RED ROSE 1915	Chaucer School, Wordsworth Avenue, Sheffield S5 8NH
FRECHEVILLE C.A.	Davy Sports Club, Princ eof Wales Road, Darnall, Sheffield S9 4ER
GRIMETHORPE LL UK	Bruce Dyer LLUK Sports Ground, Cemetery Road, Grimethorpe S72 7EQ
HEPWORTH UNITED	Far Lane, Hepworth HD9 1RN
HIGH GREEN VILLA	St George Park Thorncliffe, Packhouse Lane, High Green, Sheffield S35 3HU
HOUGHTON MAIN	Middlecliffe Lane, Little Houghton, Barnsley S72 0HN
JUBILEE SPORTS	Jubilee Sports Ground, Claywheels Lane, Sheffield
NORTH GAWBER COLLIERY	Woolley MW, Wolley Colliery Road, Darton, Barnsley S75 5JA
OUGHTIBRIDGE WAR MEMORIAL	Oughtibridge War Mem. Ground, off Waterside Gardens, Oughtibridge, Sheffield S35 0JS
PENISTONE CHURCH RES	Memorial Ground, Church View Road, Penistone, Sheffield S36 6AT
STOCKSBRIDGE P.S. RESERVES	Look Local Stadium, Bracken Moor Lane, Stocksbridge, Sheffield S36 2AN
SWINTON ATHLETIC	Mexborough Athletic Ground, New Oxford Road, Mexborough S64 0JL
WAKEFIELD AFC	Dorothy Hyman Stadium, Syndale Road, Cudworth, Barnsley S72 8HL
WOMBWELL MAIN	Wombwell Main CC, Houghton Lane, Wombwell S73 8PW

Somerset County League Premier Division

CHARD TOWN	Denning Sports Field, Zembard Lane, Chard, Somerset TA20 1JL
CHILCOMPTON SPORTS	Chilcompton Sports Ground, Bennell Wells Road, Chilcompton BA3 4EZ
CLEVEDON UNITED	Coleridge Vale, Clevedon, North Somerset
CLUTTON	Warwick Fields, Upper Bristol Rd , Behind Warwick Arms, Clutton, Bristol BS39 5TA
FRY CLUB	Cadbury's, Somerdale, Keynsham, Bristol BS31 2AU
ILMINSTER TOWN	The Archie Gooch Pavilion, Canal Way, Ilminster TA19 9FE
KEYNSHAM TOWN RESERVES	The Crown Field, Bristol Road, Keynsham, Bristol BS31 2BE
MENDIP BROADWALK	Creswicke Road, Knowle, Bristol BS4 1UQ
MIDDLEZOY ROVERS	The Aerodrome, Westonzoyland, Somerset TA7 0ES
NAILSEA AND TICKENHAM	Fryth Way, Pound Lane, Nailsea BS48 2AS
NAILSEA UNITED	Grove Sports Ground, Old Church, Nailsea BS48 4ND
SHIREHAMPTON	Bristol Manor Farm FC, The Creek, Portway, Sea Mills, Bristol BS9 2HS
STOCKWOOD GREEN	Hursley Lane, Woolard Lane, Whitchurch, Bristol BS14 0QY
STOCKWOOD WANDERERS	Stockers Stadium, Stockwood lane, Bristol BS14 8SJ
WATCHET TOWN	Memorial Ground, Doniford Road, Watchet TA23 0YE
WESTFIELD	Charlton Lane, Midsomer Norton, Radstock BA3 4BD
WORLE	Station Road, Worle BS22 6AN

St Piran League East

AFC ST AUSTELL RESERVES	Poltair Park, Poltair Road, St Austell PL25 4LR
BUDE TOWN	Broad Close Park, Bude EX23 8DR
CALLINGTON RESERVES	Ginsters Marshfield Parc, Launceston Road, Callington PL17 7DR
LANREATH	Rally Park, Lanreath, Looe PL13 2NX
LAUNCESTON RESERVES	Pennygillam Way, Pennygillam Industrial Estate, Launceston PL15 7ED
LISKEARD ATHLETIC RES	Lux Park Leisure Centre, Coldstyle Road, Liskeard PL14 3HZ
MILLBROOK AFC RESERVES	Mill Park, Parsons Court, Southdown Road, Millbrook, Torpoint PL10 1FE
MORWENSTOW AFC	The Playing Field, Shop, Morwenstow, Bude EX23 9SL
POLPERRO AFC	Killgarth, Brentfields, Looe PL13 2JQ
SALTASH BOROUGH	Saltmill Park, Salt Mill, Saltash PL12 6LG
SALTASH UNITED RESERVES	Kimberley Stadium, Callington Road, Saltash PL12 6DX
ST DENNIS AFC RESERVES	Boscawen Park, St Dennis, St Austell PL26 8DT
ST MAWGAN AFC	Trevarrian Holiday Park, Trevarrin, Newquay TR8 4AQ
STICKERS RESERVES	Burngullow Park, Tre-End, Sticker, St Austell PL26 7EN
TORPOINT ATHLETIC RESERVES	The Mill, Mill Lane, Torpoint PL11 2RE
WADEBRIDGE TOWN RESERVES	Bodieve Park, Bedueve Road, Wadebridge PL27 6DJ

St Piran League West

FALMOUTH TOWN RESERVES	Bickland Park, Bickland Hill, Falmouth TR11 4PB
HAYLE	Trevassack Park, Viaduct Hill, Hayle TR27 5HT
HELSTON ATHLETIC RESERVES	Kellaway Park, Clodgey Lane, Helston TR13 8PJ
ILLOGAN RBL	Oxland Park, Meadowside Richards Lane, Paynters Lane, Redruth TR16 4DQ
LUDGVAN	Jubilee Hall, Fairfield, Ludgvan TR20 8ES
MOUSEHOLE RESERVES	Trungle Parc, Paul, Penzance TR19 6AZ
MULLION	Clifden Park, Clifden Close, Mullion TR12 7EQ
PENRYN ATHLETIC	Kernick Road, Penryn TR10 8QE
PERRANPORTH	Ponsmere Valley, Budnic, Perranporth TR6 0BP
PERRANWELL	King George V Memorial Playing Field, Perranwell Station, Truro TR3 7JX
REDRUTH UNITED	Clijah Croft, Redruth TR15 2NR
ST AGNES AFC	Enys Park, Tregease Road, St Agnes TR5 0SL
ST DAY	Vogue Playing Field, Nampara Vogue Hill, St Day, Redruth TR16 5NQ
ST IVES TOWN	Lelant Saltings, Saltings Reach, Lelant, St Ives TR27 6GH
ST JUST AFC	Lafrowda Park, Regent Terrace, St Just, Penzance TR19 7LE
WENDROM UNITED RESERVES	Wendron Cricket Club, Underlane, Helston TR13 0EH

Staffordshire County Senior League Premier Division

ABBEY HULTON UNITED RES	Birches Head Road, Birches Head, Stoke-on-Trent ST2 8DD
ALSAGER TOWN RESERVES	Wood Park Stadium, Woodland Court, Alsager, Staffordshire ST7 2DP
ASHBOURNE	Rocester FC, Mill Street, Rocester, Staffordshire ST14 5JX
AUDLEY & DISTRICT	Old Road, Bignall End, Newcastle under Lyme ST7 8QH
BRERETON SOCIAL	Brereton Sports and Social Club, Armitage Lane, Rugeley, Staffordshire WS15 1ED
CHEADLE TOWN	Thorley Drive, Cheadle, Staffordshire. ST10 1SA
CITY OF STOKE	Bradwell Community Centre, Riceyman Road, Newcastle ST5 8LF
EASTWOOD HANLEY	Northwood Sports Centre, Keelings Road, Hanley ST1 6PA
FOLEY MEIR	Whitcombe Road, Meir, Staffordshire ST3 6AU
HANLEY TOWN RESERVES	Potteries Park, Abbey Lane, Bucknall, Staffordshire ST2 8AJ
LEEK CSOB	Pointon Park, Felthouse Lane, Cheddleton, Leek ST13 7BP
REDGATE CLAYTON	Clayton Comm. Centre, Northwood Lane, Clayton, Newcastle-under-Lyme ST5 4BN
SILVERDALE ATHLETIC	Kents Lane Football Ground, Sutton Ave, Staffordshire ST5 6TA
STONE DOMINOES	Wellbeing Centre, Stone Dominoes, Staffordshire ST15 0NF
WALSALL PHOENIX	The Green, off Little Aston Road, Aldridge, Staffordshire WS9 8NH
WOLSTANTON UNITED	Bradwell Comm. Centre, Riceyman Road, Bradwell, Newcastle-under-Lyme ST5 8LD

Suffolk & Ipswich League Senior Division

ACHILLES	Pauls Social Club, Salmet Close, Ipswich IP2 9BA
BENHALL ST MARY	Benhall Club, School Lane, Benhall IP17 1HE
BILDESTON RANGERS	Consent Lane, Sportsfield, Bildeston IP7 7SB
BOURNE VALE UNITED	Bourne Vale Sports & Social Club, Halifax Road, Ipswich IP2 8RE
BRAMFORD UNITED	Acton Road Playing Field, Bramford, Ipswich IP8 4HU
CAPEL PLOUGH	Friars, Capel St Mary, Ipswich IP9 2XS
CLAYDON	Blue Circle Ground, Great Blakenham Ipswich IP6 0JZ
COPLESTONIANS	Gresham Sports & Social Club, Tuddenham Road, Ipswich IP4 3QJ
CRANE SPORTS	Gresham Sports & Social Club, Tuddenham Road, Ipswich IP4 3QJ
EAST BERGHOLT UNITED	Gandish Road, East Bergholt, Colchester CO7 6TP
HAUGHLEY UNITED	National Playing Field, Green Road, Haughley IP14 3QZ
HENLEY ATHLETIC	Henley Community Centre, Church Meadows, Henley IP6 0RP
LEISTON ST MARGARETS	Junction Meadow, Abbey Road, Leiston IP16 4RD
OLD NEWTON UNITED	Church Road, Old Newton, Stowmarket IP14 4ED
TRIMLEY RED DEVILS	Stennetts Playing Field, Stennetts Close, Trimley St Mary IP11 0TZ
WESTERFIELD UNITED	Rushmere Sports Centre, The Street, Rushmere St Andrew, Ipswich IP5 1DE

Surrey Elite Intermediate League

AFC CUBO	Southfields Academy (3G), 333 Merton Road, Southfields, London SW18 5JU
AFC SPELTHORNE SPORTS	296 Staines Road West, Ahford Common, Ashford TW15 1RY
BATTERSEA IRONSIDES	Battersea Ironsides S&S Club, Burntwood Lane, Earlsfield SW17 0AW
CHESSINGTON KC	Tolworth Court Sports Ground, Old Kingston Road, Tolworth KT4 7QH
FARLEIGH ROVERS	Parsonage Field, Harrow Road, Warlingham CR6 9EX
HORSLEY	Toms Field Horsley, Long Reach, West Horsley, Surrey KT24 6PG
LYNE	Ascot United, Winkfield Roar, Ascot SL5 7LJ
MERROW	The Urnfield, Downside Road, Guildford, Surrey, GU4 8PH
NPL	NPL Sports Club, Queens Road, Teddington, TW11 0LW
OLD RUTLISHIANS	Mayfield Stadium, Mayfield Road, Thornton Heath, Surrey CR7 6DH
RIPLEY VILLAGE	The Green, Ripley, Woking GU23 6AN
ROYAL HOLLOWAY OLD BOYS	Royal Holloway College Sports Centre (Nobles Fields), Prune Hill, Egham TW20 0ES
SPARTANS YOUTH	Carville Hall Park North, Lionel Road North, Brentford TW8 9QT
STAINES LAMMAS	The Lucan Pavilion, The Boradway, Laleham, Staines, Middlesex TW18 1RZ
WORCESTER PARK	Skinners Field, Green Lane, Worcester Park, Surrey KT4 8AJ

Thames Valley Premier League

BERKS COUNTY	Lowther Road, Wokingham RG41 1JB
BURGHFIELD	Recreation Road, Reading RG7 3EN
COOKHAM DEAN	Alfred Major Rec Ground, Hillcrest Avenue, Cookham Rise , Maidenhead SL6 9NB
FINCHAMPSTEAD	Memorial Ground, Finchampstead
MAIDENHEAD TOWN	Bisham Village, Marlow Road, Bisham SL7 1RR
MORTIMER	Alfred Palmer Memorial PF, West End Road, Mortimer, Reading RG7 3TW
NEWBURY	Faraday Road, Newbury RG14 2AD
READING CITY U23	
RICHINGS PARK	Wellesley Avenue, Iver SL0 9BN
WESTWOOD WANDERERS	Mapledurham Playing Fields, Reading RG4 7LH
WINDLESHAM UNITED	Field of Remembrance, Updown Hill, Windlesham GU20 6DT
WOODCOTE	Woodcote Recreation Ground, Reading Road, Woodcote RG8 0RA
WOODLEY UNITED ROYALS	Bulmershe Pavilion, Woodlands Avenue, Woodley, Reading RG5 3EU
WRAYSBURY VILLAGE	The Memorial Ground, Staines-upon-Thames, Wraysbury TW19 5NA

Wearside League

ANNFIELD PLAIN	Derwent Park , West Road , Annfield Plain DH9 8PZ
BOLDON C.A.	Boldon Colliery Welfare, New Road, Boldon Colliery NE35 9DS
COXHOE ATHLETIC	Beechfield Park Commercial Road East Coxhoe County Durham DH6 4LF
DARLINGTON R.A.	Brinkburn Road, Darlington, Co. Durham DL3 9LF
DARLINGTON TOWN	Eastbourne Sports Complex (4G), Bourne Avenue, Darlington DL1 1LJ
DURHAM UNITED	New Ferens Park, Belmont Park Durham DH1 1GG
FARRINGTON DETACHED	Leyburn Grove, Houghton
FC HARTLEPOOL	Grayfields Enclosure, Jesmond Gardens, Hartlepool TS24 8PJ
GATESHEAD LEAM RANGERS	Hilltop Playing Field, Gateshead, Tyne and Wear NE10 8LT
HEBBURN TOWN RESERVES	The Energy Check Sports Ground, South Drive Hebburn Tyne & Wear NE31 1UN
HORDEN COMMUNTIY WELFARE	Horden Welfare Park, Eden Street, Horden SR8 4LX
RICHMOND TOWN	Earls Orchard Playing Field. DL10 4RH
SILKSWORTH COLLIERY WELFARE	Silksworth Welfare Park, Blind Lane, Sliksworth, Sunderland SR3 1AX
WEST AUCKLAND TUNNS	PC Sports Pavillion, Coronation Terrace Cockfield DL13 5EB
WINDSCALE	Falcon Complex, Croadalla Avenue Egremont Cumbria CA22 2QN
WOLVISTON	Metcalfe Park, Wynyard Road, Wolviston, Billingham TS22 5NE

West Cheshire League Division One

ASHVILLE	Villa Park, Cross Lane, Wallasey Village, Wallasey CH45 8RH
CAPENHURST VILLA	Capenhurst Sports Ground, South Wirral
CHESTER NOMADS	Boughton Hall Cricket Club, Boughton, Chester, CH3 5EL
ELLESMERE PORT TOWN	Whitby Sports & Social Club, Chester Road, Whitby, Ellesmere Port, CH65
HALE	Hale Park, Hale Village, Liverpool L24 4AX
MAGHULL	Old Hall Field, Hall Lane, Maghull L31 7DY
MARSHALLS	Heron Eccles Sports Ground, Abbottshey Avenue, Allerton, Liverpool L18 7JT
MOSSLEY HILL ATHLETIC	Mossley Hill Athletic Club, Mossley Hill Road, Liverpool L18 8BX
NESTON NOMADS	Vauxhall Sports & Social Club, Rivacre Road, Hooton, South Wirral CH66 1NJ
NEWTON	Millcroft, Frankby Road, Greasby CH49 3PE
RAINHILL TOWN	Prescot Soccer Centre, Warrington Road, Prescot L35 5AD
REDGATE ROVERS	JMO Sports Park, Blaguegate Playing Fields, Liverpool Road, Skelmersdale WN8 8BX
RICHMOND RAITH ROVERS	St John Bosco School, Storrington Avenue, Liverpool L11 9DQ
SOUTH LIVERPOOL	North Field, Jericho Lane, Aigburth, Liverpool L17 5AR
UPTON A.A.	Chester County Sports & Social Club, Plas Newton Lane, Chester CH2 1PR
VAUXHALL MOTORS RESERVES	Vauxhall Sports & Social Club, Rivacre Road, Hooton, South Wirral CH66 1NJ

West Lancashire League Premier Division

BLACKPOOL WREN ROVERS	Bruce Park, School Road, Marton, Blackpool FY4 5DX
BURSCOUGH RICHMOND	Richmond Park, Junction Lane, Burscough, West Lancashire L40 5SN
CMB	CMB Sports Ground, Tempest Road, Lostock, Bolton BL6 4ER
COPPULL UNITED	Springfield Road, Coppull PR7 5EJ
EUXTON VILLA	Jim Fowler Memorial Ground, Runshaw Hall Lane, Euxton, Chorley PR7 6HH
FULWOOD AMATEURS	Lightfoot Lane, Fulwood, Preston PR2 0AE
HURST GREEN	San Smithy Ground, Avenue Road, Hurst Green BB7 9QB
LYTHAM TOWN	Ballam Road Ground, Ballam Road, Lytham FY8 4LE
POULTON	Cottam Hall, Poulton Le Fylde, FY6 7RH
SLYNE WITH HEST	Bottomdale Road, Slyne, Lancaster LA2 6BG
SOUTHPORT HESKETH	Bankfield Lane, Southport, Merseyside PR9 7NJ
TEMPEST UNITED	Tempest Road, Chew Moor Village, Lostock, Bolton BL6 4HL
THORNTON CLEVELEYS	Bourne Road, Cleveleys, Thornton Cleveleys FY5 4QA
TURTON	Thomasson Fold, Turton, Bolton BL7 0PD
VICKERSTOWN CC	Park Vale, Mill Lane, Walney, Barrow-in-Furness LA14 3XY
WHITEHAVEN	Focus Scaffolding Sports Complex, Coach Road, Whitehaven, CA28 9DD

West Yorkshire League Premier Division

BEESTON ST ANTHONY'S	St Antony's Road, Beeston, Leeds LS11 8DP
BOROUGHBRIDGE	Sports Pavilion, Aldborough Road, Boroughbridge YO51 9EB
CARLTON ATHLETIC	Carlton Cricket Club, Town Street, Carlton WF3 3QU
FIELD	Field Sports & Social Club, Hollingwood Lane, Bradford BD7 2RE
HALL GREEN UNITED	Crigglestone Sports Club, Painthorpe Lane, Hall Green, Wakefield WF4 3LA
HEADINGLEY	Weetwood Playing Fields, Weetwood, Leeds LS16 5AU
HORBURY TOWN	Slazengers Sports Complex, Southfields, Horbury WF4 5BH
HUDDERSFIELD AMATEUR	Old Earth, Lower Edge, Elland HX5 9ES
HUNSLET CLUB	The Hunslet Club, Hillidge Road LS10 1BP
ILKLEY TOWN	Ben Rhydding Sports Club, Leeds Road, ILKLEY LS29 8AW
KNARESBOROUGH TOWN	Manse Lane, Knaresborough HG5 8LF
LEEDS CITY	Adel War Memorial Association, Church Lane, Adel, Leeds LS16 8DE
NEWSOME	The Westgate Arena, Cross Lane, Huddersfield HD4 6DW
ROBIN HOOD ATHLETIC	Behind Coach & Horses Hotel, Rothwell Haigh LS26 0SF
SHERBURN WHITE ROSE	Finkle Hill, Recreation Ground, Finkle Hill, Sherburn-in-Elmet LS25 6EL
WHITKIRK WANDERERS	Whitkirk Social & Sports Club, Selby Road, Whitkirk, Leeds LS15 0AA

Wiltshire League Premier Division

CORSHAM TOWN RESERVES	Southbank Ground, Lacock Road, Corsham SN13 9HS
CRICKLADE TOWN	Cricklade Leisure Centre, Stones Lane, Cricklade SN6 6JW
FROME COLLEGIANS	The Old Showfield, Rodden Road, Frome BA11 2AH
HOLT	Meadow Lane, Westbury BA13 3AF
KINTBURY RANGERS	Recreation Ground, Inkpen Road RG17 9UA.
LUDGERSHALL SPORTS	Astor Crescent, Ludgershall SP11 9QE
MALMESBURY VICTORIA DEV.	Flying Monk Ground Gloucester Road SN16 9JS
MARLBOROUGH TOWN	Elcot Lane, Marlborough, SN8 2BG
MELKSHAM TOWN RESERVES	Oakfields, Eastern Way, Melksham SN12 7GU
PEWSEY VALE DEVELOPMENT	Recreation Ground, Ball Road, Pewsey SN9 5BS
PURTON	The Red House, Church Street, Purton SN5 4DY
ROYAL WOOTTON BASSETT T DEV.	Gerrard Buxton Sports Ground, Rylands Way, Royal Wootton Bassett SN4 8DS
SHREWTON UNITED	Shrewton Recreation Ground, Mill Lane, Shrewton SP3 4JY
STRATTON JUNIOR	Meadowcroft, Addison Crescent, Stratton SN2 7JX
TROWBRIDGE TOWN	Woodmarsh, Bradley Road, Trowbridge BA14 0SB
WROUGHTON	The Weir Field, Devizes Road, Wroughton SN4 0SA

York League Premier Division

CHURCH FENTON	Church Fenton Sportsground, Busk Lane, Church Fenton, Nr Tadcaster LS24 9RJ
COPMANTHORPE	Copmanthorpe RecreatioN Ground YO23 3YR
DRINGHOUSES	Dringhouses Sports & Social Club, St Helens Road, Dringhouses, York YO24 1HR
DUNNINGTON	Dunnington Sports Club, Common Road, Dunnington, York YO19 5NG
EASINGWOLD TOWN	Easingwold YO61 3FB
F1 RACING	York St Johns Sports Centre, Mille Crux YO31 8TA
HEMINGBROUGH UNITED	Hemingbrough YO8 6QS
HUNTINGTON ROVERS	Huntington SportsClub, North Lane, Huntington, York YO32 9RU
KIRKBYMOORSIDE	Kirkbymoorside YO62 6DX
OLD MALTON ST MARY'S	FitzWilliam Sportsfield Old Malton YO17 7EY
POPPLETON UNITED	The Poppleton Centre, Main Street, Poppleton, York YO26 6QG
SPORTING KNAVESMIRE	Poppleton Com. Sports Pavilion, Millfield Lane, Nether Poppleton, Nr York YO26 6NY
TADCASTER MAGNETS	Magnets Sports Ground, Leeds Road, Tadcaster, North Yorkshire LS24 9HD
THORPE UNITED	Willoughby Field Lane, Thorpe YO8 9FL
WIGGINTON GRASSHOPPERS	Mill Lane, Wigginton, York YO32 2PY

Yorkshire Amateur League

ALWOODLEY	WRCFA, Fleet Lane, Woodlesford, Leeds LS26 8NX
ATHLETICO	Bradford Academy (3G), Lister Street, BD4 7QS
CALVERLEY UNITED	Calverley Park, Calverley, Leeds LS28 5PY
DRIGHLINGTON	Adwalton Moor, Moorland Road, Drighlington BD11 1JY
FARSLEY CELTIC JUNIORS	Bradford Academy, Lister Street BD4 7QS
HORSFORTH ST MARGARETS	Leeds trinity University, Horsforth
LEEDS MEDICS & DENTISTS	Weetwood Sports Park, Ring Road, Weetwood, Leeds LS16 5AU
LITTLETOWN	Beck Lane, Heckmondwike WF15 7BH
LOWER HOPTON	Wood End Road, Mirfield WF14 8PR
OVENDEN WEST RIDING	
RAYBURN UNITED	
ROUTE ONE ROVERS	
STANLEY UNITED	WRCFA, Fleet Lane, Woodlesford, Leeds LS26 8NX
STEETON AFC	Steeton BD20 6RX
TOLLER	
WORTLEY	Blue Hill Lane, Leeds LS12 4NZ

CLUB INDEX

Over 1700 senior clubs as they line up for the 2019-20 season across Steps 1 -7